SUMMARIES – Where To Look For Help

PREREQUISITES

Your algebra, trigonometry, or precalculus textbooks, if you kept them, are good places to look because you are used to the notation and presentation. If you do not have these books for reference, we have provided the necessary review in the *Student Mathematics Handbook.* Also see:

LIMITS, DIFFERENTIATION, AND GRAPHING

INTEGRATION

INFINITE SERIES

ANALYTIC GEOMETRY, VECTORS, AND THREE DIMENSIONS

FUNCTIONS OF TWO VARIABLES

DIFFERENTIAL EQUATIONS

INSTRUCTOR'S EDITION
CALCULUS

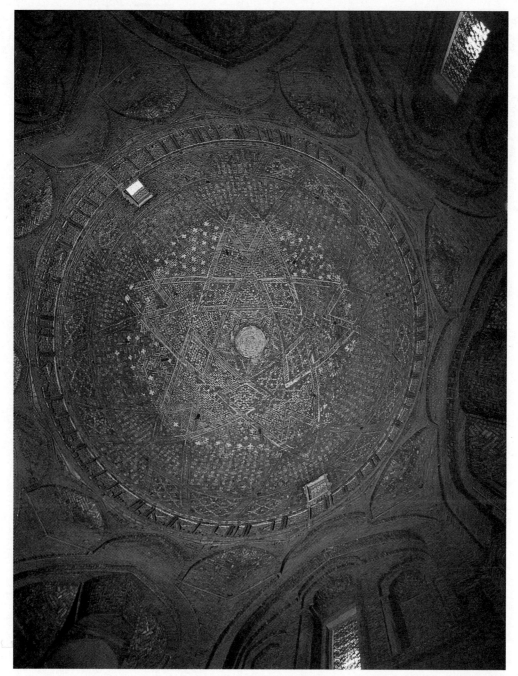

Northeast dome ceiling, Masjid-i-Jami, Isfahan, Iran. This structure was built entirely of brick in the year 1088 and has stood firmly in an earthquake zone for more than 900 years. It was designed with a sophisticated knowledge of geometry (by solving the problem of mounting a nearly perfect hemisphere on a square base) and engineered through trial and error (some earlier buildings simply collapsed). Architecture critic Eric Schroeder has written: "European dome-builders never approached their skill. How ingeniously the Western builder compensated his ignorance of the mechanics of dome construction is attested by the ten chains round the base of St. Peter's, and the concealed cone which fastens the haunch of St. Paul's. But engineers could not hope to prescribe an ideally light dome of plain masonry before Newton's work on the calculus (late in the seventeenth century)." Read on, and upon completion of this text you will be qualified, at least mathematically, to do more than design domes. (photo credit: Seherr-Thoss)

INSTRUCTOR'S EDITION
CALCULUS

Gerald L. Bradley

Claremont McKenna College

Karl J. Smith

Santa Rosa Junior College

Prentice Hall

Englewood Cliffs, New Jersey 07632

Library of Congress has cataloged another edition as follows:

Bradley, Gerald L., 1940–
    Calculus / Gerald Bradley, Karl Smith.—1st ed.
      p. cm.
    Includes index.
    ISBN 0-13-178617-2
    1. Calculus. I. Smith, Karl J. II. Title.
QA303.B88218 1995
515—dc20   94-27258
                            CIP

Acquisition Editor: George Lobell
Editor in Chief: Jerome Grant
Development Editor: Alan MacDonell
Production Editor: Edward Thomas
Marketing Manager: Frank Nicolazzo
Supplements Editor: Audra Walsh
Product Manager: Trudy Pisciotti
Design Director: Paula Maylahn
Text Designer: Lee Goldstein
Page layout: Lee Goldstein, Karen Noferi
Cover Designer: Jeanette Jacobs
Art Director: Amy Rosen
Photo Editor: Lorinda Morris-Nantz
Photo research: Melinda Reo, Page Poore-Kidder
Editorial Assistant: Mary DeLuca
Text composition: Black Dot Graphics
Art studio: Tech Graphics
Portrait artist: Bonnie J. Miljour
Copy Editor: Linda Thompson

Cover photo: Koji Horiuchi, courtesy Pei Cobb Freed and Partners

Printed in the United States of America
10 9 8 7 6 5 4 3 2 1

ISBN 0-13-330325-X

Prentice-Hall International (UK) Limited, London
Prentice-Hall of Australia Pty. Limited, Sydney
Prentice-Hall Canada Inc., Toronto
Prentice-Hall Hispanoamericana, S.A., Mexico
Prentice-Hall of India Private Limited, New Delhi
Prentice-Hall of Japan, Inc., Tokyo
Simon & Schuster Asia Pte, Ltd., Singapore
Editora Prentice-Hall do Brasil, Ltda., Rio de Janeiro

Contents

8 Infinite Series   489

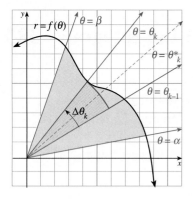

9 Polar Coordinates and Parametric Forms 569

10 Vectors in the Plane and in Space   630

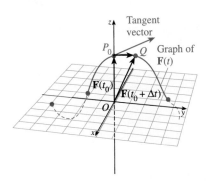

Tangent vector

P_0

Q

Graph of $\mathbf{F}(t)$

$\mathbf{F}(t_0)$ $\mathbf{F}(t_0 + \Delta t)$

O

11 Vector Calculus   684

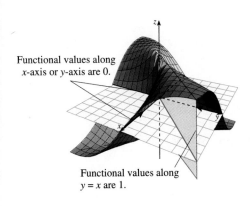

Functional values along x-axis or y-axis are 0.

Functional values along $y = x$ are 1.

12 Partial Differentiation   838

Solid S

d

y_k

Δy_k

c

Rectangle R

a b

Cross-sectional area $A(y_k)$

13 Multiple Integration   821

Curl **v**

The rotunda of City Hall, in Manhattan, New York City. Designed by John McComb, Jr., reputedly the first American-born architect, and built in the early nineteenth century in the neoclassical style. (photo credit: Behrenholtz)

About the Authors

Gerald L. Bradley

Karl J. Smith

Gerald L. Bradley received his M.S. in mathematics from Harvey Mudd College in 1962 and his Ph.D. from the California Institute of Technology in 1966. A former NSF fellow, Professor Bradley has taught at Claremont McKenna College since 1966 and has served as chairman of the mathematics department for two tours of duty. His field of research has been matrix theory. He is the author of *A Primer of Linear Algebra* and co-author of a top-selling business calculus text.

Karl J. Smith received his B.A. and M.A. (in 1967) degrees in mathematics from UCLA. Then he moved in 1968 to northern California to teach at Santa Rosa Junior College, where he has been ever since. Along the way, he served as department chair, and he received a Ph.D. in 1979 in mathematics education at Southeastern University. A past president of the American Mathematical Association of Two-Year Colleges, Professor Smith is very active nationally in mathematics education. He was founding editor of *Western AMATYC News,* a chairperson of the committee on Mathematics Excellence, and a NSF grant reviewer. He was a recipient in 1979 of an Outstanding Young Men of America Award, in 1980 of an Outstanding Educator Award, and in 1989 of an Outstanding Teacher Award. Professor Smith is the author of several successful textbooks. In fact, over one million students have learned mathematics from his textbooks.

Preface

Calculus teaching is undergoing great changes, most of which will be of lasting benefit to students. This text was written to blend many of the best aspects of calculus reform with the reasonable goals and methodology of traditional calculus. In incorporating so much of calculus reform, we made a deliberate effort *not* to "throw the baby out with the bath water." Calculus should not be a terminal course but rather one that prepares students of engineering, science, and math to move on to more advanced and necessary professional courses. This text presents most traditional topics, such as continuity, the mean value theorem, l'Hôpital's rule, parametric equations, polar coordinates, sequences, and series. In short, this text is an attempt at *Reform with Reason.*

The major issue driving calculus reform is the poor performance of students trying to master the concepts of calculus. Much of this failure can be attributed to ways in which students study and learn mathematics in high school. The high school mathematics textbooks published over the last twenty years have increasingly focused on reducing mathematics to a series of small repeatable steps. Process is stressed over insight and understanding. In these same books we often find problems matched to worked-out sample problems, which encourages students to memorize a series of problem-solving algorithms. Unfortunately, this reduces mathematics to taxonomy; students show up for calculus generally willing to work hard, but for many, this translates into working hard at rote memorization! The task of getting students *to think conceptually* falls to the teachers of calculus, and we have provided you with a calculus book that will help you focus on learning by providing you with sound development of concepts, challenging problems, and a well-developed pedagogy.

Conceptual Understanding Through Verbalization

Besides developing some minimal skills in algebraic manipulation and problem solving, a calculus text today should require students to develop verbal skills in a mathematical setting. This is not just because real mathematics wields its words precisely and compactly, but because verbalization should help students think conceptually.

Cooperative Learning (Group Research Projects) There is a great deal of interest in encouraging students to work in small groups as an alternative mode of teaching from the traditional lecture method. In July 1991, the National Science Foundation funded a group of instructors who met on the campus of New Mexico State University to discuss the topic "Discovering Calculus Through Student Projects." We believe that students should be encouraged to think independently and in small groups. Students need to be put into classroom situations that help to prepare them for a working environment. They need to be able to read and write mathematics and to ask whether an answer is reasonable without looking in the back of the book for an answer. To that end, we provide several examples of group research projects. We are indebted to those who have constructed and class tested these projects, and we thank them for their contribution to our book. Each group research project is loosely tied to the material contained in the chapter in which it is presented. Also note that the complexity of the projects increases as we progress through the book and the mathematical maturity of the student develops. In addition to doing the group research projects, the students could be encouraged to collaborate on the Putnam and journal problems.

Mathematical Communication   Students should be encouraged to communicate mathematically, and in addition to the group research projects we have included other opportunities for mathematical communication in terms that can be understood by nonprofessionals. Shorter problems encouraging written communication are included in nearly all of the problem sets. The guest essays provide alternative viewpoints. The questions that follow are called MATHEMATICAL ESSAYS and are included to encourage individual writing assignments and mathematical exposition. We believe that students will benefit from individual writing and research in mathematics. Theorems and definitions are frequently followed by short, intuitive explanations, and students are encouraged to provide their own verbal explanations of mathematics in the problem sets, where they are asked to summarize procedures and processes or to describe a mathematical result in everyday terms. Mathematics is more than working problems and getting answers, and mathematics education *must* include the communication of mathematical ideas.

Integration of Technology

Computational Windows   Reform is driven partly by the need to maximize the benefits technology brings to the learning of mathematics. Simply adding a lab course to the traditional calculus is probably pointless and may lead to unacceptable workloads for all involved. Instead, we choose to include technology as an aid to the understanding of calculus, rather than to write a calculus course developed around the technology. Although we have included over 60 pages devoted to the use of technology, we have kept such references "platform-neutral" because specific calculators and computer programs frequently change and are better considered in separate technology manuals. The technology in the book is organized under the title COMPUTATIONAL WINDOW to give insight into how technological advances can be used to help understand calculus. COMPUTATIONAL WINDOWS also appear in the student exercises: These WINDOWS contain problems requiring a graphing calculator or software and computer. Many of the problems were prepared by Jack Cohen and Frank Hagin, both of the Colorado School of Mines.

Technology Laboratory Manuals   For those students with access to a computer or graphing calculator, companion Technology Manuals are available and can be wrapped with the text at a small charge. The manuals differ from each other by being "platform specific"—that is, the key stroke instruction is specific to that technology. The five different platforms (manuals) are: Texas Instruments graphing calculators, Hewlett-Packard graphing calculators, MATLAB, Maple, and Mathematica. Each manual picks up the same technology examples from this textbook and provides the specific keystrokes needed. Also, each manual has additional technology questions (which are the same for each manual), some of which are given with the keystrokes. Thus, the instructor need not be involved in teaching the students basic key strokes or syntax in a given technology: the appropriate manual will do so. All of these manuals were prepared by Jack Cohen and Frank Hagin, both of the Colorado School of Mines.

Greater Text Visualization   Related to (but not exclusively driven by) the use of technology is the greater use of graphs and other mathematical pictures throughout this text. Over 1,700 graphs appear—more than in nearly any other calculus text. This increased visualization is intended to help develop greater student intuition. Much of this visualization appears in the wide margins to accompany the text. Its purpose is to provide explanation to supplement that of the text prose. Additional graphs are related to the student problems, including answer art.

Significant Digits   With the availability of calculators and computers, we were necessarily faced with the question of how to treat significant digits in this book. Even though our experience tells us that a thorough treatment of that topic is better left to chemistry and physics classes, we have included a brief treatment in Appendix C. On occasion, we show the entire calculator or computer output of 12 digits for clarity, even though such a display may exceed the requisite number of significant digits. Our thanks to Neil Berger, of the University of Illinois at Chicago, for his contribution to our treatment of significant digits and to Appendix C.

Problem Solving

Problems   We believe that students learn mathematics by *doing* mathematics. Therefore, the problems and applications are perhaps the most important feature of any calculus book, and you will find that the problems in this book extend from routine practice to challenging. The problem sets are divided into A Problems (routine), B Problems (requiring independent thought), and C Problems (theory problems). In this book we also include past Putnam examination problems as well as problems found in current mathematical journals. The worked out examples in the text are A and B problems. We believe very strongly that success in understanding calculus depends on having students struggle with a healthy number of challenging problems, which includes the journal and Putnam problems as well as the C problems.

You will find the scope and depth of the problems in this book to be extraordinary. Even though engineering and physics examples and problems play a prominent role, applications from a wide variety of fields—such as economics, ecology, psychology, and sociology—are included. The problems have been in the developmental stages for more than ten years, and most of them have been class tested. In addition, the chapter summaries provide not only topical review, but also many miscellaneous exercises. Although the chapter reviews are typical of examinations, the miscellaneous problems are presented not as graded problems, but rather as a random list of problems loosely tied to the ideas of the chapter. In addition, the cumulative reviews occur at natural breaking points in the text: at the ends of Chapters 6, 11, and 14.

Journal Problems   In an effort to show that mathematicians work problems too, we have reprinted problems from leading mathematics journals. We have chosen problems that are within reach of the intended audience of this book. If students need help or hints for these problems, they can search out the original presentation and solution in the cited journal. In addition, we have included problems from various **Putnam Examinations.** These problems, which are more challenging, are offered in the miscellaneous problems at the end of various chapters and are provided to give insight into the type of problems asked in mathematical competitions. The Putnam Examination is a national annual examination given under the auspices of the Mathematical Association of America and is designed to recognize mathematically talented college and university students.

Think Tank Problems   It has been said that mathematical discovery is directed toward two major goals: the formulation of proofs and the construction of counterexamples. Most calculus books focus only on the first goal (the body of proofs and true statements), but we think that some attention should be paid to the formulation of counterexamples for false statements. Throughout this book we ask the student to formulate examples satisfying certain conditions. We have designated this type of problem as a think tank problem.

Additional Features

Student Mathematics Handbook   We begin *Calculus* with a minimum of review. The prerequisite material that is often included in a calculus textbook has been bound separately in a companion book, *Student Mathematics Handbook*. We think this is an important supplement to the textbook because we have found that most errors our students make in a calculus class are not errors in calculus but errors in basic algebra and trigonometry. A unified and complete treatment of this prerequisite material, easily referenced and keyed to the textbook, has been a valuable tool for our students taking calculus. Those portions of the text that benefit from an appropriate precalculus review are marked by the symbol $\text{s}^{\text{M}}\text{H}$. Thus, the review portion of the handbook functions as a series of "help screens" that appear as the student reads the text. Our handbook is offered *free of charge* with every new copy of the textbook. The handbook not only includes the necessary review material and formulas but also contains a catalog of curves and a complete integral table.

Differential equations   We also include differential equations early (in Section 4.4) and then develop methods of solutions of differential equations in a spiral manner throughout the book. The reasons are twofold. First, differential equations make some of the best applications for calculus. Second, learning the differential equations is easier when they are seen in their most appropriate context. The multivariable paperback version of the text has an additional chapter on differential equations for those instructors who choose to teach a more substantial course.

Sequence of topics   Some colleges and universities prefer reversing Chapters 5 and 6. For this reason, we have written these chapters so that they may be interchanged without causing any difficulties. We resisted the temptation to label certain sections as optional, because that is a prerogative of individual instructors and schools. However, the following sections could be skipped without any difficulty: 1.8, 3.8, 5.7, 6.3 (delay until Sec. 13.6), 7.6, 12.8, and 13.8. Differential equations (4.4 and 6.4) could be delayed for a subsequent course. To assist instructors with the pacing of the course, we have written the material so each section can reasonably be covered in one classroom day.

Proofs   All the theorems are repeated in Appendix B for easy reference, but it is important to note that we do not pretend to prove every theorem in this book. In fact, we often refer the reader to Appendix C for some longer proofs, or sometimes to an advanced calculus text. Why then do we include the heading PROOF after each theorem? It is because we want the student to *know* that for a result to be a theorem there *must* be a proof. We use the heading not necessarily to give a complete proof in the text, but to give some direction to where a proof can be found or an indication of how it can be constructed.

Supplementary Materials

■ *A Student Survival Manual*   by Ken Seydel offers a running commentary of hints and suggestions to help assure the students' success in calculus. In addition, this manual contains detailed solutions to most odd-numbered problems in the book.

■ *Student Mathematics Handbook*   by Karl J. Smith offers a review of prerequisite material, a catalog of curves, and a complete integral table. This handbook is presented free of charge along with the purchase of a new book.

■ *Technology Manuals*   by Jack Cohen and Frank Hagin offer technology-based applications keyed to the sections in the book. These manuals are identical except for the specific keystrokes. The following manuals are available at low cost when wrapped with the text:

> Calculus Explorations with TI Calculators
> Calculus Explorations with HP Calculators
> Calculus Explorations with MATLAB
> Calculus Explorations with Maple
> Calculus Explorations with Mathematica

Each of these manuals is closely keyed to the text. Selected computational windows from each text chapter are repeated in the manual with the appropriate key strokes provided. Additional technology problem sets and projects are also provided. Students *could* pick the technology manual that matches *their* technology choice and all students would still receive the same calculus course.

■ *Instructor's Technology Manual*   by Jack Cohen and Frank Hagin. Solutions to the Technology Manuals problem sets. Available free to instructors upon request.

■ *A Complete Solutions Manual*   by Henri Feiner, available free to instructors upon text adoption, contains a brief solution for every problem in the book.

■ *Instructor's Guide*   offers sample tests and reviews for each chapter in the book. This guide also includes sample transparency masters.

■ *Computerized Testing Program*   is available in both IBM and Macintosh formats.

■ *Visual Calculus,*   by David Schneider (University of Maryland), is a superb piece of software that offers a highly student-friendly approach to graphics and is closely keyed to the text.

■ *Resources for Calculus, Volumes 1-5,*   A. Wayne Roberts (Project Director) is available from the Mathematical Association of America, 1993:

> Dudley, Underwood (ed), *Readings for Calculus,* MAA Notes, No. 31
> Fraga, Robert (ed), *Calculus Problems for a New Century,* MAA Notes, No. 28
> Jackson, Michael B., and Ramsay, John, (eds) *Problems for Student Investigation,* MAA Notes, No. 30
> Snow, Anita E. (ed), *Learning by Discovery: A Lab Manual for Calculus,* MAA Notes No. 27
> Straffin, Philip (ed), *Applications of Calculus,* MAA Notes, No. 29

This is a valuable collection of resource materials for calculus instructors. All material may be reproduced for classroom use.

Acknowledgements

The writing and publishing of a calculus book is a tremendous undertaking. We take this responsibility very seriously, because a calculus book is instrumental in transmitting knowledge from one generation to the next. We would like to thank the many people who helped us in the preparation of this book. First, we thank our editor George Lobell, who led us masterfully through the development and

publication of this book. Our sincere appreciation to development editor Alan
MacDonell, who read and critiqued each word of the manuscript, pored over each
and every figure, often several times, and worked tirelessly on the project (except
when he went to Paris!). We also appreciate the work of production editor Ed
Thomas, who kept us all on track. Ed's meticulous attention to detail was
extraordinary. We would also like to thank Priscilla McGeehon, who helped a
great deal in the early stages, and Ray Mullaney, director of development for
engineering, math, and science textbooks.

Of primary concern is the accuracy of the book. We had the assistance of
many: Henri Feiner, who worked all of the problems (sometimes more than once),
Ken Seydel, who offered us many valuable suggestions, Diana Gerardi, who read
every word and checked the accuracy of the problems, and Kurt Norlin and Terri
Bittner at Laurel Technical and Mary Toscano at Toscano, who provided us a
double back-up check of all of the problems.

Members of the focus group: We would like to acknowledge and thank each
member of the focus group who met with us one weekend in San Francisco to
critique the manuscript on a page-by-page basis. We are convinced that the book is
better because of their contributions.

Neil Berger, University of Illinois at Chicago
Dan Chiddix, Ricks College
Lawrence J. Kratz, Idaho State University
John C. Michels, Chemeketa Community College

Reviewers of this edition:

Neil Berger, University of Illinois at Chicago
Michael L. Berry, West Virginia Wesleyan College
Barbara H. Briggs, Tennessee Technical University
Robert Broschat, South Dakota State University
Robert D. Brown, University of Kansas
Dan Chiddix, Ricks College
Philip Crooke, Vanderbilt University
Ken Dunn, Dalhousie University
John H. Ellison, Grove City College
William P. Francis, Michigan Technological University
Harvey Greenwald, California Polytechnic San Luis Obispo
Richard Hitt, University of South Alabama
Joel W. Irish, University of Southern Maine
Clement T. Jeske, University of Wisconsin–Platteville
Lawrence Kratz, Idaho State University
Sam Lessing, Northeast Missouri University
Estela S. Llinas, University of Pittsburgh at Greensburg
Pauline Lowman, Western Kentucky University
William E. Mastrocola, Colgate University
Philip W. McCartney, Northern Kentucky University
E.D. McCune, Stephen F. Austin State University
John C. Michels, Chemeketa Community College
Pamela B. Pierce, College of Wooster
Connie Schrock, Emporia State University
Tatiana Shubin, San Jose State University
Tingxiu Wang, Oakton Community College

Gerald L. Bradley
Karl J. Smith

INSTRUCTOR'S EDITION
CALCULUS

1

Preview of Calculus: Functions and Limits

PREVIEW

This chapter introduces you to those concepts that are essential for the study of calculus. We begin by asking the question, "What is Calculus?" We shall see that calculus is used to model many aspects of the world about us, so we spend a little time discussing what is meant by mathematical modeling. The necessary prerequisites for this course are reviewed in a companion book, *Student Mathematics Handbook and Integration Table for CALCULUS*, and are briefly discussed in this chapter.

Most ideas in calculus have useful geometric interpretations and can be visualized in terms of functions. Therefore, we complete this preliminary chapter by discussing the basic properties of functions and by showing how functions can be represented geometrically. An essential feature of calculus involves making "infinitesimally small" changes in a quantity, and we give precise meaning to this notion by introducing and exploring the *limit of a function* and a related concept known as *continuity*.

PERSPECTIVE

Change is a fact of our daily lives. Physical scientists use mathematical models to investigate phenomena such as the motion of planets, the decay of radioactive substances, chemical reaction rates, ocean currents, and weather patterns. Economists and business managers examine consumer trends; psychologists study learning tendencies; and ecologists explore patterns of pollution and population changes involving complex relationships among species. Even areas such as political science and medicine use mathematical models in which change is the key ingredient.

Although modern science requires the use of many different skills and procedures, calculus is the primary mathematical tool for dealing with change. Sir Isaac Newton, one of the discoverers of calculus, once remarked that to accomplish his results, he "stood on the shoulders of giants." Indeed, calculus was not born in a moment of divine inspiration, but developed gradually, as a variety of apparently different ideas and methods merged into a coherent pattern. The purpose of this initial chapter is to lay the foundation for the development of calculus.

1.1 WHAT IS CALCULUS?

IN THIS SECTION   The limit: Zeno's paradox, the derivative: the tangent problem, the integral: the area problem, mathematical modeling
We informally introduce you to the three main topics of calculus: the concepts of limit, derivative, and integral.

ELEMENTARY MATHEMATICS

1. Slope of a line

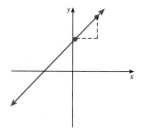

2. Tangent line to a circle

3. Area of a region bounded by line segments

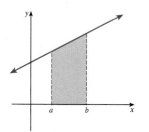

4. Average changes in position and velocity

5. Average of a finite collection of numbers

Figure 1.1 Topics from elementary mathematics

In the article "The Calculus According to Newton and Leibniz," C. H. Edwards writes

> *If there is an event that marked the coming of age of mathematics in Western culture, it must surely be the essentially simultaneous development of the calculus by Newton and Leibniz in the seventeenth century.* Before this remarkable synthesis, mathematics had often been viewed as merely a strange but harmless pursuit, indulged in by those with an excess of leisure time. After the calculus, mathematics became virtually the only acceptable language for describing the physical universe. This view of mathematics and its association with the scientific method has come to dominate the Western view of how the world ought to be explained. This domination is so complete that it is virtually impossible for us to understand how earlier cultures explained what happened around them.†*

What distinguishes calculus from your previous mathematics courses of algebra, geometry, and trigonometry is the transition from static or discrete applications (see Figure 1.1) to those that are dynamic or continuous (see Figure 1.2). For example, in elementary mathematics you considered the slope of a line, but in calculus we define the (nonconstant) slope of a nonlinear curve. In elementary mathematics you found average changes in quantities such as the position and velocity of a moving object, but in calculus we can find instantaneous changes in the same quantities. In elementary mathematics you found the average of a finite collection of numbers, but in calculus we can find the average value of a function with infinitely many values over an interval.

You might think of calculus as the culmination of all of your mathematical studies. To a certain extent that is true, but it is also the beginning of your study of mathematics as it applies to the real world around us. Calculus is a three-semester or four-quarter course that *begins* your college work in mathematics. All your prior work in mathematics is considered elementary mathematics, with calculus the dividing line between elementary mathematics and mathematics as it is used in a variety of theoretical and applied topics. It is the mathematics of motion and change.

The development of calculus in the seventeenth century by Newton and Leibniz was the result of their attempt to answer some fundamental questions about the world and the way things work. These investigations led to two fundamental concepts of calculus—namely, the idea of a *derivative* and that of an *integral*. The breakthrough in the development of these concepts was the formulation of a mathematical tool called a *limit*.

1. Limit: The limit is a mathematical tool for studying the *tendency* of a function as its variable *approaches* some value. Calculus is based on the concept of limit. We introduce the limit of a function informally in Section 1.5 and then examine the concept more formally in Section 1.8.

2. Derivative: The derivative is defined as a limit, and it is used initially to

*For a brief history of calculus see the Guest Essay at the end of this chapter.
†C. H. Edwards, Jr., "The Calculus According to Newton and Leibniz," in *The Historical Development of the Calculus* (New York: Springer-Verlag, 1979).

compute rates of change and slopes of tangent lines to curves. The study of derivatives is called *differential calculus.* Derivatives can be used in sketching graphs and in finding the extreme (largest and smallest) values of functions. The derivative is introduced and developed in Chapter 2, and its applications are examined in Chapter 3.

3. **Integral:** The integral is found by taking a special limit of a sum of terms, and the study of this process is called *integral calculus.* Area, volume, arc length, work, and hydrostatic force are a few of the many quantities that can be expressed as integrals. Integrals and their applications are studied in Chapters 4 and 6.

We will briefly describe each of these concepts later in this section. First, let us return to Edwards's description about the foundation of calculus:

One might naturally suppose that an event so momentous must involve ideas so profound that average mortals can hardly hope to comprehend them. In fact, nothing could be further from the truth. The essential ideas of calculus—the derivative and the integral—are quite straightforward and had been known prior to either Newton or Leibniz. The contribution of Newton and Leibniz was to recognize that the idea of finding tangents (the derivative) and the idea of finding areas (the integral) are related and that this relation can be used to give a simple and unified description of both processes. When calculus is described in this way one might wonder what all the fuss is about.

Let us begin by taking an intuitive look at each of these three essential ideas of calculus.

■ THE LIMIT: ZENO'S PARADOX

In the guest essay at the end of this chapter, John Troutman mentions Zeno's paradoxes, which are concerned with infinite processes. Zeno (ca. 500 B.C.) was a Greek philosopher who is known primarily for his famous paradoxes. One of these concerns a race between Achilles, a legendary Greek hero, and a tortoise. When the race begins, the (slower) tortoise is given a head start, as shown in Figure 1.3.

CALCULUS

1. Slope of a curve

2. Tangent line to a general curve

3. Area of a region bounded by curves

4. Instantaneous changes in position and velocity
5. Average of an infinite collection of numbers

Figure 1.2 Topics from calculus

Figure 1.3 Achilles and the tortoise

Is it possible for Achilles to overtake the tortoise? Zeno pointed out that by the time Achilles reaches the tortoise's starting point, $a_1 = t_0$, the tortoise will have moved ahead to a new point t_1. When Achilles gets to this next point, a_2, the tortoise will be at a new point t_2. The tortoise, even though much slower than Achilles, keeps moving forward. Although the distance between Achilles and the tortoise is getting smaller and smaller the tortoise will apparently always be ahead.

Of course, common sense tells us that Achilles will overtake the slow tortoise,

Historical Note

The numeration system we use evolved over a long period of time. It is often called the *Hindu-Arabic* system because its origins can be traced back to the Hindus in Bactria (now Afghanistan). Later, in A.D. 700, India was invaded by the Arabs, who used and modified the Hindu numeration system and in turn introduced it to Western civilization. The Hindu Brahmagupta stated the rules for operations with positive and negative numbers in the seventh century A.D. There are some indications that the Chinese had some knowledge of negative numbers as early as 200 B.C. On the other hand, the Western mathematician Girolamo Cardan (1501–1576) was calling numbers such as (-1) absurd as late as 1545.

but where is the error in reasoning? The error is in the assumption that an infinite amount of time is required to cover a distance divided into an infinite number of segments. This discussion is getting at an essential idea in calculus, the notion of a limit.

Consider the successive positions for both Achilles and the tortoise:

$$Starting\ position$$
$$\downarrow$$

Achilles: $a_0, a_1, a_2, a_3, a_4, \ldots$
Tortoise: $t_0, t_1, t_2, t_3, t_4, \ldots$

After the start, the positions for Achilles, as well as those for the tortoise, form sets of positions that are ordered with positive integers. Such ordered listings are called *sequences*.

For Achilles and the tortoise we have two sequences $\{a_1, a_2, a_3, \ldots, a_n, \ldots\}$ and $\{t_1, t_2, t_3, \ldots, t_n, \ldots\}$ where $a_n < t_n$ for all values of n. We will see in Chapter 8 that both the sequence for Achilles' position and the sequence for the tortoise's position have limits, and it is precisely at that limit point that Achilles overtakes the tortoise. The idea of limit is introduced in this chapter and is used to define the other two basic concepts of calculus: the derivative and the integral. Even if the solution to Zeno's paradox using limits seems unnatural at first, do not be discouraged. It took over 2000 years to refine the ideas of Zeno and provide conclusive answers to those questions about limits that will be introduced in this chapter. We revisit Zeno's paradox in Problem Set 8.2.

EXAMPLE 1   An intuitive preview of a limit

The sequence

$$\tfrac{1}{2}, \tfrac{2}{3}, \tfrac{3}{4}, \tfrac{4}{5}, \ldots$$

can be described by writing a *general term*: $\dfrac{n}{n+1}$ where $n = 1, 2, 3, 4, \ldots$.
Can you guess the limit, L, of this sequence?

Solution
PREVIEW: The *limit* is an important idea in calculus, and we discuss this concept extensively later in this chapter. We will say that L is the number that the sequence with general term $\dfrac{n}{n+1}$ tends toward as n becomes large without bound. We will define a notation to summarize this idea:

$$L = \lim_{n \to \infty} \frac{n}{n+1}$$

As you consider larger and larger values for n you find a sequence of fractions:

$$\tfrac{1}{2}, \tfrac{2}{3}, \tfrac{3}{4}, \ldots, \tfrac{1{,}000}{1{,}001}, \tfrac{1{,}001}{1{,}002}, \ldots, \tfrac{9{,}999{,}999}{10{,}000{,}000}, \ldots$$

It is reasonable to guess that the sequence of fractions is approaching the number 1.   ▬

■ THE DERIVATIVE: THE TANGENT PROBLEM

A **tangent line** (or, if the context is clear, simply tangent) to a circle at a given point P is a line that intersects the circle at P and only at P. This characterization does not apply for curves in general, as you can see by looking at Figure 1.4.

At each point P on a circle, there is only one line that intersects the circle exactly once.

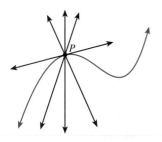

At a point P on a curve, there may be several lines that intersect the curve only once.

Figure 1.4 Tangent line

In order to find a tangent line, begin by considering a line that passes through two points on the curve, as shown in Figure 1.5a. This line is called a **secant line.**

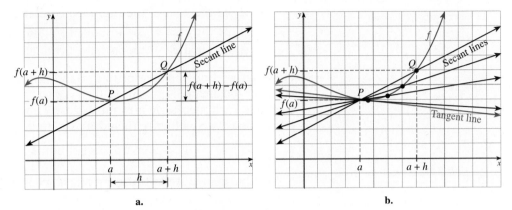

a.   b.

Figure 1.5 Secant line

The coordinates of the two points P and Q are $P(a, f(a))$ and $Q(a + h, f(a + h))$. The slope of the secant line is

$$m = \frac{f(a + h) - f(a)}{h}$$

Recall from algebra that the slope of any line is defined to be rise/run. Can you see how this formula for the slope of the secant line fits the model of "rise/run"? Now imagine that Q moves along the curve toward P, as shown in Figure 1.5b. You can see that the secant line approaches a limiting position as h approaches zero. In Section 2.1 we define this limiting position to be the tangent line. The slope of the tangent line is defined as a limit of the sequence of slopes of a set of secant lines.

PREVIEW: Once again, we can use limit notation to summarize this idea: We say that the slopes of the secant lines as h becomes small, tend toward a number which we call the slope of the tangent line. We will define the following notation to summarize this idea:

$$\lim_{h \to 0} \frac{f(a + h) - f(a)}{h}$$

■ THE INTEGRAL: THE AREA PROBLEM

You probably know the formula for the area of a circle with radius r:

$$A = \pi r^2$$

The Egyptians were the first to use this formula over 5,000 years ago, but the Greek Archimedes (287?–212 B.C.) showed how to derive the formula for the area of a circle by using a limiting process. Consider the area of inscribed polygons, as shown in Figure 1.6.

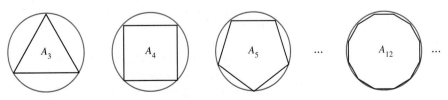

Figure 1.6 Approximating the area of a circle

Even though Archimedes did not use the following notation, here is the essence of what he did, using a method called "exhaustion":

Let A_3 be the area of the inscribed equilateral triangle;
  A_4 be the area of the inscribed square; and
  A_5 be the area of the inscribed regular pentagon.

How can we find the area of this circle? As you can see from Figure 1.6, if we consider the area of A_3, then A_4, then A_5, . . . we should have a sequence of areas such that each successive area more closely approximates that of the circle. Later in this book, we will write this idea as a limit statement:

$$A = \lim_{n \to \infty} A_n$$

In this course we will use limits in yet a different way to find the area of regions enclosed by curves. For example, consider the area shown in color in Figure 1.7. We can approximate the area by using rectangles. If A_n is the area of the nth rectangle, then the total area can be approximated by finding the sum

$$A_1 + A_2 + A_3 + \cdots + A_{n-1} + A_n$$

This process is shown in Figure 1.8.

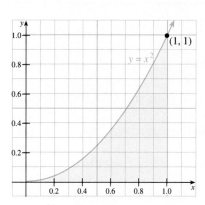

Figure 1.7 Area under a curve

a. 8 approximating rectangles

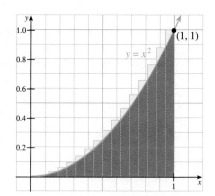

b. 16 approximating rectangles

Figure 1.8 Approximating the area using circumscribed rectangles

The area problem leads to a process called *integration*, and the study of integration forms what is called **integral calculus.** Similar reasoning allows us to calculate such things as volumes, the length of a curve, the average value of a function, or the amount of work required for a particular task.

■ MATHEMATICAL MODELING

A real-life situation is usually far too complicated to be precisely and mathematically defined. When confronted with a problem in the real world, therefore, it is usually necessary to develop a mathematical framework based on certain assumptions about the real world. This framework can then be used to find a solution to the real-world problem. The process of developing this body of mathematics is referred to as **mathematical modeling.**

Some mathematical models are quite accurate, particularly those used in the physical sciences. For example, one of the first models we will consider in calculus is a model for the path of a projectile. Other rather precise models predict such things as the time of sunrise and sunset, or the speed at which an object falls in a vacuum. Some mathematical models, however, are less accurate, especially those that involve examples from the life sciences and social sciences. Only recently has modeling in these disciplines become precise enough to be expressed in terms of calculus.

What, precisely, is a mathematical model? Sometimes, mathematical modeling can mean nothing more than a textbook word problem. But mathematical modeling can also mean choosing appropriate mathematics to solve a problem that has previously been unsolved. In this book, we use the term mathematical modeling to mean something between these two extremes. That is, it is a process we will apply to some real-life problem that does not have an obvious solution. It usually cannot be solved by applying a single formula.

The first step of what we call mathematical modeling involves *abstraction*.

With the method of abstraction, certain assumptions about the real world are made, variables are defined, and appropriate mathematics is developed. The next step is to simplify the mathematics or derive related mathematical facts from the mathematical model.

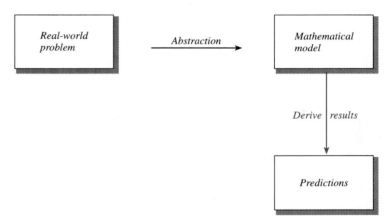

The results derived from the mathematical model should lead us to some predictions about the real world. The next step is to gather data from the situation being modeled and then to compare those data with the predictions. If the two do

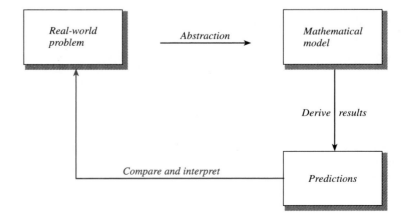

How Global Climate Is Modeled

We find a good example of mathematical modeling by looking at the work being done with weather prediction. In theory, if the correct assumptions could be programmed into a computer, along with appropriate mathematical statements of the ways global climate conditions operate, we would have a model to predict the weather throughout the world. In the global climate model, a system of equations calculates time-dependent changes in wind as well as temperature and moisture changes in the atmosphere and on the land. The model may also predict alterations in the temperature of the ocean's surface. At the National Center for Atmospheric Research, they use a CRAY supercomputer to do this modeling.

From *Scientific American*, March 1991.

not agree, then the gathered data are used to modify the assumptions used in the model.

Mathematical modeling is an ongoing process. As long as the predictions match the real world, the assumptions made about the real world are regarded as correct, as are the defined variables. On the other hand, as discrepancies are noticed, it is necessary to construct a closer and more dependable mathematical model. You might wish to read the article from *Scientific American* quoted in the margin.

PROBLEM SET 1.1   See *Student Survival Manual* for hints to odd-numbered problems.

A 1. ■ **What Does This Say?*** What is a mathematical model?

2. ■ **What Does This Say?** Why are mathematical models necessary or useful?

3. ■ **What Does This Say?** An analogy to Zeno's tortoise paradox can be made as follows. A woman standing in a room cannot walk to a wall. In order to do so, she would first have to go half the distance, then half the remaining distance, and then again half of what still remains. This process can always be continued and thus never ends. Draw an appropriate figure for this problem and then present some sort of an argument using sequences to show that the woman will, indeed, reach the wall.

4. ■ **What Does This Say?** Zeno's paradoxes remind us of an argument that might lead to an absurd conclusion: *Suppose I am playing baseball and decide to steal second base. To run from first to second base, I must first go half the distance, then half the remaining distance, and then again half of what remains. This process is continued so that I never reach second base. Therefore it is pointless to steal second base.* Draw an appropriate figure for this problem, and then present a mathematical argument using sequences to show that the conclusion is absurd.

5. Consider the sequence 0.3, 0.33, 0.333, 0.3333, ... What do you think is the appropriate limit of this sequence?

6. Consider the sequence 0.2, 0.27, 0.272, 0.2727, ... What do you think is the appropriate limit of this sequence?

7. Consider the sequence 3, 3.1, 3.14, 3.141, 3.1415, 3.14159, 3.141592, ... What do you think is the appropriate limit of this sequence?

8. Consider the sequence 1, 1.4, 1.41, 1.412, 1.41421, 1.414213, 1.4142135, ... What do you think is the appropriate limit of this sequence?

In Problems 9–12, guess the requested limits.

9. $\lim\limits_{n \to \infty} \dfrac{2n}{n + 4}$ 10. $\lim\limits_{n \to \infty} \dfrac{2n}{3n + 1}$

11. $\lim\limits_{n \to \infty} \dfrac{3n}{n^2 + 2}$ 12. $\lim\limits_{n \to \infty} \dfrac{3n^2 + 1}{2n^2 - 1}$

13. Copy the following figures on your paper. Draw what you think is an appropriate tangent line for each curve at the point *P*.

a.

b.

c.

d.

B 14. Suppose the circle in Figure 1.6 has radius 1. We know from the area formula that the area of the circle is $A = \pi(1)^2 = \pi$. Find the sequence of areas for the inscribed polygons $A_3, A_4, A_5, \ldots$ and show that these areas form a sequence of numbers that seems to have a limit π.

15. Repeat Problem 14 for a circle with radius 2. What is the apparent value of the new limit?

16. Calculate the sum of the areas of the rectangles shown in Figure 1.8a.

17. Calculate the sum of the areas of the rectangles shown in Figure 1.8b.

18. Use the results of Problems 16 and 17 to see if you can make a guess about the shaded area under the curve $y = x^2$ from $x = 0$ to $x = 1$.

* Many problems in this book are labeled **What Does This Say?** Following the question will be a question for you to answer in your own words, or a statement for you to rephrase in your own words. These problems are intended to be similar to the "What This Says" boxes that appear throughout the book.

1.2 PRELIMINARIES

> **IN THIS SECTION** Distance on a number line, absolute value, distance in the plane, trigonometry
> We begin by reviewing one- and two-dimensional coordinate systems, absolute value, absolute value equations and inequalities, and trigonometric equations. These topics are needed for our work in calculus.

Every mathematical book that is worth reading must be read "backwards and forwards," if I may use the expression. I would modify Lagrange's advice a little and say, "Go on, but often return to strengthen your faith." When you come on a hard and dreary passage, pass it over; come back to it after you have seen its importance or found its importance or found the need for it further on.

George Chrystal, *Algebra*, Part 2
(Edinburgh, 1889)

This section provides a quick review of some fundamental concepts and techniques from precalculus mathematics. If you have recently had a precalculus course you could skip over this section.

Algebra, geometry, and trigonometry are important ingredients of calculus. Even though we will review many ideas from algebra, geometry, and trigonometry, we will not be able to develop every idea from these courses before we use it in calculus. For example, the law of cosines from trigonometry may be needed to solve a problem in a section that never mentions trigonometry in the exposition. For this reason, we have made available a separate reference manual *Student Mathematics Handbook and Integration Table for CALCULUS*, which includes the background material you will need for this course. We suggest that you keep it close at hand. References to this handbook are indicated by the logo (SMH) .

■ DISTANCE ON A NUMBER LINE

You are probably familiar with the set of **real numbers** as well as with various of its subsets, including the counting or natural numbers, the integers, the rational numbers, and the irrational numbers.

The real numbers can most easily be visualized by using a **one-dimensional coordinate system** called a **real number line,** as shown in Figure 1.9.

Notice that a number a is less than a number b if it is to the left of b on a real number line, as shown in Figure 1.10.

Figure 1.9 Real number line

Figure 1.10 Geometric definition of *less than*

Similar definitions can be given for $a > b$, $a \leq b$, and $a \geq b$.

The location of the number 0 is chosen arbitrarily, and a unit distance is picked (meters, feet, inches, . . .). Numbers are ordered on the real number line according to the following order properties.

⊘ Watch for these symbols. We use them to warn you of common mistakes as well as those things you should remember. ⊘

Order Properties

For all real numbers a, b, and c:

Trichotomy law: Exactly one of the following is true:
$$a < b, \ a > b, \text{ or } a = b$$

Transitive law of inequality: If $a < b$ and $b < c$, then $a < c$.

Additive law of inequality: If $a < c$ and $b < d$, then $a + b < c + d$.

Multiplicative law of inequality: If $a < b$, then
$$ac < bc \text{ if } c > 0 \text{ and } ac > bc \text{ if } c < 0$$

■ ABSOLUTE VALUE

Absolute Value

The **absolute value** of a real number a, denoted by $|a|$, is

$$|a| = \begin{cases} a & \text{if } a \geq 0 \\ -a & \text{if } a < 0 \end{cases}$$

⊘ $|a|$ is NOT the number a without its sign. ⊘

The number x is located $|x|$ units away from 0 — to the right if $x > 0$ and to the left if $x < 0$.

Absolute value is used to describe the distance between points on a number line.

Distance Between Two Points on a Number Line

The **distance** between the numbers x_1 and x_2 on a number line is

$$|x_2 - x_1|$$

⊘ Recall that
$|x_2 - x_1| = |x_1 - x_2|$ ⊘

For example, the distance between 2 and -3 is $|2 - (-3)| = 5$ units.

Several properties of absolute value that you will need in this course are summarized in Table 1.1.

TABLE 1.1 Properties of Absolute Value

Let a and b be any real numbers:

Property	Comment
1. $|a| \geq 0$	**1.** Absolute value is nonnegative.
2. $|-a| = |a|$	**2.** The absolute value of a number and the absolute value of its opposite are equal.
3. $|a|^2 = a^2$	**3.** If an absolute value is squared, the absolute value can be dropped because both squares are nonnegative.
4. $|ab| = |a||b|$	**4.** The absolute value of a product is the product of the absolute values.
5. $\left|\dfrac{a}{b}\right| = \dfrac{|a|}{|b|}, b \neq 0$	**5.** The absolute value of a quotient is the quotient of the absolute values.
6. $-|a| \leq a \leq |a|$	**6.** Any number a is between the absolute value of that number and its opposite, inclusive.
7. Let $b \geq 0$; $|a| = b$ if and only if $a = \pm b$	**7.** This property is useful in solving absolute value equations.
8. Let $b > 0$; $|a| < b$ if and only if $-b < a < b$	**8 and 9.** These are the main properties used in solving absolute value inequalities.
9. Let $b > 0$; $|a| > b$ if and only if $a > b$ or $a < -b$	
10. $|a + b| \leq |a| + |b|$	**10.** This property is called the **triangle inequality**. It is used in both theory and numerical computations involving inequalities.

⊘ "p if and only if q" is used to mean that both a statement and its converse are true; that is: If p, then q, *and* if q, then p. For example, Property 8 has two parts:
1. If $|a| < b$, then $-b < a < b$.
2. If $-b < a < b$, then $|a| < b$. ⊘

Property 7 is sometimes stated as $|a| = |b|$ if and only if $a = \pm b$. Since $|b| = \pm b$, it follows that this property is equivalent to Property 7. Also, Properties 8 and 9 are true for $\leq$ and $\geq$ inequalities. Specifically, if $b > 0$, then

$$|a| \leq b \text{ if and only if } -b \leq a \leq b$$

and

$$|a| \geq b \text{ if and only if } a \geq b \text{ or } a \leq -b$$

A convenient notation for representing intervals on a number line is called *interval notation* and is summarized in the accompanying table. Note that a solid dot (•) at an endpoint of an interval indicates that the endpoint is included in the interval, while an open dot (∘) indicates that the endpoint is excluded. An interval is *bounded* if both its endpoints are real numbers. A bounded interval is *open* if it includes neither endpoint, *half-open* if it includes only one endpoint, and *closed* if it includes both endpoints. The symbol "∞" (pronounced *infinity*) is used for intervals that are not limited in one direction or another. In particular, $(-\infty, \infty)$ denotes the entire number line. If this notation is new to you, please check the *Handbook* for further examples. We will use interval notation to write the solutions of absolute value equations and inequalities.

$\boxed{\text{s}^{\text{M}}\text{H}}$

Name of Interval	Inequality Notation	Interval Notation	Graph
Closed interval	$a \leq x \leq b$	$[a, b]$	
	$a \leq x$	$[a, \infty)$	
	$x \leq b$	$(-\infty, b]$	
Open interval	$a < x < b$	(a, b)	
	$a < x$	(a, ∞)	
	$x < b$	$(-\infty, b)$	
Half-open interval	$a < x \leq b$	$(a, b]$	
	$a \leq x < b$	$[a, b)$	
Real number line	All real numbers	$(-\infty, \infty)$	

Absolute Value Equations Absolute value property 7 allows us to solve absolute value equations easily. Here is an example.

EXAMPLE 1 **Solving an equation with an absolute value on one side**

Solve $|2x - 6| = x$.

Solution   If $2x - 6 \geq 0$, then $2x - 6 = x$ or $x = 6$

   If $2x - 6 < 0$, then $-(2x - 6) = x$

$$-3x = -6$$
$$x = 2$$

The solutions are $x = 6$ and $x = 2$.

Computational Window—Graphing Calculators

You can solve equations to any reasonable degree of accuracy by graphing on a calculator or computer. Look at Example 1. You can graph two functions, $y_1 = |2x - 6|$ and $y_2 = x$, and then find their intersection. For the absolute value function, look for a key labeled (ABS). Enter Y1=ABS(2X − 6) and Y2=X. When we show calculator graphs in this book we will show them just as you will see them on a calculator, without scale and without labeling. There are many considerations of scale, limitations on the x-axis and the y-axis, which we will discuss from time to time in these special computational window boxes.

The (TRACE) key allows us to find approximate coordinates of points on the curves. For Example 1 we find X=2, Y=2 and X=6, Y=6 as possible points of intersection. Checking $x = 2$ and $x = 6$ in the original equation, we can verify the solution. There is also a key called (ZOOM) that allows you to enlarge (zoom in) or shrink (zoom out). Finally, you can press (RANGE) to reset the scale. Example 1, with a scale with $0 \le x \le 10$ and $0 \le y \le 10$, is shown at the right. We will frequently show you a graph similar to the one you would obtain on your calculator but with some scale and other designations to help you relate the geometric solution to the algebraic one. We will do this without using a special computational window format, as shown after the following example.

```
Y1Babs (2X-6)
Y2BX
Xmin=-10  Ymin=-10
Xmax=10   Ymax=10
Xscl=1    Yscl=1
```

```
Y1Babs (2X-6)
Y2BX
Xmin=0    Ymin=0
Xmax=10   Ymax=10
Xscl=1    Yscl=1
```

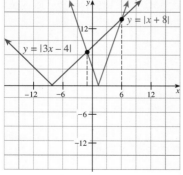

The points of intersection of $y = |x + 8|$ and $y = |3x - 4|$ are at $x = -1$ and $x = 6$.

If you are solving an absolute value equation with absolute value on both sides of the equation, then you still use Property 7 and proceed as shown in Example 1.

EXAMPLE 2   Solving an equation with absolute value on both sides

Solve $|x + 8| = |3x - 4|$

Solution

$$x + 8 = 3x - 4 \qquad \text{or} \qquad x + 8 = -(3x - 4) \quad \textit{Property 7}$$
$$-2x = -12 \qquad\qquad\qquad 4x = -4$$
$$x = 6 \qquad\qquad\qquad\qquad x = -1$$

A graphical solution for Example 2 is shown in the margin. Notice that the points of intersection of the graphs of the functions on the left and the right sides represents the solution.

The absolute value expression $|x - a|$ can be interpreted as the distance between x and a on a number line. An equation of the form

$$|x - a| = b$$

is satisfied by two values of x that are a given distance b from a when represented on a number line. For example, $|x - 5| = 3$ states that x is 3 units from 5 on a number line. Thus, x is either 2 or 8.

Geometric representation   *Algebraic representation*

$$|x - 5| = 3$$
$$x - 5 = \pm 3$$
$$x = 5 \pm 3$$
$$= 8 \text{ or } 2$$

Absolute Value Inequalities Because $|x - 5| = 3$ states that the distance from x to 5 is 3 units, the inequality $|x - 5| < 3$ states that the distance from x to 5 is less than 3 units, while $|x - 5| > 3$ states that the distance from x to 5 is greater than 3 units.

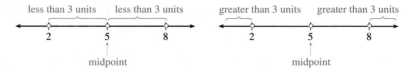

This number-line solution is a one-dimensional interpretation of an absolute value inequality. For a two-dimensional interpretation with a graphing calculator, graph $y_1 = |x - 5|$ and $y_2 = 3$, and then look at the x-values for which $y_1 = y_2$, $y_1 < y_2$, or $y_1 > y_2$, as shown in Figure 1.11.

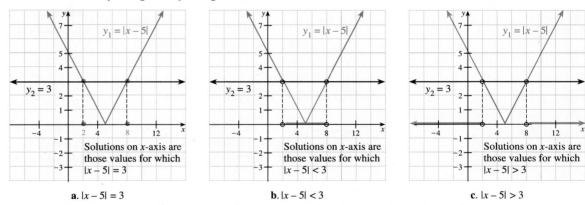

Figure 1.11 Two-dimensional graphs for absolute value inequalities

EXAMPLE 3   Solving an absolute value inequality

Solve $|2x - 3| \leq 4$.

Solution   Algebraic solution:

$$-4 \leq 2x - 3 \leq 4 \qquad \textit{Property 8}$$
$$-4 + 3 \leq 2x - 3 + 3 \leq 4 + 3$$
$$-1 \leq 2x \leq 7$$
$$-\frac{1}{2} \leq \frac{2x}{2} \leq \frac{7}{2}$$
$$-\frac{1}{2} \leq x \leq \frac{7}{2}$$

The solution is the interval $\left[-\frac{1}{2}, \frac{7}{2}\right]$.

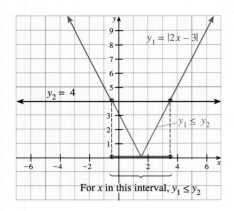

For x in this interval, $y_1 \leq y_2$

Geometric solution: Graph $y_1 = |2x - 3|$ and $y_2 = 4$. Because we are looking for $|2x - 3| \leq 4$, we note those x-values on the real number line for which the graph of y_1 is below the graph of y_2. We see that the interval is $[-0.5, 3.5]$ or $\left[-\frac{1}{2}, \frac{7}{2}\right]$.   ▬

When absolute value is applied to measurement it is called **tolerance**. Tolerance is an allowable deviation from a standard. An example of a cement bag with a weight of w lb is "90 lb plus or minus 2 lb" might be described as having a weight given by $|w - 90| \leq 2$. When considered as a tolerance, the expression $|x - a| \leq b$ may be interpreted as x being compared to a having an **absolute error** of measurement of b units. Consider the following example.

EXAMPLE 4   Absolute value as a tolerance

Suppose a 90-lb bag of cement is purchased. It will not be exactly 90 lb. The material must be measured, and the measurement is approximate. Some bags will be a little over 90 lb, and some will be a little under 90 lb, perhaps by a couple of pounds. If so, the bag could weigh as much as 92 lb and as little as 88 lb. State this as an absolute value inequality.

Solution   Let w = weight of the bag of cement in pounds. Then

$$88 \leq \quad w \quad \leq 92$$
$$88 - 90 \leq w - 90 \leq 92 - 90 \qquad \textit{Subtract 90 from each}$$
$$-2 \leq w - 90 \leq 2 \qquad \qquad \textit{member, because this is the}$$
$$\textit{average of the extremes.}$$

Equivalently, $|w - 90| \leq 2$.   ▬

■ DISTANCE IN THE PLANE

Absolute value is used to find the distance between two points on a number line. In order to find the distance between two points in a coordinate plane, we use the *distance formula*, which is derived by using the Pythagorean theorem.

THEOREM 1.1   Distance between two points in the plane

The distance d between the points $P_1(x_1, y_1)$ and $P_2(x_2, y_2)$ in the plane is given by

$$d = \sqrt{(\Delta x)^2 + (\Delta y)^2} = \sqrt{(x_2 - x_1)^2 + (y_2 - y_1)^2}$$

where Δx (read "delta x") is the **horizontal change** defined by the distance $x_2 - x_1$ and Δy (read "delta y") is the **vertical change** defined by $y_2 - y_1$.

Proof: Using the two points, form a right triangle by drawing lines through the given points parallel to the coordinate axes, as shown in Figure 1.12. The length of the horizontal side of the triangle is $|x_2 - x_1| = |\Delta x|$ and the length of the vertical side is $|y_2 - y_1| = |\Delta y|$. Then

$$d^2 = |\Delta x|^2 + |\Delta y|^2 \qquad \textit{Pythagorean theorem}$$
$$\textit{Absolute value property 3}$$
$$d^2 = (\Delta x)^2 + (\Delta y)^2$$
$$d = \sqrt{(\Delta x)^2 + (\Delta y)^2}$$

■

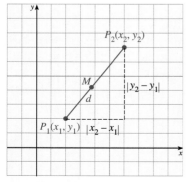

Figure 1.12 Distance formula

Midpoint Formula Related to the distance between two points is the formula for finding the midpoint of a line segment, as shown in Figure 1.12.

Midpoint Formula

The **midpoint**, M, of the segment with endpoints $P_1(x_1,y_1)$ and $P_2(x_2,y_2)$ has coordinates

$$M\left(\frac{x_1 + x_2}{2}, \frac{y_1 + y_2}{2}\right)$$

Notice that the coordinates of the midpoint of a segment are found by averaging the first and second components of the coordinates of the endpoints, respectively. You are asked to derive this formula in Problem 74.

Relationship Between an Equation and a Graph **Analytic geometry** is that branch of geometry that ties together the geometric concept of position with an algebraic representation, namely coordinates. For example, you remember from algebra that a line can be represented by an equation. Precisely what does this mean? Can we make a statement that is true for any curve, not just for lines? We answer in the affirmative with the following definition.

Graph of an Equation

The **graph of an equation,** in two variables x and y is the collection of all points $P(x, y)$ whose coordinates (x, y) satisfy the equation.

There are two frequently asked questions in analytic geometry:

1. Given a graph (a geometrical representation), find the corresponding equation.
2. Given an equation (an algebraic representation), find the corresponding graph.

In Example 5 we use the distance formula to derive the equation of a circle. This means that if x and y are numbers that satisfy the equation, then the point (x, y) will lie on the circle. Conversely, the coordinates of any point on the circle will satisfy the equation.

EXAMPLE 5   **Using the distance formula to derive an equation of a graph.**

Find the equation of a circle with center (h, k) and radius r.

Solution   Let (x, y) be any point on a circle. Recall that a circle is the set of all points in the plane a given distance from a given point. The given point, called the center, is (h, k) and the given distance, the radius, is r.

$$r = \text{DISTANCE FROM } (h, k) \text{ TO } (x, y)$$
$$r = \sqrt{(x - h)^2 + (y - k)^2}$$
$$r^2 = (x - h)^2 + (y - k)^2, \quad \text{or} \quad (x - h)^2 + (y - k)^2 = r^2 \qquad \blacksquare$$

Note that if $(h, k) = (0, 0)$ and $r = 1$, then the circle is called a **unit circle** and the equation is $x^2 + y^2 = 1$.

EXAMPLE 6   Finding the equation of a circle

Find the equation of the circle with center $(3, -5)$ that passes through the point $(1, 8)$.

Solution   See Figure 1.13. The radius is the distance from the center to the given point:

$$r = \sqrt{(1 - 3)^2 + [8 - (-5)]^2}$$
$$= \sqrt{4 + 169}$$
$$= \sqrt{173}$$

Thus, the equation of the circle is

$$(x - 3)^2 + [y - (-5)]^2 = (\sqrt{173})^2$$
$$(x - 3)^2 + (y + 5)^2 = 173$$

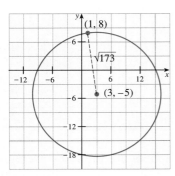

Figure 1.13 Circle with center $(3, -5)$ passing through $(1, 8)$

EXAMPLE 7   Finding the graph of a circle given its equation

Sketch the graph of the circle whose equation is

$$4x^2 + 4y^2 - 4x + 8y - 5 = 0$$

Solution   We need to convert this equation into standard form. To do this we use a process called **completing the square** (see *Student Mathematics Handbook*).

$$4x^2 + 4y^2 - 4x + 8y - 5 = 0$$

$$x^2 + y^2 - x + 2y = \tfrac{5}{4} \quad \text{\textit{Coefficients of squared terms should be 1.}}$$

$$(x^2 - x \quad\;) + (y^2 + 2y \quad\;) = \tfrac{5}{4} \quad \text{\textit{Associate x-terms and y-terms.}}$$

$$\left[x^2 - x + \left(-\tfrac{1}{2}\right)^2\right] + (y^2 + 2y + 1^2) = \tfrac{5}{4} + \tfrac{1}{4} + 1 \quad \text{\textit{Complete the squares by adding $\tfrac{1}{4}$ and 1 to both sides.}}$$

$$\left(x - \tfrac{1}{2}\right)^2 + (y + 1)^2 = \tfrac{10}{4} = \tfrac{5}{2}$$

This is a circle with center at $\left(\tfrac{1}{2}, -1\right)$ and radius $\sqrt{\tfrac{5}{2}}$. The graph is shown in Figure 1.14.

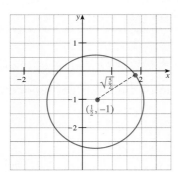

Figure 1.14 Sketch of $4x^2 + 4y^2 - 4x + 8y - 5 = 0$

■ TRIGONOMETRY

One of the prerequisites for this book is trigonometry. If you need some review, consult a text on trigonometry or the *Student Mathematics Handbook* that accompanies this book. Angles are commonly measured in degrees and radians. A degree is defined to be $\tfrac{1}{360}$ revolution and a radian $\tfrac{1}{2\pi}$ revolution. Thus, to convert between degree and radian measure use the following formula:

$$\frac{\theta \text{ measured in degrees}}{360} = \frac{\theta \text{ measured in radians}}{2\pi}$$

EXAMPLE 8   Converting degree measure to radian measure

Convert $255°$ to radian measure.

⊘ When angles are measured in calculus, radian measure is generally preferable to degree measure. For example, in Chapter 2 we will use the formula for the area of a sector, which requires that the angle be measured in radians. You may assume that when we write expressions such as $\sin x$, $\cos x$, and $\tan x$, the angle x is in radians unless otherwise specified by a degree symbol. ⊘

Solution
$$\frac{255}{360} = \frac{\theta}{2\pi}$$
$$\theta = \left(\frac{\pi}{180}\right)(255)$$
$$\approx 4.450589593$$

EXAMPLE 9   Converting radian measure to degree measure

Express 1 radian in terms of degrees.

Solution
$$\frac{\theta}{360} = \frac{1}{2\pi}$$
$$\theta = \left(\frac{180}{\pi}\right)(1) \quad \theta \text{ in degrees}$$
$$\approx 57.29577951°$$

Solving Trigonometric Equations There will be many times in calculus when you will need to solve a trigonometric equation. As you may remember from trigonometry, solving a trigonometric equation is equivalent to evaluating an inverse trigonometric relation. Because these inverse functions will not be introduced in this book until Section 5.6, we will, for now, solve trigonometric equations whose solutions involve the values in Table 1.2 (called a **table of exact values**). These exact values from trigonometry are reviewed in *Student Mathematics Handbook*.

TABLE 1.2 Exact Trigonometric Values

Function \ Angle θ	0	$\frac{\pi}{6}$	$\frac{\pi}{4}$	$\frac{\pi}{3}$	$\frac{\pi}{2}$
$\cos\theta$	1	$\frac{\sqrt{3}}{2}$	$\frac{\sqrt{2}}{2}$	$\frac{1}{2}$	0
$\sin\theta$	0	$\frac{1}{2}$	$\frac{\sqrt{2}}{2}$	$\frac{\sqrt{3}}{2}$	1
$\tan\theta$	0	$\frac{\sqrt{3}}{3}$	1	$\sqrt{3}$	undefined

It is customary to use the values from Table 1.2 whenever possible, and the approximate calculator values will be given only when necessary.

EXAMPLE 10   Evaluating sine, cosine, tangent, secant, cosecant, and cotangent

Evaluate $\cos\frac{\pi}{3}$; $\sin\frac{5\pi}{6}$; $\tan\left(-\frac{5\pi}{4}\right)$; $\sec 1.2$; $\csc(-4.5)$; and $\cot 180°$.

Solution $\cos\frac{\pi}{3} = \frac{1}{2}$ *Exact value; Quadrant I*

$\sin\frac{5\pi}{6} = \frac{1}{2}$ *Exact value; Quadrant II*

$\tan\left(-\frac{5\pi}{4}\right) = -1$ *Exact value; Quadrant II*

$\sec 1.2 \approx 2.759703601$ *Approximate calculator value*

$\csc(-4.5) \approx 1.022986384$ *Approximate calculator value*

$\cot 180°$ is not defined.

EXAMPLE 11   Solving a trigonometric equation by factoring

Solve $2 \cos\theta \sin\theta = \sin\theta$ on $[0, 2\pi)$

Solution $2 \cos\theta \sin\theta - \sin\theta = 0$

$$\sin\theta(2 \cos\theta - 1) = 0$$

$$\sin\theta = 0 \qquad\quad 2\cos\theta - 1 = 0$$

$$\theta = 0, \pi \qquad\qquad \cos\theta = \tfrac{1}{2}$$

$$\theta = \tfrac{\pi}{3}, \tfrac{5\pi}{3}$$

⊘ Do not divide both sides by $\sin\theta$, because you might lose a solution. Notice that if $\theta = 0$ or π, then $\sin\theta = 0$. You cannot divide by 0. ⊘

Computational Window—Graphing Calculators

The procedure for solving trigonometric equations using calculators is quite similar to solving equations with absolute values. For Example 11, graph $Y1 = 2 \ COS(X) \ SIN(X)$ and $Y2 = SIN(X)$. We see there are four points of intersection of the curves on the interval $[0, 2\pi)$: By inspection we can see the curves intersect at 0 and π. (Note that the curves also intersect at $x = 2\pi$, but that value is not in the domain.)
By using the (ZOOM) we can find answers with better accuracy. We see that the approximate solution is X ≈ 0, 3.1, 1.0, 5.2.

```
Y1∎2cos Xsin X
Y2∎sin X

Xmin=0
Xmax=6.2831853…
Xscl=.5

Ymin=-1.5
Ymax=1.5
Yscl=.5
```

EXAMPLE 12   Solving a trigonometric equation using identities

Solve $\tan x + \sqrt{3} = \sec x$ on $[0, 2\pi)$.

Solution
$$\tan x + \sqrt{3} = \sec x$$

$$\tan^2 x + 2\sqrt{3}\,\tan x + 3 = \sec^2 x \qquad \textit{Square both sides.}$$

$$\tan^2 x + 2\sqrt{3}\,\tan x + 3 = 1 + \tan^2 x \qquad \textit{Use the identity } 1 + \tan^2 x = \sec^2 x \textit{ to write the equation using } \tan x \textit{ alone.}$$

$$2\sqrt{3}\,\tan x = -2$$

$$\tan x = \frac{-1}{\sqrt{3}} = -\tfrac{1}{3}\sqrt{3}$$

$$x = \tfrac{5\pi}{6}, \tfrac{11\pi}{6}$$

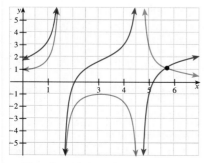

There is one intersection point: $x \approx 5.8$.

However, since we squared both sides we need to check for extraneous roots by substituting into the original equation. Checking, we see that $x = \tfrac{5\pi}{6}$ is extraneous, and the only solution is $x = \tfrac{11\pi}{6}$.

PROBLEM SET 1.2

Ⓐ 1. Fill in the missing parts in the following table.

Inequality Notation	Interval Notation
$-3 < x < 4$	a.
b.	$[3, 5]$
c.	$[-2, 1)$
$2 < x \le 7$	d.

2. Fill in the missing parts in the following table.

Inequality Notation	Interval Notation
a.	$(-\infty, -2)$
b.	$\left[\frac{\pi}{4}, \sqrt{2}\right]$
$x > -3$	c.
$-1 \le x \le 5$	d.

3. Represent each of the following on a number line.
 a. $-1 \le x < 4$ **b.** $-1 \le t \le 3$
 c. $(0, 2)$ **d.** $[-2, 1)$
4. Represent each of the following on a number line.
 a. $(-\infty, 2) \cup (2, \infty)$ **b.** $x > -2$
 c. $z \le 4$ **d.** $-2 < x \le 3$ or $x \ge 5$

In Problems 5–8, plot the given points P and Q on a Cartesian plane, find the distance between them, and find the coordinates of the midpoint of the line segment $\overline{PQ}$.
 5. a. $P(1, 0)$, $Q(5, 0)$ **b.** $P(2, 3)$, $Q(-2, 5)$
 6. a. $P(-2, 3)$, $Q(4, 1)$ **b.** $P(-5, 3)$, $Q(-5, -7)$
 7. a. $P(-1, 1)$, $Q(3, -2)$ **b.** $P(-2, -1)$, $Q(-1, -2)$
 8. a. $P(-4, 3)$, $Q(3, -4)$ **b.** $P(-5, -2)$, $Q(-6, -8)$

Solve each equation in Problems 9–26. Assume that a, b, and c are known constants.
 9. $x^2 - x = 0$ **10.** $2y^2 + y - 3 = 0$
 11. $y^2 - 5y + 3 = 17$ **12.** $x^2 + 5x + a = 0$
 13. $3x^2 - bx = c$ **14.** $4x^2 + 20x + 25 = 0$
 15. $|2x + 4| = 16$ **16.** $|5y + 2| = 12$
 17. $|3 - 2w| = 7$ **18.** $|5 - 3t| = 14$
 19. $|3x + 1| = -4$ **20.** $|1 - 5x| = -2$
 21. $\sin x = -\frac{1}{2}$ on $[0, 2\pi)$
 22. $(\sin x)(\cos x) = 0$ on $[0, 2\pi)$
 23. $(2 \cos x + \sqrt{2})(2 \cos x - 1) = 0$ on $[0, 2\pi)$
 24. $(3 \tan x + \sqrt{3})(3 \tan x - \sqrt{3}) = 0$ on $[0, 2\pi)$
 25. $\cot x + \sqrt{3} = \csc x$ on $[0, 2\pi)$
 26. $\sec^2 x - 1 = \sqrt{3} \tan x$ on $[0, 2\pi)$

Solve each inequality in Problems 27–38, and give your answer using interval notation.
 27. $3x + 7 < 2$ **28.** $5(3 - x) > 3x - 1$
 29. $-5 < 3x < 0$ **30.** $3 \le -y < 8$
 31. $-3 < y - 5 \le 2$ **32.** $-5 \le 3 - 2x < 18$
 33. $t^2 - 2t \le 3$ **34.** $s^2 + 3s - 4 > 0$
 35. $\dfrac{x(2x - 1)}{5 - x} > 0$ **36.** $\dfrac{x(x + 5)(x - 3)}{(x + 3)(x - 4)} \ge 0$
 37. $|x - 8| \le 0.001$ **38.** $|x - 5| < 0.01$

Convert each angle in Problems 39–42 to degrees if it is given in radians or to radians if it is given in degrees.
 39. (exact)   **a.** $30°$ **b.** $45°$
 40. (nearest hundredth of a radian)   **a.** $67°$ **b.** $275°$
 41. (exact)   **a.** $\frac{\pi}{3}$ **b.** $\frac{\pi}{6}$
 42. (nearest degree)   **a.** 4   **b.** -1
 43. Find the length of the arc subtended (cut off) by an angle of 2 radians in a circle of radius 2 cm.
 44. Find the arc length (measured to the nearest inch) of the arc subtended by an angle of $30°$ in a circle of radius 10 in.

Evaluate the trigonometric functions in Problems 45–48. Use exact values when possible; otherwise round to four decimal places.
 45. a. $\cos\frac{\pi}{4}$ **b.** $\sec\frac{3\pi}{4}$ **c.** $\tan\frac{2\pi}{3}$
 46. a. $\sin(-2)$ **b.** $\cos(-1.5)$ **c.** $\tan 0.5$
 47. a. $\tan 1$ **b.** $\sin 3.2$ **c.** $\cos 6.02$
 48. a. $\cos\left(-\frac{\pi}{3}\right)$ **b.** $\tan\frac{7\pi}{3}$ **c.** $\cot\left(-\frac{2\pi}{3}\right)$

In Problems 49–52, find an equation of a circle with given center C and radius r.
 49. $C(-1, 2)$; $r = 3$ **50.** $C(3, 0)$; $r = 2$
 51. $C(0, 1.5)$; $r = 0.25$ **52.** $C(-1, -5)$; $r = 4.1$

Graph the circles in Problems 53–56.
 53. $x^2 - 2x + y^2 + 2y + 1 = 0$ **54.** $4x^2 + 4y^2 + 4y - 15 = 0$
 55. $x^2 + y^2 + 2x - 10y + 25 = 0$
 56. $2x^2 + 2y^2 + 2x - 6y - 9 = 0$

Use the sum and difference formulas from trigonometry to find the exact values of the expressions in Problems 57–60.
 57. $\sin\left(-\frac{\pi}{12}\right)$ **58.** $\cos\frac{7\pi}{12}$ **59.** $\tan\frac{\pi}{12}$ **60.** $\sin 165°$

Ⓑ 61. ■ **What Does This Say?** Describe a process for solving a quadratic equation.
62. ■ **What Does This Say?** Describe a process for solving absolute value equations.
63. ■ **What Does This Say?** Describe a process for solving absolute value inequalities.
64. ■ **What Does This Say?** Describe a process for solving trigonometric equations.
Ⓒ 65. ■ **What Does This Say?** If $ax + b = 0$, what effect does changing b have on the solution ($a \ne 0$)?
66. ■ **What Does This Say?** If $ax^2 + bx + c = 0$, what effect does changing c have on the solution ($a \ne 0$)?

67. ■ **What Does This Say?**   If $\sin ax = b$, what effect does changing a have on the solution $(a \neq 0)$?

68. If $c \geq 0$, show that $|x| \leq c$ if and only if $-c \leq x \leq c$.

69. Show that $-|x| \leq x \leq |x|$ for any number x.

70. Prove that $|a| = |b|$ if and only if $a = b$ or $a = -b$.

71. Prove that if $|a| < b$ and $b > 0$, then $-b < a < b$.

72. Prove the triangle inequality: $|x + y| \leq |x| + |y|$

73. Show that $\big\| |x| - |y| \big\| \leq |x - y|$ for all x and y.

74. Derive the **midpoint formula**

$$M\left(\frac{x_1 + x_2}{2}, \frac{y_1 + y_2}{2}\right)$$

for the midpoint of a segment with endpoints $P(x_1, y_1)$ and $P(x_2, y_2)$.

1.3 LINES IN THE PLANE

Historical Note
RENÉ DESCARTES (1596–1650)

The Cartesian coordinate system is named in honor of the French mathematician René Descartes. Tradition tells us that he thought of his coordinate system while lying in bed watching a fly crawl around on the ceiling of his bedroom. He noticed that the path of the fly could be described if he knew the relation connecting the fly's distance from each of the walls. This idea of a coordinate system ties together the two great branches of mathematics, algebra and geometry, to form what is known as **analytic geometry.** Plane analytic geometry is that subject devoted primarily to the graphing of equations in two variables and finding the equations of points in the plane.

IN THIS SECTION Slope of a line, forms for equations of lines, parallel and perpendicular lines

A line is one of the simplest geometric concepts yet one of the most useful from the standpoint of calculus. In this section we review some of the basic facts about lines in a plane.

■ SLOPE OF A LINE

A distinguishing feature of a line is the fact that its *inclination* with respect to the horizontal is constant. It is common practice to specify inclination by means of a concept called *slope*. A carpenter might describe a roof line that rises 1 ft for every 3 ft of horizontal "run" as having a slope or pitch of 1 to 3.

Let Δx and Δy represent, as before, the amount of change in the variables x and y, respectively. Then a nonvertical line ℓ that rises (or falls) Δy units measured from bottom to top for every Δx units of run (measured from left to right) is said to have a *slope* of $m = \Delta y / \Delta x$. (*Recall*: If Δy is negative, then the "rise" is actually a fall; and if Δx is negative then the run is actually right to left.) In particular, if $P(x_1, y_1)$ and $Q(x_2, y_2)$ are two distinct points on ℓ, then the changes in the variables x and y are given by $\Delta x = x_2 - x_1$ and $\Delta y = y_2 - y_1$, and the slope of ℓ is

$$m = \frac{\Delta y}{\Delta x} = \frac{y_2 - y_1}{x_2 - x_1} \text{ for } \Delta x \neq 0 \quad \textit{See Figure 1.15.}$$

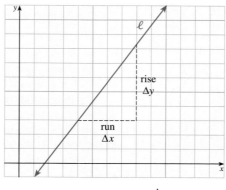

a. The slope of ℓ is $m = \dfrac{\Delta y}{\Delta x}$.

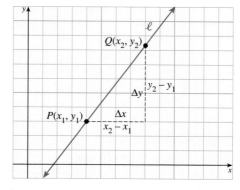

b. The slope is given by $m = \dfrac{y_2 - y_1}{x_2 - x_1}$.

Figure 1.15 The slope of a line

Slope of a Line

A nonvertical line that contains the points $P(x_1, y_1)$ and $Q(x_2, y_2)$ has **slope**

$$m = \frac{\Delta y}{\Delta x} = \frac{y_2 - y_1}{x_2 - x_1}$$

We say that a line with slope m is *rising* (when viewed from left to right) if $m > 0$, *falling* if $m < 0$, and *horizontal* if $m = 0$.

There is a useful trigonometric formulation of slope. The **angle of inclination** of a line ℓ is defined to be the nonnegative angle ϕ ($0 \le \phi < \pi$) formed between ℓ and the positively directed x-axis.

Angle of Inclination

The **angle of inclination** of a line ℓ is the angle ϕ ($0 \le \phi < \pi$) between line ℓ and the positive x-axis. Then the **slope** of line ℓ with inclination ϕ is

$$m = \tan \phi$$

We see that the line ℓ is *rising* if $0 < \phi < \frac{\pi}{2}$ and is *falling* if $\frac{\pi}{2} < \phi < \pi$. The line is *horizontal* if $\phi = 0$ and is *vertical* if $\phi = \frac{\pi}{2}$. Notice that if $\phi = \frac{\pi}{2}$, $\tan \phi$ is not defined; therefore m is not defined for a vertical line. A **vertical line** is said to have **no slope.**

⊘ Sometimes we say a vertical line has **infinite slope.** Pay special attention to the fact that if we say a line has no slope (vertical line), that is NOT the same as saying the line has 0 slope (horizontal line). ⊘

To derive the trigonometric representation for slope we need to find the slope of the line through $P(x_1, y_1)$ and $Q(x_2, y_2)$, where ϕ is the angle of inclination. From the definition of the tangent, we have

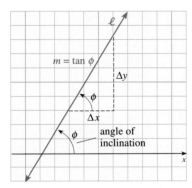

Figure 1.16 Trigonometric form for the slope of a line

$$\tan \phi = \frac{y_2 - y_1}{x_2 - x_1} = \frac{\Delta y}{\Delta x} = m \qquad \textit{See Figure 1.16.}$$

Lines with various slopes are shown in Figure 1.17.

Positive slope; line rises.

Negative slope; line falls.

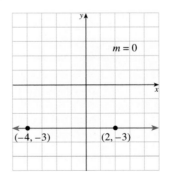

Zero slope ($\Delta y = 0$); line is horizontal.

Slope is undefined; ($\Delta x = 0$) line is vertical.

Figure 1.17 Examples of slope

■ FORMS FOR EQUATIONS OF LINES

In algebra you studied several forms of the equation of a line. The derivations of some of these are reviewed in the problems, and the rest are reviewed in the *Student Mathematics Handbook*. Here is a summary of the forms most frequently used in calculus.

Forms of a Linear Equation

STANDARD FORM:	$Ax + By + C = 0$	A, B, C constants (A and B not both 0)
SLOPE-INTERCEPT FORM:	$y = mx + b$	Slope m, y-intercept $(0, b)$
POINT-SLOPE FORM:	$y - k = m(x - h)$	Slope m, through point (h, k)
HORIZONTAL LINE:	$y = k$	Slope 0
VERTICAL LINE:	$x = h$	No slope (slope is not defined for vertical lines)

EXAMPLE 1   Deriving the two-intercept form of the equation of a line

Derive the equation of the line with intercepts $(a, 0)$ and $(0, b)$, $a \neq 0$, $b \neq 0$.

Solution   The slope of the equation passing through the given points is

$$m = \frac{b - 0}{0 - a} = -\frac{b}{a}$$

Use the point-slope form with $h = 0$, $k = b$. (You can use either of the given points.)

$$y - b = -\frac{b}{a}(x - 0)$$

$$ay - ab = -bx$$

$$bx + ay = ab$$

$$\frac{x}{a} + \frac{y}{b} = 1 \qquad\qquad \textit{Divide both sides by ab.} \quad \blacksquare$$

Two quantities x and y that satisfy a linear equation $Ax + By + C = 0$ (A and B not both 0) are said to be *linearly related*. This terminology is illustrated in Example 2.

EXAMPLE 2   Linearly related variables

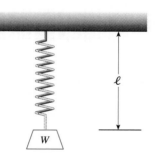

When a weight is attached to a helical spring, it causes the spring to lengthen. According to Hooke's law, the length ℓ of the spring is linearly related to the weight w.* If $\ell = 4$ cm when $w = 3$ g and $\ell = 6$ cm when $w = 6$ g, what is the original length of the spring, and what weight will cause the spring to lengthen to 5 cm?

Solution   Because ℓ is linearly related to w, we know that points (w, ℓ) lie on a line, and the given information tells us that two such points are $(3, 4)$ and $(6, 6)$ as shown in Figure 1.18 on page 23.

We first find the slope of the line and then use the point-slope form to derive its equation.

$$m = \frac{6 - 4}{6 - 3} = \frac{2}{3}$$

*Hooke's law is useful for small displacements, but for larger displacements, it may not be a good model.

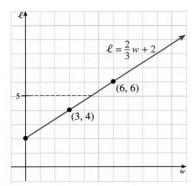

Figure 1.18 The length ℓ of the spring is linearly related to the weight w of the attached object.

Next, substitute into the point-slope form with $h = 3$ and $k = 4$:

$$\ell - 4 = \tfrac{2}{3}(w - 3)$$

$$\ell = \tfrac{2}{3}w + 2$$

The original length of the spring is found for $w = 0$:

$$\ell = \tfrac{2}{3}(0) + 2 = 2$$

The original length was 2 cm. To find the weight that corresponds to $\ell = 5$, we solve the equation

$$5 = \tfrac{2}{3}w + 2$$

$$3 = \tfrac{2}{3}w$$

$$\tfrac{9}{2} = w$$

Therefore, the weight that corresponds to a length of 5 cm is 4.5 g. ▬

■ PARALLEL AND PERPENDICULAR LINES

It is often useful to know whether two given lines are either parallel or perpendicular. A vertical line can be parallel only to other vertical lines and perpendicular only to horizontal lines. Cases involving nonvertical lines may be handled by the criteria given in the following theorem.

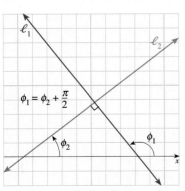

a. Parallel lines have equal slope: $m_1 = m_2$.

b. Perpendicular lines have negative reciprocal slopes: $m_1 m_2 = -1$.

Figure 1.19

THEOREM 1.2 Slope criteria for parallel and perpendicular lines

If ℓ_1 and ℓ_2 are nonvertical lines with slopes m_1 and m_2, then

ℓ_1 and ℓ_2 are **parallel** if and only if $m_1 = m_2$;

ℓ_1 and ℓ_2 are **perpendicular** if and only if $m_1 m_2 = -1$, or $m_1 = -\dfrac{1}{m_2}$.

In other words, lines are parallel if and only if their slopes are equal and are perpendicular if and only if their slopes are negative reciprocals of each other.

Proof: The key ideas behind these two slope criteria are displayed in Figure 1.19. The criterion for parallel lines follows from the fact that lines are parallel whenever their angles of inclination are equal (see Figure 1.19a). On the other hand, if ℓ_1 and ℓ_2 are perpendicular (see Figure 1.19b), one angle of inclination, say ϕ_2, must be an acute angle and must satisfy

$$\phi_1 = \phi_2 + \tfrac{\pi}{2}$$

Then

$$m_1 = \tan \phi_1$$

$$= \tan \left(\phi_2 + \frac{\pi}{2} \right)$$

$$= \tan \left[\frac{\pi}{2} - (-\phi_2) \right]$$

$$= \cot(-\phi_2)$$

$$= -\cot \phi_2$$

$$= \frac{-1}{\tan \phi_2}$$

$$= \frac{-1}{m_2}$$

Thus, $m_1 m_2 = -1$. We leave it to you to show that ℓ_1 and ℓ_2 are perpendicular if $m_1 m_2 = -1$. ∎

EXAMPLE 3   Finding equations for parallel and perpendicular lines

Let ℓ be the line $3x + 2y = 5$.
  a. Find an equation of the line that is parallel to ℓ and passes through $P(4, 7)$.
  b. Find an equation of the line that is perpendicular to ℓ and passes through $P(4, 7)$.

Solution   By rewriting the equation of ℓ as $y = -\frac{3}{2}x + \frac{5}{2}$, we see that the slope of ℓ is $m = -\frac{3}{2}$.

  a. Any line that is parallel to ℓ must also have slope $m_1 = -\frac{3}{2}$. The required line contains the point $P(4, 7)$. Use the point-slope form to find the equation and write your answer in standard form:

$$y - 7 = -\frac{3}{2}(x - 4)$$

$$2y - 14 = -3x + 12$$

$$3x + 2y - 26 = 0$$

  b. Any line perpendicular to ℓ must have slope $m_2 = \frac{2}{3}$ (negative reciprocal of the slope of ℓ). Once again, the required line contains the point $P(4, 7)$, and we find

$$y - 7 = \frac{2}{3}(x - 4)$$

$$3y - 21 = 2x - 8$$

$$2x - 3y + 13 = 0$$

These lines are shown in Figure 1.20. ▬

Figure 1.20 Graph of lines parallel and perpendicular to the given line $3x + 2y = 5$

PROBLEM SET 1.3

Ⓐ **1.** ■ **What Does This Say?** Outline a procedure for graphing a linear equation.

In Problems 2–15, find the equation in standard form for the line that satisfies the given requirements.
  2. passing through $(1, 4)$ and $(3, 6)$

  3. passing through $(-1, 7)$ and $(-2, 9)$

  4. horizontal line through $(-2, -5)$

  5. passing through the point $\left(1, \frac{1}{2} \right)$ with slope 0

  6. slope 2 and y-intercept $(0, 5)$

7. vertical line through $(-2, -5)$

8. slope -3, x-intercept $(5, 0)$

9. x-intercept $(7, 0)$ and y-intercept $(0, -8)$

10. x-intercept $(4.5, 0)$ and y-intercept $(0, -5.4)$

11. passing through $(-1, 8)$ parallel to $3x + y = 7$

12. passing through $(3, -2)$ perpendicular to $4x - 3y + 2 = 0$

13. passing through $(4, 5)$ parallel to the line passing through $(2, 1)$ and $(5, 9)$

14. passing through $(-1, 6)$ perpendicular to the line through the origin with slope 0.5

15. perpendicular to the line whose equation is $x - 4y + 5 = 0$ where it intersects the line whose equation is $2x + 3y - 1 = 0$

In Problems 16–23, find, if possible, the slope, the y-intercept, and the x-intercept of the line whose equation is given. Sketch the graph of each equation.

16. $5x + 3y - 15 = 0$

17. $3x + 5y + 15 = 0$

18. $\frac{x}{2} + \frac{y}{3} = 2$

19. $\frac{x}{2} - \frac{y}{3} = 1$

20. $y = 2x$

21. $x = 5y$

22. $y - 5 = 0$

23. $x + 3 = 0$

B 24. Find an equation for a vertical line ℓ such that a region bounded by ℓ, the x-axis, and the line $2y - 3x = 6$ has area 3.

25. Three vertices of a parallelogram are $(1, 3)$, $(4, 11)$, and $(3, -2)$. If $(1, 3)$ and $(3, -2)$ lie on the same side, what is the fourth vertex? What are the equations of the lines that form the sides of the parallelogram?

26. A life insurance table indicates that a woman who is now A years old can expect to live E years longer. Suppose that A and E are linearly related and that $E = 50$ when $A = 24$ and $E = 20$ when $A = 60$.

   a. At what age may a woman expect to live 30 years longer?

   b. What is the life expectancy of a newborn female child?

   c. At what age is the life expectancy zero?

27. On the Fahrenheit temperature scale, water freezes at $32°$ and boils at $212°$; the corresponding temperatures on the Celsius scale are $0°$ and $100°$. Given that the Fahrenheit and Celsius temperatures are linearly related, first find numbers r and s so that $F = rC + s$, and then answer these questions.

   a. Mercury freezes at $-39°C$. What is the corresponding Fahrenheit temperature?

   b. For what value of C is $F = 0$?

   c. What temperature is the same in both scales?

28. The average SAT mathematics scores of incoming students at an eastern liberal arts college have been declining in recent years. In 1987 the average SAT score was 575, and in 1992 it was 545. Assuming the SAT score varies linearly with time, answer these questions.

   a. Express the average SAT score in terms of time.

   b. If the trend continues, what will the average SAT score of incoming students be in the year 2000?

   c. When will the average SAT score be 527?

29. A manufacturer's total cost consists of a fixed overhead of $5,000 plus production costs of $60 per unit. Assuming the cost varies linearly with the level of production, express the total cost in terms of the number of units produced and draw the graph.

30. A certain car rental agency charges $40 per day with 100 free miles plus 34¢ per mile after the first 100 miles. First express the cost of renting a car from this agency for one day in terms of the number of miles driven. Then draw the graph and use it to check your answers to these questions.

   a. How much does it cost to rent a car for a 1-day trip of 50 mi?

   b. How many miles were driven if the daily rental cost was $92.36?

31. A manufacturer buys $200,000 worth of machinery that depreciates linearly so that its trade-in value after 10 years will be $10,000. Express the value of the machinery as a function of its age and draw the graph. What is the value of the machinery after 4 years?

32. Show that if the point $P(x, y)$ is equidistant from $A(1, 3)$ and $B(-1, 2)$, its coordinates must satisfy the equation $4x + 2y - 5 = 0$. Sketch the graph of this equation.

33. Let $P_1(2, 6)$, $P_2(-1, 3)$, $P_3(0, -2)$, and $P_4(a, b)$ be points in the plane that are located so that $P_1P_2P_3P_4$ is a parallelogram.

   a. There are three possible choices for P_4. One is $P_4(3, 1)$. What are the others?

   b. Show that for $P_4(3, 1)$, the diagonals bisect each other.

34. Since the beginning of the month, a local reservoir has been losing water at a constant rate (that is, the amount of water in the reservoir is a linear function of time). On the 12th of the month, the reservoir held 200 million gallons of water; on the 21st, it held only 164 million gallons. How much water was in the reservoir on the 8th of the month?

35. To encourage motorists to form car pools, the transit authority in a certain metropolitan area has been offering a special reduced rate at toll bridges for vehicles containing four or more persons. When the program began 30 days ago, 157 vehicles qualified for the reduced rate during the morning rush hour. Since then, the number of vehicles qualifying has increased at a constant rate (that is, the number is a linear function of time), and 247 vehicles qualified today. If the trend continues, how many vehicles will qualify during the morning rush hour 14 days from now?

36. The value of a certain rare book doubles every 10 years. The book was originally worth $3.

   a. How much is the book worth when it is 30 years old? When it is 40 years old?

   b. Is the relationship between the value of the book and its age linear? Explain.

C 37. Show that, in general, a line passing through $P(h, k)$ with slope m has the equation $y - k = m(x - h)$.

38. If $A(x_1, y_1)$ and $B(x_2, y_2)$ with $x_1 \neq x_2$ are two points on the graph of the line $y = mx + b$, show that

$$m = \frac{y_2 - y_1}{x_2 - x_1}$$

Use this to show that the graph of $y = mx + b$ is a line with slope m; show that the line has y-intercept $(0, b)$.

39. Show that the distance s from the point (x_0, y_0) to the line $Ax + By + C = 0$ is given by the formula

$$s = \left| \frac{Ax_0 + By_0 + C}{\sqrt{A^2 + B^2}} \right|$$

40. Let L_1 and L_2 have slopes m_1 and m_2, respectively, and let ϕ be the angle from L_1 and L_2, as shown in Figure 1.21. Show that

$$\tan \phi = \frac{m_2 - m_1}{1 + m_1 m_2}$$

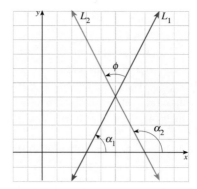

Figure 1.21 Angle ϕ between given lines

41. JOURNAL PROBLEM*: *Ontario Secondary School Mathematics Bulletin*. Show that there is just one line in the family $y - 8 = m(x + 1)$ that is five units from the $(2, 4)$.

1.4 FUNCTIONS AND THEIR GRAPHS

> **IN THIS SECTION** Definition of a function, functional notation, domain and range of a function, composition of functions, graph of a function, transformation of functions, classification of functions
> The concept of function is the backbone of a calculus course. A thorough understanding of this section is essential for your work in calculus.

Scientists, economists, and other researchers study relationships between quantities. For example, an engineer may need to know how the illumination from a light source on an object is related to the distance between the object and the source; a biologist may wish to investigate how the population of a bacterial colony varies with time in the presence of a toxin; an economist may wish to determine the relationship between demand for a certain commodity and its market price. The mathematical study of such relationships involves the concept of a *function*.

■ DEFINITION OF A FUNCTION

Function   A **function** f is a rule that assigns to each element x of a set X a unique element y of a set Y. The element y is called the **image** of x under f and is denoted by $f(x)$ (read as "f of x"). The set X is called the **domain** of f, and the set of all images of elements of X is called the **range** of the function.

A function whose *name* is f can be thought of as the set of ordered pairs (x, y) for which each member x of the domain is associated with exactly one member $y = f(x)$. The function can also be regarded as a rule that assigns a unique "output" in the set Y to each "input" from the set X.

*Most mathematics journals have problem sections that solicit interesting problems and solutions for publication. From time to time we will reprint a problem from a mathematics journal. If you have difficulty solving a journal problem, you may wish to use a library to find the problem and solution as printed in the journal. The title of the journal is included as part of the problem, and we will generally give you a reference as a footnote. This problem is found in Volume 18, 1982, issue 2, p. 7.

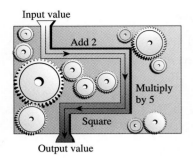

Input value

Add 2

Multiply by 5

Square

Output value

| *What this says*: To be called a function, the rule must have the property that it assigns one and only one output to each input.

A visual representation of a function is shown in Figure 1.22. Note that it is quite possible for two different elements in the domain X to map into the same element in the range, and that it is possible for Y to include elements not in the range of f. If the range of f does, however, consist of all of Y, then f is said to map **X onto Y.** Furthermore, if each element in the range is the image of one and only one element in the domain, then f is said to be a **one-to-one function.** We shall have more to say about these terms in Chapter 5. A function is called a **real-valued function** if the range is a subset of the set of real numbers.* In this book, we work with real-valued functions of a real variable which restrict both the domain and range to the set of real numbers. A function f is said to be **bounded** on $[a, b]$ if there exists a number B so that $|f(x)| \le B$ for all x in $[a, b]$.

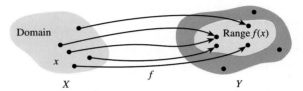

Domain

Range $f(x)$

x

X f Y

Figure 1.22 A function as a mapping

■ FUNCTIONAL NOTATION

Functions can be represented in several ways, but usually they are defined by using a mathematical formula. It is traditional to let x denote the input and y the corresponding output, and to write an equation relating x and y. The letters x and y that appear in such an equation are called **variables.** Because the value of the variable y is determined by that of the variable x, we call y the **dependent variable** and x the **independent variable.**

In this book, when we define functions by expressions such as

$$f(x) = 2x + 3 \text{ or } g(x) = x^2 + 4x + 5$$

we mean the functions f and g are the sets of all ordered pairs (x, y), satisfying the equations $y = 2x + 3$ and $y = x^2 + 4x + 5$, respectively. To **evaluate** a function f means to find the value of f for some particular value in the domain. For example, to evaluate f at $x = 2$ is to find $f(2)$.

EXAMPLE 1   Using functional notation

Suppose $f(x) = 2x^2 - x$. Find $f(-1)$, $f(0)$, $f(2)$, $f(x + h)$, and $\dfrac{f(x + h) - f(x)}{h}$, where x and h are real numbers and $h \ne 0$.

Solution   In this case, the defined function f tells us to subtract the independent

*The functions that appear in this book belong to a very special class called **elementary functions,** defined by Joseph Liouville (1809–1882). You will study some nonelementary functions in complex analysis and in advanced calculus. Many functions that appear in physics and higher mathematics are not elementary functions.

variable x from twice its square. Thus, we have

$$f(-1) = 2(-1)^2 - (-1) = 3$$
$$f(0) = 2(0)^2 - (0) = 0$$
$$f(2) = 2(2)^2 - 2 = 6$$

To find $f(x + h)$ we begin by writing the formula for f in more neutral terms, say as

$$f(\square) = 2(\square)^2 - (\square)$$

Then we insert the expression $x + h$ inside each box, obtaining

$$f(\boxed{x + h}) = 2(\boxed{x + h})^2 - (\boxed{x + h})$$
$$= 2(x^2 + 2xh + h^2) - (x + h)$$
$$= 2x^2 + 4xh + 2h^2 - x - h$$

Finally, if $h \neq 0$,

$$\frac{f(x + h) - f(x)}{h} = \frac{[2x^2 + 4xh + 2h^2 - x - h] - [2x^2 - x]}{h}$$
$$= \frac{4xh + 2h^2 - h}{h} = 4x + 2h - 1$$

The expression $\dfrac{f(x + h) - f(x)}{h}$ is called a **difference quotient** and is used in Chapter 2 to compute the *derivative*.

Sometimes functions need to be defined in pieces because they have a split domain. These functions require more than one formula to define the function, and therefore are called **piecewise-defined functions.**

EXAMPLE 2   Evaluating a piecewise-defined function

If $f(x) = \begin{cases} x \sin x & \text{if } x < 2 \\ 3x^2 + 1 & \text{if } x \geq 2 \end{cases}$

find $f(-0.5)$, $f\left(\frac{\pi}{2}\right)$, and $f(2)$.

Solution   To find $f(-0.5)$ we use the first line of the formula because $-0.5 < 2$:

$$f(-0.5) = -0.5 \sin(-0.5) = 0.5 \sin 0.5 \quad \text{This is the exact value.}$$
$$\approx 0.2397 \quad \text{This is the approximate value.}$$

To find $f\left(\frac{\pi}{2}\right)$ we use the first line of the formula because $\frac{\pi}{2} \approx 1.57 < 2$:

$$f\left(\tfrac{\pi}{2}\right) = \tfrac{\pi}{2} \sin \tfrac{\pi}{2} = \tfrac{\pi}{2} \quad \text{This is the exact value.}$$

Finally, because $2 \geq 2$, we use the second line of the formula to find $f(2)$.

$$f(2) = 3(2)^2 + 1 = 13$$

Functional notation can be used in a wide variety of applied problems, as shown by Example 3 and again in the problem set.

EXAMPLE 3   Applying functional notation

It is known that an object dropped from a height in a vacuum will fall a distance of s ft in t seconds according to the formula

$$s(t) = 16t^2, \quad t \geq 0$$

a. How far will the object fall in the first second? In the *next* 2 seconds?

b. How far will it fall during the time interval $t = 1$ to $t = 1 + h$ seconds?

c. What is the average rate of change of distance (in feet per second) during the time $t = 1$ sec to $t = 3$ sec?

d. What is the average rate of change of distance during the time $t = x$ seconds to $t = x + h$ seconds?

Solution

a. $s(1) = 16(1)^2 = 16$

In the first second the object will fall 16 ft. In the next two seconds the object will fall

$$s(1 + 2) - s(1) = s(3) - s(1) = 16(3)^2 - 16(1)^2 = 128$$

The object will fall 128 ft in the next 2 sec.

b. $s(1 + h) - s(1) = 16(1 + h)^2 - 16(1)^2$
$$= 16 + 32h + 16h^2 - 16 = 32h + 16h^2$$

c. AVERAGE RATE $= \dfrac{\text{CHANGE IN DISTANCE}}{\text{CHANGE IN TIME}} = \dfrac{s(3) - s(1)}{3 - 1} = \dfrac{128}{2} = 64$

The average rate of change is 64 ft/sec.

d. $\dfrac{s(x + h) - s(x)}{(x + h) - x} = \dfrac{s(x + h) - s(x)}{h}$ *Does this look familiar? See Example 1.*

$$= \frac{16(x + h)^2 - 16x^2}{h} = \frac{16x^2 + 32xh + 16h^2 - 16x^2}{h} = 32x + 16h$$

■ DOMAIN AND RANGE OF A FUNCTION

⊘ Notice this agreement about the domain of a function, which will be used throughout the book. ⊘

In this book, unless otherwise specified, the domain of a function is the set of real numbers for which the function is defined. We call this the **domain convention.** If a function f is **undefined** at x, it means that x is not in the domain of f. The most frequent exclusions from the domain are those values that cause division by 0 and negative values under a square root. In applications, the domain is often specified by the context. For example, if x is the number of people on an elevator, the context requires that negative numbers and nonintegers be excluded from the domain; therefore, x must be an integer such that $0 \leq x \leq c$ where c is the maximum capacity of the elevator.

EXAMPLE 4   Domain of a function

Find the domain for the given functions.

a. $f(x) = 2x - 1$ **b.** $g(x) = 2x - 1, \; x \neq -3$

c. $h(x) = \dfrac{(2x - 1)(x + 3)}{x + 3}$ **d.** $F(x) = \sqrt{x + 2}$ **e.** $G(x) = \dfrac{4}{5 - \cos x}$

Solution

a. All real numbers; $D = (-\infty, \infty)$

b. All real numbers except -3

c. Because the expression is meaningful for all $x \neq -3$, the domain is all real numbers except -3.

d. F has meaning if and only if $x + 2$ is nonnegative; therefore the domain is $x \geq -2$, or $D = [-2, \infty)$.

e. G is defined whenever $5 - \cos x \neq 0$. This imposes no restriction on x since $|\cos x| \leq 1$. Thus, the domain of G is the set of all real numbers; $D = (-\infty, \infty)$. ▄

Equality of Functions

> Two functions f and g are **equal** if and only if
> **1.** f and g have the same domain.
> **2.** $f(x) = g(x)$ for all x in the domain.

$f(x) = 2x - 1$
$g(x) = 2x - 1, \; x \neq -3$
$h(x) = \dfrac{(2x - 1)(x + 3)}{x + 3}$

In Example 4 (repeated in the margin here) the functions g and h are equal. A common mistake is to "reduce" the function h to the function f:

⊘ WRONG: $h(x) = \dfrac{(2x - 1)(x + 3)}{x + 3} = 2x - 1 = f(x)$ ⊘

RIGHT: $h(x) = \dfrac{(2x - 1)(x + 3)}{x + 3} = 2x - 1, \; x \neq -3$; therefore, $h(x) = g(x)$.

The following concept can be used to reduce (by half) the amount of work necessary on many problems.

Even and Odd Functions

> A function f is called
>   **even** if $f(-x) = f(x)$, and
>   **odd** if $f(-x) = -f(x)$
> for all x in the domain of f.

Just as not every real number is even or odd (2 is even, 3 is odd, but 2.5 is neither), not every function is even or odd. For example:

$$f(x) = x^2 \text{ is } even, \text{ because } f(-x) = (-x)^2 = x^2 = f(x)$$

$$g(x) = x^3 \text{ is } odd, \text{ because } g(-x) = (-x)^3 = -x^3 = -g(x)$$

$$h(x) = x^2 + x \text{ is } neither \text{ because } h(-x) = (-x)^2 + (-x) = x^2 - x$$

Note that $h(-x) \neq h(x)$ and $h(-x) \neq -h(x)$.

■ COMPOSITION OF FUNCTIONS

There are many situations in which a quantity is given as a function of one variable that, in turn, can be written as a function of a second variable. Suppose, for example, that your job is to ship x packages of a product via Federal Express to a variety of addresses. Let x be the number of packages to ship, and let f be the weight of the x objects and g be the cost of shipping. Then

The weight is a function of the number of objects: $f(x)$;
The cost is a function of the weight: $g[f(x)]$.

This process of evaluating a function of a function illustrates the idea of *composition of functions*.

Composition of Functions

The **composite function** $f \circ g$ is defined by

$$(f \circ g)(x) = f[g(x)]$$

for each x in the domain of g for which $g(x)$ is in the domain of f.

■ *What this says*: To visualize how functional composition works, think of $f \circ g$ in terms of an "assembly line" in which g and f are arranged in series, with output $g(x)$ becoming the input of f, as illustrated in Figure 1.23.

Assembly line interpretation of composite functions

Figure 1.23 Composition of functions

EXAMPLE 5   Finding the composition of functions

If $f(x) = 3x + 5$ and $g(x) = \sqrt{x}$, find the composite functions $f \circ g$ and $g \circ f$.

⊘ Example 5 illustrates that *functional composition is not commutative.* ⊘ That is, $f \circ g$ is not, in general, the same as $g \circ f$.

Solution   The function $f \circ g$ is defined by $f[g(x)]$.

$$(f \circ g)(x) = f[g(x)] = f(\sqrt{x}) = 3\sqrt{x} + 5$$

The function $g \circ f$ is defined by $g[f(x)]$.

$$(g \circ f)(x) = g[f(x)] = g(3x + 5) = \sqrt{3x + 5}$$

Computational Window

In addition to using function machines to visualize the composition of functions, we can also visualize composition in terms of "boxes" or "spreadsheet cells":

A **spreadsheet** is a computer program to manipulate data and carry out calculations or chains of calculations (as in composition of functions). If you have access to a computer and software such as Excel, Lotus 1-2-3, or Quattro-Pro, you might wish to look at the *Technology Manual* accompanying this book.

Initial value   Output value from "some formula" in cell A1

CELL   A1   ⟶   A2

⟶

B

Output from "second formula, A2" is the *composition* of the formulas.

composite value

EXAMPLE 6   An application of composite functions

Air pollution is a problem for many metropolitan areas. Suppose that carbon monoxide is measured as a function of the number of people according to the following information:

Number of People	Daily Carbon Monoxide Level (in parts per million)
100,000	1.41
200,000	1.83
300,000	2.43
400,000	3.05
500,000	3.72

Further studies show that a refined formula for the average daily level of carbon monoxide in the air is

$$L(p) = 0.7\sqrt{p^2 + 3}$$

Further assume that the population of a given metropolitan area is growing according to the formula $p(t) = 1 + 0.02t^3$, where t is the time from now (in years) and p is the population (in hundred thousands). Based on these assumptions, what level of air pollution should be expected in 4 years?

Solution   The level of pollution is $L(p) = 0.7\sqrt{p^2 + 3}$, *where* $p(t) = 1 + 0.02t^3$. Thus, the pollution level at time t is given by the composite function

$$(L \circ p)(t) = L[p(t)] = L(1 + 0.02t^3) = 0.7\sqrt{(1 + 0.02t^3)^2 + 3}$$

In particular, when $t = 4$, we have

$$(L \circ p)(4) = 0.7\sqrt{[1 + 0.02(4)^3]^2 + 3} \approx 2.0 \text{ ppm} \quad \blacksquare$$

In calculus, it is frequently necessary to express a function as the composite of two simpler functions.

EXAMPLE 7   Expressing a given function as the composite of two functions

Express each of the following functions as the composite of two functions u and g so that $f(x) = g[u(x)]$.

a. $f(x) = (x^2 + 5x + 1)^5$ **b.** $f(x) = \cos^3 x$
c. $f(x) = \sin x^3$ **d.** $f(x) = \sqrt{5x^2 - x}$

Solution

Given Function $f(x) = g[u(x)]$	Inner Function $u(x)$	Outer Function $g[u(x)]$
a. $f(x) = (x^2 + 5x + 1)^5$	$u(x) = x^2 + 5x + 1$	$g[u(x)] = [u(x)]^5$
b. $f(x) = \cos^3 x$	$u(x) = \cos x$	$g[u(x)] = [u(x)]^3$
c. $f(x) = \sin x^3$	$u(x) = x^3$	$g[u(x)] = \sin[u(x)]$
d. $f(x) = \sqrt{5x^2 - x}$	$u(x) = 5x^2 - x$	$g[u(x)] = \sqrt{u(x)}$

$\blacksquare$

⊘ Consider Example 7 and this paragraph carefully. ⊘

There are often other ways to express a composite function, but the most common procedure is to choose the function u to be the "inside" portion of the given function f. Notice that in part **a** the "inside" portion is the portion inside the parentheses. Compare parts **b** and **c**: the inside portion of **b** is $\cos x$ because $f(x) = \cos^3 x = (\cos x)^3$. In part **c**, on the other hand, $u(x) = x^3$ is the inside portion because $\sin x^3 = \sin(x^3)$. Finally, notice in part **d** that $u(x)$ is the part "inside" the radical sign.

■ GRAPH OF A FUNCTION

Graphs have visual impact. They also reveal information that may not be evident from verbal or algebraic descriptions. Two graphs depicting practical relationships are shown in Figure 1.24.

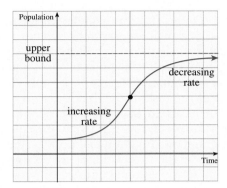

a. A production function
This graph describes the variation in total industrial production in a certain country over a five year time span. The fact that the graph has a peak suggests that production is greatest at the corresponding time.

b. Bounded population growth
This graph represents the growth of a population when environmental factors impose an upper bound on the possible size of the population. It indicates that the rate of population growth increases at first and then decreases as the size of the population gets closer and closer to the upper bound.

Figure 1.24 Examples of functions

To represent a function $y = f(x)$ geometrically as a graph, it is traditional to use a Cartesian coordinate system on which units for the independent variable x are marked on the horizontal axis and units for the dependent variable y on the vertical axis.

Graph of a Function

> The **graph** of a function f consists of all points whose coordinates (x, y) satisfy $y = f(x)$, for all x in the domain of f.

In Chapter 3 we will discuss efficient techniques involving calculus that you can use to draw accurate graphs of functions. In beginning algebra you began sketching lines by plotting points, but you quickly found out that this is not a very efficient way to draw more complicated graphs, especially without the aid of a graphing calculator or computer. Table 1.3 includes a few common graphs you have probably encountered in previous courses. We will assume that you are familiar with their general shape and know how to sketch each of them.

Intercepts The points where a graph intersects the coordinate axes are called intercepts. Here is a definition.

Intercepts

> If the number zero is in the domain of f and $f(0) = b$, then the point $(0, b)$ is called the **y-intercept** of the graph of f. If a is a real number in the domain of f such that $f(a) = 0$, then $(a, 0)$ is an **x-intercept** of f.
>
> ■ **What this says**: To find the x-intercepts, set y equal to 0, and solve for x. To find the y-intercept, set x equal to 0 and solve for y.

Computational Window—Computer or Calculator Graphing

If you use a computer or a calculator to help you draw graphs, you will need to pay particular attention to Xmin, Xmax, and Xscl, as well as Ymin, Ymax, and Yscl. These selections will determine the region of the plane you will see on your screen. Computers and graphing calculators rely heavily on the technique of graphing by plotting points. When you use a computer or a calculator the graph is quite often the easiest part of the task; the difficult part is choosing a scale on the axes so that the shape of the graph can be ascertained. In this text, we will frequently show you the graph of a function and how the graph looks when using a graphing calculator. In Example 4, we asked you to find the domain and not the range. In order to find the range of a function algebraically, we need to solve for x and then look for values of y that cause the function to be undefined (division by 0 or a negative number under a square root, for example). However, a graphing calculator or computer can help you determine the range once you have found the domain.

a. $f(x) = 2x - 1$

Domain: $(-\infty, \infty)$
Range: $(-\infty, \infty)$

```
Y₁■2X-1
Xmin=-10  Ymin=-10
Xmax=10   Ymax=10
Xscl=1    Yscl=1
```

b. $g(x) = 2x - 1, \; x \neq -3$

Calculators do not show the deleted point. The graph looks the same as the one in part **a.** *You* must add the circle at the point $(-3, -7)$.

c. $h(x) = \dfrac{(2x - 1)(x + 3)}{x + 3}$

The graph is the same as the one in part **b.**

Domain: $x = -3$
Range: $y \neq -7$

```
Y₁■(2X-1)(X+3)/(
X+3)
Xmin=-10  Ymin=-10
Xmax=10   Ymax=10
Xscl=1    Yscl=1
```

d. $F(x) = \sqrt{x + 2}$

Domain: $[-2, \infty)$
Range: $[0, \infty)$

```
Y₁■√(X+2)
Xmin=-10  Ymin=-10
Xmax=10   Ymax=10
Xscl=1    Yscl=1
```

e. $G(x) = \dfrac{4}{5 - \cos x}$

In part **e**, it is easy to see the maximum value of y to be 1, but the minimum value cannot be easily seen from the graph. However, by using the TRACE function on a calculator we can find an appropriate minimum value (approximately):

Domain: $(-\infty, \infty)$
Range: $(0.666, 1)$

```
Y₁■4/(5-cos X)
Xmin=-8   Ymin=0
Xmax=8    Ymax=1.2
Xscl=1    Yscl=.1
```

TABLE 1.3 Directory of Curves

Identity Function $y = x$	Standard Quadratic Function $y = x^2$	Standard Cubic Function $y = x^3$

Absolute Value Function $y = |x| = \sqrt{x^2}$	Square Root Function $y = \sqrt{x}$	Cube Root Function $y = \sqrt[3]{x}$

Standard Reciprocal $y = \dfrac{1}{x}$	Standard Reciprocal Squared $y = \dfrac{1}{x^2}$	Standard Square Root Reciprocal $y = \dfrac{1}{\sqrt{x}}$

Cosine Function $y = \cos x$	Sine Function $y = \sin x$	Tangent Function $y = \tan x$

Secant Function $y = \sec x$	Cosecant Function $y = \csc x$	Cotangent Function $y = \cot x$

EXAMPLE 8   Finding the intercepts

Find all intercepts of the function $f(x) = -x^2 + x + 2$.

Solution   The y-intercept is $(0, f(0)) = (0, 2)$. To find the x-intercepts, solve the equation $f(x) = 0$. Factoring, we find that

$$-x^2 + x + 2 = 0$$

$$x^2 - x - 2 = 0$$

$$(x + 1)(x - 2) = 0$$

$$x = -1 \text{ or } x = 2$$

Thus, the intercepts are $(0, 2)$, $(-1, 0)$ and $(2, 0)$.

Vertical Line Test   Functions can have several x-intercepts but can have at most one y-intercept. Thus follows a very useful technique for deciding if a given curve is the graph of a function. The graph of a typical function is shown in Figure 1.25. Notice that for each a in the domain there is only *one point* $(a, f(a))$ on the graph. This means that a given vertical line passes through the graph of a function in at most one point. This is the **vertical line test** for the graph of a function, as shown in Figure 1.26.

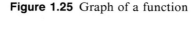

Figure 1.25 Graph of a function

| The Vertical Line Test | A curve in the plane is the graph of a function if and only if it intersects a vertical line no more than once. |

Function   Function   Function   Not a function   Not a function

a. The graph of a function: No vertical line intersects the curve more than once.   **b.** Not the graph of a function: The curve intersects at least one vertical line more than once.

Figure 1.26 The vertical line test

■ TRANSFORMATION OF FUNCTIONS

Sometimes the graph of a function can be sketched by translating or reflecting the graph of a related function. We call these translations and reflections *transformations* of a function. This procedure is illustrated in Figure 1.27, in which we have sketched the graph of $y = x^2$ and then translated and reflected that graph.

Functional Transformations

The graph defined by the equation
$$y - k = f(x - h)$$
is said to be a **translation** of the graph defined by $y = f(x)$.
    The translation (shift, as shown in Figure 1.27) is

to the right if $h > 0$ up if $k > 0$
to the left if $h < 0$ down if $k < 0$

> A **reflection in the *x*-axis** of the graph of $y = f(x)$ is the graph of
> $$y = -f(x)$$
> A **reflection in the *y*-axis** of the graph of $y = f(x)$ is the graph of
> $$y = f(-x)$$
>
> ■ *What this says*: If we replace x by $x - h$ and y by $y - k$, the graph is translated so the origin $(0, 0)$ is moved to the point (h, k). Also, the graph is reflected in the *x*-axis if we replace y by $-y$ in its equation, and it is reflected in the *y*-axis if we replace x by $-x$.

Given curve

Shift up

Shift down

$y = -x^2$ Reflection

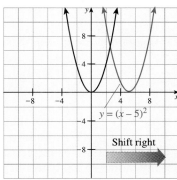

$y = (x - 5)^2$ Shift right

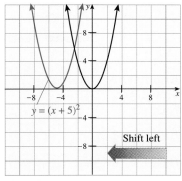

$y = (x + 5)^2$ Shift left

Figure 1.27 Transformations of $y = x^2$

EXAMPLE 9   Graphing with a translation

Graph $y + 2 = \sin(x - 1)$.

Solution   By inspection, the desired graph may be obtained by translating the standard sine curve $y = \sin x$ to the right by $h = 1$ unit and vertically by $k = -2$ units—that is, the origin $(0, 0)$ is moved to the point $(1, -2)$. The graph is shown in Figure 1.28.

Figure 1.28 Translation of $y = \sin x$ from $(0, 0)$ to $(h, k) = (1, -2)$ ■

EXAMPLE 10   Graphing with a reflection

Graph $y = -\sqrt{x}$.

Solution   The graph of this function is a reflection in the *x*-axis of the graph of $y = \sqrt{x}$, as shown in Figure 1.29. ■

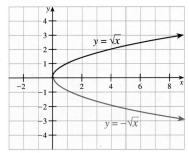

Figure 1.29 Reflection in the *x*-axis of $y = \sqrt{x}$

■ CLASSIFICATION OF FUNCTIONS

The functions shown in Table 1.3 are examples of **elementary functions.** We will now describe some of the common types of functions we use in this course.

Polynomial Function

A **polynomial function** is a function of the form

$$f(x) = a_n x^n + a_{n-1} x^{n-1} + \cdots + a_2 x^2 + a_1 x + a_0$$

where n is a nonnegative integer and $a_n, \ldots, a_2, a_1, a_0$ are constants. If $a_n \neq 0$, the integer n is called the **degree** of the polynomial. The constant a_n is called the **leading coefficient** and the constant a_0 is called the **constant term** of the polynomial function. In particular,

Examples of Polynomial Functions:
$f(x) = 5$
$f(x) = 2x - \sqrt{2}$
$f(x) = 3x^2 + 5x - \frac{1}{2}$
$f(x) = \sqrt{2}x^3 - \pi x$

    A constant function is zero degree: $f(x) = a$
    A linear function is first degree: $f(x) = ax + b$
    A quadratic function is second degree: $f(x) = ax^2 + bx + c$
    A cubic function is third degree: $f(x) = ax^3 + bx^2 + cx + d$
    A quartic function is fourth degree: $f(x) = ax^4 + bx^3 + cx^2 + dx + e$

The identity function, standard quadratic function, and standard cubic function in Table 1.3 on page 35 are examples of polynomial functions.

A second important algebraic function is a *rational function.*

Rational Function

A **rational function** is the quotient of two polynomial functions, $p(x)$ and $d(x)$:

$$f(x) = \frac{p(x)}{d(x)}, \qquad d(x) \neq 0$$

Examples of Rational Functions:
$f(x) = x^{-1}$
$f(x) = \dfrac{x - 5}{x^2 + 2x - 3}$
$f(x) = x^{-3} + \sqrt{2}x$

When we write $d(x) \neq 0$ we mean that all values c for which $d(c) = 0$ are excluded from the domain of d. The standard reciprocal and standard reciprocal squared functions in Table 1.3 are examples of rational functions.

If r is any nonzero real number, the function $f(x) = x^r$ is called a **power function** with exponent r. You should be familiar with the following cases:

Examples of Power Functions:
$f(x) = x^6$

$f(x) = x^{-4}$

$f(x) = x^{3/4}$

$f(x) = \sqrt[3]{x^2}$

Integral powers ($r = n$, a positive integer): $f(x) = x^n = \underbrace{x \cdot x \cdot \cdots \cdot x}_{n \text{ factors}}$

Reciprocal powers (r is a negative integer): $f(x) = x^{-n} = \dfrac{1}{x^n}$ for $x \neq 0$

Roots ($r = \dfrac{m}{n}$ is a rational number): $f(x) = x^{m/n} = \sqrt[n]{x^m} = (\sqrt[n]{x})^m$ for

$x \geq 0$ if n even, $n \neq 0$ $\left(\dfrac{m}{n} \text{ is reduced}\right)$

Power functions can also have irrational exponents (such as $\sqrt{2}$ or π), but such functions must be defined in a special way and are introduced in Chapter 5.

A function is called **algebraic** if it can be constructed using algebraic operations (such as adding, subtracting, multiplying, dividing, or taking roots) starting with polynomials. Any rational function is an algebraic function.

Functions that are not algebraic are called **transcendental.** The following functions are transcendental functions:

Trigonometric functions are the functions sine, cosine, tangent, secant, cosecant, and cotangent. These functions are reviewed in the *Student Mathematics Handbook*. You can also review these functions by consulting a trigonometry or precalculus textbook.

Exponential functions are functions of the form $f(x) = b^x$, where b is a positive constant. We will study these functions in Chapter 5.

Logarithmic functions are functions of the form $f(x) = \log_b x$, where b is a positive constant. We will also study these functions in Chapter 5.

PROBLEM SET 1.4

In Problems 1–12, find the domain of f and compute the indicated values or state that the corresponding x-value is not in the domain.

Ⓐ **1.** $f(x) = 2x + 3$; $f(-2)$, $f(1)$, $f(0)$

2. $f(x) = -x^2 + 2x + 3$; $f(0)$, $f(1)$, $f(-2)$

3. $f(x) = 3x^2 + 5x - 2$; $f(1)$, $f(0)$, $f(-2)$

4. $f(x) = x + \frac{1}{x}$; $f(-1)$, $f(1)$, $f(2)$

5. $f(x) = \frac{(x + 3)(x - 2)}{x + 3}$; $f(2)$, $f(0)$, $f(-3)$

6. $f(x) = (2x - 1)^{-3/2}$; $f(1)$, $f\left(\frac{1}{2}\right)$, $f(13)$

7. $f(x) = \sqrt{x^2 + 2x}$; $f(-1)$, $f\left(\frac{1}{2}\right)$, $f(1)$

8. $f(x) = \sqrt{x^2 + 5x + 6}$; $f(0)$, $f(1)$, $f(-2)$

9. $f(x) = \sin(1 - 2x)$; $f(-1)$, $f\left(\frac{1}{2}\right)$, $f(1)$

10. $f(x) = \sin x - \cos x$; $f(0)$, $f\left(-\frac{\pi}{2}\right)$, $f(\pi)$

11. $f(x) = \begin{cases} -2x + 4 & \text{if } x \le 1 \\ x + 1 & \text{if } x > 1 \end{cases}$

$f(3)$, $f(1)$, $f(0)$

12. $f(x) = \begin{cases} 3 & \text{if } x < -5 \\ x + 1 & \text{if } -5 \le x \le 5 \\ \sqrt{x} & \text{if } x > 5 \end{cases}$

$f(-6)$, $f(-5)$, $f(16)$

In Problems 13–20, evaluate the difference quotient $\frac{f(x + h) - f(x)}{h}$ for the given function f.

13. $f(x) = 9x + 3$ **14.** $f(x) = 5 - 2x$

15. $f(x) = 5x^2$ **16.** $f(x) = 3x^2 + 2x$

17. $f(x) = |x|$ if $x < -1$ and $0 < h < 1$

18. $f(x) = |x|$ if $x > 1$ and $0 < h < 1$

19. $f(x) = \frac{1}{x}$ **20.** $f(x) = \frac{x + 1}{x - 1}$

State whether the functions f and g in Problems 21–23 are equal.

21. a. $f(x) = \frac{2x^2 + x}{x}$; $g(x) = 2x + 1$

b. $f(x) = \frac{2x^2 + x}{x}$; $g(x) = 2x + 1$, $x \ne 0$

22. a. $f(x) = \frac{2x^2 - x - 6}{x - 2}$; $g(x) = 2x + 3$, $x \ne 2$

b. $f(x) = \frac{3x^2 - 7x - 6}{x - 3}$; $g(x) = 3x + 2$, $x \ne 3$

23. a. $f(x) = \frac{3x^2 - 5x - 2}{x - 2}$; $g(x) = 3x + 1$

b. $f(x) = \frac{(3x + 1)(x - 2)}{x - 2}$, $x \ne 6$;

$g(x) = \frac{(3x + 1)(x - 6)}{x - 6}$, $x \ne 2$

Classify the functions defined in Problems 24–27 as even, odd, or neither.

24. a. $f_1(x) = x^2 + 1$ **b.** $f_2(x) = \sqrt{x^2}$

25. a. $f_3(x) = \frac{1}{3x^3 - 4}$ **b.** $f_4(x) = x^3 + x$

26. a. $f_5(x) = \frac{1}{(x^3 + 3)^2}$ **b.** $f_6(x) = \frac{1}{(x^3 + x)^2}$

27. a. $f_7(x) = |x|$ **b.** $f_8(x) = |x| + 3$

In Problems 28–33, find the composite functions $f \circ g$ and $g \circ f$.

28. $f(x) = x^2 + 1$ and $g(x) = 2x$

29. $f(x) = \sin x$ and $g(x) = 1 - x^2$

30. $f(t) = \sqrt{t}$ and $g(t) = t^2$

31. $f(u) = \frac{u - 1}{u + 1}$ and $g(u) = \frac{u + 1}{1 - u}$

32. $f(x) = \sin x$ and $g(x) = 2x + 3$

33. $f(x) = \frac{1}{x}$ and $g(x) = \tan x$

In Problems 34–37, express f as the composition of two functions u and g such that $f(x) = g[u(x)]$.

34. a. $f(x) = (2x^2 - 1)^4$ **b.** $f(x) = \sqrt{5x - 1}$

35. a. $f(x) = \tan^2 x$ **b.** $f(x) = \tan x^2$

36. a. $f(x) = \sin \sqrt{x}$ **b.** $f(x) = \sqrt{\sin x}$

37. a. $f(x) = \sin\left(\frac{x + 1}{2 - x}\right)$ **b.** $f(x) = \tan\left(\frac{2x}{1 - x}\right)$

Use the directory of curves (Table 1.3) and the ideas of translation and reflection to sketch the graphs of the functions given in Problems 38–51.

38. $f(x) = x^2 + 4$ **39.** $f(x) = (x + 4)^2$

40. $y = -x^3$ **41.** $y = -|x|$

42. $y = \dfrac{1}{x - 3}$

43. $y + 1 = \dfrac{1}{x}$

44. $y = \sqrt[3]{x + 2}$

45. $y = \sqrt[3]{x} + 2$

46. $y = \cos(x - 1)$

47. $y = \cos x - 1$

48. $y = \sin(x + 2)$

49. $y = \sin x + 2$

50. $y = \tan(x + 1)$

51. $y = \tan x + 1$

52. If point A in Figure 1.30 has coordinates $(2, f(2))$, what are the coordinates of P and Q?

Problem 52   Problem 53

Figure 1.30

53. If point B in Figure 1.30 has coordinates $(3, g(3))$, what are the coordinates of R and S?

54. A ball is thrown directly upward from the edge of a cliff in such a way that t seconds later, it is $s = -16t^2 + 96t + 144$ feet above the ground at the base of the cliff. Sketch the graph of this equation (making the t-axis the horizontal axis) and then answer these questions:

a. How high is the cliff?

b. When (to the nearest tenth of a second) does the ball hit the ground at the base of the cliff?

c. Estimate the time it takes for the ball to reach its maximum height. What is the maximum height?

55. Suppose the total cost (in dollars) of manufacturing q units of a certain commodity is given by

$$C(q) = q^3 - 30q^2 + 400q + 500 \text{ for } 0 \le q \le 30$$

a. Compute the cost of manufacturing 20 units.

b. Compute the cost of manufacturing the twentieth unit.

56. An efficiency study of the morning shift at a certain factory indicates that an average worker who arrives on the job at 8:00 A.M. will have assembled $f(x) = -x^3 + 6x + 15x^2$ CD players x hours later ($0 \le x \le 8$).

a. How many players will such a worker have assembled by 10:00 A.M.?

b. How many players will such a worker assemble between 9:00 A.M. and 10:00 A.M.?

57. In physics, a light source of luminous intensity K candles is said to have *illuminance* $I = K/s^2$ on a flat surface s ft away. Suppose a small, unshaded lamp of luminous intensity 30 candles is connected to a rope that allows it to be raised and lowered between the floor and the top of a 10-ft-high ceiling. Assume that the lamp is being raised and lowered in such a way that at time t (in min) it is $s = 6t - t^2$ ft above the floor.

a. Express the illuminance on the floor as a composite function of t for $0 < t < 6$.

b. What is the illuminance when $t = 1$? When $t = 4$?

58. It is estimated that t years from now, the population of a certain suburban community will be $P(t) = 20 - \dfrac{6}{t + 1}$ thousand people.

a. What will the population be nine years from now?

b. By how much will the population increase during the ninth year?

c. What will happen to the size of the population in the "long run"?

59. To study the rate at which animals learn, a psychology student performs an experiment in which a rat is sent repeatedly through a laboratory maze. Suppose that the time (in minutes) required for the rat to traverse the maze on the nth trial is approximately $f(n) = 3 + \dfrac{12}{n}$.

a. What is the domain of the function f?

b. For what values of n does $f(n)$ have meaning in the context of the psychology experiment?

c. How long does it take the rat to traverse the maze on the third trial?

d. On which trial does the rat first traverse the maze in 4 minutes or less?

e. According to the function f, what will happen to the time required for the rat to traverse the maze as the number of trials increases? Will the rat ever be able to traverse the maze in less than three minutes?

60. Biologists have found that the speed of blood in an artery is a function of the distance of the blood from the artery's central axis. According to *Poiseuille's law*, the speed (cm/sec) of blood that is r cm from the central axis of an artery is given by the function $S(r) = C(R^2 - r^2)$, where C is a constant and R is the radius of the artery.* Suppose that for a certain artery, $C = 1.76 \times 10^5$ cm/s^2 and $R = 1.2 \times 10^{-2}$ cm.

a. Compute the speed of the blood at the central axis of this artery.

b. Compute the speed of the blood midway between the artery's wall and central axis.

61. At a certain factory, the total cost of manufacturing q units during the daily production run is $C(q) = q^2 + q + 900$ dollars. On a typical workday, the numbers of units manufactured during the first t hours of a production run can be modeled by the function $q(t) = 25t$.

a. Express the total manufacturing cost as a function of t.

b. How much will have been spent on production by the end of the third hour?

c. When will the total manufacturing cost reach $11,000?

*The law and the unit poise, a unit of viscosity, are both named for the French physician Jean Louis Poiseuille (1799–1869).

Computational Window

62. Define the functions $f(x) = x^2 + 1$ and $g(x) = x^3 - x^2 - 9x + 9$ and plot them on the same graph. From your graph, estimate the three values of x where the plots cross.

63. Form the rational function $r(x) = \dfrac{g(x)}{f(x)}$ and plot it on $[-20, 20]$. Make a hand sketch of what you see. The graph of $r(x)$ looks linear for "large" x. Can you figure out *what* linear function approximates r for large x?

64. Define the function $G(x) = x^5 + 2x^4 - 9x - 18$ and plot G on several x-values to get a good idea of its behavior.

   a. Zoom in on the largest x-value for which $G = 0$. Does the function become "almost linear" as you zoom in?

   b. One way or another, factor G to find the exact x-values at which $G = 0$. *Hint*: $G(2) = 0$.

   c. Define a new rational function, $R = G/F$, where $F(x) = x^3 + 3$. Decide if R is "almost linear" for x large (as was the case with the r discussed in Problem 63). Discuss briefly.

65. Imagine a sphere of unknown radius r with a meter stick sitting upright at the "north pole." A wire is strung from the top of the stick to a point of tangency of the sphere; and when paced off along the surface, this distance is 25 meters.

   a. Show that one gets the following equation for r:

   $$\cos\frac{25}{r} - \frac{r}{r+1} = 0$$

   b. Graphically estimate, say to one decimal place accuracy, the meaningful value of r. *Note*: there are many solutions, but the one that you want is greater than 25; why?

Ⓒ 66. JOURNAL PROBLEM:* *The Mathematics Student Journal.* Given that $f(11) = 11$ and

$$f(x + 3) = \frac{f(x) - 1}{f(x) + 1}$$

for all x, find $f(2000)$.

1.5 THE LIMIT OF A FUNCTION

IN THIS SECTION Intuitive notion of limits, limits by graphing, limits by table, limits that do not exist

This section introduces you to the limit of a function, a concept that gives calculus its power and distinguishes it from other areas of mathematics, such as algebra.

Our goal in this section is to give an intuitive introduction to the *limit of a function*. A more rigorous treatment will be given in Section 1.8, and variations of the limit concept will be introduced later in the text.

The development of the limit concept was a major mathematical breakthrough in the history of mathematics, and it is unrealistic for you to expect to understand everything about this concept immediately. Have patience, read the examples carefully, and work as many problems as possible, and eventually, the limit concept will become a useful part of your mathematical toolkit.

■ INTUITIVE NOTION OF A LIMIT

The limit of a function f is a tool for investigating the behavior of $f(x)$ as x gets closer and closer to a particular number c. To visualize this concept we begin with an example.

---

†Volume 28, 1980, issue 3, p. 2; note the journal problem requests $f(1979)$, which, no doubt, was related to the publication date. We have taken the liberty of updating the requested value.

Let Y1 = $(16X^2 - 64)/(X - 2)$

Y1**8**(16X²-64)/(X-
2)

Xmin=0   Ymin=0
Xmax=3   Ymax=100
Xscl=.5   Yscl=10

Using **TRACE** we find:
X=2.021056, Y=64.336842
X=1.9894737,
Y=63.831579

EXAMPLE 1   Velocity as a limit

A freely falling body experiencing no air resistance falls $s(t) = 16t^2$ feet in t seconds. Express the body's velocity at time $t = 2$ as a limit.

Solution   We need to define some sort of "mathematical speedometer" for measuring the *instantaneous velocity* of the body at time $t = 2$. Toward this end, we first compute the *average velocity* $\bar{v}(t)$ of the body between time $t = 2$ and any other time t by the formula

$$\bar{v}(t) = \frac{\text{DISTANCE TRAVELED}}{\text{ELAPSED TIME}} = \frac{s(t) - s(2)}{t - 2}$$

$$= \frac{16t^2 - 16(2)^2}{t - 2} = \frac{16t^2 - 64}{t - 2}$$

As t gets closer and closer to 2, it is reasonable to expect the average velocity $\bar{v}(t)$ to approach the value of the required instantaneous velocity at time $t = 2$.

$$\lim_{t \to 2} \bar{v}(t) = \underbrace{\lim_{t \to 2} \frac{16t^2 - 64}{t - 2}}$$
This is the instantaneous velocity at $t = 2$.

Notice that we cannot find the instantaneous velocity at time $t = 2$ by simply substituting $t = 2$ into the average velocity formula because this would yield the meaningless form 0/0.   ▬

We now devote the remainder of this section to an intuitive introduction of how we can find the value of limits such as the one that appears in Example 1.

Limit of a Function (Informal Definition)

The notation

$$\lim_{x \to c} f(x) = L$$

is read "the limit of $f(x)$ as x approaches c is L" and means that the functional values $f(x)$ can be made arbitrarily close to L by choosing x sufficiently close to c (but not equal to c).

■ *What this says*: If $f(x)$ becomes arbitrarily close to a single number L as x approaches c from either side, then we say that L is the limit of $f(x)$ as x approaches c. The limit $\lim_{x \to c} f(x)$ exists if and only if the limiting value from the left equals the limiting value from the right.

This informal definition of limit cannot be used in proofs until we give precise meaning to terms such as "arbitrarily close to L" and "sufficiently close to c." This will be done in Section 1.8. For now, we shall use this informal definition to gain a working knowledge of limits.

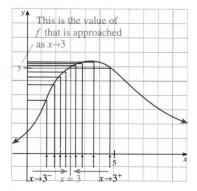

Figure 1.31 Limit as x approaches c

■ LIMITS BY GRAPHING

Figure 1.31 shows the graph of a function f and the number $c = 3$. The arrowheads are used to illustrate possible sequences of numbers along the x-axis, approaching from both the left and the right. As x approaches $c = 3$, $f(x)$ gets closer and closer to 5. We write this as

$$\lim_{x \to 3} f(x) = 5$$

As x approaches 3 from the left we write $x \to 3^-$, and as x approaches 3 from the right we write $x \to 3^+$. We say that the limit at $x = 3$ exists only if the value approached from the left is the same as the value approached from the right.

EXAMPLE 2   Estimating limits by graphing

Given the function f defined by the graph in Figure 1.32, find the following limits by inspection, if they exist:

a. $\displaystyle\lim_{x\to3^-} f(x)$ **b.** $\displaystyle\lim_{x\to-2^+} f(x)$ **c.** $\displaystyle\lim_{x\to0} f(x)$

Solution   Take a good look at the given graph; notice the open circles on the graph at $x = 0$ and $x = -2$ and also notice that $f(0) = 5$.

a. $\displaystyle\lim_{x\to3^-} f(x)$ is the value that f approaches as x tends toward 3 from the left. From Figure 1.32 we see that this value is -2. We write $\displaystyle\lim_{x\to3^-} f(x) = -2$.

b. $\displaystyle\lim_{x\to-2^+} f(x)$ is the value that f approaches as x tends toward -2 from the right. We see that this value is 4, so
$$\lim_{x\to-2^+} f(x) = 4$$

c. To find $\displaystyle\lim_{x\to0} f(x)$ we need to look at both the left and right limits. Look at Figure 1.32 to find
$$\lim_{x\to0^-} f(x) = 1 \quad\text{and}\quad \lim_{x\to0^+} f(x) = 1$$

so $\displaystyle\lim_{x\to0} f(x)$ exists and $\displaystyle\lim_{x\to0} f(x) = 1$. Notice here that *the value of the limit as $x \to 0$ is not the same as the value of the function at $x = 0$.* ■

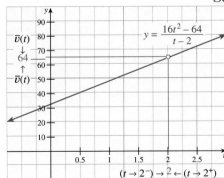

Figure 1.32 Limits from a graph

EXAMPLE 3   Finding the limit from Example 1 by graphing

Find $\displaystyle\lim_{t\to2} \frac{16t^2 - 64}{t - 2}$ by graphing.

Solution

$$\bar{v}(t) = \frac{16t^2 - 64}{t - 2} = \frac{16(t^2 - 4)}{t - 2} = \frac{16(t - 2)(t + 2)}{t - 2} = 16(t + 2), \quad t \neq 2$$

The graph of $\bar{v}(t)$ is a line with a deleted point, as shown in Figure 1.33. If you have a graphing calculator, compare this with the graph shown on your calculator (see the computational window for Example 1).

The limit can now be seen:

$$\lim_{t\to2} \bar{v}(t) = 64$$

That is, the instantaneous velocity of the falling body in Example 1 is 64 ft/sec. ■

Notice from the preceding examples that when we write

$$\lim_{x\to c} f(x) = L$$

we do not require c itself to be in the domain of f, nor do we require $f(c)$, if it is defined, to be equal to the limit. Functions with the special property that

$$\lim_{x\to c} f(x) = f(c)$$

are said to be **continuous at $x = c$**. This idea is considered in Section 1.7.

Figure 1.33 $\displaystyle\lim_{t\to2} \frac{16t^2 - 64}{t - 2} = 64$

⊘ The limit of a function as the independent variable approaches a point does not depend on the value of the function at that point. ⊘

■ LIMITS BY TABLE

It is not always convenient (or even possible) to first draw a graph in order to find limits. You can also use a calculator or a computer to construct a table of values for f as $x \to c$.

EXAMPLE 4   Finding a limit with a table

Find $\lim\limits_{t \to 2} \dfrac{16t^2 - 64}{t - 2}$ by using a table.

Solution   You will recognize this limit from Examples 1 and 3. We need to begin by selecting sequences of numbers for $t \to 2^-$ and $t \to 2^+$:

	t approaches from the left; $t \to 2^-$. $\longrightarrow$				$\longleftarrow t$ approaches from the right; $t \to 2^+$.		
t	1.950	1.995	1.999	2	2.001	2.015	2.100
$\bar{v}(t)$	63.200	63.920	63.984	Undefined	64.016	64.240	65.600
	$v(t)$ approaches 64 from the left. $\longrightarrow$				$\longleftarrow v(t)$ approaches 64 from the right.		

That is, the pattern of numbers suggests

$$\lim_{t \to 2} \frac{16t^2 - 64}{t - 2} = 64$$

as we found using a graphical approach in Example 3.   ▬

EXAMPLE 5   Finding limits of trigonometric functions

Evaluate $\lim\limits_{x \to 0} \sin x$ and $\lim\limits_{x \to 0} \cos x$.

Solution   We can evaluate these limits by table or by graph.
By table:

x	1	0.5	0.1	0.01	-0.5	-0.1	-0.01
$\sin x$	0.8415	0.4794	0.0998	0.0099998	-0.4794	-0.0998	-0.0099998
$\cos x$	0.5413	0.8776	0.9950	0.9985	0.8776	0.9950	0.99995

The pattern of numbers in the table suggests that

$$\lim_{x \to 0} \sin x = 0 \quad \text{and} \quad \lim_{x \to 0} \cos x = 1$$ ▬

EXAMPLE 6   Evaluating a trigonometric limit using a table

Evaluate $\lim\limits_{x \to 0} \dfrac{\sin x}{x}$.

Solution $f(x) = \dfrac{\sin x}{x}$ is an even function because

$$f(-x) = \frac{\sin(-x)}{-x} = \frac{-\sin x}{-x} = \frac{\sin x}{x} = f(x)$$

Computational Window ▼ ▲

It is easy to find the limits of $\sin x$ and $\cos x$ as $x \to 0$ by looking at the graphs.

Y₁＝sin X

```
Xmin=-6.152285…
Xmax=6.1522856…
Xscl=1.5707963…
Ymin=-1.5
Ymax=1.5
Yscl=.5
```

Y₁＝cos X

```
Xmin=-6.152285…
Xmax=6.1522856…
Xscl=1.5707963…
Ymin=-1.5
Ymax=1.5
Yscl=.5
```

This means that we only need to find the right-hand limit because the limiting behavior from the left will be the same as that of the right-hand limit. These values are shown in the following table.

	x approaches 0 from the right. $\longrightarrow$				
x	0.1	0.05	0.01	0.001	0
$f(x)$	0.998334	0.999583	0.9999833	0.99999983	undefined
	$f(x)$ approaches 1 from below. $\longrightarrow$				

The table suggests that $\lim\limits_{x \to 0^+} \dfrac{\sin x}{x} = 1$; therefore, $\lim\limits_{x \to 0} \dfrac{\sin x}{x} = 1$. We shall consider this limit more completely in Section 2.3.

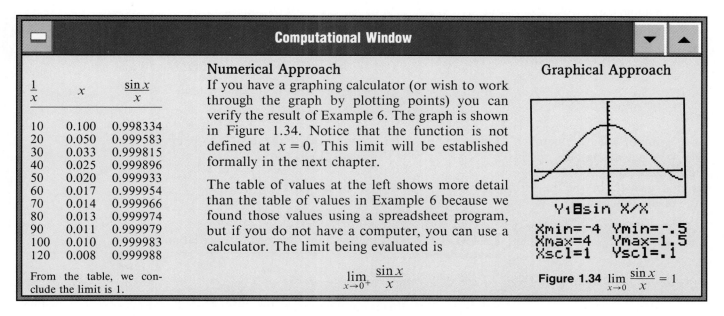

Computational Window

$\dfrac{1}{x}$	x	$\dfrac{\sin x}{x}$
10	0.100	0.998334
20	0.050	0.999583
30	0.033	0.999815
40	0.025	0.999896
50	0.020	0.999933
60	0.017	0.999954
70	0.014	0.999966
80	0.013	0.999974
90	0.011	0.999979
100	0.010	0.999983
120	0.008	0.999988

From the table, we conclude the limit is 1.

Numerical Approach

If you have a graphing calculator (or wish to work through the graph by plotting points) you can verify the result of Example 6. The graph is shown in Figure 1.34. Notice that the function is not defined at $x = 0$. This limit will be established formally in the next chapter.

The table of values at the left shows more detail than the table of values in Example 6 because we found those values using a spreadsheet program, but if you do not have a computer, you can use a calculator. The limit being evaluated is

$$\lim_{x \to 0^+} \frac{\sin x}{x}$$

Graphical Approach

Y₁=sin X/X
Xmin=-4   Ymin=-.5
Xmax=4   Ymax=1.5
Xscl=1   Yscl=.1

Figure 1.34 $\lim\limits_{x \to 0} \dfrac{\sin x}{x} = 1$

We should note that when we use a table (using either calculator or computer values) we may be misled. All we can say is that if a limit exists, then it can be calculated using a table. That is why when we find a limit from a table we must be cautious about the possibility of erroneous results. For example, if the table method is used with Example 8 (given at the end of this section), an erroneous conclusion is possible.

■ **LIMITS THAT DO NOT EXIST**

It may happen that a function f does not have a (finite) limit as $x \to c$. When $\lim\limits_{x \to c} f(x)$ fails to exist, we say that $f(x)$ **diverges** as x approaches c. The following examples illustrate how divergence may occur.

EXAMPLE 7   A function that diverges

Evaluate $\lim\limits_{x \to 0} \dfrac{1}{x^2}$.

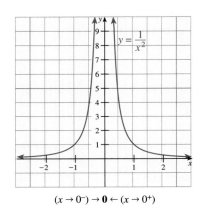

$(x \to 0^-) \to 0 \leftarrow (x \to 0^+)$

Figure 1.35 $\lim\limits_{x \to 0} \dfrac{1}{x^2}$ does not exist, and the graph illustrates that f rises without bound.

A Function Diverges to Infinity

⊘ It is important to remember that ∞ is **not** a number, but is merely a symbol denoting unrestricted growth in the magnitude of the function. ⊘

Solution   As $x \to 0$, the corresponding functional values of $f(x) = \dfrac{1}{x^2}$ grow arbitrarily large, as indicated in the following table.

x approaches 0 from the left; $x \to 0^-$ →				← x approaches 0 from the right; $x \to 0^+$		
x	-0.1	-0.05	-0.001	0	0.001	0.005	0.01
$f(x) = \dfrac{1}{x^2}$	100	400	1×10^6	undefined	1×10^6	4×10^4	1×10^4

The graph of f is shown in Figure 1.35.

Geometrically, the graph of $y = f(x)$ rises without bound as $x \to 0$. Thus, $\lim\limits_{x \to 0} \dfrac{1}{x^2}$ does not exist, so we say f diverges as $x \to 0$.   ▬

A function f that increases or decreases without bound as x approaches c is said to **diverge to infinity** (∞) at c. We indicate this behavior by writing

$\lim\limits_{x \to c} f(x) = +\infty$ if f increases without bound and by

$\lim\limits_{x \to c} f(x) = -\infty$ if it decreases without bound.

Using this notation, we can rewrite the answer to Example 7 as

$$\lim\limits_{x \to 0} \frac{1}{x^2} = +\infty$$

EXAMPLE 8   A function that diverges by oscillation

Evaluate $\lim\limits_{x \to 0} \sin\dfrac{1}{x}$.

Solution   Note this is not the same as $\lim\limits_{x \to 0} \dfrac{\sin x}{x}$. The values of $f(x) = \sin\dfrac{1}{x}$ oscillate infinitely often between 1 and -1 as x approaches 0. For example, $f(x) = 1$ for $x = 2/\pi, 2/(5\pi), 2/(9\pi), \ldots$ and $f(x) = -1$ for $x = 2/(3\pi), 2/(7\pi), 2/(11\pi), \ldots$. The graph of $f(x)$ is shown in Figure 1.36.

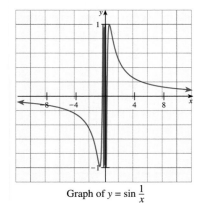

Graph of $y = \sin\dfrac{1}{x}$

Detail of left hand graph on $[-1, 1]$

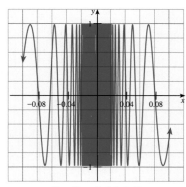

Detail on $[-0.1, 0.1]$

Figure 1.36 $\lim\limits_{x \to 0} \sin\dfrac{1}{x}$ diverges by oscillation.

Because the values of $f(x)$ do not approach a unique number L as $x \to 0$, the limit does not exist. This kind of function limiting behavior is called *divergence by oscillation.*

In the next section, we will introduce some properties of limits that will help us evaluate limits efficiently. In the following problem set remember that the emphasis is on an intuitive understanding of limits, including their evaluation by graphing and by table.

PROBLEM SET 1.5

Ⓐ *Given the functions defined by the graphs in Figure 1.37, find the limits in Problems 1–12.*

| Graph of f | Graph of g | Graph of t |

Figure 1.37 Graphs of the functions f, g, and t

1. $\lim\limits_{x \to 3} f(x)$ 2. $\lim\limits_{x \to 2} f(x)$ 3. $\lim\limits_{x \to 0} f(x)$

4. $\lim\limits_{x \to -3} g(x)$ 5. $\lim\limits_{x \to -1} g(x)$ 6. $\lim\limits_{x \to 2^+} g(x)$

7. $\lim\limits_{x \to 3^+} g(x)$ 8. $\lim\limits_{x \to 2^-} t(x)$ 9. $\lim\limits_{x \to 2^+} t(x)$

10. $\lim\limits_{x \to 2} t(x)$ 11. $\lim\limits_{x \to 4} t(x)$ 12. $\lim\limits_{x \to -4} t(x)$

Find the limits by filling in the appropriate values in the tables in Problems 13–15.

13. $\lim\limits_{x \to 5^-} f(x)$, where $f(x) = (4x - 5)$

x	2	3	4	4.5	4.9	4.99
$f(x)$	3					

14. $\lim\limits_{x \to 2^-} g(x)$, where $g(x) = \dfrac{x^3 - 8}{x^2 + 2x + 4}$

x	1	1.5	1.9	1.99	1.999	1.9999
$g(x)$	-1					

15. $\lim\limits_{x \to 2} h(x)$, where $h(x) = \dfrac{3x^2 - 2x - 8}{x - 2}$

x	1	1.9	1.99	1.999	3	2.5	2.1	2.001
$h(x)$	7							

16. Find $\lim\limits_{x \to 0} \dfrac{\tan 2x}{\tan 3x}$ using the following procedure based on the fact that $f(x) = \tan x$ is an odd function:

If $f(x) = \dfrac{\tan 2x}{\tan 3x}$, then

$f(-x) = \dfrac{\tan(-2x)}{\tan(-3x)} = \dfrac{-\tan 2x}{-\tan 3x} = f(x).$

Thus, we simply need to check for $x \to 0^+$. Find the limit by completing the following table.

x	1	0.5	0.1	0.01	0.001	0.0001
$f(x)$	15.33					

Describe each illustration in Problems 17–22 using a limit statement.

17.   18.

19.   20.

21.   22.

Ⓑ 23. ■ **What Does This Say?** Explain a process for finding a limit.

Evaluate the limits in Problems 24–58 to two decimal places by graphing or by using a table of values. If the limit does not exist, explain why.

24. $\lim\limits_{x \to 0^+} x^4$ 25. $\lim\limits_{x \to 0^+} \cos x$

26. $\lim\limits_{x \to 2^-} (x^2 - 4)$ 27. $\lim\limits_{x \to 3^-} (x^2 - 4)$

28. $\lim\limits_{x \to 1^+} \dfrac{1}{x - 3}$ 29. $\lim\limits_{x \to -3^+} \dfrac{1}{x - 3}$

30. $\lim\limits_{x \to 3} \dfrac{1}{x - 3}$ 31. $\lim\limits_{x \to \pi/2} \tan x$

32. $\lim\limits_{x\to 0} \dfrac{\cos x}{x}$

33. $\lim\limits_{x\to \pi} \dfrac{\cos x}{x}$

34. $\lim\limits_{x\to 0.4} |x|\,\sin\dfrac{1}{x}$

35. $\lim\limits_{x\to 0} |x|\,\sin\dfrac{1}{x}$

36. $\lim\limits_{x\to 0} \dfrac{1-\cos x}{x}$

37. $\lim\limits_{x\to \pi} \dfrac{1-\cos x}{x}$

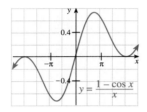

38. $\lim\limits_{x\to 3} \dfrac{x^2+3x-10}{x-2}$

39. $\lim\limits_{x\to 3} \dfrac{x^2+3x-10}{x-3}$

40. $\lim\limits_{x\to 1} \dfrac{x^5-1}{x-1}$

41. $\lim\limits_{x\to 0} \dfrac{x}{\sin x}$

42. $\lim\limits_{x\to \pi/2} \dfrac{2x-\pi}{\cos x}$

43. $\lim\limits_{x\to 1} \dfrac{\sin\frac{\pi}{x}}{x-1}$

44. $\lim\limits_{x\to 9} \dfrac{\sqrt{x}-3}{x-9}$

45. $\lim\limits_{x\to 9} \dfrac{\sqrt{x}-3}{x-3}$

46. $\lim\limits_{x\to 2} \dfrac{\sqrt{x+2}-2}{x-2}$

47. $\lim\limits_{x\to 1} \dfrac{\sqrt[3]{x}-1}{\sqrt{x}-1}$

48. $\lim\limits_{x\to 3^+} \dfrac{\sqrt{x-3}+x}{3-x}$

49. $\lim\limits_{x\to 4^+} \dfrac{\frac{1}{\sqrt{x}}-\frac{1}{2}}{x-4}$

50. $\lim\limits_{x\to 0} \dfrac{\sin 2x}{x}$

51. $\lim\limits_{x\to 0} \dfrac{\sin 3x}{x}$

52. $\lim\limits_{x\to 0} \dfrac{1-\frac{1}{x+1}}{x}$

53. $\lim\limits_{x\to 1} \dfrac{1-\frac{1}{x}}{x-1}$

54. $\lim\limits_{x\to 0}(1+x)^{1/x}$

55. $\lim\limits_{x\to 1}(1+x)^{1/x}$

56. $\lim\limits_{x\to 0}\left(x^2-\dfrac{2^x}{2{,}000}\right)$

57. $\lim\limits_{x\to 0} \dfrac{\tan x - x}{x^2}$

58. $\lim\limits_{x\to 0} \cos\dfrac{1}{x}$

59. A ball is thrown directly upward from the edge of a cliff and travels in such a way that t seconds later, its height above the ground at the base of the cliff is

$$s(t) = -16t^2 + 40t + 24 \text{ ft}$$

a. Compute the limit
$$v(t) = \lim_{x\to t} \frac{s(x)-s(t)}{x-t}$$
to find the instantaneous velocity of the ball at time t.

b. What is the ball's initial velocity?

c. When does the ball hit the ground, and what is its impact velocity?

d. When does the ball have velocity 0? What physical interpretation should be given to this time?

60. Tom and Sue are driving along a straight, level road in a car whose speedometer needle is broken but which has a trip odometer that can measure the distance traveled from an arbitrary starting point in tenths of a mile. At 2:50 P.M., Tom says he would like to know how fast they are traveling at 3:00 P.M., so Sue takes down the odometer readings listed in the table below, makes a few calculations, and announces the desired velocity. What is her result?

time t	2:50	2:55	2:59	3:00	3:01	3:03	3:06
odometer reading	33.9	38.2	41.5	42.4	43.2	44.9	47.4

Computational Window

In Problems 61–64, estimate the limits by plotting points or by using tables.

61. $\lim\limits_{x\to 13} \dfrac{x^3-9x^2-45x-91}{x-13}$

62. $\lim\limits_{x\to 13} \dfrac{x^3-9x^2-39x-86}{x-13}$

63. $\lim\limits_{x\to 13} \dfrac{x^4-26x^3+178x^2-234x+1{,}521}{x-13}$

64. $\lim\limits_{x\to 0}(\sin x)^x$

65. The tabular approach is a convenient device for discussing limits informally, but if it is not used very carefully, it can be misleading. For example, for $x \neq 0$, let

$$f(x) = \sin\frac{1}{x}$$

a. Construct a table showing the values of $f(x)$ for $x = \dfrac{-2}{\pi}, \dfrac{-2}{9\pi}, \dfrac{-2}{13\pi}, \dfrac{2}{19\pi}, \dfrac{2}{7\pi}, \dfrac{2}{3\pi}$. Based on this table, what would you say about $\lim\limits_{x\to 0} f(x)$?

b. Construct a second table, this time showing the values of $f(x)$ for $x = \dfrac{-1}{2\pi}, \dfrac{-1}{11\pi}, \dfrac{-1}{20\pi}, \dfrac{1}{50\pi}, \dfrac{1}{30\pi}, \dfrac{1}{5\pi}$.

c. What conclusions can you make about $\lim\limits_{x\to 0} f(x)$?

1.6 PROPERTIES OF LIMITS

> **IN THIS SECTION** Computations with limits, using algebra to find limits, limits of piecewise-defined functions
>
> It is important to be able to find limits easily and efficiently, but the methods of graphing and table construction of the previous section are not always easy or efficient. In this section we state some limit rules and then show how to use these rules along with algebra to evaluate limits.

■ COMPUTATIONS WITH LIMITS

Here is a list of properties that can be used to evaluate a variety of limits.

Basic Properties and Rules for Limits

For any real number c, suppose the functions f and g both have limits at $x = c$.

Constant rule $\lim\limits_{x \to c} k = k$ for any constant k

Limit of x rule $\lim\limits_{x \to c} x = c$

Multiple rule $\lim\limits_{x \to c} [sf(x)] = s \lim\limits_{x \to c} f(x)$ for any constant s
The limit of a constant times a function is the constant times the limit of the function.

Sum rule $\lim\limits_{x \to c} [f(x) + g(x)] = \lim\limits_{x \to c} f(x) + \lim\limits_{x \to c} g(x)$
The limit of a sum is the sum of the limits.

Difference rule $\lim\limits_{x \to c} [f(x) - g(x)] = \lim\limits_{x \to c} f(x) - \lim\limits_{x \to c} g(x)$
The limit of a difference is the difference of the limits.

Product rule $\lim\limits_{x \to c} [f(x)g(x)] = \left[\lim\limits_{x \to c} f(x)\right]\left[\lim\limits_{x \to c} g(x)\right]$
The limit of a product is the product of the limits.

Quotient rule $\lim\limits_{x \to c} \dfrac{f(x)}{g(x)} = \dfrac{\lim\limits_{x \to c} f(x)}{\lim\limits_{x \to c} g(x)}$ if $\lim\limits_{x \to c} g(x) \neq 0$
The limit of a quotient is the quotient of the limits, as long as the limit of the denominator is not zero.

Power rule $\lim\limits_{x \to c} \left[f(x)\right]^n = \left[\lim\limits_{x \to c} f(x)\right]^n$ n is a rational number and the limit on the right exists.
The limit of a power is the power of the limit.

Another property that will be especially important to us in our future work is given in the following box.

Squeeze Rule

If on some interval about c,

$$g(x) \leq f(x) \leq h(x) \text{ and } \lim_{x \to c} g(x) = \lim_{x \to c} h(x) = L,$$

then $\lim_{x \to c} f(x) = L$.

■ *What this says*: If a function can be squeezed between two functions with equal limits, then that function must also have that same limit.

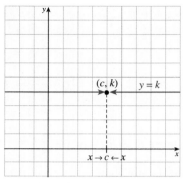

a. Limit of a constant: $\lim_{x \to c} k = k$

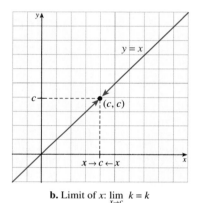

b. Limit of x: $\lim_{x \to c} k = k$

Figure 1.38 Two basic limits

These limit rules can be used to evaluate a variety of limits. We shall not prove any of these results until Section 1.8, but it is fairly easy graphically to justify the rules for the limit of a constant and the limit of x, as shown in Figure 1.38.

EXAMPLE 1   Finding the limit of a polynomial function

Evaluate $\lim_{x \to 2}(2x^5 - 9x^3 + 3x^2 - 11)$.

Solution $\lim_{x \to 2}(2x^5 - 9x^3 + 3x^2 - 11) = \lim_{x \to 2}(2x^5) - \lim_{x \to 2}(9x^3) + \lim_{x \to 2}(3x^2) - \lim_{x \to 2}(11)$
Sum and difference rules

$$= 2[\lim_{x \to 2} x^5] - 9[\lim_{x \to 2} x^3] + 3[\lim_{x \to 2} x^2] - 11$$
Multiple and constant rules

$$= 2 [\lim_{x \to 2} x]^5 - 9[\lim_{x \to 2} x]^3 + 3[\lim_{x \to 2} x]^2 - 11$$
Power rule

$$= 2(2)^5 - 9(2)^3 + 3(2)^2 - 11 = -7$$
Limit of x rule

COMMENT: If you consider Example 1 carefully, it is easy to see that if f is any polynomial, then the limit at $x = c$ can be found by substituting $x = c$ into the formula for $f(x)$.

Limit of a Polynomial Function

If P is a polynomial function, then

$$\lim_{x \to c} P(x) = P(c)$$

⊘ You must be careful about when you write the word "limit" and when you do not; pay particular attention to this when looking at the examples in this section. ⊘

EXAMPLE 2   Finding the limit of a rational function

Evaluate $\lim_{z \to -1} \dfrac{z^3 - 3z + 7}{5z^2 + 9z + 6}$.

Solution $\lim_{z \to -1} \dfrac{z^3 - 3z + 7}{5z^2 + 9z + 6} = \dfrac{\lim_{z \to -1}(z^3 - 3z + 7)}{\lim_{z \to -1}(5z^2 + 9z + 6)}$ *Quotient rule*

$$= \dfrac{(-1)^3 - 3(-1) + 7}{5(-1)^2 + 9(-1) + 6}$$

$$= \dfrac{9}{2} \quad \textit{Both numerator and denominator are polynomial functions.}$$

Notice that if the denominator of the rational function is not zero, the limit can be found by substitution.

Limit of a Rational Function

If Q is a rational function defined by $Q(x) = \dfrac{P(x)}{D(x)}$, then

$$\lim_{x \to c} Q(x) = \frac{P(c)}{D(c)}$$

provided $D(c) \neq 0$.

EXAMPLE 3   Finding the limit of a power (or root) function

Evaluate $\displaystyle\lim_{x \to -2} \sqrt[3]{x^2 - 3x - 2}$.

Solution
$$\lim_{x \to -2} \sqrt[3]{x^2 - 3x - 2} = \lim_{x \to -2} (x^2 - 3x - 2)^{1/3}$$

$$= \left[\lim_{x \to -2} (x^2 - 3x - 2) \right]^{1/3} \quad \textit{Power rule}$$

$$= [(-2)^2 - 3(-2) - 2]^{1/3} = 8^{1/3} = 2 \quad \rule[0.5ex]{2em}{0.4ex}$$

Once again, for values of the function for which $f(c)$ is defined, the limit can be found by substitution.

In the last section we found that $\displaystyle\lim_{x \to 0} \sin x = 0$ and $\displaystyle\lim_{x \to 0} \cos x = 1$ using a table. In the following example we use this information, along with the properties of limits to find other trigonometric limits.

EXAMPLE 4   Finding trigonometric limits algebraically

Given that $\displaystyle\lim_{x \to 0} \sin x = 0$ and $\displaystyle\lim_{x \to 0} \cos x = 1$, evaluate:

a. $\displaystyle\lim_{x \to 0} \sin^2 x$ **b.** $\displaystyle\lim_{x \to 0} (1 - \cos x)$

Solution   **a.**
$$\lim_{x \to 0} \sin^2 x = \left[\lim_{x \to 0} \sin x \right]^2 \quad \textit{Power rule}$$

$$= 0^2 \qquad\qquad \lim_{x \to 0} \sin x = 0$$

$$= 0$$

b.
$$\lim_{x \to 0} (1 - \cos x) = \lim_{x \to 0} 1 - \lim_{x \to 0} \cos x \quad \textit{Difference rule}$$

$$= 1 - 1 \qquad\qquad \textit{Constant rule and}$$

$$= 0 \qquad\qquad\qquad \lim_{x \to 0} \cos x = 1 \quad \rule[0.5ex]{2em}{0.4ex}$$

The following theorem states that we can find limits of trigonometric functions by direct substitution, as long as the number that x is approaching is in the domain of the given function. The proof of the theorem makes use of the limit formulas $\displaystyle\lim_{x \to 0} \sin x = 0$ and $\displaystyle\lim_{x \to 0} \cos x = 1$.

Computational Window

It is easy to find the limits of $\sin^2 x$ and $1 - \cos x$ as $x \to 0$ by looking at the graphs.

Y₁■(sin X)²

Xmin=-8   Ymin=-1
Xmax=8   Ymax=2
Xscl=1   Yscl=.5

Y₁■1-cos X

Xmin=-8   Ymin=-1
Xmax=8   Ymax=2
Xscl=1   Yscl=.5

THEOREM 1.3 Limits of trigonometric functions

If c is any number in the domain of the given trigonometric function, then

$$\lim_{x \to c} \cos x = \cos c \qquad \lim_{x \to c} \sec x = \sec c$$

$$\lim_{x \to c} \sin x = \sin c \qquad \lim_{x \to c} \csc x = \csc c$$

$$\lim_{x \to c} \tan x = \tan c \qquad \lim_{x \to c} \cot x = \cot c$$

Proof: We shall show that $\lim_{x \to c} \sin x = \sin c$. The other five limit formulas may be proved in a similar fashion (see Problems 71–72). Let $h = x - c$. Then $x = h + c$, and as $h \to 0$, $x \to c$. Thus,

$$\lim_{x \to c} \sin x = \lim_{h \to 0} \sin (h + c)$$

Using the trigonometric identity $\sin (A + B) = \sin A \cos B + \cos A \sin B$ and the limit formulas for sums and products, we find that

$$\lim_{x \to c} \sin x = \lim_{h \to 0} \sin (h + c)$$
$$= \lim_{h \to 0} [\sin h \cos c + \cos h \sin c]$$
$$= \lim_{h \to 0} \sin h \cdot \lim_{h \to 0} \cos c + \lim_{h \to 0} \cos h \cdot \lim_{h \to 0} \sin c$$
$$= 0 \cdot \cos c + 1 \cdot \sin c \qquad \lim_{h \to 0} \sin h = 0 \text{ and}$$
$$\qquad\qquad\qquad\qquad\qquad\qquad \lim_{h \to 0} \cos h = 1$$
$$= \sin c$$

Note that $\sin c$ and $\cos c$ do not change as $h \to 0$ because these are constants with respect to h. ∎

■ USING ALGEBRA TO FIND LIMITS

Sometimes the limit of $f(x)$ as $x \to c$ *cannot* be evaluated by direct substitution. In such a case, we look for another function that agrees with f for all values of x *except at the troublesome value* $x = c$. We illustrate with some examples.

EXAMPLE 5 Evaluating a limit using fraction reduction

Evaluate $\lim\limits_{x \to 2} \dfrac{x^2 + x - 6}{x - 2}$.

Solution If you try substitution on this limit, you will obtain:

$$\lim_{x \to 2} \frac{x^2 + x - 6}{x - 2} \begin{array}{l} \nearrow \text{ If } x = 2, \text{ then } x^2 + x - 6 = 0 \\[1em] \searrow \text{ If } x = 2, \text{ then } x - 2 = 0 \end{array}$$

The form 0/0 is called an **indeterminate form** because the form does not help us determine the limit of the expression. In other words, we cannot evaluate a limit for which direct substitution yields 0/0.

If the expression is a rational expression, the next step is to simplify the function by factoring and simplifying to see if the reduced form is a polynomial.

$$\lim_{x \to 2} \frac{x^2 + x - 6}{x - 2} = \lim_{x \to 2} \frac{(x + 3)(x - 2)}{x - 2} = \lim_{x \to 2} (x + 3)$$

This simplification is valid only if $x \neq 2$. Now complete the evaluation of the

Computational Window

Y₁ ⊟ (X²+X-6)/(X-2)

Xmin= -10 Ymin= -10
Xmax= 10   Ymax= 10
Xscl= 1   Yscl= 1

reduced function by direct substitution. This is not a problem, because $\lim_{x \to 2}$ is concerned with values *as x approaches 2,* not the value where $x = 2$.

$$\lim_{x \to 2} \frac{x^2 + x - 6}{x - 2} = \lim_{x \to 2} (x + 3) = 5$$

Another algebraic technique for finding limits is to rationalize either the numerator or the denominator to obtain an algebraic form that is not indeterminate.

EXAMPLE 6 Evaluating a limit by rationalizing

Evaluate $\lim_{x \to 4} \dfrac{\sqrt{x} - 2}{x - 4}$.

⊘ This method will work only if the resulting numerator allows the fraction to be simplified. ⊘

Solution Once again, notice that both the numerator and denominator of this rational expression are 0 when $x = 4$, so that we cannot evaluate the limit by direct substitution. Instead, we multiply by 1, its form chosen so that the numerator is rationalized.

$$\lim_{x \to 4} \frac{\sqrt{x} - 2}{x - 4} = \lim_{x \to 4} \frac{\sqrt{x} - 2}{x - 4} \cdot \frac{\sqrt{x} + 2}{\sqrt{x} + 2} \quad \textit{Multiply by 1.}$$

$$= \lim_{x \to 4} \frac{x - 4}{(x - 4)(\sqrt{x} + 2)}$$

$$= \lim_{x \to 4} \frac{1}{\sqrt{x} + 2}$$

$$= \frac{1}{\sqrt{4} + 2} = \frac{1}{4}$$

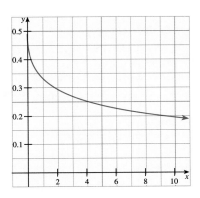

EXAMPLE 7 Evaluating a trigonometric function by multiplying by the conjugate

Evaluate $\lim_{x \to 0} \dfrac{1 - \cos x}{x}$.

This was Problem 36 of the previous section.

Solution Both the numerator and the denominator of this quotient are 0 when $x = 0$. However, if we multiply both the numerator and denominator of $f(x)$ by $1 + \cos x$ (the conjugate), we can rewrite the quotient $\dfrac{1 - \cos x}{x}$ in a form in which its limit can be found.

$$\lim_{x \to 0} \frac{1 - \cos x}{x} = \lim_{x \to 0} \left(\frac{1 - \cos x}{x} \cdot \frac{1 + \cos x}{1 + \cos x} \right)$$

$$= \lim_{x \to 0} \frac{1 - \cos^2 x}{x(1 + \cos x)}$$

$$= \lim_{x \to 0} \frac{\sin^2 x}{x(1 + \cos x)} \quad 1 - \cos^2 x = \sin^2 x$$

$$= \lim_{x \to 0} \left[\left(\frac{\sin x}{x} \right) \left(\frac{\sin x}{1 + \cos x} \right) \right]$$

$$= \lim_{x \to 0} \left(\frac{\sin x}{x} \right) \lim_{x \to 0} \left(\frac{\sin x}{1 + \cos x} \right) \quad \textit{Remember } \lim_{x \to 0} \frac{\sin x}{x} = 1 \textit{ and}$$

$$= 1 \cdot 0 \quad\quad\quad\quad\quad\quad\quad\quad \textit{evaluate the other limit by direct}$$

$$= 0 \quad\quad\quad\quad\quad\quad\quad\quad\quad \textit{substitution of } \sin 0 = 0 \textit{ and}$$

$$\quad\quad\quad\quad\quad\quad\quad\quad\quad\quad\quad \cos 0 = 1.$$

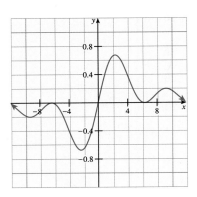

■ LIMITS OF PIECEWISE-DEFINED FUNCTIONS

It is easy to see that the left- and right-hand limits are not the same.

In Section 1.4 we defined a *piecewise-defined function*. To evaluate

$$\lim_{x \to c} f(x)$$

where the domain of f is divided into pieces, we first look to see if c is a critical value separating two of the pieces. If so, we need to consider one-sided limits, as illustrated by the following examples.

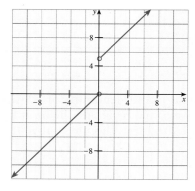

EXAMPLE 8   Limit of a piecewise-defined function

Find $\lim_{x \to 0} f(x)$ where $f(x) = \begin{cases} x + 5 & \text{if } x > 0 \\ x & \text{if } x < 0 \end{cases}$

Solution   Notice that $f(0)$ is not defined, and that it is necessary to consider left- and right-hand limits.

$$\lim_{x \to 0^-} f(x) = \lim_{x \to 0^-} x \qquad f(x) = x \text{ to the left of } 0.$$
$$= 0$$

$$\lim_{x \to 0^+} f(x) = \lim_{x \to 0^+} (x + 5) \quad f(x) = x + 5 \text{ to the right of } 0.$$
$$= 5$$

Because the left- and right-hand limits are not the same, we conclude that $\lim_{x \to 0} f(x)$ does not exist.   ▬

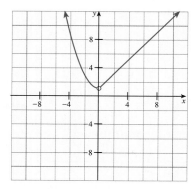

Compare this graph with the graph in Example 8.

EXAMPLE 9   Limit of a piecewise-defined function

Find $\lim_{x \to 0} g(x)$ where $g(x) = \begin{cases} x + 1 & \text{if } x > 0 \\ x^2 + 1 & \text{if } x < 0 \end{cases}$

$$\lim_{x \to 0^-} g(x) = \lim_{x \to 0^-} (x^2 + 1) = 1$$
$$\lim_{x \to 0^+} g(x) = \lim_{x \to 0^+} (x + 1) = 1$$

Because the left- and right-hand limits are equal, we conclude that $\lim_{x \to 0} g(x) = 1$.   ▬

PROBLEM SET 1.6

Ⓐ *In Problems 1–30, evaluate each limit.*

1. $\lim_{x \to -2} (x^2 + 3x - 7)$

2. $\lim_{t \to 0} (t^3 - 5t^2 + 4)$

3. $\lim_{x \to 3} (x + 5)(2x - 7)$

4. $\lim_{x \to 4} \left(\dfrac{1}{x} + \dfrac{3}{x - 5} \right)$

5. $\lim_{x \to 1} \dfrac{z^2 + z - 3}{z + 1}$

6. $\lim_{x \to 3} \dfrac{x^2 + 3x - 10}{3x^2 + 5x - 7}$

7. $\lim_{x \to \pi/3} \sec x$

8. $\lim_{x \to \pi/4} \dfrac{1 + \tan x}{\csc x + 2}$

9. $\lim_{x \to 1/3} \dfrac{x \sin \pi x}{1 + \cos \pi x}$

10. $\lim_{x \to 6} \dfrac{\tan (\pi/x)}{x - 1}$

11. $\lim_{u \to -2} \dfrac{4 - u^2}{2 + u}$

12. $\lim_{x \to 2} \dfrac{x^2 - 4x + 4}{x^2 - x - 2}$

13. $\lim_{x \to 1} \dfrac{\frac{1}{x} - 1}{x - 1}$

14. $\lim_{x \to 0} \dfrac{(x + 1)^2 - 1}{x}$

15. $\lim_{x \to 1} \left(\dfrac{x^2 - 3x + 2}{x^2 + x - 2} \right)^2$

16. $\lim_{x \to 3} \sqrt{\dfrac{x^2 - 2x - 3}{x - 3}}$

17. $\lim_{x \to 1} \dfrac{\sqrt{x} - 1}{x - 1}$

18. $\lim_{y \to 2} \dfrac{\sqrt{y + 2} - 2}{y - 2}$

19. $\lim_{x \to 0} \dfrac{1 - \sin x}{\cos^2 x}$

20. $\lim_{x \to 0} \dfrac{1 - 2 \cos x}{\sqrt{3} - 2\sin x}$

21. $\lim_{x \to 0} \dfrac{\sin 2x}{x}$

22. $\lim_{x \to 0} \dfrac{\sin 3x}{2x}$

23. $\lim_{x \to 0} \dfrac{\tan x}{x}$

24. $\lim_{x \to 0} \dfrac{\sin^2 x}{x^2}$

25. $\lim_{x \to 0} \dfrac{\frac{1}{x + 3} - \frac{1}{3}}{x}$

26. $\lim_{x \to 3} \dfrac{\frac{1}{x} - \frac{1}{3}}{x - 3}$

27. $\lim_{x \to 0} \dfrac{\sec x - 1}{x \sec x}$

28. $\lim_{x \to \pi/4} \dfrac{1 - \tan x}{\sin x - \cos x}$

29. $\lim_{x \to 0} \dfrac{\tan^2 x}{x}$

30. $\lim_{x \to \pi} \dfrac{\tan x}{1 + \sec x}$

B 31. ■ **What Does This Say?** How do you find the limit of a polynomial function?

32. ■ **What Does This Say?** How do you find the limit of a rational function?

33. ■ **What Does This Say?** How do you find $\lim\limits_{x \to 0} \dfrac{\sin ax}{x}$?

In Problems 34–41, compute the one-sided limit.

34. $\lim\limits_{x \to 2^-} (x^2 - 2x)$

35. $\lim\limits_{x \to 1^+} \dfrac{\sqrt{x-1} + x}{1 - 2x} = -1$

36. $\lim\limits_{x \to 0^-} \dfrac{|x|}{x}$

37. $\lim\limits_{x \to 0^+} \dfrac{|x|}{x}$

38. $\lim\limits_{x \to 2^-} f(x)$ where $f(x) = \begin{cases} 3 - 2x & \text{if } x \le 2 \\ x^2 - 5 & \text{if } x > 2 \end{cases}$

39. $\lim\limits_{x \to 2^+} f(x)$ where $f(x) = \begin{cases} 3 - 2x & \text{if } x \le 2 \\ x^2 - 5 & \text{if } x > 2 \end{cases}$

40. $\lim\limits_{s \to 1^-} g(s)$ where $g(s) = \begin{cases} \dfrac{s^2 - s}{s - 1} & \text{if } s < 1 \\ \sqrt{1 - s} & \text{if } s \ge 1 \end{cases}$

41. $\lim\limits_{s \to 1^+} g(s)$ where $g(s) = \begin{cases} \dfrac{s^2 - s}{s - 1} & \text{if } s < 1 \\ \sqrt{1 - s} & \text{if } s \ge 1 \end{cases}$

■ **What Does This Say?** *In Problems 42–49, explain why the given limit does not exist.*

42. $\lim\limits_{x \to 1} \dfrac{1}{x - 1}$

43. $\lim\limits_{x \to 2^+} \dfrac{1}{\sqrt{x - 2}}$

44. $\lim\limits_{t \to 2} \dfrac{t^2 - 4}{t^2 - 4t + 4}$

45. $\lim\limits_{x \to 0} \dfrac{|x|}{x}$

46. $\lim\limits_{x \to 1} f(x)$ where $f(x) = \begin{cases} 2 & \text{if } x \ge 1 \\ -5 & \text{if } x < 1 \end{cases}$

47. $\lim\limits_{t \to -1} g(t)$ where $g(t) = \begin{cases} 2t + 1 & \text{if } t \ge -1 \\ 5t^2 & \text{if } t < -1 \end{cases}$

48. $\lim\limits_{x \to \pi/2} \tan x$

49. $\lim\limits_{x \to 1} \csc \pi x$

We can use algebra, graphs, or tables to find limits. Find the limits in Problems 50–53.

50. $\lim\limits_{x \to 3} \dfrac{x^2 - 9}{x - 3}$

51. $\lim\limits_{x \to 0} \dfrac{x - \sin x}{x^3}$

52. $\lim\limits_{x \to 1} \dfrac{x^5 - 1}{x - 1}$

53. $\lim\limits_{x \to 1} \dfrac{\sqrt{x} - 1}{x - 1}$

In Problems 54–59, either evaluate the limit or explain why it does not exist.

54. $\lim\limits_{x \to 1} \dfrac{\frac{1}{x} - 1}{\sqrt{x} - 1}$

55. $\lim\limits_{x \to 0} \left(\dfrac{1}{x} - \dfrac{1}{x^2} \right)$

56. $\lim\limits_{x \to 5} f(x)$ where $f(x) = \begin{cases} x + 3 & \text{if } x \ne 5 \\ 4 & \text{if } x = 5 \end{cases}$

57. $\lim\limits_{t \to 2} g(t)$ where $g(t) = \begin{cases} t^2 & \text{if } -1 \le t < 2 \\ 3t - 2 & \text{if } t \ge 2 \end{cases}$

58. $\lim\limits_{x \to 2} f(x)$ where $f(x) = \begin{cases} 2(x + 1) & \text{if } x < 3 \\ 4 & \text{if } x = 3 \\ x^2 - 1 & \text{if } x > 3 \end{cases}$

59. $\lim\limits_{x \to 3} f(x)$ where $f(x) = \begin{cases} 2(x + 1) & \text{if } x < 3 \\ 4 & \text{if } x = 3 \\ x^2 - 1 & \text{if } x > 3 \end{cases}$

60. THINK TANK PROBLEM Evaluate
$$\lim\limits_{x \to 0} \left[x^2 - \dfrac{\cos x}{1{,}000{,}000{,}000} \right]$$
Explain why a calculator solution might lead you to an incorrect conclusion about the limit.

In the next chapter we will formally define the quantity
$$\dfrac{\Delta f}{\Delta x} = \dfrac{f(x + \Delta x) - f(x)}{\Delta x}$$
*to be the **difference quotient** of a function f. The number Δx is an arbitrary number (usually assumed to be very small). In each of Problems 61–64, first find $\Delta f/\Delta x$; then compute**
$$\lim\limits_{\Delta x \to 0} \dfrac{\Delta f}{\Delta x}$$

61. $f(x) = 3x - 5$

62. $f(x) = x^2$

63. $f(x) = \dfrac{3}{x}$

64. $f(x) = \sqrt{x}$

Verify the limit statements in Problems 65–66. You may use $\lim\limits_{u \to 0} \dfrac{\sin u}{u} = 1$ *and* $\lim\limits_{u \to 0} \dfrac{u}{\sin u} = 1$ *without proof.*

65. $\lim\limits_{x \to 0} \dfrac{\sin ax}{\sin bx} = \dfrac{a}{b}$ for constants a, b, with $b \ne 0$

66. $\lim\limits_{x \to 0} \dfrac{\tan ax}{\tan bx} = \dfrac{a}{b}$ for constants a, b, with $b \ne 0$

C 67. Let $f(x) = \dfrac{1}{x^2}$ with $x \ne 0$, and let L be any fixed positive integer. Show that
$$f(x) > 100L \quad \text{if} \quad |x| < \dfrac{1}{10\sqrt{L}}$$
What does this imply about $\lim\limits_{x \to 0} f(x)$?

68. THINK TANK PROBLEM Give an example for which neither $\lim\limits_{x \to c} f(x)$ nor $\lim\limits_{x \to c} g(x)$ exists, but $\lim\limits_{x \to c} [f(x) + g(x)]$ does exist.

69. THINK TANK PROBLEM It is not necessarily true that $\lim\limits_{x \to c} f(x)$ and $\lim\limits_{x \to c} g(x)$ exist whenever $\lim\limits_{x \to c} [f(x) \cdot g(x)]$ or $\lim\limits_{x \to c} \dfrac{f(x)}{g(x)}$ exists.

   a. Find functions f and g such that $\lim\limits_{x \to c} [f(x) \cdot g(x)]$ exists and $\lim\limits_{x \to c} g(x) = 0$, but $\lim\limits_{x \to c} f(x)$ does not exist.

   b. Find functions f and g such that $\lim\limits_{x \to 0} \dfrac{f(x)}{g(x)}$ exists, but neither $\lim\limits_{x \to 0} f(x)$ nor $\lim\limits_{x \to 0} g(x)$ exists.

70. Use the sum rule to show that if $\lim\limits_{x \to c} [f(x) + g(x)]$ and $\lim\limits_{x \to c} f(x)$ both exist, then so does $\lim\limits_{x \to c} g(x)$.

71. Show that $\lim\limits_{x \to x_0} \cos x = \cos x_0$.
   Hint: You will need to use the trigonometric identity $\cos(A + B) = \cos A \cos B - \sin A \sin B$.

72. Show that $\lim\limits_{x \to x_0} \tan x = \tan x_0$ whenever $\cos x_0 \ne 0$.

*This kind of limit will be used to define an idea called a derivative in Section 2.1.

1.7 CONTINUITY

> **IN THIS SECTION** Intuitive notion of continuity, definition of continuity, continuity theorems, continuity on an interval, the intermediate value theorem, approximation by the bisection method
>
> Informally, a continuous function is one whose graph has no "breaks" or "jumps." However, do not be misled by this simple geometric characterization. Continuity is an important and complex concept that plays a central role in the further development of calculus.

■ INTUITIVE NOTION OF CONTINUITY

The idea of *continuity* may be thought of informally as the quality of having parts that are in immediate connection with one another. The idea evolved from the vague or intuitive notion of a curve "without breaks or jumps" to a rigorous definition first given toward the end of the 19th century (see the historical note on page 59).

We begin with a discussion of *continuity at a point*. It may seem strange to talk about continuity *at a point*, but it should seem natural to talk about a curve being "discontinuous at a point," as illustrated by Figure 1.39.

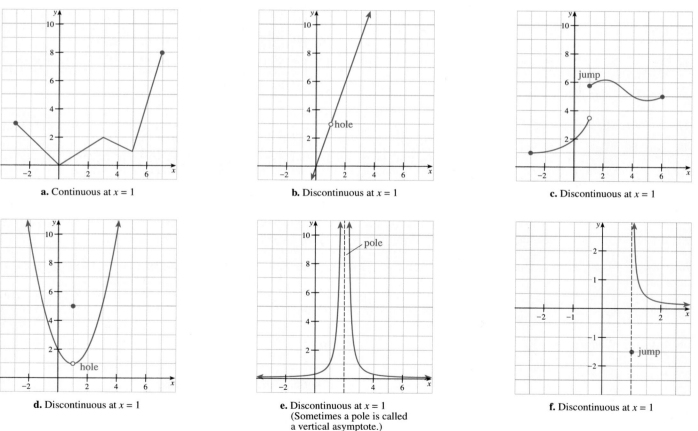

a. Continuous at $x = 1$

b. Discontinuous at $x = 1$

c. Discontinuous at $x = 1$

d. Discontinuous at $x = 1$

e. Discontinuous at $x = 1$
(Sometimes a pole is called a vertical asymptote.)

f. Discontinuous at $x = 1$

Figure 1.39 The curves in b, c, d, e, and f have a discontinuity at the point $x = 1$.

Figure 1.39 shows some curves that illustrate the idea of continuity from an intuitive standpoint, but we need to define this idea more precisely.

■ DEFINITION OF CONTINUITY

Let us consider the conditions that must be satisfied for a function f to be continuous at a point c. First, $f(c)$ must be defined. For example, the curves in Figures 1.39b and 1.39e are not continuous at $x = 1$ because they are not defined for $x = 1$. (An open dot indicates an excluded point). A second condition for continuity at a point $x = c$ is that the function makes no jumps there. This means that if "x is close to c," then "$f(x)$ must be close to $f(c)$." This condition is satisfied if $\lim_{x \to c} f(x)$ exists and is equal to $f(c)$. Looking at Figure 1.39, we see that the graphs in parts c, d, and f have a jump at the point $x = 1$.

Continuity of a Function at a Point

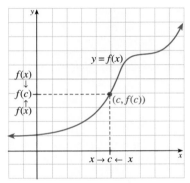

If f is continuous at c, the points $(x, f(x))$ converge to $(c, f(c))$ as $x \to c$.

Figure 1.40 The geometric interpretation of continuity

A function f is **continuous at a point $x = c$** if

1. $f(c)$ is defined;
2. $\lim_{x \to c} f(x)$ exists;
3. $\lim_{x \to c} f(x) = f(c)$.

A function that is not continuous at c is said to have a **discontinuity** at that point.

■ *What this says*: Step 1 refers to the domain of the function and ignores what happens at points $x \neq c$, whereas step 2 refers to points close to c, but ignores the point $x = c$. Continuity looks at the whole picture — at $x = c$ and at points close to $x = c$ — and checks to see if they are somehow "alike."

If f is continuous at $x = c$, the difference between $f(x)$ and $f(c)$ is small whenever x is close to c because $\lim_{x \to c} f(x) = f(c)$. Geometrically, this means that the points $(x, f(x))$ on the graph of f converge to the point $(c, f(c))$ as $x \to c$, and this is what guarantees that the graph is unbroken at $(c, f(c))$ with no "gap" or "hole," as shown in Figure 1.40.

There are three common ways for a function to be discontinuous at $x = c$. (A fourth way a function can be discontinuous is by oscillation.) These can be remembered as *holes, poles, and jumps* and are summarized in Table 1.4.

EXAMPLE 1   Testing the definition of continuity with a given function

Test the continuity of each of the following functions at $x = 1$. If it is not continuous at $x = 1$, explain.

a. $f(x) = \dfrac{x^2 + 2x - 3}{x - 1}$

b. $g(x) = \dfrac{x^2 + 2x - 3}{x - 1}$ if $x \neq 1$ and $g(x) = 6$ if $x = 1$

c. $h(x) = \dfrac{x^2 + 2x - 3}{x - 1}$ if $x \neq 1$ and $h(x) = 4$ if $x = 1$

d. $F(x) = \dfrac{x + 3}{x - 1}$ if $x \neq 1$ and $F(x) = 4$ if $x = 1$

e. $G(x) = 7x^3 + 3x^2 - 2$

f. $H(x) = 2 \sin x - \tan x$

Solution   We verify that the three criteria for continuity are satisfied for $c = 1$.

a. The function f is not continuous at $x = 1$ (hole; $f(c)$ not defined) because it is not defined at this point.

b. 1. $g(1)$ is defined; $g(1) = 6$.

2. $\lim\limits_{x \to 1} g(x) = \lim\limits_{x \to 1} \dfrac{x^2 + 2x - 3}{x - 1}$

$\qquad = \lim\limits_{x \to 1} \dfrac{(x - 1)(x + 3)}{x - 1}$

$\qquad = \lim\limits_{x \to 1} (x + 3) = 4$

3. $\lim\limits_{x \to 1} g(x) \neq g(1)$, so g is not continuous at $x = 1$ (hole; $g(c)$ defined).

c. Compare h with g of part **b.** We see that all three conditions of continuity are satisfied, so h is continuous at $x = 1$.

TABLE 1.4 Holes, Poles, Jumps, and Continuity

$f(c)$ Defined	$f(c)$ Not Defined
Not continuous at $x = c$: Hole $\lim\limits_{x \to c} f(x)$ exists and is not equal to $f(c)$. 	*Not continuous at $x = c$: Hole* $\lim\limits_{x \to c} f(x)$ exists. 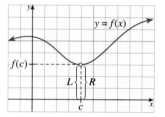
Not continuous at $x = c$: Pole $\lim\limits_{x \to c} f(x)$ does not exist. 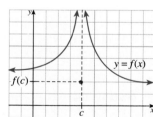	*Not continuous at $x = c$: Pole* $\lim\limits_{x \to c} f(x)$ does not exist. 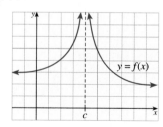
Not continuous at $x = c$: Jump $\lim\limits_{x \to c} f(x)$ does not exist. 	*Not continuous at $x = c$: Jump* $\lim\limits_{x \to c} f(x)$ does not exist. 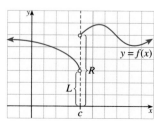

Continuous at $x = c$:
$\lim\limits_{x \to c} f(x)$ exists and is equal to $f(c)$.

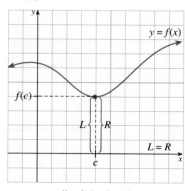

$\lim\limits_{x \to c^-} f(x) = L$ and
$\lim\limits_{x \to c^+} f(x) = R$

d. 1. $F(1)$ is defined; $F(1) = 4$.

2. $\lim\limits_{x \to 1} F(x) = \lim\limits_{x \to 1} \dfrac{x + 3}{x - 1}$; the limit does not exist.

The function F is not continuous at $x = 1$ (pole).

e. 1. $G(1)$ is defined; $G(1) = 8$.

2. $\lim\limits_{x \to 1} G(x) = 7(\lim\limits_{x \to 1} x)^3 + 3(\lim\limits_{x \to 1} x)^2 - \lim\limits_{x \to 1} 2 = 8$.

3. $\lim\limits_{x \to 1} G(x) = G(1)$.

Because the three conditions of continuity are satisfied, G is continuous at $x = 1$.

f. 1. $H(1)$ is defined; $H(1) = 2 \sin 1 - \tan 1 \approx 0.1255$ (approximate value).

2. $\lim\limits_{x \to 1} H(x) = 2 \lim\limits_{x \to 1} \sin x - \lim\limits_{x \to 1} \tan x = 2 \sin 1 - \tan 1$ (exact value).

3. $\lim\limits_{x \to 1} H(x) = H(1)$.

Because the three conditions of continuity are satisfied, H is continuous at $x = 1$. ▬

■ CONTINUITY THEOREMS

It is often difficult to determine whether a given function is continuous at a specified number. However, many common functions are continuous wherever they are defined.

THEOREM 1.4   Continuity theorem

If f is a polynomial or a rational function, a power function, or a trigonometric function, then f is continuous at any number $x = c$ for which $f(c)$ is defined.

Proof: The proof of the continuity theorem is based on the limit properties stated in the last section. That is, a polynomial is a function of the form

$$P(x) = a_n x^n + a_{n-1} x^{n-1} + \ldots + a_1 x + a_0$$

where $a_0, a_1, \ldots a_n$ are constants. We know that $\lim\limits_{x \to c} a_0 = a_0$ and that $\lim\limits_{x \to c} x^m = c^m$ for $m = 1, 2, \ldots, n$. This is precisely the statement that the function $g(x) = ax^m$ is continuous at any number $x = c$, or simply continuous. Because P is a sum of functions of this form and a constant function, it follows from the limit properties that P is continuous.

The proofs of the other parts (rational, power, and trigonometric functions) follow similarly. ■

The limit properties of the last section can also be used to prove a second continuity theorem. This theorem tells us that continuous functions may be combined in various ways *without creating a discontinuity.*

THEOREM 1.5   Properties of continuous functions

If s is a real number (called a *scalar*) and f and g are functions that are continuous at $x = c$, then the following functions are also continuous at $x = c$.

Scalar multiple	sf
Sum and difference	$f + g$ and $f - g$
Product	fg

Quotient	$\dfrac{f}{g}$	provided $g(c) \neq 0$
Composition	$f \circ g$	provided f is continuous at $g(c)$

Proof: The first four properties in this theorem follow directly from the basic limit rules given in Section 1.6. For instance, to prove the product property, note that since f and g are given to be continuous at $x = c$, we have

$$\lim_{x \to c} f(x) = f(c) \quad \text{and} \quad \lim_{x \to c} g(x) = g(c)$$

If $P(x) = f(x)g(x)$, then

$$\begin{aligned}
\lim_{x \to c} P(x) &= \lim_{x \to c} f(x)g(x) & \text{\textit{Product rule for limits}} \\
&= \left[\lim_{x \to c} f(x)\right]\left[\lim_{x \to c} g(x)\right] & \text{\textit{Continuity of f and g at x = c}} \\
&= f(c)g(c) = P(c)
\end{aligned}$$

so $P(x)$ is continuous at $x = c$, as required.

The continuous composition property is proved in a similar fashion but requires the following limit rule, whose proof is outlined in Problem 25 of Section 1.8.

Composition Limit Rule:

If f is continuous at L and $\lim_{x \to c} g(x) = L$, then

$$\lim_{x \to c} f(g(x)) = f(L) = f(\lim_{x \to c} g(x))$$

Now we can prove the continuous composition property of Theorem 1.5. Let $h(x) = (f \circ g)(x)$. Then we have

$$\begin{aligned}
\lim_{x \to c} h(x) = \lim_{x \to c} (f \circ g)(x) &= \lim_{x \to c} f[g(x)] & \text{\textit{Definition of composition}} \\
&= f[\lim_{x \to c} g(x)] & \text{\textit{Composition limit rule}} \\
&= f[g(c)] & \text{\textit{g is continuous at x = c.}} \\
&= (f \circ g)(c) = h(c)
\end{aligned}$$

■ **What this says:** Roughly speaking, the composition limit rule says that the limit of a continuous function is the function of the limiting value. The continuous composition property says that a continuous function of a continuous function is continuous.

We need to talk about a function being continuous on some interval. In order to do so we must first know how to handle continuity at the endpoints of the interval, which leads to the following definition.

One-Sided Continuity

The function f is **continuous from the right at a** if and only if

$$\lim_{x \to a^+} f(x) = f(a)$$

and it is **continuous from the left at b** if and only if

$$\lim_{x \to b^-} f(x) = f(b)$$

■ **CONTINUITY ON AN INTERVAL**

The function f is said to be **continuous on the open interval (a, b)** if it is continuous at each number in this interval. If f is also continuous from the right at a, we say it is **continuous on the half-open interval $[a, b)$**. Similarly, f is **continuous on the half-open interval $(a, b]$** if it is continuous at each number between a and b and is continuous from the left at the endpoint b. Finally, f is **continuous on the closed interval [a, b]** if it is continuous at each number between a and b and is both continuous from the right at a and continuous from the left at b.

EXAMPLE 2   Testing for continuity on an interval

Find the intervals on which each of the given functions is continuous.

a. $f_1(x) = \dfrac{x^2 - 1}{x^2 - 4}$ **b.** $f_2(x) = |x^2 - 4|$ **c.** $f_3(x) = \csc x$

d. $f_4(x) = \sin\dfrac{1}{x}$ **e.** $f_5(x) = \begin{cases} x \sin\dfrac{1}{x} & \text{if } x \neq 0 \\ 0 & \text{if } x = 0 \end{cases}$

   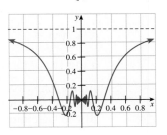

Solution

   a. Function f_1 is not defined when $x^2 - 4 = 0$ or when $x = 2$ or $x = -2$. The curve is continuous on $(-\infty, -2) \cup (-2, 2) \cup (2, \infty)$.

   b. Function f_2 is continuous on $(-\infty, \infty)$.

   c. The cosecant function is not defined at $x = n\pi$, n an integer. At all other points it is continuous. Thus f_3 is continuous on

$$\ldots \cup (-2\pi, -\pi) \cup (-\pi, 0) \cup (0, \pi) \cup (\pi, 2\pi) \cup \ldots$$

   d. Because $1/x$ is continuous except at $x = 0$ and the sine function is continuous everywhere, we need only check continuity at $x = 0$.

$$\lim_{x \to 0} \sin\frac{1}{x} \text{ does not exist.}$$

Therefore, $f(x) = \sin\dfrac{1}{x}$ is continuous on $(-\infty, 0) \cup (0, \infty)$.

   e. It can be shown that

$$-|x| \leq x \sin\frac{1}{x} \leq |x|, \qquad x \neq 0$$

(see Figure 1.41 to see the plausibility of this inequality). We can now use the squeeze rule. Because $\lim_{x \to 0} |x| = 0$ and $\lim_{x \to 0}(-|x|) = 0$, it follows that $\lim_{x \to 0} x \sin\dfrac{1}{x} = 0$. Because $f_5(0) = 0$ we see that f is continuous at $x = 0$ and therefore is continuous on $(-\infty, \infty)$.

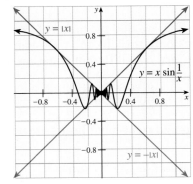

Figure 1.41 The graph of $y = \sin\dfrac{1}{x}$ and $y = -|x|$

Because we do not always have the graph of a function readily available, as we did in Example 2, and because the task of checking for continuity will focus on certain values, we consider a procedure involving identifying and then checking those values of concern. To help us describe the situation, we define a **suspicious point** as a point having an x-value for which the definition of the function changes, or a value that causes division by zero for the given function.

For Example 2 the suspicious points can be listed:

a. $\dfrac{x^2 - 1}{x^2 - 4}$ has suspicious points for division by zero when $x = 2$ and $x = -2$.

b. $|x^2 - 4| = x^2 - 4$ when $x^2 - 4 \geq 0$ and $|x^2 - 4| = 4 - x^2$ when $x^2 - 4 < 0$. This means the definition of the function changes when $x^2 - 4 = 0$, namely, when $x = 2$ and $x = -2$.

c. The points $x = n\pi$ are suspicious points because these are the values for which the function is not defined.

d. $\sin\dfrac{1}{x}$ has a suspicious point when $x = 0$ (division by 0).

e. Here, the only suspicious point is when $x = 0$.

EXAMPLE 3   Checking continuity at suspicious points

Let $f(x) = \begin{cases} 3 - x & \text{if } -5 \leq x < 2 \\ x - 2 & \text{if } 2 \leq x < 5 \end{cases}$ and $g(x) = \begin{cases} 2 - x & \text{if } -5 \leq x < 2 \\ x - 2 & \text{if } 2 \leq x < 5 \end{cases}$

Find the intervals on which f and g are continuous.

Solution   The domain for both functions is $[-5, 5)$; the continuity theorem tells us both functions are continuous everywhere on that interval except possibly at the suspicious points. Examining f, we see

$f(x) = 3 - x$ on $[-5, 2)$,   which is a polynomial function and thus is continuous

$f(x) = x - 2$ on $[2, 5)$,   which is a polynomial function and thus is continuous

The suspicious point on the real number line is the x-value for which the definition of f changes—in this case, $x = 2$.

For g we likewise see that the function is continuous except possibly at the suspicious point $x = 2$, the value where the definition of the function changes.

1. Because $f(2) = 2 - 2 = 0$ and $g(2) = 2 - 2 = 0$, both functions are defined at $x = 2$.

2. The second condition for continuity requires that we find the limits of f and g as $x \to 2$. To find this limit we need to check both the left- and right-hand limits because the value of the function is defined by a different equation if we approach from the left or from the right.

$$\lim_{x \to 2^-} f(x) = \lim_{x \to 2^-} (3 - x) = 1 \text{ and } \lim_{x \to 2^+} f(x) = \lim_{x \to 2^+} (x - 2) = 0$$

Thus $\lim_{x \to 2} f(x)$ does not exist, because the left- and right-hand limits are not the same.

$$\lim_{x \to 2^-} g(x) = \lim_{x \to 2^-} (2 - x) = 0 \text{ and } \lim_{x \to 2^+} g(x) = \lim_{x \to 2^+} (x - 2) = 0$$

Therefore, $\lim_{x \to 2} g(x) = 0$.

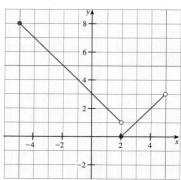

Although a graph is not part of the derivation, it can often be helpful in finding suspicious points. This is the graph of f.

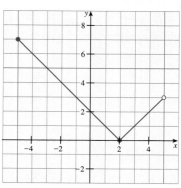

This is the graph of g. Does the graph reinforce our conclusions?

3. The third condition of continuity cannot hold at $x = 2$ for the function f, because the required limit in step 2 does not exist. It is continuous on $[-5, 2)$ and on $[2, 5)$, but not on the entire interval $[-5, 5)$. The function g also satisfies the third continuity property, namely, that $\lim_{x \to 2} g(x) = g(2)$; g therefore is continuous on $[-5, 5)$. ▬

◼ THE INTERMEDIATE VALUE THEOREM

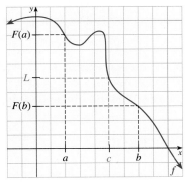

Figure 1.42 If L lies between $f(a)$ and $f(b)$, then $f(c) = L$ for some c between a and b.

Intuitively, if f is continuous throughout an entire interval, its graph on that interval may be drawn "without the pencil leaving the paper." That is, if $f(x)$ varies continuously from $f(a)$ to $f(b)$ as x increases from a to b, then it must hit every number L between $f(a)$ and $f(b)$, as shown in Figure 1.42.

Here is an example illustrating the property shown in Figure 1.42. Suppose f is a function defined as the weight of a person at age x. If we assume that weight varies continuously with time, a person who weighs 50 pounds at age 6 and 120 pounds at age 15 must weigh 100 pounds at some time between ages 6 and 15. This feature of continuous functions is known as the *intermediate value property*. A formal statement of this property is contained in the following theorem.

THEOREM 1.6   The intermediate value theorem

If f is a continuous function on the closed interval $[a, b]$ and L is some number strictly between $f(a)$ and $f(b)$, then there exists at least one number c on the open interval (a, b) such that $f(c) = L$.

Proof: This theorem is intuitively obvious, but it is not at all easy to prove. A proof may be found in most advanced calculus textbooks. ◼

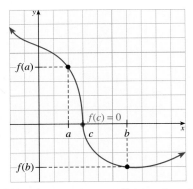

Figure 1.43 Because $f(a) > 0$ and $f(b) < 0$, then $f(c) = 0$ for some c between a and b.

> ◼ *What this says*: If f is a continuous function (with emphasis on the word *continuous*) on some *closed* interval, and if x takes on all values between a and b, then $f(x)$ must take on all values between $f(a)$ and $f(b)$. I'm reminded of my calculus instructor who asked me my height, "Six foot," I answered. "This means," said he, "that at one time you were *exactly* 2 ft tall; why?" The answer, of course, is because of the intermediate value theorem.

One important consequence of the intermediate value theorem is the fact that it allows us to find, or estimate, roots of the equation $f(x) = 0$. If, for example, there is some positive value of a continuous function f (the graph of f at this point is above the x-axis) and another value of f is negative (the graph of f at this point is below the x-axis), then there must be at least one number c between a and b for which $f(x) = 0$ (the graph crosses the x-axis). This is shown in Figure 1.43 and is summarized in the following theorem.

THEOREM 1.7   Root location theorem

If f is continuous on the closed interval $[a, b]$ and if $f(a)$ and $f(b)$ have opposite algebraic signs (one positive and the other negative), then $f(c) = 0$ for at least one number c on the open interval (a, b).

Proof: This follows directly from the intermediate value theorem (see Figure 1.43). The details of this proof are left as a problem. ◼

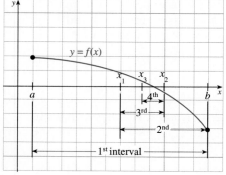

Graph of $y = x^4 - 2\sqrt[3]{x} - 1$

EXAMPLE 4   Using the root location theorem

Show that $x^4 - 2\sqrt[3]{x} = 1$ for at least one number c on $[-1, 1]$.

Solution   Notice that the function $f(x) = x^4 - 2\sqrt[3]{x} - 1$ is continuous on $[-1, 1]$. Also notice that $f(-1) = 2$ (it is positive) and $f(1) = -2$ (it is negative), so the conditions of the root location theorem apply.

Therefore, there is at least one number c on $(-1, 1)$ for which $f(c) = 0$. This means that $c^4 - 2\sqrt[3]{c} - 1 = 0$, or, equivalently, $c^4 - 2\sqrt[3]{c} = 1$ as required.   ▬

The intermediate value theorem and the root location theorem are called **existence theorems.** That is, they tell us certain values exist, but they do not give us a method for finding c. We conclude this section by giving one possible method for finding c.

■ APPROXIMATION BY THE BISECTION METHOD

The intermediate value theorem is the basis for a procedure that can be used to approximate roots of equations to any desired degree of accuracy. Suppose f is a continuous function on the closed interval $[a, b]$ with, for example, $f(a) > 0$ and $f(b) < 0$. Then, by the intermediate value theorem, the equation $f(x) = 0$ has a root somewhere between $x = a$ and $x = b$. To estimate the location of this root with more precision, evaluate f at the midpoint

$$x_1 = \frac{a + b}{2}$$

of the interval $[a, b]$. There are three possibilities, as shown in Figure 1.44.

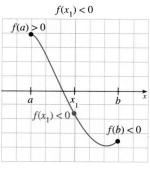

Figure 1.44 Approximation of a root by bisection

Either x_1 is the root or you have found a new interval, one that is only half as wide as the original interval and that must also contain the desired root. This is shown in Figure 1.45.

As you consider Example 5, notice that at each stage of the procedure, the midpoint x_n of the interval approximates the root with a maximum error E_n that is no greater than the width of the $(n + 1)$th interval.

Figure 1.45 The bisection method

EXAMPLE 5   Using the bisection method

The equation $x^3 - x^2 - 1 = 0$ has one real root. Find this root with an error no greater than $\frac{1}{16}$.

Solution The goal is to find a root of the equation $f(x) = 0$, where

$$f(x) = x^3 - x^2 - 1$$

In other words, you are to find the value(s) of x for which $f(x) = 0$. Note that $f(1) = 1^3 - 1^2 - 1 = -1 < 0$ and $f(2) = 2^3 - 2^2 - 1 = 3 > 0$. Therefore, the real root must lie on the interval $[1, 2] = [a, b]$, with positive values of $f(x)$ on the right and negative values on the left.

 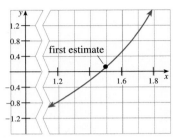

Step 1: Apply the bisection method by assigning the midpoint of the interval $[1, 2]$ to x_1: $x_1 = \frac{1+2}{2} = \frac{3}{2} = 1.5$. Because $f(x_1) = f\left(\frac{3}{2}\right) = 1.5^3 - 1.5^2 - 1 = 0.125$, we see that $f(x_1) > 0$. Therefore, $\frac{3}{2}$ replaces 2 as the right, positive-yielding endpoint of the interval, and the root must be on $\left[1, \frac{3}{2}\right]$. The first estimate is $x_1 = 1.5$ and the error is no more than $\frac{1}{2}$ (that is, the length of the interval).

Step 2: We know that at the left endpoint, $a = 1$, $f(1) < 0$ and at the right endpoint, $x_1 = \frac{3}{2}$, $f(x_1) = 0.125 > 0$. Therefore, we will assign the midpoint of this interval to x_2:

$$x_2 = \frac{1 + \frac{3}{2}}{2} = \frac{5}{4} = 1.25$$

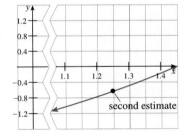

Now calculate $f(x_2) = f\left(\frac{5}{4}\right) = -0.609375$.

Because this value is negative, $\frac{5}{4}$ replaces 1 as the left, negative-yielding endpoint of the interval, which is narrowed down to $\left[\frac{5}{4}, \frac{3}{2}\right]$. The second estimate is $x_2 = 1.25$, and the error is no more than $\frac{1}{4}$.

Step 3: Because the root must lie on the interval $\left[\frac{5}{4}, \frac{3}{2}\right]$, that is where we will seek the next estimate.

$$x_3 = \frac{\frac{5}{4} + \frac{3}{2}}{2} = \frac{11}{8}; f(x_3) = -0.291015625 < 0$$

The third estimate is $x_3 = \frac{11}{8} = 1.375$ and the error is no more than $\frac{1}{8}$.

Step 4: On $\left[\frac{11}{8}, \frac{3}{2}\right]$ we find $x_4 = \frac{\frac{11}{8} + \frac{3}{2}}{2} = \frac{23}{16}; f(x_4) \approx -0.095947265 < 0$

The fourth estimate is $x_4 = \frac{23}{16} = 1.4375$ and the error is no more than $\frac{1}{16}$, as requested in the problem. We estimate the root to be 1.4375. ▄

Convergence of the Bisection Method When you estimate a root such as the one in Example 5, be sure you are not misled about the accuracy of the answers.

When you write 1.4375, the error could be as large as 0.0625. Here is what we mean: If r represents the root, x_n is the estimate of the root, and ε_n is the maximum error for the nth estimate, then $x_n - \varepsilon < r < x_n + \varepsilon$. For this answer we see that the root is contained in the interval $\left(x_4 - \frac{1}{16}, x_4 + \frac{1}{16}\right) = (1.375, 1.500)$.

The approximations $x_1, x_2, \ldots$ generated by the bisection method converge on the true value of the desired root. However, the rate of this convergence is often fairly slow when compared to other methods. After four steps in Example 5, for example, the maximum possible error is $E_4 = 0.0625$. After n steps, the maximum error would be $1/2^n$, and more than 14 steps would be required to guarantee four-decimal-place accuracy.

PROBLEM SET 1.7

Ⓐ *Which of the functions described in Problems 1–6 represent continuous functions? State the domain, if possible, for each example.*

  1. the temperature on a specific day at a given location considered as a function of time

  2. the humidity on a specific day at a given location considered as a function of time

  3. the selling price of ATT stock on a specific day considered as a function of time

  4. the number of unemployed people in the United States during the month of January 1995 considered as a function of time

  5. the charges for a taxi ride across town considered as a function of mileage

  6. the charges to mail a package considered as a function of its weight

Identify all suspicious points and determine all points of discontinuity in Problems 7–20.

  7. $f(x) = x^3 - 7x + 3$

  8. $f(x) = \dfrac{3x + 5}{2x - 1}$

  9. $f(x) = \dfrac{3x}{x^2 - x}$

  10. $f(t) = 3 - (5 + 2t)^3$

  11. $h(x) = \sqrt{x} + \dfrac{3}{x}$

  12. $f(u) = \sqrt[3]{u^2 - 1}$

  13. $f(t) = \dfrac{1}{t} - \dfrac{3}{t + 1}$

  14. $g(x) = \dfrac{x^2 - 1}{x^2 + x - 2}$

  15. $f(x) = \begin{cases} x^2 - 2 & \text{if } x > 1 \\ 2x - 3 & \text{if } x \le 1 \end{cases}$

  16. $g(t) = \begin{cases} 3t^2 - 1 & \text{if } t > 3 \\ 5 & \text{if } 1 < t \le 3 \\ 3t + 2 & \text{if } t \le 1 \end{cases}$

  17. $f(x) = 3 \tan x - 5 \sin x \cos x$

  18. $g(x) = \dfrac{\cot x}{\sin x - \cos x}$

  19. $h(x) = \csc x \cot x$

  20. $f(x) = \dfrac{\sec x}{\sin x \tan x}$

In Problems 21–26, the given function is defined everywhere except at $x = 2$. In each case, find what value should be assigned to $f(2)$, if any, in order to guarantee that f will be continuous at 2.

  21. $f(x) = \dfrac{x^2 - x - 2}{x - 2}$

  22. $f(x) = \sqrt{\dfrac{x^2 - 4}{x - 2}}$

  23. $f(x) = \dfrac{\sin(\pi x)}{x - 2}$

  24. $f(x) = \dfrac{\cos \frac{\pi}{x}}{x - 2}$

  25. $f(x) = \begin{cases} 2x + 5 & \text{if } x > 2 \\ 15 - x^2 & \text{if } x < 2 \end{cases}$

  26. $f(x) = \dfrac{\frac{1}{x} - 1}{x - 2}$

In Problems 27–34, determine whether or not the given function is continuous on the prescribed interval.

  27. $f(x) = \dfrac{1}{x}$ on $[1, 2]$

  28. $f(x) = \dfrac{1}{x}$ on $[0, 1]$

  29. $f(t) = \dfrac{1}{t}$ on $[-3, 0)$

  30. $g(x) = \dfrac{1}{1 - x}$ on $[0, 7)$

  31. $f(x) = \begin{cases} x^2 & \text{if } 0 \le x < 2 \\ 3x + 1 & \text{if } 2 \le x < 5 \end{cases}$

  32. $g(t) = \begin{cases} 2t & \text{if } 0 < t \le 3 \\ 15 - t^2 & \text{if } -3 \le t \le 0 \end{cases}$

  33. $f(x) = x \sin x$ on $(0, \pi)$

  34. $f(x) = \dfrac{\sin x}{x}$ on $[0, \pi]$

Ⓑ 35. Let $f(x) = \begin{cases} x & \text{if } x \ne 0 \\ 2 & \text{if } x = 0 \end{cases}$ and $g(x) = \begin{cases} 3x & \text{if } x \ne 0 \\ -2 & \text{if } x = 0 \end{cases}$

  Show that $f + g$ is continuous at $x = 0$ even though f and g are both discontinuous there.

  36. Show that if f/g and g are both continuous at $x = c$, then f must also be continuous there.

  37. THINK TANK PROBLEM   Find functions f and g such that f is discontinuous at $x = 1$ but fg is continuous there.

  38. THINK TANK PROBLEM   Give an example of a function defined for all real numbers which is continuous at only one point.

In Problems 39–44, show that the given equation has at least one solution on the indicated interval.

39. $\sqrt[3]{x} = x^2 + 2x - 1$ on $[0, 1]$ **40.** $\dfrac{1}{x + 1} = x^2 - x - 1$ on $[1, 2]$

41. $\sqrt[3]{x - 8} + 9x^{2/3} = 29$ on $[0, 8]$ **42.** $\tan x = 2x^2 - 1$ on $\left[-\frac{\pi}{4}, 0\right]$

43. $\cos x - \sin x = x$ on $\left[0, \frac{\pi}{2}\right]$

44. $\cos x = x^2 - 1$ on $[0, \pi]$

45. Let $f(x) = \begin{cases} x^2 & \text{if } x > 2 \\ x + 1 & \text{if } x \leq 2 \end{cases}$

Show that f is continuous from the left at 2, but not from the right.

46. Find constants a and b such that $f(2) = f(0)$ and f is continuous at $x = 1$.

$$f(x) = \begin{cases} ax + 3 & \text{if } x > 1 \\ 4 & \text{if } x = 1 \\ x^2 + b & \text{if } x < 1 \end{cases}$$

47. ■ **What Does This Say?** Use the intermediate value theorem to explain why the hands of a clock coincide at least once every hour.

48. The population (in thousands) of a colony of bacteria t minutes after the introduction of a toxin is given by the function

$$P(t) = \begin{cases} t^2 + 1 & \text{if } 0 \leq t < 5 \\ -8t + 66 & \text{if } t \geq 5 \end{cases}$$

a. When does the colony die out?
b. Show that at some time between $t = 2$ and $t = 7$, the population is 9,000.

In Problems 49–54, find constants a and b so that the given function will be continuous for all x. You may use the result of Problem 62.

49. $f(x) = \begin{cases} ax + 3 & \text{if } x > 5 \\ 8 & \text{if } x = 5 \\ x^2 + bx + 1 & \text{if } x < 5 \end{cases}$

50. $f(t) = \begin{cases} \dfrac{at - 4}{t - 2} & \text{if } t \neq 2 \\ b & \text{if } t = 2 \end{cases}$

51. $f(x) = \begin{cases} \dfrac{\sqrt{x} - a}{x - 1} & \text{if } x > 0, x \neq 1 \\ b & \text{if } x = 1 \end{cases}$

52. $g(x) = \begin{cases} \dfrac{ax^2 - 3}{x + 5} & \text{if } x > -5 \\ bx + 2 & \text{if } x \leq -5 \end{cases}$

53. $g(x) = \begin{cases} \dfrac{\sin ax}{x} & \text{if } x < 0 \\ 5 & \text{if } x = 0 \\ x + b & \text{if } x > 0 \end{cases}$

54. $f(x) = \begin{cases} \dfrac{\tan ax}{\tan bx} & \text{if } x < 0 \\ 4 & \text{if } x = 0 \\ ax + b & \text{if } x > 0 \end{cases}$

Computational Window

In Problems 55–60, use the bisection method, a graphing calculator, or a computer to approximate a solution to $f(x) = 0$. If you use the bisection method, estimate the root with error no greater than $\frac{1}{16}$; if you use a computer, estimate the root with error no greater than $\frac{1}{1000}$.

55. the root of $x^2 - x - 1 = 0$ between 1 and 2
56. the root of $x^2 - 3x + 1 = 0$ between 0 and 1
57. the negative root of $x^2 - 2x - 1 = 0$
58. the root of $x^3 + x^2 - 1 = 0$
59. the zero of $f(x) = x^3 + 2x^2 + x - 5$
60. the zero of $f(x) = x^3 + 2x^2 - x + 1$

The functions in Problems 61–62 are undefined at an obvious point. If possible, define the function there so it is continuous for all x. If not possible, explain why.

61. $\dfrac{\sin x - x}{x^3}$

62. $\dfrac{x^4 - 2x^3 + 3x^2 - 5x - 2}{|x - 2|}$

Ⓒ 63. Prove the root location theorem.
64. Show that f is continuous at c if and only if it is both continuous from the right and continuous from the left at c.

65. Let $u(x) = x$ and $f(x) = \begin{cases} 0 & \text{if } x \neq 0 \\ 1 & \text{if } x = 0 \end{cases}$.

Show that $\lim\limits_{x \to 0} f[u(x)] \neq f\left[\lim\limits_{x \to 0} u(x)\right]$.

1.8 INTRODUCTION TO THE THEORY OF LIMITS*

IN THIS SECTION Limit of a function (formal definition), the believer/doubter format, epsilon-delta proofs, selected theorems with formal proofs

This section gives a firm footing for calculus by making precise the notion of a limit. The techniques of this section will be important if you take future courses in advanced mathematics, but they are not required for the material that follows in this text.

*This section can be omitted without disrupting the development of the remainder of the text.

In Section 1.5 we defined the limit of a function as follows:

> The notation
> $$\lim_{x \to c} f(x) = L$$
> is read "the limit of $f(x)$ as x approaches c is L" and means that the function values $f(x)$ can be made arbitrarily close to L by choosing x sufficiently close to c but not equal to c.

This informal definition was valuable because it gave you an intuitive feeling for the limit of a function and allowed you to develop a working knowledge of this fundamental concept. For theoretical work, however, this definition will not suffice, because it gives no precise, quantifiable meaning to the terms "arbitrarily close to L" and "sufficiently close to c." The following definition, derived from the work of Cauchy and Weierstrass, gives precision to the limit definition.

■ LIMIT OF A FUNCTION (FORMAL DEFINITION)

> The limit statement
> $$\lim_{x \to c} f(x) = L$$
> means that for each $\varepsilon > 0$, there corresponds a number $\delta > 0$ with the property that
> $$|f(x) - L| < \varepsilon \text{ whenever } 0 < |x - c| < \delta$$

Because the Greek letters ε (epsilon) and δ (delta) are traditionally used in this context, the formal definition of limit is sometimes called the **epsilon-delta** definition of the limit. The goal of this section is to show how this formal definition embodies our intuitive understanding of the limit process and how it can be used rigorously to establish a variety of results.

Do not be discouraged if this material seems difficult—it is. Probably your best course of action is to read this section carefully and examine a few examples closely. Then, using the examples as models, try some of the exercises. This material often takes several attempts, but if you persevere, you should come away with an appreciation of the epsilon-delta process—and a better understanding of calculus. We begin by restating the formal definition graphically.

Behind the formal language is a fairly straightforward idea. In particular, to establish a specific limit, say $\lim_{x \to c} f(x) = L$, a number $\varepsilon > 0$ is chosen first to establish a desired degree of proximity to L, and then a number $\delta > 0$ is found that determines how close x must be to c to ensure that $f(x)$ is within ε units of L.

For each $\varepsilon > 0$ This forms an interval around L on the y-axis.	**there is a $\delta > 0$ such that** This forms an interval around c on the x-axis.	**if $0 < |x - c| < \delta$,** This says that if x is in the interval on the x-axis, . . .	**then $|f(x) - L| < \varepsilon$.** then $f(x)$ is in the interval on the y-axis.

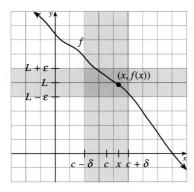

Figure 1.46 The epsilon-delta definition of limit

The situation is illustrated in Figure 1.46, which shows a function that satisfies the conditions of the definition. Notice that whenever x is within δ units of c (but not equal to c), the point $(x, f(x))$ on the graph of f must lie in the rectangle (purple region) formed by the intersection of the horizontal band of width 2ε (blue screen) centered at L and the vertical band of width 2δ (red region) centered at c. The smaller the ε-interval around the proposed limit L, generally the smaller the δ-interval will need to be in order for L to lie in the ε-interval. If such a δ can be found, no matter how small ε is, then L must be the limit.

■ THE BELIEVER/DOUBTER FORMAT

The limit process can be thought of as a "contest" between a "believer" who claims that $\lim_{x \to c} f(x) = L$ and a "doubter" who disputes this claim. The contest begins with the doubter choosing a positive number ε so that whenever x is a number (other than c) within δ units of c (the red region), the corresponding function value $f(x)$ is within ε units of L (the blue region). Naturally, the doubter tries to choose ε so small that no matter what δ the believer chooses, it will not be possible to satisfy the accuracy requirement. When will the doubter win and when will the believer win the argument? As you can see from Figure 1.46, if the believer has the "correct limit" L, it will be in the intersection (the purple portion) no matter what ε the doubter chooses. On the other hand, if the believer has an "incorrect limit," as shown in Figure 1.47, the limit may be in the purple portions for some choices of ε, but for other choices of ε the doubter can force the believer to be the loser of this contest by prohibiting the believer from making a choice within the purple portion.

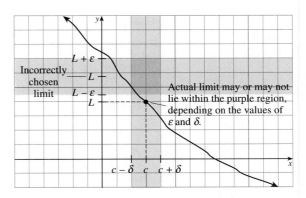

Figure 1.47 False limit scenario

To avoid an endless series of ε-δ challenges, the believer usually tries to settle the issue by producing a formula relating the choice of δ to the doubter's ε that will satisfy the requirement no matter what ε is chosen. The believer/doubter format is used in Example 1 to verify a given limit statement (believer "wins") and in Example 2 to show that a certain limit does not exist (doubter "wins").

EXAMPLE 1   Verifying a limit claim (believer wins)

Show that $\lim_{x \to 2} (2x + 1) = 5$.

Solution   To verify the given limit statement, we begin by having the doubter choose a positive number ε. Before picking δ, the believer might entertain the thought process shown in the following screen.

Figure 1.48a

Figure 1.48 $\lim\limits_{x \to 2} (2x + 1) = 5$

a.

b.

c.

Figure 1.49 Example of an incorrectly chosen limit

Write $|f(x) - L|$ in terms of $|x - c|$ (where $c = 2$) as follows:

$$|f(x) - L| = |(2x + 1) - 5| = |2x - 4| = 2|x - 2|$$

Thus, if $0 < |x - c| < \delta$ or $0 < |x - 2| < \delta$, then $|f(x) - L| < 2\delta$

The believer *wants* $|f(x) - L| < \varepsilon$, so we see that the believer should choose $2\delta = \varepsilon$, or $\delta = \frac{\varepsilon}{2}.$*

With the information shown in this screen, we can now make the following argument, which uses the formal definition of limit:

Let $\varepsilon > 0$ be given. Choose $\delta = \frac{\varepsilon}{2} > 0$. It follows that if

$$0 < |x - 2| < \delta = \frac{\varepsilon}{2}, \text{ then}$$

$$|(2x + 1) - 5| = 2|x - 2| < 2\left(\frac{\varepsilon}{2}\right) = \varepsilon$$

Thus, the conditions of the definition of limit are satisfied, and we have

$$\lim\limits_{x \to 2} (2x + 1) = 5$$

This is shown graphically in Figure 1.48a.

Notice that no matter what ε is chosen the doubter, by choosing a number that is one-half of that ε, the believer will force the function to stay within the purple portion of the graph, as shown in Figure 1.48b. ▬

EXAMPLE 2   Disproving a limit claim (doubter wins)

Determine whether $\lim\limits_{x \to 2} \dfrac{2x^2 - 3x - 2}{x - 2} = 6$.

Solution   Once again, the doubter will choose a positive number ε and the believer must respond with a δ. As before, the believer does some preliminary work with $f(x) - L$:

$$\left| \frac{2x^2 - 3x - 2}{x - 2} - 6 \right| = \left| \frac{2x^2 - 3x - 2 - 6x + 12}{x - 2} \right|$$

$$= \left| \frac{2x^2 - 9x + 10}{x - 2} \right|$$

$$= \left| \frac{(2x - 5)(x - 2)}{x - 2} \right|$$

$$= |2x - 5|$$

The believer wants to write this expression in terms of $x - 2$. This example does not seem to "fall into place" as did Example 1. Suppose the doubter chooses $\varepsilon = 1.5$ (not a very small ε). Then we must find a δ so that whenever x is within this δ distance of 2, $f(x)$ will be within 1.5 units of 6. This is shown in Figure 1.49a. However, if the doubter chooses $\varepsilon = 0.5$ (still not a very small ε), then the believer is defeated, because no δ can be found, as shown in Figure 1.49b. ▬

*In fact, there are other choices that would work; for example, $\delta = \frac{\varepsilon}{a}$ where $a \geq 2$.

The believer/doubter format is a useful device for dramatizing the way certain choices are made in epsilon-delta arguments, but it is customary to be less "chatty" in formal mathematical proofs.

■ EPSILON-DELTA PROOFS

The following examples illustrate epsilon-delta proofs, two in which the function has a limit and one in which it does not.

EXAMPLE 3 An epsilon-delta proof of a limit of a linear function

Show that $\lim\limits_{x \to 2} (4x - 3) = 5$.

Solution We have
$$|f(x) - L| = |4x - 3 - 5|$$
$$= |4x - 8|$$
$$= \underbrace{4|x - 2|}$$

This must be less than ε
whenever $|x - 2| < \delta$.

Choose $\delta = \frac{\varepsilon}{4}$; then
$$|f(x) - L| = 4|x - 2| < 4\delta = 4\left(\frac{\varepsilon}{4}\right) = \varepsilon$$

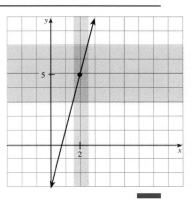

EXAMPLE 4 An epsilon-delta proof of a limit of a rational function

Show that $\lim\limits_{x \to 2} \dfrac{x^2 - 2x + 2}{x - 4} = -1$.

Solution We have $|f(x) - L| = \left| \dfrac{x^2 - 2x + 2}{x - 4} - (-1) \right|$

$$= \left| \frac{x^2 - x - 2}{x - 4} \right|$$

$$= \underbrace{|x - 2| \left| \frac{x + 1}{x - 4} \right|}$$

This must be less than the given ε
whenever x is near 2.

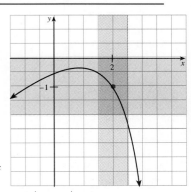

Certainly $|x - 2|$ is small if x is near 2, and the factor $\left| \dfrac{x + 1}{x - 4} \right|$ is not large $\Big($it is close to $\frac{3}{2}\Big)$. Note that if $|x - 2|$ is small it is reasonable to assume

$$|x - 2| < 1 \text{ so that } 1 < x < 3$$

The largest value of the fraction $\dfrac{x + 1}{x - 4}$ is

$$\frac{1 + 1}{1 - 4} = \frac{2}{-3}$$

and the smallest value of the fraction $\dfrac{x + 1}{x - 4}$ is

$$\frac{3 + 1}{3 - 4} = \frac{4}{-1} = -4$$

Thus, if $|x - 2| < 1$, we have

$$-4 < \frac{x + 1}{x - 4} < -\frac{2}{3}$$

so that

$$-4 < \frac{x+1}{x-4} < 4 \quad \textit{Because } -\frac{2}{3} < 4$$

and

$$\left|\frac{x+1}{x-4}\right| < 4$$

Now let $\varepsilon > 0$ be given. If simultaneously

$$|x-2| < \frac{\varepsilon}{4} \quad \text{and} \quad \left|\frac{x+1}{x-4}\right| < 4$$

then

$$|f(x) - L| = |x - 2|\left|\frac{x+1}{x-4}\right| < \frac{\varepsilon}{4}(4) = \varepsilon$$

Thus, we have only to take δ to be the smaller of the two numbers 1 and $\frac{\varepsilon}{4}$ in order to guarantee that

$$|f(x) - L| < \varepsilon$$

That is, given $\varepsilon > 0$, choose δ to be the smaller of the numbers 1 and $\frac{\varepsilon}{4}$. We write this as $\delta = \min\left(1, \frac{\varepsilon}{4}\right)$.   ▬

EXAMPLE 5   An epsilon-delta proof that a limit does not exist

Show that $\lim\limits_{x\to 0} \frac{1}{x}$ does not exist.

Solution   Let $f(x) = \frac{1}{x}$ and L be any number. Suppose that $\lim\limits_{x\to 0} f(x) = L$. Look at the graph of f, as shown in Figure 1.50. It would seem that no matter what value of ε is chosen, it would be impossible to find a corresponding δ. Consider the absolute value expression required by the definition of limit: If

$$|f(x) - L| < \varepsilon, \text{ or, for this example, } \left|\frac{1}{x} - L\right| < \varepsilon$$

then

$$-\varepsilon < \frac{1}{x} - L < \varepsilon \quad \textit{Property of absolute value (Table 1.1, p. 10)}$$

and

$$L - \varepsilon < \frac{1}{x} < L + \varepsilon$$

If $\varepsilon = 1$ (not a particularly small ε), then

$$\left|\frac{1}{x}\right| < |L| + 1$$

$$|x| > \frac{1}{|L| + 1}$$

which proves (because L was chosen arbitrarily) that $\lim\limits_{x\to 0} \frac{1}{x}$ does not exist. In other words, because ε can be chosen very small, $|x|$ will be very large, and it will be impossible to squeeze $\frac{1}{x}$ between $L - \varepsilon$ and $L + \varepsilon$.   ▬

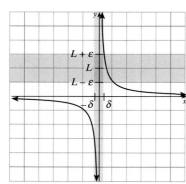

Figure 1.50 $\lim\limits_{x\to 0} \frac{1}{x}$

If $f(x) \geq 0$ for all x near c, then $\lim\limits_{x\to c} f(x) \geq 0$.

Figure 1.51 Limit limitation theorem

■ SELECTED THEOREMS WITH FORMAL PROOFS

Next, we shall prove several theoretical results using the formal definition of the limit.

The next two theorems are useful tools in the development of calculus. The first states that the points on a graph that are on or above the x-axis cannot possibly "tend toward" a point *below* the axis, as shown in Figure 1.51.

THEOREM 1.8   Limit limitation theorem

Suppose $\lim\limits_{x \to c} f(x)$ exists and $f(x) \geq 0$ throughout an open interval containing the number c, except possibly at c itself. Then

$$\lim_{x \to c} f(x) \geq 0$$

Proof: Let $L = \lim\limits_{x \to c} f(x)$. To show that $L \geq 0$, assume, on the contrary, that $L < 0$. According to the definition of limit (with $\varepsilon = -L$), there is a number $\delta > 0$ such that

$$|f(x) - L| < -L \quad \text{whenever} \quad 0 < |x - c| < \delta$$

In particular,

$$f(x) - L < -L$$

or

$$f(x) < 0$$

Thus

$$f(x) < 0 \quad \text{whenever} \quad 0 < |x - c| < \delta$$

However, this contradicts the hypothesis that $f(x) \geq 0$ throughout an open interval containing c. Therefore, we reject the assumption that $L < 0$ and conclude that $L \geq 0$, as required. ∎

⊘ It may seem reasonable to conjecture that if $f(x) > 0$ throughout an open interval containing c, then $\lim\limits_{x \to c} f(x) > 0$. This is not necessarily true, and the most that can be said in this situation is that $\lim\limits_{x \to c} f(x) \geq 0$, if the limit exists. For example, if

$$f(x) = \begin{cases} x^2 & \text{for } x \neq 0 \\ 1 & \text{for } x = 0 \end{cases}$$

then $f(x) > 0$ for all x, but $\lim\limits_{x \to 0} f(x) = 0$. ⊘

Useful information about the limit of a given function f can often be obtained by examining other functions that bound f from above and below. For example, in Section 1.5 we found

$$\lim_{x \to 0} \frac{\sin x}{x} = 1$$

by using a table. This will be proved in Section 2.3 by first showing that

$$\cos x \leq \frac{\sin x}{x} \leq 1$$

for all x near 0 and then noting that because $\cos x$ and 1 both tend toward 1 as x approaches 0, the function

$$\frac{\sin x}{x}$$

which is "squeezed" between them, must converge to 1 as well. Theorem 1.9 provides the theoretical basis for this method of proof.

THEOREM 1.9   The squeeze theorem

If $g(x) \leq f(x) \leq h(x)$ for all x in an open interval containing c (except possibly at c itself) and if

$$\lim_{x \to c} g(x) = \lim_{x \to c} h(x) = L$$

then $\lim\limits_{x \to c} f(x) = L$.

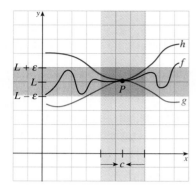

Figure 1.52 The squeeze theorem

Proof: Let $\varepsilon > 0$ be given. Since $\lim_{x \to c} g(x) = L$ and $\lim_{x \to c} h(x) = L$, there are positive numbers δ_1 and δ_2 such that

$$|g(x) - L| < \varepsilon \quad \text{and} \quad |h(x) - L| < \varepsilon$$

whenever
$$0 < |x - c| < \delta_1 \quad \text{and} \quad 0 < |x - c| < \delta_2$$

respectively. Let δ be the smaller of the numbers δ_1 and δ_2. Then, if x is a number that satisfies $0 < |x - c| < \delta$, we have

$$-\varepsilon < g(x) - L \le f(x) - L \le h(x) - L < \varepsilon$$

and it follows that $|f(x) - L| < \varepsilon$. Thus, $\lim_{x \to c} f(x) = L$, as claimed. ∎

The geometric interpretation of the squeeze theorem is shown in Figure 1.52. Notice that because $g(x) \le f(x) \le h(x)$, the graph of f is "squeezed" between those of g and h in the neighborhood of c. Thus, if the bounding graphs converge to a common point P as x approaches c, then the graph of f must also converge to P as well.

PROBLEM SET 1.8

Ⓑ *In Problems 1–6, use the believer/doubter format to prove or disprove the given limit statement.*

1. $\lim_{x \to 1} (2x - 5) = -3$
2. $\lim_{x \to -2} (3x + 7) = 1$
3. $\lim_{x \to 1} (3x + 1) = 5$
4. $\lim_{x \to 2} (x^2 - 2) = 5$
5. $\lim_{x \to 2} (x^2 + 2) = 6$
6. $\lim_{x \to 1} (x^2 - 3x + 2) = 0$

In Problems 7–12, use the formal definition of the limit to prove or disprove the given limit statement.

7. $\lim_{x \to 2} (x + 3) = 5$
8. $\lim_{t \to 0} (3t - 1) = 0$
9. $\lim_{x \to -2} (3x + 7) = 1$
10. $\lim_{x \to 1} (2x - 5) = -3$
11. $\lim_{x \to 2} (x^2 + 2) = 6$
12. $\lim_{x \to 2} \frac{1}{x} = \frac{1}{2}$

13. Prove that $f(x) = \begin{cases} \sin \dfrac{1}{x} & \text{if } x \ne 0 \\ 0 & \text{if } x = 0 \end{cases}$
is not continuous at $x = 0$. *Hint*: To show that $\lim_{x \to 0} f(x) \ne 0$, choose $\varepsilon = 0.5$ and note that for any $\delta > 0$, there exists an x of the form $x = \dfrac{2}{\pi(2n + 1)}$ with n a natural number for which $0 < |x| < \delta$.

Ⓒ *In Problems 14–19, construct a formal ε-δ proof to show that the given limit statement is valid for any number c.*

14. If $\lim_{x \to c} f(x)$ exists and k is a constant, then $\lim_{x \to c} kf(x) = k \lim_{x \to c} f(x)$.

15. If $\lim_{x \to c} f(x)$ and $\lim_{x \to c} g(x)$ both exist, then $\lim_{x \to c} [f(x) - g(x)] = \lim_{x \to c} f(x) - \lim_{x \to c} g(x)$.

16. If $\lim_{x \to c} f(x)$ and $\lim_{x \to c} g(x)$ both exist and a, b are constants, then $\lim_{x \to c} [af(x) + bg(x)] = a \lim_{x \to c} f(x) + b \lim_{x \to c} g(x)$.

17. If $\lim_{x \to c} f(x) = 0$ and $\lim_{x \to c} g(x) = 0$, then $\lim_{x \to c} f(x)g(x) = 0$.

18. If $f(x) \ge g(x) \ge 0$ for all x and $\lim_{x \to c} f(x) = 0$, then $\lim_{x \to c} g(x) = 0$.

19. If $f(x) \ge g(x)$ for all x in an open interval containing the number c and $\lim_{x \to c} f(x)$ and $\lim_{x \to c} g(x)$ both exist, then

$\lim_{x \to c} f(x) \ge \lim_{x \to c} g(x)$. *Hint*: Apply the limit limitation theorem (Theorem 1.8) to the function $h(x) = f(x) - g(x)$.

Problems 20–23 lead to a proof of the product rule for limits.

20. If $\lim_{x \to c} f(x) = L$, show that $\lim_{x \to c} |f(x)| = |L|$. *Hint*: Note that
$$\big| |f(x)| - |L| \big| \le |f(x) - L|.$$

21. If $\lim_{x \to c} f(x) = L$, $L \ne 0$, show that there exists a $\delta > 0$ such that $\frac{1}{2}|L| < |f(x)| < \frac{3}{2}|L|$ for all x for which $0 < |x - c| < \delta$.
Hint: Use $\varepsilon = \frac{1}{2}|L|$ in Problem 20.

22. If $\lim_{x \to c} f(x) = L$ and $L \ne 0$, show that $\lim_{x \to c} [f(x)]^2 = L^2$ by completing these steps:
   a. Use Problem 21 to show that there exists a $\delta_1 > 0$ so that $|f(x) + L| < \frac{5}{2}|L|$ whenever $0 < |x - c| < \delta_1$.
   b. Given $\varepsilon > 0$, show that there exists a $\delta_2 > 0$ such that $|[f(x)]^2 - L^2| < \frac{5}{2}|L|\varepsilon$ whenever $0 < |x - c| < \delta_2$.
   c. Complete the proof that $\lim_{x \to c} [f(x)]^2 = L^2$.

23. Prove the product rule for limits: If $\lim_{x \to c} f(x) = L$ and $\lim_{x \to c} g(x) = M$, then $\lim_{x \to c} f(x)g(x) = LM$. *Hint*: Use the result of Problem 22 along with the identity
$$fg = \tfrac{1}{4}[(f + g)^2 - (f - g)^2]$$

24. Show that if f is continuous at c and $f(c) > 0$, then $f(x) > 0$ throughout an open interval containing c. *Hint*: Note that $\lim_{x \to c} f(x) = f(c)$ and use $\varepsilon = \frac{1}{2}f(c)$ in the definition of limit.

25. Show that if f is continuous at L and $\lim_{x \to c} g(x) = L$, then $\lim_{x \to c} f(g(x)) = f(L)$ by completing the following steps:
   a. Explain why there exists a $\delta_1 > 0$ such that $|f(w) - f(L)| < \varepsilon$ whenever $|w - L| > \delta_1$.
   b. Complete the proof by setting $w = g(x)$ and using part (a).

Computational Window ▼ ▲

26. For linear functions, the relation between ε and δ is clear; but for complicated functions, it is not. However, the correct graph can illustrate this relationship. For the following function, illustrate not only that f is continuous at $x = 3$, but determine graphically how you would pick δ to accommodate a given ε. (For example, $\delta = K\varepsilon$.)

$$f(x) = \frac{x^4 - 2x^3 + 3x^2 - 5x + 2}{x - 2}$$

CHAPTER 1 REVIEW

IN THIS REVIEW Proficiency examination, supplementary problems
Problems 1–21 of the proficiency examination test your knowledge of the concepts of this chapter, and Problems 22–30 test your understanding of those concepts by asking you to work sample practice problems. The supplementary problems present questions relating to the material of this chapter in a wide variety of settings.

PROFICIENCY EXAMINATION

Concept Problems

1. Characterize the following sets of numbers: natural numbers, whole numbers, integers, rational numbers, irrational numbers, and real numbers.

2. Define absolute value.

3. State the triangle inequality.

4. State the distance formula for points $P(x_1, y_1)$ and $Q(x_2, y_2)$.

5. Define slope; include a discussion of angle of inclination.

6. List the following forms of the equation of a line:
   a. standard form   **b.** slope-intercept form
   c. point-slope form   **d.** horizontal line
   e. vertical line

7. State the slope criteria for parallel and for perpendicular lines.

8. Define function.

9. Define the composition of functions.

10. What is meant by the graph of a function?

11. Draw a quick sketch of an example of each of the following functions.
   a. identity function   **b.** standard quadratic function
   c. standard cubic function **d.** absolute value function
   e. cube root function   **f.** standard reciprocal
   g. standard reciprocal squared **h.** cosine function
   i. sine function   **j.** tangent function
   k. secant function   **l.** cosecant function
   m. cotangent function

12. What is a polynomial function?

13. What is a rational function?

14. State the informal definition of a limit of a function. Discuss this informal definition.

15. State the following basic formulas and rules for limits:
   a. limit of a constant   **b.** multiple rule
   c. sum rule   **d.** difference rule
   e. product rule   **f.** quotient rule
   g. power rule

16. Define the continuity of a function at a point and discuss.

17. State the continuity theorem as well as the properties of continuous functions.

18. State the intermediate value theorem.

19. What is the bisection method?

20. State the formal definition of a limit.

21. State the squeeze theorem for limits in formal terms.

Practice Problems

22. Find an equation for the lines satisfying the following conditions:
   a. through $\left(-\frac{1}{2}, 5\right)$ with slope $m = -\frac{3}{4}$
   b. through $(-3, 5)$ and $(7, 2)$
   c. with x-intercept $(4, 0)$ and y-intercept $\left(0, -\frac{3}{7}\right)$
   d. through $\left(-\frac{1}{2}, 5\right)$ and parallel to the line $2x + 5y - 11 = 0$
   e. the perpendicular bisector of the line segment joining $P(-3, 7)$ and $Q(5, 1)$

23. Sketch the graph of each of the following equations:
   a. $3x + 2y - 12 = 0$ **b.** $y = x^2 - 4x - 10$
   c. $y - 3 = |x + 1|$ **d.** $y = 2\cos(x - 1)$
   e. $y + 1 = \tan(2x + 3)$

24. If $f(x) = \dfrac{1}{x+1}$, what values of x satisfy

$$f\left(\frac{1}{x+1}\right) = f\left(\frac{2x+1}{2x+4}\right)?$$

25. If $f(x) = \sqrt{\dfrac{x}{x-1}}$ and $g(x) = \dfrac{\sqrt{x}}{\sqrt{x-1}}$, does $f = g$? Why or why not?

26. If $f(x) = \sin x$ and $g(x) = \sqrt{1-x^2}$, find the composite functions $f \circ g$ and $g \circ f$.

27. An efficiency expert has found that when XYZ Corporation employs N workers ($N > 3$), it takes

$$T = \frac{3N+4}{2N-5}$$

hours to complete a certain job. If each worker earns $25 per hour, express the total labor cost C as a function of N.

28. Evaluate each of the following limits.

a. $\displaystyle\lim_{x\to 3} \frac{x^2 - 4x + 9}{x^2 + x - 8}$ **b.** $\displaystyle\lim_{x\to 4} \frac{\sqrt{x} - 2}{x - 4}$

c. $\displaystyle\lim_{x\to 2} \frac{x^2 - 5x + 6}{x^2 - 4}$ **d.** $\displaystyle\lim_{x\to 0} \frac{1 - \cos x}{2\tan x}$

29. Find constants A and B such that f is continuous for all x:

$$f(x) = \begin{cases} Ax + 3 & \text{if } x < 1 \\ 2 & \text{if } x = 1 \\ x^2 + B & \text{if } x > 1 \end{cases}$$

30. Show that the equation

$$x + \sin x = \frac{1}{\sqrt{x+3}}$$

has at least one solution on the interval $[0, \pi]$.

SUPPLEMENTARY PROBLEMS*

In Problems 1–3, find the perimeter and area of the given figure.

1. the right triangle with vertices $(-1, 3)$, $(-1, 8)$, and $(11, 8)$

2. the triangle bounded by the lines $y = 5$, $3y - 4x = 11$, and $12x + 5y = 25$

3. the trapezoid with vertices $(-3, 0)$, $(5, 0)$, $(0, 8)$, and $(2, 8)$

In Problems 4–7, find an equation for the indicated line or circle.

4. the vertical line through the point where the line $y = 2x - 7$ is tangent to the parabola $y = x^2 + 6x - 3$

5. the circle that is tangent to the x-axis and is centered at $(5, 4)$

6. the circle that contains the origin and is tangent to the line $3x + 4y - 40 = 0$

7. the line through the two points where the circles $x^2 + y^2 - 5x + 7y = 3$ and $x^2 + y^2 + 4y = 0$ intersect

8. In each of the following cases, find constants A and B so that the given equation will be true whenever both sides are defined:

a. $\tan\left(x + \frac{\pi}{3}\right) = \dfrac{A + \tan x}{1 + B\tan x}$

b. $\sin^3 x = A \sin 3x + B \sin x$

9. In a triangle, the perpendicular segment drawn from a given vertex to the opposite side is called the *altitude* on that side. Consider the triangle with vertices $(-2, 1)$, $(5, 6)$, and $(3, -2)$.

a. Find an equation for each line containing an altitude of this triangle.

b. Show that the three lines found in part **a** intersect at the same point. Find the coordinates of this point.

The supplementary problems are presented in a somewhat random order, not necessarily in order of difficulty.

10. Let $f(x) = x^2 + 5x - 9$. For what values of x is it true that $f(2x) = f(3x)$?

11. If an object is shot up from the ground with an initial velocity of 256 ft/sec, its distance in feet above the ground at the end of t seconds is given by $s(t) = 256t - 16t^2$ (neglecting air resistance). What is the highest point for this projectile?

12. It is estimated that t years from now, the population of a certain suburban community will be

$$P(t) = \frac{11t + 12}{2t + 3}$$

thousand people. What is the current population of the community? What will the population be in 6 years? When will there be 5,000 people in the community?

In Problems 13–16, evaluate the given limit.

13. $\displaystyle\lim_{x\to 1^+} \sqrt{\frac{x^2 - x}{x - 1}}$ **14.** $\displaystyle\lim_{x\to 1} \frac{x^3 - 1}{x^2 - 1}$

15. $\displaystyle\lim_{x\to 1} \frac{x^2 - 3x + 2}{x^2 - 1}$ **16.** $\displaystyle\lim_{x\to 1/\pi} \frac{1 + \cos\frac{1}{x}}{\pi x - 1}$

Evaluate $\displaystyle\lim_{\Delta x\to 0} \dfrac{f(x + \Delta x) - f(x)}{\Delta x}$ for the function f in Problems 17–20.

17. $f(x) = 3x + 5$ **18.** $f(x) = \sqrt{2x}$

19. $f(x) = x(x + 1)$ **20.** $f(x) = \dfrac{4}{x}$

21. Find constants A and B so that the following function $f(x)$ will be continuous for all x:

$$f(x) = \begin{cases} \dfrac{x^2 - Ax - 6}{x - 2} & \text{if } x > 2 \\ x^2 + B & \text{if } x \le 2 \end{cases}$$

22. A bus charter company offers a travel club the following arrangements: If no more than 100 people go on a certain tour, the cost will be $500 per person, but the cost per person will be reduced by $4 for each person in excess of 100 who takes the tour.

    a. Express the total revenue R obtained by the charter company as a function of the number of people who go on the tour.

    b. Sketch the graph of R. Estimate the number of people that results in the greatest total revenue for the charter company.

23. Many materials, such as brick, steel, aluminum, and concrete, expand due to increases in temperature. This is why spaces are placed between the cement slabs in sidewalks. Suppose you have a 100-ft length of material securely fastened at both ends, and assume that the buckle is linear. (It is not, but this assumption will serve as a worthwhile approximation.) If the height of the buckle is x ft, and the percentage of swelling is y, then x and y are related as shown in Figure 1.53.

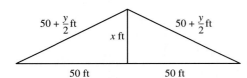

Figure 1.53 Buckling of a given material

Find the amount of buckling (to the nearest inch) for the following materials:

    a. brick; $y = 0.03$ b. steel; $y = 0.06$
    c. aluminum; $y = 0.12$ d. concrete; $y = 0.05$

24. A ball has been dropped from the top of a building. Its height (in feet) after t seconds is given by the function

$$h(t) = -16t^2 + 256$$

    a. How high will the ball be after 2 sec?
    b. How far will the ball travel during the third second?
    c. How tall is the building?
    d. When will the ball hit the ground?

25. Suppose the number of worker-hours required to distribute new telephone books to x percent of the households in a certain rural community is given by the function

$$f(x) = \frac{600x}{300 - x}$$

    a. What is the domain of the function f?
    b. For what values of x does $f(x)$ have a practical interpretation in this context?
    c. How many worker-hours were required to distribute new telephone books to the first 50% of the households?
    d. How many worker-hours were required to distribute new telephone books to the entire community?

    e. What percentage of the households in the community had received new telephone books by the time 150 worker-hours had been expended?

26. First sketch the graph of $y = -x^2 + 5x - 6$. Next, use your graph to obtain the graphs of the related functions:

    a. $y = -x^2 + 5x$
    b. $y = x^2 - 5x + 6$
    c. $y = (x + 1)^2 + 5(x + 1) - 6$

27. Find the area of each of the following plane figures:

    a. the circle $x^2 + y^2 = 9$
    b. the rectangle with vertices $(0, 0)$, $(3, 0)$, $(3, 2)$, and $(0, 2)$

28. Find the volume and the surface area of each of the following solid figures:

    a. a sphere with radius 4
    b. a rectangular parallelepiped (box) with sides of length 2, 3, and 5

29. Find the volume and the surface area of each of these solid figures:

    a. the right circular cylinder with height 4 and radius 2
    b. the inverted cone with height 5 and top radius 3

30. Show that the tangent line to the circle $x^2 + y^2 = r^2$ at the point (x_0, y_0) has the equation $y_0y + x_0x = r^2$. *Hint:* Recall that the tangent line at a point P on a circle with center C is the line that passes through P and is perpendicular to the line segment CP.

31. a. Consider the triangle with vertices $A(-1, 4)$, $B(3, 2)$, and $C(3, -6)$. Determine the midpoints M_1 and M_2 of sides $\overline{AB}$ and $\overline{AC}$, respectively, and show that the line segment M_1M_2 is parallel to side $\overline{BC}$ with half its length.

    b. Generalize the procedure of part **a** to show that the line segment joining the midpoints of any two sides of a given triangle is parallel to the third side and has half its length.

32. Let $ABCD$ be a quadrilateral in the plane, and let P, Q, R, and S be the midpoints of sides $\overline{AB}$, $\overline{BC}$, $\overline{CD}$, and $\overline{DA}$, as shown in Figure 1.54. Show that $PQRS$ is a parallelogram.

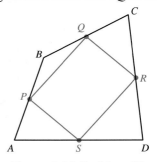

Figure 1.54 Problem 32

33. Find a constant c that guarantees that the graph of the equation

$$x^2 + xy + cy = 4$$

will have a y-intercept of $(0, -5)$. What are the x-intercepts of the graph?

34. A manufacturer estimates that when the price for each unit is p dollars, the profit will be $N = -p^2 + 14p - 48$ thousand dollars. Sketch the graph of the profit formula and answer these questions.

  a. For what values of p is this a profitable operation? (That is, when is $N > 0$?)

  b. What price results in maximum profit? What is the maximum profit?

35. When analyzing experimental data involving two variables, a useful procedure is to pass a smooth curve through a number of plotted data points and then perform computations as if the curve were the graph of an equation relating the variables. Suppose the following data are gathered as a result of a physiological experiment in which skin tissue is subjected to external heat for t seconds, and a measurement is made of the change in temperature ΔT required to cause a change of 2.5°C at a depth of 0.5 mm in the skin:

t (sec)	1	2	3	4	10	20	25	30
ΔT (°C)	12.5	7.5	5.8	5	4.5	3.5	2.9	2.8

Plot the data points in a coordinate plane and then answer these questions.

  a. What temperature difference ΔT would be expected if the exposure time is 2.2 sec?

  b. Approximately what exposure time t corresponds to a temperature difference $\Delta T = 8°C$?

36. A mural 7 feet high is hung on a wall in such a way so that its lower edge is 5 feet higher than the eye of an observer standing 12 feet from the wall. (See Figure 1.55.) Find tan θ, where θ is the angle subtended by the mural at the observer's eye.

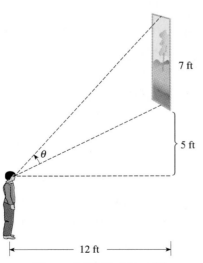

7 ft

5 ft

θ

12 ft

Figure 1.55 Problem 36

37. In Figure 1.56, ship A is at point P at noon and sails due east at 9 km/hr. Ship B arrives at point P at 1:00 P.M. and sails at 7 km/hr along a course that forms an angle of 60° with the course of ship A. Find a formula for the distance $s(t)$ separating the ships t hours after noon. Approximately how far apart (to the nearest kilometer) are the ships at 4:00 P.M.?

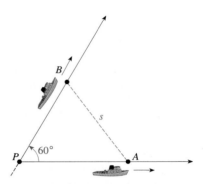

B

s

P 60° A

Figure 1.56 Problem 37

38. Under the provisions of a proposed property tax bill, a homeowner will pay $100 plus 8% of the assessed value of the house. Under the provisions of a competing bill, the homeowner will pay $1,900 plus 2% of the assessed value. If only financial considerations are taken into account, how should a homeowner decide which bill to support?

39. SPY PROBLEM   The hero of a popular spy story has escaped from the headquarters of an international diamond-smuggling ring in the tiny Mediterranean country of Azusa. Our hero, driving a stolen milk truck at 72 km/hr, has a 40-minute head start on his pursuers, who are chasing him in a Ferrari going 168 km/hr. The distance from the smugglers' headquarters in Azusa to the border, and freedom, is 83.8 km. Will he make it?

40. Two jets bound for Los Angeles leave New York 30 minutes apart. The first travels 550 mph, while the second goes 650 mph. How long will it take the second plane to pass the first?

41. To raise money, a service club has been collecting used bottles that it plans to deliver to a local glass company for recycling. Since the project began 8 days ago, the club has collected 2,400 pounds of glass, for which the glass company currently offers 15¢ per pound. However, since bottles are accumulating faster than they can be recycled, the company plans to reduce the price they pay by 1¢ per pound each day until the price reaches 0¢ fifteen days from now. Assuming that the club can continue to collect bottles at the same rate and that transportation costs make more than one trip to the glass company unfeasible, express the club's revenue from its recycling project as a function of the number of additional days the project runs. Draw the graph and estimate when the club should conclude the project and deliver the bottles in order to maximize its revenue.

42. An open box with a square base is to be built for $48. The sides of the box will cost $3 per square ft and the base will cost $4 per square ft. Express the volume of the box as a function of the length of its base.

43. A regular polygon of n sides is inscribed in a circle of radius R as shown in Figure 1.57.

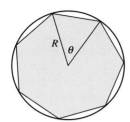

Figure 1.57 A regular polygon of seven sides with central angle θ (Problem 43)

a. Show that the perimeter of the polygon is given by $P(\theta)$ $= \dfrac{4\pi R}{\theta} \sin\dfrac{\theta}{2}$ where $\theta = \dfrac{2\pi}{n}$ is the central angle subtended by one side of the polygon.

b. Use the formula in part **a** together with the fact that $\displaystyle\lim_{x\to 0} \dfrac{\sin x}{x} = 1$ to show that a circle of radius R has circumference $2\pi R$.

c. Modify the approach suggested in parts **a** and **b** to show that a circle of radius R has area πR^2. *Hint*: First express the area of the shaded polygon in Figure 1.58 as a function of θ.

44. A cylindrical tank containing 50 ℓ of water is drained into an empty rectangular trough that can hold 75 ℓ. Explain why there must be a time when the height of water in the tank is the same as that in the trough.

45. The famous author John Uptight must decide between two publishers who are vying for the rights to his new book, *Zen and the Art of Taxidermy*. Publisher A offers royalties of 12% of net proceeds on the first 30,000 copies sold and 17% on all copies in excess of that figure, and expects to net $5 on each copy sold. Publisher B will pay no royalties on the first 4,000 copies sold but will pay 15% on the net proceeds of all copies sold in excess of 4,000 copies, and expects to net $6 on each copy sold.

a. With whom should John sign if he expects to sell 30,000 copies?

b. What if he expects to sell 100,000 copies?

c. Derive a formula for determining which publisher John should choose if he expects to sell N copies.

d. For what value of N are the two publishers' offers equivalent? This is called the **break-even point.**

46. A function f is said to satisfy a *Lipschitz condition* (named for the 19th century mathematician, Rudolf Lipschitz) on a given interval if there is a positive constant M such that

$$|f(x) - f(y)| < M|x - y|$$

for all x and y in the interval (with $x \neq y$). Suppose f satisfies a Lipschitz condition on an interval and let c be a fixed number chosen arbitrarily from the interval. Use the formal definition of limit to prove that f is continuous at c.

Computational Window

47. In this problem, you are to find the tangent line to a curve using the idea that the tangent line is the limit of secant lines. As a nontrivial example, consider the function defined by

$$f(x) = \frac{(x^3 - 5)(x^2 - 1)}{x^2 + 1}$$

and graphically find the tangent line at the specific point $(2, f(2)) = (2, 1.8)$. To this end, consider two points on the graph, namely $(2, f(2))$ and $(b, f(b))$, where b is close to, but not equal to 2. The slope of the secant line (the line that connects the two points) is

$$\frac{f(b) - f(2)}{b - 2.0}$$

To find the secant line for a given b, the slope is

$$m = \frac{f(b) - f(2)}{b - 2}$$

and hence the secant is expressed as $y = f(2.0) + m(x - 2.0)$. Experimentally find b so that the secant is effectively tangent to the curve at $(2, f(2))$. Record your choice of b and m, and if possible, hand in a graph.

48. Here you investigate a function whose tangent at a particular point is problematic. Consider $f(x) = (x - 2)^{2/3} + 2x^3$ near $x = 2$. As in Problem 49, chose b close to, but not equal to 2 (try both $b < 2$ and $b > 2$). Report on your findings. Next try to explain what is happening by zooming the graph of $f(x)$ near $(2, f(2))$.

---

*49. PUTNAM EXAMINATION PROBLEM If f and g are real-valued functions of one real variable, show that there exist numbers x, y such that

$$0 \leq x \leq 1,\ 0 \leq y \leq 1,\ \text{and}\ |xy - f(x) - g(y)| \geq \tfrac{1}{4}$$

*50. PUTNAM EXAMINATION PROBLEM Consider a polynomial $f(x)$ with real coefficients having the property $f(g(x)) = g(f(x))$ for every polynomial $g(x)$ with real coefficients. What is $f(x)$?

*Putnam examination problems should be considered optional.

Calculus Was Inevitable

by John L. Troutman, Professor of Mathematics at Syracuse University

Historical Note

Isaac Newton (1642–1727)
Sir Isaac Newton was one of
the greatest mathematicians of
all time. He was a genius of the
highest order but was often
absent-minded. One story
about Newton is that when he
was a boy, he was sent to cut a
hole in the bottom of the barn
door for the cats to go in and
out. He cut two holes—a large
one for the cat and a small one
for the kittens. Newton considered himself a theologian rather
than a mathematician or a
physicist. He spent years
searching for clues about the
end of the world and the geog-
raphy of hell. One of Newton's
quotations about himself is, "I
seem to have been only like a
boy playing on the seashore and
diverting myself in now and
then finding a smoother pebble
or prettier shell than ordinary,
whilst the great ocean of truth
lay all undiscovered before
me."

The invention of calculus is now credited jointly to Isaac Newton (1642–1727)
and Gottfried W. Leibniz (1646–1716); when they produced their separate
publications, however (around 1685), there was a bitter controversy about who
created it. Part of the explanation for this is the fact that each had done his actual
work earlier (Newton in 1669; Leibniz, a little later); some can be attributed to the
rivalry between scientists in England who championed Newton and those in
Europe who supported Leibniz; but much simply reflects how ripe the intellectual
climate was for the blooming of calculus. Indeed, even if neither of these great
mathematicians had existed, it seems almost certain that the principles of
calculus—including the fundatmenta theorem (introduced in Chapter 4)—would
have been announced by the end of the seventeenth century.

Emergence of calculus was effectively demanded by the philosophical spirit of the
times. Natural philosophers had long believed that the universe was constructed
according to understandable mathematical principles, although they disagreed
about just what these principles were and how they might be formulated. For
example, the Pythagorean school (ca. 600 B.C.) maintained that everything
consisted of (whole) numbers and their ratios; hence their consternation upon
discovering that different entities such as $\sqrt{2}$ could be constructed. Next, the early
astronomers announced that heavenly bodies move in circular orbits around the
Earth as center, and later that the Earth itself must be a perfect sphere to reflect
the divine hand of its Creator. Both of these assertions are now known to be false,
and by 1612, Kepler had already explained why. Galileo (1564–1642) announced
that the distance traveled by a heavy body falling from rest is proportional to the
square of the elapsed time, and Fermat asserted (in 1657) that light moves along
those paths that minimize the time of travel. The question was whether such laws
could be formulated and justified mathematically, and what kind of mathematics
would be appropriate to describe these phenomena.

For already from antiquity there was the warning of Zeno (ca. 450 B.C.), in the
form of paradoxes, against unwise speculation about phenomena whose analysis
involved infinite processes. In particular, he "proved" that motion was impossible
if time consisted of indivisible instants, and conversely, that covering a given
distance was impossible if length was capable of infinite subdivision (see Chapter
8). Thus, although 17th-century scientists and philosophers might propose such
principles, it was evident that there must be underlying subtleties in the mathematics required to support them (that, in fact, required another two centuries for
satisfactory clarification).

To understand better how the mathematics developed, we must examine some of
the previous attempts to solve the twin problems of classical origin that motivated
the emergence of the calculus—those of finding the tangent line to a given planar
geometrical curve and finding the area under the curve. Newton himself acknowl-
edged that his greater vision resulted from his "standing on the shoulders of

giants." Who were these giants, and what had they contributed? First, there were the efforts of the Greek mathematicians, principally Eudoxus, Euclid, and Archimedes, who had originated the geometric concepts of tangency and area between 400 B.C. and 200 B.C., together with examples of each, such as the construction of tangent lines to a circle and the area under a parabolic curve. The Hindu and Arabic mathematicians had extended the number system and the formal language of algebra with certain of its laws by A.D. 1300, but it was not until Newton's own era that the methods of algebra and geometry were combined satisfactorily in the analytic geometry of René Descartes (1596–1650) to produce the recognition that a geometrical curve could be regarded as the locus of points whose coordinates satisfied an algebraic equation. This provided potential numerical exactitude to geometric constructions as well as the possibility of giving geometric proofs for limiting algebraic arguments. Since Euclidian geometry was then generally regarded as the only reliable mathematics, it was the latter direction that was most frequently taken. And it was this direction that was taken in the seventeenth century by de Roberval, Fermat, Cavalieri, Huygens, Wallis, and others, not the least of whom was Newton's own teacher at Cambridge, Isaac Barrow (1630–1677). These giants, as Newton called them, obtained equations for tangent lines to, and the (correct) areas under, polynomial curves with equations $y = x^n$ for $n = 1, 2, 3, \ldots, 9$, and certain other geometrically defined curves such as the spiral and the cycloid.

In his analysis of tangency, Barrow incorporated the approximating infinitesimal triangle with sides Δx, Δy, Δs that is now standard in expositions of calculus, and Cavalieri attempted to "count" an indefinite number of parallel equidistant lines to obtain areas. It was known that in specific cases these problems were related, and that they were equivalent, respectively, to the kinematic problems of characterizing velocity and distance traveled during a motion, problems which directly confronted the paradoxes of Zeno.

All that remained was for some mathematicians to sense the generality underlying these specific constructions and to devise a usable notation for presenting the results. This was accomplished essentially independently by Newton (who, justly mistrusting the required limiting arguments, suppressed his own contributions until he could validate them geometrically) and by the only slightly less cautious Leibniz. However, as we have argued, by this time (about 1670), it was almost inevitable that someone should do so.

What calculus has provided is a mathematical language that, by means of the derivative, can describe the rates of change used to characterize various physical processes (such as velocity) and, by means of the integral, can show how macroscopic entities (such as area or distance) can emerge from properly assembled microscopic elements. Moreover, the fundamental theorem, which states that these are inverse operations, supplies an exact method for passing between these types of description. Finally, the ability to relate the results of limiting arguments by simple algebraic formulas permits the correct use of calculus while retaining skepticism regarding its foundations. This has enabled applications to go forward while mathematicians have sought an appropriate axiomatic basis.

Our present technological age attests to the success of this endeavor, and to the value of calculus.

Historical Note

Gottfried Leibniz (1646–1716) At the age of 14, Leibniz attempted to reform Aristotelian logic. He wanted to create a general method of reasoning by calculation. At the age of 20, he applied for his doctorate at the university in Leipzig and was refused (because they said he was too young). He received his doctorate the next year at the University of Altdorf, where he made such a favorable impression that he was offered a professorship, which he declined, saying he had very different things in view. Leibniz went on to invent calculus, but not without a bitter controversy developing between Leibniz and Newton. Most historians agree that the bitterness over who invented calculus materially affected the history of mathematics. J. S. Mill characterized Leibniz by saying, "It would be difficult to name a man more remarkable for the greatness and universality of his intellectual powers than Leibniz."

MATHEMATICAL ESSAYS

Use a library or references other than this textbook to research the information necessary to answer the questions in Problems 1–11.

1. Write an essay about Isaac Newton and his discovery of calculus. This essay should be at least 500 words.

2. Write a 500-word essay about Gottfried Leibniz and his discovery of calculus.

3. Write a 500-word essay about the controversy surrounding the discovery of calculus by Newton and Leibniz.

4. The Greek mathematicians mentioned in this guest essay include Eudoxus, Euclid, and Archimedes. Write a short paper about contributions they made that might have been used by Newton.

5. Write a paper about the contributions of René Descartes that are needed for the development of calculus.

6. What is the definition of elementary functions as given by Joseph Liouville?

7. The guest essay mentions the contributions of de Roberval, Fermat, Cavalieri, Huygens, Wallis, and Barrow toward the invention of calculus. Write a short paper about these contributions.

8. In this guest essay, Troutman argues that the invention of calculus was inevitable, and even if Newton and Leibniz had not invented it, someone else would have. Write a 500-word essay either defending or refuting this thesis.

9. For years women were prohibited from serious study in mathematics. Write a paper on the history of women mathematicians and their achievements. Your paper should include a list of many prominent women mathematicians and their primary contribution. It should also include a lengthy profile of at least one woman mathematician.

10. "There are, in every culture, groups or individuals who think more about some ideas than do others. For other cultures, we know about the ideas of some professional groups or some ideas of the culture at large. We know little, however, about the mathematical thoughts of individuals in those cultures who are specially inclined toward mathematical ideas. In Western culture, on the other hand, we focus on, and record much about, those special individuals while including little about everyone else. Realization of this difference should make us particularly wary of any comparisons across cultures. Even more important, it should encourage finding out more about the ideas of mathematically oriented innovators in other cultures and, simultaneously, encourage expanding the scope of Western history to recognize and include mathematical ideas held by different groups within our culture or by our culture as a whole." From *Ethnomathematics* by Marcia Ascher (Pacific Grove: Brooks/Cole, 1991), pp. 188–189. Write a paper discussing this quotation.

11. **Book report** "Ethnomathematics, as it is being addressed here, has the goal of broadening the history of mathematics to one that has a multicultural, global perspective." Read the book *Ethnomathematics* by Marcia Ascher (Pacific Grove: Brooks/Cole, 1991), and prepare a book report.

12. Make up a word problem involving a limit or continuity. Send your problems to:

Mathematics Editor,
re: Bradley, Smith: *CALCULUS*
Prentice Hall
113 Sylvan Ave., Route 9W
Englewood Cliffs, NJ 07632

The best ones submitted will appear in the next edition (along with credit to the problem poser).

2

Techniques of Differentiation with Selected Applications

PREVIEW

In this chapter, we develop the main ideas of differential calculus. We begin by defining the *derivative,* which is the central concept of differential calculus. Then we develop a list of rules and formulas for finding the derivative of a variety of expressions, including polynomial functions, rational functions, root functions, and trigonometric functions. We then see how the derivative can be interpreted as a rate of change, and we develop a method for making approximations using the derivative.

PERSPECTIVE

In this chapter we focus on the concept of a derivative and are introduced to efficient ways of finding the derivative. The derivative is one of the fundamental ideas in all of calculus and is the cornerstone of more advanced mathematics.

If you have been introduced to the mechanics of *finding* a derivative in another course, you may feel that you already know the content of this chapter; **but there is much more to the idea of a derivative than finding the derivative of a polynomial function.** W. Dale Compton of the National Academy of Engineering stated at the National Colloquium on Calculus for a New Century (1987): *Engineering, in the words of the Accreditation Board for Engineering and Technology, is "the profession in which knowledge of the mathematical and natural sciences gained by study, experience, and practice is applied with judgment to develop ways to utilize, economically, the materials and forces of nature for the benefit of mankind."* The operative words in this statement are knowledge and judgment. Whereas mathematics has most often been considered as a requirement for **knowledge,** it is time for us to begin to consider its role in **judgment.** In addition to *finding* derivatives, you need to understand the *concept* of a derivative if you ever hope to be able to use mathematics in making judgments in scientific investigations. **Your success in a large portion of the material of this book rests on your success in this chapter.**

2.1 AN INTRODUCTION TO THE DERIVATIVE: TANGENTS

> **IN THIS SECTION** **Tangent lines, slope of a tangent, the derivative, existence of derivatives, continuity and differentiability, and derivative notation.** Ancient Greek mathematicians were able to construct tangents to circles and a few other simple curves, but before the 17th century there was no general procedure for finding the equation of a tangent to the graph of a function at a given point. To solve this "tangent problem," Sir Isaac Newton (see Historical Note on page 80) used an approach originally developed by the French mathematician Pierre de Fermat (see Historical Note on page 483). This approach leads to the definition of the *derivative*.

■ TANGENT LINES

In elementary mathematics a **tangent to a circle** is defined as a line in the plane of the circle that intersects the circle in exactly one point. However, this is much too narrow a view for our purposes in calculus. We will now consider the concept of a line tangent to a given curve (not necessarily a circle) at a given point. In general, it is not a simple matter to find the slope of a tangent line at a given point $P_0(x_0, y_0)$. This is because the formula

$$\text{slope} = m = \frac{\Delta y}{\Delta x} = \frac{y_1 - y_0}{x_1 - x_0}$$

requires knowledge not only of the point of tangency (x_0, y_0), but of at least one other point (x_1, y_1) on the line as well.

■ SLOPE OF A TANGENT

The limit procedure for finding the slope of a tangent was originally developed by Pierre de Fermat and was later used by Isaac Newton. The brilliance of the Fermat–Newton approach was the use of the "dynamic" limit process to attack the "static" problem of finding tangents.

Suppose we wish to find the slope of the tangent to $y = f(x)$ at the point $P(x_0, f(x_0))$. The strategy is to approximate the tangent by other lines whose slopes can be computed directly. In particular, consider the line joining the given point P to the neighboring point Q on the graph of f, as shown in Figure 2.1. This line is called a **secant** (a line that intersects, but is not tangent to, a curve). Compare the secants shown in Figure 2.1.

⊘ Δx is a single symbol and does not mean delta times x. ⊘

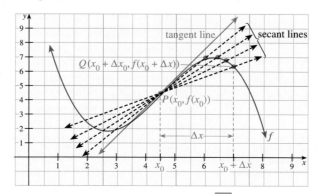

Figure 2.1 The secant $\overline{PQ}$

Notice that a secant is a good approximation to the tangent at point P as long as Q is close to P.

To compute the slope of a secant, first label the coordinates of the neighboring point Q, as indicated in Figure 2.1. In particular, let Δx denote the change in the x-coordinate between the given point $P(x_0, f(x_0))$ and the neighboring point $Q(x_0 + \Delta x, f(x_0 + \Delta x))$. The slope of this secant, m_{sec}, is easy to calculate:

$$m_{sec} = \frac{\Delta y}{\Delta x} = \frac{f(x_0 + \Delta x) - f(x_0)}{\Delta x}$$

To bring the secant closer to the tangent, let Q approach P *on the graph of f* by letting Δx approach 0. As this happens, the slope of the secant should approach the slope of the tangent at P. We denote the slope of the tangent by m_{tan} to distinguish it from the slope of a secant. These observations suggest the following definition.

Slope of a Line Tangent to a Graph at a Point

At the point $P(x_0, f(x_0))$, the tangent line to the graph of f has **slope** given by the formula

$$m_{tan} = \lim_{\Delta x \to 0} \frac{f(x_0 + \Delta x) - f(x_0)}{\Delta x}$$

provided that this limit exists.

EXAMPLE 1   Slope of a tangent at a particular point

Find the slope of the tangent to the graph of $f(x) = x^2$ at the point $P(-1, 1)$.

Solution   Figure 2.2a shows the tangent to f at $x = -1$.

The slope of the tangent is given by

$$
\begin{aligned}
m_{tan} &= \lim_{\Delta x \to 0} \frac{f(-1 + \Delta x) - f(-1)}{\Delta x} && \textit{Because } f(x) = x^2, \\
&&& f(-1 + \Delta x) = (-1 + \Delta x)^2. \\
&= \lim_{\Delta x \to 0} \frac{(-1 + \Delta x)^2 - (-1)^2}{\Delta x} \\
&= \lim_{\Delta x \to 0} \frac{1 - 2\Delta x + (\Delta x)^2 - 1}{\Delta x} \\
&= \lim_{\Delta x \to 0} \frac{-2\Delta x + (\Delta x)^2}{\Delta x} \\
&= \lim_{\Delta x \to 0} \frac{(-2 + \Delta x)\Delta x}{\Delta x} && \textit{Factor out } \Delta x \textit{ and reduce.} \\
&= \lim_{\Delta x \to 0} (-2 + \Delta x) = -2
\end{aligned}
$$

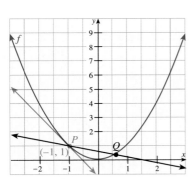

a. Tangent line at $(-1, 1)$

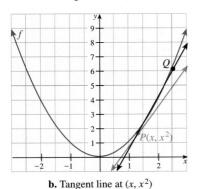

b. Tangent line at (x, x^2)

Figure 2.2 Tangent lines to the graph of $y = x^2$

In Example 1 we found the slope of the tangent $y = x^2$ at the point $(-1, 1)$. In Example 2, we perform the same calculation again, this time representing the given point algebraically as (x, x^2). This is the situation shown in Figure 2.2b for the slope of the tangent to $y = x^2$ at *any* point (x, x^2).

EXAMPLE 2   Slope of a tangent at an arbitrary point

Derive a formula for the slope of the tangent to the graph of $f(x) = x^2$, and then use the formula to compute the slope at $(4, 16)$.

Solution   Figure 2.2b shows a tangent at an arbitrary point $P(x, x^2)$ on the curve.

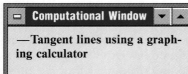

—Tangent lines using a graphing calculator

We can use a calculator to graph $\dfrac{f(x_0 + \Delta x) - f(x_0)}{\Delta x}$ for a small value of Δx. The resulting graph can be used to approximate the slope of the tangent line at a point x_0. Using $f(x) = x^2$ from Example 2, we created the calculator graph by graphing

$$Y1 = ((X + 0.01)^2 - X^2)/0.01$$

Note this is

$$\frac{f(x_0 + 0.01) - f(x_0)}{0.01}$$

$$= \frac{(x_0 + 0.01)^2 - x_0{}^2}{0.01}$$

```
Y1▤((X+.01)²-X²)
/.01
Xmin=-10  Ymin=-10
Xmax=10   Ymax=10
Xscl=1    Yscl=1
```

Use the (TRACE) to find the approximate slope of f at various values of x.

Compare the results with those obtained in Example 2.
Hint: Try resetting the (RANGE) value Xmin = −9 and note the trace values.

From the definition of slope of the tangent,

$$m_{\tan} = \lim_{\Delta x \to 0} \frac{f(x + \Delta x) - f(x)}{\Delta x} \qquad \textit{Because } f(x) = x^2,\ f(x + \Delta x) = (x + \Delta x)^2.$$

$$= \lim_{\Delta x \to 0} \frac{(x + \Delta x)^2 - x^2}{\Delta x}$$

$$= \lim_{\Delta x \to 0} \frac{x^2 + 2x\Delta x + (\Delta x)^2 - x^2}{\Delta x}$$

$$= \lim_{\Delta x \to 0} \frac{2x\Delta x + (\Delta x)^2}{\Delta x}$$

$$= \lim_{\Delta x \to 0} \frac{(2x + \Delta x)\Delta x}{\Delta x} \qquad \textit{Factor and reduce.}$$

$$= \lim_{\Delta x \to 0} (2x + \Delta x) = 2x$$

At the point $(4, 16)$, $x = 4$, so $m_{\tan} = 2(4) = 8$. ▬

The result of Example 2 gives a general formula for the slope of a line tangent to the graph of $f(x) = x^2$, namely, $m_{\tan} = 2x$. The answer from Example 1 can now be verified using this formula; if $x = -1$, then $m_{\tan} = 2(-1) = -2$.

PREVIEW

Knowledge of tangent lines at various points of a function f will give us some idea about the shape of the curve, as shown in Figure 2.3. We will consider this concept later in this chapter.

Figure 2.3 Tangent lines to a curve indicate the shape of the curve.

■ THE DERIVATIVE

The expression $\dfrac{f(x + \Delta x) - f(x)}{\Delta x}$

which gives a formula for the slope of a secant to the graph of a function f, is called the **difference quotient** of f. The limit of the difference quotient

$$\lim_{\Delta x \to 0} \frac{f(x + \Delta x) - f(x)}{\Delta x}$$

which gives a formula for the slope of the tangent to the graph of f at the point $(x, f(x))$ is called the **derivative** of f and is frequently denoted by the symbol $f'(x)$ (read "eff prime of x"). To **differentiate** a function f at x means to find its derivative at the point $(x, f(x))$.

Derivative

The **derivative** of f at x is given by

$$f'(x) = \lim_{\Delta x \to 0} \frac{f(x + \Delta x) - f(x)}{\Delta x}$$

provided this limit exists.

The derivative is one of the fundamental concepts in calculus, and it is important to make some observations regarding this definition.

1. If the limit for the difference quotient exists, then we say that the function f is **differentiable at x.**
2. The value of a derivative depends only on the limit process and not on the symbols used in that process. In Example 2, we found that if $f(x) = x^2$, then $f'(x) = 2x$. This means that we also know

$$\text{If } g(t) = t^2, \text{ then } g'(t) = 2t.$$
$$\text{If } h(u) = u^2, \text{ then } h'(u) = 2u.$$
$$\vdots$$

3. Notice that the derivative of a function is itself a function.

Computational Window—Derivatives by difference quotient and graphing

A graphing calculator can help us "guess" the appropriate derivative, which can then be found using the definition (or derivative theorems to be developed later in this chapter). For example, suppose we wish to find the derivative of $f(x) = x^3$ at $x = 1$.

Graph Y1 = $((X + 0.01)^3 − X^3)/0.01$.

Y₁⊟((X+.01)^3−X^
3)/.01

Xmin=-3   Ymin=0
Xmax=3   Ymax=8
Xscl=.5   Yscl=1

Recognize this as the difference quotient $\dfrac{f(x + \Delta x) − f(x)}{\Delta x}$ for $f(x) = x^3$ and $\Delta x = 0.01$. Remember, this approximates the derivative and *not* the graph of $f(x) = x^3$. We use the (TRACE) to find

X = 1.0212766, Y = 3.159756. This means the slope of the secant line passing through the points where $x = 1$ and $x = 1 + 0.01 = 1.01$ is about 3.2; this could be used as an approximation for the slope of the tangent line. Later, we will show that the derivative of $f(x) = x^3$ is $f'(x) = 3x^2$. We might "guess" this by looking at the graph of the difference quotient. Can you improve this approximation? Also, if you use different (RANGE) values you can see a different-sized or differently centered graph. Try once again by setting Xmin = −9, Xmax = 10, and note the different appearance of the graph. Also note that the (TRACE) gives X = 1, Y = 3.0301.

Another way of using a graphing calculator to approximate the derivative is to consider Δx as the variable in the difference quotient. For this example, $f(x) = x^3$ at $x = 1$, so you look at

$$\frac{f(x + \Delta x) − f(x)}{\Delta x} = \frac{(1 + \Delta x)^3 − 1^3}{\Delta x}$$

Trace values of Δx as $\Delta x \to 0$. You can use the table or graph functions of your calculator. Graphically, we say we are looking at

$$\frac{(1 + \Delta x)^3 − 1}{\Delta x} \quad \textit{in the neighborhood of } \Delta x = 0.$$

Besides giving the slope of the tangent at a point, the derivative has a variety of other important applications that we will see in subsequent sections. For example, the derivative can be used to study rates of change, rectilinear motion, marginal analysis in economics, maximum and minimum values and concavity of a function, to mention just a few applications.

EXAMPLE 3   Derivative using the definition

Differentiate $f(t) = \sqrt{t}$.

Solution $f'(t) = \lim_{\Delta t \to 0} \dfrac{f(t + \Delta t) - f(t)}{\Delta t}$

$\qquad = \lim_{\Delta t \to 0} \dfrac{\sqrt{t + \Delta t} - \sqrt{t}}{\Delta t}$

$\qquad = \lim_{\Delta t \to 0} \dfrac{\sqrt{t + \Delta t} - \sqrt{t}}{\Delta t} \left(\dfrac{\sqrt{t + \Delta t} + \sqrt{t}}{\sqrt{t + \Delta t} + \sqrt{t}} \right)$ *Rationalize numerator.*

$\qquad = \lim_{\Delta t \to 0} \dfrac{(t + \Delta t) - t}{\Delta t(\sqrt{t + \Delta t} + \sqrt{t})}$

$\qquad = \lim_{\Delta t \to 0} \dfrac{\Delta t}{\Delta t(\sqrt{t + \Delta t} + \sqrt{t})}$

$\qquad = \lim_{\Delta t \to 0} \dfrac{1}{\sqrt{t + \Delta t} + \sqrt{t}}$ *Reduce fraction.*

$\qquad = \dfrac{1}{2\sqrt{t}}$ *For $t > 0$*

⊘ Notice that $f(t) = \sqrt{t}$ is defined for all $t \geq 0$, whereas its derivative $f'(t) = \dfrac{1}{2\sqrt{t}}$ is defined for all $t > 0$. This shows that a function need not be differentiable throughout its entire domain. ⊘

THEOREM 2.1   Equation of a line tangent to a curve at a point

If f is a differentiable function at x_0, the graph of $y = f(x)$ has a tangent line at the point $P(x_0, f(x_0))$ with slope $f'(x_0)$ and equation

$$y = f'(x_0)(x - x_0) + f(x_0)$$

Proof: To find the equation of the tangent to the curve $y = f(x)$ at the point $P(x_0, y_0)$, we use the fact that the slope of the tangent is the derivative $f'(x_0)$ and apply the point-slope formula for the equation of a line:

$\qquad y - k = m(x - h)$ *Point-slope formula*

$\qquad y - y_0 = m(x - x_0)$ *Given point (x_0, y_0)*

$\qquad y - f(x_0) = f'(x_0)(x - x_0)$ *$y_0 = f(x_0)$ and $m_{\text{tan}} = f'(x_0)$*

$\qquad y = f'(x_0)(x - x_0) + f(x_0)$ *Add $f(x_0)$ to both sides.*   ■

EXAMPLE 4   Equation of a tangent

Find an equation of the tangent to the graph of $f(x) = \dfrac{1}{x}$ at the point where $x = 2$.

Solution   The graph of the function $y = \dfrac{1}{x}$, the point where $x = 2$, and the tangent at the point are shown in Figure 2.4. First, find $f'(x)$.

$f'(x) = \lim_{\Delta x \to 0} \dfrac{f(x + \Delta x) - f(x)}{\Delta x}$ *Definition of derivative*

$\qquad = \lim_{\Delta x \to 0} \dfrac{\dfrac{1}{x + \Delta x} - \dfrac{1}{x}}{\Delta x}$ *$f(x) = \dfrac{1}{x}; f(x + \Delta x) = \dfrac{1}{x + \Delta x}$*

$\qquad = \lim_{\Delta x \to 0} \dfrac{x - (x + \Delta x)}{x \Delta x (x + \Delta x)}$ *Simplify the fraction.*

$\qquad = \lim_{\Delta x \to 0} \dfrac{-1}{x(x + \Delta x)}$ *Cancel factor of Δx.*

$\qquad = \dfrac{-1}{x^2}$

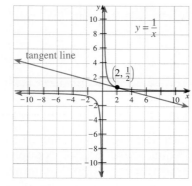

Figure 2.4 tangent to $y = \frac{1}{x}$ at $\left(2, \frac{1}{2}\right)$

Next, find the slope of the tangent at $x = 2$: $m_{\tan} = f'(2) = -\frac{1}{4}$. Finally, find the point of tangency $(2, f(2)) = \left(2, \frac{1}{2}\right)$. The equation of the tangent can now be found by using Theorem 2.1:

$$y = -\tfrac{1}{4}(x - 2) + \tfrac{1}{2} \text{ or, in standard form, } x + 4y - 4 = 0 \qquad \blacksquare$$

⊘   The slope of f at $x = x_0$ is not the derivative f' but the *value* of the derivative at $x = x_0$. In Example 4 the function is defined by $f(x) = 1/x$, the derivative is $f'(x) = -1/x^2$, and the slope at $x = 2$ is the *number* $f'(2) = -\frac{1}{4}$. ⊘

EXAMPLE 5   A line that is perpendicular to a tangent

Find the equation of the line that is perpendicular to the tangent of $f(x) = \dfrac{1}{x}$ at $x = 2$ and intersects it at the point of tangency.

Solution   From Example 4, we found that the slope of the tangent is $f'(2) = -\frac{1}{4}$ and that the point of tangency is $\left(2, \frac{1}{2}\right)$. In Section 1.3, we saw that two lines are perpendicular if and only if their slopes are negative reciprocals of each other. Thus, the perpendicular line we seek has slope 4 $\left(\text{the negative reciprocal of } -\frac{1}{4}\right)$, as shown in Figure 2.5. The desired equation is

$$y - \tfrac{1}{2} = 4(x - 2) \qquad \textit{Point-slope formula} \qquad \blacksquare$$

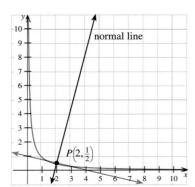

Figure 2.5 Graph for Example 5

The line we found in Example 5 has a name:

Normal Line to a Graph

> The **normal line** to the graph of f at the point P is the line that is perpendicular to the tangent to the graph at P.

■ EXISTENCE OF DERIVATIVES

We observed that a function is differentiable only if the limit in the definition of derivative exists. At points where a function f is not differentiable, we say that *the derivative of f does not exist*. The three common ways for a derivative to fail to exist are shown in Figure 2.6.

a. Corner point   **b.** Vertical tangent   **c.** Point of discontinuity

Figure 2.6 Common examples where a derivative does not exist

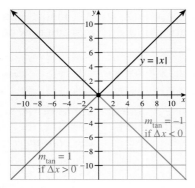

Figure 2.7 $f(x) = |x|$ is not differentiable at $x = 0$, because the slope from the left does not equal the slope from the right.

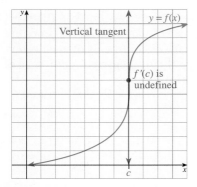

Figure 2.8 Vertical tangent line at $x = c$

EXAMPLE 6   A function that does not have a derivative because of a corner

Show that the absolute value function $f(x) = |x|$ is not differentiable at $x = 0$.

Solution   The graph of $f(x) = |x|$ is shown in Figure 2.7. Note that because the slope "from the left" at $x = 0$ is -1 while the slope "from the right" is $+1$, the graph has a corner at the origin, which prevents a unique tangent from being drawn there.

We can show this algebraically by using the definition of derivative:

$$f'(0) = \lim_{\Delta x \to 0} \frac{f(0 + \Delta x) - f(0)}{\Delta x}$$

$$= \lim_{\Delta x \to 0} \frac{f(\Delta x) - f(0)}{\Delta x}$$

$$= \lim_{\Delta x \to 0} \frac{|\Delta x|}{\Delta x}$$

We must now consider one-sided limits, because

$$|\Delta x| = \Delta x \text{ when } \Delta x > 0, \text{ and } |\Delta x| = -\Delta x \text{ when } \Delta x < 0.$$

$$\lim_{\Delta x \to 0^-} \frac{|\Delta x|}{\Delta x} = \lim_{\Delta x \to 0^-} \frac{-\Delta x}{\Delta x} = -1 \quad \textit{Derivative from the left}$$

$$\lim_{\Delta x \to 0^+} \frac{|\Delta x|}{\Delta x} = \lim_{\Delta x \to 0^+} \frac{\Delta x}{\Delta x} = 1 \quad \textit{Derivative from the right}$$

The left- and right-hand limits are not the same; therefore, the limit does not exist. This means that the derivative does not exist at $x = 0$.   ▬

The continuous function $f(x) = |x|$ in Example 6 failed to be differentiable at $x = 0$ because the one-sided limits of its difference quotients were unequal. A continuous function may also fail to be differentiable at $x = c$ if its difference quotient diverges to infinity. In this case, the function is said to have a *vertical tangent* at $x = c$, as illustrated in Figure 2.8.

Vertical Tangent Line

The graph of f has a **vertical tangent** at $x = c$ if f is continuous at c and

$$\lim_{\Delta x \to c} |f'(x)| = \infty$$

(that is, the derivative function increases or decreases without bound).

We will have more to say about such functions when we discuss curve sketching with derivatives in Chapter 3.

■ CONTINUITY AND DIFFERENTIABILITY

If the graph of a function has a tangent at a point, we would expect the function to be continuous at that point. The following theorem confirms this expectation, for nonvertical tangents.

THEOREM 2.2   Differentiability implies continuity

If a function f is differentiable at c, then it is also continuous at c.

Proof: There are three conditions for establishing continuity: (1) $f(c)$ is defined; (2) $\lim\limits_{x \to c} f(x)$ exists; and (3) $\lim\limits_{x \to c} f(x) = f(c)$. Because $f(x)$ is differentiable at c, $f(c)$ must be defined. Therefore, to establish continuity, it suffices to show that $\lim\limits_{x \to c} f(x) = f(c)$, because doing so also implies that $\lim\limits_{x \to c} f(x)$ exists. This is equivalent to showing

$$\lim_{\Delta x \to 0} f(c + \Delta x) = f(c) \text{ or } \lim_{\Delta x \to 0} [f(c + \Delta x) - f(c)] = 0$$

Because f is a differentiable function at $x = c$, $f'(c)$ exists and

$$\lim_{\Delta x \to 0} \frac{f(c + \Delta x) - f(c)}{\Delta x} = f'(c)$$

Therefore, by applying the product rule for limits, we find that

$$\lim_{\Delta x \to 0}[f(c + \Delta x) - f(c)] = \lim_{\Delta x \to 0}\left[\frac{f(c + \Delta x) - f(c)}{\Delta x} \cdot \Delta x\right]$$

$$= \left[\lim_{\Delta x \to 0} \frac{f(c + \Delta x) - f(c)}{\Delta x}\right]\left[\lim_{\Delta x \to 0} \Delta x\right]$$

$$= f'(c) \cdot 0 = 0$$

Thus $\lim\limits_{x \to c} f(x) = f(c)$, and the conditions for continuity are satisfied. ∎

⊘ Be sure you understand what we have just shown with Example 6 and Theorem 2.2: If a function is differentiable at $x = c$, then it must be continuous at that point. The converse is not true: If a function is continuous at $x = c$, then it may or may not be differentiable at that point. Finally, if a function is discontinuous at $x = c$, then it cannot possibly have a derivative at that point. (See Figure 2.9c.) ⊘

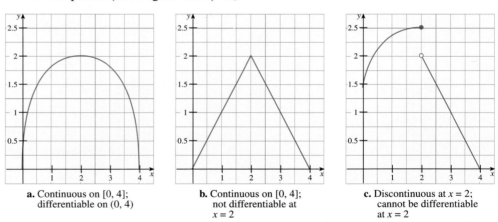

a. Continuous on [0, 4]; differentiable on (0, 4)

b. Continuous on [0, 4]; not differentiable at $x = 2$

c. Discontinuous at $x = 2$; cannot be differentiable at $x = 2$

Figure 2.9 A function continuous at $x = 2$ may or may not be differentiable at $x = 2$. A function discontinuous at $x = 2$ cannot be differentiable at $x = 2$.

■ DERIVATIVE NOTATION

Symbols other than $f'(x)$ are often used to denote the derivative. In particular, if y rather than $f(x)$ is used to denote the function itself, the symbol $\dfrac{dy}{dx}$ (suggesting the slope $\Delta y/\Delta x$) is frequently used instead of $f'(x)$ or y'. Because the notation $\frac{dy}{dx}$ was originally used by Leibniz, it is known as the *Leibniz notation* for the derivative. For example, if $y = x^2$, the derivative is $y' = 2x$ and the Leibniz notation is $\frac{dy}{dx} = 2x$. The symbol $\frac{dy}{dx}$ is read "the derivative of y with respect to x." When we wish to denote the value of the derivative at c in the Leibniz notation, we shall write

$$\frac{dy}{dx}\bigg|_{x=c}$$

For instance, we would evaluate $\frac{dy}{dx} = 4x^2$ at $x = 3$ by writing

$$4x^2\big|_{x=3} = 4(3)^2 = 36$$

By omitting reference to y and f altogether, we can combine these two statements and write

$$\frac{d}{dx}(x^2) = 2x$$

which is read "the derivative of x^2 with respect to x is $2x$."

⊘ Despite its appearance, $\frac{dy}{dx}$ is a single symbol and is *not* a fraction. In Section 2.8, we introduce a concept called a *differential* that will provide independent meaning to symbols like dy and dx, but for now, these symbols have meaning only in connection with the Leibniz derivative symbol $\frac{dy}{dx}$. ⊘

EXAMPLE 7   Derivative at a point with Leibniz notation

Find $\frac{dy}{dx}\bigg|_{x=-1}$ if $y = x^3$.

Solution
$$\frac{dy}{dx} = \frac{d}{dx}(x^3)$$

$$= \lim_{\Delta x \to 0} \frac{(x + \Delta x)^3 - x^3}{\Delta x}$$

$$= \lim_{\Delta x \to 0} \frac{[x^3 + 3x^2\Delta x + 3x(\Delta x)^2 + (\Delta x)^3] - x^3}{\Delta x}$$

$$= \lim_{\Delta x \to 0} [3x^2 + 3x(\Delta x) + (\Delta x)^2]$$

$$= 3x^2$$

At $x = -1$,

$$\frac{dy}{dx}\bigg|_{x=-1} = 3x^2\big|_{x=-1} = 3$$

EXAMPLE 8   Estimating a derivative using a table

Estimate the derivative of $f(x) = \cos x$ at $x = \frac{\pi}{6}$ by evaluating the difference quotient

$$\frac{\Delta y}{\Delta x} = \frac{f(x + \Delta x) - f(x)}{\Delta x}$$

near the point $x = \frac{\pi}{6}$.

Computational Window ▼ ▲

Many calculators will find numerical values for derivatives. Check your owner's manual. Typically, you will need to input (*expression, variable, value*). For $f(x) = \cos(x)$ at $x = \frac{\pi}{6}$, input

(COS X, X, $\pi/6$)

The output is $-.5$.

Solution $\dfrac{\Delta y}{\Delta x} = \dfrac{\cos\left(\frac{\pi}{6} + \Delta x\right) - \cos\frac{\pi}{6}}{\Delta x}$

Choose a sequence of values for $\Delta x \to 0$: say $1, \frac{1}{2}, \frac{1}{4}, \frac{1}{8}, \ldots$ and use a calculator (or a computer) to estimate the difference quotient by table. We show selected elements from this sequence of calculations.

Δx	$\frac{\pi}{6} + \Delta x$	Difference Quotient $\frac{\Delta y}{\Delta x}$
1	1.523598776	-0.81885
0.5	1.023598776	-0.69146
0.125	0.648598776	-0.55276
0.0625	0.586098776	-0.52673
0.015625	0.539223776	-0.50675
0.00195313	0.525551906	-0.50085
0.00012207	0.523720846	-0.50005
0.00000763	0.523606405	-0.50000
↓	↓	↓
0	$\frac{\pi}{6} \approx 0.5235987756$	$-\frac{1}{2}$

From the table, we would guess that $f'\left(\frac{\pi}{6}\right) = -0.5$.

PROBLEM SET 2.1

 1. ■ **What Does This Say?*** Describe the process of finding a derivative using the definition.

2. ■ **What Does This Say?** What is the definition of a derivative?

Find the difference quotient for the functions given in Problems 3–8, and then use the limit definition of derivative to find $f'(c)$ for the given number c.

3. $f(x) = 3$ at $c = -5$
4. $f(x) = x$ at $c = 2$
5. $f(x) = 2x$ at $c = 1$
6. $f(x) = 2x^2$ at $c = 1$
7. $f(x) = 2 - x^2$ at $c = 0$
8. $f(x) = -x^2$ at $c = 2$

Use the definition to differentiate the functions given in Problems 9–20, and then describe the set of all numbers for which the function is differentiable.

9. $f(x) = 5$
10. $g(x) = 3x$
11. $f(t) = 3t - 7$
12. $f(u) = 4 - 5u$
13. $g(r) = 3r^2$
14. $h(x) = 2x^2$
15. $f(x) = x^2 - x$
16. $g(t) = 4 - t^2$
17. $f(s) = (s - 1)^2$
18. $f(x) = \dfrac{1}{2x}$

*Many problems in this book are labeled **What Does This Say?** Following the question will be a question for you to answer in your own words, or a statement for you to rephrase in your own words. These problems are intended to be similar to the "What This Says" boxes that appear throughout the book.*

19. $f(x) = \sqrt{5x}$
20. $f(x) = \sqrt{x + 1}$

Find an equation for the tangent to the graph of the function at the specified point in Problems 21–26.

21. $f(x) = 3x - 7$ at $(3, 2)$
22. $g(t) = 3t^2$ at $(-2, 12)$
23. $f(s) = s^3$ at $s = -\frac{1}{2}$
24. $h(x) = 9 - x^2$ at $x = 0$
25. $f(x) = \dfrac{1}{x + 3}$ at $x = 2$
26. $g(t) = \sqrt{t - 5}$ at $t = 9$

Find an equation of the normal line to the graph of the function at the specified point in Problems 27–30.

27. $f(x) = 5x - 2$ at $(3, 13)$
28. $g(t) = 2t - 3$ at $(0, -3)$
29. $g(t) = \dfrac{1}{t + 5}$ at $t = 1$
30. $f(x) = \sqrt{4x}$ at $x = 1$

Find $\left.\dfrac{dy}{dx}\right|_{x=c}$ for the functions and values of c given in Problems 31–34.

31. $y = 2x, c = -1$
32. $y = 4 - x, c = 2$
33. $y = 1 - x^2, c = 0$
34. $y = \dfrac{4}{x}, c = 1$

B 35. Suppose $f(x) = x^2$.
   a. Compute the slope of the secant joining the points on the graph of f whose x-coordinates are -2 and -1.9.
   b. Use calculus to compute the slope of the line that is tangent to the graph when $x = -2$ and compare this slope with your answer in part **a**.

36. Suppose $f(x) = x^3$.
  a. Compute the slope of the secant joining the points on the graph of f whose x-coordinates are 1 and 1.1.
  b. Use calculus to compute the slope of the line that is tangent to the graph when $x = 1$ and compare this slope to your answer from part **a**.

37. Sketch the graph of the function $y = x^2 - x$. Determine the value of x for which the derivative is 0. What happens to the graph at the corresponding point(s)?

38. a. Find the derivative of $f(x) = x^2 - 3x$.
  b. Recall that a horizontal line has slope 0. Show that the parabola whose equation is $y = x^2 - 3x$ has one horizontal tangent and find the equation of this line.
  c. Find a point on the parabola whose equation is $y = x^2 - 3x$ where the tangent is parallel to the line $3x + y = 11$.
  d. Sketch the graph of the parabola whose equation is $y = x^2 - 3x$. Display the horizontal tangent and the tangent found in part **c**.

39. a. Find the derivative of $f(x) = 4 - 2x^2$.
  b. The parabola whose equation is $y = 4 - 2x^2$ has one horizontal tangent. What is its equation?
  c. At what point on the parabola whose equation is $y = 4 - 2x^2$ is the tangent parallel to the line $8x + 3y = 4$?

40. Let
$$f(x) = \begin{cases} -x^2 & \text{if } x < 0 \\ x^2 & \text{if } x \geq 0 \end{cases}$$
Does $f'(0)$ exist? *Hint*: Find the difference quotient and take the limit as $\Delta x \to 0$ from the left and from the right.

41. Let
$$f(x) = \begin{cases} \sqrt{x} - 3 & \text{if } x \geq 1 \\ -2x & \text{if } x < 1 \end{cases}$$
  a. Sketch the graph of f.
  b. Show that f is continuous but not differentiable at 1.

42. THINK TANK PROBLEM   Give an example of a function continuous on $(-\infty, \infty)$ but not differentiable at $x = 5$.

Estimate the derivative $f'(x)$ in Problems 43–46 by evaluating the difference quotient
$$\frac{\Delta y}{\Delta x} = \frac{f(c + \Delta x) - f(c)}{\Delta x}$$
at a succession of numbers near c.

43. $f(x) = (2x - 1)^2$ for $c = 1$
44. $f(x) = \dfrac{1}{x + 1}$ for $c = 2$
45. $f(x) = \sqrt{x}$ for $c = 4$
46. $f(x) = \sqrt[3]{x}$ for $c = 8$

47. Show that the tangent to the parabola $y = Ax^2$ (for $A \neq 0$) at the point where $x = c$ will intersect the x-axis at the point $(c/2, 0)$. Where does it intersect the y-axis?

48. a. Find the derivatives of the functions $y = x^2$ and $y = x^2 - 3$ and account geometrically for their similarity.
  b. Without further computation, find the derivative of $y = x^2 + 5$.

49. a. Find the derivative of $y = x^2 + 3x$.
  b. Find the derivatives of the functions $y = x^2$ and $y = 3x$ separately. How are these derivatives related to the derivative in part **a**?

  c. In general, if $f(x) = g(x) + h(x)$, what would you guess is the relationship between the derivative of f and the derivatives of g and h?

50. Find the point on the graph of $f(x) = -x^2$ such that the tangent at that point passes through the point $(0, -9)$.

Computational Window

It is often helpful to draw the graph of a function and its derivatives. Graphing complicated functions has been made relatively easy by calculators and computers. Use a graphing utility to graph the functions given in Problems 51–54.

51. $f(x) = x + \sin x$ on $[0, 6\pi]$
52. $f(x) = x \sin x$ on $\left[0, \frac{\pi}{2}\right]$
53. $f(x) = x^3 - 4x^2 + 5x - 2$ on $[-1, 4]$
54. $f(x) = \sin(2\pi \cos x)$ on $[0, \pi]$

55. For the functions given in Problems 51–54, use the *differentiation program* of your calculus software to draw the graph of the first derivative of each function. Print out the graphs, if possible. For each graph, note the following:
  a. On the graph, plot the points where the derivative is 0 and note where the derivative is positive and where it is negative.
  b. Compare the graphs of $f(x)$ and $f'(x)$. Can you see a correlation between the sign of f' and the interval on which f is increasing or decreasing?

56. Return to a function seen earlier (Problem 47, page 79)
$$f(x) = \frac{(x^3 - 5)(x^2 - 1)}{x^2 + 1}$$
With the help of a computing device, you can compute $f'(2)$ by, in it's definition, making Δx sufficiently small. Do so; then find the equation of the tangent to the curve $(2, f(2))$.

57. Return to another function seen earlier (Problem 48, page 79)
$$f(x) = (x - 2)^{2/3} + 2x^3$$
which gives trouble in seeking the tangent at $(2, f(2))$. Attempt to compute $f'(2)$, either "by hand" or using a computer. Describe what happens; in particular, do you see why the tangent there is meaningless?

Ⓒ 58. If $f'(c) \neq 0$, find the equation of the normal line to $y = f(x)$ at point $P(c, f(c))$? What is the equation if $f'(c) = 0$?

59. Suppose a parabola is given in the plane along with its axis of symmetry. Explain how you could construct the tangent at a given point P on the parabola using only compass and straightedge methods. *Hint*: Use Problem 47. You may assume that the parabola has an equation of the form $y = Ax^2$ in which the y-axis is the axis of symmetry and the vertex of the parabola is at the origin.

2.2 TECHNIQUES OF DIFFERENTIATION

IN THIS SECTION Derivative of a constant function, derivative of a power function, procedural rules for finding derivatives, higher derivatives
In Section 2.1, you learned how to find the derivative of a function f by computing the limit of its difference quotient

$$f'(x) = \lim_{\Delta x \to 0} \frac{f(x + \Delta x) - f(x)}{\Delta x}$$

For even the simplest functions, this process is tedious and time-consuming. In this section, we will describe some rules that simplify the process of differentiation.

■ DERIVATIVE OF A CONSTANT FUNCTION

We begin by proving that the derivative of any constant function is zero. Notice that this is plausible because the graph of the constant function $f(x) = k$ is a horizontal line, and its slope is zero. Thus, for example, if $f(x) = 5$, then $f'(x) = 0$.

THEOREM 2.3   Constant rule

A constant function $f(x) = k$ has a derivative $f'(x) = 0$; in Leibniz notation,

$$\frac{d}{dx}(k) = 0$$

Proof: Note that if $f(x) = k$, then $f(x + \Delta x) = k$ for all Δx. Therefore, the difference quotient is

$$\frac{f(x + \Delta x) - f(x)}{\Delta x} = \frac{k - k}{\Delta x} = 0$$

and

$$f'(x) = \lim_{\Delta x \to 0} \frac{f(x + \Delta x) - f(x)}{\Delta x} = \lim_{\Delta x \to 0} 0 = 0$$

as claimed.   ■

■ DERIVATIVE OF A POWER FUNCTION

Recall that a **power function** is a function of the form $f(x) = x^n$ where n is a real number. For example, $f(x) = x^2$, $g(x) = x^{-3}$, $h(x) = x^{1/2}$ are all power functions. So are

$$F(x) = \frac{1}{x^2} = x^{-2} \text{ and } G(x) = \sqrt[3]{x^2} = x^{2/3}$$

Here is a simple rule for finding the derivative of any power function.

THEOREM 2.4   Power rule

For any real number n, the power function $f(x) = x^n$ has the derivative $f'(x) = nx^{n-1}$; in Leibniz notation,

$$\frac{d}{dx}(x^n) = nx^{n-1}$$

Proof: If the exponent n is a positive integer, we can prove the power rule by using the binomial theorem with the definition of derivative. Begin with the difference quotient:

$$\frac{f(x + \Delta x) - f(x)}{\Delta x} = \frac{(x + \Delta x)^n - x^n}{\Delta x}$$

$$= \frac{[x^n + nx^{n-1} \Delta x + \frac{n(n-1)}{2}x^{n-2}(\Delta x)^2 + \cdots + (\Delta x)^n] - x^n}{\Delta x}$$

$$= \frac{nx^{n-1} \Delta x + \frac{n(n-1)}{2} x^{n-2}(\Delta x)^2 + \cdots + (\Delta x)^n}{\Delta x}$$

$$= nx^{n-1} + \frac{n(n-1)}{2} x^{n-2} \Delta x + \cdots + (\Delta x)^{n-1}$$

Note that Δx is a factor of every term in this expression except the first. Hence, as $\Delta x \to 0$, we have

$$f'(x) = \lim_{\Delta x \to 0} \frac{f(x + \Delta x) - f(x)}{\Delta x}$$

$$= \lim_{\Delta x \to 0} \left[nx^{n-1} + \frac{n(n-1)}{2} x^{n-2} \Delta x + \cdots + (\Delta x)^{n-1} \right]$$

$$= nx^{n-1}$$

If $n = 0$, then $f(x) = x^0 = 1$, so $f'(x) = 0$. We shall prove the power rule for negative integer exponents later in this section, and we shall deal with the case in which the exponent is a rational number in Section 2.6. Note, however, that we have already verified the power rule for the rational exponent $\frac{1}{2}$ in Example 3 of Section 2.1, when we showed that the derivative of $f(t) = \sqrt{t} = t^{1/2}$ is $f'(t) = \frac{1}{2}t^{-1/2} = \frac{1}{2\sqrt{t}}$ for $t > 0$. We shall introduce power functions with irrational exponents (for example, $x^{\sqrt{2}}$ or x^{π}) in Chapter 5, and at the same time we shall derive the power rule for such functions. For now, however, we will assume that the power rule holds when the exponent is a real number. ∎

EXAMPLE 1   Using the power rule to find a derivative

Differentiate each of the following functions.

a. $f(x) = x^8$ **b.** $g(x) = x^{3/2}$ **c.** $h(x) = \dfrac{\sqrt[3]{x}}{x^2}$

Solution

a. Applying the power rule with $n = 8$, we find that

$$\frac{d}{dx}(x^8) = 8x^{8-1} = 8x^7$$

b. Applying the power rule with $n = \frac{3}{2}$, we get

$$\frac{d}{dx}(x^{3/2}) = \frac{3}{2}x^{(3/2)-1} = \frac{3}{2} x^{1/2} = \frac{3}{2} \sqrt{x}$$

c. For this part you need to recognize that $h(x) = \dfrac{x^{1/3}}{x^2} = x^{-5/3}$. Applying the power rule with $n = -\frac{5}{3}$, we find that

$$\frac{d}{dx}(x^{-5/3}) = -\frac{5}{3} x^{-5/3-1} = -\frac{5}{3} x^{-8/3}$$

■ PROCEDURAL RULES FOR FINDING DERIVATIVES

The next theorem expands the class of functions that we can differentiate easily by giving rules for differentiating certain combinations of functions, such as sums, differences, products, and quotients. We shall see that the derivative of a sum (difference) is the sum (difference) of derivatives, but the derivative of a product or a quotient does not have such a simple form.

For example, to convince yourself that the derivative of a product is not the product of the separate derivatives, consider the power functions

$$f(x) = x \quad \text{and} \quad g(x) = x^2$$

⊘ Note the product and quotient rules do not behave as you might expect. ⊘

and their product

$$p(x) = f(x)g(x) = x^3$$

Because $f'(x) = 1$ and $g'(x) = 2x$, the product of the derivatives is

$$f'(x)g'(x) = (1)(2x) = 2x$$

whereas the actual derivative of $p(x) = x^3$ is $p'(x) = 3x^2$. The product rule tells us how to find the derivative of a product.

THEOREM 2.5   Basic rules for combining derivatives—procedural forms

If f and g are differentiable functions at all x, and a, b, and c are any real numbers, then the functions cf, $f + g$, fg, and f/g (for $g(x) \neq 0$) are also differentiable, and their derivatives satisfy the following formulas:

Name of Rule	Prime Notation	Function Notation	Leibniz Notation
Constant multiple	$(cf)' = cf'$	$[cf(x)]' = cf'(x)$	$\dfrac{d}{dx}(cf) = c\dfrac{df}{dx}$
Sum rule	$(f + g)' = f' + g'$	$[f(x) + g(x)]' = f'(x) + g'(x)$	$\dfrac{d}{dx}(f + g) = \dfrac{df}{dx} + \dfrac{dg}{dx}$
Difference rule	$(f - g)' = f' - g'$	$[f(x) - g(x)]' = f'(x) - g'(x)$	$\dfrac{d}{dx}(f - g) = \dfrac{df}{dx} - \dfrac{dg}{dx}$

The constant multiple, sum, and difference rules can be combined into a single rule, which is called the *linearity rule*.

Name of Rule	Prime Notation	Function Notation	Leibniz Notation
Linearity rule	$(af + bg)' = af' + bg'$	$[af(x) + bg(x)]' = af'(x) + bg'(x)$	$\dfrac{d}{dx}(af + bg) = a\dfrac{df}{dx} + b\dfrac{dg}{dx}$
Product rule	$(fg)' = fg' + f'g$	$[f(x)g(x)]' = f(x)g'(x) + f'(x)g(x)$	$\dfrac{d}{dx}(fg) = f\dfrac{dg}{dx} + g\dfrac{df}{dx}$
Quotient rule	$\left(\dfrac{f}{g}\right)' = \dfrac{gf' - fg'}{g^2}$	$\left[\dfrac{f(x)}{g(x)}\right]' = \dfrac{g(x)f'(x) - f(x)g'(x)}{[g(x)]^2}$	$\dfrac{d}{dx}\left(\dfrac{f}{g}\right) = \dfrac{g\dfrac{df}{dx} - f\dfrac{dg}{dx}}{g^2}$

Proof of the Product Rule: We shall prove the product rule in detail, leaving the other rules as problems. We begin by rearranging the difference quotient of the product function $p = fg$ so that it appears in a form involving the difference quotients of f and g. We do this by considering areas, and to help with the geometric representation, we assume that $\Delta x > 0$ and that f and g are both increasing functions. It should be noted that the algebraic steps stand alone without considering area.

Begin with the difference quotient for the function p.

$$\underbrace{p(x)}_{\text{Area of rectangle}} = \underbrace{f(x)}_{\text{Length}} \; \underbrace{g(x)}_{\text{Width}}$$

The product of p can be represented as the area of a rectangle:

$$\underbrace{p(x + \Delta x)}_{\text{Area of large rectangle}} = \underbrace{f(x + \Delta x)}_{\text{Length}} \; \underbrace{g(x + \Delta x)}_{\text{Width}}$$

$$\overbrace{p(x + \Delta x) - p(x)}^{\text{Area of L-shaped region}} = f(x + \Delta x)g(x + \Delta x) - f(x)g(x)$$

This difference is the "outside (larger)" rectangle minus the "inside (smaller)" rectangle, giving the L-shaped region shown in color.

Area of I: $[g(x + \Delta x) - g(x)]f(x + \Delta x)$

Area of II: $[f(x + \Delta x) - f(x)]g(x)$

Area of $p(x + \Delta x) - p(x)$ = Area of I + Area of II

The key to the proof of the product rule is to rewrite the difference. We can write this as the sum of regions I and II.

$$p(x + \Delta x) - p(x) = \overbrace{[g(x + \Delta x) - g(x)]f(x + \Delta x)}^{\text{area of I}} + \overbrace{[f(x + \Delta x) - f(x)]g(x)}^{\text{area of II}}$$

Divide both sides by Δx (where $\Delta x \neq 0$):

$$\frac{p(x + \Delta x) - p(x)}{\Delta x} = \frac{[g(x + \Delta x) - g(x)]}{\Delta x}f(x + \Delta x) + \frac{[f(x + \Delta x) - f(x)]}{\Delta x}g(x)$$

The last step in deriving the product rule is to take the limit as $\Delta x \to 0$.

$$p'(x) = \frac{dp}{dx} = \lim_{\Delta x \to 0} \frac{p(x + \Delta x) - p(x)}{\Delta x}$$

$$= \lim_{\Delta x \to 0} \left\{ f(x + \Delta x)\left[\frac{g(x + \Delta x) - g(x)}{\Delta x}\right] + g(x)\left[\frac{f(x + \Delta x) - f(x)}{\Delta x}\right] \right\}$$

$$= \lim_{\Delta x \to 0} f(x + \Delta x) \underbrace{\lim_{\Delta x \to 0}\left[\frac{g(x + \Delta x) - g(x)}{\Delta x}\right]}_{\text{This is the derivative of } g} + \lim_{\Delta x \to 0} g(x) \underbrace{\lim_{\Delta x \to 0}\left[\frac{f(x + \Delta x) - f(x)}{\Delta x}\right]}_{\text{This is the derivative of } f}$$

$$= f(x)\,g'(x) + g(x)\,f'(x) \qquad\qquad \lim_{\Delta x \to 0} f(x + \Delta x) = f(x) \; \textit{because f is continuous} \; \blacksquare$$

We might point out that in proving the previous theorem we are both proving that the derivative of the sum, difference, product, and quotient exist and finding appropriate formulas. For example, if we assume $q(x) = f(x)/g(x)$ where $g(x) \neq 0$, along with the existence of $f'(x)$ and $g'(x)$, we need to prove two parts:

1. $q'(x)$ exists

2. $q'(x) = \dfrac{g(x)f'(x) - f(x)g'(x)}{[g(x)]^2}$

EXAMPLE 2 Using the basic rules to find a derivative

Differentiate each of the following functions.

a. $f(x) = 2x^2 - 5\sqrt{x}$ **b.** $p(x) = (3x^2 - 1)(7 + 2x^3)$

c. $q(x) = \dfrac{4x - 7}{3 - x^2}$ **d.** $g(x) = (4x + 3)^2$

e. $F(x) = \dfrac{2}{3x^2} - \dfrac{x}{3} + \dfrac{4}{5} + \dfrac{x + 1}{x}$

Solution

Historical Note

When working with rational forms, we need to be careful about division by zero and the possibility of obtaining an indeterminate form. One of the earliest recorded treatments of indeterminate equations is attributed to the Hindu mathematician Āryabhaṭa (476–550?). He gave rules for approximations of square roots and sums of arithmetic progressions as well as rules for basic algebraic manipulations. One example of his work is the following calculation for π: "Add four to one hundred, multiply by eight and add again sixty-two thousand; the result is the approximate value of the circumference of a circle whose diameter is twenty-thousand." It is remarkable that today, most of us would not attempt such a verification of the approximation 3.1416 without using a calculator. The first Indian satellite was named ARYABHAT in his honor.

a. Apply the linearity rule (constant multiple, sum, and difference) and power rules:

$$f'(x) = 2(x^2)' - 5(x^{1/2})' = 2(2x) - 5\left(\tfrac{1}{2}\right)(x^{-1/2}) = 4x - \tfrac{5}{2}x^{-1/2}$$

b. Apply the product rule; then apply the linearity and power rules:

$$p'(x) = (3x^2 - 1)(7 + 2x^3)' + (3x^2 - 1)'(7 + 2x^3)$$
$$= (3x^2 - 1)[0 + 2(3x^2)] + [3(2x) - 0](7 + 2x^3)$$
$$= (3x^2 - 1)(6x^2) + (6x)(7 + 2x^3)$$
$$= 6x(5x^3 - x + 7)$$

c. Apply the quotient rule, then the linearity and power rules:

$$q'(x) = \frac{(3 - x^2)(4x - 7)' - (4x - 7)(3 - x^2)'}{(3 - x^2)^2}$$
$$= \frac{(3 - x^2)(4 - 0) - (4x - 7)(0 - 2x)}{(3 - x^2)^2}$$
$$= \frac{12 - 4x^2 + 8x^2 - 14x}{(3 - x^2)^2} = \frac{4x^2 - 14x + 12}{(3 - x^2)^2}$$

d. Apply the product rule:

$$g'(x) = (4x + 3)(4x + 3)' + (4x + 3)'(4x + 3)$$
$$= (4x + 3)(4) + (4)(4x + 3) = 8(4x + 3)$$

Sometimes when the exponent is 2, it is easier to expand before differentiating:

$$g(x) = (4x + 3)^2 = 16x^2 + 24x + 9$$
$$g'(x) = 32x + 24$$

e. Write the function using negative exponents for rational expressions:

$$F(x) = \tfrac{2}{3}x^{-2} - \tfrac{1}{3}x + \tfrac{4}{5} + 1 + x^{-1}$$

Then apply the power rule term by term to obtain

$$F'(x) = \tfrac{2}{3}(-2x^{-3}) - \tfrac{1}{3} + 0 + 0 + (-1)x^{-2}$$
$$= -\tfrac{4}{3}x^{-3} - \tfrac{1}{3} - x^{-2}$$

■

In applying the power rule term by term in Example 2e, we really used the following generalization of the linearity rule.

COROLLARY TO THEOREM 2.5   The extended linearity rule

If $f_1, f_2, \ldots, f_n$ are differentiable functions and $a_1, a_2, \ldots, a_n$ are constants, then

$$\frac{d}{dx}[a_1f_1 + a_2f_2 + \cdots + a_nf_n] = a_1\frac{df_1}{dx} + a_2\frac{df_2}{dx} + \cdots + a_n\frac{df_n}{dx}$$

Proof: The proof is a straightforward extension of the proof of the linearity rule of Theorem 2.5. ∎

Example 3 illustrates how the extended linearity rule can be used to differentiate a polynomial.

EXAMPLE 3   Derivative of a polynomial function

Differentiate the polynomial function $p(x) = 2x^5 - 3x^2 + 8x - 5$.

Solution $p'(x) = \frac{d}{dx}[2x^5 - 3x^2 + 8x - 5]$

$\qquad = 2\frac{d}{dx}(x^5) - 3\frac{d}{dx}(x^2) + 8\frac{d}{dx}(x) - \frac{d}{dx}(5)$ *Extended linearity rule*

$\qquad = 2(5x^4) - 3(2x) + 8(1) - 0$ *Power rule; constant rule*

$\qquad = 10x^4 - 6x + 8$

EXAMPLE 4   Derivative of a product of polynomials

Differentiate $p(x) = (x^3 - 4x + 7)(3x^5 - x^2 + 6x)$.

Solution   We could expand the product function $p(x)$ as a polynomial and proceed as in Example 3, but it is easier to use the product rule.

$p'(x) = (x^3 - 4x + 7)(3x^5 - x^2 + 6x)' + (x^3 - 4x + 7)'(3x^5 - x^2 + 6x)$

$\qquad = (x^3 - 4x + 7)(15x^4 - 2x + 6) + (3x^2 - 4)(3x^5 - x^2 + 6x)$

EXAMPLE 5   Equation of a tangent line

Find the standard form equation for the line tangent to the graph of

$$f(x) = \frac{3x^2 + 5}{2x^2 + x - 3}$$

at the point where $x = -1$.

Solution   Evaluating $f(x)$ at $x = -1$, we find that $f(-1) = -4$ (verify); therefore, the point of tangency is $(-1, -4)$. The slope of the tangent line at $(-1, -4)$ is $f'(-1)$. Find $f'(x)$ by applying the quotient rule:

$f'(x) = \dfrac{(2x^2 + x - 3)(3x^2 + 5)' - (3x^2 + 5)(2x^2 + x - 3)'}{(2x^2 + x - 3)^2}$

$\qquad = \dfrac{(2x^2 + x - 3)(6x) - (3x^2 + 5)(4x + 1)}{(2x^2 + x - 3)^2}$

$\qquad = \dfrac{12x^3 + 6x^2 - 18x - 12x^3 - 3x^2 - 20x - 5}{(2x^2 + x - 3)^2}$

$\qquad = \dfrac{3x^2 - 38x - 5}{(2x^2 + x - 3)^2}$

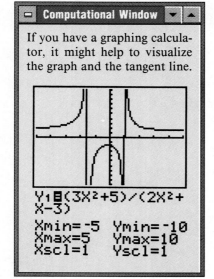

Computational Window

If you have a graphing calculator, it might help to visualize the graph and the tangent line.

Y1◘(3X²+5)/(2X²+
X-3)

Xmin=-5   Ymin=-10
Xmax=5   Ymax=10
Xscl=1   Yscl=1

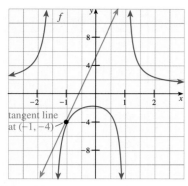

Figure 2.10 Graph of f and the tangent line at the point $(-1, -4)$

The slope of the tangent line is $f'(-1) = \dfrac{3(-1)^2 - 38(-1) - 5}{[2(-1)^2 + (-1) - 3]^2} = 9$.

From the formula (Theorem 2.1) $y = f'(x_0)(x - x_0) + f(x_0)$, we find that an equation for the tangent line is

$$y = 9(x + 1) + (-4)$$

or in standard form $9x - y + 5 = 0$. The graphs of both f and its tangent line at $(-1, -4)$ are shown in Figure 2.10.   ▬

EXAMPLE 6   Finding horizontal tangent lines

Let $y = (x - 2)(x^2 + 4x - 7)$. Find all points on this curve where the tangent line is horizontal.

Solution   The tangent line will be horizontal when $dy/dx = 0$, because the derivative dy/dx is the slope and a horizontal line has slope 0. Applying the product rule, we find

$$\frac{dy}{dx} = (x - 2)(x^2 + 4x - 7)' + (x - 2)'(x^2 + 4x - 7)$$

$$= (x - 2)(2x + 4) + (1)(x^2 + 4x - 7) = 2x^2 - 8 + x^2 + 4x - 7$$

$$= 3x^2 + 4x - 15 = (3x - 5)(x + 3)$$

Thus, $\dfrac{dy}{dx} = 0$ when $x = \frac{5}{3}$ or $x = -3$. The corresponding points $\left(\frac{5}{3}, \frac{-22}{27}\right)$ and $(-3, 50)$ are the points on the curve at which the tangent is horizontal.   ▬

In the following example, we use the quotient rule to extend the proof of the power rule to the case in which the exponent n is a negative integer.

EXAMPLE 7   Proof of the power rule for negative exponents

Show that $\dfrac{d}{dx}(x^n) = nx^{n-1}$ if $n = -m$, where m is a positive integer.

Solution   We have $f(x) = x^n = x^{-m} = 1/x^m$, so apply the quotient rule:

$$\frac{d}{dx}(x^n) = \frac{d}{dx}\left(\frac{1}{x^m}\right) = \frac{x^m(1)' - (1)(x^m)'}{(x^m)^2} = \frac{x^m(0) - mx^{m-1}}{x^{2m}}$$

$$= -mx^{(m-1)-2m} = -mx^{-m-1} = nx^{n-1} \qquad \textit{Substitute } -m = n.$$

▬

■ HIGHER DERIVATIVES

Occasionally, it is useful to differentiate the derivative of a function. In this context, we shall refer to f' as the **first derivative** of f and to the derivative of f' as the **second derivative** of f. We could denote the second derivative by $(f')'$, but for simplicity we write f''. Other higher derivatives are defined and denoted similarly. Thus, the **third derivative** of f is the derivative of f'' and is denoted by f'''. In general, for $n > 3$, the nth derivative of f is denoted by $f^{(n)}$, for example, $f^{(4)}$ or $f^{(5)}$. In Leibniz notation, higher derivatives for $y = f(x)$ are denoted as follows:

				Leibniz Notation	
First derivative:	y'	$f'(x)$	$\dfrac{dy}{dx}$	$\dfrac{d}{dx} f(x)$
Second derivative:	y''	$f''(x)$	$\dfrac{d^2y}{dx^2}$	$\dfrac{d^2}{dx^2} f(x)$
Third derivative:	y'''	$f'''(x)$	$\dfrac{d^3y}{dx^3}$	$\dfrac{d^3}{dx^3} f(x)$
Fourth derivative:	$y^{(4)}$	$f^{(4)}(x)$	$\dfrac{d^4y}{dx^4}$	$\dfrac{d^4}{dx^4} f(x)$
⋮	⋮	⋮	⋮	⋮
nth derivative	$y^{(n)}$	$f^{(n)}(x)$	$\dfrac{d^ny}{dx^n}$	$\dfrac{d^n}{dx^n} f(x)$

> ▪ **What this says:** Because the derivative of a function is a function, differentiation can be applied over and over, as long as the derivative itself is a differentiable function.
>   Notice also that for derivatives higher than the third, the parentheses distinguish a derivative from a power. For example, $f^4 \neq f^{(4)}$.

You should also note that all higher derivatives of a polynomial $p(x)$ will also be polynomials, and if p has degree n, then $p^{(k)}(x) = 0$ for $k \geq n + 1$.

EXAMPLE 8   Higher derivatives for a polynomial function

Find the first and all higher derivatives of

$$p(x) = -2x^4 + 9x^3 - 5x^2 + 7$$

Solution

$$p'(x) = -8x^3 + 27x^2 - 10x; \quad p''(x) = -24x^2 + 54x - 10;$$
$$p'''(x) = -48x + 54; \quad p^{(4)}(x) = -48; \quad p^{(5)}(x) = 0; \ldots$$
$$p^{(n)}(x) = 0 \ (n \geq 5)$$

PROBLEM SET 2.2

Ⓐ *In order to demonstrate the power of the theorems of this section, Problems 1–4 ask you to go back and rework some problems in Section 2.1, using the material of this section instead of the definition of derivative.*

1. Find the derivatives of the functions given in Problems 3–8 of Problem Set 2.1.

2. Find the derivatives of the functions given in Problems 9–14 of Problem Set 2.1.

3. Find the derivatives of the functions given in Problems 15–20 of Problem Set 2.1.

4. Find the derivatives of the functions given in Problems 21–26 of Problem Set 2.1.

Differentiate the functions given in Problems 5–20. Assume that C is a constant.

5. **a.** $f(x) = 3x^4 - 9$ **b.** $g(x) = 3(9)^4 - x$

6. **a.** $f(x) = 5x^2 + x$ **b.** $g(x) = \pi^3$

7. **a.** $f(x) = x^3 + C$ **b.** $g(x) = C^2 + x$

8. **a.** $f(t) = 10t^{-1}$ **b.** $g(t) = \dfrac{7}{t}$

9. $r(t) = t^2 - \dfrac{1}{t^2} + \dfrac{5}{t^4}$ 10. $f(x) = \pi^3 - 3\pi^2$

11. $f(x) = \dfrac{7}{x^2} + x^{2/3} + C$ 12. $g(x) = \dfrac{1}{2\sqrt{x}} + \dfrac{x^2}{4} + C$

13. $f(x) = \dfrac{x^3 + x^2 + x - 7}{x^2}$ 14. $g(x) = \dfrac{2x^5 - 3x^2 + 11}{x^3}$

15. $f(x) = (2x + 1)(1 - 4x^3)$ 16. $g(x) = (x + 2)(2\sqrt{x} + x^2)$

17. $f(x) = \dfrac{3x + 5}{x + 9}$ 18. $f(x) = \dfrac{x^2 + 3}{x^2 + 5}$

19. $g(x) = x^2(x + 2)^2$ 20. $f(x) = x^2(2x + 1)^2$

In Problems 21–24, find f', f'', f''', and $f^{(4)}$.
21. $f(x) = x^5 - 5x^3 + x + 12$

22. $f(x) = \frac{1}{4}x^8 - \frac{1}{2}x^6 - x^2 + 2$

23. $f(x) = \frac{-2}{x^2}$

24. $f(x) = \frac{4}{\sqrt{x}}$

25. Find $\frac{d^2y}{dx^2}$, where $y = 3x^3 - 7x^2 + 2x - 3$.

26. Find $\frac{d^2y}{dx^2}$, where $y = (x^2 + 4)(1 - 3x^3)$.

In Problems 27–32, find the standard form equation for the tangent line to $y = f(x)$ at the specified point.

27. $f(x) = x^2 - 3x - 5$, where $x = -2$

28. $f(x) = x^5 - 3x^3 - 5x + 2$, where $x = 1$

29. $f(x) = (x^2 + 1)(1 - x^3)$, where $x = 1$

30. $f(x) = \frac{x + 1}{x - 1}$, where $x = 0$

31. $f(x) = \frac{x^2 + 5}{x + 5}$, where $x = 1$

32. $f(x) = 1 - \frac{1}{x} + \frac{2}{\sqrt{x}}$, where $x = 4$

Find the coordinates of every point of the graph of the functions given in Problems 33–39 where there is a horizontal tangent line.

33. $f(x) = 2x^3 - 7x^2 + 8x - 3$ **34.** $g(x) = (3x - 5)(x - 8)$

35. $f(t) = \frac{1}{t^2} - \frac{1}{t^3}$ **36.** $f(t) = t^4 + 4t^3 - 8t^2 + 3$

37. $f(x) = \sqrt{x}(x - 3)$ **38.** $h(x) = \frac{x^2 - 2x + 1}{x - 1}$

39. $h(x) = \frac{4x^2 + 12x + 9}{2x + 3}$

B **40.** **a.** Differentiate the function $f(x) = 2x^2 - 5x - 3$.

   b. Factor the function in part **a** and differentiate by using the product rule. Show that the two answers are the same.

41. **a.** Use the quotient rule to differentiate

$$f(x) = \frac{2x - 3}{x^3}$$

   b. Rewrite the function in part **a** as

$$f(x) = x^{-3}(2x - 3)$$

   and differentiate by using the product rule.

   c. Rewrite the function in part **a** as

$$f(x) = 2x^{-2} - 3x^{-3}$$

   and differentiate.

   d. Show the answers to parts **a**, **b**, and **c** are all the same.

42. Find numbers a, b, and c that guarantee that the graph of the function $f(x) = ax^2 + bx + c$ will have x-intercepts at $(0, 0)$ and $(5, 0)$ and a tangent with slope 1 where $x = 2$.

43. Find the equation for the tangent to the curve with equation $y = x^4 - 2x + 1$ that is parallel to the line $2x - y - 3 = 0$.

44. Find equations for two tangent lines to the graph of

$$f(x) = \frac{3x + 5}{1 + x}$$

that are perpendicular to the line $2x - y - 1 = 0$.

45. Let $f(x) = (x^3 - 2x^2)(x + 2)$.

   a. Find an equation for the tangent to the graph of f at the point where $x = 1$.

   b. Find an equation for the normal line to the graph of f at the point where $x = 0$.

46. Find an equation for a normal line to the graph of $f(x) = (x^3 - 2x^2)(x + 2)$ that is parallel to the line $x - 16y + 17 = 0$.

47. Find all points (x, y) on the graph of $y = 4x^2$ with the property that the tangent at (x, y) passes through the point $(2, 0)$.

48. Find the equations of all the tangents to the graph of the function

$$f(x) = x^2 - 4x + 25$$

that pass through the origin.

Determine which (if any) of the functions $y = f(x)$ given in Problems 49–52 satisfy the equation $y''' + y'' + y' = x + 1$

49. $f(x) = x^2 + 2x - 3$ **50.** $f(x) = x^3 + x^2 + x$

51. $f(x) = \frac{1}{2}x^2 + 3$ **52.** $f(x) = 2x^2 + x$

C **53.** What is the relationship between the degree of a polynomial function P and the value of k for which $P^{(k)}(x)$ is first equal to 0?

54. Prove the constant multiple rule $(cf)' = cf'$.

55. Prove the sum rule $(f + g)' = f' + g'$.

56. Prove the difference rule $(f - g)' = f' - g'$.

57. Use the definition of derivative to find the derivative of f^2, given that f is a differentiable function.

58. Prove the product rule by using the result of Problem 57 and the identity

$$fg = \frac{1}{2}\left[(f + g)^2 - f^2 - g^2\right]$$

59. If $q(x) = f(x)/g(x)$, where $g(x) \neq 0$, prove that $q'(x)$ exists if $f'(x)$ and $g'(x)$ exist.

60. Prove the quotient rule

$$\left(\frac{f}{g}\right)' = \frac{gf' - fg'}{g^2}$$

where $g(x) \neq 0$. *Hint:* First show that the difference quotient for f/g can be expressed as

$$\frac{\left(\frac{f}{g}\right)(x + \Delta x) - \left(\frac{f}{g}\right)(x)}{\Delta x} = \frac{f(x + \Delta x)g(x) - f(x)g(x + \Delta x)}{(\Delta x)g(x + \Delta x)g(x)}$$

and then subtract and add the term $g(x)f(x)$ in the numerator.

61. Show that the reciprocal function $r(x) = 1/f(x)$ has the derivative $r'(x) = -f'(x)/[f(x)]^2$ at each point x where f is differentiable and $f(x) \neq 0$.

62. If f, g, and h are differentiable functions, show that the product fgh is also differentiable and

$$(fgh)' = fgh' + fg'h + f'gh$$

63. Let f be a function that is differentiable at x.
  a. If $g(x) = [f(x)]^3$, show that

$$g'(x) = 3[f(x)]^2 f'(x)$$

  Hint: Write $g(x) = [f(x)]^2 f(x)$ and use the product rule.
  b. Show that $p(x) = [f(x)]^4$ has the derivative

$$p'(x) = 4[f(x)]^3 f'(x)$$

64. Find constants A, B, and C so that

$$y = Ax^3 + Bx + C$$

satisfies the equation

$$y''' + 2y'' - 3y' + y = x$$

65. JOURNAL PROBLEM: *The Amatyc Review** by Michael W. Ecker. Let $f(x)$ be a polynomial of degree n with the property that $f(x) \geq 0$ for all x. Prove that

$$f(x) + f'(x) + f''(x) + \cdots + f^{(n)}(x) \geq 0$$

for all x.

2.3 DERIVATIVES OF THE TRIGONOMETRIC FUNCTIONS

IN THIS SECTION Two special trigonometric limits, derivatives of the sine and the cosine, differentiation of the other trigonometric functions
In Section 2.2, we developed general rules for differentiation and applied those rules to various algebraic functions involving power functions, polynomials, and rational functions. In this section, we develop differentiation formulas for the trigonometric functions.

■ TWO SPECIAL TRIGONOMETRIC LIMITS

We will need the following two basic limit properties (from Theorem 1.3) involving the cosine and sine functions.

$$\lim_{x \to c} \cos x = \cos c \quad \text{and} \quad \lim_{x \to c} \sin x = \sin c$$

In Example 6 of Section 1.5, we found $\lim\limits_{x \to 0} \dfrac{\sin x}{x}$ by using a table. We will now prove this same result by using a geometric argument.

THEOREM 2.6   Special limits involving sine and cosine

$$\lim_{h \to 0} \frac{\sin h}{h} = 1 \qquad \lim_{h \to 0} \frac{\cos h - 1}{h} = 0$$

Proof: To prove the sine limit theorem requires some principles that are not entirely obvious (see Problem 68). However, we can demonstrate its plausibility by considering Figure 2.11 in which AOC is a sector of a circle of radius 1. (See *Student Mathematics Handbook* for a review of the terminology about sectors.) This derivation requires that θ be measured in radians. The line segments $\overline{AD}$ and $\overline{BC}$ are drawn perpendicular to segment $\overline{OC}$.

Assume $0 < h < \frac{\pi}{2}$; that is, h is in Quadrant I.

$$|\overarc{AC}| = h$$

$$|AD| = \sin h$$

$$|BC| = \tan h = \frac{\sin h}{\cos h}$$

$$|OD| = \cos h$$

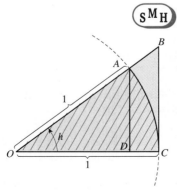

Figure 2.11 Trigonometric relationships in the proof that
$$\lim_{h \to 0} \frac{\sin h}{h} = 1$$

Now, compare the area of the sector AOC with those of $\triangle AOD$ and $\triangle BOC$. In particular, since the area of the circular sector of radius r and central angle θ is $\frac{1}{2}r^2\theta$ (see page 2 of the *Handbook*), sector AOC must have area

$$\tfrac{1}{2}(1)^2 h = \tfrac{1}{2}h$$

We also find that $\triangle AOD$ has area

$$\tfrac{1}{2}|OD||AD| = \tfrac{1}{2}\cos h \sin h$$

and $\triangle BOC$ has area

$$\tfrac{1}{2}|BC||OC| = \tfrac{1}{2}\frac{\sin h}{\cos h} = \frac{\sin h}{2\cos h}$$

By comparing areas (see Figure 2.11) we have:

$$\underbrace{\vphantom{\frac{1}{2}}}_{\substack{\text{AREA OF }\triangle AOD \\ \frac{1}{2}\cos h \sin h}} \leq \underbrace{\vphantom{\frac{1}{2}}}_{\substack{\text{AREA OF SECTOR }AOC \\ \frac{1}{2}h}} \leq \underbrace{\vphantom{\frac{1}{2}}}_{\substack{\text{AREA OF }\triangle BOC \\ \frac{\sin h}{2\cos h}}}$$

Divide all parts of these inequalities by $\frac{1}{2}\sin h$:

$$\cos h \leq \frac{h}{\sin h} \leq \frac{1}{\cos h}$$

Take reciprocals and reverse the inequality symbols:

$$\cos h \leq \frac{\sin h}{h} \leq \frac{1}{\cos h}$$

This same inequality holds in the interval $-\frac{\pi}{2} < h < 0$. This can be shown by using the trigonometric identities $\cos(-h) = \cos h$ and $\sin(-h) = -\sin h$. Finally, we take the limit of all parts as $h \to 0$ to find

$$\lim_{h\to 0}\cos h \leq \lim_{h\to 0}\frac{\sin h}{h} \leq \lim_{h\to 0}\frac{1}{\cos h}$$

By Theorem 1.3, $\lim\limits_{h\to 0}\cos h = \cos 0 = 1$. Thus,

$$1 \leq \lim_{h\to 0}\frac{\sin h}{h} \leq \frac{1}{1}$$

From the squeeze theorem (Theorem 1.9, Section 1.8), we conclude that $\lim\limits_{h\to 0}\frac{\sin h}{h} = 1$.

The second part of this theorem is left as a problem, but consider*

$$0 < \frac{1-\cos h}{h} < \frac{\sin h}{h}\sin h < k\sin h$$

for some constant k for which $\frac{\sin h}{h} < k$. ∎

Examples 1 and 2 show how the two special limits in Theorem 2.6 can be used to compute trigonometric limits.

EXAMPLE 1 Evaluation of a trigonometric limit

Find $\lim\limits_{x\to 0}\dfrac{\sin 3x}{5x}$.

*This string of inequalities was suggested by Leonard Gillman in the *American Mathematical Monthly*, April 1991.

Computational Window

You might want to reinforce your intuition about the $\lim\limits_{x\to 0}\dfrac{\sin x}{x}$ by looking at the graph:

Y₁=sin X/X

Xmin=-5   Ymin=-1
Xmax=5   Ymax=1
Xscl=1   Yscl=.1

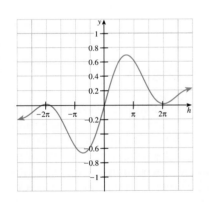

Graph of $y = \dfrac{1-\cos h}{h}$

What is $\lim\limits_{h\to 0}\dfrac{1-\cos h}{h}$?

Solution   We prepare the limit for evaluation by Theorem 2.6 by writing

$$\frac{\sin 3x}{5x} = \frac{3}{5}\left(\frac{\sin 3x}{3x}\right)$$

Because $3x \to 0$ as $x \to 0$, we can set $h = 3x$ in Theorem 2.6 to obtain

$$\lim_{x \to 0}\frac{\sin 3x}{5x} = \lim_{x \to 0}\frac{3}{5}\left(\frac{\sin 3x}{3x}\right) = \frac{3}{5}\lim_{h \to 0}\frac{\sin h}{h} = \frac{3}{5}(1) = \frac{3}{5}$$

EXAMPLE 2   Evaluation of a trigonometric limit

Find $\displaystyle\lim_{x \to 0}\frac{\tan 2x}{\sin 7x}$

Solution   As in Example 1, we first prepare the limit for evaluation by Theorem 2.6:

$$\frac{\tan 2x}{\sin 7x} = \left(\frac{\sin 2x}{\cos 2x}\right)\left(\frac{1}{\sin 7x}\right) = \frac{2}{7}\left(\frac{\sin 2x}{2x}\right)\left(\frac{7x}{\sin 7x}\right)\left(\frac{1}{\cos 2x}\right)$$

Because $2x \to 0$ and $7x \to 0$ as $x \to 0$, we have

$$\lim_{x \to 0}\frac{\tan 2x}{\sin 7x} = \lim_{x \to 0}\left[\frac{2}{7}\left(\frac{\sin 2x}{2x}\right)\left(\frac{7x}{\sin 7x}\right)\left(\frac{1}{\cos 2x}\right)\right]$$

$$= \frac{2}{7}\left(\lim_{x \to 0}\frac{\sin 2x}{2x}\right)\left(\lim_{x \to 0}\frac{7x}{\sin 7x}\right)\left(\lim_{x \to 0}\frac{1}{\cos 2x}\right)$$

$$= \frac{2}{7}\left(\lim_{x \to 0}\frac{\sin 2x}{2x}\right)\left(\frac{1}{\displaystyle\lim_{x \to 0}\frac{\sin 7x}{7x}}\right)\left(\lim_{x \to 0}\frac{1}{\cos 2x}\right)$$

$$= \frac{2}{7}(1)\left(\frac{1}{1}\right)(1) = \frac{2}{7}$$

■ DERIVATIVES OF THE SINE AND THE COSINE

(s**M**h)

⊘ The formulas we state and derive assume radian measure. ⊘

By combining the limits in Theorem 2.6 with some elementary trigonometric identities (see *Student Mathematics Handbook* for a review of the elementary trigonometric identities), we obtain the following differentiation formulas for the cosine and sine functions. In calculus we assume that the trigonometric functions are functions of real numbers or of angles measured in radians. We make this assumption because the trigonometric differentiation formulas become more complicated if degree measurement is used instead of radians.

THEOREM 2.7   Derivatives of the sine and cosine functions

The functions $\sin x$ and $\cos x$ are differentiable for all x and

$$\frac{d}{dx}\sin x = \cos x \qquad \frac{d}{dx}\cos x = -\sin x$$

Proof: The proofs of these two formulas are similar. We shall prove the first using the trigonometric identity

$$\sin(\alpha + \beta) = \sin\alpha\cos\beta + \cos\alpha\sin\beta$$

and leave the proof of the second formula as a problem. From the definition of the derivative

$$\frac{d}{dx}\sin x = \lim_{\Delta x \to 0} \frac{\sin(x + \Delta x) - \sin x}{\Delta x}$$

$$= \lim_{\Delta x \to 0} \frac{\sin x \cos \Delta x + \cos x \sin \Delta x - \sin x}{\Delta x}$$

$$= \lim_{\Delta x \to 0} \left[\sin x \left(\frac{\cos \Delta x}{\Delta x} \right) + \cos x \left(\frac{\sin \Delta x}{\Delta x} \right) - \frac{\sin x}{\Delta x} \right]$$

$$= (\sin x) \lim_{\Delta x \to 0} \left(\frac{\cos \Delta x - 1}{\Delta x} \right) + (\cos x) \lim_{\Delta x \to 0} \frac{\sin \Delta x}{\Delta x}$$

$$= \sin x \, (0) + \cos x \, (1)$$

$$= \cos x \qquad\qquad\qquad ■$$

Computational Window

Before stating the theorem that derives the derivative of sine and cosine, suppose we look at the graph of the difference quotient. Consider $f(x) = \sin x$. Then

$$\frac{\sin(x + \Delta x) - \sin x}{\Delta x} = \frac{\sin(x + 0.01) - \sin x}{0.01}$$

is the difference quotient. The graph shown at the right is

$$Y1 = (\sin(X + 0.01) - \sin(X))/0.01$$

By looking at the graph of this difference quotient, it looks like the derivative of $f(x) = \sin x$ is $f'(x) = \cos x$. We now verify this with the following theorem.

```
Y1B(sin (X+.01)-
sin X)/.01
Xmin=-9.424777…
Xmax=9.4247779…
Xscl=1.5707963…
Ymin=-1
Ymax=1
Yscl=.1
```

EXAMPLE 3   Derivative involving a trigonometric function

Differentiate $f(x) = 2x^4 + 3\cos x + \sin a$, for *constant* a

Solution $f'(x) = \dfrac{d}{dx}(2x^4 + 3\cos x + \sin a)$

$$= 2\frac{d}{dx}(x^4) + 3\frac{d}{dx}(\cos x) + \frac{d}{dx}(\sin a) \qquad \textit{Linearity rule}$$

$$= 2(4x^3) + 3(-\sin x) + 0 \qquad \textit{Power rule, derivative of cosine, and}$$
$$\textit{derivative of a constant}$$

$$= 8x^3 - 3\sin x \qquad\qquad\qquad ▬$$

EXAMPLE 4   Derivative of a trigonometric function with product rule

Differentiate $f(x) = x^2 \sin x$.

Solution $f'(x) = \dfrac{d}{dx}(x^2 \sin x)$

$$= x^2 \frac{d}{dx}(\sin x) + \sin x \frac{d}{dx}(x^2) \qquad \textit{Product rule}$$

$$= x^2 \cos x + 2x \sin x \qquad\qquad \textit{Power rule and derivative of sine} ▬$$

EXAMPLE 5   **Derivative of a trigonometric function with quotient rule**

Differentiate $h(t) = \dfrac{\sqrt{t}}{\cos t}$.

Solution   Write $\sqrt{t}$ as $t^{1/2}$.

$$h'(t) = \frac{d}{dt}\left[\frac{t^{1/2}}{\cos t}\right]$$

$$= \frac{\cos t \dfrac{d}{dt}(t^{1/2}) - t^{1/2}\dfrac{d}{dt}\cos t}{\cos^2 t} \qquad \textit{Quotient rule}$$

$$= \frac{\frac{1}{2}t^{-1/2}\cos t - t^{1/2}(-\sin t)}{\cos^2 t} \qquad \begin{array}{l}\textit{Power rule and}\\ \textit{derivative of sine}\end{array}$$

$$= \frac{\frac{1}{2}t^{-1/2}(\cos t + 2t\sin t)}{\cos^2 t} \qquad \textit{Common factor } \tfrac{1}{2}t^{-1/2}$$

$$= \frac{\cos t + 2t\sin t}{2\sqrt{t}\cos^2 t}$$

■ DIFFERENTIATION OF THE OTHER TRIGONOMETRIC FUNCTIONS

You will need to be able to differentiate not only the sine and cosine functions, but also the other trigonometric functions. In order to find the derivatives of these functions you must remember the following identities, which are given in the *Student Mathematics Handbook*.

$$\tan x = \frac{\sin x}{\cos x} \qquad \cot x = \frac{\cos x}{\sin x}$$

$$\sec x = \frac{1}{\cos x} \qquad \csc x = \frac{1}{\sin x}$$

You will also need the following identity:

$$\cos^2 x + \sin^2 x = 1$$

THEOREM 2.8   **Derivatives of the trigonometric functions**

The six basic trigonometric functions $\sin x$, $\cos x$, $\tan x$, $\csc x$, $\sec x$, and $\cot x$ are all differentiable wherever they are defined, and

$$\frac{d}{dx}\sin x = \cos x \qquad\qquad \frac{d}{dx}\cos x = -\sin x$$

$$\frac{d}{dx}\tan x = \sec^2 x \qquad\qquad \frac{d}{dx}\cot x = -\csc^2 x$$

$$\frac{d}{dx}\sec x = \sec x \tan x \qquad\qquad \frac{d}{dx}\csc x = -\csc x \cot x$$

Proof: The derivatives for sine and cosine were given in Theorem 2.7. All the other derivatives in this theorem are proved by using the appropriate quotient rules along with formulas for the derivatives of the sine and cosine. We will obtain the derivative of the tangent function and leave the rest as problems.

$$\frac{d}{dx}\tan x = \frac{d}{dx}\frac{\sin x}{\cos x} \qquad \textit{Trigonometric identity}$$

$$= \frac{\cos x \frac{d}{dx}\sin x - \sin x \frac{d}{dx}\cos x}{\cos^2 x} \qquad \textit{Quotient rule}$$

$$= \frac{\cos x(\cos x) - \sin x(-\sin x)}{\cos^2 x} \qquad \textit{Derivative of } \sin x \textit{ and } \cos x$$

$$= \frac{\cos^2 x + \sin^2 x}{\cos^2 x}$$

$$= \frac{1}{\cos^2 x} \qquad \cos^2 x + \sin^2 x = 1$$

$$= \sec^2 x \qquad 1/\cos^2 x = \sec^2 x \qquad \blacksquare$$

EXAMPLE 6   Derivative of a trigonometric function with the product rule

Differentiate $f(\theta) = 3\theta \sec \theta$.

Solution $f'(\theta) = \frac{d}{d\theta}(3\theta \sec \theta)$

$$= 3\theta \frac{d}{d\theta}\sec\theta + \sec\theta \frac{d}{d\theta}(3\theta) \qquad \textit{Product rule}$$

$$= 3\theta \sec\theta \tan\theta + 3 \sec\theta \qquad \blacksquare$$

EXAMPLE 7   Derivative of a product of trigonometric functions

Differentiate $f(x) = \sec x \tan x$.

Solution $f'(x) = \frac{d}{dx}(\sec x \tan x)$

$$= \sec x \frac{d}{dx}\tan x + \tan x \frac{d}{dx}\sec x \qquad \textit{Product rule}$$

$$= \sec x (\sec^2 x) + \tan x (\sec x \tan x)$$

$$= \sec^3 x + \sec x \tan^2 x \qquad \blacksquare$$

EXAMPLE 8   Equation of a tangent line involving a trigonometric function

Find the equation of the tangent to the curve $y = \cot x - 2 \csc x$ at the point where $x = \frac{\pi}{3}$.

Solution   The slope of the tangent is the derivative of y with respect to x at the point $x = \frac{\pi}{3}$.

$$\frac{dy}{dx} = \frac{d}{dx}(\cot x - 2 \csc x)$$

$$= \frac{d}{dx}\cot x - 2\frac{d}{dx}\csc x \qquad \textit{Linearity rule}$$

$$= -\csc^2 x - 2(-\csc x \cot x)$$

$$= 2 \csc x \cot x - \csc^2 x$$

Writing this expression in terms of sine and cosine, we find

$$2 \csc x \cot x - \csc^2 x = 2\left(\frac{1}{\sin x}\right)\left(\frac{\cos x}{\sin x}\right) - \frac{1}{\sin^2 x}$$

$$= \frac{2\cos x - 1}{\sin^2 x}$$

$$\left.\frac{dy}{dx}\right|_{x=\pi/3} = \frac{2\cos\frac{\pi}{3} - 1}{\sin^2\frac{\pi}{3}} = \frac{2(\frac{1}{2}) - 1}{\left(\frac{\sqrt{3}}{2}\right)^2} = \frac{0}{\frac{3}{4}} = 0$$

Thus, the tangent line at the point where $x = \frac{\pi}{3}$ has slope 0, which means that the tangent line is horizontal. When $x = \frac{\pi}{3}$, we have

$$y = \cot\frac{\pi}{3} - 2\csc\frac{\pi}{3} = \frac{\sqrt{3}}{3} - 2\left(\frac{2\sqrt{3}}{3}\right) = \frac{-3\sqrt{3}}{3} = -\sqrt{3}$$

so the point of tangency is $\left(\frac{\pi}{3}, -\sqrt{3}\right)$. The desired equation is

$$y + \sqrt{3} = 0$$

Computational Window

If you are using a software program to calculate derivatives, such as Mathematica, Derive, or Maple, the form of the derivative may vary. For example, you might obtain

$$\frac{d}{dx}(\tan x) = \tan^2 x + 1 \qquad \frac{d}{dx}(\cot x) = -\cot^2 x - 1 \qquad \frac{d}{dx}(\sec x) = \frac{\sin x}{\cos^2 x} \qquad \frac{d}{dx}(\csc x) = -\frac{\cos x}{\sin^2 x}$$

Although these are different forms than those shown in this section, you should notice that they are equivalent by recalling some of the fundamental identities from trigonometry.

PROBLEM SET 2.3

A *Evaluate the limits in Problems 1–12.*

1. $\lim\limits_{x\to 0} \dfrac{\sin 2x}{x}$

2. $\lim\limits_{x\to 0} \dfrac{\sin 4x}{9x}$

3. $\lim\limits_{x\to 0} \dfrac{\sin 3x}{\sin 2x}$

4. $\lim\limits_{t\to 0} \dfrac{\sin 3t}{\cos t}$

5. $\lim\limits_{t\to 0} \dfrac{\tan 5t}{\tan 2t}$

6. $\lim\limits_{x\to 0} \dfrac{\cot 3x}{\cot x}$

7. $\lim\limits_{x\to 0} \dfrac{1 - \cos x}{\sin x}$

8. $\lim\limits_{x\to 0} \dfrac{\sin^2 x}{2x}$

9. $\lim\limits_{x\to 0} \dfrac{\sin(\cos x)}{\sec x}$

10. $\lim\limits_{x\to 0} \tan 2x \cot x$

11. $\lim\limits_{x\to 0} \dfrac{\sin^2 x}{x^2}$

12. $\lim\limits_{x\to 0} \dfrac{x^2\cos 2x}{1 - \cos x}$

Differentiate the functions given in Problems 13–38.

13. $f(x) = \sin x + \cos x$

14. $f(x) = 2\sin x + \tan x$

15. $g(t) = t^2 + \cos t + \cos\frac{\pi}{4}$

16. $g(t) = 2\sec t + 3\tan t - \tan\frac{\pi}{3}$

17. $p(x) = x^2\cos x$

18. $p(t) = (t^2 + 2)\sin t$

19. $f(t) = \sin^2 t$. *Hint*: Use the product rule on $(\sin t)(\sin t)$.

20. $g(x) = \cos^2 x$. *Hint*: Use the product rule on $(\cos x)(\cos x)$.

21. $f(x) = \sqrt{x}\cos x + x\cot x$

22. $f(x) = 2x^3\sin x - 3x\cos x$

23. $q(x) = \dfrac{\sin x}{x}$

24. $r(x) = \dfrac{x}{\sin x}$

25. $h(t) = \dfrac{\tan t}{t}$

26. $f(\theta) = \dfrac{\sec\theta}{\theta}$

27. $f(x) = \dfrac{\tan x}{1 - 2x}$

28. $g(t) = \dfrac{1 + \sin t}{\sqrt{t}}$

29. $f(t) = \dfrac{2 + \sin t}{t + 2}$

30. $f(\theta) = \dfrac{\theta - 1}{2 + \cos\theta}$

31. $f(x) = \dfrac{\sin x}{1 - \cos x}$

32. $f(x) = \dfrac{x}{1 - \sin x}$

33. $f(x) = \dfrac{1 + \sin x}{2 - \cos x}$

34. $g(x) = \dfrac{\cos x}{1 + \cos x}$

35. $f(x) = \dfrac{\sin x + \cos x}{\sin x - \cos x}$

36. $f(x) = \dfrac{x^2 + \tan x}{3x + 2 \tan x}$

37. $g(x) = \sec^2 x - \tan^2 x + \cos x$

38. $g(x) = \cos^2 x + \sin^2 x + \sin x$

Find the second derivative of each function given in Problems 39–48.

39. $f(\theta) = \sin \theta$

40. $f(\theta) = \cos \theta$

41. $f(\theta) = \tan \theta$

42. $f(\theta) = \cot \theta$

43. $f(\theta) = \sec \theta$

44. $f(\theta) = \csc \theta$

45. $f(x) = \sin x + \cos x$

46. $f(x) = x \sin x$

47. $g(y) = \csc y - \cot y$

48. $g(t) = \sec t - \tan t$

▬ Computational Window ▼ ▲

49. Graph the difference quotient for $f(x) = \sin x$, where $\Delta x = 0.1$, and the cosine function on the same axis with Xmin = 0 and Xmax = 2π. That is, let

$$Y1 = (\sin(X + .1) - \sin(X))/.1$$

$$Y2 = \cos X$$

Use (**TRACE**) to compare the values of the difference quotient and the cosine function. What do you notice?

50. Repeat Problem 49 for $\Delta x = 0.01$ and then for $\Delta x = 0.001$. What do you notice?

Find the equation for the tangent line at the prescribed point for each function in Problems 51–57.

51. $f(\theta) = \tan \theta$ at $\left(\frac{\pi}{4}, 1\right)$

52. $f(\theta) = \sec \theta$ at $\left(\frac{\pi}{3}, 2\right)$

53. $f(x) = \sin x$, where $x = \frac{\pi}{6}$

54. $f(x) = \cos x$, where $x = \frac{\pi}{3}$

55. $y = x + \sin x$, where $x = 0$

56. $x = t \sec t$, where $t = 0$

57. $y = x \cos x$, where $x = \frac{\pi}{3}$

Ⓑ 58. If $y = 2 \sin x + 3 \cos x$, what is $\dfrac{d^2y}{dx^2} + y$?

59. If $y = 4 \cos x - 2 \sin x$, what is $\dfrac{d^2y}{dx^2} + y$?

60. For what values of A and B does $y = A \cos x + B \sin x$ satisfy $y'' + 2y' + 3y = 2 \sin x$?

61. For what values of A and B does

$$y = Ax \cos x + Bx \sin x$$

satisfy $y'' + y = -3 \cos x$?

Ⓒ 62. THINK TANK PROBLEM Give an example of a differentiable function with a discontinuous derivative.

63. Prove that

$$\lim_{h \to 0} \frac{\cos h - 1}{h} = 0$$

64. Complete the proof of Theorem 2.7 by showing that $\dfrac{d}{dx} \cos x = -\sin x$. *Hint*: You will need to use the identity $\cos(\alpha + \beta) = \cos \alpha \cos \beta - \sin \alpha \sin \beta$.

Prove the requested parts of Theorem 2.8 in Problems 65–67.

65. $\dfrac{d}{dx} \cot x = -\csc^2 x$

66. $\dfrac{d}{dx} \sec x = \sec x \tan x$

67. $\dfrac{d}{dx} \csc x = -\cot x \csc x$

68. JOURNAL PROBLEM The theorem

$$\lim_{h \to 0} \frac{\sin h}{h} = 1$$

stated in this section has been the subject of much discussion in mathematical journals:

W. B. Gearhart, and H. S. Shultz, "The Function $\sin x/x$," *College Mathematics Journal* (1990): 90–99.

L. Gillman, "π and the Limit of $(\sin \alpha)/\alpha$," *American Mathematical Monthly* (1991): 345–348.

F. Richman, "A Circular Argument," *College Mathematics Journal* (1993): 160–162.

D. A. Rose, "The Differentiability of $\sin x$," *College Mathematics Journal* (1991): 139–142.

P. Ungar, "Reviews," *American Mathematical Monthly* (1986): 221–230.

Some of these articles argue that the demonstration shown in the text is circular, since we use the fact that the area of a circle is πr^2. How do we know the area of a circle? The answer, of course, is that we learned it in elementary school, but that does not constitute a proof. On the other hand, some of these articles argue that the reasoning is not necessarily circular. Read one or more of these journal articles and write a report.

69. a. Show that $\sin x < x$ if $0 < x \leq \frac{\pi}{2}$. Refer to Figure 2.12. *Hint*: Compare the area of an appropriate triangle and sector.

b. Show that $|\sin x| < |x|$ if $0 < |x| < \frac{\pi}{2}$.

c. Use the definition of continuity to show that $\sin x$ is continuous at $x = 0$.

d. Use the formula $\sin(\alpha + \beta) = \sin \alpha \cos \beta + \sin \beta \cos \alpha$ to show that $\sin x$ is continuous for all real x.

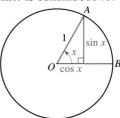

Figure 2.12 Figure for Problems 69 and 70

70. Follow the procedure outlined in Problem 69 to show that $\cos x$ is continuous for all x. *Hint:* After showing that

$$\lim_{x \to 0} \cos x = 1$$

you may need the identity

$$\cos(x + h) = \cos x \cos h - \sin x \sin h$$

71. Use the squeeze theorem to prove that

$$\lim_{h \to 0} \frac{\tan h}{h} = 1$$

Hint: Start with Figure 2.11 (the same figure as the one used in the proof of Theorem 2.6).

72. Use the limit of a difference quotient to prove that

$$\frac{d}{dx} \tan x = \sec^2 x$$

73. JOURNAL PROBLEM   Write a short paper on difficulties of differentiating trignometric functions measured in degrees.*

74. JOURNAL THINK TANK PROBLEM   (From the *American Mathematical Monthly*). Suppose f and g are differentiable real-valued functions defined on $(-\infty, +\infty)$. Must there exist a differentiable real-valued function h defined on $(-\infty, +\infty)$ such that $h' = f'g'$?

2.4 RATES OF CHANGE: RECTILINEAR MOTION

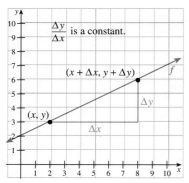

a. Linear function: rate of change $\Delta y/\Delta x$ is constant.

b. Nonlinear function: rate of change $\Delta y/\Delta x$ depends on chosen points.

Figure 2.13 Rate of change is measured by the slope of a tangent line.

⊘ The formula for Δy is important. Note the change in y in Figure 2.14. ⊘

IN THIS SECTION **Rate of change (geometric interpretation), average and instantaneous rate of change, rectilinear motion (physics application), falling body problem.**
The derivative can be interpreted as a rate of change, which leads to a wide variety of applications. Viewed as rates of change, derivatives may represent such quantities as the speed of a moving object, the rate at which a population grows, a manufacturer's marginal cost, the rate of inflation, or the rate at which natural resources are being depleted.

■ RATE OF CHANGE—GEOMETRIC INTERPRETATION

Let us begin by thinking of rate of change in geometric terms. Intuitively, a **rate of change** means how fast one variable changes with respect to another variable.

The rate of change of a linear function $f(x) = ax + b$ with respect to its independent variable x is measured by the steepness or slope of its straight-line graph, as shown in Figure 2.13a. For the graph of a linear function, the slope or rate of change is constant. However, if the function under consideration is not linear, its rate of change varies from point to point, as shown in Figure 2.13b. Because the slope of the tangent is given by the derivative of the function, the preceding geometric observations suggest that the rate of change of a function is measured by its derivative. This connection will be made more precise in the following discussion.

■ AVERAGE AND INSTANTANEOUS RATE OF CHANGE

Suppose that y is a function of x, say, $y = f(x)$. Corresponding to a change from x to $x + \Delta x$, the variable y changes from $f(x)$ to $f(x + \Delta x)$. Thus the change in y is $\Delta y = f(x + \Delta x) - f(x)$, and then the **average rate of change of y with respect to x** is

$$\text{AVERAGE RATE OF CHANGE} = \frac{\text{change in } y}{\text{change in } x} = \frac{\Delta y}{\Delta x} = \frac{f(x + \Delta x) - f(x)}{\Delta x}$$

As the interval over which we are averaging becomes shorter (that is, as $\Delta x \to 0$), the average rate of change approaches what we would intuitively call the

*See, for example, "Fallacies, Flaws, and Flimflam," *The College Mathematics Journal*, Vol. 23, No. 3, May 1992 and Vol. 24, No. 4, September 1993.

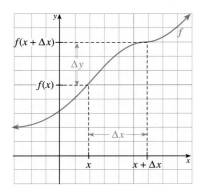

Figure 2.14 A change in Δy corresponding to a change Δx

instantaneous rate of change of y with respect to x, and the difference quotient approaches the derivative $f'(x)$, or $\dfrac{dy}{dx}$. Thus, we have

$$\begin{array}{c} \text{INSTANTANEOUS} \\ \text{RATE OF CHANGE} \end{array} = \lim_{\Delta x \to 0} \frac{\Delta y}{\Delta x} = \lim_{\Delta x \to 0} \frac{f(x + \Delta x) - f(x)}{\Delta x} = f'(x)$$

To summarize:

> **Instantaneous Rate of Change**
> If $y = f(x)$, the **instantaneous rate of change** of y with respect to x, is given by the derivative of f:
>
> $$\text{INSTANTANEOUS RATE OF CHANGE OF } y = f'(x) = \frac{dy}{dx}$$

EXAMPLE 1 Instantaneous rate of change

Find the rate at which the function $y = x^2 \sin x$ is changing with respect to x when $x = \pi$.

Solution For any x, the instantaneous rate of change is the derivative,

$$\frac{dy}{dx} = 2x \sin x + x^2 \cos x$$

Thus, the rate when $x = \pi$ is

$$\frac{dy}{dx}\bigg|_{x = \pi} = 2\pi \sin \pi + \pi^2 \cos \pi = 2\pi(0) + \pi^2(-1) = -\pi^2$$

The negative sign indicates that when $x = \pi$, the function is *decreasing* at the rate of $\pi^2 \approx 9.9$ units of y for each one-unit increase in x. ▬

Let us consider an example comparing the average rate of change and the instantaneous rate of change.

EXAMPLE 2 Comparison between average rate and instantaneous rate of change

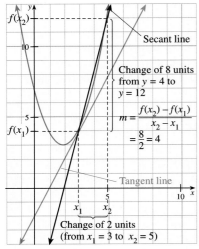

Figure 2.15 Comparison of instantaneous and average rates of change from x_1 to x_2

Let $f(x) = x^2 - 4x + 7$.

a. Find the instantaneous rate of change of f at $x = 3$.
b. Find the average rate of change of f with respect to x between $x = 3$ and 5.

Solution

a. The instantaneous rate of change of the function with respect to x is the derivative of the function; that is,

$$f'(x) = 2x - 4$$

The instantaneous rate of change of f at $x = 3$ is

$$f'(3) = 2(3) - 4 = 2$$

The tangent line at $x = 3$ has slope 2, as shown in Figure 2.15.

b. The (average) rate of change from $x = 3$ to $x = 5$ is found by dividing the change in f by the change in x. That is, the change in f from $x = 3$ to $x = 5$ is

$$f(5) - f(3) = [5^2 - 4(5) + 7] - [3^2 - 4(3) + 7] = 8$$

The average rate of change is

$$\frac{f(5) - f(3)}{5 - 3} = \frac{8}{2} = 4.$$

The slope of the secant line is 4, as shown in Figure 2.14. ▬▬

■ AN APPLICATION TO PHYSICS—RECTILINEAR MOTION

Rectilinear motion is motion along a straight line. For example, the up and down motion of a yo-yo may be regarded as rectilinear, as may the motion of a rocket early in its flight.

When studying rectilinear motion, we may assume that the object is moving along a coordinate line. The position or **displacement** of the object from the origin in relation to the line is a function of time t and is often expressed as $s(t)$. The rate of change of the displacement with respect to time is the object's **velocity** $v(t)$, and the rate of change of the velocity with respect to t is its **acceleration** $a(t)$. Interpreting these rates as derivatives, we see that

$$\text{Velocity is } v(t) = \frac{ds}{dt}.$$

$$\text{Acceleration is } a(t) = \frac{dv}{dt} = \frac{d^2s}{dt^2}.$$

If $v(t) > 0$, we say that the object is *advancing* and if $v(t) < 0$, the object is *retreating*. If $v(t) = 0$, the object is neither advancing nor retreating, and we say it is *stationary*. The object is *accelerating* when $a(t) > 0$ and is *decelerating* when $a(t) < 0$. The significance of the acceleration is that it gives the rate at which the velocity is changing. These ideas are summarized in the following box.

Rectilinear Motion

> An object that moves along a straight line with *displacement* $s(t)$ has *velocity* $v(t) = \frac{ds}{dt}$ and *acceleration* $a(t) = \frac{dv}{dt} = \frac{d^2s}{dt^2}$ when these derivatives exist. The **speed** of the object is $|v(t)|$.

⊘ Rectilinear motion involves *displacement*, *velocity*, and *acceleration*. Sometimes there is confusion between the words speed and velocity. Because speed is the absolute value of the velocity, it indicates how fast an object is moving, whereas velocity indicates both speed and direction (relative to a given coordinate system). ⊘

NOTATIONAL COMMENT: If distance is measured in meters and time in seconds, velocity is measured in meters per second (m/s) and acceleration in meters per second per second (m/s/s). The notation m/s/s is awkward, so m/s^2 is more commonly used. Similarly, if distance is measured in feet, velocity is measured in feet per second (ft/s) and acceleration in feet per second per second (ft/s^2).

When you are riding in a car, moving along a straight road, you do not feel the velocity, but you do feel the acceleration. That is, you feel *changes* in the velocity.

EXAMPLE 3   The position, velocity, and acceleration of a moving object

Assume that the displacement at time t of an object moving along a line is given by

$$s(t) = 3t^3 - 40.5t^2 + 162t$$

for t on $[0, 8]$. Find the position, velocity, and acceleration.

Computational Window

You can use a graphing calculator or computer to look at the graphs of the position, velocity, and acceleration functions.

Y1 = 3X^3 − 40.5X^2 + 162X

Y2 = 9X^2 − 81X + 162

Y3 = 18x − 81

s: increasing   increasing
         decreasing

d: decreasing   increasing

a: increasing

Notice that the velocity is increasing when both the position and acceleration functions have the same sign.

Computational Window

The table shows representative values of s, v, and a.

t	s	v	a
0	0	162	−81
1	124.5	90	−63
2	186	36	−45
3	202.5	0	−27
4	192	−18	−9
4.5	182.25	−20.25	0
5	172.5	−18	9
6	162	0	27
7	178.5	36	45
8	240	90	63

Solution   The position at time t is given by the function s. The starting position is found at time $t = 0$, so

$$s(0) = 0 \qquad \textit{The object starts at the origin.}$$

The velocity is determined by finding the derivative of the position function.

$$v(t) = s'(t) = 9t^2 - 81t + 162$$
$$= 9(t^2 - 9t + 18)$$
$$= 9(t - 3)(t - 6)$$

The starting velocity is 162, which is found by evaluating $v(0)$.

When $t = 3$ and when $t = 6$, v the velocity is 0, which means the *object is stationary* at those times. Furthermore,

$v(t) > 0$	on $[0, 3)$	*Object is advancing.*
$v(t) < 0$	on $(3, 6)$	*Object is retreating.*
$v(t) > 0$	on $(6, 8]$	*Object is advancing.*

$$a(t) = s''(t) = v'(t) = 18t - 81 = 18(t - 4.5)$$

We see that

$a(t) < 0$	on $[0, 4.5)$	*Velocity is decreasing; that is, the object is decelerating.*
$a(t) = 0$	at $t = 4.5$	*Velocity is not changing.*
$a(t) > 0$	on $(4.5, 8]$	*Velocity is increasing; that is, the object is accelerating.*

The table (computational window) shown in the margin gives values for s, v, and a. We use these values to plot a few points, as shown in Figure 2.16. The actual path of the object is back and forth on the axis and the figure is for clarification only.

a. Position of the object: when $v > 0$, the object advances, and when $v < 0$, the object retreats.

b. Velocity of the object: when $a > 0$, the velocity increases, and when $a < 0$, the velocity decreases.

Figure 2.16 Analysis of rectilinear motion

Recall that the *speed* of the particle is the absolute value of its velocity. The speed decreases from 162 to 0 between $t = 0$ and $t = 3$, and it increases from 0 to 20.25 as the velocity becomes negative between $t = 3$ and $t = 4.5$. Then, for $4.5 < t < 6$, the particle slows down again, from 20.25 to 0, after which it speeds up. ▬

A common mistake is to think that a particle moving on a straight line speeds up when its acceleration is positive and slows down when the acceleration is negative, but this is not quite correct. Instead, the following is generally true:

- The speed *increases* (particle speeds up) when the velocity and acceleration have the same signs.
- The speed *decreases* (particle slows down) when the velocity and acceleration have opposite signs.

■ FALLING BODY PROBLEM

As a second example of rectilinear motion, we shall consider a *falling body problem*. In such a problem, it is assumed that an object is projected (that is, thrown, fired, dropped, etc.) vertically in such a way that the only acceleration acting on the object is the constant downward acceleration g due to gravity, which on the earth near sea level is approximately 32 ft/s^2 or 9.8 m/s^2. At time t, the height of the object is given by the following formula:

Formula for the Height of an Object

$$\underbrace{v_0 \text{ is the initial velocity.}}$$
$$h(t) = -\tfrac{1}{2}gt^2 + v_0 t + s_0 \qquad \{s_0 \text{ is the initial height.}$$
$$\underbrace{g \text{ is the acceleration due to gravity.}}$$

where s_0 and v_0 are the object's initial height and velocity, respectively. We shall derive this formula in Chapter 4.

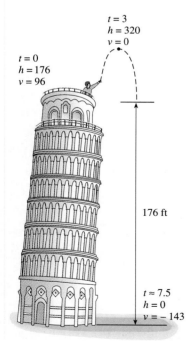

$t = 3$
$h = 320$
$v = 0$

$t = 0$
$h = 176$
$v = 96$

176 ft

$t \approx 7.5$
$h = 0$
$v = -143$

Figure 2.17 The motion of a ball thrown upward from the Tower of Pisa

---

EXAMPLE 4   Position, velocity, and acceleration of a falling object

Suppose a person standing at the top of the Tower of Pisa (176 ft high) throws a ball directly upward with an initial speed of 96 ft/s.

a. Find the ball's height, its velocity, and acceleration at time t.
b. When does the ball hit the ground, and what is its impact velocity?
c. How far does the ball travel during its flight?

Solution   First, draw a picture such as the one shown in Figure 2.17 to help you understand the problem.

a. Substitute the known values into the height of an object formula:

$$v_0 = 96 \text{ ft/s: } \textit{Initial velocity}$$
$$\downarrow$$
$$h(t) = -\tfrac{1}{2}(32)t^2 + 96t + 176 \leftarrow h_0 = 176 \text{ ft: } \textit{Height of tower}$$
$$\uparrow$$
$$g = 32 \text{ ft/s}^2\text{: } \textit{Constant downward gravitational acceleration}$$
$$h(t) = -16t^2 + 96t + 176 \qquad \textit{This is the displacement, or position,}$$
$$\textit{function.}$$
$$\textit{It gives the height of the ball.}$$

The velocity at time t is the derivative:

$$v(t) = \frac{dh}{dt} = -32t + 96$$

The acceleration is the derivative of the velocity function:

$$a(t) = \frac{dv}{dt} = \frac{d^2h}{dt^2} = -32$$

This means that the velocity of the ball is always decreasing at the rate of 32 ft/s².

b. The ball hits the ground when $h(t) = 0$. Solve the equation

$$-16t^2 + 96t + 176 = 0$$

to find that this occurs when $t \approx -1.47$ $(t = 3 - 2\sqrt{5})$ and $t \approx 7.47$ $(t = 3 + 2\sqrt{5})$. Disregarding the negative value we see that impact occurs at $t = 3 + 2\sqrt{5}$ sec. The impact velocity is

$$v(3 + 2\sqrt{5}) = -32(3 + 2\sqrt{5}) + 96 \approx -143 \text{ ft/s}$$

The negative sign here means the ball is coming down at the moment of impact.

c. The ball travels upward for some time and then falls downward to the ground, as shown in Figure 2.17. We need to find the distance it travels upward plus the distance it falls to the ground. The turning point at the top (the highest point) occurs when the velocity is zero. Solve the equation

$$-32t + 96 = 0$$

to find that this occurs when $t = 3$. For $t < 3$, the velocity is positive and the ball is rising, and for $t > 3$, the ball is falling. It follows that the ball is at the highest point when $t = 3$. The ball starts at $h(0) = 176$ ft and rises to a maximum height when $t = 3$:

$$h(3) = -16(3)^2 + 96(3) + 176 = 320$$

Thus, the total distance traveled is

$$\underbrace{(320 - 176)}_{\text{Upward distance}} + \underbrace{320}_{\text{Downward distance}} = 464$$

$$\uparrow$$
$$\text{Initial height}$$

The total distance traveled is 464 ft.   ▬

PROBLEM SET 2.4

A *For each function f given in Problems 1–14, find the rate of change with respect to x at $x = x_0$.*

1. $f(x) = x^2 - 3x + 5$ when $x_0 = 2$

2. $f(x) = 14 + x - x^2$ when $x_0 = 1$

3. $f(x) = -2x^2 + x + 4$ for $x_0 = 1$

4. $f(x) = \frac{-2}{x + 1}$ for $x_0 = 1$

5. $f(x) = \frac{2x - 1}{3x + 5}$ when $x_0 = -1$

6. $f(x) = (x^2 + 2)(x + \sqrt{x})$ when $x_0 = 4$

7. $f(x) = x \cos x$ when $x_0 = \pi$

8. $f(x) = (x + 1) \sin x$ when $x_0 = \frac{\pi}{2}$

9. $f(x) = x + \frac{3}{2 - 4x}$ when $x_0 = 0$

10. $f(x) = \frac{1}{x + 1} - \frac{1}{x - 1}$ when $x_0 = 3$

11. $f(x) = \sin x \cos x$ when $x_0 = \frac{\pi}{2}$

12. $f(x) = \frac{x^2}{x^2 + 1}$ when $x_0 = 1$

13. $f(x) = \left(x - \frac{2}{x}\right)^2$ when $x_0 = 1$

14. $f(x) = \sin^2 x$ when $x_0 = \frac{\pi}{4}$

Give both exact and approximate values.

The function s(t) in Problems 15–22 gives the displacement of an object moving along a line. In each case:

a. *Find the velocity at time t.*

b. *Find the acceleration at time t.*

c. *Describe the motion of the object; that is, tell where is it advancing and where it is retreating. Compute the total distance traveled by the object during the indicated time interval.*

d. *Tell where the object is accelerating and where it is decelerating.*

For a review of solving equations see Sections 2.5, 2.6, and 3.7 of the Student Mathematics Handbook.

15. $s(t) = t^2 - 2t + 6$ on $[0, 2]$

16. $s(t) = 3t^2 + 2t - 5$ on $[0, 1]$

17. $s(t) = t^3 - 9t^2 + 15t + 25$ on $[0, 6]$

18. $s(t) = t^4 - 4t^3 + 8t$ on $[0, 4]$

19. $s(t) = \dfrac{2t + 1}{t^2}$ for $1 \le t \le 3$

20. $s(t) = \dfrac{t^2 + 1}{t^2}$ for $1 \le t \le 2$

21. $s(t) = 3 \cos t$ for $0 \le t \le 2\pi$

22. $s(t) = 1 + \sec t$ for $0 \le t \le \frac{\pi}{4}$

 23. It is estimated that x years from now, $0 \le x \le 10$, the average SAT mathematics score of the incoming students at a certain eastern liberal arts college will be

$$f(x) = -6x + 582$$

a. Derive an expression for the rate at which the average SAT score will be changing with respect to time x years from now.

b. What is the significance of the fact that the expression in part **a** is a negative constant?

24. A particle moving on the x-axis has displacement

$$x(t) = 2t^3 + 3t^2 - 36t + 40$$

after an elapsed time of t seconds.

a. Find the velocity of the particle at time t.

b. Find the acceleration at time t.

c. What is the total distance traveled by the particle during the first 3 sec?

25. An object moving on the x-axis has displacement

$$x(t) = t^3 - 9t^2 + 24t + 20$$

after t seconds. What is the total distance traveled by the object during the first 8 sec?

26. A car has velocity

$$v(t) = \frac{90t}{3t + 12}$$

ft/s after t seconds of motion. What is its acceleration (to the nearest hundredth ft/s^2) after 10 sec?

27. An object moves along a straight line so that after t minutes, its distance from its starting point (in meters) is

$$s(t) = 10t + \frac{5}{t + 1}$$

a. At what speed (to the nearest tenth m/min) is the object moving at the end of 4 min?

b. How far (to the nearest tenth m) does the object actually travel during the 5th minute?

28. A bucket containing 5 gal of water has a leak. After t seconds, there are

$$Q(t) = 5\left(1 - \frac{t}{25}\right)^2$$

gallons of water in the bucket.

a. At what rate (to the nearest hundredth gal) is water leaking from the bucket after 2 sec?

b. How long does it take for all the water to leak out of the bucket?

c. At what rate is the water leaking when the last drop leaks out?

29. A person standing at the edge of a cliff throws a rock directly upward. It is observed that 2 sec later the rock is at its maximum height (in feet) and that 5 sec after that, it hits the ground at the base of the cliff.

a. What is the initial velocity of the rock?

b. How high is the cliff?

c. What is the velocity of the rock at time t?

d. With what velocity does the rock hit the ground?

30. A projectile is shot upward from the earth with an initial velocity of 320 ft/s.

a. What is its velocity after 5 sec?

b. What is its acceleration after 3 sec?

31. A rock is dropped from a height of 90 ft. One second later another rock is dropped from height H. What is H (to the nearest foot) if the two rocks hit the ground at the same time?

32. A ball is thrown vertically upward from the ground with an initial velocity of 160 ft/s.

a. When will the ball hit the ground?

b. With what speed will the ball hit the ground?

c. When will the ball reach its maximum height?

d. What is the speed of the ball as it hits the ground?

33. An object is dropped (initial velocity $v_0 = 0$) from the top of a building and falls 3 seconds before hitting the pavement below. Find the height of the building in feet.

34. An astronaut standing at the edge of a cliff on the moon throws a rock directly upward and observes that it passes her on the way down exactly 4 sec later. Three seconds after that, the rock hits the ground at the base of the cliff. Use this information to determine the initial velocity v_0 and the height of the cliff. *Note:* $g = 5.5$ ft/s^2 on the moon.

35. Answer the questions in Problem 34 assuming the astronaut is on Mars, where $g = 12$ ft/s^2.

36. A car is traveling at 88 ft/s (60 mph) when the driver applies the brakes to avoid hitting a child. After t seconds, the car is $s(t) = 88t - 8t^2$ feet from the point where the brakes were first applied. How long does it take for the car to come to a stop, and how far does it travel before stopping?

37. It is estimated that t years from now, the circulation of a local newspaper will be

$$C(t) = 100t^2 + 400t + 5{,}000$$

   a. Find an expression for the rate at which the circulation will be changing with respect to time t years from now.

   b. At what rate will the circulation be changing with respect to time 5 years from now?

   c. By how much will the circulation actually change during the 6th year?

38. An efficiency study of the morning shift at a certain factory indicates that an average worker who arrives on the job at 8:00 A.M. will have assembled

$$f(x) = -\tfrac{1}{3}x^3 + \tfrac{1}{2}x^2 + 50x$$

units x hours later.

   a. Find a formula for the rate at which the worker will be assembling the units after x hours.

   b. At what rate will the worker be assembling units at 9:00 A.M.?

   c. How many units will the worker actually assemble between 9:00 A.M. and 10:00 A.M.?

39. An environmental study of a suburban community suggests that t years from now, the average level of carbon monoxide in the air will be $q(t) = 0.05t^2 + 0.1t + 3.4$ parts per million.

   a. At what rate will the carbon monoxide level be changing with respect to time one year from now?

   b. By how much will the carbon monoxide level change in the first year?

   c. By how much will the carbon monoxide level change over the next (second) year?

40. According to *Newton's law of universal gravitation*, if an object of mass M is separated by a distance r from a second object of mass m, then the two objects are attracted to one another by a force that acts along the line joining them and has magnitude

$$F = \frac{GmM}{r^2}$$

where G is a positive constant. Show the rate of change of F with respect to r is inversely proportional to r^3.

41. The population of a bacterial colony is approximately $P(t) = P_0 + 61t + 3t^2$ thousand t hours after observation begins, where P_0 is the initial population. Find the rate at which the colony is growing after 5 hours.

If $y = f(x)$, the percentage rate of change of y with respect to x is defined by the expression

$$\frac{f'(x)}{f(x)} \cdot 100$$

Use this definition in Problems 42–47.

42. The gross domestic product (GDP) of a country was $g(t) = t^2 + 5t + 106$ billion dollars t years after 1990.

   a. At what rate was the GDP changing in 1992?

   b. At what percentage rate was the GDP changing in 1992?

43. It is projected that x months from now, the population of a certain town will be $P(x) = 2x + 4x^{3/2} + 5{,}000$.

   a. At what rate will the population be changing with respect to time 9 months from now?

   b. At what percentage rate will the population be changing with respect to time 9 months from now?

44. Assume that your starting salary is $30,000 and you get a raise of $3,000 each year.

   a. Express the percentage rate of change of your salary as a function of time and draw the graph.

   b. At what percentage rate will your salary be increasing after one year?

   c. What will happen to the percentage rate of change of your salary in the long run?

45. The gross domestic product (GDP) of a certain country is growing at a constant rate. In 1990 the GDP was 125 billion dollars, and in 1992 it was 155 billion dollars. At what percentage rate will the GDP be growing in 1995?

46. If y is a linear function of x, what will happen to the percentage rate of change of y with respect to x as x increases without bound?

Computational Window

47. A disease is spreading in such a way that after t weeks for $0 \le t \le 6$, it has affected

$$N(t) = 5 - t^2(t - 6)$$

hundred people. Health officials declare that this disease will reach epidemic proportions when the percentage rate of increase of $N(t)$ at the start of a particular week is at least 30% per week. The epidemic designation level is dropped when the percentage rate falls below this level.

   a. Find the percentage rate of change of $N(t)$ at time t.

   b. Between what weeks is the disease at the epidemic level?

48. An object attached to a helical spring is pulled down from its equilibrium position and then released, as shown in Figure 2.18.

Figure 2.18 Helical spring

Suppose that t seconds later, its displacement (in centimeters measured in relation to the equilibrium position) is given by

$$s(t) = 7 \cos t$$

a. Find the velocity and acceleration of the object at time t.

b. Find the length of time required for one complete oscillation. This is called the *period* of the motion.

c. What is the distance between the highest point reached by the object and the lowest point? Half of this distance is called the *amplitude* of the motion.

49. Two cars leave a town at the same time and travel at constant speeds along straight roads that meet at an angle of 60° in the town. If one car travels twice as fast as the other and the distance between them increases at the rate of 45 mi/hr, how fast is the slower car traveling?

50. SPY PROBLEM   Our friend the spy, who escaped from the diamond smugglers in Problem 39 of Chapter 1 Supplementary Problems, is on a secret mission in space. An encounter with an enemy agent leaves him with a mild concussion that causes him to forget where he is. Fortunately, he remembers the formula for the height of a projectile,

$$h(t) = -\frac{1}{2} gt^2 + v_0 t + s_0$$

and the values of g for various heavenly bodies. Therefore, to deduce his whereabouts, he throws a rock directly upward (from ground level) and notes that it reaches a maximum height of 37.5 ft and hits the ground 5 sec after leaving his hand. Where is he? *Note*: You will need to know that g is 32 ft/s² on earth, 5.5 ft/s² on the moon, 12 ft/s² on Mars, and 28 ft/s² on Venus.

© 51. Find the rate of change of the volume of a cube with respect to the length of one of its edges. How is this rate related to the surface area of the cube?

52. Show that the rate of change of the volume of a sphere with respect to its radius is equal to its surface area.

53. Van der Waal's equation states that a gas that occupies a volume V at temperature T (Kelvin) exerts pressure P, where

$$\left(P + \frac{A}{V^2}\right)(V - B) = kT$$

and A, B, and k are physical constants. Find the rate of change of pressure with respect to volume, assuming fixed temperature.

54. According to Debye's formula in physical chemistry, the orientation polarization P of a gas satisfies

$$P = \frac{4}{3}\pi N\left(\frac{\mu^2}{3kT}\right)$$

where μ, k, and N are constants and T is the temperature of the gas. Find the rate of change of P with respect to T.

2.5 THE CHAIN RULE

> **IN THIS SECTION** Introduction to the chain rule, differentiation of composite functions, generalized derivative formulas, justification of the chain rule
>
> In many practical situations, a quantity is given as a function of one variable, which, in turn, can be thought of as a function of a second variable. In such cases, we shall find that the rate of change of the quantity with respect to the second variable is equal to a product of rates.

■ INTRODUCTION TO THE CHAIN RULE

Suppose it is known that the carbon monoxide pollution in the air is changing at the rate of 0.02 ppm (parts per million) for each person in a town whose population is growing at the rate of 1,000 people per year. To find the rate at which the level of pollution is increasing with respect to time, we form the product

$$(0.02 \text{ ppm/person})(1,000 \text{ people/year}) = 20 \text{ ppm/year}$$

In this example, the level of pollution L is a function of the population p, which is itself a function of time t. Thus, L is a function of t, and:

$$\begin{bmatrix} \text{RATE OF CHANGE OF } L \\ \text{WITH RESPECT TO } t \end{bmatrix} = \begin{bmatrix} \text{RATE OF CHANGE OF } L \\ \text{WITH RESPECT TO } p \end{bmatrix} \begin{bmatrix} \text{RATE OF CHANGE OF } p \\ \text{WITH RESPECT TO } t \end{bmatrix}$$

Expressing each of these rates in terms of an appropriate derivative in Leibniz form, we obtain the following equation:

$$\frac{dL}{dt} = \frac{dL}{dp}\frac{dp}{dt}$$

These observations anticipate the following important theorem.

THEOREM 2.9   Chain rule

If $y = f(u)$ is a differentiable function of u and $u = g(x)$ is a differentiable function of x, then $y = f[g(x)]$ is a differentiable function of x and

$$\frac{dy}{dx} = \frac{dy}{du}\frac{du}{dx}$$

■ **What this says**: The derivative of y with respect to x is the derivative of y with respect to u times the derivative of u with respect to x. This is one of the most important derivative rules in calculus, and you must make sure you understand it thoroughly. We have noted that $\frac{dy}{dx}$ is not a fraction, but in Section 2.8 we *will* define dy and dx. Thus, one way to remember the chain rule is to pretend that the derivatives $\frac{dy}{du}$ and $\frac{du}{dx}$ are quotients and "cancel" du, reducing the expression $\frac{dy}{du}\frac{du}{dx}$ on the right-hand side of the equation to the expression $\frac{dy}{dx}$ on the left-hand side. Remember that this is only a mnemonic device, and no actual reducing of fractions occurs.

Proof: A proof of the chain rule is included in Appendix B. We give a justification at the end of this section. ■

EXAMPLE 1   The chain rule

Find $\frac{dy}{dx}$ if $y = u^3 - 3u^2 + 1$ and $u = x^2 + 2$.

Solution   Because $\frac{dy}{du} = 3u^2 - 6u$ and $\frac{du}{dx} = 2x$

it follows from the chain rule that

$$\frac{dy}{dx} = \frac{dy}{du}\frac{du}{dx} = (3u^2 - 6u)(2x) = (2x)(3u)(u - 2) = 6xu(u - 2)$$

Notice that this derivative is expressed in terms of the variables x and u. To express dy/dx in terms of x alone, we substitute $u = x^2 + 2$ as follows:

$$\frac{dy}{dx} = 6xu(u - 2) = 6x(x^2 + 2)[(x^2 + 2) - 2] = 6x(x^2 + 2)(x^2)$$

$$= 6x^3(x^2 + 2)$$

■ DIFFERENTIATION OF COMPOSITE FUNCTIONS

The chain rule is actually a rule for differentiating composite functions. In particular, if $y = f(u)$ and $u = u(x)$, then y is the composite function $y = (f \circ u)(x) = f[u(x)]$, and the chain rule can be rewritten as follows:

THEOREM 2.9a   The chain rule (alternate form)

If u is differentiable at x and f is differentiable at $u(x)$, then the composite function $f \circ u$ is differentiable at x and

$$(f \circ u)'(x) = f'[u(x)]u'(x) \quad \text{or} \quad \frac{d}{dx}f[u(x)] = \frac{d}{du}f(u)\frac{du}{dx} \qquad ■$$

> ■ *What this says*: In Section 1.4 when we introduced composite functions, we talked about the "inner" and "outer" functions. Using this terminology, the chain rule says that the derivative of the composite function $f[u(x)]$ is equal to the derivative of the inner function u times the derivative of the outer function f evaluated at the inner function. You might wish to review Section 1.4 where this idea was introduced.

EXAMPLE 2   The chain rule applied to a power

Differentiate $y = (3x^4 - 7x + 5)^3$.

Solution $y' = \boxed{3}(3x^4 - 7x + 5)^{\boxed{3-1}}(3x^4 - 7x + 5)'$

This step is usually done mentally. Note that we are thinking of $u(x) = 3x^4 - 7x + 5$. *What you write down is*:

$$y' = 3(3x^4 - 7x + 5)^2(12x^3 - 7)$$

━━

You could, with a lot of work, have found the derivative in Example 2 without using the chain rule, either by expanding the polynomial or by using the product rule. The answer would be the same but would involve much more algebra. In order to compare these methods, however, consider the following problem with a simpler function.

EXAMPLE 3   Comparison of differentiation with and without the chain rule

Differentiate $y = (3x + 2)^2$.

   a. by expansion   **b.** by the product rule   **c.** by the chain rule.

Solution   **a.** $y = (3x + 2)^2 = 9x^2 + 12x + 4$

$$y' = 18x + 12 = 6(3x + 2)$$

b. $y = (3x + 2)^2 = (3x + 2)(3x + 2)$

$$y' = (3x + 2)(3x + 2)' + (3x + 2)'(3x + 2)$$
$$= (3x + 2)(3) + (3)(3x + 2) = 6(3x + 2)$$

c. $y = (3x + 2)^2$

$$y' = 2(3x + 2)(3) = 6(3x + 2)$$

━━

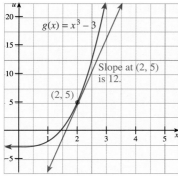

a. Graph of $u = g(x)$

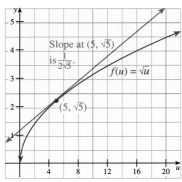

b. Graph of $y = f(u)$

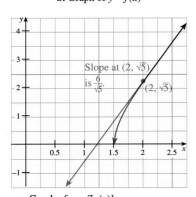

c. Graph of $y = f[g(x)]$
Slope at the point $(2, \sqrt{5})$ product of slopes of g and f: $12\left(\frac{1}{2\sqrt{5}}\right) = \frac{6}{\sqrt{5}}$

Figure 2.19 Graphical representation of chain rule

Generalized Derivative Formulas

It is worthwhile to interpret the chain rule using slopes. Let

$$u = g(x) = x^3 - 3; \quad \text{if } x = 2, \text{ then } u = g(2) = 5$$
$$y = f(u) = \sqrt{u}; \quad \text{if } u = 5, \text{ then } y = f(5) = \sqrt{5}$$

We are interested in the slope of the line tangent to $y = f[g(x)]$ at $x = 2$. The graphs of these functions, along with the slope of their tangent lines, are shown in Figure 2.19. The slope of the composite function $y = f[g(x)]$ at the point $x = 2$ is the product of the slopes of the functions f and g:

$$\underbrace{\frac{dy}{dx}}_{\text{Slope of } y = f[g(x)]} = \underbrace{\frac{dy}{du}}_{\text{Slope of } y = f(u)} \cdot \underbrace{\frac{du}{dx}}_{\text{Slope of } u = g(x)}$$

$$= \underbrace{\frac{1}{2}(x^3 - 3)^{-1/2}}_{\text{Slope of } f} \quad \underbrace{(3x^2)}_{\text{Slope of } g}$$

The chain rule allows us to find derivatives that would otherwise be very difficult to handle.

EXAMPLE 4 Differentiation with quotient rule inside the chain rule

Differentiate $g(x) = \sqrt[4]{\dfrac{x}{1 - 3x}}$.

Solution Write $g(x) = \left(\dfrac{x}{1 - 3x}\right)^{1/4}$.

$$g'(x) = \frac{1}{4}\left(\frac{x}{1 - 3x}\right)^{-3/4}\left(\frac{x}{1 - 3x}\right)' \quad \begin{array}{l} \textit{The inside function is } u = \dfrac{x}{1 - 3x} \\ \textit{and the outside function is } u^{1/4}. \end{array}$$

$$= \frac{1}{4}\left(\frac{x}{1 - 3x}\right)^{-3/4}\left[\frac{(1 - 3x)(1) - x(-3)}{(1 - 3x)^2}\right] \quad \textit{Quotient rule}$$

$$= \frac{1}{4}\left(\frac{1 - 3x}{x}\right)^{3/4}\left[\frac{1}{(1 - 3x)^2}\right] = \frac{1}{4x^{3/4}(1 - 3x)^{5/4}}$$

■ GENERALIZED DERIVATIVE FORMULAS

The chain rule can be used to derive the generalizations of the power rule and the rules for differentiating the trigonometric functions, as summarized in the following box:

$$\frac{d}{dx} u^n = nu^{n-1} \frac{du}{dx}$$

$$\frac{d}{dx} \sin u = \cos u \frac{du}{dx} \qquad \frac{d}{dx} \cos u = -\sin u \frac{du}{dx}$$

$$\frac{d}{dx} \tan u = \sec^2 u \frac{du}{dx} \qquad \frac{d}{dx} \cot u = -\csc^2 u \frac{du}{dx}$$

$$\frac{d}{dx} \sec u = \sec u \tan u \frac{du}{dx} \qquad \frac{d}{dx} \csc u = -\csc u \cot u \frac{du}{dx}$$

The chain rule is so important that you need to see several examples, with a few variations.

EXAMPLE 5   Chain rule with a trigonometric function

Differentiate $f(x) = \sin(3x^2 + 5x - 7)$.

Solution   Think of this as $f(u) = \sin u$, where $u = 3x^2 + 5x - 7$, and apply the chain rule:

$$f'(x) = \cos(3x^2 + 5x - 7) \cdot (3x^2 + 5x - 7)'$$
$$= (6x + 5)\cos(3x^2 + 5x - 7)$$

EXAMPLE 6   Chain rule with other rules

Differentiate $g(x) = \cos x^2 + 5\left(\dfrac{3}{x} + 4\right)^6$.

Solution
$$\frac{dg}{dx} = \frac{d}{dx}\cos x^2 + 5\frac{d}{dx}(3x^{-1} + 4)^6$$

$$= -\sin x^2 \frac{d}{dx}(x^2) + 5\left[6(3x^{-1} + 4)^5 \frac{d}{dx}(3x^{-1} + 4)\right]$$

$$= (-\sin x^2)(2x) + 30(3x^{-1} + 4)^5(-3x^{-2})$$

$$= -2x\sin x^2 - 90x^{-2}(3x^{-1} + 4)^5$$

EXAMPLE 7   Power of a trigonometric function using the chain rule

Differentiate $y = \cos^4(3x + 1)^2$.

Solution $\dfrac{dy}{dx} = 4\cos^3(3x + 1)^2 \dfrac{d}{dx}\cos(3x + 1)^2$ *Power rule for cosine function*

$$= 4\cos^3(3x + 1)^2 \cdot [-\sin(3x + 1)^2] \cdot \frac{d}{dx}(3x + 1)^2$$

Derivative of cosine function

$$= -4\cos^3(3x + 2)^2 \sin(3x + 1)^2 \cdot 2(3x + 1)(3)$$

Derivative of $(3x + 1)^2$

$$= -24(3x + 1)\cos^3(3x + 1)^2 \sin(3x + 1)^2$$

EXAMPLE 8   Differentiation with chain rule inside quotient rule

Differentiate $p(x) = \dfrac{\tan 7x}{(1 - 4x)^5}$.

Solution $\dfrac{dp}{dx} = \dfrac{(1 - 4x)^5 \frac{d}{dx}\tan 7x - \tan 7x \frac{d}{dx}(1 - 4x)^5}{[(1 - 4x)^5]^2}$

$$= \frac{(1 - 4x)^5(\sec^2 7x)\frac{d}{dx}(7x) - (\tan 7x)[5(1 - 4x)^4 \frac{d}{dx}(1 - 4x)]}{(1 - 4x)^{10}}$$

$$= \frac{(1 - 4x)^5(\sec^2 7x)(7) - (\tan 7x)(5)(1 - 4x)^4(-4)}{(1 - 4x)^{10}}$$

$$= \frac{(1 - 4x)^4[7(1 - 4x)\sec^2 7x + 20\tan 7x]}{(1 - 4x)^{10}}$$

$$= \frac{7(1 - 4x)\sec^2 7x + 20\tan 7x}{(1 - 4x)^6}$$

EXAMPLE 9 Chain rule with a radical

Differentiate $h(x) = \sqrt{\sec x^3}$.

Solution Write $h(x) = (\sec x^3)^{1/2}$.

$$\frac{dh}{dx} = \frac{1}{2}(\sec x^3)^{-1/2}\frac{d}{dx}(\sec x^3) = \frac{1}{2}(\sec x^3)^{-1/2}(\sec x^3 \tan x^3)\frac{d}{dx}(x^3)$$

$$= \frac{1}{2}(\sec x^3)^{-1/2}(\sec x^3 \tan x^3)(3x^2) = \frac{3}{2}x^2\sqrt{\sec x^3}\tan x^3$$

EXAMPLE 10 Finding a horizontal tangent

Find the x-coordinate of each point on the curve

$$y = (x + 1)^3(2x + 3)^2$$

where the tangent is horizontal.

Solution Because horizontal tangents have zero slope, we need to solve the equation $f'(x) = 0$. First use the product rule and the extended power rule to find the derivative.

$$f'(x) = (x + 1)^3\frac{d}{dx}(2x + 3)^2 + (2x + 3)^2\frac{d}{dx}(x + 1)^3$$

$$= (x + 1)^3(2)(2x + 3)^1\frac{d}{dx}(2x + 3) + (2x + 3)^2(3)(x + 1)^2\frac{d}{dx}(x + 1)$$

$$= (x + 1)^3(2)(2x + 3)(2) + (2x + 3)^2(3)(x + 1)^2(1)$$

$$= (x + 1)^2(2x + 3)[4(x + 1) + 3(2x + 3)]$$

$$= (x + 1)^2(2x + 3)(10x + 13)$$

From the final factored form, we see that $f'(x) = 0$ when $x = -1, -\frac{3}{2}$, or $-\frac{13}{10}$, and these are the x-coordinates of all the points on the graph where horizontal tangents occur.

Computational Window

It is worth taking a moment to discuss graphing the function in Example 10 to verify the answer graphically. If you input $Y=(X+1)^3(2X+3)^2$ and graph with a standard scale, the graph is not satisfactory.

This might be a good place to experiment with the (ZOOM) feature of your calculator. What scale is necessary to obtain a graph similar to the following?

Y₁☰(X+1)^3(2X+3)^2

Y₁☰(X+1)^3(2X+3)^2
Xmin=-10 Ymin=-10
Xmax=10   Ymax=10
Xscl=1   Yscl=1

EXAMPLE 11   An application of the chain rule

An environmental study of a certain suburban community suggests that the average daily level of carbon monoxide in the air is described by the formula

$$C(p) = \sqrt{0.5p^2 + 17}$$

parts per million when the population is p thousand. It is estimated that t years from now, the population of the community will be

$$p(t) = 3.1 + 0.1t^2$$

thousand. At what rate will the carbon monoxide level be changing with respect to time 3 years from now?

Solution
$$\frac{dC}{dt} = \frac{dC}{dp}\frac{dp}{dt} = \left[\tfrac{1}{2}(0.5p^2 + 17)^{-1/2}(0.5(2p))\right][0.1(2t)]$$

When $t = 3$, $p(t) = 3.1 + 0.1(3)^2 = 4$, so

$$\frac{dC}{dt}\bigg|_{t=3} = \left[\tfrac{1}{2}(0.5 \cdot 4^2 + 17)^{-1/2}(0.5(2 \cdot 4))\right][0.1(2 \cdot 3)] = 0.24$$

The carbon monoxide level will be changing at the rate of 0.24 parts per million.

■ JUSTIFICATION OF THE CHAIN RULE

To get a better feel for why the chain rule is true, suppose x is changed by a small amount Δx. This will cause u to change by an amount Δu, which, in turn, will cause y to change by an amount Δy. *If Δu is not zero*, we can write

$$\frac{\Delta y}{\Delta x} = \frac{\Delta y}{\Delta u}\frac{\Delta u}{\Delta x}$$

By letting $\Delta x \to 0$, we force Δu to approach zero as well, because

$$\Delta u = \left(\frac{\Delta u}{\Delta x}\right)\Delta x \quad \text{so} \quad \lim_{\Delta x \to 0} \Delta u = \left(\frac{du}{dx}\right)(0) = 0$$

It follows that

$$\lim_{\Delta x \to 0} \frac{\Delta y}{\Delta x} = \left(\lim_{\Delta u \to 0} \frac{\Delta y}{\Delta u}\right)\left(\lim_{\Delta x \to 0} \frac{\Delta u}{\Delta x}\right)$$

or, equivalently,

$$\frac{dy}{dx} = \frac{dy}{du}\frac{du}{dx}$$

Unfortunately, there is a flaw in this "proof" of the chain rule. At the beginning we assumed that $\Delta u \neq 0$. However, it is theoretically possible for a small change in x to produce no change in u so that $\Delta u = 0$. This is the case that we consider in the proof in Appendix B.

Historical Note
A calculus book written by the famous mathematician G. H. Hardy (1877–1947) contained essentially this "incorrect" proof rather than the one given in Appendix B. It is even more remarkable that the error was not noticed until the fourth edition.

PROBLEM SET 2.5

Ⓐ 1. ■ **What Does This Say?** What is the chain rule?
2. ■ **What Does This Say?** When do you need to use the chain rule?

In Problems 3–8, use the chain rule to compute the derivative dy/dx and write your answer in terms of x only.

3. $y = u^2 + 1$; $u = 3x - 2$ 4. $y = 2u^2 - u + 5$; $u = 1 - x^2$

5. $y = \dfrac{2}{u^2}; \quad u = x^2 - 9$ **6.** $y = \dfrac{u + 3}{2u + 5}; \quad u = \dfrac{5x - 3}{1 - 2x}$

7. $y = \cos u; \quad u = x^2 + 7$ **8.** $y = u \tan u; \quad u = 3x + \dfrac{6}{x}$

Differentiate the given function in Problems 9–32 with respect to the given variable of the function.

9. a. $g(u) = u^5$ **b.** $u(x) = 3x - 1$
   c. $f(x) = (3x - 1)^5$

10. a. $g(u) = u^3$ **b.** $u(x) = x^2 + 1$
   c. $f(x) = (x^2 + 1)^3$

11. a. $g(u) = u^{15}$ **b.** $u(x) = 3x^2 + 5x - 7$
   c. $f(x) = (3x^2 + 5x - 7)^{15}$

12. a. $g(u) = u^7$ **b.** $u(x) = 5 - 8x - 12x^2$
   c. $f(x) = (5 - 8x - 12x^2)^7$

13. a. $f(x) = \sin(2x)$
   b. $g(x) = \sin(2 \cos x)$

14. a. $f(\theta) = \sin(\sin \theta)$ **b.** $f(\theta) = \sin(\cos \theta)$

15. $s(\theta) = \sin(4\theta + 2)$ **16.** $c(\theta) = \cos(5 - 3\theta)$

17. $f(x) = x^2 \tan x^2$ **18.** $h(x) = x^2(2x - 5)^3$

19. $p(x) = \sin x^2 \cos x^2$ **20.** $f(x) = \csc^2(\sqrt{x})$

21. $f(x) = (2x^2 + 1)^4(x^2 - 2)^5$ **22.** $f(x) = (x^3 + 1)^5(2x^3 - 1)^6$

23. $f(t) = (1 - t^2)\sin t^2$ **24.** $f(x) = \sin^2(\sqrt{x + 3})$

25. $f(t) = (t^2 - 1)^3 \cos(3t + 2)$ **26.** $f(x) = \sqrt{\dfrac{x^2 + 3}{x^2 - 5}}$

27. $f(x) = \sqrt{\dfrac{2x^2 - 1}{3x^2 + 2}}$

28. a. $f(x) = \sqrt{\sin x^2}$ **b.** $f(x) = \sin^2(\sqrt{x})$

29. a. $f(x) = \dfrac{1}{\sqrt{\cos x^2}}$ **b.** $f(x) = \sqrt{\dfrac{1}{\cos^2 x}}$

30. $f(x) = \sqrt{x + \sqrt{x}}$ **31.** $f(x) = \sqrt[3]{x^2 + 2\sqrt{x}}$

32. $f(x) = \sin(\sin(\sin x))$

For each function in Problems 33–38, find an equation for the tangent to the graph at the prescribed point.

33. $f(x) = \sqrt{x^2 + 5}$ at $(2, 3)$

34. $f(x) = (5x + 4)^3$ at $(-1, -1)$

35. $f(x) = x^2(x - 1)^2$ where $x = \frac{1}{2}$

36. $f(x) = \sin(3x - \pi)$ where $x = \frac{\pi}{2}$

37. $f(x) = x^2 \tan(4 - 3x)$ where $x = 0$

38. $f(x) = \left(\dfrac{5 - x^2}{3x - 1}\right)^2$ where $x = 0$

Find the x-coordinate of each point in Problems 39–42 where the graph of the given function has a horizontal tangent line.

39. $f(x) = x\sqrt{1 - 3x}$ **40.** $g(x) = x^2(2x + 3)^2$

41. $q(x) = \dfrac{(x - 1)^2}{(x + 2)^3}$ **42.** $f(x) = (2x^2 - 7)^3$

Ⓑ 43. Let $f(x) = (x + 3)^2(x - 2)^2$.
   a. Compute $f'(x)$ and determine all values of x for which $f'(x) = 0$.
   b. Compute $f''(x)$ and find all solutions of $f''(x) = 0$.

44. The graphs of $u = g(x)$ and $y = f(u)$ are shown in Figure 2.20.

a. $u = g(x)$ **b.** $y = f(u)$

Figure 2.20 Find slope of $y = f[g(x)]$

a. Find the approximate value of y at $x = 2$. What is the slope of the tangent line at that point?

b. Find the approximate value of y at $x = 5$. What is the slope of the tangent line at that point?

c. Find the slope of $y = f[g(x)]$ at $x = 2$.

45. Assume that a snowball melts in such a way that its radius decreases at a constant rate (that is, the radius is a linear function of time). Suppose it begins with a radius of 10 cm and takes 2 hours to disappear. (Assume the snowball is a sphere, and recall that $V = \frac{4}{3}\pi r^3$, $S = 4\pi r^2$.)

a. What is the rate of change of its volume after 1 hour?

b. At what rate is its surface area changing after 1 hour?

46. It is estimated that t years from now, the population of a certain suburban community will be

$$p(t) = 20 - \frac{6}{t + 1}$$

thousand persons. An environmental study indicates that the average daily level of carbon monoxide in the air will be

$$L(p) = 0.5\sqrt{p^2 + p + 58}$$

ppm when the population is p thousand. Find the rate at which the level of carbon monoxide will be changing with respect to time two years from now.

47. At a certain factory, the total cost of manufacturing q units during the daily production run is

$$C(q) = 0.2q^2 + q + 900$$

dollars. From experience, it has been determined that approximately

$$q(t) = t^2 + 100t$$

units are manufactured during the first t hours of a production run. Compute the rate at which the total manufacturing cost is changing with respect to time one hour after production begins.

48. An importer of Brazilian coffee estimates that local consumers will buy approximately

$$D(p) = \frac{4,374}{p^2}$$

pounds of the coffee per week when the price is p dollars per pound. It is estimated that t weeks from now, the price of Brazilian coffee will be

$$p(t) = 0.02t^2 + 0.1t + 6$$

dollars per pound. At what rate will the weekly demand for the coffee be changing with respect to time 10 weeks from now? Will the demand be increasing or decreasing?

49. When electric blenders are sold for p dollars apiece, local consumers will buy

$$D(p) = \frac{8{,}000}{p}$$

blenders per month. It is estimated that t months from now, the price of the blenders will be

$$p(t) = 0.04t^{3/2} + 15$$

dollars. Compute the rate at which the monthly demand for the blenders will be changing with respect to time 25 months from now. Will the demand be increasing or decreasing?

50. The equation $\dfrac{d^2s}{dt^2} + ks = 0$ is called a **differential equation of simple harmonic motion.** Let A be any number. Show that the function $s(t) = A \sin 2t$ satisfies the equation

$$\frac{d^2s}{dt^2} + 4s = 0$$

51. Suppose $L(x)$ is a function with the property that $L'(x) = x^{-1}$. Use the chain rule to find the derivatives of the following functions.

    a. $f(x) = L(x^2)$ **b.** $f(x) = L\left(\dfrac{1}{x}\right)$

    c. $f(x) = L\left(\dfrac{2}{3\sqrt{x}}\right)$ **d.** $f(x) = L\left(\dfrac{2x+1}{1-x}\right)$

When a point source of light of luminous intensity K (candles) shines directly on a point on a surface s meters away, the illuminance on the surface is given by the formula $I = Ks^{-2}$. Use this formula to answer the questions in Problems 52–53. (Note that 1 lux = 1 candle/m^2.)

52. Suppose a person carrying a 20-candlepower light walks toward a wall in such a way that at time t (seconds) the person is $s(t) = 28 - t^2$ meters from the wall.

    a. How fast is the illuminance on the wall increasing when the person is 19 m from the wall?

    b. How fast is the illuminance at a point on the wall increasing when the person is 3 m from the wall? Your answer should be in lux/sec rounded to two decimal places.

53. A lamp of luminous intensity 40 candles is 10 m above the floor of a room and is being lowered at the constant rate of 2 m/s. At what rate will the illuminance at the point on the floor directly under the lamp be increasing when the lamp is 15 m above the floor? Your answer should be in lux/sec rounded to the nearest hundredth.

54. To form a *simple pendulum*, a weight is attached to a rod which is then suspended by one end in such a way that it can swing freely in a vertical plane. Let θ be the angular displacement of the rod from the vertical as shown in Figure 2.21.

Figure 2.21 Problem 54

It can be shown that as long as the maximum displacement θ_M is small, it is reasonable to assume that $\theta = \theta_M \sin kt$ at time t, where k is a constant that depends on the length of the rod. Show that

$$\frac{d^2\theta}{dt^2} + k^2\theta = 0$$

55. A lighthouse is located 2 km directly across the sea from a point O on the shoreline, as shown in Figure 2.22.

Figure 2.22 Problem 55

A beacon in the lighthouse makes 3 complete revolutions (that is, 6π radians) each minute, and during part of each revolution, the light sweeps across the face of a row of cliffs lining the shore.

    a. Show that t minutes after it passes point O, the beam of light is at a point P located $s(t) = 2 \tan(6\pi t)$ km from O.

    b. How fast is the beam of light moving at the time it passes a point on the cliff that is 4 km from the lighthouse?

Ⓒ 56. Using only the formula

$$\frac{d}{dx}\sin u = \cos u \,\frac{du}{dx}$$

and the identities $\cos x = \sin\left(\frac{\pi}{2} - x\right)$ and $\sin x = \cos\left(\frac{\pi}{2} - x\right)$, show that

$$\frac{d}{dx}\cos u = -\sin u \,\frac{du}{dx}$$

57. THINK TANK PROBLEM Let $g(x) = f[u(x)]$, where $u(-3) = 5$, $u'(-3) = 2$, $f(5) = 3$, and $f'(5) = -3$. Find an equation for the tangent to the graph of g at the point where $x = -3$.

58. Let f be a function for which
$$f'(x) = \frac{1}{x^2 + 1}$$
a. If $g(x) = f(3x - 1)$, what is $g'(x)$?
b. If $h(x) = f\left(\frac{1}{x}\right)$, what is $h'(x)$?

59. Let f be a function for which $f(2) = -3$ and $f'(x) = \sqrt{x^2 + 5}$. If
$$g(x) = x^2 f\left(\frac{x}{x-1}\right)$$
what is $g'(2)$?

60. If $\dfrac{df}{dx} = \dfrac{\sin x}{x}$ and $u(x) = \cot x$, what is $\dfrac{df}{du}$?

61. Suppose that f is twice differentiable for all x (that is, $f''(x)$ exists for all x). Use the chain rule to find
$$\frac{d}{dx} f'[f(x)] \quad \text{and} \quad \frac{d}{dx} f[f'(x)].$$

62. Show that if a particle moves along a straight line with displacement $s(t)$ and velocity $v(t)$, then its acceleration satisfies
$$a(t) = v(t) \frac{dv}{ds}$$
Use this formula to find $\dfrac{dv}{ds}$ in the case where
$$s(t) = -2t^3 + 4t^2 + t - 3.$$

2.6 IMPLICIT DIFFERENTIATION

IN THIS SECTION General procedure for implicit differentiation, higher implicit differentiation
In this section we introduce implicitly defined functions and show how such functions can be differentiated when their derivatives exist, without first solving for y explicitly.

■ GENERAL PROCEDURE FOR IMPLICIT DIFFERENTIATION

An equation of the form $y = f(x)$ is said to define y **explicitly** as a function of x. On the other hand, if an equation involves both x and y, as in $x = y^2 + 1$, and if y is thought of as the dependent variable, then we say that y is defined **implicitly** as a function of x. Suppose we have an equation that defines y *implicitly* as a function of x, and we want to find the derivative dy/dx. For example, we may be interested in the slope of a line that is tangent to the graph of the equation at a particular point. One approach might be to solve the equation for y *explicitly* and then differentiate using the techniques we have already developed. For functions that are defined implicitly, it may not be possible to solve for y. For example, there is no obvious way to solve for y in equations such as
$$x^2 y + 2y^3 = 3x + 2y$$

Moreover, even when we can solve for y explicitly, the resulting formula is often complicated and unpleasant to differentiate. For example, the equation
$$x^2 y^3 - 6 = 5y^3 + x$$
can be solved for y to yield
$$y = \left(\frac{x + 6}{x^2 - 5}\right)^{1/3}$$

The computation of dy/dx for this function in explicit form would be routine but tedious, involving both the chain rule and the quotient rule.

Fortunately, there is a simple technique based on the chain rule that allows us to find dy/dx without first solving for y explicitly. This technique is known as **implicit differentiation**. It consists of differentiating both sides of the (unsolved) equation with respect to x and *then* solving algebraically for dy/dx.

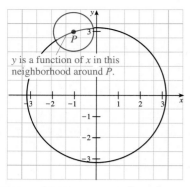

y is a function of x in this neighborhood around P.

Figure 2.23 Graph of $x^2 + y^2 = 10$ showing a neighborhood about $P(-1, 3)$

EXAMPLE 1   Slope of a tangent using implicit differentiation

Find the slope of the tangent to the circle $x^2 + y^2 = 10$ at the point $P(-1, 3)$.

Solution   We recognize the graph of $x^2 + y^2 = 10$ as not being the graph of a function. However, if we look at a small neighborhood around the point $(-1, 3)$, as shown in Figure 2.23, we see that this part of the graph *does pass the vertical line test* for functions. Thus, the required slope can be found by evaluating the derivative dy/dx at $x = -1$. Instead of solving for y and finding the derivative, we *take the derivative of both sides of the equation*:

$$x^2 + y^2 = 10 \qquad \text{Given equation}$$

$$\frac{d}{dx}[x^2 + y^2] = \frac{d}{dx}(10)$$

$$\frac{d}{dx}(x^2) + \frac{d}{dx}(y^2) = 0 \qquad \text{Derivative of a sum; derivative of a constant is zero.}$$

$$2x + 2y\frac{dy}{dx} = 0 \qquad \text{Because } y \text{ is a function of } x, \text{ apply the generalized power rule to find the derivative of } y^2.$$

$$\frac{dy}{dx} = -\frac{2x}{2y} \qquad \text{Solve the equation for } \frac{dy}{dx}.$$

$$= -\frac{x}{y}$$

The slope of the tangent at $P(-1, 3)$ is

$$\frac{dy}{dx}\bigg|_{\substack{x=-1 \\ y=3}} = -\frac{x}{y}\bigg|_{(-1,\,3)} = -\frac{-1}{3} = \frac{1}{3}$$

Here is a general description of the procedure for implicit differentiation:

Procedure for Implicit Differentiation

Suppose an equation defines y implicitly as a differentiable function of x. To find $\frac{dy}{dx}$:

Step 1. Differentiate both sides of the equation with respect to x. Remember that y is really a function of x for part of the curve and use the chain rule when differentiating terms containing y.

Step 2. Solve the differentiated equation algebraically for $\frac{dy}{dx}$.

EXAMPLE 2   Implicit differentiation

Find $\frac{dy}{dx}$ if $x^2y + 2y^3 = 3x + 2y$.

Solution   The process is to differentiate both sides of the given equation with respect to x. To help you remember that y is a function of x, we will replace y with the symbol $y(x)$.

$$x^2y(x) + 2[y(x)]^3 = 3x + 2y(x)$$

Differentiate both sides of this equation term by term with respect to x:

$$\frac{d}{dx}\{x^2 y(x) + 2[y(x)]^3\} = \frac{d}{dx}[3x + 2y(x)]$$

$$\frac{d}{dx}[x^2 y(x)] + 2\frac{d}{dx}[y(x)]^3 = 3\frac{d}{dx}x + 2\frac{d}{dx}y(x)$$

$$\underbrace{x^2 \frac{d}{dx}y(x) + y(x)\frac{d}{dx}x^2}_{\text{Product rule}} + \underbrace{2\left\{3[y(x)]^2 \frac{d}{dx}y(x)\right\}}_{\text{Generalized power rule}} = 3 + 2\frac{d}{dx}y(x)$$

$$x^2 \frac{d}{dx}y(x) + 2xy(x) + 6[y(x)]^2 \frac{d}{dx}y(x) = 3 + 2\frac{d}{dx}y(x)$$

Now replace $y(x)$ by y and $\frac{d}{dx}y(x)$ by $\frac{dy}{dx}$ and rewrite the equation:

$$x^2 \frac{dy}{dx} + 2xy + 6y^2 \frac{dy}{dx} = 3 + 2\frac{dy}{dx}$$

Finally, solve this equation for $\frac{dy}{dx}$:

$$x^2 \frac{dy}{dx} + 6y^2 \frac{dy}{dx} - 2\frac{dy}{dx} = 3 - 2xy$$

$$(x^2 + 6y^2 - 2)\frac{dy}{dx} = 3 - 2xy$$

$$\frac{dy}{dx} = \frac{3 - 2xy}{x^2 + 6y^2 - 2}$$

Notice that the formula for dy/dx contains both the independent variable x and the dependent variable y. This is usual when derivatives are computed implicitly. ▬▬

In Example 2 it was suggested that you temporarily replace y by $y(x)$, so you would not forget to use the chain rule when first learning implicit differentiation. In the following example, we eliminate this unnecessary step and differentiate the given equation directly. Just keep in mind that y is really a function of x and remember to use the chain rule when it is appropriate.

EXAMPLE 3   Implicit differentiation; simplified notation

Find $\frac{dy}{dx}$ if y is a differentiable function of x that satisfies

$$\sin(x^2 + y) = y^2(3x + 1)$$

Solution There is no obvious way to solve the given equation explicitly for y. Differentiate implicitly to obtain

$$\frac{d}{dx}[\sin(x^2 + y)] = \frac{d}{dx}[y^2(3x + 1)]$$

$$\underbrace{\cos(x^2 + y)\frac{d}{dx}(x^2 + y)}_{\text{Chain rule}} = \underbrace{y^2 \frac{d}{dx}(3x + 1) + (3x + 1)\frac{d}{dx}y^2}_{\text{Product rule}}$$

$$\cos(x^2 + y)\left(2x + \frac{dy}{dx}\right) = y^2(3) + (3x + 1)\left(2y\frac{dy}{dx}\right)$$

Finally, solve for $\frac{dy}{dx}$:

$$2x \cos(x^2 + y) + \cos(x^2 + y)\frac{dy}{dx} = 3y^2 + 2y(3x + 1)\frac{dy}{dx}$$

$$[\cos(x^2 + y) - 2y(3x + 1)]\frac{dy}{dx} = 3y^2 - 2x \cos(x^2 + y)$$

$$\frac{dy}{dx} = \frac{3y^2 - 2x \cos(x^2 + y)}{\cos(x^2 + y) - 2y(3x + 1)}$$

EXAMPLE 4   Slope of a line tangent to a given curve

Find the slope of a line tangent to the circle $x^2 + y^2 = 5x + 4y$ at the point $P(5, 4)$.

Solution   The slope of a curve $y = f(x)$ is $\frac{dy}{dx}$, which we find implicitly.

$$x^2 + y^2 = 5x + 4y$$

$$\frac{d}{dx}(x^2 + y^2) = \frac{d}{dx}(5x + 4y)$$

$$2x + 2y\frac{dy}{dx} = 5 + 4\frac{dy}{dx}$$

$$2y\frac{dy}{dx} - 4\frac{dy}{dx} = 5 - 2x$$

$$(2y - 4)\frac{dy}{dx} = 5 - 2x$$

$$\frac{dy}{dx} = \frac{5 - 2x}{2y - 4}$$

At $(5, 4)$, the slope of the tangent line is

$$\left.\frac{dy}{dx}\right|_{(5, 4)} = \left.\frac{5 - 2x}{2y - 4}\right|_{(5, 4)} = \frac{5 - 2(5)}{2(4) - 4} = \frac{-5}{4}$$

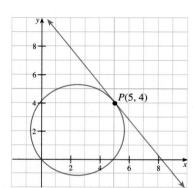

Note that the expression is undefined at $y = 2$. This makes sense when you see that the tangent is vertical there. Look at the graph and see if you should exclude any other values.

■ HIGHER IMPLICIT DIFFERENTIATION

The use of implicit differentiation to find higher derivatives is illustrated in the following example.

EXAMPLE 5   Second derivative by implicit differentiation

Find $\frac{d^2y}{dx^2}$ if $x^2 + y^2 = 10$.

Solution   In Example 1 we found (implicitly) that $\frac{dy}{dx} = -\frac{x}{y}$. Thus

$$\frac{d^2y}{dx^2} = \frac{d}{dx}\left(\frac{-x}{y}\right) = \underbrace{\frac{y\frac{d}{dx}(-x) - (-x)\frac{d}{dx}y}{y^2}}_{\text{Quotient rule}} = \frac{-y + x\frac{dy}{dx}}{y^2}$$

Note that the expression for the second derivative contains the first derivative dy/dx. To simplify the answer, substitute the algebraic expression previously found for dy/dx:

$$\frac{d^2y}{dx^2} = \frac{-y + x\frac{dy}{dx}}{y^2} = \frac{-y + x\left(\frac{-x}{y}\right)}{y^2} \qquad \textit{Substitute } \frac{dy}{dx} = -\frac{x}{y}.$$

$$= \frac{-y^2 - x^2}{y^3}$$

$$= \frac{-(x^2 + y^2)}{y^3}$$

$$= \frac{-10}{y^3} \qquad \textit{Substitute } x^2 + y^2 = 10.$$

Implicit differentiation is a valuable theoretical tool. For example, in Section 2.2 we proved the power rule for the case in which the exponent is an integer. We are now able to prove this result for rational exponents by using implicit differentiation.

THEOREM 2.10   Power rule for rational exponents

If $n = \frac{p}{q}$ is a rational number, then $\frac{d}{dx}(x^n) = nx^{n-1}$.

Proof: If $y = x^n = x^{p/q}$ is differentiable at x, then $y^q = x^{q(p/q)} = x^p$. Differentiate both sides of this equation with respect to x:

$$\frac{d}{dx}(y^q) = \frac{d}{dx}(x^p)$$

$$qy^{q-1}\frac{dy}{dx} = px^{p-1} \qquad \textit{Power rule for integer exponents}$$

$$\frac{dy}{dx} = \frac{px^{p-1}}{qy^{q-1}} \qquad \textit{Solve for } \frac{dy}{dx}.$$

$$= \frac{px^{p-1}}{q(x^{p/q})^{q-1}} \qquad \textit{Substitute } y = x^{p/q}.$$

$$= \frac{p}{q}x^{p-1-p+p/q}$$

$$= \frac{p}{q}x^{-1+p/q}$$

$$= nx^{n-1} \qquad \textit{Substitute } n = \frac{p}{q}.$$

⊘ It is important to realize that implicit differentiation is a technique for finding dy/dx that is valid only if y is a differentiable function of x, and careless application of the technique can lead to errors. For example, there is clearly no real-valued function y that satisfies the equation $x^2 + y^2 = -1$, yet formal application of implicit differentiation yields the "derivative" $dy/dx = -x/y$. To be able to evaluate this "derivative," we must find some values for which $x^2 + y^2 = -1$. Because no such values exist, the derivative does *not* exist. ⊘

PROBLEM SET 2.6

Ⓐ *Find dy/dx by implicit differentiation in Problems 1–14.*

1. $x^2 + y^2 = 25$ **2.** $x^2 + y = x^3 + y^3$

3. $xy = 25$ **4.** $xy(2x + 3y) = 2$

5. $x^2 + 3xy + y^2 = 15$ **6.** $x^3 + y^3 = x + y$

7. $(x + y)^3 + 3y = 3$ **8.** $x^3 + xy + y^3 = x$

9. $\dfrac{1}{y} + \dfrac{1}{x} = 1$ **10.** $(2x + 3y)^2 = 10$

11. $\sin(x + y) = x - y$ **12.** $\tan\dfrac{x}{y} = y$

13. $\cos xy = 1 - x^2$ **14.** $(x^2 + 3y^2)^5 = 2xy$

In Problems 15–18, find $\dfrac{dy}{dx}$ in two ways:

a. *By implicit differentiation of the equation*

b. *By differentiating an explicit formula for y*

15. $x^2 + y^3 = 12$ **16.** $xy + 2y = x^2$

17. $x + \dfrac{1}{y} = 5$ **18.** $xy - x = y + 2$

In Problems 19–22, find an equation of the tangent to the graph of each equation at the prescribed point.

19. $x^2 + y^2 = 13$ at $(-2, 3)$

20. $x^3 + y^3 = y + 21$ at $(3, -2)$

21. $\sin(x - y) = xy$ at $(0, \pi)$

22. $\sec\dfrac{y}{x} = \sqrt{x + 1}$ at $(3, \pi)$

Find the slope of the tangent to the graph at the points indicated in Problems 23–26.

23. Bifolium: $(x^2 + y^2)^2 = 4x^2y$ at $(1, 1)$

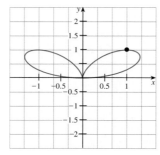

24. Lemniscate of Bernoulli:

$$(x^2 + y^2)^2 = \frac{25}{3}(x^2 - y^2) \text{ at } (2, 1)$$

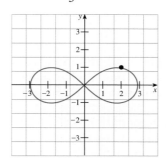

25. Folium of Descartes:

$$x^3 + y^3 - \frac{9}{2}xy = 0 \text{ at } (2, 1)$$

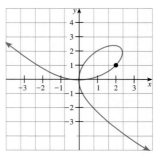

26. Cissoid of Dioceles:

$$y^2(6 - x) = x^3 \text{ at } (3, 3)$$

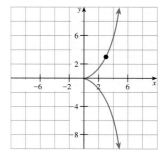

27. Find an equation of the normal line to the curve $x^2 + 2xy = y^3$ at $(1, -1)$.

28. Find an equation of the normal line to the curve $x^2\sqrt{y - 2} = y^2 - 3x - 1$ at $(1, 2)$.

Use implicit differentiation to find the second derivative y'' of the functions given in Problems 29–32.

29. $7x + 5y^2 = 1$ **30.** $x^2 + 2y^3 = 4$

31. $4x^2 - 3y^2 = 9$ **32.** $x^2 + 5xy - y^2 = 1$

33. Let $\dfrac{u^2}{a^2} + \dfrac{v^2}{b^2} = 1$, where a and b are nonzero constants. Find

     a. $\dfrac{du}{dv}$ **b.** $\dfrac{dv}{du}$

34. Let $(a - b)u^3 - (a + b)v^2 = c$, where a, b, and c are constants. Find

     a. $\dfrac{du}{dv}$ **b.** $\dfrac{dv}{du}$

Ⓑ **35.** Show that the tangent at the point (a, b) on the curve whose equation is $2x^2 + 3xy + y^2 = -2$ is horizontal if $4a + 3b = 0$. Find two such points on the curve.

36. Find two points on the curve whose equation is $x^2 - 3xy + 2y^2 = -2$ where the tangent is vertical.

37. Let g be a differentiable function of x that satisfies $g(x) < 0$ and $x^2 + g^2(x) = 10$ for all x.

     a. Use implicit differentiation to show that

$$\frac{dg}{dx} = \frac{-x}{g(x)}$$

b. Show that

$$g(x) = -\sqrt{10 - x^2}$$

satisfies the given requirements. Then use the chain rule to verify that
$$\frac{dg}{dx} = \frac{-x}{g(x)}$$

38. Find the equation of the tangent and the normal line to the curve
$$x^3 + y^3 = 2Axy$$

at the point (A, A), where A is a constant.

39. THINK TANK PROBLEM

a. If $x^2 + y^2 = 6y - 10$ and $\frac{dy}{dx}$ exists, show that
$$\frac{dy}{dx} = \frac{x}{3 - y}.$$

b. Show that there are no real numbers x, y that satisfy the equation
$$x^2 + y^2 = 6y - 10$$

c. What can you conclude from the result found in part a in light of this observation in part b?

40. Find all points on the lemniscate
$$(x^2 + y^2)^2 = 4(x^2 - y^2)$$

where the tangent is horizontal. (See Figure 2.24.)

Figure 2.24 Lemniscate:
$(x^2 + y^2)^2 = 4(x^2 - y^2)$

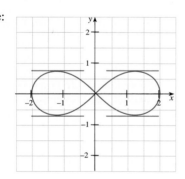

41. Find all points on the cardioid
$$(x^2 + y^2)^{3/2} = \sqrt{x^2 + y^2} + x$$

where the tangent is vertical. (See Figure 2.25.)

Figure 2.25 Cardioid:
$(x^2 + y^2)^{3/2} =$
$$\sqrt{x^2 + y^2} + x$$

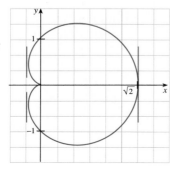

42. The tangent to the curve
$$x^{2/3} + y^{2/3} = 8$$

at the point $(8, 8)$ and the coordinate axes form a triangle, as shown in Figure 2.26. What is the area of this triangle?

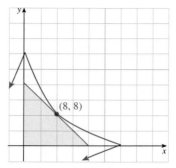

Figure 2.26 Problem 42

43. THINK TANK PROBLEM Find two differentiable functions f that satisfy the equation
$$x - [f(x)]^2 = 9$$

Give the explicit form of each function, and sketch its graph.

44. Show that the tangent to the ellipse
$$\frac{x^2}{a^2} + \frac{y^2}{b^2} = 1$$

at the point (x_0, y_0) is
$$\frac{x_0 x}{a^2} + \frac{y_0 y}{b^2} = 1$$

(See Figure 2.27.)

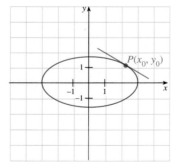

Figure 2.27 Ellipse: $\frac{x^2}{a^2} + \frac{y^2}{b^2} = 1$

45. Find an equation of the tangent to the hyperbola
$$\frac{x^2}{a^2} - \frac{y^2}{b^2} = 1$$

at the point (x_0, y_0). (See Figure 2.28.)

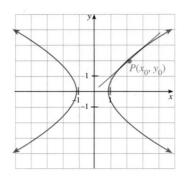

Figure 2.28 Hyperbola: $\dfrac{x^2}{a^2} - \dfrac{y^2}{b^2} = 1$

46. Use implicit differentiation to find the second derivative y'', where y is a differentiable function of x that satisfies

$$ax^2 + by^2 = c$$

(a, b, and c are constants).

47. Show that the sum of the x-intercept and the y-intercept of any tangent to the curve

$$\sqrt{x} + \sqrt{y} = C$$

is equal to C^2.

*The **angle between curves C_1 and C_2** at the point of intersection P is defined as the angle $\theta \leq \frac{\pi}{2}$ between the tangent lines. Specifically, the angle from C_1 to C_2 is the angle from the tangent line to C_1 at P, to the tangent line to C_2 at P, as shown in Figure 2.29. Use this information for Problems 48–49.*

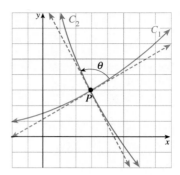

Figure 2.29 The angle θ from C_1 to C_2 at P

48. If θ is the acute angle from curve C_1 to curve C_2 at P and the tangent lines to C_1 and C_2 at P, have slopes m_1 and m_2, respectively, show that

$$\tan \theta = \frac{|m_1 - m_2|}{1 + m_1 m_2}$$

49. Find the angle from the circle

$$x^2 + y^2 = 1$$

to the circle

$$x^2 + (y - 1)^2 = 1$$

at each of the two points of intersection.

50. JOURNAL PROBLEM: *The Pi Mu Epsilon Journal** by Bruce W. King.   When a professor asked the calculus class to find the derivative of y^2 with respect to x^2 for the function $y = x^2 - x$, one student found

$$\frac{dy}{dx} \cdot \frac{y}{x}$$

and obtained the correct answer. Help the professor to enlighten the student about taking derivatives.

2.7 RELATED RATES

IN THIS SECTION   Related rates and applications
In many practical applications of implicit differentiation, the derivatives represent rates of change (often with respect to time). In a typical situation, two or more quantities that vary with time may be related to each other, and implicit differentiation allows us to obtain corresponding relationships among their respective rates without first finding explicit formulas for the quantities as functions of time. Techniques for solving such problems are discussed in this section.

When working a related rate problem you must distinguish between the general situation and the specific situation. The *general situation* comprises properties that are true at *every* instant of time, whereas the *specific situation* refers to those properties that are guaranteed to be true only at the *particular* instant of time that the problem investigates. Here is an example.

EXAMPLE 1   An application involving related rates

A spherical balloon is being filled with a gas in such a way that when the radius is 2 ft, the radius is increasing at the rate of $\frac{1}{6}$ ft/min. How fast is the volume changing at this time?

Solution

The general situation: Let V denote the volume and r the radius, both of which are functions of time t (minutes). Since the container is a sphere, its volume is given by

$$V = \tfrac{4}{3}\pi r^3$$

Differentiating both sides implicitly with respect to time t yields

$$\frac{dV}{dt} = \frac{d}{dt}\left(\frac{4}{3}\pi r^3\right)$$

$$= 4\pi r^2 \frac{dr}{dt} \qquad \text{\textit{Do not forget to use the chain rule because r is also a function of time.}}$$

The specific situation: Our goal is to find $\dfrac{dV}{dt}$ at the time when $r = 2$ and $\dfrac{dr}{dt} = \dfrac{1}{6}$.

$$\frac{dV}{dt} = 4\pi(2)^2\left(\frac{1}{6}\right) = \frac{8\pi}{3} \approx 8.37758041$$

This means that the volume of the container is increasing with respect to time at the rate of about 8.38 ft³/min. ▬

Although each related rate problem has its own "personality," many can be handled by the following summary:

Procedure for Solving Related Rate Problems

The General Situation

Step 1. *Draw a figure, if appropriate, and assign variables to the quantities that vary.* Because rates involve variables and not constants, be careful not to label a quantity with a number unless it *never* changes in the problem.

Step 2. *Find a formula or equation that relates the variables.* Eliminate unnecessary variables; some of these "extra" variables may be constants, but others may be eliminated because of given relationships among the variables.

Step 3. *Differentiate the equations.* Often this involves differentiating implicitly with respect to time.

The Specific Situation

Step 4. *Substitute specific numerical values and solve algebraically for any required rate.* List the known quantities; list as unknown the quantity you wish to find. Substitute all values into the formula. The only remaining variable should be the unknown, which may be a variable or a rate. Solve for the unknown.

EXAMPLE 2   Related rates

A person 6 ft tall is walking away from a streetlight 20 ft high at the rate of 7 ft/s. At what rate is the length of the person's shadow increasing?

Solution

The general situation: Step 1: Let x denote the length (in feet) of the person's shadow and y, the distance between the person and the streetlight, as shown in Figure 2.30. Let t denote the time (in seconds).

Step 2: Because $\triangle ABC$ and $\triangle DEC$ are similar, we have

$$\frac{x + y}{20} = \frac{x}{6}$$

Step 3: Write this equation as $x + y = \frac{20}{6}x$, or $y = \frac{7}{3}x$, and differentiate both sides with respect to t.

$$\frac{dy}{dt} = \frac{7}{3}\frac{dx}{dt}$$

The specific situation: Step 4: List the known quantities. We know that $\frac{dy}{dt} = 7$. Our goal is to find $\frac{dx}{dt}$. Substitute and then solve for the unknown value:

$$\frac{dy}{dt} = \frac{7}{3}\frac{dx}{dt}$$

$$7 = \frac{7}{3}\frac{dx}{dt} \quad \textit{Substitute.}$$

$$3 = \frac{dx}{dt} \quad \textit{Multiply both sides by } \tfrac{3}{7}.$$

The length of the person's shadow is increasing at the rate of 3 ft/s.   ▬

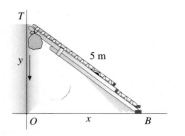

Figure 2.30 A person walking away from a street lamp.

EXAMPLE 3   Related rates

A bag is tied to the top of a 5-m ladder resting against a vertical wall. Suppose the ladder begins sliding down the wall in such a way that the foot of the ladder is moving away from the wall. How fast is the bag descending at the instant the foot of the ladder is 4 m from the wall and the foot is moving away at the rate of 2 m/s?

Solution

The general situation: Let x and y be the distances from the base of the wall to the foot and top of the ladder, respectively, as shown in Figure 2.31.

Notice that $\triangle TOB$ is a right triangle, so a relevant formula is the Pythagorean theorem:

$$x^2 + y^2 = 25$$

Differentiate both sides of this equation with respect to t:

$$2x\frac{dx}{dt} + 2y\frac{dy}{dt} = 0$$

The specific situation: At the particular instant in question, $x = 4$ and $y = \sqrt{25 - 4^2} = 3$. We also know that $\frac{dx}{dt} = 2$, and the goal is to find $\frac{dy}{dt}$ at this

Figure 2.31 A ladder sliding down a wall

instant. We have

$$2(4)(2) + 2(3)\frac{dy}{dt} = 0$$

$$\frac{dy}{dt} = -\tfrac{8}{3}$$

This tells us that at the instant in question, the bag is descending (because dy/dt is negative) at the rate of $\tfrac{8}{3} \approx 2.7$ m/s.   ▬

EXAMPLE 4   A physical application involving related rates

When air expands *adiabatically* (that is, with no change in heat), the pressure P and the volume V satisfy the relationship

$$PV^{1.4} = C$$

where C is a constant. At a certain instant, the pressure is 20 lb/in.^{2} and the volume is 280 in^3. If the volume is decreasing at the rate of 5 in.^{3}/s at this instant, what is the rate of change of the pressure?

Solution

The general situation: The required equation was given, so we begin by differentiating both sides with respect to t. Remember, because C is a constant, its derivative with respect to t is zero.

$$1.4PV^{0.4}\frac{dV}{dt} + V^{1.4}\frac{dP}{dt} = 0 \quad \textit{Product rule}$$

The specific situation: At the instant in question, $P = 20$, $V = 280$, and $dV/dt = -5$ (negative because the volume is decreasing). The goal is to find dP/dt. First substitute.

$$(20)(1.4)(280)^{0.4}(-5) + (280)^{1.4}\frac{dP}{dt} = 0$$

Now, solve for $\frac{dP}{dt}$.

$$\frac{dP}{dt} = \frac{5(20)(1.4)(280)^{0.4}}{(280)^{1.4}}$$

$$\frac{dP}{dt} = 0.5$$

Thus, at the instant in question, the pressure is increasing (because its derivative is positive) at the rate of 0.5 lb/in.^{2} per second.   ▬

EXAMPLE 5   Related rates

A tank filled with water is in the shape of an inverted cone 20 ft high with a circular base (on top) whose radius is 5 ft. Water is running out of the bottom of the tank at the constant rate of 2 ft^3/min. How fast is the water level falling when the water is 8 ft deep?

Solution

The general situation: Consider a conical tank with height 20 ft and circular base of radius 5 ft, as shown in Figure 2.32. Suppose that the water level is h ft and that the radius of the surface of the water is *r*.

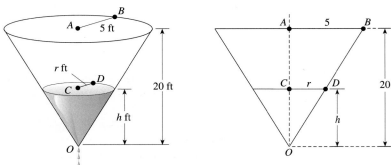

Figure 2.32 A conical water tank

Let *V* denote the volume of water in the tank after *t* minutes. We know that

$$V = \tfrac{1}{3}\pi r^2 h$$

(See *Student Mathematics Handbook* for appropriate formulas.) Once again, we use similar triangles (see Figure 2.32) to write $\frac{5}{20} = \frac{r}{h}$, or $r = \frac{h}{4}$. We substitute this into the formula to obtain

$$V = \tfrac{1}{3}\pi \left(\frac{h}{4}\right)^2 h = \tfrac{1}{48}\pi h^3$$

and then differentiate both sides of this equation with respect to *t*.

$$\frac{dV}{dt} = \frac{\pi}{16} h^2 \frac{dh}{dt}$$

The specific situation: Begin with the known quantities: we know that $dV/dt = -2$ (negative, because the volume is decreasing). The goal is to find dh/dt. At the particular instant in question, $h = 8$ and we substitute to find:

$$-2 = \frac{\pi}{16}(8)^2 \frac{dh}{dt}$$

$$\frac{-1}{2\pi} = \frac{dh}{dt}$$

At the instant when the water is 8 ft deep, the water level is falling (because dh/dt is negative) at a rate of $\frac{1}{2\pi} \approx 0.16$ ft/min ≈ 1.9 in./min.   ▬

⊘ A common error in solving related-rate problems is to substitute numerical values too soon or, equivalently, to use relationships that apply only at a particular moment in time. This explains why we have separated related-rate problems into two distinct parts. Be careful to work with general relationships among the variables and substitute specific numerical values only after you have found general rate relationships by differentiation. ⊘

(s^MH)

EXAMPLE 6   Related rates

Every day, a flight from Los Angeles to New York flies directly over my home at a constant altitude of 4 mi. If I assume that the plane is flying at a constant speed of 400 mi/hr, at what rate is the angle of elevation of my line of sight changing with respect to time when the horizontal distance between the approaching plane and my location is exactly 3 mi?

Solution

The general situation: Let *x* denote the horizontal distance between the plane and the observer, as shown in Figure 2.33a. The height of the observer is insignificant when compared to the height of the plane.

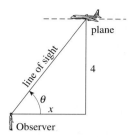

a. Observer of an approaching plane

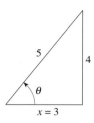

b. Triangle for computing $\sin\theta$ when $x = 3$

Figure 2.33 Angle of elevation problem

A general relationship is

$$\cot\theta = \tfrac{1}{4}x$$

Differentiate both sides of this equation with respect to t to obtain

$$-\csc^2\theta\,\frac{d\theta}{dt} = \tfrac{1}{4}\frac{dx}{dt}$$

The specific situation:. Solving for $\dfrac{d\theta}{dt}$, we obtain

$$\frac{d\theta}{dt} = -\tfrac{1}{4}\sin^2\theta\,\frac{dx}{dt}$$

At the instant when $x = 3$, we are given that $\dfrac{dx}{dt} = -400$ (negative because the distance is decreasing), and from Figure 2.33b we see $\sin\theta = 4/5$. Thus, the angle of elevation is changing at the rate of

$$\frac{d\theta}{dt} = -\tfrac{1}{4}\left(\tfrac{4}{5}\right)^2(-400) = 64 \text{ rad/hr}$$

The angle of elevation is increasing at the rate of 64 radians per hour or, equivalently,

$$(64 \text{ rad/hr})\left(\frac{360 \text{ deg}}{2\pi \text{ rad}}\right)\left(\frac{1 \text{ hr}}{3600 \text{ sec}}\right) \approx 1.02 \text{ deg/sec}$$

PROBLEM SET 2.7

Ⓐ *Find the indicated rate in Problems 1–9, given the other information. Assume $x > 0$ and $y > 0$.*

1. Find $\dfrac{dy}{dt}$ where $x^2 + y^2 = 25$ and $\dfrac{dx}{dt} = 4$, when $x = 3$.

2. Find $\dfrac{dx}{dt}$ where $x^2 + y^2 = 25$ and $\dfrac{dy}{dt} = 2$, when $x = 4$.

3. Find $\dfrac{dy}{dt}$ where $5x^2 - y = 100$ and $\dfrac{dx}{dt} = 10$, when $x = 10$.

4. Find $\dfrac{dx}{dt}$ where $4x^2 - y = 100$ and $\dfrac{dy}{dt} = -6$, when $x = 1$.

5. Find $\dfrac{dx}{dt}$ where $y = 2\sqrt{x} - 9$ and $\dfrac{dy}{dt} = 5$, when $x = 9$.

6. Find $\dfrac{dy}{dt}$ where $y = 5\sqrt{x+9}$ and $\dfrac{dx}{dt} = 2$, when $x = 7$.

7. Find $\dfrac{dy}{dt}$ where $xy = 10$ and $\dfrac{dx}{dt} = -2$, when $x = 5$.

8. Find $\dfrac{dy}{dt}$ where $5xy = 10$ and $\dfrac{dx}{dt} = -2$, when $x = 1$.

9. Find $\dfrac{dx}{dt}$ where $x^2 + xy - y^2 = 11$ and $\dfrac{dy}{dt} = 5$, when $x = 4$ and $y > 0$.

In physics, Hooke's law says that when a spring is stretched x units beyond its natural length, the elastic force $F(x)$ exerted by the spring is $F(x) = -kx$, where k is a constant that depends on the spring. Assume $k = 12$ in Problems 10 and 11.

10. If a spring is stretched at the constant rate of a $\frac{1}{4}$ in./s, how fast is the force $F(x)$ changing when $x = 2$ in.?

11. If a spring is stretched at the constant rate of a $\frac{1}{4}$ in./s, how fast is the force $F(x)$ changing when $x = 3$ in.?

12. A particle moves along the parabolic path given by $y^2 = 4x$ in such a way that when it is at the point $(1, -2)$, its horizontal velocity (in the direction of the x-axis) is 3 ft/s. What is its vertical velocity (in the direction of the y-axis) at this instant?

13. A particle moves along the elliptical path given by $4x^2 + y^2 = 4$ in such a way that when it is at the point $(\sqrt{3}/2, 1)$ its x-coordinate is increasing at the rate of 5 units per second. How fast is the y-coordinate changing at that instant?

14. A rock is dropped into a lake and an expanding circular ripple results. When the radius of the ripple is 8 in., the radius is increasing at a rate of 3 in./s. At what rate is the area enclosed by the ripple changing at this time?

15. A pebble dropped into a pond causes a circular ripple. Find the rate at which the radius of the ripple is changing at a time when the radius is one foot and the area enclosed by the ripple is increasing at the rate of 4 ft²/s.

16. An environmental study of a certain community indicates that there will be $Q(p) = p^2 + 3p + 1{,}200$ units of a harmful pollutant in the air when the population is p thousand. The population is currently 30,000 and is increasing at a rate of 2,000 per year. At what rate is the level of air pollution increasing?

17. It is estimated that the annual advertising revenue received by a newspaper will be $R(x) = 0.5x^2 + 3x + 160$

thousand dollars when its circulation is x thousand. The circulation of the paper is currently 10,000 and is increasing at a rate of 2,000 per year. At what rate will the annual advertising revenue be increasing with respect to time 2 years from now?

18. Hospital officials estimate that approximately $N(p) = p^2 + 5p + 900$ people will seek treatment in the emergency room each year if the population of the community is p thousand. The population is currently 20,000 and is growing at the rate of 1,200 per year. At what rate is the number of people seeking emergency room treatment increasing?

19. Boyle's law states that when gas is compressed at constant temperature, the pressure P of a given sample satisfies the equation $PV = C$, where V is the volume of the sample and C is a constant. Suppose that at a certain time the volume is 30 in.^{3}, the pressure is 90 lb/in.^{2}, and the volume is increasing at the rate of 10 in.^{3}/s. How fast is the pressure changing at this instant? Is it increasing or decreasing?

B 20. ■ **What Does This Say?**   What do we mean by a related-rate problem?

21. ■ **What Does This Say?**   Outline a procedure for solving related-rate problems.

22. The volume of a spherical balloon is increasing at a constant rate of 3 in.^{3}/s. At what rate is the radius of the balloon increasing when the radius is 2 in.?

23. Can you stretch your imagination to consider a piece of ice in the shape of a sphere? Suppose such a piece of ice is melting at the rate of 5 in.^{3}/min. How fast is the radius changing at the instant when the radius is 4 in.? How fast is the surface area of the sphere changing at the same instant? Assume the ice retains its spherical shape at all times.

24. The surface area of a sphere is decreasing at the constant rate of 3π cm^2/s. At what rate is the volume of the sphere decreasing at the instant its radius is 2 cm?

25. A certain medical procedure requires that a spherical balloon be inserted into the stomach and then be inflated. If the radius of the balloon is increasing at the rate of 0.3 cm/min, how fast is the volume changing when the radius is 4 cm?

26. A person 6 ft tall walks away from a street light at the rate of 5 ft/s. If the light is 18 ft above ground level, how fast is the person's shadow lengthening?

27. A ladder 13 ft long rests against a vertical wall and is sliding down the wall at the rate of 3 ft/s at the instant the foot of the ladder is 5 ft from the base of the wall. At this instant, how fast is the foot of the ladder moving away from the wall?

28. A car traveling north at 40 mi/hr and a truck traveling east at 30 mi/hr leave an intersection at the same time. At what rate will the distance between them be changing 3 hr later?

29. A very peculiar water tank is built in the shape of a cone 40 ft high with a circular base of radius 20 ft with the point on top. Water is flowing into the tank at a constant rate of 80 ft^3/min. How fast is the water level rising when the water is 12 ft deep?

30. Suppose that in Problem 29, water is also flowing out the bottom of the tank. At what rate should the water be allowed to flow out so that the water level will be rising at a rate of only 0.05 ft/min when the water is 12 ft deep? Give your answer to the nearest hundredth of a cubic foot per minute.

31. A person is standing at the end of a pier 12 ft above the water and is pulling in a rope attached to a rowboat at the water line at the rate of 6 ft of rope per minute, as shown in Figure 2.34. How fast is the boat moving in the water when it is 16 ft from the pier?

12 ft

|← 16 ft →|

Figure 2.34 Problem 31

32. One end of a rope is fastened to a boat and the other end is wound around a windlass located on a dock at a point 4 m above the level of the boat. If the boat is drifting away from the dock at the rate of 2 m/min, how fast is the rope unwinding at the instant when the length of the rope is 5 m?

33. A ball is dropped from a height of 160 ft. A light is located at the same level, 10 ft away from the initial position of the ball. The height of the ball after t seconds is $H(t) = -16t^2 + 160$ ft. How fast is the ball's shadow moving along the ground one second after the ball is dropped?

34. A point $P(x, y)$ moves along the curve $xy = 100$ in the first quadrant of the xy-plane. Let A be the area of the triangle with vertices P, $Q(1, 0)$, and $R(0, 2)$. If the x-coordinate of P is increasing at the rate of 3 units per second, how fast is the area changing at the time the x-coordinate of P is four times the y-coordinate? Is the area increasing or decreasing at this time?

35. A person 6 ft tall stands 10 ft from point P directly beneath a lantern hanging 30 ft above the ground, as shown in Figure 2.35.

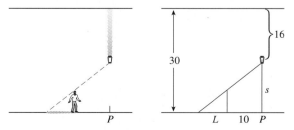

Figure 2.35 Problem 35

The lantern starts to fall, thus causing the person's shadow to lengthen. Given that the lantern falls $16t^2$ ft in t sec, how fast will the shadow be lengthening when $t = 1$?

36. A race official is watching a race car approach the finish line at the rate of 200 km/hr. Suppose the official is sitting at the finish line, 20 m from the point where the car will cross, and let θ be the angle between the finish line and the official's line of sight to the car, as shown as Figure 2.36. At what rate is θ changing when the car crosses the finish line?

Figure 2.36 Problem 36

37. At noon on a certain day, a truck is 250 mi due east of a car. The truck is traveling west at a constant speed of 25 mi/hr, whereas the car is traveling north at 50 mi/hr.
    a. At what rate is the distance between them changing at time t?
    b. At what time is the distance between the car and the truck neither increasing nor decreasing?
    c. What is the minimal distance between the car and the truck? *Hint*: This distance must occur at the time found in part **b**. Do you see why?

38. A weather balloon is rising vertically at the rate of 10 ft/s. An observer is standing on the ground 300 ft horizontally from the point where the balloon was released. At what rate is the distance between the observer and the balloon changing when the balloon is 400 ft high?

39. An observer watches a plane approach at a speed of 500 mi/hr and an altitude of 3 mi. At what rate is the angle of elevation of the observer's line of sight changing with respect to time when the horizontal distance between the plane and the observer is 4 mi? Give your answer in radians per hour or in degrees per minute.

40. A person 6 ft tall is watching a streetlight 18 ft high while walking toward it at a speed of 5 ft/s, as shown in Figure 2.37.

Figure 2.37 Problem 40

At what rate is the angle of elevation of the person's line of sight changing with respect to time when the person is 9 ft from the base of the light?

41. A revolving searchlight in a lighthouse 2 mi off shore is following a beachcomber along the shore, as shown in Figure 2.38.

Figure 2.38 Problem 41

When the beachcomber is 1 mi from the point on the shore that is closest to the lighthouse, the searchlight is turning at the rate of 0.25 rev/hr. How fast is the beachcomber walking at that moment? *Hint*: Note that 0.25 rev/hr is the same as $\frac{\pi}{2}$ rad/hr.

42. A water trough is 2 ft deep and 10 ft long and has a trapezoidal cross section with base lengths 2 ft and 5 ft, as shown in Figure 2.39.

Figure 2.39 Problem 42

    a. Find a relationship between the volume of water in the trough at any given time and the depth of the water at that time.
    b. If the water enters the trough at the rate of 10 ft³/min, how fast is the water level rising (to the nearest $\frac{1}{2}$ in./min) when the trough is 1 ft deep?

43. At noon, a ship sails due north from a point P at 8 knots (nautical miles per hour). Another ship, sailing at 12 knots, leaves the same point 1 h later on a course 60° east of north. How fast is the distance between the ships increasing at 2 P.M.? At 5 P.M.? *Hint*: Use the law of cosines.

44. A swimming pool is 60 ft long and 25 ft wide. Its depth varies uniformly from 3 ft at the shallow end to 15 ft at the deep end, as shown in Figure 2.40.

Figure 2.40 Problem 44

Suppose the pool is being filled with water at the rate of 800 ft³/min. At what rate is the depth of water increasing at the deep end when it is 5 ft deep at that end?

45. A water bucket has the shape of the frustum of a cone with height 1 ft and upper and lower radii of 1 ft and 9 in., respectively, as shown in Figure 2.41.

1 ft
1 ft
9 in

Figure 2.41 Problem 45

If water is leaking from the bottom of the bucket at the rate of 8 in.³/min, at what rate is the water level falling when the depth of water in the bucket is 6 in.? *Hint:* The volume of the frustum of a cone with height h and base radii r and R is

$$V = \frac{\pi h}{3}(R^2 + rR + r^2)$$

Ⓒ 46. A lighthouse is located 2 km directly across the sea from a point S on the shoreline. A beacon in the lighthouse makes 3 complete revolutions (6π radians) each minute, and during part of each revolution, the light sweeps across the face of a row of cliffs lining the shore.

a. Show that t minutes after it passes point S, the beam of light is at a point P located $s(t) = 2 \tan 6\pi t$ km from S.

b. How fast is the beam of light moving at the time it passes a point on the cliff located 4 km from the lighthouse?

47. A car is traveling at the rate of 40 ft/s along a straight, level road that parallels the seashore. A rock with a family of seals is located 50 yd offshore.

a. Find an expression for the rate of change of the angle θ between the road and the driver's line of sight to the seals.

b. As the distance x in Figure 2.42 approaches 0, what happens to $d\theta/dt$?

50 yd
θ
x

Figure 2.42 Problem 47

c. Suppose the car is traveling at v ft/sec. Now what happens to $d\theta/dt$ as $x \to 0$? What effect does this have on a passenger looking at the seals if the car is traveling at a high rate of speed?

2.8 DIFFERENTIALS AND TANGENT LINE APPROXIMATIONS

IN THIS SECTION Tangent line approximation, the differential, error propagation, marginal analysis in economics

The material of this section was historically motivated by the desire to make certain approximations by using the derivative. However, because fast, accurate calculators and computers are now commonplace and because computations can usually be made without the use of calculus approximations, we now study approximations to provide insight into the nature of the derivative. We also introduce a new symbol, dx, called the differential, which is used to estimate changes in functional values. A special case of the approximation procedure is the concept of marginal analysis, which plays an important role in business and economics.

■ TANGENT LINE APPROXIMATION

Consider the graph of a function that is differentiable at a point $x = a$. (Three examples are shown in Figure 2.43.) Next, look at successive enlargements, and notice that the curve eventually looks linear. In fact, if we draw that tangent line at some point $(a, f(a))$ on the curve, we see that for a small interval on the x-axis, the y-values along the tangent line give good approximations to the y-values on the curve. It is for this reason that we call the equation of the tangent line to a function f at a point a **linearization** of the function at a point $x = a$.

a. $y = x^3 - 2x + 5$

  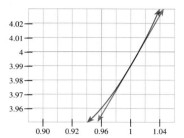

b. $y = \sqrt{15 + x}$

  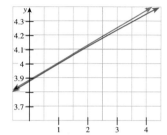

c. $y = \sin x - \sin 1 + 4$

  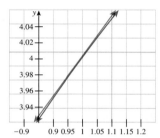

Figure 2.43 Comparison of graphs and tangent lines for functions passing through $(1, 4)$

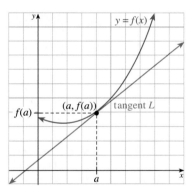

Figure 2.44 Equation of the tangent line is
$y = f(a) + f'(a)(x - a)$.

In order to find the equation of the tangent line at the point $(a, f(a))$, we note that the slope is $f'(a)$ and use the point-slope form of the equation of a line:

$$y - f(a) = f'(a)(x - a)$$
$$y = f(a) + f'(a)(x - a)$$

We can use this line as an approximation of f as long as the line remains close to the graph of f, as shown in Figure 2.44.

Linearization of a Function

If $y = f(x)$ is differentiable at $x = a$, then

$$L(x) = f(a) + f'(a)(x - a)$$

is the **linearization** of f at a.

EXAMPLE 1   Finding a linearization of a given function

Find the linearization of the function defined by $f(x) = x^3 - 2x + 5$ at $a = 1$ (see Figure 2.43a).

Solution   The derivative of f is $f'(x) = 3x^2 - 2$. We also find

$$f(1) = 1^3 - 2(1) + 5 = 4 \qquad f'(1) = 3(1)^2 - 2 = 1$$

so that the linearization of f at $a = 1$ is

$$L(x) = f(1) + f'(1)(x - 1) = 4 + 1(x - 1) = x + 3 \qquad \blacksquare$$

We might ask about the accuracy of the linearization in Example 1. The variable Δx is called the **increment of x.** The accuracy of the approximation $f(x) \approx L(x)$ is found by considering

$$x^3 - 2x + 5 \approx x + 3$$

If $\Delta x = 1$, then $a + \Delta x = 1 + 1 = 2$. Also,

$$f(a + \Delta x) = f(2) = 2^3 - 2(2) + 5 = 9 \qquad \text{and}$$

$$L(a + \Delta x) = L(2) = 2 + 3 = 5$$

These (along with other) values are summarized in the following table:

a	Δx	$a + \Delta x$	$f(a + \Delta x)$	$L(a + \Delta x)$	$\lvert L(a + \Delta x) - f(a + \Delta x)\rvert$
1	1	2	9	5	4
1	0.1	1.1	4.131	4.1	0.031
1	0.01	1.01	4.010301	4.01	0.000301

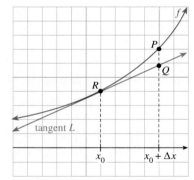

a. Tangent line to f at R

Let us consider a geometric interpretation. Let f be a differentiable function at $x = x_0$. You can see from Figure 2.45a that as Δx becomes small, Q becomes a good approximation of P. To find an expression for the y-value of Q, look at Figure 2.45b. You can see that the y-value of Q is equal to $f(x_0) + \Delta y$. Because the slope of the tangent at R is the derivative of f at x_0, we have

$$f'(x_0) = \frac{\Delta y}{\Delta x}$$

$$\Delta y = f'(x_0)\,\Delta x$$

Thus, the y-value of Q is

$$f(x_0) + f'(x_0)\,\Delta x$$

Because Q is a good approximation of P if Δx is small,

$$\underbrace{f(x_0) + \Delta x}_{y\text{-value of }P} \approx \underbrace{f(x_0) + f'(x_0)\,\Delta x}_{y\text{-value of }Q}$$

If we wish to find the change in the function f that corresponds to a change in x, we use the following notation:

$\Delta x =$ increment of x (that is, change in x)
$\Delta f =$ increment of f (that is, change in f caused by a change Δx in x)

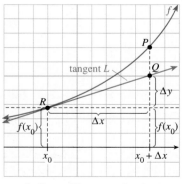

b. Tangent line approximation

Figure 2.45 Tangent line approximation

Then,

$$\Delta f = f(x_0 + \Delta x) - f(x_0)$$

so that

$$\Delta f \approx f'(x_0)\,\Delta x$$

We call this the **incremental approximation formula.**

Incremental Approximation
Formula

If f is differentiable at x_0 and Δx is small, then the corresponding change (in functional notation) in f satisfies

$$\Delta f = f(x_0 + \Delta x) - f(x_0) \approx f'(x_0)\,\Delta x$$

▮ *What this says*: At a point where the function is differentiable, the change in the function is approximately the derivative of the function at that point times the change in the independent variable.

EXAMPLE 2 Incremental approximation

Show that if $f(x) = \sin x$, the function $g(x) = \Delta f / \Delta x$ approximates the function $f'(x) = \cos x$ for small values of Δx.

Solution The approximation formula $\Delta f = f(x_0 + \Delta x) - f(x_0) \approx f'(x_0)\Delta x$ implies that

$$\frac{\Delta f}{\Delta x} = \frac{f(x_0 + \Delta x) - f(x_0)}{\Delta x} \approx f'(x_0)$$

Because $f(x) = \sin x$, $f'(x) = \cos x$, and

$$\frac{\sin(x + \Delta x) - \sin x}{\Delta x} \approx \cos x$$

Figure 2.46 shows the graphs of f and g for three different choices of Δx. Notice as Δx becomes smaller, it is more difficult to see the difference between f and g. In fact, for very small Δx, the graphs are indistinguishable.

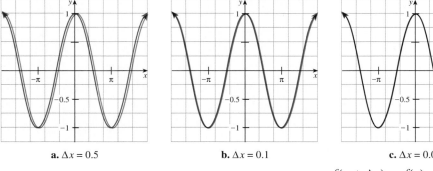

a. $\Delta x = 0.5$ **b.** $\Delta x = 0.1$ **c.** $\Delta x = 0.01$

Figure 2.46 Graphs of $f'(x) = \cos x$ and $g(x) = \dfrac{f(x + \Delta x) - f(x)}{\Delta x}$ ▬

▦ THE DIFFERENTIAL

We have already observed that writing the derivative of $f(x)$ in the Leibniz notation df/dx suggests that the derivative may be incorrectly regarded as a quotient of "df" by "dx." It is a tribute to the genius of Leibniz that this erroneous interpretation of his notation often turns out to make good sense.

To give dx and dy meaning as separate quantities, let x be fixed and define dx to be an independent variable equal to Δx, the change in x. That is, define dx, called the **differential of x,** to be an independent variable equal to Δx, the change in x. Then, if f is differentiable at x, we define dy, called the **differential of y,** by the formula

$$dy = f'(x)\,dx \quad \text{or, equivalently,} \quad df = f'(x)\,dx$$

If we relate differentials to Figure 2.47, we see that $dx = \Delta x$ and that Δy is the rise of f that occurs for a change of Δx, whereas dy is the rise of a tangent relative to the same change in x. It is important to note that Δy and Δx are generally not the same (see Figure 2.47).

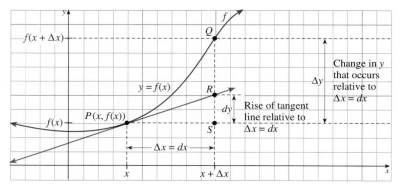

Figure 2.47 Geometrical definition of dx and dy

We now restate the standard rules and formulas for differentiation in terms of differentials. Remember that a and b are constants, while f and g are functions.

Differential Rules

Linearity rule $\quad\quad\quad\quad\quad d(af + bg) = a\,df + b\,dg$

Product rule $\quad\quad\quad\quad\quad\quad d(fg) = f\,dg + g\,df$

Quotient rule $\quad\quad\quad\quad\quad d\left(\dfrac{f}{g}\right) = \dfrac{g\,df - f\,dg}{g^2}\quad\quad (g \neq 0)$

Power rule $\quad\quad\quad\quad\quad\quad d(x^n) = nx^{n-1}\,dx$

Trigonometric rules

$\quad\quad d(\sin x) = \cos x\,dx \quad\quad\quad d(\cos x) = -\sin x\,dx$

$\quad\quad d(\tan x) = \sec^2 x\,dx \quad\quad\quad d(\cot x) = -\csc^2 x\,dx$

$\quad\quad d(\sec x) = \sec x \tan x\,dx \quad\quad d(\csc x) = -\csc x \cot x\,dx$

EXAMPLE 3 **Differential involving a product and a trigonometric function**

Find $d(x^2\sin x)$.

Solution $\quad\quad\quad d(x^2\sin x) = x^2 d(\sin x) + \sin x\,d(x^2)$

$\quad\quad\quad\quad\quad\quad\quad\quad = x^2(\cos x\,dx) + \sin x(2x\,dx)$

$\quad\quad\quad\quad\quad\quad\quad\quad = (x^2\cos x + 2x \sin x)\,dx$

Next, we use differentials to make an approximation. Keep in mind that we are using a numerical example to help us understand the differential. If all we wanted to do was to evaluate the expression, we would use a calculator and not differentials.

EXAMPLE 4 **Using a differential to approximate a function**

Use differentials to approximate $\sqrt[3]{8.02}$ and check by using a calculator.

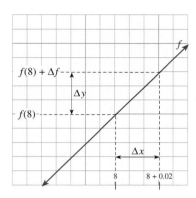

Solution In order to use differentials, we need to write this problem using functional notation. If $f(x) = \sqrt[3]{x}$, then we want to approximate $f(8.02)$.

$$f(8.02) = f(8 + 0.02)$$
$$= f(8) + \Delta f$$

We now approximate Δf by using differentials:

$$\Delta f \approx df = f'(x)\,dx$$
$$= \tfrac{1}{3}x^{-2/3}\,dx$$

Let $x = 8$ and $dx = 0.02$. Then,

$$df = \tfrac{1}{3}(8)^{-2/3}(0.02) = \frac{0.005}{3} \approx 0.001666667$$

Therefore, since $\Delta f = f(8.02) - f(8)$, we have

$$f(8.02) = f(8) + \Delta f$$
$$\approx f(8) + df$$
$$\approx 2 + 0.001666667$$
$$\approx 2.0016667$$

Our calculator tells us that $\sqrt[3]{8.02} = 2.0016653$ to 7 digits, so the error in the approximation is less than 0.00001. ▬

■ ERROR PROPAGATION

In the next example, the approximation formula is used to study **propagation of error,** which is the term used to describe an error that accumulates from other errors in an approximation. In particular, in the next example, the derivative is used to estimate the maximum error in a calculation that is based on figures obtained by imperfect measurement.

EXAMPLE 5   Propagation of error in a volume measurement

You measure the side of a cube and find it to be 10 cm long. From this you conclude that the volume of the cube is $10^3 = 1,000$ cm^3. If your original measurement of the side is accurate to within 2%, approximately how accurate is your calculation of volume?

Solution The volume of the cube is $V(x) = x^3$, where x is the length of a side. If you take the length of a side to be 10 when it is really $10 + \Delta x$, your error is Δx; and your corresponding error when computing the volume will be ΔV, given by

$$\Delta V = V(10 + \Delta x) - V(10) \approx V'(10)\,\Delta x$$

Now, $V'(x) = 3x^2$, so $V'(10) = 300$. Also, your measurement of the side can be off by as much as 2%—that is, by as much as $0.02(10) = 0.2$ cm in either direction. Substituting $\Delta x = \pm 0.2$ in the incremental approximation formula for ΔV, we get

$$\Delta V \approx \underbrace{3(10)^2}_{V'(10)}\underbrace{(\pm 0.2)}_{\Delta x} = \pm 60$$

Thus the propagated error in computing the volume is approximately ± 60 cm^3. ▬

Error Propagation

If x_0 represents the measured value of a variable and $x_0 + \Delta x$ represents the exact value, then Δx is the **error in measurement**. The difference between $f(x + \Delta x)$ and $f(x)$ is called the **propagated error** and is defined by

$$\Delta f = f(x + \Delta x) - f(x)$$

Relative Error

The **relative error** is $\dfrac{df}{f} \approx \dfrac{\Delta f}{f}$.

Percentage Error

The **percentage error** is $100\dfrac{\Delta f}{f}$%.

In Example 5, the approximate propagated error in measuring the volume is ± 60, the approximate relative error is

$$\frac{\Delta V}{V} \approx \frac{\pm 60}{(10)^3} = \pm 0.06$$

and the approximate percentage error is $\pm 6\%$

EXAMPLE 6   Relative error and percentage error

The height of a certain right circular cylinder is twice the radius of the base. The radius is measured to be 17.3 cm, with a maximum measurement error of 0.02 cm. Estimate the corresponding propagated error, the relative error, and the percentage error when calculating the surface area.

Solution   We have (Figure 2.48)

$$S = \underbrace{2\pi r}_{\text{Circumference}} \overset{\text{Height}}{\overbrace{2r}} + \underbrace{\pi r^2}_{\text{Top}} + \underbrace{\pi r^2}_{\text{Bottom}} = 6\pi r^2$$

$$\underbrace{\qquad\qquad\qquad}_{\text{Lateral side}}$$

where r is the radius of the cylinder's base. Then the *propagated error* is

$$\Delta S \approx S'(r)\,\Delta r = 12\pi r\,\Delta r = 12\pi(17.3)(\pm 0.02) \approx \pm 13.0438927$$

Thus, the maximum error in the measurement of the surface area is about 13.04 cm². Is this a large or a small error? The *relative error* is found by computing the ratio

$$\frac{\Delta S}{S} = \frac{12\pi r\,\Delta r}{6\pi r^2} = 2r^{-1}\Delta r = 2(17.3)^{-1}(\pm 0.02) \approx \pm 0.0023121387$$

This tells us that the maximum error of approximately 13.04 is fairly small relative to the surface area S. The corresponding *percentage error* is found by

$$100\left|\frac{\Delta S}{S}\right| \approx 100(\pm 0.0023121) \pm 0.23121$$

This means that the percentage error is about $\pm 0.23\%$.

$$V = 2\pi r^3$$

Figure 2.48 Surface area of a right circular cylinder

■ MARGINAL ANALYSIS IN ECONOMICS

When the derivative is used in economics to study the rate of change of one quantity with respect to another, the procedure is called **marginal analysis.**

Marginal cost is the instantaneous rate of change of production cost, C, with respect to the number of units produced, x.

Marginal revenue is the instantaneous rate of change of revenue, R, with respect to the number of units produced, x.

In economics, we are often interested in knowing the change in cost or the change in revenue caused by a unit change in production. That is, if $\Delta x = 1$, then

Change in cost due to a unit change in x:
$$\Delta C = C(x + \Delta x) - C(x) = C(x + 1) - C(x)$$

Change in revenue due to a unit change in x:
$$\Delta R = R(x + \Delta x) - R(x) = R(x + 1) - R(x)$$

In practice, these functions are approximated using marginal cost and marginal revenue, respectively. Because $\Delta x = 1$ we have the following approximations:

$$\Delta C = C(x + \Delta x) - C(x) \approx C'(x)\,\Delta x = C'(x)$$

$$\Delta R = R(x + \Delta x) - R(x) \approx R'(x)\,\Delta x = R'(x)$$

▓ **What this says:** If $C(x)$ is the total cost of manufacturing x units and $R(x)$ is the total revenue from the sale of x units, then:

The **marginal cost,** $C'(x)$, approximates the cost of producing the $(x + 1)$st unit. The **marginal revenue,** $R'(x)$, approximates the revenue derived from the sale of the $(x + 1)$st unit.

EXAMPLE 7 **Approximation by marginal cost and marginal revenue**

A manufacturer estimates that when x units $(0 \le x \le 50)$ of a particular commodity are produced, the total cost will be

$$C(x) = \tfrac{1}{8}x^2 + 3x + 98$$

dollars and that all x items will be sold if the price used by the manufacturer is

$$p(x) = \tfrac{1}{3}(75 - x)$$

dollars per unit.

a. Find the marginal cost and the marginal revenue.
b. Use marginal cost to estimate the cost of producing the 9th unit.
c. What is the actual cost of producing the 9th unit?
d. Use marginal revenue to estimate the revenue derived from producing the 9th unit.
e. What is the actual revenue derived from producing the 9th unit?

Solution

a. The marginal cost is

$$C'(x) = \tfrac{1}{4}x + 3$$

To find the marginal revenue, we must first find the revenue function:

$$R(x) = xp(x) = x\left(\tfrac{1}{3}\right)(75 - x) = -\tfrac{1}{3}x^2 + 25x$$

Thus the marginal revenue is

$$R'(x) = -\tfrac{2}{3}x + 25$$

b. The cost of producing the 9th unit is the change in cost as x increases from 8 to 9 and is estimated by

$$C'(8) = \tfrac{1}{4}(8) + 3 = 5$$

We estimate the cost of producing the 9th unit to be $5.

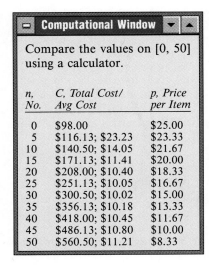

▭ Computational Window ▼ ▲

Compare the values on [0, 50] using a calculator.

n, No.	C, Total Cost/ Avg Cost	p, Price per Item
0	$98.00	$25.00
5	$116.13; $23.23	$23.33
10	$140.50; $14.05	$21.67
15	$171.13; $11.41	$20.00
20	$208.00; $10.40	$18.33
25	$251.13; $10.05	$16.67
30	$300.50; $10.02	$15.00
35	$356.13; $10.18	$13.33
40	$418.00; $10.45	$11.67
45	$486.13; $10.80	$10.00
50	$560.50; $11.21	$8.33

c. Actual cost is

$$\Delta C = C(9) - C(8) = \left[\tfrac{1}{8}(9)^2 + 3(9) + 98 \right] - \left[\tfrac{1}{8}(8)^2 + 3(8) + 98 \right]$$

$$= 5\tfrac{1}{8} = 5.125$$

The actual cost of producing the 9th unit (to the nearest cent) is $5.13. Notice that this is approximated fairly well by the marginal cost in part b.

d. The revenue (to the nearest cent) obtained from the sale of the 9th unit is approximated by the marginal revenue:

$$R'(8) = -\tfrac{2}{3}(8) + 25 = \tfrac{59}{3} \approx 19.67$$

e. The actual revenue (nearest cent) obtained from the sale of the 9th unit is

$$\Delta R = R(9) - R(8) = \tfrac{58}{3} \approx 19.33$$

Remember that the revenue from the sale of the 9th item is *not* the price of one item if 9 are sold. Rather, it is the additional revenue the company has earned by selling the 9th item—that is, the total revenue of 9 items minus the total revenue of 8 items.   ▬

PROBLEM SET 2.8

Ⓐ *In Problems 1–14*

a. *Use a calculator to approximate the value of the given quantity;*

b. *Choose an appropriate value for x and for Δx so that you can use the approximation formula*

$$f(x_0 + \Delta x) \approx f(x_0) + f'(x) \, \Delta x$$

Suggested values are given in Problems 1 and 2.

1. $\sqrt{17}$; let $f(x) = \sqrt{x}$ where $x_0 = 16$, $\Delta x = 1$.
2. $\sqrt[3]{28}$; let $f(x) = \sqrt[3]{x}$ where $x_0 = 27$, $\Delta x = 1$.

3. $\sqrt[4]{15}$ **4.** $\sqrt[3]{26}$

5. $\dfrac{1}{\sqrt{4.5}}$ **6.** $\dfrac{1}{\sqrt[3]{7.8}}$

7. $(1.1)^4$ **8.** 1.9^5
9. $\sqrt{0.99}$ **10.** 0.99^{100}

11. $\cos\left(\tfrac{\pi}{2} + 0.01\right)$ **12.** $\sin\left(\tfrac{\pi}{2} - 0.01\right)$

13. $\sin\left(\tfrac{\pi}{4} - 0.001\right)$ **14.** $\cos\left(\tfrac{\pi}{3} + 0.001\right)$

In Problems 15–20, use the approximation formula to approximate Δf, the change in f that occurs as x varies from a to b.
15. $f(x) = x^2 + x - 2$, $a = 1$, $b = 1.001$
16. $f(x) = 3x^2 - x + 2$, $a = 2$, $b = 2.01$
17. $f(x) = x^{10} + x^5$, $a = 1$, $b = 0.99$
18. $f(x) = 3x^7 + x^4$, $a = 1$, $b = 0.999$
19. $f(x) = \sqrt{x} + x^{3/2}$, $a = 4$, $b = 4.001$
20. $f(x) = \sqrt[3]{x} + x^2$, $a = 8$, $b = 7.99$

Find the differentials indicated in Problems 21–30.
21. $d(2x^3)$ **22.** $d(3 - 5x^2)$
23. $d(2\sqrt{x})$ **24.** $d(x^5 + \sqrt{x^2 + 5})$

25. $d(x \cos x)$ **26.** $d(x \sin 2x)$
27. $d\left(\dfrac{\tan 3x}{2x}\right)$ **28.** $d\left(\dfrac{x^2 \sec x}{x - 3}\right)$
29. $d(x\sqrt{x^2 - 1})$ **30.** $d\left(\dfrac{x - 5}{\sqrt{x + 4}}\right)$

Ⓑ 31. ■ **What Does This Say?** What is a differential?
32. ■ **What Does This Say?** Discuss error propagation, including relative and percentage error.
33. Use differentials to approximate the value of $(3.01)^5 - 2(3.01)^3 + 3(3.01)^2 - 2$ and determine the error as compared to the calculator value.
34. Use differentials to approximate the value of

$$\sqrt[4]{4{,}096} + \sqrt[3]{4{,}096} + 3\sqrt{4{,}096}$$

and determine the error as compared to the calculator value.

Use calculus to obtain the required estimates in Problems 35–49.
35. You measure the radius of a circle to be 12 cm and use the formula $A = \pi r^2$ to calculate the area. If your measurement of the radius is accurate to within 3%, approximately how accurate (to the nearest percent) is your calculation of the area?

36. Experiment Suppose a 12-oz can of Coke has a height of 4.5 in. Determine the radius with an accuracy to within 1%. Check your answer by examining a Coke can.

37. You measure the radius of a sphere to be 6 in. and use the formula $V = \tfrac{4}{3}\pi r^3$ to calculate the volume. If your measurement of the radius is accurate to within 1%, approximately how accurate (to the nearest percent) is your calculation of the volume?

38. It is projected that t years from now the circulation of a local newspaper will be

$$C(t) = 100t^2 + 400t + 5,000$$

Estimate the amount by which the circulation will increase during the next 6 months.

39. An environmental study of a certain community suggests that t years from now, the average level of carbon monoxide in the air will be

$$Q(t) = 0.05t^2 + 0.1t + 3.4$$

parts per million (ppm). By approximately how much will the carbon monoxide level change during the next 6 months?

40. A manufacturer's total cost (in dollars) is

$$C(q) = 0.1q^3 - 0.5q^2 + 500q + 200$$

when the level of production is q units. The current level of production is 4 units, and the manufacturer is planning to decrease this to 3.9 units. Estimate how the total cost will change as a result.

41. At a certain factory, the daily output is

$$Q(L) = 60,000L^{1/3}$$

units, where L denotes the size of the labor force measured in worker-hours. Currently 1,000 worker-hours of labor are used each day. Estimate the effect on output that will be produced if the labor force is cut to 940 worker-hours.

42. The speed of blood flowing along the central axis of a certain artery is

$$S(R) = 1.8 \times 10^5 R^2$$

cm/s, where R is the radius of the artery measured in cm. A medical researcher measures the radius of the artery to be 1.2×10^{-2} cm and makes an error of 5×10^{-4} cm. Estimate the amount by which the calculated value of the speed of the blood will differ from the true speed if the incorrect value of the radius is used in the formula.

43. A soccer ball made of leather $\frac{1}{8}$ in. thick has an inner diameter of $8\frac{1}{2}$ in. Estimate the volume of its leather shell.

44. A cubical box is to be constructed from three kinds of building materials. The material used in the four sides of the box costs 2¢/in.^{2}, the material in the bottom costs 3¢/in.^{2}, and the material used for the lid costs 4¢/in.^{2} Estimate the additional total cost of all the building materials if the length of a side is increased from 20 in. to 21 in.

45. In a healthy person of height x in., the average pulse rate in beats per minute is approximated by

$$P(x) = \frac{596}{\sqrt{x}} \qquad 30 \le x \le 100$$

Estimate the change in pulse rate that corresponds to a height change from 59 to 60 in.

46. A drug is injected into a patient's bloodstream. The concentration of the drug in the bloodstream t hours after the drug is injected is given by

$$C(t) = \frac{0.12t}{t^2 + t + 1}$$

milligrams per cubic centimeter. Estimate the change in concentration over the time period from 30 to 35 minutes after injection.

47. According to Poiseuille's law, the speed of blood flowing along the central axis of an artery of radius R is $S(R) = cR^2$, where c is a constant. What percentage error (rounded to the nearest percent) will you make in the calculation of $S(R)$ from this formula if you make a 1% error in the measurement of R?

48. The period of a pendulum is given by the formula

$$T = 2\pi\sqrt{\frac{L}{g}}$$

where L is the length of the pendulum in feet, $g = 32$ ft/s^2 is the acceleration due to gravity, and T is time in seconds. If the pendulum has been heated enough to increase its length by 0.4%, what is the approximate percentage change in its period?

49. A thin horizontal beam of alpha particles strikes a thin vertical foil, and the alpha particles that are scattered through an angle θ will travel along a cone of vertex angle θ as shown in Figure 2.49.

Time 1: Stream is focused.

Time 2: Stream hits foil.

Time 3: Stream is scattered after colliding with foil and disperses in the shape of a cone.

Figure 2.49 Paths of alpha particles

A vertical screen is placed at a fixed distance from the point of scattering. Physical theory predicts that the number N of alpha particles falling on a unit area of the screen is proportional to the reciprocal of $\sin^4\left(\frac{\theta}{2}\right)$. Suppose

$$N = \frac{1}{\sin^4\left(\dfrac{\theta}{2}\right)}$$

Estimate the change in the number of alpha particles per unit area of the screen if θ changes from 1 to 1.1.

50. Suppose the total cost of manufacturing q units is

$$C(q) = 3q^2 + q + 500$$

dollars.

a. Use marginal analysis to estimate the cost of manufacturing the 41st unit.

b. Compute the actual cost of manufacturing the 41st unit.

51. A manufacturer's total cost is

$$C(q) = 0.1q^3 - 5q^2 + 500q + 200$$

dollars, where q is the number of units produced.

a. Use marginal analysis to estimate the cost of manufacturing the 4th unit.

b. Compute the actual cost of manufacturing the 4th unit.

52. Suppose the total cost of producing x units of a particular commodity is

$$C(x) = \tfrac{1}{7}x^2 + 4x + 100$$

and that each unit of the commodity can be sold for

$$p(x) = \tfrac{1}{4}(80 - x)$$

dollars.

a. What is the marginal cost?

b. What is the price when the marginal cost is \$10?

c. Estimate the cost of producing the 11th unit.

d. Find the actual cost of producing the 11th unit.

53. Suppose the total cost of producing x units of a particular commodity is

$$C(x) = \tfrac{2}{5}x^2 + 3x + 10$$

and that each unit of the commodity can be sold for

$$p(x) = \tfrac{1}{5}(45 - x)$$

dollars.

a. What is the marginal cost?

b. What is the price when the marginal cost is \$23?

c. Estimate the cost of producing the 11th unit.

d. Find the actual cost of producing the 11th unit.

54. At a certain factory, the daily output is

$$Q(L) = 360L^{1/3}$$

units, where L is the size of the labor force measured in worker-hours. Currently, 1,000 worker-hours of labor are used each day. Use differentials to estimate the effect that one additional worker-hour will have on the daily output.

55. Suppose that when x units of a certain commodity are produced, the total cost is $C(x)$ and the total revenue is $R(x)$. Let $P(x)$ denote the total profit, and let

$$A(x) = \frac{C(x)}{x}$$

be the average cost.

a. Show that $P'(x) = 0$ when marginal revenue equals marginal cost.

b. Show that $A'(x) = 0$ when average cost equals marginal cost.

56. The radius R of a spherical ball is measured as 14 in.

a. If the maximum error in measuring R is $\tfrac{1}{8}$ in., what is the maximum propagated error in computing the volume V of the ball?

b. With what accuracy must the radius R be measured to guarantee an error of at most 2 in.^{3} in the calculated volume?

C **57.** Show that if h is sufficiently small, then

a. $\sqrt{1 + h}$ is approximately equal to $1 + \dfrac{h}{2}$.

b. $\dfrac{1}{1 + h}$ is approximately equal to $1 - h$.

58. If h is sufficiently small, find an approximate value for $\sqrt[n]{A^n + h}$ for constant A.

59. Tangent line approximations are useful only if Δx is small. Illustrate this fact by trying to approximate $\sqrt{97}$ by regarding 97 as being near 81 (instead of 100).

2.9 THE NEWTON–RAPHSON METHOD FOR APPROXIMATING ROOTS

IN THIS SECTION **The Newton–Raphson method, when the Newton–Raphson method fails**
Solving equations of the form $f(x) = 0$ can sometimes be very difficult, if not impossible. Often, the most we can hope for is to obtain approximate solutions by using a computer, calculator, or by following a regular procedure, such as the bisection method discussed in Section 1.7. Another such approximation procedure is called the *Newton–Raphson* method, because it was first used by Newton and then was refined and improved by Joseph Raphson (1648–1715). This method uses tangent lines to the graph of f to approximate roots of the equation $f(x) = 0$.

■ THE NEWTON–RAPHSON METHOD

The basic idea behind the Newton–Raphson method is illustrated in Figure 2.50. In this figure, r is a root of the equation $f(x) = 0$, x_0 is an approximation to r, and

x_1 is a better approximation obtained by taking the x-intercept of the line that is tangent to the graph of f at $(x_0, f(x_0))$.

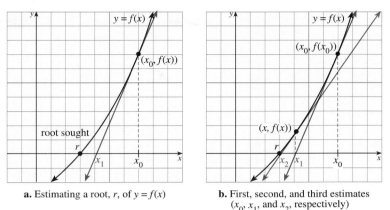

a. Estimating a root, r, of $y = f(x)$

b. First, second, and third estimates (x_0, x_1, and x_2, respectively)

Figure 2.50 The Newton–Raphson method

THEOREM 2.11   The Newton–Raphson method

To approximate a root of the equation $f(x) = 0$, start with a preliminary estimate x_0 and generate a sequence of increasingly accurate approximations $x_1, x_2, x_3, \ldots$ using the formula

$$x_{n+1} = x_n - \frac{f(x_n)}{f'(x_n)} \qquad f'(x_n) \neq 0$$

Either this sequence of approximations will approach a limit that is a root of the equations or else the sequence does not have a limit.

Proof: Rather than present a formal proof, we will present a geometric description of the procedure to help you understand what is happening. Let x_0 be an initial approximation such that $f'(x_0) \neq 0$. To find a formula for the improved approximation x_1, recall that the slope of the tangent line through $(x_0, f(x_0))$ is the derivative $f'(x_0)$. Therefore (see Figure 2.50b),

$$\underbrace{f'(x_0)}_{\text{Slope of the tangent through } (x_0,\, f(x_0))} = \frac{\Delta y}{\Delta x} = \frac{f(x_0) - 0}{x_0 - x_1}$$

or, equivalently (by solving the equation for x_1),

$$x_1 = x_0 - \frac{f(x_0)}{f'(x_0)} \qquad f'(x_0) \neq 0$$

If this procedure is repeated using x_1 as the initial approximation, an even better approximation may often be obtained (see Figure 2.50b). This approximation, x_2, is related to x_1 as x_1 was related to x_0. That is,

$$x_2 = x_1 - \frac{f(x_1)}{f'(x_1)}$$

If this process produces a limit, it can be continued until the desired degree of accuracy is obtained. In general, the nth approximation x_n is related to the $(n-1)$th by the formula

$$x_n = x_{n-1} - \frac{f(x_{n-1})}{f'(x_{n-1})}$$

EXAMPLE 1   Estimating a root with the Newton–Raphson method

Approximate a real root of the equation $x^3 + x + 1 = 0$ on $[-2, 2]$.

Solution   Let $f(x) = x^3 + x + 1$. Our goal is to find the root of the equation $f(x) = 0$. The derivative of f is $f'(x) = 3x^2 + 1$, and so

$$x - \frac{f(x)}{f'(x)} = x - \frac{x^3 + x + 1}{3x^2 + 1} = \frac{2x^3 - 1}{3x^2 + 1}$$

Thus, for $n = 0, 1, 2, 3, \ldots,$

$$x_{n+1} = x_n - \frac{f(x_n)}{f'(x_n)} = \frac{2x_n^3 - 1}{3x_n^2 + 1}$$

A convenient choice for the preliminary estimate is $x_0 = -1$. Then

$$x_1 = \frac{2x_0^3 - 1}{3x_0^2 + 1} = -0.75$$

You will need a calculator or a spreadsheet to help you with these calculations.

$$x_2 = \frac{2x_1^3 - 1}{3x_1^2 + 1} \approx -0.6860465$$

$$x_3 = \frac{2x_2^3 - 1}{3x_2^2 + 1} \approx -0.6823396$$

In general, we shall stop finding new estimates when successive approximations x_n and x_{n+1} are within a desired tolerance of each other. Specifically, if we wish to have the solutions to be within ε ($\varepsilon > 0$) of each other, we compute approximations until $|x_{n+1} - x_n| < \varepsilon$ is satisfied. Using the Newton–Raphson formula (Theorem 2.11), we see that this condition is equivalent to

$$|x_{n+1} - x_n| = \left| \frac{-f(x_n)}{f'(x_n)} \right| < \varepsilon$$

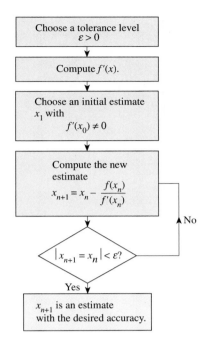

Figure 2.51 Flowchart for the Newton–Raphson method

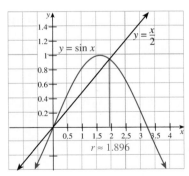

Figure 2.52 The Newton–Raphson method applied to the equation $\sin x = \frac{x}{2}$

⊘ Do not round yet; work with all the accuracy you have available.

$$|x_2 - x_1| \approx 0.0054839 \;⊘$$

Now we can describe a step-by-step procedure for applying the Newton–Raphson method. A flow chart for the method appears in Figure 2.51.

Procedure for Applying the Newton–Raphson Method to Solve the Equation $f(x) = 0$

1. Choose a number $\varepsilon > 0$ that determines the allowable tolerance for estimated solutions.
2. Compute $f'(x)$ and choose a number x_0 (with $f'(x_0) \neq 0$) "close" to a solution of $f(x) = 0$ as an initial estimate.
3. Compute a new approximation with the formula

$$x_{n+1} = x_n - \frac{f(x_n)}{f'(x_n)}$$

4. Repeat step 3 until $|x_{n+1} - x_n| < \varepsilon$. The estimate $\bar{x} = x_n$ then has the required accuracy.

EXAMPLE 2 The Newton–Raphson method with error analysis

Estimate a solution of the equation $\sin x = \frac{x}{2}$. Use the Newton–Raphson method until successive approximations agree to 3 decimal places.

Solution Geometrically, we are looking for the x-coordinate of the point where the curve $y = \sin x$ intersects the line $y = \frac{1}{2}x$, as shown in Figure 2.52. If we set $f(x) = x - 2\sin x$, the problem can be restated as "solve $f(x) = 0$." We find $f'(x) = 1 - 2\cos x$, and

$$x_{n+1} = x_n - \frac{f(x_n)}{f'(x_n)} = x_n - \frac{x_n - 2\sin x_n}{1 - 2\cos x_n}$$

As a first approximation we choose $x_0 = 2$. Then,

$$x_1 = 2 - \frac{2 - 2\sin 2}{1 - 2\cos 2} \approx 1.9009956; \; |x_1 - x_0| \approx 0.0990044$$

$$x_2 = 1.9009956 - \frac{1.9009956 - 2\sin 1.9009956}{1 - 2\cos 1.9009956} \approx 1.8955116$$

$$x_3 = 1.8955116 - \frac{1.8955116 - 2\sin 1.8955116}{1 - 2\cos 1.8955116} \approx 1.8954943;$$

$$|x_3 - x_2| \approx 0.0000174$$

The error for x_3 is less than the required three decimal places, so the approximate solution is $x \approx 1.895$.

■ WHEN THE NEWTON–RAPHSON METHOD FAILS

We have already observed that for the Newton–Raphson method to work, we cannot have $f'(x_n) = 0$ for any estimate of x_n; and the method may also fail if the initial estimate x_0 is too far from the desired solution of $f(x) = 0$, as shown in Figure 2.53b. Usually, these problems can be overcome by simply making another choice for the initial estimate, x_0. However, there are other more troublesome ways for the method to fail. In particular, it can happen that no matter how we choose x_0, the method will produce a sequence of estimates $x_1, x_2, x_3, \ldots$ such that $|x_{n+1} - x_n|$ will get larger instead of smaller (see Figure 2.53b) as n increases. This case is illustrated by the following example.

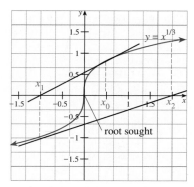

a. The Newton–Raphson method gives an approximation for the root sought.

b. The Newton–Raphson method fails.

Figure 2.53 The Newton–Raphson method (part a) might fail (part b).

EXAMPLE 3 Failure of the Newton–Raphson method

Try to find a zero for the function $f(x) = x^{1/3}$ by using the Newton–Raphson method.

Solution According to the Newton–Raphson method,

$$x_{n+1} = x_n - \frac{f(x_n)}{f'(x_n)} = x_n - \frac{x_n^{1/3}}{\frac{1}{3}x_n^{-2/3}} = x_n - 3x_n = -2x_n$$

We see that x_{n+1} is always twice as big as x_n in absolute value. The graph of $f(x) = x^{1/3}$ is shown in Figure 2.53b. Notice how the shape of the graph causes the estimates to disperse instead of converging. That is, the difference of successive estimates $|x_{n+1} - x_n|$ does not decrease as n increases. ■

The sequence of estimates $x_1, x_2, x_3, \ldots$ produced by the Newton–Raphson method is said to **converge** to a root of $f(x) = 0$ if for any choice of $\varepsilon > 0$, we have $|x_{n+1} - x_n| < \varepsilon$ for n sufficiently large. In a more advanced course, called numerical analysis, it is shown that the sequence of estimates will converge to a solution if

$$\left| \frac{f(x)f''(x)}{[f'(x)]^2} \right| < 1$$

on an open interval containing the solution. Note that the function $f(x) = x^{1/3}$ fails the test because we have

$$f'(x) = \tfrac{1}{3}x^{-2/3} \quad \text{and} \quad f''(x) = -\tfrac{2}{9}x^{-5/3}$$

so that (for $x \neq 0$)

$$\left| \frac{f(x)f''(x)}{[f'(x)]^2} \right| = \left| \frac{x^{1/3}\left(-\frac{2}{9}\right)x^{-5/3}}{\left[\frac{1}{3}x^{-2/3}\right]^2} \right| = |-2| = 2$$

which is not less than 1.

PROBLEM SET 2.9

A *Find estimate x_3 in the Newton–Raphson method for $f(x) = 0$ with the initial estimate x_0 given in Problems 1–10.*

1. $f(x) = x^3 - 29$ for $x_0 = 3$
2. $f(x) = x^3 - 29$ for $x_0 = 3.1$
3. $f(x) = x^3 - 3$ for $x_0 = 1$
4. $f(x) = x^5 - 33$ for $x_0 = 2$
5. $f(x) = x^4 - 16.2$ for $x_0 = 2$
6. $f(x) = x^3 - 17$ for $x_0 = 2$
7. $f(x) = \sin x$ for $x_0 = 1$
8. $f(x) = \tan x$ for $x_0 = 0.2$
9. $f(x) = x^3 + 2x - 1$ for $x_0 = 0$
10. $f(x) = x^5 - x^4 - x^2 + 13$ for $x_0 = 2$

B 11. ■ **What Does This Say?** Discuss the Newton–Raphson method. Include a discussion of the shortcomings of this method.

Use the Newton–Raphson method to estimate a solution of the equations on the intervals given in Problems 12–19. In each case, continue the process until two successive approximations differ by less than $\varepsilon = 0.001$.

12. $x^3 - 3x^2 + 3 = 0$ on $(2, 3)$

13. $x^3 + 3x - 1 = 0$ on $(0, 1)$

14. $x^3 + 2x - 1 = 0$ on $(0, 1)$

15. $x^3 + 2x^2 - x + 1 = 0$ on $(-3, -2)$

16. $\sqrt[3]{x + 2} = x - 1$ on $[2, 4]$

17. $\sqrt[3]{x - 3} = x + 1$ on $[-3, -2]$

18. $\cos x = x - 1$ on $\left[0, \frac{\pi}{2}\right]$ **19.** $\sin x = x^2$ on $(0, \pi)$

Show that the Newton–Raphson method fails in Problems 20–23 for the equation $f(x) = 0$ and the initial estimate x_0.

20. $f(x) = 9x^2 + 2x + 3$ for $x_0 = -\frac{1}{9}$

21. $f(x) = 1 - \frac{1}{x}$ for $x_0 = 2$ **22.** $f(x) = x^{1/6}$ for any $x_0 \neq 0$

23. $f(x) = 9x^4 - 16x^3 - 36x^2 + 96x - 60$ for $x_0 = \frac{4}{3}$

24. Use the Newton–Raphson method to estimate a solution of the equation

$$\sin(x^3 + 2) = \frac{1}{x} \text{ for } 0 < x < 2$$

25. Use the Newton–Raphson method to estimate a solution to the equation

$$x^3 - 3x = \cos x - \sin x$$

on the interval $\left[0, \frac{\pi}{2}\right]$.

26. Consider the equation $\cos x = \frac{x}{6}$.

a. Sketch the graphs of $y = \cos x$ and $y = \frac{x}{6}$. How many times do these graphs intersect?

b. Use the Newton–Raphson method to estimate each root of the equation $\cos x = \frac{x}{6}$.

27. First show that there exists at least one solution of the equation $x^6 - x^5 + x^3 = 3$. *Hint:* Recall the intermediate value theorem. Then use the Newton–Raphson method to estimate a root of this equation.

28. A wire 10 inches long is to be cut into two pieces, one of which is bent to form a square and the other to form a circle. If the circle is to have twice the area of the square, where should the wire be cut? Use the Newton–Raphson method.

In Problems 29–30, use the Newton–Raphson method to estimate at least one root of the given equation.

29. $4x^3 + 3x^2 - 12x + 7 = 0$

30. $13x^5 + x^4 - 15x^3 + 8x^2 + 4x - 7 = 0$

In Problems 31 and 32, $s(t)$ is the displacement of a moving object. Use the Newton–Raphson method to estimate a value of t where the object is stationary (that is, where $s'(t) = 0$).

31. $s(t) = 3t^4 + 4t^3 - 30t^2 + t + 4$ **32.** $s(t) = t^3 - 2t^2 - 5t + 3$

33. Let $f(x) = -2x^4 + 3x^2 + \frac{11}{8}$.

a. Show that the equation $f(x) = 0$ has at least 2 solutions. *Hint:* Use the intermediate value theorem.

b. Show that the Newton–Raphson method fails if you choose $x_0 = \frac{1}{2}$ as the initial estimate. *Hint:* You should obtain $x_1 = -x_0$; $x_2 = x_0$; . . . .

34. The volume of a spherical segment is given by

$$V = \frac{\pi}{3}H^2(3R - H)$$

where R is the radius of the sphere and H is the height of the segment, as shown in Figure 2.54.

Figure 2.54 Problem 34

a. If $V = 8$ and $R = 2$, use the Newton–Raphson method to estimate the corresponding H.

b. A celebrated problem of the Greek geometer Archimedes (ca. 287–212 B.C.) asks where a sphere should be cut in order to divide it into two pieces whose volumes have a given ratio. Show that if a plane at distance x_c from the center of a sphere with $R = 1$ divides the sphere into two parts, one with volume *twice* that of the other, then $3x_c^3 - 9x_c^2 - 4 = 0$. Use the Newton–Raphson method to estimate x_c.

c. In part b, suppose the plane is located so that it divides the sphere in the ratio of 1:3. Find an equation for x_c, and estimate the value of x_c by the Newton–Raphson method.

▭ Computational Window ▼ ▲

In Problems 35–36 we look at the speed at which Newton's method converges. Let $e_n = |x_{\text{exact}} - x_n|$ denote the error after n applications of Newton's method. Typically, the error in each iteration tends to be the square of the previous error; that is, $e_{n+1} = Ke_n^2$ where K is some constant. You are to investigate this relationship.

35. Do 3 or 4 iterations of Newton's method toward finding the positive root of $x^2 - 2 = 0$, starting with $x_0 = 2$. You should see the above convergence pattern. What is K?

36. Take several iterations of Newton's method in looking for the obvious solution of $(x - 5)^2 = 0$, starting with $x_0 = 4$. Comment on the rate of convergence. Why is this problem not "typical" in its rate of convergence?

C 37. THINK TANK PROBLEM Let $f(x) = -x^4 + x^2 + A$ for constant A. What value of A should be chosen that guarantees that if $x_0 = \frac{1}{3}$ is chosen as the initial estimate, the Newton–Raphson method produces $x_1 = -x_0$; $x_2 = x_0$; $x_3 = -x_0$; . . . , as in Problem 33b?

38. Can you solve the equation $\sqrt{x} = 0$ using the Newton–Raphson method with the initial estimate $x_0 = 0.05$? Does it make any difference if we choose another initial estimate (other than $x_0 = 0$)?

39. Suppose that when we try to use the Newton–Raphson method to approximate a solution of $f(x) = 0$, we find that $f(x_n) = 0$, but $f'(x_n) \neq 0$ for some x_n. What does this imply about

$$x_{n+1}, x_{n+2}, \ldots ?$$

Explain.

40. The ancient Babylonians (ca. 1700 B.C.) approximated $\sqrt{N}$ by applying the formula

$$x_{n+1} = \tfrac{1}{2}\left(x_n + \frac{N}{x_n}\right) \text{ for } n, = 1, 2, \ldots$$

a. Apply the Newton–Raphson method to $f(x) = x^2 - N$ to justify this formula.

b. Apply the formula to estimate $\sqrt{1{,}265}$ correct to 5 decimal places.

41. Use the Newton–Raphson method to derive a formula like the one in Problem 40 for the reciprocal function $f(x) = 1/x$. Then apply your formula to find the reciprocal

$$\frac{1}{2.355673}$$

correct to 5 decimal places. This method permits you to do a division just by doing a multiplication.

CHAPTER 2 REVIEW

> **IN THIS REVIEW**   **Proficiency examination; supplementary problems**
> Problems 1–14 of the proficiency examination test your knowledge of the concepts of this chapter, and Problems 15–25 test your understanding of those concepts by asking you to work sample practice problems. The supplementary problems present questions relating to the material of this chapter in a wide variety of settings.

PROFICIENCY EXAMINATION

Concept Problems

1. What is the slope of a tangent? How does this compare to the slope of a secant?
2. Define the derivative of a function.
3. What is a normal line to a graph?
4. State the following derivative rules.

   a. constant rule **b.** power rule   **c.** constant multiple

   d. sum rule   **e.** difference rule **f.** linearity rule

   g. product rule **h.** quotient rule   **i.** cosine rule

   j. sine rule   **k.** tangent rule   **l.** secant rule

   m. cosecant rule **n.** cotangent rule

5. What is a higher derivative? List some of the different notations for higher derivatives.
6. How do you find the velocity and the acceleration for an object with displacement $s(t)$?
7. State the chain rule.
8. Outline a procedure for implicit differentiation.
9. Outline a procedure for solving related rate problems.
10. State the tangent line approximation formula.
11. What is meant by marginal analysis?
12. Define the differential of x and the differential of y for a function $y = f(x)$. Draw a sketch showing Δx, Δy, dx, and dy.
13. Define the terms propagated error, relative error, and percentage error.
14. What is the Newton–Raphson method?

Practice Problems

Find $\dfrac{dy}{dx}$ in Problems 15–19.

15. $y = x^3 + x\sqrt{x} + \cos 2x$ **16.** $y = \left(\sqrt{3}x + \dfrac{3}{x^2}\right)^{-4}$

17. $y = \sqrt{\sin(3 - x^2)}$ **18.** $xy + y^3 = 10$

19. $y = \sin^2(x^{10} + \sqrt{x}) + \cos^2(x^{10} + \sqrt{x})$

20. Find $\dfrac{dy^2}{dx^2}$, where $x^2 + xy - 2y^2 = 4$.

21. Use the definition of derivative to find $\dfrac{d}{dx}(x - 3x^2)$.

22. Find the equation of the tangent to the graph of

$$y = (x^2 + 3x - 2)(7 - 3x) \text{ at } (1, 8)$$

23. Let $f(x) = \sin^2\left(\dfrac{\pi x}{4}\right)$. Find equations of the tangent and the normal line to the graph of f at $x = 1$.

24. A rock tossed into a stream causes a circular ripple of water whose radius increases at a constant rate of 0.5 ft/s. How fast is the area contained inside of the ripple changing when the radius is 2 ft?

25. Use the Newton–Raphson method to estimate a solution of the equation $x^3 - x^2 - x = 13$ on $[0, 3]$. Continue the process until two successive approximations differ by less than 0.001.

SUPPLEMENTARY PROBLEMS

Find the derivative $\dfrac{dy}{dx}$ in Problems 1–24.

1. $y = x^4 + 3x^2 - 7x + 5$

2. $y = x^5 + 3x^3 - 11$

3. $y = \sqrt{\dfrac{x^2 - 1}{x^2 - 5}}$

4. $y = \dfrac{1 - \cos 3x}{x + \sin x}$

5. $2x^2 - xy + 2y = 5$

6. $y = x\sqrt{\sin(3 - x^2)}$

7. $y = \left(\sqrt{3x} + \dfrac{3}{x^2}\right)^{-4}$

8. $y = (x^2 + 3x - 5)^7$.

9. $y = (x^3 + x)^{10}$

10. $y = \sqrt{x}(x^2 + 5)^{10}$

11. $y = \sqrt[3]{x}(x^3 + 1)^5$

12. $y = (x^3 + 3)^5(x^3 - 5)^8$

13. $y = (x^4 - 1)^{10}(2x^4 + 3)^7$

14. $y = \sqrt{\sin 5x}$

15. $y = \sqrt{\cos \sqrt{x}}$

16. $y = (\sin x + \cos x)^3$

17. $y = (\sqrt{x} + \sqrt[3]{x})^5$

18. $y = \sqrt{\dfrac{x^3 - x}{4 - x^2}}$

19. $y = \sin(\sin x)$

20. $y = \cos(\sin x)$

21. $x^{1/2} + y^{1/2} = x$

22. $4x^2 - 16y^2 = 64$

23. $\sin xy = y + x$

24. $\sin(x + y) + \cos(x - y) = xy$

Find $\dfrac{dy^2}{dx^2}$ in Problems 25–28.

25. $y = x^5 - 5x^4 + 7x^3 - 3x^2 + 17$

26. $y = \dfrac{x - 5}{2x + 3} + (3x - 1)^2$

27. $x^2 + y^3 = 10$

28. $x^2 + \sin y = 2$

In Problems 29–36, find an equation of the tangent to the curve at the indicated point.

29. $y = x^4 - 7x^3 + x^2 - 3$ at $(0, -3)$

30. $y = (3x^2 + 5x - 7)^3$ where $x = 1$

31. $y = x \cos x$ where $x = \dfrac{\pi}{2}$

32. $y = \dfrac{\sin x}{\sec x \tan x}$ where $x = \pi$

33. $xy^2 + x^2y = 2$ at $(1, 1)$

34. $y = (x^3 - 3x^2 + 4)^2$ where $x = 1$

35. $y = \dfrac{3x - 4}{3x^2 + x - 5}$ where $x = 1$

36. $x^{2/3} + y^{2/3} = 2$ at $(1, 1)$

37. Let $f(x) = (x^3 - x^2 + 2x - 1)^4$. Find equations of the tangent and normal lines to the graph of f at $x = 1$.

38. Find equations for the tangent and normal lines to the graph of $y = \left(2x + \dfrac{1}{x}\right)^3$ at the point $(1, 27)$.

39. Use the chain rule to find $\dfrac{dy}{dt}$ and $\dfrac{d^2y}{dt^2}$ when $y = x^3 - 7x$ and $x = t \sin t$.

40. Find $f''(x)$ if $f(x) = x^2\sin x^2$.

41. Find f', f'', f''' and $f^{(4)}$ if $f(x) = x^4 - \dfrac{1}{x^4}$.

42. Find f', f'', and f''' if $f(x) = x(x^2 + 1)^{7/2}$.

43. Let
$$f(x) = \sqrt[3]{\dfrac{x^4 + 1}{x^4 - 2}}.$$
Find $f'(x)$ by using implicit differentiation to differentiate $[f(x)]^3$.

44. Find y' and y'' if $x^3y^3 + x - y = 1$. For y'', leave your answer in terms of x, y, and y'.

45. Find y' and y'' if $x^2 + 4xy - y^2 = 8$. Your answer may involve x and y, but not y'.

46. Find the derivative of
$$f(x) = \begin{cases} x^2 + 5x + 4 & \text{for } x \le 0 \\ 5x + 4 & \text{for } 0 < x < 6 \\ x^2 - 2 & \text{for } x \ge 6 \end{cases}$$

47. Find equations of the tangent and normal lines to the curve given by $x^3 - y^3 = 2xy$ at the point $(-1, 1)$.

48. Use differentials to approximate $(16.01)^{3/2} + 2\sqrt{16.01}$.

49. Use differentials to approximate $\cos \dfrac{101\pi}{600}$. Use the approximations $\sqrt{3} \approx 1.7321$ and $\pi \approx 3.1416$.

50. Use differentials to estimate the change in the volume of a cone if the height of the cone is increased from 10 cm to 10.01 cm while the radius of the base stays fixed at 2 cm.

51. The newspaper clipping below was taken from the *Wall Street Journal*. Restate the headline, "Effective Marginal Tax Rates," using calculus.

*Senate Finance Committee
Source: Harris Bank Economic Research Office

52. On New Year's Eve, a network TV camera is focusing on the descent of a lighted ball from the top of a building that is 600 ft away. The ball is falling at the rate of 20 ft/min. At what rate is the angle of elevation of the camera's line of sight changing with respect to time when the ball is 800 ft from the ground?

53. Suppose f is a differentiable function whose derivative satisfies $f'(x) = 2x^2 + 3$. Find $\dfrac{d}{dx}f(x^3 - 1)$.

54. Suppose f is a differentiable function such that $f'(x) = x^2 + x$. Find $\dfrac{d}{dx} f(x^2 + x)$.

55. Let $f(x) = 3x^2 + 1$ for all x. Use the chain rule to find $\dfrac{d}{dx}(f \circ f)(x)$.

56. Let $f(x) = \sin 2x + \cos 3x$ and $g(x) = x^2$. Use the chain rule to find $\dfrac{d}{dx}(f \circ g)(x)$.

57. Let

$$f(x) = \begin{cases} x \sin\dfrac{1}{x} & \text{if } x \neq 0 \\ 0 & \text{if } x = 0 \end{cases}$$

Use the definition of the derivative to find $f'(x)$ if it exists.

58. A car and a truck leave an intersection at the same time. The car travels north at 60 mi/hr and the truck travels east at 45 mi/hr. How fast is the distance between them changing after 45 minutes?

59. A truck leaves an intersection going north at 45 mi/h. At the same time a car leaves the intersection and is traveling east at 60 mi/hr. How fast is the distance between the car and the truck changing after 1 hour?

60. A spherical balloon is being filled with air in such a way that its radius is increasing at a constant rate of 2 cm/s. At what rate is the volume of the balloon increasing at the instant when its surface has area 4π cm^2?

61. A block of ice in the shape of a cube originally having volume 1,000 cm^3 is melting in such a way that the length of each of its edges is decreasing at the rate of 1 cm/hr. At what rate is its surface area decreasing at the time its volume is 27 cm^3? Assume that the block of ice maintains its cubical shape.

62. Show that the rate of change of the area of a circle with respect to its radius is equal to the circumference.

63. A charged particle is projected into a linear accelerator. The particle undergoes a constant acceleration that changes its velocity from 1,200 m/s to 6,000 m/s in 2×10^{-3} sec. Find the acceleration of the particle.

64. A rocket is launched vertically from a point on the ground that is 3,000 horizontal feet from an observer with binoculars. If the rocket is rising vertically at the rate of 750 ft/s at the instant it is 4,000 ft above the ground, how fast must the observer change the angle of elevation of her line of sight in order to keep the rocket in sight at that instant?

65. Assume that a certain artery in the body is a circular tube whose cross section has radius 1.2 mm. Fat deposits are observed to build up uniformly on the inside wall of the artery. Find the rate at which the cross-sectional area of the artery is decreasing relative to the thickness of the fat deposit at the instant when the deposit is 0.3 mm thick.

66. A processor who sells a certain raw material has analyzed the market and determined that the unit price should be

$$p(x) = 60 - x^2$$

(thousand dollars) for x tons ($0 \leq x \leq 7$) produced. Estimate the change in the unit price that accompanies each change in sales:

a. From 2 tons to 2.05 tons

b. From 2 tons to 2.1 tons

c. From 2 tons to 1.95 tons

67. A company sends out a truck to deliver its products. When traveling at a constant rate of x mi/hr (with $x \geq 5$), the truck consumes gasoline at the rate of

$$\frac{1}{300}\left(\frac{1,500}{x} + x\right)$$

gal/mi. The driver is paid \$16 per hour to drive the truck 300 mi. Gasoline costs \$2 per gallon.

a. Find an expression for the total cost $C(x)$ of the trip.

b. Use increments to estimate the additional cost if the truck is driven at 57 mi/hr instead of 55 mi/hr.

68. A viewer standing at ground level and 30 ft from a platform watches an object rise from that platform at the constant rate of 3 ft/s. (See Figure 2.55.) How fast is the angle of sight between the viewer and the object changing at the instant when $\theta = \frac{\pi}{4}$?

Figure 2.55 Problem 68

69. A particle of mass m moves along the x-axis. The velocity $v = \dfrac{dx}{dt}$ and position $x = x(t)$ satisfy the equation

$$m(v^2 - v_0{}^2) = k(x_0{}^2 - x^2)$$

where k, x_0, and v_0 are positive constants. The force F acting on the object is defined by $F = ma$, where a is the object's acceleration. Show that $F = -kx$.

70. Let f and g be differentiable functions such that $f[g(x)] = x$ and $g[f(x)] = x$ for all x (such functions are said to be inverses). Show that

$$\frac{dg}{dx} = \frac{1}{\dfrac{df}{dx}}$$

71. A baseball player is stealing second base. He runs at 30 ft/s and when he is 25 ft from second base, the catcher, while standing at home plate, throws the ball toward the base at a speed of 120 ft/s. At what rate is the distance between the ball and the player changing at the time the ball is thrown?

90 ft

72. A rod $\overline{OA}$ 2 m long is rotating counterclockwise in a plane about O at the rate of 3 rev/s as shown in Figure 2.56.

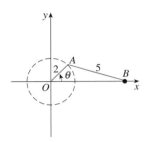

Figure 2.56 Problem 72

The rod $\overline{AB}$ is attached to $\overline{OA}$, and the end B slides along the x-axis. Suppose $\overline{AB}$ is 5 meters long. What are the velocity and the acceleration of the motion of the point B along the x-axis?

73. The ideal gas law states that for an ideal gas, $PV = kT$ where P is the pressure, V is the volume, T is the temperature, and k is a constant. Suppose the temperature is kept fixed at 100 °C, and the pressure decreases at the rate of 7 lb/in.^{2} per min. At what rate is the volume changing at the instant the pressure is 25 lb/in.^{2} and the volume is 30 in.^{3}?

Computational Window ▼ ▲

74. This problem deals with the function
$$f(x) = \frac{x^3 - 2.1x^2 + x - 2}{x^6 + 1}$$

a. Prove that f has at least one zero in the interval $[-10, 10]$.

b. Graphically show that f has only one zero in this interval. *Note:* This will require some careful specification of domains and ranges.

c. Pick a reasonable starting x_0-value (for example, the closest integer), and do enough iterations of the Newton–Raphson method to get at least six significant figure precision. Hand in computer outputs showing all the x_n values.

d. Pick x_0 bigger (for example, $x_0 = 3$, or larger). Do several iterations and explain the results.

e. Try x_0 around 0.5, and explain what happens, and why it happens.

f. Try x_0 around -1.0 and tell what happens, and why.

75. Chaos Here we investigate the notion of *chaos* using the Newton–Raphson method. Basically, in mathematical terms, this means that the outcome of a problem is extremely sensitive to starting values. Here we apply the Newton–Raphson method (unnecessarily) to the function

$$f(x) = x^3 - x = x(x - 1)(x + 1)$$

Investigate what happens as we change the starting value, x_0.

a. Two important x-values in our study are

$$s_3 = \frac{1}{\sqrt{3}} \quad \text{and} \quad s_5 = \frac{1}{\sqrt{5}}$$

One would *not* want to pick x_0 as either $\pm s_3$. Why not? Also, what happens if one picks $x_0 = s_5$? That is, what are $x_1, x_2, \ldots$?

b. Generate a good plot of $f(x)$ on $[-2, 2]$. Explain from the plots why you would *expect* that an initial value $x_0 > s_3$ would lead to $\lim_{n \to \infty} x_n = 1$. (Also, by symmetry, $x_0 < -s_3$ leads to $\lim_{n \to \infty} x_n = -1$).

c. Explain why if $|x_0| < s_5$, you would expect $x_n \to 0$.

d. Numerically verify your assertions of parts **b** and **c**.

e. Now to see the "chaos," use the following x_0 values and take 6 to 10 iterations, until convergence occurs, and report what happens: 0.448955; 0.447503; 0.447262; 0.447222; 0.4472215; 0.4472213.

76. P<small>UTNAM</small> E<small>XAMINATION</small> P<small>ROBLEM</small> Suppose $f(x) = ax^2 + bx + c$, where a, b, and c are real numbers and $|f(x)| \le 1$ for $x \le 1$. Show that $|f'(x)| \le 4$ for $|x| \le 1$.

77. P<small>UTNAM</small> E<small>XAMINATION</small> P<small>ROBLEM</small> A point P is taken on the curve $y = x^3$. The tangent at P meets the curve again at Q. Prove that the slope of the curve at Q is four times the slope at P.

78. P<small>UTNAM</small> E<small>XAMINATION</small> P<small>ROBLEM</small> A particle of unit mass moves on a straight line under the action of a force that is a function $f(v)$ of the velocity v of the particle, but the form of this function is not known. A motion is observed, and the distance x covered in time t is found to be related to t by the formula $x = at + bt^2 + ct^3$, where a, b, and c have numerical values determined by observation of the motion. Find the function $f(v)$ for the range of v covered by this experiment.

"Ups and Downs"

Mathematics is one of the oldest of the sciences; it is also one of the most active, for its strength is the vigor of perpetual youth.

A. R. Forsyth
Nature 84 (1910): 285

This project is to be done in groups of three or four students. Each group will submit a single written report.

You have been hired by Two Flags to help with the design of their new roller coaster. You are to plan the path design of ups and downs for a straight stretch with horizontal length of 185 ft. One possible design is shown below, and here is the information you will need:

a. There must be a support every 10 ft.

b. The descent can be no steeper than 80° at any point (angles refer to the angle that the path makes with a horizontal).

c. The design must start with a 45° incline.

d. The amount of material needed for a support is the square of the height of the support. For example, a support that is 20 ft high requires $20^2 = 400$ ft of material.

We also define the **thrill** of the coaster as the sum of the angle of steepest descent in each fall in radians plus the number of tops.

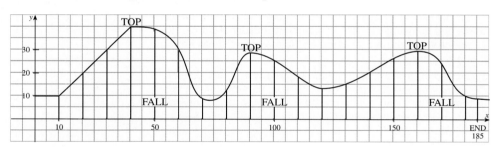

The whole of mathematics consists in the organization of a series of aids to the imagination in the process of reasoning.

A. N. Whitehead
Universal Algebra (Cambridge, 1898), p. 12

Your paper should include, but is not limited to, the following concerns: You should design two roller coaster paths; one should be the most thrilling, and the other should use the least material for supports. Your paper should address where the path is increasing at an increasing rate, and decreasing at a decreasing rate. You should address the safety criteria (a-d listed above) and show the graphs of the path, the slope, and the rate of change of the slope.

*This group project is from Diane Schwartz from Ithaca College, Ithaca, N.Y.

Additional Applications of the Derivative

PREVIEW

In Chapter 2, we used the derivative to find tangent lines and to compute rates of change. The primary goal of this chapter is to examine the use of calculus in curve sketching, optimization, and other applications.

■ PERSPECTIVE

Homing pigeons and certain other birds are known to avoid flying over large bodies of water whenever possible. The reason for this behavior is not entirely known. However, it is reasonable to speculate that it may have something to do with minimizing the energy expended in flight, because the air over a lake is often "heavier" than that over land. Suppose a pigeon is released from a boat at point B on the lake shown in the accompanying figure.* It will fly to its loft at point L on the lakeshore by heading across water to a point P on the shore and then flying directly from P to L along the shore. If the pigeon expends e_w units of energy per mile over water and e_L units over land, where should P be located in order to minimize the total energy expended in flight?†

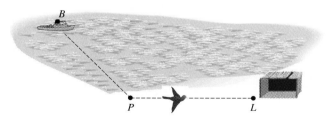

Optimization (finding the maximum or minimum values) is one of the most important applications we will study in calculus. From maximizing profit and minimizing cost, to maximizing the strength of a structure or minimizing the distance traveled, it is easy to think of optimization problems that can be solved with calculus. Optimization problems are considered in Sections 3.7 and 3.8.

*Edward Batschelet, *Introduction to Mathematics for Life Scientists,* 2nd ed. (New York: Springer-Verlag, 19), pp. 276–277.
†See Problem 25, Section 3.8.

3.1 EXTREME VALUES OF A CONTINUOUS FUNCTION

IN THIS SECTION Extreme value theorem, relative extrema, absolute extrema, optimization

It is often very important to know what the largest and smallest values of a function are and where these extreme values occur. In this section, we shall see how the derivative may be used to locate extreme values.

■ EXTREME VALUE THEOREM

One of the principal goals of calculus is to investigate the behavior of various functions. As part of this investigation, we will be laying the groundwork for solving a large class of problems that involve finding the maximum or minimum value of a function. Such problems are called **optimization problems.** Let us begin by introducing some useful terminology.

Absolute Maximum
Absolute Minimum

Let f be a function defined on a set D that contains the number c. Then

$f(c)$ is the **absolute maximum** of f on D if
$$f(c) \geq f(x) \text{ for all } x \text{ in } D$$
$f(c)$ is the **absolute minimum** of f on D if
$$f(c) \leq f(x) \text{ for all } x \text{ in } D$$

a. The continuous function $g(x) = x$ has no extrema on the open interval (0, 1).

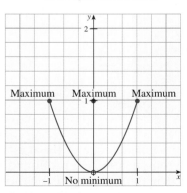

b. The discontinuous function h has a maximum, but not a minimum on the closed interval [−1, 1].

Figure 3.1 Functions that lack one or both extreme values

Together, the absolute maximum and minimum of f on the interval I are called the **extreme values,** or the **absolute extrema,** of f on I. A function does not necessarily have extreme values on a given interval. For instance, the continuous function $g(x) = x$ has neither a maximum nor a minimum on the open interval (0, 1), as shown in Figure 3.1a.

The discontinuous function defined by

$$h(x) = \begin{cases} x^2 & \text{for } x \neq 0 \\ 1 & \text{for } x = 0 \end{cases}$$

has a maximum on the closed interval [−1, 1] but no minimum, as shown in Figure 3.1b. Incidentally, this graph also illustrates the fact that a function may assume an absolute extremum at more than one point. In this case, the maximum is at (−1, 1), (0, 1), and (1, 1). If a function f is continuous and the interval I is closed and bounded, it can be shown that both an absolute maximum and an absolute minimum *must* occur. This result, called the **extreme value theorem,** plays an important role in our work.

THEOREM 3.1   Extreme value theorem

A continuous function f on a closed, bounded interval $[a, b]$ has an absolute maximum and an absolute minimum.

Proof: Even though this result may seem quite natural (see Figure 3.2), its proof requires concepts beyond the scope of this text and will be omitted.

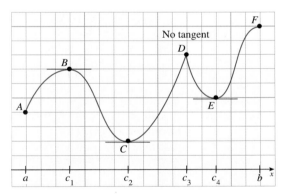

Absolute maximum at $x = c_1$ and $x = c_2$
Absolute minimum at $x = d$

Figure 3.2 Extreme value theorem

This theorem does *not* apply if the function is not continuous and it also does not apply if the interval is not closed. You will be asked for appropriate counterexamples in the problem set.

If we compare a function with its graph, we note that the maximum of a function occurs at the highest point on the graph and the minimum occurs at the lowest point. These properties are illustrated in Example 1.

EXAMPLE 1   Extreme values of a continuous function

Using the graph in Figure 3.3, locate the extreme values of the function f defined on the closed interval $[a, b]$.

Figure 3.3 A continuous function on a closed interval $[a, b]$

Solution   The highest point on the graph occurs at the right endpoint F, and the lowest point occurs at C. Thus, the absolute maximum is $f(b)$, and the absolute minimum is $f(c_2)$.

EXAMPLE 2   Conditions of the extreme value theorem

Explain why each of the following examples does not contradict the extreme value theorem:

a. $f(x) = \begin{cases} 2x & \text{if } 0 \le x < 1 \\ 0 & \text{if } 1 \le x \le 2 \end{cases}$ **b.** $g(x) = x^2$ for $0 < x \le 2$

Solution

a. The function f has no maximum. It takes on all values arbitrarily close to 2, but it never reaches the value 2. The extreme value theorem is not violated because f is not continuous on $[0, 2]$.

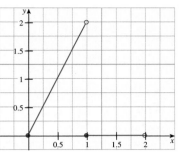

f does not have a maximum value.

b. Although the functional values $g(x)$ become arbitrarily small as x approaches 0, it never reaches the value 0, so it has no minimum. The function g is continuous on the interval $(0, 2]$, but the extreme value theorem is not violated because the interval is not closed.

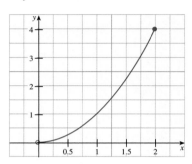

g does not have a minimum value (but it does have a maximum value).

■ RELATIVE EXTREMA

Typically, the extrema of a continuous function occur either at endpoints of the interval or at points where the graph has a "peak" or a "valley" (points where the graph is higher or lower than all nearby points). For example, the function f in Figure 3.3 has "peaks" at B and D and "valleys" at C and E. Peaks and valleys are what we call *relative extrema*.

Relative Maximum
Relative Minimum

> The function f is said to have a **relative maximum** at the point c if $f(c) \geq f(x)$ for all x in an open interval containing c. Also, f is said to have a **relative minimum** at d if $f(d) \leq f(x)$ for all x in an open interval containing d. Relative maxima and relative minima are called, in general, **relative extrema.**

We would like to formulate a procedure for finding relative extrema. By looking at Figure 3.3, we see that there are horizontal tangents at B, C, and E, whereas a tangent does not exist at D. This suggests that the relative extrema of f occur either where the derivative is zero (horizontal tangent) or where the derivative does not exist (no tangent). This notion leads us to the following definition.

Critical Values and Critical Points

> Suppose f is defined at c and either $f'(c) = 0$ or $f'(c)$ does not exist. Then the number c is called a **critical value** of f, and the point $P(c, f(c))$ on the graph of f is called a **critical point.**

⊘ Note that if $f(c)$ is not defined, then c *cannot* be a critical value. ⊘

If there is a relative maximum at c, then the functional value, $f(c)$, is that maximum value. Similarly, if there is a relative minimum at c, then that minimum value is $f(c)$.

EXAMPLE 3 Finding critical values

Find the critical values for the given functions.

a. $f(x) = 4x^3 - 5x^2 - 8x + 20$ **b.** $f(x) = \dfrac{x^2}{x-2}$ **c.** $f(x) = 12x^{1/2} - 2x^{3/2}$

Solution

a. $f'(x) = 12x^2 - 10x - 8$ is defined for all values of x. Solve

$$12x^2 - 10x - 8 = 0$$

$$2(3x - 4)(2x + 1) = 0$$

$$x = \tfrac{4}{3}, -\tfrac{1}{2} \quad \textit{These are the critical values.}$$

b. $f'(x) = \dfrac{(x-2)(2x) - x^2(1)}{(x-2)^2} = \dfrac{x(x-4)}{(x-2)^2}$

The derivative is not defined at $x = 2$, but f is not defined at 2 either; so $x = 2$ is not a critical value. The actual critical values are found by solving $f'(x) = 0$.

$$\dfrac{x(x-4)}{(x-2)^2} = 0$$

$$x = 0, 4 \quad \textit{These are the critical values.}$$

c. $f'(x) = 6x^{-1/2} - 3x^{1/2}$

The derivative is not defined at $x = 0$. We have $f(0) = 12(0)^{1/2} - 2(0)^{3/2} = 0$, so we see that f *is* defined at $x = 0$, which means that $x = 0$ is a critical value. For other critical values, solve $f'(x) = 0$:

$$6x^{-1/2} - 3x^{1/2} = 0$$

$$3x^{-1/2}(2 - x) = 0$$

$$x = 2$$

The critical values are $x = 0, 2$. ▬

EXAMPLE 4 Critical values and critical points

Find the critical values and the critical points for the function

$$f(x) = (x - 1)^2(x + 2)$$

Solution Because the function f is a polynomial, we know that it is continuous and that the derivative exists for all x. Thus, we find the critical values by using the product rule and chain rule to solve the equation $f'(x) = 0$.

$$f'(x) = (x - 1)^2(1) + 2(x - 1)(1)(x + 2)$$

$$= (x - 1)[(x - 1) + 2(x + 2)]$$

$$= (x - 1)(3x + 3)$$

$$= 3(x - 1)(x + 1)$$

The critical values are $x = \pm 1$. To find the critical points, we need to find the y-component for each critical value.

$$f(1) = (1 - 1)^2(1 + 2) = 0$$

$$f(-1) = (-1 - 1)^2(-1 + 2) = 4$$

Thus, the critical points are $(1, 0)$ and $(-1, 4)$. ▬

Figure 3.4 The graph of
$f(x) = (x - 1)^2(x + 2)$

We will use the critical points to help us draw a graph in Section 3.3. However, if we use a computer or calculator to graph f in Example 4, we can see that the relative extrema are related to the critical points as shown in Figure 3.4.

Our observation that relative extrema occur only at points on a graph where there is either a horizontal tangent line or no tangent at all is equivalent to the following result.

THEOREM 3.2 Critical value theorem

If a continuous function f has a relative extremum at c, then c must be a critical value of f.

> ■ *What this says*: If a point is a relative maximum or a relative minimum value for a function, then either the derivative is 0 or it does not exist at that point.

Proof: If $f'(c)$ does not exist, then c is a critical value by definition ($f(c)$ must exist). We shall show that if $f'(c)$ exists and a relative maximum occurs at c, then $f'(c) = 0$. Our approach will be to examine the difference quotient. (The case where $f'(c)$ exists and a relative minimum occurs at c is handled similarly in Problem 56 of Problem Set 3.1.)

Because a relative maximum occurs at c, we have $f(c) \geq f(x)$ for every number x in an open interval (a, b) containing c. Thus, if Δx is small enough so $c + \Delta x$ is in (a, b), then

$$f(c) \geq f(c + \Delta x) \quad \textit{Because a relative maximum occurs at } c$$

$$f(c) - f(c + \Delta x) \geq 0$$

$$f(c + \Delta x) - f(c) \leq 0 \quad \textit{Multiply both sides by } -1.$$
$$\textit{(Remember to reverse the inequality.)}$$

For the next step we want to divide both sides by Δx (in order to write the left side as a difference quotient). However, as this is an inequality, we need to consider two possibilities:

1. Suppose $\Delta x > 0$ (the inequality does not reverse):

$$\frac{f(c + \Delta x) - f(c)}{\Delta x} \leq 0 \quad \textit{Divide both sides by } \Delta x.$$

Now we take the limit of both sides as Δx approaches from the right (because Δx is positive).

$$\underbrace{\lim_{\Delta x \to 0^+} \frac{f(c + \Delta x) - f(c)}{\Delta x}}_{f'(c)} \leq \underbrace{\lim_{\Delta x \to 0^+} 0}_{0}$$

$$f'(c) \leq 0$$

2. Next, suppose $\Delta x < 0$ (the inequality reverses). Then

$$\frac{f(c + \Delta x) - f(c)}{\Delta x} \geq 0 \quad \textit{Divide both sides by } \Delta x.$$

This time we take the limit of both sides as Δx approaches 0 from the left (because Δx is negative).

$$\lim_{\Delta x \to 0^-} \frac{f(c + \Delta x) - f(c)}{\Delta x} \geq \lim_{\Delta x \to 0^-} 0$$

Because we have shown that $f'(c) \leq 0$ and $f'(c) \geq 0$, it follows that $f'(c) = 0$. ■

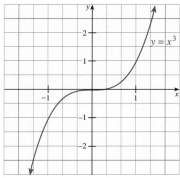

a. The graph of $f(x) = x^3$
No relative extremum occurs
at $c = 0$ even though $f'(0) = 0$

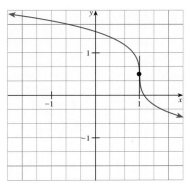

b. Although $g'(1)$ does not exist,
no relative extremum occurs
at $c = 1$.

Figure 3.5 A relative extremum
may not occur at each critical
value.

⊘ Theorem 3.2 tells us that a relative extremum of a continuous function f can occur *only* at a critical value, but *it does not say that a relative extremum must occur at each critical value.*

For example, if $f(x) = x^3$, then $f'(x) = 3x^2$ and $f'(0) = 0$, but there is no relative extremum at $c = 0$ on the graph of f because the graph is rising for $x < 0$ and also for $x > 0$, as shown in Figure 3.5a. It is also quite possible for $g'(c)$ not to exist for a continuous function g that has no relative extremum at c, as shown in Figure 3.5b. ⊘

EXAMPLE 5 Critical values where the derivative does not exist

Find the critical values for $f(x) = |x + 1|$ on $[-5, 5]$.

Solution If $x > -1$, then $f(x) = x + 1$ and $f'(x) = 1$. However, if $x < -1$, then $f(x) = -x - 1$ and $f'(x) = -1$. Because these are not the same,

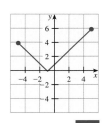

$$\lim_{x \to -1^-} f'(x) \neq \lim_{x \to -1^+} f'(x)$$

the derivative does not exist at $x = c = -1$. Because $f(-1)$ is defined, -1 must be a critical value.

■ ABSOLUTE EXTREMA

Suppose we are looking for the absolute extrema of a continuous function f on the closed, bounded interval $[a, b]$. We know that these extrema exist by Theorem 3.1. Also, Theorem 3.2 enables us to narrow the list of "candidates" for points where extrema can occur from the entire interval $[a, b]$ to just the endpoints $x = a$, $x = b$, and the critical values c between a and b. This suggests the following procedure.

Procedure for Finding Absolute Extrema
To find the absolute extrema of a continuous function f on $[a, b]$:
Step 1. Compute $f'(x)$ and find all critical values of f on $[a, b]$.
Step 2. Evaluate f at the endpoints a and b and at each critical value c.
Step 3. Compare the values in Step 2.
The largest value is the absolute maximum of f on $[a, b]$.
The smallest value is the absolute minimum of f on $[a, b]$.

Figure 3.6 shows some of the possibilities in the application of this procedure.

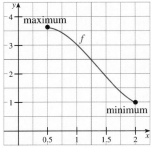

$f(x) = x^3 - 4x^2 + 3x + 3$ on $[0.5, 2]$
a. f is continuous; both
extrema at endpoints

$g(x) = \sin x$ on $[0, 2\pi]$
b. g is continuous; neither
extremum at an endpoint

$h(x) = x^2 - 4x + 1$ on $[0, 3]$
c. h is continuous; one
extremum at an endpoint

Figure 3.6 Absolute extrema

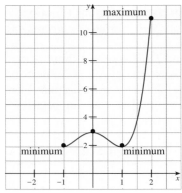

Figure 3.7 The graph of
$f(x) = x^4 - 2x^2 + 3$ on $[-1, 2]$

EXAMPLE 6   Absolute extrema of a polynomial function

Find the absolute extrema of the function defined by the equation
$f(x) = x^4 - 2x^2 + 3$ on the closed interval $[-1, 2]$.

Solution   Because f is a polynomial function, it is continuous on the closed
interval $[-1, 2]$. Theorem 3.1 tells us that there must be an absolute maximum
and an absolute minimum on the interval.

Step 1: $f'(x) = 4x^3 - 2(2x)$
$\qquad\qquad = 4x(x^2 - 1)$
$\qquad\qquad = 4x(x - 1)(x + 1)$

The critical values are $x = 0$, 1, and -1.

Step 2: Values at endpoints: $f(-1) = 2, f(2) = 11$
$\qquad\qquad$ Critical values: $f(0) = 3, f(1) = 2$

Step 3: The absolute maximum of f occurs at $x = 2$ and is $f(2) = 11$; the
absolute minima of f occur at $x = 1$ and $x = -1$ and are $f(1) = f(-1) = 2$. The
graph of f is shown in Figure 3.7.

EXAMPLE 7   Absolute extrema when the derivative does not exist

Find the absolute extrema of $f(x) = x^{2/3}(5 - 2x)$ on the interval $[-1, 2]$.

Solution   **Step 1:** In order to find the derivative, rewrite the given function as
$f(x) = 5x^{2/3} - 2x^{5/3}$. Then

$$f'(x) = \tfrac{10}{3}x^{-1/3} - \tfrac{10}{3}x^{2/3} = \tfrac{10}{3}x^{-1/3}(1 - x)$$

Critical values are found by solving $f'(x) = 0$ and by locating the places where
the derivative does not exist. First,

$$f'(x) = 0 \text{ when } x = 1$$

Even though $f(0)$ exists, we note that $f'(x)$ does not exist at $x = 0$ (notice the
division by zero when $x = 0$). Thus, the critical values are $x = 0$ and $x = 1$.

Step 2: Values at endpoints: $f(-1) = 7$
$\qquad\qquad\qquad\qquad\qquad\quad f(2) = 2^{2/3} \approx 1.587401052$
$\qquad\qquad$ Critical values: $f(0) = 0$
$\qquad\qquad\qquad\qquad\qquad\quad f(1) = 3$

Step 3: The absolute maximum of f occurs at $x = -1$ and is $f(-1) = 7$; the
absolute minimum of f occurs at $x = 0$ and is $f(0) = 0$, as shown in Figure 3.8.

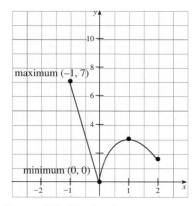

Figure 3.8 Graph of
$f(x) = 5x^{2/3} - 2x^{5/3}$ on $[-1, 2]$

EXAMPLE 8   Absolute extrema for a trigonometric function

Find the absolute extrema of the following continuous function on $\left[0, \frac{\pi}{2}\right]$:
$T(x) = \frac{1}{2}(\sin^2 x + \cos x) + 2 \sin x - x$.

Solution   **Step 1:** We have $T'(x) = \frac{1}{2}(2 \sin x \cos x - \sin x) + 2(\cos x) - 1$

$\qquad\qquad\qquad\qquad = \frac{1}{2}(2 \sin x \cos x - \sin x + 4 \cos x - 2)$

$\qquad\qquad\qquad\qquad = \frac{1}{2}[2 \cos x(\sin x + 2) - (\sin x + 2)]$

$\qquad\qquad\qquad\qquad = \frac{1}{2}[(\sin x + 2)(2 \cos x - 1)]$

Set each factor equal to zero and solve to obtain $x = \frac{\pi}{3}$.

Step 2: Evaluate the function at the endpoints:

$$T(0) = \tfrac{1}{2}(\sin^2 0 + \cos 0) + 2 \sin 0 - 0 = \tfrac{1}{2}(0 + 1) + 2(0) - 0 = 0.5$$

$$T\left(\tfrac{\pi}{2}\right) = \tfrac{1}{2}\left(\sin^2 \tfrac{\pi}{2} + \cos \tfrac{\pi}{2}\right) + 2 \sin \tfrac{\pi}{2} - \tfrac{\pi}{2}$$

$$= \tfrac{1}{2}(1 + 0) + 2(1) - \tfrac{\pi}{2} = \tfrac{5}{2} - \tfrac{\pi}{2} \approx 0.9292036732$$

Critical value:

$$T\left(\tfrac{\pi}{3}\right) = \tfrac{1}{2}\left(\sin^2 \tfrac{\pi}{3} + \cos \tfrac{\pi}{3}\right) + 2 \sin \tfrac{\pi}{3} - \tfrac{\pi}{3}$$

$$= \tfrac{1}{2}\left(\tfrac{3}{4} + \tfrac{1}{2}\right) + 2\left(\tfrac{\sqrt{3}}{2}\right) - \tfrac{\pi}{3} = \tfrac{5}{8} + \sqrt{3} - \tfrac{\pi}{3} \approx 1.309853256$$

Step 3: The absolute maximum of T is approximately 1.31 at $x = \frac{\pi}{3}$ and the absolute minimum of T is 0.5 at $x = 0$. The graph is shown in Figure 3.9 as part of the computational window. ▬

Computational Window

If you have a graphing calculator, you can find approximate maximum and minimum values. For Example 8:
The maximum value can be found using the (TRACE) and it appears to be in the neighborhood of

   X=1.0360572,   Y=1.3096998   and
   X=1.0527678,   Y=1.3098147

More accurate values could be obtained using the (ZOOM).

Figure 3.9 The graph of
$T(x) = \frac{1}{2}(\sin^2 x + \cos x) + 2 \sin x - x$ on $\left[0, \frac{\pi}{2}\right]$

Y1◻.5((sin X)²+cos X)+2sin X-X

Xmin=0
Xmax=1.5707963...
Xscl=1.5707963...
Ymin=0
Ymax=2
Yscl=1

X=1.0360572 _Y=1.3096998

X=1.0527678 _Y=1.3098147

■ OPTIMIZATION

In our next two examples, we examine two applications involving optimization. Such problems are investigated in more depth in Sections 3.7 and 3.8.

EXAMPLE 9   Maximum and minimum velocity of a moving particle

A particle moves along the t-axis with displacement

$$s(t) = t^4 - 8t^3 + 18t^2 + 60t - 8$$

Find the largest and smallest values of its velocity for $1 \le t \le 5$.

Solution   The velocity is

$$v(t) = s'(t) = 4t^3 - 24t^2 + 36t + 60$$

Y1■4X^3-24X²+36X +60

Xmin=1   Ymin=30
Xmax=5   Ymax=160
Xscl=1   Yscl=1

Y1■4X^3-24X²+36X +60

Xmin=1   Ymin=30
Xmax=5   Ymax=160
Xscl=1   Yscl=1

Using the (TRACE), find the maximum is 140 when $t = 5$ and the minimum is 60 when $t = 3$.

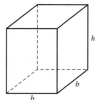

Figure 3.10 Volume of a box

To find the largest value of $v(t)$, we compute the derivative of v:

$$v'(t) = 12t^2 - 48t + 36$$
$$= 12(t - 3)(t - 1)$$

Setting $v'(t) = 0$, we find that the critical values of $v(t)$ are $t = 3, 1$. (*Note*: v is a polynomial function, so it has a derivative for all t.) Now we evaluate v at the critical values and endpoints.

$t = 1$ is both a critical value and an endpoint:

$$v(1) = 4(1)^3 - 24(1)^2 + 36(1) + 60 = 76$$

$t = 5$ is an endpoint:

$$v(5) = 4(5)^3 - 24(5)^2 + 36(5) + 60 = 140$$

$t = 3$ is a critical value:

$$v(3) = 4(3)^3 - 24(3)^2 + 36(3) + 60 = 60$$

The largest value of the velocity is 140 at the endpoint where $t = 5$, and the smallest value is 60 when $t = 3$.   ▬

EXAMPLE 10   An applied maximum value problem

A box with a square base is constructed so that the length of one side of the base plus the height is 10 in. What is the largest possible volume of such a box?

Solution   We let b be the length of one side of the base and h be the height of the box, as shown in Figure 3.10. The volume, V, is

$$V = b^2h$$

Because our methods apply only to functions of one variable, it may seem that we cannot deal with V as a function of two variables. However, we know that $b + h = 10$; therefore, $h = 10 - b$, and we can now write V as a function of b alone:

$$V(b) = b^2(10 - b)$$

The domain is not stated, but we must have $b \geq 0$ and $10 - b = h \geq 0$, so that $0 \leq b \leq 10$. First, we find the critical values. Note that V is a polynomial function, so the derivative exists everywhere in the domain. Write $V(b) = 10b^2 - b^3$ and find $V'(b) = 20b - 3b^2$. Then

$$V'(b) = 0$$
$$20b - 3b^2 = 0$$
$$b(20 - 3b) = 0$$
$$b = 0, \tfrac{20}{3}$$

Checking the endpoints and the critical values, we have

$$V(0) = 0$$
$$V(10) = 10^2(10 - 10) = 0$$
$$V\left(\tfrac{20}{3}\right) = \left(\tfrac{20}{3}\right)^2\left(10 - \tfrac{20}{3}\right) = \tfrac{4{,}000}{27}$$

Thus the largest value for the volume V is $\tfrac{4{,}000}{27} \approx 148.1$ in³. It occurs when the square base has a side of length $\tfrac{20}{3}$ in. and the height is $h = 10 - \tfrac{20}{3} = \tfrac{10}{3}$ in.   ▬

PROBLEM SET 3.1

A *In Problems 1–12, find the largest and smallest values of each continuous function on the given closed, bounded interval.*

1. $f(x) = 5 + 10x - x^2$ on $[-3, 3]$
2. $f(x) = 10 + 6x - x^2$ on $[-4, 4]$
3. $f(x) = x^3 - 3x^2$ on $[-1, 3]$
4. $f(t) = t^4 - 8t^2$ on $[-3, 3]$
5. $f(x) = x^3$ on $\left[-\frac{1}{2}, 1\right]$
6. $g(x) = x^3 - 3x$ on $[-2, 2]$
7. $f(x) = x^5 - x^4$ on $[-1, 1]$
8. $g(t) = 3t^5 - 20t^3$ on $[-1, 3]$
9. $f(x) = |x|$ on $[-1, 1]$
10. $f(x) = |x - 3|$ on $[-4, 4]$
11. $f(u) = \sin^2 u + \cos u$ on $[0, 2]$
12. $g(u) = \sin u - \cos u$ on $[0, \pi]$
13. ■ **What Does This Say?** Outline a procedure for finding the absolute extrema of a function. Include in your outline a discussion of what is meant by critical values.

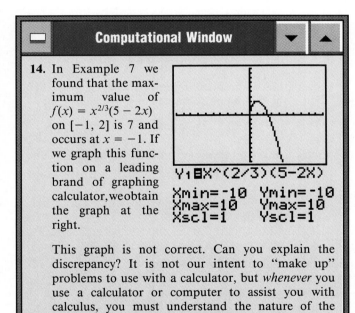

Computational Window

14. In Example 7 we found that the maximum value of $f(x) = x^{2/3}(5 - 2x)$ on $[-1, 2]$ is 7 and occurs at $x = -1$. If we graph this function on a leading brand of graphing calculator, we obtain the graph at the right.

Y₁⊟X^(2/3)(5-2X)

Xmin=-10 Ymin=-10
Xmax=10   Ymax=10
Xscl=1   Yscl=1

This graph is not correct. Can you explain the discrepancy? It is not our intent to "make up" problems to use with a calculator, but *whenever* you use a calculator or computer to assist you with calculus, you must understand the nature of the functions with which you are working and not rely only on the calculator or computer output.

In Problems 15–30, find the largest and smallest values of each continuous function on the closed, bounded interval. If the function is not continuous on the interval, so state.

15. $f(u) = 1 - u^{2/3}$ on $[-1, 1]$
16. $g(t) = (50 + t)^{2/3}$ on $[-50, 14]$
17. $f(\theta) = \cos^3 \theta - 4 \cos^2 \theta$ on $[-0.1, \pi + 0.1]$
18. $g(\theta) = \theta \sin \theta$ on $[-2, 2]$
19. $f(x) = 20 \sin(378\pi x)$ on $[-1, 1]$

20. $g(x) = 2x^3 - 3x^2 - 36x + 4$ on $[-4, 4]$
21. $g(x) = x^3 + 3x^2 - 24x - 4$ on $[-4, 4]$
22. $f(x) = \frac{8}{3}x^3 - 5x^2 + 8x - 5$ on $[-4, 4]$
23. $f(x) = \frac{1}{6}(x^3 - 6x^2 + 9x + 1)$ on $[0, 2]$
24. $g(u) = 98u^3 - 4u^2 + 72u$ on $[0, 4]$
25. $f(w) = \sqrt{w}(w - 5)^{1/3}$ on $[0, 4]$
26. $h(x) = \sqrt[3]{x} \sqrt[3]{(x - 3)^2}$ on $[-1, 4]$
27. $h(x) = \tan x + \sec x$ on $[0, 2\pi]$
28. $s(t) = t \cos t - \sin t$ on $[0, 2\pi]$
29. $f(x) = \begin{cases} 9 - 4x & \text{if } x < 1 \\ -x^2 + 6x & \text{if } x \geq 1 \end{cases}$ on $[-1, 4]$
30. $f(x) = \begin{cases} 8 - 3x & \text{if } x < 2 \\ -x^2 + 3x & \text{if } x \geq 2 \end{cases}$ on $[-1, 4]$

Find the required extrema in Problems 31–35.
31. The smallest value of $f(x) = x^2$ on $[-1, 1]$
32. The largest value of $f(x) = \dfrac{1}{x(x + 1)}$ on $[-0.5, 0]$
33. The smallest value of $g(x) = \dfrac{9}{x} + x - 3$ on $[1, 9]$
34. The smallest value of $g(x) = \dfrac{x^2 - 1}{x^2 + 1}$ on $[-1, 1]$
35. The largest value of
$$f(t) = \begin{cases} -t^2 - t + 2 & \text{if } t < 1 \\ 3 - t & \text{if } t \geq 1 \end{cases} \text{ on } [-2, 3]$$

B *Find a function that not only meets the conditions specified in Problems 36–39, but also meets each of the following conditions:*

  a. a minimum but no maximum
  b. a maximum but no minimum
  c. both a maximum and a minimum
  d. neither a maximum nor a minimum

That is, each of these parts a–d may need a different example to satisfy the conditions requested in Problems 36–39.

36. THINK TANK PROBLEM Find a function that is discontinuous and defined on an open interval.
37. THINK TANK PROBLEM Find a function that is discontinuous and defined on a closed interval.
38. THINK TANK PROBLEM Find a function that is continuous on an open interval.
39. THINK TANK PROBLEM Find a function that is continuous on a closed interval.
40. THINK TANK PROBLEM Give a counterexample to show that the extreme value theorem does not necessarily apply if one disregards the condition that f be continuous (that is, f need not be continuous).
41. THINK TANK PROBLEM Give a counterexample to show that the extreme value theorem does not necessarily apply if one disregards the condition that f be defined on a closed interval (that is, f may be defined on an open interval).

42. An object moves along the t-axis with displacement

$$s(t) = t^3 - 6t^2 - 15t + 11$$

Find the largest value of its velocity on $[0, 4]$.

43. An object moves along the t-axis with displacement

$$s(t) = t^4 - 2t^3 - 12t^2 + 60t - 10$$

Find the largest value of its velocity on $[0, 3]$.

44. Find two nonnegative numbers whose sum is 8 and the product of whose squares is as large as possible.

45. Find two nonnegative numbers such that the sum of one and twice the other is 12 if it is required that their product be as large as possible.

46. Under the condition that $3x + y = 80$, maximize the product xy^3 when $x \geq 0$, $y \geq 0$.

47. Under the condition that $3x + y = 126$, maximize xy when $x \geq 0$ and $y \geq 0$.

48. Under the condition that $2x - 5y = 18$, maximize x^2y when $x \geq 0$ and $y \leq 0$.

49. Show that if a rectangle with fixed perimeter P is to enclose the greatest area, it must be a square.

50. Find all points on the circle $x^2 + y^2 = a^2$ ($a \geq 0$) such that the product of the x-coordinate and y-coordinate is as large as possible.

51. A commodity has a cost function given by

$$C(x) = 0.125x^2 + 20,000$$

where x is the number of units produced. Show that the average cost,

$$A(x) = \frac{C(x)}{x}$$

is minimized when the average cost is equal to $C'(x)$. (Recall from Chapter 2 that $C'(x)$ is called the marginal cost.)

52. a. Show that $\frac{1}{2}$ is the number that exceeds its own square by the greatest amount.

b. Which nonnegative number exceeds its own cube by the greatest amount?

c. Which nonnegative number exceeds its own nth power ($n > 0$) by the greatest amount?

53. Given the constants $a_1, a_2, \ldots, a_n$, find the value of x that guarantees that the sum

$$S(x) = (a_1 - x)^2 + (a_2 - x)^2 + \cdots + (a_n - x)^2$$

will be as small as possible.

54. Find the smallest value of m so that the line $y = mx$ will lie above the curve

$$y = 1 - \frac{1}{x}$$

for all $x > 0$. *Hint*: Begin by locating the value of x that minimizes

$$f(x) = mx - 1 + \frac{1}{x}$$

55. Explain why the function

$$f(x) = \frac{8}{\sin x} + \frac{27}{\cos x}$$

must attain a minimum in the open interval $\left(0, \frac{\pi}{2}\right)$. Show that if the minimum is attained at $x = \theta$, then

$$\tan \theta = \frac{2}{3}$$

56. Show that if $f'(c)$ exists and a relative minimum occurs at c, then c must be a critical value of f.

3.2 THE MEAN VALUE THEOREM

IN THIS SECTION   Rolle's theorem and a proof of the MVT, some uses of the mean value theorem
The mean value theorem is an extremely important result in calculus, both in theory and for practical applications. The goal of this section is to prove the mean value theorem and to examine some of its consequences.

If an automobile averages 60 mi/hr on a trip, it is reasonable to expect that the speedometer must read exactly 60 *at least once* during the trip. More generally, suppose an object moves along a straight line so that its distance is $s(t)$ from its starting point at time t. The average velocity of the object from time $t = a$ to time $t = b$ is given by the ratio

$$\frac{s(b) - s(a)}{b - a}$$

Just as in the case of the automobile, we expect that there should be at least one time t_0 between a and b when the instantaneous velocity equals this average velocity. That is, there exists some t_0 such that

$$\underbrace{s'(t_0)}_{\text{Instantaneous velocity}} = \underbrace{\frac{s(b) - s(a)}{b - a}}_{\text{Average velocity}}$$

This is an example of the *mean value theorem for derivatives*, which we shall refer to simply as the **mean value theorem.**

Mean Value Theorem (MVT)

> If f is continuous on the closed interval $[a, b]$ and differentiable on the open interval (a, b), then there exists at least one number c such that
>
> $$\frac{f(b) - f(a)}{b - a} = f'(c) \qquad \text{for } a < c < b$$

The proof of this theorem follows later in this section.

> ■ *What this says*: Under reasonable conditions, there must be at least one number c between a and b such that the derivative $f'(c)$ actually equals the difference quotient
>
> $$\frac{f(b) - f(a)}{b - a}$$

The equation in the MVT may or may not be easy to solve. Example 1 illustrates one method of finding such a number c.

EXAMPLE 1   Finding the number c specified by the MVT

Show that the function $f(x) = x^3 + x^2$ satisfies the hypotheses of the MVT on the closed interval $[1, 2]$, and find a number c between 1 and 2 such that

$$f'(c) = \frac{f(2) - f(1)}{2 - 1}$$

Solution   Because f is a polynomial function, it is differentiable and hence also continuous on the entire interval $[1, 2]$. Thus, the hypotheses of the MVT are satisfied.

By differentiating f, we find that

$$f'(x) = 3x^2 + 2x$$

for all x. Therefore, we have $f'(c) = 3c^2 + 2c$, and the MVT equation

$$f'(c) = \frac{f(2) - f(1)}{2 - 1}$$

is satisfied when

$$3c^2 + 2c = \frac{f(2) - f(1)}{2 - 1} = \frac{12 - 2}{1} = 10$$

Solving the resulting equation $3c^2 + 2c - 10 = 0$ by the quadratic formula, we obtain

$$c = \frac{-1 \pm \sqrt{31}}{3}$$

The negative value is not in the open interval $(1, 2)$, but the positive value

$$c = \frac{-1 + \sqrt{31}}{3} \approx 1.522588121$$

satisfies the requirements of the MVT.   ▬

■ ROLLE'S THEOREM* AND A PROOF OF THE MVT

The key to the proof of the mean value theorem is the following result, which is really just the MVT in the special case where $f(b) = f(a)$.

THEOREM 3.3   Rolle's theorem

Suppose f is continuous on the closed interval $[a, b]$ and differentiable on the open interval (a, b). Then if $f(a) = f(b)$, there exists at least one number c between a and b such that $f'(c) = 0$.

Proof: If f is constant on the closed interval $[a, b]$, then $f'(x) = 0$ for *all* x between a and b. If f is not constant throughout the interval $[a, b]$, the largest and smallest values of f on $[a, b]$ cannot be the same. Because $f(a) = f(b)$, at least one extreme value of f does not occur at an endpoint. According to the extreme value theorem and the critical value theorem (Theorems 3.1 and 3.2 of Section 3.1), such an extreme value must occur at a critical value between a and b. Recall that a critical value c has the property that $f'(c) = 0$ or else $f'(c)$ does not exist. Because $f'(x)$ is assumed to exist throughout the interval (a, b), it follows that $f'(c) = 0$ for some number between a and b, as claimed.   ■

The proof of Rolle's theorem makes much more sense if it is considered geometrically, as shown in Figure 3.11. Figure 3.11a shows that if f is constant on the closed interval $[a, b]$, then $f'(x) = 0$ for all x in the interval.

However, if f is not constant, as shown in Figure 3.11b, its graph must change direction at least once in order to begin and end on the same level. [Remember that f is continuous and $f(a) = f(b)$.] The graph must have a horizontal tangent (with a derivative of zero) wherever the direction changes. Figure 3.11b shows that it is quite possible for the graph to have several such transition points, even though the theorem asserts only that at least one exists.

The mean value theorem has a similar geometric interpretation, as shown in Figure 3.12. Rolle's theorem can be viewed as saying that if $f(a) = f(b) = d$, then for at least one number c between a and b, the tangent line at $(c, f(c))$ is parallel to the line $y = d$ through the endpoints (a, d) and (b, d). It is reasonable to expect a similar result to hold if the endpoints of the graph are not necessarily at the same height. Note that in Figure 3.12b, the graph of Figure 3.12a has been "lifted and tilted," but the tangent line at $(c, f(c))$ is still parallel to the line L through the endpoints $P(a, f(a))$ and $Q(b, f(b))$. Because the tangent line at $(c, f(c))$ has slope

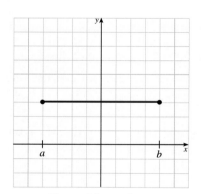

a. The special case where
$f(a) = f(b)$; f is
constant for this example.

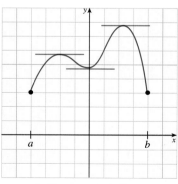

b. The case where f is
not constant on $[a, b]$

Figure 3.11 A geometric interpretation of Rolle's theorem

*Rolle's theorem is named for Michel Rolle (1652–1719), a French mathematician who investigated a special case of the mean value theorem in a book on the algebra of equations published in 1690.

$f'(c)$, it follows that

$$f'(c) = \frac{f(b) - f(a)}{b - a}$$

Now we are ready to prove the mean value theorem.

THEOREM 3.4   The mean value theorem (MVT) for derivatives

If f is continuous on the closed interval $[a, b]$ and differentiable on the open interval (a, b), then there exists at least one number c such that

$$\frac{f(b) - f(a)}{b - a} = f'(c) \qquad \text{for } a < c < b$$

Proof: The proof of the MVT uses Rolle's theorem. Suppose f is continuous on $[a, b]$ and differentiable on (a, b). Define a new function g as follows:

$$g(x) = \left[\frac{f(b) - f(a)}{b - a}\right](x - a) + f(a) - f(x)$$

for $a \le x \le b$. Because f satisfies the hypotheses of the MVT, the function g is also continuous on the closed interval $[a, b]$ and differentiable on the open interval (a, b). In addition, we find that

$$g(a) = \left[\frac{f(b) - f(a)}{b - a}\right](a - a) + f(a) - f(a) = 0$$
$$g(b) = \left[\frac{f(b) - f(a)}{b - a}\right](b - a) + f(a) - f(b)$$
$$= [f(b) - f(a)] + f(a) - f(b) = 0$$

Thus, g satisfies the hypotheses of Rolle's theorem, so there exists at least one number c between a and b for which $g'(c) = 0$. Differentiating the function g, we find that

$$g'(x) = \frac{f(b) - f(a)}{b - a} - f'(x)$$

Because $g'(c) = 0$, we have

$$0 = g'(c) = \frac{f(b) - f(a)}{b - a} - f'(c)$$

This means that

$$f'(c) = \frac{f(b) - f(a)}{b - a}$$

as required.   ■

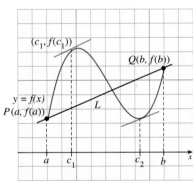

a. Rolle's theorem

b. Mean value theorem

Figure 3.12 A geometrical comparison of Rolle's theorem and the mean value theorem

■ SOME USES OF THE MEAN VALUE THEOREM

The MVT has many different uses. In Example 2, we use it to establish a trigonometric inequality.

EXAMPLE 2   Using the MVT to prove a trigonometric inequality

Show that $|\sin x - \sin y| \le |x - y|$ for numbers x and y by applying the mean value theorem.

Solution The inequality is true if $x = y$. Suppose $x \ne y$; then $f(\theta) = \sin \theta$ is differentiable and hence continuous for all θ, with $f'(\theta) = \cos \theta$. By applying the MVT to f on the closed interval with endpoints x and y, we see that

$$\frac{f(x) - f(y)}{x - y} = f'(c)$$

for some c between x and y. Because $f'(c) = \cos c$ and

$$f(x) - f(y) = \sin x - \sin y$$

we have

$$\frac{\sin x - \sin y}{x - y} = \cos c$$

Finally, we take the absolute value of the expression on each side, remembering that $|\cos c| \leq 1$ for any number c:

$$\left| \frac{\sin x - \sin y}{x - y} \right| = |\cos c| \leq 1$$

Thus, $|\sin x - \sin y| \leq |x - y|$, as claimed.

The MVT is usually used to prove certain key theoretical results of calculus. For example, in Theorem 3.5 we will use the MVT to prove that a function whose derivative is always zero on an interval must be constant on that interval. This apparently simple result and its corollary (Theorem 3.6) turn out to be crucial to our development of the integral in Chapter 4.

THEOREM 3.5   Zero derivative theorem

Suppose f is a continuous function on the closed interval $[a, b]$ and is differentiable on the open interval (a, b). Then if $f'(x) = 0$ for all x on (a, b), the function f is constant on $[a, b]$.

Proof: Let x_1 and x_2 be two distinct numbers ($x_1 \neq x_2$) chosen arbitrarily from the closed interval $[a, b]$. The function f satisfies the requirements of the MVT on the interval with endpoints x_1 and x_2, which means that there exists a number c between x_1 and x_2 such that

$$\frac{f(x_2) - f(x_1)}{x_2 - x_1} = f'(c)$$

By hypothesis, $f'(x) = 0$ throughout the open interval (a, b), and because c lies within this interval, we have $f'(c) = 0$. Thus, by substitution we have

$$\frac{f(x_2) - f(x_1)}{x_2 - x_1} = 0$$

$$f(x_2) = f(x_1)$$

Because x_1 and x_2 were chosen arbitrarily from $[a, b]$, we conclude that $f(x) = k$, a constant, for all x, as required. ∎

THEOREM 3.6   Constant difference theorem

Suppose the functions f and g are continuous on the closed interval $[a, b]$ and differentiable on the open interval (a, b). Then if $f'(x) = g'(x)$ for all x on (a, b), there exists a constant C such that

$$f(x) = g(x) + C$$

for all x on $[a, b]$.

Proof: Let $h(x) = f(x) - g(x)$; then

$$h'(x) = f'(x) - g'(x)$$

$$= 0 \qquad \textit{Because } f'(x) = g'(x)$$

Thus, by Theorem 3.5, $h(x) = C$ for some constant C and all x on $[a, b]$, and because $h(x) = f(x) - g(x)$, it follows that

$$f(x) - g(x) = C$$

$$f(x) = g(x) + C \quad \textit{Add } g(x) \textit{ to both sides.} \qquad \blacksquare$$

> ■ **What this says:** Two functions with derivatives that are equal on an open interval differ by a constant on that interval.

PROBLEM SET 3.2

Ⓐ **1.** ■ **What Does This Say?** What does Rolle's theorem say, and why is it important?

2. ■ **What Does This Say?** Without looking, state the hypothesis for the MVT. How are the hypotheses used in the proof? Can the conclusion of the MVT be true if all or part of the hypotheses are not satisfied?

In Problems 3–14, verify that the given function f satisfies the hypotheses of the MVT on the given interval $[a, b]$. Then find all numbers c between a and b for which

$$\frac{f(b) - f(a)}{b - a} = f'(c)$$

3. $f(x) = 2x^2 + 1$ on $[0, 2]$ **4.** $f(x) = -x^2 + 4$ on $[-1, 0]$

5. $f(x) = x^3 + x$ on $[1, 2]$ **6.** $f(x) = 2x^3 - x^2$ on $[0, 2]$

7. $f(x) = x^4 + 2$ on $[-1, 2]$ **8.** $f(x) = x^5 + 3$ on $[2, 4]$

9. $f(x) = \sqrt{x}$ on $[1, 4]$ **10.** $f(x) = \frac{1}{\sqrt{x}}$ on $[1, 4]$

11. $f(x) = \frac{1}{x + 1}$ on $[0, 2]$ **12.** $f(x) = 1 + \frac{1}{x}$ on $[1, 4]$

13. $f(x) = \cos x$ on $[0, \frac{\pi}{2}]$ **14.** $f(x) = \sin x + \cos x$ on $[0, 2\pi]$

Decide whether Rolle's theorem can be applied to f on the interval indicated in Problems 15–23.

15. $f(x) = |x - 2|$ on $[0, 4]$ **16.** $f(x) = \tan x$ on $[0, 2\pi]$

17. $f(x) = \sin x$ on $[0, 2\pi]$ **18.** $f(x) = |x| - 2$ on $[0, 4]$

19. $f(x) = \sqrt[3]{x} - 1$ on $[-8, 8]$ **20.** $f(x) = \frac{1}{x - 2}$ on $[-1, 1]$

21. $f(x) = \frac{1}{x - 2}$ on $[1, 2]$ **22.** $f(x) = 3x + \sec x$ on $[-\pi, \pi]$

23. $f(x) = \sin^2 x$ on $\left[-\frac{\pi}{2}, \frac{\pi}{2}\right]$

Ⓑ **24.** **Alternative form of the mean value theorem:** If f is continuous on $[a, b]$ and differentiable on (a, b), then there exists a number c in (a, b) such that

$$f(b) = f(a) + (b - a)f'(c)$$

Derive this alternative form of the MVT.

25. Let u and v be any two numbers between $-\frac{\pi}{2}$ and $\frac{\pi}{2}$. Use the MVT to show that

$$|\tan u - \tan v| \geq |u - v|$$

26. If $f(x) = \frac{1}{x}$ on $[-1, 1]$, does the mean value theorem apply? Why or why not?

27. If $g(x) = |x|$ on $[-2, 2]$, does the mean value theorem apply? Why or why not?

28. THINK TANK PROBLEM   Is it true that

$$|\cos x - \cos y| \leq |x - y|$$

for all x and y? Either prove that the inequality is always valid or find a counterexample.

29. THINK TANK PROBLEM   Consider

$$f(x) = \begin{cases} 1 & \text{if } x \geq 0 \\ -1 & \text{if } x < 0 \end{cases}$$

$f'(x) = 0$ for all x in the domain, but f is not a constant. Does this example contradict the zero derivative theorem? Why or why not?

30. a. Let n be a positive integer. Show that there is a number c between 0 and x for which

$$\frac{(1 + x)^n - 1}{x} = n(1 + c)^{n-1}$$

b. Use part **a** to evaluate

$$\lim_{x \to 0} \frac{(1 + x)^n - 1}{x}$$

31. a. Show that there is a number h between 0 and x for which

$$\cos x - 1 = (-\sin h)x$$

b. Use part **a** to evaluate

$$\lim_{x \to 0} \frac{\cos x - 1}{x}$$

32. Evaluate

$$\lim_{x \to \pi^+} \frac{\cos x + 1}{x - \pi}$$

33. Let $f(x) = 1 + \frac{1}{x}$. If a and b are constants such that $a < 0$ and $b > 0$, show that there is no number w between a and b for which

$$f(b) - f(a) = f'(w)(b - a)$$

34. Show that for any $x > 4$, there is a number w between 4 and x such that

$$\frac{\sqrt{x} - 2}{x - 4} = \frac{1}{2\sqrt{w}}$$

Use this fact to show that if $x > 4$, then

$$\sqrt{x} < 2 + \frac{x - 4}{4}$$

35. Show that if an object moves along a straight line in such a way that its velocity is the same at two different times (that is, $v(t_1) = v(t_2)$ for $t_1 \neq t_2$), then there is some intermediate time when the acceleration is zero.

36. Two radar patrol cars are located at fixed positions 6 mi apart on a long, straight road where the speed limit is 55 mi/hr. A sports car passes the first patrol car traveling at 53 mi/hr, and then 5 min later, it passes the second patrol car going 48 mi/hr. Use the MVT to show that at some time between the two clockings, the sports car exceeded the speed limit.

37. The total profit from sales of a commodity is given by

$$P(x) = R(x) - C(x)$$

where $R(x)$ is the revenue and $C(x)$ is the cost associated with a production level of x units. Suppose that a and b are equally profitable levels of production—that is, $P(a) = P(b)$. If $R(x)$ and $C(x)$ are both differentiable for

$a < x < b$, show that there is at least one level of production between a and b where marginal cost equals marginal revenue—that is, $C'(x) = R'(x)$.

38. Use Rolle's theorem to show that the equation

$$\tan x = 1 - x$$

has at least one solution for $0 < x < 1$.

39. Use the MVT to show that

$$\sqrt{1 + x} < 4 + \frac{x - 15}{8} \qquad \text{if } x > 15$$

Hint: Let $f(x) = \sqrt{1 + x}$ and observe that $f(15) = 4$.

40. Use the MVT to show that

$$\frac{1}{2x + 1} > \frac{1}{5} + \frac{2}{25}(2 - x)$$

if $0 \leq x \leq 2$.

Ⓒ 41. Let $f(x) = \tan x$. Note that

$$f(\pi) = f(0) = 0$$

Show that there is no number w between 0 and π for which $f'(w) = 0$. Why does this fact not contradict the MVT?

42. Use Rolle's theorem or the MVT to show that there is no number a for which the equation

$$x^3 - 3x + a = 0$$

has *two* distinct solutions in the interval $[0, 1]$.

43. If $a > 0$ is a constant, show that the equation

$$x^3 + ax - 1 = 0$$

has exactly one real solution. *Hint*: Let $f(x) = x^3 + ax - 1$ and use the intermediate value theorem to show that there is at least one root. Then assume there are two roots, and use Rolle's theorem to obtain a contradiction.

44. If $a > 0$ and n is a positive integer, use Rolle's theorem or the MVT to show that the polynomial

$$p(x) = x^{2n+1} + ax + b$$

can have at most one real root for constants a and b. *Hint*: See the hint for Problem 43.

45. Suppose f and g are differentiable functions on the closed interval $[a, b]$ and that

$$f(a) = g(a) \quad \text{and} \quad f(b) = g(b)$$

Prove that there is a number c between a and b for which

$$f'(c) = g'(c)$$

46. Show that if $f''(x) = 0$ for all x, then f is a linear function. (That is, $f(x) = Ax + B$ for constants $A \neq 0$ and B.)

47. Show that if $f'(x) = Ax + B$ for constants $A \neq 0$ and B, then $f(x)$ is a quadratic function. (That is, $f(x) = ax^2 + bx + c$ for constants a, b, and c, where $a \neq 0$.)

3.3 FIRST-DERIVATIVE TEST

> **IN THIS SECTION** Increasing and decreasing functions, the first-derivative test, curve sketching with the first derivative
> The sign of the derivative of a function can be used to determine whether the function is increasing or decreasing on a given interval. We shall use this information to develop a procedure called *the first-derivative test* for classifying a given critical point as a relative maximum, a relative minimum, or neither. Finally, we shall use these ideas to begin the development of a procedure for sketching the graph of a function; this procedure will be refined and extended in the next three sections.

■ INCREASING AND DECREASING FUNCTIONS

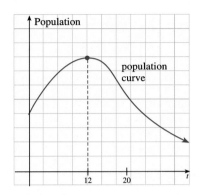

Figure 3.13 A population curve

Suppose an ecologist has determined the size of a population of a certain species as a function f of time t (months). If it turns out that the population is increasing until the end of the first year and is decreasing thereafter, it is reasonable to expect the population to be maximized at time $t = 12$ and for the population curve to have a high point at $t = 12$, as shown in Figure 3.13. If the graph of a function f, such as this population curve, is rising throughout the interval $0 < x < 12$ (and never flattens out on that interval), we say that f is *strictly increasing* on that interval. Similarly, the graph of the function in Figure 3.13 is *strictly decreasing* on the interval $12 < t < 20$. These terms may be defined more formally as follows:

Strictly Increasing

Strictly Decreasing

> The function f is **strictly increasing** on an interval I if
> $$f(x_1) < f(x_2) \quad \text{whenever} \quad x_1 < x_2$$
> for x_1 and x_2 on I. Likewise, f is **strictly decreasing** on I if
> $$f(x_1) > f(x_2) \quad \text{whenever} \quad x_1 < x_2$$
> for x_1 and x_2 on I.

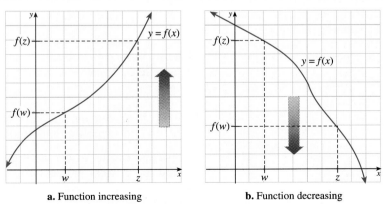

a. Function increasing   **b.** Function decreasing

Figure 3.14 Increasing and decreasing functions

A function f is said to be (strictly) **monotonic** on an interval I if it is either strictly increasing on all of I or strictly decreasing on I. Monotonic behavior is closely related to the sign of the derivative f'. In particular, if the graph of a function has tangent lines with only positive slopes on I, the graph will be tilted upward and f will be increasing on I (see Figure 3.15). Because the slope of the tangent at each point on the graph is measured by the derivative f', it is reasonable to expect f to be increasing on intervals where $f' > 0$. Similarly, it is reasonable to expect f to be decreasing on an interval where $f' < 0$. These observations are established formally in Theorem 3.7.

Figure 3.15 The graph is rising where $f' > 0$ and falling where $f' < 0$. Notice that the small flags indicate the slopes at various points on the graph.

THEOREM 3.7   Increasing and decreasing function theorem

Let f be differentiable on the open interval (a, b). Then the *function f is strictly increasing* on (a, b) if

$$f'(x) > 0 \quad \text{for } a < x < b$$

and f is *strictly decreasing* on (a, b) if

$$f'(x) < 0 \quad \text{for } a < x < b.$$

Proof: We shall prove that f is strictly increasing on (a, b) if $f'(x) > 0$ throughout the interval. The strictly decreasing case is similar and is left as an exercise for the reader.

Suppose $f'(x) > 0$ throughout the interval (a, b), and let x_1 and x_2 be two numbers chosen arbitrarily from this interval, with $x_1 < x_2$. The MVT tells us that

$$\frac{f(x_2) - f(x_1)}{x_2 - x_1} = f'(c) \quad \text{or} \quad f(x_2) - f(x_1) = f'(c)(x_2 - x_1)$$

for some number c between x_1 and x_2. Because both $f'(c) > 0$ and $x_2 - x_1 > 0$, it follows that $f'(c)(x_2 - x_1) > 0$, and therefore

$$f(x_2) - f(x_1) > 0 \quad \text{or} \quad f(x_2) > f(x_1)$$

That is, if x_1 and x_2 are any two numbers in (a, b) such that $x_1 < x_2$, then $f(x_1) < f(x_2)$, which means that f is strictly increasing on (a, b).   ∎

To determine where a function f is increasing or decreasing, we begin by finding the critical values (where the derivative is zero or does not exist). These values divide the x-axis into intervals, and we test the sign of f' in each of these intervals. Finally, if $f'(x) > 0$ in an interval, then f is increasing in that entire interval; and if $f'(x) < 0$ in an interval, then f is decreasing in that same interval. This procedure is illustrated in the following example.

EXAMPLE 1   Finding intervals on which a function is increasing or decreasing

Determine where the function defined by $f(x) = x^3 - 3x^2 - 9x + 1$ is strictly increasing and where it is strictly decreasing.

Solution   First, we find the derivative:

$$f'(x) = 3x^2 - 6x - 9 = 3(x + 1)(x - 3)$$

Next, we determine the critical values: $f'(x)$ exists for all x and $f'(x) = 0$ at $x = -1$ and $x = 3$ (by inspection). These critical values divide the x-axis into three parts, as shown in Figure 3.16a, and we select a typical number from each of these intervals. For example, we select -2, 0, and 4, evaluate the derivative at these values, and mark each interval as increasing (↑) or decreasing (↓), according to whether the derivative is positive or negative, respectively. This is shown in Figure 3.16b.

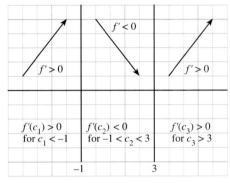

a. Intervals where f is increasing and where it is decreasing

b. The graph of f along with the sign graphs for f and f'

Figure 3.16 $f(x) = x^3 - 3x^2 - 9x + 1$

The function f is increasing for $x < -1$ and for $x > 3$; f is decreasing for $-1 < x < 3$.

EXAMPLE 2   Comparison of the graphs of a function and its derivative

Graph $f(x) = x^3 - 3x^2 - 9x + 1$ and $f'(x) = 3x^2 - 6x - 9$ and compare.

a. When f' is positive, what does that mean in terms of the graph of f?

b. When the graph of f is decreasing, what does that mean in terms of the graph of f'?

Solution   The graphs of f and f' are shown in Figure 3.17.

⊘ Notice that critical values of f are intercepts for the graph of f'. ⊘

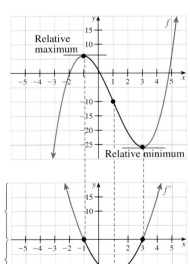

a. When f' is positive, f is increasing.

b. When f' is negative, f is decreasing.

Figure 3.17 Graphs of f and f'

■ THE FIRST-DERIVATIVE TEST

Every relative extremum is a critical point. However, as we saw in Section 3.1, not every critical point is necessarily a relative extremum. If the derivative is positive to the left of a critical value and negative to its right, the graph changes from increasing to decreasing and the critical point must be a relative maximum, as shown in Figure 3.18a. If the derivative is negative to the left of a critical value and positive to its right, the graph changes from decreasing to increasing and the critical point is a relative minimum (Figure 3.18b). However, if the sign of the derivative is the same on both sides of the critical value, then it is neither a relative maximum nor a relative minimum (Figure 3.18c). These observations are summarized in a procedure called the *first-derivative test for relative extrema*.

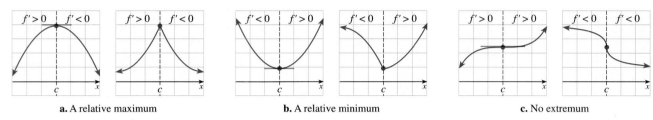

a. A relative maximum   b. A relative minimum   c. No extremum

Figure 3.18 Three patterns of behavior near a critical value

The First-Derivative Test for Relative Extrema

Step 1. Find all critical values of f. That is, find all numbers c such that $f(c)$ is defined and either $f'(c) = 0$ or $f'(c)$ does not exist.

Step 2. Classify each critical point $(c, f(c))$ as follows:

    a. The point $(c, f(c))$ is a **relative maximum** if $f'(x) > 0$ (rising) for all x in an open interval (a, c) to the left of c, and $f'(x) < 0$ (falling) for all x in an open interval (c, b) to the right of c.

    b. The point $(c, f(c))$ is a **relative minimum** if $f'(x) < 0$ (falling) for all x in an open interval (a, c) to the left of c, and $f'(x) > 0$ (rising) for all x in an open interval (c, b) to the right of c.

    c. The point $(c, f(c))$ is **not an extremum** if the derivative $f'(x)$ has the same sign in open intervals (a, c) and (c, b) on both sides of c.

Suppose we apply this first-derivative test to the polynomial

$$f(x) = x^3 - 3x^2 - 9x + 1$$

In Example 2 we found that this function has the critical values -1 and 3 and that f is increasing when $x < -1$ and $x > 3$ and decreasing when $-1 < x < 3$ (see the arrow pattern above). The first derivative test tells us there is a relative maximum at -1 (↗ ↘ pattern) and a relative minimum at 3 (↘ ↗ pattern).

EXAMPLE 3   Relative extrema using the first-derivative test

Find all critical values of $g(t) = t - 2 \sin t$ for $0 \le t \le 2\pi$, and determine whether each corresponds to a relative maximum, a relative minimum, or neither.

Solution   Because $g'(t) = 1 - 2 \cos t$ exists for all t, the only critical values occur when $g'(t) = 0$; that is, when $\cos t = \frac{1}{2}$. Solving, we find that the critical values for $g(t)$ on the interval $[0, 2\pi]$ are $\frac{\pi}{3}$ and $\frac{5\pi}{3}$.

Next, we examine the sign of $g'(t)$. Because $g'(t)$ is continuous, it is enough to check the sign of $g'(t)$ at convenient numbers on each side of the critical values, as shown in Figure 3.19a. Notice that the arrows show the increasing and decreasing pattern for g. According to the first-derivative test, there is a relative minimum at $\frac{\pi}{3}$ and a relative maximum at $\frac{5\pi}{3}$. The graph of g is shown in Figure 3.19b. Note that $g\left(\frac{\pi}{3}\right) = \frac{\pi}{3} - \sqrt{3} \approx -0.68$ and $g\left(\frac{5\pi}{3}\right) = \frac{5\pi}{3} + \sqrt{3} \approx 6.97$.

 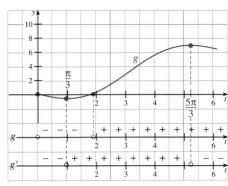

Figure 3.19 The first-derivative test for $g(t) = t - 2 \sin t$

a. Intervals where $g(t) = t - 2 \sin t$ is increasing or decreasing

b. The graph of $g(t) = t - 2 \sin t$ for $0 \le t \le 2\pi$

■ CURVE SKETCHING WITH THE FIRST DERIVATIVE

The ability to draw a quick and accurate sketch is one of the most important skills you can learn in mathematics. It has been said that René Descartes revolutionized *thinking* when he introduced the coordinate system. Today, nearly every aspect of mathematics, engineering, physics, industry, education, and the social sciences is enhanced by the use of graphs.

In calculus, we use graphs to help us understand analysis, and we use analysis to help us understand graphs. Plotting points, although useful in introducing a curve, is a very poor method for drawing a graph. You also cannot rely solely on graphing technology to do your graphing. As we have seen, there are many properties of curves that require analysis or calculus, and those properties could easily be overlooked if we relied only on graphing technology. Software and graphing calculators are helpful but incomplete ways of visualizing mathematics. For example, the relatively simple function $y = \sin\left(\frac{x}{50\pi}\right)$ is difficult to sketch using most graphing calculators. We now consider some graphing techniques that should help you to sketch curves quickly and accurately.

The First-Derivative Procedure for Sketching the Graph of a Continuous Function

Step 1. Compute the derivative $f'(x)$.

Step 2. Find the critical values: values of x for which $f(x)$ is defined but $f'(x)$ is zero or undefined. Substitute each critical value into $f(x)$ to find the y-coordinate of the corresponding critical point. Plot these critical points on a coordinate plane.

Step 3. Determine where the function is increasing or decreasing by checking the sign of the derivative on the intervals whose endpoints are the critical values found in step 2.

Step 4. Sketch the graph so that it increases on the intervals where $f'(x) > 0$, decreases on the intervals where $f'(x) < 0$, passes through the critical points, and has a horizontal tangent where $f'(x) = 0$.

EXAMPLE 4   Sketching the graph of a polynomial using the first-derivative procedure

Sketch the graph of $f(x) = 2x^3 + 3x^2 - 12x - 5$.

Solution   We begin by computing and factoring the derivative:

$$f'(x) = 6x^2 + 6x - 12 = 6(x + 2)(x - 1)$$

We see that $f'(x)$ exists for all x, and from the factored form of the derivative we see that $f'(x) = 0$ when $x = -2$ and when $x = 1$. The corresponding critical points are found as follows:

$$f(-2) = 2(-2)^3 + 3(-2)^2 - 12(-2) - 5 = 15;\quad \text{critical point } (-2, 15)$$

$$f(1) = 2(1)^3 + 3(1)^2 - 12(1) - 5 = -12;\quad \text{critical point } (1, -12)$$

Next, to find the intervals of increase and decrease of the function, we plot the critical numbers on a number line and check the sign of the derivative at values to the left and right of -2 and 1. We find that f is increasing and decreasing, as indicated in Figure 3.20.

The arrow pattern in Figure 3.20 suggests that the graph of f has a relative maximum at $(-2, 15)$ and a relative minimum at $(1, -12)$. We begin the sketch by plotting these points on a coordinate plane. We put a "cap" at the relative maximum $(-2, 15)$ and a "cup" at the relative minimum $(1, -12)$, as shown in Figure 3.21a. Finally, we note that because $f(0) = -5$, the graph has its y-intercept at $(0, -5)$. We complete the sketch by drawing the curve so that it increases for $x < -2$ to the relative maximum at $(-2, 15)$, decreases for $-2 < x < 1$, passing through the y-intercept $(0, -5)$ on its way to the relative minimum at $(1, -12)$, and then increases again for $x > 1$. The completed graph is shown in Figure 3.21b.

Figure 3.20 Intervals of increase and decrease for $f(x) = 2x^3 + 3x^2 - 12x - 5$

Computational Window

The graphs of most of the functions in this section can be checked by drawing them with a graphing calculator. Use **GRAPH** and **ZOOM**.

Y₁ ⊟ 2X^3+3X^2−12X
−5

Xmin=-3   Ymin=-20
Xmax=3   Ymax=20
Xscl=.5   Yscl=5

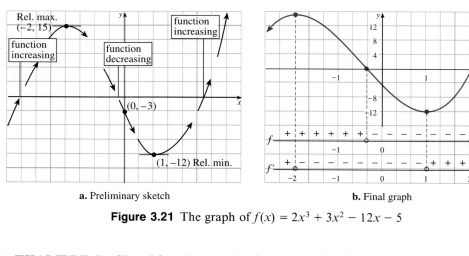

a. Preliminary sketch   **b.** Final graph

Figure 3.21 The graph of $f(x) = 2x^3 + 3x^2 - 12x - 5$

EXAMPLE 5   Sketching the graph of a trigonometric function using the first-derivative procedure

Sketch the graph of $f(x) = \cos^2 x + \cos x$ on $[0, 2\pi]$.

Solution   The derivative of f is

$$f'(x) = -2 \cos x \sin x - \sin x$$

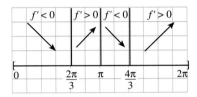

Figure 3.22 Intervals of increase and decrease for
$f(x) = \cos^2 x + \cos x$

Because $f'(x)$ exists for all x, we solve $f'(x) = 0$ to find the critical values:

$$-2 \cos x \sin x - \sin x = 0$$

$$\sin x(2 \cos x + 1) = 0$$

$$\sin x = 0 \quad \text{or} \quad \cos x = -\tfrac{1}{2}$$

The critical values on the interior of the interval $[0, 2\pi]$ are $x = \frac{2\pi}{3}$, π, and $\frac{4\pi}{3}$. Because $f\left(\frac{2\pi}{3}\right) = -\frac{1}{4}$, $f(\pi) = 0$ and $f\left(\frac{4\pi}{3}\right) = -\frac{1}{4}$, the corresponding critical points are $\left(\frac{2\pi}{3}, -\frac{1}{4}\right)$, $(\pi, 0)$, and $\left(\frac{4\pi}{3}, -\frac{1}{4}\right)$.

Next, we plot the critical values on a number line and determine the sign of the derivative $f'(x)$ in each interval, as indicated in Figure 3.22.

The arrow pattern in the diagram indicates that we have relative minima at $\left(\frac{2\pi}{3}, -\frac{1}{4}\right)$ and $\left(\frac{4\pi}{3}, -\frac{1}{4}\right)$, and a relative maximum at $(\pi, 0)$. We plot these points on a coordinate plane and place "cups" at the relative minima and a "cap" at the relative maximum. Finally, we sketch a smooth curve through these points, obtaining the graph shown in Figure 3.23. If the curve is defined over a particular interval, then you should also plot the endpoints.

Figure 3.23 The graph of
$f(x) = \cos^2 x + \cos x$

EXAMPLE 6 Sketching a graph using the first-derivative procedure

Sketch the graph of $f(x) = x^{1/3}(x - 4)$.

Solution Rewrite the given function as $f(x) = x^{4/3} - 4x^{1/3}$ and differentiate:

$$f'(x) = \tfrac{4}{3}x^{1/3} - \tfrac{4}{3}x^{-2/3} = \tfrac{4}{3}x^{-2/3}(x - 1)$$

We see that $f'(x)$ does not exist when $x = 0$ and that $f'(x) = 0$ only when $x = 1$. Because $f(0) = 0$ and $f(1) = -3$, the critical points are $(0, 0)$ and $(1, -3)$.

We plot the critical values on a number line and determine the sign of $f'(x)$ for each interval determined by the critical values, as shown in Figure 3.24.

Figure 3.24 Intervals of increase and decrease for $f(x) = x^{1/3}(x - 4)$

We see that there is a relative minimum at $(1, -3)$ and neither kind of extremum at $(0, 0)$. We plot the critical points on a coordinate plane with a "cup" at $(1, -3)$, as shown in Figure 3.25a. Finally, we pass a smooth curve

⊘ In Section 2.1, we showed that the derivative does not exist at a vertical tangent, and you might wish to verify that the derivative does not exist at $x = 0$. On the other hand, you must be careful; just because the derivative does not exist does not mean that it must have a vertical tangent. It may have a corner or cusp, for example. ⊘

through these points, obtaining the graph shown in Figure 3.25b. Note that at (0, 0) the curve looks like it has a vertical tangent.

a. Preliminary sketch

b. Final graph

Figure 3.25 The graph of $f(x) = x^{1/3}(x - 4)$

PROBLEM SET 3.3

A 1. ■ **What Does This Say?** What is the first-derivative test?

2. ■ **What Does This Say?** What is the relationship between the graph of a function and the graph of its derivative?

In Problems 3–4, identify which curve represents a function $y = f(x)$ and which curve represents its derivative $y = f'(x)$.

3.

4.
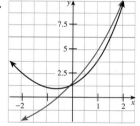

Draw a curve that represents the derivative of the function defined by the curves shown in Problems 5–8.

5.

6.

7.

8.

In Problems 9–12 draw the graph of a function whose derivative matches the graph shown.

9.

10.

11.

12.
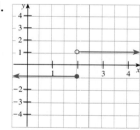

In Problems 13–34,

a. *find the critical values;*

b. *show where the function is increasing and where it is decreasing;*

c. *plot each critical point and label it as a relative maximum, a relative minimum, or neither;*

d. *sketch the graph.*

13. $f(x) = x^3 + 3x^2 + 1$

14. $f(x) = \frac{1}{3}x^3 - 9x + 2$

15. $f(x) = x^3 + 35x^2 - 125x - 9{,}375$

16. $f(x) = x^5 + 5x^4 - 550x^3 - 2{,}000x^2 + 60{,}000x$

17. $f(x) = x^5 - 5x^4 + 100$

18. $f(x) = x + \frac{1}{x}$ **19.** $f(x) = \frac{x - 1}{x^2 + 3}$ **20.** $f(x) = \frac{x + 1}{x^2 + 1}$

21. $f(t) = (t + 1)^2(t - 5)$ **22.** $f(t) = (2t - 1)^2(t^2 - 9)$

23. $f(x) = (x - 3)(x - 7)(2x + 1)$ **24.** $f(x) = 16(x - 3)^2(x - 7)^2$

25. $f(x) = \sqrt{x^2 + 1}$ **26.** $f(x) = \sqrt{x^2 - 2x + 2}$

27. $g(x) = x^{2/3}(2x - 5)$ **28.** $g(x) = x^{1/3}\sqrt{x + 15}$

29. $f(\theta) = 2\cos\theta - \theta$ on $[0, 2\pi]$

30. $c(\theta) = \theta + \cos 2\theta$ for $0 \le t \le \pi$

31. $t(x) = \tan^2 x$ for $-\frac{\pi}{4} \le x \le \frac{\pi}{4}$

32. $f(x) = 9\cos x - 4\cos^2 x$ on $[0, \pi]$

33. $f(x) = \sin(x/50\pi)$ on $[0, 1000]$ **34.** $f(x) = (x - 2)^3$

35. ■ **What Does This Say?** For n a counting number, consider the graph of $f(x) = (x - 2)^n$. What is the effect of n on these graphs?

In Problems 36–39, determine whether the given function has a relative maximum, a relative minimum, or neither at the given critical value(s).

36. $f(x) = (x^3 - 3x + 1)^7$ at $x = 1; x = -1$

37. $f(x) = (x^4 - 4x + 2)^5$ at $x = 1$

38. $f(x) = (x^2 - 4)^4(x^2 - 1)^3$ at $x = 1; x = 2$

39. $f(x) = \sqrt[3]{x^3 - 48x}$ at $x = 4$

Ⓑ 40. Suppose f is a differentiable function with derivative
$$f'(x) = (x - 1)^2(x - 2)(x - 4)(x + 5)^4$$
Find all critical values of f and determine whether each corresponds to a relative maximum, a relative minimum, or neither.

41. Suppose f is a differentiable function with derivative
$$f'(x) = \frac{(2x - 1)(x + 3)}{(x - 1)^2}$$
Find all critical values of f and determine whether each corresponds to a relative maximum, a relative minimum, or neither.

42. Sketch a graph of a function f that is differentiable on the interval $[-1, 4]$ and satisfies the following conditions:

i. The function f is decreasing on $(1, 3)$ and increasing elsewhere on $[-1, 4]$.

ii. The largest value of f is 5 and the smallest is 0.

iii. The graph of f has relative extrema at $(1, 4)$ and $(3, 1)$.

43. Sketch a graph of a function f that satisfies the following conditions:

i. $f'(x) > 0$ when $x < -5$ and when $x > 1$.

ii. $f'(x) < 0$ when $-5 < x < 1$.

iii. $f(-5) = 4$ and $f(1) = -1$.

44. Sketch a graph of a function f that satisfies the following conditions:

i. $f'(x) < 0$ when $x < -1$.

ii. $f'(x) > 0$ when $-1 < x < 3$ and when $x > 3$.

iii. $f'(-1) = 0$ and $f'(3) = 0$.

45. Find constants a, b, and c such that the graph of $f(x) = ax^2 + bx + c$ has a relative maximum at $(5, 12)$ and crosses the y-axis at $(0, 3)$.

46. Use calculus to prove that the relative extremum of the quadratic function
$$y = ax^2 + bx + c \quad (a \ne 0)$$
occurs at $x = -b/(2a)$.

47. Use calculus to prove that the relative extremum of the quadratic function
$$f(x) = (x - p)(x - q)$$
occurs midway between its x-intercepts.

48. The formula
$$I = I_0\left(\frac{\sin\theta}{\theta}\right)^2$$
with I_0 a positive constant, occurs in physics in connection with the study of Fraunhofer diffraction. (If $\theta = 0$, then $I = I_0$.) Assuming the graph of I is continuous, sketch the graph for $[-3\pi, 3\pi]$.

49. At a temperature of T (in degrees Celsius), the speed of sound in air is given by
$$v = v_0\sqrt{1 + \tfrac{1}{273}T}$$
where v_0 is the speed at $0°C$. Sketch the graph of v for $T > 0$.

50. Find constants a, b, and c that guarantee that the graph of
$$f(x) = x^3 + ax^2 + bx + c$$
will have a relative maximum at $(-3, 18)$ and a relative minimum at $(1, -14)$.

51. Find constants A, B, C, and D that guarantee that the graph of
$$f(x) = 3x^4 + Ax^3 + Bx^2 + Cx + D$$
will have horizontal tangents at $(2, 1)$ and $(0, -15)$. Classify each critical point as a relative maximum, a relative minimum, or neither.

52. Let
$$f(x) = (x - A)^m(x - B)^n$$
where A and B are real numbers and m and n are positive integers with $m > 1$ and $n > 1$. Find the critical values of f and classify each as a relative maximum, a relative minimum, or neither.

53. Let
$$f(x) = x^{1/3}\sqrt{Ax + B}$$
where A and B are positive constants. Find all critical values of f.

| ▭ | **Computational Window** | ▼ | ▲ |

54. Given that $f(x) = x^3 - \cos x$, find $f'(x)$ and then use the bisection method, the Newton–Raphson method, or a calculator to find all real critical values of f correct to the nearest hundredth. Sketch the graph of f.

55. Given that $f(x) = x^5 + \sin x^2$, find $f'(x)$ and then use the bisection method, the Newton–Raphson method, or a calculator to find all real critical values of f correct to the nearest hundredth. Sketch the graph of f.

Ⓒ 56. Suppose $f(x)$ and $g(x)$ are both continuous for all x and differentiable at $x = c$. Show that if c is a critical value for both f and g, then it is also a critical value for the product function fg. If a relative maximum occurs at c for both f and g, is it true that a relative maximum of fg occurs at c?

57. Show that if $f(x)$ is strictly increasing on an open interval I where it is differentiable, then $f'(x) \geq 0$ for all x in I. *Hint:* You may use the fact that if $f(x) > 0$ for every x in an interval except perhaps for c, and if $\lim_{x \to c} f(x)$ exists, then $\lim_{x \to c} f(x) \geq 0$.

58. Let f and g be strictly increasing functions on the interval $[a, b]$.

  a. If $f(x) > 0$ and $g(x) > 0$ on $[a, b]$, show that the product fg is also strictly increasing on $[a, b]$.

  b. If $f(x) < 0$ and $g(x) < 0$ on $[a, b]$, is fg strictly increasing, strictly decreasing, or neither? Explain.

59. a. Suppose f is strictly increasing for $x > 0$. Let n be a positive integer and define $g(x) = x^n f(x)$ for $x > 0$. If $f(x) > 0$ on an interval $[a, b]$ with $a > 0$, show that g is strictly increasing on the same interval.

  b. Let $g(x) = x^n \sin x$ for $0 < x < \frac{\pi}{2}$, where n is a positive integer. Explain why g is strictly increasing on this interval.

60. Complete the proof of the increasing and decreasing function theorem (Theorem 3.7). Specifically, show that if f is differentiable on (a, b) and $f'(x) < 0$ throughout the interval $[a, b]$, then f is strictly decreasing on $[a, b]$.

THINK TANK PROBLEMS: *Problems 61–67 are statements about continuous functions. In each case, either show that the statement is generally true or find a counterexample.*

61. If f and g both have a relative maximum at c, then so does $f + g$.

62. If f and g are both differentiable and f and g both have a relative extremum at c, then $f'(c) = g'(c) = 0$.

63. If f is strictly increasing for $x > c$ and strictly decreasing for $x < c$, then $f'(c) = 0$.

64. If $f'(0) = 0$, $f'\left(-\frac{1}{2}\right) < 0$, and $f'\left(\frac{1}{2}\right) > 0$, then f has a relative minimum at $(0, f(0))$.

65. If f' is nonnegative on an interval I, then f is strictly increasing on I.

66. If f is strictly decreasing on an interval I, then $-f$ is strictly increasing on I.

67. If f and g are each strictly increasing on an interval I, then $f - g$ is also strictly increasing on I.

68. JOURNAL PROBLEM: *Mathematics Magazine.** Give an elementary proof that

$$f(x) = \frac{1}{\sin x} - \frac{1}{x}, \qquad 0 < x \leq \frac{\pi}{2}$$

is positive and increasing.

3.4 CONCAVITY AND THE SECOND-DERIVATIVE TEST

IN THIS SECTION Concavity, inflection points, curve sketching with the second derivative, the second-derivative test for relative extrema

Knowing where a given graph is rising and falling gives only a partial picture of the graph. For example, suppose we wish to sketch the graph of $f(x) = x^3 + 3x + 1$. The derivative $f'(x) = 3x^2 + 3$ is positive for all x so the graph is always rising. But in what *way* is it rising? Each of the graphs in Figure 3.26 is a possible graph of f, but they are quite different from one another. Later in this section we shall show that the correct graph is the one in Figure 3.26c. The focus of our work is a characteristic of graphs called *concavity* that will allow us to distinguish among graphs such as these. In addition, we shall develop a *second-derivative test* that enables us to classify a critical point P of a function f as a relative maximum or a relative minimum by examining the sign of the second derivative f'' at P.

a.

b.

c.

Figure 3.26 Which curve is the graph of $f(x) = x^3 + 3x + 1$?

*Volume 55, 1982, p. 300. "Elementary proof" in the question means that you should use only techniques from beginning calculus. For our purposes, you simply need to give a reasonable argument to justify the conclusion.

■ CONCAVITY

A portion of graph that is cupped upward is called *concave up*, and a portion that is cupped downward is *concave down*. Figure 3.27 shows a graph that is concave up between A and C and concave down between C and E. At various points on the graph, the slope is indicated by "flags," and we observe that the slope increases from A to C and decreases from C to E. This is no accident! *The slope of a graph increases on an interval where the graph is concave up and decreases where the graph is concave down.*

Conversely, a graph will be concave up on any interval where the slope is increasing and concave down where the slope is decreasing. Because the slope is found by computing the derivative, it is reasonable to expect the graph of a given function f to be concave up where the derivative f' is strictly increasing. According to the increasing and decreasing function theorem (Theorem 3.7), this occurs when $(f')' > 0$, which means that the graph of f is concave up where the *second derivative* f'' satisfies $f'' > 0$. Similarly, the graph is concave down where $f'' < 0$. We use this observation to *define* concavity.

Figure 3.27 The slope of a graph increases or decreases, depending on its concavity.

Concavity

> The graph of a function f is **concave upward** on any open interval I where $f''(x) > 0$, and it is **concave downward** where $f''(x) < 0$.

EXAMPLE 1   Concavity for a polynomial function

Find where the graph of $f(x) = x^3 + 3x + 1$ is concave up and where it is concave down.

Solution   We find that $f'(x) = 3x^2 + 3$ and $f''(x) = 6x$. Therefore, $f''(x) < 0$ if $x < 0$ and $f''(x) > 0$ if $x > 0$, so the graph of f is concave down for $x < 0$ and concave up for $x > 0$. Using this information, we can now answer the question asked in Figure 3.26—the correct graph is c.   ■

■ INFLECTION POINTS

In Figure 3.27, notice that the graph changes from concave up to concave down at the point C. It will be convenient to give a name to such a transition point.

Inflection Point

> Suppose the graph of a function f has a tangent line (possibly vertical) at the point $P(c, f(c))$ and that the graph is concave up on one side of P and concave down on the other side. Then P is called an **inflection point** of the graph.

Returning to Example 1, notice that the graph of $f(x) = x^3 + 3x + 1$ has exactly one inflection point, at $(0, 1)$, where the concavity changes from down to up.

Various kinds of graphical behavior are illustrated in Figure 3.28. Note that the graph is rising on the interval $[a, c_1]$, falling on $[c_1, c_2]$, rising on $[c_2, c_3]$, falling on $[c_3, c_4]$, rising on $[c_4, c_5]$, and falling on $[c_5, b]$. The concavity is up on $[p_1, p_2]$ and $[p_3, p_4]$ and down otherwise.

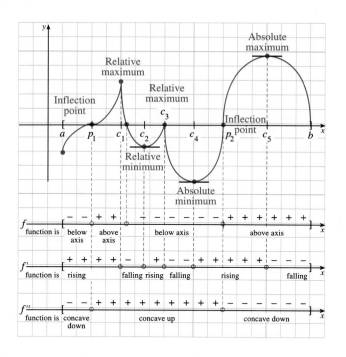

Figure 3.28 A graph of a function showing critical values and inflection points

The graph has relative maxima at c_1, c_3, and c_5 and relative minima at c_2 and c_4. There are horizontal tangents ($f' = 0$) at all of these points except c_1 and c_3, where there are sharp points called cusps ($f'(c_1)$ and $f'(c_3)$ do not exist). There is also a horizontal tangent at p_1 ($f'(p_1) = 0$) but no relative extrema appear there. Instead, we have points of inflection at p_1 and p_2, because the concavity changes direction at each of these points.

In general, the concavity of the graph of f will change only at points where $f'' = 0$ or f'' does not exist; that is, at critical values of the derivative f'. We shall call the number c a **second-order critical value** if $f''(c) = 0$ or $f''(c)$ does not exist, and in this context an "ordinary" critical value (where $f' = 0$ or f' does not exist) will be referred to as a **first-order critical value**. Inflection points correspond to second-order critical values and must actually be on the graph of f. Specifically, a number c such that $f''(c)$ is not defined and the concavity of f changes at c will correspond to an inflection point only if $f(c)$ is defined.

⊘ A continuous function f does not have to have an inflection point where $f'' = 0$. For instance, if $f(x) = x^4$, we have $f''(x) = 12x^2$, so $f''(0) = 0$, but the graph of f is always concave up (see Figure 3.29). ⊘

EXAMPLE 2   Concavity and inflection points

Figure 3.29 The graph of $f(x) = x^4$ has no inflection point at $(0, 0)$ even though $f''(0) = 0$.

Discuss the concavity of $f(x) = \dfrac{x^2}{2\sqrt{2}} + \sin x$ on the interval $\left[0, \frac{\pi}{2}\right]$ and find all the inflection points of f.

Solution   Find f' and f'':

$$f'(x) = \frac{x}{\sqrt{2}} + \cos x \qquad f''(x) = \frac{1}{\sqrt{2}} - \sin x$$

Both $f'(x)$ and $f''(x)$ are defined for all x on the interval $\left[0, \frac{\pi}{2}\right]$ and $f''(x) = 0$ when $\sin x = \frac{1}{\sqrt{2}}$. Thus, the only possible location for an inflection point is where $x = \frac{\pi}{4}$. Testing to the left and right of $\frac{\pi}{4}$ we see that the concavity changes (from up to down) at $x = \frac{\pi}{4}$, so a point of inflection occurs there, and this is the only such point on the interval $\left[0, \frac{\pi}{2}\right]$. The graph of f is shown in Figure 3.30.

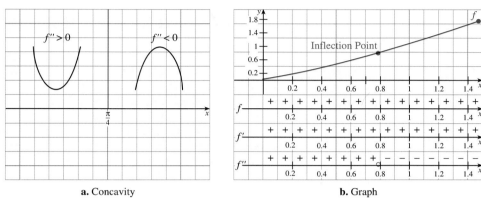

a. Concavity   b. Graph

Figure 3.30 Concavity and graph of $f(x) = \dfrac{x^2}{2\sqrt{2}} + \sin x$

Here is an example of one way inflection points may appear in practical applications.

EXAMPLE 3   Finding the maximum rate of production

An efficiency study of the morning shift at a factory indicates that an average worker who arrives on the job at 8:00 A.M. will have turned out $Q(t) = -t^3 + 9t^2 + 12t$ units t hours later. At what time in the morning is the worker performing most efficiently?

Solution   The worker's rate of production is the derivative

$$R(t) = Q'(t) = -3t^2 + 18t + 12$$

Assuming the morning shift runs from 8:00 A.M. until noon, the goal is to maximize the function $R(t)$ on the closed interval $[0, 4]$. The derivative of R is

$$R'(t) = Q''(t) = -6t + 18$$

which is zero when $t = 3$; this is the critical value. Using the optimization criterion of Section 3.1, we know that the extrema of $R(t)$ on the closed interval $[0, 4]$ must occur at either the interior critical value 3 or at one (or both) of the endpoints (which are 0 and 4). We find that

$$R(0) = 12 \qquad R(3) = 39 \qquad R(4) = 36$$

so the rate of production $R(t)$ is greatest and the worker is performing most efficiently when $t = 3$, that is, at 11:00 A.M. The graphs of the output function Q and its derivative, the rate-of-production function R, are shown in Figure 3.31. Notice that the production curve is steepest and the rate of production is greatest when $t = 3$.

In Example 3, note how the rate of assembly, as measured by the slope of the graph of the average worker's output, increases from 0 to the inflection point I and then decreases from I to E, as shown in Figure 3.31a. Because the point I marks

---

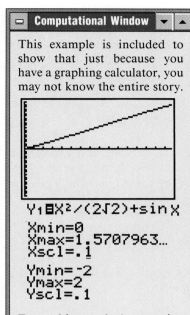

Computational Window

This example is included to show that just because you have a graphing calculator, you may not know the entire story.

Y₁◻X²/(2√2)+sinX
Xmin=0
Xmax=1.5707963...
Xscl=.1

Ymin=-2
Ymax=2
Yscl=.1

From this graph (even using the (TRACE) and (ZOOM)), it is not possible to find the inflection point at $x = \frac{\pi}{4}$. Even if we use the standard scale we still cannot discover the inflection point.

Y₁◻X²/(2√2)+sin
Xmin=-10 Ymin=-10
Xmax=10   Ymax=10
Xscl=1   Yscl=1

a. A production curve

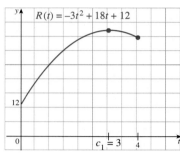

b. Rate of production

Figure 3.31 Graph of a production curve showing the point of diminishing returns

the point where the rate of production "peaks out," it is natural to refer to I as a point of **diminishing returns.** It is also an inflection point on the graph of Q. Knowing that this point occurs at 11:00 A.M., the manager of the factory might be able to increase the overall output of the labor force by scheduling a break near this time. (Remember that the domain for Example 3 is $[0, 4]$.)

■ CURVE SKETCHING WITH THE SECOND DERIVATIVE

In Section 3.3, we learned how to find where a graph is rising and where it is falling by examining the sign of the first derivative. Now, by examining the sign of the second derivative, we can determine the concavity of the graph, which gives us a more refined picture of the graph's appearance.

EXAMPLE 4   Graph of a polynomial function

Determine where the function $f(x) = x^4 - 4x^3 + 10$ is increasing and decreasing and where its graph is concave up and concave down. Find the relative extrema and inflection points and sketch the graph of f.

Solution   The first derivative,

$$f'(x) = 4x^3 - 12x^2 = 4x^2(x - 3)$$

is zero when $x = 0$ and when $x = 3$. Because $4x^2 > 0$ for $x \neq 0$, we have $f'(x) < 0$ for $x < 3$ (except for $x = 0$) and $f'(x) > 0$ for $x > 3$. The pattern showing where f is increasing and where it is decreasing is displayed in Figure 3.32a.

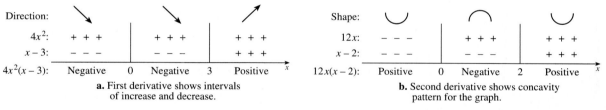

a. First derivative shows intervals of increase and decrease.

b. Second derivative shows concavity pattern for the graph.

Figure 3.32 First and second derivatives of $f(x) = x^4 - 4x^3 + 10$

Next, to determine the concavity of the graph we compute

$$f''(x) = 12x^2 - 24x = 12x(x - 2)$$

If $x < 0$ or $x > 2$, then $f''(x) > 0$ and the graph is concave up. It is concave down when $0 < x < 2$, because $f''(x) < 0$ on this interval. The concavity of the graph of f is shown in Figure 3.32b.

The two diagrams in Figure 3.32 tell us that there is a relative minimum at $x = 3$ and inflection points at $x = 0$ and $x = 2$ (because the second derivative changes sign at these points).

To find the critical points and the inflection points, evaluate f at $x = 0, 2,$ and 3:

$$f(0) = (0)^4 - 4(0)^3 + 10 = 10$$

$$f(2) = (2)^4 - 4(2)^3 + 10 = -6$$

$$f(3) = (3)^4 - 4(3)^3 + 10 = -17$$

Finally, to sketch the graph of f, we first place a "cup" ($\cup$) at the minimum point $(3, -17)$ and note that $(0, 10)$ and $(2, -6)$ are inflection points;

remember there is also a horizontal tangent at $(0, 10)$. The preliminary graph is shown in Figure 3.33a. Complete the sketch by passing a smooth curve through these points, using the two diagrams in Figure 3.32 as a guide for determining where the graph is rising and falling and where it is concave up and down. The completed graph is shown in Figure 3.33b.

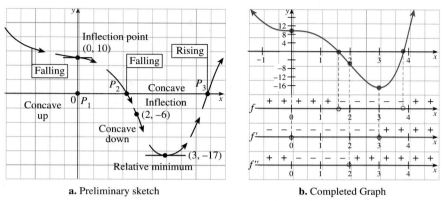

| a. Preliminary sketch | b. Completed Graph |

Figure 3.33 Graphing $f(x) = x^4 - 4x^3 + 10$

EXAMPLE 5   Using the first and second derivative to graph a function

Sketch the graph of $f(x) = x^{2/3}(2x + 5)$.

Solution   Find the first and second derivative and write them in factored form. To do this, write $f(x) = 2x^{5/3} + 5x^{2/3}$.

$$f'(x) = 2\left(\tfrac{5}{3}\right)x^{2/3} + 5\left(\tfrac{2}{3}\right)x^{-1/3} = \tfrac{10}{3}x^{-1/3}(x + 1)$$

$$f''(x) = \tfrac{10}{3}\left(\tfrac{2}{3}\right)x^{-1/3} + \tfrac{10}{3}\left(-\tfrac{1}{3}\right)x^{-4/3} = \tfrac{10}{9}x^{-4/3}(2x - 1)$$

From these equations we see

$f'(x) = 0$ when $x = -1$; $f'(x)$ does not exist at $x = 0$. The first-order critical values are -1 and 0.

$f''(x) = 0$ when $x = \tfrac{1}{2}$; $f''(x)$ does not exist at $x = 0$. The second-order critical values are $\tfrac{1}{2}$ and 0.

Check the intervals of increase and decrease (Figure 3.34a) and of concavity (Figure 3.34b).

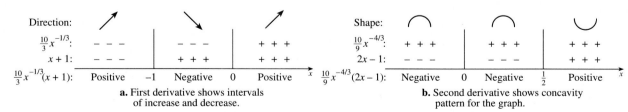

| a. First derivative shows intervals of increase and decrease. | b. Second derivative shows concavity pattern for the graph. |

Figure 3.34 Preliminary work for graphing $f(x) = x^{2/3}(2x + 5)$

The diagrams in Figure 3.34 suggest that the graph of f has a relative maximum at $x = -1$, a relative minimum at $x = 0$, and an inflection point at $x = \tfrac{1}{2}$. We must find the y-coordinates of these points by evaluating f:

$$f(-1) = 3 \qquad f(0) = 0 \qquad f\left(\tfrac{1}{2}\right) = \frac{6}{\sqrt[3]{4}} \approx 3.77976315$$

Plot and label the points $(-1, 3)$, $(0, 0)$, and $(0.5, 3.8)$ on the preliminary graph, as shown in Figure 3.35a. Note that because the graph is concave down on both sides of the origin and because the first derivative grows large without bound as $x \to 0$ from both the left and the right, there is a vertical tangent at $(0, 0)$. By plotting the relative extrema and the inflection point on a coordinate plane and passing a smooth curve through these points, we obtain the graph shown in Figure 3.35b.

a. Preliminary sketch

b. Completed graph

Figure 3.35 Graph of $f(x) = x^{2/3}(2x + 5)$

EXAMPLE 6   Using the first and second derivatives to graph a trigonometric function

Sketch the graph of $T(x) = \sin x + \cos x$ on $[0, 2\pi]$.

Solution   You probably graphed this function in trigonometry by adding ordinates. However, with this example we wish to illustrate the power of calculus to complete the graph. Thus, we begin by finding the first and second derivatives.

$$T'(x) = \cos x - \sin x$$
$$T''(x) = -\sin x - \cos x$$

From these equations we find the critical values (both T' and T'' are defined for all values of x):

$T'(x) = 0$ when $\cos x = \sin x$;   thus, $x = \frac{\pi}{4}$ and $x = \frac{5\pi}{4}$.
$T''(x) = 0$ when $\cos x = -\sin x$;   thus, $x = \frac{3\pi}{4}$ and $x = \frac{7\pi}{4}$.

We check the intervals of increase and decrease as well as the concavity pattern, as shown in Figure 3.36.

Find the critical points, as well as the points of inflection.

Relative maximum: $T\left(\frac{\pi}{4}\right) = \sqrt{2}$; the critical point is $\left(\frac{\pi}{4}, \sqrt{2}\right)$.

Relative minimum: $T\left(\frac{5\pi}{4}\right) = -\sqrt{2}$; the critical point is $\left(\frac{5\pi}{4}, -\sqrt{2}\right)$.

Inflection: $T\left(\frac{3\pi}{4}\right) = 0$; the inflection point is $\left(\frac{3\pi}{4}, 0\right)$.

$T\left(\frac{7\pi}{4}\right) = 0$; the inflection point is $\left(\frac{7\pi}{4}, 0\right)$.

Finally, find the value of T at the endpoints:

$$T(0) = 1 \quad \text{and} \quad T(2\pi) = 1$$

This information is shown in Figure 3.37.

a. Intervals of increase and decrease

b. Concavity pattern

Figure 3.36 Preliminary work for sketching $T(x) = \sin x + \cos x$

a. Preliminary sketch   **b. Completed sketch**

Figure 3.37 Graph of $T(x) = \sin x + \cos x$ on $[0, 2\pi]$

■ THE SECOND-DERIVATIVE TEST FOR RELATIVE EXTREMA

It is often possible to classify a critical point $P(c, f(c))$ on the graph of f by examining the sign of $f''(c)$. Specifically, suppose $f'(c) = 0$ and $f''(c) > 0$. Then there is a horizontal tangent line at P and the graph of f is concave up in the neighborhood of P. This means that the graph of f is cupped upward from the horizontal tangent at P, and it is reasonable to expect P to be a relative minimum, as shown in Figure 3.38a. Similarly, we expect P to be a relative maximum if $f'(c) = 0$ and $f''(c) < 0$, because the graph is cupped down beneath the critical point P, as shown in Figure 3.38b.

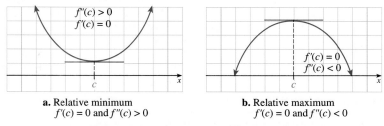

a. Relative minimum
$f'(c) = 0$ and $f''(c) > 0$

b. Relative maximum
$f'(c) = 0$ and $f''(c) < 0$

Figure 3.38 Second-derivative test for relative extrema

These observations lead to the *second-derivative test* for relative extrema.

The Second-Derivative Test for Relative Extrema

Let f be a function such that $f'(c) = 0$ and the second derivative exists on an open interval containing c.
If $f''(c) > 0$, there is a **relative minimum** at $x = c$.
If $f''(c) < 0$, there is a **relative maximum** at $x = c$.
If $f''(c) = 0$, then the second-derivative test fails and gives no information.

EXAMPLE 7   Second-derivative test to find extrema

Use the second-derivative test to determine whether each critical value of the function $f(x) = 3x^5 - 5x^3 + 2$ corresponds to a relative maximum, a relative minimum, or neither.

Solution   Once again, we begin by finding the first and second derivatives:

$$f'(x) = 15x^4 - 15x^2 = 15x^2(x - 1)(x + 1)$$

$$f''(x) = 60x^3 - 30x = 30x(2x^2 - 1)$$

To apply the second-derivative test, evaluate the second derivative for the critical values $x = 0$, 1, and -1:

$f''(0) = 0$;   test fails at $x = 0$.

$f''(1) = 30$;   positive; test tells us that there is a relative minimum at $x = 1$.

$f''(-1) = -30$;   negative, so test tells us that there is a relative maximum at $x = -1$.

When the second-derivative test fails (in this case at $x = 0$), revert to the first-derivative test:

The derivative is negative to the right of 0 and negative to the left of 0.

Neither kind of extremum occurs at $x = 0$ ($\searrow\searrow$ pattern). Actually, there is an inflection point at $x = 0$ because the second derivative is negative to the right of 0 and positive to the left of zero. The graph is shown in Figure 3.39.

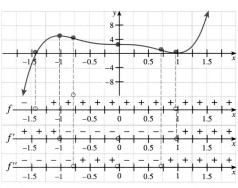

Figure 3.39 Graph of $f(x) = 3x^5 - 5x^3 + 2$

Example 7 demonstrates both the strength and the weakness of the second-derivative test. In particular, when it is relatively easy to find the second derivative (as with a polynomial) and if the zeros of this function are easy to find, then the second-derivative test provides a quick means for classifying the critical points. However, if it is difficult to compute $f''(c)$ or if $f''(c) = 0$, it may be easier, or even necessary, to apply the first-derivative test.

TABLE 3.1 Summary of the First-Derivative and Second-Derivative Tests

Find the **critical values** c such that $f(c)$ is defined and either $f'(c) = 0$ or $f'(c)$ does not exist.

Second-Derivative Test

If $f''(c) < 0$, relative maximum at $x = c$.	If $f''(c) > 0$, relative minimum at $x = c$.	If $f''(c) = 0$, second-derivative test fails.

$f''(c) < 0$

$f''(c) > 0$

First-Derivative Test

If the first derivative changes from positive to negative (left to right) at c, then f has a relative maximum at $x = c$.	If the first derivative changes from negative to positive (left to right) at c, then f has a relative minimum at $x = c$.

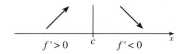

$f' > 0$ c $f' < 0$

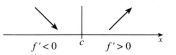

$f' < 0$ c $f' > 0$

Inflection Points

There is an inflection point at c if f'' (the concavity) changes sign there. This may occur if $f''(c) = 0$ or if $f''(c)$ is not defined.

PROBLEM SET 3.4

A 1. ■ **What Does This Say?** What is the second-derivative test?

2. ■ **What Does This Say?** What is the relationship between concavity, points of inflection, and the second derivative?

3. ■ **What Does This Say?** The cartoon on page 196 exclaims, "Our prices are increasing slower than any of our competitors!" Restate using calculus.

Find all critical points of the given function in Problems 4–27, and determine where the graph of the function is rising, falling, concave up, or concave down. Sketch the graph.

4. $f(x) = x^2 + 5x - 3$

5. $f(x) = 2(x + 20)^2 - 8(x + 20) + 7$

6. $f(x) = x^3 - 3x - 4$

7. $f(x) = \frac{1}{3}x^3 - 9x + 2$

8. $f(x) = (x - 12)^4 - 2(x - 12)^3$

9. $f(x) = 1 + 2x + \frac{18}{x}$

10. $f(u) = 3u^4 - 2u^3 - 12u^2 + 18u - 5$

11. $g(u) = u^4 + 6u^3 - 24u^2 + 26$

12. $f(x) = \dfrac{x^2}{x - 3}$

13. $f(x) = \dfrac{x^2 - 3x}{x + 1}$

14. $f(x) = \sqrt{x^2 + 1}$

15. $g(t) = (t^3 + t)^2$

16. $f(t) = (t^3 + 3t^2)^3$

17. $f(t) = t^3 - 3t^4$

18. $f(t) = 4t^5 - 5t^4$

19. $g(t) = 5t^6 - 6t^3$

20. $f(x) = \dfrac{1}{x^2 + 3}$

21. $f(x) = \dfrac{x}{x^2 + 1}$

22. $f(t) = 2t^{4/3} + 9t + 1$

23. $f(x) = x^{4/3}(x - 27)$

24. $t(\theta) = \sin \theta - 2 \cos \theta$ for $0 \le \theta \le 2\pi$

25. $t(\theta) = \theta + \cos 2\theta$ for $0 \le \theta \le \pi$

26. $h(u) = \dfrac{\sin u}{2 + \cos u}$ for $0 \le u \le 2\pi$

27. $f(t) = -\frac{1}{4} \sin 2t + \cos t$ for $0 \le t \le \pi$

B 28. THINK TANK PROBLEM Sketch the graph of a function with the following properties:

$f'(x) > 0$ when $x < -1$ and when $x > 3$

$f'(x) < 0$ when $-1 < x < 3$

$f''(x) < 0$ when $x < 2$

$f''(x) > 0$ when $x > 2$

29. THINK TANK PROBLEM Sketch the graph of a function with the following properties:

$f'(x) > 0$ when $x < 2$ and when $2 < x < 5$

$f'(x) < 0$ when $x > 5$

$f'(2) = 0$

$f''(x) < 0$ when $x < 2$ and when $4 < x < 7$

$f''(x) > 0$ when $2 < x < 4$ and when $x > 7$

30. THINK TANK PROBLEM Sketch the graph of a function with the following properties:

$f'(x) > 0$ when $x < 1$

$f'(x) < 0$ when $x > 1$

$f''(x) > 0$ when $x < 1$

$f''(x) > 0$ when $x > 1$

What can you say about the derivative of f when $x = 1$?

31. THINK TANK PROBLEM Sketch the graph of a function with the following properties: There are relative extrema at $(-1, 7)$ and $(3, 2)$. There is an inflection point at $(1, 4)$. The graph is concave down only if $x < 1$. The intercepts are $(-4, 0)$ and $(0, 5)$.

32. ■ **What Does This Say?** Consider the graphs of

a. $f(x) = (x + 1)^{1/3}$

b. $f(x) = (x + 1)^{2/3}$

c. $f(x) = (x + 1)^{4/3}$

d. $f(x) = (x + 1)^{5/3}$

Generalize to make a statement about the effect of a positive integer n on the graph of $f(x) = (x + 1)^{n/3}$.

33. Use calculus to show that the graph of the quadratic function $y = Ax^2 + Bx + C$ is concave up if $A > 0$ and concave down if $A < 0$.

34. Find constants A, B, and C that guarantee that the function $f(x) = Ax^3 + Bx^2 + C$ will have a relative extremum at $(2, 11)$ and an inflection point at $(1, 5)$. Sketch the graph of f.

35. ■ **What Does This Say?** Consider the graph of $y = x^3 + bx^2 + cx + d$ for constants b, c, and d. What happens to the graph as b changes?

36. At noon on a certain day, Frank sets out to assemble five stereo sets. His rate of assembly increases steadily throughout the afternoon until 4 P.M., at which time he has completed 3 sets. After that, he assembles sets at a slower and slower rate until he finally completes the fifth set at 8 P.M. Sketch a rough graph of a function that represents the number of sets Frank has completed after t hours of work.

37. The deflection of a hardwood beam of length ℓ is given by

$$D(x) = \tfrac{9}{4}x^4 - 7\ell x^3 + 5\ell^2 x^2$$

where x is the distance from one end of the beam. What value of x yields the maximum deflection?

38. A manufacturer estimates that if x units of a particular commodity are produced, the total cost (in dollars) will be

$$C(x) = x^3 - 24x^2 + 350x + 400$$

At what level of production will the marginal cost C' be minimized?

39. The total cost of producing x thousand units of a certain commodity is

$$C(x) = 2x^4 - 6x^3 - 12x^2 - 2x + 1$$

Determine the largest and smallest values of the marginal cost C' for $0 \le x \le 3$.

40. Let f be a function that is differentiable at 0 and satisfies $f(0) = 0$. If $y = f(x)$, suppose

$$\frac{dy}{dx} = \frac{3y^2 + x}{y^2 + 2}$$

a. Find an equation for the tangent line to the graph of f at the point where $x = 0$.

b. Note that the origin is a critical point. What kind of relative extremum (if any) occurs at this point?

41. An industrial psychologist conducts two efficiency studies at the Chilco appliance factory. The first study indicates the average worker who arrives on the job at 8 A.M. will have assembled

$$-t^3 + 6t^2 + 13t$$

blenders in t hours (without a break), for $0 \le t \le 4$. The second study suggests that after a 15-minute coffee break, the average worker can assemble

$$-\tfrac{1}{3}t^3 + \tfrac{1}{2}t^2 + 25t$$

blenders in t hours after the break for $0 < t \le 4$.
Note: The 15-minute break is not part of the work time.

a. Verify that if the coffee break occurs at 10 A.M., the average worker will assemble 42 blenders before the break and $49\tfrac{1}{3}$ blenders for the two hours after the break.

b. Suppose the coffee break is scheduled to begin x hours after 8 A.M. Find an expression for the total number of blenders $N(x)$ assembled by the average worker during the morning shift (8 A.M. to 12:15 P.M.).

c. At what time should the coffee break be scheduled so

that the average worker will produce the maximum number of blenders during the morning shift? How is this optimum time related to the point of diminishing returns?

Ⓒ 42. In a paper published in 1969,* C. J. Pennycuick provided experimental evidence to show that the power P required by a bird to maintain flight is given by the formula

$$P = \frac{w^2}{2\rho S v} + \frac{1}{2}\rho A v^3$$

where v is the relative speed of the bird, w is its weight, ρ is the density of air, and S and A are constants associated with the bird's size and shape. What speed will minimize the power? You may assume that w, ρ, S, and A are all positive.

43. Show that if f is concave up on an interval I, then the graph of f lies above all its tangents on I. *Hint:* Use the mean value theorem to show that if c is a point in I, then

$$f(x) > f(c) + f'(c)(x - c)$$

for all x in I. This property is sometimes used as the definition of concave up.

44. ■ **What Does This Say?** Rephrase in your own words what Problem 43 is all about.

| ▬ | **Computational Window** | ▼ | ▲ |

In Problems 45–48, find $f'(x)$ and $f''(x)$, then use the bisection method, the Newton–Raphson method, or a calculator to find (correct to the nearest hundredth) all critical values of f and f'. Find all inflection points and sketch the graph of f.

45. $f(x) = x^4 - 3x^3 + x - 5$

46. $f(x) = x^3 + \sin x$ on $[-\pi, \pi]$

47. $f(x) = \tan x - x^2 + 3$ on $[-2\pi, 2\pi]$

48. $f(x) = x^5 + 2x^3 - x^2 + 11$

3.5 INFINITE LIMITS AND ASYMPTOTES

IN THIS SECTION Asymptotes, limits involving infinity, graphs with asymptotes
In order to complete our discussion of curve sketching we need to introduce two concepts, asymptotes and limits involving infinity.

■ ASYMPTOTES

Recall from Chapter 1 that $\lim\limits_{x \to c} f(x)$ does not exist when $f(x)$ increases or decreases without bound as x approaches c. This is one kind of *limit involving infinity*, and a

*"The Mechanics of Bird Migration," Ibis III, pp. 525–556.

goal of this section is to examine such limits and to see how they may be used in curve sketching.

As a preview of the ideas we plan to explore, let us examine the graph shown in Figure 3.40.

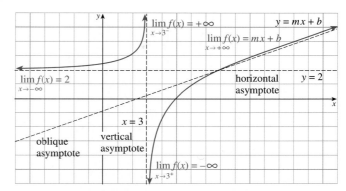

Figure 3.40 A typical graph with asymptotes

Suppose the graph shown in Figure 3.40 is the graph of a function we will call *f*. Notice that as *x* approaches 3 from either side, the corresponding functional values of *f* get large without bound (in absolute value), and the graph of *f* approaches the vertical line *x* = 3. This approach is through positive values ("up") as *x* approaches 3^- (from the left) and through negative values ("down") as *x* approaches 3^+ (from the right). We indicate the behavior of *f* for *x* near 3 by writing*

$$\lim_{x \to 3^-} f(x) = +\infty \quad \text{and} \quad \lim_{x \to 3^+} f(x) = -\infty$$

and we describe the corresponding geometric behavior by saying that the line *x* = 3 is a **vertical asymptote** of the graph of *f*.

Note also that as *x* increases without bound (that is, as *x* moves toward the right on the *x*-axis), the graph of *f* follows the line *y* = *mx* + *b*. For this reason, the line *y* = *mx* + *b* (where *m* ≠ 0) is called an **oblique** (or **slant**) **asymptote.**

At the other end of the *x*-axis (as *x* decreases without bound), the graph approaches the line *y* = 2. We write

$$\lim_{x \to -\infty} f(x) = 2$$

and say that the line *y* = 2 is a **horizontal asymptote** of the graph.

More specifically, an **asymptote** is a line having the property that the distance from a point *P* on the curve to the line approaches zero as the distance from *P* to the origin increases without bound, and *P* is *on a suitable part of the curve.* This last phrase (in italics) is best illustrated by considering Figure 3.41, where *L* is an asymptote for the function *f*.

Consider *P* and *d*, the distance from *P* to the line *L*, as shown in Figure 3.41a. Now, the distance from *P* to the origin can increase in two ways, depending on whether *P* moves along the curve in direction 1 or direction 2. In direction 1, the distance *d* increases without bound, but in direction 2 the distance *d* approaches zero. Thus, if you consider the portion of the curve in the shaded region of Figure 3.41b, you see that the distance decreases as *P* moves along the curve in a certain direction.

There are three types of asymptotes that occur frequently enough when sketching curves to merit our consideration: *vertical*, *horizontal*, and *oblique*

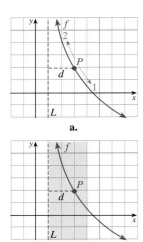

Figure 3.41 An asymptote to a curve

*Many books simply write ∞ to mean +∞. For now, we use +∞ to remind you that +∞ is not the same as −∞.

(*slant*) *asymptotes.* An example of each is shown in Figure 3.42. A graph may pass through a horizontal or oblique (slant) asymptote.

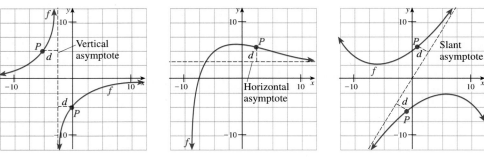

Figure 3.42 Asymptotes

We will define the concepts formally later in this section, and we will also examine examples of graphs with asymptotes. However, we first need to discuss limits involving infinity.

■ LIMITS INVOLVING INFINITY

If the functional values of f get closer and closer to the number L as x increases without bound, we say that $f(x)$ *approaches L as x approaches infinity* and we write $\lim_{x \to +\infty} f(x) = L$. If $f(x)$ approaches L as x decreases without bound, we write $\lim_{x \to -\infty} f(x) = L$. These concepts may be defined formally as follows:

Limits to Infinity

The limit statement $\lim_{x \to +\infty} f(x) = L$ means that for any number $\varepsilon > 0$, there exists a number N_1 such that

$$|f(x) - L| < \varepsilon \quad \text{whenever} \quad x > N_1$$

for x in the domain of f. Similarly, $\lim_{x \to -\infty} f(x) = M$ means that for any $\varepsilon > 0$, there exists a number N_2 such that

$$|f(x) - M| < \varepsilon \quad \text{whenever} \quad x < N_2$$

This definition can be illustrated graphically, as shown in Figure 3.43.

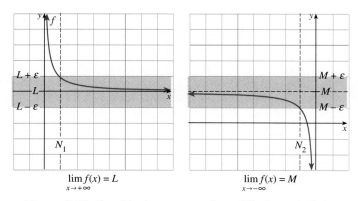

$$\lim_{x \to +\infty} f(x) = L \qquad \lim_{x \to -\infty} f(x) = M$$

Figure 3.43 Graphical representation of limits to infinity

With this formal definition, we can show that all the rules for limits established in Chapter 1 also apply to $\lim_{x \to +\infty} f(x)$ and $\lim_{x \to -\infty} f(x)$. We now state those limit rules for $x \to +\infty$.

Limit Rules

If $\lim_{x \to +\infty} f(x)$ exists, then for constants a and b:

Power rule: $\lim_{x \to +\infty} [f(x)]^n = \left[\lim_{x \to +\infty} f(x) \right]^n$

Linearity rule: $\lim_{x \to +\infty} [af(x) + bg(x)] = a \lim_{x \to +\infty} f(x) + b \lim_{x \to +\infty} g(x)$

Product rule: $\lim_{x \to +\infty} [f(x)g(x)] = \left[\lim_{x \to +\infty} f(x) \right]\left[\lim_{x \to +\infty} g(x) \right]$

Quotient rule: $\lim_{x \to +\infty} \dfrac{f(x)}{g(x)} = \dfrac{\lim_{x \to +\infty} f(x)}{\lim_{x \to +\infty} g(x)}$ if $\lim_{x \to +\infty} g(x) \neq 0$

The same results hold for $\lim_{x \to -\infty} f(x)$, if it exists.

The following theorem will allow us to evaluate certain limits to infinity with ease.

THEOREM 3.8 Limits to infinity

If n is a positive rational number, and A is any nonzero real number, then

$$\lim_{x \to +\infty} \frac{A}{x^n} = 0$$

Furthermore, if x^n is defined when $x < 0$, then

$$\lim_{x \to -\infty} \frac{A}{x^n} = 0$$

Proof: We begin by proving that $\lim_{x \to +\infty} \frac{1}{x} = 0$. For $\varepsilon > 0$, let $N = \frac{1}{\varepsilon}$. Then for $x > N$ we have

$$x > N = \frac{1}{\varepsilon} \quad \text{so that} \quad \frac{1}{x} < \varepsilon$$

This means that $\left| \frac{1}{x} - 0 \right| < \varepsilon$ so that from the definition of limit we have $\lim_{x \to +\infty} \frac{1}{x} = 0$. Now let n be a rational number—say, $n = \frac{p}{q}$. Then

$$\lim_{x \to +\infty} \frac{A}{x^n} = \lim_{x \to +\infty} \frac{A}{x^{p/q}} = A \lim_{x \to +\infty} \left[\frac{1}{\sqrt[q]{x}} \right]^p$$

$$= A \left[\sqrt[q]{\lim_{x \to +\infty} \frac{1}{x}} \right]^p = A \left[\sqrt[q]{0} \right]^p = A \cdot 0 = 0$$

The second part of the proof follows similarly. ∎

Example 1 illustrates how Theorem 3.8 can be used along with the other limit properties to evaluate limits to infinity.

EXAMPLE 1 Evaluating limits to infinity

Evaluate

$$\lim_{x \to +\infty} \sqrt{\frac{3x - 5}{x - 2}} \quad \text{and} \quad \lim_{x \to -\infty} \left(\frac{3x - 5}{x - 2} \right)^3$$

Computational Window

You can use a graphing calculator to help with limits to infinity.

```
Y₁⊟√((3X-5)/(X-2
))
Xmin=-10  Ymin=-10
Xmax=10   Ymax=10
Xscl=1    Yscl=1
```

```
Y₁⊟((3X-5)/(X-2)
)^3
Xmin=-100  Ymin=0
Xmax=100   Ymax=50
Xscl=10    Yscl=10
```

Solution   Notice that for $x \neq 0$,

$$\frac{3x - 5}{x - 2} = \frac{x\left(3 - \frac{5}{x}\right)}{x\left(1 - \frac{2}{x}\right)} = \frac{3 - \frac{5}{x}}{1 - \frac{2}{x}}$$

Also, according to Theorem 3.8, we know that

$$\lim_{x \to +\infty} \frac{5}{x} = \lim_{x \to +\infty} \frac{2}{x} = 0$$

We now find the limits using the quotient rule, the power rule, and Theorem 3.8:

$$\lim_{x \to +\infty} \sqrt{\frac{3x - 5}{x - 2}} = \lim_{x \to +\infty} \left(\frac{3x - 5}{x - 2}\right)^{1/2} = \left(\lim_{x \to +\infty} \frac{3x - 5}{x - 2}\right)^{1/2}$$

$$= \left(\frac{\lim_{x \to +\infty}\left(3 - \frac{5}{x}\right)}{\lim_{x \to +\infty}\left(1 - \frac{2}{x}\right)}\right)^{1/2} = \left(\frac{3 - 0}{1 - 0}\right)^{1/2} = \sqrt{3}$$

Similarly,

$$\lim_{x \to -\infty} \left(\frac{3x - 5}{x - 2}\right)^3 = 3^3 = 27$$

When evaluating a limit of the form

$$\lim_{x \to +\infty} \frac{p(x)}{d(x)} \quad \text{or} \quad \lim_{x \to -\infty} \frac{p(x)}{d(x)}$$

where $p(x)$ and $d(x)$ are polynomials, it is often useful to divide both $p(x)$ and $d(x)$ by the highest power of x that occurs in either. The limit can then be found by applying Theorem 3.8. This process is illustrated by the following examples.

EXAMPLE 2   Evaluating a limit to (positive) infinity

Evaluate $\displaystyle\lim_{x \to +\infty} \frac{3x^3 - 5x + 9}{5x^3 + 2x^2 - 7}$.

Solution   We may assume $x \neq 0$, because we are interested only in very large values of x. Dividing both the numerator and denominator of the given expressions by x^3, we find

$$\frac{3x^3 - 5x + 9}{5x^3 + 2x^2 - 7} = \frac{3x^3 - 5x + 9}{5x^3 + 2x^2 - 7} \cdot \frac{\frac{1}{x^3}}{\frac{1}{x^3}} = \frac{3 - \frac{5}{x^2} + \frac{9}{x^3}}{5 + \frac{2}{x} - \frac{7}{x^3}}$$

Thus,

$$\lim_{x \to +\infty} \frac{3x^3 - 5x + 9}{5x^3 + 2x^2 - 7} = \lim_{x \to +\infty} \frac{3 - \frac{5}{x^2} + \frac{9}{x^3}}{5 + \frac{2}{x} - \frac{7}{x^3}}$$

$$= \frac{\lim_{x \to +\infty}\left(3 - \frac{5}{x^2} + \frac{9}{x^3}\right)}{\lim_{x \to +\infty}\left(5 + \frac{2}{x} - \frac{7}{x^3}\right)}$$

$$= \frac{3 - 0 + 0}{5 + 0 - 0} = \frac{3}{5}$$

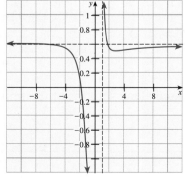

Graph of $y = \dfrac{3x^3 - 5x + 9}{5x^3 + 2x^2 - 7}$.

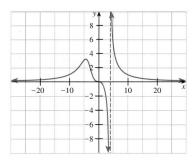

Graph of $y = \dfrac{95x^3 + 57x + 30}{x^5 - 1,000}$

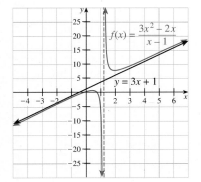

Compare the graphs of $f(x)$ $= \dfrac{3x^2 - 2x}{x - 1}$ and $y = 3x + 1$.

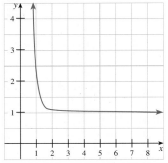

Figure 3.44 Graphs of y_1, y_2, and y_3; with the given scale, the three graphs look the same.

EXAMPLE 3   Evaluating a limit to negative infinity

Evaluate $\displaystyle\lim_{x \to -\infty} \dfrac{95x^3 + 57x + 30}{x^5 - 1,000}$.

Solution   Dividing the numerator and the denominator by the highest power, x^5, we find that

$$\lim_{x \to -\infty} \frac{95x^3 + 57x + 30}{x^5 - 1,000} = \lim_{x \to -\infty} \frac{95x^3 + 57x + 30}{x^5 - 1,000} \cdot \frac{\frac{1}{x^5}}{\frac{1}{x^5}}$$

$$= \lim_{x \to -\infty} \frac{\frac{95}{x^2} + \frac{57}{x^4} + \frac{30}{x^5}}{1 - \frac{1,000}{x^5}} = \frac{0 + 0 + 0}{1 - 0} = 0$$

EXAMPLE 4   A limit to infinity that does not exist

Evaluate $\displaystyle\lim_{x \to +\infty} \dfrac{3x^2 - 2x}{x - 1}$.

Solution   We note that the degree of the numerator is greater than the degree of the denominator. Intuitively, we expect that the limit does not exist because the numerator is growing faster than the denominator. If we divide the numerator by the denominator we find

$$\lim_{x \to +\infty} \frac{3x^2 - 2x}{x - 1} = \lim_{x \to +\infty} \left[(3x + 1) + \frac{1}{x - 1} \right]$$

$$= \lim_{x \to +\infty} (3x + 1) + \lim_{x \to +\infty} \frac{1}{x - 1}$$

$$= +\infty$$

EXAMPLE 5   A limit where technology may fail

Evaluate $\displaystyle\lim_{x \to +\infty} \dfrac{x^{4.359} + 1}{x^{\sqrt{19}}}$.

Solution   Consider three similar functions:

$$y_1 = \frac{x^{4.359} + 1}{x^{\sqrt{19}}} \qquad y_2 = \frac{x^{4.359} + 1}{x^{4.36}} \qquad y_3 = \frac{x^{4.359} + 1}{x^{4.359}}$$

If you begin with a calculator (table) or a graph you might obtain a faulty conclusion. Look at the graph of these three functions in Figure 3.44. From the graph you might be led to the *incorrect* conclusion that the limits as $x \to +\infty$ for y_1, y_2, and y_3 are all 1. Let us consider the situation more carefully. We note $\sqrt{19} \approx 4.358898944$.

If we use the approximation $\sqrt{19} \approx 4.36$, we obtain y_2:

$$\lim_{x \to +\infty} \frac{x^{4.359} + 1}{x^{4.36}} = \lim_{x \to +\infty} \left(\frac{1}{x^{0.001}} + \frac{1}{x^{4.36}} \right) = 0 + 0 = 0$$

Let's use a better approximation. With $\sqrt{19} \approx 4.359$, we obtain y_3:

$$\lim_{x \to +\infty} \frac{x^{4.359} + 1}{x^{4.359}} = \lim_{x \to +\infty} \left(1 + \frac{1}{x^{4.359}} \right) = 1$$

We note that our preliminary conclusion that these limits were the same was incorrect. Let's look at some better graphs (which we might not consider if we relied only on the technology), as shown in Figure 3.45.

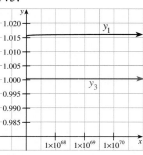

Figure 3.45 Detail of Figure 3.4

a. As $x \to +\infty$ we see that y_2 starts to drop away.

b. As $x \to +\infty$ we see that y_1 starts to rise.

c. For large enough x, we can make y_1 as large as we wish.

Instead of using a numerical approximation (which is what most calculators or computers would use), we confirm what we begin to expect from Figure 3.45c.

$$\lim_{x \to +\infty} \frac{x^{4.359} + 1}{x^{\sqrt{19}}} = \lim_{x \to +\infty} \left(\frac{x^{4.359}}{x^{\sqrt{19}}} + \frac{1}{x^{\sqrt{19}}} \right) = +\infty \quad \textit{Because } \sqrt{19} < 4.359$$

In mathematics, we use the symbol ∞ to describe the situation in Example 5 or whenever it is necessary to indicate either the process of unrestricted growth or the end result of such growth. With this understanding, we can speak of *infinite limits*—that is, limits that increase or decrease without bound. The limit statement $\lim_{x \to c} f(x) = +\infty$ may be defined formally as follows.

> **Infinite Limit**
>
> We write $\lim_{x \to c} f(x) = +\infty$ if for any number $N > 0$ (no matter how large), it is possible to find a number $\delta > 0$ such that $f(x) > N$ whenever $0 < |x - c| < \delta$.
>
> ⊘ ▇ *What this does not say:* An infinite limit does not exist in the sense that limits were defined in Chapter 1. The symbolism $\lim_{x \to c} f(x) = +\infty$ *does not mean* that $f(x)$ approaches a *number* $+\infty$ as x approaches c. That is, ∞ is **not** a *number*. Nevertheless, writing $\lim_{x \to c} f(x) = +\infty$ or $\lim_{x \to c} f(x) = -\infty$ conveys more specific information than simply saying "the limit of $f(x)$ as x approaches c does not exist." ⊘

A similar definition holds for the infinite limit statement $\lim_{x \to c} f(x) = -\infty$ (see Problem 62, Problem Set 3.5). For example,

$$\lim_{x \to 5^-} \frac{4}{x - 5} = -\infty \quad \text{and} \quad \lim_{x \to 5^+} \frac{4}{x - 5} = +\infty \quad \text{or} \quad \lim_{x \to -4^-} \frac{-7}{x + 4} = +\infty \quad \text{and} \quad \lim_{x \to -4^+} \frac{-7}{x + 4} = -\infty$$

are infinite limits. The graphs of these functions are shown in Figure 3.46.

Figure 3.46 Graphs showing infinite limits

a. Graph of $y = \dfrac{4}{x - 5}$

b. Graph of $y = \dfrac{-7}{x + 4}$

EXAMPLE 6 Infinite limit

Find $\lim\limits_{x \to 2^-} \dfrac{3x - 5}{x - 2}$ and $\lim\limits_{x \to 2^+} \dfrac{3x - 5}{x - 2}$.

Solution Notice that $\dfrac{1}{x - 2}$ increases without bound as x approaches 2 from the right and $\dfrac{1}{x - 2}$ decreases without bound as x approaches 2 from the left. That is,

$$\lim_{x \to 2^+} \frac{1}{x - 2} = +\infty \quad \text{and} \quad \lim_{x \to 2^-} \frac{1}{x - 2} = -\infty$$

We also have $\lim\limits_{x \to 2} (3x - 5) = 1$, and it follows that

$$\lim_{x \to 2^+} \frac{3x - 5}{x - 2} = +\infty \quad \text{and} \quad \lim_{x \to 2^-} \frac{3x - 5}{x - 2} = -\infty$$

■ GRAPHS WITH ASYMPTOTES

We shall now show how limits involving infinity can be used along with the curve-sketching techniques developed in the last two sections to sketch graphs with asymptotes. We need the following definitions:

Vertical Asymptote The line $x = c$ is a **vertical asymptote** of the graph of f if either of the one-sided limits

$$\lim_{x \to c^-} f(x) \quad \text{or} \quad \lim_{x \to c^+} f(x)$$

Horizontal Asymptote is infinite. The line $y = L$ is a **horizontal asymptote** of the graph of f if

$$\lim_{x \to +\infty} f(x) = L \quad \text{or} \quad \lim_{x \to -\infty} f(x) = L$$

Oblique Asymptote The line $y = mx + b$ is an **oblique asymptote** of the graph of f if f is a rational function such that the numerator and denominator have no common factors and

$$f(x) = \frac{p(x)}{d(x)} = mx + b + \frac{r}{d(x)}$$

where $\lim\limits_{x \to +\infty} \dfrac{r}{d(x)} = 0$.

EXAMPLE 7 Graphing a rational function using asymptotes

Sketch the graph of $f(x) = \dfrac{3x - 5}{x - 2}$.

Solution

Vertical Asymptotes. First, make sure the given function is written in simplified form. Because vertical asymptotes for $f(x) = \dfrac{3x - 5}{x - 2}$ occur at values of x for which f is not defined, we look for values that cause the denominator to be zero; that is, we solve $d(c) = 0$ and then evaluate $\lim\limits_{x \to c^-} f(x)$ and $\lim\limits_{x \to c^+} f(x)$ to ascertain the behavior of the function at $x = c$. For this example, $x = 2$ is a value that causes division by zero, so we find

$$\lim_{x \to 2^-} \frac{3x - 5}{x - 2} = -\infty \quad \text{and} \quad \lim_{x \to 2^+} \frac{3x - 5}{x - 2} = +\infty$$

(We found these limits in Example 6.) This means that $x = 2$ is a vertical asymptote and that the graph is moving downward as $x \to 2$ from the left and upward as $x \to 2$ from the right. This information is recorded on the preliminary graph shown in Figure 3.47a by a dashed vertical line with upward ($\uparrow$) and downward ($\downarrow$) arrows.

Horizontal Asymptotes. In order to find the horizontal asymptotes we compute

$$\lim_{x \to +\infty} \frac{3x - 5}{x - 2} = \lim_{x \to +\infty} \frac{3x - 5}{x - 2} \cdot \frac{\frac{1}{x}}{\frac{1}{x}} = \lim_{x \to +\infty} \frac{3 - \frac{5}{x}}{1 - \frac{2}{x}} = \frac{3 - 0}{1 - 0} = 3$$

and

$$\lim_{x \to -\infty} \frac{3x - 5}{x - 2} = 3 \qquad \text{(The steps here are the same as for } x \to +\infty.)$$

This means that $y = 3$ is a horizontal asymptote. This information is recorded on the preliminary graph shown in Figure 3.47a by a dashed horizontal line with outbound arrows ($\leftarrow$, $\rightarrow$).

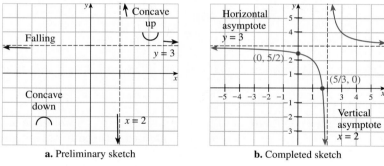

a. Preliminary sketch   **b.** Completed sketch

Figure 3.47 Graph of $f(x) = \dfrac{3x - 5}{x - 2}$

Oblique Asymptotes. This function does not have oblique asymptotes. (Do you see why?)

The preliminary sketch gives us some valuable information about the graph, but it does not present the entire picture. Next, we use calculus to find where the function is increasing and decreasing (first derivative) and where it is concave upward and concave downward (second derivative).

$$f'(x) = \frac{-1}{(x - 2)^2} \quad \text{and} \quad f''(x) = \frac{2}{(x - 2)^3} \qquad \textit{The details for finding these derivatives are not shown.}$$

Neither derivative is ever zero, and both are undefined at $x = 2$. Checking the signs of the first and second derivatives, we find that this curve has no points of inflection (the function is not defined at $x = 2$). This information is added to the preliminary sketch shown in Figure 3.47a. The completed graph is shown in Figure 3.47b.

PROBLEM SET 3.5

Ⓐ *Evaluate the limits in Problems 1–36.*

1. $\displaystyle\lim_{x\to+\infty}\frac{2,000}{x+1}$

2. $\displaystyle\lim_{x\to+\infty}\frac{7,000}{\sqrt{x}+1}$

3. $\displaystyle\lim_{x\to+\infty}\frac{3x+5}{x-2}$

4. $\displaystyle\lim_{x\to+\infty}\frac{x+2}{3x-5}$

5. $\displaystyle\lim_{t\to-\infty}\frac{5+t}{7-t}$

6. $\displaystyle\lim_{s\to-\infty}\frac{3s+4}{7-2s}$

7. $\displaystyle\lim_{x\to+\infty}\frac{3x^2-7x+5}{-2x^2+x-9}$

8. $\displaystyle\lim_{t\to+\infty}\frac{9t^5+50t^2+800}{t^5-1,000}$

9. $\displaystyle\lim_{t\to+\infty}\frac{17t^5+800t^2+1,000}{t^6-1}$

10. $\displaystyle\lim_{x\to-\infty}\frac{100\,x^6+x^2-x+500}{x^7+2}$

11. $\displaystyle\lim_{x\to+\infty}\frac{8x^3-9x+5}{x^2+300x}$

12. $\displaystyle\lim_{x\to+\infty}\frac{5,000x^4+300x^3+1,000}{x^5+3}$

13. $\displaystyle\lim_{x\to-\infty}\frac{(2x+5)(x-3)}{(7x-2)(4x+1)}$

14. $\displaystyle\lim_{x\to+\infty}\frac{(3x^2-10)(x^2+x)}{(4x^3-x^2+1)(x-7)}$

15. $\displaystyle\lim_{x\to-\infty}\frac{(2x+1)(x+5)(x-3)}{x^4+9}$

16. $\displaystyle\lim_{x\to+\infty}\frac{x(x+1)(x+2)}{x^4-4}$

17. $\displaystyle\lim_{t\to+\infty}\left(\frac{8t+1}{7t}-\frac{1-t}{t+5}\right)$

18. $\displaystyle\lim_{x\to+\infty}\left(\frac{x}{x+1}-\frac{2x}{x-1}\right)$

19. $\displaystyle\lim_{t\to+\infty}\left(\frac{8t+5}{3-2t}\right)^3$

20. $\displaystyle\lim_{t\to+\infty}\sqrt{\frac{18t^2+t-4}{3t+2t^2}}$

21. $\displaystyle\lim_{x\to+\infty}\frac{x}{\sqrt{x^2+1,000}}$

22. $\displaystyle\lim_{x\to-\infty}\frac{3x}{\sqrt{4x^2+10}}$

23. $\displaystyle\lim_{x\to+\infty}\frac{x^{5.916}+1}{x^{\sqrt{35}}}$

24. $\displaystyle\lim_{x\to+\infty}\frac{x^{6.083}+1}{x^{\sqrt{37}}}$

25. $\displaystyle\lim_{x\to+\infty}\frac{x^{5.831}+1}{x^{\sqrt{34}}}$

26. $\displaystyle\lim_{x\to+\infty}\frac{x^{5.744}+1}{x^{\sqrt{33}}}$

27. $\displaystyle\lim_{x\to-2^-}\frac{x^2-3x+4}{x+2}$

28. $\displaystyle\lim_{x\to1^-}\frac{x-1}{|x^2-1|}$

29. $\displaystyle\lim_{x\to3^+}\frac{x^2-4x+3}{x^2-6x+9}$

30. $\displaystyle\lim_{x\to3^+}\left(\frac{1}{x-7}-\frac{1}{x-3}\right)$

31. $\displaystyle\lim_{x\to0^+}\frac{x^2-x+1}{x-\sin x}$

32. $\displaystyle\lim_{x\to\frac{\pi}{4}^+}\frac{\sec x}{\tan x-1}$

33. $\displaystyle\lim_{x\to+\infty}\left(x\sin\frac{1}{x}\right)$

34. $\displaystyle\lim_{x\to0^+}\frac{x^2-x}{x-\sin x}$

35. $\displaystyle\lim_{x\to0^+}\frac{x^2\csc x}{1-\cos x}$

36. $\displaystyle\lim_{x\to0^+}\frac{x-\sin x}{\sqrt{\sin x}}$

Find all vertical and horizontal asymptotes of the graphs of the functions given in Problems 37–46. Find where each graph is rising and where it is falling, determine concavity, and locate all critical points and points of inflection. Finally, sketch the graph.

37. $f(x)=\dfrac{3x+5}{7-x}$

38. $g(x)=\dfrac{15}{x+4}$

39. $f(x)=4+\dfrac{2x}{x-3}$

40. $g(x)=x-\dfrac{x}{4-x}$

41. $h(x)=x^2+\dfrac{2}{x}$

42. $f(x)=\dfrac{x^2+2x-3}{x+1}$

43. $f(x)=\dfrac{x^3+1}{x^3-8}$

44. $f(x)=\dfrac{2x^2-5x+7}{x^2-9}$

45. $g(x)=\dfrac{8}{x-1}+\dfrac{27}{x+4}$

46. $f(x)=\dfrac{1}{x+1}+\dfrac{1}{x-1}$

Sketch the graphs of the piecewise-defined functions in Problems 47–50.

47. $f(x)=\begin{cases}x^2-3x & \text{if } x\le 1\\ \sqrt{x} & \text{if } x>1\end{cases}$

48. $f(t)=\begin{cases}\sqrt{t}(t-1) & \text{if } t>0\\ 1+t^3 & \text{if } t\le 0\end{cases}$

49. $f(t)=\begin{cases}\cos t-\sin t & \text{if } t\le 0\\ \cos^2 t & \text{if } t>0\end{cases}$

50. $f(x)=\begin{cases}x^2-3x & \text{if } x\le 1\\ \frac{1}{2}(3x-7) & \text{if } 1<x<3\\ \dfrac{3x-1}{x+5} & \text{if } x\ge 3\end{cases}$

Ⓑ 51. THINK TANK PROBLEM Sketch the graph of a function f with all the following properties:

The graph has $y=1$ and $x=3$ as asymptotes;

f is increasing for $x<3$ and $3<x<5$ and is decreasing elsewhere;

The graph is concave up for $x<3$ and for $x>7$ and concave down for $3<x<7$;

$f(0)=4=f(5)$ and $f(7)=2$.

52. THINK TANK PROBLEM Sketch a graph of a function g with all of the following properties:

The graph has no inflection points and only one critical point $(1,1)$;

$\displaystyle\lim_{x\to-\infty}g(x)=\lim_{x\to+\infty}g(x)=2$; and

$\displaystyle\lim_{x\to-1^+}g(x)=\lim_{x\to3^-}g(x)=-\infty$;

g is increasing for $x<-1$ and is decreasing only for $-1<x<1$.

53. ■ What Does This Say? Frank Kornerkutter has put off doing his math homework until the last minute, and he is now trying to evaluate

$$\lim_{x\to0^+}\left(\frac{1}{x^2}-\frac{1}{x}\right)$$

At first he is stumped, but suddenly he has an idea: Because

$$\lim_{x\to0^+}\frac{1}{x^2}=+\infty \quad \text{and} \quad \lim_{x\to0^+}\frac{1}{x}=+\infty$$

it must surely be true that the limit in question has the value $+\infty - (+\infty) = 0$. Having thus "solved" his problem he celebrates by taking a nap. Is he right, and if not, what is wrong with his argument?

54. Find constants a and b that guarantee that the graph of the function defined by

$$f(x) = \frac{ax + 5}{3 - bx}$$

will have a vertical asymptote at $x = 5$ and a horizontal asymptote at $y = -3$.

55. JOURNAL PROBLEM: *College Mathematics Journal** by Michael G. Murphy. Find the oblique asymptote of the curve with equation

$$y = \frac{x^2 + 3x + 7}{x + 2}$$

Solution 1. By division,

$$\frac{x^2 + 3x + 7}{x + 2} = x + 1 + \frac{5}{x + 2}$$

Because the final term tends to zero as x grows, the asymptote is the line of equation $y = x + 1$.

Solution 2. Following a procedure frequently used in calculating limits at infinity,

$$\frac{x^2 + 3x + 7}{x + 2} = \frac{x + 3 + \frac{7}{x}}{1 + \frac{2}{x}}$$

For large x, the value is approximately $x + 3$, so the asymptote should be the line of equation $y = x + 3$.

Reconcile these solutions. What is wrong?

56. JOURNAL PROBLEM: *Parabola*†.   Draw a careful sketch of the curve

$$y = \frac{x^2}{x^2 - 1}$$

indicating clearly any vertical or horizontal asymptotes, turning points, or points of inflection.

57. Let

$$P(x) = a_n x^n + a_{n-1} x^{n-1} + \cdots + a_1 x + a_0$$

be a polynomial with $a_n \neq 0$ and let

$$L = \lim_{x \to -\infty} P(x) \quad \text{and} \quad M = \lim_{x \to +\infty} P(x).$$

Fill in the missing entries in the following table:

Sign of a_n	n	L	M
+	even	a.	$+\infty$
+	odd	$-\infty$	b.
−	even	c.	d.
−	odd	e.	$-\infty$

*Volume 22, May 1991, p. 221.

†Volume 20, Issue 1, 1984. A *turning point* is what we have called a relative extrema.

58. A town planning commission estimates that t years from now, the population of the town will be p thousand people given by the formula

$$p(t) = \frac{57t + 8}{3t + 4}$$

a. What is the population of the town? What will it be in 10 years?

b. Sketch the graph of the population function p. What is the "ultimate population" of the town—that is, what is $\lim_{t \to +\infty} p(t)$?

59. a. Show that, in general, the graph of the function

$$f(x) = \frac{ax^2 + bx + c}{rx^2 + sx + t}$$

will have $y = \frac{a}{r}$ as a horizontal asymptote and that when $br \neq as$, the graph will cross this asymptote at the point where

$$x = \frac{at - cr}{br - as}$$

b. What can be said about the case where $br = as$?

c. Sketch the graph of each of the following functions:

$$g(x) = \frac{x^2 - 4x - 5}{2x^2 + x - 10}$$

$$h(x) = \frac{3x^2 - x - 7}{-12x^2 + 4x + 8}$$

Ⓒ 60. Let $f(x) = p(x)/d(x)$ be a rational function, and let c be a number for which $d(c) = 0$ but $p(c) \neq 0$. Explain why $\lim_{x \to c^-} f(x)$ and $\lim_{x \to c^+} f(x)$ must both be infinite. Note that this means $x = c$ is a vertical asymptote of the graph of f.

61. Consider the rational function

$$f(x) = \frac{a_n x^n + a_{n-1} x^{n-1} + \cdots + a_1 x + a_0}{b_m x^m + b_{m-1} x^{m-1} + \cdots + b_1 x + b_0}$$

a. If $m > n$ and $b_m \neq 0$, show that the x-axis is the only horizontal asymptote of the graph of f.

b. If $m = n$, show that the line $y = a_n/b_m$ is the only horizontal asymptote of the graph of f.

c. If $m < n$, is it possible for the graph to have a horizontal asymptote? Explain.

62. ■ **What Does This Say?**   State what you think should be the formal definition of each of the following limit statements:

a. $\lim_{x \to c^+} f(x) = -\infty$ b. $\lim_{x \to c^-} f(x) = +\infty$

63. Prove that if

$$\lim_{x \to +\infty} f(x) \quad \text{and} \quad \lim_{x \to +\infty} g(x)$$

both exist, so does

$$\lim_{x \to +\infty} [f(x) + g(x)]$$

and

$$\lim_{x \to +\infty} [f(x) + g(x)] = \lim_{x \to +\infty} f(x) + \lim_{x \to +\infty} g(x)$$

Hint: The key is to show that if

$$|f(x) - L| < \frac{\varepsilon}{2}$$

for $x > N_1$ and

$$|g(x) - M| < \frac{\varepsilon}{2}$$

for $x > N_2$, then

$$|[f(x) + g(x)] - (L + M)| < \varepsilon$$

whenever $x > N$ for some number N. You should also show that N relates to N_1 and N_2.

64. Prove the following limit rule. If $\lim_{x \to c} f(x) = +\infty$ and

$$\lim_{x \to c} g(x) = A \qquad A > 0$$

then $\lim_{x \to c} [f(x)g(x)] = +\infty$

Hint: Notice that because $\lim_{x \to c} g(x) = A$, the function $g(x)$ is near A when x is near c. Therefore, because $\lim_{x \to +\infty} f(x) = +\infty$, the product $f(x)g(x)$ is large if x is near c. Formalize these observations for the proof.

65. Prove the following limit rule. If $\lim_{x \to c} f(x) = +\infty$ and $\lim_{x \to c} g(x) = A$ where $A < 0$, then

$$\lim_{x \to c} \frac{f(x)}{g(x)} = -\infty$$

3.6 SUMMARY OF CURVE SKETCHING

> **IN THIS SECTION** General curve sketching, graphing strategy
> In this section we tie together your graphing skills from previous courses as well as the calculus-based curve sketching developed in this chapter.

■ GENERAL CURVE SKETCHING

It is worthwhile to combine the techniques of curve sketching from calculus with those techniques studied in precalculus courses. You may be familiar with **extent** (finding the domain and the range of the function) or **symmetry** (with respect to the *x*-axis, *y*-axis, or origin). These features are reviewed in the *Student Mathematics Handbook and Integration Table for CALCULUS*. We now have all the tools we need to describe a general procedure for curve sketching, and this procedure is summarized in Table 3.2 on page 216.

(S^M_H)

EXAMPLE 1   Sketching a curve with an oblique asymptote

Discuss and sketch the graph of $y = \dfrac{x^2 - x - 2}{x - 3}$.

Solution   Performing the division, we write

$$y = \frac{x^2 - x - 2}{x - 3} = x + 2 + \frac{4}{x - 3}$$

Find the first and second derivatives, along with the critical values for y' and y'':

Derivatives	*Critical values*
$y' = 1 - 4(x - 3)^{-2}$	$1 - 4(x - 3)^{-2} = 0$
	$1 = 4(x - 3)^{-2}$
	$(x - 3)^2 = 4$
	$x - 3 = \pm 2$
	$x = 5, 1$
$y'' = 8(x - 3)^{-3}$	$8(x - 3)^{-3} = 0$
	No second-order critical values

Computational Window

Y₁⊟(X²−X−2)/(X−3)

Xmin=-10   Ymin=-10
Xmax=10   Ymax=10
Xscl=1   Yscl=1

The second derivative test: $f''(5) > 0$; relative minimum at $x = 5$.
$f''(1) < 0$; relative maximum at $x = 1$.

The intervals of increase and decrease, relative extrema, and concavity are indicated the the preliminary sketch in Figure 3.48a. Note that there is a vertical asymptote at $x = 3$ and an oblique asymptote $y = x + 2$, because $y = x + 2 + \dfrac{4}{x - 3}$. There are no horizontal asymptotes. Finally, plot a few additional points and then draw a smooth curve, as shown in Figure 3.48b.

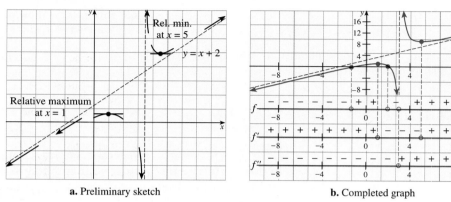

a. Preliminary sketch   b. Completed graph

Figure 3.48 Graph of $y = \dfrac{x^2 - x - 2}{x - 3}$

EXAMPLE 2   Sketching a trigonometric curve

Discuss and sketch the graph of $y = 20 \sin(378\pi x)$.

Solution   We recognize this as a standard sine curve, but we need to pay some attention to the domain and range. We note that this sine curve has amplitude 20 and period $2\pi/(378\pi) = \frac{1}{189}$. These numbers help us set the scale on both the axes. We find the critical values for y':

$$y' = [20 \cos(378\pi x)](378\pi) = 7560\pi \cos(378\pi x)$$

$$y' = 0 \quad \text{whenever} \quad \cos(378\pi x) = 0 \quad \text{or} \quad 378\pi x = \frac{\pi}{2} + n\pi \quad \text{for an integer } n$$

Because of our knowledge of the shape of a sine curve, it is not necessary for us to find the concavity or points of inflection. The graph is shown in Figure 3.49.

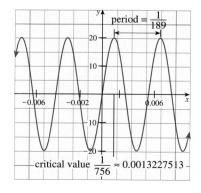

Figure 3.49 Graph of $y = 20 \sin(378\pi x)$

TABLE 3.2 Graphing Strategy for a Function Defined by $y = f(x)$

Step	Procedure
Simplify.	If possible, simplify algebraically the function you wish to graph.
Find derivatives and critical values.	Compute the first and second derivatives; factor, if possible, and find the first- and second-order critical values.
Apply the second-derivative test.	Use the second-derivative test to find the relative maxima or minima: substitute the first-order critical values, c_1, with the following test: $f''(c_1) > 0,$ relative minimum $f''(c_1) < 0,$ relative maximum $f''(c_1) = 0,$ test fails; use first-derivative test
Determine concavity and points of inflection.	Use the second-order critical values, c_2, to determine concavity: Substitute $f''(c_2) > 0$, concave up; $f''(c_2) < 0$, concave down. Find the points of inflection. These are located where the concavity changes from up to down or down to up, and are found at the x-intercepts of the second derivative.
Apply the first-derivative test.	Use the first-derivative test if the second-derivative test fails or is too complicated. **1.** Let c be a first-order critical value of f. **2. a.** $(c, f(c))$ is a relative minimum if $f'(x) < 0$ for all x in an open interval (a, c) to the left of c and $f'(x) > 0$ for all x in an open interval (c, b) to the right of c. **b.** $(c, f(c))$ is a relative maximum if $f'(x) > 0$ for all x in an open interval (a, c) to the left of c and $f'(x) < 0$ for all x in an open interval (c, b) to the right of c. **c.** $(c, f(c))$ is not an extremum if $f'(x)$ has the same sign in open intervals (a, c) and (c, b) on both sides of c.
Determine intervals of increase and decrease.	Use the first-order critical values of f to determine intervals of increase and decrease: $f'(x) > 0,$ curve rising (indicate these regions by ↑) $f'(x) < 0,$ curve falling (indicate these regions by ↓)
Find asymptotes.	**1.** *Vertical asymptote*—The vertical asymptote, if one exists, will occur at a value $x = c$ for which f is not defined. Use the limits $\lim_{x \to c^-} f(x)$ and $\lim_{x \to c^+} f(x)$ to determine the behavior of the graph near $x = c$. Show this behavior with arrows (↑ ↓). **2.** *Horizontal asymptote*—Compute $\lim_{x \to +\infty} f(x)$ and $\lim_{x \to -\infty} f(x)$. If either is finite, plot the associated horizontal asymptote. **3.** *Oblique asymptote*—If f is a rational function with no common factors and with the degree of the numerator 1 more than the degree of the denominator, then write $f(x) = mx + b + r(x)/d(x)$ and plot the asymptote $y = mx + b$.
Plot points.	**1.** If c is a relative maximum, relative minimum, or inflection point, plot $(c, f(c))$. Show the relative maximum points by using a "cap" (∩), and relative minimum points by using a "cup" (∪). **2.** x-intercepts: Set $y = 0$ and if $x = a$ is a solution, plot $(a, 0)$. y-intercepts: Set $x = 0$ and if $y = b$ is a solution, plot $(0, b)$; a function will have, at most, one y-intercept. **3.** Asymptote intercepts: Plot those points where f intersects horizontal or oblique asymptotes.
Sketch the curve.	Draw a smooth curve through the plotted points.

Computational Window

Once again, we present our often-repeated warning about relying on technology. The following screens show some variations we obtained on graphing calcu- lators and software after inputting the function shown in Example 2. Remember, technology alone is not sufficient; use *both* calculus and technology.

Y₁■20(sin (378πX))	Y₁■20(sin (378πX))	Y₁■20(sin (378πX))	Y₁■20(sin (378πX))
Xmin=0 Ymin=⁻20	Xmin=0 Ymin=⁻20	Xmin=0	Xmin=0
Xmax=3 Ymax=20	Xmax=3.1 Ymax=20	Xmax=2208.5	Xmax=1104.25
Xscl=1 Yscl=1	Xscl=1 Yscl=1	Xscl=1	Xscl=1
		Ymin=⁻20	Ymin=⁻20
		Ymax=20	Ymax=20
		Yscl=1	Yscl=1

$Y_1 = 20(\sin(378\pi X))$

Computational Window

$Y_1 = 2 + 7/(3(X-2)) - 10/(3(X+1))$

Xmin=⁻10	Ymin=⁻10
Xmax=10	Ymax=10
Xscl=1	Yscl=1

It is sometimes difficult to choose the necessary informa- tion without using calculus. On the other hand, sometimes the calculator graph will suffice. This example shows that the calculus can sometimes be very tedious; on the other hand, a calculator will not supply $9 \pm \sqrt{70}$.

EXAMPLE 3   Sketching a curve with asymptotes

Discuss and graph $f(x) = 2 + \dfrac{7}{3(x-2)} - \dfrac{10}{3(x+1)}$.

Solution   We first simplify the algebraic representation of the given function.

$$f(x) = \frac{2(3)(x+1)(x-2) + 7(x+1) - 10(x-2)}{3(x+1)(x-2)} = \frac{2x^2 - 3x + 5}{(x+1)(x-2)}$$

Find the first and second derivatives, along with the critical values for f and f':

$$f'(x) = \frac{(x^2 - x - 2)(4x - 3) - (2x^2 - 3x + 5)(2x - 1)}{(x+1)^2(x-2)^2} = \frac{x^2 - 18x + 11}{(x+1)^2(x-2)^2}$$

To find the critical values for f, solve

$$\frac{x^2 - 18x + 11}{(x+1)^2(x-2)^2} = 0$$

$$x^2 - 18x + 11 = 0$$

$$x = 9 \pm \sqrt{70}$$

The first derivative is not defined when $x = -1$ and $x = 2$, but these values are not in the domain of f. Thus the first-order critical values are $9 + \sqrt{70}$, and $9 - \sqrt{70}$. Next, find the second derivative (we will not show the intermediate steps).

$$f''(x) = \frac{2(-x^3 + 27x^2 - 33x + 29)}{(x+1)^3(x-2)^3}$$

To find the second-order critical values, solve

$$\frac{2(-x^3 + 27x^2 - 33x + 29)}{(x + 1)^3(x - 2)^3} = 0$$

$$-x^3 + 27x^2 - 33x + 29 = 0$$

You can approximate the roots of this cubic equation by using a spreadsheet, the bisection method, or the Newton-Raphson method: there is one real root, namely, $x \approx 25.8$. Additional second-order critical values are where the second derivative is not defined, namely, $x = -1$ and $x = 2$, but as we have seen, these are not in the domain of f.

The second-derivative test gives us the following information:

$$f''(9 + \sqrt{70}) > 0; \quad \text{relative minimum at } x = 9 + \sqrt{70}$$
$$f''(9 - \sqrt{70}) < 0; \quad \text{relative maximum at } x = 9 - \sqrt{70}$$

The function has vertical asymptotes at $x = -1$ and $x = 2$:

$$\lim_{x \to -1^-} \frac{2x^2 - 3x + 5}{(x + 1)(x - 2)} = +\infty \qquad \lim_{x \to -1^+} \frac{2x^2 - 3x + 5}{(x + 1)(x - 2)} = -\infty$$

$$\lim_{x \to 2^-} \frac{2x^2 - 3x + 5}{(x + 1)(x - 2)} = -\infty \qquad \lim_{x \to 2^+} \frac{2x^2 - 3x + 5}{(x + 1)(x - 2)} = +\infty$$

These asymptotes (along with the appropriate arrows) are shown in the preliminary sketch in Figure 3.50a.

The function has a horizontal asymptote:

$$\lim_{x \to +\infty} \frac{2x^2 - 3x + 5}{(x + 1)(x - 2)} = 2$$

$$\lim_{x \to -\infty} \frac{2x^2 - 3x + 5}{(x + 1)(x - 2)} = 2$$

The horizontal asymptote is $y = 2$. This is shown in Figure 3.50a.

Plot a few important points:

Critical Values

$x = 9 + \sqrt{70} \qquad f(9 + \sqrt{70}) \approx f(17.4) \approx 1.97$
Plot relative minimum point $(17.4, 1.97)$ and label it with a "cup" ($\cup$).
$x = 9 - \sqrt{70} \qquad f(9 - \sqrt{70}) \approx f(0.6) \approx -1.7$
Plot relative maximum point $(0.6, -1.7)$ and label it with a "cap" ($\cap$).

Intercepts

$$x = 0 \qquad\qquad\qquad f(0) = -\tfrac{5}{2} \ Plot \left(0, -\tfrac{5}{2}\right).$$

$$y = 0 \qquad\qquad \frac{2x^2 - 3x + 5}{(x + 1)(x - 2)} = 0 \quad No\ real\ roots;\ thus\ there\ are\ no\ x\text{-}intercepts.$$

$$\text{asymptote } y = 2 \qquad \frac{2x^2 - 3x + 5}{(x + 1)(x - 2)} = 2 \quad Root\ x = 9$$

$$f(9) = 2 \qquad The\ curve\ crosses\ the\ horizontal\ asymptote\ at\ (9, 2).$$

If necessary, you can plot a few additional points to draw a smooth curve, as shown in Figure 3.50b.

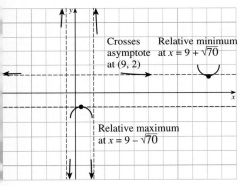

Crosses asymptote at (9, 2) Relative minimum at $x = 9 + \sqrt{70}$

Relative maximum at $x = 9 - \sqrt{70}$

a. Preliminary sketch

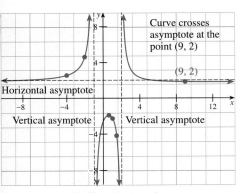

Curve crosses asymptote at the point (9, 2)

(9, 2)

Horizontal asymptote

Vertical asymptote   Vertical asymptote

b. Completed graph

Figure 3.50 Graph of

$$f(x) = 2 + \frac{7}{3(x - 2)} - \frac{10}{3(x + 1)}$$

EXAMPLE 4   Sketching a trigonometric curve

Discuss and graph $T(x) = \dfrac{\cos x}{1 - 2 \sin x}$ on $[0, \pi]$.

Solution   The first and second derivatives are found to be

$$T'(x) = \frac{2 - \sin x}{(1 - 2 \sin x)^2} \quad \text{and} \quad T''(x) = \frac{\cos x(7 - 2 \sin x)}{(1 - 2 \sin x)^3}$$

None of the functions T, T', or T'' is defined where $(1 - 2 \sin x)$ is 0. Solve

$$1 - 2 \sin x = 0$$
$$\sin x = \tfrac{1}{2}$$

The roots in $[0, \pi]$ are $x = \frac{\pi}{6}$ and $\frac{5\pi}{6}$. We find that $T'(x) > 0$ for all other x in the interval, so there are no other critical values for T. We also note from this information that T must be increasing for all defined points.

The critical values of T'' (other than those for which it is not defined) are found by solving

$$7 - 2 \sin x = 0 \quad \text{and} \quad \cos x = 0$$
$$\sin x = \tfrac{7}{2} \qquad\qquad x = \tfrac{\pi}{2}$$

Because $\sin x$ is never $\frac{7}{2}$, we see that the only second order critical value of t is $x = \frac{\pi}{2}$.

By checking the sign of T'' on each side of $\frac{\pi}{2}$, we see that the concavity changes, so it corresponds to a point of inflection.

The graph has a vertical asymptote when the denominator of T is 0; namely, when $\sin x = \frac{1}{2}$ or when $x = \frac{\pi}{6}$ or $x = \frac{5\pi}{6}$. We find that

$$\lim_{x \to \pi/6^-} T(x) = +\infty \qquad \lim_{x \to \pi/6^+} T(x) = -\infty$$
$$\lim_{x \to 5\pi/6^-} T(x) = +\infty \qquad \lim_{x \to 5\pi/6^+} T(x) = -\infty$$

There are no horizontal or oblique asymptotes.

Finally, plot some points:

$T(0) = 1$; plot the point $(0, 1)$.   *This is an endpoint.*

$T(\pi) = -1$; plot the point $(\pi, -1)$.   *This is an endpoint.*

$T\left(\frac{\pi}{2}\right) = 0$; plot the point $\left(\frac{\pi}{2}, 0\right)$.   *This is an inflection point.*

The preliminary graph is shown in Figure 3.51a and the completed graph in Figure 3.51b.

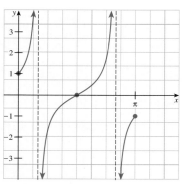

a. Preliminary sketch

b. Completed graph

Figure 3.51 Graph of $T(x) = \dfrac{\cos x}{1 - 2 \sin x}$ on $[0, \pi]$

PROBLEM SET 3.6

Ⓐ **1.** ■ **What Does This Say?** Outline a method for curve sketching.

2. ■ **What Does This Say?** Discuss the importance of critical values in curve sketching.

3. ■ **What Does This Say?** Discuss the importance of concavity and points of inflection in curve sketching.

4. ■ **What Does This Say?** Discuss the importance of asymptotes in curve sketching.

Sketch the graphs of the functions in Problems 5–22.

5. $f(x) = 3x^4 - 8x^3 + 6x^2 + 2$ **6.** $f(x) = 324x - 72x^2 + 4x^3$

7. $f(x) = 2x^3 + 6x^2 + 6x + 5$

8. $f(x) = 10x^6 + 24x^5 + 15x^4 + 3$

9. $f(t) = (t + 1)^2(t - 5)$ **10.** $f(z) = (1 - z)^2(z + 2)$

11. $g(x) = 2x^3 - 3x^2 - 12x + 14$ **12.** $h(x) = x^3 + 3x^2 - 6x + 2$

13. $g(t) = (t^3 + t)^2$

14. $f(x) = x\sqrt{16 - x^2}$

15. $f(x) = 12x(x - 1)^2 + (9x + 2)(x - 2)^3$

16. $g(u) = u^4 + 6u^3 - 24u^2 - 62u - 15$

17. $f(t) = 4t^5 + 5t^4$

18. $g(t) = t^{-1/2} + \frac{1}{3}t^{3/2}$

19. $f(x) = \dfrac{1}{x^2 + 12}$

20. $f(x) = \dfrac{2x^2 + 3x + 6}{x + 2}$

21. $c(x) = 25 \cos(450\pi x)$

22. $s(x) = 30 \sin\left(\dfrac{x}{180\pi}\right)$

B *Find the first- and second-order critical values of the functions given in Problems 23–43, and classify each such value as a relative maximum, a relative minimum, or neither. Sketch the graph of each function.*

23. $f(x) = x^3 + 3x^2 + 1$

24. $f(x) = x^4 - 2x^2 + 3$

25. $f(x) = (x^2 - 9)^2$

26. $g(x) = x(x^2 - 12)$

27. $f(x) = 2x + 1 + \dfrac{18}{x}$

28. $f(x) = 2x^3 - 3x^2 - 12x + 13$

29. $f(x) = (x + 1)^2(5 - x)$

30. $f(t) = (t - 3)^2(t - 4)^2$

31. $f(x) = 3x^4 - 2x^3 - 12x^2 + 18x$

32. $f(x) = x^{1/3}(x - 4)$

33. $f(u) = u^{2/3}(u - 7)$

34. $g(u) = (u^2 + u + 1)^{-2}$

35. $f(x) = \dfrac{x^2}{x - 2}$

36. $t(\theta) = \sin\theta - \cos\theta$ for $0 \le \theta \le 2\pi$

37. $f(x) = x - \sin 2x$ for $0 \le x \le \pi$

38. $g(t) = \tan t - \sec t$ for $0 \le t \le \frac{\pi}{3}$

39. $f(x) = \sin^2 x - 2\sin x + 1$ for $0 \le x \le \pi$

40. $g(t) = \dfrac{t + 4}{\sqrt{t}}$

41. $g(t) = \dfrac{t}{\sqrt{t^2 + 1}}$

42. $g(x) = \sin x \tan x$ on $[-\pi, \pi]$

43. $g(x) = \dfrac{\sin x}{1 + \cos x}$ on $[-2\pi, 2\pi]$

44. The *ideal speed v* for a banked curve on a highway satisfies the equation
$$v^2 = gr \tan\theta$$

where g is the constant acceleration due to gravity, r is the radius of the curve, and θ is the angle of the bank. Assuming that r is constant, sketch the graph of v as a function of θ for $0 \le \theta \le \frac{\pi}{2}$.*

45. According to Einstein's special theory of relativity, the mass of a body satisfies the equation

$$m = \dfrac{m_0}{\sqrt{1 - \dfrac{v^2}{c^2}}}$$

where m_0 is the mass of the body at rest in relation to the observer, m is the mass of the body when it moves with speed v in relation to the observer, and c is the speed of light. Sketch the graph of m as a function of v.

Computational Window

In Problems 46–47, use the bisection method, the Newton-Raphson method, or a computer to find all asymptotes of f, correct to the nearest hundredth. Sketch the graph.

46. $f(x) = \dfrac{x^2 + x - 3}{x^2 + 3x + 5}$

47. $f(x) = \dfrac{x^3 - x + 1}{x^5 + x^2 + 2}$

C THINK TANK PROBLEMS *In Problems 48–51, either show that the statement is generally true or find a counterexample.*

48. If f and g are concave up on the interval I, then so is $f + g$.

49. If f is concave up and g is concave down on an interval I, then fg is neither concave up nor concave down on I.

50. If $f(x) < 0$ and $f''(x) > 0$ for all x on I, then the function $g = f^2$ is concave up on I.

51. If $f(x) > 0$ and $g(x) > 0$ for all x on I and if f and g are concave up on I, then fg is also concave up on I.

3.7 OPTIMIZATION IN THE PHYSICAL SCIENCES AND ENGINEERING

IN THIS SECTION **Optimization procedure, Fermat's principle of optics and Snell's law**
In Chapter 1 we introduced the processes involved with model-building. Now that we have developed the necessary calculus skills, we shall use those skills in solving practical optimization problems.

■ OPTIMIZATION PROCEDURE

Nothing takes place in the world whose meaning is not that of some maximum or minimum.
Leonhard Euler

It is common to ask for the best procedure, the greatest value, the least cost, or the shortest path. The process of developing something to the utmost extent is called **optimization.** Entire courses in mathematics are devoted to this topic, and in this section and the next we will develop procedures involving calculus to solve real-

*In physics it is shown that if one travels around the curve at the ideal speed, no frictional force is required to prevent slipping. This greatly reduces wear on tires and contributes to safety.

life problems that seek the maximum or minimum value. We will model our procedure after one attributed to George Polya.

Optimization Procedure

Step 1: Understand the problem. Ask yourself if you can separate the given quantities and those you must find. What is unknown? Draw a picture to help you understand the problem.

Step 2: Choose the variables. Decide which quantity is to be optimized (that is, maximized or minimized) and call it Q. Choose other variables for unknown quantities and label your diagram using these symbols.

Step 3: Express Q in terms of the variables defined in Step 2. Use the information given in the problem and the principle of substitution to rewrite Q in terms of a single variable, say x. **In other words,** Q may begin as a formula involving several variables, but by using given information or known formulas, the goal is to write Q as a function of *one* variable so that $Q = f(x)$.

Step 4: Find the domain for the function $Q = f(x)$.

Step 5: Use calculus to find the *absolute* maximum or minimum value of f. In particular, if the domain of f is a closed interval $[a, b]$, then the procedure outlined in Section 3.1 can be used:

   a. Compute $f'(x)$ and find all critical values of f on $[a, b]$.

   b. Evaluate f at the endpoints a, b, and at each critical value, c.

   c. Compare the values in step b to find either the largest or smallest value.

Step 6: Convert the result obtained in Step 5 back into the context of the original problem, making all appropriate interpretations. Be sure to answer the question asked.

EXAMPLE 1   Maximizing a constrained area

You need to fence in a rectangular play zone for children, to fit into a right-triangular plot with sides measuring 4 m and 12 m. What is the maximum area for this play zone?

Solution   A picture of the play zone is shown in Figure 3.52. Let x and y denote the length and width of the inscribed rectangle. The appropriate formula for the area is

$$A = \ell w = xy$$

We wish to maximize Q where $Q = A = xy$. Now, write this as a function of a single variable. To do this, note that

$$\triangle ABC \sim \triangle ADF$$

This means that corresponding sides of these triangles are proportional; therefore

$$\frac{4 - y}{4} = \frac{x}{12}$$

$$4 - y = \tfrac{1}{3}x$$

$$y = 4 - \tfrac{1}{3}x$$

We can now write Q as a function of x alone:

$$Q(x) = x\left(4 - \tfrac{1}{3}x\right) = 4x - \tfrac{1}{3}x^2$$

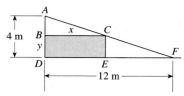

Figure 3.52 Children's play zone

The domain for x is $0 \le x \le 12$. The critical values for Q are values such that $Q'(x) = 0$ (since there are no places where the derivative does not exist). Because

$$Q'(x) = 4 - \frac{2}{3}x$$

the critical value is $x = 6$. Evaluate $Q(x)$ at the endpoints and the critical value:

$$Q(6) = 4(6) - \tfrac{1}{3}(6)^2 = 12; \qquad Q(0) = 0; \qquad Q(12) = 0$$

The maximum area occurs when $x = 6$. This means that

$$y = 4 - \tfrac{1}{3}(6) = 2$$

The largest rectangular play zone that can be built in the triangular plot is a rectangle 6 m long and 2 m wide, so the maximum area is 12 m². ■

EXAMPLE 2   Maximizing profits

A manufacturer can produce a pair of earrings at a cost of $3. The earrings have been selling for $5 per pair, and at this price, consumers have been buying 4,000 per month. The manufacturer is planning to raise the price of the earrings and estimates that for each $1 increase in the price, 400 fewer pairs of earrings will be sold each month. At what price should the manufacturer sell the earrings to maximize profit?

Solution   Let x denote the number of $1 price increases, and let $P(x)$ represent the corresponding profit.

PROFIT = REVENUE − COST

= (NUMBER SOLD)(PRICE PER PAIR) − (NUMBER SOLD)(COST PER PAIR)

= (NUMBER SOLD)(PRICE PER PAIR − COST PER PAIR)

Recall that 4,000 pairs of earrings are sold each month when the price is $5 per pair and 400 fewer pairs will be sold each month for each added dollar in the price. Thus,

NUMBER OF PAIRS SOLD = 4,000 − 400(NUMBER OF $1 INCREASES)

= 4,000 − 400x

Knowing that the price per pair is $5 + x$, write the profit as a function of x:

$$P(x) = (\text{NUMBER SOLD})(\text{PRICE PER PAIR} - \text{COST PER PAIR})$$
$$= (4,000 - 400x)[(5 + x) - 3] = 400(10 - x)(2 + x)$$

To find the domain, we note that $x \ge 0$. And $400(10 - x)$, the number of pairs sold, should be nonnegative, so $x \le 10$. Thus, the domain is [0, 10].

The critical values are found when the derivative is 0 (P is a polynomial function, so there are no values for which the derivative is not defined):

$$P'(x) = 400(10 - x)(1) + 400(-1)(2 + x) = 400(10 - x - 2 - x)$$
$$= 400(8 - 2x) = 800(4 - x)$$

The critical value is $x = 4$ and the endpoints are $x = 0$ and $x = 10$. Checking for the maximum profit:

$$P(4) = 400(10 - 4)(2 + 4) = 14,400; \qquad P(0) = 8,000; \qquad P(10) = 0$$

The maximum possible profit is $14,400, which will be generated if the earrings are sold for $9.00 per pair. The graph of the profit function is shown in Figure 3.53. ■

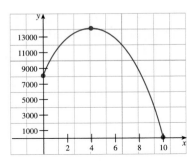

Figure 3.53 The profit function $P(x)$

Figure 3.54 A box cut from a 24 in. by 45 in. piece of tin

Computational Window ▼ ▲

The necessity of knowing the endpoints of the interval is emphasized when you use a graphing calculator. For example, the TI-85 finds the approximate maximum value of a given function but requires that you enter *function, variable, lower limit, and upper limit*. For $V'(x)$ in Example 3, we obtain the answers 5.00231626223 with a tolerance of 0.01 and $\delta = 0.001$.

EXAMPLE 3   Maximizing a volume

A carpenter wants to make an open-topped box out of a rectangular sheet of tin 24 in. wide and 45 in. long. The carpenter plans to cut congruent squares out of each corner of the sheet and then bend the edges of the sheet upward to form the sides of the box, as shown in Figure 3.54. If the box is to have the greatest possible volume, what should its dimensions be?

Solution   If each square corner cut out has side x, the box will be x inches deep, $45 - 2x$ inches long, and $24 - 2x$ inches wide. The volume of the box shown in Figure 3.54 is

$$V(x) = x(45 - 2x)(24 - 2x) = 4x^3 - 138x^2 + 1{,}080x$$

To find the domain, we note that the dimensions must all be nonnegative; therefore, $x \geq 0$, $45 - 2x \geq 0$ (or $x \leq 22.5$), and $24 - 2x \geq 0$ (or $x \leq 12$). This implies that the domain is $[0, 12]$. To find the critical values (the derivative is defined everywhere in the domain), we find values for which the derivative is 0:

$$V'(x) = 12x^2 - 276x + 1{,}080 = 12(x - 18)(x - 5)$$

The critical values are $x = 5$ and $x = 18$, but $x = 18$ is not in the domain, so the only relevant critical value is $x = 5$. Evaluating $V(x)$ at the critical value $x = 5$ and the endpoints $x = 0$, $x = 12$, we find

$$V(5) = 5(45 - 10)(24 - 10) = 2{,}450; \qquad V(0) = 0; \qquad V(12) = 0$$

Thus, the box with the largest volume is found when $x = 5$. Such a box has dimensions 5 in. × 14 in. × 35 in.

EXAMPLE 4   Maximizing an area using trigonometry

Two sides of a triangle are 4 inches long. What should the angle between these sides be to make the area of the triangle as large as possible?

Solution   The triangle is shown in Figure 3.55. In general, the area of a triangle is given by

$$A = \tfrac{1}{2}bh$$

In this case, the base b is 4 and, because $\sin \theta = \dfrac{h}{4}$, the height h is $4 \sin \theta$. Thus,

$$A = \tfrac{1}{2}(4)(4 \sin \theta) = 8 \sin \theta$$

To find the domain, we note that the largest angle in a triangle is π; therefore, $0 \leq \theta \leq \pi$. Also, because $A'(\theta)$ is defined throughout this interval, the critical values are found when the derivative is 0. We have

$$A'(\theta) = 8 \cos \theta$$

which is zero only when $\theta = \frac{\pi}{2}$. Because

$$A\left(\tfrac{\pi}{2}\right) = 8 \sin \tfrac{\pi}{2} = 8, \qquad A(0) = 8 \sin 0 = 0, \qquad A(\pi) = 8 \sin \pi = 0$$

we see that the area is maximized when the angle θ is $\frac{\pi}{2}$—that is, when the triangle is a right triangle.

Figure 3.55 Triangle with two 4-in. sides

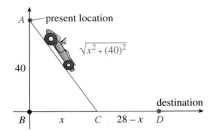

Figure 3.56 A path traveled by a dune buggy

EXAMPLE 5   Minimizing time of travel

A dune buggy is on the desert at a point A located 40 km from a point B, which lies on a long, straight road, as shown in Figure 3.56. The driver can travel at 45 km/hr on the desert and 75 km/hr on the road. The driver will win a prize if she arrives at the finish line (point D) in less than 1 hr. If the distance from B to D is 28 km, is it possible for her to choose a route so that she can collect the prize?

Solution   Suppose the driver heads for a point C located x km down the road from B toward her destination, as shown in Figure 3.56. We want to minimize the time. We will need to remember the formula $d = rt$, or in terms of time, $t = d/r$.

$$\text{TIME} = \text{TIME FROM } A \text{ TO } C + \text{TIME FROM } C \text{ TO } D$$

$$T(x) = \frac{\text{DISTANCE FROM } A \text{ TO } C}{\text{RATE FROM } A \text{ TO } C} + \frac{\text{DISTANCE FROM } C \text{ TO } D}{\text{RATE FROM } C \text{ TO } D}$$

$$= \frac{\sqrt{x^2 + 1{,}600}}{45} + \frac{28 - x}{75}$$

The domain for x is $[0, 28]$. Next, find the derivative of time T with respect to x.

$$T'(x) = \frac{1}{45}\left[\frac{1}{2}(x^2 + 1{,}600)^{-1/2}(2x)\right] + \frac{1}{75}(-1)$$

$$= \frac{x}{45\sqrt{x^2 + 1{,}600}} - \frac{1}{75}$$

$$= \frac{5x - 3\sqrt{x^2 + 1{,}600}}{225\sqrt{x^2 + 1{,}600}}$$

The derivative exists for all x and is zero when

$$5x - 3\sqrt{x^2 + 1{,}600} = 0$$

Solving this equation, we find $x = 30$ (-30 is extraneous), which must be rejected because it is not within the interval $[0, 28]$. Evaluating $T(x)$ at the endpoints, we find that

$$T(0) = \frac{\sqrt{0^2 + 1{,}600}}{45} + \frac{28 - 0}{75} \approx 1.26$$

$$T(28) = \frac{\sqrt{28^2 + 1{,}600}}{45} + \frac{28 - 28}{75} \approx 1.09$$

The driver can minimize the total driving time by heading directly across the desert from A to D. Even so, she takes a little more than an hour for the trip, so she does not win the prize.

EXAMPLE 6   Optimizing a constrained area

A wire of length L is to be cut into two pieces, one of which will be bent to form a circle and the other, to form a square. How should the cut be made to

a. maximize the sum of the areas enclosed by the two pieces?
b. minimize the sum of the areas enclosed by the two pieces?

Computational Window

A standard window will not suffice. You will need to set both the domain and the range:

```
Y₁■√(X²+1600)/45
+(28-X)/75

Xmin=0     Ymin=0
Xmax=100   Ymax=1.5
Xscl=10    Yscl=.1
```

The TRACE will give you a first estimate for the minimum time:

```
X=29.787234  Y=1.0844509

Y₁■√(X²+1600)/45
+(28-X)/75

Xmin=0     Ymin=0
Xmax=100   Ymax=1.5
Xscl=10    Yscl=.1
```

Because 29.787234 is not in the domain, the minimum value occurs at the endpoint, $x = 28$.

Solution   In order to understand the problem we draw a sketch, as shown in Figure 3.57, and label the radius of the circle r and the side of the square s.

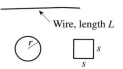

Figure 3.57 Forming a circle and a square from a wire with length L

We find that the combined area is

$$\text{AREA} = \text{AREA OF CIRCLE} + \text{AREA OF SQUARE}$$

$$= \pi r^2 + s^2$$

We need to write the radius r and the side s in terms of the length of wire, L.

$$L = \text{CIRCUMFERENCE OF CIRCLE} + \text{PERIMETER OF SQUARE}$$

$$= 2\pi r + 4s$$

Thus, $s = \frac{1}{4}(L - 2\pi r)$. Remember, L is a given constant, so the variable for the area function is r (although the problem could just as easily have been done in terms of s). By substitution,

$$A(r) = \pi r^2 + \left[\tfrac{1}{4}(L - 2\pi r)\right]^2 = \pi r^2 + \tfrac{1}{16}(L - 2\pi r)^2$$

To find the domain, we note that $r \geq 0$ and that $L - 2\pi r \geq 0$, so the domain is $0 \leq r \leq \frac{L}{2\pi}$. The derivative of $A(r)$ is

$$A'(r) = 2\pi r + \tfrac{1}{8}(L - 2\pi r)(-2\pi)$$

$$= 2\pi r - \tfrac{\pi}{4}(L - 2\pi r) = \tfrac{\pi}{4}(8r - L + 2\pi r)$$

We solve $A'(r) = 0$ to find $r = \dfrac{L}{2(\pi + 4)}$.

Thus, the extreme values of the area function on $\left[0, \dfrac{L}{2\pi}\right]$ must occur either at the endpoints or at the critical value $\dfrac{L}{2\pi + 8}$. Evaluating $A(r)$ at each of these numbers, we find

$$A(0) = \pi(0)^2 + \tfrac{1}{16}[L - 2\pi(0)]^2 = \tfrac{L^2}{16} = 0.0625L^2$$

$$A\left(\frac{L}{2\pi}\right) = \pi\left(\frac{L}{2\pi}\right)^2 + \tfrac{1}{16}\left[L - 2\pi\left(\frac{L}{2\pi}\right)\right]^2 = \tfrac{L^2}{4\pi} \approx 0.079\,577\,471L^2$$

$$A\left(\frac{L}{2\pi + 8}\right) = \pi\left(\frac{L}{2\pi + 8}\right)^2 + \tfrac{1}{16}\left[(L - 2)\left(\frac{L}{2\pi + 8}\right)\right]^2 = \frac{L^2}{4(\pi + 4)}$$

$$\approx 0.035\,006\,197L^2$$

Comparing these values, we see that the smallest area occurs at $x = \dfrac{L}{2\pi + 8}$ and the largest area occurs at $x = \dfrac{L}{2\pi}$. To summarize:

1. To maximize the sum of the areas, do not cut the wire at all. Bend the wire to form a circle of radius $r = \dfrac{L}{2\pi}$.

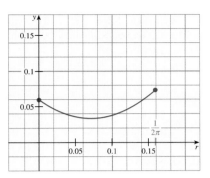

Figure 3.58 Graph of
$A(r) = \pi r^2 + \frac{1}{16}[1 - 2\pi r]^2$

2. To minimize the sum of the areas, cut the wire at the point located $\dfrac{2\pi L}{2\pi + 8}$ units from one end, and form the circular part with radius $r = \dfrac{L}{2\pi + 8}$.

If you use a graphing calculator or a computer, you can verify this result (for $L = 1$) by looking at the graph of the area function, as shown in Figure 3.58. ■

■ PHYSICS: FERMAT'S PRINCIPLE OF OPTICS AND SNELL'S LAW

Light travels at different rates in different media; the more optically dense the medium, the slower the speed of transit. Consider the situation shown in Figure 3.59, in which a beam of light originates at a point A in one medium, then strikes the upper surface of a second, denser medium at a point P, and is refracted to a point B in the second medium.

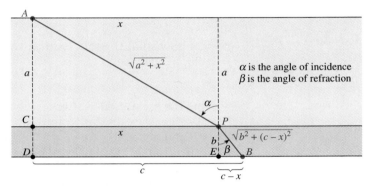

Figure 3.59 The path of a light beam through two media of different density

Suppose light travels with speed v_1 in the first medium and speed v_2 in the second. What can be said about the path followed by the beam of light?

Our method of investigating this question is based on the following optical property.

Fermat's Principle of Optics

Light travels between two points in such a way as to minimize the time of transit.

This problem is very similar to the dune buggy problem of Example 5: Light minimizes the time, and minimum time was the goal of Example 5. In Figure 3.59, let $a = \overline{AC}$, $b = \overline{CD}$, and $c = \overline{DB}$, and let x denote the distance from C to P. Because A and B are fixed points, the path APB is determined by the location of P, which, in turn, is determined by x. Because v_1 is a constant, the time required for the light to travel from A to P is given by

$$T_1 = \frac{|\overline{AP}|}{v_1} = \frac{\sqrt{a^2 + x^2}}{v_1}$$

and the time required for the light to go from P to B is

$$T_2 = \frac{|\overline{PB}|}{v_2} = \frac{\sqrt{b^2 + (c - x)^2}}{v_2}$$

Therefore, the total time of transit is

$$T = T_1 + T_2 = \frac{\sqrt{a^2 + x^2}}{v_1} + \frac{\sqrt{b^2 + (c - x)^2}}{v_2}$$

where it is clear that $0 \le x \le c$. According to Fermat's principle, the path followed by the beam of light is the one that corresponds to the smallest possible value of T; that is, we want to minimize T as a function of x.

Toward this end, we begin by finding $\dfrac{dT}{dx}$.

$$\frac{dT}{dx} = \frac{x}{v_1 \sqrt{a^2 + x^2}} - \frac{c - x}{v_2 \sqrt{b^2 + (c - x)^2}}$$

Note from Figure 3.59 that if α is the angle of incidence of the beam of light and β is the angle of refraction, then (from the definition of sine)

$$\sin \alpha = \frac{x}{\sqrt{a^2 + x^2}} \quad \text{and} \quad \sin \beta = \frac{c - x}{\sqrt{b^2 + (c - x)^2}}$$

Therefore (by substitution), we see the derivative of T can be expressed as

$$\frac{dT}{dx} = \frac{\sin \alpha}{v_1} - \frac{\sin \beta}{v_2}$$

and it follows that the only critical value occurs when

$$\frac{\sin \alpha}{\sin \beta} = \frac{v_1}{v_2}$$

By using the second-derivative test in the interval $[0, c]$, it can be shown that this critical value is an absolute minimum. The corresponding value of x enables us to locate P and hence to determine the path followed by the beam of light. We have established the following law of optics.

Snell's Law of Refraction

If a beam of light strikes the boundary between two media with angle of incidence α and is refracted through an angle β, then

$$\frac{\sin \alpha}{\sin \beta} = \frac{v_1}{v_2}$$

where v_1 and v_2 are the rates at which light travels through the first and second medium, respectively. The constant ratio

$$n = \frac{\sin \alpha}{\sin \beta}$$

is called the **relative index of refraction** of the two media.

PROBLEM SET 3.7

A 1. ■ What Does This Say? Describe an optimization procedure.

2. ■ What Does This Say? Why is it important to check end values when finding an optimum value?

B 3. A woman plans to fence off a rectangular garden whose area is 64 ft². What should be the dimensions of the garden if she wants to minimize the amount of fencing used?

4. The highway department is planning to build a rectangular picnic area for motorists along a major highway. It is to have an area of 5,000 yd² and is to be fenced off on the three sides not adjacent to the highway. What is the least amount of fencing that will be needed to complete the job?

5. A farmer wishes to enclose a rectangular pasture with 320 ft of fence. Find the dimensions that give the maximum area in these situations:

   a. The fence is on all four sides of the pasture.

   b. The fence is on three sides of the pasture and the fourth side is bounded by a wall.

6. EXPERIMENT Pull out a sheet of $8\frac{1}{2}$-in. by 11-in. binder paper. Cut squares from the corners and fold the sides up to form a container. Show that the maximum volume of such a container is about 1 liter.

7. JOURNAL PROBLEM: *Parabola*.* Farmer Jones has to build a fence to enclose a 1200 m² rectangular area

* Volume 19, Issue 1, 1983, p. 22.

ABCD. Fencing costs $3 per meter, but Farmer Smith has agreed to pay half the cost of fencing $\overline{CD}$, which borders the property. Given *x* is the length of side $\overline{BC}$, what is the maximum amount (to the nearest cent) Jones has to pay?

8. Find the rectangle of largest area that can be inscribed in a semicircle of radius *R*, assuming that one side of the rectangle lies on the diameter of the semicircle.

9. A tinsmith wants to make an open-topped box out of a rectangular sheet of tin 24 in. wide and 45 in. long. The tinsmith plans to cut congruent squares out of each corner of the sheet and then bend the edges of the sheet upward to form the sides of the box. What are the dimensions of the largest box that can be made in this fashion?

10. Find the dimensions of the right circular cylinder of largest volume that can be inscribed in a sphere of radius *R*.

11. Given a sphere of radius *R*, find the radius *r* and altitude *h* of the right circular cylinder with largest lateral surface area that can be inscribed in the sphere. *Hint*: The lateral surface area is $S = 2\pi rh$.

12. Each edge of a square has length *L*. Determine the edge of the square of largest area that can be circumscribed about the given square.

13. Find the dimensions of the right circular cylinder of largest volume that can be inscribed in a right circular cone of radius *R* and altitude *H*.

14. A truck is 250 mi due east of a sports car and is traveling west at a constant speed of 60 mi/hr. Meanwhile, the sports car is going north at 80 mi/hr. When will the truck and the car be closest to each other? What is the minimum distance between them? *Hint*: Minimize the square of the distance.

15. Show that of all rectangles with a given perimeter, the square has the largest area.

16. Show that of all rectangles with a given area, the square has the smallest perimeter.

17. A closed box with square base and vertical sides is to be built to house an ant colony. The bottom of the box and all four sides are to be made of material costing $1/ft^2, and the top is to be constructed of glass costing $5/ft^2. What are the dimensions of the box of greatest volume that can be constructed for $72?

18. According to postal regulations, the girth plus the length of a parcel sent by fourth class mail may not exceed 108 in. What is the largest possible volume of a rectangular parcel with two square sides that can be sent by fourth class mail?

19. SPY PROBLEM   It is noon. The spy has returned from space (Problem 50 of Section 2.4) and is driving a jeep through the sandy desert in the tiny principality of Alta Loma. He is 32 km from the nearest point on a straight, paved road. Down the road 16 km is a power plant in which a band of international terrorists has placed a time bomb set to explode at 12:50 P.M. The jeep can travel at 48 km/hr in the sand and at 80 km/hr on the paved road. If he arrives at the power plant in the shortest possible time, how long will our hero have to defuse the bomb?

20. Missy Smith is at a point *A* on the north bank of a long, straight river 6 mi wide. Directly across from her on the south bank is a point *B*, and she wishes to reach a cabin *C* located *s* mi down the river from *B*. Given that Missy can row at 6 mi/hr (including the effect of the current) and run at 10 mi/hr, what is the minimum time (to the nearest minute) required for her to travel from *A* to *C* in each case?   **a.** *s* = 4   **b.** *s* = 6

21. Two towns *A* and *B* are 12 mi apart and are located 5 mi and 3 mi, respectively, from a long, straight highway. A construction company has a contract to build a road from *A* to the highway and then to *B*. How long is the *shortest* (to the nearest mile) road that meets these requirements?

22. A poster is to contain 108 cm^2 of printed matter, with margins of 6 cm each at top and bottom and 2 cm on the sides. What is the minimum cost of the poster if it is to be made of material costing 20¢/cm^2?

23. An isosceles trapezoid has a base of 14 cm and slant sides of 6 cm, as shown in Figure 3.60. What is the largest area of such a trapezoid?

Figure 3.60 Area of a trapezoid

24. EXPERIMENT   Use the fact that 12 fl oz is approximately 6.89π in.³ to find the dimensions of the 12-oz Coke® can that can be constructed using the least amount of metal. Compare these dimensions with a Coke from your refrigerator. What do you think accounts for the difference?

An interesting article that discusses a similar question regarding tuna fish cans is "What manufacturers say about a max/min application" by Robert F. Cunningham, Trenton State College, *The Mathematics Teacher*, March 1994, pp. 172–175.

25. A cylindrical container with no top is to be constructed to hold a fixed volume of liquid. The cost of the material used for the bottom is 50¢/in.², and the cost of the material used for the curved side is 30¢/in². Use calculus to find the radius (in terms of the volume) of the least expensive container.

26. Light emanating from a source A is reflected by a mirror to a point B, as shown in Figure 3.61. Use Fermat's principle of optics to show that the angle of incidence α equals the angle of reflection β.

Figure 3.61 Angle of incidence is equal to the angle of reflection.

27. A stained glass window in the form of an equilateral triangle is built on top of a rectangular window, as shown in Figure 3.62. The window is of clear glass and transmits twice as much light per ft² as the triangular window, which is made of stained glass. If the entire window has a perimeter of 20 ft, find the dimensions (to the nearest ft) of the rectangular window that will admit the most light.

Figure 3.62 Maximizing the amount of light

28. Figure 3.63 shows a thin lens located p cm from an object AB and q cm from the image RS.

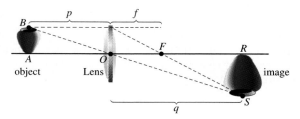

Figure 3.63 Image from a lens

The distance f from the center O of the lens to the point labeled F is called the **focal length** of the lens.

a. Using similar triangles, show that

$$\frac{1}{p} + \frac{1}{q} = \frac{1}{f}$$

b. Suppose a lens maker wished to have $p + q = 24$. What is the largest value of f for which this condition can be satisfied?

29. When a mechanical system is at rest in an equilibrium position, its potential energy is minimized with respect to any small change in its position. Figure 3.64 shows a system involving a pulley, two small weights of mass m and a larger weight of mass M.

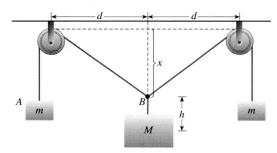

Figure 3.64 A pulley system

It can be shown that the total potential energy of the system is given by

$$E = -Mg(x + h) - 2mg(L - \sqrt{x^2 + d^2})$$

where x, h, and d are the distances shown in Figure 3.64, L is the length of the cord from A around one pulley to B, and g is the constant acceleration due to gravity. All the other symbols represent constants. Use this information to find the value of x for which E is minimized.

30. One end of a cantilever beam of length L is built into a wall, but the other end is supported by a single post. The deflection, or "sag," of the beam at a point located x units from the built-in end is given by the formula

$$D = k(2x^4 - 5Lx^3 + 3L^2x^2)$$

where k is a positive constant. Where does the maximum deflection occur on the beam?

31. A resistor of R ohms is connected across a battery of E volts whose internal resistance is r ohms. According to the principles of electricity, a current of

$$I = \frac{E}{R + r}$$

amperes will flow in the circuit and will generate

$$P = I^2R$$

watts of power in the external resistor. Assuming that E and r are constant, what value of R will result in maximum power in the external resistor?

32. A lamp with adjustable height hangs directly above the center of a circular kitchen table that is 8 ft in diameter. The illumination at the edge of the table is directly proportional to the cosine of the angle θ and inversely proportional to the square of the distance d, given θ and d as shown in Figure 3.65

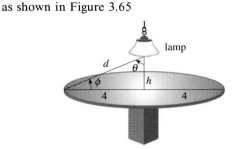

Figure 3.65 Illumination on a kitchen table

a. Let I denote the illumination at the edge of the table. Show that

$$I(\theta) = \frac{k}{16} \cos\theta \sin^2\theta$$

Find $I'(\theta)$.

b. Show that $I'(\theta) = 0$ when $\tan\theta = \sqrt{2}$. What are $\sin\theta$ and $\cos\theta$?

c. How close to the table (to the nearest ft) should the lamp be pulled to maximize the illumination at the edge of the table?

33. In Problem 32, suppose the illumination is directly proportional to the sine of the angle ϕ and inversely proportional to the square of the distance d, where ϕ is the angle at which the ray of light meets the table. How close to the table (to the nearest ft) should the lamp be pulled to maximize the illumination at the edge of the table? Is your answer the same as in Problem 32? Explain why or why not.

Ⓒ 34. The lower right-hand corner of a piece of paper is folded over to reach the leftmost edge, as shown in Figure 3.66.

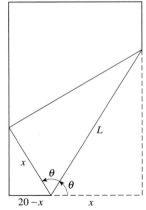

Figure 3.66 Paper folding problem

If the page is 20 cm wide and 30 cm long, what is the length L of the shortest possible crease? *Hint*: First

express $\cos\theta$ and $\cos 2\theta$ in terms of x and then use the trigonometric identity

$$\cos 2\theta = 2\cos^2\theta - 1$$

to eliminate θ and express L in terms of x alone.

35. Find the length of the longest pipe that can be carried horizontally around a corner joining two corridors that are $2\sqrt{2}$ ft wide, as shown in Figure 3.67.

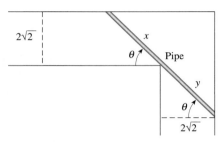

Figure 3.67 Problem 35

36. Congruent triangles are cut out of a square piece of paper 20 in. on a side, leaving a star-like figure that can be folded to form a pyramid, as indicated in Figure 3.68.

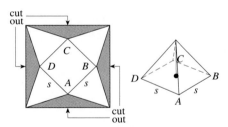

Figure 3.68 Constructing a pyramid

What is the largest volume of the pyramid that can be formed in this manner?

37. It is known that water expands and contracts according to its temperature. Physical experiments suggest that an amount of water that occupies 1 liter at 0 °C will occupy

$$V(T) = 1 - 6.42 \cdot 10^{-5}T + 8.51 \cdot 10^{-6}T^2 - 6.79 \times 10^{-8}T^3$$

liters when the temperature is T °C. At what temperature is $V(T)$ minimized? This seems to suggest that the maximum density of water occurs at a temperature above its freezing point (0 °), and explains why ice forms only at the upper levels of a lake during winter.

3.8 OPTIMIZATION IN BUSINESS, ECONOMICS, AND THE LIFE SCIENCES

> **IN THIS SECTION**   Optimization of discrete functions, economics: two principles of business management; marginal analysis; an inventory model; physiology: the optimal angle for vascular branching
> Optimization problems appear in many different areas that use calculus as a method of analysis. We have already examined a few of these applications in Section 3.7, and this section deals with more specialized applications.

■ OPTIMIZATION OF DISCRETE FUNCTIONS

Sometimes the function to be maximized has practical meaning only when its independent variable is a positive integer. This can lead to certain problems when applying the processes of calculus, because the theorems we have developed require continuous functions. If we model a function whose variable is defined as a positive integer, but as part of the modeling process we assume the function is defined for all real values (so that it is continuous), it may happen that the optimization procedure leads to a nonintegral value of the independent variable, and additional analysis is needed to obtain a meaningful solution.

EXAMPLE 1   Maximizing a discrete revenue function

x	No.	Fare	Revenue
0	35	60	2,100
1	36	59	2,124
2	37	58	2,146
3	38	57	2,166
4	39	56	2,184
5	40	55	2,200
6	41	54	2,214
7	42	53	2,226
8	43	52	2,236
9	44	51	2,244
10	45	50	2,250
11	46	49	2,254
12	47	48	2,256
13	48	47	2,256
14	49	46	2,254
15	50	45	2,250

A bus company will charter a bus that holds 50 people to groups of 35 or more. If a group contains exactly 35 people, each person pays $60. In larger groups, everybody's fare is reduced by $1 for each person in excess of 35. Determine the size of the group for which the bus company's revenue will be the greatest.

Solution   We wish to maximize the revenue:

REVENUE = (NUMBER OF PEOPLE IN THE GROUP)(FARE PER PERSON)

Let x be the number of people in excess of 35 who take the trip. Then,

NUMBER OF PEOPLE IN THE GROUP $= 35 + x$
FARE PER PERSON $= 60 - x$

Let $R(x)$ be the revenue for the bus company:

$$R(x) = (35 + x)(60 - x) = 2,100 + 25x - x^2$$

Next, find the domain: We note that there must be at least 35 people ($x = 0$) and at most 50 people ($x = 15$); thus $0 \le x \le 15$, *but because x represents a number of people, it must also be an integer.*
The critical values are found by looking at the derivative.

$$R'(x) = 25 - 2x$$

Because the derivative exists throughout the interval, the only critical value is $x = 12.5$. But x must be an integer, so $x = 12.5$ is not in the domain. To find the optimal *integer* solution, observe that R is increasing on $(0, 12.5)$ and decreasing on $(12.5, 15)$, as shown in Figure 3.69. If follows that the opti-

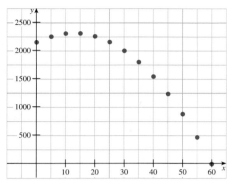

Figure 3.69 Graphs of $R(x) = -x^2 + 25x + 2{,}100$

a. The continuous revenue function

b. The discrete revenue function

mal integer value of x is either $x = 12$ or $x = 13$. Because

$$R(12) = 2{,}256 \quad \text{and} \quad R(13) = 2{,}256$$

we conclude that the bus company's revenue will be greatest when the group contains either 12 or 13 people in excess of 35—that is, for groups of 47 or 48. In either case, the revenue will be $2,256.

The graph of revenue as a function of x is a collection of discrete points corresponding to the integer values of x, as indicated in Figure 3.69b. Technically, calculus cannot be used to study such a function, so instead, we worked with the differentiable function $R(x) = -x^2 + 25x + 2{,}100$, which is defined for all values of x and whose graph "connects" the points in the discrete graph. After applying calculus to this continuous model, we obtained a mathematical solution that was not the solution of the discrete practical problem, but that did suggest where to look for the required solution. To verify that this integer solution is correct, we can look at the margin table, p. 230, which shows all possibilities from $x = 0$ (35 people) to $x = 15$ (50 people). For each number of travelers, the total revenue is calculated, and we see that the maximum value 2,256 is obtained when $x = 12$ and again when $x = 13$. ▃▃

■ ECONOMICS: TWO GENERAL PRINCIPLES OF MARGINAL ANALYSIS

In Chapter 2, we described *marginal analysis* as that branch of economics that is concerned with the way quantities such as price, cost, revenue, and profit vary with small changes in the level of production. Specifically, recall that if $C(x)$ is the total cost and $p(x)$ is the market price per unit when x units of a particular commodity are produced, then $R(x) = xp(x)$ is the **total revenue** and $P(x) = R(x) - C(x)$ is the profit function. These functions are shown in Figure 3.70.

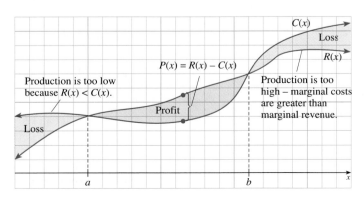

Figure 3.70 Cost, revenue, and profit functions

In Section 2.8, we worked with marginal quantities and their role as rates of change, namely, $C'(x)$, the *marginal cost*, and $R'(x)$, the *marginal revenue*.*

We will now consider these functions in optimization problems. For example, the manufacturer certainly would like to know what level of production results in maximum profit. To solve this problem, we want to maximize the profit function

$$P(x) = R(x) - C(x)$$

We differentiate with respect to x and find that

$$P'(x) = R'(x) - C'(x)$$

Thus, $P'(x) = 0$ when $R'(x) = C'(x)$, and by using economic arguments we can show that a maximum occurs at the corresponding critical point.

Maximum Profit

> Profit is maximized when marginal revenue equals marginal cost.

EXAMPLE 2   Maximum profit

A manufacturer estimates that when x units of a particular commodity are produced each month, the total cost (in dollars) will be

$$C(x) = \tfrac{1}{8}x^2 + 4x + 200$$

and all units can be sold at a price of $p(x) = 49 - x$ dollars per unit. Determine the price that corresponds to the maximum profit.

Solution   The marginal cost is $C'(x) = \tfrac{1}{4}x + 4$. The revenue is

$$R(x) = xp(x) = x(49 - x) = 49x - x^2$$

The marginal revenue is $R'(x) = 49 - 2x$. The profit is maximized when $R'(x) = C'(x)$:

$$R'(x) = C'(x)$$
$$49 - 2x = \tfrac{1}{4}x + 4$$
$$x = 20$$

Thus, the price that corresponds to the maximum profit is

$$p(20) = 49 - 20 = 29 \text{ dollars} \qquad \blacksquare$$

A second general principle of economics involves the following relationship between marginal cost and the *average cost* $A(x) = C(x)/x$.

Minimum Average Cost

> Average cost is minimized at the level of production where the marginal cost equals the average cost.

To justify this second business principle, find the derivative of the average cost function:

$$A'(x) = \frac{xC'(x) - C(x)}{x^2} = \frac{C'(x) - \frac{C(x)}{x}}{x} = \frac{C'(x) - A(x)}{x}$$

---

*Recall (from Section 2.8) that marginal cost is the instantaneous rate of change of production cost C with respect to the number of units x produced, and the marginal revenue is the instantaneous rate of change of revenue with respect to the number of units x produced.

Thus, $A'(x) = 0$ when $C'(x) = A(x)$, and once again, economic theory justifies this result as a minimum (rather than a maximum, which would seem possible using only calculus).

EXAMPLE 3   Minimizing average cost

A manufacturer estimates that when x units of a particular commodity are produced each month, the total cost (in dollars) will be

$$C(x) = \tfrac{1}{8}x^2 + 4x + 200$$

and they can all be sold at a price of $p(x) = 49 - x$ dollars per unit. Determine the level of production where the average cost is minimized.

Solution The average cost is $A(x) = \dfrac{C(x)}{x} = \tfrac{1}{8}x + 4 + 200x^{-1}$ and $A(x)$ is minimized when $C'(x) = A(x)$. Thus,

$$\tfrac{1}{4}x + 4 = \tfrac{1}{8}x + 4 + 200x^{-1}$$

$$x^2 = 1600 \qquad \textit{Multiply both sides by } 8x \textit{ and simplify.}$$

If we disregard the negative solution, it follows that the minimal average cost occurs when $x = 40$ units. You might have noticed that we did not use the information $p(x) = 49 - x$ in arriving at the solution. It is included, because when doing real-world modeling it is often necessary to make a choice about which parts of the available information are necessary to solve the problem. ▬

The average cost, marginal cost, marginal revenue, and total profit graphs for Examples 2 and 3 are shown in Figure 3.71.

a. Profit function $P(x) = -\dfrac{9}{8}x^2 + 45x - 200$ **b.** Detail of graph **a**

Figure 3.71 Average cost, marginal cost, marginal revenue, and profit functions

Notice that the marginal revenue and marginal cost graphs intersect below the peak of the profit graph and that the marginal cost graph intersects the average cost graph at the lowest point of the average cost graph, as predicted by the theory.

■ BUSINESS MANAGEMENT: AN INVENTORY MODEL

Sometimes mathematical methods can be used to assist managers in making certain business decisions. As an illustration, we shall show how calculus can be applied to a problem involving inventory control.

For each shipment of raw materials, a manufacturer must pay an ordering fee to cover handling and transportation. When the raw materials arrive, they must be stored until needed and storage costs result. If each shipment of raw materials is large, few shipments will be needed and ordering costs will be low, but storage costs will be high. If each shipment is small, ordering costs will be high because many shipments will be needed, but storage cost will be low. A manufacturer would like to determine the shipment size that will minimize the total cost. Here is an example of how the problem may be solved using calculus.

EXAMPLE 4   Placing orders to minimize cost

A retailer buys 6,000 calculator batteries a year from a distributor and is trying to decide how often to order the batteries. The ordering fee is $20 per shipment, the storage cost is $0.96 per battery per year, and each battery costs the retailer $0.25. Suppose that the batteries are sold at a constant rate throughout the year, and that each shipment arrives just as the preceding shipment has been used up. How many batteries should the retailer order each time to minimize the total cost?

Solution   We begin by writing the cost function:

$$\text{TOTAL COST} = \text{STORAGE COST} + \text{ORDERING COST} + \text{COST OF BATTERIES}$$

We need to find an expression for each of these unknowns. Assume that the same number of batteries must be ordered each time an order is placed; denote this number by x so that $C(x)$ is the corresponding total cost.

$$\text{STORAGE COST} = \begin{pmatrix} \text{AVERAGE NUMBER} \\ \text{IN STORAGE PER YR} \end{pmatrix}\begin{pmatrix} \text{COST OF STORING 1} \\ \text{BATTERY FOR 1 YR} \end{pmatrix} = \left(\frac{x}{2}\right)(0.96) = 0.48x$$

Figure 3.72 Inventory graph

The average number of batteries in storage during the year is half of a given order, that is, $x/2$. Thus, the total yearly storage cost is the same as if $x/2$ batteries were kept in storage for the entire year. This situation is shown in Figure 3.72. In order to find the total ordering cost, we can multiply the ordering cost per shipment by the number of shipments. We also note that because 6,000 batteries are ordered during the year and because each shipment contains x batteries, the number of shipments is $6,000/x$.

$$\text{ORDERING COST} = \begin{pmatrix} \text{ORDERING COST} \\ \text{PER SHIPMENT} \end{pmatrix}\begin{pmatrix} \text{NUMBER OF} \\ \text{SHIPMENTS} \end{pmatrix} = (20)\left(\frac{6,000}{x}\right) = \frac{120,000}{x}$$

$$\text{COST OF BATTERIES} = \begin{pmatrix} \text{TOTAL NUMBER} \\ \text{OF BATTERIES} \end{pmatrix}\begin{pmatrix} \text{COST PER} \\ \text{BATTERY} \end{pmatrix} = 6,000(0.25) = 1,500$$

Thus the total cost function is

$$C(x) = 0.48x + \frac{120,000}{x} + 1,500$$

The goal is to minimize $C(x)$ on $(0, 6,000]$. To find the critical values, we differentiate $C(x)$

$$C'(x) = 0.48 - 120,000x^{-2}$$

and then solve $C'(x) = 0$ to find

$$0.48x^2 = 120,000$$

$$x = \pm 500$$

Figure 3.73 The total cost function
$C(x) = 0.48x + 120,000x^{-1} + 1,500$

The root $x = -500$ does not lie in the interval $(0, 6000]$. It is easy to check that C is decreasing on $(0, 500)$ and increasing on $(500, 6000]$, as shown in Figure 3.73. Thus, the absolute minimum of C on the interval $(0, 6000]$ occurs when $x = 500$, and we conclude that to minimize cost, the manufacturer should order the batteries in lots of 500.   ■

The simple inventory model analyzed in Example 4 allows no *shortages*; that is, inventory is never allowed to become depleted during the order cycle. An inventory model that allows shortages is more realistic, but it is also more difficult to analyze.

■ PHYSIOLOGY: THE OPTIMAL ANGLE FOR VASCULAR BRANCHING

Figure 3.74 Vascular branching

The blood vascular system operates in such a way that the circulation of blood—from the heart, through the organs of the body, and back to the heart—is accomplished with as little expenditure of energy as possible. Thus, it is reasonable to expect that when an artery branches, the angle between the "parent" artery and its "daughter" should minimize the total resistance to the flow of blood. Figure 3.74 shows a small artery of radius r branching from a larger artery of radius R. Blood flows in the direction of the arrows from point A to the branch at B and then to points C and D. For simplicity, we assume that C and D are located in such a way that $\overline{CB}$ is perpendicular to the main line through A, B, and D. We wish to find the value of the branching angle θ that minimizes the total resistance to the flow of blood as it moves from A to B and then to point C, which is located a fixed perpendicular distance h from the line through A and B.*

Poiseuille's Law

The resistance to the flow of blood in an artery is directly proportional to the artery's length and inversely proportional to the fourth power of its radius.

According to Poiseuille's law, the resistance to flow from A to B is

$$f_1 = \frac{ks_1}{R^4}$$

and the resistance from B to C is

$$f_2 = \frac{ks_2}{r^4}$$

where k is a viscosity constant, $s_1 = |\overline{AB}|$, and $s_2 = |\overline{BC}|$. Thus, the total resistance to flow is

$$f = f_1 + f_2 = \frac{ks_1}{R^4} + \frac{ks_2}{r^4} = k\left(\frac{s_1}{R^4} + \frac{s_2}{r^4}\right)$$

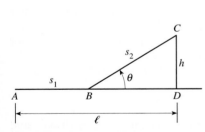

Figure 3.75 Minimizing the resistance to blood flow

The next task is to write f as a function of θ. In order to do this, reconsider Figure 3.74 by labeling s_1, s_2, h, and ℓ as shown in Figure 3.75. We want to find equations for s_1 and s_2 in terms of h and θ; to this end we notice that

$$\sin \theta = \frac{h}{s_2} \qquad \tan \theta = \frac{h}{\ell - s_1}$$

$$s_2 = \frac{h}{\sin \theta} \qquad \ell - s_1 = \frac{h}{\tan \theta}$$

$$= h \csc \theta \qquad s_1 = \ell - \frac{h}{\tan \theta}$$

$$= \ell - h \cot \theta$$

*The key to solving this problem is a result due to work of the 19th-century French physiologist, Jean Louis Poiseuille (1789–1869). Our discussion of vascular branching is adapted from *Introduction to Mathematics for Life Scientists*, 2nd ed., by Edward Batschelet (New York: Springer-Verlag, 1976, pp. 278–280). In this excellent little book, Batschelet develops a number of interesting applications of calculus, several of which appear in the problem set.

We can now write f as a function of θ:

$$f(\theta) = k\left(\frac{s_1}{R^4} + \frac{s_2}{r^4}\right) = k\left(\frac{\ell - h\cot\theta}{R^4} + \frac{h\csc\theta}{r^4}\right)$$

To minimize f we need to find the critical values (remember that h, ℓ, and k are constants):

$$\frac{df}{d\theta} = k\left[\frac{-h(-\csc^2\theta)}{R^4} + \frac{h(-\csc\theta\cot\theta)}{r^4}\right] = kh\csc\theta\left(\frac{\csc\theta}{R^4} - \frac{\cot\theta}{r^4}\right)$$

Because $\csc\theta$, k, and h are never zero, we see that the derivative is zero when

$$\left(\frac{\csc\theta}{R^4} - \frac{\cot\theta}{r^4}\right) = 0$$

$$\frac{\csc\theta}{R^4} = \frac{\cot\theta}{r^4}$$

$$\frac{1}{R^4\sin\theta} = \frac{\cos\theta}{r^4\sin\theta}$$

$$\frac{r^4}{R^4} = \cos\theta$$

By finding the second derivative and noting that r and R are both positive, we can show that any value θ_m that satisfies this equation yields a value $f(\theta_m)$ that is a minimum.

PROBLEM SET 3.8

Ⓐ *In Problems 1–3, we give the cost C of producing x units of a particular commodity and the selling price p when x units are produced. In each case, find the profit function P and determine the level of production that maximizes profit.*

1. $C(x) = \frac{1}{8}x^2 + 5x + 98$ and $p(x) = \frac{1}{2}(75 - x)$

2. $C(x) = \frac{2}{5}x^2 + 3x + 10$ and $p(x) = \frac{1}{5}(45 - x)$

3. $C(x) = \frac{1}{5}(x + 30)$ and $p(x) = \frac{70 - x}{x + 30}$

4. Suppose the total cost of producing x units of a certain commodity is

$$C(x) = 2x^4 - 10x^3 - 18x^2 + x + 5$$

Determine the largest and smallest values of the marginal cost for $0 < x < 5$.

5. Suppose the total cost of manufacturing x units of a certain commodity is

$$C(x) = 3x^2 + x + 48$$

dollars. Determine the minimum average cost.

6. A toy manufacturer produces an inexpensive doll (Flopsy) and an expensive doll (Mopsy) in units of x hundreds and y hundreds, respectively. Suppose it is possible to produce the dolls in such a way that

$$y = \frac{82 - 10x}{10 - x} \qquad 0 \le x \le 8$$

and that the company receives *twice* as much for selling a Mopsy doll as for selling a Flopsy doll. Find the level of production for both x and y for which the total revenue derived from selling these dolls is maximized. You may assume that the company sells every doll it produces.

7. A manufacturer knows that when p dollars are charged for every unit of a product, the sales will be $x = 380 - 20p$ units. At this level of production, the average cost is

$$A(x) = 5 + \frac{x}{50}$$

a. Find the total revenue and total cost functions, and express the profit as a function of x.

b. What price should the manufacturer charge to maximize profit? What is the maximum profit?

Ⓑ **8.** The owner of the Pill Boxx drug store expects to sell 600 bottles of hair spray each year. Each bottle costs \$4, and the ordering fee is \$30 per shipment. In addition, it cost 90¢ per year to store each bottle. Assuming that the hair spray sells at a uniform rate throughout the year and that each shipment arrives just as the last bottle from the previous shipment is sold, how frequently should shipments of hair spray be ordered to minimize the total cost?

9. An electronics firm uses 18,000 cases of connectors each year. The cost of storing one case for a year is \$4.50, and the ordering fee is \$20 per shipment. Assume that the connectors are used at a constant rate throughout the year and that each shipment arrives just as the preceding shipment has been used up. How many cases should the firm order each time to keep total cost to a minimum?

10. Suppose the total cost (in dollars) of manufacturing x units of a certain commodity is

$$C(x) = 3x^2 + 5x + 75$$

a. At what level of production is the average cost per unit the smallest?

b. At what level of production is the average cost per unit equal to the marginal cost?

c. Graph the average cost and the marginal cost functions on the same set of axes, for $x > 0$.

11. Suppose the total revenue (in dollars) from the sale of x units of a certain commodity is

$$R(x) = -2x^2 + 68x - 128$$

a. At what level of sales is the average revenue per unit equal to the marginal revenue?

b. Verify that the average revenue is increasing if the level of sales is less than the level in part a and decreasing if the level of sales is greater than the level in part a.

c. On the same set of axes, graph the relevant portions of the average and marginal revenue functions.

12. A manufacturer finds that the demand function for a certain product is

$$x(p) = \frac{73}{\sqrt{p}}$$

Should the price p be raised or lowered in order to increase consumer expenditure? Explain your answer.

13. A store owner expects to sell Q units of a certain commodity each year. The cost of each unit is n dollars; it costs s dollars to order each new shipment of N units; and it costs t dollars to store each unit for a year. Assuming that the commodity is used at a constant rate throughout the year and that each shipment arrives just as the preceding shipment has been used up, show that the total cost of maintaining inventory is minimized when the ordering cost equals the storage cost.

14. A commuter train carries 600 passengers each day from a suburb to a city. It now costs $5 per person to ride the train. A study shows that 50 additional people will ride the train for each 25¢ reduction in fare. What fare should be charged in order to maximize total revenue?

15. A store has been selling skateboards at the price of $40 per board, and at this price skaters have been buying 50 boards a month. The owner of the store wishes to raise the price and estimates that for each $1 increase in price, 3 fewer boards will be sold each month. If each board costs the store $25, at which price should the store sell the boards in order to maximize profit?

16. As more and more industrial areas are constructed, there is a growing need for standards ensuring control of the pollutants released into the air. Suppose that the pollution at a particular location is based on the distance from the source of the pollution according to the principle that for distances greater than or equal to 1 mi, the concentration of particulate matter (in parts per million, ppm) decreases as the reciprocal of the distance from the source. This means that if you live 3 mi from a plant emitting 60 ppm,

the pollution at your home is $\frac{60}{3} = 20$ ppm. On the other hand, if you live 10 miles from the plant, the pollution at your home is $\frac{60}{10} = 6$ ppm. Suppose that two plants 10 mi apart are releasing 60 and 240 ppm, respectively. At what point between the plants is the pollution a minimum?

17. A tour agency is booking a tour and has 100 people signed up. The price of a ticket is $2,000 per person. The agency has booked a plane seating 150 people at a cost of $125,000. Additional costs to the agency are incidental fees of $500 per person. For each $5 that the price is lowered, a new person will sign up. How much should the price be lowered for all participants to maximize the profit to the tour agency?

18. A bookstore can obtain the best seller *20,000 Leagues Under the Majors* from the publisher at a cost of $6 per book. The store has been offering the book at a price of $30 per copy and has been selling 200 copies a month at this price. The bookstore is planning to lower its price to stimulate sales and estimates that for each $2 reduction in the price, 20 more books will be sold per month. At what price should the bookstore sell the book to generate the greatest possible profit?

19. A Florida citrus grower estimates that if 60 orange trees are planted, the average yield per tree will be 400 oranges. The average yield will decrease by 4 oranges for each additional tree planted on the same acreage. How many trees should the grower plant to maximize the total yield?

20. Farmers can get $2 per bushel for their potatoes on July 1, and after that the price drops 2¢ per bushel per day. On July 1, a farmer has 80 bu of potatoes in the field and estimates that the crop is increasing at the rate of 1 bu per day. When should the farmer harvest the potatoes to maximize revenue?

21. A viticulturist estimates that if 50 grapevines are planted per acre, each grapevine will product 150 lb of grapes. Each additional grapevine planted per acre (up to 20), reduces the average yield per vine by 2 lb. How many grapevines should be planted to maximize the yield per acre?

22. To raise money, a service club has been collecting used bottles, which it plans to deliver to a local glass company for recycling. Because the project began 80 days ago, the club has collected 24,000 pounds of glass, for which the glass company offers 1¢ per pound. However, because bottles are accumulating faster than they can be recycled, the company plans to reduce the price it will pay by 1¢ per 100 pounds of used glass. What is the most advantageous time for the club to conclude its project and deliver all the bottles? (Assume that the club can continue to collect bottles at the same rate and that they plan on making only one trip to the glass company.)

23. Suppose that the demand function for a certain commodity is expressed as

$$p(x) = \sqrt{\frac{120 - x}{0.1}} \quad 0 \le x \le 120$$

   a. Find the total revenue function explicitly and use its first derivative to determine its intervals of increase and decrease and the price at which revenue is maximized.

   b. Graph the relevant portions of the demand and revenue functions.

24. Suppose the demand equation for a certain commodity is linear—that is,

$$p(x) = \frac{b - x}{a} \quad \text{for} \quad 0 \le x \le b$$

   where a and b are positive constants.

   a. Find the total revenue function explicitly and use its first derivative to determine its intervals of increase and decrease.

   b. Graph the relevant portions of the demand and revenue functions.

25. Homing pigeons will rarely fly over large bodies of water unless forced to do so, presumably because it requires more energy to maintain altitude in flight over the cool water. Suppose a pigeon is released from a boat floating on a lake 3 mi from a point A on the shore and 10 mi away from the pigeon's loft, as shown in Figure 3.76.

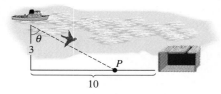

Figure 3.76 Flight path for a pigeon

If the pigeon requires twice as much energy to fly over water as over land and it follows a path that minimizes total energy, find the angle θ of its heading as it leaves the boat. This is the situation in the perspective section of the chapter introduction.

26. In an experiment, a fish swims s meters upstream at a constant velocity v m/sec relative to the water, which itself has velocity v_1 relative to the ground. The results of the experiment suggest that if the fish takes t seconds to reach its goal (that is, to swim s meters), the energy it expends is given by

$$E = cv^k t$$

   where $c > 0$ and $k > 2$ are physical constants. Assuming v_1 is known, what velocity v minimizes the energy?

27. In certain tissues, cells exist in the shape of circular cylinders. Suppose such a cylinder has radius r and height h. If the volume is fixed (say, at v_0), find the value of r that minimizes the total surface area ($S = 2\pi rh + 2\pi r^2$) of the cell.

28. In a learning model, two responses (A and B) are possible for each of a series of observations. If there is a probability p of getting response A in any observation, the probability of getting a response A exactly n times in a series of M observations is

$$F(p) = p^n (1 - p)^{M-n}$$

   The *maximum likelihood estimate* is the value of p that maximizes $F(p)$ on $[0, 1]$. For what value of p does this occur?

29. During coughing, the diameter of the trachea decreases. The velocity v of air in the trachea during a cough is related to the radius r of the trachea during the cough by the equation

$$v = Ar^2(r_0 - r)$$

   where A is a constant and r_0 is the radius of the trachea in a relaxed state. Find the radius of the trachea when the velocity is greatest, and find the maximum velocity of air. (Notice $0 \le r \le r_0$.)

30. The work of V. A. Tucker and K. Schmidt-Koenig[*] indicates that the energy expended in flight by a certain kind of bird is given by

$$E = \frac{1}{v}[a(v - b)^2 + c]$$

   where a, b, and c are positive constants, v is the velocity of the bird, and the domain of v is $[16, 60]$. What value of v will minimize the energy expenditure in the case where $a = 0.04$, $b = 36$, and $c = 9$?

31. A plastics firm has received an order from the city recreation department to manufacture 8,000 special styrofoam kickboards for its summer swimming program. The firm owns 10 machines, each of which can produce 50 kickboards per hour. The cost of setting up the machines to produce the kickboards is $800 per machine. Once the machines have been set up, the operation is fully

*Tucker, V. A. and Schmidt-Koening, K., "Flight of Birds in Relation to Energetics and Wind Directions," *The Auk* 88 (1971): 97–107.

automated and can be overseen by a single production supervisor earning $35 per hour.

a. How many machines should be used to minimize the cost of production? Remember, the answer should be a positive integer.

b. How much will the supervisor earn during the production run if the optimal number of machines is used?

C 32. Generalize Problem 31. Specifically, a manufacturing firm received an order for Q units of a certain commodity. Each of the firm's machines can produce n units per hour. The setup cost is s dollars per machine, and the operating cost is p dollars per hour.

a. Derive a formula for the number of machines that should be used to minimize the total cost of filling the order.

b. Show that when the total cost is minimal, the setup cost is equal to the cost of operating the machines.

33. An important quantity in economic analysis is *elasticity of demand*, defined by $E(x) = \dfrac{p}{x}\dfrac{dx}{dp}$, where x is the number of units of a commodity demanded when the price is p dollars. Show that

$$\frac{dR}{dx} = \frac{R}{x}\left[1 - \frac{1}{E(p)}\right]$$

That is, show that the marginal revenue is $[1 - 1/E(p)]$ times average revenue.

3.9 L'HÔPITAL'S RULE

Historical Note

GUILLAUME FRANCOIS
ANTOINE DE L'HÔPITAL
(1661–1704)

The French mathematician Marquis de l'Hôpital published the rule in the late 17th century in what is often regarded as the first calculus text. Actually, the rule was discovered by l'Hôpital's teacher, Johann Bernoulli. Not only did l'Hôpital neglect to cite his sources in his book, but there is also evidence that he paid Bernoulli for his results and for keeping their arrangements for payment confidential. In a letter dated March 17, 1694, he asked Bernoulli "to communicate to me your discoveries . . ."—with the request not to mention them to others—". . . it would not please me if they were made public."

IN THIS SECTION l'Hôpital's rule, indeterminate form 0/0, indeterminate form ∞/∞, l'Hôpital's rule for other forms

We can use limit theorems for sums, differences, products, and quotients (with nonzero division) provided certain meaningless expressions are not involved. For example, $\displaystyle\lim_{x\to 0}\frac{\sin x}{x}$ results in the meaningless form $\frac{0}{0}$ when the quotient limit theorem is applied. In such cases, we have had to use other means to evaluate the limit (see Sections 1.6 and 2.3). Johann Bernoulli (1667–1748) developed an easier method, involving derivatives. We shall introduce this procedure, called l'Hôpital's rule, and illustrate its use in a variety of problems.

In curve sketching, optimization, and other applications, it is often necessary to evaluate a limit of the general form

$$L = \lim_{x\to c}\frac{f(x)}{g(x)}$$

where c is either a finite number or $+\infty$ or $-\infty$. If $\displaystyle\lim_{x\to c} g(x) \neq 0$, then the quotient rule can be used. However, if *both* the numerator and denominator approach zero, the limit can be any real number or it can diverge to $+\infty$ or $-\infty$. For this reason, a limit of this kind is said to be a $\dfrac{0}{0}$ **indeterminate form.** Similarly, if $\displaystyle\lim_{x\to c} f(x)$ and $\displaystyle\lim_{x\to c} g(x)$ are both infinite, $\displaystyle\lim_{x\to c} g(x)$ is called an $\dfrac{\infty}{\infty}$ **indeterminate form.** For example:

$$\lim_{x\to 0}\frac{\sin x}{x} \text{ is a } \frac{0}{0} \text{ indeterminate form.}$$

$$\lim_{x\to\infty}\frac{2x^2 - 3x + 1}{3x^2 + 5x - 2} \text{ is an } \frac{\infty}{\infty} \text{ indeterminate form.}$$

■ L'HÔPITAL'S RULE

Earlier in this text, we evaluated certain indeterminate forms such as $\displaystyle\lim_{x\to 1}\frac{x^2 - 1}{x - 1}$ using algebraic procedures, but not all indeterminate forms can be handled in this manner. Fortunately, there is a procedure, called **l'Hôpital's rule,** that allows us to relate an indeterminate form $\lim\limits_{x \to c} \dfrac{f(x)}{g(x)}$ to the limit of the ratio of derivatives, $\lim\limits_{x \to c} \dfrac{f'(x)}{g'(x)}$. Here is a formal statement of the rule.

THEOREM 3.9   l'Hôpital's rule

Computational Window ▼ ▲

An interesting article on l'Hôpital's rule with the computer program *Mathematica* can be found in *The AMATYC Review*, Fall 1991, p. 40.

Let f and g be functions that are differentiable on an open interval containing c (except possibly at c itself). If

$$\lim_{x \to c} \frac{f(x)}{g(x)}$$

produces an indeterminate form $\dfrac{0}{0}$ or $\dfrac{\infty}{\infty}$, then

$$\lim_{x \to c} \frac{f(x)}{g(x)} = \lim_{x \to c} \frac{f'(x)}{g'(x)}$$

provided the limit on the right-hand side of the equation exists (or is infinite). L'Hôpital's rule also applies in the case where $x \to +\infty$ (or $x \to -\infty$) instead of $x \to c$.

> ■ *What this says*: If the $\lim\limits_{x \to c} \dfrac{f(x)}{g(x)}$ yields one of the indeterminate forms of the type $\dfrac{0}{0}$ or $\dfrac{\infty}{\infty}$, then you can evaluate the limit by replacing f with f' and g with g'. This *does not* mean you use the quotient rule for derivatives on $f(x)/g(x)$. Moreover, you can use l'Hôpital's rule on a reduced rational expression as long as you still get one of the forms
>
> $$\frac{0}{0} \quad \text{or} \quad \frac{+\infty}{+\infty} \quad \text{or} \quad \frac{+\infty}{-\infty} \quad \text{or} \quad \frac{-\infty}{+\infty} \quad \text{or} \quad \frac{-\infty}{-\infty}$$
>
> at $x = c$. Because l'Hôpital's rule can be applied repeatedly, you can keep applying it until you get something other than these forms (for *either* the numerator or the denominator).

Proof: This proof follows from a more general result called the extended mean value theorem, which is stated in Appendix B. The proofs of l'Hôpital's rule for the $\dfrac{0}{0}$ case, as well as the extended mean value theorem are found in Appendix B. ■

■ INDETERMINATE FORM 0/0

EXAMPLE 1   l'Hôpital's rule of the type 0/0

Evaluate

$$\lim_{x \to 1} \frac{x^2 - 1}{x - 1}.$$

Solution   It is easy to use the algebraic method of Chapter 1 to show that this limit has the value 2, but as a first example, we will verify that we obtain the same result using l'Hôpital's rule instead of algebraic simplification. We first note that the conditions for l'Hôpital's rule apply; this is of the form 0/0. Then,

$$\lim_{x \to 1} \frac{x^2 - 1}{x - 1} = \lim_{x \to 1} \frac{2x}{1} = 2$$

EXAMPLE 2   l'Hôpital's rule of the type 0/0

Evaluate

$$\lim_{x \to 2} \frac{x^7 - 128}{x^3 - 8}$$

Solution   For this example,

$$f(x) = x^7 - 128 \quad \text{and} \quad g(x) = x^3 - 8$$

and the form is 0/0. Notice that l'Hôpital's rule tells us that

$$\lim_{x \to 2} \frac{x^7 - 128}{x^3 - 8} = \lim_{x \to 2} \frac{7x^6}{3x^2} = \lim_{x \to 2} \frac{7x^4}{3} = \frac{7(2)^4}{3} = \frac{112}{3}$$

EXAMPLE 3   l'Hôpital's rule with trigonometric functions

Evaluate

$$\lim_{x \to 0} \frac{1 - \cos^3 x}{\sin^2 x}$$

Solution   This is the indeterminate form 0/0; by applying l'Hôpital's rule, we obtain

$$\lim_{x \to 0} \frac{1 - \cos^3 x}{\sin^2 x} = \lim_{x \to 0} \frac{-3 \cos^2 x(-\sin x)}{2 \sin x \cos x} = \lim_{x \to 0} \frac{3 \cos x}{2} = \frac{3}{2}$$

Computational Window

You can use a graphing calculator to help find many of these limits. For example, the graph of

$$y = \frac{1 - \cos^3 x}{\sin^2 x}$$ is shown at the right. Note that as

$x \to 0$ from either the left or the right, the limit is the same, 1.5. The graphs of some of the functions for the remainder of the examples of this section are shown so that you can note the relationship between the requested limit, the function, and l'Hôpital's rule. Such analysis using a graphing calculator is not essential when working these problems, especially because graphing many of these functions is more difficult than finding the limits. However, if you have access to a graphing calculator, it is worthwhile looking at the graph.

Y₁=(1-(cos X)^3)/(sin X)^2

Xmin=-10 Ymin=-1
Xmax=10   Ymax=5
Xscl=1   Yscl=1

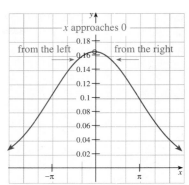

By looking at the graph, you can reinforce the result obtained using l'Hôpital's rule.

EXAMPLE 4   l'Hôpital's rule applied more than one time

Evaluate $\lim\limits_{x \to 0} \dfrac{x - \sin x}{x^3}$.

Solution   This is a 0/0 indeterminate form, and we find that

$$\lim_{x \to 0} \frac{x - \sin x}{x^3} = \lim_{x \to 0} \frac{1 - \cos x}{3x^2}$$

This is still the indeterminate form 0/0, so l'Hôpital's rule can be applied once again:

$$\lim_{x \to 0} \frac{1 - \cos x}{3x^2} = \lim_{x \to 0} \frac{-(-\sin x)}{6x} = \frac{1}{6} \lim_{x \to 0} \frac{\sin x}{x} = \frac{1}{6}(1) = \frac{1}{6}$$

EXAMPLE 5   Limit is not an indeterminate form

Evaluate $\lim\limits_{x \to 0} \dfrac{1 - \cos x}{\sec x}$.

Solution

⊘   If you apply l'Hôpital's rule blindly, you obtain the WRONG answer:

$$\lim_{x \to 0} \frac{1 - \cos x}{\sec x} = \lim_{x \to 0} \frac{\sin x}{\sec x \tan x} \qquad \textit{This is NOT correct.}$$

$$= \lim_{x \to 0} \frac{\cos x}{\sec x} = \frac{1}{1} = 1 \quad ⊘$$

l'Hôpital's rule does not apply here, because this limit is *not* an indeterminate form. In fact,

$$\lim_{x \to 0} \frac{1 - \cos x}{\sec x} = \frac{\lim\limits_{x \to 0}(1 - \cos x)}{\lim\limits_{x \to 0} \sec x} = \frac{0}{1} = 0$$

EXAMPLE 6   Substitution with l'Hôpital's rule

Evaluate $\lim\limits_{x \to +\infty} x \tan \dfrac{1}{x}$.

Solution   This is an $\infty \cdot 0$ indeterminate form, but we can convert it into a 0/0 form by using the substitution $u = 1/x$ and noting that $u \to 0$ as $x \to +\infty$.

$$\lim_{x \to +\infty} x \tan \frac{1}{x} = \lim_{u \to 0} \frac{1}{u} \tan u = \lim_{u \to 0} \frac{\tan u}{u} \quad \textit{This is a } \tfrac{0}{0} \textit{ form.}$$

$$= \lim_{u \to 0} \frac{\sec^2 u}{1} = 1$$

■ INDETERMINATE FORM ∞ / ∞

EXAMPLE 7   l'Hôpital's rule of the type ∞ / ∞

Evaluate $\lim\limits_{x \to +\infty} \dfrac{2x^2 - 3x + 1}{3x^2 + 5x - 2}$.

Solution Using the methods of Section 3.5, we can compute this limit by multiplying by $(1/x^2)/(1/x^2)$. Instead, let us note that this is of the form ∞/∞ and apply l'Hôpital's rule.

$$\lim_{x \to +\infty} \frac{2x^2 - 3x + 1}{3x^2 + 5x - 2} = \lim_{x \to +\infty} \frac{4x - 3}{6x + 5} \qquad \textit{Apply l'Hôpital's rule again.}$$

$$= \lim_{x \to +\infty} \frac{4}{6} = \frac{2}{3}$$

⊘ You must be careful when applying l'Hôpital's rule. Pay particular attention to the following points to avoid common mistakes;

1. l'Hôpital's rule involves differentiation of the numerator and the denominator *separately*. A common mistake is to differentiate the quotient as a whole by using the quotient rule.

2. l'Hôpital's rule applies only to the indeterminate forms $0/0$ and ∞/∞. Indiscriminate use of l'Hôpital's rule often leads to erroneous results. For example, note that $\lim_{x \to 0} \dfrac{x + 5}{x + 1} = 5$, but if you try to apply l'Hôpital's rule to this limit, you will obtain an incorrect result. ⊘

EXAMPLE 8   l'Hôpital's rule with a one-sided limit

Show that $\displaystyle \lim_{x \to (\pi/2)^-} \frac{a + \sec x}{b + \tan x} = 1$ for any constants a and b.

Solution The limit is indeterminate of the form ∞/∞. By applying l'Hôpital's rule,

$$\lim_{x \to (\pi/2)^-} \frac{a + \sec x}{b + \tan x} = \lim_{x \to (\pi/2)^-} \frac{\sec x \tan x}{\sec^2 x} = \lim_{x \to (\pi/2)^-} \frac{\tan x}{\sec x}$$

If you apply l'Hôpital's rule again, you will obtain

$$\lim_{x \to (\pi/2)^-} \frac{\tan x}{\sec x} = \lim_{x \to (\pi/2)^-} \frac{\sec^2 x}{\sec x \tan x} = \lim_{x \to (\pi/2)^-} \frac{\sec x}{\tan x}$$

Finally, applying l'Hôpital's rule once again;

$$\lim_{x \to (\pi/2)^-} \frac{\sec x}{\tan x} = \lim_{x \to (\pi/2)^-} \frac{\sec x \tan x}{\sec^2 x} = \lim_{x \to (\pi/2)^-} \frac{\tan x}{\sec x}$$

You see that for this example, l'Hôpital's rule leads us in circles. Instead, use trigonometric identities to write

$$\frac{\tan x}{\sec x} = \frac{\frac{\sin x}{\cos x}}{\frac{1}{\cos x}} = \sin x$$

Thus,

$$\lim_{x \to (\pi/2)^-} \frac{\tan x}{\sec x} = \lim_{x \to (\pi/2)^-} \sin x = 1$$

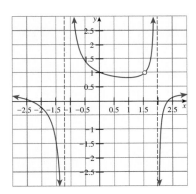

The curve has a deleted point at $x = \pi/2$. However, if you evaluate the function for $x = 1.57$, you will find the function has a value very close to 1. Note that left- and right-hand limits to $\pi/2$ are the same. Is this true for $x \to 2$?

■ L'HÔPITAL'S RULE FOR OTHER FORMS

Certain limits that do not have either of the standard forms of $0/0$ or ∞/∞ do not allow direct use of l'Hôpital's rule. However, the expression can sometimes be manipulated algebraically into a standard indeterminate form and then can be evaluated by applying l'Hôpital's rule.

EXAMPLE 9   l'Hôpital's rule with the form $\infty - \infty$

Evaluate $\lim\limits_{x \to 0^+} \left(\dfrac{1}{x} - \dfrac{1}{\sin x} \right)$.

Solution   As it stands, this has the form $\infty - \infty$, because

$$\frac{1}{x} \to +\infty \quad \text{and} \quad \frac{1}{\sin x} \to +\infty \quad \text{as } x \to 0 \text{ from the right.}$$

However, using a little algebra we find

$$\lim_{x \to 0^+} \left(\frac{1}{x} - \frac{1}{\sin x} \right) = \lim_{x \to 0^+} \frac{\sin x - x}{x \sin x}$$

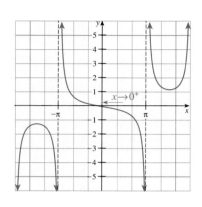

This limit is now of the form $0/0$, so the hypotheses of l'Hôpital's rule are satisfied. Thus

$$\lim_{x \to 0^+} \frac{\sin x - x}{x \sin x} = \lim_{x \to 0^+} \frac{\cos x - 1}{\sin x + x \cos x} \qquad \textit{Again, the form } \frac{0}{0}$$

$$= \lim_{x \to 0^+} \frac{-\sin x}{\cos x + x(-\sin x) + \cos x} = \frac{0}{2} = 0$$

EXAMPLE 10   l'Hôpital's rule with the form $0 \cdot \infty$

Evaluate $\lim\limits_{x \to \pi/2^-} \left(x - \dfrac{\pi}{2} \right) \tan x$.

Solution   This limit has the form $0 \cdot \infty$, because

$$\lim_{x \to \pi/2^-} \left(x - \frac{\pi}{2} \right) = 0 \quad \text{and} \quad \lim_{x \to \pi/2^-} \tan x = +\infty$$

Write $\tan x = \dfrac{1}{\cot x}$ to obtain

$$\lim_{x \to \pi/2^-} \left(x - \frac{\pi}{2} \right) \tan x = \lim_{x \to \pi/2^-} \frac{x - \frac{\pi}{2}}{\cot x} \qquad \textit{Form } 0/0$$

$$= \lim_{x \to \pi/2^-} \frac{1}{-\csc^2 x} \qquad \textit{l'Hôpital's rule}$$

$$= \lim_{x \to \pi/2^-} (-\sin^2 x) = -1$$

Look at the graph as $x \to \dfrac{\pi}{2}$ from both the left and the right.

It may happen that even when l'Hôpital's rule applies to a limit, it is not the best way to proceed, as illustrated by Example 11.

EXAMPLE 11   Using l'Hôpital's rule with other limit properties

Evaluate $\lim\limits_{x \to 0} \dfrac{(1 - \cos x) \sin 4x}{x^3 \cos x}$.

Solution   This limit has the form $0/0$, but direct application of l'Hôpital's rule leads to a real mess (try it!). Instead, we compute the given limit by using the product rule for limits along with two simple applications of l'Hôpital's rule. Specifically, using the product rule for limits (assuming the limits exist), we have

$$\lim_{x \to 0} \frac{(1 - \cos x) \sin 4x}{x^3 \cos x} = \left[\lim_{x \to 0} \frac{1 - \cos x}{x^2} \right] \left[\lim_{x \to 0} \frac{\sin 4x}{x} \right] \left[\lim_{x \to 0} \frac{1}{\cos x} \right]$$

$$= \left[\lim_{x \to 0} \frac{\sin x}{2x} \right] \left[\lim_{x \to 0} \frac{4 \cos 4x}{1} \right] \left[\lim_{x \to 0} \frac{1}{\cos x} \right] = \left(\tfrac{1}{2} \right)(4)(1) = 2$$

l'Hôpital's rule

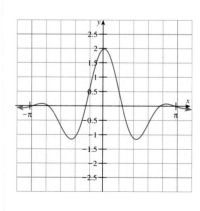

EXAMPLE 12   Hypotheses of l'Hôpital's rule are not satisfied

Evaluate $\displaystyle\lim_{x\to+\infty}\frac{x+\sin x}{x-\cos x}$.

Solution   This limit has the indeterminate form ∞/∞. If you try to apply l'Hôpital's rule, you find

$$\lim_{x\to+\infty}\frac{x+\sin x}{x-\cos x}=\lim_{x\to+\infty}\frac{1+\cos x}{1+\sin x}$$

The limit on the right does not exist, because both $\sin x$ and $\cos x$ oscillate between -1 and 1 as $x\to+\infty$. Recall that l'Hôpital's rule applies only if this limit exists. This does not mean that the limit of the original expression does not exist or that we cannot find it; it simply means that we cannot apply l'Hôpital's rule. To find this limit, factor out an x from the numerator and denominator and proceed as follows:

$$\lim_{x\to+\infty}\frac{x+\sin x}{x-\cos x}=\lim_{x\to+\infty}\frac{x\left(1+\frac{\sin x}{x}\right)}{x\left(1-\frac{\cos x}{x}\right)}=\lim_{x\to+\infty}\frac{1+\frac{\sin x}{x}}{1-\frac{\cos x}{x}}=\frac{1+0}{1-0}=1$$

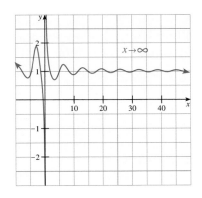

PROBLEM SET 3.9

A **1.** ■ **What Does This Say?** An incorrect use of l'Hôpital's rule is illustrated in the following limit computations. In each case, explain what is wrong and find the correct value of the limit.

a. $\displaystyle\lim_{x\to\pi}\frac{1-\cos x}{x}=\lim_{x\to\pi}\frac{\sin x}{1}=0$

b. $\displaystyle\lim_{x\to\pi/2}\frac{\sin x}{x}=\lim_{x\to\pi/2}\frac{\cos x}{1}=0$

2. ■ **What Does This Say?** Sometimes l'Hôpital's rule leads to inconclusive computation. For example, observe what happens when the rule is applied to

$$\lim_{x\to+\infty}\frac{x}{\sqrt{x^2-1}}$$

Use any method you wish to evaluate this limit.

Use l'Hôpital's rule to evaluate the limits given in Problems 3–37.

3. $\displaystyle\lim_{x\to2}\frac{x^4-16}{x^2-4}$

4. $\displaystyle\lim_{x\to1}\frac{x^4-1}{x^2-1}$

5. $\displaystyle\lim_{x\to2}\frac{x^3-27}{x^2-9}$

6. $\displaystyle\lim_{x\to1}\frac{x^3-1}{x^2-1}$

7. $\displaystyle\lim_{x\to1}\frac{x^{10}-1}{x-1}$

8. $\displaystyle\lim_{x\to-1}\frac{x^{10}-1}{x+1}$

9. $\displaystyle\lim_{x\to0}\frac{1-\cos^2 x}{\sin^3 x}$

10. $\displaystyle\lim_{x\to0}\frac{1-\cos^2 x}{3\sin x}$

11. $\displaystyle\lim_{x\to\pi}\frac{\cos\frac{x}{2}}{\pi-x}$

12. $\displaystyle\lim_{x\to0}\frac{1-\cos x}{x^2}$

13. $\displaystyle\lim_{x\to0}\frac{\sin ax}{\cos bx}, ab\neq0$

14. $\displaystyle\lim_{x\to0}\frac{\tan 3x}{\sin 5x}$

15. $\displaystyle\lim_{x\to0}\frac{x-\sin x}{\tan x-x}$

16. $\displaystyle\lim_{x\to0}\frac{1-\cos^2 x}{x\tan x}$

17. $\displaystyle\lim_{t\to\pi/2}\frac{3\sec t}{2+\tan t}$

18. $\displaystyle\lim_{x\to0}\frac{x+\sin^3 x}{x^2+2x}$

19. $\displaystyle\lim_{x\to0}\frac{3x+\sin^3 x}{x\cos x}$

20. $\displaystyle\lim_{x\to0}\frac{x-\sin ax}{x+\sin bx}$

21. $\displaystyle\lim_{x\to0}\frac{x^2+\sin x^2}{x^2+x^3}$

22. $\displaystyle\lim_{x\to+\infty}x^2\sin\frac{1}{x}$

23. $\displaystyle\lim_{x\to+\infty}x^{3/2}\sin\frac{1}{x}$

24. $\displaystyle\lim_{x\to1}(1-x)\cot x$

25. $\displaystyle\lim_{x\to1}\frac{(x-1)\sin(x-1)}{1-\cos(x-1)}$

26. $\displaystyle\lim_{\theta\to0}\frac{\theta-1+\cos^2\theta}{\theta^2+5\theta}$

27. $\displaystyle\lim_{x\to0}\frac{x+\sin(x^2+x)}{3x+\sin x}$

28. $\displaystyle\lim_{x\to\pi/2^-}\sec 3x\cos 9x$

B **29.** $\displaystyle\lim_{x\to0}\left(\frac{1}{x}-\frac{1}{x\sin x}\right)$

30. $\displaystyle\lim_{x\to0}\left(\frac{1}{\sin 2x}-\frac{1}{2x}\right)$

31. $\displaystyle\lim_{x\to0}\left(\frac{1}{\sin^2 x}-\frac{1}{x}\right)$

32. $\displaystyle\lim_{x\to0}\left(\cot x-\frac{1}{x}\right)$

33. $\displaystyle\lim_{x\to0^+}\left(\frac{2\cos x}{\sin 2x}-\frac{1}{x}\right)$

34. $\displaystyle\lim_{x\to+\infty}\left(\frac{x^2}{x-1}-\frac{x^2}{x+1}\right)$

35. $\displaystyle\lim_{x\to+\infty}\left(\frac{x^3}{x^2-x+1}-\frac{x^3}{x^2+x-1}\right)$

36. $\displaystyle\lim_{x\to0}\frac{\sin 3x\sin 2x}{x\sin 4x}$

37. $\displaystyle\lim_{x\to\pi/2}\frac{\sin 2x\cos x}{x\sin 4x}$

C **38.** Find constants a and b so that

$$\lim_{x\to0}\left(\frac{\sin 2x}{x^3}+\frac{a}{x^2}+b\right)=1$$

39. A weight hanging by a spring is made to vibrate by applying a sinusoidal force, and the displacement at time t is given by

$$f(t)=\frac{C}{\alpha^2-\beta^2}(\sin\alpha t-\sin\beta t)$$

where C, α, and β are constants such that $\alpha\neq\beta$. What happens to $f(t)$ as $\alpha\to\beta$? You may assume that β is fixed.

3.10 ANTIDERIVATIVES

> **IN THIS SECTION** Reversing differentiation, antiderivative notation, antidifferentiation formulas, applications
> Our goal in this section is to study a process called *antidifferentiation*, which reverses differentiation in much the same way that division reverses multiplication. We shall examine algebraic properties of the process and several useful applications.

■ REVERSING DIFFERENTIATION

A physicist who knows the acceleration of a particle may want to determine its velocity or its position at a particular time. An ecologist who knows the rate at which a certain pollutant is being absorbed by a particular species of fish might want to know the actual amount of pollutant in the fish's system at a given time. In each of these cases, a derivative f' is given and the problem is that of finding the corresponding function f. Toward this end, we make the following definition.

Antiderivative

An **antiderivative** of a function f is a function F that satisfies

$$F' = f$$

Suppose we know $f(x) = 3x^2$. We want to find a function $F(x)$ so that $F'(x) = 3x^2$. It is not difficult to use the power rule in reverse to discover that $F(x) = x^3$ is such a function. However, that is not the only possibility:

Given: $\quad F(x) = x^3 \qquad G(x) = x^3 - 5 \qquad H(x) = x^3 + \pi^2$
Find: $\quad\; F'(x) = 3x^2 \qquad G'(x) = 3x^2 \qquad H'(x) = 3x^2$

Are there other functions that have a derivative equal to f? Clearly, there are infinitely many, and they all seem to differ by a constant. If F is an antiderivative of f, then so is $F + C$ for any constant C, because

$$[F(x) + C]' = F'(x) + 0 = f(x)$$

Conversely, the following theorem shows that any antiderivative of f can be expressed in this form. This is the constant difference theorem we proved in Section 3.2.

THEOREM 3.10 Antiderivatives differ by a constant

If F is an antiderivative of the continuous function f, then any other antiderivative of f must have the form
$$G(x) = F(x) + C$$

> ■ **What this says:** Two antiderivatives of the same function differ by a constant (which may be 0).

Proof: If F and G are both antiderivatives of f, then $F' = f$ and $G' = f$ and Theorem 3.5 (the constant difference theorem) tells us that $G(x) - F(x) = C$, so $G(x) = F(x) + C$. ∎

Also, keep in mind the difference between a particular antiderivative and a general antiderivative. For the function defined by $f(x) = 3x^2$ we note that $F(x) = x^3$ is a particular antiderivative and $G(x) = x^3 + C$ is a general antiderivative.

EXAMPLE 1 Finding antiderivatives

Find general antiderivatives for the given functions.

a. $f(x) = x^5$ **b.** $s(x) = \sin x$

Solution

a. If $F(x) = x^6$, then $F'(x) = 6x^5$, so we see that a particular antiderivative of f is $F(x) = \dfrac{x^6}{6}$ in order to obtain $F'(x) = \dfrac{6x^5}{6} = x^5$. By Theorem 3.10, the most general antiderivative is $G(x) = \dfrac{x^6}{6} + C$.

b. If $S(x) = -\cos x$, then $S'(x) = \sin x$, so $G(x) = -\cos x + C$.   ▬

■ ANTIDERIVATIVE NOTATION

It is worthwhile to define a notation to indicate the operation of antidifferentiation.

Indefinite Integral

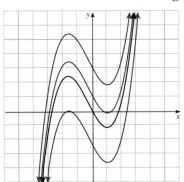

Figure 3.77 Several members of the family of curves $y = F(x) + C$

⊘ It is important to remember that $\int f(x)\, dx$ represents a family of functions. ⊘

The notation
$$\int f(x)\, dx = F(x) + C$$
where C is an arbitrary constant means that F is an antiderivative of f. It is called the **indefinite integral of f** and satisfies the condition that $F'(x) = f(x)$ for all x in the domain of f.

■ **What This Says:** This is nothing more than the definition of antiderivative, along with a convenient notation. We also agree that in the context of antidifferentiation, C is an arbitrary constant.

The graph of $F(x) + C$ for different values of C is called **a family of functions** (see Figure 3.77). Because each member of the family $y = F(x) + C$ has the same derivative at x, the slope of each graph at x is the same. This means that the graph of all functions of the form $y = F(x) + C$ is a collection of curves, as shown in Figure 3.77.

The process of finding indefinite integrals is called **indefinite integration.** Notice that this process amounts to finding an antiderivative of f and adding on an arbitrary constant C, which is called the **constant of integration.**

EXAMPLE 2 Antidifferentiation

Find

a. $\displaystyle\int 5x^3\, dx$ **b.** $\displaystyle\int \sec^2 x\, dx$ **c.** $\displaystyle\int \sec x \tan x\, dx$

Solution **a.** Because $\dfrac{d}{dx}(x)^4 = 4x^3$, it follows that $\dfrac{d}{dx}\left(\dfrac{5}{4}x^4\right) = 5x^3$. Thus, $\displaystyle\int 5x^3\, dx = \dfrac{5x^4}{4} + C$.

b. Because $\dfrac{d}{dx}(\tan x) = \sec^2 x$, we have $\displaystyle\int \sec^2 x\, dx = \tan x + C$

c. Since $\dfrac{d}{dx}(\sec x) = \sec x \tan x$, we have $\displaystyle\int \sec x \tan x\, dx = \sec x + C$ ▬

■ ANTIDIFFERENTIATION FORMULAS

Example 2 leads us to state formulas for antidifferentiation. Theorem 3.11 summarizes several fundamental properties of indefinite integrals, each of which can be derived by reversing an appropriate differentiation formula.

THEOREM 3.11   Basic integration rules

PROCEDURAL RULES	Differentiation Formulas	Integration Formulas
Constant multiple:	$\dfrac{d}{du}(cf) = c\dfrac{df}{du}$	$\displaystyle\int cf(u)\,du = c\int f(u)\,du$
Sum rule:	$\dfrac{d}{du}(f + g) = \dfrac{df}{du} + \dfrac{dg}{du}$	$\displaystyle\int [f(u) + g(u)]\,du = \int f(u)\,du + \int g(u)\,du$
Difference rule:	$\dfrac{d}{du}(f - g) = \dfrac{df}{du} - \dfrac{dg}{du}$	$\displaystyle\int [f(u) - g(u)]\,du = \int f(u)\,du - \int g(u)\,du$
Linearity rule:	$\dfrac{d}{du}(af + bg) = a\dfrac{df}{du} + b\dfrac{dg}{du}$	$\displaystyle\int [af(u) + bg(u)]\,du = a\int f(u)\,du + b\int g(u)\,du$
Constant rule:	$\dfrac{d}{du}(c) = 0$	$\displaystyle\int 0\,du = c$
Power rule:	$\dfrac{d}{du}(u^n) = nu^{n-1}$	$\displaystyle\int u^n\,du = \dfrac{u^{n+1}}{n + 1} + C;\ n \neq -1$
Trigonometric rules:	$\dfrac{d}{du}(\cos u) = -\sin u$	$\displaystyle\int \sin u\,du = -\cos u + C$
	$\dfrac{d}{du}(\sin u) = \cos u$	$\displaystyle\int \cos u\,du = \sin u + C$
	$\dfrac{d}{du}(\tan u) = \sec^2 u$	$\displaystyle\int \sec^2 u\,du = \tan u + C$

Proof: Each of these parts can be derived by reversing the accompanying derivative formula. For example, to obtain the power rule, note that if n is any number other than -1, then

$$\frac{d}{du}\left[\frac{1}{n + 1}\,u^{n+1}\right] = \frac{1}{n + 1}[(n + 1)u^n] = u^n$$

so that $\dfrac{1}{n + 1}\,u^{n+1}$ is an antiderivative of u^n and

$$\int u^n\,du = \frac{1}{n + 1}\,u^{n+1} + C \qquad \text{for } n \neq -1$$

Now we shall use these rules to compute a number of indefinite integrals.

EXAMPLE 3   Indefinite integral of a polynomial function

Evaluate $\displaystyle\int (x^5 - 3x^2 - 7)\,dx$.

Solution   The first two steps are usually done mentally:

$$\int (x^5 - 3x^2 - 7)\,dx = \int x^5\,dx - 3\int x^2\,dx - 7\int dx$$

$$= \frac{x^{5+1}}{5 + 1} - 3\,\frac{x^{2+1}}{2 + 1} - 7x + C = \tfrac{1}{6}x^6 - x^3 - 7x + C$$

EXAMPLE 4   Indefinite integral with a mixture of forms

Evaluate $\int (5\sqrt{x} + 4 \sin x)\, dx$.

Solution $\int (5\sqrt{x} + 4 \sin x)\, dx = 5\int x^{1/2}\, dx + 4 \int \sin x\, dx$

$$= 5\frac{x^{3/2}}{\frac{3}{2}} + 4(-\cos x) + C$$

$$= \tfrac{10}{3}x^{3/2} - 4 \cos x + C$$

This concept of antiderivative will be used extensively in integration, and in the next chapter it will be related to a marvelous result called the fundamental theorem of calculus.

■ APPLICATIONS

In Chapter 2, we used differentiation to compute the slope at each point on the graph of a function. Example 5 shows how this procedure can be reversed.

EXAMPLE 5   Given the slope, find the function

The graph of a certain function F has slope $4x^3 - 5$ at each point (x, y) and contains the point $(1, 2)$. Find the function F.

Solution   Because the slope of the tangent at each point (x, y) is given by $F'(x)$, we have

$$F'(x) = 4x^3 - 5$$

and it follows that

$$\int F'(x)\, dx = \int (4x^3 - 5)\, dx$$
$$F(x) = 4\left(\frac{x^4}{4}\right) - 5x + C$$
$$= x^4 - 5x + C$$

The family of curves is $y = x^4 - 5x + C$. To find the one that passes through $(1, 2)$, substitute:

$$2 = 1^4 - 5(1) + C$$
$$6 = C$$

The curve is $y = x^4 - 5x + 6$.

In Section 2.4, we observed that an object moving along a straight line with displacement $s(t)$ has velocity $v(t) = \frac{ds}{dt}$ and acceleration $a(t) = \frac{dv}{dt}$. Thus, we have

$$v(t) = \int a(t)\, dt \quad \text{and} \quad s(t) = \int v(t)\, dt$$

These formulas are used in Example 6.

EXAMPLE 6   Stopping distance for an automobile

The brakes of a certain automobile produce a constant deceleration of 22 ft/s². If the car is traveling at 60 mi/h (88 ft/s) when the brakes are applied, how far will it travel before coming to a complete stop?

Solution　Let $a(t)$, $v(t)$, and $s(t)$ denote the acceleration, velocity, and displacement of the car t seconds after the brakes are applied. We shall assume that s is measured from the point where the brakes are applied, so that $s(0) = 0$.

$$v(t) = \int a(t)\, dt$$

$$= \int (-22)\, dt \quad \textit{Negative because the car is decelerating}$$

$$= -22t + C_1 \quad v(0) = -22(0) + C_1 = 88,\ \text{so that}\ C_1 = 88.$$
$$\textit{Starting velocity is 88.}$$
$$= -22t + 88$$

Similarly,

$$s(t) = \int v(t)\, dt$$

$$= \int (-22t + 88)\, dt$$

$$= -11t^2 + 88t + C_2$$

$$s(0) = -11(0)^2 + 88(0) + C_2 = 0\ \textit{so that}\ C_2 = 0$$

$$= -11t^2 + 88t \qquad \textit{Starting distance is 0.}$$

Finally, the car comes to rest when its velocity is 0, so we need to solve $v(t) = 0$ for t:

$$-22t + 88 = 0$$

$$t = 4$$

This means that the car decelerates for 4 s before coming to rest, and in that time it travels

$$s(4) = -11(4)^2 + 88(4) = 176\ \text{ft}$$
　■

Indefinite integration also has applications in business and economics. Recall that the *demand function* for a particular commodity is the function $p(x)$, which gives the price p that consumers will pay for each unit of the commodity when x units are brought to market. Then the total revenue is $R(x) = xp(x)$, and the marginal revenue is $R'(x)$. Our final example of this section shows how the demand function can be determined from the marginal revenue.

EXAMPLE 7　**Finding the demand function given the marginal revenue**

A manufacturer estimates that the marginal revenue of a commodity is $R'(x) = 240 + 0.1x$ when x units are produced. Find the demand function $p(x)$.

Solution　$R(x) = \displaystyle\int R'(x)\, dx$

$$= \int (240 + 0.1x)\, dx = 240x + 0.1\left(\tfrac{1}{2}x^2\right) + C = 240x + 0.05x^2 + C$$

Because $R(x) = xp(x)$ where $p(x)$ is the demand function, we must have $R(0) = 0$ so that

$$240(0) + 0.05(0)^2 + C = 0 \quad \text{or} \quad C = 0$$

Thus, $R(x) = 240x + 0.05x^2$. It follows that the demand function is

$$p(x) = \frac{R(x)}{x} = \frac{240x + 0.05x^2}{x} = 240 + 0.05x$$
　■

PROBLEM SET 3.10

A *Find the indefinite integral in Problems 1–22.*

1. $\displaystyle\int 2\,dx$

2. $\displaystyle\int -4\,dx$

3. $\displaystyle\int (2x + 3)\,dx$

4. $\displaystyle\int (4 - 5x)\,dx$

5. $\displaystyle\int (4t^3 + 3t^2)\,dt$

6. $\displaystyle\int (-8t^3 + 15t^5)\,dt$

7. $\displaystyle\int (6u^2 - 3\cos u)\,du$

8. $\displaystyle\int (5t^3 - \sqrt{t})\,dt$

9. $\displaystyle\int \sec^2\theta\,d\theta$

10. $\displaystyle\int \sec\theta\tan\theta\,d\theta$

11. $\displaystyle\int 2\sin\theta\,d\theta$

12. $\displaystyle\int 3\cos\theta\,d\theta$

13. $\displaystyle\int (u^{3/2} - u^{1/2} + u^{-10})\,du$

14. $\displaystyle\int (x^3 - 3x + \sqrt[4]{x} - 5)\,dx$

15. $\displaystyle\int x(x + \sqrt{x})\,dx$

16. $\displaystyle\int y(y^2 - 3y)\,dy$

17. $\displaystyle\int \left(\frac{1}{t^2} - \frac{1}{t^3} + \frac{1}{t^4}\right)dt$

18. $\displaystyle\int \frac{1}{t}\left(\frac{2}{t^2} - \frac{3}{t^3}\right)dt$

19. $\displaystyle\int (2x^2 + 5)^2\,dx$

20. $\displaystyle\int (3 - 4x^3)^2\,dx$

21. $\displaystyle\int \left(\frac{x^2 + 3x - 1}{x^4}\right)dx$

22. $\displaystyle\int \frac{x^2 + \sqrt{x} + 1}{x^2}\,dx$

The slope $F'(x)$ at each point on a graph is given in Problems 23–26 along with one point (x_0, y_0) on the graph. Use this information to find F.

23. slope $x^2 + 3x$ with point $(0, 0)$

24. slope $(\sqrt{x} + 3)^2$ with point $(4, 36)$

25. slope $(2x - 1)^2$ with point $(1, 3)$

26. slope $3 - 2\sin x$ with point $(0, 1)$

B **27. a.** If $F(x) = \displaystyle\int \left(\frac{1}{\sqrt{x}} - 4\right)dx$ find F so that $F(1) = 0$.

   b. Sketch the graphs of $y = F(x)$, $y = F(x) + 3$, and $y = F(x) - 1$.

   c. Find a constant C_0 so that the largest value of $G(x) = F(x) + C_0$ is 0.

28. A ball is thrown directly upward from ground level with an initial velocity of 96 ft/s. Assuming that the ball's only acceleration is that due to gravity (that is, $a(t) = -32$ ft/s^2), determine the maximum height reached by the ball and the time it takes to return to ground level.

29. The marginal cost of a certain commodity is $C'(x) = 6x^2 - 2x + 5$, where x is the level of production. If it costs \$5 to produce 1 unit, what is the total cost of producing 5 units?

30. The marginal revenue of a certain commodity is $R'(x) = -3x^2 + 4x + 32$, where x is the level of production (in thousands). Assume $R(x) = 0$ when $x = 0$.

   a. Find the demand function $p(x)$.

   b. Find the level of production that results in maximum revenue. What is the market price per unit at this level of production?

31. It is estimated that t months from now the population of a certain town will be changing at the rate of $4 + 5t^{2/3}$ people per month. If the current population is 10,000, what will the population be 8 months from now?

32. A particle travels along the x-axis so that its acceleration at time t is $a(t) = \sqrt{t} + t^2$. If it starts at the origin (that is, $s(0) = 0$) with an initial velocity of 2 (that is, $v(0) = 2$), determine its position and velocity when $t = 4$.

33. An automobile starts from rest (that is, $v(0) = 0$) and travels with constant acceleration $a(t) = k$ in such a way that 6 s after it begins to move, it has traveled 360 ft from its starting point. What is k?

34. The price of bacon is currently \$1.80/lb pound in Styxville. A consumer service has conducted a study which predicts that t months from now, the price will be changing at the rate of $0.984 + 0.012\sqrt{t}$ cents per month. How much will a pound of bacon cost 4 mo from now?

35. An airplane has a constant acceleration while moving down the runway from rest. What is the acceleration of the plane at liftoff if the plane requires 100 mi/h and 1.2 mi of runway before lifting off?

36. The brakes of a certain automobile produce a constant deceleration of k ft/s^2. The car is traveling at 60 m/h (88 ft/s) when the driver is forced to hit the brakes, and it comes to rest at a point 121 ft from the point where the brakes were applied. What is k?

C **37.** If a, b, and c are constants, use the linearity rule twice to show that

$$\int [af(x) + bg(x) + ch(x)]\,dx$$
$$= a\int f(x)\,dx + b\int g(x)\,dx + c\int h(x)\,dx$$

CHAPTER 3 REVIEW

IN THIS REVIEW Proficiency examination, supplementary problems
Problems 1–13 of the proficiency examination test your knowledge of the concepts of this chapter, and Problems 14–25 test your understanding of those concepts by asking you to work sample practice problems. The supplementary problems present questions relating to the material of this chapter in a wide variety of settings.

PROFICIENCY EXAMINATION

Concept Problems

1. What is the difference between absolute and relative extrema of a function?
2. State the extreme value theorem.
3. What are the critical values of a function? What is the difference between critical values and critical points?
4. Outline a procedure for finding the absolute extrema of a function on a closed interval $[a, b]$.
5. State both Rolle's theorem and the mean value theorem, and discuss the relationship between the two.
6. State the first-derivative test.
7. State the second-derivative test.
8. What is an asymptote?
9. Define $\lim_{x \to +\infty} f(x) = L$ and $\lim_{x \to c} f(x) = +\infty$.
10. Outline a graphing strategy for a function defined by $y = f(x)$.
11. What do we mean by optimization? Outline an optimization procedure.
12. State l'Hôpital's rule.
13. What do we mean by antidifferentiation?

Practice Problems

Evaluate the limits in Problems 14–17.

14. $\lim_{x \to \pi/2} \dfrac{\sin 2x}{\cos x}$　　15. $\lim_{x \to 1} \dfrac{1 - \sqrt{x}}{x - 1}$

16. $\lim_{x \to +\infty} \left(\dfrac{1}{x} - \dfrac{1}{\sqrt{x}} \right)$　　17. $\lim_{x \to +\infty} \left(\dfrac{x^3}{x^2 - 2} - \dfrac{x^3}{x^2 + 2} \right)$

Sketch the graph of the function in Problems 18–21. Include all key features, such as relative extrema, inflection points, asymptotes, and intercepts.

18. $f(x) = x^3 + 3x^2 - 9x + 2$　　19. $f(x) = x^{1/3}(27 - x)$
20. $f(x) = \sin^2 x - 2 \cos x$ for $0 \le x \le 2\pi$
21. $f(x) = \dfrac{x^2 - 1}{x^2 - 4}$

22. If $f'(x) = 3x^2 + 1$, use antidifferentiation to find f. Graph both f and f' on the same coordinate grid. Suppose $f(0) = 10$.
23. Determine the largest and smallest values of

$$f(x) = x^4 - 2x^5 + 5$$

on the closed interval $[0, 1]$.
24. A box is to have a square base, an open top, and volume of 2 ft^3. Find the dimensions (to the nearest inch) of the box that uses the least amount of material.
25. It is projected that t years from now, the population of a certain suburban community will be

$$P(t) = 20 - \dfrac{6}{t + 1}$$

thousand people. Use increments to estimate how much the population will change during the next quarter-year.

SUPPLEMENTARY PROBLEMS

Sketch the graph of each function in Problems 1–14. Show all of the key features, such as relative extrema, inflection points, asymptotes, and intercepts.

1. $f(x) = x^3 + 6x^2 + 9x - 1$　　2. $f(x) = x^4 + 4x^3 + 4x^2 + 1$
3. $f(x) = 3x^4 - 4x^3 + 1$　　4. $f(x) = 3x^4 - 4x^2 + 1$
5. $f(x) = 6x^5 - 15x^4 + 10x^3$
6. $f(x) = 3x^5 - 10x^3 + 15x + 1$
7. $f(x) = \dfrac{9 - x^2}{3 + x^2}$　　8. $f(x) = \dfrac{x}{1 - x}$
9. $f(x) = \sin 2x - \sin x$　　10. $f(x) = \sin x \sin 2x$
11. $f(x) = \dfrac{x^2 - 4}{x^2}$　　12. $f(x) = \dfrac{x^2 + 2x - 3}{x^2 - 3x + 2}$
13. $f(x) = \dfrac{3x - 2}{(x + 1)^2(x - 2)}$　　14. $f(x) = \dfrac{x^3 + 3}{x(x + 1)(x + 2)}$

Determine the maximum and minimum value of each function on the interval given in Problems 15–16.
15. $f(x) = x^4 - 8x^2 + 12$ on $[-1, 2]$
16. $f(x) = \sqrt{x}(x - 5)^{1/3}$ on $[0, 6]$

Evaluate the limits in Problems 17–30.

17. $\lim_{x \to +\infty} \dfrac{x \sin^2 x}{x^2 + 1}$　　18. $\lim_{x \to +\infty} \dfrac{2x^4 - 7}{6x^4 + 7}$

19. $\lim_{x \to +\infty} \left(\sqrt{x^2 - x} - x \right)$　　20. $\lim_{x \to +\infty} \left[\sqrt{x(x + b)} - x \right]$
21. $\lim_{x \to 0} \dfrac{x \sin x}{x + \sin^3 x}$　　22. $\lim_{x \to 0} \dfrac{x \sin x}{x^2 - \sin^3 x}$
23. $\lim_{x \to 0} \dfrac{x \sin^2 x}{x^2 - \sin^2 x}$　　24. $\lim_{x \to 0} \dfrac{x - \sin x}{\tan^3 x}$
25. $\lim_{x \to 0} \dfrac{\sin^2 x}{\sin x^2}$　　26. $\lim_{x \to 0} \left(\dfrac{1}{x^2} - \dfrac{1}{x^2 \sec x} \right)$
27. $\lim_{x \to \pi/2} -\dfrac{\sec^2 x}{\sec^2 3x}$　　28. $\lim_{x \to \pi/2} -(1 - \sin x)\tan x$
29. $\lim_{x \to \pi/2} -(\sec x - \tan x)$　　30. $\lim_{x \to +\infty} \left(\sqrt{x^2 + 4} - \sqrt{x^2 - 4} \right)$

Find the indefinite integrals of the functions in Problems 31–34.

31. $\displaystyle\int (5x - 6)\, dx$

32. $\displaystyle\int (t - 1)(t + 2)\, dt$

33. $\displaystyle\int \dfrac{1}{x^3}\, dx$

34. $\displaystyle\int \dfrac{5x^2 - 2x + 1}{\sqrt{x}}\, dx$

35. JOURNAL PROBLEM *Mathematics Teacher.** Which of the graphs is the derivative and which is the function?

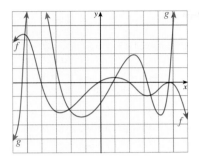

36. Determine a, b, and c such that the graph of $f(x) = ax^2 + bx^2 + c$ has an inflection point and slope 1 at $(-1, 2)$.

37. ■ **What Does This Say?** Explain why the graph of a quadratic polynomial cannot have a point of inflection. How many inflection points does the graph of a cubic polynomial have?

38. Find the points on the hyperbola $x^2 - y^2 = 4$ that are closest to the point $(0, 1)$.

39. A Norman window consists of a rectangle with a semicircle surmounted on the top. What are the dimensions of the Norman window of largest area with a fixed perimeter of P_0 meters?

40. Find numbers A, B, C, and D that guarantee that the function

$$f(x) = Ax^3 + Bx^2 + Cx + D$$

will have a relative maximum at $(-1, 1)$ and a relative minimum at $(1, -1)$.

41. Find the area of the rectangle of maximum area that can be inscribed in the semicircle defined by the equation

$$y = \sqrt{a^2 - x^2}$$

for fixed $a > 0$.

42. An apartment complex has 200 units. When the monthly rent for each unit is $600, all units are occupied. Experience indicates that for each $20-per-month increase in rent, 5 units will become vacant. Each rented apartment costs the owners of the complex $80 per month to maintain. What monthly rent should be charged to maximize the owner's profit? What is maximum profit? How many units are rented when profit is a maximum?

43. A peach grower has determined that if 30 trees are planted per acre, each tree will average 200 lb of peaches per season. However, for each tree grown in addition to the 30 trees, the average yield for each of the trees in the grove drops by 5 lb per tree. How many peach trees should be planted on each acre in order to maximize the yield of peaches per acre? What is the maximum yield?

Shore

44. Oil from an offshore rig located 3 mi from the shore is to be pumped to a location on the edge of the shore that is 8 mi east of the rig. The cost of constructing a pipe in the ocean from the rig to the shore is 1.5 times more expensive than the cost of construction on land. How should the pipe be laid to minimize cost?

45. In order to obtain the maximum price, a shipment of fruit should reach the market as early as possible after the fruit has been picked. If a grower picks the fruit immediately for shipment, 100 cases can be shipped at a profit of $10 per case. By waiting, the grower estimates that the crop will yield an additional 25 cases per week, but because the competitor's yield will also increase, the grower's profit will decrease by $1 per case per week. Use calculus to determine when the grower should ship the fruit in order to maximize profit. What will be the maximum profit?

46. The owner of a novelty store can obtain joy buzzers from the manufacturer for 40¢ apiece. It is estimated that 60 buzzers will be sold when the price is $1.20 per buzzer and that 10 more buzzers will be sold for every 10¢ decrease in price. What price should be charged in order to maximize profit?

47. Westel Corporation manufactures telephones and has developed a new cellular phone. Production analysis shows that its price must not be less than $50; if x units are sold, then the price is given by the formula $p(x) = 150 - x$. The total cost of producing x units is given by the formula $C(x) = 2,500 + 30x$. Find the maximum profit, and determine the price that should be charged to maximize the profits.

48. The cost of producing a certain book is $25 per copy. The number of books sold is given by the formula

$$n = \frac{50,000}{x + 20} - 2,000$$

where x is the price of the book. The profit $P(x)$ is the number of books sold times the price less $29. That is,

$$P(x) = (x - 29)n$$

In order to maximize the profit, what should be the selling price of the book if the domain for x is $[29, 150]$?

49. A manufacturer receives an order for 5,000 items. There are 12 machines available, each of which can produce 25 items per hour. The cost of setting up a machine for a production run is $50. Once the machines are in operation, the procedure is fully automated and can be supervised by a single worker earning $20 per hour. Find the number of machines that should be used in order to minimize the total cost of filling the order.

50. The personnel manager of a department store estimates that if N temporary salespersons are hired for the holiday season, the total net revenue derived (in hundreds of dollars) from their efforts will be

$$R(N) = -3N^4 + 50N^3 - 261N^2 + 540N$$

for $0 \leq N \leq 9$. How many salespersons should be hired in order to maximize total net revenue? *Hint:* A critical value for $R(N)$ is 2.

51. Show that the graph of a polynomial of degree n, with $n > 2$, has at most $n - 2$ inflection points.

52. Show that the graph of the function $f(x) = x^n$ with $n > 1$ has either one or no inflection points, depending on whether n is odd or even.

53. Each tangent line to the circle $x^2 + y^2 = 1$ at a point in the first quadrant will intersect the coordinate axes at points $(x_1, 0)$ and $(0, y_1)$. Determine the line for which $x_1 + y_1$ is a minimum.

54. An accelerated particle moving at speed close to the speed of light emits power P in the direction θ given by

$$P(\theta) = \frac{a \sin \theta}{(1 - b \cos \theta)^5} \quad \text{for} \quad 0 < b < 1$$

Find the value of $\cos \theta$ for which P has the greatest value.

55. Suppose that f is a continuous function defined on the closed interval $[a, b]$ and that $f'(x) = c$ on the open interval (a, b) for some constant c. Use MVT to show that

$$f(x) = c(x - a) + f(a)$$

for all x in the interval $[a, b]$.

56. Suppose that $f''(x)$ exists and that $f''(x) + c^2 f(x) = 0$, with $f'(0) = 1$. Show that for any x_0, there is a number w between 0 and x for which $f'(x_0) + c^2 f(x_0)x = 1$.

57. An electric charge Q_0 is distributed uniformly over a ring of radius R. The electric field intensity at any point x along the axis of the ring is given by

$$E(x) = \frac{Q_0 x}{(x^2 + R^2)^{3/2}}$$

At what point on the axis is $E(x)$ maximized?

Computational Window ▼ ▲

Using the graphing and differentiation programs of your computer software, graph $f(x)$, $f'(x)$, $f''(x)$ for each function in Problems 58–61. Print out a copy, if possible. On each graph, indicate the intervals where

a. $f'(x) > 0$ **b.** $f'(x) < 0$ **c.** $f''(x) > 0$

d. $f''(x) < 0$ **e.** $f'(x) = 0$

f. $f'(x)$ does not exist   **g.** $f''(x) = 0$

Describe how these inequalities qualitatively determine the shape of the graph of the functions over the given interval.

58. $f(x) = \sin 2x$ on $[-\pi, \pi]$

59. $f(x) = x^3 - x^2 - x + 1$ on $\left[-\frac{3}{2}, 2\right]$

60. $f(x) = x^4 - 2x^2$ on $[-2, 2]$

61. $f(x) = x^3 - x + \frac{1}{x} + 1$ on $[-2, 2]$

62. Consider a string 60 in. long that is formed into a rectangle. Using a graphing calculator or a graphing program, graph the area $A(x)$ enclosed by the string as a function of the length x of a given side ($0 < x < 30$). From the graph, deduce that the maximum area is enclosed when the rectangle is a square. What is the minimum area enclosed? Compare this problem to the exact solution. What conclusions do you draw about the desirability of analytical solutions and the role of the computer?

63. The shore of a lake follows contours that are approximated by the curve $4x^2 + y^2 = 1$, and a nearby road lies along the curve $y = 1/x$ for $x > 0$. Using your graphing calculator or computer software, determine the closest approach of the road to the lake in the north-south direction. Take the positive y-axis as pointing north.

64. Using your graphing and differentiation programs, locate and identify all the relative extrema for the function defined by

$$f(x) = \tfrac{1}{5}x^5 - \tfrac{5}{4}x^4 + 2x^2$$

This may require a few judicious choices of the plotting interval.

65. Suppose you are a manager of a fleet of delivery trucks. Each truck has a minimum speed of 15 mi/h and a maximum speed of 55 mi/h. Suppose the truck burns gas at the rate of

$$\frac{1}{250} \left(\frac{750}{x} + x \right)$$

gal/mi when traveling x mi/h. Using a graphing and differentiation program (and/or root-solving program on your computer or calculator), answer the following questions:

a. If gas costs $1.70/gal, estimate the steady speed that will minimize the cost of fuel for a 500-mi trip.

b. Estimate the steady speed that will minimize the cost if the driver is paid $28 per hour and the price of gasoline remains constant at $1.70/gal.

66. **A mechanics problem** The sketch shows a circular wheel of radius 1 ft moving at an angular speed of 2 radians/s in a counterclockwise direction. A rod of length L is attached to the circumference, and the

other end of the rod can move only vertically, as shown in Figure 3.78.

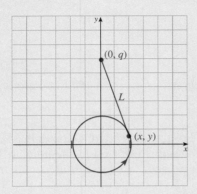

Figure 3.78 A rod attached to a circular wheel

a. Argue that a point on the circumference can be expressed as $(x, y) = (\cos 2t, \sin 2t)$.

b. Derive the equation for q:

$$q(t) = \sin 2t + \sqrt{L^2 - \cos^2 2t}$$

c. Compute $q'(t)$ without a calculator or computer.

d. From the physics of the problem, argue that velocity $q'(t) = 0$ when the (x, y) point is at the top or the bottom of the wheel. Then conjecture at what point(s) q' will achieve its maximum value.

From now on, use some computing help.

e. Compute $q'(t)$ and compare it with your answer in part **c.**

f. For $L = 2$, plot $q(t)$ and $a'(t)$ and comment on what you see. Any surprises?

g. Now, for L slightly larger than 1 (that is, 1.1. or 1.01) repeat part **f.**

h. Find for what values of t, $q'(t)$ achieves its maximum value. Specifically, find at least one t value to two-decimal-place accuracy. Compare with your answer in part **d.** *Hint:* You may want to look for zeros of $q''(t)$.

i. Compare the maximum speed of point $(0, q)$ with that of the other end of the rod, (x, y).

j. **Exploratory** What do you think happens to q'_{max} as $L \to 1.0$?

67. Measuring a sphere In Chapter 1, you were introduced to a method of finding the radius of a sphere by using a meter stick and a wire. This led to the equation for r:

$$f(r) = \cos\frac{25}{r} - \frac{r}{r+1} = 0$$

where 25 represents the distance on the surface from the meter stick to a point of tangency. Recall that from the geometry involved, $r > 25$.

a. Make a plot of $f(r)$, thus obtaining a rough estimate of the desired "zero" of f.

b. Use the Newton-Raphson method to find the radius of the sphere to 5-decimal-place accuracy.

68. PUTNAM EXAMINATION PROBLEM Given the parabola $y^2 = 2mx$, what is the length of the shortest chord that is normal to the curve at one end? *Hint:* If $\overline{AB}$ is normal to the parabola, where A and B are the points $(2mt^2, 2mt)$ and $(2ms^2, 2ms)$, show that the slope of the tangent at A is $1/2t$.

69. PUTNAM EXAMINATION PROBLEM Prove that the polynomial

$$(a - x)^6 - 3a(a - x)^5 + \tfrac{5}{2}a^2(a - x)^4 - \tfrac{1}{2}a^4(a - x)^2$$

has only negative values for $0 < x < a$. *Hint:* Show that if $x = g(1 - y)$, the polynomial becomes $a^6y^2g(y)$ where

$$g(y) = y^4 - 3y^3 + \tfrac{5}{2}y^2 - \tfrac{1}{2}$$

and then prove that $g(y) < 0$ for $0 < y < 1$.

70. PUTNAM EXAMINATION PROBLEM Find the maximum value of $f(x) = x^3 - 3x$ on the set of all real numbers x satisfying $x^4 + 36 \le 13x^2$.

71. PUTNAM EXAMINATION PROBLEM Let T be an acute triangle with inscribed rectangles R and S, as shown in Figure 3.79.

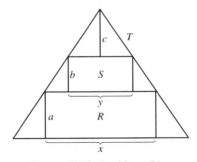

Figure 3.79 Problem 71

Let a, b, c and x, y, z be the lengths as indicated in Figure 3.79. Let $A(x)$ denote the area of polygon X (rectangle or triangle). Find the maximum value of the ratio

$$\frac{A(R) + A(S)}{A(T)}$$

for all possible choices of the acute triangle T and the inscribed rectangles R and S. *Hint:* Show that the problem can be restated as, "Maximize $ab + ac + bc$, subject to $a + b + c = h$."

"Wine Barrel Capacity"

This project is to be done in groups of three or four students. Each group will submit a single written report.

A wine barrel has a hole in the middle of its side called a **bung hole.** To determine the volume of wine in the barrel, a **bung rod** is inserted in the hole until it hits the lower seam. Determine how to calibrate such a rod so that it will measure the volume of the wine in the barrel.

You should make the following assumptions:

1. The barrel is cylindrical.

2. The distance from the bung hole to the corner is λ.

3. The ratio of the height to the diameter of the barrel is t. This ratio should be chosen so that for a given λ value, the volume of the barrel is maximal.

Your paper is not limited to the following questions, but it should include these concerns: You should show that the volume of the cylindrical barrel is $V = 2\pi\lambda^3 t(4 + t^2)^{-3/2}$, and you should find the approximate ideal value for t. Johannes Kepler was the first person to show mathematically why coopers were guided in their construction of wine barrels by one rule: *make the staves* (the boards that make up the sides of the barrel) *one and one-half times as long as the diameter.* (This is the approximate t-value.) You should provide dimensions for the barrel as well as for the bung rod.

Johannes Kepler (1571–1630) is usually remembered for his work in astronomy, in particular for his three laws of planetary motion. However, Kepler was also a renowned mathematician and served as court mathematician to the Austrian emperor Matthew I. While at Matthew I's court, Kepler observed with admiration the ability of a young vintner to declare quickly and easily the capacities of a number of different wine casks. He describes how this can be done in his book *The New Stereometry of Wine Barrels, Mostly Austrian.*

YE OLDE BUNG ROD

bung rod

*The idea for this group research project comes from research done at Iowa State University as part of a National Science Foundation grant. Our thanks to Elgin Johnston of Iowa State University.

4

Integration

CONTENTS

PREVIEW

If an object moves along a straight line with velocity $v(t)$, what is its position $s(t)$ at time t? If $f(x) \geq 0$ on the interval $[a, b]$, what is the area under the curve $y = f(x)$ over this interval? On Christmas Day, it starts snowing at a steady rate. A snowplow starts out at noon, going 2 miles during the first hour and 1 mile during the second. What time did it start snowing? At first glance, these problems may appear to have little in common, but they are all typical of what we shall encounter in our study of *integral calculus*. In Section 1.1, we pointed out that there are two fundamental concepts in calculus, namely, the idea of a *derivative* and that of an *integral*. With this chapter we formally introduce you to this second fundamental concept of calculus.

PERSPECTIVE

The key concept in integral calculus is *integration*, a procedure that involves computing a special kind of limit of sums called the *definite integral*. We shall find that such limits can often be computed by reversing the process of differentiation; that is, given a function f, we find a function F such that $F' = f$. This is called *indefinite integration*, and the equation $F' = f$ is an example of a *differential equation*.

Finding integrals and solving differential equations are extremely important processes in calculus. We begin our study of these topics by defining definite and indefinite integration and showing how they are connected by a remarkable result called the *fundamental theorem of calculus*. Then we examine several techniques of integration and show how area, average value, and other quantities can be set up and analyzed by integration. Our study of differential equations begins in this chapter and will continue in appropriate sections throughout this text. We also establish a mean value theorem for integrals and develop numerical procedures for estimating the value of a definite integral.

We close the chapter by showing how integration can be used to find the area between two curves and to compute certain useful quantities in economics.

4.1 AREA AS THE LIMIT OF A SUM; SUMMATION NOTATION

IN THIS SECTION Area as the limit of a sum, the general approximation scheme, summation notation, area using summation formulas
In elementary school you were introduced to the concept of area, and you calculated the areas of certain plane figures with straight-line boundaries. You were even given a formula for the area of a circle, but, in general, you were not taught to find the area of a plane region with curved boundaries. The process of finding an area of a region with curved boundaries is called **quadrature**. The area under a curve plays a central role in integral calculus. In this section, we shall show that it is reasonable to *define* area as the limit of a sum. In the process, we shall introduce ideas that play a key role in our general development of integral calculus.

■ AREA AS THE LIMIT OF A SUM

Computing area has been a problem of both theoretical and practical interest since ancient times; except for a few special cases, the problem is not easy. For example, you may know the formulas for computing the area of a rectangle, square, triangle, circle, or even a trapezoid. You have probably found the areas of regions that were more complicated but could be broken up into parts using these formulas. However, how would you find the area between the parabola whose equation is $y = x^2$ and the x-axis on the interval [0, 1]? By solving this problem, we shall demonstrate a general procedure for computing area.

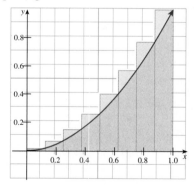

a. *Problem*: Compute the area under the curve $y = x^2$, above the x-axis and between the lines $x = 0$ and $x = 1$.

b. The required area is approximately the same as the total area bounded by the shaded rectangles.

Figure 4.1 Example of the area problem

EXAMPLE 1   Estimating the area under a parabola using rectangles and right endpoints

Estimate the area under the parabola $y = x^2$ on the interval [0, 1].

Solution Observe that although we cannot compute the area by applying a simple formula, we can certainly *estimate* the area by adding the area of approximating rectangles constructed on subintervals of [0, 1], as shown in Figure 4.1b. To simplify computations, we shall require all approximating rectangles to have the same width and shall take the height of each rectangle to be the y-

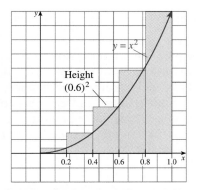

Figure 4.2a Detail of Figure 4.1b.

Figure 4.2b Detail of area under $y = x^2$ on [0, 1]

coordinate of the parabola above the *right endpoint* of the subinterval on which it is based.* For the first estimate, we divide the interval [0, 1] into 5 subintervals, as shown in Figure 4.2a. Because the approximating rectangles all have the same width, the right endpoints are $x_1 = 0.2$, $x_2 = 0.4$, $x_3 = 0.6$, $x_4 = 0.8$ and $x_5 = 1$. This subdivision is called *partitioning the interval*. The width of each subdivision is denoted by Δx and is found by taking the length of the interval divided by the number of subintervals:

$$\Delta x = \frac{1-0}{5} = \frac{1}{5} = 0.2$$

If we let S_n be the total area of n rectangles, we find for the case where $n = 5$ that

$$S_5 = f(x_1)\Delta x + f(x_2)\Delta x + f(x_3)\Delta x + f(x_4)\Delta x + f(x_5)\Delta x$$
$$= [f(x_1) + f(x_2) + f(x_3) + f(x_4) + f(x_5)]\Delta x$$
$$= [f(0.2) + f(0.4) + f(0.6) + f(0.8) + f(1)](0.2)$$
$$= [0.2^2 + 0.4^2 + 0.6^2 + 0.8^2 + 1^2](0.2) = 0.44$$

Even though $S_5 = 0.44$ serves as a reasonable approximation of the area, we see from Figure 4.2b in the margin that this area is too large. Let us rework Example 1 using a general scheme rather than a specified number of rectangles. Partition the interval [0, 1] into n equal parts, each with width

$$\Delta x = \frac{1-0}{n} = \frac{1}{n}$$

For $k = 1, 2, 3, \ldots, n$, the kth subinterval is

$$\left[\frac{k-1}{n}, \frac{k}{n}\right]$$

and on this subinterval, we then construct an approximating rectangle with width $\Delta x = \frac{1}{n}$ and height $\left(\frac{k}{n}\right)^2$, because $y = x^2$. The total area bounded by all n rectangles is

$$S_n = \left[\left(\frac{1}{n}\right)^2 + \left(\frac{2}{n}\right)^2 + \cdots + \left(\frac{n}{n}\right)^2\right]\left(\frac{1}{n}\right)$$

Consider different choices for n, as shown in Figure 4.3.

$n = 4$

$n = 16$

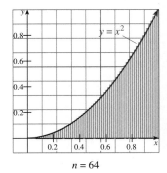

$n = 64$

Figure 4.3 The area estimate is improved by taking more rectangles.

---

*Actually, there is nothing special about right endpoints, and we could just as easily have used any other well-defined point in the base subinterval—say, the left endpoint or the midpoint.

n	S_n
5	0.440
10	0.385
50	0.343
100	0.338
1,000	0.334
5,000	0.333

If we increase the number of subdivisions n, the width $\Delta x = \frac{1}{n}$ of each approximating rectangle will decrease, and we would expect the area estimates S_n to improve. Thus, it is reasonable to *define* the area A under the parabola to be the *limit of S_n* as $\Delta x \to 0$ or, equivalently, as $n \to +\infty$. Although we now have no way of formally computing this limit, we can attempt to predict its value by seeing what happens to the sum as n grows large without bound. It is both tedious and difficult to evaluate such sums by hand, but fortunately we can use a calculator or computer to obtain some (rounded) values for S_n as shown in the margin. Notice that for $n = 5$, the value 0.44 corresponds to the calculation in Example 1.

Computational Window

These computer-generated drawings show the area under the curve $y = x^2$ on [1, 5] as approximated by rectangles using left endpoints (in contrast to right endpoints used in Example 1). The sums in this output are called *Riemann sums*, which we will define in the next section.

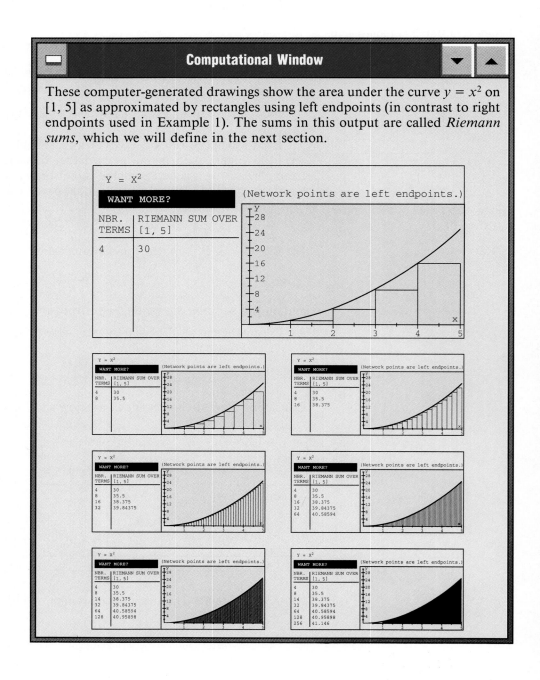

■ THE GENERAL APPROXIMATION SCHEME

We now compute the area under any curve $y = f(x)$ on an interval $[a, b]$ where f is a nonnegative continuous function. We first partition the interval $[a, b]$ into n equal subintervals, each of width

$$\Delta x = \frac{b - a}{n}$$

For $k = 1, 2, 3, \ldots, n$ the kth subinterval is $[a + (k - 1)\Delta x, a + k\Delta x]$, and the kth approximating rectangle is constructed with width Δx and height $f(a + k\Delta x)$ equal to the altitude of the curve $y = f(x)$ above the right endpoint of the subinterval. Adding the areas of these n rectangles, we obtain

$$S_n = \overbrace{f(a + \Delta x)\,\Delta x}^{\substack{\text{Area of} \\ \text{first rectangle}}} + \overbrace{f(a + 2\Delta x)\,\Delta x}^{\substack{\text{Area of} \\ \text{second rectangle}}} + \cdots + \overbrace{f(a + n\Delta x)\,\Delta x}^{\substack{\text{Area of} \\ n\text{th rectangle}}}$$

as an estimate of the area under the curve. In advanced calculus, it is shown that the continuity of f guarantees the existence of $\lim_{\Delta x \to 0} S_n$, and we use this limit to define the required area, as shown in the following box.

Area As the Limit of a Sum

> Suppose f is continuous and $f(x) \geq 0$ throughout the interval $[a, b]$. Then the **area** of the region under the curve $y = f(x)$ over this interval is
>
> $$A = \lim_{\Delta x \to 0} [f(a + \Delta x) + f(a + 2\Delta x) + \cdots + f(a + n\Delta x)]\,\Delta x \text{ where } \Delta x = \frac{b - a}{n}.$$

The definition of area as a limit of a sum is consistent with the area concept introduced in plane geometry. For example, it would not be difficult to use this formula to show that a rectangle has area $A = \ell w$ or that a triangle has area $A = \frac{1}{2}bh$. You will also note that we maintained everyday usage in saying that the *formula* for the area of a rectangle is $A = \ell w$ or the *area* of the region under the curve $y = f(x)$ is a limit, but it is actually more proper to say that the limit *is the definition* of the area of the region.

The problem we now face is how to implement this definition of area as the limit of a sum. The immediate answer (discussed in this section) is to use summation formulas and technology. The long-range goal is to develop integral calculus, which is discussed in the next section.

■ SUMMATION NOTATION

The expanded form of the sum for the definition of area makes it awkward to use. Therefore, we shall digress to introduce a more compact notation for sums. Using this **summation notation,** we express the sum $a_1 + a_2 + \cdots + a_n$ as follows:

$$a_1 + a_2 + \cdots + a_n = \sum_{k=1}^{n} a_k$$

The summation notation is sometimes called the **sigma notation** because the uppercase Greek letter sigma (Σ) is used to denote the summation process. The index k is called the **index of summation** (or *running index*). The terminology used in connection with the summation notation is shown:

Upper limit of summation

$$\sum_{k=1}^{n} \overset{\text{General term}}{\widehat{a_k}}$$

Index of summation

Lower limit of summation

Note that as far as the summation process is concerned, the choice of summation index is immaterial. For example, the following sums are all exactly the same:

$$\sum_{k=3}^{7} k^2 = \sum_{j=3}^{7} j^2 = \sum_{i=3}^{7} i^2 = \sum_{\lambda=3}^{7} \lambda^2$$

In general, an index (k, j, i, or λ) that represents a process in which it has no direct effect on the result is called a **dummy variable.**

Several useful properties of sums and sum formulas are listed in Theorem 4.1. We shall use the summation notation throughout the rest of this text, especially in this chapter, Chapter 6, and Chapter 8.

THEOREM 4.1   Basic rules and formulas for sums

For any numbers c and d, and positive integers k, m, and n

1. **Constant term rule** $\displaystyle\sum_{k=1}^{n} c = \underbrace{c + c + \ldots + c}_{n \text{ terms}} = nc$

2. **Sum rule** $\displaystyle\sum_{k=1}^{n} (a_k + b_k) = \sum_{k=1}^{n} a_k + \sum_{k=1}^{n} b_k$

3. **Scalar multiple rule** $\displaystyle\sum_{k=1}^{n} ca_k = c\sum_{k=1}^{n} a_k = \left(\sum_{k=1}^{n} a_k\right)c$

4. **Linearity rule** $\displaystyle\sum_{k=1}^{n} (ca_k + db_k) = c\sum_{k=1}^{n} a_k + d\sum_{k=1}^{n} b_k$

5. **Subtotal rule**   If $1 < m < n$, then
$$\sum_{k=1}^{n} a_k = \sum_{k=1}^{m} a_k + \sum_{k=m+1}^{n} a_k$$

6. **Dominance rule**   If $a_k \le b_k$ for $k = 1, 2, \ldots, n$, then
$$\sum_{k=1}^{n} a_k \le \sum_{k=1}^{n} b_k$$

Proof: These properties can all be established by applying well-known algebraic rules (see Problem 47 of Problem Set 4.1).   ∎

Using summation notation, we can streamline the symbolism in the formula for the area under the curve $y = f(x)$ on the interval $[a, b]$. In particular, note that the approximating sum S_n is

$$S_n = [f(a + \Delta x) + f(a + 2\Delta x) + \cdots + f(a + n\Delta x)]\Delta x$$

$$= \sum_{k=1}^{n} f(a + k\Delta x)\Delta x$$

where $\Delta x = \dfrac{b-a}{n}$. Thus, the formula for the definition of area can be written as

Area under $y = f(x)$ above the x-axis n is the number of approximating rectangles
between $x = a$ and $x = b$ $\downarrow$ $\downarrow$ Width of each rectangle

$$A = \lim_{n \to +\infty} S_n = \lim_{\Delta x \to 0} \sum_{k=1}^{n} \underbrace{f(a + k\Delta x)}\,\widehat{\Delta x}$$

Height of the kth rectangle

■ AREA USING SUMMATION FORMULAS

From algebra we recall certain summation formulas (proved using mathematical induction) that we will need in order to find areas using the limit definition of area.

Summation Formulas

$$\sum_{k=1}^{n} 1 = n$$

$$\sum_{k=1}^{n} k = 1 + 2 + 3 + \cdots + n = \frac{n(n+1)}{2}$$

$$\sum_{k=1}^{n} k^2 = 1^2 + 2^2 + 3^2 + \cdots + n^2 = \frac{n(n+1)(2n+1)}{6}$$

$$\sum_{k=1}^{n} k^3 = 1^3 + 2^3 + 3^3 + \cdots + n^3 = \frac{n^2(n+1)^2}{4}$$

EXAMPLE 2   Area using summation and the definition

Use the summation definition of area to find the area under the parabola $y = x^2$ on the interval $[0, 1]$. You estimated this area in Example 1.

Solution   Partition the interval $[0, 1]$ into n subintervals with width $\Delta x = \dfrac{1-0}{n}$.
The right endpoint of the kth subinterval is $a + k\Delta x = \dfrac{k}{n}$, and $f\left(\dfrac{k}{n}\right) = \dfrac{k^2}{n^2}$. Thus, from the definition of area we have

$$A = \lim_{\Delta x \to 0} \sum_{k=1}^{n} f(a + k\Delta x)\Delta x = \lim_{n \to +\infty} \sum_{k=1}^{n} \left(\frac{k^2}{n^2}\right)\left(\frac{1}{n}\right)$$

$$= \lim_{n \to +\infty} \sum_{k=1}^{n} \frac{k^2}{n^3}$$

$$= \lim_{n \to +\infty} \frac{1}{n^3} \sum_{k=1}^{n} k^2 \qquad \textit{Scalar multiple rule}$$

$$= \lim_{n \to +\infty} \frac{1}{n^3} \left[\frac{n(n+1)(2n+1)}{6}\right] \qquad \textit{Summation formula for squares}$$

$$= \lim_{n \to +\infty} \frac{n(n+1)(2n+1)}{6n^3} = \lim_{n \to +\infty} \frac{n(n+1)(2n+1)\left(\frac{1}{n^3}\right)}{6n^3\left(\frac{1}{n^3}\right)}$$

$$= \lim_{n \to +\infty} \frac{\dfrac{n}{n}\left(\dfrac{n+1}{n}\right)\left(\dfrac{2n+1}{n}\right)}{6} = \lim_{n \to +\infty} \frac{\left(1 + \dfrac{1}{n}\right)\left(2 + \dfrac{1}{n}\right)}{6} = \frac{2}{6} = \frac{1}{3} \qquad \blacksquare$$

Computational Window

Sometimes the summation formulas cannot be used as shown in Example 2, but by using a computer you can find a pattern leading to the appropriate limit, just as we used tables to find limits in Chapter 1. Consider the following example.

EXAMPLE 3   Tabular approach for finding area

Use a computer to estimate the area under the curve $y = \sin x$ on the interval $\left[0, \frac{\pi}{2}\right]$.

Solution   We see $a = 0$ and $b = \frac{\pi}{2}$, so $\Delta x = \frac{\frac{\pi}{2} - 0}{n} = \frac{\pi}{2n}$. The right endpoints are

$$a + \Delta x = 0 + \left(\frac{\pi}{2n}\right) = \frac{\pi}{2n}$$

$$a + 2\Delta x = \frac{2\pi}{2n} = \frac{\pi}{n}$$

$$a + 3\Delta x = \frac{3\pi}{2n}$$

$$\vdots$$

$$a + n\Delta x = \frac{n\pi}{2n} = \frac{\pi}{2} = b$$

Thus, $S_n = \sum\limits_{k=1}^{n} f\left(0 + \frac{k\pi}{2n}\right)\left(\frac{\pi}{2n}\right) = \sum\limits_{k=1}^{n} \left[\sin\left(\frac{k\pi}{2n}\right)\right]\left(\frac{\pi}{2n}\right)$

Now we know from the definition that the actual area is

$$S = \lim_{n \to +\infty} \sum_{k=1}^{n} \left[\sin\left(\frac{k\pi}{2n}\right)\right]\left(\frac{\pi}{2n}\right)$$

n	S_n
10	1.07648
20	1.03876
50	1.01563
100	1.00783
500	1.00157

which we can estimate by computing S_n for successively large values of n, as summarized in the table in the margin. Note that the pattern of numbers in this table suggests that

$$\lim_{\Delta x \to 0} S_n = \lim_{n \to +\infty} S_n = 1$$

Thus, we expect the actual area under the curve to be 1 square unit. ▬

PROBLEM SET 4.1

A *Evaluate the sums in Problems 1–8 by using the summation formulas.*

1. $\sum\limits_{k=1}^{6} 1$ **2.** $\sum\limits_{k=1}^{250} 1$ **3.** $\sum\limits_{k=1}^{15} k$ **4.** $\sum\limits_{k=1}^{10} k$

5. $\sum\limits_{k=1}^{5} k^3$ **6.** $\sum\limits_{k=1}^{7} k^2$ **7.** $\sum\limits_{k=1}^{100} (2k - 3)$ **8.** $\sum\limits_{k=1}^{100} (k - 1)^2$

Use the properties of sigma notation in Problems 9–12 to evaluate the given limits.

9. $\lim\limits_{n \to +\infty} \sum\limits_{k=1}^{n} \dfrac{k}{n^2}$ **10.** $\lim\limits_{n \to +\infty} \sum\limits_{k=1}^{n} \dfrac{k^2}{n^3}$

11. $\lim\limits_{n \to +\infty} \sum\limits_{k=1}^{n} \left(1 + \dfrac{k}{n}\right)\left(\dfrac{2}{n}\right)$ **12.** $\lim\limits_{n \to +\infty} \sum\limits_{k=1}^{n} \left(1 + \dfrac{2k}{n}\right)^2\left(\dfrac{2}{n}\right)$

First sketch the region under the graph of $y = f(x)$ on the interval [a, b] in Problems 13–21. Then approximate the area of each region by using right endpoints and the formula

$$S_n = \sum_{k=1}^{n} f(a + k\Delta x)\Delta x$$

for $\Delta x = \dfrac{b - a}{n}$ and the indicated values of n.

13. $f(x) = 4x + 1$ on [0, 1] for
    a. $n = 4$ **b.** $n = 8$

14. $f(x) = 3 - 2x$ on [0, 1] for
    a. $n = 3$ **b.** $n = 6$

15. $f(x) = x^2$ on [1, 2] for
    a. $n = 4$ **b.** $n = 6$

16. $f(x) = \cos x$ on $\left[-\frac{\pi}{2}, 0\right]$ for $n = 4$

17. $f(x) = x + \sin x$ on $\left[0, \frac{\pi}{4}\right]$ for $n = 3$

18. $f(x) = \frac{1}{x^2}$ on [1, 2] for $n = 4$

19. $f(x) = \frac{2}{x}$ on [1, 2] for $n = 4$

20. $f(x) = \sqrt{x}$ on [1, 4] for $n = 4$
21. $f(x) = \sqrt{1 + x^2}$ on [0, 1] for $n = 4$

Ⓑ *Find the exact area under the given curve on the interval prescribed in Problems 22–27 by using the summation formulas.*
22. $y = 4x^3 + 2x$ on [0, 2]
23. $y = 4x^3 + 2x$ on [1, 2]
24. $y = 6x^2 + 2x + 4$ on [0, 3]
25. $y = 6x^2 + 2x + 4$ on [1, 3]
26. $y = 3x^2 + 2x + 1$ on [0, 1]
27. $y = 4x^3 + 3x^2$ on [0, 1]

THINK TANK PROBLEMS   *Show that each statement in Problems 28–33 about area is generally true or provide a counterexample. It will probably help to sketch the indicated region for each problem.*
28. If $C > 0$ is a constant, the region under the line $y = C$ on the interval [a, b] has area $A = C(b - a)$.
29. If $C > 0$ is a constant and $b > a \geq 0$, the region under the line $y = Cx$ on the interval [a, b] has area $A = \frac{1}{2}C(b - a)$.
30. The region under the parabola $y = x^2$ on the interval [a, b] has area less than
$$\tfrac{1}{2}(b^2 + a^2)(b - a)$$
31. The region under the curve $y = \sqrt{1 - x^2}$ on the interval [−1, 1] has area $A = \frac{\pi}{2}$.
32. Let f be a function that satisfies $f(x) \geq 0$ for x in the interval [a, b]. Then the area under the curve $y = [f(x)]^2$ on the interval [a, b] must always be greater than the area under $y = f(x)$ on the same interval.
33. If f is an even function [that is, f satisfies $f(x) = f(-x)$] and $f(x) \geq 0$ throughout the interval [−a, a], then the area under the curve $y = f(x)$ on this interval is *twice* the area under $y = f(x)$ on [0, a].
34. Show that the region under the curve $y = x^3$ on the interval [0, 1] has area $\frac{1}{4}$ square units.
35. Use the definition of area to show that the area of a rectangle equals the product of its length ℓ and its width w.

36. Show that the triangle with vertices (0, 0), (0, h), and (b, 0) has area $A = \frac{1}{2}bh$.
37. **a.** Compute the area under the parabola $y = 2x^2$ on the interval [1, 2] as the limit of a sum.
    b. Let $f(x) = 2x^2$ and note that $g(x) = \frac{2}{3}x^3$ defines a function that satisfies $g'(x) = f(x)$ on the interval [1, 2]. Verify that the area computed in part **a** satisfies $A = g(2) - g(1)$.
    c. The function defined by
$$h(x) = \tfrac{2}{3}x^3 + C$$
    for any constant C also satisfies $h'(x) = f(x)$. Is it true that the area in part **a** satisfies $A = h(2) - h(1)$?

Computational Window

Use a tabular approach to compute the area under the curve $y = f(x)$ on each interval given in Problems 38–42 as the limit of a sum of terms.
38. $f(x) = 4x$ on [0, 1]
39. $f(x) = x^2$ on [0, 4]
40. $f(x) = \cos x$ on $\left[-\frac{\pi}{2}, 0\right]$. Compare with Problem 16.
41. $f(x) = x + \sin x$ on $\left[0, \frac{\pi}{4}\right]$. Compare with Problem 17.
42. **a.** Use the tabular approach to compute the area under the curve $y = \sin x + \cos x$ on the interval $\left[0, \frac{\pi}{2}\right]$ as the limit of a sum.
    b. Let $f(x) = \sin x + \cos x$ and note that $g(x) = -\cos x + \sin x$ satisfies $g'(x) = f(x)$ on the interval $\left[0, \frac{\pi}{2}\right]$. Verify that the area computed in part **a** satisfies $A = g\left(\frac{\pi}{2}\right) - g(0)$.
    c. The function $h(x) = -\cos x + \sin x + C$ for constant C also satisfies $h'(x) = f(x)$. Is it true that the area in part **a** satisfies $A = h\left(\frac{\pi}{2}\right) - h(0)$?

Ⓒ 43. Derive the formula
$$\sum_{k=1}^{n} k = 1 + 2 + 3 + \cdots + n = \frac{n(n + 1)}{2}$$
by completing these steps:
a. Use the properties of sum in Theorem 4.1 to show that
$$\sum_{k=1}^{n} k = \frac{1}{2} \sum_{k=1}^{n} [k^2 - (k - 1)^2] + \frac{1}{2} \sum_{k=1}^{n} 1$$
$$= \frac{1}{2} \sum_{k=1}^{n} [k^2 - (k - 1)^2] + \frac{1}{2} n$$
b. Show that $\sum_{k=1}^{n} [k^2 - (k - 1)^2] = n^2$

Hint: Expand the sum by writing out a few terms. Note the internal cancellation.

c. Combine parts **a** and **b** to show that $\sum_{k=1}^{n} k = \dfrac{n(n+1)}{2}$.

44. First find constants a, b, c, and d such that

$$k^3 = a[k^4 - (k-1)^4] + bk^2 + ck + d$$

and then modify the approach outlined in Problem 43 to establish the formula

$$\sum_{k=1}^{n} k^2 = \frac{n(n+1)(2n+1)}{6}$$

45. The purpose of this problem is to show that the definition of area that uses the right endpoint of each subinterval is not the only way to approximate the area under a curve. Specifically, we shall find the area A under the parabola $y = x^2$ on the interval $[0, 1]$ in several ways.
Verify that

$$\lim_{n \to +\infty} \sum_{k=1}^{n} \left(\frac{k-1}{n}\right)^2 \left(\frac{1}{n}\right) = \frac{1}{3}$$

Compare this with the procedure outlined in Problem 43. Note that when the interval $[0, 1]$ is subdivided into n

equal parts, the kth subinterval is

$$\left(\frac{k-1}{n}, \frac{k}{n}\right)$$

This formula uses approximating rectangles with heights taken at the *left* endpoints.

46. Develop a formula for area based on approximating rectangles with heights taken at the *midpoints* of subintervals.

47. Use the properties of real numbers to establish the summation formulas in Theorem 4.1. For example, to prove the linearity rule, use the associative, commutative, and distributive properties of real numbers to note that

$$\sum_{k=1}^{n}(ca_k + db_k) = (ca_1 + db_1)$$
$$+ (ca_2 + db_2) + \cdots + (ca_n + db_n)$$
$$= (ca_1 + ca_2 + \cdots + ca_n) + (db_1 + db_2 + \cdots + db_n)$$
$$= c(a_1 + a_2 + \cdots a_n) + d(b_1 + b_2 + \cdots b_n)$$
$$= c\sum_{k=1}^{n} a_k + d\sum_{k=1}^{n} b_k$$

4.2 RIEMANN SUMS AND THE DEFINITE INTEGRAL

Historical Note

GEORG FRIEDRICH BERNHARD
RIEMANN (1826–1866)

We meet Riemann in this section in the context of what we call Riemann sums. In his personal life he was frail, bashful, and timid, but in his professional life he was one of the giants in mathematical history. He is known for his work in geometry (for example, Riemannian geometry and Riemann surfaces) and analysis. In

IN THIS SECTION Riemann sum, definite integral, area as an integral, distance as an integral, properties of the definite integral
We shall soon discover that not just area, but also such useful quantities as distance, volume, mass, and work, can be first approximated by sums and then obtained exactly by taking a limit involving the approximating sums. The special kind of limit of a sum that appears in this context is called the *definite integral*, and the process of finding integrals is called *definite integration* or *Riemann integration* in honor of the German mathematician Bernhard Riemann (1826–1866), who pioneered this approach. In this section, we describe integration as a generalization of the method for computing area introduced in Section 4.1. You should also note the last paragraph of the Preview on page 273 in anticipation of one of the greatest labor-saving devices known to humankind—namely, the fundamental theorem of calculus, which will be developed in Section 4.3.

■ RIEMANN SUMS

Recall from Section 4.1 that to find the area under the continuous curve $y = f(x)$ on the closed interval $[a, b]$ where $f(x) \geq 0$, we first partitioned the interval into n subintervals of equal width $\Delta x = \dfrac{b-a}{n}$. Then we evaluated f at the right endpoint $a + k\Delta x$ of the kth subinterval for $k = 1, 2, \ldots, n$ and formed the approximating sum of the areas of the n rectangles, which we denoted by S_n. Because we expect the estimates S_n to improve as Δx decreases, we *defined* the area A under the curve, above the x-axis, and bounded by the lines $x = a$ and $x = b$ to be the limit of S_n as $\Delta x \to 0$. Thus, we write

$$A = \lim_{n \to +\infty} \sum_{k=1}^{n} f(a + k\Delta x)\,\Delta x$$

his book, *Space Through the Ages*, Cornelius Lanczos said, "Although Riemann's collected papers fill only one single volume of 538 pages, this volume weighs tons if measured intellectually. Every one of his many discoveries was destined to change the course of mathematical science."

if this limit exists. This means that A can be estimated to any desired degree of accuracy by approximating the sum S_n with Δx sufficiently small (or, equivalently, n sufficiently large).

This approach to the area problem contains the essentials of integration, but there is no compelling reason for the partition points to be evenly spaced or to insist on evaluating f at right endpoints. These conventions are for convenience of computation, but to accommodate applications other than area, it is necessary to consider a more general type of approximating sum and to specify what is meant by the limit of such sums. The approximating sums that occur in integration problems are called **Riemann sums,** and the following definition contains a step-by-step description of how such sums are formed.

Riemann Sum

Suppose a function f is given, along with a closed interval $[a, b]$ on which f is defined. Then:

Step 1: Partition the interval $[a, b]$ into n subintervals by choosing points $\{x_0, x_1, \ldots, x_n\}$ arranged in such a way that

$$a = x_0 < x_1 < x_2 < \cdots < x_{n-1} < x_n = b$$

Call this partition P. For $k = 1, 2, \ldots, n$, the kth subinterval width is $\Delta x_k = x_k - x_{k-1}$. The largest of these widths is called the **norm** of the partition P and is denoted by $\|P\|$; that is,

$$\|P\| = \max_{k=1,2,\ldots,n} \{\Delta x_k\}$$

Step 2: Choose a number arbitrarily from each subinterval. For $k = 1, 2, \ldots, n$, the number x_k^* chosen from the kth subinterval is called the kth *subinterval representative* of the partition P.

Step 3: Form the sum

$$R_n = f(x_1^*)\Delta x_1 + f(x_2^*)\Delta x_2 + \cdots + f(x_n^*)\Delta x_n = \sum_{k=1}^{n} f(x_k^*)\Delta x_k$$

This is the **Riemann sum** associated with f, the given partition P, and the chosen subinterval representatives $x_1^*, x_2^*, \ldots, x_n^*$.

■ *What This Says*: This is a generalization of the area calculations of the last section. *Whenever* we formulate the sum

$$\sum_{k=1}^{n} f(x_k^*)\Delta x_k$$

it is called a *Riemann sum*. Riemann sums are generally used to produce the correct integral for a particular application. Note that the Riemann sum *does not* require that the function f be nonnegative and also allows that x_k^* is *any* point in the kth subinterval.

EXAMPLE 1   Formation of the Riemann sum for a given function

Suppose the interval $[-2, 1]$ is partitioned into 6 subintervals with subdivision points $a = x_0 = -2$, $x_1 = -1.6$, $x_2 = -0.93$, $x_3 = -0.21$, $x_4 = 0.35$, $x_5 = 0.82$, and $x_6 = 1 = b$. Find the norm of this partition P and the Riemann sum associated with the function $f(x) = 2x$, the given partition, and the subinterval representatives $x_1^* = -1.81$, $x_2^* = -1.12$, $x_3^* = -0.55$, $x_4^* = -0.17$, $x_5^* = 0.43$, and $x_6^* = 0.94$.

Solution   Before we can find the norm of the partition or the required Riemann sum, we must compute the subinterval width Δx_k and evaluate f at each subinterval representative x_k^*. These values are shown in Figure 4.4 and the table of computations on page 268.

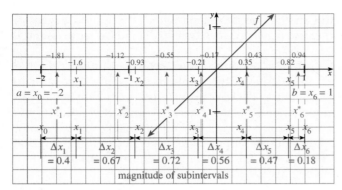

Figure 4.4 Partition for a Riemann sum

k	Given $x_k - x_{k-1} = \Delta x_k$	Given $\downarrow$ x_k^*	$f(x_k^*) = 2(x_k^*)$
1	$-1.6 - (-2) = 0.40$	-1.81	-3.62
2	$-0.93 - (-1.6) = 0.67$	-1.12	-2.24
3	$-0.21 - (-0.93) = 0.72$	-0.55	-1.10
4	$0.35 - (-0.21) = 0.56$	-0.17	-0.34
5	$0.82 - 0.35 = 0.47$	0.43	0.86
6	$1.00 - 0.82 = 0.18$	0.94	1.88

⊘ Notice from Example 1 that the Riemann sum does not necessarily represent an area. The sum found is negative (and area must be nonnegative). ⊘

From the table, we see that the largest subinterval width is $\Delta x_3 = 0.72$, so the partition has norm $\|P\| = 0.72$. Finally, by using the definition, we compute the Riemann sum:

$$R_6 = (-3.62)(0.4) + (-2.24)(0.67) + (-1.10)(0.72) + (-0.34)(0.56)$$
$$+ (0.86)(0.47) + (1.88)(0.18) \approx -3.1886 \approx -3.19$$

■ THE DEFINITE INTEGRAL

By comparing the formula for Riemann sum with that of area in the last section, we recognize that the sum S_n used to approximate area is actually a special kind of Riemann sum which has

$$\Delta x_k = \Delta x = \frac{b-a}{n} \quad \text{and} \quad x_k^* = a + k\Delta x$$

for $k = 1, 2, \ldots, n$. Because each subinterval in the partition P associated with S_n has width Δx, the norm of the partition is

$$\|P\| = \Delta x = \frac{b-a}{n}$$

This kind of partition is called a **regular partition.** When we express the area under the curve $y = f(x)$ as $A = \lim_{\Delta x \to 0} S_n$, we are actually saying that A can be estimated to any desired accuracy by finding a Riemann sum of the form S_n with norm

$$\|P\| = \frac{b-a}{n}$$

sufficiently small. We use this interpretation as a model for the following definition.

Definite Integral

If f is defined on the closed interval $[a, b]$ we say f is **integrable** on $[a, b]$ if

$$I = \lim_{\|P\| \to 0} \sum_{k=1}^{n} f(x_k^*) \Delta x_k$$

exists. This limit is called the **definite integral** of f from a to b. The definite integral is denoted by

$$I = \int_a^b f(x)\, dx \quad \text{or} \quad I = \int_{x=a}^{x=b} f(x)\, dx$$

The latter is used if we wish to emphasize the variable of integration.

■ *What this says*: If the limit of a Riemann sum of f as $\|P\| \to 0$ exists and is finite, then we say that f is *integrable*. In particular, it means that the number I can be approximated to any prescribed degree of accuracy by any Riemann sum of f with norm sufficiently small. As long as we remember the conditions of this theorem (that is, f is defined on a closed interval and that the limit of the Riemann sum exists), it can be summarized by writing

$$\int_a^b f(x)\,dx = \lim_{\|P\|\to 0} \sum_{k=1}^{n} f(x_k^*)\Delta x_k$$

Formally, I is the definite integral of f on $[a, b]$ if for each number $\varepsilon > 0$, there exists a number $\delta > 0$ such that if

$$\sum_{k=1}^{n} f(x_k^*)\Delta x_k$$

is any Riemann sum of f whose norm satisfies $\|P\| < \delta$, then

$$\left| I - \sum_{k=1}^{n} f(x_k^*)\Delta x_k \right| < \varepsilon$$

In advanced calculus, it is shown that when this limit exists, it is unique. Moreover, its value is independent of the particular way in which the partitions of $[a, b]$ and the subinterval representatives x_k^* are chosen.

Consider the notation used in the margin. The function f that is being integrated is called the **integrand;** the interval $[a, b]$ is the **interval of integration;** and the endpoints a and b are called, respectively, the **lower and upper limits of integration.**

In the special case where $a = b$, the interval of integration $[a, b]$ is really just a point, and the integral of any function on this "interval" is defined to be 0; that is,

$$\int_a^a f(x)\,dx = 0$$

Also, at times, we shall consider integrals in which the lower limit of integration is a larger number than the upper limit. To handle this case, we specify that the integral from b to a is the *opposite* of the integral from a to b:

$$\int_b^a f(x)\,dx = -\int_a^b f(x)\,dx$$

To summarize:

Upper limit of integration
↓
integrand
$$\int_a^b \overbrace{f(x)}\,dx$$
Lower limit of integration

Definite Integral at a Point

$$\int_a^a f(x)\,dx = 0$$

Opposite of a Definite Integral

$$\int_b^a f(x)\,dx = -\int_a^b f(x)\,dx$$

At first, the definition of the definite integral may seem rather imposing. How are we to tell whether a given function f is integrable on an interval $[a, b]$? If f is integrable, how are we supposed to compute the definite integral? Answering these questions is not easy, but in advanced calculus, it is shown that f is integrable on a closed interval $[a, b]$ if it is continuous on the interval except at a finite number of points and if it is bounded on the interval (that is, there is a number $A > 0$ such that $|f(x)| < A$ for all x in the interval). We will state a special case of this result as a theorem.

THEOREM 4.2   Existence of Riemann sum

If f is continuous on an interval $[a, b]$, then f is integrable on $[a, b]$.

Proof: The proof is found in most advanced calculus textbooks.   ∎

Our next example illustrates how to use the definition to find a definite integral.

EXAMPLE 2   Evaluating a definite integral using the definition

Evaluate $\displaystyle\int_{-2}^{1} 4x \, dx$.

Solution   We note the variable of integration is x, so we interpret this as

$$\int_{x=-2}^{x=1} 4x \, dx$$

The integral exists because $f(x) = 4x$ is continuous on $[-2, 1]$. Because the integral can be computed by any partition whose norm approaches 0 (that is, the integral is independent of the sequence of partitions *and* the subinterval representatives), we shall simplify matters by choosing a partition in which the points are evenly spaced. Specifically, we divide the interval $[-2, 1]$ into n subintervals, each of width

$$\Delta x = \frac{1 - (-2)}{n} = \frac{3}{n}$$

For each k, we choose the kth subinterval representative to be the right endpoint of the kth subinterval; that is,

$$x_k^* = -2 + k\Delta x = -2 + k\left(\frac{3}{n}\right)$$

Finally, we form the Riemann sum

$$
\begin{aligned}
\int_{-2}^{1} 4x \, dx &= \lim_{\|P\|\to 0} \sum_{k=1}^{n} f(x_k^*)\Delta x \\
&= \lim_{n\to+\infty} \sum_{k=1}^{n} 4\left(-2 + \frac{3k}{n}\right)\left(\frac{3}{n}\right) \qquad n \to +\infty \text{ as } \|P\| \to 0 \\
&= \lim_{n\to+\infty} \frac{12}{n^2} \sum_{k=1}^{n} (-2n + 3k) \\
&= \lim_{n\to+\infty} \frac{12}{n^2}\left(\sum_{k=1}^{n}(-2n) + \sum_{k=1}^{n} 3k\right) \\
&= \lim_{n\to+\infty} \frac{12}{n^2}\left((-2n)n + 3\left[\frac{n(n+1)}{2}\right]\right) \qquad \textit{Formula for the sum of integers} \\
&= \lim_{n\to+\infty} \frac{12}{n^2}\left(\frac{-4n^2 + 3n^2 + 3n}{2}\right) \\
&= \lim_{n\to+\infty} \frac{-6n^2 + 18n}{n^2} = -6
\end{aligned}
$$

■ AREA AS AN INTEGRAL

Because we have used the development of area in Section 4.1 as the model for our definition of the definite integral, it is no surprise to discover that the area under a curve can be expressed as a definite integral. However, integrals can be positive, zero, or negative (as in Example 2), and we certainly would not expect the area under a curve to be a negative number! The actual relationship between integrals and area under a curve is contained in the following observation, which follows from the definition of area as the limit of a sum along with Theorem 4.2.

Area As an Integral

⊘ We will find areas using a definite integral, but not every definite integral can be interpreted as an area. ⊘

> Suppose f is continuous and $f(x) \geq 0$ on the closed interval $[a, b]$. Then the area under the curve $y = f(x)$ on $[a, b]$ is given by the definite integral of f on $[a, b]$. That is,
>
> $$\text{Area} = \int_a^b f(x)\, dx$$

Usually we find area by evaluating a definite integral, but sometimes area can be used to help us evaluate the integral. At this stage of our study, it is not easy to evaluate Riemann sums, so if you happen to recognize that the integral represents the area of some common geometric figure, you can use the known formula instead of the definite integral, as shown in Example 3.

EXAMPLE 3   Evaluating an integral using an area formula

Evaluate $\displaystyle\int_{-3}^{3} \sqrt{9 - x^2}\, dx$.

Solution   Let $f(x) = \sqrt{9 - x^2}$. The curve $y = \sqrt{9 - x^2}$ is a semicircle centered at the origin of radius 3, as shown in Figure 4.5. From geometry, we know the area of the circle is $A = \pi r^2 = \pi(3)^2 = 9\pi$. Thus, the area of the semicircle is $\frac{9\pi}{2}$, so

$$\int_{-3}^{3} \sqrt{9 - x^2}\, dx = \frac{9\pi}{2}$$

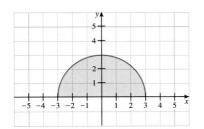

Figure 4.5 The curve $y = \sqrt{9 - x^2}$ is a semicircle of radius 3.

■ DISTANCE AS AN INTEGRAL

Many quantities other than area can be computed as the limit of a sum. For example, suppose an object moving along a line is known to have continuous velocity $v(t)$ for each time t between $t = a$ and $t = b$, and we wish to compute the total distance traveled by the object during this time period.

Suppose the interval $[a, b]$ is partitioned into n equal subintervals, each of length $\Delta t = \dfrac{b - a}{n}$, as indicated in Figure 4.6. The kth subinterval is

The distance is $\Delta s = v[a + (k - 1)\Delta t](\Delta t)$.

Figure 4.6 The distance traveled during the kth time subinterval

$[a + (k - 1)\Delta t, a + k\Delta t]$, and if Δt is small enough, the velocity $v(t)$ will not change much over the subinterval; so it is reasonable to approximate $v(t)$ by the constant value $v[a + (k - 1)\Delta t]$ throughout the entire subinterval.

The corresponding change in the object's position will be approximated by the product

$$v[a + (k - 1)\Delta t]\Delta t$$

This change will be positive if $v[a + (k - 1)\Delta t]$ is positive and negative otherwise. Both cases may be summarized by the formula

$$|v[a + (k - 1)\Delta t]|\Delta t$$

and the total distance traveled by the object as t varies from $t = a$ to $t = b$ is given by the sum

$$S_n = \sum_{k=1}^{n} |v[a + (k - 1)\Delta t]|\Delta t$$

We recognize this as a Riemann sum and can make it more and more precise by taking more refined partitions (that is, shorter time intervals Δt). Therefore, it is reasonable to *define* the exact distance S traveled as the limit of the sum S_n as $\Delta t \to 0$, or, equivalently, as $n \to +\infty$, so that

$$S = \lim_{n \to +\infty} \sum_{k=1}^{n} |v[a + (k - 1)\Delta t]|\Delta t = \int_a^b |v(t)|dt$$

To summarize:

Distance

The **distance traveled** by an object moving with continuous velocity $v(t)$ along a straight line from time $t = a$ to $t = b$ is
$$S = \int_a^b |v(t)|dt$$

Sometimes we are more interested in where the object is at the end of a given time interval than in the total distance it has traveled. The difference between the object's final position and its initial position is called its **displacement** and is given by

$$[\text{displacement}] \quad D = \int_a^b v(t)dt$$

Thus, an object that moves forward 2 units and back 3 on a given time interval has moved a total distance of 5 units, but its displacement is -1 because it ends up 1 unit to the left of its initial position.

EXAMPLE 4   Distance moved by an object whose velocity is known

An object moves along a straight line with velocity $v(t) = t^2$ for $t > 0$. How far does the object travel between times $t = 1$ and $t = 2$?

Solution   We have $a = 1$, $b = 2$, and $\Delta t = \dfrac{2 - 1}{n} = \dfrac{1}{n}$; therefore, the required distance is

$$S = \int_{t=1}^{t=2} |v(t)|dt = \lim_{n \to +\infty} \sum_{k=1}^{n} \left|v\left[1 + (k - 1)\left(\frac{1}{n}\right)\right]\right|\left(\frac{1}{n}\right)$$

$$= \lim_{n \to \infty} \sum_{k=1}^{n} \left|v\left(\frac{n + k - 1}{n}\right)\right|\left(\frac{1}{n}\right) = \lim_{n \to \infty} \sum_{k=1}^{n} \frac{(n + k - 1)^2}{n^2}\left(\frac{1}{n}\right)$$

$$= \lim_{n \to \infty} \frac{1}{n^3} \sum_{k=1}^{n} [(n^2 - 2n + 1) + k^2 + 2(n - 1)k]$$

$$= \lim_{n \to \infty} \frac{1}{n^3} \left[(n^2 - 2n + 1) \sum_{k=1}^{n} 1 + \sum_{k=1}^{n} k^2 + 2(n - 1) \sum_{k=1}^{n} k \right]$$

$$= \lim_{n \to \infty} \frac{1}{n^3} \left[(n^2 - 2n + 1)n + \frac{n(n + 1)(2n + 1)}{6} + 2(n - 1)\frac{n(n + 1)}{2} \right]$$

$$= \lim_{n \to \infty} \frac{14n^3 - 9n^2 + n}{6n^3} = \frac{14}{6} = \frac{7}{3}$$

Thus, we expect the object to travel $\frac{7}{3}$ units during the time interval $[1, 2]$. ▬

PREVIEW

Students often become discouraged at this point, especially after looking at the amount of "work" necessary to complete Example 4, so we offer an encouraging word. Recall the definition of derivative in Chapter 1. It was difficult to find derivatives using the definition, but we soon proved some theorems to make it easier to find and evaluate derivatives. The same is true of integration. It is difficult to apply the definition of a definite integral. However, we will soon have some theorems to make your work easier when working with certain types of functions. As a preview of what is to come, consider an object moving along a straight line with displacement $s(t)$ and velocity $v(t)$. We know from Chapter 2 that these are related by the equation $v(t) = s'(t)$. If the object is always moving forward, $v(t) > 0$, for all t in the time interval $[a, b]$, then the total distance traveled by the object during this time interval is $S = s(b) - s(a)$. However, by comparing the definition of area as the limit of a sum with the formula for S:

$$S = \lim_{n \to +\infty} \sum_{k=1}^{n} v[a + (k - 1)\Delta t]\Delta t$$

we see that the total distance S also equals the area under the graph of $v(t)$ on the interval $[a, b]$. That is:

If $v(t)$ is a continuous function that satisfies $v(t) > 0$ on the interval $[a, b]$, then the area under the curve $y = v(t)$ on the interval $[a, b]$ is equal to
$$s(b) - s(a)$$
where $s(t)$ satisfies $s'(t) = v(t)$ throughout $[a, b]$.

This observation anticipates the *fundamental theorem of calculus*, which provides a vital link between differential and integral calculus. We shall formally introduce the fundamental theorem in Section 4.3 and use it in all subsequent work.

Notice how our observation applies to Example 4, where $v(t) = t^2$ and the interval is $[1, 2]$. It is easy to verify that if $g(t) = \frac{1}{3}t^3$, then $g'(t) = v(t)$. Thus, the total distance traveled by the object during the time interval $[1, 2]$ is

$$S = g(2) - g(1) = \left[\frac{1}{3}(2)^3 - \frac{1}{3}(1)^3 \right] = \frac{7}{3}$$

which coincides with the result found numerically in Example 4. Incidentally, note that $h(t) = \frac{1}{3}t^3 + C$ also satisfies $h'(t) = v(t)$ for any constant C. What happens if you try to compute the distance S using $h(t)$ instead of $g(t)$?

By considering the distance as an integral, we see that zero or negative values of a definite integral can also be interpreted physically. When $v(t) > 0$ on a time

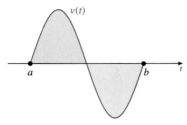

a. Net displacement of 0

There is as much area under the positive part of the velocity curve as there is above the negative part.

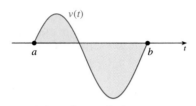

b. Negative net displacement

There is more area above the negative part of the velocity curve than there is under the positive part.

Figure 4.7 Definite integral in terms of displacement

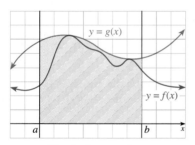

a. The *dominance rule*
If $g(x) \geq f(x)$, the area under $y = g(x)$ can be no less than the area under $y = f(x)$.

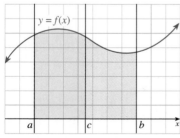

b. The *subdivision rule*
The area under $y = f(x)$ on $[a, b]$ equals the sum of the areas $[a, c]$ and $[c, b]$.

Figure 4.8 Comparison of dominance and subdivision rules

interval $[a, b]$, then the total distance S traveled by the object between times $t = a$ and $t = b$ is the same as the area under the graph of $v(t)$ on $[a, b]$.

When $v(t) > 0$, the object moves forward, but when $v(t) < 0$, it reverses direction and moves backward (to the left). In the general case where $v(t)$ changes sign on the time interval $[a, b]$, the integral

$$\int_a^b v(t)\, dt$$

measures the net displacement of the object, taking into account both forward and backward motion.

For example, for the velocity function $v(t)$ graphed in Figure 4.7a, the net distance traveled is 0 because the area above the t-axis is the same as the area below, but in Figure 4.7b, there is more area below the t-axis, which means the net distance is negative, and the object ends up "behind" (to the left of) its starting position.

■ PROPERTIES OF THE DEFINITE INTEGRAL

In computations involving integrals, it is often helpful to use the three general properties listed in the following theorem.

THEOREM 4.3   General properties of the definite integral

Linearity rule   If f and g are integrable on $[a, b]$, then so is $rf + sg$ for constants r, s.

$$\int_a^b [rf(x) + sg(x)]\, dx = r \int_a^b f(x)\, dx + s \int_a^b g(x)\, dx$$

Dominance rule   If f and g are integrable on $[a, b]$ and $f(x) \leq g(x)$ throughout this interval, then

$$\int_a^b f(x)\, dx \leq \int_a^b g(x)\, dx$$

Subdivision rule   For any number c such that $a < c < b$

$$\int_a^b f(x)\, dx = \int_a^c f(x)\, dx + \int_c^b f(x)\, dx$$

assuming all three integrals exist.

Proof: Each of these rules can be established by using a familiar property of sums with the definition of the definite integral. For example, to derive the linearity rule, we note that any Riemann sum of the function $rf + sg$ can be expressed as

$$\sum_{k=1}^n [rf(x_k^*) + sg(x_k^*)]\Delta x_k = r\left[\sum_{k=1}^n f(x_k^*)\Delta x_k\right] + s\left[\sum_{k=1}^n g(x_k^*)\Delta x_k\right]$$

and the linearity rule then follows by taking the limit on each side of this equation as the norm of the partition tends to 0.   ■

The dominance rule and the subdivision rule are interpreted geometrically for nonnegative functions in Figure 4.8.

Notice that if $f(x) \geq g(x) \geq 0$, the curve $y = g(x)$ is always above (or touching) the curve $y = f(x)$, and the dominance rule expresses the fact that the area under the upper curve $y = g(x)$ cannot be less than the area under the area under $y = f(x)$. The subdivision rule says that the area under $y = f(x)$ above $[a, b]$ is the sum of the area on $[a, c]$ and the area on $[c, b]$. We close with an example that illustrates one way of using the subdivision rule.

EXAMPLE 5   Subdivision rule

If $\displaystyle\int_{-2}^{1} f(x)\,dx = 3$ and $\displaystyle\int_{-2}^{7} f(x)\,dx = -5$, what is $\displaystyle\int_{1}^{7} f(x)\,dx$?

Solution   According to the subdivision rule, we have

$$\int_{-2}^{7} f(x)\,dx = \int_{-2}^{1} f(x)\,dx + \int_{1}^{7} f(x)\,dx$$

Therefore,

$$\int_{1}^{7} f(x)\,dx = \int_{-2}^{7} f(x)\,dx - \int_{-2}^{1} f(x)\,dx = (-5) - 3 = -8$$ ■

PROBLEM SET 4.2

A *In Problems 1–8, estimate (using right endpoints) the given integral $\displaystyle\int_{a}^{b} f(x)\,dx$ by using a Riemann sum*

$$S_n = \sum_{k=1}^{n} f(a + k\Delta x)\,\Delta x \text{ for } n = 4.$$

1. $\displaystyle\int_{0}^{1} (2x + 1)\,dx$

2. $\displaystyle\int_{0}^{1} (4x^2 + 2)\,dx$

3. $\displaystyle\int_{1}^{3} x^2\,dx$

4. $\displaystyle\int_{0}^{2} x^3\,dx$

5. $\displaystyle\int_{0}^{1} (1 - 3x)\,dx$

6. $\displaystyle\int_{1}^{3} (x^2 - x^3)\,dx$

7. $\displaystyle\int_{-\pi/2}^{0} \cos x\,dx$

8. $\displaystyle\int_{0}^{\pi/4} (x + \sin x)\,dx$

In Problems 9–12, $v(t)$ is the velocity of an object moving along a straight line. Use the formula

$$S_n = \sum_{k=1}^{n} v[a + (k-1)\Delta t]\,\Delta t$$

where $\Delta t = \dfrac{b-a}{n}$ to estimate the total distance traveled by the object during the time interval $[a, b]$. Let $n = 4$ for Problems 9–12.

9. $v(t) = 3t + 1$ on $[1, 4]$

10. $v(t) = 1 + 2t$ on $[1, 2]$

11. $v(t) = \sin t$ on $[0, \pi]$

12. $v(t) = \cos t$ on $\left[0, \frac{\pi}{2}\right]$

Evaluate each of the integrals in Problems 13–18 by using the following information together with the linearity and subdivision properties:

$$\int_{-1}^{2} x^2\,dx = 3; \int_{-1}^{0} x^2\,dx = \tfrac{1}{3}; \int_{-1}^{2} x\,dx = \tfrac{3}{2}; \int_{0}^{2} x\,dx = 2$$

13. $\displaystyle\int_{0}^{-1} x^2\,dx$

14. $\displaystyle\int_{-1}^{2} (x^2 + x)\,dx$

15. $\displaystyle\int_{-1}^{2} (2x^2 - 3x)\,dx$

16. $\displaystyle\int_{0}^{2} x^2\,dx$

17. $\displaystyle\int_{-1}^{0} x\,dx$

18. $\displaystyle\int_{-1}^{0} (3x^2 - 5x)\,dx$

Use the dominance property of integrals to establish the given inequality in Problems 19–20.

19. $\displaystyle\int_{0}^{1} x^3\,dx \leq \tfrac{1}{2}$ *Hint:* Note that $x^3 \leq x$ on $[0, 1]$.

20. $\displaystyle\int_{0}^{\pi} \sin x\,dx \leq \pi$ *Hint:* $\sin x \leq 1$ for all x.

B **21.** Given $\displaystyle\int_{-2}^{4} [5f(x) + 2g(x)]\,dx = 7$ and $\displaystyle\int_{-2}^{4} [3f(x) + g(x)]\,dx = 4$,

find $\displaystyle\int_{-2}^{4} f(x)\,dx$ and $\displaystyle\int_{-2}^{4} g(x)\,dx$.

22. Suppose $\displaystyle\int_{0}^{2} f(x)\,dx = 3$, $\displaystyle\int_{0}^{2} g(x)\,dx = -1$, and $\displaystyle\int_{0}^{2} h(x)\,dx = 3$.

a. Evaluate $\displaystyle\int_{0}^{2} [2f(x) + 5g(x) - 7h(x)]\,dx$.

b. Find s such that $\displaystyle\int_{0}^{2} [5f(x) + sg(x) - 6h(x)]\,dx = 0$

23. Evaluate $\displaystyle\int_{-1}^{2} f(x)\,dx$ given that

$$\int_{-1}^{1} f(x)\,dx = 3; \int_{2}^{3} f(x)\,dx = -2; \int_{1}^{3} f(x)\,dx = 5$$

24. Let $f(x) = \begin{cases} 2 & \text{for } -1 \leq x \leq 1 \\ 3 - x & \text{for } 1 < x < 4 \\ 2x - 9 & \text{for } 4 \leq x \leq 5 \end{cases}$

Sketch the graph of f on the interval $[-1, 5]$ and show that f is continuous on this interval. Then use Theorem 4.3 to evaluate

$$\int_{-1}^{5} f(x)\, dx$$

25. Let $f(x) = \begin{cases} 5 & \text{for } -3 \leq x \leq -1 \\ 4 - x & \text{for } -1 < x < 2 \\ 2x - 2 & \text{for } 2 \leq x \leq 5 \end{cases}$

Sketch the graph of f on the interval $[-3, 5]$ and show that f is continuous on this interval. Then use Theorem 4.3 to evaluate

$$\int_{-3}^{5} f(x)\, dx$$

© 26. Generalize the subdivision property by showing that for $a \leq c \leq d \leq b$,

$$\int_a^b f(x)\, dx = \int_a^c f(x)\, dx + \int_c^d f(x)\, dx + \int_d^b f(x)\, dx$$

whenever all these integrals exist.

27. For any constants C and D, show that

$$\int_a^b (Cx + D)\, dx = (b - a)\left[\frac{C}{2}(b + a) + D\right]$$

Hint: Sketch the region under the line $y = Cx + D$, and express the integral as an area.

28. For $b > a > 0$, show that

$$\int_a^b x^2\, dx = \frac{1}{3}(b^3 - a^3)$$

In Problems 29–31, use the partition $P = \{-1, -0.2, 0.9, 1.3, 1.7, 2\}$ on the interval $[-1, 2]$.

29. Find the subinterval widths

$$\Delta x_k = x_k - x_{k-1}$$

for $k = 1, 2, \ldots, 5$. What is the norm of P?

30. Compute the Riemann sum associated with $f(x) = 4 - 5x$, the partition P, and the subinterval representatives $x_1^* = -0.5$, $x_2^* = 0.8$, $x_3^* = 1$, $x_4^* = 1.3$, $x_5^* = 1.8$.

31. Compute the Riemann sum associated with $f(x) = x^3$, the partition P, and the subinterval representatives $x_1^* = -1$, $x_2^* = 0$, $x_3^* = 1$, $x_4^* = \frac{128}{81}$, and $x_5^* = \frac{125}{64}$.

32. If the numbers a_k and b_k satisfy $a_k \leq b_k$ for $k = 1, 2, \ldots, n$, then $\sum_{k=1}^{n} a_k \leq \sum_{k=1}^{n} b_k$. Use this dominance property of sums to establish the dominance property of integrals.

33. THINK TANK PROBLEM   Either prove that the following result is generally true or find a counterexample: If $f(x)$ is not identically zero on the interval $[a, b]$, then

$$\int_a^b f(x)\, dx \neq 0$$

for some x-value on $[a, b]$.

34. THINK TANK PROBLEM   Either prove that the following result is generally true or find a counterexample: If f and g are continuous on $[a, b]$, then

$$\int_a^b f(x)g(x)\, dx = \left[\int_a^b f(x)\, dx\right]\left[\int_a^b g(x)\, dx\right]$$

35. a. If $f(x) < 0$ on the interval $[a, b]$, show that

$$\int_a^b f(x)\, dx = -A$$

where A is the area under the graph of $y = -f(x)$ on $[a, b]$.

b. Combine the formula in part **a** with the formula of Theorem 4.3 to show that

$$\int_a^b f(x)\, dx = P - N$$

where P is the sum of the area of all positive regions ($f(x) > 0$) and N is the sum of the area of all negative regions ($f(x) < 0$).

c. Use the formula in part **b** to evaluate

$$\int_{-2}^{1} 2x\, dx.$$

4.3 THE FUNDAMENTAL THEOREM OF CALCULUS; INTEGRATION BY SUBSTITUTION

IN THIS SECTION **The fundamental theorem of calculus, substitution with indefinite integration, substitution with definite integration**
We have found that the value of a definite integral can be approximated numerically, and by using summation formulas we can compute some integrals algebraically. These methods are messy, and it is doubtful that integration would be the powerful mathematical tool it is if these were the only ways to compute integrals. The fundamental theorem of calculus, presented in this section, gives us a means of evaluating many integrals. We shall study techniques of integration in Chapter 7, but one such technique, the *method of substitution*, is so fundamental that it is useful to have it now.

■ THE FUNDAMENTAL THEOREM OF CALCULUS

In the last section we found that if $v(t)$ is the velocity of an object at time t as it moves along a straight line, then

$$\int_a^b v(t)\, dt = s(b) - s(a)$$

where $s(t)$ is the displacement of the object and satisfies $s'(t) = v(t)$. This result is an application of a general theorem discovered by the English mathematician Isaac Barrow (1630–1677), who was Newton's mentor at Cambridge.

THEOREM 4.4   The fundamental theorem of calculus

If f is continuous on the interval $[a, b]$ and F is any function that satisfies $F'(x) = f(x)$ throughout this interval, then

$$\int_a^b f(x)\, dx = F(b) - F(a)$$

Proof: Let $P = \{x_0, x_1, x_2, \ldots, x_n\}$ be a regular partition of the interval, with subinterval widths $\Delta x = \dfrac{b-a}{n}$. Note that F satisfies the hypotheses of the mean value theorem (Theorem 3.4, Section 3.2) on each of the closed subintervals $[x_{k-1}, x_k]$. Thus, the MVT tells us that there is a point x_k^* in each open subinterval (x_{k-1}, x_k) for which

$$\frac{F(x_k) - F(x_{k-1})}{x_k - x_{k-1}} = F'(x_k^*) \quad \text{or} \quad F(x_k) - F(x_{k-1}) = F'(x_k^*)(x_k - x_{k-1})$$

Because $F'(x_k^*) = f(x_k^*)$ and $x_k - x_{k-1} = \Delta x = \dfrac{b-a}{n}$, we can write $F(x_k) - F(x_{k-1}) = f(x_k^*)\Delta x$, so that

$$F(x_1) - F(x_0) = f(x_1^*)\Delta x$$
$$F(x_2) - F(x_1) = f(x_2^*)\Delta x$$
$$\vdots$$
$$F(x_n) - F(x_{n-1}) = f(x_n^*)\Delta x$$

Thus, by adding both sides of all the equations, we obtain

$$\sum_{k=1}^n f(x_k^*)\Delta x = f(x_1^*)\Delta x + f(x_2^*)\Delta x + \cdots + f(x_n^*)\Delta x$$
$$= [F(x_1) - F(x_0)] + [F(x_2) - F(x_1)] + \cdots + [F(x_n) - F(x_{n-1})]$$
$$= F(x_n) - F(x_0)$$

Because $x_0 = a$ and $x_n = b$, we have

$$\sum_{k=1}^n f(x_k^*)\Delta x = F(b) - F(a)$$

Finally, we take the limit as $\|P\| \to 0$, and because $F(b) - F(a)$ is a constant, we have

$$\int_a^b f(x)\, dx = F(b) - F(a)$$

■

Recall (from Section 3.10) that an *antiderivative of a function f* is a function F that satisfies $F' = f$.

> ■ **What this says**: The definite integral $\int_a^b f(x)\,dx$ can be computed by finding an antiderivative F on the interval $[a, b]$ and evaluating it at the limits of integration a and b. Also notice that this theorem does not say *how* to find the antiderivative, nor does it say that an antiderivative F exists.

The issue of existence of an antiderivative is important, and in Section 4.5 we shall show that such an antiderivative always exists as long as f is continuous on $[a, b]$. Indeed, we consider the issue of existence just as important as the formula in the fundamental theorem. In fact, sometimes the two results are referred to as the first and second fundamental theorems of calculus.

In order to give you some insight into why this theorem is important enough to be named *the fundamental theorem of calculus*, we repeat Example 2 from Section 4.2 in the margin and then work the same example using the fundamental theorem.

EXAMPLE 1   Evaluating an antiderivative

Evaluate $\int_{-2}^{1} 4x\,dx$ using the definition of the definite integral and also using the fundamental theorem.

Solution

Solution from Section 4.2 using Riemann sums:

$$\int_{-2}^{1} 4x\,dx = \lim_{\|P\|\to 0} \sum_{k=1}^{n} f(x_k^*)\Delta x$$

$$= \lim_{n\to+\infty} \sum_{k=1}^{n} 4\left(-2 + \frac{3k}{n}\right)\left(\frac{3}{n}\right)$$

$$= \lim_{n\to+\infty} \frac{12}{n^2} \sum_{k=1}^{n} (-2n + 3k)$$

$$= \lim_{n\to+\infty} \frac{12}{n^2}\left(\sum_{k=1}^{n} (-2n) + \sum_{k=1}^{n} 3k\right)$$

$$= \lim_{n\to+\infty} \frac{12}{n^2}\left((-2n)n + 3\left[\frac{n(n+1)}{2}\right]\right)$$

$$= \lim_{n\to+\infty} \frac{12}{n^2}\left(\frac{-4n^2 + 3n^2 + 3n}{2}\right)$$

$$= \lim_{n\to+\infty} \frac{-6n^2 + 18n}{n^2}$$

$$= -6$$

Solution using the fundamental theorem of calculus:

$$\int_{-2}^{1} 4x\,dx = F(1) - F(-2)$$

where F is an antiderivative of f. If $F(x) = 2x^2$, then $F'(x) = 4x$, so F is an antiderivative of f. Thus

$$\int_{-2}^{1} 4x\,dx = 2(1)^2 - 2(-2)^2 = -6 \qquad \blacksquare$$

Henceforth, when evaluating an integral by the fundamental theorem, we shall denote the difference

$$F(b) - F(a) \text{ by } F(x)\big|_a^b, \text{ which means } F(x)\big|_{x=a}^{x=b}$$

Sometimes we also write $[F(x)]_a^b$, where $F'(x) = f(x)$ on $[a, b]$. This notation is illustrated in Example 2.

EXAMPLE 2   Finding the area under a curve using the fundamental theorem of calculus

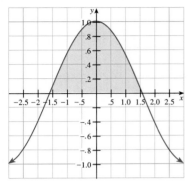

If you look at the graph of $f(x) = \cos x$ on $\left[-\frac{\pi}{2}, \frac{\pi}{2}\right]$, you can see that an area of 2 seems reasonable.

Find the area under the curve $y = \cos x$ on $\left[-\frac{\pi}{2}, \frac{\pi}{2}\right]$.

Solution   Because $f(x) = \cos x$ is continuous on $\left[-\frac{\pi}{2}, \frac{\pi}{2}\right]$, and because the derivative of $\sin x$ is $\cos x$, it follows (from the definition of antiderivative) that $\sin x$ is an antiderivative of $\cos x$. Also, because $f(x) \geq 0$, the required area is given by the integral

$$A = \int_{-\pi/2}^{\pi/2} \cos x \, dx = \sin x \Big|_{-\pi/2}^{\pi/2} = \sin \frac{\pi}{2} - \sin\left(-\frac{\pi}{2}\right) = 1 - (-1) = 2$$

The region has area $A = 2$ square units.

⊘   It is important to remember that the *definite* integral $\int_a^b f(x) \, dx$ is a number, whereas the *indefinite* integral $\int f(x) \, dx$ is a family of functions.   ⊘

The relationship between the indefinite and definite integral is given by

$$\int_a^b f(x) \, dx = \left[\int f(x) \, dx \right]\Big|_a^b$$

EXAMPLE 3   Evaluating an integral using the fundamental theorem

Evaluate   **a.** $\displaystyle\int_{-3}^{5} (-10) \, dx$ **b.** $\displaystyle\int_{4}^{9}\left[\frac{1}{\sqrt{x}} + x\right] dx$ **c.** $\displaystyle\int_{-2}^{2} |x| \, dx$

Solution

a. $\displaystyle\int_{-3}^{5} (-10) \, dx = -10x \Big|_{-3}^{5} = -10(5 + 3) = -80$

b. $\displaystyle\int_{4}^{9}\left[\frac{1}{\sqrt{x}} + x\right] dx = \int_{4}^{9} [x^{-1/2} + x] \, dx = \left[\left(\frac{x^{1/2}}{\frac{1}{2}}\right) + \frac{x^2}{2}\right]\Big|_{4}^{9}$

$$= \left(6 + \tfrac{81}{2}\right) - \left(4 + \tfrac{16}{2}\right) = 34\tfrac{1}{2}$$

c. $\displaystyle\int_{-2}^{2} |x| \, dx$ Recall,
$$|x| = x \quad \text{if } x \geq 0$$
$$|x| = -x \quad \text{if } x < 0$$

So, for
$$x \geq 0, \quad F_1(x) = \frac{x^2}{2}$$
$$x < 0, \quad F_2(x) = -\frac{x^2}{2}$$

We evaluate this integral by using the subdivision principle:

$$\int_{-2}^{2} |x| \, dx = \int_{-2}^{0} |x| \, dx + \int_{0}^{2} |x| \, dx = \int_{-2}^{0} (-x) \, dx + \int_{0}^{2} x \, dx$$

$$= -\frac{x^2}{2}\Big|_{-2}^{0} + \frac{x^2}{2}\Big|_{0}^{2} = -\left(0 - \tfrac{4}{2}\right) + \left(\tfrac{4}{2} + 0\right) = 4$$

The fundamental theorem of calculus reduces a problem of integration to a problem of antidifferentiation. We stated the antidifferentiation formulas in Theorem 3.11; they are repeated here for easy reference.

Integration Formulas

Constant rule:	$\displaystyle \int 0 \, du = C$
Power rule:	$\displaystyle \int u^n \, du = \frac{u^{n+1}}{n+1} + C; \, n \neq -1$
Trigonometric rules:	$\displaystyle \int \sin u \, du = -\cos u + C$
	$\displaystyle \int \cos u \, du = \sin u + C$
	$\displaystyle \int \sec^2 u \, du = \tan u + C$
	$\displaystyle \int \csc u \cot u \, du = -\csc u + C$
	$\displaystyle \int \csc^2 u \, du = -\cot u + C$
	$\displaystyle \int \sec u \tan u \, du = \sec u + C$

These formulas alone are not sufficient for many of the integrals we need to evaluate. A most important procedure of integration is called substitution. We now introduce this procedure with indefinite integration and then extend it to definite integration.

■ SUBSTITUTION WITH INDEFINITE INTEGRATION

The method of substitution is the integration version of the chain rule. Recall that according to the chain rule, the derivative of $(x^2 + 3x + 5)^9$ is

$$\frac{d}{dx}(x^2 + 3x + 5)^9 = 9(x^2 + 3x + 5)^8(2x + 3)$$

Thus, $\displaystyle \int 9(x^2 + 3x + 5)^8(2x + 3)\, dx = (x^2 + 3x + 5)^9 + C$

Note that the product is of the form $g(u)\dfrac{du}{dx}$ where, in this case, $g(u) = 9u^8$ and $u = x^2 + 3x + 5$.

You can integrate many products of the form $g(u)\dfrac{du}{dx}$ by applying the chain rule in reverse, as indicated by the following theorem.

THEOREM 4.5   Integration by substitution

Let f, g, and u be differentiable functions of x such that

$$f(x) = g(u)\frac{du}{dx}$$

Then

$$\int f(x) \, dx = \int g(u) \frac{du}{dx} \, dx = \int g(u) \, du = G(u) + C$$

where G is an antiderivative of g.

Proof: If G is an antiderivative of g, then $G'(u) = g(u)$ and, by the chain rule,

$$f(x) = \frac{d}{dx}[G(u)] = G'(u)\frac{du}{dx} = g(u)\,\frac{du}{dx}$$

Integrating both sides of this equation, we obtain

$$\int f(x)\,dx = \int \left[g(u)\frac{du}{dx}\right] dx = \int \left[\frac{d}{dx}G(u)\right] dx = G(u) + C$$

as required.   ■

EXAMPLE 4   Integration of an indefinite integral by substitution

Find $\int 9(x^2 + 3x + 5)^8(2x + 3)\,dx$.

Solution   Look at the problem and make the observations as shown in the boxes:

Let $u = x^2 + 3x + 5$.   ← *If* $u = x^2 + 3x + 5$, *then* $du = (2x + 3)\,dx$.

$$\int \underbrace{9(x^2 + 3x + 5)^8}_{\text{This is }g(u).}\underbrace{(2x + 3)\,dx}_{\text{This is }du.} = \int 9u^8\,du$$

Now complete the integration of $g(u)$ and, when you are finished, back-substitute to express u in terms of x:

$$\int 9u^8\,du = 9\left(\frac{u^9}{9}\right) + C = (x^2 + 3x + 5)^9 + C$$ ▬

Sometimes the value for du is not quite as obvious as that shown in Example 4, so a more general procedure is shown next:

$$\int 9(x^2 + 3x + 5)^8(2x + 3)\,dx$$

Let $u = x^2 + 3x + 5$, so $\frac{du}{dx} = 2x + 3$, which implies $dx = \frac{du}{2x + 3}$.
Substitute these values:

$$\int 9\overbrace{(x^2 + 3x + 5)}^{u}{}^8\,(2x + 3)\,\overbrace{dx}^{\frac{du}{2x+3}} = \int 9u^8(2x + 3)\,\frac{du}{2x + 3}$$
$$= \underbrace{\int 9u^8\,du}$$

The goal here is to have an expression of
the form $\int g(u)\,du$—that is, *all terms
involving x and dx should be eliminated.*

EXAMPLE 5   Substitution with a radical function

Find $\int \sqrt{3x + 7}\,dx$.

Solution   Let $u = 3x + 7$, so $du = 3\,dx$ or $dx = \frac{du}{3}$; substitute:

$$\int \sqrt{3x + 7}\,dx = \int \sqrt{u}\,\frac{du}{3} = \frac{1}{3}\int u^{1/2}\,du$$

$$= \frac{1}{3}\left(\frac{u^{3/2}}{\frac{3}{2}}\right) + C = \frac{2}{9}u^{3/2} + C = \frac{2}{9}(3x + 7)^{3/2} + C$$ ▬

⊘   After you have made your substitution and simplified, there should be no leftover x-values in the integrand.   ⊘

EXAMPLE 6   Substitution with leftover x-values

Find $\int x(4x - 5)^3 \, dx$.

Solution   Let $u = 4x - 5$, so $du = 4 \, dx$ implies $dx = \frac{du}{4}$; substitute:

$$\int x(4x - 5)^3 \, dx = \int xu^3\left(\frac{du}{4}\right) = \tfrac{1}{4} \int xu^3 \, du$$

There is a leftover x value.

We are not ready to integrate until the leftover x-term has been eliminated. Because $u = 4x - 5$, we can solve for x:

$$x = \frac{u + 5}{4}$$

so

$$\tfrac{1}{4} \int xu^3 \, du = \tfrac{1}{4} \int \left(\frac{u + 5}{4}\right)u^3 \, du = \tfrac{1}{16} \int (u^4 + 5u^3) \, du$$

$$= \tfrac{1}{16}\left(\frac{u^5}{5} + 5\,\frac{u^4}{4}\right) + C = \tfrac{1}{80}(4x - 5)^5 + \tfrac{5}{64}(4x - 5)^4 + C$$

Computational Window

If you are using a software program to integrate functions such as the one shown in Example 6, you may obtain

$$\frac{64}{5} x^5 - 60x^4 + 100x^3 - \frac{125}{2} x^2 + \frac{625}{64}$$

This does not look anything like our answer to Example 6. However, by expanding the answer shown in Example 6, you can see they are the same (except for a constant).

EXAMPLE 7   Change of variable by substitution

Find $\int \dfrac{x \, dx}{\sqrt{x^2 + 1}}$.

Solution   Let $u = x^2 + 1$, so $du = 2x \, dx$ and $dx = \frac{du}{2x}$; substitute:

$$\int \frac{x \, dx}{\sqrt{x^2 + 1}} = \int \frac{x\left(\frac{du}{2x}\right)}{\sqrt{u}} = \tfrac{1}{2} \int u^{-1/2} \, du = \tfrac{1}{2}\left(\frac{u^{1/2}}{1/2}\right) + C = (x^2 + 1)^{1/2} + C$$

EXAMPLE 8   Substitution with a trigonometric function

Find $\int (4 - 2 \cos \theta)^3 \sin \theta \, d\theta$.

Solution Let $u = 4 - 2 \cos \theta$, so $\frac{du}{d\theta} = -2(-\sin \theta)$ and $d\theta = \frac{du}{2 \sin \theta}$; substitute:

$$\int (4 - 2 \cos \theta)^3 \sin \theta \, d\theta = \int u^3 \sin \theta \, \frac{du}{2 \sin \theta} = \frac{1}{2} \int u^3 \, du$$

$$= \frac{1}{2}\left(\frac{u^4}{4}\right) + C = \frac{1}{8}(4 - 2 \cos \theta)^4 + C$$

Computational Window

As we have previously noted, the forms found by using software will sometimes differ considerably from the forms obtained without the software. For example, using software we obtain the following form for Example 8:

$$2 \cos^4 \theta - 16 \cos^3 \theta - 64 \cos \theta - 48 \sin^2 \theta$$

To show the forms are equivalent, we can change this form to cosines:

$$2 \cos^4 \theta - 16 \cos^3 \theta + 48 \cos^2 \theta - 64 \cos \theta - 48$$

Now, we expand the answer shown in Example 8 to obtain

$$\tfrac{1}{8}(4 - 2 \cos \theta)^4 + C = 2 \cos^4 \theta - 16 \cos^3 \theta + 48 \cos^2 \theta - 64 \cos \theta + 32 + C$$

You can now see that for an appropriate choice of C, these forms are the same. The process of reconciling a software answer and an answer from human calculation is not very different from the process of proving that equations in trigonometry are identities.

EXAMPLE 9 **Using a trigonometric identity with substitution**

Find $\displaystyle\int \sin 2x \, dx$.

Solution Let $u = 2x$, so $du = 2 \, dx$ so that $dx = \frac{du}{2}$; substitute:

$$\int \sin 2x \, dx = \int \sin u \, \frac{du}{2} = \frac{1}{2} \int \sin u \, du = -\frac{1}{2} \cos u + C = -\frac{1}{2} \cos 2x + C$$

If you wish to check your work with integration problems, you can check by using differentiation:

$$\frac{d}{dx}\left(-\frac{1}{2} \cos 2x + C\right) = -\frac{1}{2}(-2 \sin 2x) + 0 = \sin 2x$$

Here is a problem in which the rate of change of a quantity is known and we use the method of substitution to find an expression for the quantity itself.

EXAMPLE 10 **Find the volume when the rate of flow is known**

Water is flowing into a tank at the rate of $\sqrt{3t + 1}$ ft³/min. If the tank is empty when $t = 0$, how much water does it contain 5 min later?

Solution   Because the rate at which the volume V is changing is dV/dt,

$$\frac{dV}{dt} = \sqrt{3t+1}$$
$$dV = \sqrt{3t+1}\ dt$$
$$\int dV = \int \sqrt{3t+1}\ dt = \int \sqrt{u}\ \frac{du}{3}$$

$$u = 3t+1$$
$$du = 3\ dt$$

$$V + C_1 = \frac{1}{3}\int u^{1/2}\ du$$

$$= \frac{1}{3}\cdot\frac{2}{3}u^{3/2} + C_2 \quad \textit{We need different constants for the different integrals.}$$

$$V = \frac{2}{9}(3t+1)^{3/2} + C \text{ where } C = C_2 - C_1$$

$$V(0) = \frac{2}{9}(3\cdot 0 + 1)^{3/2} + C = 0 \text{ so that } C = -\frac{2}{9} \quad \textit{The initial volume is 0.}$$

$$V(t) = \frac{2}{9}(3t+1)^{3/2} - \frac{2}{9} \text{ and } V(5) = \frac{2}{9}(16)^{3/2} - \frac{2}{9} = 14$$

The tank contains 14 ft^3 of water.

■ SUBSTITUTION WITH DEFINITE INTEGRATION

Example 10 could be considered as a definite integral:

$$\int_0^5 \sqrt{3t+1}\ dt = \frac{2}{9}(3t+1)^{3/2}\Big|_0^5 = \frac{2}{9}(16)^{3/2} - \frac{2}{9}(1)^{3/2} = 14$$

Notice that the definite integral eliminates the need for finding C. Furthermore, the following theorem eliminates the need for returning to the original variable.

THEOREM 4.6   Substitution with the definite integral

Suppose f is continuous on the set of values taken on by g. If g' is continuous on $[a, b]$, and if f has an antiderivative F on that interval, then

$$\int_a^b f[g(x)]g'(x)\ dx = \int_{g(a)}^{g(b)} f(u)\ du \quad \text{where } u = g(x), du = g'(x)\ dx$$

provided these integrals exist.

⊘ Note that when $x = b$, then $u = g(b)$; when $x = a$, then $u = g(a)$. ⊘

Proof: Let $u = g(x)$ and let F be an antiderivative of f on the interval $[a, b]$, so that $F' = f$. By the chain rule,

$$f[g(x)]g'(x)\ dx = f(u)\ du = F'(u)\ du$$

Then the fundamental theorem of calculus tells us that

$$\int_a^b f[g(x)]g'(x)\ dx = \left[\int F'(u)\ du\right]\Big|_{x=a}^{x=b}$$

$$= F(u)\Big|_{u=g(a)}^{u=g(b)} \quad \textit{Because } u = g(x)$$

$$= F[g(b)] - F[(g(a)]$$

$$= \int_{g(a)}^{g(b)} f(u)\ du \quad \textit{Because F is an antiderivative of f}$$ ■

EXAMPLE 11   Substitution with the definite integral

Evaluate $\int_1^2 (4x - 5)^3\ dx$.

Solution   Let $u = 4x - 5$,
$du = 4\ dx$

If $x = 2$, then $u = 4(2) - 5 = 3$.

$$\int_1^2 (4x - 5)^3\ dx = \int_{-1}^3 u^3\,\frac{du}{4}$$

⊘ You cannot change variables and keep the original limits of integration. ⊘

If $x = 1$, then $u = 4(1) - 5 = -1$.

$$= \frac{1}{4} \cdot \frac{u^4}{4}\Big|_{-1}^3$$

$$= \frac{1}{16}(81 - 1) = 5$$

Notice that substitution with the definite integral does not require that you return to the original variable.

PROBLEM SET 4.3

Ⓐ *In Problems 1–22, evaluate the definite integral.*

1. $\int_{-10}^{10} 7\ dx$

2. $\int_{-5}^7 (-3)\ dx$

3. $\int_{-3}^5 (2x + a)\ dx$

4. $\int_{-2}^2 (b - x)\ dx$

5. $\int_{-1}^2 ax^3\ dx$

6. $\int_{-1}^1 (x^3 + bx^2)\ dx$

7. $\int_1^2 \frac{1}{x^3}\ dx$

8. $\int_{-2}^{-1} \frac{3}{x^2}\ dx$

9. a. $\int_0^1 (5u^7 + \pi^2)\ du$ **b.** $\int_0^1 (8x^7 + \sqrt{\pi})\ dx$

10. $\int_0^4 \sqrt{x}(x + 1)\ dx$ **11.** $\int_0^1 \sqrt{t}(t - \sqrt{t})\ dt$

12. $\int_1^2 \frac{x^3 + 1}{x^2}\ dx$ **13.** $\int_1^4 \frac{x^2 + x - 1}{\sqrt{x}}\ dx$

14. $\int_{-2}^3 (\sin^2 x + \cos^2 x)\ dx$ **15.** $\int_0^{\pi/4} (\sec^2 x - \tan^2 x)\ dx$

16. a. $\int_0^4 (2t + 4)\ dt$ **b.** $\int_0^4 (2t + 4)^{-1/2}\ dt$

17. a. $\int_0^{\pi/2} \sin\theta\ d\theta$ **b.** $\int_0^{\pi/2} \sin 2\theta\ d\theta$

18. a. $\int_0^\pi \cos t\ dt$ **b.** $\int_0^{\sqrt{\pi}} t \cos t^2\ dt$

19. a. $\int_0^4 \sqrt{x}\ dx$ **b.** $\int_{-4}^0 \sqrt{-x}\ dx$

20. a. $\int_0^{16} \sqrt[4]{x}\ dx$ **b.** $\int_{-16}^0 \sqrt[4]{-x}\ dx$

21. a. $\int_0^3 |5x|dx$ **b.** $\int_{-3}^0 |5x|\ dx$ **c.** $\int_{-3}^3 |5x|\ dx$

22. a. $\int_0^2 |x|\ dx$ **b.** $\int_{-2}^0 |x|\ dx$ **c.** $\int_{-2}^2 |x|\ dx$

Use substitution to evaluate the indefinite integrals in Problems 23–39.

23. $\int (2x + 3)^4\ dx$ **24.** $\int \sqrt{3t - 5}\ dt$

25. $\int (x - 27)^{2/3}\ dx$ **26.** $\int (11 - 2x)^{-4/5}\ dx$

27. $\int (x^2 - \cos 3x)\ dx$ **28.** $\int \csc^2 5t\ dt$

29. $\int \sin (4 - x)\ dx$ **30.** $\int s\sqrt{s^2 + 4}\ ds$

31. $\int \sqrt{t}(t^{3/2} + 5)^3\ dt$ **32.** $\int \frac{(6x - 9)\ dx}{(x^2 - 3x + 5)^3}$

33. a. $\int x(3x^2 - 5)^5\ dx$ **b.** $\int x(3x - 5)^5\ dx$

34. a. $\int x\sqrt{2x^2 - 5}\, dx$ **b.** $\int x\sqrt{2x - 5}\, dx$

35. a. $\int x\sqrt{2x^2 + 1}\, dx$ **b.** $\int x\sqrt{2x + 1}\, dx$

36. a. $\int x^2(x^3 + 9)^{1/2}\, dx$ **b.** $\int x^3(x^2 + 9)^{1/2}\, dx$

37. a. $\int x(x^2 + 4)^{1/2}\, dx$ **b.** $\int x^3(x^2 + 4)^{1/2}\, dx$

38. $\int x \sin(3 + x^2)\, dx$ **39.** $\int \sin^3 t \cos t\, dt$

Find the area of the region under the curves given in Problems 40–47.

40. $y = x^2 + 1$ on $[-1, 1]$ **41.** $y = \sqrt{t}$ on $[0, 1]$

42. $y = \cos x$ on $\left[-\dfrac{\pi}{2}, \dfrac{\pi}{2}\right]$ **43.** $y = \sin x + \cos x$ on $\left[0, \dfrac{\pi}{6}\right]$

44. $y = t\sqrt{t^2 + 9}$ on $[0, 4]$ **45.** $y = \dfrac{1}{t^2}\sqrt{5 - \dfrac{1}{t}}$ on $\left[\dfrac{1}{5}, 1\right]$

46. $y = x(x - 1)^{1/3}$ on $[2, 9]$ **47.** $y = |x|$ on $[2, 3]$

Ⓑ 48. ■ **What Does This Say?** What is the relationship between finding an area and evaluating an integral?

49. ■ **What Does This Say?** Discuss $\int_{-4}^{4} x^{1/2}\, dx$.

50. a. If $F(x) = \int \left(\dfrac{1}{\sqrt{x}} - 4\right) dx$, find F so that $F(1) = 0$.

b. Sketch the graphs of $y = F(x)$, $y = F(x) + 3$, and $y = F(x) - 1$.

c. Find a constant C such that the largest value of $G(x) = F(x) + C$ is 0.

51. THINK TANK PROBLEM   Find a function whose graph has a relative minimum when $x = 1$ and a relative maximum when $x = 4$.

52. Evaluate

$$\int_{0}^{2} f(x)\, dx, \text{ where } f(x) = \begin{cases} x^3 & \text{if } 0 \le x < 1 \\ x^4 & \text{if } 1 \le x \le 2 \end{cases}$$

53. Evaluate

$$\int_{0}^{\pi} f(x)\, dx, \text{ where } f(x) = \begin{cases} \cos x & \text{if } 0 \le x < \pi/2 \\ x & \text{if } \pi/2 < x \le \pi \end{cases}$$

54. a. Show that if f is continuous and *odd* [that is, $f(-x) = -f(x)$] on the interval $[-a, a]$, then

$$\int_{-a}^{a} f(x)\, dx = 0$$

b. Show that if f is continuous and *even* [$f(-x) = f(x)$] on the interval $[-a, a]$, then

$$\int_{-a}^{a} f(x)\, dx = 2\int_{0}^{a} f(x)\, dx = 2\int_{-a}^{0} f(x)\, dx$$

Use the results of Problem 54 to evaluate the integrals given in Problems 55–58.

55. $\int_{-\pi}^{\pi} \sin x\, dx$ **56.** $\int_{-\pi/2}^{\pi/2} \cos x\, dx$

57. $\int_{-3}^{3} x\sqrt{x^4 + 1}\, dx$ **58.** $\int_{-1}^{1} \dfrac{\sin x\, dx}{x^2 + 1}$

59. In each of the following cases, determine whether the given relationship is true or false.

a. $\int_{-175}^{175} (7x^{1001} + 14x^{99})\, dx = 0$

b. $\int_{0}^{\pi} \sin^2 x\, dx = \int_{0}^{\pi} \cos^2 x\, dx$

c. $\int_{-\pi/2}^{\pi/2} \cos x\, dx = \int_{-\pi}^{0} \sin x\, dx$

60. The slope at each point (x, y) on the graph of $y = F(x)$ is given by $x(x^2 - 1)^{1/3}$, and the graph passes through the point $(3, 1)$. Use this information to find F. Sketch the graph of F.

61. A particle moves along the x-axis in such a way that at time t, its velocity is $v(t) = t^2(t^3 - 8)^{1/3}$.

a. At what time does the particle turn around?

b. If the particle starts at rest at $x = 1$, where does it turn around?

62. A rectangular storage tank has a square base 10 ft on a side. Water is flowing into the tank at the rate of

$$t(3t^2 + 1)^{-1/2} \text{ ft}^3/\text{s}$$

at time t seconds. If the tank is empty at time $t = 0$, how much water does it contain 4 s later? What is the depth of the water (to the nearest quarter inch) at that time?

63. JOURNAL PROBLEM* Evaluate

$$\int [(x^2 - 1)(x + 1)]^{-2/3}\, dx$$

Ⓒ 64. THINK TANK PROBLEM   The purpose of this problem is to provide a counterexample showing that the integral of a product (or quotient) is not necessarily equal to the product (quotient) of the respective integrals.

a. Show that $\int x\sqrt{x}\, dx \ne (\int x\, dx)(\int \sqrt{x}\, dx)$.

b. Show that $\int \dfrac{\sqrt{x}}{x}\, dx \ne \dfrac{\int \sqrt{x}\, dx}{\int x\, dx}$.

65. Suppose f is a function with the property that $f'(x) = f(x)$ for all x.

a. Show that $\int_{a}^{b} f(x)\, dx = f(b) - f(a)$.

b. Show that $\int_{a}^{b} [f(x)]^2\, dx = \dfrac{1}{2}\left\{[f(b)]^2 - [f(a)]^2\right\}$.

*From the *College Mathematics Journal*, Sept. 1989, p. 343. Problem by Murray Klamkin.

4.4 INTRODUCTION TO DIFFERENTIAL EQUATIONS*

> **IN THIS SECTION** Introduction and terminology, separable differential equations, orthogonal trajectories, the flow of a fluid through an orifice, escape velocity of a projectile
>
> The study of differential equations is as old as calculus itself. Today, it would be virtually impossible to make a serious study of physics, astronomy, chemistry, or engineering without encountering physical models based on differential equations. In addition, differential equations are beginning to appear more frequently in the biological and social sciences, especially in economics. In this section we introduce you to the basic terminology of differential equations and show how such equations can be used to model applications. Later in the text, we shall investigate more and more sophisticated issues regarding differential equations as we develop the necessary mathematical tools.

■ INTRODUCTION AND TERMINOLOGY

Any equation that contains a derivative or differential is called a **differential equation.** For example, the equations

$$\frac{dy}{dx} = 3x^3 + 5 \qquad \frac{dP}{dt} = kP^2 \qquad \left(\frac{dy}{dx}\right)^2 + 3\frac{dy}{dx} + 2y = xy \qquad \frac{d^2x}{dt^2} + 2\frac{dx}{dt} + 5t = \sin t$$

are all differential equations.

Many practical situations, especially those involving rates, can be described mathematically by differential equations. For example, the assumption that population P grows at a rate proportional to its size can be expressed by the differential equation

$$\frac{dP}{dt} = kP$$

where t is time and k is the constant of proportionality (we will examine this equation in Chapter 6).

A **solution** of a given differential equation is a function that satisfies the equation. A **general solution** is a characterization of all possible solutions of the equation. We say that the equation is **solved** when we find a general solution.

For example, $y = x^2$ is a solution of the differential equation

$$\frac{dy}{dx} = 2x$$

because

$$\frac{dy}{dx} = \frac{d}{dx}(y) = \frac{d}{dx}(x^2) = 2x$$

Moreover, because any solution of this equation must be an indefinite integral of $2x$, it follows that

$$y = \int 2x \, dx = x^2 + C$$

is the general solution of the differential equation.

*This section is required only for Section 6.4.

EXAMPLE 1   Solving a differential equation to find future revenue

An oil well that yields 300 barrels of crude oil a day will run dry in 3 years. It is estimated that t days from now the price of the crude oil will be $p(t) = 30 + 0.3\sqrt{t}$ dollars per barrel. If the oil is sold as soon as it is extracted from the ground, what will be the total future revenue from the well?

Solution   Let $R(t)$ denote the total revenue up to time t. Then the rate of change of revenue is $\frac{dR}{dt}$, the number of dollars received per barrel is $p(t) = 30 + 0.3\sqrt{t}$, and the number of barrels sold per day is 300. Thus, we have

$$\begin{bmatrix} \text{RATE OF CHANGE} \\ \text{OF TOTAL REVENUE} \end{bmatrix} = \begin{bmatrix} \text{NUMBER OF DOLLARS} \\ \text{PER BARREL} \end{bmatrix} \begin{bmatrix} \text{NUMBER OF BARRELS} \\ \text{SOLD PER DAY} \end{bmatrix}$$

$$\frac{dR}{dt} = (30 + 0.3\sqrt{t})(300)$$

$$= 9{,}000 + 90\sqrt{t}$$

This is actually a statement of the chain rule: $\frac{dR}{dt} = \frac{dR}{dB} \cdot \frac{dB}{dt}$, where B denotes the number of barrels extracted and R denotes the revenue. It is often helpful to use the chain rule in this way when setting up similar differential equations. We solve this differential equation by integration:

$$R = \int \frac{dR}{dt}\, dt$$

$$R(t) = 9{,}000t + 60t^{3/2} + C$$

Because $R(0) = 0$, it follows that $C = 0$. We also are given that the well will run dry in 3 years or 1,095 days, so that the total revenue obtained during the life of the well is

$$R(1{,}095) = 9{,}000(1{,}095) + 60(1{,}095)^{3/2}$$

$$\approx 12{,}029{,}064.52$$

The total future revenue is $12,029,065.   ▬

■ SEPARABLE DIFFERENTIAL EQUATIONS

Many useful differential equations can be formally rewritten so that all the terms containing the independent variable appear on one side of the equation and all terms involving the dependent variable appear on the other side. Thus, such an equation has the form

$$g(x)\, dx = f(y)\, dy$$

or, equivalently (integrating both sides):

$$\int g(x)\, dx = \int f(y)\, dy$$

A differential equation that can be written in the form

$$\frac{dy}{dx} = \frac{g(x)}{f(y)}$$

is said to be **separable.** *To solve a separable differential equation, separate the variables and then separately integrate both sides of the resulting equation.* This procedure is illustrated in Example 2.

EXAMPLE 2   Separable differential equation

Solve $\dfrac{dy}{dx} = \dfrac{x}{y}$.

Solution

$$\frac{dy}{dx} = \frac{x}{y}$$

$$y\,dy = x\,dx$$

$$\int y\,dy = \int x\,dx$$

$$\tfrac{1}{2}y^2 + C_1 = \tfrac{1}{2}x^2 + C_2$$

$$x^2 - y^2 = C \qquad \text{where } C = 2(C_1 - C_2)$$

Notice the treatment of constants in Example 2. Because all constants can be combined into a single constant, it is customary not to write $C = 2(C_1 - C_2)$, but rather to simply replace all the arbitrary constants in the problem by a single arbitrary constant at the end of the problem.

The remainder of this section is devoted to selected applications involving separable differential equations.

■ ORTHOGONAL TRAJECTORIES

A curve that intersects each member of a given family of curves at right angles is called an **orthogonal trajectory** of that family. Orthogonal families arise in many applications. For example, in thermodynamics, the heat flow across a planar surface is orthogonal to the curves of constant temperature, called *isotherms*. In the theory of fluid flow, the flow lines are orthogonal trajectories of *velocity potential curves*. The basic procedure for finding orthogonal trajectories involves differential equations and is demonstrated in Example 3.

EXAMPLE 3   Finding orthogonal trajectories

Find the orthogonal trajectories of the family of curves of the form

$$xy = C$$

Solution   We are seeking a family of curves. Each curve in that family intersects each curve in the family $xy = C$ at right angles, as shown in Figure 4.10. Assume that a typical point on a given curve in the family $xy = C$ has coordinates (x, y) and that a typical point on the orthogonal trajectory curve has coordinates (X, Y).

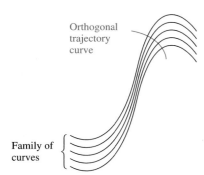

Orthogonal trajectory curve

Family of curves

Orthogonal trajectory

The orthogonal trajectory intersects each curve in the given family at right angles.

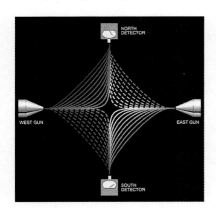

Figure 4.9 Scattering experiment can reveal the quantum mechanical behavior of particles using orthogonal trajectories. Two guns shoot particles toward one another. The particles that are deflected by 90° are recorded in two detectors. The solid lines show one set of possible trajectories for the deflected particles. The dotted lines show another set.

We use uppercase letters for one kind of curve and lowercase for the other to make it easier to tell which curve is being mentioned at each stage of the following discussion.

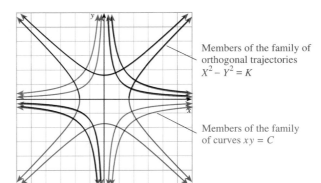

Members of the family of orthogonal trajectories $X^2 - Y^2 = K$

Members of the family of curves $xy = C$

Figure 4.10 The family of curves $xy = C$ and their orthogonal trajectories

Let P be a point where a particular curve of the form $xy = C$ intersects the orthogonal trajectory curve. At P, we have $x = X$ and $y = Y$, and the slope dY/dX of the orthogonal trajectory is the same as the negative reciprocal of the slope dy/dx of the curve $xy = C$. Using implicit differentiation, we find

$$xy = C$$

$$x\frac{dy}{dx} + y = 0 \quad \textit{Product rule}$$

$$\frac{dy}{dx} = \frac{-y}{x}$$

Thus, at the point of intersection P, the slope $\frac{dY}{dX}$ of the orthogonal trajectory is

$$\frac{dY}{dX} = -\frac{1}{dy/dx} = -\frac{1}{-y/x} = \frac{x}{y} = \frac{X}{Y}$$

According to this equation, the coordinates (X, Y) of the orthogonal trajectory curve satisfy the separable differential equation

$$\frac{dY}{dX} = \frac{X}{Y}$$

discussed in Example 2. Using the result of that example, we see that the orthogonal trajectories of the family $xy = C$ are the curves in the family

$$X^2 - Y^2 = K$$

where K is a constant. The given family of curves $xy = C$ and the family of orthogonal trajectory curves $X^2 - Y^2 = K$ are shown in Figure 4.10. ■

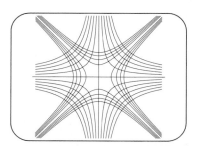

Computer-generated family
of orthogonal trajectories

■ THE FLOW OF A FLUID THROUGH AN ORIFICE

Consider a tank that is filled with a fluid being slowly drained through a small, sharp-edged hole in its base, as shown in Figure 4.11.

By using a principle of physics known as Torricelli's law,* we can show that the rate of discharge dV/dt at time t is proportional to the square root of the depth h at that time. Specifically, if all dimensions are given in terms of feet, the drain hole has area A_0, and the height above the hole is h at time t (seconds), then

$$\frac{dV}{dt} = -4.8A_0\sqrt{h}$$

is the rate of flow of water in cubic feet per second. This formula is used in Example 4.

Figure 4.11 The flow of a fluid through an orifice

EXAMPLE 4   Fluid flow through an orifice

A cylindrical tank is filled with a liquid that is draining through a small circular hole in its base. If the tank is 9 ft high with radius 4 ft, and the drain hole has radius 1 in., how long does it take for the tank to empty?

Solution   Because the drain hole is a circle of radius $\frac{1}{12}$ ft (= 1 in.), its area is $\pi r^2 = \pi\left(\frac{1}{12}\right)^2$, and the rate of flow (according to Torricelli's law) is

$$\frac{dV}{dt} = -4.8\left(\frac{\pi}{144}\right)\sqrt{h}$$

*Torricelli's law says that the stream of liquid through the orifice has velocity $v = \sqrt{2gh}$, where $g = 32$ ft/s^2 is the acceleration due to gravity and h is the height of the liquid above the orifice. The factor 4.8 that appears in the rate of flow equation is required to compensate for the effect of friction.

Because the tank is cylindrical, the amount of fluid in the tank at any particular time will form a cylinder of radius 4 ft and height h. Also, because we are using $g = 32$ ft/s^2, it is implied that the time, t, is measured in seconds. The volume of such a liquid cylinder is

$$V = \pi r^2 h = \pi(4)^2 h = 16\pi h$$

and by differentiating both sides of this equation with respect to t, we obtain

$$\frac{dV}{dt} = 16\pi \frac{dh}{dt}$$

$$-4.8\left(\frac{\pi}{144}\right)\sqrt{h} = 16\pi \frac{dh}{dt} \qquad \textit{By substituting from Torricelli's law}$$

$$\frac{dh}{dt} = \frac{-4.8\sqrt{h}}{144(16)} \approx -0.0021\sqrt{h}$$

$$\frac{1}{\sqrt{h}}\, dh = -0.0021\, dt \qquad \textit{Separate the variables.}$$

$$\int h^{-1/2}\, dh = \int (-0.0021)\, dt \qquad \textit{Integrate both sides.}$$

$$2h^{1/2} + C_1 = -0.0021t + C_2$$

$$2\sqrt{h} = -0.0021t + C$$

To evaluate C, recall that the tank is full at time $t = 0$. Thus $h = 9$ when $t = 0$, so that

$$2\sqrt{9} = -0.0021(0) + C \quad \text{and} \quad C = 6$$

Therefore, the general formula is

$$2\sqrt{h} = -0.0021t + 6$$

Now we can find the depth of the fluid at any given time or the time at which a prescribed depth occurs. In particular, the tank is empty at the time t_e when $h = 0$. By substituting $h = 0$ into this formula we find

$$2\sqrt{0} = -0.0021t_e + 6 \quad \text{so that} \quad t_e \approx 2{,}857 \text{ sec}$$

Thus roughly 0.8 hr (47.62 min) are required to drain the tank.   ▬

On April 12, 1981, the United States launched the world's first space shuttle, *Columbia*.

■ ESCAPE VELOCITY OF A PROJECTILE

Consider a projectile that is launched with initial velocity v_0 from a planet's surface along a direct line through the center of the planet, as shown in Figure 4.12.

Figure 4.12 A projectile launched from the surface of a planet

We shall find a general formula for the velocity of the projectile and the minimal value of v_0 required to guarantee that the projectile will escape the planet's gravitational attraction.

We shall assume that the only force acting on the projectile is that due to gravity, although in practice, factors such as air resistance must also be considered. With this assumption, Newton's law of gravitation can be used to show that when the projectile is at a distance s from the center of the planet, its acceleration is given by the formula

$$a = \frac{-gR^2}{s^2}$$

where R is the radius of the planet and g is the acceleration due to gravity at the planet's surface.*

Our first goal is to express the velocity v of the projectile in terms of the distance s. Because the projectile travels along a straight line, we know that

$$a = \frac{dv}{dt} \quad \text{and} \quad v = \frac{ds}{dt}$$

and by applying the chain rule, we see that

$$a = \frac{dv}{dt} = \frac{dv}{ds} \cdot \frac{ds}{dt} = \frac{dv}{ds} v$$

Therefore, by substitution for a we have

$$\frac{dv}{ds} v = \frac{-gR^2}{s^2}$$

$$v \, dv = -gR^2 s^{-2} \, ds$$

$$\int v \, dv = \int -gR^2 s^{-2} \, ds$$

$$\tfrac{1}{2}v^2 + C_1 = gR^2 s^{-1} + C_2$$

$$v^2 = 2gR^2 s^{-1} + C$$

To evaluate the constant C, recall that the projectile was fired from the planet's surface with initial velocity v_0. Thus, $v = v_0$ when $s = R$, and by substitution:

$$v_0^2 = 2gR^2 R^{-1} + C \quad \text{which implies} \quad C = v_0^2 - 2gR$$

so

$$v^2 = 2gR^2 s^{-1} + v_0^2 - 2gR$$

Because the projectile is launched in a direction away from the center of the planet, we would expect it to keep moving in that direction until it stops. In other words, *the projectile will keep moving away from the planet until it reaches a point where $v = 0$.* Because $2gR^2 s^{-1} > 0$ for all $s > 0$, v^2 will always be positive if $v_0^2 - 2gR \geq 0$. On the other hand, if $v_0^2 - 2gR < 0$, then sooner or later v will become 0 and the projectile will eventually fall back to the surface of the planet.

Therefore, we conclude that the projectile will escape from the planet's

---

*According to Newton's law of gravitation, the force of gravity acting on a projectile of mass m has magnitude $F = mk/s^2$, where k is constant. If this is the only force acting on the projectile, then $F = ma$, and we have $ma = F = mk/s^2$. By canceling the m's on each side of the equation, we obtain $a = k/s^2$.

gravitational attraction if $v_0^2 \geq 2gR$ — that is, if $v_0 \geq \sqrt{2gR}$. For this reason, the minimum speed for which this can occur, namely,

$$v_0 = \sqrt{2gR}$$

is called the **escape velocity** of the planet. In particular, for the earth, $R = 3{,}956$ mi and $g = 32$ ft/s^2 = 0.00606 mi/s^2, and the escape velocity is

$$v_0 = \sqrt{2gR} \approx \sqrt{2(0.006\,06)(3{,}956)} \approx 6.924\,357$$

The escape velocity for the earth is 6.92 mi/s.

PROBLEM SET 4.4

A *Verify in Problems 1–6 that if y satisfies the prescribed relationship with x, then it will be a solution of the given differential equation.*

1. If $x^2 + y^2 = 7$, then $\dfrac{dy}{dx} = -\dfrac{x}{y}$.

2. If $5x^2 - 2y^2 = 3$, then $\dfrac{dy}{dy} = \dfrac{5x}{2y}$.

3. If $xy = C$, then $\dfrac{dy}{dx} = \dfrac{-y}{x}$.

4. If $x^2 - 3xy + y^2 = 5$, then
$$(2x - 3y)\,dx + (2y - 3x)\,dy = 0.$$

5. If $y = \sin(Ax + B)$, then $\dfrac{d^2y}{dx^2} + A^2y = 0$.

6. If $y = \dfrac{x^4}{20} - \dfrac{A}{x} + B$, then $x\dfrac{d^2y}{dx^2} + 2\dfrac{dy}{dx} = x^3$.

Find the general solution of the separable differential equations given in Problems 7–16.

7. $\dfrac{dy}{dx} = -\dfrac{x}{y}$

8. $\dfrac{dx}{dt} = x^2\sqrt{t}$

9. $\dfrac{dy}{dx} = \sqrt{\dfrac{x}{y}}$

10. $\dfrac{dy}{dx} = \sqrt{\dfrac{y}{x}}$

11. $\dfrac{dy}{dx} = \dfrac{x}{y}\sqrt{1 - x^2}$

12. $\dfrac{dy}{dx} = (y - 4)^2$

13. $xy\,dx + \sqrt{xy}\,dy = 0$

14. $4y^3\,dz + 5z^2\,dy = 0$

15. $\dfrac{dy}{dx} = \dfrac{\sin x}{\cos y}$

16. $x^2\,dy + \sec y\,dx = 0$

In Problems 17–20, find the general solution of the given differential equation by using either the product rule or the quotient rule.

17. $x\,dy + y\,dx = 0$

18. $\dfrac{x\,dy - y\,dx}{x^2} = 0$

19. $y\,dx = x\,dy$, $x > 0$, $y > 0$
20. $x^2y\,dy + xy^2\,dx = 0$

Write a differential equation describing the situation given in Problems 21–26. Do not solve.

21. The number of bacteria in a culture grows at a rate that is proportional to the number present.

22. A sample of radium decays at a rate that is proportional to the amount of radium present in the sample.

23. The rate at which the temperature of an object changes is proportional to the difference between its own temperature and the temperature of the surrounding medium.

24. When a person is asked to recall a set of facts, the rate at which the facts are recalled is proportional to the number of relevant facts in the person's memory that have not yet been recalled.

25. The rate at which an epidemic spreads through a community of P susceptible people is proportional to the product of the number of people who have caught the disease and the number who have not.

26. The rate at which people are implicated in a government scandal is proportional to the product of the number of people already implicated and the number of people involved who have not yet been implicated.

B *Find the orthogonal trajectories of the family of curves given in Problems 27–31. In each case, sketch several members of the given family of curves and several members of the family of orthogonal trajectories on the same coordinate axes.*

27. the lines $2x - 3y = C$

28. the lines $y = x + C$

29. the cubic curves $y = x^3 + C$

30. the curves $y = x^4 + C$

31. the curves $xy^2 = C$

32. What do you think the orthogonal trajectories of the family of curves

$$x^2 - y^2 = C$$

will be? *Hint*: Take another look at Example 3.

33. The following is a list of six families of curves. Sketch several members of each family and then determine which pairs are orthogonal trajectories of one other.

a. the circles $x^2 + y^2 = A$
b. the ellipses $2x^2 + y^2 = B^2$
c. the ellipses $x^2 + 2y^2 = C$
d. the lines $y = Cx$
e. the parabolas $y^2 = Cx$
f. the parabolas $y = Cx^2$

34. A cylindrical tank of radius 3 ft is filled with water to a depth of 5 ft. Determine how long (to the nearest minute) it takes to drain the tank through a sharp-edged circular hole in the bottom with radius 2 in.

35. Rework Problem 34 for a tank with a sharp-edged drainhole that is square with length of side 1.5 in.

36. EXPERIMENT   A rectangular tank has a square base 2 ft on a side that is filled with water to a depth of 4 ft. It is being drained from the bottom of the tank through a sharp-edged square hole that is 2 in. on a side.

    a. Show that at time t, the depth h satisfies the differential equation

    $$4\frac{dh}{dt} = -4.8A_0\sqrt{h}$$

    where A_0 is the area of the drain hole.

    b. How long will it take to empty the tank?

    c. Construct this tank and then drain it out of the 2 in.^{2} hole. Is the time that it takes consistent with your answer to part b?

37. A toy rocket is launched from the surface of the earth with initial velocity $v_0 = 150$ ft/s. (The radius of the earth is roughly 3,956 mi, and $g = 32$ ft/s^2.)

    a. Determine the velocity (to the nearest ft/s) of the rocket when it is first 200 feet above the ground. (Remember, this is not the same as 200 ft from the center of the earth.)

    b. What is s when $v = 0$? Determine the maximum height above the ground that is attained by the rocket.

38. Determine the escape velocity of each of the following heavenly bodies:

    a. moon ($R = 1,080$ mi; $g = 5.5$ ft/s^2)

    b. Mars ($R = 2,050$ mi; $g = 12$ ft/s^2)

    c. Venus ($R = 3,800$ mi; $g = 28$ ft/s^2)

39. Population statistics indicate that x years after 1990, a certain city was growing at a rate of approximately $1,500t^{-1/2}$ people per year. In 1994 the population of the city was 39,000.

    a. What was the population in 1990?

    b. If this pattern continues, how many people will be living in the city in the year 1999?

40. In a certain section of the country, the price of chicken is currently $3 per pound. It is estimated that t weeks from now the price will be increasing at a rate of $\sqrt{3t + 1}$ cents per week. How much will chicken cost 8 weeks from now?

41. It is estimated that t years from now a farmer's crop will be increasing at a rate of $0.3t^2 + 0.6t + 1$ bushels per day. By how much will the value of the crop increase during the next 20 days if the market price remains fixed at $3 per bushel?

42. The radius of planet X is one-fourth that of planet Y, and the acceleration due to gravity at the surface of X is eight-ninth that at the surface of Y. If the escape velocity of planet X is 6 ft/s, what is the escape velocity of planet Y?

43. A survey indicates that the population of a certain town is growing in such a way that the rate of growth at time t is proportional to the square root of the population P at the time. If the population was 4,000 ten years ago and is observed to be 9,000 now, how long will it take before 16,000 people live in the town?

44. After its brakes are applied, a certain sports car decelerates at a constant rate of 28 ft/s^2. Compute the stopping distance if the car is going 60 mi/hr (88 ft/s) when the brakes are applied.

45. SPY PROBLEM   The spy, having defused the bomb in Problem 19, Section 3.7, is driving the sports car in Problem 44 at a speed of 60 mi/hr on Highway 1 in the remote republic of San Dimas. Suddenly he sees a camel in the road 199 ft in front of him. After a reaction time of 00.7 seconds, he steps on the brakes. Will he stop before hitting the camel?

46. A scientist has discovered a radioactive substance that disintegrates in such a way that at time t, the rate of disintegration is proportional to the *square* of the amount present.

    a. If a 100-g sample of the substance dwindles to only 80 g in 1 d, how much will be left after 6 d?

    b. When will only 10 g be left?

47. In physics, it is shown that the amount of heat Q (calories) that flows through an object by conduction will satisfy the differential equation

    $$\frac{dQ}{dt} = -kA\frac{dT}{ds}$$

    where t (seconds) is the time of flow, k is a physical constant (the *thermal conductivity* of the object), A is the surface area of the object measured at right angles to the direction of flow, and T is the temperature at a point s centimeters within the object, measured in the direction of the flow, as shown in Figure 4.13.

    Figure 4.13 Heat conduction through an object

    Direction of heat flow

    Under certain conditions (equilibrium), the rate of heat flow dQ/dt will be constant. Assuming these conditions to exist, find the number of calories that will flow each second across the face of a square pane of glass 2 cm thick and 50 cm on a side if the temperature on one side of the pane is 5° and the temperature on the other side is 60°. The thermal conductivity of glass is approximately $k = 0.0025$.

48. The shape of a tank is such that when it is filled to a depth of h feet, it contains

    $$V = 9\pi h^3 \text{ ft}^3$$

    of water. The tank is being drained through a sharp-edged circular hole of radius 1 in. If the tank is originally filled to a depth of 4 ft, how long does it take for the tank to empty?

49. A rectangular tank has a square base 4 ft on a side and is 10 ft high. Originally, it was filled with water to a depth of

6 feet, but now is being drained from the bottom of the tank through a sharp-edged square hole 1 in. on a side.

a. Find an equation involving the rate dh/dt.

b. How long will it take to drain the tank?

C **50.** A projectile is launched from the surface of a planet whose radius is R and where the acceleration due to gravity at the surface is g.

a. If the initial velocity v_0 of the projectile satisfies $v_0 < \sqrt{2gR}$, show that the projectile eventually returns to the surface of the planet. Also show that the maximum height above the surface of the planet reached by the projectile is

$$h = \frac{v_0^2 R}{2gR - v_0^2}$$

b. On a certain planet, it is known that $g = 25$ ft/s². A projectile is fired with an initial velocity of $v_0 = 2$ mi/sec and attains a maximum height of 450 mi. What is the radius of the planet?

51. A projectile is launched from the surface of a planet whose radius is R. The constant acceleration due to gravity on the surface of the planet is g. According to Newton's law of gravitation, the force of gravity acting on a projectile of mass m has magnitude

$$F = \frac{mk}{s^2}$$

where k is a constant. If this is the only force acting on the projectile, then $F = ma$. Show that

$$a = \frac{-gR^2}{s^2}$$

4.5 THE MEAN VALUE THEOREM FOR INTEGRALS; AVERAGE VALUE

IN THIS SECTION Mean value theorem for integrals, average value of a function, variable limits of integration, Leibniz's rule

The fundamental theorem of calculus simplifies the procedure for evaluating the definite integral *providing we can find an antiderivative*. However, this theorem does not tell us whether every continuous function actually has an antiderivative. In this section we prove the second fundamental theorem of calculus, which says that a continuous function on an open interval has an antiderivative on that interval. In order to prove this major result we first need to establish a result called the mean value theorem for integrals.

■ MEAN VALUE THEOREM FOR INTEGRALS

In Section 3.2 we established a very useful theoretical tool called the mean value theorem, which said that under reasonable conditions, there is at least one number c on the interval $[a, b]$ such that the value of the derivative at $x = c$ is exactly the same as

$$\frac{f(b) - f(a)}{b - a}$$

The mean value theorem for integrals is similar, and in the special case where $f(x) \geq 0$ it has a geometric interpretation that makes the theorem easy to understand. In particular, the theorem says that it is possible to find at least one number c on the interval $[a, b]$ such that the area of the rectangle with height $f(c)$ and width $(b - a)$ has exactly the same area as the region under the curve $y = f(x)$ on $[a, b]$. This is illustrated in Figure 4.14.

THEOREM 4.7   Mean value theorem for integrals

If f is continuous on the interval $[a, b]$, there is at least one number c between a and b such that

$$\int_a^b f(x)\, dx = f(c)(b - a)$$

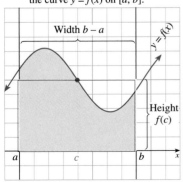

The red rectangle has the same area as the region under the curve $y = f(x)$ on $[a, b]$.

Figure 4.14 Geometric interpretation of the mean value theorem for integrals

Proof: Suppose M and m are the largest and smallest values of f, respectively, on $[a, b]$. This means that

$$m \leq f(x) \leq M \quad \text{when} \quad a \leq x \leq b$$

$$\int_a^b m \, dx \leq \int_a^b f(x) \, dx \leq \int_a^b M \, dx \quad \text{Dominance property}$$

$$m(b - a) \leq \int_a^b f(x) \, dx \leq M(b - a)$$

$$m \leq \frac{1}{b - a} \int_a^b f(x) \, dx \leq M$$

The intermediate value theorem (Section 1.7) says that because f is continuous on the closed interval $[a, b]$ and because the number

$$I = \frac{1}{b - a} \int_a^b f(x) \, dx$$

lies between m and M, there exists a number c between a and b for which $f(c) = I$; that is,

$$\frac{1}{b - a} \int_a^b f(x) \, dx = f(c)$$

$$\int_a^b f(x) \, dx = f(c)(b - a) \qquad \blacksquare$$

The mean value theorem for integrals does not specify how to determine c, it simply guarantees the existence of at least one number c in the interval. However, Example 1 shows how to find a value of c guaranteed by this theorem.

EXAMPLE 1   Finding c in the mean value theorem for integrals

Find a value of c guaranteed by the mean value theorem for integrals for $f(x) = \sin x$ on $[0, \pi]$.

Solution $\quad \int_0^\pi \sin x \, dx = -\cos x \Big|_0^\pi = -\cos \pi + \cos 0 = -(-1) + 1 = 2$

The region bounded by f and the x-axis on $[0, \pi]$ is shaded in Figure 4.15. The mean value theorem for integrals asserts the existence of a number c on $[0, \pi]$ such that $f(c)(b - a) = 2$. We can solve an equation to find this value:

$$f(c)(b - a) = 2$$

$$(\sin c)(\pi - 0) = 2$$

$$\sin c = \frac{2}{\pi}$$

$$c \approx 0.690107, \text{ or } 2.451486$$

Because c is between 0 and π, we have found the value c guaranteed by the mean value theorem for integrals. ▬

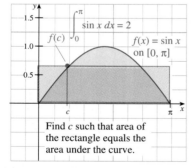

Find c such that area of the rectangle equals the area under the curve.

Figure 4.15 Graph of $f(x) = \sin x$ illustrating the mean value theorem on $[0, \pi]$

■ AVERAGE VALUE OF A FUNCTION

There are many practical situations in which one is interested in the *average value* of a continuous function on an interval, such as the average level of air pollution over a 24-hour period, the average speed of a truck during a 3-hour trip, or the average productivity of a worker during a production run. Averages of this kind can be computed by the formula in the following definition.

Average Value

If f is continuous on the interval $[a, b]$, the **average value** of f on this interval is given by the integral

$$\frac{1}{b-a} \int_a^b f(x)\, dx$$

You probably know that the average value of n numbers $x_1, x_2, \ldots, x_n$ is

$$\frac{x_1 + x_2 + \cdots + x_n}{n}$$

but what if there are infinitely many numbers? Specifically, what is the average value of $f(x)$ on the interval $a \le x \le b$? To see how the definition of finite average value can be used, imagine that the interval $[a, b]$ is divided into n equal subintervals, each of width

$$\Delta x = \frac{b-a}{n}$$

For $k = 1, 2, \ldots, n$, let x_k^* be a number chosen arbitrarily from the kth subinterval. Then the average value V of f on $[a, b]$ is estimated by the weighted sum

$$S_n = \frac{f(x_1^*) + f(x_2^*) + \cdots + f(x_n^*)}{n} = \frac{1}{n} \sum_{k=1}^{n} f(x_k^*)$$

Because $\Delta x = \dfrac{b-a}{n}$, we know that $\dfrac{1}{n} = \dfrac{1}{b-a} \Delta x$ and

$$S_n = \frac{1}{n} \sum_{k=1}^{n} f(x_k^*) = \left[\frac{1}{b-a} \Delta x \right] \sum_{k=1}^{n} f(x_k^*) = \frac{1}{b-a} \sum_{k=1}^{n} f(x_k^*) \Delta x$$

The sum on the right is a Riemann sum with norm $\|P\| = \dfrac{b-a}{n}$, and because $\|P\| \to 0$ as $n \to +\infty$, we have

$$\lim_{\|P\| \to 0} S_n = \lim_{n \to \infty} \frac{1}{b-a} \sum_{k=1}^{n} f(x_k^*) \Delta x = \frac{1}{b-a} \int_a^b f(x)\, dx$$

Finally, because it is reasonable to expect the estimating average S_n to approach the "true average value" as $n \to +\infty$, we are led to the formula given as the definition of average value.

EXAMPLE 2   Average speed of traffic

Suppose a study suggests that between the hours of 1:00 P.M. and 4:00 P.M. on a normal weekday, the speed of the traffic at a certain expressway exit is modeled by the formula

$$S(t) = 2t^3 - 21t^2 + 60t + 20$$

kilometers per hour, where t is the number of hours past noon. Compute the average speed of the traffic between the hours of 1:00 P.M. and 4:00 P.M.

Solution   Our goal is to find the average value of $S(t)$ on the interval $[1, 4]$. The average speed is

$$\frac{1}{4-1} \int_1^4 (2t^3 - 21t^2 + 60t + 20)\, dt = \frac{1}{3} \left[\frac{1}{2}t^4 - 7t^3 + 30t^2 + 20t \right]_1^4$$

$$= \frac{1}{3}(240 - 43.5) = 65.5$$

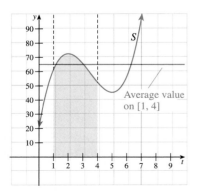

Average value on [1, 4]

Note that the mean value theorem for integrals can be interpreted as saying that the average value of $f(x)$ on $[a, b]$ equals the value of f for some number c between a and b. That is, *a function must assume its average value at least once on any closed, bounded interval $[a, b]$ where it is continuous.*

Actually, this is quite reasonable, because the intermediate value theorem of continuous functions assures us that a continuous function f assumes every value between its maximum M and minimum m, and we would expect the average value V to be between these two extremes. Example 3 illustrates one way of using these ideas.

EXAMPLE 3   **Average temperature**

Suppose that x hours after midnight, the temperature (in degrees Celsius) in Minneapolis one night can be modeled by the formula

$$T(x) = 2 - \tfrac{1}{7}(x - 13)^2$$

Find the average temperature between 2 A.M. and 2 P.M. and a time when the average temperature actually occurs.

Solution   We wish to find the average temperature of T on the interval $[2, 14]$ (because 2 P.M. is 14 hr after midnight). The average value is

$$T = \frac{1}{14 - 2} \int_2^{14} \left[2 - \tfrac{1}{7}(x - 13)^2 \right] dx = \tfrac{1}{12}\left[2x - \tfrac{1}{7} \cdot \tfrac{1}{3}(x - 13)^3 \right]\Big|_2^{14}$$

$$= \tfrac{1}{12}\left[\tfrac{587}{21} - \tfrac{1,415}{21} \right] \approx -3.2857143$$

Thus the average temperature on the given time period is approximately 3.286 °C below zero. To determine when this temperature actually occurs, solve the equation

$$\text{AVERAGE TEMPERATURE} = \text{TEMPERATURE AT TIME } x$$

$$-3.2857143 = 2 - \tfrac{1}{7}(x - 13)^2$$

$$37 = (x - 13)^2$$

$$x = 13 \pm \sqrt{37} \approx 19.082763 \quad \text{or} \quad 6.9172375$$

The first value is to be rejected because it is not in the interval $[2, 14]$, so we find that the average temperature occurs 6.917 hr after midnight, or at approximately 6:55 A.M.   ▬

■ VARIABLE LIMITS OF INTEGRATION

The fundamental theorem of calculus tells us that the definite integral can be evaluated as a difference:

$$\int_b^a f(x) \, dx = F(b) - F(a)$$

where F is an antiderivative of f on $[a, b]$. But in general, what guarantee do we have that such an antiderivative even exists? The answer is provided by the following theorem, which is often referred to as the second fundamental theorem of calculus.

THEOREM 4.8   Second fundamental theorem of calculus

Let $f(t)$ be continuous on the interval $[a, b]$ and define the function G by the integral equation

$$G(x) = \int_a^x f(t)\, dt$$

for $a \leq x \leq b$. Then G is an antiderivative of f on $[a, b]$; that is,

$$G'(x) = \frac{d}{dx}\left[\int_a^x f(t)\, dt\right] = f(x)$$

on $[a, b]$.

Proof: Apply the definition of derivative to G:

$$G'(x) = \lim_{\Delta x \to 0} \frac{G(x + \Delta x) - G(x)}{\Delta x}$$

$$= \lim_{\Delta x \to 0} \frac{1}{\Delta x}[G(x + \Delta x) - G(x)]$$

$$= \lim_{\Delta x \to 0} \frac{1}{\Delta x}\left[\int_a^{x+\Delta x} f(t)\, dt - \int_a^x f(t)\, dt\right]$$

$$= \lim_{\Delta x \to 0} \frac{1}{\Delta x}\left[\int_a^{x+\Delta x} f(t)\, dt + \int_x^a f(t)\, dt\right]$$

$$= \lim_{\Delta x \to 0} \frac{1}{\Delta x}\left[\int_x^{x+\Delta x} f(t)\, dt\right] \qquad \text{Subdivision property}$$

$$= \lim_{\Delta x \to 0} \frac{1}{\Delta x}[f(c)\Delta x] \qquad \text{This is true for } c \\ \text{between } x \text{ and } x + \Delta x; \\ \text{mean value theorem} \\ \text{for integrals.}$$

$$= \lim_{c \to x} f(c) \qquad \text{Since } c \text{ is between} \\ x \text{ and } x + \Delta x \text{ and} \\ \Delta x \to 0$$

$$= f(x) \qquad \text{Since } f \text{ is continuous at } x \quad \blacksquare$$

Notice that if F is *any* antiderivative of f on the interval $[a, b]$, then the antiderivative

$$G(x) = \int_a^x f(t)\, dt$$

found in Theorem 4.8 satisfies $G(x) = F(x) + C$ for some constant C and all x on the interval $[a, b]$. In particular, when $x = a$, we have

$$0 = \int_a^a f(t)\, dt = G(a) = F(a) + C$$

so that $C = -F(a)$. Finally, by letting $x = b$, we find that

$$\int_a^b f(t)\, dt = G(b) = F(b) + C = F(b) + [-F(a)] = F(b) - F(a)$$

This provides an alternative proof of the (first) fundamental theorem.

EXAMPLE 4   Using the second fundamental theorem

Differentiate $F(x) = \int_7^x (2t - 3)\, dt$.

Solution   From the second fundamental theorem, we can obtain $F'(x)$ by simply replacing t with x in the integrand $f(t) = 2t - 3$. Thus

$$F'(x) = \frac{d}{dx}\left[\int_7^x (2t - 3)\, dt\right] = 2x - 3$$

The second fundamental theorem of calculus can also be applied to an integral function with a variable *lower* limit of integration. For example, to differentiate

$$G(z) = \int_z^5 \frac{\sin u}{u}\, du$$

reverse the order of integration and apply the second fundamental theorem of calculus, as before:

$$G'(z) = \frac{d}{dz}\left[\int_z^5 \frac{\sin u}{u}\, du\right] = \frac{d}{dz}\left[-\int_5^z \frac{\sin u}{u}\, du\right] = -\frac{d}{dz}\left[\int_5^z \frac{\sin u}{u}\, du\right] = -\frac{\sin z}{z}$$

■ LEIBNIZ'S RULE

Occasionally, it is necessary to differentiate an integral in which one (or both) of the limits of integration is a function. More specifically, suppose $u(x)$ is a differentiable function of x and that F is the function defined by

$$F(u) = \int_a^{u(x)} f(t)\, dt$$

for a continuous function f. Then F is a function of u, and the second fundamental theorem of calculus tells us that

$$\frac{dF}{du} = \frac{d}{du}\left[\int_a^u f(t)\, dt\right] = f(u)$$

However, F can also be regarded as a composite function of x, and by applying the chain rule, we find that

$$\frac{dF}{dx} = \frac{dF}{du}\cdot\frac{du}{dx}$$

so that

$$\frac{d}{dx}\left[\int_a^{u(x)} f(t)\, dt\right] = \frac{d}{du}\left[\int_a^u f(t)\, dt\right]\frac{du}{dx} = f(u)\frac{du}{dx}$$

More generally, an integral with differentiable functions in both limits of integration can be differentiated by applying the following useful theorem.

THEOREM 4.9   Leibniz's rule

If $u(x)$ and $v(x)$ are differentiable functions of x, then

$$\frac{d}{dx}\left[\int_{v(x)}^{u(x)} f(t)\, dt\right] = f(u)\frac{du}{dx} - f(v)\frac{dv}{dx}$$

Proof: A formal proof of Leibniz's rule requires the chain rule for a function of two variables and will be given in Section 12.5. The plausibility of this rule can be demonstrated by noting that for any number a between v and u

$$\int_v^u f(t)\, dt = \int_v^a f(t)\, dt + \int_a^u f(t)\, dt = -\int_a^v f(t)\, dt + \int_a^u f(t)\, dt$$

and thus, by differentiating, we obtain

$$\frac{d}{dx}\left[\int_{v(x)}^{u(x)} f(t)\, dt\right] = \frac{d}{dx}\left[-\int_{a}^{v(x)} f(t)\, dt\right] + \frac{d}{dx}\left[\int_{a}^{u(x)} f(t)\, dt\right]$$

$$= -f(v)\frac{dv}{dx} + f(u)\frac{du}{dx} \qquad \blacksquare$$

EXAMPLE 5   Applying Leibniz's rule

Differentiate $F(x) = \int_{\sqrt{x}}^{x^2-3x} \tan t\, dt$.

Solution   We shall apply Leibniz's rule with $f(t) = \tan t$, $u(x) = x^2 - 3x$, and $v(x) = \sqrt{x}$. Accordingly,

$$\frac{du}{dx} = 2x - 3 \quad \text{and} \quad \frac{dv}{dx} = \frac{1}{2}\cdot\frac{1}{\sqrt{x}}$$

so that

$$\frac{dF}{dx} = (2x - 3)\tan(x^2 - 3x) - \tan\sqrt{x}\left(\frac{1}{2}\cdot\frac{1}{\sqrt{x}}\right)$$

$$= (2x - 3)\tan(x^2 - 3x) - \frac{\tan\sqrt{x}}{2\sqrt{x}} \qquad \rule{1.5em}{0.4ex}$$

PROBLEM SET 4.5

(A) *In Problems 1–6 find c such that*

$$\int_{a}^{b} f(x)\, dx = f(c)(b - a)$$

as guaranteed by the mean value theorem for integrals. If you cannot find such a value, explain why the theorem does not apply.

1. $f(x) = 4x^3$ on $[1, 2]$

2. $f(x) = x^2 + 4x + 1$ on $[0, 2]$

3. $f(x) = 15x^{-2}$ on $[1, 5]$

4. $f(x) = 12x^{-3}$ on $(0, 3)$

5. $f(x) = 2\csc^2 x$ on $\left[-\frac{\pi}{3}, \frac{\pi}{3}\right]$

6. $f(x) = \cos x$ on $\left[-\frac{\pi}{2}, \frac{\pi}{2}\right]$

Use the second fundamental theorem of calculus to find the derivative of F in Problems 7–12. Next, verify your answer by integrating to find F and then differentiating the result.

7. $F(x) = \int_{0}^{x} (4t + 9)\, dt$

8. $F(x) = \int_{0}^{x} (3t^2 - 4t + 5)\, dt$

9. $F(x) = \int_{4}^{x} (\sqrt[4]{t} - 4)\, dt$

10. $F(x) = \int_{1}^{x} \frac{t\, dt}{\sqrt{1 + 3t^2}}$

11. $F(x) = \int_{1}^{x} \frac{dt}{(1 - 3t)^3}$

12. $F(x) = \int_{\pi/3}^{x} \sec t \tan t\, dt$

Determine the area of the indicated region in Problems 13–18 and then draw a rectangle with base (b − a) and height f(c) for some c on [a, b] so that the area of the rectangle is equal to the area of the given region.

13. $y = \frac{1}{2}x$ on $[0, 10]$

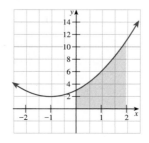

14. $y = x^2$ on $[0, 3]$

15. $y = x^2 + 2x + 3$ on $[0, 2]$

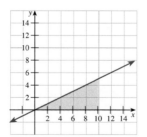

16. $y = \frac{1}{x^2}$ on $[0.5, 2]$

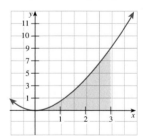

17. $y = \cos x$ on $[-1, 1.5]$ **18.** $y = x + \sin x$ on $[0.5, 2]$

Find the average value of the function given in Problems 19–30 on the prescribed interval.

19. $f(x) = x^2 - x + 1$ on $[-1, 2]$

20. $f(x) = x^3 - 3x^2$ on $[-2, 1]$

21. $f(x) = \sin x$ on $\left[0, \frac{\pi}{4}\right]$

22. $f(x) = 2 \sin x - \cos x$ on $\left[0, \frac{\pi}{2}\right]$

23. $f(x) = \sqrt{4 - x}$ on $[0, 4]$ **24.** $f(x) = \sqrt[3]{1 - x}$ on $[-7, 0]$

25. $f(x) = (2x - 3)^3$ on $[0,1]$ **26.** $f(x) = x\sqrt{2x^2 + 7}$ on $[0,1]$

27. $f(x) = x(x^2 + 1)^3$ on $[-2, 1]$ **28.** $f(x) = \dfrac{x}{\sqrt{x^2 + 1}}$ on $[0, 3]$

29. $f(x) = \sqrt{9 - x^2}$ on $[-3, 3]$
    Hint: The integral can be evaluated as part of a circle.

30. $f(x) = \sqrt{16 - x^2}$ on $[0, 4]$
    Hint: The integral can be evaluated as part of a circle.

Ⓑ *Use Leibniz's rule to differentiate the integral functions given in Problems 31–34.*

31. $F(x) = \displaystyle\int_2^x \cos t^2 \, dt$ **32.** $G(x) = \displaystyle\int_x^{-1} \frac{t^2 + 3}{t - 1} \, dt$

33. $H(t) = \displaystyle\int_{3t}^{1-t} \frac{\sin x}{x + 1} \, dx$ **34.** $G(y) = \displaystyle\int_{1-y^2}^{\sqrt{y}} \frac{dz}{z + 1}$

35. If an object is propelled upward from ground level with an initial velocity v_0, then its height at time t is given by

$$s = -\tfrac{1}{2}gt^2 + v_0 t$$

where g is the constant acceleration due to gravity. Show that between times t_0 and t_1, the average height of the object is

$$s = -\tfrac{1}{6}g[t_1^2 + t_1 t_0 + t_0^2] + \tfrac{1}{2}v_0(t_1 + t_0)$$

36. What is the average velocity for the object described in Problem 35 during the same time period?

37. Records indicate that t hours past midnight, the temperature at the local airport was

$$f(t) = -0.3t^2 + 4t + 10$$

degrees Celsius. What was the average temperature at the airport between 9:00 A.M. and noon?

38. Suppose a study indicates that t years from now, the level of carbon dioxide in the air of a certain city will be

$$L(t) = (t + 1)^2$$

parts per million (ppm).

a. What is the average level of carbon dioxide in the first 3 years?

b. At what time (or times) does the average level of carbon dioxide actually occur? Answer to the nearest month.

Ⓒ **39.** Let $f(t)$ be a function that is continuous and satisfies $f(t) \geq 0$ on the interval $\left[0, \frac{\pi}{2}\right]$. Suppose it is known that for any number x between 0 and $\frac{\pi}{2}$, the region under the graph of f on $[0, x]$ has area $A(x) = \tan x$.

a. Explain why $\displaystyle\int_0^x f(t) \, dt = \tan x$ for $0 \leq x \leq \frac{\pi}{2}$.

b. Differentiate both sides of the equation in part **a** and deduce the identity of f.

40. THINK TANK PROBLEM Suppose that $f(t)$ is continuous for all t and that for any number x it is known that the average value of f on $[-1, x]$ is

$$A(x) = \sin x$$

Use this information to deduce the identity of f.

41. Suppose that $f(t)$ is continuous for all t and that for any number x the average value of f on $[x, x^2]$ is

$$A(x) = \frac{1}{x}$$

Find $f(2)$ given that $f(4) = 2f(2)$. *Hint*: Use Leibniz's rule.

4.6 NUMERICAL INTEGRATION: THE TRAPEZOIDAL RULE AND SIMPSON'S RULE

IN THIS SECTION Approximation by rectangles, trapezoidal rule, Simpson's rule, error estimation

The fundamental theorem of calculus can be used to evaluate an integral whenever an appropriate antiderivative is known. However, certain functions have no simple antiderivative. To find a definite integral of such a function, it is often necessary to use numerical approximation. In this section, we shall examine approximation by rectangles, by trapezoids, and by parabolic arcs (through Simpson's rule). It will help if you have access to a calculator or computer.

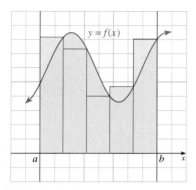

Figure 4.16 Approximation by rectangles

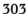

■ APPROXIMATION BY RECTANGLES

If $f(x) \geq 0$ on the interval $[a, b]$, the definite integral $\int_a^b f(x)\, dx$ is equal to area under the graph of f on $[a, b]$. As we saw in Section 4.1, one way to approximate this area is to use n rectangles, as shown in Figure 4.16. In particular, divide the interval $[a, b]$ into n subintervals, each of width $\Delta x = \dfrac{b - a}{n}$, and let x_k^* denote the right endpoint of the kth subinterval. The base of the kth rectangle is the kth subinterval, and its height is $f(x_k^*)$. Hence, the area of the kth rectangle is $f(x_k^*)\,\Delta x$. The sum of the areas of all n rectangles is an approximation for the area under the curve and hence an approximation for the corresponding definite integral. Thus,

$$\int_a^b f(x)\, dx \approx f(x_1^*)\,\Delta x + f(x_2^*)\,\Delta x + \cdots + f(x_n^*)\,\Delta x$$

This approximation improves as the number of rectangles increases, and we can estimate the integral to any desired degree of accuracy by taking n large enough. However, because fairly large values of n are usually required to achieve reasonable accuracy, approximation by rectangles is rarely used in practice.

■ THE TRAPEZOIDAL RULE

The accuracy of the approximation generally improves significantly if trapezoids are used instead of rectangles. Figure 4.17 shows the area from Figure 4.16 approximated by n trapezoids instead of rectangles. Even from these rough illustrations you can see how much better the approximation is in this case.

Suppose the interval $[a, b]$ is partitioned into n equal parts by the subdivision points $x_0, x_1, \ldots, x_n$, where $x_0 = a$ and $x_n = b$. The kth trapezoid is shown in greater detail in Figure 4.18.

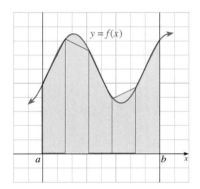

Figure 4.17 Approximation by trapezoids

Recall the formula for the area of a trapezoid:

$$A = \tfrac{1}{2}(b_1 + b_2)h$$

Figure 4.18 The kth trapezoid has area $\tfrac{1}{2}[f(x_{k-1}) + f(x_k)]\,\Delta x$.

If we let T_n denote the sum of the areas of n trapezoids, we see that

$$T_n = \tfrac{1}{2}[f(x_0) + f(x_1)]\,\Delta x + \tfrac{1}{2}[f(x_1) + f(x_2)]\,\Delta x + \cdots + \tfrac{1}{2}[f(x_{n-1}) + f(x_n)]\,\Delta x$$

$$= \tfrac{1}{2}[f(x_0) + 2f(x_1) + 2f(x_2) + \cdots + 2f(x_{n-1}) + f(x_n)]\,\Delta x$$

The sum T_n estimates the total area under the curve $y = f(x)$ on the interval $[a, b]$ and hence also estimates the integral

$$\int_a^b f(x)\, dx$$

This approximation formula is known as the *trapezoidal rule* and applies as a means of approximating the integral, even if the function f is not positive.

Trapezoidal Rule

Let f be continuous on $[a, b]$. The **trapezoidal rule** is

$$\int_a^b f(x)\, dx \approx \tfrac{1}{2}[f(x_0) + 2f(x_1) + 2f(x_2) + \cdots + 2f(x_{n-1}) + f(x_n)]\Delta x$$

where $\Delta x = \dfrac{b-a}{n}$ and, for the kth subinterval, $x_k = a + k\Delta x$. Moreover, the larger the value for n, the better the approximation.

Our first example uses the trapezoidal rule to estimate the value of an integral that we can compute exactly by using the fundamental theorem.

EXAMPLE 1   Trapezoidal rule approximation

Use the trapezoidal rule with $n = 4$ to estimate $\displaystyle\int_{-1}^{2} x^2\, dx$.

Solution   The interval is $[a, b] = [-1, 2]$, so $a = -1$ and $b = 2$. Then,

$$\Delta x = \frac{2 - (-1)}{4} = \frac{3}{4} = 0.75. \text{ Thus,}$$

$$x_0 = a = -1 \qquad\qquad f(x_0) = f(-1) = (-1)^2 = 1$$
$$x_1 = a + 1 \cdot \Delta x = -1 + \tfrac{3}{4} = -\tfrac{1}{4} \qquad 2f(x_1) = 2\left(-\tfrac{1}{4}\right)^2 = \tfrac{1}{8} = 0.125$$
$$x_2 = a + 2 \cdot \Delta x = -1 + \tfrac{6}{4} = \tfrac{1}{2} \qquad 2f(x_2) = 2\left(\tfrac{1}{2}\right)^2 = \tfrac{1}{2} = 0.5$$
$$x_3 = a + 3 \cdot \Delta x = -1 + \tfrac{9}{4} = \tfrac{5}{4} \qquad 2f(x_3) = 2\left(\tfrac{5}{4}\right)^2 = \tfrac{25}{8} = 3.125$$
$$x_4 = a + 4 \cdot \Delta x = b = 2 \qquad\qquad f(x_4) = 2^2 = 4$$
$$T_4 = \tfrac{1}{2}[1 + 0.125 + 0.5 + 3.125 + 4](0.75) = 3.28125$$

The exact value of the integral in Example 1 is

$$\int_{-1}^{2} x^2\, dx = \left.\frac{x^3}{3}\right|_{-1}^{2} = \frac{8}{3} - \frac{-1}{3} = 3$$

Therefore, the trapezoidal estimate T_4 involves an error, which we denote by E_4. We find that

$$E_4 = \int_{-1}^{2} x^2\, dx - T_4 = 3 - 3.28125 = -0.28125$$

The negative sign indicates that the trapezoidal formula *overestimated* the true value of the integral in Example 1.

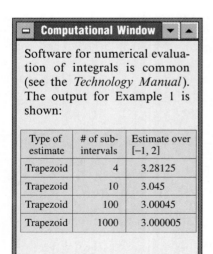

Computational Window

Software for numerical evaluation of integrals is common (see the *Technology Manual*). The output for Example 1 is shown:

Type of estimate	# of sub-intervals	Estimate over [–1, 2]
Trapezoid	4	3.28125
Trapezoid	10	3.045
Trapezoid	100	3.00045
Trapezoid	1000	3.000005

◼ SIMPSON'S RULE

Roughly speaking, the accuracy of a procedure for estimating the area under a curve depends on how well the upper boundary of each approximating strip fits the shape of the given curve. Trapezoidal strips often result in a better approximation than rectangles, and it is reasonable to expect even greater accuracy if the approximating strips have curved upper boundaries, as shown in Figure 4.19. The name given to the procedure in which the approximating strip has a parabolic arc for its upper boundary is called **Simpson's rule.**[*]

We shall derive Simpson's rule as a means for approximating, as before, the area under the curve $y = f(x)$ on the interval $[a, b]$, where f is continuous and satisfies $f(x) \geq 0$. First, we partition the given interval into a number of equal subintervals, but this time, we require the number of subdivisions to be an *even* number (because this requirement will simplify the formula associated with the final result). If $x_0, x_1, \ldots, x_n$ are the subdivision points in our partition (with $x_0 = a$ and $x_n = b$), we pass a parabolic arc through the points, three at a time (the points with x-coordinates x_0, x_1, x_2, then those with x_2, x_3, x_4, and so on). It can be shown (see Problem 31) that the region under the parabolic curve $y = f(x)$ on the interval $[x_{2k-2}, x_{2k}]$ has area

$$\tfrac{1}{3}[f(x_{2k-2}) + 4f(x_{2k-1}) + f(x_{2k})]\Delta x$$

where $\Delta x = \dfrac{b-a}{n}$. This procedure is illustrated in Figure 4.20.

a. Rectangular

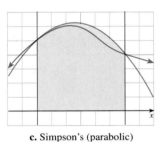

b. Trapezoidal

c. Simpson's (parabolic)

Figure 4.19 A comparison of approximating strips

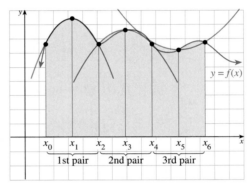

Figure 4.20 Approximation using parabolas

By adding the area of the approximating parabolic strips and combining terms, we obtain the sum S_n of n parabolic regions:

$$S_n = \tfrac{1}{3}[f(x_0) + 4f(x_1) + f(x_2)]\Delta x + \tfrac{1}{3}[f(x_2) + 4f(x_3) + f(x_4)]\Delta x$$

$$+ \cdots + \tfrac{1}{3}[f(x_{n-2}) + 4f(x_{n-1}) + f(x_n)]\Delta x$$

$$= \tfrac{1}{3}[f(x_0) + 4f(x_1) + 2f(x_2) + 4f(x_3) + \cdots + 4f(x_{n-1}) + f(x_n)]\Delta x$$

These observations are summarized in the following box:

Simpson's Rule

Let f be continuous on $[a, b]$. **Simpson's rule** is

$$\int_a^b f(x)\, dx \approx \tfrac{1}{3}[f(x_0) + 4f(x_1) + 2f(x_2) + \cdots + 4f(x_{n-1}) + f(x_n)]\Delta x$$

where $\Delta x = \dfrac{b-a}{n}$, $x_k = a + k\Delta x$, k an integer and n an even integer. Moreover, the larger the value for n, the better the approximation.

[*]This rule is named for Thomas Simpson (1710–1761), an English mathematician, who, curiously, neither discovered nor made any special use of the formula that bears his name.

EXAMPLE 2   Approximation by Simpson's rule

Use Simpson's rule with $n = 10$ to approximate $\int_1^2 \frac{dx}{x}$.

Solution   We have $\Delta x = \frac{2-1}{10} = 0.1$, and $x_0 = a = 1$, $x_1 = 1.1$, $x_2 = 1.2, \ldots,$ $x_9 = 1.9$, $x_{10} = 2$.

$$\int_1^2 \frac{1}{x}\, dx \approx S_{10}$$

$$= \frac{1}{3}\left(\frac{1}{1} + \frac{4}{1.1} + \frac{2}{1.2} + \frac{4}{1.3} + \frac{2}{1.4} + \frac{4}{1.5} + \frac{2}{1.6} + \frac{4}{1.7} + \frac{2}{1.8} + \frac{4}{1.9} + \frac{1}{2}\right)(0.1)$$

$$\approx 0.6931502$$

■

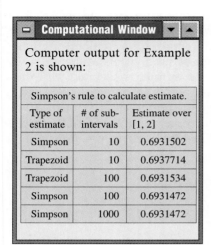

Computational Window

Computer output for Example 2 is shown:

Simpson's rule to calculate estimate.

Type of estimate	# of sub-intervals	Estimate over [1, 2]
Simpson	10	0.6931502
Trapezoid	10	0.6937714
Trapezoid	100	0.6931534
Simpson	100	0.6931472
Simpson	1000	0.6931472

■ ERROR ESTIMATION

The difference between the value of an integral and its estimated value is called its **error**. Because this error depends on n, we denote it by E_n.

THEOREM 4.10   Error in the trapezoidal rule and Simpson's rule

If f has a continuous second derivative on $[a, b]$, then the error E_n in approximating $\int_b^a f(x)\, dx$ by the trapezoidal rule satisfies

Trapezoidal error: $|E_n| \leq \dfrac{(b-a)^3}{12n^2} M$, where M is the maximum value of $|f''(x)|$ on $[a, b]$

Moreover, if f has a continuous fourth derivative on $[a, b]$, then the error E_n (n even) in approximating $\int_b^a f(x)\, dx$ by Simpson's rule satisfies

Simpson's error: $|E_n| \leq \dfrac{(b-a)^5}{180n^4} K$, where K is the maximum value of $|f^{(4)}(x)|$ on $[a, b]$

Proof: The proofs of these error estimates are beyond of scope of this book; they can be found in many advanced calculus textbooks and in most numerical analysis books.   ■

EXAMPLE 3   Estimate of error when using Simpson's rule

Estimate the accuracy of the approximation of $\int_1^2 \frac{dx}{x}$ by Simpson's rule with $n = 10$ in Example 2.

Solution   If $f(x) = \frac{1}{x}$, we find that $f^{(4)}(x) = 24x^{-5}$. The maximum value of this function will occur at a critical value (there are none on $[1, 2]$) or at an endpoint. Thus, the largest value of $|f^{(4)}(x)|$ on $[1, 2]$ is $|f^{(4)}(1)| = 24$. Now, apply the error formula with $K = 24$, $a = 1$, $b = 2$, and $n = 10$ to obtain

$$|E_n| \leq \frac{K(b-a)^5}{180n^4} = \frac{24(2-1)^5}{180(10)^4} \approx 0.0000133$$

That is, the error in the approximation in Example 2 is guaranteed to be no greater than 0.0000133.   ■

Historical Note

PIERRE SIMON LAPLACE
(1749–1827)

Newton and Leibniz have been credited with the discovery of calculus, but much of its refine-

With the aid of the error estimates, we can decide in advance how many subintervals to use in order to achieve a desired degree of accuracy.

EXAMPLE 4   Choosing number of subintervals to guarantee given accuracy

How many subintervals are required to guarantee that the error will be less than 0.00005 in the approximation of

$$\int_1^2 \frac{dx}{x}$$

on [1, 2] using the trapezoidal rule?

Solution   Because $f(x) = x^{-1}$, we have $f''(x) = 2x^{-3}$. On [1, 2] the largest value of $|f''(x)|$ is $|f''(1)| = 2$, so $M = 2$, $a = 1$, $b = 2$ and

$$|E_n| \le \frac{2(2-1)^3}{12n^2} = \frac{1}{6n^2}$$

The goal is to find the smallest positive integer n for which

$$\frac{1}{6n^2} < 0.00005$$
$$10,000 < 3n^2 \qquad \textit{Multiply by the positive number } 60{,}000n^2$$
$$10,000 - 3n^2 < 0$$
$$(100 - \sqrt{3}n)(100 + \sqrt{3}n) < 0$$
$$n < -\frac{100}{\sqrt{3}} \quad \text{or} \quad n > \frac{100}{\sqrt{3}} \approx 57.735027$$

The smallest positive integer that satisfies this condition is $n = 58$; therefore, 58 subintervals are required to ensure the desired accuracy. ▬

If f is the linear function $f(x) = Ax + B$, then $f''(x) = 0$ and we can take $M = 0$ as the error estimate. In this case, the error in applying the trapezoidal rule satisfies $|E_n| \le 0$. That is, the trapezoidal rule is *exact* for a linear function, which is what we would expect, because the region under a line on an interval is a trapezoid.

In discussing the accuracy of the trapezoidal rule as a means of estimating the value of the definite integral

$$I = \int_a^b f(x)\, dx$$

we have focused attention on the "error term," but this only measures the error that comes from estimating I by the trapezoidal or Simpson approximation sum. There are other kinds of error that must be considered in this or any other method of approximation. In particular, each time we cut off digits from a decimal, we incur what is known as a round-off error. For example, a round-off error occurs when we use 0.66666667 in place of $\frac{2}{3}$ or 3.1415927 for the number π. Round-off errors occur even in large computers and can accumulate to cause real problems. Specialized methods for dealing with these and other errors are studied in numerical analysis.

The examples of numerical integration examined in this section are intended as illustrations and thus involve relatively simple computations, whereas in practice, such computations often involve hundreds of terms and can be quite tedious. Fortunately, these computations are extremely well-suited to automatic computing, and the reader who is interested in pursuing computer methods in numerical integration will find an introduction to this topic in the computer supplement.

(sidebar)

ment was due to the mathematicians Laplace, Lagrange, and Gauss. Pierre Simon Laplace was a French mathematician who did outstanding work in differential equations, which were introduced in this chapter. He was also known for his work in celestial mechanics, geodesy, and probability. We will meet Lagrange and Gauss in other historical notes, but these three great mathematicians of calculus were contrasted by W. W. Rouse Ball.

The great masters of modern analysis are Lagrange, Laplace, and Gauss, who were contemporaries. It is interesting to note the marked contrast in their styles. Lagrange is perfect both in form and matter; he is careful to explain his procedure, and though his arguments are general they are easy to follow. Laplace on the other hand explains nothing, is indifferent to style, and, if satisfied that his results are correct, is content to leave them either with no proof or with a faulty one. Gauss is exact and elegant as Lagrange, but even more difficult to follow than Laplace, for he removes every trace of the analysis by which he reached his results, and strives to give a proof which while rigorous shall be as concise and synthetical as possible.

A Short Account of the History of Mathematics as quoted in *Mathematical Circles Adieu* by Howard Eves (Boston: Prindle, Weber & Schmidt, Inc., 1977).

PROBLEM SET 4.6

(A) *Approximate the integrals in Problems 1–2 using the trapezoidal rule and Simpson's rule with the specified number of subintervals and then compare your answers with the exact value of the definite integral.*

1. $\int_1^2 x^2 \, dx$ with $n = 4$

2. $\int_0^4 \sqrt{x} \, dx$ with $n = 6$

Approximate the integrals given in Problems 3–6 with the specified number of subintervals using: **a.** *the trapezoidal rule* **b.** *Simpson's rule.*

3. $\int_0^1 \dfrac{dx}{1 + x^2}$ with $n = 4$

4. $\int_{-1}^0 \sqrt{1 + x^2} \, dx$ with $n = 4$

5. $\int_2^4 \sqrt{1 + \sin x} \, dx$ with $n = 4$

6. $\int_0^2 x \cos x \, dx$ with $n = 6$

(B) **7.** ■ **What Does This Say?**   Describe the trapezoidal rule.
8. ■ **What Does This Say?**   Describe Simpson's rule.

Estimate the value of the integrals in Problems 9–14 to within the prescribed accuracy.

9. $\int_0^1 \dfrac{dx}{x^2 + 1}$ with error less than 0.05

10. $\int_{-1}^2 \sqrt{1 + x^2} \, dx$ with error less than 0.05

11. $\int_0^1 \cos^2 x \, dx$ accurate to three decimal places

12. $\int_1^2 x^{-1} \, dx$ accurate to three decimal places

13. $\int_0^4 x\sqrt{4 - x} \, dx$ with error less than 0.1

14. $\int_0^\pi \theta \cos^2 \theta \, d\theta$ with error less than 0.01

In Problems 15–18, determine how many subintervals are required to guarantee accuracy to within 0.00005 using **a.** *the trapezoidal rule* **b.** *Simpson's rule*

15. $\int_1^3 x^{-1} \, dx$

16. $\int_{-1}^4 (x^3 + 2x^2 + 1) \, dx$

17. $\int_1^4 \dfrac{dx}{\sqrt{x}}$

18. $\int_0^2 \cos x \, dx$

19. A quarter-circle of radius 1 has the equation $y = \sqrt{1 - x^2}$ for $0 \le x \le 1$, which means that

$$\int_0^1 \sqrt{1 - x^2} \, dx = \frac{\pi}{4}$$

Estimate π correct to one decimal place by applying the trapezoidal rule to this integral.

20. A quarter-circle of radius 1 has the equation $y = \sqrt{1 - x^2}$ for $0 \le x \le 1$, which means that

$$\int_0^1 \sqrt{1 - x^2} \, dx = \frac{\pi}{4}$$

Estimate π correct to one decimal place by applying Simpson's rule to this integral.

21. Find the smallest value of n for which the trapezoidal rule estimates the value of the integral

$$\int_1^2 x^{-1} \, dx$$

with six decimal-place accuracy.

22. The following graph (from the *Wall Street Journal*, February 26, 1986) shows the 10-year treasury bond rate for the years 1980–1985. Estimate the area in terms of the rectangles shown on the grid under this curve using a trapezoidal approximation where $n = 6$, and each year is 1 unit.

23. The width of an irregularly shaped dam is measured at 5-m intervals, with the results indicated in Figure 4.21. Use Simpson's rule to estimate the area of the face of the dam.

Figure 4.21 Area of the face of a dam

Computational Window

24. Apply the trapezoidal rule to the following data found on a spreadsheet (table):

	A	B
1	x	$f(x)$
2	0	3.7
3	0.3	3.9
4	0.6	4.1
5	0.9	4.1
6	1.2	4.2
7	1.5	4.4
8	1.8	4.6
9	2.1	4.9
10	2.4	5.2
11	2.7	5.5
12	3	6

25. Apply Simpson's rule to the following data found on a spreadsheet (table):

	A	B
1	x	$f(x)$
2	0	10
3	0.5	9.75
4	1	10
5	1.5	10.75
6	2	12
7	2.5	13.75
8	3	16
9	3.5	18.75
10	4	22
11	4.5	25.75
12	5	30

26. The idea here is to study the "order of convergence" of three numerical integration methods; that is, how the error goes to zero as $n \to \infty$. As summarized in Theorem 4.10, the error in the trapezoid rule behaves like M/n^2 and the error in Simpson's rule behaves like K/n^4; hence for large n values Simpson's rule is usually much more accurate. It can also be shown that the error in the rectangular rule (select midpoints) is about $\frac{1}{2}$ that of the trapezoid rule. In this problem, you are to demonstrate this notion.

a. By using the fundamental theorem, show that

$$\int_0^\pi \sin x \, dx = 2 \qquad \text{(exactly)}$$

b. Now, for several values of n (say, 10, 20, 40, and 80) approximate the above integral by the three numerical methods. Build a table of the errors; thus, verify the above discussed order of convergence. In particular, from your table, find approximate values of M and K.

27. a. Repeat Problem 26, except now let $f(x) = 9x - x^3$, on $[0, \pi]$. You may be surprised by the result of Simpson's rule; but, after some thought, explain this situation.

b. Simpson struggles! In contrast to part **a,** here is an example where Simpson's rule does not live up to expectations. For $n = 10, 20, 40$, and 80, use Simpson's rule and the rectangular rule (select midpoints) for this integral and make a table of errors. Then try to explain Simpson's poor performance. *Hint*: Look at the formula for the error.

$$\int_0^2 \sqrt{4 - x^2} \, dx = \pi$$

28. Show that if $p(x)$ is any polynomial of degree less than or equal to 3, then

$$\int_a^b p(x) \, dx = \frac{b-a}{6} \left[p(a) + 4p\left(\frac{a+b}{2}\right) + p(b) \right]$$

This result is often called the *prismoidal rule*.

29. Use the prismoidal rule (Problem 28) to evaluate

$$\int_{-1}^2 (x^3 - 3x + 4) \, dx$$

30. Use the prismoidal rule (Problem 28) to evaluate

$$\int_{-1}^3 (x^3 + 2x^2 - 7) \, dx$$

31. Let $p(x)$ be a polynomial of degree at most 3.
a. Show there is a number c between 0 and 1 such that

$$\int_{-1}^1 p(x) \, dx = p(c) + p(-c)$$

b. Show that there is a number c such that

$$\int_{-1/2}^{1/2} p(x) \, dx = \tfrac{1}{3}[p(-c) + p(0) + p(c)]$$

32. Let $p(x) = Ax^3 + Bx^2 + Cx + D$ be a polynomial. Show that Simpson's rule gives the exact value for

$$\int_a^b P(x) \, dx$$

33. The object of this exercise is to prove Simpson's rule for the special case involving three points.
a. Let $P_1(-h, f(-h))$, $P_2(0, f(0))$, $P_3(h, f(h))$. Find the equation of the form $y = Ax^2 + Bx + C$ for the parabola through the points $P_1, P_2,$ and P_3.
b. If $y = p(x)$ is the quadratic function found in part **a,** show that

$$\int_{-h}^h p(x) \, dx = \frac{h}{3}[P(-h) + 4P(0) + P(h)]$$

c. Let $Q_1(x_1, f(x_1))$, $Q_2(x_2, f(x_2))$, $Q_3(x_3, f(x_3))$ be points with $x_2 = x_1 + h$, and $x_3 = x_1 + 2h$. Explain why

$$\int_{x_1}^{x_3} p(x) \, dx = \frac{h}{3}[P(x_1) + 4P(x_2) + P(x_3)]$$

4.7 AREA BETWEEN TWO CURVES

IN THIS SECTION Area between curves, area by vertical strips, area by horizontal strips, two applications to economics

We have seen how the area between the curves defined by $y = f(x)$ and the x-axis can be computed by the integral $\int_a^b f(x)\, dx$ on an interval $a \leq x \leq b$ where $f(x) \geq 0$. In this section, we shall find that integration can be used to find the area of more general regions between curves. We shall also see how two important economic applications can be considered as an area between two curves.

■ AREA BETWEEN CURVES

In some practical problems, you may have to compute the area between two curves. Suppose f and g are functions such that $f(x) \geq g(x)$ on the interval $[a, b]$, as shown in Figure 4.22. Note that we do not insist that both f and g are nonnegative functions, but we begin by showing that case in Figure 4.22.

  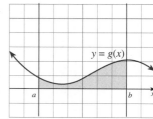

Area between $y = f(x)$ and $y = g(x)$ is equal to the area under $y = f(x)$ minus the area under $y = g(x)$

Figure 4.22 Area between two curves

a. Approximating rectangles

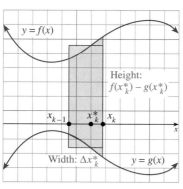

b. A typical vertical strip

Figure 4.23 Using Riemann sums to find the area between two curves

To find the area of the region R between the curves from $x = a$ to $x = b$, we subtract the area between the lower curve $y = g(x)$ from the area between the upper curve $y = f(x)$ and the x-axis; that is,

$$\text{AREA OF } R = \int_a^b f(x)\, dx - \int_a^b g(x)\, dx = \int_a^b [f(x) - g(x)]\, dx$$

This formula seems obvious in the situation where both $f(x) \geq 0$ and $g(x) \geq 0$, as shown in Figure 4.22. However, the following derivation requires only that f and g be continuous and satisfy $f(x) \geq g(x)$ on the interval $[a, b]$. We wish to find the area between the curves $y = f(x)$ and $y = g(x)$ on this interval. Choose a partition $\{x_0, x_1, x_2, \ldots, x_n\}$ of the interval $[a, b]$ and a representative number x_k^* from each subinterval $[x_{k-1}, x_k]$. Next, for each index k, with $k = 1, 2, \ldots, n$, construct a rectangle of width

$$\Delta x_k = x_k - x_{k-1}$$

and height

$$f(x_k^*) - g(x_k^*)$$

equal to the vertical distance between the two curves at $x = x_k^*$. A typical approximating rectangle is shown in Figure 4.23b. We refer to this approximating rectangle as a **vertical strip**.

The representative rectangle has area

$$[f(x_k^*) - g(x_k^*)]\Delta x_k$$

and the total area between the curves $y = f(x)$ and $y = g(x)$ can be estimated by the Riemann sum

$$\sum_{k=1}^{n} [f(x_k^*) - g(x_k^*)]\Delta x_k$$

It is reasonable to expect this estimate to improve if we increase the number of subdivision points in the partition P in such a way that the norm $\|P\|$ approaches 0. Thus, the region between the two curves has area

$$A = \lim_{\|P\| \to 0} \sum_{k=1}^{n} [f(x_k^*) - g(x_k^*)]\Delta x_k$$

which we recognize as the integral of the function $f(x) - g(x)$ on the interval $[a, b]$. These observations may be used to define the area between the curves.

Area Between Two Curves

> If f and g are continuous and satisfy $f(x) \geq g(x)$ on the closed interval $[a, b]$, then the **area between the two curves** $y = f(x)$ and $y = g(x)$ is given by
>
> $$A = \int_a^b [f(x) - g(x)]\, dx$$
>
> ■ *What this says:* To find the area between two curves on a given closed interval $[a, b]$ use the formula
>
> $$A = \int_a^b [\text{TOP CURVE} - \text{BOTTOM CURVE}]\, dx$$
>
> It is no longer necessary to require either curve to be above the x-axis. In fact, we will see later in this section that the curves might cross somewhere in the domain so that one curve is on top for part of the interval and the other curve is on top for the rest.

EXAMPLE 1 Area between two curves

Find the area of the region between the curves $y = x^3$ and $y = x^2 - x$ on the interval $[0, 1]$.

Solution The region is shown in Figure 4.24. We need to know which curve is the *top curve* on $[0, 1]$. Solve

$$x^3 = x^2 - x \quad \text{or} \quad x(x^2 - x + 1) = 0$$

The only real root is $x = 0$ ($x^2 - x + 1 = 0$ has no real roots). Thus, the same curve is on top throughout the interval $[0, 1]$. To see which curve is on top, take some representative value, such as $x = 0.5$, and note that because $(0.5)^3 > 0.5^2 - 0.5$, the curve $y = x^3$ must be above $y = x^2 - x$. Thus, the required area is given by

$$A = \int_0^1 [\underbrace{x^3}_{\substack{\text{Top} \\ \text{curve}}} - \underbrace{(x^2 - x)}_{\substack{\text{Bottom} \\ \text{curve}}}]\, dx = \left(\tfrac{1}{4}x^4 - \tfrac{1}{3}x^3 + \tfrac{1}{2}x^2\right)\Big|_0^1 = \frac{5}{12}$$

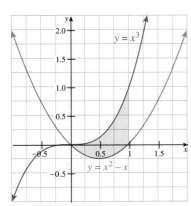

Figure 4.24 The area between the curves $y = x^3$ and $y = x^2 - x$ on $[0, 1]$

In Section 4.1 we defined area for a continuous function f with the restriction that $f(x) \geq 0$. Example 1 shows us that when considering the area between two curves, we need to be concerned no longer with the nonnegative restriction but only with whether $f(x) \geq g(x)$. We now use this idea to find the area for a function that is negative.

EXAMPLE 2   Area with a negative function

Find the area of the region bounded by the curve $y = x^2 - 4x$ and the x-axis.

Solution   We find the points of intersection of the curve and the x-axis:

$x^2 - 4x = 0$ *The curve intersects the*
x-axis where y = 0.

$x(x - 4) = 0$ so that $x = 0, 4$

The graph $f(x) \leq x^2 - 4x$ is shown in Figure 4.25. We see that on the interval $[0, 4]$, $f(x) \leq 0$, but we can find the area of the given region by considering the area between the curves defined by equations $y = 0$ and $y = x^2 - 4x$.

$$A = \int_0^4 [\underbrace{0}_{\text{Top curve}} - \underbrace{(x^2 - 4x)}_{\text{Bottom curve}}]\, dx = \left(-\frac{x^3}{3} + 2x^2\right)\Big|_0^4 = \frac{32}{3}$$

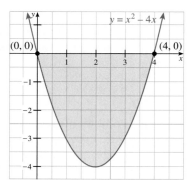

Figure 4.25 Area of region

■ AREA BY VERTICAL STRIPS

Although the only mathematically correct way to establish a formula involving integrals is to form Riemann sums and take the limit according to the definition of the definite integral, we can simulate this procedure with approximating strips. This simplification is especially useful for finding the area of a complicated region formed when two curves intersect one or more times, as shown in Figure 4.26. Note that the vertical strip has height $f(x) - g(x)$ if $y = f(x)$ is above $y = g(x)$ and height $g(x) - f(x)$ if $y = g(x)$ is above $y = f(x)$. In either case, the height can be represented by $|f(x) - g(x)|$, and the area of the vertical strip is

$$\Delta A = |f(x) - g(x)|\Delta x = |f(x) - g(x)|\, dx$$

Thus, we have a new integration formula for area; namely,

$$A = \int_a^b |f(x) - g(x)|\, dx$$

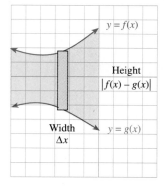

Figure 4.26 Area by vertical strips

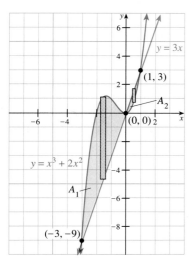

Figure 4.27 The area between the curve $y = x^3 + 2x^2$ and the line $y = 3x$.

⊘ You cannot use the formula $A = \int [f - g]\, dx$ directly here because the hypotheses $f \geq g$ is not satisfied. In order to use $A = \int |f - g|\, dx$ over the entire interval, you must remember that $|f - g|$ might be $f - g$ over part of the interval and $g - f$ over another part (see Figure 4.26). Make sure you check to see which curve is on top. Because the curves cross in Example 3, the interval must be subdivided accordingly. ⊘

EXAMPLE 3   Area by vertical strips

Find the area of the region bounded by the line $y = 3x$ and the curve $y = x^3 + 2x^2$.

Solution   The region between the curve and the line is the shaded portion of Figure 4.27. Part of the process of graphing these curves is to find which is the top curve and which is the bottom. To do this, we need to find where these curves intersect:

$$x^3 + 2x^2 = 3x \quad \text{or} \quad x(x + 3)(x - 1) = 0$$
$$x = 0, -3, 1$$

The points of intersection are $x = -3$, 0, and 1. In the subinterval $[-3, 0]$, labeled A_1 in Figure 4.27, the curve $y = x^3 + 2x^2$ is on top (test a typical point in the subinterval, such as $x = -1$), and on $[0, 1]$, the region labeled A_2, curve $y = 3x$ is on top. The representative vertical strips are shown in Figure 4.27, and the area between the curve and the line is given by the sum

$$A = \int_{-3}^{0} [(x^3 + 2x^2) - (3x)]\, dx + \int_{0}^{1} [(3x) - (x^3 + 2x^2)]\, dx$$
$$= \left(\tfrac{1}{4}x^4 + \tfrac{2}{3}x^3 - \tfrac{3}{2}x^2\right)\Big|_{-3}^{0} + \left(\tfrac{3}{2}x^2 - \tfrac{1}{4}x^4 - \tfrac{2}{3}x^3\right)\Big|_{0}^{1}$$
$$= 0 - \left(\tfrac{81}{4} - \tfrac{54}{3} - \tfrac{27}{2}\right) + \left(\tfrac{3}{2} - \tfrac{1}{4} - \tfrac{2}{3}\right) - 0$$
$$= \frac{71}{6} \text{ (or } 11.83333333 \text{ by calculator)}$$

■ AREA BY HORIZONTAL STRIPS

For many regions, it is more appropriate to form horizontal strips rather than vertical strips. The procedure for horizontal strips duplicates the procedure for vertical strips. Suppose we want to find the area between two curves of the form $x = F(y)$ and $x = G(y)$ on the interval $[c, d]$. Such a region is shown in Figure 4.28, together with a typical horizontal approximating rectangle of width Δy, which we refer to as a **horizontal strip**.

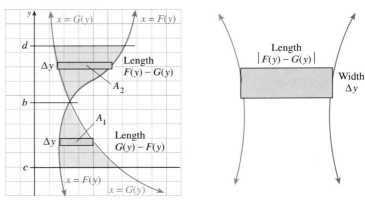

a. Approximation by horizontal strips of width Δy **b.** A typical horizontal strip

Figure 4.28 Area by horizontal strips

Note that regardless of which curve is "ahead" or "behind," the horizontal strip has length $|F(y) - G(y)|$ and area

$$\Delta A = |F(y) - G(y)|\Delta y$$

However, in practice, you must make sure to find the points of intersection of the curves and divide the integrals so that in each region one curve is the *leading curve* ("right curve") and the other is the *trailing curve* ("left curve"). Suppose the curves intersect where $y = b$ for b on the interval $[c, d]$, as shown in Figure 4.28. Then

$$A = \int_c^b \underbrace{[G(y) - F(y)]}_{G \text{ ahead of } F} \, dy + \int_b^d \underbrace{[F(y) - G(y)]}_{F \text{ ahead of } G} \, dy$$

EXAMPLE 4 Area by horizontal strips

Find the area of the region between the parabola $x = 4y - y^2$ and the line $x = 2y - 3$.

Solution Figure 4.29 shows the region between the parabola and the line, together with a typical horizontal strip. To find where the line and the parabola intersect, solve

$$4y - y^2 = 2y - 3 \quad \text{to obtain} \quad y = -1 \quad \text{and} \quad y = 3$$

Throughout the interval $[-1, 3]$, the parabola is to the right of the line (test a typical point between -1 and 3, such as $y = 0$). Thus, the horizontal strip has area

$$\Delta A = [\underbrace{(4y - y^2)}_{\text{Right curve}} - \underbrace{(2y - 3)}_{\text{Left curve}}]\Delta y$$

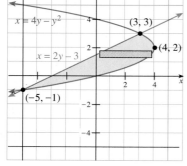

Figure 4.29 The area between the curves $x = 4y - y^2$ and $x = 2y - 3$ using horizontal strips

and the area between the parabola and the line is given by

$$A = \int_{-1}^3 [(4y - y^2) - (2y - 3)] \, dy = \int_{-1}^3 (3 + 2y - y^2) \, dy$$

$$= \left(3y + y^2 - \tfrac{1}{3}y^3\right)\Big|_{-1}^3 = (9 + 9 - 9) - \left(-3 + 1 + \tfrac{1}{3}\right) = 10\tfrac{2}{3}$$

In Example 4, the area can also be found by using vertical strips, but the procedure is more complicated. Note in Figure 4.30 that on the interval $[-5, 3]$, a representative vertical strip would extend from the bottom half of the parabola $y^2 - 4y + x = 0$ to the line $y = \tfrac{1}{2}(x + 3)$, whereas on the interval $[3, 4]$, a typical vertical strip would extend from the bottom half of the parabola $y^2 - 4y + x = 0$ to the top half. Thus, the area is given by the sum of two integrals. It can be shown that the computation of area by vertical strips gives the same result as that found by horizontal strips in Example 4.

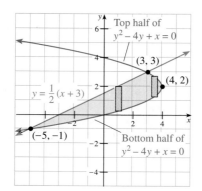

Figure 4.30 The area between the curves $x = 4y - y^2$ and $x = 2y - 3$ using vertical strips

■ TWO APPLICATIONS TO ECONOMICS

Next, we shall see how definite integration can be used in economics to compute *net earnings* generated on time and a special quantity called *consumer's surplus*.

Net Earnings. The net earnings generated by an industrial machine on a period of time is the difference between the total revenue generated by the machine and the total cost of operating and servicing the machine, as shown in Figure 4.31.

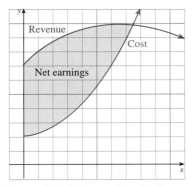

Figure 4.31 Net earnings is the difference between total revenue and total cost.

In the following example, the net earnings of a machine are calculated as a definite integral and interpreted as the area between two curves.

EXAMPLE 5   Profitability of a piece of equipment

Suppose that a piece of equipment is purchased in 1990 and will generate revenue of $R(x) = 5,000 - 20x^2$ dollars per year for x years after 1990. At the same time the cost of maintaining and operating the equipment at that time is $C(x) = 2,000 + 10x^2$ dollars.

a. For how many years will the use of the equipment remain profitable?
b. What are the net earnings generated by the machine during its period of profitability?

Solution   The cost and revenue curves are sketched in Figure 4.32.

a. Note that the revenue curve is above the cost curve until they cross, so the use of the equipment will be profitable as long as the revenue exceeds the cost; that is, until

$$5,000 - 20x^2 = 2,000 + 10x^2$$
$$30x^2 = 3,000$$
$$x = \pm 10 \qquad (-10 \text{ is not in the domain})$$

The equipment will be profitable for 10 yr.

b. The difference $P(x) = R(x) - C(x)$ represents the net earnings of the machine after x years after 1990. To obtain the *total* net earnings, we integrate over the period of profitability; that is, from $t = 0$ to $t = 10$.

$$\text{NET EARNINGS} = \int_0^{10} [R(x) - C(x)] \, dx$$

$$= \int_0^{10} [(5,000 - 20x^2) - (2,000 + 10x^2)] \, dx$$

$$= \int_0^{10} (3,000 - 30x^2) \, dx$$

$$= (3,000x - 10x^3)\Big|_0^{10} = 20,000$$

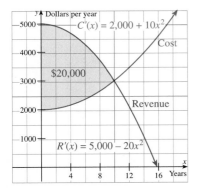

Figure 4.32 The net earnings from a piece of equipment

This piece of equipment should generate \$20,000 of net earnings for the years 1990–2000 (its 10-year period of profitability).   ▬

Consumer's Surplus.   In a competitive economy, the total amount that consumers actually spend on a commodity is usually less than the total amount they would have been willing to spend. The difference between the two amounts can be thought of as a savings realized by consumers and is known in economics as the **consumer's surplus.**

To get a better feel for the concept of consumer's surplus, consider an example of a couple who are willing to spend \$500 for their first TV set, \$300 for a second set, and only \$50 for a third set. If the market price is \$300, then the couple would buy only two sets and would spend a total of $2 \times \$300 = \$600$. This is less than the $\$500 + \$300 = \$800$ that the couple would have been willing to spend to get the two sets. The savings of $800 − $600 = $200 is the couple's consumer's surplus. Consumer's surplus has a simple geometric interpretation, shown in Figure 4.33.

(a)   (b)   (c)

Figure 4.33 Geometric interpretation of consumer's surplus

Note that p and q denote the market price and the corresponding demand, respectively. Figure 4.33a shows the region under the demand curve $p = D(q)$ from $q = 0$ to $q = q_0$, and the area of this region represents the total amount that consumers are willing to spend to get q_0 units of the commodity. The rectangle in Figure 4.33b has an area of $p_0 q_0$ and represents the actual consumer expenditure for q_0 units at p_0 dollars per unit. The difference between these two areas (Figure 4.33c) represents the consumer's surplus. That is, consumer's surplus is the area of the region between the demand curve $p = D(q)$ and the horizontal line $p = p_0$ so that

$$\int_0^{q_0} [D(q) - p_0]\, dq = \int_0^{q_0} D(q)\, dq - \int_0^{q_0} p_0\, dq = \int_0^{q_0} D(q)\, dq - p_0 q_0$$

Consumer's Surplus

If q_0 units of a commodity are sold at a price of p_0 dollars per unit and if $p = D(q)$ is the consumer's demand function for the commodity, then

$$\begin{bmatrix} \text{CONSUMER'S} \\ \text{SURPLUS} \end{bmatrix} = \begin{bmatrix} \text{TOTAL AMOUNT CONSUM-} \\ \text{ERS ARE WILLING TO} \\ \text{SPEND FOR } q_0 \text{ UNITS} \end{bmatrix} - \begin{bmatrix} \text{ACTUAL CONSUMER} \\ \text{EXPENDITURE FOR} \\ q_0 \text{ UNITS} \end{bmatrix}$$

$$= \int_0^{q_0} D(q)\, dq - p_0 q_0$$

EXAMPLE 6   Consumer's surplus

Suppose the consumer's demand function for a certain commodity is $D(q) = 4(25 - q^2)$ dollars per unit. Find the consumer's surplus if the commodity is sold for $64 per unit.

Solution   First find the number of units that will be bought by solving the demand equation $p = D(q)$ for q when $p = \$64$:

$$64 = 4(25 - q^2) \quad \text{so that} \quad q = 3 \quad \textit{Disregard} -3.$$

This says that $q_0 = 3$ units will be bought when the price is $p_0 = \$64$ per unit. The corresponding consumer's surplus is

$$\int_0^3 D(q)\, dq - 64(3) = \int_0^3 4(25 - q^2)\, dq - 192$$

$$= 4\left(25q - \tfrac{1}{3}q^3\right)\Big|_0^3 - 192 = 72$$

The consumer's surplus is the shaded area in Figure 4.34.

Figure 4.34 Consumer's demand curve $p = 4(25 - q^2)$ showing consumer's surplus

PROBLEM SET 4.7

A *Sketch a representative vertical or horizontal strip and find the area of the given region in Problems 1–6.*

1. $y = -x^2 + 6x - 5$
$y = \frac{3}{2}x - \frac{3}{2}$

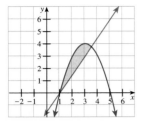

2. $x = y^2 - 6y$
$x = -y$

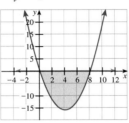

3. $x = y^2 - 5y$
$x = 0$

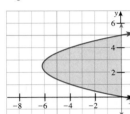

4. $y = x^2 - 8x$
$y = 0$

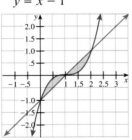

5. $y = \sin x$ on $[0, 2\pi]$
$y = 0$

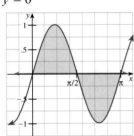

6. $y = (x - 1)^3$
$y = x - 1$

Sketch the area of the region bounded by the given equations, and find the area of each region in Problems 7–23.

7. $y = x^2, y = x, x = -1, x = 1$
8. $y = x^3, y = x, x = -1, x = 1$
9. $y = x^2, y = x^3$
10. $y = x^2, y = \sqrt[3]{x}$
11. $y = x^2 - 1, x = -1, x = 2, y = 0$
12. $y = 4x^2 - 9, x = 3, x = 0, y = 0$
13. $y = x^4 - 3x^2, y = 6x^2$
14. $x = 8 - y^2, x = y^2$
15. $x = 2 - y^2, x = y$
16. $y = x^2 + 3x - 5, y = -x^2 + x + 7$
17. $y = 2x^3 + x^2 - x - 1, y = x^3 + 2x^2 + 5x - 1$
18. $y = \sin x, y = \cos x, x = 0, x = \frac{\pi}{4}$
19. $y = \sin x, y = \sin 2x, x = 0, x = \pi$
20. $y = |x|, y = x^2 - 6$

21. $y = |4x - 1|, y = x^2 - 5, x = 0, x = 4$
22. x-axis, $y = x^3 - 2x^2 - x + 2$
23. y-axis, $x = y^3 - 3y^2 - 4y + 12$

Find the consumer's surplus for the given demand function defined by D(q) at the point that corresponds to the sales level q as given in Problems 24–27.

24. $D(q) = 3.5 - 0.5q$
   a. $q_0 = 1$ **b.** $q_0 = 1.5$
25. $D(q) = 2.5 - 1.5q$
   a. $q_0 = 1$ **b.** $q_0 = 0$
26. $D(q) = 100 - 8q$
   a. $q_0 = 4$ **b.** $q_0 = 10$
27. $D(q) = 150 - 6q$
   a. $q_0 = 5$ **b.** $q_0 = 12$

B **28.** ■ **What Does This Say?**   When finding the area between two curves, discuss reasons for deciding between vertical and horizontal strips.

29. ■ **What Does This Say?**   What is consumer's surplus?

In Problems 30–33, find the consumer's surplus at the point of market equilibrium [the level of production where supply S(q) equals demand D(q)].

Demand function	**Supply function**
30. $D(q) = 14 - q^2$	$S(q) = 2q^2 + 2$
31. $D(q) = 25 - q^2$	$S(q) = 5q^2 + 1$
32. $D(q) = 32 - 2q^2$	$S(q) = \frac{1}{3}q^2 + 2q + 5$
33. $D(q) = 27 - q^2$	$S(q) = \frac{1}{4}q^2 + \frac{1}{2}q + 5$

34. Find the area of the region that contains the origin and is bounded by the lines $2y = 11 - x$ and $y = 7x + 13$ and the curve $y = x^2 - 5$.

35. Show that the region defined by the inequalities $x^2 + y^2 \le 8$, $x \ge y$, and $y \ge 0$ has area π.

36. Find the area of the region bounded by the curve $\sqrt{x} + \sqrt{y} = 1$ and the coordinate axes.

37. Suppose an industrial machine that is x years old generates revenue

$$R(x) = 6{,}025 - 10x^2$$

dollars and costs

$$C(x) = 4{,}000 + 15x^2$$

dollars to operate and maintain.

   a. For how many years is it profitable to use this machine? [Recall that profit is $P(x) = R(x) - C(x)$].
   b. What are the net earnings generated by the machine during its period of profitability? Interpret this amount as the area between two curves.

38. After t hours on the job, one factory worker is producing

$$Q_1(t) = 60 - 2(t - 1)^2$$

units per hour, and a second is producing

$$Q_2(t) = 50 - 5t$$

units per hour. If both arrive on the job at 8:00 A.M., how many more units (to the nearest unit) will the first worker have produced by noon than the second worker? Interpret your answer as the area between two curves.

39. Suppose that x years from now, one investment plan will be generating profit at the rate of

$$P_1'(x) = 100 + x^2$$

dollars per year, whereas a second plan will be generating profit at the rate of

$$P_2'(x) = 220 + 2x$$

dollars per year.

a. For how many years will the second plan be more profitable?

b. How much excess profit will you earn if you invest in the second plan instead of the first for the period of time in part **a**? Interpret the excess profit as the area between two curves.

40. Parts for a piece of heavy machinery are sold in units of 1,000. The demand for the parts (in dollars) is given by

$$p(x) = 110 - x$$

The total cost is given by

$$C(x) = x^3 - 25x^2 + 2x + 30 \text{ (dollars)}$$

a. For what value of x is the profit

$$P(x) = xp(x) - C(x)$$

maximized?

b. Find the consumer's surplus with respect to the price that corresponds to maximum profit.

41. Repeat Problem 40 with $p(x) = 124 - 2x$ and $C(x) = 2x^3 - 59x^2 + 4x + 76$.

42. Suppose when q units of a commodity are produced, the demand is $p(q) = 45 - q^2$ dollars per unit, and the marginal cost is

$$\frac{dC}{dq} = 6 + \frac{1}{4}q^2$$

a. Find the total revenue and the marginal revenue.

b. Find the value of q (to the nearest unit) that maximizes profit.

c. Find the consumer's surplus (to the nearest unit) at the value of q where profit is maximized. *Hint*: Use the exact value (not the rounded value) of q.

43. Repeat Problem 42 with

$$p(q) = \frac{1}{4}(10 - q)^2 \quad \text{and} \quad \frac{dC}{dq} = \frac{3}{4}q^2 + 5$$

44. A company plans to hire additional personnel. Suppose it is estimated that as x new people are hired, it will cost

$C(x) = 0.2x$ thousand dollars and that these x people will bring in $R(x) = \sqrt{3x}$ thousand dollars in additional revenue. How many new people would be hired to maximize the profit? How much net revenue would the company gain by hiring these people?

45. Suppose the demand function for a certain commodity is $D(q) = 20 - 4q^2$, and that the marginal cost is $C'(q) = 2q + 6$, where q is the number of units produced. Find the consumer's surplus at the sales level q_0 where profit is maximized.

COMPUTATIONAL WINDOW

46. Imagine a cylindrical fuel tank lying on its side (of length $L = 20$ ft); the ends are circular with radius b. You will soon be asked to compute the amount of fuel in the tank for a given level.

a. Explain why the volume of the tank can be expressed by

$$V = 2L \int_{-b}^{b} \sqrt{b^2 - y^2}\, dy$$

b. Derive this formula for the volume of fuel at level h, where $-b \leq h \leq b$:

$$V(h) = 2L \int_{-b}^{h} \sqrt{b^2 - y^2}\, dy$$

c. Finally, for $b = 4$, numerically compute $V(h)$ for $h = -3, -2, \ldots, 4$. *Note*: $V(0)$ and $V(4)$ will serve as a check on your work.

47. The *supply function* represents the amount of a commodity that would be supplied to the market at a given price. If the market price is s_0, then those producers who would be willing to supply the commodity for a price less than s_0 realize a gain. For instance, if the market price is $12 and the corresponding supply is only $10, then those producers who are willing to supply the commodity at $10 gain from the fact that the price is actually $12. The **producer's surplus** is defined to be the total gain realized by all producers who are willing to supply the commodity for a price that is less than the market price.

Suppose the supply function for a certain commodity is $s(q)$, where q is the number of units of the commodity that will be supplied to the market when the price is s dollars per unit. Show that the producer's surplus with respect to the fixed price s_0 is given by

$$\int_0^{q_0} [s_0 - s(q)]\, dq$$

where q_0 is the sales level that corresponds to the price s_0; that is, $s_0 = s(q_0)$.

Chapter 4 Review

> **IN THIS REVIEW** Proficiency examination; supplementary problems
> Problems 1–18 problems of the proficiency examination test your knowledge
> of the concepts of this chapter, and Problems 19–30 test your understanding of
> those concepts by asking you to work sample practice problems. The supple-
> mentary problems present questions relating to the material of this chapter in a
> wide variety of settings.

PROFICIENCY EXAMINATION

Concept Problems

1. What is the area as the limit of a sum?
2. Complete these basic rules for sums:

   a. $\sum_{k=1}^{n} c =$ _____

   b. $\sum_{k=1}^{n} (a_k + b_k) =$ _____

   c. $\sum_{k=1}^{n} ca_k =$ _____

   d. $\sum_{k=1}^{n} (ca_k + db_k) =$ _____

   e. $\sum_{k=1}^{n} a_k =$ _____ subtotal rule

   for $1 < m < n$

   f. dominance rule: _____

   g. $\sum_{k=1}^{n} 1 =$ _____

   h. $\sum_{k=1}^{n} k =$ _____

   i. $\sum_{k=1}^{n} k^2 =$ _____

   j. $\sum_{k=1}^{n} k^3 =$ _____

3. What is a Riemann sum?
4. Define a definite integral.
5. What conditions are necessary for an integral to represent an area?
6. How can distance be expressed as an integral?
7. Complete these statements summarizing the general
   properties of the definite integral.

   a. Definite integral at a point: $\int_{a}^{a} f(x)\, dx$

   = _____

   b. Opposite of a definite integral: $\int_{b}^{a} f(x)\, dx$

   = _____

8. State the fundamental theorem of calculus.

9. Describe in your own words the process of integration
   by substitution.
10. What is a differential equation? How do you solve a
    separable differential equation?
11. What is an orthogonal trajectory?
12. State the mean value theorem for integrals.
13. What is the formula for the average value of a continu-
    ous function?
14. State the second fundamental theorem of calculus.
15. State Leibniz's rule.
16. State the following approximation rules:

    a. rectangular approximation

    b. trapezoidal rule

    c. Simpson's rule
17. How do you find the area between two curves?
18. What is consumer's surplus and how do you find it?

Practice Problems

19. Given that $\int_{0}^{1} x^4\, dx = \frac{1}{5}$, $\int_{0}^{1} x^2\, dx = \frac{1}{3}$, and $\int_{0}^{1} dx = 1$,
    find $\int_{0}^{1} [x^2(2x^2 - 3)]\, dx$.

20. Find $F'(x)$ if $F(x) = \int_{3}^{x} t^5 \sqrt{\cos(2t + 1)}\, dt$.

Evaluate the definite integral in Problems 21–24.

21. $\int_{1}^{4} (\sqrt{x} + x^{-3/2})\, dx$ 22. $\int_{0}^{1} (2x - 6)(x^2 - 6x + 2)\, dx$

23. $\int_{0}^{\pi/2} \dfrac{\sin x\, dx}{(1 + \cos x)^2}$ 24. $\int_{-2}^{1} (2x + 1)\sqrt{2x^2 + 2x + 5}\, dx$

25. a. Find the area under the curve $f(x) = 3x^2 + 2$ on
    $[-1, 3]$.

    b. Find the area between the curves $y = x^2$ and $y^3 = x$.

26. Find the average value of $y = \cos 2x$ on the interval
    $\left[0, \frac{\pi}{2}\right]$.

27. An object experiences linear acceleration given by

    $$a(t) = 2t + 1 \text{ ft/s}^2$$

Find the velocity and position of the object, given that it starts its motion (at $t = 0$) at $s = 4$ with initial velocity 2 ft/s.

28. When it is x years old, a certain industrial machine generates revenue at the rate of $R'(x) = 1{,}575 - 5x^2$ dollars per year and results in costs that accumulate at the rate of $C'(x) = 1{,}200 + 10x^2$ dollars per year.

   a. For how many years is the use of the machine profitable?

   b. What are the total net earnings generated by the machine during the period of profitability (see part **a**)?

29. Solve the differential equation $\dfrac{dy}{dx} = y^2 \sin 3x$.

30. a. Find the necessary n to estimate the value of

$$\int_0^{\pi/2} \cos x \, dx$$

   to within 0.0005 of its correct value using the trapezoidal rule.

   b. Find the necessary n if Simpson's rule is used.

SUPPLEMENTARY PROBLEMS

1. Given that $\displaystyle\int_{-1}^0 f(x) \, dx = 3$, $\displaystyle\int_0^1 f(x) \, dx = -1$, and

$\displaystyle\int_{-1}^1 g(x)\, dx = 7$ find $\displaystyle\int_{-1}^1 [3g(x) + 2f(x)] \, dx$.

2. Use the definition of definite integral to find

$$\int_0^1 (3x^2 + 2x - 1)dx$$

3. Use the definition of definite integral to find

$$\int_0^1 (4x^3 + 6x^2 + 3) \, dx$$

Find the definite and indefinite integrals in Problems 4–22. If you do not have a technique for finding a closed (exact) answer, approximate the integral using numerical integration.

4. $\displaystyle\int_0^1 (5x^4 - 8x^3 + 1) \, dx$

5. $\displaystyle\int_{-1}^2 30(5x - 2)^2 \, dx$

6. $\displaystyle\int_0^1 (x\sqrt{x} + 2)^2 \, dx$

7. $\displaystyle\int_1^2 \frac{x^2 \, dx}{\sqrt{x^3 + 1}}$

8. $\displaystyle\int_2^2 (x + \sin x)^3 \, dx$

9. $\displaystyle\int_{-1}^0 \frac{dx}{\sqrt{1 - 2x}}$

10. $\displaystyle\int_1^2 \frac{dx}{\sqrt{3x - 1}}$

11. $\displaystyle\int_{-1}^0 \frac{dx}{\sqrt[3]{1 - 2x}}$

12. $\displaystyle\int \sqrt{x}(x^2 + \sqrt{x} + 1) \, dx$

13. $\displaystyle\int (x - 1)^2 \, dx$

14. $\displaystyle\int \frac{x^2 + 1}{x^2} \, dx$

15. $\displaystyle\int (\sin^2 x + \cos^2 x) \, dx$

16. $\displaystyle\int x(x + 4)\sqrt{x^3 + 6x^2 + 2} \, dx$ **17.** $\displaystyle\int x(2x^2 + 1)\sqrt{x^4 + x^2} \, dx$

18. $\displaystyle\int \frac{dx}{\sqrt{x}(\sqrt{x} + 1)^2}$

19. $\displaystyle\int x\sqrt{1 - 5x^2} \, dx$

20. $\displaystyle\int \sqrt{\sin x - \cos x}(\sin x + \cos x) \, dx$

21. $\displaystyle\int_{-10}^{10} [3 + 7x^{73} - 100x^{101}] \, dx$

22. $\displaystyle\int_{-\pi/4}^{\pi/4} [\sin(4x) + 2 \cos(4x)] \, dx$

23. Find $F'(x)$, where $F(x) = \displaystyle\int_{x^2}^{x^3} t^2 \cos^4 t \, dt$

24. Find the area under $f(x) = x^{-2}$ on $[1, 4]$.

25. Find the area under $f(x) = 2 + x - x^2$ on $[-1, 1]$.

26. Find the area under $f(x) = x^4$ on $[0, 2]$.

27. Find the area under the curve $y = x\sqrt{x^2 + 5}$ on $[-1, 2]$.

Find the area of the regions bounded by the curves and lines in Problems 28–31.

28. $4y^2 = x$ and $2y = x - 2$

29. $y = x^3$, $y = x^4$

30. $x = y^{2/3}$, $x = y^2$

31. $y = \sqrt{3}\, \sin x$, $y = \cos x$, and the vertical lines $x = 0$ and $x = \frac{\pi}{2}$

32. a. Find $f(t)$ if $f''(t) = \sin 4t - \cos 2t$ and $f\left(\frac{\pi}{2}\right) = f'\left(\frac{\pi}{2}\right) = 1$.

   b. Find $f(x)$ if $f'''(x) = 2x^3 + x^2$, given that $f''(1) = 2$, $f'(1) = 1$, and $f(1) = 0$.

Solve the differential equations in Problems 33–40.

33. $\dfrac{dy}{dx} = (1 - y)^2$

34. $\dfrac{dy}{dx} = \dfrac{\cos 4x}{y}$

35. $\dfrac{dy}{dx} = \left(\dfrac{\cos y}{\sin x}\right)^2$

36. $\dfrac{1}{y^2} + \dfrac{dy}{dx} = \left(\dfrac{x}{y}\right)^2$

37. $\dfrac{dy}{dx} = \dfrac{x - 1}{y} + \dfrac{y - x(y - 1)}{y^2}$

38. $\dfrac{dy}{dx} = \dfrac{x}{y}\sqrt{\dfrac{y^2 + 2}{x^2 + 1}}$

39. $\dfrac{dy}{dx} = \dfrac{x \sin x^2}{y^2 \cos y^3}$

40. $\dfrac{dy}{dx} = \sqrt{\dfrac{x}{y}}$

41. Find the average value of $f(x) = \dfrac{\sin x}{\cos^2 x}$ on the interval $\left[0, \frac{\pi}{4}\right]$.

42. Find the average value of $f(x) = \sin x$

   a. on $[0, \pi]$ **b.** on $[0, 2\pi]$

43. Use the trapezoidal rule with $n = 6$ to approximate $\int_0^\pi \sin x \, dx$. Compare your result with the exact value of this integral.

44. Estimate $\int_0^1 \sqrt{1 + x^3} \, dx$ using the trapezoidal rule with $n = 6$.

45. Estimate $\int_0^1 \frac{dx}{\sqrt{1 + x^3}}$ using the trapezoidal rule with $n = 8$.

46. Estimate $\int_0^1 \sqrt{1 + x^3} \, dx$ using Simpson's rule with $n = 6$.

47. Estimate $\int_0^1 \frac{dx}{\sqrt{1 + x^3}}$ using Simpson's rule with $n = 8$.

48. Use the trapezoidal rule to estimate to within 0.00005 the value of the integral
$$\int_1^2 \sqrt{x + \frac{1}{x}} \, dx$$

49. Use the trapezoidal rule to approximate $\int_0^1 \frac{x^2 \, dx}{1 + x^2}$ with an error no greater than 0.005.

50. Use Simpson's rule to estimate to within 0.00005 the value of the integral
$$\int_1^2 \sqrt{x + \frac{1}{x}} \, dx$$

51. Find the average value of the function defined by
$$f(x) = \frac{\cos x}{1 - \frac{x^2}{2}}$$
on $\left[0, \frac{\pi}{2}\right]$. *Hint*: Use the trapezoidal rule with $n = 6$.

52. Find the area between the curves $y = \sin x$, $y = \cos x$, and the lines $x = 0$ and $x = 2\pi$.

53. The brakes of a certain automobile produce a constant deceleration of k m/s^2. The car is traveling at 25 m/s when the driver is forced to hit the brakes. If it comes to rest at a point 50 m from the point where the brakes are applied, what is k?

54. A particle moves along the x-axis in such a way that $a(t) = -4s(t)$, where $s(t)$ and $a(t)$ are its position and acceleration, respectively, at time t. The particle starts from rest at $s = 5$.
    a. Show that $v^2 + 4t^2 = 100$.
    Hint: First use the chain rule to show that $a(t) = v\frac{dv}{ds}$.
    b. What is the velocity when the particle first reaches $x = 3$? *Note*: The sign of v is determined by the direction in which the particle is moving at the time in question.

55. A manufacturer estimates marginal revenue to be $100x^{-1/3}$ dollars per unit when the level of production is x units. The corresponding marginal cost has been found to be 0.4x dollars per unit. Suppose the manufacture's profit is \$520 when the level of production is 16 units. What is the manufacturer's profit when the level of production is 25 units?

56. A tree has been transplanted and after t years is growing at a rate of
$$1 + \frac{1}{(x + 1)^2}$$
feet per year. After 2 years it has reached a height of 5 ft. How tall was the tree when it was transplanted?

57. A manufacturer estimates that the marginal revenue of a certain commodity is
$$R'(x) = \sqrt{x}(x^{3/2} + 1)^{-1/2}$$
dollars per unit when x units are produced. Assuming no revenue is obtained when $x = 0$, how much revenue is obtained from producing $x = 4$ units?

58. Find a function whose tangent has slope $x\sqrt{x^2 + 5}$ for each value of x and whose graph passes through the point $(2, 10)$.

59. A particle moves along the x-axis in such a way that after t seconds its acceleration is $a(t) = 12(2t + 1)^{-3/2}$. If it starts at rest at $x = 3$, where will it be 4 seconds later?

60. An environmental study of a certain community suggests that t years from now, the level of carbon monoxide in the air will be changing at the rate of $0.1t + 0.2$ parts per million per year. If the current level of carbon monoxide in the air is 3.4 parts per million, what will the level be 3 years from now?

61. A woman, driving on a straight, level road at the constant speed v_0 is forced to apply her brakes to avoid hitting a cow, and the car comes to a stop 3 seconds later and s_0 feet from the point where the brakes were applied. Continuing on her way, she increases her speed by 20 ft/s to make up time but is again forced to hit the brakes, and this time it takes her 5 seconds and s_1 feet to come to a full stop. Assuming that her brakes supplied a constant deceleration d each time they were used, find d and determine v_0, s_0, and s_1.

62. A company has purchased a machine at time $t = 0$ (in years). It is estimated that the machine will earn $E(t) = 180 - 0.25t^2$ thousand dollars and that in the same time, it will cost the company $C(t) = t^2$ thousand dollars to maintain and repair the machine. Finally, it is known that at time t, the *salvage value* of the machine is
$$S(t) = \frac{7,105}{t + 7}$$
thousand dollars.
    a. When should the machine be sold?
    Hint: Let $P(t) = E(t) - C(t)$ and show that $P(t) = 0$ when $t = 12$. Explain why the machine should be sold after T years, where T satisfies
    $$S(t) = \int_T^{12} P(t) \, dt$$
    Find T.

b. How much total net revenue does the machine generate in its lifetime?

63. A company plans to hire additional advertising personnel. Suppose it is estimated that if x new people are hired, they will bring in additional revenue of $R(x) = \sqrt{2x}$ thousand dollars and that the cost of adding these x people will be $C(x) = \frac{1}{3}x$ thousand dollars. How many new people should be hired? How much total net revenue (that is, revenue minus cost) is gained by hiring these people?

64. A study indicates that x months from now the population of a certain town will be increasing at the rate of $10 + 2\sqrt{x}$ people per month. By how much will the population of the town increase over the next 9 months?

65. It is estimated that t days from now a farmer's crop will be increasing at rate of $0.3t^2 + 0.6t + 1$ bushels per day. By how much will the value of the crop increase during the next 6 days if the market price remains fixed at \$2 per bushel?

66. Records indicate that t months after the beginning of the year, the price of turkey in local supermarkets was

$$P(t) = 0.06t^2 - 0.2t + 1.2$$

dollars per pound. What was the average price of turkey during the first 6 months of the year?

67. A retailer expects that x months from now, consumers will be buying 50 cameras a month at a price of $P(x) = 40 + 3\sqrt{x}$ dollars per camera. Use the characterization of the definite integral as the limit of a sum to find the total revenue the retailer can expect from the sale of the cameras over the next 9 months.

68. Economists predict that x months from now the demand for beef will be $D(x)$ pounds per months and the price will be $P(x)$ dollars per pound. Use the characterization of the definite integral as the limit of a sum to find an expression for the total amount that consumers will spend on beef this year.

69. If f is continuous on $[a, b]$, show that
$$-|f(x)| \le f(x) \le |f(x)| \quad \text{on } [a, b]$$

70. If f is continuous on $[a, b]$, show that

$$\left| \int_a^b f(x)\, dx \right| \le \int_a^b |f(x)|\, dx$$

71. Show that $\left| \displaystyle\int_0^\pi \sin x\, dx \right| \le \pi$. *Hint*: See Problem 70.

72. Solve the system of differential equations

$$\begin{cases} 2\dfrac{dx}{dt} + 5\dfrac{dy}{dt} = t \\ \dfrac{dx}{dt} + 3\dfrac{dy}{dt} = 7\cos t \end{cases}$$

Hint: Solve for $\dfrac{dx}{dt}$ and $\dfrac{dy}{dt}$ algebraically, and then integrate.

73. PUTNAM EXAMINATION PROBLEM The time-varying temperature of a certain body is given by a polynomial of the form $f(t) = at^3 + bt^2 + ct + d$, where t is time. Show that the average temperature of the body between 9 A.M. and 3 P.M. can always be found by taking the average of the temperatures at two fixed times, t_1 and t_2, which are independent of a, b, c, and d. Find t_1 and t_2 to the nearest minute.

74. PUTNAM EXAMINATION PROBLEM Where on the parabola $4ay = x^2$ ($a > 0$) should a chord be drawn so that it will be normal to the parabola and cut off a parabolic sector of minimum area? That is, find P so that the shaded area in Figure 4.35 is as small as possible.

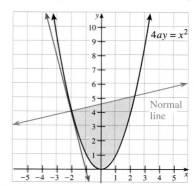

Figure 4.35 Minimum area problem

75. PUTNAM EXAMINATION PROBLEM If $a_0, a_1, \ldots, a_n$ are real numbers that satisfy

$$\frac{a_0}{1} + \frac{a_1}{2} + \cdots + \frac{a_n}{n+1} = 0$$

show that the equation $a_0 + a_1 x + a_2 x^2 + \ldots + a_n x^n = 0$ has at least one real root. *Hint*: Use the mean value theorem for integrals.

"Kinematics of Jogging" by Ralph Boas

Ralph Boas (1912–1992), Professor Emeritus of Mathematics from the Northwestern University, wrote this guest essay. Professor Boas is well known for his papers and professional activities. In addition to his work in real and complex analysis, he wrote many expository articles, such as this guest essay, about teaching or using mathematics.

Nature herself exhibits to us measurable and observable quantities in definite mathematical dependence; the conception of a function is suggested by all the processes of nature where we observe natural phenomena varying according to distance or to time. Nearly all the "known" functions have presented themselves in the attempt to solve geometrical, mechanical, or physical problems.

J. T. Mertz, *A History of European Thought in the Nineteenth Century* (Edinburgh and London, 1903), p. 696.

Some people think that calculus is dull, but it did not seem so three centuries ago, when it was invented. Then, it produced unexpected results; and, now and then, it still does. This essay is about such a result.

You have learned about the intermediate value theorem (see Section 1.6), which tells you, for instance, that if you jog at 8 min per mile, there must be some instant when your speed is exactly $\frac{1}{8}$ mi per minute—assuming, as is only natural in a course in calculus, that your elapsed time is a continuous function of the distance covered. This principle is very intuitive and was recognized before calculus was invented: Galileo was aware of it in 1638 and thought that it had been known to Plato. On the other hand, there is a question with a much less intuitive answer that was noticed only recently (and, as happens more often than mathematicians like to admit, by a physicist). Suppose that you average 8 min/mi, must you cover some one continuous mile (such as a "measured mile" on a highway) in exactly 8 min? The answer is not intuitive at all: It depends on whether or not your total distance was an integral number of miles. More precisely, if you cover an integral number of miles, then you cover exactly one mile in some 8 min. However, if you cover a nonintegral number of miles, there is not necessarily any one continuous mile that you cover in 8 min.

To prove this, let x be the distance (in miles) covered at any point during your trip, and suppose that when you stop you have covered an integral number of n miles. Let $f(x)$ be the time (in minutes) that it took to cover the first x miles; we will suppose that f is a continuous function. If you averaged 8 min/mi, then $f(x) - 8x = 0$ when $x = 0$ and when $x = n$. Now suppose that you never did cover any consecutive mile in 8 min; in mathematical terms,

$$f(x + 1) - f(x) \neq 8$$

Because

$$f(x + 1) - f(x) - 8$$

is continuous and never 0, it must either always be positive, or else always negative; let us suppose the former. Write the corresponding facts for $x = 0$, $1, \ldots, n$:

$$f(1) - f(0) > 8$$
$$f(2) - f(1) > 8$$
$$\vdots$$
$$f(n) - f(n - 1) > 8$$

If we add these inequalities we obtain

$$f(n) - f(0) > 8n$$

But we started with the assumption that $f(n) = 8n$ and $f(0) = 0$, so assuming that $f(x + 1) - f(x)$ is never 8 leads to a contradiction.

It is somewhat harder to show that only integral values of n will work. Suppose you jog so that your time to cover x miles is

$$J(x) = k \sin^2 \frac{\pi x}{n} + 8x$$

where n is *not* an integer and k is a small number. This is a legitimate assumption, because J is an increasing function (as a time has to be), if k is small enough. To be sure of this, we calculate $J'(x)$—and here we actually have to use some calculus (or have a calculator that will do it for us). We find

$$J'(x) = \frac{k\pi}{n} \sin \frac{2\pi x}{n} + 8$$

If k is small enough $\left(k < \frac{8n}{\pi}\right)$, then $J'(x) > 0$. This shows not only that J increases, but also that

$$J(x + 1) - J(x)$$

cannot be eight. Because $J(x + 1) - J(x)$ is never negative, if you jog so that your time is $J(x)$, you will never even cover a whole mile in less than 8 min.

MATHEMATICAL ESSAYS

Use a library or references other than this textbook to research the information necessary to answer questions in Problems 1–6.

1. One of the great ideas of calculus is that of derivative. Write an essay of at least 500 words about some application of the derivative that is not discussed in this text.

2. The concept of the integral is one of the great ideas of calculus. Write an essay of at least 500 words about the relationship of integration and differentiation as it relates to the history of calculus.

3. At the beginning of Chapter 2, we wrote of the Fermat–Newton approach to finding the slope of a tangent to a curve at a point. Do some research in the history of calculus and write a paper on the development of this concept. At the conclusion of this paper, discuss why the concept of derivative is so important.

4. Write a report on Georg Riemann. Include some recent developments (1984) in the solution of the Riemann hypotheses.

5. Write a report on Fermat's last theorem. Include some recent developments (1993) in the solution of this theorem.

6. Write a report on the Bernoulli family.

7. As we saw in this chapter, the mathematician Seki Kōwa was doing a form of integration at about the same time that Newton and Leibniz were inventing the calculus. Write a paper of the history of calculus from the eastern viewpoint.

8. In the guest essay it was assumed that the time to cover x miles is

$$J(x) = k \sin^2 \frac{\pi x}{n} + 8x$$

Suppose that $n = 5$. What choices for k seem reasonable?

9. Suppose that the time to cover x miles is given by

$$J(x) = \sin^2 \frac{\pi x}{5} + 8x$$

Graph this function on $[0, 8]$.

10. Use calculus to find how small k needs to be in the expression

$$J(x) = k \sin^2 \frac{\pi x}{n} + 8x$$

so that $J'(x) > 0$.

11. Find a number x, $x \neq 0$, so that when it is divided by 2 the display on your calculator shows 0. Write a paper describing your work as well as the processes or your calculator.

12. Calculate $\sqrt{2}$ using a calculator. Next, repeatedly subtract the integer part of the displayed number and multiply the result by 10. Describe the outcome, and then devise a method for finding $\sqrt{2}$ using calculus. Write a paper comparing these answers.

13. **Book Report** Eli Maor, a native of Israel, has a long-standing interest in the relations between mathematics and the arts. Read the fascinating book *To Infinity and Beyond, A Cultural History of the Infinite* (Boston: Birkhäuser, 1987), and prepare a book report.

14. Make up a word problem involving an application of the derivative. Send your problem to:

> Math Executive Editor
> Bradley and Smith *Calculus*
> Prentice-Hall
> Englewood Cliffs, NJ 07632

The best one submitted will appear in the next edition (along with credit to the problem-poser).

Exponential, Logarithmic, and Inverse Trigonometric Functions

PREVIEW

So far, all our work has been with polynomials, rational functions, root functions, trigonometric functions, and combinations of these basic functional types. However, many pure and applied mathematical topics require functions of a different kind. We begin this chapter by defining the *natural exponential* function e^x and then the *natural logarithmic* function, ln *x*. We shall find that the derivatives of these functions satisfy

$$\frac{d}{dx}(e^x) = e^x \quad \text{and} \quad \frac{d}{dx}(\ln x) = \frac{1}{x}$$

Applications of these functions as they relate to both the integral and the derivative are also considered. The fact that e^x is equal to its own derivative has important theoretical and practical uses. Indeed, it is this feature of e^x that causes mathematicians to regard it as "natural." We also introduce and study the inverse trigonometric functions, which have practical applications and also provide useful integration formulas. Finally, in Section 5.7 we provide an alternative development in which the natural logarithm is *defined* as an integral function with a variable upper limit.

PERSPECTIVE

In 1964, an earthquake measuring 8.5 on the Richter scale devastated parts of Alaska. The 1989 World Series was interrupted by a 6.5 quake, and newspaper accounts compared the two events by pointing out that the Alaska quake had been at least 100 times more powerful. But what kind of scale measures 8.5 as 100 times as large as 6.5? The Richter scale, which is often used to measure the magnitude of earthquakes, uses a *logarithmic* scale.

5.1 EXPONENTIAL FUNCTIONS; THE NUMBER e

> **IN THIS SECTION** Exponential functions, natural base e, continuous compounding of interest
> Linear, quadratic, polynomial, and rational functions are among those functions called **algebraic functions**. Functions that are not algebraic are called **transcendental functions**. Trigonometric functions are examples of transcendental functions, and in this section we introduce an additional important transcendental function, the exponential function and the irrational number e. We also discuss some graphical properties of exponential functions and an interesting application dealing with continuous compounding of interest.

■ EXPONENTIAL FUNCTIONS

Exponential Function

> The function f is an **exponential function** if
>
> $$f(x) = b^x$$
>
> where b is a positive constant other than 1 and x is any real number.

Recall that if n is a natural number, then

$$b^n = \underbrace{b \cdot b \cdot b \cdots b}_{n \; factors}$$

Furthermore, if $b \neq 0$, then

$$b^0 = 1, \quad b^{-n} = \frac{1}{b^n}, \quad \text{and} \quad b^{1/n} = \sqrt[n]{b}$$

Also, if m and n are any integers, and m/n is a reduced fraction, then

$$b^{m/n} = (b^{1/n})^m$$

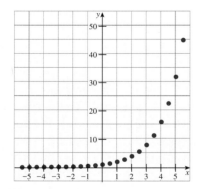

Figure 5.1 Graph of $y = 2^x$ for selected rational exponents

This means that we know what b^x means for rational values of x. However, we now wish to enlarge the domain of x to include all real numbers. To get a feeling for what is involved in this problem, let us examine the special case where $b = 2$. In Figure 5.1, we have plotted several points with coordinates $(r, 2^r)$, where r is a rational number. We must now attach meaning to b^x if x is not a rational number. In order to enlarge the domain of x to include all real numbers, we need the help of the following theorem.

THEOREM 5.1   Bracketing theorem for exponents

Suppose b is a real number greater than 1. Then for any real number x, there is a unique real number b^x. Moreover, if p and q are any two rational numbers such that $p < x < q$, then

$$b^p < b^x < b^q$$

Proof: A formal proof of this theorem is beyond the scope of this course, but we can outline the needed steps. The proof depends on a property of real numbers called the *completeness property of the real numbers*. What the completeness property says is that each real number can be approximated to any prescribed degree of accuracy by a rational number. Using mathematical notation this is equivalent to saying that if x is a real number, then for every positive integer n there exists a rational number r_n such that $|x - r_n| < \frac{1}{n}$. In other words,

$$x = \lim_{n \to +\infty} r_n$$

Then, b^x is defined by

$$b^x = \lim_{n \to +\infty} b^{r_n}$$

The bracketing theorem follows from these definitions.   ∎

The bracketing theorem gives meaning to expressions such as $2^{\sqrt{3}}$. Because

$$1.732 < \sqrt{3} < 1.733$$

the bracketing theorem says that

$$2^{1.732} < 2^{\sqrt{3}} < 2^{1.733}$$

EXAMPLE 1 Graph of an exponential function

Graph $f(x) = 2^x$.

Solution Begin by plotting points using rational x-values. We see that the graph has a fairly well defined shape (as shown in Figure 5.2a), but it is riddled with "holes" that correspond to those points whose x-coordinates are irrational numbers.

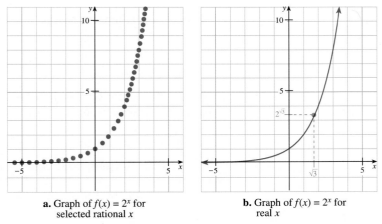

a. Graph of $f(x) = 2^x$ for selected rational x

b. Graph of $f(x) = 2^x$ for real x

Figure 5.2 Graph of $f(x) = 2^x$

We complete the graph by connecting the points with a smooth curve as shown in Figure 5.2b. However, let us take a moment to relate the completed graph to the definition of 2^x for an irrational x-value. Consider the point $(x, 2^x)$ for $x = \sqrt{3}$. Because $\sqrt{3}$ is irrational, the decimal representation is nonterminating and nonrepeating. In other words, $\sqrt{3}$ is a limit of a sequence of rational numbers, specifically,

$$1, 1.7, 1.73, 1.732, 1.7320, 1.73205, 1.732050, 1.7320508, \ldots$$

Then, $2^{\sqrt{3}}$ is the limit of the sequence of numbers

$$2^1, 2^{1.7}, 2^{1.73}, 2^{1.732}, 2^{1.7320}, 2^{1.73205}, 2^{1.732050}, 2^{1.7320508}, \ldots$$

Graphically, this means that as the rational numbers $1, 1.7, 1.73, \ldots$ tend toward $\sqrt{3}$, the points $(1, 2), (1.7, 2^{1.7}), (1.73, 2^{1.73}), \ldots$ tend toward the "hole" in the graph of $y = 2^x$ that corresponds to $x = \sqrt{3}$.   ▬

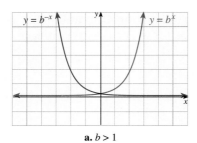

a. $b > 1$

b. $0 < b < 1$
Notice that $c = \frac{1}{b}$ satisfies $c > 1$.

Figure 5.3 Graph of $y = b^x$

The shape of the graph of $y = b^x$ for any $b > 1$ is essentially the same as that of $y = 2^x$. The graph of $y = b^x$ for a typical base $b > 1$ is shown in Figure 5.3a, and by reflecting this graph about the y-axis (see Problem 43) we obtain the graph of $y = b^{-x}$. The case where $0 < b < 1$ is shown in Figure 5.3b. In particular, notice that in this case, the reciprocal $c = 1/b$ satisfies $c > 1$, and $y = b^x$ and $y = b^{-x}$ are thus the same as $y = c^{-x}$ and $y = c^x$, respectively.

We summarize the basic properties of exponential functions with the following theorem. Many of these properties were proved in previous courses for bases with rational exponents.

THEOREM 5.2   Properties of exponential functions

Let x, y be real numbers, and a and b positive real numbers.

Equality rule   If $b \neq 1$, then $b^x = b^y$ if and only if $x = y$.

Inequality rules   If $x > y$ and $b > 1$, then $b^x > b^y$.
   If $x > y$ and $0 < b < 1$, then $b^x < b^y$.

Product rule $b^x b^y = b^{x+y}$

Quotient rule $\dfrac{b^x}{b^y} = b^{x-y}$

Power rules $(b^x)^y = b^{xy}$

$$(ab)^x = a^x b^x \text{ and } \left(\dfrac{a}{b}\right)^x = \dfrac{a^x}{b^x}$$

Limits involving exponential functions   If $b > 1$,

$$\lim_{x \to -\infty} b^x = 0 \quad \text{and} \quad \lim_{x \to +\infty} b^x = +\infty$$

$$\lim_{x \to -\infty} b^{-x} = +\infty \quad \text{and} \quad \lim_{x \to +\infty} b^{-x} = 0$$

Proof: The proof of this theorem is beyond the scope of this course. However, some special cases and parts of the theorem are considered in the problem set. ∎

Many parts of this theorem are used in the following example.

EXAMPLE 2   Exponential equations

Solve each of the following exponential equations.

a. $2^{x^2+3} = 16$ **b.** $2^x 3^{x+1} = 108$ **c.** $(\sqrt{2})^{x^2} = \dfrac{8^x}{4}$

Solution   a. $2^{x^2+3} = 16$
$2^{x^2+3} = 2^4$ *Write 16 as 2^4 so that the equality rule can be used.*
$x^2 + 3 = 4, \quad \text{or} \quad x = \pm 1$

b. $2^x 3^{x+1} = 108$
$2^x 3^x 3 = 3 \cdot 36$ *Product rule*

$(2 \cdot 3)^x = 36$ *Power rule; also divide both sides by 3.*

$6^x = 6^2$

$x = 2$ *Identity rule*

c. $(\sqrt{2})^{x^2} = \dfrac{8^x}{4}$

$(2^{1/2})^{x^2} = \dfrac{(2^3)^x}{2^2}$

$$2^{x^2/2} = 2^{3x-2} \quad \textit{Identity rule}$$
$$\frac{x^2}{2} = 3x - 2$$
$$x^2 - 6x + 4 = 0$$
$$x = \frac{6 \pm \sqrt{36 - 4(1)(4)}}{2} = 3 \pm \sqrt{5}$$

Computational Window

You can use a graphing calculator to estimate solutions to equations like those in Example 2. For example, in part **a,** you can graph both the left and right sides of the equation and then look for the intersection point(s), if any.

The (TRACE) with the cursor on the curve $y = 2^{x^2+3}$ gives the following values:

X=-1.021277 Y=16.48413 ← *A root is between*
X=-.9787234 Y=15.539837 ← *these x-values.*
and

X=.9787234 Y=15.539837 ← *A root is between*
X=1.0212766 Y=16.484131 ← *these x-values.*

```
Y₁□2^(X^2+3)
Y₂■16

Xmin=-2    Ymin=-5
Xmax=2     Ymax=20
Xscl=1     Yscl=1
```

The intermediate value theorem tells us the desired root is between the traced values, so it looks like the roots are $x = -1$ and $x = 1$. These values could be checked by substitution.

For part **b** we have:
(TRACE) with the cursor on the curve $y = 108$; we find X=1.9574468 and X=2.0425532. From the intermediate value, we see the root is between 1.9574468 and 2.0425532; you can check to verify that $x = 2$ is the root.

For part **c,** we could be very clever in setting scale to graph the given equations, but instead this example illustrates that even though you may have a graphing calculator there are many problems that still require mathematical analysis. Remember, a graphing calculator is a valuable tool, but it will not do your work for you.

```
Y₁□2^X*3^(X+1)
Y₂□108

Xmin=-4    Ymin=-50
Xmax=4     Ymax=150
Xscl=1     Yscl=10
```

◼ NATURAL BASE *e*

In elementary algebra, exponential bases are usually 2 or 10, but in calculus, we shall find it more useful to consider exponential functions with base *e*, where *e* is the following number defined as a limit.

The Number _e_

n	(1 + 1/n)^n
1	2
2	2.25
3	2.37037037
4	2.44140625
5	2.48832
6	2.521626372
7	2.546499697
8	2.565784514
9	2.581174792
10	2.59374246
20	2.653297705
30	2.674318776
40	2.685063838
50	2.691588029
60	2.695970139
70	2.699116371
80	2.701484941
90	2.703332461
100	2.704813829
200	2.711517123
300	2.713765158
400	2.714891744
500	2.715568521
600	2.716020049
700	2.716342739
800	2.716584847
900	2.716773208
1000	2.716923932
2000	2.717602569
3000	2.71782892
4000	2.717942121
5000	2.71801005
6000	2.71805535
7000	2.718087694
8000	2.718111955
9000	2.718130825
10000	2.718145927

The limit

$$\lim_{n \to +\infty} \left(1 + \frac{1}{n}\right)^n$$

exists and is denoted by _e_. The number _e_ is called the **natural exponential base.**

The letter _e_ was chosen in honor of the great Swiss mathematician Leonhard Euler (1707–1783), who investigated this limit and explored a number of applications in which this limit plays a useful role. At first glance, there may seem to be very little about the number _e_ that is "natural," but later in this section and throughout the rest of this chapter, we shall point out features that make _e_ an extremely interesting and useful exponential base.

First, let us get a better idea of the nature of this number we have called _e_. It is by no means obvious that this limit even exists (we shall show that it does in Chapter 8), but assuming that it does, it may seem to have the value 1. After all,

$$\lim_{n \to +\infty} \left(1 + \frac{1}{n}\right) = 1 \text{ and } 1^n = 1.$$

However, the limit process does not work this way, and it turns out that

$$e \approx 2.718281828459045$$

The first four digits of this limit are substantiated by the table shown in the margin (which was done on a computer). It can be shown that the number _e_ is irrational, so it does not have a terminating or repeating decimal representation.

The function $f(x) = e^x$ is called the **natural exponential function.** This function obeys all the basic rules of Theorem 5.2 for exponential functions with base $b > 1$. Because many of the applications we consider in calculus will have complicated exponents, such as

$$e^{3x^2 - 2 \sin x + 8}$$

we sometimes streamline this form by writing

$$\exp(3x^2 - 2 \sin x + 8)$$

Exp Notation

If $f(x)$ is an expression in x, the notation

$$\exp(f(x))$$

means $e^{f(x)}$.

■ CONTINUOUS COMPOUNDING OF INTEREST

One reason _e_ is called the "natural" exponential base is that many natural growth phenomena can be described in terms of e^x. As an illustration of this fact, we close this section by showing how e^x can be used to describe the accounting procedure called _continuous compounding of interest._

If a sum of money, called the **present value** or **principal,** is denoted by P and invested at an annual rate of r for t years, then the **future value** is denoted by A and is found by

$$A = P + I$$

where I denotes the amount of interest. **Interest** is an amount of money paid for the use of another's money. **Simple interest** is found by multiplication: $I = Prt$. For example, \$1,000 invested for 3 years at a 15% simple annual interest rate generates $I = \$1,000(0.15)(3) = \$450$, so the future value in 3 years is $A = \$1,000 + \$450 = \$1,450$.

Most businesses, however, pay interest on the interest as well as on the principal, and when this is done, it is called **compound interest.** For example, \$1,000 invested at 15% annual interest compounded annually for 3 years can be found as follows:

First year: $A = P + I$

$\qquad = P \cdot 1 + Pr$ $\qquad\qquad I = Prt$ and $t = 1$

$\qquad = \mathbf{P(1 + r)}$ $\qquad\qquad$ *For this example, $A = \$1,000(1 + 0.15)$*
$\qquad\qquad\qquad\qquad\qquad\qquad\qquad = \$1,150$

Second year: $A = \mathbf{P(1 + r)} + I$ $\qquad$ *The total amount from the first year becomes the principal for the second year*

$\qquad A = \mathbf{P(1 + r)} \cdot 1 + \mathbf{P(1 + r)} \cdot r$

$\qquad = P(1 + r)(1 + r)$

$\qquad = P(1 + r)^2$ $\qquad\qquad$ *For this example, $A = \$1,000(1 + 0.15)^2$*
$\qquad\qquad\qquad\qquad\qquad\qquad = \$1,322.50$

Third year: $A = P(1 + r)^2 + P(1 + r)^2 \cdot r$

$\qquad = P(1 + r)^2(1 + r)$

$\qquad = P(1 + r)^3$ $\qquad\qquad$ *For this example, $A = \$1,000(1 + 0.15)^3$*
$\qquad\qquad\qquad\qquad\qquad\qquad \approx \$1,520.88$

Notice that with simple interest the amount in 3 years is \$1,450, as compared with \$1,520.88 when interest is compounded annually.

Compound Interest Future Value Formula

If a principal of P dollars is invested at an interest rate of i per period for a total of N periods, then the future amount A is given by the formula

$$A = P(1 + i)^N$$

Compound interest is usually stated in terms of an annual interest rate r and a given number of years t. The frequency of compounding (that is, the number of compoundings per year) is denoted by n. Therefore, $i = \frac{r}{n}$ and $N = nt$, in the formula for A.

The first two graphs in Figure 5.4 show how an amount of money in an account over a one-year period of time grows, first with quarterly compounding and then with monthly compounding. Notice that these are "step" graphs, with jumps occurring at the end of each compounding period.

a. Quarterly compounding $\qquad$ **b.** Monthly compounding $\qquad$ **c.** Continuous compounding

Figure 5.4 The growth of an account over a one-year period with different compounding frequencies

With continuous compounding, we compound interest not quarterly, or monthly, or daily, or even every second, but *instantaneously*, so that the future amount of money A in the account grows continuously, as shown in Figure 5.4c.

To compute A, we take the limit as the number of compounding periods n increases without bound. That is

$$A = \lim_{n \to +\infty} P\left(1 + \frac{r}{n}\right)^{nt}$$

To evaluate this limit, let $m = \frac{n}{r}$ so that $\frac{r}{n} = \frac{1}{m}$ and $nt = mrt$. Also, as $n \to +\infty$ we see $m \to +\infty$.

$$= \lim_{m \to +\infty} P\left(1 + \frac{1}{m}\right)^{mrt}$$

$$= \lim_{m \to +\infty} P\left[\left(1 + \frac{1}{m}\right)^{m}\right]^{rt} \qquad \textit{Properties of exponents}$$

$$= P\left[\lim_{m \to +\infty} \left(1 + \frac{1}{m}\right)^{m}\right]^{rt} \qquad \textit{Scalar rule}$$

$$= Pe^{rt}$$

This is summarized in the following box.

Continuous Compounding of Interest

If P dollars are invested at an annual interest rate r **compounded continuously,** then the future value after t years is

$$A = Pe^{rt}$$

EXAMPLE 3 Compounding of interest

$12,000 is invested for 5 years at 18%; find the future value at the end of 5 years if interest is compounded

a. monthly   **b.** continuously

Solution $P = \$12,000$; $t = 5$; and $r = 18\% = 0.18$ are given.

a. $n = 12$; $A = P(1 + i)^N = \$12,000\left(1 + \frac{0.18}{12}\right)^{12 \cdot 5} \approx \$29,318.64$

b. $A = \$12,000e^{0.18(5)} \approx \$29,515.24$

PROBLEM SET 5.1

Ⓐ *Sketch the graph of the functions in Problems 1–4.*

1. $y = 3^x$

2. $y = 4^{-x}$

3. $y = -e^{-x}$

4. $y = -e^x$

Evaluate the expressions (with calculator accuracy) in Problems 5–16.

5. $32^{2/5} + 9^{3/2}$

6. $(1 + 4^{3/2})^{-1/2}$

7. $2.5^{-1/3}$

8. $(1.5)^{-2}(1.5)^{3.7}$

9. $(e^{1.3})^2$

10. $\sqrt{e^{-4.1}}$

11. $e^3 e^{2.3}$

12. $\dfrac{e^2}{e + e^{1.3}}$

13. $5{,}000\left(1 + \frac{0.135}{12}\right)^{12(5)}$

14. $145{,}000\left(1 + \frac{0.073}{365}\right)^{-365(5)}$

15. $2{,}589e^{0.45(6)}$

16. $850{,}000e^{-0.04(10)}$

Find all real numbers x that satisfy the equations in Problems 17–24.

17. $3^{x^2-x} = 9$

18. $4^{x^2+x} = 16$

19. $2^x 5^{x+2} = 25{,}000$

20. $3^x 4^{x+1/2} = 3{,}476$

21. $(\sqrt[3]{2})^{x+10} = 2^{x^2}$

22. $(\sqrt[3]{5})^{x+2} = 5^{x^2}$

23. $e^{2x+3} = 1$

24. $\dfrac{e^{x^2}}{e^{x+6}} = 1$

Ⓑ 25. In the definition of the exponential function $f(x) = b^x$, we require that b be a positive constant other than 1.

a. What happens if $b = 1$? Draw the graph of $f(x) = b^x$, where $b = 1$. Is this an algebraic or a transcendental function?

b. What happens if $b = 0$? Draw the graph of $f(x) = b^x$, where $b = 0$. Is this an algebraic or a transcendental function?

26. THINK TANK PROBLEM   In the definition of the exponential function $f(x) = b^x$, we require that b be a positive constant. What happens if $b < 0$—for example, if $b = -2$? For what values of x is f defined? Describe the graph of f in this case.

27. Let $E(x) = 2^{x^2 - 2x}$.

a. Choose a number of values of x and plot the corresponding points $(x, E(x))$ on a coordinate plane. Pass a smooth curve through the points to obtain a rough sketch of the graph of E.

b. Where does the graph cross the y-axis? What happens to the graph as $x \to +\infty$ and as $x \to -\infty$?

c. Based on your graph, what would you say is the smallest value of E?

28. If \$3,600 is invested at 15% compounded daily, how much money will there be in 7 years? (Use a 365-day year; this is known as *exact interest*).

29. If \$9,400 is invested at 14% compounded daily, how much money will there be in 6 months? (Use a 360-day year; this is known as *ordinary interest*).

30. A certain bank pays 6% interest compounded continuously. How much will a \$1,000 investment be worth after 10 years?

31. How much money must be invested at 5% interest compounded continuously in order to have \$3,000 in 4 years?

32. A bank pays 6% interest compounded monthly, and a savings institution pays 5.9% compounded continuously. Over a one-year period, which account pays more interest? What about a five-year period?

33. A manufacturer of car batteries estimates that p percent of the batteries will work for at least t months, where

$$p(t) = 100e^{-0.03t}$$

a. What percent of the batteries can be expected to last at least 40 months?

b. What percent can be expected to *fail* before 50 months?

c. What percent can be expected to fail between the 40th and 50th months?

34. If P dollars are borrowed for N months compounded monthly at an annual interest rate of r, then the monthly payment is found by the formula

$$m = \frac{P\left(\frac{r}{12}\right)}{1 - \left(1 + \frac{r}{12}\right)^{-N}}$$

Use this formula to determine the monthly car payment for a new car costing \$12,487 with a down payment of \$2,487. The car is financed for 4 years at 12%.

35. A home loan is made for \$110,000 at 6% interest for 30 years. What is the monthly payment? *Hint*: See Problem 34 for the appropriate formula.

36. A cool drink is removed from a refrigerator and is placed in a room where the temperature is 70 °F. According to a result in physics known as *Newton's law of cooling*, the temperature of the drink in t minutes will be

$$F(t) = 70 - Ae^{-kt}$$

where A and k are positive constants. Suppose the temperature of the drink was 35 °F when it left the refrigerator, and 30 minutes later, it was 50 °F (that is, $F(0) = 35$ and $F(30) = 50$).

a. Find A and e^{-30k}.

b. What will the temperature (to the nearest degree) of the drink be after one hour?

c. What would you expect to happen to the temperature as $t \to +\infty$?

37. Newton's law of cooling states that an object at temperature B surrounded by air temperature A will cool to a temperature T after t minutes according to the formula

$$T = A + (B - A)e^{-kt}$$

where k is a constant depending on the item being cooled. If you draw a tub of 120 °F water for a bath and let it stand in a 75 °F room, what is the temperature of the water (to the nearest degree) after 30 min if $k = 0.01$?

38. Biologists estimate that under ideal conditions, the population $N(t)$ of a bacterial colony at time t (minutes) is given by

$$N(t) = N_0 2^{kt}$$

where N_0 and k are positive constants. Suppose the colony contains 2,000 bacteria at time $t = 0$, and 10 min later it contains 5,000 bacteria. What is the population after 20 min? After one hour?

Ⓒ 39. Show that $b^m b^n = b^{m+n}$ for $b > 0$ and all positive integers m and n.

40. Show that $\dfrac{b^m}{b^n} = b^{m-n}$ for $b > 0$ and all positive integers m and n.

41. Show that $(b^m)^n = b^{mn}$ for $b > 0$ and all positive integers m and n.

42. Show that $(\sqrt[n]{b})^m = \sqrt[n]{b^m}$ for $b > 0$ and all positive integers m and n.

43. If (x, y) is a point on the graph of $y = f(x)$, note that $(-x, y)$ is on the graph of $y = f(-x)$. Use this fact to prove that the graph of $y = f(-x)$ can be obtained by reflecting the graph of $y = f(x)$ about the y-axis.

44. Show that $\lim\limits_{h \to 0} \dfrac{e^h - 1}{h} = 1$.

45. Prove that $\lim\limits_{x \to +\infty} e^x = +\infty$ by showing that for any $N > 0$, there is a number d such that $e^x > N$ whenever $x > d$.

5.2 INVERSE FUNCTIONS; LOGARITHMS

The inverse function f^{-1} reverses the effect of f. This relationship can be illustrated by function "machines."

> **IN THIS SECTION** Inverse functions, criteria for the existence of an inverse function f^{-1}, graph of f^{-1}, the logarithmic function, the natural logarithm
>
> Intuitively, an inverse function f^{-1} "reverses" the effect of a given function f, so that both the composite functions $f \circ f^{-1}$ and $f^{-1} \circ f$ have the effect of leaving x unchanged; that is,
>
> $$(f \circ f^{-1})(x) = x \quad \text{and} \quad (f^{-1} \circ f)(x) = x$$
>
> This idea of inverse functions is exploited in this section to define a function that is the inverse of the exponential function, namely, the logarithmic function.

■ INVERSE FUNCTIONS

⊘ The symbol f^{-1} means the *inverse* of f and does not mean $1/f$. ⊘

For a given function f, we write $y_0 = f(x_0)$ to indicate that f maps the number x_0 in its domain into the corresponding number y_0 in the range. If f has an inverse f^{-1}, it is the function that reverses the effect of f in the sense that

$$f^{-1}(y_0) = x_0$$

For example, if

$$f(x) = 2x - 3, \quad \text{then} \quad f(0) = -3, \quad f(1) = -1, \quad f(2) = 1$$

and the inverse f^{-1} reverses f so that

$$f(0) = -3 \quad \boldsymbol{f^{-1}(-3) = 0} \quad \text{that is, } f^{-1}[f(0)] = 0$$
$$f(1) = -1 \quad \boldsymbol{f^{-1}(-1) = 1} \quad \text{that is, } f^{-1}[f(1)] = 1$$
$$f(2) = 1 \quad \qquad \boldsymbol{f^{-1}(1) = 2} \quad \text{that is, } f^{-1}[f(2)] = 2$$

In the case where the inverse of a function is itself a function, we have the following definition.

Inverse Function

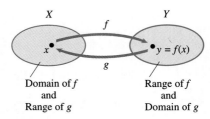

Domain of f and Range of g Range of f and Domain of g

Figure 5.5 Inverse functions f and g

> Let f be a function with domain D and range R. Then the function f^{-1} with domain R and range D is the **inverse of f** if
>
> $$f^{-1}[f(x)] = x \quad \text{for all } x \text{ in } D$$
> $$f[f^{-1}(y)] = y \quad \text{for all } y \text{ in } R$$
>
> ■ *What this says*: Suppose we consider a function defined by a set of ordered pairs $y = f(x)$. The image of x is y, as shown in Figure 5.5. If y is a member of the domain of the function $g = f^{-1}$, then $g(y) = x$. This means that f matches each element of x to exactly one y, and g matches those same elements of y back to the original values of x. If you think of a function f as a set of ordered pairs (x, y), the inverse of f is the set of ordered pairs with the components (y, x).

The language of this definition suggests that there is only one inverse function of f. Indeed, it can be shown (see Problem 61) that if f has an inverse, then the inverse is unique.

EXAMPLE 1   Inverse of a given function defined as a set of ordered pairs

Let $f = \{(0, 3), (1, 5), (3, 9), (5, 13)\}$; find f^{-1}, if it exists.

Solution   The inverse simply reverses the ordered pairs:

$$f^{-1} = \{(3, 0), (5, 1), (9, 3), (13, 5)\}$$

EXAMPLE 2   Inverse of a given function defined by an equation

Let $f(x) = 2x - 3$; find f^{-1}, if it exists.

Solution   To find f^{-1}, let $y = f(x)$ and interchange the x and y variables; *then* solve for y.

$$\text{Given function:} \quad y = 2x - 3 \qquad \text{Inverse:} \quad x = 2y - 3$$
$$2y = x + 3$$
$$y = \tfrac{1}{2}(x + 3)$$

Thus, we represent the inverse function as $f^{-1}(x) = \tfrac{1}{2}(x + 3)$. To verify that these functions are inverses of each other, we note that

$$f[f^{-1}(x)] = f\left[\tfrac{1}{2}(x + 3)\right] = 2\left[\tfrac{1}{2}(x + 3)\right] - 3 = x + 3 - 3 = x$$

and

$$f^{-1}[f(x)] = f^{-1}(2x - 3) = \tfrac{1}{2}[(2x - 3) + 3] = \tfrac{1}{2}(2x) = x$$

for all x.

■ CRITERIA FOR THE EXISTENCE OF AN INVERSE FUNCTION f^{-1}

The inverse of a function may not exist. For example,

$$f = \{(0, 0), (1, 1), (-1, 1), (2, 4), (-2, 4)\}$$

and

$$g(x) = x^2$$

do not have inverses because if we attempt to find the inverses, we obtain relations that are not functions. In the first case we find

Possible inverse of f: $\{(0, 0), (1, 1), (1, -1), (4, 2), (4, -2)\}$

This is not a function because not every member of the domain is associated with a single member in the range: $(1, 1)$ and $(1, -2)$, for example.

In the second case, if we interchange the x and y in the equation for the function g where $y = x^2$ and then solve for y we find:

$$x = y^2 \quad \text{or} \quad y = \pm\sqrt{x} \qquad \text{for } x \geq 0$$

But this is not a function of x, because for any positive value of x, there are two corresponding values of y, namely, $\sqrt{x}$ and $-\sqrt{x}$.

A function f will have an inverse f^{-1} on the interval I when there is exactly one number in the domain associated with each number in the range. That is, f^{-1} exists if $f(x_1)$ and $f(x_2)$ are equal only when $x_1 = x_2$. A function with this property is said to be **one-to-one**. This is equivalent to the graphical criterion shown in Figure 5.6.

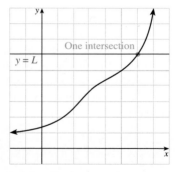

a. A function that has an inverse

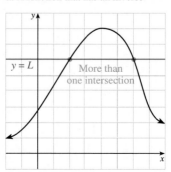

b. A function that does not have an inverse

Figure 5.6 Horizontal line test

Horizontal Line Test

A function f has an inverse if and only if each horizontal line intersects the graph of $y = f(x)$ in at most one point.

Remember that a function is strictly monotonic on some interval if it is either strictly increasing or strictly decreasing on that interval (Section 3.3). Note that a strictly monotonic function must be one-to-one and, therefore, must have an inverse. For example, if f is strictly increasing on the interval I, we know that

$$x_1 > x_2 \quad \text{implies} \quad f(x_1) > f(x_2)$$

so there is no way to have $f(x_1) = f(x_2)$ unless $x_1 = x_2$. In fact, this idea is formalized in the following theorem.

THEOREM 5.3 Existence of an inverse

Let f be a function that is continuous and strictly monotonic on an interval I. Then f^{-1} exists and is monotonic on I (increasing if f is increasing and decreasing if f is decreasing).

Proof: We have already commented on why f^{-1} exists. To show that f^{-1} is strictly increasing whenever f is increasing, let y_1 and y_2 be numbers in the range of f, with $y_2 > y_1$. We shall show that $f^{-1}(y_2) > f^{-1}(y_1)$. Because y_1, y_2 are in the range of f, there exist numbers x_1, x_2 in the domain I such that $y_1 = f(x_1)$ and $y_2 = f(x_2)$. Because $y_2 > y_1$, it follows that $f(x_2) > f(x_1)$, and because f is strictly increasing, we must have $x_2 > x_1$. Thus, $f^{-1}(y_2) > f^{-1}(y_1)$, and f^{-1} is strictly increasing. Similarly, if f is strictly decreasing, then so is f^{-1}. (The details are left for the reader.) ∎

■ GRAPH OF f^{-1}

The graphs of f and its inverse f^{-1} are closely related. In particular, if (a, b) is a point on the graph of f, then $b = f(a)$ and $a = f^{-1}(b)$, so (b, a) is on the graph of f^{-1}. It can be shown that (a, b) and (b, a) are reflections of one another in the line $y = x$. (See Figure 5.7, as well as Problem 60.) These observations yield the following procedure for sketching the graph of an inverse function.

Procedure for Obtaining the Graph of f^{-1}

If f^{-1} exists, its graph may be obtained by reflecting the graph of f in the line $y = x$.

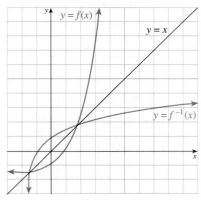

Figure 5.7 The graphs of f and f^{-1} are reflections in the line $y = x$.

EXAMPLE 3   Graphing an inverse

Explain why the function $f(x) = x^3 + 2$ has an inverse. Sketch the graph of f^{-1}.

Solution   The derivative of f is $f'(x) = 3x^2$. Because $f'(x) > 0$ for all $x \neq 0$, it follows that f is strictly increasing, and according to Theorem 5.3, f^{-1} exists.

The graph of f is shown in Figure 5.8, and in the same figure, we obtain the graph of f^{-1} by reflecting the graph of f in the line $y = x$.   ■

In general, if the graph of f has a nonhorizontal tangent line at a point $P(a, b)$, we expect the graph of the inverse function f^{-1} to have a nonvertical tangent line at the reflected point $Q(b, a)$. Thus, if f is differentiable at x_0 and $f'(x_0) \neq 0$, then f^{-1} is differentiable at $y_0 = f(x_0)$. This observation is formalized in Theorem 5.4.

THEOREM 5.4   Continuity and differentiability of inverse functions

Let f be a one-to-one function. (This means that it possesses an inverse.)

1. If f is continuous on its domain, then f^{-1} is continuous on its domain.
2. If f is differentiable at c and $f'(c) \neq 0$, then f^{-1} is differentiable at $f(c)$.

Proof: The reasonableness of this theorem follows from Figure 5.8. A proof is given in Appendix B.   ■

We can use Theorem 5.4 and the chain rule to provide a formula for the derivative of $f^{-1}(x)$ in terms of the derivative $f'(x)$.

THEOREM 5.5   Derivative of an inverse function

Suppose f is strictly monotonic and differentiable for all x in its domain. Then

$$(f^{-1})'(x) = \frac{1}{f'[f^{-1}(x)]}$$

Proof: Let $g(x) = f^{-1}(x)$. From Theorem 5.4 we know that g is differentiable. By definition of inverse functions,

$$f[g(x)] = x$$

$$\frac{d}{dx} f[g(x)] = 1 \qquad \textit{Differentiate both sides with respect to x.}$$

$$f'[g(x)] \frac{d}{dx}[g(x)] = 1 \qquad \textit{Chain rule}$$

$$\frac{d}{dx}[g(x)] = \frac{1}{f'[g(x)]} \qquad \begin{array}{l}\textit{Because f is monotonic, } f' \neq 0, \textit{ so} \\ f'[g(x)] \neq 0, \textit{ and we can divide both} \\ \textit{sides by } f'[g(x)].\end{array}$$ ■

■ ***What this says***: Geometrically, the derivatives of two functions that are inverses tell us that graphs of inverse functions have reciprocal slopes at the points (a, b) and (b, a). Also notice that in the Leibniz notation, the formula in Theorem 5.5 can be written

$$\frac{dx}{dy} = \frac{1}{\dfrac{dy}{dx}}$$

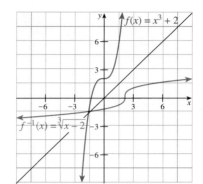

Figure 5.8 The graphs of $f(x) = x^3 + 2$ and its inverse $f^{-1}(x) = \sqrt[3]{x - 2}$

Historical Note

JOHN NAPIER (1550–1617)

Napier was the Isaac Asimov of his day, having envisioned the tank, the machine gun, and the submarine. He also predicted that the end of the world would occur between 1688 and 1700. He is best known today as the inventor of logarithms, which until the advent of the calculator were used extensively with complicated calculations. Today we use the logarithmic function to model many situations. Napier considered mathematics only a diversion from his theological work, on which he felt his reputation would solely depend.

EXAMPLE 4 Derivative of an inverse function

Let $f(x) = \sqrt[3]{x}$. Show that $f^{-1}(x)$ exists and use the derivative of an inverse function theorem to evaluate the derivative of $f^{-1}(x)$ at $x = 4$.

Solution Because $f'(x) = \frac{1}{3}x^{-2/3} > 0$ for all $x \neq 0$, it follows that f^{-1} exists. Because $f(64) = 4$, we have $f^{-1}(4) = 64$ and $f'(64) = \frac{1}{3}(64)^{-2/3} = \frac{1}{48}$. We now use the derivative of an inverse function theorem:

$$(f^{-1})'(4) = \frac{1}{f'[f^{-1}(4)]} = \frac{1}{f'(64)} = \frac{1}{\frac{1}{48}} = 48$$

To check this result, note that because $f(x) = \sqrt[3]{x}$, we have $f^{-1}(x) = x^3$. Thus,

$$(f^{-1})'(x) = 3x^2 \quad \text{and} \quad (f^{-1})'(4) = 3(4)^2 = 48$$

as we found by applying the formula for the derivative of an inverse function theorem.

■ **THE LOGARITHMIC FUNCTION**

In Section 5.1, we observed that if $b > 0$ and $b \neq 1$, the exponential function $f(x) = b^x$ is continuous and monotonic (increasing if $b > 1$ and decreasing if $0 < b < 1$). Therefore, according to Theorem 5.3 (the existence of an inverse), $f(x) = b^x$ has an inverse that is also continuous and monotonic, and we shall refer to this inverse function as the *logarithm of x to the base b*. Here is a definition, along with some notation.

Logarithmic Function

If $b > 0$ and $b \neq 1$, the **logarithm of x to the base b** is the function $y = \log_b x$ that satisfies $b^y = x$; that is

$$y = \log_b x \quad \text{means} \quad b^y = x$$

■ *What this says*: It is useful to think of a logarithm as an exponent. That is, consider the following sequence of interpretations:

$y = \log_b x$
y is the logarithm to the base b of x.
y is the **exponent on a base b** that yields x.
$b^y = x$

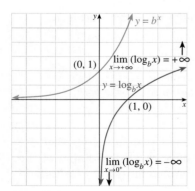

Figure 5.9 The graph of $y = \log_b x$ for $b > 1$

Notice that $y = \log_b x$ is defined only for $x > 0$ because $b^y > 0$ for all y. We have sketched the graph of $y = \log_b x$ for $b > 1$ in Figure 5.9 by reflecting the graph of $y = b^x$ in the line $y = x$. Notice that because $y = b^x$ is a continuous, increasing function that satisfies $b^x > 0$ for all x, $\log_b x$ must also be continuous and increasing, and its graph must lie entirely to the right of the y-axis. Also, because $b^0 = 1$ and $b^1 = b$, we have $\log_b 1 = 0$ and $\log_b b = 1$

so $(1, 0)$ and $(b, 1)$ lie on the logarithmic curve. Theorem 5.6 lists several general properties of logarithms.

THEOREM 5.6   Basic properties of logarithmic functions

If $b > 0$ and $b \neq 1$, then

Equality rule	If $x = y$, then $\log_b x = \log_b y$
Inequality rules	If $x > y$ and $b > 1$, then $\log_b x > \log_b y$
	If $x > y$ and $0 < b < 1$, then $\log_b x < \log_b y$
Product rule	$\log_b(xy) = \log_b x + \log_b y$
Quotient rule	$\log_b\left(\dfrac{x}{y}\right) = \log_b x - \log_b y$
Power rule	$\log_b x^p = p \log_b x \qquad$ for any real number p

⊘ Remember, the definition of logarithm requires that $x > 0$ and $y > 0$. ⊘

Proof: Each part of this theorem can be derived by using the definition of logarithm in conjunction with a suitable property of exponentials.   ■

We will also need the following properties about limits involving logarithms.

Limits of Logarithms

For $b > 1$,

$$\lim_{x \to 0^+} \log_b x = -\infty$$

$$\lim_{x \to +\infty} \log_b x = +\infty$$

⊘ Don't forget this result. ⊘

$$\lim_{x \to c} \log_b x = \log_b \left[\lim_{x \to c} x \right]$$

▮ *What this says*: A limit of a log is the log of a limit.

EXAMPLE 5   Evaluate a logarithmic expression

Evaluate $\log_2\left(\frac{1}{8}\right) + \log_2 128$.

Solution   You can evaluate this on your calculator, or you can use Theorem 5.6

$$\log_2\left(\tfrac{1}{8}\right) + \log_2 128 = \log_2 (2)^{-3} + \log_2 2^7$$

$$= \log_2 [2^{-3}(2^7)] = \log_2 2^4 = 4 \log_2 2 = 4(1) = 4$$

What we have shown here is much longer than what you would do in your work, which would probably be shortened as follows:

$$\log_2\left(\tfrac{1}{8}\right) + \log_2 128 = \log_2 16 \quad \textit{Because } \left(\tfrac{1}{8}\right)(128) = 16$$

$$= 4 \qquad\qquad \textit{Because 4 is the \textbf{exponent} on}$$
$$\textit{2 that yields 16}$$ ▬

EXAMPLE 6   Logarithmic equation

Solve the equation $\log_3(2x + 1) - 2 \log_3(x - 3) = 2$.

Solution   Use Theorem 5.6, remembering that $2x + 1 > 0$ and $x - 3 > 0$.

Computational Window

For a graphical solution:

Y₁◻log (2X+1)/lo
g 3-2*log (X-3)/
log 3

Xmin=-1   Ymin=-5
Xmax=10   Ymax=10
Xscl=1   Yscl=1

$$\log_3(2x + 1) - 2\log_3(x - 3) = 2$$
$$\log_3(2x + 1) - \log_3(x - 3)^2 = 2$$
$$\log_3 \frac{2x + 1}{(x - 3)^2} = 2$$
$$3^2 = \frac{2x + 1}{(x - 3)^2}$$
$$9(x - 3)^2 = 2x + 1$$
$$9x^2 - 56x + 80 = 0$$
$$(x - 4)(9x - 20) = 0$$
$$x = 4, \tfrac{20}{9}$$

Notice that $x - 3 < 0$ if $x = \frac{20}{9}$, so the given logarithmic equation has only $x = 4$ as a solution. Do not forget that we cannot take the logarithm of a negative number.

EXAMPLE 7   Exponential equation with base 10

Solve $10^{5x+3} = 195$.

Solution $10^{5x+3} = 195$

$$5x + 3 = \log_{10} 195 \qquad \textit{Remember that } 5x + 3 \textit{ is the } \textbf{exponent}$$
$$\textit{on a base } 10 \textit{ that yields } 195.$$
$$5x = \log_{10} 195 - 3$$
$$x = \frac{\log_{10} 195 - 3}{5}$$
$$\approx -0.141\,993\,077\,7 \quad \textit{By calculator}$$

Computational Window

Y₁◻10^(5X+3)
Y₂◻195

Xmin=-1   Ymin=-50
Xmax=1   Ymax=250
Xscl=.25 Yscl=50

■ THE NATURAL LOGARITHM

There are two frequently used bases for logarithms. If the base 10 is used, then the logarithm is called a **common logarithm;** and if the base e is used, the logarithm is called a **natural logarithm.** We use a special notation for each of these logarithms.

Common Logarithm
Natural Logarithm
(ln x is pronounced "ell n x"
or "lawn x")

The **common logarithm,** $\log_{10} x$, is denoted by **log x.**

The **natural logarithm,** $\log_e x$, is denoted by **ln x.**

EXAMPLE 8   Solving an exponential equation with base e

Solve $\frac{1}{2} = e^{-0.000\,425t}$.

Solution $\qquad \frac{1}{2} = e^{-0.000425t}$

$$-0.000\,425t = \ln 0.5 \qquad \textit{Remember that } -0.000425t \textit{ is the } \textbf{exponent}$$
$$\textit{on base } e \textit{ that yields } \tfrac{1}{2} = 0.5.$$
$$t = \frac{\ln 0.5}{-0.000\,425} \approx 1,630.934\,542$$

If a logarithmic equation has a base other than base 10 or e, you can solve it using the equality rule of Theorem 5.6. The following theorem provides a useful formula for converting from one base to another.

THEOREM 5.7 Change-of-base theorem

$$\log_a x = \frac{\log_b x}{\log_b a} \qquad \text{\textit{Remember, the definition of logarithms requires that } } b > 0, b \neq 1.$$

Proof: Let $y = \log_a x$

$$a^y = x \qquad \text{\textit{Definition of logarithm}}$$

$$\log_b a^y = \log_b x \qquad \text{\textit{Equality rule of logarithms}}$$

$$y \log_b a = \log_b x \qquad \text{\textit{Power rule of logarithms}}$$

$$y = \frac{\log_b x}{\log_b a} \qquad \text{\textit{Divide both sides by } } \log_b a. \qquad \blacksquare$$

■ *What this says*: To change from base a to another (possibly more familiar) base b, you simply change the base on the given logarithm from a to b and then divide by the logarithm to the base b of the old base a.

EXAMPLE 9 Solving an exponential equation using the change-of-base theorem

Solve $6^{3x+2} = 200$.

Solution

$$6^{3x+2} = 200$$

$$3x + 2 = \log_6 200$$

$$3x = \log_6 200 - 2$$

$$x = \frac{\log_6 200 - 2}{3} \qquad \text{\textit{To evaluate } } \log_6 200, \text{\textit{ use }} \log_6 200 = \frac{\ln 200}{\ln 6}.$$

$$\approx 0.319\,015\,741\,7 \qquad \qquad \blacksquare$$

Because we most often use base e, it is worthwhile to state some useful properties of natural logarithms.

THEOREM 5.8 Basic properties of the natural logarithm

a. $\ln 1 = 0$

b. $\ln e = 1$

c. $e^{\ln x} = x$ for all $x > 0$

d. $\ln e^y = y$ for all y

e. $\log_b x = \frac{\ln x}{\ln b}$ for any $b > 0$ $(b \neq 1)$

f. $b^x = e^{x \ln b}$ for any $b > 0$ $(b \neq 1)$

Proof: **a.** $\ln 1 = \log_e 1 = 0$ *Definition of logarithm* $e^0 = 1$

b. $\ln e = \log_e e = 1$ *Definition of logarithm* $e^1 = e$

c. $e^{\ln x} = e^y$ *Let* $y = \ln x$.

     $= x$ *Definition of logarithm: if* $y = \ln x$, *then* $e^y = x$.

d. $\ln e^y = \ln x$ *Let* $x = e^y$.

     $= y$ *Definition of logarithm: if* $x = e^y$, *then* $\ln x = y$.

e. $\log_b x = \dfrac{\ln x}{\ln b}$ *Change-of-base theorem*

f. $b^x = y$ *Let* $y = b^x$.

     $= e^{\ln y}$ *Property c of this theorem*

     $= e^{x \ln b}$ *If* $y = b^x$, *then* $x = \log_b y = \dfrac{\ln y}{\ln b}$, *so that* $\ln y = x \ln b$. ∎

Computational Window

If you are using a software package such as Mathematica, Derive, or Maple, be careful about the notation. Some versions do not distinguish between $\log x$ (common logarithm) and $\ln x$ (natural logarithm). All logarithms on these versions are assumed to be natural logarithms, so evaluating a common logarithm requires the change-of-base theorem.

We close this section with an application in which logarithms play a useful role.

EXAMPLE 10   Exponential growth

A biological colony grows in such a way that at time t, the population is

$$P(t) = P_0 e^{kt}$$

where P_0 is the initial population and k is a positive constant. Suppose the colony begins with 5,000 individuals and contains a population of 7,000 after 20 min. Find k and determine the population after 30 min.

Solution   Because $P_0 = 5,000$, the population after t minutes will be

$$P(t) = 5,000 e^{kt}$$

In particular, because the population is 7,000 after 20 min,

$$P(20) = 5,000 e^{k(20)}$$

$$7,000 = 5,000 e^{20k}$$

$$\frac{7}{5} = e^{20k}$$

$$20k = \ln\left(\tfrac{7}{5}\right)$$

$$k = \tfrac{1}{20} \ln\left(\tfrac{7}{5}\right)$$

$$\approx 0.016\,823\,6$$

Computational Window

```
Y₁⊟5000e^(.01682
36X)

    Xmin=0
    Xmax=50
    Xscl=10
    Ymin=0
    Ymax=10000
    Yscl=1000
```

Graph of $y = 5,000e^{\wedge}(kx)$ where $k = 0.0168236$

Finally, to determine the population after 30 min, substitute this value for k to find:

$$P(30) = 5,000e^{30k}$$

$$\approx 8,282.5117$$

The expected population is approximately 8,000. ▬

PROBLEM SET 5.2

Ⓐ *Determine which pairs of functions defined by the equations in Problems 1–6 are inverses of each other.*

1. $f(x) = 5x + 3$; $g(x) = \dfrac{x-3}{5}$

2. $f(x) = \frac{2}{3}x + 2$; $g(x) = \frac{3}{2}x + 3$

3. $f(x) = \frac{4}{5}x + 4$; $g(x) = \frac{5}{4}x + 3$

4. $f(x) = \dfrac{1}{x}$, $x \neq 0$; $g(x) = \dfrac{1}{x}$, $x \neq 0$

5. $f(x) = x^2$, $x < 0$; $g(x) = \sqrt{x}$, $x > 0$

6. $f(x) = x^2$, $x \geq 0$; $g(x) = \sqrt{x}$, $x \geq 0$

Find the inverse (if it exists) of each function given in Problems 7–12.

7. $f = \{(4, 5), (6, 3), (7, 1), (2, 4)\}$

8. $f(x) = 2x + 3$

9. $g(x) = x^2 - 5$, $x \geq 0$

10. $g(x) = \sqrt{x} + 5$

11. $h(x) = \dfrac{2x - 6}{3x + 3}$

12. $h(x) = \dfrac{2x + 1}{x}$

Evaluate the expressions given in Problems 13–22.

13. $\log_2 4 + \log_3 \frac{1}{9}$

14. $2^{\log_2 3 - \log_2 5}$

15. $5\log_3 9 - 2\log_2 16$

16. $\left(\log_2 \frac{1}{8}\right)(\log_3 27)$

17. $(3^{\log_3 7})(\log_5 0.04)$

18. $e^{5 \ln 2}$

19. $\log_3 3^4 - \ln e^{0.5}$

20. $\ln(\log 10^e)$

21. $\exp(\ln 3 - \ln 10)$

22. $\exp(\log_{e^2} 25)$

Solve the logarithmic and exponential equations to calculator accuracy in Problems 23–33.

23. $\log_x 16 = 2$

24. $\log x = 5.1$

25. $e^{-3x} = 0.5$

26. $\ln x^2 = 9$

27. $7^{-x} = 15$

28. $e^{2x} = \ln(4 + e)$

29. $\frac{1}{2}\log_3 x = \log_2 8$

30. $\log_2(x^{\log_2 x}) = 4$

31. $\log_3 x + \log_3(2x + 1) = 1$

32. $\ln\left(\dfrac{x^2}{1 - x}\right) = \ln x + \ln\left(\dfrac{2x}{1 + x}\right)$

33. $2^{3\log_2 x} = 4\log_3 9$

34. Let $f(x) = 3x + 5$. Show that $f^{-1}(x)$ exists and use the derivative of an inverse function theorem to evaluate the derivative of $f^{-1}(x)$ at $x = 2$.

Ⓑ **35.** Let $f(x) = \sin x$ for $0 \leq x \leq \frac{\pi}{2}$. Use Theorem 5.5 (the derivative of an inverse function theorem) to find the derivative of the inverse function.

36. If $\log_b 1{,}296 = 4$, what is $\left(\frac{3}{2}b\right)^{3/2}$?

37. If $\log_{\sqrt{b}} 106 = 2$, what is $\sqrt{b - 25}$?

Sketch the graph of f in Problems 38–44 and then use the horizontal line test to determine whether or not f has an inverse. If f^{-1} exists, sketch its graph.

38. $f(x) = x^2$, for all x

39. $f(x) = x^2$, $x \leq 0$

40. $f(x) = 10^x$, for all x

41. $f(x) = \sqrt{1 - x^2}$ on $(-1, 1)$

42. $f(x) = x(x - 1)(x - 2)$ on $[1, 2]$

43. $f(x) = \cos x$, on $[0, \pi]$

44. $f(x) = \tan x$, on $\left(-\frac{\pi}{2}, \frac{\pi}{2}\right)$

45. According to the *Bouguer–Lambert law*, a beam of light that strikes the surface of a body of water with intensity I_0 will have intensity I at a depth of x meters, where

$$I = I_0 e^{kx} \qquad k > 0$$

The constant k is called the *absorption coefficient*, and it depends on such things as the wavelength of the beam of light and the purity of the water. Suppose a given beam of light is only 5% as intense at a depth of 2 meters as it is at the surface. Find k and determine at what depth (to the nearest meter) the intensity is 1% of the intensity at the surface. (This explains why plant life exists only in the top 10 m of a lake or sea.)

46. A manufacturer of light bulbs estimates that the fraction $F(t)$ of bulbs that remain burning after t weeks is given by

$$F(t) = e^{-kt}$$

where k is a positive constant. Suppose twice as many bulbs are burning after 5 wk as after 9 wk.

a. Find k and determine the fraction of bulbs that are burning after 7 wk.

b. What fraction of the bulbs *burn out* before 10 wk?

c. What fraction of the bulbs can be expected to burn out between the 4th and 5th weeks?

47. A certain bank pays 6% interest compounded continuously. How long will it take for $835 to double?

48. If an amount of money is compounded continuously at an annual rate r, how long will it take for that amount of money to double?

49. First National Bank pays 7% interest compounded monthly, and World Savings pays 6.95% interest compounded continuously. Which bank offers a better deal?

50. A person invests $8,500 in a bank that compounds interest continuously. If the investment doubles in 10 years, what is the (annual) rate of interest (correct to the nearest hundredth percent)?

51. In 1626, Peter Minuit traded trinkets worth $24 for land on Manhattan Island. Assume that in 1990 the same land was worth $25.2 billion. Find the annual rate of interest compounded continuously at which the $24 would have had to be invested during this time to yield the same amount.

52. Biologists estimate that the population of a bacterial colony is

$$P(t) = P_0 2^{kt}$$

at time t (in minutes). Suppose the population is found to be 1,000 after 20 min and that it doubles every hour.

a. Find P_0 and k.

b. When will the population be 5,000 (correct to the nearest minute)?

53. A *decibel* (named for Alexander Graham Bell) is the smallest increase of the loudness of a sound that is detectable by the human ear. In physics, it is shown that when two sounds of intensity I_1 and I_2 (watts/cm^3) occur, the difference in loudness is D decibels, where

$$D = 10 \log_{10}\left(\frac{I_1}{I_2}\right)$$

When sound is rated in relation to the threshold of human hearing ($I_0 = 10^{-16}$) the level of normal conversation is 50 decibels, whereas that of a rock concert is 110 decibels. Show that a rock concert is 60 times as loud as normal conversation but a million times as intense.

54. The *Richter scale* measures the intensity of earthquakes. Specifically, if E is the energy (watt/cm^3) released by a quake, then it is said to have *magnitude M*, where

$$M = \frac{\log E - 11.4}{1.5}$$

a. Express E in terms of M.

b. How much more energy is released in an $M = 8.5$ earthquake (such as the devastating Alaska quake of 1964) than in an average quake of magnitude $M = 6.5$ (such as the Los Angeles quake of 1994)?

Ⓒ 55. Let b be any positive number other than 1. Show that

$$x^x = b^{x \log_b x}$$

56. Let a, b be any positive numbers other than 1. Show that

$$(\log_a b)(\log_b a) = 1$$

57. Verify directly that if (u, v) is a point on the graph of $y = \log_b x$, then (v, u) is on the graph of $y = b^x$, and vice versa.

58. Suppose that f is differentiable and that its inverse exists. Let $y = f(x)$ and show that

$$\frac{df}{dx}\frac{df^{-1}}{dy} = 1$$

Hint: Apply the chain rule to the equation $f^{-1}(y) = x$.

59. Suppose that f is differentiable and that its inverse exists. Let $y = f(x)$ and show that

$$\frac{df^{-1}}{dy} > 0$$

for all y in the domain of f^{-1} if $\frac{df}{dx} > 0$ for all x in the domain of f. *Hint*: Conclude that f^{-1} is increasing if f is increasing, and then show that f^{-1} is decreasing if f is decreasing.

60. Show that the line $y = x$ is the perpendicular bisector of the line segment joining the points (a, b) and (b, a). Notice that this means (a, b) and (b, a) are reflections of one another in the line $y = x$.

61. Show that if f^{-1} exists, it is unique. *Hint*: If g_1 and g_2 both satisfy

$$g_1[f(x)] = x = f[g_1(x)]$$
$$g_2[f(x)] = x = f[g_2(x)]$$

then show that $g_1(x) = g_2(x)$.

5.3 DERIVATIVES INVOLVING e^x AND $\ln x$

IN THIS SECTION Derivatives of natural logarithmic functions, derivatives of exponential functions, logarithmic differentiation.
The goal of this section is to develop the differential calculus of logarithmic and exponential functions. We shall begin by deriving differentiation formulas for $\ln x$ and e^x, and we shall apply these formulas to a number of differentiation problems and applications. We shall also develop a technique called *logarithmic differentiation*, which can be used to simplify the differentiation of products and quotients.

■ DERIVATIVES OF NATURAL LOGARITHMIC FUNCTIONS

THEOREM 5.9   Derivative of ln u

If $x > 0$, then $\dfrac{d}{dx}(\ln x) = \dfrac{1}{x}$.

If u is a differentiable function of x, then $\dfrac{d}{dx}(\ln u) = \dfrac{1}{u}\dfrac{du}{dx}$ for $u > 0$.

Proof: To find the derivative of $\ln x$, we apply the definition of derivative.

$$\frac{d}{dx}(\ln x) = \lim_{\Delta x \to 0} \frac{\ln(x + \Delta x) - \ln x}{\Delta x}$$

$$= \lim_{\Delta x \to 0} \frac{1}{\Delta x} \ln\left(\frac{x + \Delta x}{x}\right)$$

$$= \lim_{\Delta x \to 0} \frac{1}{\Delta x} \ln\left(1 + \frac{\Delta x}{x}\right)$$

$$= \lim_{h \to +\infty} \frac{1}{\frac{x}{h}} \ln\left(1 + \frac{\frac{x}{h}}{x}\right) \qquad \textit{Let } h = \frac{x}{\Delta x}, \textit{ so } \Delta x = \frac{x}{h}.$$
$$\textit{As } \Delta x \to 0, \; h \to \infty$$

$$= \lim_{h \to +\infty} \frac{h}{x} \ln\left(1 + \frac{1}{h}\right)$$

$$= \frac{1}{x} \lim_{h \to +\infty} h \ln\left(1 + \frac{1}{h}\right)$$

$$= \frac{1}{x} \lim_{h \to +\infty} \ln\left(1 + \frac{1}{h}\right)^h \qquad \textit{Power rule for logarithms}$$

$$= \frac{1}{x} \ln \lim_{h \to +\infty} \left(1 + \frac{1}{h}\right)^h \qquad \textit{Limit of a } \log \textit{ property}$$

$$= \frac{1}{x} \ln e \qquad \textit{Definition of e}$$

$$= \frac{1}{x} \qquad \ln e = 1, \textit{ because } e^1 = e.$$

For the second part of this theorem, let u be a differentiable function of x and apply the chain rule to $\ln u$ to find

$$\frac{d}{dx}(\ln u) = \left[\frac{d}{du}(\ln u)\right]\frac{du}{dx} = \frac{1}{u}\frac{du}{dx} \qquad ■$$

EXAMPLE 1   Derivative of a natural logarithm

Differentiate $y = \ln(5x^2 + 2x + 1)$.

Solution   Use the chain rule where $u = 5x^2 + 2x + 1$, so $\dfrac{du}{dx} = 10x + 2$ and

$$\frac{dy}{dx} = \frac{1}{5x^2 + 2x + 1}(10x + 2) = \frac{10x + 2}{5x^2 + 2x + 1} \qquad ▬$$

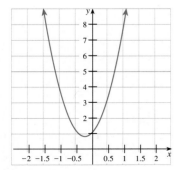

Figure 5.10 Graph of $y = 5x^2 + 2x + 1$ shows $5x^2 + 2x + 1 > 0$.

In Example 1, we did not specifically note that $5x^2 + 2x + 1 \geq 0$ but it is worth noting because $\ln u$ is defined only for $u > 0$. See Figure 5.10.

THEOREM 5.10 Derivative of ln $|u|$

If $f(x) = \ln |x|$, $x \neq 0$, then $f'(x) = \dfrac{1}{x}$.

Also, if u is a differentiable function of x, then $\dfrac{d}{dx} \ln |u| = \dfrac{1}{u} \dfrac{du}{dx}$.

Proof: Using the definition of absolute value,

$$f(x) = \begin{cases} \ln x & \text{if } x > 0 \\ \ln(-x) & \text{if } x < 0 \end{cases}$$

so

$$f'(x) = \begin{cases} \dfrac{1}{x} & \text{if } x > 0 \\ \dfrac{1}{-x}(-1) = \dfrac{1}{x} & \text{if } x < 0 \end{cases}$$

Thus, $f'(x) = \dfrac{1}{x}$ for all $x \neq 0$. The second part (for u, a differentiable function of x) follows from the chain rule. ∎

EXAMPLE 2 Derivative of a function involving a natural logarithm

---

Differentiate $f(x) = \sin x + \sqrt{\ln x}$.

Solution Write $f(x) = \sin x + (\ln x)^{1/2}$.

$$f'(x) = \cos x + \tfrac{1}{2} (\ln x)^{-1/2}\left(\frac{1}{x}\right) = \cos x + \frac{1}{2x\sqrt{\ln x}}$$

EXAMPLE 3 Derivative of a function involving a natural logarithm

---

Differentiate $f(x) = (x^2 + \ln\sqrt{x})^3$.

Solution Write $f(x) = (x^2 + \tfrac{1}{2} \ln x)^3$. *Use the power rule of logarithms.*

$$f'(x) = 3(x^2 + \tfrac{1}{2} \ln x)^2\left(2x + \frac{1}{2x}\right) = \frac{3}{2x}\left(x^2 + \ln\sqrt{x}\right)^2(4x^2 + 1)$$

■ DERIVATIVES OF EXPONENTIAL FUNCTIONS

The next theorem is easy to prove and remember and also is one of the most important results in all of differential calculus.

THEOREM 5.11 Derivative of e^u

$$\frac{d}{dx}(e^x) = e^x$$

If u is a differentiable function of x, then $\dfrac{d}{dx}(e^u) = e^u \dfrac{du}{dx}$.

Proof: Let $v = e^x$ so that

$$x = \ln v$$

$$\frac{d}{dx}(x) = \frac{d}{dx}(\ln v) \qquad \textit{Implicit differentiation}$$

$$1 = \frac{1}{v}\frac{dv}{dx}$$

$$v = \frac{dv}{dx}$$

$$e^x = \frac{dv}{dx} = \frac{d}{dx}(e^x) \quad \textit{Because } v = e^x$$

For the second part of this theorem, let u be a differentiable function of x, and apply the chain rule to e^u to find

$$\frac{d}{dx}(e^u) = \frac{d}{du}(e^u)\frac{du}{dx} = e^u\frac{du}{dx} \qquad \blacksquare$$

EXAMPLE 4 Derivative of an exponential function

Differentiate $f(x) = e^{x^2+x}$.

Solution $\qquad \frac{d}{dx}(e^{x^2+x}) = e^{x^2+x}\left[\frac{d}{dx}(x^2+x)\right] = e^{x^2+x}(2x+1)$ ▬

EXAMPLE 5 Derivative of a product involving an exponential function

Differentiate $e^{-3x}\sin x$.

Solution Use the product rule:

$$\frac{d}{dx}\left[e^{-3x}\sin x\right] = e^{-3x}\left[\frac{d}{dx}(\sin x)\right] + \left[\frac{d}{dx}(e^{-3x})\right]\sin x$$

$$= e^{-3x}(\cos x) + [e^{-3x}(-3)]\sin x$$

$$= e^{-3x}(\cos x - 3\sin x) \qquad \text{▬}$$

⊘ It is important to remember that a power function x^n has a constant exponent and a variable base, whereas an exponential function b^x has a constant base and a variable exponent. You should not expect a function like 2^x to behave like x^2. ⊘   The following theorem illustrates a major behavioral difference between the monomial x^n and the exponential b^x.

THEOREM 5.12 Derivative of an exponential function with base b

For base b $(b > 0,\ b \neq 1)$,

$$\frac{d}{dx}b^x = (\ln b)b^x$$

and if u is a differentiable function of x, then

$$\frac{d}{dx}b^u = (\ln b)b^u\frac{du}{dx} \qquad \text{for all } u.$$

Proof: Because $b^x = e^{x\ln b}$, (Theorem 5.8f), we can apply the chain rule formula $\frac{d}{dx}(e^u)$ with $u = x\ln b$ to obtain

$$\frac{d}{dx}(b^x) = \frac{d}{dx}(e^{x\ln b}) = e^{x\ln b}\frac{d}{dx}(x\ln b) = e^{x\ln b}(\ln b) = b^x(\ln b)$$

The second part of this theorem follows from the chain rule. ■

EXAMPLE 6   Derivative of an exponential function with base $b \neq e$

Differentiate $f(x) = x(2^{1-x})$.

Solution   Apply the product rule.

$$f'(x) = \frac{d}{dx}(x\, 2^{1-x}) = x\frac{d}{dx}(2^{1-x}) + 2^{1-x}\frac{d}{dx}(x)$$

$$= x(\ln 2)(2^{1-x})(-1) + 2^{1-x}(1) = 2^{1-x}(1 - x \ln 2)$$ ▬

THEOREM 5.13   Derivative of a natural logarithm with base b

For base b $(b > 0, b \neq 1)$

$$\frac{d}{dx}(\log_b x) = \frac{1}{(\ln b)\, x} \qquad \text{for all } x > 0$$

and if u is a differentiable function of x, then

$$\frac{d}{dx}(\log_b u) = \frac{1}{(\ln b)\, u}\frac{du}{dx} \qquad \text{for all } u > 0$$

Proof: Because $\log_b x = \dfrac{\ln x}{\ln b}$ and because $\dfrac{d}{dx}(\ln x) = \dfrac{1}{x}$ for $x > 0$, we have

$$\frac{d}{dx}(\log_b x) = \frac{d}{dx}\left[\frac{\ln x}{\ln b}\right] = \frac{1}{\ln b}\cdot\frac{1}{x} = \frac{1}{(\ln b)x}$$

Once again, the second part follows from the chain rule.   ▪

> ▪ **What this says:** The derivatives of b^x and $\log_b x$ are the same as the derivatives of e^x and $\ln x$, respectively, except for a factor of $\ln b$ that appears as a multiplier in the formula
>
> $$\frac{d}{dx}(b^x) = (\ln b)b^x$$
>
> and as a divisor in the formula
>
> $$\frac{d}{dx}(\log_b x) = \frac{1}{(\ln b)x}$$

EXAMPLE 7   Derivative of a logarithmic function with a base $b \neq e$

Differentiate $g(x) = \log_{3.1}|x^2 - x|$.

Solution   Let $u = x^2 - x$ and $b = 3.1$.

$$g'(x) = \frac{d}{dx}(\log_{3.1}|x^2 - x|) = \frac{1}{(\ln 3.1)(x^2 - x)}\frac{d}{dx}(x^2 - x)$$

$$= \frac{2x - 1}{(\ln 3.1)(x^2 - x)} \qquad \begin{array}{l}\textit{For all } x \textit{ such that } u = x^2 - x \neq 0;\\ \textit{that is, } x \neq 0, 1\end{array}$$ ▬

▪ LOGARITHMIC DIFFERENTIATION

Logarithmic differentiation is a procedure in which logarithms are used to trade the task of differentiating products and quotients for that of differentiating sums and differences. It is especially valuable as a means for handling complicated product or quotient functions and power functions where variables appear in both the base and the exponent.

EXAMPLE 8   Logarithmic differentiation

Find the derivative of $y = \dfrac{e^{2x}(2x - 1)^6}{(x^3 + 5)^2(4 - 7x)}$.

Solution   The procedure called logarithmic differentiation requires that we first take the logarithm of both sides and then apply properties of logarithms before attempting to take the derivative.

$$y = \frac{e^{2x}(2x - 1)^6}{(x^3 + 5)^2(4 - 7x)}$$

$$\ln y = \ln\left[\frac{e^{2x}(2x - 1)^6}{(x^3 + 5)^2(4 - 7x)}\right]$$

$$= \ln e^{2x} + \ln(2x - 1)^6 - \ln(x^3 + 5)^2 - \ln(4 - 7x)$$

$$= 2x + 6\ln(2x - 1) - 2\ln(x^3 + 5) - \ln(4 - 7x)$$

Next, differentiate both sides with respect to x and then solve for $\dfrac{dy}{dx}$.

$$\frac{1}{y}\frac{dy}{dx} = 2 + 6\left[\frac{1}{2x - 1}(2)\right] - 2\left[\frac{1}{x^3 + 5}(3x^2)\right] - \left[\frac{1}{4 - 7x}(-7)\right]$$

$$\frac{dy}{dx} = y\left[2 + \frac{12}{2x - 1} - \frac{6x^2}{x^3 + 5} + \frac{7}{4 - 7x}\right]$$

This is the derivative in terms of x and y. If we want the derivative in terms of x alone, we can substitute the value of y:

$$\frac{dy}{dx} = \frac{e^{2x}(2x - 1)^6}{(x^3 + 5)^2(4 - 7x)}\left[2 + \frac{12}{2x - 1} - \frac{6x^2}{x^3 + 5} + \frac{7}{4 - 7x}\right]$$ ▬

EXAMPLE 9   Derivative of a function with a variable in both the base term and the exponent

Find $\dfrac{dy}{dx}$, where $y = (x + 1)^{2x}$.

Solution $$y = (x + 1)^{2x}$$

$$\ln y = \ln[(x + 1)^{2x}] = 2x \ln(x + 1)$$

Differentiate both sides of this equation:

$$\frac{1}{y}\frac{dy}{dx} = 2x\left\{\frac{d}{dx}[\ln(x + 1)]\right\} + \left[\frac{d}{dx}(2x)\right]\ln(x + 1) \quad \textit{Product rule}$$

$$= 2x\left[\frac{1}{x + 1}(1)\right] + 2\ln(x + 1) = \frac{2x}{x + 1} + 2\ln(x + 1)$$

Finally, multiply both sides by $y = (x + 1)^{2x}$:

$$\frac{dy}{dx} = \left[\frac{2x}{x + 1} + 2\ln(x + 1)\right](x + 1)^{2x}$$ ▬

Logarithmic differentiation is also a valuable theoretical tool. For example, we can use it to prove that the power rule holds even when the exponent is an irrational number.

EXAMPLE 10   Proof of power rule for irrational exponents

Prove $\frac{d}{dx}(x^r) = rx^{r-1}$ holds for all real numbers r.

Solution   If $y = x^r$, then $y = e^{r \ln x}$, so that

$$\ln y = r \ln x$$

$$\frac{1}{y}\frac{dy}{dx} = r\left(\frac{1}{x}\right)$$

$$\frac{dy}{dx} = y\left(\frac{r}{x}\right)$$

$$= x^r\left(\frac{r}{x}\right) \quad \text{Substitute } y = x^r.$$

$$= rx^{r-1}$$

PROBLEM SET 5.3

Ⓐ *Differentiate the functions given in Problems 1–26.*

1. $y = e^{3x}$
2. $y = \ln 5x$
3. $y = \ln(3x^4 + 5x)$
4. $y = e^{2x+1}$
5. $y = x^2 + 2^x$
6. $y = 3^x + x^3$
7. $y = \pi^e + e^\pi + e^x + x^e$
8. $y = \pi^x + x^\pi$
9. $y = e^{x^2}$
10. $y = e^x + x^e$
11. $f(x) = e^{-4x} + e^{3-2x}$
12. $f(x) = e^{3x} - e^{-5x}$
13. $f(t) = \exp(t^2 + t + 5)$
14. $f(x) = \exp(x^2 - 3x^{-1})$
15. $f(u) = \frac{1}{2}(e^{2u} - e^{-2u})$
16. $f(t) = e^{3t+1} + e^{1-3t}$
17. $f(x) = x^2e^{-x} + e^\pi$
18. $f(x) = (x^2 + 3)e^{1+x}$
19. $g(t) = \frac{e^{2t}}{3t + 5} + \pi^2$
20. $g(t) = e^t\sin(2t + 1)$
21. $g(t) = (e^{\sqrt{t}} - t)^2$
22. $f(x) = (e^x + \ln 2x)^2$
23. $f(u) = \ln(\ln u)$
24. $f(x) = \exp[\exp(\exp x)]$
25. $y = \ln(\sin x + \cos x)$
26. $y = \ln(\sec x + \tan x)$

Use implicit differentiation to find $\frac{dy}{dx}$ in Problems 27–32.

27. $xe^{-x} = y$
28. $xe^y + ye^x = 2x$
29. $e^{xy} + 1 = x^2$
30. $\ln(xy) = e^{2x}$
31. $e^{xy} + \ln y^2 = x$
32. $\log_3\left(\frac{x^2}{y}\right) = x$

Ⓑ **33.** ■ **What Does This Say?** Compare and contrast the derivatives of the following functions.
a. $y = x^2$ **b.** $y = 2^x$ **c.** $y = e^x$ **d.** $y = x^e$

34. ■ **What Does This Say?** Compare and contrast the derivatives of the following functions:
a. $y = \log x$ **b.** $y = \ln x$

35. ■ **What Does This Say?** Discuss logarithmic differentiation.

Use logarithmic differentiation in Problems 36–47 for finding $\frac{dy}{dx}$. You may express your answer in terms of both x and y, and you do not need to simplify the resulting rational expressions.

36. $y = \sqrt[18]{(x^{10} + 1)^3(x^7 - 3)^8}$
37. $y = \frac{(2x - 1)^5}{\sqrt{x - 9}(x + 3)^2}$
38. $y = \frac{e^{2x}}{(x^2 - 3)^2\sqrt{4 - 5x}}$
39. $y = \frac{e^{3x^2}}{(x^3 + 1)^2(4x - 7)^{-2}}$
40. $y = x^x$
41. $y = x^{\ln\sqrt{x}}$
42. $y = (x^2 + 3)^{2x}$
43. $y = (\sin x)^{\sqrt{x}}$
44. $y = x^{x^x}$
45. $y = (x^x)^x$
46. $y = x^{\sin x}$
47. $y = (\sin x)^x$

Find an equation for the tangent line to the curves given in Problems 48–62 at the prescribed point.

48. $y = (\ln x)^x$ where $x = e$
49. $y = x^{\ln x}$ where $x = 1$
50. $y = (\sin x)^{\cos x}$ where $x = \frac{\pi}{2}$
51. $y = x^{x^x}$ where $x = 1$
52. $y = xe^{-x}$ where $x = 0$
53. $y = \frac{e^x}{x}$ where $x = 1$
54. $y = e^{-x}\sin x$ where $x = 0$
55. $x^2 + 2y = e^y$ at $(1, 0)$
56. $x \log_2 y = x - y$ at $(1, 1)$
57. $y = x2^{-3x}$ where $x = 1$
58. $y = x \ln x^2$ where $x = 1$
59. $y = \frac{\ln\sqrt{x}}{x}$ where $x = 4$
60. $\ln(xy) = 2(x - y)$ at $(1, 1)$
61. $y = \frac{(2x^2 - 3)(x + 2)^2}{(x^3 + 3x - 5)^5}$ where $x = 1$
62. $y = (1 - 3x)^{2x}$ where $x = -1$

63. Find the equation of the line that is normal to the graph of the equation
$$2x + y = 1 + e^y$$
at the point $(1, 0)$

64. Find an equation for the normal to the curve $y = \sqrt{x} \ln x$ at the point where $x = e^{-2}$.

Ⓒ **65. a.** If $F(x) = \ln|\cos x|$, show that $F'(x) = -\tan x$.
b. If $F(x) = \ln|\sec x + \tan x|$, show that $F'(x) = \sec x$.

66. Evaluate $\lim\limits_{h \to 0} \frac{a^h - 1}{h}$.

67. If $f(x) = e^x$, show that $f'(x) = e^x$ by using the definition of derivative. *Hint:* You will need the limit from Problem 66.

5.4 APPLICATIONS INVOLVING DERIVATIVES OF e^x AND $\ln x$

Remember, even though a graphing calculator can be very helpful, you cannot assume that the calculator will do all your work for you. Indeed, the ideas of calculus are often necessary to be sure you have the correct graph.

IN THIS SECTION **Curve sketching, optimization, evaluating limits using logarithms and l'Hôpital's rule**
We now study a few applications involving the derivatives of exponential and logarithmic functions. We begin with curve sketching, then consider examples of optimization and rectilinear motion, and, finally, use l'Hôpital's rule to evaluate limits involving exponential and logarithmic functions.

■ CURVE SKETCHING

EXAMPLE 1   **Graphing a function involving a logarithmic function**

Determine where the function $f(x) = \dfrac{\ln x}{x}$ is increasing and where it is decreasing. Sketch the graph of f.

Solution   First of all, note that f is defined only for $x > 0$ and that

$$f'(x) = \frac{x\left(\frac{1}{x}\right) - 1 \ln x}{x^2} = \frac{1 - \ln x}{x^2}$$

Because $x^2 > 0$ for all $x > 0$, it follows that $f'(x) = 0$ only when $\ln x = 1$; thus, e is the only critical number of f. We use the first-derivative test and look at the sign of $f'(x)$ to the left of e (at $x = 1$, for instance) and to the right (at $x = 3$, for example). We see that

$$f'(x) > 0 \quad \text{for} \quad x < e \quad \text{and}$$
$$f'(x) < 0 \quad \text{for} \quad x > e$$

Thus, f is increasing to the left of e and decreasing to the right, as shown in Figure 5.11a.

We now have most of the information we need to sketch the graph of f. In particular, we know that the graph lies entirely to the right of the y-axis (because f is defined only for $x > 0$) and that it rises to a relative maximum at $x = e$, after which it falls indefinitely. Moreover, because we obtain

$$\frac{\ln x}{x} = 0 \quad \text{only for} \quad x = 1$$

The graph of $f(x) = \dfrac{\ln x}{x}$ is shown:

Y₁⊟ln X/X

Xmin=-10 Ymin=-10
Xmax=10 Ymax=10
Xscl=1 Yscl=1

If we regraph with

Xmin=0 Ymin=-.1
Xmax=10 Ymax=.4
Xscl=1 Yscl=.1

a. Tendency diagram for $f(x) = \dfrac{\ln x}{x}$

b. The graph rises to a maximum at e and then "flattens out" as it falls.

c. Further analysis shows that the graph approaches the x-axis as $x \to +\infty$.

Figure 5.11 The graph of $f(x) = \dfrac{\ln x}{x}$

it follows that the graph crosses the x-axis on the way up but not on the way down, and this causes us to suspect that the graph must "flatten out" in some way as $x \to +\infty$ (see Figure 5.11b).

Note that $f(x) = \dfrac{\ln x}{x}$ becomes large and negative as x approaches 0 through positive values; that is,

$$\lim_{x \to 0^+} \frac{\ln x}{x} = -\infty$$

To see what happens to $f(x)$ as x increases without bound, we use l'Hôpital's rule (Section 3.9) and find that

$$\lim_{x \to +\infty} \frac{\ln x}{x} = \lim_{x \to +\infty} \frac{\frac{1}{x}}{1} = 0$$

The graph of f approaches the y-axis asymptotically as x tends toward 0, and approaches the x-axis as x increases without bound. The completed graph is shown in Figure 5.11c. Notice that as the graph comes down from the relative maximum at e, its concavity appears to change from down to up. Indeed,

$$f''(x) = \frac{x^2\left(-\frac{1}{x}\right) - (1 - \ln x)(2x)}{(x^2)^2} = \frac{-3 + 2 \ln x}{x^3}$$

Solving the equation $f''(x) = 0$ for x, we find:

$$\frac{-3 + 2 \ln x}{x^3} = 0$$
$$2 \ln x = 3$$
$$\ln x = \tfrac{3}{2}, \quad \text{or} \quad x = e^{3/2}$$

Because $e^{3/2} \approx 4.48$, we find $f''(4) < 0$ and $f''(5) > 0$, so that f has an inflection point at $x = e^{3/2}$.   ▬

Functions such as $\dfrac{\ln x}{x}$ or xe^{-5x}, which have the general form $\dfrac{\ln x}{x^n}$ or $x^n e^{kx}$, appear frequently in applications, and it is convenient to have the limit formulas given in the following theorem.

THEOREM 5.14   Limits involving natural logarithms and exponentials

If k and n are positive integers, then

$$\lim_{x \to 0^+} \frac{\ln x}{x^n} = -\infty \qquad \lim_{x \to +\infty} \frac{\ln x}{x^n} = 0$$

$$\lim_{x \to +\infty} \frac{e^{kx}}{x^n} = +\infty \qquad \lim_{x \to +\infty} x^n e^{-kx} = 0$$

Proof: These can all be verified directly or by applying l'Hôpital's rule. For example,

$$\lim_{x \to +\infty} \frac{\ln x}{x^n} = \lim_{x \to +\infty} \frac{\frac{1}{x}}{nx^{n-1}} = \lim_{x \to +\infty} \frac{1}{nx^n} = 0$$

The other parts are left for you to verify.   ■

EXAMPLE 2   Graphing a function involving an exponential function

Determine where the function

$$f(x) = \frac{1}{\sqrt{2\pi}} e^{-x^2/2}$$

is increasing, decreasing, concave up, and concave down. Find the relative extrema and inflection points and sketch the graph. This function plays an important role in statistics, where it is called the *standard normal density function*.

Solution   The first derivative is

$$f'(x) = \frac{-x}{\sqrt{2\pi}} e^{-x^2/2}$$

Because $e^{-x^2/2}$ is always positive, $f'(x) = 0$ if and only if $x = 0$. Hence, the corresponding point

$$\left(0, \frac{1}{\sqrt{2\pi}}\right) \approx (0, 0.4)$$

is the only critical point. Checking the sign of f' on each side of 0, we find that f is increasing for $x < 0$ and decreasing for $x > 0$, so there is a relative maximum at $x = 0$, as indicated in Figure 5.12a.

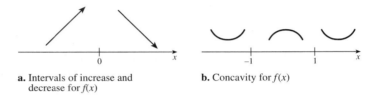

a. Intervals of increase and decrease for $f(x)$

b. Concavity for $f(x)$

Figure 5.12 Preliminary sketches for the graph of $f(x) = \frac{1}{\sqrt{2\pi}} e^{-x^2/2}$

We find that the second derivative of f is

$$f''(x) = \frac{x^2}{\sqrt{2\pi}} e^{-x^2/2} - \frac{1}{\sqrt{2\pi}} e^{-x^2/2} = \frac{1}{\sqrt{2\pi}}(x^2 - 1)e^{-x^2/2}$$

which is zero when $x = \pm 1$. We find that $f(1) = f(-1) \approx 0.24$, and that the concavity of the graph of f is as indicated in Figure 5.12b.

Finally, we draw a smooth curve through the known points, as shown in Figure 5.13. The graph of f rises to the high point at $(0, 0.4)$ and then falls indefinitely, approaching the x-axis asymptotically because $e^{-x^2/2}$ approaches 0 as $|x|$ increases without bound. Note that the graph has no x-intercepts, because $e^{-x^2/2}$ is always positive.   ▬

■ OPTIMIZATION

Optimization problems involving exponential and logarithmic functions occur in many applied areas and can be analyzed by the methods of Chapter 3. Here are two examples.

EXAMPLE 3   Maximum concentration of a drug

Let $C(t)$ denote the concentration in the blood at time t of a drug injected into the body intramuscularly. In a now classic paper by E. Heinz, it was observed that the concentration is given by

$$C(t) = \frac{k}{b - a}(e^{-at} - e^{-bt}) \qquad t \geq 0$$

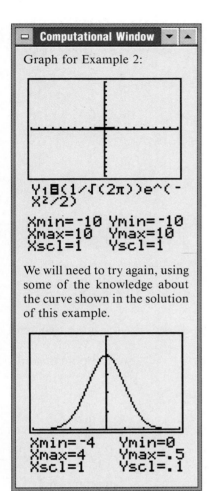

Graph for Example 2:

```
Y₁⊟(1/√(2π))e^(-
X²/2)
Xmin=-10 Ymin=-10
Xmax=10  Ymax=10
Xscl=1   Yscl=1
```

We will need to try again, using some of the knowledge about the curve shown in the solution of this example.

```
Xmin=-4   Ymin=0
Xmax=4    Ymax=.5
Xscl=1    Yscl=.1
```

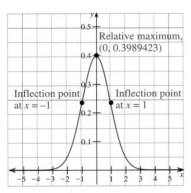

Figure 5.13 Graph of the standard normal density function:

$$f(x) = \frac{1}{\sqrt{2\pi}} e^{-x^2/2}$$

where a, b (with $b > a$) and k are positive constants that depend on the drug. At what time does the largest concentration occur? What happens to the concentration as $t \to +\infty$?

Solution   To locate the extrema, we solve $C'(t) = 0$.

$$C'(t) = \frac{d}{dt}\left[\frac{k}{b-a}(e^{-at} - e^{-bt}) \right]$$

$$= \frac{k}{b-a}[(-a)e^{-at} - (-b)e^{-bt}] = \frac{k}{b-a}(be^{-bt} - ae^{-at})$$

We see that $C'(t_c) = 0$ when

$$be^{-bt_c} = ae^{-at_c}$$

$$e^{at_c - bt_c} = \frac{a}{b}$$

$$at_c - bt_c = \ln \frac{a}{b} \qquad \text{Definition of logarithm}$$

$$t_c = \frac{1}{a-b} \ln \frac{a}{b}$$

Using the second-derivative test, it can be shown that the largest value of $C(t)$ occurs at t_c (see Problem 57).

To see what happens to the concentration as $t \to +\infty$, we compute the limit

$$\lim_{t \to +\infty} C(t) = \lim_{t \to +\infty} \frac{k}{b-a}[e^{-at} - e^{-bt}]$$

$$= \frac{k}{b-a}\left[\lim_{t \to +\infty} \frac{1}{e^{at}} - \lim_{t \to +\infty} \frac{1}{e^{bt}} \right] = \frac{k}{b-a}[0 - 0]$$

This tells us that the longer the drug is in the blood, the closer the concentration is to 0. The graph of C is shown in Figure 5.14.

Intuitively, we would expect the Heinz concentration function to begin at 0, increase to a maximum, and then gradually drop off to 0. Figure 5.14 indicates that $C(t)$ does not have these characteristics, because it does not quite get back to 0 in finite time. This suggests that the Heinz model may apply most reliably to the period of time right after the drug has been injected.

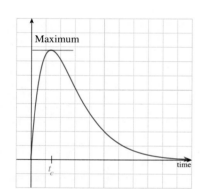

Figure 5.14 Graph of

$$C(t) = \frac{k}{b-a}(e^{-at} - e^{-bt})$$

Sales	Expenditure
0	0
10	40,936.54
20	67,032.00
30	82,321.75
40	89,865.79
→50	91,969.86 ←Maximum on list
60	90,358.26
70	86,308.94
80	80,758.61
90	74,384.50
100	67,667.64
150	37,340.30

EXAMPLE 4   Greatest consumer expenditure

Consumer demand for a certain commodity is

$$D(p) = 5{,}000e^{-0.02p}$$

units per month when the market price is p dollars per unit. Determine the market price that results in the greatest consumer expenditure.

Solution   The consumer expenditure $E(p)$ for the commodity is the price per unit p times the number of units sold; that is,

$$E(p) = pD(p) = 5{,}000pe^{-0.02p}$$

Because only nonnegative values of p are meaningful in this context, the goal is to find the absolute maximum of $E(p)$ on the interval $[0, \infty)$. The derivative of $E(p)$ is

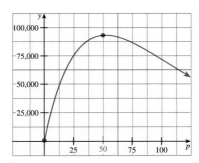

Figure 5.15 The graph of the consumer expenditure function $E(p) = 5,000pe^{-0.02p}$

$$E'(p) = 5,000(-0.02pe^{-0.02p} + e^{-0.02p})$$
$$= 5,000(1 - 0.02p)e^{-0.02p}$$

Because $e^{-0.02p}$ is never zero, $E'(p) = 0$ if and only if

$$1 - 0.02p = 0, \quad \text{or} \quad p = 50$$

The easiest way to verify that $p = 50$ actually gives the absolute maximum of $E(p)$ on the interval $p > 0$ is to check the sign of $E'(p)$ for $0 < p < 50$ and for $p > 50$:

If $0 < p < 50$, then $E'(p) = 5,000e^{-0.02p}(1 - 0.02p) > 0$.
If $p > 50$, then $E'(p) = 5,000e^{-0.02p}(1 - 0.02p) < 0$.

Hence, $E(p)$ is increasing on $(0, 50)$ and decreasing on $(50, +\infty)$, and there is an absolute maximum when $p = 50$ as shown in Figure 5.15. Thus, consumer expenditure will be greatest when the market price is \$50 per unit. ▬

■ EVALUATING LIMITS USING LOGARITHMS AND L'HÔPITAL'S RULE

Certain limits of the form $\lim\limits_{x \to +\infty} [f(x)]^{u(x)}$ will result in forms of the type 0^0, ∞^0, or 1^∞, which are **indeterminate forms** (recall Section 3.9). We shall find that logarithms can often be used to reduce such forms to forms of the type $\frac{0}{0}$ or $\frac{\infty}{\infty}$, which can then be handled by l'Hôpital's rule. The usual approach is to let L equal the limit we wish to evaluate and then take the natural logarithm of both sides, which should then allow us to use l'Hôpital's rule. This procedure is illustrated in the following example.

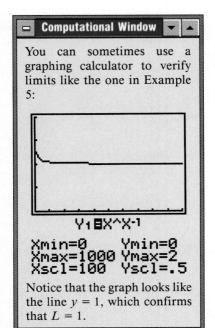

EXAMPLE 5   **Limit of the form ∞^0**

Find $\lim\limits_{x \to +\infty} x^{1/x}$.

Solution   This is a limit of the indeterminate form ∞^0.
If $L = \lim\limits_{x \to +\infty} x^{1/x}$ then

$$\ln L = \ln \lim_{x \to +\infty} x^{1/x}$$
$$= \lim_{x \to +\infty} \ln x^{1/x} \qquad \textit{The limit of a log is the log of a limit}$$
$$= \lim_{x \to +\infty} \frac{1}{x} \ln x$$
$$= \lim_{x \to +\infty} \frac{\ln x}{x}$$
$$= \lim_{x \to +\infty} \frac{\frac{1}{x}}{1} \qquad \textit{l'Hôpital's rule}$$
$$= 0$$

Thus, we have $\ln L = 0$; therefore, $L = e^0 = 1$. ▬

Computational Window

To use a graphing calculator on a limit like the one in Example 6, you can choose a value for k (such as $k = 2$) and graph the resulting function.

Y₁■(1+2/X)^X
Xmin=0   Ymin=0
Xmax=1000 Ymax=10
Xscl=100 Yscl=1

It looks like the limit is somewhere between 7 and 8. This is consistent with the answer in Example 6 (for $k = 2$):

$$L = e^2 \approx 7.389056099$$

EXAMPLE 6   Limit of the form 1^∞

Find $\displaystyle\lim_{x \to +\infty} \left(1 + \frac{k}{x}\right)^x$.

Solution   This is a limit of the indeterminate form 1^∞.

$$\text{If } L = \lim_{x \to +\infty} \left(1 + \frac{k}{x}\right)^x, \text{ then}$$

$$\ln L = \ln \lim_{x \to +\infty} \left(1 + \frac{k}{x}\right)^x$$

$$= \lim_{x \to +\infty} \ln\left(1 + \frac{k}{x}\right)^x$$

$$= \lim_{x \to +\infty} \left[x \ln\left(1 + \frac{k}{x}\right)\right]$$

To convert this $\infty \cdot 0$ indeterminate form into a $\frac{0}{0}$ form, we write x as $1/(1/x)$:

$$\ln L = \lim_{x \to +\infty} \left[x \ln\left(1 + \frac{k}{x}\right)\right] \qquad \textit{Form } \infty \cdot 0$$

$$= \lim_{x \to +\infty} \left[\frac{\ln\left(1 + \frac{k}{x}\right)}{\frac{1}{x}}\right] \qquad \textit{Form } \frac{0}{0}$$

$$= \lim_{x \to +\infty} \left[\frac{\frac{1}{1 + \frac{k}{x}}\left(\frac{-k}{x^2}\right)}{\left(\frac{-1}{x^2}\right)}\right] \qquad \textit{l'Hôpital's rule}$$

$$= \lim_{x \to +\infty} \frac{k}{1 + \frac{k}{x}} = k$$

Thus, $L = e^k$.   ▬

PROBLEM SET 5.4

Ⓐ *In Problems 1–4, the graph of the given function f(x) for x > 0 is one of the six curves shown in Figure 5.16. In each case, match the function to a graph.*

a.

b.

c.

d.

e.

f.
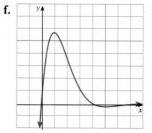

Figure 5.16 Problems 1–4

1. $f(x) = x2^{-x}$

2. $f(x) = \dfrac{\ln\sqrt{x}}{x}$

3. $f(x) = \dfrac{e^x}{x}$

4. $f(x) = e^{-x}\cos x$

In Problems 5–20, answer the following questions about the given function, and then sketch its graph.

a. *What is the domain of the function?*

b. *What are the critical numbers, and where is the graph of the function rising and falling?*

c. *What are the coordinates of all high and low points? Where does the graph cross the coordinate axes?*

d. *Where is the graph concave up and concave down? What are the second-order critical numbers?*

5. $f(x) = 3^{x-1}$

6. $f(x) = 2^{3-x}$

7. $f(x) = x - \ln x$

8. $f(x) = x \ln x$

9. $f(x) = xe^{-x}$

10. $f(u) = u^2 e^{-2u}$

11. $f(x) = \dfrac{\ln \sqrt{x}}{\sqrt{x}}$

12. $f(x) = \log_3 2x$

13. $f(x) = e^{-x^2}$

14. $f(w) = \dfrac{2^w}{w}$

15. $f(t) = \ln\left(\dfrac{t^2}{1-t}\right)$

16. $g(t) = \ln(4 - t^2)$

17. $f(x) = e^x + e^{-x}$

18. $f(x) = \dfrac{e^x - e^{-x}}{e^x + e^{-x}}$

19. $f(x) = (\ln x)^2$

20. $f(x) = \ln x^2$

21. Let $S(x) = \frac{1}{2}(e^x - e^{-x})$ and $C(x) = \frac{1}{2}(e^x + e^{-x})$. These functions are known as the *hyperbolic sine* and *cosine*, respectively, and are examined in Section 7.6.
   a. Show that $S'(x) = C(x)$ and $C'(x) = S(x)$.
   b. Sketch the graphs of S and C.

22. Find all points of intersection of the curves

$$y = 2^{x^2-2x} \quad \text{and} \quad y = 4^x$$

Sketch the two curves on the same set of coordinate axes.

23. Let b be a positive number other than 1. Sketch the graph of $y = \log_b x$ for each case.
   a. $b > 1$ **b.** $b < 1$

Find the maximum and minimum values of the functions given in Problems 24–27 on the prescribed interval.

24. $f(x) = xe^{-2x}$ on $[-1, 2]$

25. $f(x) = \dfrac{e^x}{x}$ on $\left[\frac{1}{2}, 2\right]$

26. $f(t) = \dfrac{(\ln t)^2}{t}$ on $\left[\frac{1}{2}, 9\right]$

27. $f(t) = te^{-t^2}$ on $[-1, 1]$

Use l'Hôpital's rule to evaluate the limit in Problems 28–37.

28. $\lim\limits_{x \to 0^+} x^x$

29. $\lim\limits_{x \to 0^+} x \ln x$

30. $\lim\limits_{x \to 0^+} x^{\sin x}$

31. $\lim\limits_{x \to 0^+} (\sin x) \ln x$

32. $\lim\limits_{x \to +\infty} \dfrac{\ln(\ln x)}{x}$

33. $\lim\limits_{x \to +\infty} \left(1 - \dfrac{1}{x}\right)^{2x}$

34. $\lim\limits_{x \to +\infty} (\ln x)^{1/x}$

35. $\lim\limits_{x \to 0} (e^x + x)^{1/x}$

36. $\lim\limits_{x \to 1} x^{1/(x-1)}$

37. $\lim\limits_{x \to 0} (e^x - 1 - x)^x$

38. Sketch the graph of $f(x) = e^{-x}\sin x$. Note that the graph crosses the x-axis only where $x = n\pi$ for any integer n. Where does the graph have high points and low points? What happens to the graph as $x \to +\infty$?

B 39. Show that for positive constants m, k,

$$\lim_{x \to +\infty} \left(1 + \dfrac{1}{x^k}\right)^{x^m} = \begin{cases} 1 & \text{if } k > m \\ +\infty & \text{if } k < m \end{cases}$$

What is the limit when $k = m$?

40. A function that plays a prominent role in statistics is

$$D(t) = \dfrac{1}{\sqrt{2\pi}\sigma} \exp\left[\dfrac{-1}{2}\left(\dfrac{t-m}{\sigma}\right)^2\right]$$

where m is a real number and σ is a positive constant.
   a. Find $D'(t)$ and determine all relative extrema of $D(t)$.
   b. What happens to $D(t)$ as $t \to +\infty$ and as $t \to -\infty$?
   c. Sketch the graph of $D(t)$.

41. A *Gompertz curve* is the graph of a function of the form

$$G(x) = A \exp(-Be^{-kx}) \qquad \text{for } x > 0$$

where A, B, and k are positive constants. Such graphs appear in certain population studies. Find $G'(x)$ and $G''(x)$, and sketch the graph of G.

42. In an experiment, a biologist introduces a toxin into a bacterial colony and then measures the effect on the population of the colony. Suppose that at time t (in minutes) the population is

$$P(t) = 5 + e^{-0.04t}(t + 1)$$

thousand. At what time will the population be the largest? What happens to the population in the long run (as $t \to +\infty$)? Find where the graph of P has an inflection point, and interpret this point in terms of the population. Sketch the graph of P.

43. Some psychologists believe that a child's ability to memorize is measured by a function of the form

$$g(t) = \begin{cases} t \ln t + 1 & \text{if } 0 < t \le 4 \\ 1 & \text{if } t = 0 \end{cases}$$

where t is time, measured in years. Determine when the largest and smallest values of g occur.

44. Suppose a manufacturer estimates that when the market price of a certain product is p, that

$$x = -6 \ln\left(\dfrac{p}{40}\right)$$

units will be sold. It is also estimated that the cost of producing these x units will be

$$C(x) = 4xe^{-x/6} + 30$$

   a. Find the average cost, $C(x)/x$, the marginal cost, $C'(x)$, and the marginal revenue for this production process.
   b. What level of production x corresponds to maximum profit?

In Problems 45–47 you are asked for the percentage rate. We define the percentage rate of a function f at the value x to be

$$\dfrac{100f'(x)}{f(x)}$$

45. It is projected that t years from now, the population of a certain country will be $P(t) = 50e^{0.02t}$ million.
   a. At what rate will the population be changing with respect to time 10 years from now?
   b. At what percentage rate will the population be changing with respect to time t years from now?

46. A certain industrial machine depreciates in such a way that its value after t years is

$$Q(t) = 20,000e^{-0.4t}$$

dollars.

a. At what rate is the value of the machine changing with respect to time after 5 years?

b. At what percentage rate is the value of the machine changing with respect to time after t years?

47. A quantity decreases exponentially (that is, $f(t) = Ae^{-kt}$).

a. Show that its rate of decrease is proportional to its size.

b. Show that the percentage rate of change is constant.

48. A cool drink is removed from a refrigerator on a hot summer day and placed in a room whose temperature is 30 °C. According to Newton's law of cooling, the temperature of the drink t minutes later is given by a function of the form $f(t) = 30 - Ae^{-kt}$. Show that the rate of change of the temperature of the drink with respect to time is proportional to the difference between the temperature of the room and that of the drink.

49. The mathematics editor at a major publishing house estimates that if x thousand complimentary copies are distributed to professors, the first-year sales of a new text will be

$$f(x) = 20 - 15e^{-0.2x}$$

thousand copies. Currently, the editor is planning to distribute 10,000 complimentary copies.

a. Use marginal analysis to estimate the increase in first-year sales that will result if 1,000 additional complimentary copies are distributed.

b. Calculate the actual increase in first-year sales that will result from the distribution of an additional 1,000 complimentary copies.

50. A manufacturer can produce shoes at a cost of $50 a pair and estimates that if they are sold for x dollars a pair, consumers will buy approximately

$$s(x) = 1,000e^{-0.1x}$$

pairs of shoes per week. At what price should the manufacturer sell the shoes to maximize profit?

51. It is estimated that t years from now the population of a certain country will be

$$p(t) = \frac{160}{1 + 8e^{-0.01t}}$$

million. When will the population grow most rapidly?

52. An epidemic spreads through a community in such a way that t weeks after its outbreak, the number of residents who have been infected is given by a function of the form

$$f(t) = \frac{A}{1 + Ce^{-kt}}$$

where A is the total number of susceptible residents. Show that the epidemic is spreading most rapidly when half the susceptible residents have been infected.

53. A particle moves along the x-axis in such a way that at time t it is at $x(t) = \sqrt{t}e^{-t}$.

a. Find the velocity and acceleration of the particle at time t.

b. Show that the particle initially moves in a positive direction and then at a certain time T it turns and moves back toward the origin. What is T? Where is the particle when it turns?

c. What is the total distance traveled by the particle between times $t = 0$ and $t = 1$?

54. A particle moves along the x-axis in such a way that at time t, its position is given by

$$x(t) = Ae^{kt} + Be^{-kt}$$

Show that at any given time, the acceleration of the particle is proportional to its position.

55. Suppose the percentage rate of change of the *square* of a function f is proportional to $\cos x$ and that $f(0) = 1$. What is $f(\pi)$?

a. Show that its rate of decrease is proportional to its size.

b. Show that its percentage rate of increase is constant.

56. Show that the graphs of $y = e^{-kx}$ and $y = e^{kx}$ are reflections of one another in the y-axis.

57. In this section we showed that the Heinz concentration function,

$$C(t) = \frac{k}{b - a}(e^{-at} - e^{-bt})$$

for $b > a$ has exactly one critical number, namely,

$$t_c = \frac{1}{b - a}\ln\left(\frac{b}{a}\right)$$

Find $C''(t)$ and use the second derivative test to show that a relative maximum for the concentration (lt) occurs at time $t = t_c$.

5.5 INTEGRALS INVOLVING e^x AND $\ln x$

IN THIS SECTION Integration of exponential and logarithmic functions, integration involving $\tan x$ and $\cot x$
We reverse the differentiation of exponentials and logarithms to find integration formulas and then apply these results to the motion of a particle.

■ INTEGRATION OF e^x AND $\ln x$

THEOREM 5.15   Integration of e^x

$$\int e^x\, dx = e^x + C$$

Proof: This follows directly from the differentiation formula

$$\frac{d}{dx}(e^x) = e^x$$

EXAMPLE 1   Integration involving an exponential function

Show that for any nonzero constant k

$$\int e^{kx}dx = \frac{1}{k}\, e^{kx} + C$$

Solution   Let $u = kx$, so $du = k\, dx$.

$$\int e^{kx}dx = \int e^u\, \frac{du}{k} = \frac{1}{k}\int e^u\, du = \frac{1}{k}\, e^u + C = \frac{1}{k}\, e^{kx} + C$$

EXAMPLE 2   Substitution involving an exponential function

Evaluate $\displaystyle\int_1^2 \frac{e^{\sqrt t}}{\sqrt t}\, dt$.

Solution   Let $u = \sqrt t$, so that $du = \frac{1}{2\sqrt t}dt$ and $\frac{dt}{\sqrt t} = 2\, du$. Also, if $t = 1$, then $u = 1$ and if $t = 2$, $u = \sqrt 2$, and we have

$$\int_1^2 \frac{e^{\sqrt t}}{\sqrt t}\, dt = \int_1^{\sqrt 2} e^u[2\, du] = 2e^u \Big|_1^{\sqrt 2} = 2(e^{\sqrt 2} - e^1) \approx 2.789\,937\,1$$

THEOREM 5.16   Integration of $1/x$

$$\int \frac{1}{x}\, dx = \ln|x| + C$$

Proof: This proof follows directly from Theorem 5.10. Because

$$\frac{d}{dx}(\ln|x|) = \frac{1}{x} \qquad \text{for all } x \ne 0$$

we have $\displaystyle\int \frac{1}{x}\, dx = \ln|x| + C$

In Chapter 4, we found $\int x^n dx$ for $n \ne -1$, and now we know what happens when $n = -1$, so we restate the complete power rule for integration.

Power Rule

$$\int x^n\, dx = \begin{cases} \dfrac{x^{n+1}}{n+1} + C & n \ne -1 \\[2mm] \ln|x| + C & n = -1 \end{cases}$$

EXAMPLE 3   Integration of a rational function

Find $\int \dfrac{7\, dx}{2x - 5}$.

Solution   Let $u = 2x - 5$, so that $du = 2\, dx$ and $dx = \frac{1}{2}\, du$.

$$\int \frac{7\, dx}{2x - 5} = \int \frac{7\left(\frac{1}{2}\, du\right)}{u} = \frac{7}{2} \int u^{-1}\, du = \frac{7}{2} \ln|u| + C = \frac{7}{2} \ln|2x - 5| + C \quad \rule{1em}{0.6em}$$

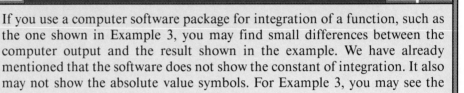

Computational Window

If you use a computer software package for integration of a function, such as the one shown in Example 3, you may find small differences between the computer output and the result shown in the example. We have already mentioned that the software does not show the constant of integration. It also may not show the absolute value symbols. For Example 3, you may see the computer result

$$\frac{7\mathrm{LN}(2\mathrm{X} - 5)}{2}$$

Compare this with the result $\frac{7}{2} \ln |2x - 5| + C$, as obtained in Example 3.

EXAMPLE 4   Integration of a trigonometric function

Find $\int \dfrac{\sin x\, dx}{3 + 2\cos x}$,

Solution   Let $u = 3 + 2\cos x$, so that $du = -2\sin x\, dx$.

$$\int \frac{\sin x\, dx}{3 + 2\cos x} = \int \frac{\frac{du}{-2}}{u} = -\frac{1}{2} \int \frac{du}{u} = -\frac{1}{2} \ln|u| + C = -\frac{1}{2} \ln|3 + 2\cos x| + C$$

$$= -\frac{1}{2} \ln(3 + 2\cos x) + C \quad \textit{Because } 3 + 2\cos x \geq 0 \quad \rule{1em}{0.6em}$$

In general, it is a good idea to begin work on an integration problem by using algebra to simplify the integrand as much as possible. This principle is illustrated in the next example.

EXAMPLE 5   Integration of an exponential to a base other than e

Find $\int 3^{5-x}\, dx$.

Solution   We have a formula for integrating exponentials to a base e, so we write

$$3^{5-x} = e^{(5-x)\ln 3} \quad \textit{Theorem 5.8f, page 341}$$

$$\int 3^{5-x}\, dx = \int e^{(5-x)\ln 3}\, dx = \int e^u\left(\frac{-du}{\ln 3}\right) = \frac{-1}{\ln 3} e^u + C$$

Let $u = (5 - x) \ln 3$;
$du = (-\ln 3)\, dx$, so $dx = \dfrac{-du}{\ln 3}$.

$$= \frac{-1}{\ln 3} e^{(5-x)\ln 3} + C = \frac{-3^{5-x}}{\ln 3} + C \quad \rule{1em}{0.6em}$$

■ INTEGRATION INVOLVING tan x AND cot x

We derived integration formulas for $\sin x$ and $\cos x$ in Chapter 4, and now that we have the natural logarithm at our disposal, we can also integrate certain expressions involving $\tan x$ and $\cot x$. The key to these integration problems is the following theorem.

THEOREM 5.17   Integral of tangent and cotangent

$$\int \tan x \, dx = -\ln|\cos x| + C \qquad \int \cot x \, dx = \ln|\sin x| + C$$

Proof: $\displaystyle\int \tan x \, dx = \int \frac{\sin x}{\cos x} \, dx$ Let $u = \cos x$; then $du = -\sin x \, dx$.

$$= \int \frac{-du}{u} = -\ln|u| + C = -\ln|\cos x| + C$$

The formula for the integral of the cotangent may be derived in a similar fashion (see Problem 62). ■

EXAMPLE 6   Substitution with a cotangent function

Find $\displaystyle\int \cot(1 - 2x) \, dx$.

Solution $\displaystyle\int \cot(1 - 2x) \, dx = \int \cot u \left(-\frac{1}{2} \, du \right)$ Let $u = 1 - 2x$; then $du = -2 \, dx$.

$$= -\frac{1}{2} \int \cot u \, du = -\frac{1}{2} \ln|\sin u| + C = -\frac{1}{2} \ln|\sin(1 - 2x)| + C$$

We complete this section with an applied example.

EXAMPLE 7   The motion of a particle

A particle moves along a coordinate axis in such a way that its acceleration at time t is $a(t) = (5 - t)^{-2}$. If the velocity of the particle is 2 when $t = 4$, how far does the particle move between times $t = 0$ and $t = 4$?

Solution   Because $a(t) = v'(t)$, it follows that

$$v(t) = \int a(t) \, dt = \int \frac{dt}{(5 - t)^2} = \int \frac{-du}{u^2} = u^{-1} + C = (5 - t)^{-1} + C$$

Let $u = 5 - t$; $du = -dt$.

Because $v(4) = 2$, we have $2 = (5 - 4)^{-1} + C$, which means $C = 1$.
Next, if $s(t)$ is the position of the particle at time t, then

$$s'(t) = v(t) = (5 - t)^{-1} + 1$$

It follows that the total distance traveled by the particle between times $t = 0$ and $t = 4$ is given by

$$s(t) = \int_0^4 |v(t)| \, dt = \int_0^4 [(5 - t)^{-1} + 1] \, dt = (-\ln|5 - t| + t) \Big|_0^4$$

Note: $v(t) > 0$ *on* $[0, 4]$

$$= -\ln|5 - 4| + 4 + \ln|5 - 0| - 0 = 4 + \ln 5 \approx 5.609\,437\,9 \qquad ■$$

PROBLEM SET 5.5

Ⓐ *Find the given integral in Problems 1–32.*

1. $\displaystyle\int e^{5x}\,dx$

2. $\displaystyle\int e^{-2x}\,dx$

3. $\displaystyle\int \frac{dx}{2x+1}$

4. $\displaystyle\int \frac{3\,dx}{2x-5}$

5. $\displaystyle\int \ln e^{x}\,dx$

6. $\displaystyle\int \ln e^{x^{2}}\,dx$

7. $\displaystyle\int (au^{2}-u^{-1}+e^{u})\,du$, for constant a

8. $\displaystyle\int (au^{4}+bu^{-1}+ce^{u})\,du$, for constants a, b, and c

9. $\displaystyle\int x\exp(1-x^{2})\,dx$

10. $\displaystyle\int (x+1)\exp(x^{2}+2x+3)\,dx$

11. $\displaystyle\int \left(\frac{x^{2}}{1-x^{3}}+xe^{x^{2}}\right)dx$

12. $\displaystyle\int \left(\frac{4x+6}{\sqrt{x^{2}+3x}}+xe^{3x^{2}}\right)dx$

13. $\displaystyle\int \frac{x\,dx}{2x^{2}+3}$

14. $\displaystyle\int \frac{x^{2}\,dx}{x^{3}+1}$

15. $\displaystyle\int \frac{2x+1}{x-5}\,dx$

16. $\displaystyle\int \frac{4x\,dx}{2x+1}$

17. $\displaystyle\int \sqrt{x}\,e^{x\sqrt{x}}\,dx$

18. $\displaystyle\int \frac{e^{\sqrt[3]{x}}\,dx}{x^{2/3}}$

19. $\displaystyle\int 2^{3+u}\,du$

20. $\displaystyle\int 10^{2t}\,dt$

21. $\displaystyle\int \frac{\ln x}{x}\,dx$

22. $\displaystyle\int \frac{\ln(x+1)}{x+1}\,dx$

23. $\displaystyle\int \frac{dx}{\sqrt{x}(\sqrt{x}+7)}$

24. $\displaystyle\int \frac{dx}{x^{2/3}(\sqrt[3]{x}+1)}$

25. $\displaystyle\int \frac{e^{t}\,dt}{e^{t}+1}$

26. $\displaystyle\int \frac{e^{\sqrt{t}}\,dt}{\sqrt{t}(e^{\sqrt{t}}+1)}$

27. $\displaystyle\int \frac{\cos x\,dx}{5+2\sin x}$

28. $\displaystyle\int \frac{\sec^{2}\theta\,d\theta}{1+\tan\theta}$

29. $\displaystyle\int \frac{\cot\sqrt{x}}{\sqrt{x}}\,dx$

30. $\displaystyle\int \frac{\tan x\,dx}{\sec x+1}$

31. $\displaystyle\int \frac{\sin x-\cos x}{\sin x+\cos x}\,dx$

32. $\displaystyle\int \frac{\sec x\tan x\,dx}{5-3\sec x}$

Evaluate the definite integrals given in Problems 33–42. Approximate the answers to Problems 41 and 42 to two significant figures.

33. $\displaystyle\int_{0}^{1} \frac{5x^{2}\,dx}{2x^{3}+1}$

34. $\displaystyle\int_{1}^{4} \frac{e^{-\sqrt{x}}\,dx}{\sqrt{x}}$

35. $\displaystyle\int_{-\ln 2}^{\ln 2} \frac{1}{2}(e^{x}-e^{-x})\,dx$

36. $\displaystyle\int_{0}^{2} (e^{x}-e^{-x})^{2}\,dx$

37. $\displaystyle\int_{1}^{2} \frac{e^{1/x}\,dx}{x^{2}}$

38. $\displaystyle\int_{1}^{2} 5^{-x}\,dx$

39. $\displaystyle\int_{0}^{\pi/6} \tan 2x\,dx$

40. $\displaystyle\int_{\pi/4}^{\pi/3} \cot x\csc x\,dx$

41. $\displaystyle\int_{0}^{5} \frac{0.58}{1+e^{-0.2x}}\,dx$

42. $\displaystyle\int_{0}^{12} \frac{5{,}000}{1+10e^{-t/5}}\,dt$

Hint for Problems 41 and 42: Multiply numerator and denominator by e^{x}.

Find the area of each region in Problems 43–46.

43. The region under the curve $y=\frac{1}{2}(e^{x}-e^{-x})$ above the x-axis such that $x\le\ln 2$.

44. The region under the curve $y=\dfrac{\ln x}{x}$ on the interval $[1,e]$.

45. The region bounded by the curves $y=2^{x}$ and $y=2^{1-x}$ and the y-axis.

46. The region under the curve $y=\cot x$ on the interval $\left[\frac{\pi}{3},\frac{\pi}{2}\right]$.

47. Find the average value of the function $f(x)=e^{3x}$ on the interval $[-1,4]$.

48. Find the average value of the function $f(x)=xe^{-x^{2}}$ on the interval $[1,3]$.

49. Find the average value of $f(x)=\tan x$ on the interval $\left[0,\frac{\pi}{4}\right]$.

Ⓑ **50.** Find $\displaystyle\int \frac{\ln^{3}x}{x}\,dx$.

51. Find $\displaystyle\int \frac{dx}{x\ln x}$.

52. Find $\displaystyle\int \frac{dx}{e^{x}+1}$. *Hint:* Rewrite the integrand as $\dfrac{e^{-x}}{1+e^{-x}}$.

53. A particle moves along the x-axis in such a way that at time t its velocity (in ft/s) is

$$v(t)=\frac{1}{t}+t$$

How far does it move (to the nearest foot) between times $t=1$ and $t=e^{2}$?

54. A manufacturer estimates that the marginal cost of a certain production process is given by

$$C'(x)=e^{0.01x}+3\sqrt{x}$$

when x units are produced. If the cost of producing 4 units is \$1,000, what does it cost to produce 9 units?

55. The operators of a new computer dating service estimate that the fraction of people who will retain their memberships in the service for at least t months is given by the function

$$f(t)=e^{-t/10}$$

There are 8,000 charter members, and the operators expect to attract 200 new members per month. How many members will the service have 10 months from now?

56. A national consumer's association has compiled statistics suggesting that the fraction of its members who are still active t months after joining is given by the function

$$f(t) = e^{-0.2t}$$

A new local chapter has 200 charter members and expects to attract new members at the rate of 10 per month. How many members can the chapter expect to have at the end of 8 months?

57. Find the enclosed area between the curve $y = \dfrac{2}{x}$ and the line $x + y = 3$.

58. Find the area between the curve $y = xe^{x^2}$ and the x-axis on $[-3, 3]$.

59. Find the area between the curve $y = \dfrac{2}{x^2}$ and the x-axis on $[1, 5]$.

ⓒ 60. Under favorable ecological conditions (that is, plenty of food and growth space), the population of a biological colony is given by

$$P = P_0 e^{kt}$$

where P_0 is the initial population and k is a positive constant. Suppose the human population of the earth has followed this pattern since A.D. 0.

a. Assuming that the world population was 1 billion in 1825 and 5 billion in 1986, find the population P_0 at A.D. 0 and the constant k.

b. The total number of people who have lived from A.D. 0 to A.D. 2000 is given by the integral

$$\int_0^{2000} P(t)\, dt$$

Evaluate this integral and determine what percentage of all people who have lived since A.D. 0 will be alive in A.D. 2000.

61. Show that for each positive integer n

$$\left(1 + \frac{1}{n}\right)^n \le e \le \left(1 + \frac{1}{n}\right)^{n+1}$$

by completing steps **a–d.**

a. Show that $\displaystyle\int_1^{1+1/n} \frac{dt}{t} \le \int_1^{1+1/n} dt$.

b. Show that $\ln\left(1 + \dfrac{1}{n}\right) \ge \dfrac{1}{n+1}$.

Hint: $\dfrac{1}{t} \ge \dfrac{1}{1 + \frac{1}{n}}$ for $1 \le t \le 1 + \dfrac{1}{n}$

c. Show that

$$\left(1 + \frac{1}{n}\right)^{n+1} \ge e$$

d. Complete the proof.

62. Derive the integration formula

$$\int \cot x\, dx = \ln|\sin x| + C$$

5.6 THE INVERSE TRIGONOMETRIC FUNCTIONS

IN THIS SECTION Definition of inverse trigonometric functions, properties of inverse trigonometric functions, derivatives and integrals involving inverse trigonometric functions

You were introduced to the inverse trigonometric functions in trigonometry, but because of their importance in calculus we define and review them in this section. We also introduce some important derivative and integral formulas involving these inverse functions.

■ DEFINITION OF INVERSE TRIGONOMETRIC FUNCTIONS

Recall from Section 5.2 that a function f has an inverse only when it is one-to-one on its domain—that is, when each number y in the range of f corresponds to exactly one number x in the domain. This condition is satisfied by the natural logarithm because $\ln x$ is monotonic on its domain $x > 0$. The trigonometric functions are not one-to-one, so their inverses do not exist. However, if we restrict the domains of the trigonometric functions, then the inverses exist. Thus, we can define the inverse trigonometric functions if we restrict their domains. In trigonometry you probably distinguished between the sine curve with unrestricted domain and the sine curve with restricted domain by writing $y = \sin x$ and $y = \mathrm{Sin}\, x$, respectively. In calculus, it is not customary to make such a distinction by using a capital letter.

Let us consider the sine function first. We know that the sine function is strictly increasing on the closed interval $\left[-\frac{\pi}{2}, \frac{\pi}{2}\right]$, and if we restrict $\sin x$ to this interval, it does have an inverse, as shown in Figure 5.17.

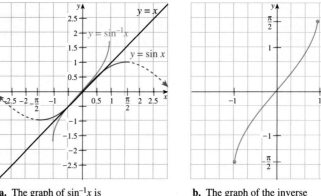

a. The graph of $\sin^{-1}x$ is obtained by reflecting the part of the sine on $\left[-\frac{\pi}{2}, \frac{\pi}{2}\right]$ about $y = x$.

b. The graph of the inverse sine function, $y = \sin^{-1}x$.

Figure 5.17 Inverse sine function

Inverse Sine Function

$$y = \sin^{-1}x \quad \text{if and only if} \quad x = \sin y \quad \text{and} \quad -\frac{\pi}{2} \le y \le \frac{\pi}{2}$$

⊘ The function $\sin^{-1}x$ is *NOT* the reciprocal of $\sin x$. To denote the reciprocal, write $(\sin x)^{-1}$. ⊘

Inverses of the other five trigonometric functions may be constructed in a similar manner. For example, by restricting $\tan x$ to the open interval $\left(-\frac{\pi}{2}, \frac{\pi}{2}\right)$ where it is one-to-one, we can define the inverse tangent function as follows.

Inverse Tangent Function

$$y = \tan^{-1}x \quad \text{if and only if} \quad x = \tan y \quad \text{and} \quad -\frac{\pi}{2} < y < \frac{\pi}{2}$$

The graph of $y = \tan^{-1}x$ is shown in Figure 5.18.

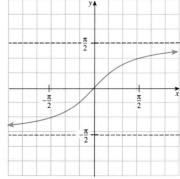

a. The graph of $\tan^{-1}x$ is obtained by reflecting the part of the tangent graph on $\left(-\frac{\pi}{2}, \frac{\pi}{2}\right)$ about the line $y = x$.

b. The graph of $\tan^{-1}x$

Figure 5.18 Graph of the inverse tangent

⊘ It is easier to remember the restrictions on the domain and the range if you do so in terms of quadrants, as shown in Table 5.1. Note the last column, which gives the range (or value of the angle y). For example, if $y = \sin^{-1} x$ and if x is positive, then y terminates in Quadrant I; in other words, $0 \leq y \leq \frac{\pi}{2} \approx 1.57$; on the other hand, if x is negative, then the terminal side of angle y is in Quadrant IV, with $-1.57 \approx -\frac{\pi}{2} \leq y \leq 0$. Finally, if x is 0, then $y = 0$. ⊘

TABLE 5.1 Definition of Inverse Trigonometric Functions

Inverse Function	Domain	Range	Value of x can be		
			Pos	Neg	Zero
			Quadrant		
$y = \sin^{-1} x$	$-1 \leq x \leq 1$	$-\frac{\pi}{2} \leq y \leq \frac{\pi}{2}$ Quadrants I and IV	I	IV	0
$y = \cos^{-1} x$	$-1 \leq x \leq 1$	$0 \leq y \leq \pi$ Quadrants I and II	I	II	$\frac{\pi}{2}$
$y = \tan^{-1} x$	$-\infty < x < +\infty$	$-\frac{\pi}{2} < y < \frac{\pi}{2}$ Quadrants I and IV	I	IV	0
$y = \sec^{-1} x$	$x \geq 1$ or $x \leq -1$	$0 \leq y \leq \pi, y \neq \frac{\pi}{2}$ Quadrants I and II	I	II	undefined
$y = \csc^{-1} x$	$x \geq 1$ or $x \leq -1$	$-\frac{\pi}{2} \leq y \leq \frac{\pi}{2}, y \neq 0$ Quadrants I and IV	I	IV	undefined
$y = \cot^{-1} x$	$-\infty < x < +\infty$	$0 < y < \pi$ Quadrants I and II	I	II	$\frac{\pi}{2}$

Definitions and graphs of four other fundamental inverse trigonometric functions are given in Figure 5.19.

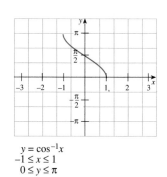

$y = \cos^{-1} x$
$-1 \leq x \leq 1$
$0 \leq y \leq \pi$

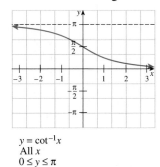

$y = \cot^{-1} x$
All x
$0 \leq y \leq \pi$

$y = \sec^{-1} x$
$|x| \geq 1$
$0 \leq y \leq \pi, y \neq \frac{\pi}{2}$

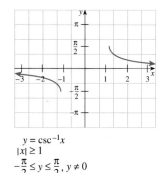

$y = \csc^{-1} x$
$|x| \geq 1$
$-\frac{\pi}{2} \leq y \leq \frac{\pi}{2}, y \neq 0$

Figure 5.19 Graphs of four inverse trigonometric functions*

EXAMPLE 1 Evaluating inverse trigonometric functions

Evaluate **a.** $\sin^{-1}\left(\frac{-\sqrt{2}}{2}\right)$ **b.** $\sin^{-1} 0.21$ **c.** $\cos^{-1} 0$ **d.** $\tan^{-1}\left(\frac{1}{\sqrt{3}}\right)$

Solution a. $\sin^{-1}\left(\frac{-\sqrt{2}}{2}\right) = -\frac{\pi}{4}$; *Think: $x = \frac{-\sqrt{2}}{2}$ is negative, so y is in Quadrant IV; the reference angle is the angle whose sine is $\frac{\sqrt{2}}{2}$; it is $\frac{\pi}{4}$, so in Quadrant IV the angle is $-\frac{\pi}{4}$.*

b. $\sin^{-1} 0.21 \approx 0.211\,575\,0$ *By calculator; be sure to use radian mode and inverse sine (not reciprocal).*

c. $\cos^{-1} 0 = \frac{\pi}{2}$ *Memorized exact value*

d. $\tan^{-1}\left(\frac{1}{\sqrt{3}}\right) = \frac{\pi}{6}$ *Think: $x = \frac{1}{\sqrt{3}}$ is positive, so y is in Quadrant I; the reference angle is the same as the value of the inverse tangent in Quadrant I.* ▬

⊘ The inversion formulas for $\sin^{-1}$ and $\tan^{-1}$ are valid only on the specified domains. ⊘

*There are no standard domain restrictions for inverse secant and inverse cosecant. Other calculus textbooks may use different restrictions from the ones we have chosen here. However, the ones we have used are the ones that are most convenient to use with standard calculators.

■ PROPERTIES OF INVERSE TRIGONOMETRIC FUNCTIONS

The definition of inverse functions yields four formulas, which we call the inversion formulas for sine and tangent.

Inversion Formulas

$$\sin(\sin^{-1}x) = x \qquad \text{for } -1 \le x \le 1$$

$$\sin^{-1}(\sin y) = y \qquad \text{for } -\tfrac{\pi}{2} \le y \le \tfrac{\pi}{2}$$

$$\tan(\tan^{-1}x) = x \qquad \text{for all } x$$

$$\tan^{-1}(\tan y) = y \qquad \text{for } -\tfrac{\pi}{2} < y < \tfrac{\pi}{2}$$

EXAMPLE 2   Inversion formula for x inside and outside domain

Evaluate the given functions.

  a. $\sin(\sin^{-1}0.5)$ **b.** $\sin(\sin^{-1}2)$ **c.** $\sin^{-1}(\sin 0.5)$ **d.** $\sin^{-1}(\sin 2)$

Solution **a.** $\sin(\sin^{-1}0.5) = 0.5$, because $-1 \le 0.5 \le 1$.

  b. $\sin(\sin^{-1}2)$ does not exist, because 2 is not between -1 and 1.

  c. $\sin^{-1}(\sin 0.5) = 0.5$, because $-\tfrac{\pi}{2} \le 0.5 \le \tfrac{\pi}{2}$.

  d. $\sin^{-1}(\sin 2) = 1.1415927$, by calculator. For exact values, notice that (reduction principle) $\sin 2 = \sin(\pi - 2)$ $\left(\text{so that } -\tfrac{\pi}{2} \le \pi - 2 \le \tfrac{\pi}{2}\right)$ and we have $\sin^{-1}(\sin 2) = \sin^{-1}[\sin(\pi - 2)] = \pi - 2$.   ▬

Some trigonometric identities correspond to inverse trigonometric identities. For example,

$$\sin^{-1}(-x) = -\sin^{-1}(x) \quad \textit{is true}$$

but

$$\oslash \quad \cos^{-1}(-x) = \cos^{-1}x \qquad \text{IS NOT TRUE} \ \oslash;$$
$$\textit{try } x = 1, \textit{ for example}$$

EXAMPLE 3   Proving an inverse identity

Show that for $-1 \le x \le 1$, $\sin^{-1}(-x) = -\sin^{-1}x$.

Solution Let
$$y = \sin^{-1}(-x)$$
$$\sin y = -x \qquad \textit{Definition of inverse sine}$$
$$-\sin y = x$$
$$\sin(-y) = x \qquad \textit{Opposite angle identity}$$
$$-y = \sin^{-1}x \qquad \textit{Definition of inverse sine}$$
$$y = -\sin^{-1}x$$

Thus, $\sin^{-1}(-x) = -\sin^{-1}x$.   ▬

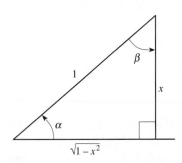

Figure 5.20 A reference triangle

A useful device for remembering inverse trigonometric relationships is the **reference triangle**. For example, suppose $\alpha = \sin^{-1}x$, so that $\sin\alpha = x$, where $0 < \alpha < \tfrac{\pi}{2}$. We construct a right triangle with an acute angle equal to α, which means we can assume the side opposite has length x and the hypotenuse has length

1, as shown in Figure 5.20. Then, if β is the angle complementary to α in this triangle, we have

$$\cos \beta = \frac{\text{ADJACENT SIDE}}{\text{HYPOTENUSE}} = \frac{x}{1} = x$$

which means that $\beta = \cos^{-1} x$. Similarly, because the side adjacent to angle α has length $\sqrt{1 - x^2}$ (by the Pythagorean theorem), we have

$$\tan \alpha = \frac{x}{\sqrt{1 - x^2}}, \quad \text{so} \quad \alpha = \tan^{-1}\left(\frac{x}{\sqrt{1 - x^2}}\right)$$

Note that the relationships displayed in the reference triangle in Figure 5.20 indicate that

$$\cos^{-1}x + \sin^{-1}x = \frac{\pi}{2} \quad \text{for } 0 \leq x \leq 1$$

because $\beta = \cos^{-1}x$, $\alpha = \sin^{-1}x$ and $\alpha + \beta = \frac{\pi}{2}$ in the reference triangle. This complementary angle relationship can be rewritten as

$$\cos^{-1}x = \frac{\pi}{2} - \sin^{-1}x$$

which is often used as the definition of the inverse cosine function.

EXAMPLE 4   Using a reference triangle

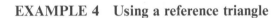

Find $\cos(\sin^{-1}x)$, where $0 < \sin^{-1}x \leq \frac{\pi}{2}$.

Solution   Let $y = \sin^{-1}x$, so we want to find $\cos y$. Form a right triangle that has an acute angle y such that $y = \sin^{-1}x$. Then

$$\cos(\sin^{-1}x) = \cos y = \frac{\sqrt{1 - x^2}}{1}$$

$$\cos(\sin^{-1}x) = \sqrt{1 - x^2}$$

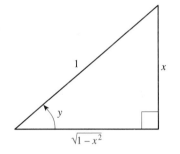

■ DERIVATIVES AND INTEGRALS INVOLVING INVERSE TRIGONOMETRIC FUNCTIONS

Differentiation formulas for the six fundamental inverse trigonometric functions are listed in Theorem 5.18. Notice that these derivatives are not inverse trigonometric functions or even trigonometric functions, but are instead rational functions or roots of rational functions.

THEOREM 5.18   Differentiation formulas for six inverse trigonometric functions

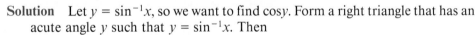

If u is a differentiable function of x, then

$$\frac{d}{dx}(\sin^{-1}u) = \frac{1}{\sqrt{1 - u^2}}\frac{du}{dx} \qquad \frac{d}{dx}(\cos^{-1}u) = \frac{-1}{\sqrt{1 - u^2}}\frac{du}{dx}$$

$$\frac{d}{dx}(\tan^{-1}u) = \frac{1}{1 + u^2}\frac{du}{dx} \qquad \frac{d}{dx}(\cot^{-1}u) = \frac{-1}{1 + u^2}\frac{du}{dx}$$

$$\frac{d}{dx}(\sec^{-1}u) = \frac{1}{|u|\sqrt{u^2 - 1}}\frac{du}{dx} \qquad \frac{d}{dx}(\csc^{-1}u) = \frac{-1}{|u|\sqrt{u^2 - 1}}\frac{du}{dx}$$

Proof: We shall prove the first formula and leave the others as problems. Let $y = \sin^{-1}x$, so $x = \sin y$. Because the sine is 1–1 and differentiable on $\left[-\frac{\pi}{2}, \frac{\pi}{2}\right]$, the inverse sine is also differentiable. To find its derivative, we proceed implicitly:

$$\sin y = x$$

$$\frac{d}{dx}(\sin y) = \frac{d}{dx}(x)$$

$$\cos y \frac{dy}{dx} = 1$$

Because $-\frac{\pi}{2} \le y \le \frac{\pi}{2}$, $\cos y \ge 0$, so

$$\frac{dy}{dx} = \frac{1}{\cos y} = \frac{1}{\sqrt{1 - \sin^2 y}} = \frac{1}{\sqrt{1 - x^2}}$$

If u is a differentiable function of x, then the chain rule gives

$$\frac{d}{dx}(\sin^{-1}u) = \frac{d}{du}(\sin^{-1}u)\frac{du}{dx} = \frac{1}{\sqrt{1 - u^2}}\frac{du}{dx}$$

∎

EXAMPLE 5   Derivatives involving inverse trigonometric functions

Differentiate each of the following functions.

a. $f(x) = \tan^{-1}\sqrt{x}$ **b.** $g(t) = \sin^{-1}(1 - t)$ **c.** $h(x) = \sec^{-1}e^{2x}$

Solution   a. Let $u = \sqrt{x}$ in the formula for $\frac{d}{dx}(\sin^{-1}u)$:

$$f'(x) = \frac{d}{dx}(\tan^{-1}\sqrt{x})$$

$$= \frac{1}{1 + (\sqrt{x})^2}\frac{d}{dx}(\sqrt{x}) = \frac{1}{1 + x}\left(\frac{1}{2}\frac{1}{\sqrt{x}}\right) = \frac{1}{2\sqrt{x}(1 + x)}$$

b. Let $u = (1 - t)$;

$$g'(t) = \frac{d}{dt}[\sin^{-1}(1 - t)]$$

$$= \frac{1}{\sqrt{1 - (1 - t)^2}}\frac{d}{dt}(1 - t) = \frac{-1}{\sqrt{1 - (1 - t)^2}} = \frac{-1}{\sqrt{2t - t^2}}$$

c. Let $u = e^{2x}$;

$$h'(x) = \frac{d}{dx}[\sec^{-1}e^{2x}] = \frac{1}{|e^{2x}|\sqrt{(e^{2x})^2 - 1}}\frac{d}{dx}(e^{2x})$$

$$= \frac{1}{e^{2x}\sqrt{e^{4x} - 1}}(2e^{2x}) = \frac{2}{\sqrt{e^{4x} - 1}} \quad \text{because } e^{2x} > 0$$

EXAMPLE 6   Graph of an inverse trigonometric function

Sketch the graph of $f(x) = \tan^{-1}x^2$.

Solution   We find that

$$f'(x) = \frac{2x}{1 + x^4}$$

$$f''(x) = \frac{(1 + x^4)(2) - 2x(4x^3)}{(1 + x^4)^2} = \frac{2 - 6x^4}{(1 + x^4)^2}$$

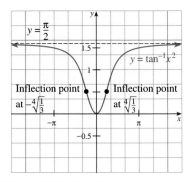

Figure 5.21 Graph of $f(x) = \tan^{-1} x^2$

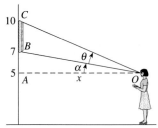

Figure 5.22 The angle θ is subtended by observer's eye.

Thus, $f'(x) = 0$ only when $x = 0$, and because $f''(0) > 0$, the graph is concave up, so there is a relative minimum at $x = 0$. Because $f(0) = \tan^{-1}(0) = 0$, the minimum occurs at $(0, 0)$.

Next, note that $f''(x) = 0$ when $6x^4 = 2$—that is, when $x = \pm \sqrt[4]{\frac{1}{3}}$ $\approx \pm 0.7598357$. Because $f''(x) < 0$ for $|x| > \sqrt[4]{\frac{1}{3}}$ and $f''(x) > 0$ for $-\sqrt[4]{\frac{1}{3}} < x < \sqrt[4]{\frac{1}{3}}$, the concavity of the graph changes at $x = \pm \sqrt[4]{\frac{1}{3}}$, and points of inflection must occur there. The graph of f is shown in Figure 5.21. ■

EXAMPLE 7   Optimization application

A painting is hung on a wall in such a way that its upper and lower edges are 10 ft and 7 ft above the floor, respectively. An observer whose eyes are 5 ft above the floor stands x feet from the wall, as shown in Figure 5.22. How far away from the wall should the observer stand to maximize the angle subtended by the painting?

Solution   In Figure 5.22, θ is the angle whose vertex occurs at the observer's eyes at a point O located x feet from the wall. Note that α is the angle between the line $\overline{OA}$ drawn directly from the observer's eyes to the wall and the line $\overline{OB}$ from the eyes to the bottom edge of the painting. In $\triangle OAB$ the angle at O is α, with $\cot \alpha = \frac{x}{2}$. In $\triangle OAC$, the angle at O is $(\alpha + \theta)$, and $\cot(\alpha + \theta) = \frac{x}{5}$. By using the definition of inverse cotangent we have

$$\theta = (\alpha + \theta) - \alpha = \cot^{-1}\left(\frac{x}{5}\right) - \cot^{-1}\left(\frac{x}{2}\right)$$

To maximize θ, we first compute the derivative

$$\frac{d\theta}{dx} = \frac{-1}{\left[1 + \left(\frac{x}{5}\right)^2\right]}\left(\frac{1}{5}\right) - \frac{-1}{\left[1 + \left(\frac{x}{2}\right)^2\right]}\left(\frac{1}{2}\right) = \frac{-5}{25 + x^2} + \frac{2}{4 + x^2}$$

Solving the equation $\frac{d\theta}{dx} = 0$ yields

$$-5(4 + x^2) + 2(25 + x^2) = 0$$
$$-3x^2 + 30 = 0$$
$$x = \pm\sqrt{10}$$

Because distance must be nonnegative, we reject the negative value. We apply the first-derivative test to show that the positive critical number $\sqrt{10}$ corresponds to a relative maximum (verify). Thus, the angle θ is maximized when the observer stands $\sqrt{10}$ ft away from the wall. ■

Each of the six derivative formulas for the inverse trigonometric functions has an integral counterpart, but as shown in the following theorem, we can pare down the list of integral formulas from six to just three.

THEOREM 5.19   Integrals involving the inverse trigonometric functions

$$\int \frac{du}{\sqrt{1 - u^2}} = \sin^{-1} u + C \qquad \text{for } |u| < 1$$
$$\int \frac{du}{1 + u^2} = \tan^{-1} u + C \qquad \text{for all } u$$
$$\int \frac{du}{|u|\sqrt{u^2 - 1}} = \sec^{-1} u + C \qquad \text{for } |u| > 1$$

Proof: The proofs are straightforward reversals of the derivatives of the inverse trigonometric formulas. We might show, however, how two of the derivative formulas can be pared down to one formula. We know, for instance, that for $-1 \leq u \leq 1$

$$\frac{d}{du}(\sin^{-1}u) = \frac{1}{\sqrt{1-u^2}} \quad \text{and} \quad \frac{d}{du}(\cos^{-1}u) = \frac{-1}{\sqrt{1-u^2}}$$

and the corresponding integration formulas are

$$\int \frac{du}{\sqrt{1-u^2}} = \sin^{-1}u + C \quad \text{and} \quad \int \frac{du}{\sqrt{1-u^2}} = -\cos^{-1}u + C$$

Clearly, only one of these integration formulas is necessary, and we choose the one involving $\sin^{-1}u$. We can even use a trigonometric identity to show these formulas are identical:

$$-\cos^{-1}u + C = \left(\sin^{-1}u - \tfrac{\pi}{2}\right) + C = \sin^{-1}u + C_1$$

where $C_1 = -\frac{\pi}{2} + C$. A similar reason applies to our choice of the integral formulas involving $\tan^{-1}u$ and $\sec^{-1}u$. ∎

EXAMPLE 8 **An integral involving an inverse trigonometric function**

Find $\displaystyle\int \frac{dx}{\sqrt{4-x^2}}$.

Solution Because the integral involves $\sqrt{a^2-x^2}$, we think of using an inverse sine, but first we must do some algebra. We write:

$$\int \frac{dx}{\sqrt{4-x^2}} = \int \frac{dx}{\sqrt{4\left(1-\frac{x^2}{4}\right)}}$$

$$= \frac{1}{2}\int \frac{dx}{\sqrt{1-\left(\frac{x}{2}\right)^2}} \qquad \begin{array}{l}\text{Let } u = \frac{x}{2};\\[4pt] du = \frac{1}{2}\,dx.\end{array}$$

$$= \frac{1}{2}\int \frac{2\,du}{\sqrt{1-u^2}} = \sin^{-1}u + C = \sin^{-1}\frac{x}{2} + C$$

The method used in Example 8 can be applied to obtain the following integration formulas for the inverse trigonometric functions.

Generalized Integration Formulas for Inverse Trigonometric Functions

For a constant $a > 0$:

$$\int \frac{du}{\sqrt{a^2-u^2}} = \sin^{-1}\frac{u}{a} + C$$

$$\int \frac{du}{a^2+u^2} = \frac{1}{a}\tan^{-1}\frac{u}{a} + C$$

$$\int \frac{du}{|u|\sqrt{u^2-a^2}} = \frac{1}{a}\sec^{-1}\left|\frac{u}{a}\right| + C$$

EXAMPLE 9 **Integrating with a generalized inverse trigonometric formula**

Find $\displaystyle\int \frac{dx}{\sqrt{9-4x^2}}$.

Solution Compare this with Example 8.

$$\int \frac{dx}{\sqrt{9 - 4x^2}} = \int \frac{dx}{\sqrt{3^2 - (2x)^2}} \qquad \text{Let } u = 2x; \\ du = 2\,dx.$$

$$= \int \frac{\frac{1}{2}\,du}{\sqrt{3^2 - u^2}}$$

$$= \frac{1}{2}\sin^{-1}\left(\frac{u}{3}\right) + C \qquad \textit{From the formula with } a = 3$$

$$= \frac{1}{2}\sin^{-1}\left(\frac{2x}{3}\right) + C$$

EXAMPLE 10   Integrating an inverse trigonometric form

Find $\displaystyle\int \frac{dx}{\sqrt{e^{2x} - 4}}$.

Solution
$$\int \frac{dx}{\sqrt{e^{2x} - 4}} = \int \frac{\frac{du}{u}}{\sqrt{u^2 - 4}} = \int \frac{du}{u\sqrt{u^2 - 4}} = \frac{1}{2}\sec^{-1}\left|\frac{u}{2}\right| + C$$

$$\text{Let } u = e^x; \qquad\qquad\qquad a = 2 \\ du = e^x\,dx; \\ dx = \frac{du}{e^x} = \frac{du}{u}.$$

$$= \frac{1}{2}\sec^{-1}\left|\frac{e^x}{2}\right| + C$$

EXAMPLE 11   Inverse trigonometric form by completing the square

Find $\displaystyle\int \frac{dx}{x^2 - 4x + 10}$.

Solution   First, we complete the square in the denominator:
$$x^2 - 4x + 10 = x^2 - 4x + 2^2 - 4 + 10$$
$$= (x - 2)^2 + 6$$

$$\int \frac{dx}{x^2 - 4x + 10} = \int \frac{dx}{(x - 2)^2 + 6} = \int \frac{du}{u^2 + 6} = \frac{1}{\sqrt{6}}\tan^{-1}\left(\frac{x - 2}{\sqrt{6}}\right) + C$$

$$\text{Let } u = x - 2; \qquad a = \sqrt{6} \\ dx = du.$$

EXAMPLE 12   Area under a curve

Find the area under the curve $y = \dfrac{1}{1 + x^2}$ on the interval $[-1, 1]$.

Solution   The region under the curve is shaded in Figure 5.23. The area is given by the integral

$$\int_{-1}^{1} \frac{dx}{1 + x^2} = \left[\tan^{-1}x\right]\Big|_{-1}^{1} = \tan^{-1}1 - \tan^{-1}(-1)$$

$$= \frac{\pi}{4} - \left(-\frac{\pi}{4}\right)$$

$$= \frac{\pi}{2}$$

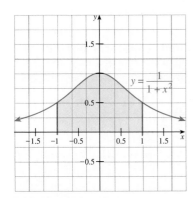

Figure 5.23 The area under $y = \dfrac{1}{1 + x^2}$ on $[-1, 1]$

PROBLEM SET 5.6

A 1. ■ **What Does This Say?** Discuss the restrictions on the domain and range in the definition of the inverse trigonometric functions.

2. ■ **What Does This Say?** Discuss the use of reference triangles in relation to the inverse trigonometric functions.

Give the exact values for functions in Problems 3–14.

3. **a.** $\cos^{-1}\frac{1}{2}$ **b.** $\sin^{-1}\left(-\frac{\sqrt{3}}{2}\right)$

4. **a.** $\sin^{-1}\left(-\frac{1}{2}\right)$ **b.** $\cos^{-1}\left(-\frac{1}{2}\right)$

5. **a.** $\tan^{-1}(-1)$ **b.** $\cot^{-1}(-\sqrt{3})$

6. **a.** $\sec^{-1}(-\sqrt{2})$ **b.** $\cot^{-1}\left(-\frac{1}{\sqrt{3}}\right)$

7. **a.** $\sin^{-1}\left(-\frac{\sqrt{3}}{2}\right)$ **b.** $\sec^{-1}(-1)$

8. **a.** $\sec^{-1}\left(\frac{2}{\sqrt{3}}\right)$ **b.** $\cot^{-1}(-1)$

9. $\cos\left(\sin^{-1}\frac{1}{2}\right)$ 10. $\sin\left(\cos^{-1}\frac{1}{\sqrt{2}}\right)$

11. $\cot\left(\tan^{-1}\frac{1}{3}\right)$ 12. $\tan\left(\sin^{-1}\frac{1}{3}\right)$

13. $\cos\left(\sin^{-1}\frac{1}{5} + 2\cos^{-1}\frac{1}{5}\right)$
Hint: Use the addition law for $\cos(\alpha + \beta)$.

14. $\sin\left(\sin^{-1}\frac{1}{5} + \cos^{-1}\frac{1}{4}\right)$
Hint: Use the addition law for $\sin(\alpha + \beta)$.

Find the derivative $\frac{dy}{dx}$ in Problems 15–30.

15. $y = \sin^{-1}(2x + 1)$ 16. $y = \cos^{-1}(4x + 3)$

17. $y = \tan^{-1}\sqrt{x^2 + 1}$ 18. $y = \cot^{-1}x^2$

19. $y = (\sin^{-1}2x)^3$ 20. $y = (\tan^{-1}x^2)^4$

21. $y = \sqrt{\tan^{-1}(2x)}$ 22. $y = \ln|\sin^{-1}x|$

23. $y = \ln|\cos^{-1}x|$ 24. $y = \sin^{-1}e^x$

25. $y = \tan^{-1}\left(\frac{1}{x}\right)$ 26. $y = \cos^{-1}(\sin x)$

27. $y = \sin^{-1}|\cos x|$ 28. $y = \ln[\sin^{-1}(e^x)]$

29. $x\sin^{-1}y + y\tan^{-1}x = x$

30. $\sin^{-1}y + y = 2xy$

Find the integral indicated in Problems 31–42.

31. $\displaystyle\int \frac{dx}{x^2 + 16}$ 32. $\displaystyle\int \frac{dx}{x\sqrt{x^2 - 9}}$

33. $\displaystyle\int \frac{dx}{\sqrt{5 - 2x^2}}$ 34. $\displaystyle\int \frac{dx}{\sqrt{4 - 7x^2}}$

35. $\displaystyle\int \frac{2x + 5}{x^2 + 4x + 5}\,dx$ 36. $\displaystyle\int \frac{2x - 3}{x^2 + 1}\,dx$

37. $\displaystyle\int \frac{x\,dx}{x^2 + x + 1}$ 38. $\displaystyle\int \frac{2x + 1}{\sqrt{1 - x^2}}\,dx$

39. $\displaystyle\int \frac{(2 + x)\,dx}{\sqrt{4 - 2x - x^2}}$ 40. $\displaystyle\int \frac{(8x - 1)\,dx}{\sqrt{1 - 4x^2}}$

41. $\displaystyle\int \frac{dx}{x^2 + 2x + 2}$ 42. $\displaystyle\int \frac{dx}{\sqrt{-x^2 + 3x - 2}}$

Evaluate the definite integrals in Problems 43–48.

43. $\displaystyle\int_{1/\sqrt{3}}^{1} \frac{dx}{x\sqrt{4x^2 - 1}}$ 44. $\displaystyle\int_{0}^{\pi/4} \frac{\sin x\,dx}{1 + \cos^2 x}$ 45. $\displaystyle\int_{0}^{\ln 2\sqrt{3}} \frac{e^x\,dx}{e^{2x} + 4}$

46. $\displaystyle\int_{1}^{e^2} \frac{dx}{x[4 + (\ln x)^2]}$ 47. $\displaystyle\int_{0}^{1/\sqrt{2}} \frac{x\,dx}{\sqrt{1 - x^4}}$ 48. $\displaystyle\int_{0}^{1} \frac{x^3\,dx}{1 + x^8}$

B *Simplify each expression in Problems 49–54.*

49. $\sin(2\tan^{-1}x)$ 50. $\tan(2\tan^{-1}x)$

51. $\tan(\cos^{-1}x)$ 52. $\cos(2\sin^{-1}x)$

53. $\sin(\sin^{-1}x + \cos^{-1}x)$

54. $\cos(\sin^{-1}x + \cos^{-1}x)$

55. Use reference triangles, if necessary, to justify each of the following identities.

a. $\cot^{-1}x = \dfrac{\pi}{2} - \tan^{-1}x$ for all x

b. $\sec^{-1}x = \cos^{-1}\left(\dfrac{1}{x}\right)$ for all $|x| \geq 1$

c. $\csc^{-1}x = \sin^{-1}\left(\dfrac{1}{x}\right)$ for all $|x| \geq 1$

56. **a.** Show that $f'(x) = 0$ where
$$f(x) = \sin^{-1}x + \cos^{-1}x$$
What does this prove about $f(x)$?

b. Show that $\tan^{-1}x + \cot^{-1}x$ is a constant by examining its derivative. What is the value of this constant?

57. Find the area under the curve
$$y = \frac{1}{x\sqrt{x^2 - 1}}$$
on the interval $(\sqrt{2}, 2)$.

58. Find the point of inflection of the curve
$$y = (x + 1)\tan^{-1}x$$

59. Find the critical values for the function and identify each as a relative maximum, relative minimum, or neither.
$$f(x) = \tan^{-1}\left(\frac{x}{a}\right) - \tan^{-1}\left(\frac{x}{b}\right), \qquad a > b$$

Sketch the graph of each function in Problems 60–63.

60. $f(x) = x + \tan^{-1}x$ 61. $f(x) = x - \tan^{-1}(2x)$

62. $f(x) = \cos^{-1}x + \sin^{-1}x$ 63. $f(x) = 2x - \sin^{-1}x$

64. A worker standing 4 m from a hoist sees the hoist at eye level. If the hoist is raised at the rate of 2 m/s, how fast is the worker's angle of sight changing when the hoist is 1.5 m above eye level?

65. The bottom of an 8-ft-high mural painted on a vertical wall is 13 ft above the ground. The lens of a camera fixed to a tripod is 4 ft above the ground. How far from the wall should the camera be placed in order to photograph the mural with the largest possible angle?

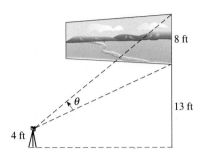

Ⓒ 66. Prove $\int \dfrac{du}{\sqrt{a^2 - u^2}} = \sin^{-1}\left(\dfrac{u}{a}\right) + C$

67. Prove $\int \dfrac{du}{a^2 + u^2} = \dfrac{1}{a}\tan^{-1}\left(\dfrac{u}{a}\right) + C$

68. Prove $\int \dfrac{du}{u\sqrt{u^2 - a^2}} = \dfrac{1}{a}\sec^{-1}\left|\dfrac{u}{a}\right| + C$

69. Use the identity $\cot^{-1}x = \dfrac{\pi}{2} - \tan^{-1}x$ for all x to find $\dfrac{d}{dx}(\cot^{-1}x)$.

70. Use the identity $\sec^{-1}x = \cos^{-1}\left(\dfrac{1}{x}\right)$ for $|x| \geq 1$ to show that

$$\frac{d}{dx}(\sec^{-1}x) = \frac{1}{|x|\sqrt{x^2 - 1}} \qquad \text{for } |x| > 1$$

5.7 AN ALTERNATIVE APPROACH: THE LOGARITHM AS AN INTEGRAL*

"When I use a word," Humpty Dumpty said, "it means just what I choose it to mean—nothing more or less."

Lewis Carroll (1832–1898)

IN THIS SECTION Definition of the natural logarithm as an integral, geometric interpretation of the natural logarithm, the natural exponential function

Charles Dodgson, whose pen name was Lewis Carroll, was a mathematician who knew that a standard procedure in mathematics is to define a function by "fitting" it to a list of desired characteristics. In this optional section, we explore an alternative treatment of the natural logarithm and exponential functions in which ln x is defined as an integral and its properties are derived by referring to properties of integrals. The natural exponential function e^x can then be defined as the inverse of ln x.

■ DEFINITION OF THE NATURAL LOGARITHM AS AN INTEGRAL

You may have noticed in Section 5.1 that we did not prove the properties of exponential functions for all real number exponents. In order to treat exponentials and logarithms *rigorously*, we use the alternative approach provided in this section. Specifically, we use a definite integral to introduce the *natural logarithmic function* and then use this function to *define* the *natural exponential function*. In this way we can develop precise meanings for b^x and $\log_b x$.

Natural Logarithm

The **natural logarithm** is the function defined by

$$\ln x = \int_1^x \frac{dt}{t} \qquad x > 0$$

At first glance, it appears there is nothing "natural" about this definition, but if this integral function has the properties of a logarithm, why should we not call it a logarithm? We begin with a theorem that shows that ln x does indeed have the properties we would expect of a logarithm.

*The material of this section is not required for subsequent sections.

Historical Note

LEONHARD EULER (1707–1783)

Euler's name is attached to almost every branch of mathematics. He was the most prolific writer on the subject of mathematics, and his mathematical textbooks were masterfully written. His writing was not at all slowed down by his total blindness for the last 17 years of his life. He possessed a phenomenal memory, had almost total recall, and could mentally calculate long and complicated problems.

   When Euler was 13 he registered at the University of Basel and was introduced to another famous mathematician, John Bernoulli, who was an instructor there at the time. If Bernoulli thought that a student was promising, he would provide, sometimes gratis, private instruction. Here is Euler's own account of this first encounter with Bernoulli:

"I soon found an opportunity to gain introduction to the famous professor John Bernoulli, whose good pleasure it was to advance me further in the mathematical sciences. True, because of his business he flatly refused me private lessons, but he gave me much wiser advice, namely, to get some more difficult mathematical books and work through them with all industry, and

THEOREM 5.20   Properties of a logarithm as defined by $\ln x = \int_1^x \dfrac{dt}{t}$

Let $x > 0$ and $y > 0$ be positive numbers. Then

   a. $\ln 1 = 0$

   b. $\ln xy = \ln x + \ln y$

   c. $\ln \dfrac{x}{y} = \ln x - \ln y$

   d. $\ln x^p = p \ln x$ for all rational numbers p

Proof: **a.** Let $x = 1$. Then $\int_1^1 \dfrac{dt}{t} = 0$.

   b. For fixed positive numbers x and y, we use the additive property of integrals as follows:

$$\ln(xy) = \int_1^{xy} \frac{dt}{t} = \int_1^x \frac{dt}{t} + \int_x^{xy} \frac{dt}{t}$$

$$= \ln x + \int_1^y \frac{x\,du}{ux}$$

$$= \ln x + \ln y$$

> Let $u = \dfrac{t}{x}$, so $t = ux$; $dt = x\,du$.
> If $t = x$, then $u = 1$; if $t = xy$, then $u = y$.

   c. and d. The proofs are outlined in the problem set.   ∎

■ GEOMETRIC INTERPRETATION OF THE NATURAL LOGARITHM

An advantage of defining the logarithm by the integral formula is that calculus can be used to study the properties of $\ln x$ from the beginning. For example, note that if $x > 1$, the integral

$$\ln x = \int_1^x \frac{dt}{t}$$

may be interpreted geometrically as the area under the graph of $y = \dfrac{1}{t}$ from $t = 1$ to $t = x$, as shown in Figure 5.24. Because the area shown in Figure 5.24 is positive, we have $\ln x > 0$ if $x > 1$. If $0 < x < 1$, then

$$\ln x = \int_1^x \frac{dt}{t} = -\int_x^1 \frac{dt}{t} < 0$$

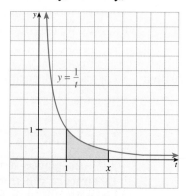

Figure 5.24 If $x > 1$, $\ln x = \displaystyle\int_1^x \dfrac{dt}{t}$ is the area under $y = \dfrac{1}{t}$ on $[1, x]$.

so that

$\ln x > 0$ if $x > 1$

$\ln 1 = 0$

$\ln x < 0$ if $0 < x < 1$

The definition $\ln x = \int_1^x \frac{dt}{t}$ makes it easy to differentiate $\ln x$. Recall from Section 4.3 that according to the second fundamental theorem of calculus, if f is continuous on $[a, b]$, then

$$F(x) = \int_a^x f(t)\, dt$$

is a differentiable function of x with derivative $\frac{dF}{dx} = f(x)$ on any interval $[a, x]$. Therefore, because $\frac{1}{t}$ is continuous for all $t > 0$, it follows that $\ln x = \int_1^x \frac{dt}{t}$ is differentiable for all $x > 0$ with derivative $\frac{d}{dx}(\ln x) = \frac{1}{x}$, and by applying the chain rule, we find that

$$\frac{d}{dx}(\ln u) = \frac{1}{u}\frac{du}{dx}$$

for any differentiable function u of x with $u > 0$.

To analyze the graph of $f(x) = \ln x$, we use the curve-sketching methods of Chapter 3:

a. $\ln x$ is continuous for all $x > 0$ (because it is differentiable), so its graph is "unbroken."

b. The graph of $\ln x$ is always *rising*, because the derivative

$$\frac{d}{dx}(\ln x) = \frac{1}{x}$$

is positive for $x > 0$. (Recall that the natural logarithm is defined only for $x > 0$.)

c. The graph of $\ln x$ is *concave down*, because the second derivative

$$\frac{d^2}{dx^2}(\ln x) = \frac{d}{dx}\left(\frac{1}{x}\right) = \frac{-1}{x^2}$$

is negative for all $x > 0$.

d. Note that $\ln 2 > 0$ (because $\int_1^2 \frac{dt}{t} > 0$) and because $\ln 2^p = p \ln 2$, it follows that $\lim\limits_{p \to +\infty} \ln 2^p = +\infty$. But the graph of $f(x) = \ln x$ is always rising, and thus $\lim\limits_{x \to +\infty} \ln x = +\infty$. Similarly, it can be shown that $\lim\limits_{x \to 0^+} \ln x = -\infty$.

e. If b is any positive number, there is exactly one number a such that $\ln a = b$ (because the graph of $\ln x$ is always rising for $x > 0$). In particular, we define $x = e$ as the unique number that satisfies $\ln x = 1$.

These features are shown in Figure 5.25.

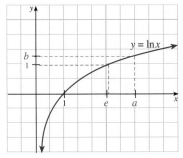

Figure 5.25 The graph of the natural logarithm function, $\ln x$

■ THE NATURAL EXPONENTIAL FUNCTION

Originally, we introduced the natural exponential function e^x and then defined the natural logarithm $\ln x$ as the inverse of e^x. In this alternative approach, we note that because the natural logarithm is an increasing function, it must be one-to-one. Therefore it has an inverse function, which we denote by $E(x)$.

Because $\ln x$ and $E(x)$ are inverses of one another, we have

$$E(x) = y \quad \text{if and only if} \quad \ln y = x$$

From the definition of inverse formulas we have

$$E(\ln x) = x \quad \text{and} \quad \ln[E(x)] = x$$

We call these formulas the **inversion formulas.** Therefore,

$$E(0) = E(\ln 1) \quad \textit{Because } \ln 1 = 0$$
$$= 1 \qquad\qquad \textit{Because } E(\ln x) = x$$

and

$$E(1) = E(\ln e) \quad \textit{Because } \ln e = 1 \text{ (see e above)}$$
$$= e \qquad\qquad \textit{Because } E(\ln e) = e$$

To obtain the graph of $E(x)$, we reflect the graph of $y = \ln x$ in the line $y = x$. The graph is shown in Figure 5.26. Notice that $\ln x = 1$ has the unique solution $x = e$.

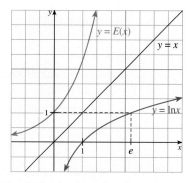

Figure 5.26 The graph of $E(x)$ is the reflection of the graph of $\ln x$ in the line $y = x$.

The following algebraic properties of the natural exponential function can be obtained by using the properties of the natural logarithm given in Theorem 5.20 along with the inversion formulas.

THEOREM 5.21   Properties of the exponential as defined by $E(x)$

For any numbers x and y,

    a. $E(x + y) = E(x)E(y)$

    b. $E(x - y) = \dfrac{E(x)}{E(y)}$

    c. $[E(x)]^p = E(px)$

Proof: **a.** We use the fact that $\ln AB = \ln A + \ln B$ to show that

$$\ln[E(x)E(y)] = \ln E(x) + \ln E(y) \quad \textit{Property of logarithms}$$
$$= x + y \qquad\qquad\qquad \textit{Inversion formula}$$
$$= \ln E(x + y) \qquad\quad \textit{Inversion formula}$$

Because $\ln x$ is a one-to-one function, we conclude that

$$E(x)E(y) = E(x + y)$$

    b. and **c.** The proofs are similar and are left as exercises.   ∎

Next, we use implicit differentiation along with the differentiation formula

$$\frac{d}{dx}(\ln x) = \frac{1}{x}$$

to obtain a differentiation formula for $E(x)$.

THEOREM 5.22   Derivative of $E(x)$

The function defined by $E(x)$ is differentiable and

$$\frac{dE}{dx} = E(x)$$

Proof: We know from Theorem 5.4 that E is differentiable because it is the inverse of the differentiable function $\ln x$. If $y = E(x)$, we know that

$$\ln y = \ln[E(x)]$$

$$\ln y = x \qquad \textit{Inversion formula}$$

$$\frac{1}{y}\frac{dy}{dx} = 1 \qquad \textit{Differentiate implicitly.}$$

$$\frac{dy}{dx} = y$$

$$\frac{dE}{dx} = E(x) \qquad \textit{Because } \frac{dy}{dx} = \frac{dE}{dx} \textit{ and } E(x) = y \qquad ∎$$

Finally, we observe that if r is a rational number, then

$$\ln(e^r) = r \ln e = r$$

so that

$$E(r) = e^r$$

This means that $E(x) = e^x$ when x is a rational number, and we **define** $E(x)$ to be e^x for irrational x as well. In particular, we now have an alternative definition for e: $E(1) = e^1 = e$.

PROBLEM SET 5.7

© **1.** Use the integral definition

$$\ln x = \int_1^x \frac{dt}{t}$$

to show that $\ln x \to -\infty$ as $x \to 0^+$. *Hint:* What happens to $\ln(2^{-N})$ as N grows large without bound?

2. Use Simpson's rule with $n = 8$ subintervals to estimate

$$\ln 3 = \int_1^3 \frac{dt}{t}$$

Compare your estimate with the value of $\ln 3$ obtained from your calculator.

3. Use the error estimate for Simpson's rule to determine the accuracy of the estimate in Problem 2. How many subinter-

vals should be used in Simpson's rule to estimate $\ln 3$ with an error not greater than 0.00005?

4. Prove the quotient rule for logarithms,

$$\ln\left(\frac{x}{y}\right) = \ln x - \ln y$$

for all $x > 0, y > 0$. *Hint:* Note that the product rule for logarithms implies

$$\ln\left[\left(\frac{x}{y}\right)y\right] = \ln\left(\frac{x}{y}\right) + \ln y$$

5. Show that $\ln(x^p) = p \ln x$ for $x > 0$ and all rational exponents p by completing the following steps.

   a. Let $F(x) = \ln(x^p)$ and $G(x) = p \ln x$. Show that $F'(x) = G'(x)$ for $x > 0$. Conclude that $F(x) = G(x) + C$.

b. Let $x = 1$ and conclude that

$$F(x) = G(x)$$

That is, that $\ln(x^p) = p \ln x$.

6. Use Rolle's theorem to show that

$$\ln M = \ln N$$

if and only if $M = N$. *Hint*: Show that if $M \neq N$, Rolle's theorem implies that

$$\frac{d}{dx}(\ln x) = 0$$

for some number c between M and N. Why is this impossible?

7. The product rule for logarithms states

$$\log_b(MN) = \log_b M + \log_b N$$

For this reason, we want the natural logarithm function $\ln x$ to satisfy the functional equation

$$f(xy) = f(x) + f(y)$$

Suppose $f(x)$ is a function that satisfies this equation throughout its domain D.

a. Show that if $f(1)$ is defined, then $f(1) = 0$.

b. Show that if $f(-1)$ is defined, then $f(-1) = 0$.

c. Show that $f(-x) = f(x)$ for all x in D.

d. If $f'(x)$ is defined for each $x \neq 0$, show that

$$f'(x) = \frac{f'(1)}{x}$$

Then show that

$$f(x) = f'(1) \int_1^x \frac{dt}{t} \qquad \text{for } x > 0$$

e. Conclude that any solution of

$$f(xy) = f(x) + f(y)$$

that is not identically 0 and has a derivative for all $x \neq 0$ must be a multiple of

$$F(x) = \int_1^{|x|} \frac{dt}{t} \qquad \text{for } x \neq 0$$

8. Show that for each number A, there is only one number x for which $\ln x = A$. *Hint*: If not, then $\ln x = \ln y = A$ for $x \neq y$. Why is this impossible?

9. By comparing areas under the curve

$$y = \frac{1}{t}$$

between $t = 2$ and $t = 3$, show that

$$\ln 2 < 1 < \ln 3$$

Why does this imply that $2 < e < 3$?

Chapter 5 Review

> **IN THIS REVIEW** Proficiency examination; supplementary problems
> Problems 1–16 of the proficiency examination test your knowledge of the concepts of this chapter, and Problems 17–25 test your understanding of those concepts by asking you to work sample practice problems. The supplementary problems present questions relating to the material of this chapter in a wide variety of settings.

PROFICIENCY EXAMINATION

Concept Problems

1. What is an exponential function?
2. What is e?
3. What is the future value formula for interest
   a. compounded n times a year?
   b. compounded continuously?
4. Define an inverse function.
5. What is the horizontal line test?
6. What is the procedure for graphing the inverse of a given function?

7. What is the formula for the derivative of an inverse function?
8. a. What is a logarithm?
   b. What is a common logarithm?
   c. What is a natural logarithm?
9. State the change of base theorem.
10. State the derivative formulas for the given functions.
    a. $\ln u$ b. $\log_b u$ c. e^u d. b^u
11. Outline the procedure for logarithmic differentiation.

12. State the integration formulas for the given functions.
    a. e^x **b.** x^n **c.** $\tan x$ **d.** $\cot x$

13. Define the six inverse trigonometric functions; include the domain, range, and graph of each.

14. State the inversion formulas for the inverse trigonometric functions.

15. State the differentiation formulas for the six inverse trigonometric functions.

16. State integration formulas involving the inverse trigonometric functions.

Practice Problems

17. Find $\dfrac{dy}{dx}$:

    a. $y = x^2 e^{-\sqrt{x}}$ **b.** $y = \dfrac{\ln 2x}{\ln 3x}$

18. Find $\dfrac{dy}{dx}$:

    a. $y = \sin^{-1}(3x + 2)$ **b.** $y = \tan^{-1} 2x$

19. Use logarithmic differentiation to find y' if
    $$y = \frac{\ln(x^2 - 1)}{\sqrt[3]{x(1 - 3x)^3}}.$$

20. Graph $y = (x^2 - 3)e^{-x}$. Be sure to show high and low points, points of inflection, intercepts, asymptotes, and endpoint behavior (for example, as $x \to +\infty$ and $x \to -\infty$).

21. Calculate the indicated integral.

    a. $\displaystyle\int_0^{\ln 2} (e^{2x} - e^{-2x})\, dx$

    b. $\displaystyle\int \frac{\ln x\, dx}{x}$ **c.** $\displaystyle\int \tan 2x\, dx$

22. Evaluate each of the given limits.

    a. $\displaystyle\lim_{x \to 0^+} (1 + x)^{4/x}$

    b. $\displaystyle\lim_{x \to 1} \left(\frac{1}{1 - x}\right)^x$ **c.** $\displaystyle\lim_{x \to 0^+} x^{\tan x}$

23. Find the area of the region above the x-axis and under $y = e^{2x} - e^x$ on $[0, 1]$.

24. How quickly will \$2,000 grow to \$5,000 when invested at an annual interest rate of 8% if interest is compounded
    a. quarterly?   **b.** monthly?   **c.** continuously?

25. A manufacturer can produce cameras at a cost of \$40 each and estimates that if they are sold for p dollars each, the consumers will buy approximately $D(p) = 800e^{-0.01p}$ cameras per week. At what price (to the nearest dollar) should the manufacturer sell the cameras to maximize profit?

SUPPLEMENTARY PROBLEMS

1. Evaluate each of the given numbers.
    a. $\ln 4.5$ **b.** $e^{2.8}$ **c.** $\tan^{-1} 2$

2. Evaluate each of the given numbers.
    a. $e^{\ln 7.4}$ **b.** $\ln e^{3.7}$ **c.** $\sin^{-1}\left(\cos \frac{\pi}{10}\right)$

3. Evaluate each of the given numbers.
    a. $\sin(2 \tan^{-1} 3)$ **b.** $\sin\left(\cos^{-1}\frac{3}{5} + \sin^{-1}\frac{5}{13}\right)$

Solve each equation in Problems 4–7 for x.

4. **a.** $4^{x-1} = 8$ **b.** $2^{x^2+4x} = \frac{1}{16}$

5. **a.** $\ln(x - 1) + \ln(x + 1) = 2 \ln\sqrt{12}$
   b. $\sqrt{x} = \cos^{-1} 0.317 + \sin^{-1} 0.317$

6. **a.** $\log_2 2^{x^2} = 4$ **b.** $\log_4 \sqrt{x(x - 15)} = 1$

7. **a.** $\log_2 x + \log_2(x - 15) = 4$ **b.** $3^{2x-1} = 6^x 3^{1-x}$

In Problems 8–9, find f^{-1} if it exists.

8. **a.** $f(x) = 2x^3 - 7$ **b.** $f(x) = \sqrt[7]{2x + 1}, x \geq -\frac{1}{2}$

9. **a.** $f(x) = \sqrt{e^x - 1}, x \geq 0$ **b.** $f(x) = \dfrac{x + 5}{x - 7}, x \neq 7$

10. Show that for any $a \neq 1$, the function $f(x) = \dfrac{x + a}{x - 1}$ is its own inverse.

11. Let $f(x) = \dfrac{ax + b}{cx + d}$. Find f^{-1} in terms of a, b, c, and d. Under what conditions does f^{-1} exist?

12. Find $f^{-1}(x)$ if $f(x) = \dfrac{x + 1}{x - 1}$. What is the domain of f^{-1}?

Find the derivative $\dfrac{dy}{dx}$ in Problems 13–27.

13. $y = \exp(2x^2 + 5x - 3)$ 14. $y = \ln(x^2 - 1)$

15. $y = x3^{2-x}$ 16. $y = \log_3(x^2 - 1)$

17. $e^{xy} + 2 = \ln \dfrac{y}{x}$ 18. $y = \sqrt{x} \sin^{-1}(3x + 2)$

19. $y = e^{\sin x}$ 20. $y = 2^x \log_2 x$

21. $y = e^{-x} \log_5 3x$ 22. $x2^y + y2^x = 3$

23. $\ln(x + y^2) = x^2 + 2y$ 24. $y = \dfrac{\sin^{-1} x}{x + \tan^{-1} x}$

25. $y = \dfrac{x}{\sin^{-1} x} + \dfrac{\tan^{-1} x}{x}$ 26. $y = e^{-x}\sqrt{\ln 2x}$

27. $y = (\sin x)(\sin^{-1} x) + x \cot^{-1} x$

Find the standard form equation for the tangent line to the given curve at the prescribed point in Problems 28–32.

28. $y = x \ln ex$ where $x = 1$

29. $y = xe^{2x-1}$ where $x = \frac{1}{2}$

30. $e^{xy} = x - y$ at $(1, 0)$

31. $y = (1 - x)^x$ where $x = 0$

32. $y = 2^x - \log_2 x$ where $x = 1$

Use logarithmic differentiation to find $\dfrac{dy}{dx}$ in Problems 33–38.

33. $y = \dfrac{5^{2-x}(x^2 - x)^3}{(2x^3 - 3x)^4}$

34. $y = \dfrac{(x^2 + 3)^{1/3}\sqrt{x^4 + x + 1}}{\sqrt[4]{x^3 + 5}}$

35. $y = (x^2 + 1)^{2x}$ **36.** $y = (\ln x)^x$

37. $y = (3x^2 + 2)^{2x}$ **38.** $y = x^{\sin x}$

Sketch the graph of each function given in Problems 39–42. Be sure to show high and low points, points of inflection, intercepts, asymptotes, and endpoint behavior (as $x \to +\infty$ and $x \to -\infty$).

39. $y = x^2 \ln\sqrt{x}$ **40.** $y = \sin^{-1}x - \cos^{-1}x$

41. $f(x) = \ln\left(\dfrac{x-1}{x+1}\right)$ **42.** $f(x) = xe^{1/x}$

Calculate the indicated integral in Problems 43–64.

43. $\displaystyle\int \dfrac{x+1}{x^2 + 2x + 5}\, dx$ **44.** $\displaystyle\int xe^{-x^2}\, dx$

45. $\displaystyle\int \dfrac{dx}{7 + x^2}$ **46.** $\displaystyle\int \dfrac{dx}{\sqrt{25 - 9x^2}}$

47. $\displaystyle\int_0^{\pi/2} \dfrac{\sin x\, dx}{2 + \cos x}$ **48.** $\displaystyle\int_0^{\ln 2} (e^{2x} - e^{-2x})\, dx$

49. $\displaystyle\int_0^{\ln 2} (e^{2x} + 5)e^x\, dx$ **50.** $\displaystyle\int_0^{\pi/6} \sec 2x\, dx$

51. $\displaystyle\int \dfrac{e^{\sqrt{x}}\, dx}{\sqrt{x}}$ **52.** $\displaystyle\int \dfrac{\sin 2x\, dx}{1 + \sin^2 x}$

53. $\displaystyle\int \dfrac{e^{2x}\, dx}{e^x + 1}$ **54.** $\displaystyle\int \dfrac{(x^2 + x + 1)\, dx}{x^2 + 1}$

55. $\displaystyle\int \dfrac{\cos x - \sin x}{\cos x + \sin x}\, dx$ **56.** $\displaystyle\int \dfrac{\sec^2 x\, dx}{1 + \tan x}$

57. $\displaystyle\int \dfrac{1 + \sqrt{1 - x^2}}{\sqrt{1 - x^2}}\, dx$ **58.** $\displaystyle\int \dfrac{(2 + x)\, dx}{1 + x^2}$

59. $\displaystyle\int \dfrac{\cos x\, dx}{1 - \sin^2 x}$ **60.** $\displaystyle\int \dfrac{x\, dx}{x^4 + 1}$

61. $\displaystyle\int \dfrac{x^2\, dx}{\sqrt{1 + x^6}}$ **62.** $\displaystyle\int \dfrac{x^4\, dx}{1 - x^{10}},\ |x| < 1$

63. $\displaystyle\int \dfrac{dx}{x + x(\ln x)^2}$ **64.** $\displaystyle\int \dfrac{dx}{x - x(\ln x)^2},\ |x| < e$

Evaluate each of the limits in Problems 65–68.

65. a. $\displaystyle\lim_{x \to 0^+} (1 + x)^{4/x}$ **b.** $\displaystyle\lim_{x \to 1} \left(\dfrac{1}{1 - x}\right)^x$

66. a. $\displaystyle\lim_{x \to 0^+} x^{\tan x}$ **b.** $\displaystyle\lim_{x \to 0} \dfrac{5^x - 1}{x}$

67. a. $\displaystyle\lim_{x \to 0} \dfrac{\ln(x^2 + 1)}{x}$ **b.** $\displaystyle\lim_{x \to +\infty} \left(\dfrac{1}{x}\right)^x$

68. a. $\displaystyle\lim_{x \to +\infty} \left(4 - \tfrac{1}{x}\right)^x$ **b.** $\displaystyle\lim_{x \to +\infty} \dfrac{e^x\cos x - 1}{x}$

In Problems 69–72, find the area of the region under each curve and above the x-axis on the prescribed interval.

69. $y = 2^{-x}$, $[0, 1]$ **70.** $y = \dfrac{\ln x}{x}$, $[1, e^2]$

71. $y = \tan x$, $\left[0, \tfrac{\pi}{4}\right]$ **72.** $y = \dfrac{x}{1 + e^{-x^2}}$, $[0, 1]$

73. Let $f'(x) = (x^2 + bx + b)e^{-x}$ for constant b. Find all critical numbers of f. Determine the relative maxima and minima of f in terms of b.

74. Find the average value of the function $f(x) = \dfrac{\ln x}{x}$ on the interval $[1, e]$.

75. How much should you invest now at an annual interest rate of 6.25% so that your balance 10 years from now will be $2,000 if interest is compounded

   a. quarterly?   **b.** continuously?

76. A lighthouse is 4,000 ft from a straight shore. Watching the beam on the shore from the point P on the shore that is closest to the lighthouse, an observer notes that the light is moving at the rate of 3 ft/s when it is 1000 ft from P. How fast is the light revolving at this instant?

77. A light is 4 mi from a straight shore line. The light revolves at the rate of 2 rev/min. Find the speed of the spot of light along the shore when the light spot is 2 mi past the point on the shore closest to the source of light.

78. First show that $\tan^{-1}x + \tan^{-1}y = \tan^{-1}\left(\dfrac{x + y}{1 - xy}\right)$ for $xy \neq 1$ whenever $-\tfrac{\pi}{2} < \tan^{-1}\left(\dfrac{x + y}{1 - xy}\right) < \tfrac{\pi}{2}$. Then establish the following equations.

   a. $\tan^{-1}\left(\tfrac{1}{2}\right) + \tan^{-1}\left(\tfrac{1}{3}\right) = \tfrac{\pi}{4}$

   b. $2\tan^{-1}\left(\tfrac{1}{3}\right) + \tan^{-1}\left(\tfrac{1}{7}\right) = \tfrac{\pi}{4}$

   c. $4\tan^{-1}\left(\tfrac{1}{5}\right) - \tan^{-1}\left(\tfrac{1}{239}\right) = \tfrac{\pi}{4}$

Note: The identity in part **c** will be used in Chapter 8 to estimate the value of π.

79. Use the identity $\cot^{-1}x = \tfrac{\pi}{2} - \tan^{-1}x$ for all x to find $\dfrac{d}{dx}(\cot^{-1}x)$.

80. Use the identity $\sec^{-1}x = \cos^{-1}\dfrac{1}{x}$ for $|x| > 1$ to verify that

$$\dfrac{d}{dx}\sec^{-1}x = \dfrac{1}{|x|\sqrt{x^2 - 1}} \quad \text{for } |x| > 1$$

81. Spy Problem The spy has finally escaped from the angry members of the Camel Lovers Club of San Dimas (Problem 45, Section 4.4) only to discover that his best friend, Sigmund ("Siggy") Leiter, has been found murdered in a freezer where the air temperature is 10 °F. The spy remembers that t hours after death, a body has temperature

$$T = T_a + (T_d - T_a)(0.97)^t$$

where T_a is the air temperature and T_d is the temperature of the body at the time of death. He is told that Siggy's body temperature was 40 °F when it was discovered at 1 P.M. on Thursday, and he knows that the dark deed was done by either Boldfinger or André Scélérat. If Scélérat was in jail from Monday until noon on Wednesday and Boldfinger was at the annual Villain's Conference from noon Wednesday until Friday, who "iced" Siggy and when? (You may assume Siggy's body temperature at the time of death was a normal 98.6 °F.)

82. A manufacturer of light bulbs estimates that the fraction $F(t)$ of bulbs that remain burning after t weeks is given by

$$F(t) = e^{-kt}$$

where k is a positive constant. Suppose twice as many bulbs are burning after 5 wk as after 9 wk.

   a. Find k and determine the fraction of bulbs still burning after 7 wk.

   b. What fraction of the bulbs burn out before 10 wk?

   c. What fraction of the bulbs can be expected to burn out between the 4th and 5th weeks?

83. First National Bank pays 7% interest compounded monthly and Fells Cargo Bank pays 6.95% interest compounded continuously. Which bank offers the better deal?

84. Let k be a fixed positive number, and suppose $A(t)$ is the area under the curve $y = e^{-kx}$ and above the x-axis on the interval $[0, t]$. Find $\lim_{t \to +\infty} A(t)$.

85. Show that for any positive number N

$$\lim_{x \to +\infty} x(N^{1/x} - 1) = \ln N$$

86. **a.** Use the definition of the definite integral to show that

$$\lim_{n \to +\infty} (e^{1/n} + e^{2/n} + \ldots + e^{n/n})\left(\frac{1}{n}\right) = e - 1$$

   b. Evaluate $\lim_{n \to +\infty} \left(\frac{1}{1+n} + \frac{1}{2+n} + \cdots + \frac{1}{n+n}\right)$.

   c. Evaluate $\lim_{n \to +\infty} \left(\frac{1}{n^2+1} + \frac{2}{n^2+4} + \cdots + \frac{n}{n^2+n^2}\right)$.

87. Show that the one-sided limits

$$\lim_{x \to 0^-} \frac{1}{1 + 2^{1/x}} \quad \text{and} \quad \lim_{x \to 0^+} \frac{1}{1 + 2^{1/x}}$$

both exist but are not equal.

88. THINK TANK PROBLEM   Each of the following equations may be either true or false. In each case, either show that the equation is generally true or find a counterexample.

   a. $\tan^{-1}x = \dfrac{\sin^{-1}x}{\cos^{-1}x}$ **b.** $e^{1/x} = e^{-1/x}$ for $x > 1$

   c. $\tan^{-1}x = \dfrac{1}{\tan x}$ **d.** $\cot^{-1}x = \dfrac{\pi}{2} - \tan^{-1}x$

   e. $\cos(\sin^{-1}x) = \sqrt{1 - x^2}$ **f.** $\sec^{-1}\left(\dfrac{1}{x}\right) = \cos^{-1}x$

▭   **Computational Window**   ▼ ▲

Use a computer or the Newton–Raphson method to estimate a solution correct to the nearest hundredth for the equations in Problems 89–90.

89. $2^x = \dfrac{1}{x}$

90. $\sin^{-1}(x - 1) = \tan^{-1}x$

91. Use a computer and the trapezoidal rule with $n = 8$ to estimate

$$\int_0^1 e^{-x^2}\, dx$$

92. The **prime number theorem** states that the number of primes between a and b (for $0 < a < b$) is approximately equal to

$$\int_a^b \frac{dx}{\ln x}$$

Use a computer and the trapezoidal rule with $n = 20$ to estimate the number of primes between $a = 50{,}000$ and $b = 60{,}000$.

---

93. PUTNAM EXAMINATION PROBLEM   A heavy object is attached to end A of a light rod AB of length a. The rod is hinged at B so that it can turn freely in a vertical plane. If the rod is balanced in the vertical position above the hinge and then slightly disturbed, show that the time required for the rod to pass from the horizontal position to the lowest position is

$$T = \sqrt{\frac{a}{g}} \ln(1 + \sqrt{2})$$

94. PUTNAM EXAMINATION PROBLEM   Which is greater

$$(\sqrt{n})^{\sqrt{n+1}} \quad \text{or} \quad (\sqrt{n+1})^{\sqrt{n}}$$

where $n > 8$? *Hint*: Use the function $f(x) = \dfrac{\ln x}{x}$, and show that $x^y > y^x$ when $e \le x < y$.

95. PUTNAM EXAMINATION PROBLEM   Show that

$$\ln\left(1 + \frac{1}{x}\right) > \frac{1}{1 + x}$$

96. PUTNAM EXAMINATION PROBLEM   The graph of the equation $x^y = y^x$ for $x > 0$, $y > 0$ consists of a straight line and a curve. Find the coordinates of the point where the line and the curve intersect.

GROUP RESEARCH PROJECT

"Quality Control"

The calculus is the greatest aid we have to the appreciation of physical truth in the broadest sense of the word.

W. F. Osgood
Bulletin American Mathematical Society.

This project is to be done in groups of three or four students. Each group will submit a single written report.

I own a plant that manufactures disk drives. My problem is to decide how many hours of labor to put into the drive. The minimum labor time required to get a drive is 5 hours, but a 5-hour drive will fail at some point during the warranty period with a probability of 10%. Any extra labor time will reduce this failure probability at an exponential rate: Specifically, each additional hour of labor cuts the failure probability by 40%. A failed disk drive is returned to us for repair, requiring an average of 2 additional hours of labor; in addition it incurs an estimated cost of $200 for handling and damage to the reputation of the product. Suppose that the labor cost is $7 per hour.

Your paper is not limited to the following questions but should include these concerns: How many hours of labor should be put into each machine to minimize my cost per machine? Suppose that hourly labor cost is *w* dollars instead of $7 per hour; answer the same question. The labor cost *w* is a parameter, and the optimum labor time depends on *w*. Exactly what is the nature of this dependence? For what *w* should we go with the basic 5-hour product, and for what *w* should this be increased, and by how much?

It is certainly true that all physical phenomena are subject to strictly mathematical conditions, and mathematical processes are unassailable in themselves. The trouble arises from the data employed. Most phenomena are so highly complex that one can never be quite sure that he is dealing with all the factors until the experiment proves it. So that experiment is rather the criterion of mathematical conclusions and must lead the way.

A. E. Dolbear
Matter, Ether, Motion (Boston, 1894), p. 89.

*This problem is from a set of course notes for an introductory calculus course taught by Peter D. Taylor of Queen's University, Kingston, Ontario.

Additional Applications of the Integral

CONTENTS

PREVIEW

In Chapter 4, we found that area and average value can be expressed in terms of the definite integral. The goal of this chapter is to consider various other applications of integration such as computing volume, arc length, surface area, work, hydrostatic force, and centroids of planar regions. We shall also see how separable differential equations can be used to study growth and decay phenomena such as population models and carbon dating. Finally, we shall introduce first-order linear differential equations and show how such equations can be used to study dilution problems and current in an electrical circuit.

PERSPECTIVE

What is the volume of the material that remains when a hole of radius of $0.5R$ is drilled into a sphere of radius R? The "center" of a rectangle is the point where its diagonals intersect, but what is the center of a quarter circle? If a reservoir is filled to the top of a dam shaped like a parabola, what is the total force of the water on the face of the dam? If a worker is carrying a bag of sand up a ladder and the bag is leaking sand through a hole in such a way that all the sand is gone when the worker reaches the top, how much work is done by the worker? If a closed electrical circuit has a resistor of 8 ohms, an inductor with 2 henries inductance, and an EMF of 5 V, what is the current in the circuit at time t? These questions are typical of the kind we shall answer in this chapter.

6.1 VOLUME: DISKS, WASHERS, AND SHELLS

IN THIS SECTION Method of cross sections, volumes of revolution: disks and washers, method of cylindrical shells, summary
We have seen how to compute area by integration, and our first goal in this chapter is to examine several methods for computing volume.

■ METHOD OF CROSS SECTIONS

A number describing the three-dimensional extent of a set is called *volume* and is measured in cubic units. We say that a cube with side 1 has *unit* volume. Table 6.1 reviews some of the common solids whose volume formulas you may remember from precalculus.

TABLE 6.1 Volume Formulas

Name of Solid	Characteristics	Volume Formula	Picture
Cube	Side s	$V = s^3$	
Sphere	Radius r	$V = \frac{4}{3}\pi r^3$	
Right circular cone	Height h Circular base of radius r	$V = \frac{1}{3}\pi r^2 h$	
Regular tetrahedron	A pyramid formed by 4 equilateral triangles, each of side a	$V = \frac{1}{12}\sqrt{2}a^3$	
Cylinder	Height h Area of base B	$V = Bh$	
Circular cylinder	Height h Circular base of radius r	$V = \pi r^2 h$	

b. Top of a single coin (a cross-section) has area B. The volume of the stack of coins is Bh.

a. Stack of coins with height h

Figure 6.1 The volume of a cylinder

A right cylinder can be regarded as a number of congruent disks stacked in a vertical pile, as shown in Figure 6.1a, and its volume can be computed by taking the product of the common cross-sectional area B and the height h of the stack. For example, a right circular cylinder of height h and radius r has circular cross sections of area $B = \pi r^2$, and its volume is $V = Bh = \pi r^2 h$.

A similar approach can be used to find the volume of other solids whose cross sections are known. However, when the cross-sectional areas are not constant, it may be necessary to use calculus.

Let S be a solid and suppose that for $a \le x \le b$, the cross section of S that is perpendicular to the x-axis at x has area $A(x)$. Think of cutting the solid with a

b. Vertical cross-section

Figure 6.2 Volumes of solids with known cross sections

knife and removing a very thin slab whose face has area $A(x)$ and whose thickness is Δx, as shown in Figure 6.2.

To find the volume of S, we first take a partition

$$P = \{x_0, x_1, \ldots, x_n\} \text{ of the interval } [a, b]$$

and choose a representative number x_k^* in each subinterval $[x_{k-1}, x_k]$.

Next, we consider a cylindrical slab with width

$$\Delta x_k = x_k - x_{k-1}$$

and constant cross-sectional area $A(x_k^*)$. This slab has volume

$$\Delta V_k = A(x_k^*) \Delta x_k$$

and by adding up the volumes of all such slabs, we obtain an approximation to the volume of the solid S:

$$\Delta V = \sum_{k=1}^{n} A(x_k^*) \Delta x_k$$

The approximation improves as the number of partition points increases, and it is reasonable to *define* the volume V of the solid S as the limit of ΔV as the norm of the partition $\|P\|$ tends to 0. That is,

$$V = \lim_{\|P\| \to 0} \sum_{k=1}^{n} A(x_k^*) \Delta x_k$$

which we recognize as the definite integral $\int_a^b A(x)\, dx$. To summarize:

Volume of a Solid with Known Cross-Sectional Area

A solid S with cross-sectional area $A(x)$ at each point perpendicular to the x-axis on the interval $[a, b]$ has **volume**

$$V = \int_a^b A(x)\, dx$$

EXAMPLE 1 Volume of a solid using square cross sections

The base of a solid is the region in the xy-plane bounded by the y-axis and the lines $y = 1 - x$, $y = 2x + 5$, and $x = 3$. Each cross section perpendicular to the x-axis is a square. Find the volume of the solid.

Solution The solid resembles a tapered brick, and it may be constructed by "gluing" together a number of thin slabs with square cross sections, like the one shown in Figure 6.3. We begin by drawing the base in two dimensions and then find the volume of the kth slice.

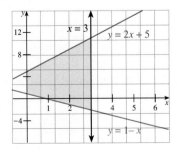

a. Two-dimensional graph of the given base

b. Three-dimensional solid

c. Cross-sectional representative element: $\Delta V = L^2 \Delta x$

Figure 6.3 A solid with a square cross section

To model this construction mathematically, we subdivide the interval [0, 3], form a vertical approximating rectangle on each resulting subinterval, and then construct a slab with square cross section on each approximating rectangle. If we choose the width of a typical slab to be Δx and the height to be

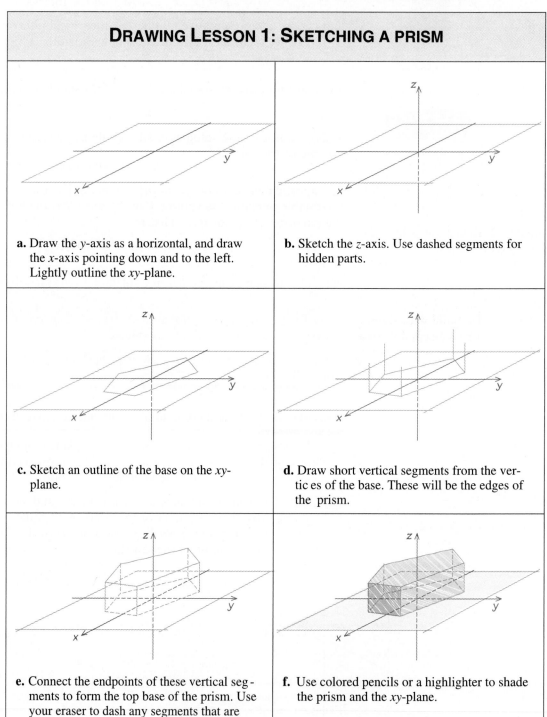

DRAWING LESSON 1: SKETCHING A PRISM

a. Draw the y-axis as a horizontal, and draw the x-axis pointing down and to the left. Lightly outline the xy-plane.

b. Sketch the z-axis. Use dashed segments for hidden parts.

c. Sketch an outline of the base on the xy-plane.

d. Draw short vertical segments from the vertices of the base. These will be the edges of the prism.

e. Connect the endpoints of these vertical segments to form the top base of the prism. Use your eraser to dash any segments that are now hidden.

f. Use colored pencils or a highlighter to shade the prism and the xy-plane.

L, the slab will have volume ΔV, where

$$\Delta V = L^2 \Delta x$$
$$= L^2(x)\Delta x$$
$$= [(2x + 5) - (1 - x)]^2 \Delta x$$
$$= (3x + 4)^2 \Delta x$$

The volume of the entire solid is obtained by integrating to "add up" all the volumes ΔV, and we find that the volume of the solid is

$$V = \int_0^3 (3x + 4)^2 \, dx$$
$$= \int_0^3 (9x^2 + 24x + 16) \, dx = (3x^3 + 12x^2 + 16x)\Big|_0^3 = 237$$

EXAMPLE 2   Volume of a regular pyramid with a square base

A regular pyramid has a square base of side L and has its apex located H units above the center of its base. Derive the formula $V = \frac{1}{3}HL^2$.

Solution   The pyramid is shown in Figure 6.4. This pyramid can be constructed by stacking a number of thin square slabs. Suppose that a representative slab has side ℓ and thickness Δh and that it is located h units above the base of the pyramid as shown in Figure 6.4. By creating a proportion from corresponding parts of similar triangles, we see that

$$\frac{\ell}{L} = \frac{H - h}{H} \quad \text{so that} \quad \ell = L\left(1 - \frac{h}{H}\right)$$

Therefore, the volume of the representative slab is

$$\Delta V = \ell^2 \Delta h = L^2\left(1 - \frac{h}{H}\right)^2 \Delta h$$

To compute the volume V of the entire pyramid, we integrate with respect to h from the base of the pyramid ($h = 0$) to the apex ($h = H$). Thus,

$$V = \int_0^H L^2\left(1 - \frac{h}{H}\right)^2 dh = L^2 \int_0^H \left[1 - \frac{2}{H}h + \frac{1}{H^2}h^2\right] dh$$
$$= L^2\left(h - \frac{h^2}{H} + \frac{h^3}{3H^2}\right)\Big|_0^H = L^2\left(H - \frac{H^2}{H} + \frac{H^3}{3H^2}\right) = \frac{1}{3}HL^2$$

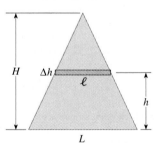

Figure 6.4 The volume of a pyramid

Other volume formulas (including those in Table 6.1) may be found in a similar fashion (see Problems 21–28).

■ VOLUMES OF REVOLUTION: DISKS AND WASHERS

A solid of revolution is a solid figure S obtained by revolving a region R in the xy plane about a line ℓ (called the axis of revolution) that lies outside R. Note that such a solid S may be thought of as having circular cross sections in the direction perpendicular to L.

Suppose the function f is continuous and satisfies $f(x) \geq 0$ on the interval $[a, b]$, and suppose we wish to find the volume of the solid S generated when the region R under the curve $y = f(x)$ on $[a, b]$ is revolved about the x-axis. That is, *the axis of revolution is horizontal and it is a boundary of the region R.* Our strategy

a. A representative vertical strip has height $f(x_k)$ and width Δx_k.

b. The representative disk is formed by revolving the representative strip about the x-axis. This disk has radius $f(x_k)$ and thickness Δx_k.

Figure 6.5 The disk method

shall be to form vertical strips and revolve them about the x-axis, generating what are called disks (that is, thin right circular cylinders) that approximate a portion of the solid of revolution S, as shown in Figure 6.5.

Now we can compute the total volume of S by using integration to sum the volumes of all the approximating disks. Recall that the formula for the volume of a cylinder of height h and cross-sectional area A is Ah. Figure 6.5a shows a typical vertical strip with height $f(x_k^*)$ and width Δx_k. You might notice that the width of the strip is the same as the thickness of the disk. The solid of revolution can be thought of as having cross sections perpendicular to the x-axis that are circular disks of volume

$$\Delta V(x) = \underbrace{\pi[f(x_k^*)]^2}_{\text{Area of circular cross section}} \Delta x_k$$

The total volume may be found by integration:

$$V = \int_a^b \overbrace{A(x)}^{\text{Area of base}} \ \overbrace{dx}^{\text{Thickness}} = \int_a^b \pi[f(x)]^2 \, dx$$

This procedure may be summarized as follows:

The Disk Method

The **disk method** is used to find a volume generated when a region R is revolved about an axis L that is *perpendicular* to a typical approximating strip in R. In particular, if the region R bounded by the curve $y = f(x)$, the x-axis, and the vertical lines $x = a$ and $x = b$ is revolved about the x-axis, it generates a solid with volume

$$V = \int_a^b \pi y^2 \, dx = \int_a^b \pi[f(x)]^2 \, dx$$

■ **What This Says:** The following diagram may help you remember the key ideas behind the disk method.

From precalculus	**Use formula to find**	**Integrate on the interval**
$\boxed{\text{KNOWN FORMULA}}$ →	$\boxed{\text{REPRESENTATIVE ELEMENT}}$ →	$\boxed{\text{INTEGRATION FORMULA}}$
Volume of disk: $V = Bh = \pi r^2 h$	$\Delta V = \pi y^2 \Delta x$	$V = \pi \int_a^b y^2 \, dx$

EXAMPLE 3   Volume of a solid of revolution: disk method

Find the volume of the solid S formed by revolving the region under the curve $y = x^2 + 1$ on the interval $[0, 2]$ about the x-axis.

Solution   The region is shown in Figure 6.6.

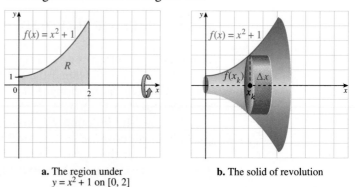

a. The region under $y = x^2 + 1$ on $[0, 2]$

b. The solid of revolution

Figure 6.6 Volume of a solid of revolution: Disk method

$$V = \pi \int_0^2 (x^2 + 1)^2 \, dx = \pi \int_0^2 (x^4 + 2x^2 + 1) \, dx$$

$$= \pi \left(\frac{1}{5}x^5 + \frac{2}{3}x^3 + x \right) \Big|_0^2 = \frac{206}{15}\pi \approx 43.14453911$$

With a small modification of the disk method, we can find the volume of a solid figure generated by revolving about the x-axis the region between two curves $y = f(x)$ and $y = g(x)$ where $f(x) \geq g(x)$ for $a \leq x \leq b$. When a typical vertical strip is revolved about the x-axis, a "washer" is formed that has cross-sectional area $\pi([f(x)]^2 - [g(x)]^2)$, as shown in Figure 6.7.

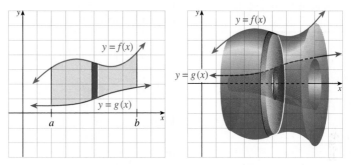

Figure 6.7 The washer method

The volume of the solid of revolution is found by the formula given in the following box.

⊘ Remember $[f^2 - g^2] \neq (f - g)^2$ ⊘

The Washer Method

Suppose f and g are continuous functions with $f(x) \geq g(x)$ on the interval $[a, b]$, and let R be the region bounded above by $y = f(x)$, below by $y = g(x)$, and on the sides by $x = a$ and $x = b$. The **washer method** says that the volume generated by revolving R about the x-axis is

$$V = \int_a^b \pi \left(\underbrace{[f(x)]^2}_{\text{Outer radius}} - \underbrace{[g(x)]^2}_{\text{Inner radius}} \right) dx$$

$$= \pi \int_a^b \left(\underbrace{[R(x)]^2}_{\text{Outer radius}} - \underbrace{[r(x)]^2}_{\text{Inner radius}} \right) dx$$

$$= \pi \int_a^b [R(x)]^2 \, dx - \pi \int_a^b [r(x)]^2 \, dx$$

The disk method and the washer method also apply when the axis of revolution is a line other than the x-axis. In Example 4, we consider what happens when a particular region R is revolved not only about the x-axis, but also about other axes.

EXAMPLE 4   **Volume of a solid of revolution: washer method**

Let R be the solid region bounded by the parabola $y = x^2$ and the line $y = x$. Find the volume of the solid generated when R is revolved about the

a. x-axis   **b.** y-axis   **c.** line $y = 2$

Solution   First, find the points of intersection of the parabola and the line by solving the following system of equations:

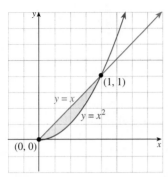

Figure 6.8 The region bounded by $y = x^2$ and $y = x$

$$\begin{cases} y = x^2 \\ y = x \end{cases}$$

This is equivalent to solving $x = x^2$, which has solution $x = 0, 1$. Draw the region R in the xy plane as shown in Figure 6.8.

a. We form the solid by rotating the region R about the x-axis. Note that the line $y = x$ is always above the parabola on the interval $[0, 1]$, so when we form a washer to approximate the volume of revolution, the outer radius is $y = R(x) = x$ and the inner radius is $y = r(x) = x^2$. Thus, the required volume is

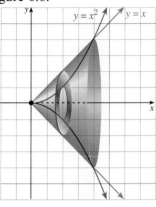

$$V = \pi \int_0^1 [x^2 - (x^2)^2] \, dx =$$
$$\pi \int_0^1 (x^2 - x^4) \, dx = \pi \left(\frac{1}{3}x^3 - \frac{1}{5}x^5\right)\Big|_0^1 = \frac{2\pi}{15}$$

b. Because we are revolving R about the y-axis, we use *horizontal* strips to approximate the solid of revolution, as shown at the right. Note that the parabola $x = \sqrt{y}$ is to the right of the line $x = y$ on the interval $[0, 1]$, so the approximating washer has outer radius $R = \sqrt{y}$ and inner radius $r = y$; thus,

$$A = \pi \int_0^1 [(\sqrt{y})^2 - (y)^2] \, dy$$
$$= \pi \int_0^1 (y - y^2) \, dy = \pi \left[\frac{y^2}{2} - \frac{y^3}{3}\right]_0^1 = \frac{\pi}{6}$$

c. The outer radius is $R = 2 - x^2$ and the inner radius is $r = 2 - x$, as shown at the right. The volume is

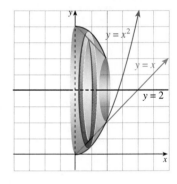

$$A = \pi \int_0^1 [(2 - x^2)^2 - (2 - x)^2] \, dx$$
$$= \pi \int_0^1 (x^4 - 5x^2 + 4x) \, dx$$
$$= \pi \left[\frac{x^5}{5} - \frac{5x^3}{3} + \frac{4x^2}{2}\right]_0^1 = \frac{8\pi}{15}$$

⊘ For the disk method or the washer method, make sure that the approximating strips are perpendicular to the axis of revolution. ⊘ ▬

■ THE METHOD OF CYLINDRICAL SHELLS

Sometimes it is easier (or even necessary) to compute a volume by taking the approximating strip parallel to the axis of rotation instead of perpendicular to the axis as in the disk or washer methods. Figure 6.9a shows a region R under the curve $y = f(x)$ on the interval $[a, b]$, with a representative vertical strip. When this strip is revolved about the y-axis, it forms a solid called a **cylindrical shell**.

When the approximating strip is rotated about the y-axis, it generates a cylindrical shell of height $f(x)$ and thickness Δx, as shown in Figure 6.9b. Because

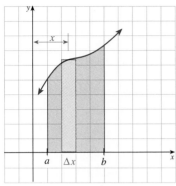

a. A vertical strip in the region R under the curve $y = f(x)$ on the interval $[a, b]$

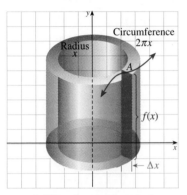

b. When the strip is revolved about the y-axis, a shell is generated.

c. The unwrapped "flattened" shell has volume $\Delta V = 2\pi x f(x)\Delta x$.

Figure 6.9 Method of cylindrical shells

the strip is x units from the axis of rotation and is assumed to be very thin, the cross section of the shell (perpendicular to the y-axis) will be a circle of radius x and circumference $2\pi x$. If we imagine the shell to be cut and flattened out, it is seen to be a rectangular slab of volume

$$\Delta V = \underbrace{2\pi x f(x)}_{\text{Area of the rectangular cross section}} \cdot \overbrace{\Delta x}^{\text{Thickness}}$$

(See Figure 6.9c.) Thus, the total volume of the solid is given by the integral

$$V = \int_a^b 2\pi x f(x)\, dx$$

The approximating shells are shown in Figure 6.10 and the formula is repeated in the following box.

Figure 6.10 Approximating a solid of revolution by cylindrical shells

Method of Cylindrical Shells

The **shell method** is used to find a volume generated when a region R is revolved about an axis L *parallel* to a typical approximating strip in R. In particular, if R is the region bounded by the curve $y = f(x)$, the x-axis, and the vertical lines $x = a$ and $x = b$ where $0 \le a < b$, then the solid generated by revolving R about the y-axis has volume

$$V = \int_a^b 2\pi x f(x)\, dx$$

EXAMPLE 5   Volume of a solid of revolution: shell method

Find the volume of the solid formed by revolving the region bounded by the graphs of $y = x^3 + x^2 + 1$, $x = 1$, and $x = 3$ about the y-axis.

Solution   This example illustrates why we need the shell method. A typical vertical strip (shown in Figure 6.11) has height $f(x) = x^3 + x^2 + 1$ so the volume, by the method of shells, is

$$V(x) = 2\pi \int_1^3 x(x^3 + x^2 + 1)\, dx$$

$$= 2\pi \int_1^3 (x^4 + x^3 + x)\, dx$$

$$= 2\pi\left(\frac{x^5}{5} + \frac{x^4}{4} + \frac{x^2}{2}\right)\Big|_1^3 = 144.8\pi$$

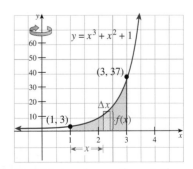

Figure 6.11 A volume of revolution by the shell method

We conclude this section with Table 6.2, which compares and contrasts the disk, washer, and shell methods for finding volume.

TABLE 6.2 Volumes of Revolution for Which the Axis of Revolution Is Either the *x*-axis or the *y*-axis

SUMMARY

a. Disk method: A representative rectangle is **perpendicular** to the axis of revolution. The axis of revolution is a boundary of the region.

Horizontal axis of revolution

Width of rectangle is Δx.

$$V = \pi \int_a^b \underbrace{[f(x)]^2}_{\text{Length (Height) of rectangle}} dx$$

Vertical axis of revolution

Width of rectangle is Δy.

$$V = \pi \int_c^d \underbrace{[g(y)]^2}_{\text{Length of rectangle}} dy$$

b. Washer method: A representative rectangle is **perpendicular** to the axis of revolution. The axis of revolution is *not* part of the boundary.

Horizontal axis of revolution

$$V = \pi \int_a^b \underbrace{\left([R(x)]^2 - [r(x)]^2\right)}_{\text{Length of rectangle}} \overbrace{dx}^{\substack{\text{Top curve} \quad \text{Bottom curve} \\ \text{Width}}}$$

Vertical axis of revolution

$$V = \pi \int_c^d \underbrace{\left([f(y)]^2 - [g(y)]^2\right)}_{\text{Length of rectangle}} \overbrace{dy}^{\substack{\text{Right curve} \quad \text{Left curve} \\ \text{Width}}}$$

c. Shell method: A representative rectangle is **parallel** to the axis of revolution.

Horizontal axis of revolution

$$V = 2\pi \int_c^d \underset{\substack{\uparrow \\ \text{Length} \\ \text{Distance to axis}}}{y} \, \overbrace{[g(y)]}^{\text{Width}} dy$$

Vertical axis of revolution

$$V = 2\pi \int_a^b \underset{\substack{\uparrow \\ \text{Length (Height)} \\ \text{Distance to axis}}}{x} \, \overbrace{[f(x)]}^{\text{Width}} dx$$

PROBLEM SET 6.1

Ⓐ *In Problems 1–6, sketch the given region and then find the volume of the solid whose base is the given region and which has the property that each cross section perpendicular to the x-axis is a **square**.*

1. the triangular region bounded by the coordinates axes and the line $y = 3 - x$

2. the region bounded by the x-axis and the semicircle $y = \sqrt{16 - x^2}$

3. the region bounded by the line $y = x + 1$ and the curve $y = x^2 - 2x + 3$

4. the region bounded above by $y = \sqrt{\sin x}$ and below by the x-axis on the interval $[0, \pi]$

5. the region bounded above by $y = \sqrt{\cos x}$ and below by the x-axis on the interval $\left[-\frac{\pi}{2}, \frac{\pi}{2}\right]$

6. the triangular region with vertices $(1, 1)$, $(3, 5)$, and $(3, -2)$

*In Problems 7–12, sketch the region and then find the volume of the solid whose base is the given region and which has the property that each cross section perpendicular to the x-axis is an **equilateral triangle**.*

7. the region bounded by the circle $x^2 + y^2 = 9$

8. the region bounded by the curves $y = x^3$ and $y = x^2$

9. the region bounded by the y-axis, the parabola $y = x^2$, and the line $2x + y - 3 = 0$

10. the region bounded above by $y = \cos x$, below by $y = \sin x$, and on the left by the y-axis

11. the region bounded above by the curve $y = \tan x$ and below by the x-axis, on the interval $\left[0, \frac{\pi}{4}\right]$

12. the region bounded by the x-axis and the curve $y = e^x$ between $x = 1$ and $x = 3$

Name the most appropriate method (disks, washers, or shells) for finding the solid of revolution in Problems 13–16. Use the representative rectangle that is shown to set up the integral, but DO NOT EVALUATE.

13. $y = 4 - x$, $0 \le x \le 4$
   a. about the x-axis
   b. about the y-axis
   c. about the line $y = -1$

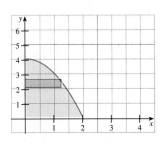

14. $y = 4 - x^2$, $0 \le x \le 2$
   a. about the x-axis
   b. about the y-axis
   c. about the line $y = -1$

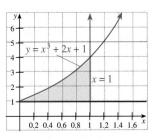

15. $y = \sqrt{4 - x^2}$, $0 \le x \le 2$
   a. about the x-axis
   b. about the y-axis
   c. about the line $x = -1$

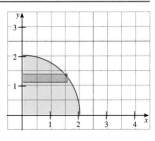

16. $y = \sqrt{4 - x^2}$, $\le x \le 2$
   a. about the x-axis
   b. about the y-axis
   c. about the line $y = -1$

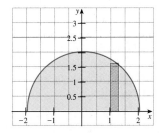

In Problems 17–20, draw a representative strip and find the integral for the volume of the solid formed by revolving the given region

   a. about the x-axis

   b. about the y-axis

Set up the integral only; DO NOT EVALUATE.

17. the region bounded by $x = y^2$ and $y = x^2$

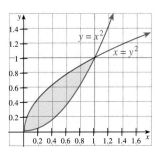

18. the region bounded by $y = x^2 - 4x + 4$, and $x = y^2$

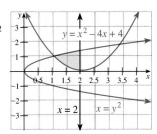

19. the region bounded by the lines $y = 1$, $x = 1$, and the curve $y = x^3 + 2x + 1$

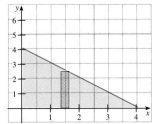

20. the region bounded by the curves $y = x^2$ and $y = -x^2 - 4x$

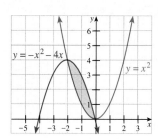

B *In Problems 21–24, find the volume of the solid whose base is bounded by the circle $x^2 + y^2 = 9$ with the indicated cross sections taken perpendicular to the x-axis.*

21. squares   **22.** equilateral triangles

23. isosceles right triangles   **24.** semicircles

In Problems 25–28, find the volume of the solid whose base is bounded by the graphs of $y = x + 1$ and $y = x^2 - 1$ with the indicated cross sections taken perpendicular to the x-axis.

25. squares   **26.** equilateral triangles

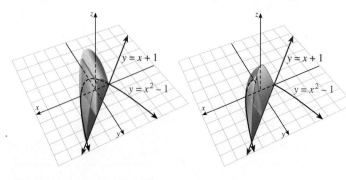

27. rectangles of height 1   **28.** semicircles

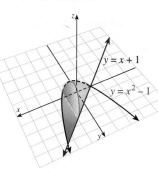

In Problems 29–38, find the volume of the solid formed when the region described is revolved about the x-axis.

29. the region under the curve $y = \sqrt{x}$ on the interval [0, 1]

30. the region under the curve $y = \sqrt[3]{x}$ on the interval [0, 8]

31. the region bounded by the lines $y = x$, $y = 2x$, and $x = 1$

32. the region bounded by the lines $x = 0$, $x = 1$, $y = x + 1$, and $y = x + 2$

33. the region under the curve $y = x^2 + x^3$ on the interval $[0, \pi]$; approximate your answer to the nearest unit

34. the region bounded by the curves $y = 2 - x^2$ and $y = x^2$

35. the region bounded by the curves $y = x^2$ and $y = x^3$

36. the region under the curve $y = \sqrt{2} \sin x$ on the interval $[0, \pi]$

37. the region under the curve $y = \sqrt{\sin x}$ on the interval $[0, \pi]$

38. the region bounded by the curves $y = e^x$ and $y = e^{-x}$ between $x = 0$ and $x = 2$; approximate your answer to the nearest unit

In Problems 39–46, find the volume of the solid formed by revolving the given regions about the y-axis.

39. the region under the line $y = 2x$ on the interval [0, 1]

40. the region under the curve $y = \sqrt{x}$ on the interval [0, 1]

41. the region bounded by the curves $y = x^2$ and $y = x^3$

42. the region bounded by the lines $y = x$, $y = 2x$, and $x = 1$

43. the region bounded by the parabola $y = 1 - x^2$, the y-axis, and the positive x-axis

44. the region bounded by the curve $y = 8 - x^3$, the y-axis, and the positive x-axis

45. the region bounded by the parabolas $y = 1 - x^2$, $y = x^2$, and the y-axis

46. the region under the curve $y = e^{-x^2}$ on the interval [0, 1]

In Problems 47–52, find the volume of the solid generated by revolving each region about the prescribed axis.

47. the region bounded by $y = x^2$ and $y = x^3$, about the line $y = -1$

48. the region bounded by $x = \sqrt{4 - y}$, $x = 0$, and $y = -1$, about the y-axis

49. the region bounded by $y = x^3$, $y = 12 - x^2$, and $x = 1$, about the line $x = -1$

50. the region bounded by $y = \frac{1}{8}(12x - x^3)$, $y = 2$, and $x = 0$, about the y-axis

51. the triangular region with vertices $(1, 1)$, $(2, 5)$, and $(4, 1)$, about the x-axis

52. the triangular region with vertices $(1, 1)$, $(3, 4)$, and $(5, 1)$, about the y-axis

In Problems 53–55, find the volume V of the solid using the given information about its cross section.

53. The base of the solid is a circle with radius 1, and the cross sections perpendicular to a fixed diameter of the base are squares.

54. The base of the solid is an equilateral triangle each side of which has length 4. The cross sections perpendicular to a given altitude of the triangle are squares.

55. The base of the solid is an isosceles right triangle whose legs a and b are each 4 units long. Each cross section perpendicular to a is a semicircle.

56. Find the volume of the solid generated when the region $y = \dfrac{1}{\sqrt{x}}$ on the interval $[1, 4]$ is revolved about

   a. the x-axis   **b.** the y-axis   **c.** the line $y = -2$

57. The great pyramid of Cheops is approximately 480 ft tall and 750 ft square at the base. Find the volume of this pyramid by using the cross-section method.

58. When viewed from above, a swimming pool has the shape of the ellipse

$$\frac{x^2}{900} + \frac{y^2}{400} = 1$$

The cross sections of the pool perpendicular to the ground and parallel to the y-axis are squares. If the units are in feet, what is the volume of the pool?

Computational Window

59. Repeat Example 1 using a spreadsheet to find the volume.

60. Repeat Example 3 using a spreadsheet to find the volume.

61. Cross-sectional areas are measured at one-foot intervals along the length of an irregularly shaped object, with the results listed in the following table (both x and A are measured in feet):

x	0	1	2	3	4	5
A	1.12	1.09	1.05	1.03	0.99	1.01

x	6	7	8	9	10
A	0.98	0.99	0.96	0.93	0.91

Estimate the volume (correct to the nearest hundredth) by using the trapezoidal rule.

62. Cross-sectional areas are measured at 1-ft intervals along the length of an irregularly shaped object, with the results listed in the following table (both x and A are measured in feet):

x	0	1	2	3	4	5
A	1.12	1.09	1.05	1.03	0.99	1.01

x	6	7	8	9	10
A	0.98	0.99	0.96	0.93	0.91

Estimate the volume (correct to the nearest hundredth) by using Simpson's rule.

© 63. A hemisphere of radius r may be regarded as a solid whose base is the region bounded by the circle $x^2 + y^2 = r^2$ and with the property that each cross-section perpendicular to the x-axis is a semicircle with a diameter in the base. Use this characterization and the method of cross-sections to show that a sphere of radius r has volume $V = \frac{4}{3}\pi r^3$. *Note:* This is a formula given in Table 6.1.

64. Use the method of cross-sections to show that the volume of a regular tetrahedron of side a is $\frac{1}{12}\sqrt{2}a^3$. *Note:* This is a formula given in Table 6.1.

65. Find the volume of the football-shaped solid (called an *ellipsoid*) formed by revolving the ellipse

$$\frac{x^2}{a^2} + \frac{y^2}{b^2} = 1$$

about the x-axis. What is the volume if the ellipse is revolved about the y-axis?

66. Find the volume of the doughnut-shaped solid (called a *torus*) formed by rotating the circle

$$(x - a)^2 + y^2 = b^2$$

about the *y*-axis. You may assume that $a > b$.

67. A "cap" is formed by truncating a sphere of radius R at a point h units from the center, as shown in Figure 6.12. Find the volume of the cap.

Figure 6.12 Volume of the cap of a sphere

68. The *frustum of a cone* is the solid region bounded by a cone and two parallel planes, as shown in Figure 6.13. If the planes are h units apart and intersect the cone in plane regions of area A_1 and A_2, use integration to show that the frustum has volume

$$V = \frac{h}{3}(A_1 + \sqrt{A_1 A_2} + A_2)$$

Figure 6.13 Volume of the frustum of a cone

69. A spherical sector (or a "gem") is formed from a section of a sphere as indicated in Figure 6.14. Assume that the spherical base has radius R and that the parallel truncating planes are h_1 and h_2 units from the center of the sphere, where

$$0 < h_1 < h_2 < R$$

Find the volume of the gem.

Figure 6.14 Volume of a section of a sphere

6.2 ARC LENGTH AND SURFACE AREA

Physical method for measuring the length of a curve

> **IN THIS SECTION** The arc length of a graph, the area of a surface of revolution
>
> If you were asked to measure the length of a given curve by hand, you might proceed by first fitting a piece of string to the curve and then measuring its length with a ruler. In this section, we see how such measurements can be carried out mathematically using integration. We also develop a general procedure for computing the surface area of certain solid figures.

■ THE ARC LENGTH OF A GRAPH

If a function f has a derivative that is continuous on some interval, then f is said to be **continuously differentiable** on the interval. The portion of the graph of a continuously differentiable function f that lies between $x = a$ and $x = b$ is called the **arc** of the graph on the interval $[a, b]$. To find the length of this arc, let P be a partition of the interval $[a, b]$, with subdivision points $x_0, x_1, \ldots, x_n$, where $x_0 = a$ and $x_n = b$. Let P_k denote the point (x_k, y_k) on the graph, where $y_k = f(x_k)$. By joining the points $P_0, P_1, \ldots, P_n$, we obtain a polygonal path whose length approximates that of the arc. Figure 6.15 demonstrates the labeling for the case where $n = 6$.

The length of the polygonal path connecting the points $P_0, P_1, \ldots, P_n$ on the graph of f is the sum

$$\sum_{k=1}^{n} s_k$$

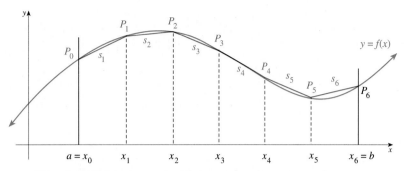

Figure 6.15 A polygonal path approximating an arc of a curve

where s_k is the length of the segment joining P_{k-1} to P_k. By applying the distance formula and rearranging terms with $\Delta x_k = x_k - x_{k-1}$ and $\Delta y_k = y_k - y_{k-1}$, we find that

$$s_k = \sqrt{(x_k - x_{k-1})^2 + (y_k - y_{k-1})^2}$$

$$= \sqrt{(\Delta x_k)^2 + (\Delta y_k)^2}$$

$$= \sqrt{\frac{(\Delta x_k)^2 + (\Delta y_k)^2}{(\Delta x_k)^2}} \, \Delta x_k$$

$$= \sqrt{1 + \left(\frac{\Delta y_k}{\Delta x_k}\right)^2} \, \Delta x_k$$

It is reasonable to expect a connection between the ratio $\Delta y_k / \Delta x_k$ and the derivative $dy/dx = f'(x)$. Indeed, it can be shown that

$$s_k = \sqrt{1 + [f'(x_k^*)]^2} \, \Delta x_k$$

for some number x_k^* between x_{k-1} and x_k. Therefore, the arc length of the graph of f on the interval $[a, b]$ may be estimated by the Riemann sum

$$\sum_{k=1}^{n} \sqrt{1 + [f'(x_k^*)]^2} \, \Delta x_k$$

This estimate may be improved by increasing the number of subdivision points in the partition P of the interval $[a, b]$ in such a way that the subinterval lengths tend to zero. Thus, it is reasonable to define the actual arc length to be the limit

$$\lim_{\|P\| \to 0} \sum_{k=1}^{n} \sqrt{1 + [f'(x_k^*)]^2} \, \Delta x_k$$

Notice that if f' is continuous on the interval $[a, b]$, then so is $\sqrt{1 + [f'(x)]^2}$. Thus, this limit exists and is the integral of $\sqrt{1 + [f'(x)]^2}$ with respect to x on the interval $[a, b]$. These observations lead us to the following definition.*

*We have used integration to obtain a meaningful definition of arc length for a function $f(x)$ with a continuous derivative $f'(x)$. It is possible to define arc length for certain curves $y = f(x)$, where $f(x)$ does not have a continuous derivative, but we will not pursue this more general topic. It may surprise you to know there are curves in the plane whose length *cannot* be defined. Curves that have length are said to be *rectifiable*, and those that do not are *nonrectifiable*. You might wish to look up references to fractals or the snowflake curve.

Arc Length

Let f be a function whose derivative f' is continuous on the interval $[a, b]$. Then the **arc length,** s, of the graph of $y = f(x)$ between $x = a$ to $x = b$ is given by the integral

$$s = \int_a^b \sqrt{1 + [f'(x)]^2}\, dx$$

Similarly, for the graph of $x = g(y)$, where g' is continuous on the interval $[c, d]$, the arc length from $y = c$ to $y = d$ is

$$s = \int_c^d \sqrt{1 + [g'(y)]^2}\, dy$$

EXAMPLE 1   Arc length of a curve

Find the arc length of the curve $y = x^{3/2}$ on the interval $[0, 4]$.

Solution   Let $f(x) = x^{3/2}$; therefore, $f'(x) = \frac{3}{2}x^{1/2}$.

$$s = \int_0^4 \sqrt{1 + \left[\tfrac{3}{2}x^{1/2}\right]^2}\, dx$$

$$= \int_0^4 \sqrt{1 + \tfrac{9}{4}x}\, dx = \left[\tfrac{4}{9} \cdot \tfrac{2}{3}\left(1 + \tfrac{9}{4}x\right)^{3/2}\right]_0^4$$

$$= \tfrac{8}{27}[(10)^{3/2} - (1)^{3/2}] \approx 9.073415289$$

Computational Window

Once again, we remind you of alternative forms common on computer software. For Example 1, an alternative form is

$$\frac{80\sqrt{10}}{27} - \frac{8}{27} \approx 9.073415289$$

EXAMPLE 2   Arc length of function of y

Find the arc length of the curve $x = \frac{1}{3}y^3 + \frac{1}{4}y^{-1}$ from $y = 1$ to $y = 3$.

Solution   Because $g(y) = \frac{1}{3}y^3 + \frac{1}{4}y^{-1}$, we have $g'(y) = y^2 - \frac{1}{4}y^{-2} = \dfrac{4y^4 - 1}{4y^2}$, which is continuous throughout the interval from $y = 1$ to $y = 3$. Therefore, the arc length is

$$\int_1^3 \sqrt{1 + [g'(y)]^2}\, dy = \int_1^3 \sqrt{1 + \left(\frac{4y^4 - 1}{4y^2}\right)^2}\, dy$$

$$= \int_1^3 \sqrt{1 + \frac{16y^8 - 8y^4 + 1}{16y^4}}\, dy$$

$$= \int_1^3 \sqrt{\frac{16y^4 + 16y^8 - 8y^4 + 1}{16y^4}}\, dy$$

$$= \int_1^3 \sqrt{\frac{(4y^4 + 1)^2}{(4y^2)^2}}\, dy = \int_1^3 \frac{4y^4 + 1}{4y^2}\, dy = \int_1^3 \left(y^2 + \tfrac{1}{4}y^{-2}\right) dy$$

$$= \left(\tfrac{1}{3}y^3 + \tfrac{1}{4} \cdot \frac{y^{-1}}{-1}\right)\bigg|_1^3 = \frac{53}{6} \approx 8.833333333$$

Computational Window

Xmin=0   Ymin=0
Xmax=10   Ymax=5
Xscl=1   Yscl=1

A graphing calculator will not give you the arc length, but you can graph the curve and imagine it to be a "piece of string." If you then measure the string, is the calculus answer reasonable?

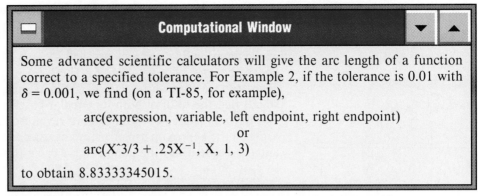

Some advanced scientific calculators will give the arc length of a function correct to a specified tolerance. For Example 2, if the tolerance is 0.01 with $\delta = 0.001$, we find (on a TI-85, for example),

arc(expression, variable, left endpoint, right endpoint)

or

arc(X^3/3 + .25X^{-1}, X, 1, 3)

to obtain 8.83333345015.

EXAMPLE 3   Estimating arc length using numerical integration

Find the length of the curve defined by $y = \sin x$ on $[0, 2\pi]$.

Solution   Because $y' = \cos x$, we have, from the arc length formula,

$$s = \int_0^{2\pi} \sqrt{1 + \cos^2 x} \; dx$$

We do not have techniques to allow us to evaluate this integral, so we turn to numerical integration. The region is shown in Figure 6.16. If we consider four rectangles we find, by various methods:

Method ($n = 4$)	Approximation
Rectangles	
Left endpoints	7.584476
Right endpoints	7.584476
Midpoints	7.695299
Trapezoids	7.584476
Simpson's rule	7.150712

Figure 6.16 Right-endpoint approximation for $n = 4$

In practice, you would choose just *one* of the methods whose approximate values are given. You might also note that, for this example, Simpson's rule performs worse than the trapezoidal, midpoint, or even the left- and right-endpoint methods. For more accurate results, you might wish to use a computer program. A simple output is shown in the computer window at left.

■ THE AREA OF A SURFACE OF REVOLUTION

When the arc of a graph is revolved about a line L, it generates a surface that we shall refer to as a **surface of revolution.** Figure 6.17 shows an arc, together with a typical approximating line segment. Notice that when the segment is revolved about L, it generates the surface of the frustum of a right circular cone.

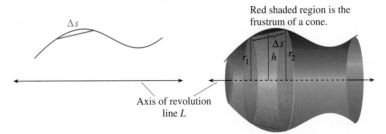

Figure 6.17 A surface of revolution

Rather than argue formally with Riemann sums, we will simply proceed intuitively. It can be shown that a frustum with slant height ℓ and base radii r_1 and r_2 has lateral surface area $\pi(r_1 + r_2)\ell$ (see Problem 32). Figure 6.17 shows an approximating line segment we shall assume has length Δs and is located h units above the axis of revolution L. Then, by revolving this segment about L, we generate a frustum whose slant height is Δs and which is so thin (because Δs is very small) that the radii of both its circular bases are essentially the same as h.

To find the area of the surface of revolution let the radii of the bases be r_1 and r_2. Then the approximating frustum has surface area $\pi(r_1 + r_2)\Delta s$. Because both r_1 and r_2 are essentially the same as h, we can estimate the surface area of the frustum by

$$\Delta S = \pi(h + h)\overbrace{\Delta s}^{\text{Lateral length}} = 2\pi h\Delta s = 2\pi f(x)\sqrt{1 + [f'(x)]^2}\,\Delta x$$

$$\underbrace{}_{\text{Distance to axis of revolution is } h = f(x).}$$

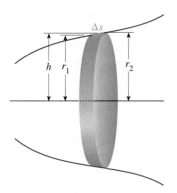

An increment of surface area ΔS

The surface area S can be obtained by integrating this expression on the interval $[a, b]$. These considerations lead us to the following definition.

Surface Area

> Suppose f' is continuous on the interval $[a, b]$. Then the surface generated by revolving about the x-axis the arc of the curve $y = f(x)$ on $[a, b]$ has **surface area**
>
> $$S = 2\pi \int_a^b f(x)\sqrt{1 + [f'(x)]^2}\,dx$$

You may find it instructive to derive this formula by the more rigorous approach used to establish the arc length formula (see Problem 34). We close with two examples that illustrate the use of the surface area formula.

EXAMPLE 4 **Area of a surface of revolution**

Find the area of the surface generated by revolving about the x-axis the arc of the curve $y = x^3$ on $[0, 1]$.

Solution Because $f(x) = x^3$, we have $f'(x) = 3x^2$, which is certainly continuous on the interval $[0, 1]$.

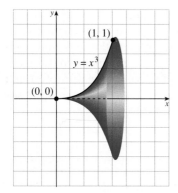

$$S = 2\pi \int_0^1 x^3\sqrt{1 + (3x^2)^2}\,dx = 2\pi \int_0^1 x^3\sqrt{1 + 9x^4}\,dx = 2\pi \int_1^{10} u^{1/2}\left(\frac{du}{36}\right)$$

Let $u = 1 + 9x^4$; $du = 36\,x^3dx$.
If $x = 1$, then $u = 10$.
If $x = 0$, then $u = 1$.

$$= \frac{\pi}{18}\left(\tfrac{2}{3}u^{3/2}\right)\Big|_1^{10} = \frac{\pi}{27}[10\sqrt{10} - 1] \approx 3.56$$

EXAMPLE 5 **Derive the formula for the surface area of a sphere**

Find a formula for the surface area of a sphere of radius r.

Solution We can generate the surface of the sphere by revolving the semicircle $y = \sqrt{r^2 - x^2}$ about the x-axis. We find that

$$y' = -x(r^2 - x^2)^{-1/2} = \frac{-x}{\sqrt{r^2 - x^2}}$$

Because the semicircle intersects the x-axis at $x = r$ and $x = -r$, the interval of integration will be $[-r, r]$. Finally, by applying the formula for the surface area, we find

$$S = 2\pi \int_{-r}^{r} \sqrt{r^2 - x^2} \sqrt{1 + \left(\frac{-x}{\sqrt{r^2 - x^2}}\right)^2} \, dx$$

$$= 2\pi \int_{-r}^{r} \sqrt{(r^2 - x^2)\left(\frac{r^2 - x^2 + x^2}{r^2 - x^2}\right)} \, dx$$

$$= 2\pi \int_{-r}^{r} r \, dx = 2\pi r(2r) = 4\pi r^2$$

To generalize the formula for surface area to apply to any vertical or horizontal axis of revolution, suppose that an axis of revolution is $R(x)$ units from a typical element of arc on the graph of $y = f(x)$, as shown in Figure 6.18.

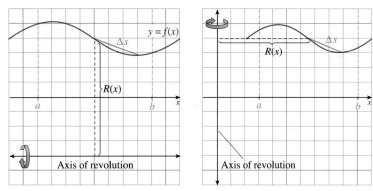

Figure 6.18 Surface of revolution about a general vertical or horizontal axis

Then $2\pi R(x)$ is the circumference of a circle of radius $R(x)$, and it can be shown that an element of surface area is

$$\Delta S = 2\pi R(x)\,\Delta s = 2\pi R(x)\sqrt{1 + [f'(x)]^2}\,\Delta x$$

Thus, the surface of revolution on the interval $[a, b]$ has area

$$S = 2\pi \int_a^b R(x)\sqrt{1 + [f'(x)]^2} \, dx$$

In particular, if the graph of $y = f(x)$ is revolved about the y-axis, an element of the arc is $R(x) = x$ units from the y-axis, and the resulting surface has area

$$S = 2\pi \int_a^b x\sqrt{1 + [f'(x)]^2} \, dx$$

PROBLEM SET 6.2

Ⓐ *Find the length of the arc of the curve $y = f(x)$ on the intervals given in Problems 1–12.*

1. $f(x) = 3x + 2$ on $[-1, 2]$

2. $f(x) = 5 - 4x$ on $[-2, 0]$

3. $f(x) = 1 - 2x$ on $[1, 3]$

4. $f(x) = x^{3/2}$ on $[0, 4]$

5. $f(x) = \frac{2}{3}x^{3/2} + 1$ on $[0, 4]$

6. $f(x) = \frac{1}{3}(2 + x^2)^{3/2}$ on $[0, 3]$

7. $f(x) = \frac{1}{12}x^5 + \frac{1}{5}x^{-3}$ on $[1, 2]$

8. $f(x) = \frac{1}{3}x^3 + \frac{1}{4}x^{-1}$ on $[1, 4]$

9. $f(x) = \frac{1}{4}x^4 + \frac{1}{8}x^{-2}$ on $[1, 2]$

10. $f(x) = x^2$ on $[0, 2]$ correct to the nearest hundredth

11. $f(x) = \frac{1}{2}x^2$ on $[0, 4]$ correct to the nearest hundredth

12. $f(x) = \sqrt{e^{2x} - 1} - \sec^{-1}(e^x)$ on $[0, \ln 2]$

13. Find the length of the curve defined by $9x^2 = 4y^3$ between the points $(0, 0)$ and $(2\sqrt{3}, 3)$.

14. Find the length of the curve defined by $(y + 1)^2 = 4x^3$ between the points $(0, -1)$ and $(1, 1)$.

15. Find the area of the surface generated when the arc of the curve

$$y = \frac{1}{3}x^3 + (4x)^{-1}$$

between $x = 1$ and $x = 3$ is revolved about

  a. the x-axis   **b.** the y-axis

16. Find the area of the surface generated when the arc of the curve

$$x = \frac{3}{5}y^{5/3} - \frac{3}{4}y^{1/3}$$

between $y = 0$ and $y = 1$ is revolved about

  a. the y-axis   **b.** the x-axis   **c.** the line $y = -1$

B *Find the surface area generated when the graph of each function given in Problems 17–20 on the prescribed interval is revolved about the x-axis.*

17. $f(x) = 2x + 1$ on $[0, 2]$

18. $f(x) = \sqrt{x}$ on $[2, 6]$

19. $f(x) = \frac{1}{3}x^3 + \frac{1}{4}x^{-1}$ on $[1, 2]$

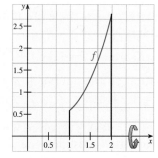

Give your answer correct to the nearest hundredth.

20. $f(x) = \frac{1}{4}x^4 + \frac{1}{8}x^{-2}$ on $[1, 2]$

Give your answer correct to the nearest hundredth.

Find the surface area generated when the graph of each function given in Problems 21–24 on the prescribed interval is revolved about the y-axis.

21. $f(x) = \frac{1}{3}(12 - x)$ on $[0, 3]$

22. $f(x) = \frac{2}{3}x^{3/2}$ on $[0, 3]$

23. $f(x) = \frac{1}{3}\sqrt{x}(3 - x)$ on $[1, 3]$

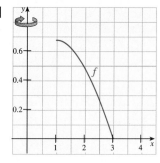

24. $f(x) = 2\sqrt{4 - x}$ on $[1, 4]$

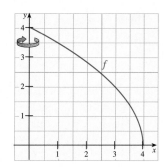

25. The graph of the equation

$$x^{2/3} + y^{2/3} = 1$$

is an **astroid**.

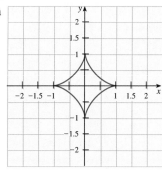

Find the length of this particular astroid by finding the length of the first quadrant portion, $y = (1 - x^{2/3})^{3/2}$ on $[0, 1]$. By symmetry, the entire curve is four times the length of the arc in the first quadrant.

26. Find the area of the surface generated by revolving the portion of the astroid with $y \geq 0$ (see Problem 25)

$$x^{2/3} + y^{2/3} = 1 \text{ on } [-1, 1]$$

about the x-axis.

27. Find the length of the curve

$$x^{2/3} + y^{2/3} = 9$$

between $x = 1$ and $x = 27$.

28. Find the area of the surface generated when the arc of the curve

$$x^{2/3} + y^{2/3} = 9$$

between $x = 1$ and $x = 27$ is revolved about the x-axis.

29. Use Simpson's rule with $n = 20$ to estimate the area of the surface obtained by revolving $y = \tan x$ about the x-axis on the interval $[0, 1]$.

Ⓒ 30. Show that when the arc of the graph of $f(x)$ between $x = a$ and $x = b$ is revolved about the y-axis, the surface generated has area

$$S = 2\pi \int_a^b x\sqrt{1 + [f'(x)]^2}\, dx$$

31. Show that a cone of radius r and height h has surface area

$$S = \pi r\sqrt{r^2 + h^2}$$

Hint: Revolve part of the line $hy = rx$ about the x-axis.

32. Figure 6.19 shows the frustum of a cone with base radii r_1 and r_2 and slant height ℓ.

Figure 6.19 Frustum of a cone

Suppose that a regular polygon of n sides is inscribed in each circular base. Each side of the polygon in the upper base has length s_1 and each side of the polygon in the lower base has length s_2. Notice that a trapezoid is formed when the ends of corresponding sides in these polygons are joined by line segments.

a. The surface area of the frustum can be estimated by adding the areas of the approximating trapezoids. Show that this estimate is

$$\tfrac{1}{2}n(s_1 + s_2)h_n$$

where h_n is the distance between corresponding sides in the polygons inscribed in the circular bases.

b. Show that the polygon inscribed in the larger base has perimeter

$$\lim_{n \to +\infty} ns_1 = 2\pi r$$

Use similar reasoning to establish the following limit statements:

$$\lim_{n \to +\infty} ns_2 = 2\pi r_2 \quad \text{and} \quad \lim_{n \to +\infty} h_n = \ell$$

c. Compare the results of parts **a** and **b** to show that the frustum has surface area

$$A = \pi(r_1 + r_2)\ell$$

33. If $f'(x)$ exists throughout the interval $[x_{k-1}, x_k]$, show that there exists a number x_k^* in this interval for which

$$\sqrt{(\Delta x_k)^2 + (\Delta y_k)^2} = \sqrt{1 + [f'(x_k^*)]^2}\, \Delta x_k$$

where $\Delta x_k = x_k - x_{k-1}$ and $\Delta y_k = f(x_k) - f(x_{k-1})$. *Hint*: Use the mean value theorem.

34. Verify the surface area formula by completing the following steps (see Figure 6.20).

a. Let $P = \{x_0, x_1, \ldots, x_n\}$ be a partition of the interval $[a, b]$, and for $k = 0, 1, \ldots, n$, let P_k denote the point (x_k, y_k) where $y_k = f(x_k)$. Show that when the line segment between P_{k-1} and P_k is revolved about the x-axis, it generates a frustum of a cone with surface area

$$\pi(y_{k-1} + y_k)\ell_k$$

where ℓ_k is the distance between P_{k-1} and P_k.

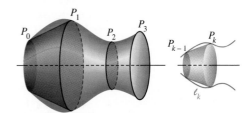

Figure 6.20 Surface area formula

b. Notice that $\tfrac{1}{2}(y_{k-1} + y_k)$ is a number between y_{k-1} and y_k. Use the intermediate value theorem (Section 1.7) to show that

$$y_{k-1} + y_k = 2f(c_k)$$

for some number c_k between x_{k-1} and x_k.

c. Explain why the surface generated when the arc of the graph of f between $x = a$ and $x = b$ is revolved about the x-axis has area

$$\lim_{\|P\| \to 0} \sum_{k=1}^n 2\pi f(c_k)\sqrt{1 + [f'(x_k^*)]^2}\, \Delta x_k$$

d. Notice that as $\|P\| \to 0$, the numbers c_k and x_k^* are "squeezed" together. Use this observation to show that the surface area is given by the integral

$$S = 2\pi \int_a^b f(x)\sqrt{1 + [f'(x)]^2}\, dx$$

35. The center of a circle of radius r is located at $(R, 0)$, where $R > r$. When the circle is revolved about the y-axis, it generates a *torus* (a doughnut-shaped solid). What is the surface area of the torus?

6.3 PHYSICAL APPLICATIONS: WORK, LIQUID FORCE, AND CENTROIDS

> **IN THIS SECTION   Work, fluid pressure and force, centroid and moment of a plane region, the volume theorem of Pappus**
>
> Integration plays an important role in many different areas of physics. **Mechanics** is the branch of physics that deals with the effects of forces on objects. In this section, we show how integration can be used to compute work and the force exerted by a liquid. We also use integration to compute centroids of plane objects and to apply a result called the *volume theorem of Pappus*. This classic result provides a simple procedure for computing the volume of certain solids of revolution.

■ WORK

In physics, considerable time is devoted to the study of *forces*. Intuitively, a **force** is that which pushes, pulls, compresses, distends, distorts, or in any way changes the state of rest or state of motion of a body. There are several types of forces, such as centrifugal force, centripetal force, and electromotive force. In order to measure forces, we define a *unit of force* to be the force that will give unit acceleration to a unit mass. When a constant force of magnitude F is applied to an object through a distance d, the *work* performed is defined to be the product of force and distance.

Work Done by a Constant Force

> If a body moves a distance d in the direction of an applied constant force F, the **work** W done by the force is
>
> $$W = Fd$$

COMMON UNITS OF WORK AND FORCE

Mass	Distance	Force Unit	WORK
kg	m	newton (N)	joule
g	cm	dyne (dyn)	erg
slug	ft	pound	ft-lb

In the U.S. system of measurements, work is typically expressed in *foot-pounds*, *inch-pounds, or foot-tons*. In the International System (SI), work is expressed in newton-meters (called *joules*), and in the centimeter-gram-second (CGS) system, the basic unit of work is the dyne-centimeter (called an *erg*).

For example, the work done in lifting a 90 lb bag of concrete 3 ft is $W = Fd = (90 \text{ lb})(3 \text{ ft}) = 270$ ft-lb. Notice that this definition does not conform to everyday use of the word work. If you labor at lifting the concrete all day but are not able to move the sack of concrete, then no work has been done.

It is not necessary for F and d to be constants, but if they are not, then calculus is used to find the work done. Suppose F is a continuous function and $F(x)$ is a variable force that acts on an object moving along the x-axis from $x = a$ to $x = b$. We shall define the work done by this force. Partition the interval $[a, b]$ into subintervals, and let Δx_k be the length of the kth subinterval I_k. If Δx_k is sufficiently small, we can expect the force to be essentially constant on I_k, equal, for instance, to $F(x_k^*)$, where x_k^* is a point chosen arbitrarily from the interval I_k. It is reasonable to expect that the work Δw_k required to move the object on the interval I_k is approximately $\Delta w_k = F(x_k^*)\Delta x_k$, and the total work is estimated by the sum

$$\sum_{k=1}^{n} F(x_k^*)\Delta x_k$$

as indicated in Figure 6.21.

The work Δw_k done when an object moves from x_{k-1} to x_k with the force F is approximately $\Delta w_k = F(x_k^*)\,\Delta x_k$.

Figure 6.21 Work performed by a variable force

By taking the limit as the norm of the partition approaches 0, we find the total work is given by

$$W = \lim_{\|P\| \to 0} \sum_{k=1}^{n} F(x_k^*)\,\Delta x_k = \int_a^b F(x)\,dx$$

Work Done by a Variable Force

The work done by the variable force $F(x)$ in moving an object along the x-axis from $x = a$ to $x = b$ is given by

$$W = \int_a^b F(x)\,dx$$

EXAMPLE 1   Work with a variable force

An object located x ft from a fixed starting position is moved along a straight road by a force of $F(x) = 3x^2 + 5$ lb. What work is done by the force to move the object:

a. through the first 4 ft?   **b.** from 1 ft to 4 ft?

Solution   **a.** $W = \displaystyle\int_0^4 (3x^2 + 5)\,dx = (x^3 + 5x)\,\Big|_0^4 = 84$ ft-lb

b. $W = \displaystyle\int_1^4 (3x^2 + 5)\,dx = (x^3 + 5x)\,\Big|_1^4 = 78$ ft-lb

Hooke's law, named for the English physicist, Robert Hooke (1635–1703), states that *when a spring is pulled x units past its equilibrium (rest) position, there is a restoring force F(x) = kx that pulls the spring back toward equilibrium.** (See Figure 6.22.) The constant k in this formula is called the **spring constant.**

Hooke's law: A force $F(x) = kx$ acts to restore the spring to its equilibrium position.

A spring at rest
(equilibrium position)

A spring stretched x units
past equilibrium

Figure 6.22 Hooke's law

---

*Actually, Hooke's law applies only in ideal circumstances, and a spring for which the law applies is sometimes called an ideal (or linear) spring.

EXAMPLE 2   Hooke's law as an application of the work formula

The natural length of a certain spring is 10 cm. If it takes 2 dyn · cm of work to stretch the spring to a total length of 18 cm, how much work will be performed in stretching the spring to a total length of 20 cm?*

Solution   Assume that the point of equilibrium is at 0 on a number line, and let x be the amount the free end of the spring is extended past equilibrium. Because the stretching force of the spring is $F(x) = kx$, the work done in stretching the spring b cm beyond equilibrium is

$$W = \int_0^b F(x)\, dx = \int_0^b kx\, dx = \tfrac{1}{2}kb^2$$

We are given that $W = 2$ when $b = 8$, so

$$2 = \tfrac{1}{2}k(8)^2 \quad \text{implies} \quad k = \tfrac{1}{16}$$

Thus, the work done in stretching the spring b cm beyond equilibrium is

$$W = \tfrac{1}{2}\left(\tfrac{1}{16}\right) b^2 = \tfrac{1}{32}b^2 \text{ dyn} \cdot \text{cm}$$

In particular, when the total length of the spring is 20 cm, it is extended $b = 10$ cm, and the required work is

$$W = \tfrac{1}{32}(10)^2 = \tfrac{25}{8} = 3.125 \text{ dyn} \cdot \text{cm}$$

10 cm

20 cm

EXAMPLE 3   Work performed in pumping out a tank of water

A tank in the shape of a right circular cone of height 12 ft and radius 3 ft is inserted into the ground with its vertex pointing down and its top at ground level, as shown in Figure 6.23a. If the tank is half-filled with water (density $\rho = 62.4$ lb/ft^3), how much work is performed in pumping all the water in the tank to ground level?

Solution   Set up a coordinate system with the origin at the vertex of the cone and the y-axis as the axis of symmetry (Figure 6.23b). Partition the interval $0 \le y \le 6$ (remember, the tank is only half full). Choose a representative point y_k^* in the kth subinterval, and construct a thin disk-like slab of water y_k^* units above the vertex of the cone. Our plan is to think of the water in the tank as a collection of these slabs of water piled on top of each other. We shall find the work done to raise a typical water disk and then compute the total work by using integration to add the contributions of all such slabs.

Note that the force required to lift the slab is equal to the weight of the slab, which equals its volume multiplied by the weight per cubic foot of water. Let x_k^* be the radius of the kth slab. By similar triangles (Figure 6.23b), we have

$$\frac{x_k^*}{y_k^*} = \frac{3}{12} \quad \text{or} \quad x_k^* = \frac{y_k^*}{4}$$

Hence, the volume of the slab is

$$\Delta V = \pi x_k^{*2}\, \Delta y_k = \pi \underbrace{\left(\frac{y_k^*}{4}\right)^2}_{\text{Radius}} \overbrace{\Delta y_k}^{\text{Thickness}}$$

a. A conical water tank

12 ft

6 ft
of water

b. A disk of water is $12 - y_k^*$ units from the top.

Figure 6.23 Work in pumping water

---

*A unit of measurement for work is the erg and is defined as 1 erg = 1 dyn · cm. It is used in the CGS system, where length is in centimeters, mass is in grams, and time is in seconds. The unit 2 dyn · cm used in this problem would be more commonly expressed as 2 ergs.

so that the weight of the slab is

$$62.4\pi \left(\frac{y_k^*}{4}\right)^2 \Delta y_k \text{ lb}$$

From Figure 6.23b, we see that the slab of water must be raised $12 - y_k^*$ feet, which means that the work ΔW required to raise this slab is

$$\Delta W = 62.4\pi \left(\frac{y_k^*}{4}\right)^2 (12 - y_k^*) \Delta y_k$$

Finally, to compute the total work, we add the work required to lift each thin slab and take the limit of the sum as the norm of the partition approaches 0, (that is, as $n \to \infty$):

$$W = \lim_{n \to +\infty 0} 62.4\pi \sum_{k=1}^{n} \left(\frac{y_k^*}{4}\right)^2 (12 - y_k^*) \Delta y_k$$

$$= 62.4\pi \int_0^6 \left(\frac{y}{4}\right)^2 (12 - y) \, dy = \frac{62.4}{16}\pi \int_0^6 (12y^2 - y^3) \, dy$$

$$= 3.9\pi \left(4y^3 - \tfrac{1}{4}y^4\right)\Big|_0^6 = 2{,}106\pi \approx 6{,}616 \text{ ft-lb}$$

■ **FLUID PRESSURE AND FORCE**

Anyone who has dived into water has probably noticed that the pressure (that is, the force per unit area) due to the water's weight increases with depth. Careful observations show that the water pressure at any given point is directly proportional to the depth at that point. The same principle applies to other fluids.

In physics, **Pascal's principle** (named for Blaise Pascal (1623–1662), a French mathematician and scientist) states that fluid pressure is the same in all directions. This means that the pressure must be the same at all points on a surface submerged horizontally, but if the surface is submerged vertically, or at an angle, the pressure varies with the depth at each point on the surface, as shown in Figure 6.24.

We can now state the following formula for fluid force.

a. Pascal's principle: In an equilibrium state, the fluid pressure is the same in all directions.

b. The pressure is constant on a horizontal surface but varies with depth on a surface submerged vertically or at an angle.

Figure 6.24 Pressure on a submerged object

Fluid Force

If a surface of area A is submerged horizontally at a depth h in a fluid, the weight of the fluid exerts a force of

$$F = (\text{PRESSURE})(\text{AREA}) = \rho h A$$

on the surface, where ρ is the fluid density (weight per unit volume). This force is called the **fluid pressure** or **hydrostatic pressure.**

It turns out that this fluid force does not depend on the shape of the container or its size. For instance, each of the containers in Figure 6.25 has the same pressure on its base because the fluid depth h and the base area A is the same in each case.

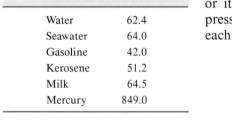

Weight-density, ρ (lb/ft^3)	
Water	62.4
Seawater	64.0
Gasoline	42.0
Kerosene	51.2
Milk	64.5
Mercury	849.0

Figure 6.25 The fluid force $F = \rho h A$ does not depend on the shape or size of the container.

a. A plate submerged vertically in a fluid of density ρ

b. A typical slab has area $A = L(h)\,\Delta h$.

Figure 6.26 Hydrostatic pressure

To see how integration can be used to compute a fluid force, let us consider a plate that is submerged vertically in a fluid of density ρ as shown in Figure 6.26.

First, we set up a coordinate system with the horizontal axis on the surface of the fluid and the positive vertical axis (the "h-axis") pointing down, so greater depths correspond to larger values of h (see Figure 6.26b). For simplicity, we assume the plate is oriented so its top and bottom are located a units and b units below the surface, respectively.

Our strategy will be to think of the plate as a pile of subplates or slabs, each so thin that we may regard it as being at a constant depth below the surface. A typical slab (a horizontal strip) is shown in Figure 6.26b. Note that it has thickness Δh and length $L = L(h)$, so that its area is $\Delta A = L\,\Delta h$. Because the slab is at a constant depth h below the surface, the fluid force on its surface is

$$\Delta F = (\text{PRESSURE})(\text{AREA}) = \rho h\,\Delta A = \rho h L(h)\,\Delta h$$

and by integrating as h varies from a to b, we obtain the total force on the plate.

Fluid (Hydrostatic) Force

Suppose a flat surface (a plate) is submerged vertically in a fluid of weight density ρ (lb/ft^3) and that the submerged portion of the plate extends from $x = a$ to $x = b$ on a vertical axis. Then the total force, F, exerted by the fluid is given by

$$F = \int_a^b \rho h(x)\, L(x)\, dx$$

where $h(x)$ is the depth at x and $L(x)$ is the corresponding length of a typical horizontal approximating strip.

EXAMPLE 4   Fluid force on a vertical surface

The cross sections of a certain trough are inverted isosceles triangles with height 6 ft and base 4 ft, as shown in Figure 6.27. If the trough contains water to a depth of 3 ft, find the total fluid force on one end.

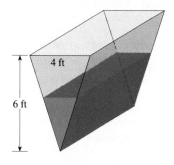

a. A trough with half-filled triangular cross sections

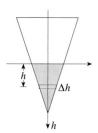

b. Side view of trough

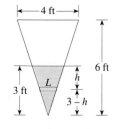

c. Use similar triangles to find $\dfrac{L}{4} = \dfrac{3-h}{6}$.

Figure 6.27 Fluid force

Solution   *First*, we set up a coordinate system in which the horizontal axis lies at the fluid surface and the positive vertical axis (the h-axis) points down (see

Figure 6.27b). *Next*, we find expressions for the length and depth of a typical thin slab (horizontal strip) in terms of the variables. We assume the slab has thickness Δh, and if its length is L, then by similar triangles (see Figure 6.27c) we have

$$\frac{L}{4} = \frac{3 - h}{6} \quad \text{so that} \quad L = \tfrac{2}{3}(3 - h)$$

We see that the approximating slab has area

$$\Delta A = L\,\Delta h = \tfrac{2}{3}(3 - h)\,\Delta h$$

Finally, multiply the product of the fluid's weight-density at a given depth (ρh) and the area of the approximating slab (ΔA) and integrate on the interval of depths occupied by the vertical plate.

$$F = \int_0^3 \underbrace{\tfrac{2}{3}\rho h(3 - h)\ dh}_{\Delta F\ =\ \text{force on a typical slab}}$$

$$= \tfrac{2}{3}(62.4)\int_0^3 (3h - h^2)\ dh \qquad \rho = 62.4\ \text{lb/ft}^3\ \text{for water}$$

$$= 41.6\left(\tfrac{3}{2}h^2 - \tfrac{1}{3}h^3\right)\Big|_0^3 = 187.2\ \text{lb}$$

The fluid force formula applies equally well if the plate is submerged in a fluid whose density varies with the depth h.

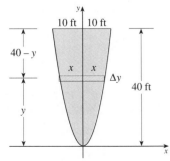

a. Cross section of a dam

b. A typical horizontal strip is $40 - y$ ft below the water surface.

Figure 6.28 Force on one face of a dam

EXAMPLE 5   Total force on one face of a dam

A reservoir is filled with water to the top of a dam. If the dam is in the shape of a parabola 40 ft high and 20 ft wide at the top, as shown in Figure 6.28, what is the total fluid force on the face of the dam?

Solution   Instead of putting the x-axis on the surface of the water (at the top of the dam), we place the origin at the vertex of the parabola and the positive y-axis along the parabola's axis of symmetry (Figure 6.28b). The advantage of this choice of axes is that the parabola can be represented by an equation of the form $y = cx^2$. Because we know that $y = 40$ when $x = 10$, it follows that

$$40 = c(10)^2 \quad \text{so that} \quad c = \tfrac{2}{5} \text{ and thus } y = \tfrac{2}{5}x^2$$

The typical horizontal strip on the face of the dam is located y feet above the x-axis, which means it is $h = 40 - y$ feet below the surface of the water. The strip is Δy feet wide and $L = 2x$ feet long. Write L as a function of y:

$$y = \tfrac{2}{5}x^2 \quad \text{so that} \quad x = \sqrt{\tfrac{5}{2}y}$$

and

$$L = 2x = 2\left(\sqrt{\tfrac{5}{2}y}\right) = \sqrt{10y}$$

Therefore

$$\Delta A = L\Delta y = 2\sqrt{\tfrac{5}{2}y}\,\Delta y = \sqrt{10y}\,\Delta y$$

Finally,

Depth below water: $h = 40 - y$

$$F = \int_0^{40} \rho h \, \underbrace{L(h) \, dh}_{\text{Area of the strip}} = \int_0^{40} (62.4)(\sqrt{10})(40 - y)\sqrt{y} \, dy$$

Density of water = 62.4

$$= 62.4\sqrt{10} \int_0^{40} (40y^{1/2} - y^{3/2}) \, dy$$

$$= 62.4\sqrt{10} \left. \left(\tfrac{80}{3}y^{3/2} - \tfrac{2}{5}y^{5/2} \right) \right|_0^{40}$$

$$= 62.4\sqrt{10} \left. (y^{3/2})\left(\tfrac{80}{3} - \tfrac{2}{5}y \right) \right|_0^{40}$$

$$= 532{,}480 \text{ lb}$$

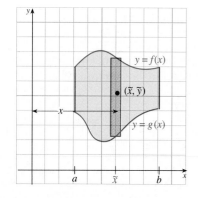

Theoretically, the lamina should balance on a point placed at its centroid.

■ CENTROID AND MOMENT OF A PLANE REGION

In mechanics, it is often important to determine the point where an irregularly shaped plate will balance. The **moment of a force** measures its tendency to produce rotation in an object and depends on the magnitude of the force and the point on the object where it is applied. Since the time of Archimedes (287–212 B.C.), it has been known that the balance point of an object occurs where all its moments cancel out (so there is no rotation).

The **mass** of an object is a measure of its **inertia;** that is, its propensity to maintain a state of rest or uniform motion. A thin plate whose material is distributed uniformly, so that its density ρ (mass per unit area) is constant, is called a **homogeneous lamina.** The balance point of such a lamina is called its **centroid** and may be thought of as its geometrical center. We shall see how centroids can be computed by integration in this section, and shall examine the topic even further in Section 13.6.

Consider a homogeneous lamina that covers a region R bounded by the curves $y = f(x)$ and $y = g(x)$ on the interval $[a, b]$, and consider a thin, vertical approximating strip within R, as shown in Figure 6.29. The mass of the strip is given by

$$\Delta m = \underset{\uparrow}{\rho} \cdot \underbrace{[f(x) - g(x)] \Delta x}_{\text{Area of strip}}$$

 Density

and the total mass of the lamina may be found by integration:

$$m = \rho \int_a^b [f(x) - g(x)] \, dx$$

The geometrical center of the approximating strip is $(\tilde{x}, \tilde{y})$, where $\tilde{x} = x$ and $\tilde{y} = \tfrac{1}{2}[f(x) + g(x)]$. The **moment of the approximating strip about the y-axis** is defined to be the product

$$\Delta M_y = \underset{\underset{\substack{\text{Distance of the} \\ \text{strip from } y\text{-axis}}}{\uparrow}}{\tilde{x}} \cdot \underbrace{\Delta m}_{\text{Mass of strip}} = \tilde{x}\{\rho[f(x) - g(x)] \Delta x\}$$

Figure 6.29 Homogeneous lamina with a vertical approximating strip

This product provides a measure of the tendency of the strip to rotate about the *y*-axis. Similarly, the **moment of the strip about the *x*-axis** is defined to be the product

$$\Delta M_x = \tilde{y}\,\Delta m = \underbrace{\tfrac{1}{2}[f(x) + g(x)]}_{\substack{\text{Average distance of the} \\ \text{strip from } x\text{-axis}}}\{\rho[f(x) - g(x)]\Delta x\}$$

$$= \tfrac{1}{2}\rho\{[f(x)]^2 - [g(x)]^2\}\,\Delta x$$

This product provides a measure of the tendency of the strip to rotate about the *x*-axis.

Integrating on [*a*, *b*], we find the moments of the entire lamina *R* about the *y*-axis and *x*-axis are given by

$$M_y = \rho \int_a^b x[f(x) - g(x)]\,dx \quad\text{and}\quad M_x = \tfrac{1}{2}\rho \int_a^b \{[f(x)]^2 - [g(x)]^2\}\,dx$$

If the entire mass *m* of the lamina *R* were located at the point $(\bar{x}, \bar{y})$, then its moment about the *x*-axis and *y*-axis would be $m\bar{y}$ and $m\bar{x}$, respectively. Thus, we have $m\bar{x} = M_y$ and $m\bar{y} = M_x$, so that

$$\bar{x} = \frac{M_y}{m} = \frac{\rho \int_a^b x[f(x) - g(x)]\,dx}{\rho \int_a^b [f(x) - g(x)]\,dx} \quad\text{and}\quad \bar{y} = \frac{M_x}{m} = \frac{\tfrac{1}{2}\rho \int_a^b \{[f(x)]^2 - [g(x)]^2\}\,dx}{\rho \int_a^b [f(x) - g(x)]\,dx}$$

We can now summarize these results.

Let *f* and *g* be continuous and satisfy $f(x) \geq g(x)$ on the interval [*a*, *b*], and consider a thin plate (lamina) of uniform density ρ that covers the region *R* between the graphs of $y = f(x)$ and $y = g(x)$ on the interval [*a*, *b*]. Then

Mass   The **mass** of *R* is: $m = \displaystyle\int_a^b \rho[f(x) - g(x)]\,dx$.

Centroid   The **centroid** of *R* is the point $(\bar{x}, \bar{y})$ such that

$$\bar{x} = \frac{M_y}{m} = \frac{\displaystyle\int_a^b \rho x[f(x) - g(x)]\,dx}{\displaystyle\int_a^b \rho[f(x) - g(x)]\,dx} \quad\text{and}\quad \bar{y} = \frac{M_x}{m} = \frac{\tfrac{1}{2}\displaystyle\int_a^b \rho\{[f(x)]^2 - [g(x)]^2\}\,dx}{\displaystyle\int_a^b \rho[f(x) - g(x)]\,dx}$$

EXAMPLE 6   Centroid on a thin plate

A homogeneous lamina *R* has constant density $\rho = 1$ and is bounded by the parabola $y = x^2$ and the line $y = x$. Find the mass and the centroid of *R*.

Solution   We see that the line and the parabola intersect at the origin and at the point (1, 1), as shown in Figure 6.30. Because $\rho = 1$, the mass is the same as the area of the region *R*. That is,

$$m = A = \int_0^1 (x - x^2)\,dx = \left(\frac{x^2}{2} - \frac{x^3}{3}\right)\Big|_0^1 = \frac{1}{6}$$

and we find that the region has moments M_y and M_x about the *y*-axis and *x*-axis, respectively, where

$$M_y = \int_0^1 x(x - x^2)\,dx = \left(\frac{x^3}{3} - \frac{x^4}{4}\right)\Big|_0^1 = \frac{1}{12}$$

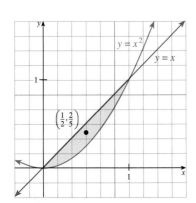

Figure 6.30 The centroid of a planar region

and

$$M_x = \frac{1}{2} \int_0^1 (x + x^2)(x - x^2)\, dx = \frac{1}{2} \int_0^1 (x^2 - x^4)\, dx$$

$$= \frac{1}{2}\left(\frac{x^3}{3} - \frac{x^5}{5}\right)\Big|_0^1 = \frac{1}{2}\left(\frac{1}{3} - \frac{1}{5}\right) = \frac{1}{15}$$

Thus, the centroid of the region R has coordinates

$$\bar{x} = \frac{M_y}{m} = \frac{\frac{1}{12}}{\frac{1}{6}} = \frac{1}{2} \quad \text{and} \quad \bar{y} = \frac{M_x}{m} = \frac{\frac{1}{15}}{\frac{1}{6}} = \frac{2}{5}$$

■ VOLUME THEOREM OF PAPPUS

In certain geometric applications, it is convenient to speak of the center of mass (x, y) without referring to a plate covering R. In this context, the center of mass is the centroid of the region R. We shall use this interpretation in the following theorem, which is usually attributed to the 4th century Greek geometer Pappus.

THEOREM 6.1   Volume theorem of Pappus

The solid generated by revolving a region R about a line outside its boundary (but in the same plane) has volume $V = As$, where A is the area of R and s is the distance traveled by the centroid of R.

Proof: First, choose a coordinate system in which the y-axis coincides with the axis of revolution. Figure 6.31 shows a typical region R together with a vertical approximating rectangle. We shall assume that this rectangle has area ΔA and that it is located x units from the y-axis.

Notice that when the rectangle is revolved about the y-axis, it generates a shell of volume $\Delta V = 2\pi x \Delta A$. Thus, by partitioning the region R into a number of rectangles and taking the limit of the sum of the volumes of all the related approximating shells as the norm of the partition approaches 0, we find that

$$V = \lim_{\|P\| \to 0} \sum_{k=1}^{n} 2\pi x_k \Delta A_k = \int 2\pi x\, dA = 2\pi \int x\, dA$$

$$= 2\pi \bar{x} \int dA \quad \textit{Because } \bar{x} = \frac{\int x\, dA}{\int dA}$$

$$= 2\pi \bar{x}\, A \qquad \textit{Because } \int dA = A$$

$$= As \qquad \textit{Where } s = 2\pi\bar{x} \textit{ is the distance traveled by the centroid (the circumference of a circle of radius } \bar{x})$$ ■

The approximating solid of revolution has volume $\Delta V = 2\pi x(\Delta A)$.

Area ΔA

Figure 6.31 The volume theorem of Pappus

We close this section with an example that illustrates the use of the volume theorem of Pappus.

EXAMPLE 7   Volume of a torus using the volume theorem of Pappus

When a circle of radius r is revolved about a line in the plane of the circle located R units from its center ($R > r$), the solid figure so generated is called a **torus,** as shown in Figure 6.32. Show that the torus has volume $V = 2\pi^2 r^2 R$.

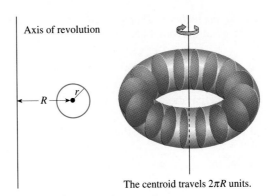

Figure 6.32 The volume of a torus

Solution The circle has area $A = \pi r^2$ and its center (which is its centroid) travels $2\pi R$ units. In this example $s = R$. Therefore, according to the theorem of Pappus, the torus has volume

$$V = (2\pi R)A = 2\pi R(\pi r^2) = 2\pi^2 r^2 R$$

Incidentally, the volume found in Example 7 using the theorem of Pappus was computed in Problem 66 of Section 6.1 by using shells.

PROBLEM SET 6.3

A 1. ■ **What Does This Say?** Discuss work and how to find it.

2. ■ **What Does This Say?** Discuss fluid pressure and how to find it.

3. ■ **What Does This Say?** What is meant by a centroid? Outline a procedure for finding both mass and centroid.

4. What is the work done in lifting a 50-lb bag of salt 5 ft?

5. What is the work done in lifting an 850-lb billiard table 15 ft?

6. How much work is done in lifting a 50-lb weight to a height of 6 ft?

7. A 5-lb force will stretch a spring 9 in. beyond its natural length. How much work is required to stretch it 1 ft beyond its natural length?

8. Suppose it takes 4 dyn · cm of work to stretch a spring 10 cm beyond its natural length. How much work is needed to stretch it 4 cm further?

9. A bucket weighing 75 lb when filled and 10 lb when empty is pulled up the side of a 100-ft building. How much more work is done in pulling up the full bucket than the empty bucket?

10. A 30-ft rope weighing 0.4 lb/ft hangs over the edge of a building 100 ft high. How much work is done in pulling the rope to the top of the building?

11. A 30-lb ball hangs at the bottom of a cable that is 50 ft long and weighs 20 lb. The entire length of cable hangs over a cliff. Find the work done to raise the cable and get the ball to the top of the cliff.

In Problems 12–17, the given figure is the vertical cross section of a tank containing the indicated substance. Find the liquid force against the end of the tank. The weight densities are given on page 407.

12. water

13. seawater

14. gasoline
Diameter of semicircle
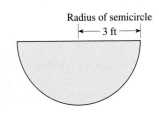

15. kerosene
Radius of semicircle

16. water
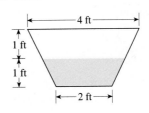

17. mercury
Radius of semicircle

Find the centroid of each planar region in Problems 18–23.

18. the region in the first quadrant bounded by the curves $y = x^3$ and $y = \sqrt[3]{x}$

19. the region bounded by the parabola $y = x^2 - 9$ and the x-axis

20. the region bounded by the parabola $y = 4 - x^2$ and the line $y = x + 2$

21. the region bounded by the curve $y = x^{-1}$, the x-axis, and the lines $x = 1$ and $x = 2$

22. the region bounded by the curve $y = x^{-1}$ and the line $2x + 2y = 5$

23. the region bounded by $y = \dfrac{1}{\sqrt{x}}$ and the x-axis on $[1, 4]$

Use the theorem of Pappus to compute the volume of the solids generated by revolving the regions given in Problems 24–27 about the prescribed axis.

24. the region bounded by the parabola $y = \sqrt{x}$, the x-axis, and the line $x = 4$ about the line $x = -1$

25. the triangular region with vertices $(-3, 0)$, $(0, 5)$, and $(2, 0)$, about the line $y = -1$

26. the semicircular region $y = \sqrt{1 - x^2}$, about the line $y = -1$

27. the semicircular region $x = \sqrt{4 - y^2}$, about the line $x = -2$

B **28.** The centroid of any triangle lies at the intersection of the medians, two-thirds the distance from each vertex to the midpoint of the opposite side. Locate the centroid of the triangle with vertices $(0, 0)$, $(7, 3)$, and $(7, -2)$ using this method, and then check your result by calculus.

29. The centroid of any triangle lies at the intersection of the medians, two-thirds the distance from each vertex to the midpoint of the opposite side. Locate the centroid for the triangle with vertices $(-2, 0)$, $(3, 5)$, and $(3, -2)$ using this method, and then check your result by calculus.

30. An object moving along the x-axis is acted upon by a force $F(x) = x^4 + 2x^2$. Find the total work done by the force in moving the object from $x = 1$ cm to $x = 2$ cm. *Note:* Distance is in cm, so force is in dynes.

31. An object moving along the x-axis is acted upon by a force $F(x) = |\sin x|$. Find the total work done by the force in moving the object from $x = 0$ cm to $x = 2\pi$ cm. *Note:* Distance is in cm, so force is in dynes.

32. A tank in the shape of an inverted right circular cone of height 6 ft and radius 3 ft is full of water. How much work is performed in pumping all the water in the tank over the top edge?

33. If water leaks from the bottom of the tank in Problem 32, how much work is done?

34. A cylindrical tank with base radius 2 ft and height 12 ft is sunk into the ground so that the top of the tank is at surface level. Find the work done to pump the liquid to the top of the tank if the liquid density is 80 lb/ft^3 and the tank is filled to the top.

35. A hemispherical bowl with radius 10 ft is filled with water to a level of 6 ft. Find the work done to the nearest 100 ft-lb to pump all the water to the top of the bowl.

36. A holding tank has the shape of a rectangular parallelepiped 20 ft by 30 ft by 10 ft. How much work is done in pumping all the water to the top of the tank? How much work is done in pumping all the water out of the tank to a height of 2 ft above the top of the tank?

37. A cylindrical tank of radius 3 ft and height 10 ft is filled to a depth of 2 ft with a liquid of density $\rho = 40$ lb/ft^3. Find the work done in pumping all the liquid to a height of 2 ft above the top of the tank.

38. An oil can in the shape of a rectangular parallelepiped is filled with oil of density 0.87 g/cm^3. What is the total force on a side of the can if it is 20 cm high and has a square base 15 cm on a side?

39. A swimming pool 20 ft by 15 ft by 10 ft deep is filled with water. A cube 1 ft on a side lies on the bottom of the pool. Find the total liquid force on a lateral face of the cube.

40. In Problem 39, suppose a log of radius 1 ft lies at the bottom of the pool. What is the total liquid force on one end of the log?

41. In Problem 39, suppose a brick with sides of lengths 2 in., 3 in., and 6 in. stands upright on the bottom of the pool. What is the total liquid force on the other five sides?

42. An object weighing 800 lb on the surface of the earth is propelled to a height of 200 mi above the earth. How much work is done against gravity? *Hint:* Assume the radius of the earth is 4,000 mi, and use Newton's law $F = -k/x^2$, for the force on an object x miles from the center of the earth.

43. A dam is in the shape of an isosceles trapezoid 200 ft at the top, 100 ft at the bottom, and 75 ft high. When water is up to the top of the dam, what is the force on its face?

44. According to Coulomb's law in physics, two similarly charged particles repel each other with a force inversely proportional to the square of the distance between them. Suppose the force is 12 dynes when they are 5 cm apart.

  a. How much work is done in moving one particle from a distance of 10 cm to a distance of 8 cm from the other?

  b. How much work is done in moving one particle from an "infinite" distance to a distance of 8 cm from the other? *Hint*: Find the work done in moving it from distance s to distance 8 and then let $s \to +\infty$.

*A region R with uniform density is said to have **moments of inertia** I_x about the x-axis and I_y about the y–axis, where*

$$I_x = \int y^2 \, dA \quad \text{and} \quad I_y = \int x^2 \, dA$$

The dA represents the area of an approximating strip. In Problems 45–46, find I_x and I_y for the given region.

45. the region bounded by the parabola $y = \sqrt{x}$, the x-axis, and the line $x = 4$.

46. the region bounded by the curve $y = \sqrt[3]{1 - x^3}$ and the coordinate axes

47. If a region has area A and moment of inertia I_y about the y-axis, then it is said to have a **radius of gyration**

$$\rho_y = \sqrt{\frac{I_y}{A}}$$

with respect to the y-axis. Compute the radius of gyration for the triangular region bounded by the line $y = 4 - x$ and the coordinate axes.

---

c. Derive this formula for the volume of the fuel at level h, where $-b \le h \le b$:

$$V(h) = 2La \int_{-b}^{h} \sqrt{1 - \left(\frac{y}{b}\right)^2} \, dy$$

  Hint: Recall that the volume of a cylinder, of any shape, is the "area × length."

d. Finally, for $a = 5$ and $b = 4$, numerically compute $V(h)$ for $h = -3, -2, \ldots, 3, 4$. *Note*: $V(0)$ and $V(4)$ will serve as a check on your work.

49. We think of the last part of Problem 48 as the "direct" problem: Given a value of h, compute $V(h)$ by a formula. Now we turn to the "inverse" problem: For a set value of V, say V_0, find h such that $V(h) = V_0$. Typically, the inverse problem is more difficult than the direct problem and requires some sort of iterative method to approximate the solution (for example, Newton–Raphson's method). For example, if $V_0 = 500$ ft^3, we could define

$$f(h) = V(h) - 500$$

and seek the relevant "zero" of f. Set up the necessary computer program to do this and find the h values, to two-decimal place accuracy corresponding to these values of V:

  a. 500   **b.** 800

  Hint: A key to this problem is thinking about $V'(h)$, where $V(h)$ is expressed in 48**c.** Also, for starting values h_0, refer to your work in Problem 48**d.**

Computational Window ▼ ▲

In these computational problems we revisit a problem similar to the one we considered at the end of Chapter 4, but add a couple of complications. Imagine a cylindrical fuel tank lying on its side (of length L = 20 ft); the ends are elliptically shaped and are defined by the equation

$$\left(\frac{x}{a}\right)^2 + \left(\frac{y}{b}\right)^2 = 1$$

We are concerned with the amount of fuel in the tank for a given level.

48. a. Explain why the area of an end of the tank can be expressed by

$$A = 2a \int_{-b}^{b} \sqrt{1 - \left(\frac{y}{b}\right)^2} \, dy$$

  b. By making the right substitution in the integral in part **a,** one can get an integral representing half the area inside the circle (with unit radius). Do this and obtain the area inside the above ellipse to be πab.

© **50.** Show that the centroid of a rectangle is the point of intersection of its diagonals.

51. A right circular cone is generated when the region bounded by the line $y = x$ and the vertical lines $x = 0$ and $x = r$ is revolved about the x-axis. Show that the volume of this cone is

$$V = \tfrac{1}{3}\pi r^3$$

52. Find the volume of the solid figure generated when a square of side L is revolved about a line that is outside the square and parallel to two of its sides, and located s units from the closer side.

53. Find the volume of the solid figure generated by revolving an equilateral triangle of side L about one of its sides.

54. Let R be a region in the plane, and suppose that R can be partitioned into two subregions R_1 and R_2. Let $(\bar{x}_1, \bar{y}_1)$ and $(\bar{x}_2, \bar{y}_2)$ be the centroids of R_1 and R_2 respectively, and let A_1 and A_2 be the areas of the subregions. Show that $(\bar{x}, \bar{y})$ is the centroid of R, where

$$\bar{x} = \frac{A_1 x_1 + A_2 x_2}{A_1 + A_2} \quad \text{and} \quad \bar{y} = \frac{A_1 y_1 + A_2 y_2}{A_1 + A_2}$$

6.4 GROWTH, DECAY, AND FIRST-ORDER LINEAR DIFFERENTIAL EQUATIONS

> **IN THIS SECTION** Radioactive decay: carbon dating, exponential and logistic growth, first-order linear differential equations, applications of first-order linear equations
>
> We investigate applications involving separable differential equations of the general forms
>
> $$\frac{dy}{dx} = my + b \quad \text{and} \quad \frac{dy}{dx} = (my + b)y$$
>
> We also see how to solve equations of the form
>
> $$\frac{dy}{dx} + P(x)y = Q(x)$$
>
> We see how this type of differential equation can be used to model dilution problems and problems involving electrical circuits.

■ RADIOACTIVE DECAY: CARBON DATING

The decomposition of a radioactive substance is a very complicated process, but experiments indicate that such substances disintegrate at a rate proportional to the amount present at each instant. Thus, if $Q(t)$ is the amount of a given radioactive substance present at time t, we have

$$\frac{dQ}{dt} = -kQ$$

where k is a positive constant (the minus sign indicates that Q decreases with time). This is called the **decay equation** for the substance. Let Q_0 be the initial amount of the substance present.

To solve the decay equation, separate the variables and integrate both sides.

$$\frac{dQ}{dt} = -kQ$$

$$\int \frac{dQ}{Q} = \int -k \, dt$$

$$\ln|Q| = -kt + C_1$$

$$e^{-kt+C_1} = Q \qquad \textit{Definition of natural logarithm}$$

$$e^{-kt}e^{C_1} = Q$$

Thus, $Q = Ce^{-kt}$, where $C = e^{C_1}$. Finally, because $Q = Q_0$ when $t = 0$, we see that

$$Q_0 = Ce^0 \quad \text{or} \quad C = Q_0$$

Decay Equation

> The **decay equation** of a radioactive substance is
>
> $$Q(t) = Q_0 e^{-kt}$$
>
> where $Q(t)$ is the amount of the substance present at time t, Q_0 is the initial amount of the substance, and k is a positive constant that depends on the substance.

We shall refer to the graph of the decay equation as the **decay curve.** Such a curve is shown in Figure 6.33. In Figure 6.33 we have also indicated the time t_h required for half of a given substance to disintegrate. The time t_h is called the **half-life** of the substance, and it provides a measure of the substance's rate of disintegration.

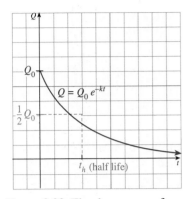

Figure 6.33 The decay curve for a radioactive substance

There is a simple relationship between k and the half-life t_h. In particular, because a sample Q_0 grams will contain only $\frac{1}{2}Q_0$ grams after t_h years, we have

$$Q(t_h) = Q_0 e^{-kt_h} = \tfrac{1}{2}Q_0$$

so that

$$e^{-kt_h} = \tfrac{1}{2}$$

By taking logarithms on both sides of this equation, we find that

$$-kt_h = \ln \tfrac{1}{2} = -\ln 2$$

$$t_h = \frac{\ln 2}{k}$$

Half-Life Formula

A radioactive substance that decays according to the decay equation $Q = Q_0 e^{-kt}$ has half-life

$$t_h = \frac{\ln 2}{k}$$

This formula can be used to determine t_h if we know k or k if we know t_h. Note that the half-life t_h is independent of the initial amount Q_0.

EXAMPLE 1   Amount of a radioactive substance present, given half-life

A particular radioactive substance has a half-life of 600 yr. Find k for this substance and determine how much of a 50-gm sample will remain after 125 yr.

Solution   According to the half-life formula, we have

$$k = \frac{\ln 2}{t_h} = \frac{\ln 2}{600} \approx 0.001\,155\,245\,3$$

Next, to see how much of a 50-gm sample will remain after 125 yr, substitute $Q_0 = 50$, $k = 0.001\,155\,245\,3$, and $t = 125$ into the decay equation:

$$Q(125) = 50e^{-0.001\,155\,245\,3(125)} \approx 43.27682805$$

There will be about 43 gm present.

One of the more interesting applications of radioactive decay is a technique known as **carbon dating,** which is used by geologists, anthropologists, and archeologists to estimate the age of fossils and other objects.* The technique is based on the fact that all animal and vegetable systems (whether living or dead) contain both stable carbon ^{12}C and a radioactive isotope ^{14}C. Scientists assume that the ratio of ^{14}C to ^{12}C in the air has remained approximately constant throughout history. Living systems absorb carbon dioxide from the air, and so the ratio of ^{14}C to ^{12}C in a living system is the same as that in the air itself. When a living system dies, the absorption of carbon dioxide ceases. The ^{12}C already in the system remains while the ^{14}C decays, and the ratio of ^{14}C to ^{12}C decreases exponentially. The half-life of ^{14}C is approximately 5,730 years. The ratio of ^{14}C to

*Carbon dating is used primarily for estimating the age of relatively "recent" specimens. For example, it was used (along with other methods) to determine that the Dead Sea Scrolls were written and deposited in the Caves of Qumran approximately 2,000 years ago. For dating older specimens, it is better to use techniques based on radioactive substances with longer half-lives. In particular, potassium 40 is often used as a "clock" for events that occurred between 5 and 15 million years ago. Paleoanthropologists find this substance especially valuable because it often occurs in volcanic deposits and can be used to date fossils trapped in such deposits.

^{12}C in a fossil t years after it was alive is approximately

$$R = R_0 e^{-kt}$$

where $k = \dfrac{\ln 2}{5,730}$ and R_0 is the ratio of ^{14}C to ^{12}C in the atmosphere. By comparing $R(t)$ with R_0, the age of the object can be estimated.

EXAMPLE 2   Carbon dating

An archaeologist has found a fossil in which the ratio of ^{14}C to ^{12}C is $\frac{1}{5}$ the ratio found in the atmosphere. Approximately how old is the fossil?

Solution   The age of the fossil is the value of t for which $R(t) = \frac{1}{5}R_0$:

$$\tfrac{1}{5}R_0 = R_0 e^{-kt}$$

$$\tfrac{1}{5} = e^{-kt}$$

$$-kt = \ln \tfrac{1}{5}$$

$$t = -\tfrac{1}{k} \ln 0.2 \qquad k = \frac{\ln 2}{5,730}$$

$$\approx 13,304\ 64798$$

The fossil is approximately 13,305 yr old.   ▬

▪ EXPONENTIAL AND LOGISTIC GROWTH

When the population $P(t)$ of a colony of living organisms (humans, bacteria, etc.) is small, it is reasonable to expect the relative rate of change of the population to be constant. In other words,

$$\frac{\frac{dP}{dt}}{P} = k \quad \text{or} \quad \frac{dP}{dt} = kP$$

where k is a constant (the **unrestricted growth rate**). This is called **exponential growth.** As long as the colony has plenty of food and living space, its population will obey this unrestricted growth rate formula and $P(t)$ will grow exponentially.

However, in practice, there always comes a time when environmental factors begin to restrict the further expansion of the colony, and at this point, the growth ceases to be purely exponential in nature. To construct a population model that takes into account the effect of diminishing resources and cramping, we assume that the relative rate of change in population is decreased by a braking factor that is proportional to the population itself. Thus, we have

$$\frac{\frac{dP}{dt}}{P} = k - LP \quad \text{or} \quad \frac{dP}{dt} = (k - LP)P$$

where L is a positive constant (the **braking rate**). This is called a **logistic equation,** and it arises not only in connection with population models, but in a variety of other situations. The following example illustrates one way such an equation can arise.

EXAMPLE 3   Logistic equation for inhibited growth

The rate at which an epidemic spreads through a community is proportional to the product of the number of residents who have been infected and the number of susceptible residents who have not. Express the number of residents who have been infected as a function of time.

Solution   Let $Q(t)$ denote the number of residents who have been infected by time t and B the total number of susceptible residents. Then the number of susceptible residents who have not been infected is $B - Q$, and the differential equation describing the spread of the epidemic is

$$\frac{dQ}{dt} = kQ(B - Q) \qquad \text{\textit{k is the constant of proportionality.}}$$

$$\frac{dQ}{Q(B - Q)} = k \, dt$$

$$\int \frac{dQ}{Q(B - Q)} = \int k \, dt$$

The integral on the right causes no difficulty, but the integral on the left is not easy to integrate in its present form. Consider the following algebraic manipulation, which allows us to rewrite the troublesome integral in a useful form for our purposes in this application:

$$\frac{1}{B}\left(\frac{1}{Q} + \frac{1}{B - Q}\right) = \frac{1}{B}\left[\frac{B - Q + Q}{Q(B - Q)}\right] = \frac{1}{Q(B - Q)}$$

We now substitute the form on the left into the equation and complete the integration:

$$\frac{1}{B} \int \frac{dQ}{Q} + \frac{1}{B} \int \frac{dQ}{B - Q} = \int k \, dt$$

$$\frac{1}{B} \ln|Q| - \frac{1}{B} \ln|B - Q| = kt + C \qquad \text{\textit{Integrate each.}}$$

$$\frac{1}{B} \ln\left|\frac{Q}{B - Q}\right| = kt + C \qquad \text{\textit{Division property of logs}}$$

$$\ln\left(\frac{Q}{B - Q}\right) = Bkt + BC \qquad \text{\textit{Multiply both sides by B. (Note that $Q > 0$, $B > Q$.)}}$$

$$\frac{Q}{B - Q} = e^{Bkt + BC} \qquad \text{\textit{Definition of ln}}$$

$$Q = (B - Q)e^{Bkt}e^{BC} \qquad \text{\textit{Because e^{BC} is a constant, we can let $A_1 = e^{BC}$.}}$$

$$Q = A_1 Be^{Bkt} - A_1 Qe^{Bkt}$$

$$Q + A_1 Qe^{Bkt} = A_1 Be^{Bkt}$$

$$Q = \frac{A_1 Be^{Bkt}}{1 + A_1 e^{Bkt}}$$

To simplify the equation, we make another substitution; let $A = \frac{1}{A_1}$, so that (after several simplification steps) we have

$$Q = \frac{\dfrac{Be^{Bkt}}{A}}{1 + \dfrac{e^{Bkt}}{A}} = \frac{B}{1 + Ae^{-Bkt}}$$

The graph of $Q(t)$ is shown in Figure 6.34. Note that the curve has an inflection point where

$$Q(t) = \frac{B}{2}$$

(The details are left for the reader.) This corresponds to the fact that the epidemic is spreading most rapidly when half the susceptible residents have been infected. ▬

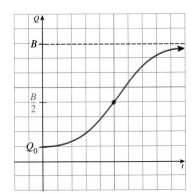

Figure 6.34 A logistic curve:
$Q(t) = \dfrac{B}{1 + Ae^{-Bkt}}$

TABLE 6.3 Summary of Growth Models

Graph	Growth Model	Equation and Solution	Sample Applications
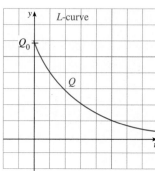	**Uninhibited growth** $(k > 0)$ Rate is proportional to the amount present.	$\dfrac{dQ}{dt} = kQ$ Solution: $Q = Q_0 e^{kt}$	Exponential growth; short-term population growth; interest compounded continuously; inflation; price/supply curves
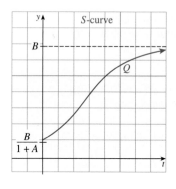	**Uninhibited decay** $(k > 0)$ Rate is proportional to the amount present.	$\dfrac{dQ}{dt} = -kQ$ Solution: $Q = Q_0 e^{-kt}$	Radioactive decay; depletion of natural resources; price/demand curves
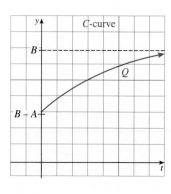	**Inhibited growth or logistic growth** Rate is jointly proportional to the amount present and to the difference between the amount present and a fixed amount $(k > 0)$.	$\dfrac{dQ}{dt} = kQ(B - Q)$ Solution: $Q = \dfrac{B}{1 + Ae^{-Bkt}}$	Long-term population growth (with a limiting value); spread of a disease in a population; sale of fad items (for example, singing flowers); growth of a business
	Limited growth Rate is proportional to the difference between the amount present and a fixed limit $(k > 0)$.	$\dfrac{dQ}{dt} = k(B - Q)$ Solution: $Q = B - Ae^{-kt}$	Learning curve; diffusion of information by mass media; intravenous infusion of a medication; Newton's law of cooling; sales of new products; growth of a business

■ FIRST-ORDER LINEAR DIFFERENTIAL EQUATIONS

Equations that can be expressed in the form

$$\frac{dy}{dx} + P(x)y = Q(x)$$

are called **first-order linear** differential equations. For example,

$$x^2 \frac{dy}{dx} - (x^2 + 2)y = x^5$$

is such an equation, with

$$P(x) = -\left(\frac{x^2 + 2}{x^2}\right) = -1 - 2x^{-2} \quad \text{and} \quad Q(x) = \frac{x^5}{x^2} = x^3$$

The following theorem shows how the general solution of a first-order linear differential equation $y' + P(x)y = Q(x)$ may be obtained.

THEOREM 6.2   General solution of a first-order linear differential equation

---

The general solution of the first-order linear differential equation

$$\frac{dy}{dx} + P(x)y = Q(x)$$

is given by

$$y = \frac{1}{I(x)}\left[\int Q(x)I(x)\, dx + C\right]$$

where $I(x) = e^{\int P(x)\, dx}$.

Proof: First, note that

$$\frac{dI(x)}{dx} = e^{\int P(x)dx}\left[\frac{d}{dx}\int P(x)\, dx\right] = e^{\int P(x)dx} P(x) = I(x)P(x)$$

because $\frac{d}{dx}e^u = e^u \frac{du}{dx}$. We also will need to note that

$$\frac{d}{dx}[I(x)y] = I(x)\frac{dy}{dx} + y\frac{d}{dx}I(x) = I(x)\frac{dy}{dx} + yI(x)\,P(x) \quad \textit{Product rule}$$

We now begin the proof by starting with the given differential equation.

$$\frac{dy}{dx} + P(x)y = Q(x) \qquad\qquad\qquad \textit{Given}$$

$$I(x)\left[\frac{dy}{dx} + P(x)y\right] = I(x)Q(x) \qquad\qquad \textit{Multiply both sides by } I(x).$$

$$I(x)\frac{dy}{dx} + I(x)P(x)y = I(x)Q(x)$$

$$\frac{d}{dx}[I(x)y] = I(x)Q(x) \qquad\qquad\qquad \textit{Substitute.}$$

$$\int \frac{d}{dx}[I(x)y]\, dx = \int I(x)Q(x)\, dx \qquad\qquad \textit{Integrate both sides.}$$

$$I(x)y = \int I(x)Q(x)\, dx + C$$

$$y = \frac{1}{I(x)}\int I(x)Q(x)\, dx + C$$

■

Because multiplying both sides of the differential equation

$$\frac{dy}{dx} + P(x)y = Q(x)$$

by $I(x)$ makes the left side an exact derivative, the function $I(x)$ is called an **integrating factor** of the differential equation.

A first-order linear differential equation together with the condition $y = y_0$ when $x = x_0$ is called an **initial value problem.** Here is an example of such a problem.

EXAMPLE 4   First-order linear differential equation

Solve $\dfrac{dy}{dx} = e^{-x} - 2y$, $x \geq 0$, subject to the initial condition $y = 2$ when $x = 0$.

Solution   The differential equation can be expressed in the proper form by adding $2y$ to both sides:

$$\frac{dy}{dx} + 2 \cdot y = e^{-x} \qquad \text{for } x \geq 0$$

We have $P(x) = 2$ and $Q(x) = e^{-x}$. Both $P(x)$ and $Q(x)$ are continuous in the domain $x \geq 0$. An integrating factor is given by

$$I(x) = e^{\int P(x)\,dx} = e^{\int 2\,dx} = e^{2x} \qquad \text{for } x \geq 0$$

We now use the first order linear differential equation theorem, where $I(x) = e^{2x}$ and $Q(x) = e^{-x}$, to find y.

$$y = \frac{1}{e^{2x}}\left[\int e^{2x}e^{-x}\,dx + C\right]$$

$$= \frac{1}{e^{2x}}\left[e^{x} + C\right] = e^{-x} + e^{-2x}C \qquad \text{for } x \geq 0$$

To find C, note that because $y = 2$ when $x = 0$, $1 = C$. So the solution is $y = e^{-x} + e^{-2x}$, $x \geq 0$.   ▬

■ APPLICATIONS OF FIRST-ORDER LINEAR EQUATIONS

EXAMPLE 5   A dilution problem

A tank contains 20 lb of salt dissolved in 50 gal of water. Suppose 3 gal of brine containing 2 lb of dissolved salt per gallon runs into the tank every minute and that the mixture (kept uniform by stirring) runs out of the tank at the rate of 2 gal/min. Find the amount of salt in the tank at any time t. How much salt is in the tank at the end of one hour?

Solution   Let $S(t)$ denote the amount of salt in the tank at the end of t minutes. Because 3 gal of brine flows into the tank each minute and each gallon contains 2 lb of salt, it follows that $(3)(2) = 6$ lb of salt flow into the tank each minute (see Figure 6.35). This is the inflow rate.

For the outflow, note that at time t, there are $S(t)$ lb of salt and $50 + (3 - 2)t$ gallons of solution (because solution flows in at 3 gal/min and out at 2 gal/min). Thus, the concentration of salt in the solution at time t is

$$\frac{S(t)}{50 + t} \text{ lb/gal}$$

Inflow rate of salt:
6 lb/min

Outflow rate of salt:

$\dfrac{S(t)}{50 + t}$ lb/min

Figure 6.35 Rate of flow equals inflow rate minus outflow rate.

and the outflow rate of salt is

$$\left[\frac{S(t)}{50 + t} \text{ lb/gal}\right] [2 \text{ gal/min}] = \frac{2S(t)}{50 + t} \text{ lb/min}$$

Combining these observations, we see that the net rate of change of salt dS/dt is given by the first-order linear differential equation

$$\frac{dS}{dt} = \underset{\underset{\text{Inflow}}{\uparrow}}{6} - \underbrace{\frac{2S}{50 + t}}_{\text{Outflow}}$$

This differential equation can be written as

$$\frac{dS}{dt} + \frac{2S}{50 + t} = 6$$

which we recognize as a first-order linear differential equation with

$$P(t) = \frac{2}{50 + t}$$

and $Q(t) = 6$. The integrating factor is

$$I(t) = e^{\int P(t)\, dt} = e^{\int (2\, dt)/(50 + t)} = e^{2 \ln|50 + t|} = (50 + t)^2$$

and the general solution is

$$S(t) = \frac{1}{(50 + t)^2}\left[\int 6(50 + t)^2\, dt + C\right]$$

$$= \frac{1}{(50 + t)^2}[2(50 + t)^3 + C]$$

$$= 2(50 + t) + \frac{C}{(50 + t)^2}$$

To evaluate C, we recall that there are 20 lb of salt initially in the solution. This means $S(0) = 20$, so that

$$S(0) = 2(50 + 0) + \frac{C}{(50 + 0)^2}$$

$$20 = 100 + \frac{C}{50^2}$$

$$-80(50^2) = C$$

Thus, the solution to the given differential equation, subject to the initial condition $S(0) = 20$, is

$$S(t) = 2(50 + t) - \frac{80(50^2)}{(50 + t)^2}$$

Specifically, at the end of 1 hour (60 min), the tank contains

$$S(60) = 2(50 + 60) - \frac{80(50)^2}{(50 + 60)^2} \approx 203.471\,0744$$

The tank contains about 200 lb of salt. ▬

A second application of first-order linear differential equations involves the current in an RL electric circuit. An RL circuit is one with a constant resistance,

Figure 6.36 An *RL* circuit diagram

R, and a constant inductance, *L*. Figure 6.36 shows an electric circuit with an electromotive force (EMF), a resistor, and an inductor connected in series. The EMF source, which is usually a battery or generator, supplies voltage that causes a current to flow in the circuit. According to Kirchhoff's second law, if the circuit is closed at time $t = 0$, then the applied electromotive force is equal to the sum of the voltage drops in the rest of the circuit. It can be shown that this implies that the current* $I(t)$ that flows in the circuit at time t must satisfy the first-order linear differential equation

$$L\frac{dI}{dt} + RI = E$$

where E is the EMF and L (the inductance) and R (the resistance) are positive constants. Write

$$\frac{dI}{dt} + \frac{R}{L}I = \frac{E}{L}$$

to see that $P(x) = \frac{R}{L}$ (a constant) and $Q(x) = \frac{E}{L}$ (a constant). Then,

$$I(t) = e^{-\int (R/L)dt}\left[\int \frac{E}{L}e^{\int (R/L)\,dt}dt + C\right]$$

$$= e^{-(R/L)t}\left[\frac{E}{L}\int e^{(R/L)t}\,dt + C\right]$$

$$= e^{-(R/L)t}\left[\frac{E}{L}\cdot\frac{L}{R}e^{(R/L)t} + C\right]$$

$$= \frac{E}{R} + Ce^{-(R/L)t}$$

It is reasonable to assume that no current flows when $t = 0$. That is, $I = 0$ when $t = 0$, so we have $0 = \frac{E}{R} + Ce^0$ and $C = -E/R$. The solution of the differential equation is

$$I = \frac{E}{R} - \left(\frac{E}{R}\right)e^{-Rt/L}$$

Notice that because $e^{-(Rt/L)} \to 0$ as $t \to +\infty$, we have

$$\lim_{t\to +\infty} I(t) = \frac{E}{R} - \lim_{t\to +\infty}\left(\frac{E}{R}\right)e^{-Rt/L} = \frac{E}{R}$$

This means that, in the long run, the current I must approach E/R. The solution of the differential equation consists of two parts, which are given special names:

$\frac{E}{R}$ is the **steady-state current.**

$-\left(\frac{E}{R}\right)e^{-Rt/L}$ is the **transient current.**

Figure 6.37 shows how the current $I(t)$ varies with time t.

We have seen four common growth and decay models, which are summarized in Table 6.3. This presentation only touches on a topic that could fill an entire course.

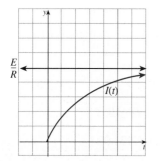

Figure 6.37 The current in an *RL* circuit with constant EMF

---

*It is common practice in physics and applied mathematics to use I as the symbol for current. Naturally, this has nothing to do with the concept of integrating factor introduced earlier in this section.

PROBLEM SET 6.4

Ⓐ *Find the general solution of each separable differential equation given in Problems 1–10.*

1. $\dfrac{dy}{dx} = 3y$ **2.** $\dfrac{dy}{dx} = y^2$ **3.** $\dfrac{dy}{dx} = e^y$

4. $\dfrac{dy}{dx} = e^{x+y}$ **5.** $\dfrac{dy}{dx} = \dfrac{y}{x}$ **6.** $\dfrac{dy}{dx} = xy$

7. $\dfrac{dy}{dx} = \dfrac{\cos x}{\cos y}$ **8.** $\dfrac{dy}{dx} = e^x$ **9.** $\dfrac{dy}{dx} - y = 10$

10. $\dfrac{dy}{dx} + y = 80$

11. Each function on the left satisfies exactly one differential equation on the right. Match each function with the proper equation.

a. $y = e^{-2x}$ *i.* $y''' + 3y'' - 4y' = 0$
b. $y = e^x - e^{-4}$ *ii.* $y'' - 4y = 0$
c. $y = e^{-x}\sin x$ *iii.* $y'' + 2y' - 3y = 0$
d. $y = xe^{3x}$ *iv.* $y'' - 6y' + 9y = 0$
e. $y = e^x + e^{-3x}$ *v.* $y'' + 2y' + 2y = 0$

Solve the differential equations in Problems 12–17.

12. $\dfrac{dy}{dx} + \dfrac{3y}{x} = x$ **13.** $\dfrac{dy}{dx} + \dfrac{2y}{x} = \sqrt{x} + 1$

14. $x^4\dfrac{dy}{dx} + 2x^3y = 5$ **15.** $x^2\dfrac{dy}{dx} + xy = 2$

16. $x\dfrac{dy}{dx} + 2y = xe^{x^3}$ **17.** $\dfrac{dy}{dx} + \left(\dfrac{2x+1}{x}\right)y = e^{-2x}$

In Problems 18–19, solve the initial value problems.

18. $x\dfrac{dy}{dx} - 2y = 2x^3$, $x > 0$ with $y = 2$ when $x = 1$

19. $y' + \dfrac{y}{x} = 0$, $x > 0$ with $y = 2$ when $x = 2$

Ⓑ *In Problems 20–23, find the orthogonal trajectories of the given family of curves. Recall from Section 4.4 that a curve is an orthogonal trajectory of a given family if it intersects each member of that family at right angles.*

20. the family of parabolas $y^2 = 4kx$
21. the family of hyperbolas $xy = c$
22. the family of circles $x^2 + y^2 = r^2$
23. the family of exponential curves $y = Ce^{-x}$

24. The Dead Sea Scrolls were written on parchment at about 100 B.C. What percentage of ^{14}C originally contained in the parchment remained when the scrolls were discovered in 1947?

25. Tests of an artifact discovered at the Debert site in Nova Scotia show that 28% of the original ^{14}C is still present. What is the probable age of the artifact?

26. In 1990 the gross domestic product (GDP) of the United States was \$5,465 billion. If the growth rate from 1989 to 1990 was 5.08%, predict the GDP in 2000.

27. In 1980 the gross domestic product (GDP) of the United States in constant 1972 dollars was \$1,481 billion. If the growth rate from 1980 to 1984 was 2.5% per year, predict the GDP in 1990. Consult an almanac to see if this prediction is correct.

28. According to the Department of Health and Human Services, the divorce rate in 1984 in the United States was 4.9% and there were 1,155,000 divorces that year. How many divorces will there be in 1996 if the divorce rate is constant?

29. According to the Department of Health and Human Services, the marriage rate in 1984 in the United States was 10.5% and there were 2,487,000 marriages that year. How many marriages will there be in 1996 if the marriage rate is constant?

30. A tank contains 10 lb of salt dissolved in 30 gal of water. Suppose 2 gal of brine containing 1 lb of dissolved salt per gallon runs into the tank every minute and that the mixture (kept uniform by stirring) runs out at the same rate.

   a. Find the amount of salt in the tank at time t.

   b. How long does it take (to the nearest second) for the tank to contain 15 lb of salt?

31. In Problem 30, suppose the tank has a capacity of 100 gal and that the mixture flows out at the rate of 1 gal/min (instead of 2 gal/min).

   a. How long will it take for the tank to fill?

   b. How much salt will be in the tank when it is full?

32. The rate at which a drug is absorbed into the blood system is given by

$$\frac{db}{dt} = \alpha - \beta b$$

where $b(t)$ is the concentration of the drug in the bloodstream at time t. What does $b(t)$ approach in the long run (that is, as $t \to +\infty$)? At what time is $b(t)$ equal to half this limiting value? Assume that $b(0) = 0$.

33. An RL-circuit has a resistor of R ohms, inductance of L henries, and emf of E volts where R, L, and E are constant. Suppose no current flows in the circuit at time $t = 0$. If L is doubled and E and R are held constant, what effect does this have on the "long-run" current in the circuit (that is, the current as $t \to +\infty$)?

34. If the 1990 census recorded 16,098,000 Hispanics and if growth is proportional to the population, how many Hispanics will be recorded in 2000 if the 1984 population was 15,575,000?

35. A population of animals on Catalina Island is limited by the amount of food available. If there were 1,800 animals present in 1980 and 2,000 in 1986 and it is estimated that the population cannot exceed 5,000, estimate the population in the year 2000.

36. In 1986 the Chernobyl nuclear disaster in the Soviet Union contaminated the atmosphere. The buildup of radioactive material in the atmosphere satisfies the differential equation

$$\frac{dM}{dt} = r\left(\frac{k}{r} - M\right) \qquad M = 0 \quad \text{when} \quad t = 0$$

where M = mass of radioactive material in the atmosphere after time t (in years); k is the rate at which the radioactive material is introduced into the atmosphere; r is the annual decay rate of the radioactive material. Find the solution, $M(t)$, of this differential equation in terms of k and r.

37. SPY PROBLEM Sweet revenge! The spy has finally tracked down Boldfinger and is ready to pay him back for killing his friend, Siggy Leiter (See Problem 81 in the Supplementary problems from Chapter 5). He is in an airplane flying at 10,000 ft, when he sees the chateau of his nemesis. There is no place to land, so he decides to parachute into Boldfinger's lair. In order to have some control over the spot where he lands, he plans to free-fall for 40 seconds before opening his parachute, but for safety's sake, he doesn't want his speed, v, to be greater than 20 ft/s when he lands. If the spy weighs 192 lb and the air resistance is $0.75v(t)$ until the parachute opens and $10v(t)$ afterward, does he land safely? *Hint:* See Problem 43.

38. An *RL*-circuit has a resistance of $R = 10$ ohms and an inductance of $L = 5$ henries. Find the current $I(t)$ in the circuit at time t if $I(0) = 0$ and the electromotive force (emf) is:

    a. $E = 15$ volts   **b.** $E = 5e^{-2t} \sin t$

▭   Computational Window   ▼ ▲

In the following two problems we pursue the logistic growth equation from a couple of new perspectives. First, by simply studying the differential equation $Q'(t) = kQ (B - Q)$, we can make some important conclusions about the solutions, without actually finding the solutions. Second, many populations do not reproduce throughout the year. In fact, most of animal, insect, and planet life breed and reproduce periodically (for example, once a year). In this case the correct model is no longer a differntial equation, but rather a "difference equation," which you will see in Problem 40. This latter model has a rather surprising complication.

39. By simply examining the differential equation itself, make these arguments:

    a. Argue that $Q(t) = B$ is a solution to $Q'(t) = kQ (B - Q)$.

    b. If $0 < Q(0) < B$, then $Q(t)$ will increase for all t; but, it can never exceed B.

    c. Similarly, what happens if $Q(0) > B$? *Note:* Since all solutions are funneled toward the solution $Q = B$, we say that this solution is highly *stable*.

40. Now, suppose the population $Q(t)$ only produces offspring once each Δt period of time. This could be 1 year or 3 weeks, for instance.

---

    a. Replace the derivative $Q'(t)$ in the differential equation in Problem 39 by the difference quotient

$$\frac{Q(t + \Delta t) - Q(t)}{\Delta t}$$

    Now, for simplicity, take $\Delta t = 1$, thus obtaining

$$Q(t + 1) = Q(t)[1 + k(B - Q(t))]$$

    b. Starting with $Q(0)$, we can compute $Q(1)$, then $Q(2)$, and so on. Write a simple program to generate a sequence of $Q(n)$. For example, the following *Mathematica* code sets the parameters and $Q(0)$, and generates $Q(1)$, $Q(2)$, . . . ,$Q(16)$. Your own code should be similar.

    $k = 0.05$; $B = 6.0$; $Q[0] = 5.0$; Table $[Q[n + 1] = Q[n](1.0 + k(B - Q[n])), \{n, 0, 15\}$

    (Your sequence of $Q(n)$ should move toward the solution $Q = B$.)

    c. In the above difference equation you may encounter a difficulty not seen in the corresponding differential equation; it can become *unstable*. In fact, if the product kB exceeds 2, the problem becomes unstable. This can have serious implications for such populations. To see this, pick k and B so that $kB > 2$ (but not too big!) and run the program. Comment on your results; including your interpretation of the parameters k and B, which will lead to this instability.

    d. A challenge problem. To see why $kB > 2$ leads to instability, you must do the following. We want to study what happens as solution $Q(n)$ get close to the key value B. So let $y(n) = Q(n) - B$, and look at *small* $y(n)$. Replace $Q(n)$ and $y(n) + B$ in the difference equation and discard the $y(n)^2$ term (since it is assumed to be very small). Thus, you obtain the new simple equation:

$$y(n + 1) = y(n)(1 - kB)$$

    Comment on what will happen to the sequence $y(n)$ in the unfortunate event that $kB > 2$. In particular, see if you can explain why we say that the solution $y(n) = 0$ is unstable (thus, the corresponding solution $Q(n) = B$ is unstable).

Ⓒ 41. A **Bernoulli equation** is a differential equation of the form

$$y' + P(x)y = Q(x)y^n$$

where n is a real number, $n \neq 0$, $n \neq 1$.

    a. Show that the change of variable $u = y^{1-n}$ transforms such an equation into one of the form

$$u'(x) + (1 - n) P(x)u(x) = (1 - n) Q(x)$$

    This transformed equation is a first-order linear differential equation in u and can be solved by the methods of this section, yielding a solution to the given Bernoulli equation.

b. Use the change of variable suggested to solve the Bernoulli equation

$$y' + \frac{y}{x} = 2y^2$$

42. Consider a curve with the property that when horizontal and vertical lines are drawn from each point $P(x, y)$ on the curve to the coordinate axes, the area A_1 under the curve is *twice* the area A_2 above the curve, as shown in Figure 6.38.

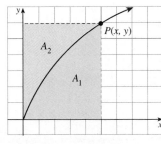

Figure 6.38 Problem 42

Show that x and y satisfy the differential equation

$$\frac{dy}{dx} = \frac{y}{2x}$$

Solve the equation and characterize the family of all curves that satisfy the given geometric condition.

43. **The Motion of a Body Falling Through a Resisting Medium** To discuss the motion of a body falling through the earth's atmosphere, we assume that the only forces acting on the body are gravitational attraction and air resistance that is proportional to the velocity of the body.

a. Suppose the body has weight W so that

$$\underbrace{m\frac{dv}{dt}}_{\text{Force on body}} = \overbrace{W}^{\text{Weight of body}} - \underbrace{kv}_{\text{Air resistance}}$$

Remember $W = mg$ where m is the object's mass and $g = 32$ ft/s^2 is the acceleration due to gravity. Also, $v_0 = v(0)$. Solve this differential equation to express velocity v in terms of time t.

b. Use integration to find the displacement s of the body at time t. (Assume that $s = s_0$ when $t = 0$.)

CHAPTER 6 REVIEW

> **IN THIS REVIEW** Proficiency examination; supplementary problems
> In Chapter 1 we introduced the idea of mathematical modeling, and in Chapter 4 we introduced one of the most important and revolutionary ideas in the history of mathematics, namely, that of a Riemann sum. In this chapter we put these two ideas together to model a great many real-life situations. Table 6.4 summarizes this relationship between modeling and the Riemann sum.
> Problems 1–12 of the proficiency examination test your knowledge of the concepts of this chapter, and Problems 13–25 test your understanding of those concepts by asking you to work sample practice problems. The supplementary problems present questions relating to the material of this chapter in a wide variety of settings.

TABLE 6.4 Modeling Applications Involving Integration

Section	Situation	Riemann Sum Model	Outcome
4.2	**Introduction** Model something in terms of one or more continuous functions on a closed interval $[a, b]$.	1. Partition interval. 2. Choose a number x_k^* arbitrarily from each subinterval of width Δx_k. 3. Form a sum of the type $$R_n = \sum_{k=1}^{n} f(x_k^*)\Delta x_k$$	The approximations improve as the norm of the partitions goes to 0. The Riemann sums approach a limiting integral. Use this integral to define and calculate the quantity we originally wanted to measure.
4.2	**Area** Find the area under a curve defined by $y = f(x)$ where $f(x) \geq 0$, above the x-axis and bounded by the lines $x = a$ and $x = b$.	Find the sum of n rectangles. $$\sum_{k=1}^{n} \underbrace{f(x_k^*)\,\Delta x_k}_{\text{Area of } k\text{th rectangle}}$$	Area $= \displaystyle\int_a^b f(x)\,dx$
4.2	**Displacement** An object is moving along a line having continuous velocity $v(t)$ for each time t between $t = a$ and $t = b$.	Find the sum of n distances. $$\sum_{k=1}^{n} \underbrace{v(t_k^*)\,\Delta t}_{\substack{\text{Distance traveled over} \\ k\text{th time interval}}}$$	Displacement $= \displaystyle\int_a^b v(t)\,dt$

TABLE 6.4 (continued) Modeling Applications Involving Integration

Section	Situation	Riemann Sum Model	Outcome
4.6	**Average value** Find the average of a continuous function on an interval.	Find the average of a weighted sum of n values. $$\frac{1}{n}\sum_{k=1}^{n} f(x_k^*)$$ $$=\frac{1}{b-a}\sum_{k=1}^{n} f(x_k^*)\,\Delta x$$	$\text{Average} = \dfrac{1}{b-a}\displaystyle\int_a^b f(x)\,dx$
4.7	**Area between curves** Find the area between the curves $y = f(x)$ and $y = g(x)$	$$\sum_{k=1}^{n} \underbrace{[f(x_k^*) - g(x_k^*)]\,\Delta x_k}_{\substack{\text{Top curve minus}\\\text{bottom curve}}}$$	$\text{Area} = \displaystyle\int_a^b [f(x) - g(x)]\,dx$
6.1	**Volume by cross section** Find the volume of a solid with a cross section perpendicular to the x-axis with face area $A(x)$.	$$\sum_{k=1}^{n} A(x_k^*)\,\Delta x_k$$	$\text{Volume} = \displaystyle\int_a^b A(x)\,dx$
6.1	**Volumes of revolution** Find the volume of a region revolved about the specified axis. **Disks:** x-axis	$$\sum_{k=1}^{n} \pi\,[f(x_k^*)]^2\,\Delta x_k$$	$\text{Volume} = \pi\displaystyle\int_a^b [f(x)]^2\,dx$
	Washers: x-axis	$$\sum_{k=1}^{n} \pi\big([f(x_k^*)]^2 - [g(x_k^*)]^2\big)\,\Delta x_k$$	$V = \pi\displaystyle\int_a^b ([f(x)]^2 - [g(x)]^2)\,dx$
	Shells: y-axis	$$\sum_{k=1}^{n} 2\pi x_k f(x_k^*)\Delta x_k$$	$\text{Volume} = 2\pi\displaystyle\int_a^b xf(x)\,dx$
6.2	**Arc length** Find the length of a continuously differentiable curve $y = f(x)$ on $[a, b]$.	$$\sum_{k=1}^{n} \sqrt{1 + [f'(x_k^*)]^2}\,\Delta x_k$$	$\text{Length} = \displaystyle\int_a^b \sqrt{1 + [f'(x)]^2}\,dx$
6.2	**Area of a surface of revolution** Find the area of a surface of revolution (about the x-axis).	$$\sum_{k=1}^{n} 2\pi f(x_k^*)\,\Delta s_k$$	$\text{Area} = 2\pi\displaystyle\int_a^b f(x)\sqrt{1 + [f'(x)]^2}\,dx$
6.3	**Mass** Find the mass of a thin plate with constant density ρ.	$$\sum_{k=1}^{n} \rho[f(x_k^*) - g(x_k^*)]\,\Delta x_k$$	$m = \rho\displaystyle\int_a^b [f(x) - g(x)]\,dx$
6.3	**Moment** Find the moment of a thin plate with constant density ρ (about the y-axis). **Centroid** Find the centroid of a homogeneous lamina.	Moment about the y-axis $$\sum_{k=1}^{n} \rho x_k^*[f(x_k^*) - g(x_k^*)]\,\Delta x_k$$ Moment about the x-axis $$\sum_{k=1}^{n} \frac{\rho}{2}\{[f(x_k^*)]^2 - [g(x_k^*)]^2\}\,\Delta x_k$$	$M_y = \rho\displaystyle\int_a^b x[f(x) - g(x)]dx$ $M_x = \dfrac{\rho}{2}\displaystyle\int_a^b \{[f(x)]^2 - [g(x)]^2\}dx$ $(\bar{x}, \bar{y}) = \left(\dfrac{M_y}{m}, \dfrac{M_x}{m}\right)$
6.3	**Work** Find the work done by a variable force $F(x)$ directed along the x-axis from a to b.	$$\sum_{k=1}^{n} F(x_k^*)\,\Delta x_k$$	$\text{Work} = \displaystyle\int_a^b F(x)\,dx$
6.3	**Hydrostatic force** Find the total force of a fluid against one side of a vertical plate.	$$\sum_{k=1}^{n} \rho(h_k^*)L(h_k^*)\,\Delta h_k$$	$F = \displaystyle\int_a^b \rho hL(h)\,dh$

PROFICIENCY EXAMINATION

Concept Problems

1. Describe the process of finding volumes of solids with a known cross-sectional area.
2. Compare and contrast the methods of finding volumes by disks, washers, and shells.
3. What is the formula for arc length of a graph?
4. What is the formula for area of a surface of revolution?
5. How do you find the work done by a variable force?
6. How do you find the force exerted by a liquid on an object submerged vertically?
7. What are the formulas for the mass and centroid of a homogeneous lamina?
8. State the volume theorem of Pappus.
9. State Hooke's law.
10. What is Pascal's principle?
11. What is the formula for solving the first-order linear differential equation $y' + P(x)y = Q(x)$?
12. What is an RL circuit?

Practice Problems

JOURNAL PROBLEMS (*Mathematics Teacher*, December 1990, p. 695.) *Use the integrals A–G to answer the questions in Problems 13–18.*

A. $\pi \int_a^b [f(x)]^2 \, dx$ **B.** $\pi \int_c^d [f(y)]^2 \, dy$ **C.** $\int_a^b A(x) \, dx$

D. $\int_c^d A(y) \, dy$ **E.** $\pi \int_a^b [f(x) - g(x)] \, dx$

F. $\pi \int_a^b \{[f(x)]^2 - [g(x)]^2\} \, dx$ **G.** $\pi \int_c^d \{[f(y)]^2 - [g(y)]^2\} \, dy$

13. Which formula does not seem to belong to this list?
14. Which expressions represent volumes of solids of revolution?
15. Which expressions represent volumes of solids containing holes?
16. Which expressions represent volumes of a solid with parallel cross sections that are perpendicular to an axis?
17. Which expressions represent volumes of solids of revolution revolved about the x-axis?
18. Which expressions represent volumes of solids of revolution revolved about the y-axis?
19. Let R be a region bounded by the graphs of the equations $y = (x - 2)^2$ and $y = 4$.
    a. Sketch the graph of R and find its area.
    b. Find the volume of a solid of revolution of R about the x-axis.
    c. Find the volume of a solid of revolution of R about the y-axis.
20. The base of a solid in the xy-plane is the circular region given by $x^2 + y^2 = 4$. Every cross section perpendicular to the x-axis is a rectangle whose height is twice the length of the side that lies in the xy-plane. Find the volume of this solid.
21. Find the arc length of the curve $y = 2 - x^{3/2}$ from $(0, 2)$ to $(1, 1)$.
22. Find the surface area obtained by revolving the parabolic arc $y^2 = x$ from $(0, 0)$ to $(1, 1)$ about the x-axis. Give answer to the nearest hundredth unit.
23. Solve the first-order linear differential equation

$$\frac{dy}{dx} + \frac{xy}{x + 1} = e^{-x}$$

subject to the condition $y = 1$ when $x = 0$.
24. A tank contains 200 gal of saturated brine with 2 lb of salt per gallon. A salt solution containing 1.3 lb of salt per gallon flows in at the rate of 5 gal/min, and the uniform mixture flows out at 3 gal/min. Find the maximum concentration of salt in the tank and the time required to reach 2/3 the maximum concentration.
25. Find the centroid of the region between $y = x^2 - x$ and $y = x - x^3$ on $[0, 1]$.

SUPPLEMENTARY PROBLEMS

Find the volume of a solid of revolution obtained by revolving the region R about the indicated axis in Problems 1–4.

1. R is bounded by $y = \sqrt{x}$, $x = 9$, $y = 0$; about the x-axis.
2. R is bounded by $y = x^2$, $y = 9 - x^2$; $x = 0$ about the y-axis.
3. R is bounded by $y = x^2$ and $y = x^4$; about the x-axis.
4. R is bounded by $y = \sqrt{\cos x}$, $x = \frac{\pi}{4}$, $x = \frac{\pi}{3}$, and $y = 0$; about the x-axis.
5. The base of a solid is the region in the xy plane that is bounded by the curve $y = 4 - x^2$ and the x-axis. Every cross section of the solid perpendicular to the y-axis is a rectangle whose height is twice the length of the side that lies in the xy plane. Find the volume of the solid.
6. The base of a solid is the region R in the xy plane bounded by the curve $y^2 = x$ and the line $y = x$. Find the volume of the solid if each cross section perpendicular to the x-axis is a semicircle with a diameter in the xy-plane.
7. Find the centroid of a homogeneous lamina covering the region R that is bounded by the parabola $y = 2 - x^2$ and the line $y = x$.
8. A force of 100 lb is required to compress a spring from its natural length of 10 in. to a length of 8 in. Find the work required to compress it to a length of 7 in.
9. A force of 1000 lb is required to compress a spring from its natural length of 10 in. to a length of 8 in. Find the work required to stretch it to a length of 11 in.
10. A tank has the shape of the solid obtained by revolving the parabolic arc $y = 2x^2$ from $x = 0$ to $x = 2$ about the

y-axis (units are in feet). The tank is filled with water. Find the work done in pumping the water to the top of the tank.

11. A tank has the shape of the solid obtained by revolving the parabolic arc $y = 2x^2$ from $x = 0$ to $x = 2$ about the *y*-axis (units are in feet). The tank is filled with water. Find the work done in pumping the water to a point 5 ft above the top of the tank.

12. Find the volume of a sphere of radius *a* by revolving the region bounded by the semicircle $y = \sqrt{a^2 - x^2}$ about the *x*-axis.

13. Find the volume of a sphere of radius *a* by revolving the region bounded by the semicircle $x = \sqrt{a^2 - y^2}$ about the *y*-axis.

14. Two solids S_1 and S_2 have as their base the region in the *xy*-plane bounded by the parabola $y = x^2$ and the line $y = 1$. For solid S_1, each cross section perpendicular to the *x*-axis is a square, and for S_2, each cross section perpendicular to the *y*-axis is a square. Find the volumes of S_1 and S_2.

15. Use calculus to find the lateral surface area of a right circular cylinder with radius *r* and height *h*.

16. Use calculus to find the surface area of a right circular cone with (top) radius *r* and height *h*.

17. A 20-lb bucket in a well is attached to the end of a 60-ft chain that weighs 16 lb. If the bucket is filled with 50 lb of dirt, how much work is done in lifting the bucket and chain to the top of the well?

18. A conical tank whose vertex points down is 10 ft high with (top) diameter 4 ft. The tank is filled with a fluid of density $\rho = 22$ lb/ft³. Find the work required to pump all the fluid to the top of the tank.

19. A swimming pool is 3 ft deep at one end and 8 ft deep at the other, as shown in Figure 6.39. The pool is 30 ft long and 25 ft wide with vertical sides. Find the fluid force against one of the 30-ft sides.

Figure 6.39 Diagram of a swimming pool

20. The ends of a container filled with water have the shape of the region *R* bounded by the curve $y = x^4$ and the line $y = 16$. Find the fluid force exerted by the water on one end of the container.

21. An observation porthole on a ship is circular with diameter 2 ft and is located so that its center is 3 ft below the water line. Find the fluid force on the porthole, assuming that the boat is in seawater (density 64 lb/ft³).

22. A conical tank whose vertex points down is 12 ft high with (top) diameter 6 ft. The tank is filled with a fluid of density $\rho = 22$ lb/ft³. If the tank is only half full, find the

work required to pump all the fluid to a height of 2 ft above the top of the tank.

23. Each end of a container filled with water has the shape of an isosceles triangle, as shown in Figure 6.40. Find the force exerted by the water on an end of the container.

Figure 6.40 Water pressure

24. A container has the shape of the solid formed by rotating the region bounded by the curve $y = x^3$ ft and the lines $x = 0$ ft and $y = 1$ ft about the *y*-axis. If the container is filled with water, how much work is required to pump all the water out of the container?

25. A gate of a water main has the shape of a circle with diameter 10 ft. If water stands 2 ft high in the main, what is the force exerted by the water on the gate?

Suppose a particle of mass m moves along a number line under the influence of a variable force F, which always acts in a direction parallel to the line of motion. Then, at a given time the particle is said to have **kinetic energy**

$$K = \tfrac{1}{2}mv^2$$

where v is the particle's velocity, and it has **potential energy**

$$P = -\int_{s_0}^{s} F \, dx$$

relative to the point s on the line of motion. Use these definitions in Problems 26–27.

26. A spring at rest has potential energy $P = 0$. If the spring constant is 30 lb/ft, how far must the spring be stretched so that its potential energy is 20 ft-lb?

27. A particle with mass *m* falls freely near the earth's surface. At time $t = 0$, the particle is s_0 units above the ground and is falling with velocity v_0.

   a. Find the potential energy *P* of the particle in terms of *s* if the potential energy is 0 when $s = s_0$.

   b. Find the potential energy *P* and the kinetic energy *K* of the particle in terms of time *t*.

28. An object weighs $w = 1,000r^{-2}$ grams, where *r* is the object's distance from the center of the earth. What work is required to lift the object from the surface of the earth ($r = 6,400$ km) to a point 3,600 km above the surface of the earth?

29. A certain species has population $P(t)$ at time *t*. The growth rate of the population is affected by seasonal variations in the food supply and may be modeled by the differential equation

$$\frac{dP}{dt} = k(P - A)\cos t$$

where k and A are physical constants. Solve the differential equation and express $P(t)$ in terms of k, A, and P_0, the initial population.

30. A company plans to hire additional advertising personnel. Suppose it is estimated that if x new people are hired, they will bring in addition revenue of $R(x) = \sqrt{2x}$ thousand dollars and that the cost of adding these x people will be $C(x) = \frac{1}{3}x$ thousand dollars. How many new people should be hired? How much total net revenue (that is, revenue minus cost) is gained by hiring these people?

31. Find the center of mass of a thin plate of constant density if the plate occupies the region bounded by the lines $2y = x$, $x + 3y = 5$, and the x-axis.

32. The portion of the ellipse

$$\frac{x^2}{a^2} + \frac{y^2}{b^2} = 1$$

that lies in the first quadrant between $x = r$ and $x = a$, for $0 < r < a$, is revolved about the x-axis to form a solid S_e. Find the volume of S_e.

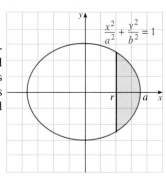

33. The portion of the hyperbola

$$\frac{x^2}{a^2} - \frac{y^2}{b^2} = 1$$

that lies in the first quadrant between $x = a$ and $x = r$, for $0 < a < r$, is revolved about the x-axis to form a solid S_h. Find the volume of S_h.

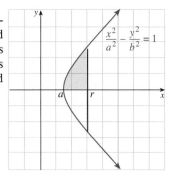

34. Let R be the part of the ellipse

$$\frac{x^2}{a^2} + \frac{y^2}{b^2} = 1$$

that lies in the first quadrant. Use the theorem of Pappus to find the coordinates of the centroid of R. You may use the facts that R has area $A = \frac{1}{4}\pi\, ab$, and the semiellipsoid it generates when it is revolved about the x-axis has volume $V = \frac{2}{3}\pi ab^2$.

35. A container of a certain fluid is raised from the ground on a pulley. While resting on the ground, the container and fluid together weigh 200 lb. However, as the container is raised, fluid leaks out in such a way that at height x feet above the ground, the total weight of the container and fluid is $200 - 0.5x$ lb. Find the work done in raising the container 100 ft.

36. A bag of sand is being lifted vertically upward at the rate of 31 ft/min. If the bag originally weighed 40 lb and leaks at the rate of 0.2 lb/s, how much work is done in raising it until it is empty?

37. The vertical end of a trough is an equilateral triangle, 3 ft on a side. Assuming the trough is filled with a fluid of density $\rho = 40$ lb/ft^3, find the force on the end of the trough.

38. The radius of a circular water main is 2 ft. Assuming the main is half full of water, find the total force exerted by the water on a gate that crosses the main at one end.

39. The force acting on an object moving along a straight line is known to be a linear function of its position. Find the force function F if it is known that 13 ft-lb of work is required to move the object over 6 ft and 44 ft-lb of work is required to move it 12 ft.

40. A tank has the shape of a rectangular parallelepiped with length 10 ft, width 6 ft, and height 8 ft. The tank contains a liquid of density $\rho = 20$ lb/ft^3. Find the level of the liquid in the tank if it will require 2,400 ft-lb of work to move all the liquid in the tank to the top.

41. A tank is constructed by placing a right circular cylinder of height 10 ft and radius 2 ft on top of a hemisphere with the same radius. If the tank is filled with a fluid of density $\rho = 24$ lb/ft^3, how much work is done in bringing all the fluid to the top of the tank?

42. A piston in a cylinder causes a gas either to expand or to contract. Assume the pressure P and the volume of gas V in the cylinder satisfy the adiabatic law (no exchange of heat)

$$PV^{1.4} = C$$

where C is a constant.

a. If the gas goes from volume V_1 to volume V_2, show that the work done is given by

$$W = \int_{V_1}^{V_2} CV^{-1.4}\, dV$$

b. How much work is done if 0.6 m³ of steam at a pressure of 2,500 newtons/m² expands 50%?

43. A thin sheet of tin is in the shape of a square, 16 cm on a side. A rectangular corner of area 156 cm² is cut from the square, and the centroid of the portion that remains is found to be 4.88 cm from one side of the original square, as shown in Figure 6.41. How far is it from the other three sides?

Figure 6.41 Centroid of a square

44. The front and back faces of a container are parabolic surfaces with vertical axes and the vertex of the parabola at the bottom (assume the coordinate axes are located so the parabola has the form $y = kx^2$). Each parabolic face is 10 ft across the top and 15 ft deep. If the container is filled with a liquid of density $\rho = 40$ lb/ft³, find the force on either parabolic face.

45. Solve the differential equation

$$\frac{dy}{dx} = \frac{y}{x + c^y y^2}$$

by reversing the roles of x and y (in other words, treat y as the independent variable).

46. Let R be the region bounded by the semicircle $y = \sqrt{4 - x^2}$ and the x-axis, and let S be the solid with base R and trapezoidal cross sections perpendicular to the x-axis. Assume that the two slant sides and the shorter parallel sides are all half as long as the side that lies in the base of each cross-sectional trapezoid are congruent as shown in Figure 6.42. Set up but do not evaluate an integral for the volume of S.

Cross section

Figure 6.42 Volume of a region S

47. A child is building a sand structure at the beach. Find the work done if the density of the sand is $\rho = 140$ lb/ft³ and the structure has the shape of a cone of height 1 ft and diameter 2 ft.

48. A child is building a sand structure at the beach. Find the work done if the density of the sand is $\rho = 140$ lb/ft³ and the structure is a tower (cylinder) of height 1 ft and radius 4 in.

49. Let S be the solid generated by revolving about the x-axis the region bounded by the parabola $y = x^2$ and the line $y = x$. Find the number A so that the plane perpendicular to the x-axis at $x = A$ divides S in half. That is, the volume on one side of A equals the volume on the other side.

50. A plate in the shape of an isosceles triangle is submerged vertically in water, as shown in Figure 6.43. Find the force on one side of the plate if the two equal sides have length 3, the third side has length 5, and the top vertex of the triangle is 4 units below the surface.

Figure 6.43 Hydrostatic pressure

51. Repeat Problem 50 for equal sides of length A, the third side with length B, and the top vertex D units below the surface, as shown in Figure 6.43.

52. Find the arc length of the curve

$$y = Ax^3 + \frac{B}{x}$$

on the interval $[a, b]$, where A and B are positive constants with $AB = \frac{1}{12}$.

53. THINK TANK PROBLEM When the line segment $y = x - 2$ between $x = 1$ and $x = 3$ is revolved about the x-axis, it generates part of a cone. Explain why the surface area of this cone is *not* given by the integral

$$\int_1^3 2\pi(x - 2)\sqrt{2}\, dx$$

What is the actual surface area?

54. An object below the surface of the earth is attracted by a gravitational force that is directly proportional to the distance from the object to the center of the earth. Find the work done in lifting an object weighing W lb from a depth of s feet (below the surface) to the surface. Assume the earth's radius is 4,000 miles.

In Problems 55–56, consider a continuous curve $y = f(x)$ that passes through $(-1, 4), (0, 3), (1, 4), (2, 6), (3, 5), (4, 6), (5, 7), (6, 6), (7, 4),$ and $(8, 3)$.

55. Use Simpson's rule to estimate the volume of the solid formed by revolving this curve about the x-axis for $[-1, 9]$.

56. Use the trapezoidal rule to estimate the volume of the solid formed by revolving this curve about the line $y = -1$ on $[-1, 9]$.

57. Find the centroid of a right triangle whose legs have lengths a and b. *Hint*: Use the theorem of Pappus.

58. The largest of the pyramids at Giza in Egypt is roughly 480 ft high and has a square base, 750 ft on a side. If the rock in the pyramid averages 160 lb/ft^3, how much work was required to lift the stones into place to construct the pyramid?

59. The half-life of the radioactive isotope cobalt-60 is 5.25 yr.

  a. What percentage of a given sample of cobalt 60 remains after 5 yr?

  b. How long will it take for 90% of a given sample to disintegrate?

60. The rate at which salt dissolves in water is directly proportional to the amount that remains undissolved. If 8 lb of salt is placed in a container of water and 2 lb dissolves in 30 min, how long will it take for 1 lb to dissolve?

61. Scientists are observing a species of insect in a certain swamp region. The insect population is estimated to be 10 million and is expected to grow at the rate of 2% per year. Assuming that the growth is exponential and stays that way for a period of years, what will the insect population be in 10 yr? How long will it take to double?

62. Find the length of the curve $y = e^x$ on the interval $[0, 1]$.

63. Find the volume of the solid generated when the region under the curve

$$y = \frac{1}{\sqrt{9 - x^2}}$$

on the interval $[0, 2]$ is revolved about the y-axis.

64. Find the volume of the solid formed by revolving about the x-axis the region bounded by the curve

$$y = \frac{2}{\sqrt{3x - 2}}$$

the x-axis, and the lines $x = 1$ and $x = 2$.

65. Find the area between the curves $y = \tan^2 x$ and $y = \sec^2 x$ on the interval $\left[0, \frac{\pi}{4}\right]$.

66. Find the surface area of the solid generated by revolving the region bounded by the x-axis and the curve

$$y = e^x + \tfrac{1}{4}e^{-x}$$

on $[0, 1]$ about the x-axis.

67. Find the volume of the solid whose base is the region R bounded by the curve $y = e^x$ and the lines $y = 0$, $x = 0$, $x = 1$, if cross sections perpendicular to the x-axis are equilateral triangles.

68. Find the length of the curve $y = \ln \sec x$ on the interval $\left[0, \frac{\pi}{3}\right]$.

69. Find the length of the curve

$$x = \frac{ay^2}{b^2} - \frac{b^2}{8a} \ln \frac{y}{b}$$

between $y = b$ and $y = 2b$.

70. **Snowplow Problem of R. P. Agnew** (This problem was mentioned in the preview for Chapter 4.) One day it starts snowing at a steady rate sometime before noon. At noon, a snowplow starts to clear a straight, level section of road. If the plow clears 1 mi of road during the first hour but requires 2 hr to clear the second mile, at what time did it start snowing? Answer this question by completing the following steps:

  a. Let t be the time (in hours) from noon. Let h be the depth of the snow at time t, and let s be the distance moved by the plow. If the plow has width w and clears snow at the constant rate p, explain why

$$wh\frac{ds}{dt} = p$$

  b. Suppose it started snowing t_0 hours before noon. Let r denote the (constant) rate of snowfall. Explain why

$$h(t) = r(t + t_0)$$

  By combining this equation with the differential equation in part **a,** note that

$$wr(t + t_0)\frac{ds}{dt} = p$$

  Solve this differential equation (with appropriate conditions) to obtain t_0 and answer the question posed in the problem.

71. Putnam Examination Problem Find the length of the curve $y^2 = x^3$ from the origin to the point where the tangent makes an angle of 45° with the x-axis.

72. Putnam Examination Problem A solid is bounded by two bases in the horizontal planes $z = h/2$ and $z = -h/2$, and by a surface with the property that every horizontal cross section has area given by an expression of the form

$$A = a_0z^3 + a_1z^2 + a_2z + a_3$$

  a. Show that the solid has volume $V = \tfrac{1}{6}h(B_1 + B_2 + 4M)$ where B_1 and B_2 are the area of the bases and M is the area of the middle horizontal cross section.

  b. Show that the formulas for the volume of a cone and a sphere can be obtained from the formula in part **a** for certain special choices of a_0, a_1, a_2, and a_3.

"Houdini's Escape"

HARRY HOUDINI (born Ehrich Weiss) (1874–1926)

Mathematics is the gate and key of the sciences. . . . Neglect of mathematics works injury to all knowledge, since he who is ignorant of it cannot know the other sciences or the things of this world. And what is worse, those who are thus ignorant are unable to perceive their own ignorance and so do not seek a remedy.

Roger Bacon
Opus Majus, Part 4, Distinctia Prima, cap. 1

It seems to be expected of every pilgrim up the slopes of the mathematical Parnassus, that he will at some point or other of his journey sit down and invent a definite integral or two towards the increase of the common stock.

J. J. Sylvester
Notes to the Meditation on Poncelet's Theorem; Mathematical Papers, Vol. 2, p. 214

This project is to be done in groups of three or four students. Each group will submit a single written report.

Harry Houdini was a famous escape artist. In this project we relive a trick of his that challenged his mathematical prowess, as well as his skill and bravery. It may challenge these qualities in you as well.

Houdini had his feet shackled to the top of a concrete block which was placed on the bottom of a giant laboratory flask. The cross sectional radius of the flask, measured in feet, was given as a function of height z from the ground by the formula $r(z) = 10z^{-1/2}$, with the bottom of the flask at $z = 1$ ft. The flask was then filled with water at a steady rate of 22π ft^3/min. Houdini's job was to escape the shackles before he was drowned by the rising water in the flask.

Now Houdini knew it would take him exactly 10 minutes to escape the shackles. For dramatic impact, he wanted to time his escape so it was completed precisely at the moment the water level reached the top of his head. Houdini was exactly 6 ft tall. In the design of the apparatus, he was allowed to specify only one thing: the height of the concrete block he stood on.

Your paper is not limited to the following questions but should include these concerns: How high should the block be? (You can neglect Houdini's volume and the volume of the block.) How fast is the water level changing when the flask first starts to fill? How fast is the water level changing at the instant when the water reaches the top of his head? You might also help Houdini with any size flask by generalizing the derivation: Consider a flask with cross-sectional radius $r(z)$ an arbitrary function of z with a constant inflow rate of $dV/dt = A$. Can you find dh/dt as a function of $h(t)$?

*MAA Notes 17 (1991), "Priming the Calculus Pump: Innovations and Resources," by Marcus S. Cohen, Edward D. Gaughan, R. Arthur Knoebel, Douglas S. Kurtz, and David J. Pengelley.

CUMULATIVE REVIEW FOR CHAPTERS 1–6

1. ■ **What Does This Say?** Define limit. Explain what this definition is saying using your own words.

2. ■ **What Does This Say?** Define derivative. Explain what this definition is saying using your own words.

3. ■ **What Does This Say?** Define a definite integral. Explain what this definition is saying using your own words.

4. ■ **What Does This Say?** Define a differential equation, and in your own words describe the procedure for solving a first-order linear differential equation.

Evaluate the limits in Problems 5–13.

5. $\lim\limits_{x \to 2} \dfrac{3x^2 - 5x - 2}{3x^2 - 7x + 2}$

6. $\lim\limits_{x \to +\infty} \dfrac{3x^2 + 7x + 2}{5x^2 - 3x + 3}$

7. $\lim\limits_{x \to +\infty} (\sqrt{x^2 + x} - x)$

8. $\lim\limits_{x \to \pi/2} \dfrac{\cos^2 x}{\cos x^2}$

9. $\lim\limits_{x \to 0} \dfrac{x \sin x}{x + \sin^2 x}$

10. $\lim\limits_{x \to 0} \dfrac{\sin 3x}{x}$

11. $\lim\limits_{x \to +\infty} (1 + x)^{2/x}$

12. $\lim\limits_{x \to 0} \dfrac{\ln(x^2 + 50)}{2x}$

13. $\lim\limits_{x \to 0^+} x^{\sin x}$

Find the derivatives in Problems 14–22.

14. $y = 6x^3 - 4x + 2$

15. $y = (x^2 + 1)^3 (3x - 4)^2$

16. $y = \dfrac{x^2 - 4}{3x + 1}$

17. $y = \dfrac{x}{x + \cos x}$

18. $x^2 + 3xy + y^2 = 0$

19. $y = \csc^2 3x$

20. $y = e^{5x - 4}$

21. $y = \ln(5x^2 + 3x - 2)$

22. $y = \cos^{-1}(x^2 - 3)$

Find the integrals in Problems 23–28.

23. $\displaystyle\int_4^9 d\theta$

24. $\displaystyle\int_{-1}^1 50(2x - 5)^3 \, dx$

25. $\displaystyle\int_0^1 \dfrac{x \, dx}{\sqrt{9 + x^2}}$

26. $\displaystyle\int \csc 3\theta \cot 3\theta \, d\theta$

27. $\displaystyle\int \dfrac{e^x \, dx}{e^x + 2}$

28. $\displaystyle\int \dfrac{x^3 + 2x - 5}{x} \, dx$

29. Evaluate $\displaystyle\int_0^4 \dfrac{dx}{\sqrt{1 + x^3}}$ using Simpson's rule with $n = 6$.

30. Sketch the graph of $y = x^3 - 5x^2 + 2x + 8$.

31. Sketch the graph of $y = \dfrac{4 - x^2}{4 + x^2}$.

32. Find the maximum value of
$f(x) = \frac{1}{3}x^3 - 2x^2 + 3x - 10$ on $[0, 6]$.

33. Find the area bounded by the curve $y = x\sqrt{x^2 + 8}$ and the x-axis on $[-2, 1]$.

34. Find the area between the curves $y = \sin x$ and $y = \cos x$ and the lines $x = 0$ and $x = 1$.

35. Find the slope of the curve $y = \dfrac{\sin x}{x}$ at the point $x = \frac{\pi}{4}$.

Solve the differential equations in Problems 36–37.

36. $\dfrac{dy}{dx} = x^2 y^2 \sqrt{4 - x^3}$

37. $y \, dx - x \, dy = x \ln x \, dx$

Find the particular solution of the differential equations in Problems 38–39.

38. $\dfrac{dy}{dx} = 2(5 - y)$; $y = 3$ when $x = 0$

39. $\dfrac{dy}{dx} = e^y \sin x$ with $y = 5$ when $x = 0$

40. Find the volume of the solid formed by revolving about the x-axis the region bounded by the curve
$$y = \dfrac{2}{\sqrt{3x - 2}}$$
the x-axis, and the lines $x = 1$ and $x = 2$.

41. Find the arc length of the curve
$$y = \sqrt{e^{2x} - 1} - \sec^{-1} e^x$$
on the interval $[0, 1]$.

42. A mason lifts a 25-lb bucket of mortar from ground level to the top of a 50-ft-high building using a rope that weighs 0.25 lb/ft. Find the work done in lifting the bucket.

43. A rocket is launched vertically from a point on the ground 5,000 ft from a TV camera. If the rocket is rising vertically at the rate of 850 ft/s at the instant the rocket is 4,000 ft above the ground, how fast must the TV camera change the angle of elevation in order to keep the rocket in the picture?

44. A lighthouse is 4,000 ft from a straight shore. Measuring the beam on the shore from the point P on the shore that is closest to the lighthouse, it is observed that the rotating light is moving at the rate of 5 ft/s when it is 1000 ft from P. How fast is the light revolving at this instant?

45. A tank contains 50 gal of pure water. Brine containing 3 lb of dissolved salt per gallon runs into the tank at the rate of 2 gal/min, and the well-stirred mixture runs out at the rate of 1 lb per gallon. How much salt does the tank contain after 15 min?

7

Methods of Integration

PREVIEW

In this chapter we increase the number of techniques and procedures for integrating a function. One of the most important techniques, substitution, is reviewed in the first section and is then expanded in several different contexts. Other important integration procedures include using tables, integration by parts, and partial fractions. In addition, improper integrals, hyperbolic functions, and inverse hyperbolic functions are discussed.

PERSPECTIVE

It is possible to differentiate most functions that arise in practice by applying a fairly short list of rules and formulas, but integration is a more complicated process. The purpose of this chapter is to increase your ability to integrate a variety of different functions. Learning to integrate is like learning to play a musical instrument: At first, it may seem impossibly complicated, but if you persevere, after a while music starts to happen. It should be noted that as technology becomes more available, *techniques* become less important and *ideas* become more important. If you have such technology available, you might wish to consult the *Technology Manual*.

7.1 REVIEW OF SUBSTITUTION AND INTEGRATION BY TABLE

> **IN THIS SECTION** Review of substitution, integral tables, trigonometric substitutions
>
> In Chapter 4 we derived a number of integration formulas and examined various algebraic procedures for reducing a given integral to a form that can be handled by these formulas. In this section we review those formulas as well as the important method of integration by substitution. Today's technology has greatly enhanced the ability of professional mathematicians and scientists in techniques of integration, thereby minimizing the need for spending hours learning rarely used integration techniques. Along with this new technology, the use of integral tables has increased in importance. Most mathematical handbooks contain extensive integral tables, and we have included a complete integration table in the accompanying book, *Student Mathematics Handbook*. For your convenience, we have also included a short table of integrals in Appendix D.

For convenient reference, the most important integration rules and formulas are listed inside the back cover. Notice that the first four integration formulas are the procedural rules, which allow us to break up integrals into simpler forms, whereas those on the remainder of the page form the building blocks of integration.

■ REVIEW OF SUBSTITUTION

Remember when doing substitution that you must choose u, calculate du, and then substitute to make the form you are integrating look *exactly like* one of the known integration formulas. We will review substitution by looking at different situations and special substitutions that prove useful.

EXAMPLE 1 Integration by substitution

Find $\displaystyle\int \frac{x^2\,dx}{(x^3-2)^5}$.

Solution Let u be the value in parentheses; that is, let $u = x^3 - 2$. Then $du = 3x^2\,dx$, so by substitution:

$$\int \frac{x^2\,dx}{(x^3-2)^5} = \int \frac{\frac{du}{3}}{u^5} = \frac{1}{3}\int u^{-5}\,du = \frac{1}{3}\frac{u^{-4}}{-4} + C = -\frac{1}{12}(x^3-2)^{-4} + C$$ ▬

EXAMPLE 2 Fitting the form of a known integration formula by substitution

Find $\displaystyle\int \frac{t\,dt}{\sqrt{1-t^4}}$.

Solution We notice the similarity between this and the formula for inverse sine if we let $a = 1$ and $u = t^2$. If $u = t^2$, then $du = 2t\,dt$ and

$$\int \frac{t\,dt}{\sqrt{1-t^4}} = \int \frac{\frac{du}{2}}{\sqrt{1-u^2}} \qquad \text{If } u = t^2 \text{, then } du = 2t\,dt, \ t\,dt = \frac{du}{2}, \text{ and } \sqrt{1-t^4} = \sqrt{1-(t^2)^2} = \sqrt{1-u^2}.$$

$$= \frac{1}{2}\int \frac{du}{\sqrt{1-u^2}} = \frac{1}{2}\sin^{-1}u + C = \frac{1}{2}\sin^{-1}t^2 + C$$ ▬

The art of substitution (Section 4.3) is very important, because many of the techniques developed in this chapter will be used in conjunction with substitution. Examples 3 and 4 illustrate additional ways substitution can be used in integration problems.

EXAMPLE 3   Substitution to derive an integration formula

Find $\int \sec x \, dx$.

Solution   Multiply the integrand $\sec x$ by $\sec x + \tan x$ and divide by the same quantity:

$$\int \sec x \, dx = \int \frac{\sec x (\sec x + \tan x)}{\sec x + \tan x} \, dx = \int \frac{\sec x \tan x + \sec^2 x}{\sec x + \tan x} \, dx$$

The advantage of this rearrangement is that the numerator is now the derivative of the denominator. That is, using the substitution

$$u = \sec x + \tan x$$
$$du = (\sec x \tan x + \sec^2 x) \, dx$$

we find

$$\int \frac{\sec x \tan x + \sec^2 x}{\sec x + \tan x} \, dx = \int \frac{du}{u} = \ln|u| + C = \ln|\sec x + \tan x| + C$$

You may wonder why anyone would think to multiply and divide the integrand $\sec x$ in Example 3 by $\sec x + \tan x$. To say that we do it "because it works" is probably not a very satisfying answer. However, techniques like this are passed on from generation to generation, and it should be noted that multiplication by 1 is a common method in mathematics for changing the form of an expression.

EXAMPLE 4   Substitution after an algebraic manipulation

Find $\int \frac{dx}{1 + e^x}$.

Solution   The straightforward substitution $u = 1 + e^x$ does not work:

$$\int \frac{dx}{1 + e^x} = \int \frac{\frac{du}{e^x}}{u} = \int \frac{du}{e^x u} \qquad \begin{array}{l}\textit{This is not an appropriate form} \\ \textit{because } x \textit{ has not been eliminated.}\end{array}$$

$u = 1 + e^x; \quad du = e^x \, dx$

Instead of the straightforward substitution, rewrite the integrand as follows:

$$\frac{1}{1 + e^x} = \frac{e^{-x}}{e^{-x}}\left(\frac{1}{1 + e^x}\right) = \frac{e^{-x}}{e^{-x} + 1}$$

$u = e^{-x} + 1; \quad du = -e^{-x} \, dx$

$$\int \frac{dx}{1 + e^x} = \int \frac{e^{-x} dx}{e^{-x} + 1} = \int \frac{-du}{u} = -\ln|u| + C = -\ln(e^{-x} + 1) + C$$

Remember, $e^{-x} + 1 > 0$ for all x, so $\ln|e^{-x} + 1| = \ln(e^{-x} + 1)$.

Algebraic procedures can also be used to handle integrals of the form

$$\int \frac{dx}{Ax^2 + Bx + C}$$

Computational Window ▾ ▲

A computer form for the integral in Example 3 is $\ln\left|\tan\left(\frac{\pi + 2x}{4}\right)\right|$. Note that the constant C is assumed to be 0 in many software programs.

If $B^2 - 4AC \geq 0$, the quadratic $Ax^2 + Bx + C$ can be factored using only real numbers, and the integral can be evaluated by a *method of partial fractions*, which is developed in Section 7.3. If $B^2 - 4AC < 0$, the denominator cannot be factored using only real numbers, and we proceed by first completing the square, as shown in the following example.

EXAMPLE 5   Substitution by completing the square

Find $\displaystyle\int \frac{dx}{2x^2 + 4x + 5}$.

Solution   You might begin by trying the "obvious" substitution $u = 2x^2 + 4x + 5$, but this substitution does not work (try it). Notice, however, that the denominator is a quadratic form with $A = 2$, $B = 4$, and $C = 5$. Because

$$B^2 - 4AC = 4^2 - 4(2)(5) < 0$$

we complete the square in the denominator of the integrand:

$$2x^2 + 4x + 5 = 2\left[(x^2 + 2x) + \tfrac{5}{2}\right] = 2\left[(x^2 + 2x + 1) - 1 + \tfrac{5}{2}\right] = 2\left[(x + 1)^2 + \tfrac{3}{2}\right]$$

Thus,

$$\int \frac{dx}{2x^2 + 4x + 5} = \int \frac{dx}{2\left[(x+1)^2 + \tfrac{3}{2}\right]} = \int \frac{du}{2\left[u^2 + \tfrac{3}{2}\right]}$$

$$u = x + 1; \qquad du = dx$$

Compare this with the rule for the inverse tangent $\left(\text{with } a^2 = \tfrac{3}{2}\right)$.

$$\int \frac{du}{2\left(u^2 + \tfrac{3}{2}\right)} = \tfrac{1}{2}\left(\frac{1}{\sqrt{\tfrac{3}{2}}} \tan^{-1} \frac{u}{\sqrt{\tfrac{3}{2}}}\right) + C = \tfrac{1}{2}\sqrt{\tfrac{2}{3}} \tan^{-1} \sqrt{\tfrac{2}{3}}(x + 1) + C \qquad \blacksquare$$

When the integrand involves terms with fractional exponents, it is usually a good idea to choose the substitution $x = u^n$, where n is the smallest integer that is divisible by all the denominators of the exponents. For example, if the integrand involves terms such as $x^{1/4}$, $x^{2/3}$, and $x^{1/6}$, then the substitution $x = u^{12}$ is suggested, because 12 is the smallest integer divisible by the exponential denominators 4, 3, and 6. The advantage of this policy is that it guarantees that each fractional power of x becomes an integral power of u. Thus,

$$x^{1/6} = (u^{12})^{1/6} = u^2, \qquad x^{1/4} = (u^{12})^{1/4} = u^3, \qquad x^{2/3} = (u^{12})^{2/3} = u^8$$

EXAMPLE 6   Substitution with fractional exponents

Find $\displaystyle\int \frac{dx}{x^{1/3} + x^{1/2}}$.

Solution   Because 6 is the smallest integer divisible by the denominators 2 and 3, we set $u = x^{1/6}$, so that $u^6 = x$ and $6u^5\, du = dx$. We now use substitution

$$\int \frac{dx}{x^{1/3} + x^{1/2}} = \int \frac{6u^5\, du}{(u^6)^{1/3} + (u^6)^{1/2}} \qquad\qquad \textit{Let } x = u^6.$$

$$= \int \frac{6u^5\, du}{u^2 + u^3} = \int \frac{6u^5\, du}{u^2(u + 1)} = \int \frac{6u^3\, du}{1 + u}$$

Substitution does not guarantee an integrable form. When the degree of the numerator is larger than the degree of the denominator, division is often

helpful. By long division

$$\frac{6u^3}{1 + u} = 6u^2 - 6u + 6 + \frac{-6}{1 + u}$$

$$\int \frac{6u^3\,du}{1 + u} = \int \left(6u^2 - 6u + 6 + \frac{-6}{1 + u}\right) du$$

$$= 2u^3 - 3u^2 + 6u - 6\,\ln|1 + u| + C$$

$$= 2(x^{1/6})^3 - 3(x^{1/6})^2 + 6x^{1/6} - 6\,\ln|1 + x^{1/6}| + C \qquad \textit{Because } u = x^{1/6}$$

$$= 2x^{1/2} - 3x^{1/3} + 6x^{1/6} - 6\,\ln|1 + x^{1/6}| + C$$

■ USING TABLES OF INTEGRALS

Example 6 (especially the part involving long division) seems particularly lengthy. When faced with the necessity of integrating a function such as

$$\int \frac{6u^3\,du}{1 + u}$$

most would turn to a computer, calculator, or a table of integrals. If you look, for example, at the short integration table (Appendix D), you will find (formula 37)

$$\int \frac{u^3\,du}{au + b} = \frac{(au + b)^3}{3a^4} - \frac{3b(au + b)^2}{2a^4} + \frac{3b^2(au + b)}{a^4} - \frac{b^3}{a^4}\ln(au + b)$$

If we let $a = 1$ and $b = 1$, we find

$$\int \frac{6u^3\,du}{1 + u} = 6\left[\frac{(u + 1)^3}{3} - \frac{3(u + 1)^2}{2} + \frac{3(u + 1)}{1} - \ln|u + 1|\right]$$

$$= 2(u + 1)^3 - 9(u + 1)^2 + 18(u + 1) - 6\,\ln|u + 1|$$

We note that when using most tables, it is necessary to add the constant C to the form given by the table. We also note that the algebraic form does not always match the form we obtain by direct integration. You might wish to show algebraically that the form we have just found and the form

$$2u^3 - 3u^2 + 6u - 6\,\ln|1 + u| + C$$

from Example 6 are the same.

***

Computational Window

If we use some computer software (such as Derive, Maple, or Mathematica), for $\int \dfrac{6u^3\,du}{1 + u}$ we obtain

$$-6\,\text{LN}(u + 1) + 2u^3 - 3u^2 + 6u$$

On the other hand, if we are using computer software, we would not need the simplified form for Example 6, and we find

$$\int \frac{dx}{x^{1/3} + x^{1/2}} = -6\,\text{LN}(x^{1/6} + 1) + 2\sqrt{x} - 3x^{1/3} + 6x^{1/6}$$

If we compare this answer with the one we found in Example 6, we note that most software programs do not necessarily give the terms in the usual order, they do not show the absolute value symbols, and they also do not provide the constant C.

To use an integral table, first classify the integral by form. The forms listed in the table of integrals included in the *Student Mathematics Handbook* are as follows:

Elementary forms (formulas 1–29; these were developed in the text)

Linear and quadratic forms (formulas 30–134)
Forms involving $au + b$; $u^2 + a^2$; $u^2 - a^2$; $a^2 - u^2$; $au + b$
and $pu + q$; $au^2 + bu + c$

Radical forms (formulas 135–270)
Forms involving $\sqrt{au + b}$; $\sqrt{au + b}$ and $pu + q$; $\sqrt{au + b}$ and
$\sqrt{pu + q}$; $\sqrt{u^2 + a^2}$; $\sqrt{u^2 - a^2}$; $\sqrt{a^2 - u^2}$; $\sqrt{au^2 + bu + c}$

Higher degree binomials (formulas 271–310)
Forms involving $u^3 + a^3$; $u^4 + a^4$ and $u^4 - a^4$;
$u^n + a^n$ and $u^n - a^n$

Trigonometric forms (formulas 311–444)
Forms involving $\cos au$; $\sin au$; $\sin au$ and $\cos au$; $\tan au$;
$\cot au$; $\sec au$; $\csc au$

Inverse trigonometric forms (formulas 445–482)

Exponential and logarithmic forms (formulas 483–513)
Forms involving e^{au}; $\ln |u|$

Hyperbolic forms (formulas 514–619; we study these in Section 7.6)
Forms involving $\cosh au$; $\sinh au$; $\sinh au$ and $\cosh au$;
$\tanh au$; $\coth au$; $\operatorname{sech} au$; $\operatorname{csch} au$

Inverse hyperbolic forms (formulas 620–650; Section 7.6)

A condensed version of this table is provided in Appendix D.

There is a common misconception that integration will be easy if a table is provided, but even with a table available there is a considerable amount of work. After deciding which form applies, match the individual type with the problem at hand by making appropriate choices for the arbitrary constants. More than one form may apply, but the results derived by using different formulas will be the same (except for the constants) even though they may look quite different. We shall not include the constants in the table listing, but you should remember to include it with your answer when using the table for integration.

 Take a few moments to look at the integration table in the *Student Mathematics Handbook* (or Appendix D). Notice that the table has two basic forms of integration formulas. The first gives a formula that is the antiderivative, whereas the second, called a *reduction formula* simply rewrites the integral in another form.

8.4

Table of Integrals

INTEGRALS INVOLVING au + b

---

30. $\displaystyle \int (au + b)^n \, du = \frac{(au + b)^{n+1}}{(n + 1)a}$

31. $\displaystyle \int u(au + b)^n \, du = \frac{(au + b)^{n+2}}{(n + 2)a^2} - \frac{b(au + b)^{n+1}}{(n + 1)a^2}$

32. $\displaystyle \int u^2(au + b)^n \, du = \frac{(au + b)^{n+3}}{(n + 3)a^3} - \frac{2b(au + b)^{n+2}}{(n + 2)a^3} + \frac{b^2(au + b)^{n+1}}{(n + 1)a^3}$

INTEGRALS INVOLVING $au + b$

$$
33. \int u^m(au + b)^n du = \begin{cases} \dfrac{u^{m+1}(au + b)^n}{m + n + 1} + \dfrac{nb}{m + n + 1} \int u^m(au + b)^{n-1} du \\[2ex] \dfrac{u^m(au + b)^{n+1}}{(m + n + 1)a} - \dfrac{mb}{(m + n + 1)a} \int u^{m-1}(au + b)^n du \\[2ex] \dfrac{-u^{m+1}(au + b)^{n+1}}{(n + 1)b} + \dfrac{m + n + 2}{(n + 1)b} \int u^m(au + b)^{n+1} du \end{cases}
$$

$$
34. \int \frac{du}{au + b} = \frac{1}{a} \ln|au + b|
$$

EXAMPLE 7   Integration using a table of integrals—antiderivative given

Find $\displaystyle\int x^2(3 - x)^5\, dx$.

Solution   This is an integral of the form $au + b$; we find that this is formula 32, where $u = x$, $a = -1$, $b = 3$, and $n = 5$. Remember, that the integral table does not show the added constant, so do not forget it when writing your answers using the table.

$$
\int x^2(3 - x)^5 dx = \frac{(3 - x)^{5+3}}{(5 + 3)(-1)^3} - \frac{2(3)(3 - x)^{5+2}}{(5 + 2)(-1)^3} + \frac{3^2(3 - x)^{5+1}}{(5 + 1)(-1)^3} + C
$$

$$
= -\frac{1}{8}(3 - x)^8 + \frac{6}{7}(3 - x)^7 - \frac{3}{2}(3 - x)^6 + C
$$

This form is acceptable as an answer. However, you may wish to complete the algebraic simplification:

$$
\int x^2(3 - x)^5 dx = -\frac{1}{56}(3 - x)^6[7(3 - x)^2 - 48(3 - x) + 84] + C
$$

$$
= -\frac{1}{56}(3 - x)^6(7x^2 + 6x + 3) + C
$$

One of the difficult considerations when using tables or computer software to carry out integration is recognizing the variety of different forms for acceptable answers. Note that it is not easy to show that these forms are algebraically equivalent. If we use computer software for this evaluation, we find yet another algebraically equivalent form:

$$
\int x^2(3 - x)^5 dx = -\frac{x^8}{8} + \frac{15x^7}{7} - 15x^6 + 54x^5 - \frac{405x^4}{4} + 81x^3
$$

Once again, remember that you must add the $+ C$ to the computer software form. ■

EXAMPLE 8   Integration using a table of integrals—reduction formula

Find $\displaystyle\int (\ln x)^4\, dx$.

Solution   The integrand is in logarithmic form; from the table of integrals we see that formula 501 applies, where $u = x$ and $n = 4$. Note that tables of integrals do not usually show the absolute value symbols. You need to remember that $\ln x$ is defined only for positive x.

Take a close look at formulas 499 to 502, and note that formula 501 gives another integral as part of the result. This is called a **reduction formula** because it enables us to compute the given integral in terms of an integral of a similar type, only with a lower power in the integral.

INTEGRALS INVOLVING $\ln|u|$

499. $\displaystyle\int \ln|u|\; du = u\,\ln|u| - u$ **500.** $\displaystyle\int (\ln|u|)^2 \; du = u\,(\ln|u|)^2 - 2u\,\ln|u| + 2u$

501. $\displaystyle\int (\ln|u|)^n \; du = u\,(\ln|u|)^n - n\int (\ln|u|)^{n-1}\; du$ **502.** $\displaystyle\int u\,\ln|u|\; du = \frac{u^2}{2}\left(\ln|u| - \frac{1}{2}\right)$

$$\int (\ln x)^4 \; dx = x(\ln x)^4 - 4\int (\ln x)^{4-1}\; dx$$

$$= x(\ln x)^4 - 4\left[x(\ln x)^3 - 3\int (\ln x)^{3-1}\; dx\right] \quad \text{Formula 501 again}$$

$$= x(\ln x)^4 - 4x(\ln x)^3 + 12\int (\ln x)^2 \; dx$$

$$= x(\ln x)^4 - 4x(\ln x)^3 + 12[x(\ln x)^2 - 2x\,\ln x + 2x] + C$$
$$\qquad\qquad\qquad\qquad\qquad\qquad\qquad \textit{This is formula 500.}$$

$$= x(\ln x)^4 - 4x(\ln x)^3 + 12x(\ln x)^2 - 24x\,\ln x + 24x + C \quad \blacksquare$$

Note from the previous example that we follow the convention of adding the constant C only after eliminating the last integral sign (rather than being technically correct and writing $C_1, C_2, \ldots$ for *each* integral). The reason we can do this is because $C_1 + C_2 + \cdots = C$, for arbitrary constants.

It is often necessary to make substitutions before using one of the integration formulas, as shown in the following example.

EXAMPLE 9   Using an integral table after substitution

Find $\displaystyle\int \frac{x\; dx}{\sqrt{8 - 5x^2}}$.

Solution   This is an integral of the form $\sqrt{a^2 - u^2}$, but it does not exactly match any of the formulas.

INTEGRALS INVOLVING $\sqrt{a^2 - u^2}$

224. $\displaystyle\int \frac{du}{\sqrt{a^2 - u^2}} = \sin^{-1}\frac{u}{a}$ **225.** $\displaystyle\int \frac{u\; du}{\sqrt{a^2 - u^2}} = -\sqrt{a^2 - u^2}$

226. $\displaystyle\int \frac{u^2\; du}{\sqrt{a^2 - u^2}} = -\frac{u\sqrt{a^2 - u^2}}{2} + \frac{a^2}{2}\sin^{-1}\frac{u}{a}$

Note, however, that except for the coefficient of 5, it is like formula 225. Let $u = \sqrt{5}\,x$ (so $u^2 = 5x^2$); then $du = \sqrt{5}\; dx$:

$$\int \frac{x\; dx}{\sqrt{8 - 5x^2}} = \int \frac{\frac{u}{\sqrt{5}} \cdot \frac{du}{\sqrt{5}}}{\sqrt{8 - u^2}} \qquad \text{Let } u = \sqrt{5}\,x \text{ so that } x = \frac{u}{\sqrt{5}};$$

$$\qquad\qquad\qquad\qquad\qquad du = \sqrt{5}\; dx, \text{ so that } dx = \frac{du}{\sqrt{5}}.$$

$$= \frac{1}{5}\int \frac{u\; du}{\sqrt{8 - u^2}}$$

Now apply formula 225 where $a^2 = 8$:

$$\frac{1}{5} \int \frac{u\,du}{\sqrt{8 - u^2}} = \frac{1}{5}(-\sqrt{8 - u^2}) + C = -\frac{1}{5}\sqrt{8 - 5x^2} + C$$

As you can see from Example 9, using an integral table is not a trivial task. In fact, other methods of integration may be preferable. For Example 9, you can let $u = 8 - 5x^2$ and integrate by substitution:

Let $u = 8 - 5x^2$;
$du = -10x\,dx$.

$$\int \frac{x\,dx}{\sqrt{8 - 5x^2}} = \int \frac{x \cdot \left(\frac{du}{-10x}\right)}{\sqrt{u}} = -\frac{1}{10} \int u^{-1/2}\,du$$

$$= -\frac{1}{10}(2u^{1/2}) + C = -\frac{1}{5}\sqrt{8 - 5x^2} + C$$

Of course, this answer is the same as the one we obtained in Example 9. The point of this calculation is to emphasize that you should try simple methods of integration before turning to the table of integrals.

Sometimes, by choosing different formulas you may obtain two different-looking (but equivalent) forms.

EXAMPLE 10　Integration by table (multiple forms with substitution)

Find $\displaystyle\int 5x^2 \sqrt{3x^2 + 1}\,dx$.

Solution　This is similar to formula 170, but you must take care of the 5 (constant multiple) and the 3 (by making a substitution).

$\mathbf{S^M_H}$

INTEGRALS INVOLVING $\sqrt{u^2 + a^2}$
168. $\displaystyle\int \sqrt{u^2 + a^2}\,du = \frac{u\sqrt{u^2 + a^2}}{2} + \frac{a^2}{2}\ln\lvert u + \sqrt{u^2 + a^2}\rvert$
169. $\displaystyle\int u\sqrt{u^2 + a^2}\,du = \frac{(u^2 + a^2)^{3/2}}{3}$
170. $\displaystyle\int u^2\sqrt{u^2 + a^2}\,du = \frac{u(u^2 + a^2)^{3/2}}{4} - \frac{a^2 u\sqrt{u^2 + a^2}}{8} - \frac{a^4}{8}\ln\lvert u + \sqrt{u^2 + a^2}\rvert$

Let $u = \sqrt{3}\,x$; then $du = \sqrt{3}\,dx$.

$$\int 5x^2\sqrt{3x^2 + 1}\,dx = 5 \int \left(\frac{u^2}{3}\right)\sqrt{u^2 + 1}\,\frac{du}{\sqrt{3}}$$

$u^2 = 3x^2$, so that $x^2 = \frac{u^2}{3}$

$$= \frac{5}{3\sqrt{3}} \int u^2\sqrt{u^2 + 1}\,du \quad \text{\textit{Use formula} 170 \textit{where} } a = 1.$$

$$= \frac{5}{3\sqrt{3}} \left[\frac{u(u^2 + 1)^{3/2}}{4} - \frac{u\sqrt{u^2 + 1}}{8} - \frac{1}{8}\ln\lvert u + \sqrt{u^2 + 1}\rvert \right] + C$$

$$= \frac{5}{24\sqrt{3}} \left[2\sqrt{3}x(3x^2 + 1)^{3/2} - \sqrt{3}x\sqrt{3x^2 + 1} - \ln\lvert\sqrt{3}\,x + \sqrt{3x^2 + 1}\rvert \right] + C$$

$$= \frac{5}{24} \left[2x(3x^2 + 1)^{3/2} - x\sqrt{3x^2 + 1} - \frac{1}{\sqrt{3}}\ln\lvert\sqrt{3}\,x + \sqrt{3x^2 + 1}\rvert \right] + C$$

Computational Window ▼ ▲

The form that we obtain when using computer software can be shown:

We now show how one of the formulas in a table of integrals might be derived by using substitution.

EXAMPLE 11   Deriving an integral formula

Derive a formula for $\int \tan^3 ax \, dx$ (formula 405).

Solution   We will derive this form by using substitution and a trigonometric identity.

$$\int \tan^3 ax \, dx = \int \tan ax(\tan^2 ax) \, dx = \int \tan ax \, (\sec^2 ax - 1) \, dx$$

$$= \int \tan ax \sec^2 ax \, dx - \int \tan ax \, dx$$

$$\boxed{\begin{array}{l} \text{Let } u = \tan ax, \\ \text{so } du = a \sec^2 ax \, dx. \end{array}}$$

$$= \int u \, \frac{du}{a} - \int \tan ax \, dx$$

$$= \frac{u^2}{2a} - \left(-\frac{1}{a} \ln|\cos ax|\right) + C \quad \textit{Formula 403}$$

$$= \frac{\tan^2 ax}{2a} + \frac{1}{a} \ln|\cos ax| + C$$

This corresponds to formula 405 in the *Student Mathematics Handbook.*

■ TRIGONOMETRIC SUBSTITUTIONS

Another useful type of substitution is known as a **trigonometric substitution.** In order to see why trigonometric substitutions can be useful, suppose an integrand contains the term $\sqrt{a^2 - u^2}$, where $a > 0$. Then by setting $u = a \sin \theta$ and using the identity $\cos^2 \theta = 1 - \sin^2 \theta$, we obtain

$$\sqrt{a^2 - u^2} = \sqrt{a^2 - a^2 \sin^2 \theta} = a\sqrt{1 - \sin^2 \theta} = a \cos \theta$$

Thus, the substitution $u = a \sin \theta$, $du = a \cos \theta \, d\theta$ eliminates the square root and converts the given integral into one involving only sine and cosine. This substitution can best be remembered by setting up a reference triangle. This process is illustrated by the following example.

EXAMPLE 12   Trigonometric substitution with form $\sqrt{a^2 - u^2}$

Find $\int \sqrt{4 - x^2} \, dx$.

Solution   First, using a table of integration we find (formula 231; $a = 2$)

$$\int \sqrt{4 - x^2} \, dx = \frac{x\sqrt{4 - x^2}}{2} + 2 \sin^{-1}\left(\frac{x}{2}\right) + C$$

Our goal with this example is to show how we might obtain this formula with a trigonometric substitution. Refer to the triangle shown in Figure 7.1. Notice

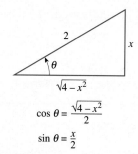

Figure 7.1 Reference triangle with form $\sqrt{4 - x^2}$

$\cos \theta = \frac{\sqrt{4 - x^2}}{2}$

$\sin \theta = \frac{x}{2}$

that $\sin \theta = \frac{x}{2}$, so that $x = 2 \sin \theta$. Then

$$\cos \theta = \frac{\sqrt{4 - x^2}}{2} \quad \text{so that} \quad \sqrt{4 - x^2} = 2 \cos \theta$$

$$\int \sqrt{4 - x^2} \, dx = \int (2 \cos \theta)(2 \cos \theta \, d\theta)$$

Let $x = 2 \sin \theta$ so $\sqrt{4 - x^2} = 2 \cos \theta$; $dx = 2 \cos \theta \, d\theta$.

$$= 4 \int \cos^2 \theta \, d\theta$$

$$= 4 \int \frac{1 + \cos 2\theta}{2} \, d\theta \qquad \textit{Half-angle identity}$$

$$= 2 \int (1 + \cos 2\theta) \, d\theta$$

$$= 2 \int d\theta + 2 \int \cos 2\theta \, d\theta$$

Let $u = 2\theta$; $du = 2 \, d\theta$.

$$= 2\theta + 2 \frac{\sin 2\theta}{2} + C$$

$$= 2\theta + \sin 2\theta + C$$

The final step is to convert this answer back in terms of x. Because $x = 2 \sin \theta$, we know

$$\frac{x}{2} = \sin \theta$$

$$\theta = \sin^{-1}\left(\frac{x}{2}\right)$$

To simplify $\sin 2\theta$ we need a double-angle identity:

$$\sin 2\theta = 2 \sin \theta \cos \theta = x \sqrt{1 - \sin^2 \theta} = x\sqrt{1 - \left(\frac{x}{2}\right)^2} = \frac{x}{2}\sqrt{4 - x^2}$$

Thus,

$$\int \sqrt{4 - x^2} \, dx = 2\theta + \sin 2\theta + C = 2 \sin^{-1}\left(\frac{x}{2}\right) + \frac{x}{2}\sqrt{4 - x^2} + C \quad \rule{1cm}{1mm}$$

Similar methods can be used to convert integrals that involve terms of the form $\sqrt{a^2 + u^2}$ or $\sqrt{u^2 - a^2}$ into trigonometric integrals.

PROBLEM SET 7.1

Ⓐ *Find each integral in Problems 1–12.*

1. $\displaystyle\int \frac{2x - 1}{(4x^2 - 4x)^2} \, dx$

2. $\displaystyle\int \frac{2x + 5}{\sqrt{x^2 + 5x}} \, dx$

3. $\displaystyle\int \frac{\ln x}{x} \, dx$

4. $\displaystyle\int \frac{\ln(x + 1)}{x + 1} \, dx$

5. $\displaystyle\int \cos x \, e^{\sin x} \, dx$

6. $\displaystyle\int \frac{x \, dx}{4 + x^4}$

7. $\displaystyle\int \frac{t^2 \, dt}{9 + t^6}$

8. $\displaystyle\int (1 + \cot x)^4 \csc^2 x \, dx$

9. $\displaystyle\int \frac{4x^3 - 4x}{x^4 - 2x^2 + 3} \, dx$

10. $\displaystyle\int \frac{x^3 - x}{(x^4 - 2x^2 + 3)^2} \, dx$

11. $\displaystyle\int \frac{2x + 4}{x^2 + 4x + 3} \, dx$

12. $\displaystyle\int \frac{2x + 1}{x^2 + x + 1} \, dx$

Integrate the expressions in Problems 13–24 using the short table of integrals given in Appendix D.

13. $\displaystyle\int \frac{dx}{x^2\sqrt{x^2 - a^2}}$

14. $\displaystyle\int \frac{dx}{x^2\sqrt{a^2 - x^2}}$

15. $\int x \ln x \, dx$ **16.** $\int \ln x \, dx$ **17.** $\int x \, e^{ax} \, dx$

18. $\int \dfrac{dx}{a + be^{2x}}$ **19.** $\int \dfrac{x^2 \, dx}{\sqrt{x^2 + 1}}$ **20.** $\int \dfrac{dx}{x^2\sqrt{x^2 + 16}}$

21. $\int \dfrac{x \, dx}{\sqrt{4x^2 + 1}}$ **22.** $\int \dfrac{dx}{x\sqrt{1 - 9x^2}}$ **23.** $\int e^{-4x}\sin 5x \, dx$

24. $\int x \sin^{-1} x \, dx$

Evaluate the integrals in Problems 25–34. If you use an integral table, state the number of the formula used, and if you use substitution, show each step. If you use an alternative table of integrals, then cite the source as well as the formula number.

25. $\int (1 + bx)^{-1} \, dx$ **26.** $\int \dfrac{x \, dx}{\sqrt{a^2 - x^2}}$ **27.** $\int x(1 + x)^3 \, dx$

28. $\int x\sqrt{1 + x} \, dx$ **29.** $\int x \, e^{4x} dx$ **30.** $\int x \ln 2x \, dx$

31. $\int \dfrac{dx}{\sqrt{5 - 4x - x^2}}$ **32.** $\int \dfrac{dx}{1 + e^{2x}}$ **33.** $\int \ln^3 x \, dx$

34. $\int \dfrac{x^3 \, dx}{\sqrt{4x^4 + 1}}$

Work Problems 35–38 by two methods.

35. $\int \dfrac{dx}{\sqrt{9 - x^2}}$ **36.** $\int \dfrac{x + 1}{\sqrt{4 + x^2}} \, dx$

37. $\int (9 + x^2)^{1/2} \, dx$ **38.** $\int \dfrac{dx}{\sqrt{x^2 - 7}}$

Ⓑ *Use the Student Mathematics Handbook or other available integration table to integrate the integrals given in Problems 39–44.*

39. $\int \dfrac{\sqrt{4x^2 + 1}}{x} \, dx$ **40.** $\int \sec^3\left(\dfrac{x}{2}\right) \, dx$

41. $\int \sin^6 x \, dx$ **42.** $\int \dfrac{dx}{9x^2 + 6x + 1}$

43. $\int (9 - x^2)^{3/2} \, dx$ **44.** $\int \dfrac{\sin^2 x}{\cos x} \, dx$

45. Derive the **sine squared formula** shown on the inside back cover (formula 348):

$$\int \sin^2 x \, dx = \tfrac{1}{2}x - \tfrac{1}{4}\sin 2x$$

Hint: Use the identity $\sin^2 x = \dfrac{1 - \cos 2x}{2}$.

46. Derive the **cosine squared formula** shown on the inside back cover (formula 317):

$$\int \cos^2 x \, dx = \tfrac{1}{2}x + \tfrac{1}{4}\sin 2x$$

Hint: Use the identity $\cos^2 x = \dfrac{1 + \cos 2x}{2}$.

Problems 47–49 use substitution to integrate certain powers of sine and cosine.

47. $\int \sin^4 x \cos x \, dx$ *Hint*: Let $u = \sin x$.

48. $\int \sin^3 x \cos^4 x \, dx$ *Hint*: Let $u = \cos x$.

49. $\int \sin^2 x \cos^2 x \, dx$ *Hint*: Use the identities shown in Problems 45 and 46.

50. ■ **What Does This Say?** Using Problems 47–49, formulate a procedure for integrals of the form

$$\int \sin^m x \cos^n x \, dx$$

51. ■ **What Does This Say?** Explain the process of using a trigonometric substitution on integrals involving $\sqrt{a^2 - u^2}$.

52. ■ **What Does This Say?** Explain the process of using a trigonometric substitution on integrals involving $\sqrt{a^2 + u^2}$.

53. ■ **What Does This Say?** Explain the process of using a trigonometric substitution on integrals involving $\sqrt{u^2 - a^2}$.

Find each integral in Problems 54–59.

54. $\int \dfrac{e^x \, dx}{1 + e^{x/2}}$ **55.** $\int \dfrac{dx}{x^{1/2} + x^{1/4}}$

56. $\int \dfrac{18 \tan^2 t \sec^2 t}{(2 + \tan^3 t)^2} \, dt$ **57.** $\int \dfrac{4dx}{x^{1/3} + 2x^{1/2}}$

58. $\int \dfrac{dx}{\left(x + \frac{1}{2}\right)\sqrt{4x^2 + 4x}}$ **59.** $\int \dfrac{e^{-x} - e^x}{e^{2x} + e^{-2x} + 2} \, dx$

60. Find the area of the region bounded by the graphs of $y = \dfrac{2x}{\sqrt{x^2 + 9}}$, $y = 0$ from $x = 0$ to $x = 4$.

61. Find the area of the region bounded by the graphs of $y = \cos 2x$, $y = 0$, $x = 0$, and $x = \frac{\pi}{4}$.

62. Find the volume of the solid generated when the curve $y = x(1 - x^2)^{1/4}$ from $x = 0$ to $x = 1$ is revolved about the x-axis.

63. Find the volume of the solid generated when the curve

$$y = \dfrac{x^{3/2}}{\sqrt{x^2 + 9}}$$

between $x = 0$ and $x = 9$ is revolved about the x-axis.

64. Find the volume of the solid generated when the curve

$$x = \sqrt[4]{4 - y^2}$$

between $y = 1$ and $y = 2$ is revolved about the y-axis.

65. Find the arc length of the curve $y = x^2$ on the interval $[0, 1]$.

66. Find the arc length of the curve $y = \ln(\cos x)$ on the interval $[0, \pi/4]$.

67. Find the surface area of the surface generated when the curve $y = x^2$ on the interval $[0, 1]$ is revolved about the x-axis.

68. Find the surface area of the surface generated when the curve $y = x^2$ on the interval $[0, 1]$ is revolved about the y-axis.

© 69. Show that

$$\int \csc x \, dx = -\ln|\csc x + \cot x| + C$$

Hint: Multiply the integrand by

$$\frac{\csc x + \cot x}{\csc x + \cot x}.$$

70. Find $\int 2 \sin x \cos x \, dx$ by using the indicated substitution.

    a. Let $u = \cos x$.   **b.** Let $u = \sin x$.

    c. Write $2 \sin x \cos x = \sin 2x$ and carry out the integration.

    d. Show that the answers you obtained for parts **a–c** are the same.

Derive the integral formulas in Problems 71–73. Assume that m and n are integers.

71. $\displaystyle\int_0^\pi x f(\sin x) \, dx = \frac{\pi}{2} \int_0^\pi f(\sin x) \, dx$

72. $\displaystyle\int_{-\pi}^\pi \sin nx \sin mx \, dx = \begin{cases} 0 & \text{if } m \neq n \\ \pi & \text{if } m = n \end{cases}$

73. $\displaystyle\int_{-\pi}^\pi \cos nx \cos mx \, dx = \begin{cases} 0 & \text{if } n \neq m \\ \pi & \text{if } n = m \end{cases}$

74. Find the surface area of the torus generated when the curve

$$x^2 + (y - b)^2 = 1, \qquad b > 1$$

is revolved about the x-axis.

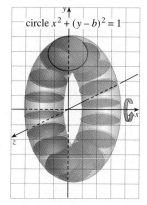

circle $x^2 + (y - b)^2 = 1$

7.2 INTEGRATION BY PARTS

IN THIS SECTION Integration by parts formula, repeated use of integration by parts, definite integration by parts, solving a differential equation by parts

Integration by parts is a procedure based on reversing the product rule for differentiation. We present this section not as a technique of integration but as a procedure that is useful in a variety of different applications.

■ INTEGRATION BY PARTS FORMULA

Recall the formula for differentiation of a product. If u and v are differentiable functions, then

$$d(uv) = u \, dv + v \, du$$

Integrate both sides of this equation to find the formula for integration by parts:

$$\int d(uv) = \int u \, dv + \int v \, du$$

$$uv = \int u \, dv + \int v \, du$$

If we rewrite this last equation, we obtain the formula summarized in the following box.

Formula for Integration by Parts

$$\int u \, dv = uv - \int v \, du$$

EXAMPLE 1   Integration by parts

Find $\int xe^x \, dx$.

Solution   To use integration by parts, we must choose u and dv so that the new integral is easier to integrate than the original.

$$\int \underset{u}{\underbrace{x}} \, \overset{}{\underbrace{e^x \, dx}_{dv}}$$

Let $u = x$ and $dv = e^x \, dx$
$du = dx$ $v = \int e^x \, dx = e^x$

$$\int xe^x \, dx = \underset{u \ v}{\underbrace{x \, e^x}} - \int \underset{v}{\underbrace{e^x}} \, \underset{du}{\underbrace{dx}} = xe^x - e^x + C$$

You can check our work with integration by parts by differentiating, using software, or an integration table. This is found in Appendix D or the *Student Mathematics Handbook* (formula 484, with $a = 1$).   ■

COMMENT: You may wonder why an arbitrary constant (call it K) was not included when performing the integration associated with $\int dv$ in integration by parts. The reason is that when applying integration by parts, we need just *one* function v whose derivative is dv, so we take the simplest one—the one with $K = 0$. You may find it instructive to see that taking $v = e^x + K$ gives the same result.

Integration by parts is often difficult the first time you try to do it, because there is no absolute choice for u and dv. In Example 1, you might have chosen

$$u = e^x \qquad \text{and} \quad dv = x \, dx$$
$$du = e^x \, dx \qquad\qquad v = \int x \, dx = \frac{x^2}{2}$$

Then

$$\int xe^x \, dx = \underset{u \ v}{\underbrace{e^x \, \frac{x^2}{2}}} - \int \underset{v}{\underbrace{\frac{x^2}{2}}} \, \underset{du}{\underbrace{e^x \, dx}}$$

$$= \tfrac{1}{2} x^2 e^x - \tfrac{1}{2} \int x^2 e^x \, dx$$

Note, however, that this choice of u and dv leads to a more complicated form than the original. In general, when you are integrating by parts, if you make a choice for u and dv that leads to a more complicated form than when you started, consider going back and making another choice for u and dv.

EXAMPLE 2   When the differentiable part is the entire integrand

Find $\int \ln x \, dx$ for $x > 0$.

Solution   Let $u = \ln x$ and $dv = dx$
$du = \dfrac{1}{x} \, dx$ $v = x$

$$\int \ln x \, dx = (\ln x)x - \int x\left(\frac{1}{x} \, dx\right) = x \ln x - \int dx = x \ln x - x + C$$

Check with formula 499 (Appendix D) where $a = 1$, which we worked as Problem 16 of Problem Set 7.1.   ■

■ REPEATED USE OF INTEGRATION BY PARTS

Sometimes integration by parts must be applied several times in order to evaluate a given integral.

EXAMPLE 3   Repeated integration by parts

Find $\int x^2 e^{-x} dx$.

Solution

Let $u = x^2$ and $dv = e^{-x} dx$
$du = 2x\,dx$ $\quad$ $v = -e^{-x}$

$$\int x^2 e^{-x} dx = x^2(-e^{-x}) - \int (-e^{-x})(2x\,dx)$$

$$= -x^2 e^{-x} + 2 \int x e^{-x} dx$$

Let $u = x$ and $dv = e^{-x} dx$
$du = dx$ $\quad$ $v = -e^{-x}$

$$= -x^2 e^{-x} + 2\left[x(-e^{-x}) - \int (-e^{-x})\,dx \right]$$

$$= -x^2 e^{-x} - 2x e^{-x} + 2\left(\frac{e^{-x}}{-1}\right) + C$$

$$= -e^{-x}(x^2 + 2x + 2) + C$$

Check with formula 485 where $a = -1$. $\qquad\qquad$ ■

In the following example it is necessary to apply integration by parts more than once, but as you will see, when we do so a second time we return to the original integral. Note carefully how this situation can be handled algebraically.

EXAMPLE 4   Substitution with an algebraic manipulation

Find $\int e^{2x} \sin x \, dx$.

Solution   For this problem you will see that it will be useful to call the original integral I. That is, we let

$$I = \int e^{2x} \sin x \, dx$$

Let $u = e^{2x}$ and $dv = \sin x \, dx$
$du = 2e^{2x} dx$ $\quad$ $v = -\cos x$

$$I = \int e^{2x} \sin x \, dx = e^{2x}(-\cos x) - \int (-\cos x)(2e^{2x} dx)$$

$$= -e^{2x}\cos x + 2 \int e^{2x}\cos x \, dx$$

Let $u = e^{2x}$ and $dv = \cos x \, dx$
$du = 2e^{2x} dx$ $\quad$ $v = \sin x$

$$= -e^{2x}\cos x + 2\left[e^{2x}(\sin x) - \int \sin x (2e^{2x} dx) \right]$$

$$= -e^{2x}\cos x + 2e^{2x}\sin x - 4 \int e^{2x}\sin x \, dx$$

Notice that this last integral is I. Thus, we have

$$I = -e^{2x}\cos x + 2e^{2x}\sin x - 4I \quad \textit{Solve this equation for I.}$$

$$5I = -e^{2x}\cos x + 2e^{2x}\sin x$$

$$I = \tfrac{1}{5}e^{2x}(2\sin x - \cos x)$$

Thus, $\displaystyle\int e^{2x}\sin x\, dx = \tfrac{1}{5}e^{2x}(2\sin x - \cos x) + C$

Check with the integration table (formula 492, where $a = 2$ and $b = 1$). ▬

■ DEFINITE INTEGRATION BY PARTS

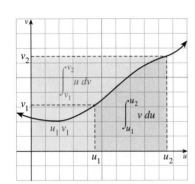

Figure 7.2 Integration by parts using areas

In order to get a clear picture of the integration by parts formula for definite integrals, it is instructive to interpret the integration by parts formula in terms of area. Consider the area of the rectangle with sides u_2 and v_2, as shown in Figure 7.2.

$$\underbrace{\text{AREA OF RECTANGLE}}_{\substack{\text{Entire colored rectangle}}} = \underbrace{\text{BLUE AREA}}_{} + \underbrace{\text{PINK AREA}}_{} + \underbrace{\text{PURPLE AREA}}_{}$$

$$u_2 v_2 \quad = \quad u_1 v_1 \quad + \quad \int_{u_1}^{u_2} v\, du \quad + \quad \int_{v_1}^{v_2} u\, dv$$

This equation can be written as

$$\int_{v_1}^{v_2} u\, dv = u_2 v_2 - u_1 v_1 - \int_{u_1}^{u_2} v\, du$$

This relationship is summarized in the following box, where we use the usual limits of integration, namely, $x = a$ to $x = b$.

Integration by Parts for Definite Integrals

$$\int_a^b u\, dv = uv\Big|_a^b - \int_a^b v\, du$$

You should recognize that this formula for definite integrals is the same as the formula for indefinite integrals, where the first term after the equal sign has been evaluated at the appropriate limits of integration. This is illustrated by the following example.

EXAMPLE 5   Integration by parts with a definite integral

Evaluate $\displaystyle\int_0^1 xe^{2x}\, dx$.

Solution Let $u = x$ and $dv = e^{2x}dx$
$$du = dx \qquad v = \tfrac{1}{2}e^{2x}$$

$$\int_0^1 xe^{2x}dx = \tfrac{1}{2}xe^{2x}\Big|_0^1 - \tfrac{1}{2}\int_0^1 e^{2x}\, dx$$

It is usually easier to simplify the algebra and then do one evaluation here at the end of the integration part of the problem.
$$\downarrow$$
$$= \left(\tfrac{1}{2}xe^{2x} - \tfrac{1}{4}e^{2x}\right)\Big|_0^1 = \tfrac{1}{4}e^2 + \tfrac{1}{4}$$

Check in Appendix D (formula 484, with $a = 2$). ▬

□ Computational Window ▼ ▲

You can use computer software or many calculators to evaluate definite integrals. For example, with CONVERGE software and 1,000 subintervals, we evaluate the integral in Example 5 as 2.093571. Compare with the decimal approximation of $\tfrac{1}{4}e^2 + \tfrac{1}{4} \approx 2.097264025$.

EXAMPLE 6   Integration by parts followed by substitution

Evaluate $\int_0^{\pi/4} \tan^{-1} x \, dx$.

Solution

Let $u = \tan^{-1} x \qquad dv = dx$

$\qquad du = \dfrac{dx}{1 + x^2} \quad$ and $\quad v = x$

$$\int_0^{\pi/4} \underbrace{\tan^{-1} x}_{u} \underbrace{dx}_{dv} = \underbrace{(\tan^{-1} x)}_{u} \underbrace{x}_{v}\Big|_0^{\pi/4} - \int_0^{\pi/4} \underbrace{\dfrac{x \, dx}{1 + x^2}}_{v \; du}$$

$$= \left[x \tan^{-1} x - \tfrac{1}{2} \ln(1 + x^2) \right]_0^{\pi/4}$$

Use substitution where $w = 1 + x^2$ and $dw = 2x \, dx$.

$\int \dfrac{x \, dx}{1 + x^2} = \int \dfrac{dw}{2w} = \tfrac{1}{2} \ln w = \tfrac{1}{2} \ln(1 + x^2)$

$$= \left[\tfrac{\pi}{4}\left(\tan^{-1} \tfrac{\pi}{4}\right) - \tfrac{1}{2} \ln\left(1 + \tfrac{\pi^2}{16}\right) \right] - \left[0 - \tfrac{1}{2} \ln 1 \right]$$

$$= \tfrac{\pi}{4} \tan^{-1} \tfrac{\pi}{4} - \tfrac{1}{2} \ln\left(1 + \tfrac{\pi^2}{16}\right)$$

Check with an integration table (formula 457, for example, with $a = 1$). ▬

Computational Window

For $n = 1,000$, we find

$$\int_0^{\pi/4} \tan^{-1} x \, dx \approx 0.282396$$

as compared to the answer in Example 6:

$$\tfrac{\pi}{4}\tan^{-1}\left(\tfrac{\pi}{4}\right) - 0.5 \ln\left(1 + \tfrac{\pi^2}{16}\right)$$

$$\approx 0.2826574895$$

You must think about the answers you obtain when using computer software. There are entire courses that discuss the accuracy of various computer approximations.

■ SOLVING DIFFERENTIAL EQUATIONS BY PARTS*

Integration by parts can be used in any of the applications we have considered. The following example involves a differential equation.

EXAMPLE 7   First-order linear differential equation

Solve the differential equation $\dfrac{dy}{dx} + \dfrac{y}{x} = e^{2x}$.

Solution   Recall from Section 6.4 that the general solution of the equation

$$\dfrac{dy}{dx} + P(x)y = Q(x) \quad \text{is given by} \quad y = \dfrac{1}{I(x)}[\textstyle\int Q(x)I(x) \, dx + C]$$

where $I(x) = e^{\int P(x)dx}$ is the integrating factor. For the differential equation in this example, we have $P(x) = x^{-1}$, $Q(x) = e^{2x}$, and

$$I(x) = e^{\int x^{-1} dx} = e^{\ln x} = x$$

Thus, the general solution is

$$y = \tfrac{1}{x}\left[\int x e^{2x} \, dx + C \right] \qquad \text{Integrate } \int x e^{2x} \, dx \text{ by parts.}$$

$$= \tfrac{1}{x}\left[\tfrac{1}{2} x e^{2x} - \tfrac{1}{4} e^{2x} + C \right] \quad \text{See Example 5 for details.}$$

$$= \tfrac{1}{2} e^{2x} - \dfrac{e^{2x}}{4x} + \dfrac{C}{x}$$

▬

*This material is not required for subsequent material.

PROBLEM SET 7.2

Ⓐ *Find each integral in Problems 1–14.*

1. $\int xe^{-2x}\,dx$ **2.** $\int x\sin x\,dx$ **3.** $\int x\ln x\,dx$

4. $\int x\tan^{-1}x\,dx$ **5.** $\int \sin^{-1}x\,dx$ **6.** $\int x^2\sin x\,dx$

7. $\int \dfrac{\ln\sqrt{x}}{\sqrt{x}}\,dx$ **8.** $\int e^{2x}\sin 3x\,dx$ **9.** $\int x\cos^2 x\,dx$

10. $\int \dfrac{x^3\,dx}{\sqrt{x^2+1}}$ **11.** $\int x^2\ln x\,dx$ **12.** $\int (x+\sin x)^2\,dx$

13. $\int e^{2x}\sqrt{1-e^x}\,dx$ **14.** $\int x\sin x\cos x\,dx$

Evaluate the definite integrals in Problems 15–20.

15. $\int_1^4 \sqrt{x}\ln x\,dx$ **16.** $\int_1^e x^3\ln x\,dx$

17. $\int_1^e (\ln x)^2\,dx$ **18.** $\int_{1/3}^e 3(\ln 3x)^2\,dx$

19. $\int_0^\pi e^{2x}\cos 2x\,dx$ **20.** $\int_0^\pi x(\sin x+\cos x)\,dx$

Ⓑ 21. ■ **What Does This Say?** Describe the process known as *integration by parts.*

In Problems 22–25 first use an appropriate substitution and then integrate by parts to evaluate the integral. Remember to give your answers in terms of x.

22. $\int \dfrac{\ln x\sin(\ln x)}{x}\,dx$ **23.** $\int [\sin 2x\ln(\cos x)]dx$

24. $\int e^{2x}\sin e^x\,dx$ **25.** $\int [\sin x\ln(2+\cos x)]dx$

26. a. Evaluate $\int \dfrac{x^3}{x^2-1}\,dx$ by parts.

   b. Evaluate the integral in part **a** by first dividing the integrand.

Evaluate the integrals in Problems 27–28 by parts.

27. $\int \sin^2 x\,dx$ **28.** $\int \cos^2 x\,dx$

29. Find $\int x^n\ln x\,dx$, where n is any positive real number.

30. After t seconds, an object is moving at a speed of $te^{-t/2}$ meters per second. Express the distance the object travels as a function of time.

31. After t hours on the job, a factory worker can produce $100te^{-0.5t}$ units per hour. How many units does the worker produce during the first 3 hours?

32. After t weeks, contributions in response to a local fund-raising campaign were coming in at the rate of $2{,}000te^{-0.2t}$ dollars per week. How much money was raised during the first 5 weeks?

33. Find the volume of the solid generated when the region under the curve $y=e^{-x}$ on the interval $[0, 2]$ is revolved about the y-axis.

34. Find the volume of the solid generated when the region under the curve $y=\sin x+\cos x$ on the interval $\left[0,\frac{\pi}{4}\right]$ is revolved about the y-axis.

35. Find the volume of the solid generated when the region under the curve $y=\ln x$ on the interval $[1, e]$ is revolved about the indicated axis.

   a. x-axis   **b.** y-axis

36. Find the centroid (with coordinates rounded to the nearest hundredth) of the region bounded by the curves $y=\sin x$ and $y=\cos x$ and the y-axis on $0\le y\le 1$.

37. Find the centroid (with coordinates rounded to the nearest hundredth) of the region bounded by the curves $y=e^x$, $y=e^{-x}$, and the line $x=1$.

Problems 38–42 require the material dealing with differential equations.

38. Solve $\dfrac{dy}{dx}+\dfrac{xy}{1+x}=x(1+x)$.

39. Solve $\dfrac{dy}{dx}+\dfrac{2xy}{1+x^2}=\sin x$ subject to the condition $y=1$ where $x=0$.

40. Find a function $f(x)$ whose graph passes through $(1, 1)$ and has the property that at each point (x, y) on the graph, the slope of the tangent line is x^2+2y.

41. Suppose it is known that $f(0)=3$ and

$$\int_0^\pi [f(x)+f''(x)]\sin x\,dx=0$$

What is $f(\pi)$?

42. Because a rocket burns fuel in flight, its mass decreases with time and this in turn affects its velocity. It can be shown that the velocity $v(t)$ of the rocket at time t in its flight is given by

$$v(t)=-r\ln\frac{w-kt}{w}-gt$$

where w is the initial weight of the rocket (including its fuel) and r and k are, respectively, the expulsion speed and the rate of consumption of the fuel, which are assumed to be constant. As usual, $g=32$ ft/s^2 is the constant acceleration due to gravity. Suppose $w=30{,}000$ lb, $r=8{,}000$ ft/s, and $k=200$ lb/s. What is the height of rocket after 2 min (120 sec)?

43. In a medium for which air resistance is proportional to the velocity of a falling body, the velocity of a body with mass m satisfies the differential equation

$$m\frac{dv}{dt}=mg-kv$$

where k is a positive constant and g is the constant of acceleration due to gravity. Find $v(t)$ if the initial velocity of the body is v_0 in feet per second.

44. A lake has a volume of 6 billion ft^3, and its initial pollutant content is 0.22%. A river whose waters contain only 0.06% pollutants flows into the lake at the rate of 350 million ft³/day, and another river flows out of the lake also carrying 350 million ft³/day. Assume that the water in the two rivers and the lake is always well mixed. How long does it take for the pollutant content to be reduced to 0.15%?

45. The displacement from equilibrium of a mass oscillating at the end of a spring hanging from the ceiling is given by

$$y = 2.3e^{-0.25t}\cos 5t$$

feet. What is the average displacement (rounded to the nearest hundredth) of the mass between times $t = 0$ and $t = \pi/5$ seconds?

46. A photographer is taking a picture of a clever sign on the back of a truck. The sign is 5 ft high and its lower edge is 1 ft above the lens of the camera. At first the truck is 4 ft away from the photographer, but then it begins to move away. What is the average value of the angle θ subtended by the camera lens as the truck moves from 4 ft to 20 ft away from the photographer?

47. If n moles of an ideal gas expand at constant temperature T, then its pressure p and volume V satisfy the equation $pV = nRT$, for constant R. It can be shown that the work done by the gas in expanding from volume V_1 to V is

$$W = nRT \ln \frac{V}{V_1}$$

What is the average work done as V increases from V_1 to $V_2 = 10V_1$?

48. In physics, it is known that loudness L of a sound is related to its intensity I by the equation

$$L = 10 \log \frac{I}{I_0}$$

decibels where $I_0 = 12^{-12}$ watt/m² is the threshold of audibility (the lowest intensity that can be heard). What is the average value of L as the intensity of a TV show ranges between I_0 and $I_1 = 3 \cdot 10^{-5}$ watt/m²?

C 49. Derive the formula

$$\int x^n e^x \, dx = x^n e^x - n \int x^{n-1} e^x \, dx$$

(This is formula 486 with $a = 1$.)

50. Derive the formula

$$\int (\ln x)^n dx = x(\ln x)^n - n \int (\ln x)^{n-1} \, dx$$

(This is formula 501.)

51. Wallis's formula If $n > 0$ is an even integer, use reduction formulas to show

$$\int_0^{\pi/2} \sin n \, dx = \int_0^{\pi/2} \cos n \, dx = \left[\frac{1 \cdot 3 \cdot 5 \cdots (n-1)}{2 \cdot 4 \cdot 6 \cdots n} \right] \frac{\pi}{2}$$

52. State and prove a result similar to the one in Problem 51 for the case for odd exponents.

7.3 THE METHOD OF PARTIAL FRACTIONS

> **IN THIS SECTION** Decomposition, integrating rational functions by partial-fraction decomposition, substitution with partial fractions, rational trigonometric integrals
> Partial-fraction decomposition has great value as a tool for integration. This process may be thought of as the "reverse" of adding fractional algebraic expressions, and it allows us to break up rational expressions into simpler terms.

■ **DECOMPOSITION**

Partial-fraction decomposition is an algebraic procedure for expressing a reduced rational function as a sum of fractional parts. For example, consider a typical algebraic process of adding rational expressions (and the necessity of finding a common denominator):

$$\frac{2}{x+1} + \frac{-3}{x+2} = \frac{2(x+2) + (-3)(x+1)}{(x+1)(x+2)} = \frac{-x+1}{x^2+3x+2}$$

In partial-fraction decomposition, we do just the opposite: We start with the reduced fraction

$$\frac{-x+1}{x^2+3x+2}$$

and write it as the sum of fractions

$$\frac{2}{x+1} + \frac{-3}{x+2}$$

The rational expression

$$f(x) = \frac{P(x)}{D(x)}$$

can be **decomposed** into partial fractions if P and D have no common factors and if the degree of P is less than the degree of D. If the degree of P is greater than or equal to the degree of D, then use division to obtain a polynomial plus a proper fraction. For example,

$$\frac{x^4 + 2x^3 - 4x^2 + x - 3}{x^2 - x - 2} = \underbrace{x^2 + 3x + 1}_{\text{polynomial}} + \underbrace{\frac{8x-1}{x^2-x-2}}_{\substack{\text{Proper fraction:} \\ \text{This is the part} \\ \text{that is decomposed} \\ \text{into partial fractions.}}}$$ *This was found by long division.*

Partial-fraction decomposition has great value as a tool for integration. In Example 5, we shall find

$$\int \frac{x^4 + 2x^3 - 4x^2 + x - 3}{x^2 - x - 2}\, dx$$

which is difficult (if not impossible) without partial-fraction decomposition or appropriate computer software. The process consists of dividing to find a polynomial (which is easy to integrate) plus a proper fraction, which is simplified using partial-fraction decomposition.

In algebra, it is shown that a proper fraction can be written as the sum $F_1 + F_2 + \cdots + F_m$, where each F_j is of the form

$$\frac{A}{(x-r)^n} \quad \text{or} \quad \frac{Ax+B}{(x^2+sx+t)^m}$$

for constants r, s, and t. Also assume that $x^2 + sx + t$ is an irreducible (that is, can not be factored into linear factors) quadratic term. We begin by focusing on the first form.

Partial-Fraction Decomposition: A Single Linear Power

$$\frac{A_1}{x-r} + \frac{A_2}{(x-r)^2} + \cdots + \frac{A_n}{(x-r)^n}$$

EXAMPLE 1   Partial-fraction decomposition with a single linear power

Decompose $\dfrac{x^2 - 6x + 3}{(x-2)^3}$ into a sum of partial fractions.

Software programs will decompose rational expressions quite handily using the direction "expand."

Solution

$$\frac{x^2 - 6x + 3}{(x - 2)^3} = \frac{A_1}{x - 2} + \frac{A_2}{(x - 2)^2} + \frac{A_3}{(x - 2)^3}$$

Multiply both sides by $(x - 2)^3$ to obtain:

$$x^2 - 6x + 3 = A_1(x - 2)^2 + A_2(x - 2) + A_3$$

Let $x = 2$:

$$2^2 - 6(2) + 3 = A_1(0) + A_2(0) + A_3$$

$$-5 = A_3$$

Substitute $A_3 = -5$ and expand the right side to obtain

$$x^2 - 6x + 3 = A_1 x^2 + (-4A_1 + A_2)x + (4A_1 - 2A_2 - 5)$$

This implies (by equating the coefficients of the similar terms) that

$$1 = A_1 \qquad\qquad x^2 \text{ terms}$$

$$-6 = -4A_1 + A_2 \qquad x \text{ terms}$$

$$3 = 4A_1 - 2A_2 - 5 \qquad \text{Constants}$$

Because $A_1 = 1$, we find $A_2 = -2$, so the decomposition is

$$\frac{x^2 - 6x + 3}{(x - 2)^3} = \frac{1}{x - 2} + \frac{-2}{(x - 2)^2} + \frac{-5}{(x - 2)^3}$$

If there are two or more linear factors in the denominator, the fraction should be decomposed into distinct linear powers. For example,

$$\frac{P(x)}{(x - r_1)(x - r_2) \cdots (x - r_n)}$$

is decomposed into separate terms

$$\frac{A_1}{x - r_1} + \frac{A_2}{x - r_2} + \cdots + \frac{A_n}{x - r_n}$$

This process is illustrated with the following example.

EXAMPLE 2   Partial-fraction decomposition with distinct linear factors

Decompose $\dfrac{8x - 1}{x^2 - x - 2}$.

Solution

$$\frac{8x - 1}{x^2 - x - 2} = \frac{8x - 1}{(x - 2)(x + 1)}$$

First factor the denominator, if possible, and make sure there are no common factors.

$$= \frac{A_1}{x - 2} + \frac{A_2}{x + 1}$$

Break up the fraction in parts, each with a linear denominator. The task is to find A_1 and A_2.

$$= \frac{A_1(x + 1) + A_2(x - 2)}{(x - 2)(x + 1)}$$

Obtain a common denominator on the right.

⊘ Note that the degree of the denominator is the same number as the number of arbitrary constants, A_1 and A_2. This provides a quick intermediate check on the correct procedure. Make this check a standard step in your developmental task. ⊘

Now, *multiply both sides of this equation by the least common denominator*, which is $(x - 2)(x + 1)$ for this example.

$$8x - 1 = A_1(x + 1) + A_2(x - 2)$$

Substitute, one at a time, the values that cause each of the factors in the least common denominator to be zero.

Let $x = -1$: $\qquad 8x - 1 = A_1(x + 1) + A_2(x - 2)$

$$8(-1) - 1 = A_1(-1 + 1) + A_2(-1 - 2)$$

$$-9 = -3A_2$$

$$3 = A_2$$

Let $x = 2$: $\qquad 8x - 1 = A_1(x + 1) + A_2(x - 2)$

$$8(2) - 1 = A_1(2 + 1) + A_2(2 - 2)$$

$$15 = 3A_1$$

$$5 = A_1$$

Thus, $\dfrac{8x - 1}{x^2 - x - 2} = \dfrac{5}{x - 2} + \dfrac{3}{x + 1}$.

■

If there is a mixture of distinct and repeated linear factors, we combine the procedure illustrated in the preceding examples. For example,

$$\frac{5x^2 + 21x + 4}{(x + 1)^2(x - 3)} \quad \text{is decomposed as} \quad \frac{A_1}{x + 1} + \frac{A_2}{(x + 1)^2} + \frac{A_3}{x - 3}.$$

Note that the degree of the denominator is three and we use three arbitrary constants A_1, A_2, and A_3.

$$\frac{5x^2 + 21x + 4}{(x + 1)^3(x - 3)} \quad \text{is decomposed as} \quad \frac{A_1}{x + 1} + \frac{A_2}{(x + 1)^2} + \frac{A_3}{(x + 1)^3} + \frac{A_4}{x - 3}.$$

The degree of the denominator is four, so we use four constants.

If some of the factors of the denominator are irreducible quadratic factors, then the numerators have the form $Ax + B$, as indicated in the following box.

Partial-Fraction Decomposition: A Single Irreducible Quadratic Factor

$$\frac{A_1x + B_1}{x^2 + sx + t} + \frac{A_2x + B_2}{(x^2 + sx + t)^2} + \cdots + \frac{A_mx + B_m}{(x^2 + sx + t)^m}$$

Because the degree of the denominator is $2m$, we have $2m$ arbitrary constants, namely, $A_1, A_2, \ldots, A_m, B_1, B_2, \ldots, B_m$.

EXAMPLE 3 **Partial-fraction decomposition with a single quadratic power**

Decompose $\dfrac{-3x^3 - x}{(x^2 + 1)^2}$.

Solution The decomposition gives

$$\frac{-3x^3 - x}{(x^2 + 1)^2} = \frac{A_1x + B_1}{(x^2 + 1)^2} + \frac{A_2x + B_2}{x^2 + 1}$$

Multiply both sides of this equation by $(x^2 + 1)^2$, and simplify algebraically.

$$-3x^3 - x = (A_1x + B_1) + (A_2x + B_2)(x^2 + 1)$$

$$= A_2x^3 + B_2x^2 + (A_1 + A_2)x + (B_1 + B_2)$$

Next, equate the coefficients on each side of this equation and solve the resulting system of equations to find $A_1 = 2$, $A_2 = -3$, $B_1 = 0$, and $B_2 = 0$. This means that

$$\frac{-3x^3 - x}{(x^2 + 1)^2} = \frac{2x}{(x^2 + 1)^2} + \frac{-3x}{x^2 + 1}$$ ▬

Many of the examples we encounter will offer a mixture of linear and quadratic factors. For example,

$$\frac{x^2 + 4x - 23}{(x^2 + 4)(x + 3)^2} \quad \text{is decomposed as} \quad \frac{A_1 x + B_1}{x^2 + 4} + \frac{A_2}{x + 3} + \frac{A_3}{(x + 3)^2}.$$

The degree of the denominator is four, and there are four constants.

In algebra, the theory of equations tells us that any polynomial P with real coefficients can be expressed as a product of linear and irreducible quadratic powers, some of which may be repeated. This fact can be used to justify the following general procedure for obtaining the partial-fraction decomposition of a rational function.

Partial-Fraction Decomposition of the Rational Function $P(x)/D(x)$

Let $f(x) = \dfrac{P(x)}{D(x)}$, where $P(x)$ and $D(x)$ have no common factors and $D(x) \neq 0$.

Step 1. If the degree of P is greater than or equal to the degree of D, use long (or synthetic) division to express $\dfrac{P(x)}{D(x)}$ as the sum of a polynomial and a fraction $\dfrac{R(x)}{D(x)}$ in which the degree of the remainder polynomial $R(x)$ is less than the degree of the denominator polynomial $D(x)$.

Step 2. Factor the denominator $D(x)$ into the product of linear and irreducible quadratic powers.

Step 3. Express $\dfrac{P(x)}{D(x)}$ as a cascading sum of partial fractions of the form

$$\frac{A_i}{(x - r)^n} \quad \text{and} \quad \frac{A_j x + B_k}{(x^2 + sx + t)^m}$$

Verify that the number of constants used is identical to the degree of the denominator.

■ INTEGRATING RATIONAL FUNCTIONS BY PARTIAL-FRACTION DECOMPOSITION

We will now apply the procedure of partial-fraction decomposition to integration.

EXAMPLE 4   Integrating a rational function with a repeated factor

Find $\displaystyle\int \frac{x^2 - 6x + 3}{(x - 2)^3} \, dx$.

Solution   From Example 1, we have

$$\int \frac{x^2 - 6x + 3}{(x - 2)^3} \, dx = \int \left[\frac{1}{x - 2} + \frac{-2}{(x - 2)^2} + \frac{-5}{(x - 2)^3} \right] dx$$

$$= \int (x - 2)^{-1} dx - 2 \int (x - 2)^{-2} dx - 5 \int (x - 2)^{-3} dx$$

$$= \ln|x - 2| + \frac{2}{x - 2} + \frac{5}{2(x - 2)^2} + C$$ ▬

EXAMPLE 5   **Integrating a rational fraction with distinct linear factors**

Find $\int \dfrac{x^4 + 2x^3 - 4x^2 + x - 3}{x^2 - x - 2}\, dx$.

Solution   We have $P(x) = x^4 + 2x^3 - 4x^2 + x - 3$ and $D(x) = x^2 - x - 2$; because the degree of P is higher than the degree of D, we carry out the long division and write

$$\int \frac{x^4 + 2x^3 - 4x^2 + x - 3}{x^2 - x - 2}\, dx = \int \left(x^2 + 3x + 1 + \frac{8x - 1}{x^2 - x - 2} \right) dx$$

The polynomial part is easy to integrate. The rational expression was decomposed into partial fractions in Example 2.

$$\int \frac{x^4 + 2x^3 - 4x^2 + x - 3}{x^2 - x - 2}\, dx = \int \left(x^2 + 3x + 1 + \frac{8x - 1}{x^2 - x - 2} \right) dx$$

$$= \int \left(x^2 + 3x + 1 + \frac{5}{x - 2} + \frac{3}{x + 1} \right) dx$$

$$= \int x^2 dx + 3 \int x\, dx + \int dx + 5 \int (x - 2)^{-1} dx + 3 \int (x + 1)^{-1} dx$$

$$= \frac{x^3}{3} + \frac{3x^2}{2} + x + 5 \ln|x - 2| + 3 \ln|x + 1| + C$$

EXAMPLE 6   **Repeated quadratic factors**

Find $\int \dfrac{-3x^3 - x}{(x^2 + 1)^2}\, dx$.

Solution   From Example 3,

$$\int \frac{-3x^3 - x}{(x^2 + 1)^2}\, dx = \int \frac{2x}{(x^2 + 1)^2}\, dx + \int \frac{-3x}{x^2 + 1}\, dx$$

Let $u = x^2 + 1$;
$du = 2x\, dx$.

$$= \int u^{-2}\, du - \frac{3}{2} \int u^{-1} du$$

$$= -u^{-1} - \frac{3}{2} \ln |u| + C$$

$$= \frac{-1}{x^2 + 1} - \frac{3}{2} \ln (x^2 + 1) + C$$

EXAMPLE 7   **Repeated linear factors**

Find $\int \dfrac{5x^2 + 21x + 4}{(x + 1)^2(x - 3)}\, dx$.

Solution   The partial-fraction decomposition of the integrand is

$$\frac{5x^2 + 21x + 4}{(x + 1)^2(x - 3)} = \frac{A_1}{(x + 1)^2} + \frac{A_2}{x + 1} + \frac{A_3}{x - 3}$$

Multiply both sides by $(x + 1)^2(x - 3)$:

$$5x^2 + 21x + 4 = A_1(x - 3) + A_2(x + 1)(x - 3) + A_3(x + 1)^2$$

As in Example 1, we substitute $x = -1$ and $x = 3$ into both sides of the equation to obtain $A_1 = 3$ and $A_3 = 7$, but A_2 cannot be obtained in this fashion. To find A_2, multiply out the polynomial on the right:

$$5x^2 + 21x + 4 = (A_2 + A_3)x^2 + (A_1 - 2A_2 + 2A_3)x + (-3A_1 - 3A_2 + A_3)$$

Equate the coefficients of x^2, x, and 1 (the constant term) on each side of the equation:

$$5 = A_2 + A_3 \qquad x^2 \text{ terms}$$
$$21 = A_1 - 2A_2 + 2A_3 \qquad x \text{ terms}$$
$$4 = -3A_1 - 3A_2 + A_3 \qquad \text{Constants}$$

Because we already know that $A_1 = 3$ and $A_3 = 7$, we use the equation $5 = A_2 + A_3$ to obtain $A_2 = -2$. We now turn to the integration:

$$\int \frac{5x^2 + 21x + 4}{(x+1)^2(x-3)}\, dx = \int \frac{3\, dx}{(x+1)^2} + \int \frac{-2\, dx}{x+1} + \int \frac{7\, dx}{x-3}$$
$$= -3(x+1)^{-1} - 2\ln|x+1| + 7\ln|x-3| + C \;\blacksquare$$

EXAMPLE 8   Distinct linear and quadratic factors

Find $\displaystyle\int \frac{x^2 + 4x - 23}{(x^2 + 4)(x + 3)}\, dx$.

Solution   The partial-fraction decomposition of the integrand has the form

$$\frac{x^2 + 4x - 23}{(x^2 + 4)(x + 3)} = \frac{A_1 x + B_1}{x^2 + 4} + \frac{A_2}{x + 3}$$

Multiply both sides by $(x^2 + 4)(x + 3)$ and then combine the terms on the right:

$$x^2 + 4x - 23 = (A_1 x + B_1)(x + 3) + A_2(x^2 + 4)$$
$$= (A_1 + A_2)x^2 + (3A_1 + B_1)x + (3B_1 + 4A_2)$$

Equate the coefficients to set up the following system of equations:

$$\begin{cases} A_1 + A_2 = 1 & x^2 \text{ terms} \\ 3A_1 + B_1 = 4 & x \text{ terms} \\ 3B_1 + 4A_2 = -23 & \text{Constants} \end{cases}$$

Solve this system (the details are not shown) to find $A_1 = 3$, $B_1 = -5$, and $A_2 = -2$. We now turn to the integration:

$$\int \frac{x^2 + 4x - 23}{(x^2 + 4)(x + 3)}\, dx = \int \frac{3x - 5}{x^2 + 4}\, dx + \int \frac{-2\, dx}{x + 3}$$
$$= 3 \underbrace{\int \frac{x\, dx}{x^2 + 4}}_{\uparrow} - 5 \int \frac{dx}{x^2 + 4} - 2 \int \frac{dx}{x + 3}$$

Let $u = x^2 + 4$; $du = 2x\, dx$.

$$= 3\left[\tfrac{1}{2}\ln(x^2 + 4)\right] - 5\left[\tfrac{1}{2}\tan^{-1}\left(\tfrac{x}{2}\right)\right] - 2\ln|x + 3| + C$$

■ SUBSTITUTION WITH PARTIAL FRACTIONS

The method of partial fractions can also be used in conjunction with substitution and other methods of integration.

EXAMPLE 9 Substitution followed by partial-fraction decomposition

Find $\int \dfrac{dx}{x^{2/3} - x^{5/3}}$.

Solution In order to guarantee an integral with integer powers, we use the substitution $x = u^3$ and $dx = 3u^2\ du$:

$$\int \frac{dx}{x^{2/3} - x^{5/3}} = \int \frac{3u^2\ du}{u^2 - u^5} = \int \frac{3u^2\ du}{u^2(1 - u^3)} = \int \frac{-3\ du}{(u - 1)(u^2 + u + 1)}$$

We use partial-fraction decomposition:

$$\frac{-3}{(u - 1)(u^2 + u + 1)} = \frac{A_1}{u - 1} + \frac{A_2 u + B_1}{u^2 + u + 1}$$

$$-3 = A_1(u^2 + u + 1) + (A_2 u + B_1)(u - 1)$$

$$-3 = (A_1 + A_2)u^2 + (A_1 - A_2 + B_1)u + (A_1 - B_1)$$

By equating the coefficients, we obtain the system of equations

$$\begin{cases} A_1 + A_2 = 0 & u^2\ terms \\ A_1 - A_2 + B_1 = 0 & u\ terms \\ A_1 - B_1 = -3 & Constants \end{cases}$$

with the solution $A_1 = -1$, $A_2 = 1$, and $B_1 = 2$.

We now continue with the integration:

$$\int \frac{dx}{x^{2/3} - x^{5/3}} = \int \frac{-3\ du}{(u - 1)(u^2 + u + 1)}$$

$$= \int \frac{-du}{u - 1} + \int \frac{u + 2}{u^2 + u + 1}\ du \quad \textit{By partial fractions}$$

$$= \int \frac{-du}{u - 1} + \int \frac{u + 2}{u^2 + u + \frac{1}{4} - \frac{1}{4} + 1}\ du$$

$$= \int \frac{-du}{u - 1} + \int \frac{u + 2}{\left(u + \frac{1}{2}\right)^2 + \frac{3}{4}}\ du \quad \boxed{\text{Let } v = u + \tfrac{1}{2};\ dv = du.}$$

$$= \int \frac{-du}{u - 1} + \int \frac{v - \frac{1}{2} + 2}{v^2 + \frac{3}{4}}\ dv$$

$$= \int \frac{-du}{u - 1} + \int \frac{v\ dv}{v^2 + \frac{3}{4}} + \frac{3}{2} \int \frac{dv}{v^2 + \frac{3}{4}} \quad \boxed{\text{Let } w = v^2 + \tfrac{3}{4};\ dw = 2v\ dv.}$$

$$= \int \frac{-du}{u - 1} + \frac{1}{2} \int \frac{dw}{w} + \frac{3}{2} \int \frac{dv}{v^2 + \left(\frac{\sqrt{3}}{2}\right)^2}$$

$$= -\ln|u - 1| + \frac{1}{2} \ln|w| + \frac{3}{2} \left(\frac{1}{\frac{\sqrt{3}}{2}}\right) \tan^{-1}\left(\frac{v}{\frac{\sqrt{3}}{2}}\right) + C$$

$$= -\ln|u - 1| + \tfrac{1}{2} \ln\left|v^2 + \tfrac{3}{4}\right| + \sqrt{3}\, \tan^{-1}\left(\frac{2v}{\sqrt{3}}\right) + C$$

$$= -\ln|u - 1| + \tfrac{1}{2} \ln\left|u^2 + u + 1\right| + \sqrt{3}\, \tan^{-1}\left(\frac{2u + 1}{\sqrt{3}}\right) + C$$

$$= -\ln\left|x^{1/3} - 1\right| + \tfrac{1}{2} \ln\left|x^{2/3} + x^{1/3} + 1\right| + \sqrt{3}\, \tan^{-1}\left(\frac{2x^{1/3} + 1}{\sqrt{3}}\right) + C \quad \rule[0.5ex]{1.5em}{0.3ex}$$

■ RATIONAL TRIGONOMETRIC INTEGRALS

$$\tan \frac{x}{2} = u$$

$$\cos \frac{x}{2} = \frac{1}{\sqrt{1 + u^2}}$$

$$\sin \frac{x}{2} = \frac{u}{\sqrt{1 + u^2}}$$

Figure 7.3 Weierstrass substitution

The German mathematician Karl Weierstrass (1815–1897; see the historical note on page 59) noticed that the substitution

$$u = \tan \frac{x}{2} \qquad -\pi < x < \pi$$

will convert any rational function of $\sin x$ and $\cos x$ into an ordinary rational function.

In order to show why this is a worthwhile substitution we use the double-angle identities for sine and cosine (see Figure 7.3):

$$\sin x = 2 \sin \frac{x}{2} \cos \frac{x}{2} \qquad \text{and} \qquad \cos x = \cos^2 \frac{x}{2} - \sin^2 \frac{x}{2}$$

$$= 2\left(\frac{u}{\sqrt{1 + u^2}}\right)\left(\frac{1}{\sqrt{1 + u^2}}\right) \qquad\qquad = \left(\frac{1}{\sqrt{1 + u^2}}\right)^2 - \left(\frac{u}{\sqrt{1 + u^2}}\right)^2$$

$$= \frac{2u}{1 + u^2} \qquad\qquad\qquad = \frac{1 - u^2}{1 + u^2}$$

Finally, because $u = \tan \frac{x}{2}$, we have $x = 2 \tan^{-1} u$, so $dx = \frac{2}{1 + u^2}\, du$.

Weierstrass Substitution

For $-\pi < x < \pi$, let $u = \tan \frac{x}{2}$ so that

$$\sin x = \frac{2u}{1 + u^2}, \qquad \cos x = \frac{1 - u^2}{1 + u^2}, \qquad \text{and} \qquad dx = \frac{2}{1 + u^2}\, du$$

This is called the **Weierstrass substitution.**

The following example illustrates how this substitution can be used along with partial fractions to integrate a rational trigonometric function.

EXAMPLE 10   Integrating a rational trigonometric function

Find $\displaystyle\int \frac{dx}{3 \cos x - 4 \sin x}$.

Solution   Use the Weierstrass substitution, that is, let $u = \tan \frac{x}{2}$.
Remember, $dx = \dfrac{2\, du}{1 + u^2}$; $\cos x = \dfrac{1 - u^2}{1 + u^2}$; and $\sin x = \dfrac{2u}{1 + u^2}$.

$$\int \frac{dx}{3 \cos x - 4 \sin x} = \int \frac{\dfrac{2\, du}{1 + u^2}}{3\left(\dfrac{1 - u^2}{1 + u^2}\right) - 4\left(\dfrac{2u}{1 + u^2}\right)} \qquad \textit{Simplify.}$$

$$= \int \frac{-2\, du}{3u^2 + 8u - 3} = \int \frac{-2\, du}{(3u - 1)(u + 3)}$$

This integral can be handled by the method of partial fractions.

$$\frac{-2}{(3u - 1)(u + 3)} = \frac{A_1}{3u - 1} + \frac{A_2}{u + 3}$$

Solve this to find $A_1 = -\frac{3}{5}$ and $A_2 = \frac{1}{5}$. We continue with the integration.

$$\int \frac{dx}{3 \cos x - 4 \sin x} = \int \frac{-2\, du}{(3u - 1)(u + 3)}$$

$$= \int \frac{-\frac{3}{5}\, du}{3u - 1} + \int \frac{\frac{1}{5}\, du}{u + 3}$$

$$= -\frac{3}{5} \cdot \frac{1}{3} \ln|3u - 1| + \frac{1}{5} \cdot \ln|u + 3| + C$$

$$= -\frac{1}{5} \ln|3 \tan \tfrac{x}{2} - 1| + \frac{1}{5} \ln|\tan \tfrac{x}{2} + 3| + C$$

Once again, observe that when carrying out integration, you may obtain very different forms for the result. For Example 10, you might use an integration table (formula 393 in the *Student Mathematics Handbook*) to find

$$\int \frac{du}{p \sin au + q \cos au} = \frac{1}{a\sqrt{p^2 + q^2}} \ln \left| \tan \left(\frac{au + \tan^{-1}\left(\frac{q}{p}\right)}{2} \right) \right|$$

Let $p = -4$, $q = 3$, $a = 1$, so that

$$\int \frac{dx}{3 \cos x - 4 \sin x} = \frac{1}{5} \ln \left| \tan \left(\frac{x + \tan^{-1}\left(-\frac{3}{4}\right)}{2} \right) \right| + C$$

Computational Window ▼ ▲

To illustrate further the point of alternative forms for the same integral, we add still another form for the indefinite integral of Example 10. Computer software programs often give alternative forms. For Example 10, we obtained

$$\frac{\text{LN}(3\cos(x) + \sin(x) + 3)}{5} - \frac{\text{LN}(\cos(x) - 3 \sin(x) + 1)}{5}$$

Problem 64 asks you to derive the formula

$$\int \sec x\, dx = \ln|\sec x + \tan x| + C$$

from scratch. You might recall that we derived this formula using an unusual algebraic step in Example 3 of Section 7.1. You can now derive this by using a Weierstrass substitution.

PROBLEM SET 7.3

Ⓐ *Write each rational function given in Problems 1–12 as a sum of partial fractions.*

1. $\dfrac{1}{x(x - 3)}$

2. $\dfrac{3x - 1}{x^2 - 1}$

3. $\dfrac{3x^2 + 2x - 1}{x(x + 1)}$

4. $\dfrac{2x^2 + 5x - 1}{x(x^2 - 1)}$

5. $\dfrac{4}{2x^2 + x}$

6. $\dfrac{x^2 - x + 3}{x^2(x - 1)}$

7. $\dfrac{4x^3 + 4x^2 + x - 1}{x^2(x + 1)^2}$

8. $\dfrac{x^2 - 5x - 4}{(x^2 + 1)(x - 3)}$

9. $\dfrac{x^3 + 3x^2 + 3x - 4}{x^2(x + 3)^2}$

10. $\dfrac{1}{x^3 - 1}$

11. $\dfrac{1}{1 - x^4}$

12. $\dfrac{x^4 - x^2 + 2}{x^2(x - 1)}$

Compute the integrals given in Problems 13–18. Notice that in each case, the integrand is a rational function decomposed into partial fractions in Problems 1–6.

13. $\displaystyle\int \frac{dx}{x(x-3)}$

14. $\displaystyle\int \frac{3x-1}{x^2-1}\,dx$

15. $\displaystyle\int \frac{3x^2+2x-1}{x(x+1)}\,dx$

16. $\displaystyle\int \frac{2x^2+5x-1}{x(x^2-1)}\,dx$

17. $\displaystyle\int \frac{4\,dx}{2x^2+x}$

18. $\displaystyle\int \frac{x^2-x+3}{x^2(x-1)}\,dx$

Find the indicated integrals in Problems 19–34.

19. $\displaystyle\int \frac{2x^3+9x-1}{x^2(x^2-1)}\,dx$

20. $\displaystyle\int \frac{x^4-x^2+2}{x^2(x-1)}\,dx$

21. $\displaystyle\int \frac{x^2+1}{x^2+x-2}\,dx$

22. $\displaystyle\int \frac{dx}{x^3-8}$

23. $\displaystyle\int \frac{x^4+1}{x^4-1}\,dx$

24. $\displaystyle\int \frac{x^3+1}{x^3-1}\,dx$

25. $\displaystyle\int \frac{x\,dx}{(x+1)^2}$

26. $\displaystyle\int \frac{2x\,dx}{(x-2)^2}$

27. $\displaystyle\int \frac{dx}{x(x+1)(x-2)}$

28. $\displaystyle\int \frac{x+2}{x(x-1)^2}\,dx$

29. $\displaystyle\int \frac{x\,dx}{(x+1)(x+2)^2}$

30. $\displaystyle\int \frac{x+1}{x(x^2+2)}\,dx$

31. $\displaystyle\int \frac{5x+7}{x^2+2x-3}\,dx$

32. $\displaystyle\int \frac{5x\,dx}{x^2-6x+9}$

33. $\displaystyle\int \frac{3x^2-2x+4}{x^3-x^2+4x-4}\,dx$

34. $\displaystyle\int \frac{3x^2+4x+1}{x^3+2x^2+x-2}\,dx$

ⓑ 35. ■ **What Does This Say?**   Describe the process of partial-fraction decomposition.

Find the indicated integral in Problems 36–53.

36. $\displaystyle\int \frac{\cos x\,dx}{\sin^2 x-\sin x-2}$

37. $\displaystyle\int \frac{e^x\,dx}{2e^{2x}-5e^x-3}$

38. $\displaystyle\int \frac{e^x\,dx}{e^{2x}-1}$

39. $\displaystyle\int \frac{\sin x\,dx}{(1+\cos x)^2}$

40. $\displaystyle\int \frac{\tan x\,dx}{\sec^2 x+4}$

41. $\displaystyle\int \frac{\sec^2 x\,dx}{\tan x+4}$

42. $\displaystyle\int \frac{dx}{x^{1/4}-x}$

43. $\displaystyle\int \frac{dx}{x^{1/4}-x^{5/4}}$

44. $\displaystyle\int \frac{dx}{\sin x-\cos x}$

45. $\displaystyle\int \frac{dx}{3\cos x+4\sin x}$

46. $\displaystyle\int \frac{dx}{5\sin x+4}$

47. $\displaystyle\int \frac{\sin x-\cos x}{\sin x+\cos x}\,dx$

48. $\displaystyle\int \frac{dx}{4\cos x+5}$

49. $\displaystyle\int \frac{dx}{\sec x-\tan x}$

50. $\displaystyle\int \frac{dx}{3\sin x+4\cos x+5}$

51. $\displaystyle\int \frac{dx}{4\sin x-3\cos x-5}$

52. $\displaystyle\int \frac{dx}{2\csc x-\cot x+2}$

53. $\displaystyle\int \frac{dx}{x(3-\ln x)(1-\ln x)}$

54. Find the area under the curve

$$y=\frac{1}{x^2+5x+4}$$

between $x=0$ and $x=3$.

55. Find the area of the region bounded by the curve

$$y=\frac{1}{6-5x+x^2}$$

and the lines $x=\frac{4}{3}$, $x=\frac{7}{4}$, and $y=0$.

56. Find the volume of the solid generated when the curve

$$y=\frac{1}{x^2+5x+4}, \qquad 0\le x\le 1$$

is revolved about the y-axis.

57. Find the volume (rounded to four decimal places) of the solid generated when the curve

$$y=\frac{1}{x^2+5x+4}, \qquad 0\le x\le 1$$

is revolved about the x-axis.

58. Find the volume of the solid generated when the region under the curve

$$y=\frac{1}{\sqrt{x^2+4x+3}}$$

on the interval $[0, 3]$ is revolved about the x-axis.

59. Find the volume of the solid generated when the region under the curve

$$y^2=x^2\left(\frac{4-x}{4+x}\right)$$

on the interval $[0, 4]$ is revolved about the x-axis.

60. Find the volume of the solid generated when the region under the curve

$$y=\frac{1}{\sin x+\cos x}$$

on the interval $\left[0, \frac{\pi}{4}\right]$ is revolved about the x-axis.

61. **SPY PROBLEM**   The spy manages to parachute safely into the small village next to Boldfinger's castle (see Problems 37 in Section 6.4). He lands at night and is observed by two villagers, the Redselig twins, who promise to keep silent. The spy cleverly disguises himself as an old duck plucker, but despite his best efforts, word begins to circulate among the 60 citizens of the village about the spy's true identity. His keen mind determines that the rate at which the rumor concerning his identity will spread is jointly proportional to the product of the number N of those who know already and the number $60-N$ who do not, so that

$$\frac{dN}{dt}=kN(60-N)$$

for a constant k. He needs a week to get the information he requires, but he figures that as soon as 20 or more villagers know his identity, Boldfinger is sure to find out and he will be a dead duck plucker. If three people know his secret after one day, will he be able to complete his mission?

ⓒ 62. Use partial fractions to derive the integration formula

$$\int \frac{dx}{a^2-x^2}=\frac{1}{2a}\ln\left|\frac{a+x}{a-x}\right|+C$$

63. Use partial fractions to derive the integration formula

$$\int \frac{dx}{x(ax + b)} = \frac{1}{b} \ln \left| \frac{x}{ax + b} \right| + C$$

64. Derive the formula

$$\int \sec x \, dx = \ln|\sec x + \tan x| + C$$

using a Weierstrass substitution.

65. Derive the formula

$$\int \csc x \, dx = -\ln|\csc x + \cot x| + C$$

using a Weierstrass substitution.

66. Recall from Section 6.4 that a population $P(t)$ follows a *logistic growth pattern* if the rate of population change is proportional to the product $P(A - P)$, where A is a positive constant. Set up and solve an appropriate differential equation for P. Assume that the initial population is P_0.

7.4 SUMMARY OF INTEGRATION TECHNIQUES

> **IN THIS SECTION** Integration strategy
>
> It is worthwhile to step back from our discussion of integration techniques and to take some time summarizing what we have done. In this section, we present a mixed bag of integration problems with no hints about how to carry out the integration.

We conclude our study of integration techniques with a table summarizing integration techniques.

TABLE 7.1 Integration Strategy

Step 1: Simplify.	Simplify the integrand, if possible, and use one of the procedural rules (see the inside back cover or the table of integrals).
Step 2: Use basic formulas.	Use the basic integration formulas (1–29 in the integration table). These are the fundamental building blocks for integration. Almost every integration will involve some basic formulas somewhere in the process, which means that you should memorize these forms.
Step 3: Substitute.	Make any substitution that will transform the integral into one of the basic forms.
Step 4: Classify.	Classify the integrand according to form in order to use a table of integrals. You may need to use substitution to transform the integrand into a form contained in the integration table. Some special types of substitution are contained in the following list:

    I. Integration by parts

        A. Forms $\int x^n e^{ax} \, dx$, $\int x^n \sin ax \, dx$, $\int x^n \cos ax \, dx$
           Let $u = x^n$.

        B. Forms $\int x^n \ln x \, dx$, $\int x^n \sin^{-1} ax \, dx$, $\int x^n \tan^{-1} ax \, dx$
           Let $dv = x^n \, dx$.

        C. Forms $\int e^{ax} \sin bx \, dx$, $\int e^{ax} \cos bx \, dx$
           Let $dv = e^{ax} \, dx$.

    II. Trigonometric functions

        A. $\int \sin^m x \cos^n x \, dx$
           m odd: **Let $u = \cos x$.**
           n odd: **Let $u = \sin x$.**
           m and n both even: **Use half-angle identities.**

        B. $\int \tan^m x \sec^n x \, dx$
           m odd: **Let $u = \sec x$.**
           n even: **Let $u = \tan x$.**
           m even, n odd: Write using powers of secant and **use integration tables (Formula 428).**

C. For a rational trigonometric integral, try the Weierstrass substitution.

Let $u = \tan\frac{x}{2}$, so that $\sin x = \dfrac{2u}{1 + u^2}$, $\cos x = \dfrac{1 - u^2}{1 + u^2}$, and $du = \dfrac{2}{1 + u^2}\, dx$.

III. Radical function; try a trigonometric substitution.
   A. Form $\sqrt{a^2 - u^2}$: **Let $u = a \sin \theta$.**
   B. Form $\sqrt{a^2 + u^2}$: **Let $u = a \tan \theta$.**
   C. Form $\sqrt{u^2 - a^2}$: **Let $u = a \sec \theta$.**

IV. Rational function; try partial-fraction decomposition.

Step 5: Try again.

Still stuck?
1. Manipulate the integrand.
   Multiply by 1 (clever choice of numerator or denominator).
   Rationalize the numerator.
   Rationalize the denominator.
2. Relate the problem to a previously worked problem.
3. Look at another table of integrals or consult computer software that does integration.
4. Some integrals do not have simple antiderivatives, so all these methods may fail. We will look at some of these forms later in the text.
5. If dealing with a definite integral, an approximation may suffice. It may be appropriate to use a calculator, computer, or the techniques introduced in Section 4.6.

EXAMPLE 1   Deciding on an integration procedure

Indicate a procedure to set up each integral. It is not necessary to carry out the integration.

a. $\displaystyle\int \frac{\sin \sqrt{x}}{\sqrt{x}}\, dx$ **b.** $\displaystyle\int (1 + \tan^2 \theta)\, d\theta$ **c.** $\displaystyle\int \sin^3 x \cos^2 x\, dx$

d. $\displaystyle\int 4x^2 \cos 3x\, dx$ **e.** $\displaystyle\int \frac{x\, dx}{\sqrt{9 - x^2}}$ **f.** $\displaystyle\int \frac{x^2\, dx}{\sqrt{9 - x^2}}$

g. $\displaystyle\int \frac{dx}{x\sqrt{x^2 - 9}}$ **h.** $\displaystyle\int e^{3x} \sin 2x\, dx$ **i.** $\displaystyle\int \frac{\cos^4 x\, dx}{1 - \sin^2 x}$

Solution   Keep in mind that there may be several correct approaches, and the way you proceed from problem to solution is often a matter of personal preference. However, in order to give you some practice, we will show several hints and suggestions in the context of this example.

a. $\displaystyle\int \frac{\sin \sqrt{x}}{\sqrt{x}}\, dx$ The integrand is simplified and is not a fundamental type. Substitution will work well for this problem if you let $u = \sqrt{x}$. After you make this substitution you can integrate using a basic formula.

b. $\displaystyle\int (1 + \tan^2 \theta)\, d\theta$ The integrand can be simplified using a trigonometric identity ($1 + \tan^2 \theta = \sec^2 \theta$), so that it can now be integrated using a basic formula.

c. $\displaystyle\int \sin^3 x \cos^2 x\, dx$ The integrand is simplified, it is not a basic formula, and there does not seem to be an easy substitution. Next, try to classify the integrand. It involves powers of trigonometric functions of the type $\int \sin^m x \cos^n x\, dx$, where $m = 3$ (odd) and $n = 2$ (even), so we make the substitution $u = \cos x$.

d. $\displaystyle\int 4x^2 \cos 3x \, dx$

The integrand is simplified (you can bring the 4 out in front of the integral, if you wish), it is not a basic formula, and there is no easy substitution. It does not seem to have an easy classification, so we check the table of integrals and find it to be formula 313.

e. $\displaystyle\int \frac{x \, dx}{\sqrt{9 - x^2}}$

The integrand is simplified and is not a basic formula. However, it looks like we might try the substitution $u = 9 - x^2$. It looks like this will work because the degree of the numerator is one less (namely x). You might also find this in a table of integrals (formula 225).

f. $\displaystyle\int \frac{x^2 \, dx}{\sqrt{9 - x^2}}$

The integrand is simplified, it is not a basic formula, and it does not look as though a substitution will work because of the degree of the numerator. It also does not seem to have an easy classification, so we turn to formula 226 of the table of integrals.

g. $\displaystyle\int \frac{dx}{x\sqrt{x^2 - 9}}$

The integrand is simplified, and it is a basic formula for inverse secant (formula 26).

h. $\displaystyle\int e^{3x} \sin 2x \, dx$

The integrand is simplified, is not a basic formula, and there does not seem to be an easy formula. If we try to classify the integrand, we see that integration by parts will work with $u = \sin 2x$ and $dv = e^{3x} \, dx$. We also find that this form is formula 492 in the integration table.

i. $\displaystyle\int \frac{\cos^4 x \, dx}{1 - \sin^2 x}$

The integration can be simplified by writing $1 - \sin^2 x = \cos^2 x$. After doing this substitution you will obtain

$$\int \frac{\cos^4 x \, dx}{1 - \sin^2 x} = \int \frac{\cos^4 x \, dx}{\cos^2 x} = \int \cos^2 x \, dx$$

This form can be integrated by using a half-angle identity or formula 317 in the table of integrals. ▬

PROBLEM SET 7.4

Ⓐ *Find each integral in Problems 1–50.*

1. $\displaystyle\int \frac{2x - 1}{(x - x^2)^3} \, dx$

2. $\displaystyle\int \frac{2x + 3}{\sqrt{x^2 + 3x}} \, dx$

3. $\displaystyle\int (x \sec 2x^2) \, dx$

4. $\displaystyle\int (x^2 \csc^2 2x^3) \, dx$

5. $\displaystyle\int (e^x \cot e^x) \, dx$

6. $\displaystyle\int \frac{\tan \sqrt{x} \, dx}{\sqrt{x}}$

7. $\displaystyle\int \frac{\tan (\ln x) \, dx}{x}$

8. $\displaystyle\int \sqrt{\cot x} \, \csc^2 x \, dx$

9. $\displaystyle\int \frac{3 + 2 \sin t}{\cos t} \, dt$

10. $\displaystyle\int \frac{2 + \cos x}{\sin x} \, dx$

11. $\displaystyle\int \frac{e^{2t} \, dt}{1 + e^{4t}}$

12. $\displaystyle\int \frac{\sin 2x \, dx}{1 + \sin^4 x}$

13. $\displaystyle\int \frac{x^2 + x + 1}{x^2 + 9} \, dx$

14. $\displaystyle\int \frac{3x + 2}{\sqrt{4 - x^2}} \, dx$

15. $\displaystyle\int \frac{1 + e^x}{1 - e^x} \, dx$

16. $\displaystyle\int \frac{e^{1 - \sqrt{x}} \, dx}{\sqrt{x}}$

17. $\displaystyle\int \frac{2t^2 \, dt}{\sqrt{1 - t^6}}$

18. $\displaystyle\int \frac{t^3 \, dt}{2^8 + t^8}$

19. $\displaystyle\int \frac{dx}{1 + e^{2x}}$

20. $\displaystyle\int \frac{dx}{4 - e^{-x}}$

21. $\displaystyle\int \frac{dx}{x^2 + 2x + 2}$

22. $\displaystyle\int \frac{dx}{x^2 + x + 4}$

23. $\displaystyle\int \frac{dx}{x^2 + x + 1}$

24. $\displaystyle\int \frac{dx}{x^2 - x + 1}$

25. $\displaystyle\int \tan^{-1} x \, dx$

26. $\displaystyle\int xe^x \sin x \, dx$

27. $\displaystyle\int e^{-x} \cos x \, dx$

28. $\displaystyle\int e^{2x} \sin 3x \, dx$

29. $\displaystyle\int \cos^{-1}(-x) \, dx$

30. $\displaystyle\int \sin^{-1} 2x \, dx$

31. $\displaystyle\int \sin^3 x \, dx$

32. $\displaystyle\int \cos^5 x \, dx$

33. $\displaystyle\int \sin^3 x \cos^2 x \, dx$

34. $\displaystyle\int \sin^3 x \cos^3 x \, dx$

35. $\displaystyle\int \sin^2 x \cos^4 x \, dx$

36. $\displaystyle\int \sin^2 x \cos^5 x \, dx$

37. $\displaystyle\int \sin^5 x \cos^4 x \, dx$

38. $\displaystyle\int \sin^4 x \cos^2 x \, dx$

39. $\displaystyle\int \tan^5 x \sec^4 x \, dx$

40. $\displaystyle\int \tan^4 x \sec^4 x \, dx$

41. $\displaystyle\int \frac{\sqrt{1 - x^2}}{x} \, dx$

42. $\displaystyle\int \frac{dx}{\sqrt{x^2 - 16}}$

43. $\displaystyle\int \frac{2x + 3}{\sqrt{2x^2 - 1}} \, dx$

44. $\displaystyle\int \frac{dx}{x\sqrt{x^2 - 1}}$

45. $\int \dfrac{dx}{x\sqrt{x^2+1}}$

46. $\int x\sqrt{x^2+1}\,dx$

47. $\int \dfrac{(2x+1)\,dx}{\sqrt{4x-x^2-2}}$

48. $\int \sqrt{3+4x-4x^2}\,dx$

49. $\int \dfrac{\cos x\,dx}{\sqrt{1+\sin^2 x}}$

50. $\int \dfrac{\sec^2 x\,dx}{\sqrt{\sec^2 x-2}}$

Evaluate the definite integrals in Problems 51–64.

51. $\displaystyle\int_0^2 \sqrt{4-x^2}\,dx$

52. $\displaystyle\int_0^1 \dfrac{dx}{\sqrt{9-x^2}}$

53. $\displaystyle\int_0^1 \dfrac{dx}{(x^2+2)^{3/2}}$

54. $\displaystyle\int_0^1 \dfrac{dt}{4t^2+4t+5}$

55. $\displaystyle\int_1^2 \dfrac{dx}{x^4\sqrt{x^2+3}}$

56. $\displaystyle\int_0^2 \dfrac{x^3}{(3+x^2)^{3/2}}\,dx$

57. $\displaystyle\int_{-2}^{2\sqrt{3}} x^3\sqrt{x^2+4}\,dx$

58. $\displaystyle\int_0^{\sqrt{5}} x^2\sqrt{5-x^2}\,dx$

59. $\displaystyle\int_0^{\ln 2} e^t\sqrt{1+e^{2t}}\,dt$

60. $\displaystyle\int_1^4 \dfrac{\sqrt{x^2+9}}{x^3}\,dx$

61. $\displaystyle\int_0^{\pi/4} \sin^5 x\,dx$

62. $\displaystyle\int_0^{\pi/4} \cos^6 x\,dx$

63. $\displaystyle\int_0^{\pi/4} \tan^4 x\,dx$

64. $\displaystyle\int_0^{\pi/3} \sec^4 x\,dx$

Ⓑ *Find each integral in Problems 65–77.*

65. $\int \dfrac{e^x\,dx}{\sqrt{1+e^{2x}}}$

66. $\int \dfrac{dx}{x\sqrt{4x^2+4x+2}}$

67. $\int \dfrac{x^2+4x+3}{x^3+x^2+x}\,dx$

68. $\int \dfrac{6x^2+8x}{x^3+2x^2}\,dx$

69. $\int \dfrac{5x^2+18x+34}{(x-7)(x+2)^2}\,dx$

70. $\int \dfrac{-3x^2+9x+21}{(x+2)^2(2x+1)}\,dx$

71. $\int \dfrac{3x+5}{x^2+2x+1}\,dx$

72. $\int \dfrac{x^2+4x+3}{x^3+x^2+x}\,dx$

73. $\int \dfrac{5x^2+3x-2}{x^3+2x^2}\,dx$

74. $\int \dfrac{6x+5}{4x^2+4x+1}\,dx$

75. $\int \dfrac{x\,dx}{(x+1)(x+2)(x+3)}$

76. $\int \dfrac{5x^2-4x+9}{x^3-x^2+4x-4}\,dx$

77. $\int \dfrac{dx}{5\cos x-12\sin x}$

Ⓑ 78. Find the area (to the nearest hundredth) under the curve $y=\sin x+\cos 2x$ on $[0,4]$.

79. Find the average value (to the nearest hundredth) of the function $f(x)=x\sin^3 x^2$ between $x=0$ and $x=1$.

80. An object moves along the x-axis in such a way that its velocity at time t is $v(t)=\sin t+\sin^2 t\cos^3 t$. Find the distance moved by the object between times $t=0$ and $t=\frac{\pi}{3}$.

81. ■ **What Does This Say?** Integrals of the general form

$$\int \cot^m x\,\csc^n x\,dx$$

are handled in much the same way as those of the form

$$\int \tan^m x\,\sec^n x\,dx$$

a. What substitution would you use in the case where m and n are both odd?

b. What substitution would you use if n is even?

c. What would you do if n is odd and m is even?

82. Find the volume of the solid generated when the region under the curve $y=\cos x$ between $x=0$ and $x=\frac{\pi}{2}$ is revolved about the x-axis.

83. Find the average value of $\sec x$ on $\left[0,\frac{\pi}{4}\right]$.

84. Find the average value (to the nearest hundredth) of $\csc x$ on $[1,2]$.

85. Find the area of the region bounded by the graphs of
$$y=\dfrac{2x}{\sqrt{x^2+9}},\ y=0,\ x=0,\text{ and }x=4.$$

86. What is the volume of the solid obtained when the region bounded by $y=\sqrt{x}e^{-x^2}$, $y=0$, $x=0$, and $x=2$ is revolved about the x-axis?

87. What is the volume of the solid obtained when the region bounded by $y=x\sqrt{9-x^2}$ and $y=0$ is revolved about the x-axis?

88. Find the length of the curve $y=\ln(\sec x)$ from $x=0$ to $x=\frac{\pi}{4}$.

89. Find the centroid (to the nearest hundredth) of the region bounded by the curve $y=x^2e^{-x}$ and the x-axis, between $x=0$ and $x=1$ revolved about the x-axis.

Ⓒ 90. Use integration by parts to verify that

$$\int e^{ax}\sin bx\,dx=\dfrac{(a\sin bx-b\cos bx)e^{ax}}{a^2+b^2}+C$$

(This is formula 492.)

91. Use integration by parts to verify that

$$\int e^{ax}\cos bx\,dx=\dfrac{(a\cos bx+b\sin bx)e^{ax}}{a^2+b^2}+C$$

(This is formula 493.)

92. Let f'' be continuous on the closed interval $[a,b]$. Use integration by parts to show that

$$\int_a^b xf''(x)\,dx=bf'(b)-af'(a)-f(b)+f(a)$$

93. Derive the integration formula

$$\int x^m(\ln x)^n\,dx=\dfrac{x^{m+1}(\ln x)^n}{m+1}-\dfrac{n}{m+1}\int x^m(\ln x)^{n-1}\,dx$$

where m and n are positive integers. (This is formula 510.) Use the formula to find

$$\int x^2(\ln x)^3\,dx$$

94. Derive the integration formula

$$\int \sin^n Ax\,dx=\dfrac{-\sin^{n-1}Ax\cos Ax}{An}+\dfrac{n-1}{n}\int \sin^{n-2}Ax\,dx$$

(This is formula 352.) Use this formula to evaluate

$$\int \sin^3 4x\,dx$$

7.5 IMPROPER INTEGRALS

IN THIS SECTION Improper integrals with infinite limits of integration, improper integrals with unbounded integrands

We have defined the definite integral $\int_a^b f(x)\,dx$ on a closed, finite interval $[a, b]$ where the integrand $f(x)$ is bounded. In this section, we extend the concept of integral to the case where the interval of integration is infinite and also to the case where f is unbounded at a finite number of points on the interval of integration. Collectively, these are called **improper integrals.**

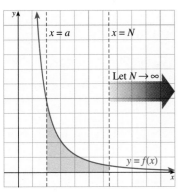

Figure 7.4 Finding the area under a curve on an unbounded region

■ IMPROPER INTEGRALS WITH INFINITE LIMITS OF INTEGRATION

In physics, economics, probability and statistics, and other applied areas, it is useful to have a concept of integral that is defined on the entire real line or on half-lines of the form $x \ge a$ or $x \le a$. If $f(x) \ge 0$, the integral of f on the interval $x \ge a$ can be thought of as the area under the curve $y = f(x)$ on this unbounded interval, as shown in Figure 7.4. A reasonable strategy for finding this area is first to use a definite integral to compute the area from $x = a$ to some finite number $x = N$ and then to let N approach infinity in the resulting expression. Here is a definition.

Improper Integrals (First Type)

Let a be a fixed number and assume $\int_a^N f(x)\,dx$ exists for all $N \ge a$. Then if

$$\lim_{N \to +\infty} \int_a^N f(x)\,dx$$ exists, we define the **improper integral**

$$\int_a^{+\infty} f(x)\,dx = \lim_{N \to +\infty} \int_a^N f(x)\,dx$$

The improper integral $\int_a^{+\infty} f(x)\,dx$ is said to **converge** if this limit is a finite number and to **diverge** otherwise.

EXAMPLE 1 Converging improper integral

Evaluate $\int_1^{+\infty} \dfrac{dx}{x^2}$.

Solution We draw the graph of $y = 1/x^2$, as shown in Figure 7.5. This region is unbounded, so it might seem reasonable to conclude that the area is also infinite. Begin by computing the integral from 1 to t.

$$Consider \int_1^t \frac{dx}{x^2} = -\frac{1}{x}\Big|_1^t = -\frac{1}{t} + 1.$$

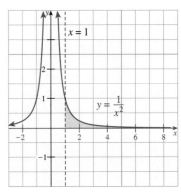

Figure 7.5 Graph of $y = \dfrac{1}{x^2}$

Let us consider the situation more carefully, as shown in Figure 7.6. For $t = 2$, 3, 10, or 100, it appears that the area is not infinite, but rather is finite.

Let $t = 2$, $A = 1/2$.

Let $t = 3$, $A = 2/3$.

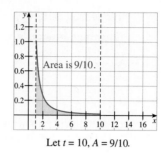

Let $t = 10$, $A = 9/10$.

Let $t = 100$, $A = 99/100$.

Figure 7.6 Area enclosed by $y = \dfrac{1}{x^2}$, the x-axis, $y = 1$, and $y = t$

Instead of picking a particular t, suppose we find the limit as $t \to \infty$, as shown in Figure 7.7.

$$\int_1^{+\infty} \frac{dx}{x^2} = \lim_{t \to +\infty} \int_1^t \frac{dx}{x^2}$$
$$= \lim_{t \to +\infty} \left[-x^{-1}\right]\Big|_1^t$$
$$= \lim_{t \to +\infty} \left[-t^{-1} + 1\right]$$
$$= 1$$

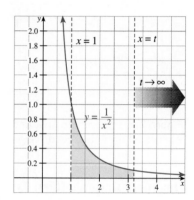

Figure 7.7 The area bounded by the curve $y = 1/x^2$, the line $x = 1$, and the x-axis is finite.

Thus, the improper integral converges and has the value 1.   ▬

EXAMPLE 2   Diverging improper integral

Evaluate $\displaystyle\int_1^{+\infty} \frac{dx}{x}$.

Solution   The graph of $y = 1/x$, shown in Figure 7.8, looks very much like the graph of $y = 1/x^2$ in Figure 7.7. We compute the integral from 1 to t and then let t go to infinity.

$$\int_1^{+\infty} \frac{dx}{x} = \lim_{t \to +\infty} \int_1^t \frac{dx}{x}$$
$$= \lim_{t \to +\infty} \ln|x|\Big|_1^t$$
$$= \lim_{t \to +\infty} \ln t = +\infty$$

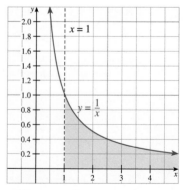

Figure 7.8 The area bounded by the curve $y = 1/x$, the line $x = 1$, and the x-axis is infinite.

The limit is not a finite number, which means the improper integral diverges.   ▬

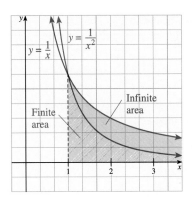

Figure 7.9 An unbounded region may have either a finite or an infinite area.

We have shown that the improper integral

$\int_1^{+\infty} \dfrac{dx}{x^2}$ converges and that the improper integral $\int_1^{+\infty} \dfrac{dx}{x}$ diverges.

In geometric terms, this says that the area to the right of $x = 1$ under the curve $y = 1/x^2$ is finite, whereas the corresponding area under the curve $y = 1/x$ is infinite. The reason for the difference is that as x increases, $1/x^2$ approaches zero more quickly than does $1/x$, as shown in Figure 7.9.

EXAMPLE 3   Determining convergence of an improper integral

Show that the improper integral $\int_1^{+\infty} \dfrac{dx}{x^p}$ converges only for $p > 1$.

> *What this says:* The improper integral
> $$\int_1^{+\infty} \frac{dx}{x^p} = \begin{cases} \dfrac{1}{p-1} & \text{if } p > 1 \\ \text{diverges} & \text{if } p \leq 1 \end{cases}$$

Solution   We already know the integral diverges for $p = 1$ (Example 2), so we can assume $p \neq 1$.

$$\int_1^{+\infty} \frac{dx}{x^p} = \lim_{t \to +\infty} \int_1^t \frac{dx}{x^p} = \lim_{t \to +\infty} \left[\frac{x^{-p+1}}{-p+1} \right]\Big|_1^t = \lim_{t \to +\infty} \frac{1}{1-p}[t^{1-p} - 1]$$

If $p > 1$, then $1 - p < 0$, so $t^{1-p} \to 0$ as $t \to +\infty$, and

$$\int_1^{+\infty} \frac{dx}{x^p} = \lim_{t \to +\infty} \frac{1}{1-p}[t^{1-p} - 1] = \frac{1}{1-p}[-1] = \frac{1}{p-1}$$

If $p < 1$, then $1 - p > 0$, so $t^{1-p} \to +\infty$ as $t \to +\infty$, and

$$\int_1^{+\infty} \frac{dx}{x^p} = \lim_{t \to +\infty} \frac{1}{1-p}[t^{1-p} - 1] = +\infty$$

Thus, the improper integral diverges for $p \leq 1$ and converges for $p > 1$. ▬

EXAMPLE 4   Improper integral for which technology may give an incorrect result

Evaluate the given integrals.

a. $\displaystyle\int_1^{\infty} \frac{x^{\sqrt{5}} + 1}{x^{3.236}}\, dx$ **b.** $\displaystyle\int_1^{\infty} \frac{x^{\sqrt{5}} + 1}{x^{3.24}}\, dx$ **c.** $\displaystyle\int_1^{\infty} \frac{x^{\sqrt{5}} + 1}{x^{1+\sqrt{5}}}\, dx$

Solution   We note that $\sqrt{5} \approx 2.236\,067\,978$; consider $\dfrac{x^{\sqrt{5}} + 1}{x^{3.236}} = \dfrac{1}{x^{3.236 - \sqrt{5}}} + \dfrac{1}{x^{3.236}}$.

a. Because $3.236 - \sqrt{5} < 1$, the integral diverges.

b. Because $3.24 - \sqrt{5} > 1$, the integral converges:

$$\int_1^{\infty} \frac{x^{\sqrt{5}} + 1}{x^{3.24}}\, dx = \int_1^{\infty} \left[\frac{1}{x^{3.24 - \sqrt{5}}} + \frac{1}{x^{3.24}} \right] = \frac{1}{(3.24 - \sqrt{5}) - 1} \approx 254.322$$

c. Because $1 + \sqrt{5} - \sqrt{5} = 1$, the integral diverges. ▬

EXAMPLE 5   Improper integral using l'Hôpital's rule

Evaluate $\displaystyle\int_0^{+\infty} xe^{-2x}\,dx$.

Solution $\displaystyle\int_0^{+\infty} xe^{-2x}\,dx = \lim_{t\to+\infty}\int_0^t \underbrace{x}_{u}\,\underbrace{e^{-2x}\,dx}_{dv}$

> By parts:
> Let $u = x$ and $dv = e^{-2x}\,dx$
> $du = dx$ $\qquad v = \frac{1}{-2}e^{-2x}$

$$= \lim_{t\to+\infty}\left[\left(\frac{x}{-2}e^{-2x}\right)\Big|_0^t - \int_0^t \frac{1}{-2}e^{-2x}\,dx\right]$$

overbrace: $uv \quad - \quad \int v\,du$

$$= \lim_{t\to+\infty}\left[\frac{-xe^{-2x}}{2} - \frac{e^{-2x}}{4}\right]\Big|_0^t$$

$$= \lim_{t\to+\infty}\left[-\tfrac{1}{2}te^{-2t} - \tfrac{1}{4}e^{-2t} + 0 + \tfrac{1}{4}\right]$$

$$= -\frac{1}{2}\lim_{t\to+\infty}\left(\frac{t}{e^{2t}}\right) + \frac{1}{4} \qquad \textit{Because } \lim_{t\to+\infty}\left(-\tfrac{1}{4}e^{-2t}\right) = 0 \textit{ and } \lim_{t\to+\infty}\tfrac{1}{4} = \tfrac{1}{4}$$

$$= -\frac{1}{2}\lim_{t\to+\infty}\left(\frac{1}{2e^{2t}}\right) + \frac{1}{4} \qquad \textit{l'Hôpital's rule: } \lim_{t\to+\infty}\left(\frac{t}{e^{2t}}\right) = \lim_{t\to+\infty}\left(\frac{1}{2e^{2t}}\right)$$

$$= \frac{1}{4}$$

EXAMPLE 6   THINK TANK example: Gabriel's horn, a solid with a finite volume but infinite surface area

Gabriel's horn is the name given to the solid formed by revolving about the x-axis the unbounded region under the curve $y = \frac{1}{x}$ for $x \geq 1$. Show that this solid has finite volume but infinite surface area.

Solution We will find the volume by using disks, as shown in Figure 7.10.

$$V = \pi\int_1^{+\infty}(x^{-1})^2\,dx = \pi\lim_{t\to+\infty}\int_1^t x^{-2}\,dx = \pi\lim_{t\to+\infty}\left(-\frac{1}{t}+1\right) = \pi$$

$$S = 2\pi\int_1^{+\infty} f(x)\sqrt{1+[f'(x)]^2}\,dx = 2\pi\int_1^{+\infty}\frac{1}{x}\sqrt{1+\frac{1}{x^4}}\,dx$$

$$= 2\pi\int_1^{+\infty}\frac{1}{x}\sqrt{\frac{x^4+1}{x^4}} = 2\pi\int_1^{+\infty}\frac{\sqrt{x^4+1}}{x^3}\,dx \qquad \begin{array}{l}\text{Let } u = x^2 \\ du = 2x\,dx\end{array}$$

$$= 2\pi\int_1^{+\infty}\frac{\sqrt{u^2+1}}{2u^2}\,du = \pi\lim_{t\to+\infty}\int_1^t\frac{\sqrt{u^2+1}}{u^2}\,du$$

$$= \pi\lim_{t\to+\infty}\left[\frac{-\sqrt{u^2+1}}{u} + \ln\left|u+\sqrt{u^2+1}\right|\right]\Big|_1^t$$

$$= +\infty \quad \text{(The details are left for the reader.)}$$

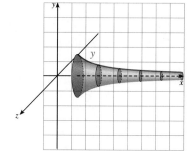

Figure 7.10 Gabriel's horn. You can fill Gabriel's horn with a finite amount of paint, but it takes an infinite amount of paint to color the inside of the horn!

We can also define an improper integral on an interval that is unbounded to the left or on the entire real number line.

Improper Integrals (First Type, Extended)

Let b be a fixed number and assume $\int_t^b f(x)\,dx$ exists for all $t < b$. Then if $\lim\limits_{t \to -\infty} \int_t^b f(x)\,dx$ exists, we define the **improper integral**

$$\int_{-\infty}^b f(x)\,dx = \lim_{t \to -\infty} \int_t^b f(x)\,dx$$

The improper integral $\int_{-\infty}^b f(x)\,dx$ is said to **converge** if this limit is a finite number and to **diverge** otherwise. If both

$$\int_a^{+\infty} f(x)\,dx \qquad \text{and} \qquad \int_{-\infty}^a f(x)\,dx$$

converge for some number a, the improper integral of $f(x)$ on the entire x-axis is defined by

$$\int_{-\infty}^{+\infty} f(x)\,dx = \int_{-\infty}^a f(x)\,dx + \int_a^{+\infty} f(x)\,dx$$

EXAMPLE 7   Improper integral to negative infinity

Find $\int_{-\infty}^0 e^x\,dx$.

Solution
$$\int_{-\infty}^0 e^x\,dx = \lim_{t \to -\infty} \int_t^0 e^x\,dx = \lim_{t \to -\infty} (1 - e^t) = 1$$

■ IMPROPER INTEGRALS WITH UNBOUNDED INTEGRANDS

A function f is **unbounded** at c if it has arbitrarily large values near c. Geometrically, this occurs when the line $x = c$ is a vertical asymptote to the graph of f at c, as shown in Figure 7.11.

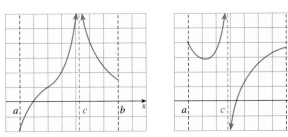

Figure 7.11 Two functions that are unbounded at c

If f is unbounded at c and $a < c < b$, the Riemann integral $\int_a^b f(x)\,dx$ is not even defined (only bounded functions are Riemann integrable). However, it may still be possible to define $\int_a^b f(x)\,dx$ as an improper integral in certain cases.

Let us examine a specific problem. Suppose

$$f(x) = \frac{1}{\sqrt{x}} \qquad \text{for } 0 < x \le 1$$

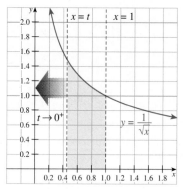

Figure 7.12 Graph of $y = \dfrac{1}{\sqrt{x}}$

Then f is unbounded at $x = 0$ and $\int_0^1 f(x)\,dx$ is not defined. However,

$$f(x) = \frac{1}{\sqrt{x}}$$

is continuous on every interval $[t, 1]$ for $t > 0$, as shown in Figure 7.12. For any such interval $[t, 1]$ we have

$$\int_t^1 \frac{dx}{\sqrt{x}} = \int_t^1 x^{-1/2}\,dx = 2\sqrt{x}\,\Big|_t^1 = 2 - 2\sqrt{t}$$

If we let $t \to 0$ through positive values, we see that

$$\lim_{t \to 0^+} \int_t^1 \frac{dx}{\sqrt{x}} = \lim_{t \to 0^+} (2 - 2\sqrt{t}) = 2$$

This is called a **convergent improper integral** with value 2, and it seems reasonable to say

$$\int_0^1 \frac{dx}{\sqrt{x}} = \lim_{t \to 0^+} \int_t^1 \frac{dx}{\sqrt{x}} = 2$$

In this example, f is unbounded at the left endpoint of the interval of integration, but similar reasoning would apply if it were unbounded at the right endpoint or at an interior point. Here is a definition of this kind of improper integral.

Improper Integral (Second Type)

If f is unbounded at a and $\int_t^b f(x)\,dx$ exists for all t such that $a < t \le b$, then

$$\int_a^b f(x)\,dx = \lim_{t \to a^+} \int_t^b f(x)\,dx$$

If the limit exists (as a finite number) we say that the improper integral **converges;** otherwise, the improper integral **diverges.** Similarly, if f is unbounded at b and $\int_a^t f(x)\,dx$ exists for all t such that $a \le t < b$, then

$$\int_a^b f(x)\,dx = \lim_{t \to b^-} \int_a^t f(x)\,dx$$

If f is unbounded at c, where $a < c < b$ and the improper integrals $\int_a^c f(x)\,dx$ and $\int_c^b f(x)\,dx$ both converge, then

$$\int_a^b f(x)\,dx = \int_a^c f(x)\,dx + \int_c^b f(x)\,dx$$

We say that the integral on the left diverges if *either* of the integrals on the right diverges.

◼ *What this says:* If a continuous function is unbounded at one of its endpoints, then replace that endpoint by t, evaluate the integral, and then take the limit as t approaches that endpoint. On the other hand, if f is continuous on the interval $[a, b]$, except for some c in (a, b) at which f has an infinite discontinuity, then rewrite the integral as

$$\int_a^b f(x)\,dx = \int_a^c f(x)\,dx + \int_c^b f(x)\,dx$$

You will then need limits to evaluate each of the integrals on the right.

EXAMPLE 8   **Improper integral at a right endpoint**

Find $\displaystyle\int_0^1 \frac{dx}{(x-1)^{2/3}}$.

Solution   Let $f(x) = (x-1)^{-2/3}$. This function is unbounded at the right endpoint of the interval of integration and is continuous on $[0, t]$ for any t with $0 \le t < 1$. We find that

$$\int_0^1 \frac{dx}{(x-1)^{2/3}} = \lim_{t \to 1^-} \int_0^t \frac{dx}{(x-1)^{2/3}} = \lim_{t \to 1^-} \left[3(x-1)^{1/3}\right]\Big|_0^t$$

$$= 3 \lim_{t \to 1^-} [(t-1)^{1/3} - (-1)] = 3$$

That is, the improper integral converges and has the value 3.   ▬

EXAMPLE 9   **Improper integral at a left endpoint**

Find $\displaystyle\int_{\pi/2}^\pi \sec x \, dx$.

Solution   Because $\sec x$ is unbounded at the left endpoint $\frac{\pi}{2}$ of the interval of integration and is continuous on $[t, \pi]$ for any t with $\frac{\pi}{2} < t \le \pi$, we find that

$$\int_{\pi/2}^\pi \sec x \, dx = \lim_{t \to (\pi/2)^+} \int_t^\pi \sec x \, dx = \lim_{t \to (\pi/2)^+} \ln|\sec x + \tan x|\Big|_t^\pi$$

$$= \lim_{t \to (\pi/2)^+} [\ln|-1 + 0| - \ln|\sec t + \tan t|] = -\infty$$

Thus, the integral diverges.   ▬

EXAMPLE 10   **Improper integral at an interior point**

Find $\displaystyle\int_0^3 (x-2)^{-1} dx$.

Solution   The integral is improper because the integrand is unbounded at $x = 2$. If the improper integral converges, we have

$$\int_0^3 (x-2)^{-1} dx = \int_0^2 (x-2)^{-1} dx + \int_2^3 (x-2)^{-1} dx$$

$$= \lim_{t \to 2^-} \int_0^t (x-2)^{-1} dx + \lim_{t \to 2^+} \int_t^3 (x-2)^{-1} dx$$

If either of these limits fails to exist, then the original integral diverges. Because

$$\lim_{t \to 2^-} \int_0^t (x-2)^{-1} dx = \lim_{t \to 2^-} \ln|x-2|\Big|_0^t$$

$$= \lim_{t \to 2^-} [\ln(2-t) - \ln 2]$$

$$= -\infty$$

we find that the original integral diverges.   ▬

⊘ A common mistake is to fail to notice the discontinuity at $x = 2$. It is WRONG to write

$$\int_0^3 (x-2)^{-1} dx$$

$$= \ln|x-2|\Big|_0^3 = \ln 1 - \ln 2$$

$$= -\ln 2$$

Notice that this mistake leads to the conclusion that the integral converges, which, as you can see, is incorrect. ⊘

Computational Window

⊘ You must be cautious in using computer software with improper integrals, because it may not detect that the integral is improper. ⊘

For Example 10,

$$\int_0^3 (x-2)^{-1}dx$$

one popular software package shows:

Type of Estimate	No. of Subintervals	Estimate on [0, 3]
Riemann	10	0.8900878
Riemann	100	1.098096
Riemann	1000	1.118402
Riemann	10000	1.120427
Trapezoid	10000	1.120652
Simpson	10000	2.329852

We must, once again, emphasize the need to understand the mathematics and not rely solely on available technology. For this reason, a graphing calculator can be an excellent tool for exposing the need for evaluating an integral at an interior point. For Example 10, simply input $y = (x-2)^{-1}$ and graph:

Using a graph in this fashion may help you to avoid mistakes.

Y₁ᗺ(X-2)⁻¹

Xmin=-5   Ymin=-5
Xmax=5   Ymax=5
Xscl=1   Yscl=1

PROBLEM SET 7.5

A   1. ■ **What Does This Say?**   What is an improper integral?
   2. ■ **What Does This Say?**   Discuss the different types of improper integrals.

In Problems 3–42, either show that the improper integral converges and find its value, or show that it diverges.

3. $\int_1^{+\infty} \dfrac{dx}{x^3}$

4. $\int_1^{+\infty} \dfrac{dx}{\sqrt[3]{x}}$

5. $\int_1^{+\infty} \dfrac{dx}{x^{0.99}}$

6. $\int_1^{+\infty} \dfrac{dx}{\sqrt{x}}$

7. $\int_1^{+\infty} \dfrac{dx}{x^{1.1}}$

8. $\int_1^{+\infty} x^{-2/3}\, dx$

9. $\int_3^{+\infty} \dfrac{dx}{2x-1}$

10. $\int_3^{+\infty} \dfrac{dx}{\sqrt[3]{2x-1}}$

11. $\int_3^{+\infty} \dfrac{dx}{(2x-1)^2}$

12. $\int_0^{+\infty} e^{-x}\, dx$

13. $\int_0^{+\infty} 5e^{-2x}\, dx$

14. $\int_1^{+\infty} e^{1-x}\, dx$

15. $\int_1^{+\infty} \dfrac{x^2\, dx}{(x^3+2)^2}$

16. $\int_1^{+\infty} \dfrac{x^2\, dx}{x^3+2}$

17. $\int_1^{+\infty} \dfrac{x^2\, dx}{\sqrt{x^3+2}}$

18. $\int_0^{+\infty} xe^{-x^2}\, dx$

19. $\int_1^{+\infty} \dfrac{e^{-\sqrt{x}}\, dx}{\sqrt{x}}$

20. $\int_0^{+\infty} xe^{-x}\, dx$

21. $\int_0^{+\infty} 5xe^{10-x}\, dx$

22. $\int_1^{+\infty} \dfrac{\ln x\, dx}{x}$

23. $\int_2^{+\infty} \dfrac{dx}{x \ln x}$

24. $\int_2^{+\infty} \dfrac{dx}{x\sqrt{\ln x}}$

25. $\int_0^{+\infty} x^2 e^{-x}\, dx$

26. $\int_0^{+\infty} x^3 e^{-x^2}\, dx$

27. $\displaystyle\int_{-\infty}^{0} \frac{2x\,dx}{x^2+1}$

28. $\displaystyle\int_{1}^{\infty} \frac{x\,dx}{(1+x^2)^2}$

29. $\displaystyle\int_{-\infty}^{0} \frac{dx}{\sqrt{2-x}}$

30. $\displaystyle\int_{-\infty}^{4} \frac{dx}{(5-x)^2}$

31. $\displaystyle\int_{-\infty}^{\infty} xe^{-|x|}\,dx$

32. $\displaystyle\int_{-\infty}^{\infty} \frac{dx}{x^2+1}$

33. $\displaystyle\int_{0}^{1} \frac{dx}{x^{1/5}}$

34. $\displaystyle\int_{0}^{4} \frac{dx}{x\sqrt{x}}$

35. $\displaystyle\int_{0}^{1} \frac{dx}{(1-x)^{1/2}}$

36. $\displaystyle\int_{-\infty}^{+\infty} \frac{3x\,dx}{(3x^2+2)^3}$

37. $\displaystyle\int_{0}^{1} \ln x\,dx$

38. $\displaystyle\int_{1}^{\infty} \ln x\,dx$

39. $\displaystyle\int_{e}^{+\infty} \frac{dx}{x(\ln x)^2}$

40. $\displaystyle\int_{0}^{1} \frac{x\,dx}{1-x^2}$

41. $\displaystyle\int_{0}^{1} e^{-(1/2)\ln x}dx$

42. $\displaystyle\int_{0}^{+\infty} \frac{dx}{e^x+e^{-x}}$

B 43. Find the area of the unbounded region between the x-axis and the curve

$$y = \frac{2}{(x-4)^3} \quad \text{for } x \geq 6$$

44. Find the area of the unbounded region between the x-axis and the curve

$$y = \frac{2}{(x-4)^3} \quad \text{for } x \leq 2$$

45. The total amount of radioactive material present in the atmosphere at time T is given by

$$A = \int_{0}^{T} Pe^{-rt}\,dt$$

where P is a constant and t is the number of years. A recent United Nations publication indicates that at the present time $r = 0.002$ and $P = 200$ millirads. Estimate the total future buildup of radioactive material in the atmosphere if these values remain constant.

46. Suppose that an oil well produces $P(t)$ thousand barrels of crude oil per month according to the formula

$$P(t) = 100e^{-0.02t} - 100e^{-0.1t}$$

where t is the number of months the well has been in production. What is the total amount of oil produced by the oil well?

47. Let $f(x) = \begin{cases} \frac{1}{x^2} & \text{for } x \geq 1 \\ 1 & \text{for } -1 < x < 1 \\ e^{x+1} & \text{for } x \leq -1 \end{cases}$

Sketch the graph of f and evaluate

$$\int_{-\infty}^{+\infty} f(x)\,dx$$

48. Find all values of p for which $\displaystyle\int_{2}^{+\infty} \frac{dx}{x(\ln x)^p}$ converges, and find the value of the integral when it exists.

49. Find all values of p for which $\displaystyle\int_{0}^{1} \frac{dx}{x^p}$ converges, and find the value of the integral when it exists.

50. Find all values of p for which $\displaystyle\int_{0}^{1/2} \frac{dx}{x(\ln x)^p}$ converges, and find the value of the integral when it exists.

51. Discuss the calculation

$$\int_{-1}^{1} \frac{dx}{x^2} = \frac{-1}{x}\Big|_{-1}^{1} = -[1-(-1)] = -2$$

Is the calculation correct? Explain.

52. JOURNAL PROBLEM.* Peter Lindstrom of North Lake College in Irving, Texas, had a student who handled an improper form as follows:

$$\int_{1}^{\infty} (x-1)e^{-x}\,dx = \int_{1}^{\infty} \frac{x-1}{e^x}\,dx$$

$$= \int_{1}^{\infty} \frac{1}{e^x}\,dx \qquad l'H\hat{o}pital's\ rule$$

$$= \frac{1}{e}$$

What is wrong, if anything, with this student's solution?

53. Find $\displaystyle\int_{0}^{2} f(x)\,dx$, where

$$f(x) = \begin{cases} \dfrac{1}{\sqrt[4]{x^3}} & \text{for } 0 \leq x \leq 1 \\ \dfrac{1}{\sqrt[4]{(2-x)^3}} & \text{for } 1 < x < 2 \end{cases}$$

C 54. THINK TANK PROBLEM Give an example of a region of finite surface area that has an infinite volume—that is, it can be painted with a finite amount of paint, but holds an infinite amount of paint.

*The **Laplace transform** of the function f is defined by the improper integral*

$$F(s) = \mathcal{L}\{f(t)\} = \int_{0}^{\infty} e^{-st} f(t)\,dt$$

where s is a constant. This notation is used in Problems 55–60.

55. Show that for constant a (with $s - a > 0$):

   a. $\mathcal{L}\{e^{at}\} = \dfrac{1}{s-a}$ b. $\mathcal{L}\{a\} = \dfrac{a}{s}$

   c. $\mathcal{L}\{\sin at\} = \dfrac{a}{s^2+a^2}$

   d. $\mathcal{L}\{\cos at\} = \dfrac{s}{s^2+a^2}$

56. Show that $\mathscr{L}\{af + bg\} = a\mathscr{L}\{f\} + b\mathscr{L}\{g\}$

57. Let $\mathscr{L}^{-1}\{F(s)\}$ denote the *inverse* Laplace transform of $F(s)$. That is, $\mathscr{L}^{-1}\{F(s)\} = f(t)$ if and only if $\mathscr{L}\{f(t)\} = F(s)$. Find (use Problems 55 and 56):

a. $\mathscr{L}^{-1}\left\{\dfrac{5}{s}\right\}$ **b.** $\mathscr{L}^{-1}\left\{\dfrac{s+2}{s^2+4}\right\}$

c. $\mathscr{L}^{-1}\left\{\dfrac{2s^2 - 3s + 3}{s^2(s-1)}\right\}$

Hint: Use partial-fraction decomposition.

d. $\mathscr{L}^{-1}\left\{\dfrac{3s^3 + 2s^2 - 3s - 17}{(s^2+4)(s^2-1)}\right\}$

58. If $F(s) = \mathscr{L}\{f(t)\}$, show $\mathscr{L}\{e^{at}f(t)\} = F(s - a)$.

59. Use the result in Problem 58 to find the following Laplace transforms and inverse transforms. For example,

$$\mathscr{L}\{t\} = \int_0^\infty e^{-st}t\,dt \quad (\text{because } f(t) = t)$$

Evaluate this improper integral to find $\mathscr{L}\{t\} = \dfrac{1}{s^2}$. From this, and Problem 58, we know $\mathscr{L}\{te^{3t}\} = \dfrac{1}{(s-3)^2}$.

a. $\mathscr{L}\{t^3 e^{-2t}\}$ **b.** $\mathscr{L}\{e^{-3t}\cos 2t\}$

c. $\mathscr{L}^{-1}\left\{\dfrac{5}{(s-1)^2}\right\}$ **d.** $\mathscr{L}^{-1}\left\{\dfrac{4s}{s^2+4s+5}\right\}$

Hint: Complete the square.

60. If $F(s) = \mathscr{L}\{f(t)\}$, show that

$$\mathscr{L}\{tf(t)\} = -F'(s)$$

You may assume that

$$\frac{d}{ds}\int_0^\infty e^{-st}f(t)\,dt = \int_0^\infty \frac{d}{ds}[e^{-st}f(t)\,dt]$$

7.6 THE HYPERBOLIC AND INVERSE HYPERBOLIC FUNCTIONS

> **IN THIS SECTION** **Hyperbolic functions, derivatives and integrals involving hyperbolic functions, inverse hyperbolic functions**
> Hyperbolic and inverse hyperbolic functions are introduced and studied; integration formulas to be used throughout the rest of the text are derived.

■ HYPERBOLIC FUNCTIONS

Figure 7.13 The hanging cable problem

In physics, it is shown that a heavy, flexible cable (for example, a power line) that is suspended between two points at the same height assumes the shape of a curve called a **catenary** (see Figure 7.13), with an equation of the form

$$y = \frac{a}{2}(e^{x/a} + e^{-x/a})$$

This is one of several important applications that involve combinations of exponential functions. The goal of this section is to study such combinations and their inverses.

In certain ways, the functions we shall study are analogous to the trigonometric functions, and they have essentially the same relationship to the hyperbola that the trigonometric functions have to the circle. For this reason, these functions are called **hyperbolic functions**. Three basic hyperbolic functions are the **hyperbolic sine** (denoted "sinh x" and pronounced "cinch"), the **hyperbolic cosine** (cosh x; pronounced "kosh"), and the **hyperbolic tangent** (tanh; pronounced "tansh"). They are defined as follows.

Hyperbolic Functions

$\sinh x = \dfrac{e^x - e^{-x}}{2}$	for all x
$\cosh x = \dfrac{e^x + e^{-x}}{2}$	for all x
$\tanh x = \dfrac{\sinh x}{\cosh x} = \dfrac{e^x - e^{-x}}{e^x + e^{-x}}$	for all x

Graphs of the three basic hyperbolic functions are shown in Figure 7.14.

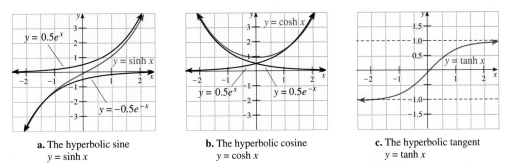

a. The hyperbolic sine
$y = \sinh x$

b. The hyperbolic cosine
$y = \cosh x$

c. The hyperbolic tangent
$y = \tanh x$

Figure 7.14 Graphs of the three basic hyperbolic functions

The list of properties in the following theorem shows how the basic hyperbolic functions are similar to the trigonometric functions.

THEOREM 7.1   Properties of the basic hyperbolic functions

⊘ A major difference between the trigonometric and hyperbolic functions is that the trigonometric functions are periodic, but the hyperbolic functions are not. ⊘

$$\cosh^2 x - \sinh^2 x = 1$$

$$\sinh(-x) = -\sinh x \qquad (\sinh x \text{ is odd})$$

$$\cosh(-x) = \cosh x \qquad (\cosh x \text{ is even})$$

$$\tanh(-x) = -\tanh x \qquad (\tanh x \text{ is odd})$$

$$\sinh(x + y) = \sinh x \cosh y + \cosh x \sinh y$$

$$\cosh(x + y) = \cosh x \cosh y + \sinh x \sinh y$$

Proof: We will verify the first identity and leave the others for the reader.

$$\cosh^2 x - \sinh^2 x = \left(\frac{e^x + e^{-x}}{2}\right)^2 - \left(\frac{e^x - e^{-x}}{2}\right)^2$$

$$= \frac{e^{2x} + 2 + e^{-2x}}{4} - \frac{e^{2x} - 2 + e^{-2x}}{4} = 1 \qquad \blacksquare$$

There are three additional hyperbolic functions, the **hyperbolic cotangent** (coth x), the **hyperbolic secant** (sech x), and the **hyperbolic cosecant** (csch x). These functions are defined as follows:

$$\coth x = \frac{1}{\tanh x} = \frac{e^x + e^{-x}}{e^x - e^{-x}}$$

$$\text{sech } x = \frac{1}{\cosh x} = \frac{2}{e^x + e^{-x}}$$

$$\text{csch } x = \frac{1}{\sinh x} = \frac{2}{e^x - e^{-x}}$$

Computational Window

In Derive, these simplified forms are shown:

$$\coth x = \frac{e^{2x} + 1}{e^{2x} - 1}$$

$$\text{sech } x = \frac{2e^x}{e^{2x} + 1}$$

$$\text{csch } x = \frac{2e^x}{e^{2x} - 1}$$

Two identities involving these functions are

$$\text{sech}^2 x = 1 - \tanh^2 x \quad \text{and} \quad \text{csch}^2 x = \coth^2 x - 1$$

You will be asked to verify these identities in Problem 58.

■ DERIVATIVES AND INTEGRALS INVOLVING HYPERBOLIC FUNCTIONS

Rules for differentiating the hyperbolic functions are listed in Theorem 7.2.

THEOREM 7.2   Rules for differentiating hyperbolic functions

Let u be a differentiable function of x. Then:

$$\frac{d}{dx}(\sinh u) = \cosh u \, \frac{du}{dx} \qquad\qquad \frac{d}{dx}(\cosh u) = \sinh u \, \frac{du}{dx}$$

$$\frac{d}{dx}(\tanh u) = \operatorname{sech}^2 u \, \frac{du}{dx} \qquad\qquad \frac{d}{dx}(\coth u) = -\operatorname{csch}^2 u \, \frac{du}{dx}$$

$$\frac{d}{dx}(\operatorname{sech} u) = -\operatorname{sech} u \tanh u \, \frac{du}{dx} \quad \frac{d}{dx}(\operatorname{csch} u) = -\operatorname{csch} u \coth u \, \frac{du}{dx}$$

Proof: Each of these rules can be obtained by differentiating the exponential functions that make up the appropriate hyperbolic function. For example, to differentiate $\sinh x$, we use the definition of $\sinh x$:

$$\frac{d}{dx}(\sinh x) = \frac{d}{dx}\frac{e^x - e^{-x}}{2}$$

$$= \tfrac{1}{2}e^x - \tfrac{1}{2}e^{-x}(-1) = \tfrac{1}{2}(e^x + e^{-x}) = \cosh x$$

The proofs for the other derivatives can be handled similarly. ■

EXAMPLE 1   Derivatives involving hyperbolic functions

Find $\dfrac{dy}{dx}$ for each of the following functions:

a. $y = \cosh Ax$ (A is constant)
b. $y = \tanh(x^2 + 1)$
c. $y = \ln(\sinh x)$

Solution   **a.** We have

$$\frac{d}{dx}(\cosh Ax) = \sinh(Ax) \, \frac{d}{dx}(Ax) = A \sinh Ax$$

b. We find that

$$\frac{d}{dx}[\tanh(x^2 + 1)] = \operatorname{sech}^2(x^2 + 1) \, \frac{d}{dx}(x^2 + 1) = 2x \operatorname{sech}^2(x^2 + 1)$$

c. Using the chain rule, with $u = \sinh x$, we obtain

$$\frac{d}{dx}[\ln(\sinh x)] = \frac{1}{\sinh x} \, \frac{d}{dx}(\sinh x) = \frac{1}{\sinh x}(\cosh x) = \coth x \quad \blacksquare$$

Each basic differentiating formula for hyperbolic functions corresponds to a basic integration formula. These formulas are listed in the following theorem.

THEOREM 7.3 Integration formulas involving the hyperbolic functions

$$\int \sinh x \, dx = \cosh x + C \qquad \int \cosh x \, dx = \sinh x + C$$

$$\int \operatorname{sech}^2 x \, dx = \tanh x + C \qquad \int \operatorname{csch}^2 x \, dx = -\coth x + C$$

$$\int \operatorname{sech} x \tanh x \, dx = -\operatorname{sech} x + C \qquad \int \operatorname{csch} x \coth x \, dx = -\operatorname{csch} x + C$$

Proof: The proof of each of these formulas follows directly from the corresponding derivative formula. ∎

EXAMPLE 2 Integration involving hyperbolic forms

Find each of the following integrals:

a. $\int \cosh^3 x \sinh x \, dx$ **b.** $\int x \operatorname{sech}^2(x^2) \, dx$ **c.** $\int \tanh x \, dx$

Solution **a.** $\int \cosh^3 x \sinh x \, dx = \int u^3 \, du = \dfrac{u^4}{4} + C = \tfrac{1}{4} \cosh^4 x + C$

> Let $u = \cosh x$;
> $du = \sinh x \, dx$.

b. $\int x \operatorname{sech}^2(x^2) \, dx = \int \operatorname{sech}^2(x^2) \, (x \, dx)$

> Let $u = x^2$;
> $du = 2x \, dx$.

$$= \int \operatorname{sech}^2 u \left(\tfrac{1}{2} \, du\right)$$

$$= \tfrac{1}{2} \tanh u + C$$

$$= \tfrac{1}{2} \tanh x^2 + C$$

c. $\int \tanh x \, dx = \int \dfrac{\sinh x \, dx}{\cosh x}$

> Let $u = \cosh x$;
> $du = \sinh x \, dx$.

$$= \int \dfrac{du}{u} = \ln|u| + C = \ln(\cosh x) + C$$

The graph of $y = \sinh^{-1} x$ is obtained by reflecting $y = \sinh x$ in the line $y = x$.

Figure 7.15 The graph of $y = \sinh^{-1} x$

■ INVERSE HYPERBOLIC FUNCTIONS

Inverse hyperbolic functions are also of interest, mainly because they enable us to express certain integrals in simple terms.

Because $\sinh x$ is continuous and strictly monotonic (increasing), it is one-to-one and has an inverse, which is defined by

$$y = \sinh^{-1} x \quad \text{if and only if} \quad x = \sinh y$$

for all x and y. This is called the **inverse hyperbolic sine** function, and its graph is obtained by reflecting the graph of $y = \sinh x$ in the line $y = x$, as shown in Figure 7.15. Other inverse hyperbolic functions are defined in a similar manner (see Problem 60).

Because the hyperbolic functions are defined in terms of exponential functions, we may expect to be able to express the inverse hyperbolic functions in terms of logarithmic functions. We summarize this relationship in the following theorem.

THEOREM 7.4 Logarithmic formulas for inverse hyperbolic functions

---

$$\sinh^{-1} x = \ln(x + \sqrt{x^2 + 1}), \text{ all } x \qquad \operatorname{csch}^{-1} x = \ln\left(\frac{1}{x} + \frac{\sqrt{1 + x^2}}{|x|}\right), x \neq 0$$

$$\cosh^{-1} x = \ln(x + \sqrt{x^2 - 1}), x \geq 1 \qquad \operatorname{sech}^{-1} x = \ln\left(\frac{1 + \sqrt{1 - x^2}}{x}\right), 0 < x \leq 1$$

$$\tanh^{-1} x = \tfrac{1}{2} \ln \frac{1 + x}{1 - x}, |x| < 1 \qquad \coth^{-1} x = \tfrac{1}{2} \ln \frac{x + 1}{x - 1}, |x| > 1$$

Proof: We will prove the first part and leave the next two parts for you to verify (see Problem 61). The other parts are proved similarly. Let $y = \sinh^{-1} x$; then its inverse is

$$x = \sinh y$$

$$= \tfrac{1}{2}(e^y - e^{-y})$$

$$2x = e^y - \frac{1}{e^y}$$

$$e^{2y} - 2xe^y - 1 = 0$$

$$e^y = \frac{2x \pm \sqrt{4x^2 + 4}}{2} \qquad \textit{Quadratic formula with } a = 1, b = -2x, c = -1$$

$$= x \pm \sqrt{x^2 + 1}$$

Because $e^y > 0$ for all y, the only solution is $e^y = x + \sqrt{x^2 + 1}$, and from the definition of logarithms,

$$y = \ln(x + \sqrt{x^2 + 1}) \qquad \blacksquare$$

Differentiation and integration formulas involving inverse hyperbolic functions are listed in Theorem 7.5.

THEOREM 7.5 Differentiation and integration formulas involving the inverse hyperbolic functions

---

$$\frac{d}{dx}(\sinh^{-1} u) = \frac{1}{\sqrt{1 + u^2}} \frac{du}{dx} \qquad\qquad \int \frac{du}{\sqrt{1 + u^2}} = \sinh^{-1} u + C$$

$$\frac{d}{dx}(\cosh^{-1} u) = \frac{1}{\sqrt{u^2 - 1}} \frac{du}{dx}, \text{ if } |u| > 1 \qquad \int \frac{du}{\sqrt{u^2 - 1}} = \cosh^{-1} u + C$$

$$\frac{d}{dx}(\tanh^{-1} u) = \frac{1}{1 - u^2} \frac{du}{dx}, \text{ if } |u| < 1 \qquad \int \frac{du}{1 - u^2} = \tanh^{-1} u + C, \text{ if } |u| < 1$$

$$\frac{d}{dx}(\operatorname{csch}^{-1} u) = \frac{-1}{|u|\sqrt{1 + u^2}} \frac{du}{dx} \qquad \int \frac{du}{u\sqrt{1 + u^2}} = -\operatorname{csch}^{-1} |u| + C$$

$$\frac{d}{dx}(\operatorname{sech}^{-1} u) = \frac{-1}{u\sqrt{1 - u^2}} \frac{du}{dx}, \ 0 < u < 1 \qquad \int \frac{du}{u\sqrt{1 - u^2}} = -\operatorname{sech}^{-1} u + C$$

$$\frac{d}{dx}(\coth^{-1} u) = \frac{1}{1 - u^2} \frac{du}{dx}, \text{ if } |u| > 1 \qquad \int \frac{du}{1 - u^2} = \coth^{-1} u + C, \text{ if } |u| > 1$$

Proof: The derivative of each inverse hyperbolic function can be found either by differentiating the appropriate logarithmic function or by using the definition in terms of hyperbolic functions. We will show how this is done for $y = \sinh^{-1} x$, and then will leave it for you to apply the chain rule for u, a differentiable function of x. By definition of inverse, we see that

$$x = \sinh y \quad \text{and} \quad \frac{dx}{dy} = \cosh y$$

Thus,

$$\frac{d}{dx}(\sinh^{-1} x) = \frac{dy}{dx} = \frac{1}{\frac{dx}{dy}} = \frac{1}{\cosh y} = \frac{1}{\sqrt{1 + \sinh^2 y}} = \frac{1}{\sqrt{1 + x^2}}$$

because $\cosh^2 y = \sinh^2 y + 1$ and $\sinh y = x$.

The integration formula that corresponds to this differentiation formula is

$$\int \frac{dx}{\sqrt{1 + x^2}} = \sinh^{-1} x + C$$

The other differentiation and integration formulas follow similarly.   ∎

EXAMPLE 3   Derivatives involving inverse hyperbolic functions

Find $\dfrac{dy}{dx}$ for **a.** $y = \sinh^{-1}(ax + b)$, and **b.** $y = \cosh^{-1}(\sec x)$, $0 \le x \le \frac{\pi}{2}$.

Solution   **a.** $\dfrac{d}{dx}[\sinh^{-1}(ax + b)] = \dfrac{1}{\sqrt{1 + (ax + b)^2}} \dfrac{d}{dx}(ax + b)$

$$= \frac{a}{\sqrt{1 + (ax + b)^2}}$$

b. $\dfrac{d}{dx}[\cosh^{-1}(\sec x)] = \dfrac{1}{\sqrt{\sec^2 x - 1}} \dfrac{d}{dx}(\sec x)$

$$= \frac{\sec x \tan x}{\sqrt{\tan^2 x}} = \sec x$$

▬

Note that the result of Example 3b implies

$$\int \sec x \, dx = \cosh^{-1}(\sec x) + C$$
$$= \ln(\sec x + \sqrt{\sec^2 x - 1}) + C$$
$$= \ln(\sec x + \tan x) + C$$

Notice that we do not need absolute values because $0 \le x \le \frac{\pi}{2}$. We will use this formula in the next chapter.

EXAMPLE 4   Integral involving an inverse hyperbolic function

Evaluate $\displaystyle\int_0^1 \frac{dx}{\sqrt{1 + x^2}}$.

Solution
$$\int_0^1 \frac{dx}{\sqrt{1 + x^2}} = [\sinh^{-1} x]\Big|_0^1$$
$$= \ln(x + \sqrt{x^2 + 1})\Big|_0^1$$
$$= \ln(1 + \sqrt{2}) - \ln(1)$$
$$= \ln(1 + \sqrt{2})$$

▬

PROBLEM SET 7.6

Ⓐ *Evaluate (correct to four decimal places) the indicated hyperbolic or inverse hyperbolic function in Problems 1–12.*

1. $\sinh 2$ **2.** $\cosh 3$ **3.** $\tanh(-1)$

4. $\sinh^{-1} 0$ **5.** $\coth 1.2$ **6.** $\tanh^{-1} 0$

7. $\cosh^{-1} 1.5$ **8.** $\sinh(\ln 2)$ **9.** $\cosh(\ln 3)$

10. $\operatorname{sech}^{-1} 0.2$ **11.** $\operatorname{sech} 1$ **12.** $\coth^{-1}(-3)$

Find $\dfrac{dy}{dx}$ in Problems 13–29.

13. $y = \sinh 3x$

14. $y = \cosh(1 - 2x^2)$

15. $y = \cosh(2x^2 + 3x)$

16. $y = \sinh \sqrt{x}$

17. $y = \sinh \dfrac{1}{x}$

18. $y = \cosh^{-1}(x^2)$

19. $y = \sinh^{-1}(x^3)$

20. $y = x \tanh^{-1}(3x)$

21. $y = \sinh^{-1}(\tan x)$

22. $y = \cosh^{-1}(\sec x)$

23. $y = \tanh^{-1}(\sin x)$

24. $y = \operatorname{sech}\left(\dfrac{1-x}{1+x}\right)$

25. $y = \dfrac{\sinh^{-1} x}{\cosh^{-1} x}$

26. $y = \sinh^{-1} x - \sqrt{1 + x^2}$

27. $y = x \cosh^{-1} x - \sqrt{x^2 - 1}$

28. $x \cosh y = y \sinh x + 5$

29. $e^x \sinh^{-1} x + e^{-x} \cosh^{-1} y = 1$

Compute the integrals in Problems 30–45.

30. $\displaystyle\int x \cosh(1 - x^2)\,dx$

31. $\displaystyle\int \dfrac{\sinh \frac{1}{x}\,dx}{x^2}$

32. $\displaystyle\int \dfrac{\operatorname{sech}^2(\ln x)\,dx}{x}$

33. $\displaystyle\int \coth x\,dx$

34. $\displaystyle\int \dfrac{dx}{\sqrt{4x^2 + 16}}$

35. $\displaystyle\int \dfrac{dt}{\sqrt{9t^2 - 16}}$

36. $\displaystyle\int \dfrac{dt}{36 - 16t^2}$

37. $\displaystyle\int \dfrac{\cos x\,dx}{\sqrt{1 + \sin^2 x}}$

38. $\displaystyle\int \dfrac{x\,dx}{\sqrt{1 + x^4}}$

39. $\displaystyle\int \dfrac{x^2\,dx}{1 - x^6}$

40. $\displaystyle\int_0^{1/2} \dfrac{dx}{1 - x^2}$

41. $\displaystyle\int_2^3 \dfrac{dx}{1 - x^2}$

42. $\displaystyle\int_0^1 \dfrac{t^5\,dt}{\sqrt{1 + t^{12}}}$

43. $\displaystyle\int_1^2 \dfrac{e^x\,dx}{\sqrt{e^{2x} - 1}}$

44. $\displaystyle\int_0^{\ln 2} \sinh 3x\,dx$

45. $\displaystyle\int_0^1 x \operatorname{sech}^2 x^2\,dx$

Ⓑ
46. Show that $\tanh(x + y) = \dfrac{\tanh x + \tanh y}{1 + \tanh x \tanh y}$

47. Show that
   a. $\sinh 2x = 2 \sinh x \cosh x$
   b. $\cosh 2x = \cosh^2 x + \sinh^2 x$

48. Show that
   a. $-1 < \tanh x < 1$ for all x
   b. $\lim\limits_{x \to +\infty} \tanh x = 1$ and $\lim\limits_{x \to -\infty} \tanh x = -1$

49. Determine where the graph of $y = \tanh x$ is rising and falling and where it is concave up and concave down. Sketch the graph and compare with Figure 7.14c.

50. Sketch the graph of $y = \coth x$. Be sure to show key features such as intercepts, high and low points, and points of inflection.

51. First show that $\cosh x + \sinh x = e^x$, and then use this result to prove that

$$(\sinh x + \cosh x)^n = \cosh nx + \sinh nx$$

for positive integers n.

52. If $x = a \cosh t$ and $y = b \sinh t$ where a, b are positive constants and t is any number, show that

$$\frac{x^2}{a^2} - \frac{y^2}{b^2} = 1$$

53. a. Verify that $y = a \cosh cx + b \sinh cx$ satisfies the differential equation

$$y'' - c^2 y = 0$$

   b. Use part **a** to find a solution of the differential equation

$$y'' - 4y = 0$$

subject to the initial conditions $y(0) = 1$, $y'(0) = 2$.

54. Find the area of the region bounded by the curves $y = \sinh x$ and $y = \cosh x$, the y-axis, and the line $x = 1$.

55. Find the length of the catenary

$$y = a \cosh \frac{x}{a}$$

between $x = -a$ and $x = a$.

56. Find the volume of the solid formed by revolving the region bounded by the curve $y = \tanh x$ on the interval $[0, 1]$ about the x-axis.

57. Find the surface area of the solid generated by revolving the curve $y = \cosh x$ on the interval $[-1, 1]$ about the x-axis.

Ⓒ **58.** Prove the formulas
   a. $\operatorname{sech}^2 x + \tanh^2 x = 1$ **b.** $\coth^2 x - \operatorname{csch}^2 x = 1$

59. Derive the differentiation formulas for $\cosh u$, $\tanh u$, and $\operatorname{sech} u$, where u is a differentiable function of x.

60. First give definitions for $\cosh^{-1} x$, $\tanh^{-1} x$, and $\operatorname{sech}^{-1} x$, and then derive the differentiation formulas for these functions by using these definitions.

61. Prove
   a. $\cosh^{-1} x = \ln(x + \sqrt{x^2 - 1})$
   b. $\tanh^{-1} x = \frac{1}{2} \ln \dfrac{1 + x}{1 - x}$

62. Show that

$$\int \frac{dx}{\sqrt{x^2 + a^2}} = \sinh^{-1} \frac{x}{a} + C$$

for constant $a > 0$. State and prove a similar formula for

$$\int \frac{dx}{\sqrt{a^2 - x^2}}$$

with $a > 0$ and $|x| < a$.

Chapter 7 Review

> **IN THIS REVIEW** Proficiency examination; supplementary problems
> Problems 1–13 of the proficiency examination test your knowledge of the
> concepts of this chapter, and Problems 14–30 test your understanding of those
> concepts by asking you to work sample practice problems. The supplementary
> problems present questions relating to the material of this chapter in a wide
> variety of settings.

PROFICIENCY EXAMINATION

Concept Problems

1. Discuss the method of integration by substitution for both indefinite and definite integrals.
2. What is the formula for integration by parts?
3. What is a reduction integration formula?
4. When should you consider a trigonometric substitution?
5. When should you consider the method of partial fractions?
6. What are the substitutions to use when integrating rational trigonometric integrals?
7. Outline a strategy for integration.
8. What is an improper integral?
9. Define the hyperbolic sine, hyperbolic cosine, and hyperbolic tangent.
10. State the rules for differentiating the hyperbolic functions.
11. State the rules for integrating the hyperbolic functions.
12. What are the logarithmic formulas for the inverse hyperbolic formulas?
13. State the differentiation and integration formulas for the inverse hyperbolic functions.

Practice Problems

14. Evaluate each of the given numbers.

   a. $\tanh^{-1}(0.5)$ **b.** $\sinh(\ln 3)$ **c.** $\coth^{-1}(2)$

Find the integrals in Problem 15–20.

15. $\displaystyle\int \frac{2x+3}{\sqrt{x^2+1}}\,dx$

16. $\displaystyle\int x \sin 2x\,dx$

17. $\displaystyle\int \sinh(1-2x)\,dx$

18. $\displaystyle\int \frac{dx}{\sqrt{4-x^2}}$

19. $\displaystyle\int \frac{x^2\,dx}{(x^2+1)(x-1)}$

20. $\displaystyle\int \frac{x^3\,dx}{x^2-1}$

Evaluate the definite integrals in Problems 21–24.

21. $\displaystyle\int_1^2 x \ln x^3\,dx$

22. $\displaystyle\int_2^3 \frac{dx}{(x-1)^2(x+2)}$

23. $\displaystyle\int_3^4 \frac{dx}{2x-x^2}$

24. $\displaystyle\int_0^{\pi/4} \sec^3 x \tan x\,dx$

Determine whether each improper integral in Problems 25–28 converges, and if it does, find its value.

25. $\displaystyle\int_0^{+\infty} x\,e^{-2x}\,dx$

26. $\displaystyle\int_0^{\pi} \frac{\cos x\,dx}{1-\cos x}$

27. $\displaystyle\int_0^1 \frac{2x+3}{x^2(x-2)}\,dx$

28. $\displaystyle\int_0^{+\infty} e^{-x}\sin x\,dx$

29. Find $\dfrac{dy}{dx}$ for $y = \sqrt{\tanh^{-1} 2x}$.

30. Find the volume of the solid generated when the region under the curve

$$y = \frac{1}{\sqrt{9-x^2}}$$

on the interval $[0, 2]$ is revolved about the y-axis.

SUPPLEMENTARY PROBLEMS

Find the derivative $\dfrac{dy}{dx}$ in Problems 1–5.

1. $y = \tanh^{-1}\dfrac{1}{x}$

2. $y = x \cosh^{-1}(3x+1)$

3. $y = \dfrac{\sinh x}{e^x}$

4. $y = \sinh x \cosh x$

5. $y = x \sinh x + \sinh(e^x + e^{-x})$

Find the integrals in Problems 6–35.

6. $\displaystyle\int \cos^{-1} x\,dx$

7. $\displaystyle\int \frac{x^2\,dx}{\sqrt{4-x^2}}$

8. $\displaystyle\int \frac{x\,dx}{x^2-2x+5}$

9. $\displaystyle\int \frac{3x-2}{x^3-2x^2}\,dx$

10. $\displaystyle\int \frac{dx}{(x^2 + x + 1)^{3/2}}$

11. $\displaystyle\int \frac{dx}{\sqrt{x}(1 + \sqrt[4]{x})}$

12. $\displaystyle\int \frac{\sqrt{9x^2 - 1}\,dx}{x}$

13. $\displaystyle\int x^2 \tan^{-1} x\,dx$

14. $\displaystyle\int \frac{dx}{\sin x + \tan x}$

15. $\displaystyle\int e^x\sqrt{4 - e^{2x}}\,dx$

16. $\displaystyle\int \cos\frac{x}{2} \sin\frac{x}{3}\,dx$

17. $\displaystyle\int \frac{1}{x^5}\sqrt{1 + \frac{1}{x^2}}\,dx$

18. $\displaystyle\int \frac{\sin x\,dx}{\cos^5 x}$

19. $\displaystyle\int \sqrt{1 + \sin x}\,dx$

20. $\displaystyle\int \cos x\,\ln(\sin x)\,dx$

21. $\displaystyle\int \sin(\ln x)\,dx$

22. $\displaystyle\int e^{2x}\,\text{sech}\,(e^{2x})\,dx$

23. $\displaystyle\int \frac{\sinh x\,dx}{2 + \cosh x}$

24. $\displaystyle\int \frac{\tanh^{-1} x\,dx}{1 - x^2}$

25. $\displaystyle\int x^2\cot^{-1} x\,dx$

26. $\displaystyle\int x(1 + x)^{1/3}\,dx$

27. $\displaystyle\int \frac{x^2 + 2}{x^3 + 6x + 1}\,dx$

28. $\displaystyle\int \frac{\sin x - \cos x}{(\sin x + \cos x)^{1/4}}\,dx$

29. $\displaystyle\int \cos(\sqrt{x + 2})\,dx$

30. $\displaystyle\int \sqrt{5 + 2\sin^2 x}\,\sin 2x\,dx$

31. $\displaystyle\int \frac{x^3 + 2x}{x^4 + 4x^2 + 3}\,dx$

32. $\displaystyle\int \frac{x\,dx}{\sqrt{5 - x^2}}$

33. $\displaystyle\int \frac{\sqrt{5 - x^2}\,dx}{x}$

34. $\displaystyle\int \frac{\sqrt{x^2 + x}\,dx}{x}$

35. $\displaystyle\int x^3(x^2 + 4)^{-1/2}\,dx$

Determine whether the improper integral in Problems 36–39 converges, and if it does, find its value.

36. $\displaystyle\int_0^{\pi/2} \frac{\cos x\,dx}{\sqrt{\sin x}}$

37. $\displaystyle\int_{-\infty}^{+\infty} \frac{dx}{4 + x^2}$

38. $\displaystyle\int_{-\infty}^{+\infty} \frac{dx}{x^2 + 4x + 6}$

39. $\displaystyle\int_1^{+\infty} \frac{dx}{x^4 + x^2}$

40. If n is a positive integer and a is a positive number, find

$$\int_0^{+\infty} x^n e^{-ax}\,dx$$

41. Find $\displaystyle\int \frac{\sin x\,dx}{1 + \cos^2 x}$.

42. Show that $\displaystyle\int_0^1 x^m(1 - x)^n dx = \int_0^1 x^n(1 - x)^m dx$ for positive integers m, n.

43. Think Tank Problem   Each of the following equations may be either true or false. In each case, either show that the equation is generally true or find a number x for which it fails.

a. $\tanh\left(\frac{1}{2}\ln x\right) = \dfrac{x - 1}{x + 1}$ $x > 0$

b. $\sinh^{-1}(\tan x) = \tanh^{-1}(\sin x)$ for $-\frac{\pi}{2} < x < \frac{\pi}{2}$

44. Compute $\displaystyle\int_0^1 x\,f''(3x)\,dx$, given that $f'(0)$ is defined, $f(0) = 1$, $f(3) = 4$, and $f'(3) = -2$.

45. What is $\displaystyle\int_0^{\pi/2} [f(x) + f''(x)]\cos x\,dx$ if $f(0)$ is defined, $f(\frac{\pi}{2}) = 5$ and $f'(0) = -1$?

46. Spy Problem   After plucking the spy from the village (Problem 61, Section 7.3), Boldfinger has him thrown into the Closet of Doom in the confines of his castle dungeon. He is tied to a chain inside the Closet and poison gas is slowly pumped in at the rate of 0.2 ft³/min. He quickly determines that the Closet has volume 400 ft³ and that a mixture of gas and fresh air is continuously escaping from the Closet at the same rate the gas is being pumped in. He knows that the gas becomes deadly when the air in the Closet contains at least 0.8 ft³ of poison gas. If he takes 3 min to get untied and another 45 sec to kick open the door, will our hero survive to reach Chapter 8?

47. A prime number is a positive number n with exactly two divisors. In number theory, it is shown that the total number of primes less than or equal to x is approximated by the function

$$L(x) = \int_2^x \frac{dt}{\ln t} \qquad x \geq 2$$

Use the trapezoidal rule to estimate the number of primes between $x = 2$ and $x = 1{,}000$.

48. Find the centroid of a thin plate of constant density δ that occupies the region bounded by the graph of $y = \sin x + \cos x$, the coordinate axes, and the line $x = \pi/4$.

49. Repeat Problem 48 for a plate that occupies the region bounded by $y = \sec^2 x$, the coordinate axes, and the line $x = \pi/3$.

50. Find the volume obtained by revolving about the y-axis the region bounded by the curve $y = \sinh x$, the x-axis, and the line $x = 1$.

51. Find the volume obtained by revolving about the y-axis the region bounded by the curve $y = \cosh x$, the y-axis, and the line $y = 2$.

52. The region bounded by the graph of $y = \sin x$ and the x-axis between $x = 0$ and $x = \pi$ is revolved about the x-axis to generate a solid. Find the volume of the solid and its surface area.

53. Find the length of the arc of the curve $y = \frac{4}{5}x^{5/4}$ that lies between $x = 0$ and $x = 1$.

54. Find the volume of the solid obtained by revolving about the x-axis, the region bounded by the curve $y = (9 - x^2)^{1/4}$ and the x-axis.

55. Find the volume of the solid formed by revolving about the y-axis the region bounded by the curve

$$y = \frac{1}{1 + x^4}$$

between $x = 0$ and $x = 4$.

56. Find the volume of the solid formed by revolving about the x-axis the region bounded by the curve
$$y = \frac{2}{\sqrt{3x - 2}}$$
the x-axis, and the lines $x = 1$ and $x = 2$.

57. Find the surface area of the solid generated by revolving the region bounded by the curve
$$y = e^x + \tfrac{1}{4}e^{-x}$$
on [0, 1] about the x-axis.

58. Find the volume of the solid whose base is the region R bounded by the curve $y = e^x$ and the lines $y = 0$, $x = 0$, $x = 1$, if cross sections perpendicular to the x-axis are equilateral triangles.

59. Show that the area under $y = \frac{1}{x}$ on the interval $[1, a]$ equals the area under the same curve on $[k, ka]$ for any number $k > 0$.

60. Find the length of the curve $y = \ln(\sec x)$ on the interval $\left[0, \frac{\pi}{3}\right]$.

61. Find the length of the curve
$$x = \frac{ay^2}{b^2} - \frac{b^2}{8a} \ln \frac{y}{b}$$
between $y = b$ and $y = 2b$.

62. If $s > 0$, the integral function defined by
$$\Gamma(s) = \int_0^{+\infty} e^{-t}t^{s-1}\, dt$$
is called the *gamma function*. It was introduced by Leonhard Euler in 1729 and has some useful properties.

   a. Show that $\Gamma(s)$ converges for all $s > 0$.

   b. Show that $\Gamma(s + 1) = s\Gamma(s)$.

   c. Show that $\Gamma(n + 1) = n!$ for any positive integer n.

Computational Window

63. This problem is a continuation of Problem 62.

   a. Show that for a positive integer n:
   $$\Gamma(x + n) = (x + n - 1)\cdots(x + 1)x\Gamma(x)$$

   b. Suppose we need to approximate $\Gamma(x)$ by numerically integrating over an inteval $(0, T)$, for T quite large. Of course, you want T to be no larger than necessary. For $0 < x \le 1$, find T so that
   $$\int_T^{\infty} e^{-t}t^{x-1}\, dt < 0.005$$
   Thus, your approximation to $\Gamma(x)$ by integrating over $(0, T)$ is accurate to within 0.005 units. *Note:* in general, $t^{x-1} \le 1$.

   c. We will now use part **a**. Suppose you need to approximate $\Gamma(7.3)$. Explain how to use part **a** to numerically compute $\Gamma(0.3)$, and thus $\Gamma(7.3)$, and be sure the resulting *relative* error is less than 0.005.

   d. Explain why you would rather computer $\Gamma(0.3)$ than $\Gamma(7.3)$.

   e. Numerically compute $\Gamma(7.3)$ by the method suggested here. If your computer can compute $\Gamma(7.3)$ explicitly, compare with your approximate result.

64. **Stirling's formula** This problem requires Problem 62 and a rapid evaluation of $\Gamma(x)$, see Problem 63. You have probably noticed that $n!$ grows incredibly fast (that is, faster than exponentials, even e^{n^5}). This problem investigates this fact. It has been shown that
$$\Gamma(x + 1) \approx Cx^{x+1/2}e^{-x}$$
for large x; so the major growth factor is x^x. You are to find the constant C.

   a. By plotting, for large x, the ratio of $\Gamma(x + 1)$ and $x^{x+1/2}e^{-x}$, find a numerical estimate of C.

   b. Given that C is the square root of a familiar number, find C. When you are finished you will have Stirling's formula.

   c. Stirling's formula is called an *asymptotic* result; that is, it becomes more accurate as $x \to +\infty$. To see this (provided your computer can handle very large numbers), approximate $n!$ for $n = 10$ and $n = 100$, and calculate the relative error in each case. *Hint:* The ratio of the two values works well for this calculation of relative error.

65. Derive the integration formula
$$\int (a^2 - x^2)^n dx = \frac{x(a^2 - x^2)^n}{2n + 1} + \frac{2a^2n}{2n + 1}\int (a^2 - x^2)^{n-1}dx$$
Use this formula to find $\int (9 - x^2)^{5/2}dx$

66. Derive the integration formula
$$\int \frac{\sin^n x\, dx}{\cos^m x} = \frac{1}{m - 1}\frac{\sin^{n-1} x}{\cos^{m-1} x} - \frac{n - 1}{m - 1}\int \frac{\sin^{n-2} x\, dx}{\cos^{m-2} x}$$

67. Derive an integration formula for $\int \frac{\cos^n x\, dx}{\sin^m x}$.

68. Derive an integration formula for $\int x^n(x^2 + a^2)^{-1/2}dx$.

69. Derive the integration formula
$$\int \frac{dx}{x^n\sqrt{ax + b}} = \frac{-\sqrt{ax + b}}{(n - 1)bx^{n-1}} - \frac{(2n - 3)a}{(2n - 2)b}\int \frac{dx}{x^{n-1}\sqrt{ax + b}}$$

70. The improper integral $\int_1^{+\infty}\left[\frac{2Ax^3}{x^4 + 1} - \frac{1}{x + 1}\right] dx$ converges for exactly one value of the constant A. Find A and then compute the value of the integral.

71. Evaluate $\int_0^{+\infty} \frac{\sqrt{x}\, \ln x\, dx}{(x + 1)(x^2 + x + 1)}$ if it exists.

72. PUTNAM EXAMINATION PROBLEM Show that
$$\frac{22}{7} - \pi = \int_0^1 \frac{x^4(1 - x)^4\, dx}{1 + x^2}$$

73. PUTNAM EXAMINATION PROBLEM Evaluate
$$\int_0^{\pi/2} \frac{dx}{1 + (\tan x)^{\sqrt{2}}}$$

74. PUTNAM EXAMINATION PROBLEM Evaluate
$$\int_0^{+\infty} t^{-1/2} exp[-1985(t + \tfrac{1}{2})]\, dt$$
You may assume that $\int_{-\infty}^{\infty} e^{-x^2}dx = \sqrt{\pi}$.

GROUP RESEARCH PROJECT

"Buoy Design"

The book of nature is written in the language of mathematics.

Galileo

The pseudomath is a person who handles mathematics as a monkey handles the razor. The creature tried to shave himself as he had seen his master do; but, not having any notion of the angle at which the razor was to be held, he cut his own throat. He never tried it a second time, poor animal! But the pseudomath keeps on in his work, proclaims himself clean shaved, and all the rest of the world hairy.

A. De Morgan
Budget of Paradoxes (London, 1872), p. 473.

This project is to be done in groups of three or four students. Each group will submit a single written report.

You have been hired as a special consultant by the U.S. Coast Guard to evaluate some proposed new designs for navigational aids (buoys).

The buoys are floating cans that need to be visible from some distance away, without rising too far out of the water. Each buoy has a circular cross section and will be fitted with a superstructure that carries equipment such as lights and batteries.

To be acceptable, a fully equipped buoy must float with not less than 1.5 ft nor more than 3 ft of freeboard. (Freeboard is the distance from the water level to the top of the device.)

You should make the following assumptions:
   a. A floating object will displace a volume of water whose weight equals the weight of the floating object. (This is Archimedes' principle.)
   b. Your devices will be floating in salt water, which weighs 65.5500 lb/ft^3.
   c. The buoys will be constructed of $\frac{1}{2}$ in. thick sheet metal that weighs 490 lb/ft^3.
   d. You can estimate an additional 20% in weight attributable to welds, bolts, and the like.
   e. Each buoy will be fitted with a superstructure and equipment weighing a total of 2,000 lb.
   f. Each design you are given to evaluate will be presented to you in the form of a curve $x = f(y)$, to be revolved about the y-axis.

Your paper is not limited to the following questions but should include these concerns: You are to design your evaluation procedure using a top-down structured approach. The design should take the form of an outline of the procedure used, with headings and subheadings as appropriate.

*This project is adapted from a computer project used at the U.S. Coast Guard Academy.

8

Infinite Series

PREVIEW

Is it possible for the sum of infinitely many numbers to be finite? This concept, which may seem paradoxical at first, plays a central role in mathematics and has a variety of important applications. The goal of this chapter is to examine the theory and applications of infinite sums, which shall be referred to as *infinite series*. Geometric series, introduced in Section 8.2, are among the simplest infinite series we shall encounter and, in some ways, the most important. In Sections 8.3–8.6, we shall develop *convergence tests*, which provide ways of determining quickly whether or not certain infinite series have a finite sum. Next, we shall turn our attention to series in which the individual terms are functions instead of numbers. We shall be especially interested in the properties of *power series*, which may be thought of as polynomials of infinite degree, although some of their properties are quite different from those of polynomials. We shall find that many common functions, such as e^x, $\ln(x + 1)$, $\sin x$, $\cos x$, and $\tan^{-1} x$ can be represented as power series, and we shall discuss some important theoretical and computational aspects of this kind of representation.

PERSPECTIVE

Series, or sums, arise in many different ways. For example, suppose it is known that a certain pollutant is released into the atmosphere at weekly intervals and is dissipated at the rate of 2% per week. If m grams of pollutant are released each week, then at the beginning of the first week, there will be $S_1 = m$ grams in the atmosphere, and at the beginning of the second, there will be $0.98m$ grams of "old" pollutant left plus m grams of "new" pollutant, to yield a total of $S_2 = m + 0.98m$ grams. Continuing, at the beginning of the nth week there will be

$$S_n = m + 0.98m + (0.98)^2 m + \cdots + (0.98)^{n-1} m$$

grams. It is natural to wonder how much pollutant will accumulate in the "long run" (as $n \to +\infty$), and the answer is given by the infinite sum

$$S_{+\infty} = m + 0.98m + (0.98)^2 m + \cdots$$

But just exactly what do we mean by such a sum, and if the total is a finite number, how can we compute its value?

We seek answers to these questions in this chapter.

8.1 SEQUENCES AND THEIR LIMITS

> **IN THIS SECTION**   Sequences; the limit of a sequence; bounded, monotonic sequences
>
> Most phenomena we have considered occur continuously, but in practically every field of inquiry, there are situations that can be described by cataloging individual items in a numerical listing. In this section we define a mathematical tool, called a sequence, in order to do this cataloging, and then we define what we mean by the limit of a sequence. In the next section we shall use our knowledge of sequences to define and study infinite sums.

This drawing represents consecutive frames from a 16-mm movie film showing a golfer from the moment he is at the top of his backswing until he hits the ball. If this film were projected at a rate of several frames per second, the viewer would have the illusion of seeing the golfer in action as he makes his downswing.

The making of a motion picture is a complex process, and editing the film into a movie requires that all the frames of the action be labeled in chronological order. For example, R21-435 might signify the 435th frame of the 21st reel. A mathematician might refer to the movie editor's labeling procedure by saying the frames are arranged in a *sequence*.

■ SEQUENCES

A sequence is a succession of numbers that are listed according to a given prescription or rule. Specifically, if n is a positive integer, the sequence whose nth term is the number a_n can be written as

$$a_1, a_2, \ldots, a_n, \ldots$$

or, more simply,

$$\{a_n\}$$

The number a_n is called the **general term** of the sequence. We will deal only with infinite sequences, so each term a_n has a **successor** a_{n+1} and for $n > 1$, a **predecessor** a_{n-1}. For example, by associating each positive integer n with its reciprocal $\frac{1}{n}$, we obtain the sequence denoted by

$$\left\{\frac{1}{n}\right\}, \quad \text{which represents the succession of numbers} \quad 1, \tfrac{1}{2}, \tfrac{1}{3}, \ldots, \tfrac{1}{n}, \ldots$$

The general term is denoted by $a_n = \frac{1}{n}$.

The following examples illustrate the notation and terminology used in connection with sequences.

EXAMPLE 1   Given the general term, find particular terms of a sequence

Find the 1st, 2nd, and 15th terms of the sequence $\{a_n\}$, where the general term is

$$a_n = \left(\tfrac{1}{2}\right)^{n-1}$$

Solution   If $n = 1$, then $a_1 = \left(\tfrac{1}{2}\right)^{1-1} = 1$. Similarly,

$$a_2 = \left(\tfrac{1}{2}\right)^{2-1} = \tfrac{1}{2}$$

$$a_{15} = \left(\tfrac{1}{2}\right)^{15-1} = \left(\tfrac{1}{2}\right)^{14} = 2^{-14}$$

The reverse question, that of finding a general term given certain terms of a sequence, is a more difficult task, and even if we find a general term, we have no assurance that the general term is unique. For example, consider the sequence

$$2, 4, 6, 8, \ldots$$

This seems to have a general term $a_n = 2n$. However, the general term

$$a_n = (n - 1)(n - 2)(n - 3)(n - 4) + 2n$$

has the same first four terms, but $a_5 = 34$ (not 10, as we would expect from the sequence 2, 4, 6, 8).

It is sometimes useful to start a sequence with a_0 instead of a_1; that is, to have a sequence of the form

$$a_0, a_1, a_2, \ldots$$

So far, we have been discussing the concept of a sequence informally, without a definition. We have observed that a sequence $\{a_n\}$ associates the number a_n with the positive integer n. Hence, a sequence is really a special kind of function, one whose domain is the set of all positive (or possibly, nonnegative) integers.

Sequence

> A **sequence** $\{a_n\}$ is a function whose domain is a set of nonnegative integers and whose range is a subset of the real numbers. The functional values a_1, a_2, a_3, . . . are called the **terms** of the sequence, and a_n is called the **nth term,** or **general term,** of the sequence.

⊘ Even though we write a_n, remember this is a function, $a(n) = \dfrac{n}{n + 1}$ where the domain is the set of nonnegative integers. ⊘

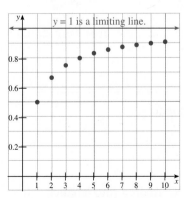

a. Graphing a sequence in one dimension

b. Graphing a sequence in two dimensions

Figure 8.1 Graphing the sequence $a_n = \dfrac{n}{n + 1}$

In this text, we shall only consider *real-valued sequences*—that is, sequences in which each a_n is a real number. Unless otherwise specified, "sequence" will always mean "real-valued sequence." Although a sequence is a function, we usually represent sequences as $\{a_n\}$ rather than with functional notation.

■ THE LIMIT OF A SEQUENCE

It is often desirable to examine the behavior of a given sequence $\{a_n\}$ as n gets arbitrarily large. For example, consider the sequence

$$a_n = \frac{n}{n + 1}$$

Because $a_1 = \frac{1}{2}$, $a_2 = \frac{2}{3}$, $a_3 = \frac{3}{4}$, . . . , we can plot the terms of this sequence on a number line, as shown in Figure 8.1a, or the sequence can be plotted in two dimensions, as shown in Figure 8.1b. By looking at either graph in Figure 8.1, we see that it appears the terms of the sequence are approaching 1. In general, if the terms of the sequence approach the number L as n increases without bound, we say that the sequence *converges to the limit L* and write

$$L = \lim_{n \to \infty} a_n$$

(Note that for simplicity, the limiting behavior is denoted by $n \to \infty$ instead of the usual $n \to +\infty$). For instance, in our example, we would expect

$$\lim_{n \to \infty} \frac{n}{n + 1} = 1$$

This limiting behavior is analogous to the continuous case (discussed in Section 3.5), and may be defined formally as follows.

Convergent Sequence

a. one dimension

b. two dimensions

Figure 8.2 Geometric interpretation of a converging sequence

> The sequence $\{a_n\}$ **converges** to the number L, and we write
>
> $$L = \lim_{n \to \infty} a_n$$
>
> if for every $\varepsilon > 0$, there is an integer N such that
>
> $$|a_n - L| < \varepsilon \quad \text{whenever} \quad n > N$$
>
> Otherwise, the sequence **diverges**.
>
> ■ *What this says:* The notation $L = \lim_{n \to \infty} a_n$ means that the terms of the sequence $\{a_n\}$ can be made as close to L as may be desired by taking n sufficiently large.

A geometric interpretation of this definition is shown in Figure 8.2.
Note that if

$$L = \lim_{n \to \infty} a_n$$

the numbers a_n may be practically anywhere at first (that is, for "small" n), but eventually, the a_n must "cluster" near the limiting value L.

The theorem on limits of functions carries over to sequences. We have the following useful result.

THEOREM 8.1   Limit theorem for sequences

If $\lim_{n \to \infty} a_n = L$ and $\lim_{n \to \infty} b_n = M$, then the following limits exist, and:

Linearity rule	$\lim_{n \to \infty} (ra_n + sb_n) = rL + sM$	
Product rule	$\lim_{n \to \infty} (a_n b_n) = LM$	
Quotient rule	$\lim_{n \to \infty} \dfrac{a_n}{b_n} = \dfrac{L}{M}$	*provided $M \neq 0$*
Root rule	$\lim_{n \to \infty} \sqrt[m]{a_n} = \sqrt[m]{L}$	*provided $\sqrt[m]{a_n}$ is defined for all n and $\sqrt[m]{L}$ exists*

Proof: The proof of these rules follows from the limit rules that were stated in Section 3.5.   ■

EXAMPLE 2   Convergent sequences

Find the limit of each of these convergent sequences:

a. $\left\{ \dfrac{100}{n} \right\}$ **b.** $\left\{ \dfrac{2n^2 + 5n - 7}{n^3} \right\}$ **c.** $\left\{ \dfrac{3n^4 + n - 1}{5n^4 + 2n^2 + 1} \right\}$

Solution   a. As n grows arbitrarily large, $100/n$ gets smaller and smaller. Thus,

$$\lim_{n \to \infty} \frac{100}{n} = 0$$

A graphical representation is shown in Figure 8.3.

Figure 8.3 Graphical representation of $a_n = 100/n$

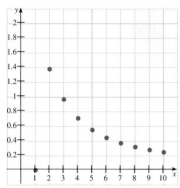

Figure 8.4 Graph of
$$a_n = \frac{2n^2 + 5n - 7}{n^3}$$

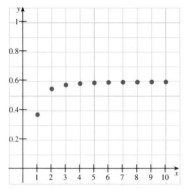

Figure 8.5 Graph of
$$a_n = \frac{3n^4 + n - 1}{5n^4 + 2n^2 + 1}$$

b. We cannot use the quotient rule of Theorem 8.1 because neither the limit in the numerator nor the one in the denominator exists. However,

$$\frac{2n^2 + 5n - 7}{n^3} = \frac{2}{n} + \frac{5}{n^2} - \frac{7}{n^3}$$

and by using the linearity rule, we find that

$$\lim_{n \to \infty} \frac{2n^2 + 5n - 7}{n^3} = \lim_{n \to \infty} \frac{2}{n} + 5 \lim_{n \to \infty} \frac{1}{n^2} - 7 \lim_{n \to \infty} \frac{1}{n^3}$$

$$= 0 + 0 + 0$$

$$= 0$$

A graph is shown in Figure 8.4.

c. Divide the numerator and denominator by n^4 to obtain

$$\lim_{n \to \infty} \frac{3n^4 + n - 1}{5n^4 + 2n^2 + 1} = \lim_{n \to \infty} \frac{3 + \frac{1}{n^3} - \frac{1}{n^4}}{5 + \frac{2}{n^2} + \frac{1}{n^4}} = \frac{3}{5}$$

A graph of this sequence is shown in Figure 8.5.

EXAMPLE 3 Divergent sequences

Show that the following sequences diverge:

a. $\{(-1)^n\}$ **b.** $\left\{ \dfrac{n^5 + n^3 + 2}{7n^4 + n^2 + 3} \right\}$

Solution   **a.** The sequence defined by $\{(-1)^n\}$ is $-1, 1, -1, 1, \ldots$. This sequence diverges by oscillation because the nth term is always either 1 or -1, so a_n cannot approach one specific number L as n grows large. The graph is shown in Figure 8.6a.

b. $\lim\limits_{n \to \infty} \dfrac{n^5 + n^3 + 2}{7n^4 + n^2 + 3} = \dfrac{1 + \frac{1}{n^2} + \frac{2}{n^5}}{\frac{7}{n} + \frac{1}{n^3} + \frac{3}{n^5}}$

The numerator tends toward 1 as $n \to \infty$, and the denominator approaches 0. Hence the quotient increases without bound, and the sequence must diverge. The graph is shown in Figure 8.6b.

a. $a_n = (-1)^n$

b. $a_n = \dfrac{n^5 + n^3 + 2}{7n^4 + n^2 + 3}$

Figure 8.6 Graph and values for two divergent sequences

If $\lim\limits_{n\to\infty} a_n$ does not exist because the numbers a_n become arbitrarily large as $n\to\infty$, we write $\lim\limits_{n\to\infty} a_n = \infty$. We summarize this more precisely in the following box.

Limit Notation

$\lim\limits_{n\to\infty} a_n = \infty$	means that for any real number A, we have $a_n > A$ for all sufficiently large n.
$\lim\limits_{n\to\infty} b_n = -\infty$	means that for any real number B, we have $b_n < B$ for all sufficiently large n.

Rewriting the answer to Example 3b in this notation, we find that

$$\lim_{n\to\infty} \frac{n^5 + n^3 + 2}{7n^4 + n^2 + 3} = +\infty$$

Also notice that $\lim\limits_{n\to\infty} (-5n) = -\infty$ (that is, decreases without bound) whereas $\lim\limits_{n\to\infty} (-1)^n$ does not exist. Thus, the answer to Example 3a is *neither* $+\infty$ or $-\infty$.

EXAMPLE 4   Determining the convergence or divergence of a sequence

Determine the convergence or divergence of the sequence $\{\sqrt{n^2 + 3n} - n\}$.

Solution   Consider

$$\lim_{n\to\infty} (\sqrt{n^2 + 3n} - n)$$

It would not be correct to apply the linearity property for sequences (because neither $\lim\limits_{n\to\infty} \sqrt{n^2 + 3n}$ nor $\lim\limits_{n\to\infty} n$ exists). It is also not correct to use this as a reason to say that the limit does not exist. You might even try some values of n (shown in the Figure 8.7) to guess that there is some limit. In order to find the limit, however, we shall rewrite the general term algebraically as follows:

$$\sqrt{n^2 + 3n} - n = (\sqrt{n^2 + 3n} - n)\frac{\sqrt{n^2 + 3n} + n}{\sqrt{n^2 + 3n} + n}$$

$$= \frac{n^2 + 3n - n^2}{\sqrt{n^2 + 3n} + n}\frac{\frac{1}{n}}{\frac{1}{n}} = \frac{3}{\frac{\sqrt{n^2 + 3n}}{n} + 1} = \frac{3}{\sqrt{\frac{n^2 + 3n}{n^2}} + 1} = \frac{3}{\sqrt{1 + \frac{3}{n}} + 1}$$

Hence, $$\lim_{n\to\infty} (\sqrt{n^2 + 3n} - n) = \lim_{n\to\infty} \frac{3}{\sqrt{1 + \frac{3}{n}} + 1} = \frac{3}{2}$$

Figure 8.7 Graph of $a_n = \sqrt{n^2 + 3n} - n$: convergent or divergent?

Note the graph of the sequence in Example 4. The graph of a sequence consists of a succession of isolated points. This can be compared with the graph of $y = \sqrt{x^2 + 3x} - x$, $x \geq 1$, which is a continuous curve (shown in Figure 8.8). The only difference between $\lim\limits_{n\to\infty} a_n = L$ and $\lim\limits_{x\to\infty} f(x) = L$ is that n is required to be an integer. This is stated in the hypothesis of the following theorem.

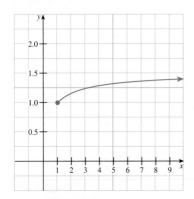

Figure 8.8 Graph of $f(x) = \sqrt{x^2 + 3x} - x$, $x \geq 1$

THEOREM 8.2   Limit of a sequence

Suppose f is a function such that $a_n = f(n)$ for $n = 1, 2, \ldots$. If $\lim\limits_{x\to\infty} f(x)$ exists and $\lim\limits_{x\to\infty} f(x) = L$, the sequence $\{a_n\}$ converges and $\lim\limits_{n\to\infty} a_n = L$.

Proof: Let $\varepsilon > 0$ be given. Because $\lim\limits_{x\to\infty} f(x) = L$, there exists a number $N > 0$ such that

$$|f(x) - L| < \varepsilon \quad \text{whenever } x > N$$

In particular, if $n > N$, it follows that $|f(n) - L| = |a_n - L| < \varepsilon$.   ∎

Be sure you read this theorem correctly. In particular, note that it *does not* say that if $\lim\limits_{n\to\infty} a_n = L$, then $\lim\limits_{x\to\infty} f(x) = L$ (see Figure 8.9b).

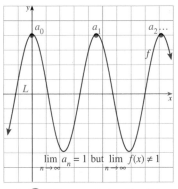

a. If $\lim\limits_{n\to\infty} f(x) = L$, then $\lim\limits_{n\to\infty} a_n = L$.

b. ⊘ If $\lim\limits_{n\to\infty} a_n = L$, then $\lim\limits_{n\to\infty} f(x)$ does NOT necessarily equal L. ⊘

Figure 8.9 Graphical comparison of $\lim\limits_{n\to\infty} a_n$ and $\lim\limits_{x\to\infty} f(x)$, where $f(n) = a_n$ for $n = 1, 2, \ldots$

EXAMPLE 5   Convergence using l'Hôpital's rule

Given that the sequence $\left\{ \dfrac{n^2}{1 - e^n} \right\}$ converges, evaluate $\lim\limits_{n\to\infty} \dfrac{n^2}{1 - e^n}$.

Solution   Let $L = \lim\limits_{x\to\infty} f(x)$, where $f(x) = \dfrac{x^2}{1 - e^x}$. Because $f(n) = a_n$ for $n = 1, 2, \ldots$, Theorem 8.2 tells us that $\lim\limits_{n\to\infty} \dfrac{n^2}{1 - e^n}$ is the same as $\lim\limits_{n\to\infty} f(x)$.

$$\lim_{x\to\infty} \frac{x^2}{1 - e^x} = \lim_{x\to\infty} \frac{2x}{-e^x} \quad \textit{l'Hôpital's rule}$$

$$= \lim_{x\to\infty} \frac{2}{-e^x} \quad \textit{l'Hôpital's rule again}$$

$$= 0$$

Thus, by Theorem 8.2, $\lim\limits_{n\to\infty} \dfrac{n^2}{1 - e^n} = \lim\limits_{x\to\infty} f(x) = L = 0$.   ▬

The squeeze theorem (Theorem 1.9) can be reformulated in terms of sequences.

THEOREM 8.3   Squeeze theorem for sequences

If $a_n \le b_n \le c_n$ for all $n > N$, and $\lim\limits_{n\to\infty} a_n = \lim\limits_{n\to\infty} c_n = L$, then $\lim\limits_{n\to\infty} b_n = L$

Proof: The proof follows from Theorem 1.9 and Theorem 8.2.   ∎

EXAMPLE 6   Using l'Hôpital's rule and the squeeze theorem

Show that the following sequences converge, and find their limits.

a. $\lim\limits_{n\to\infty} n^{1/n}$ **b.** $\lim\limits_{n\to 0} \dfrac{n!}{n^n}$

Solution   **a.** Let $L = \lim\limits_{n\to\infty} n^{1/n}$; then $\ln L = \lim\limits_{n\to\infty} \dfrac{\ln n}{n} = \lim\limits_{n\to\infty} \dfrac{\frac{1}{n}}{1} = 0$ (l'Hopital's rule)

Thus, $L = e^0 = 1$.

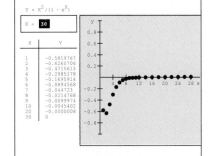

From the graph, it looks like $\lim\limits_{x\to\infty} f(a_n) \le 0$.

b. We cannot use l'Hôpital's rule because $x!$ is not defined as an elementary function when x is not an integer. Instead, we use the squeeze theorem for sequences. Accordingly, note that

$$b_n = \frac{n!}{n^n} \quad \text{so that} \quad b_1 = 1, \ b_2 = \frac{2 \cdot 1}{2 \cdot 2}, \ b_3 = \frac{3 \cdot 2 \cdot 1}{3 \cdot 3 \cdot 3}, \ \dots,$$

$$b_n = \frac{n \cdot (n-1) \cdots 3 \cdot 2 \cdot 1}{\underbrace{n \cdot n \cdot n \cdots n}_{n \text{ factors}}} = \left[\underbrace{\frac{n(n-1) \cdots 3 \cdot 2}{n \cdot n \cdot n \cdots n}}_{n-1 \text{ factors}} \right]\left(\frac{1}{n}\right)$$

Thus, if $a_n = 0$, and $c_n = \frac{1}{n}$, for all n, we have

$$\overset{a_n}{\overbrace{0}} \leq \overset{b_n}{\overbrace{\frac{n!}{n^n}}} \leq \overset{c_n}{\overbrace{\frac{1}{n}}} \qquad \frac{n!}{n^n} \leq \frac{1}{n} \text{ because } n \cdot n! < n^n$$

Because $\lim\limits_{n \to \infty} a_n = 0$ and $\lim\limits_{n \to \infty} c_n = 0$, it follows from the squeeze theorem that $\lim\limits_{n \to \infty} \frac{n!}{n^n} = 0$. ▬

■ BOUNDED, MONOTONIC SEQUENCES

A sequence $\{a_n\}$ is said to be

Increasing	**Increasing** if $a_1 < a_2 < a_3 < \cdots < a_{k-1} < a_k < \cdots$
Nondecreasing	**Nondecreasing** if $a_1 \leq a_2 \leq \cdots \leq a_{k-1} \leq a_k \leq \cdots$
Decreasing	**Decreasing** if $a_1 > a_2 > a_3 > \cdots > a_{k-1} > a_k > \cdots$
Nonincreasing	**Nonincreasing** if $a_1 \geq a_2 \geq \cdots \geq a_{k-1} \geq a_k \geq \cdots$
Monotonic	**Monotonic** if it is nondecreasing or nonincreasing
Strictly Monotonic	**Strictly monotonic** if it is increasing or decreasing
Bounded Above	**Bounded above** by M if $a_n \leq M$ for $n = 1, 2, 3, \dots$
Bounded Below	**Bounded below** by m if $m \leq a_n$ for $n = 1, 2, 3, \dots$
Bounded	**Bounded** if it is bounded both above and below

In general, it is difficult to tell whether or not a given sequence converges or diverges, but thanks to the following theorem, it is easy to make this determination if we know the sequence is monotonic.

THEOREM 8.4   BMCT: The bounded, monotonic convergence theorem

A monotonic sequence $\{a_n\}$ converges if it is bounded and diverges otherwise.

Proof: A formal proof of the BMCT is outlined in Problem 54. For the following informal argument we will assume that $\{a_n\}$ is a nondecreasing sequence. (You might wish to see whether you can give a similar informal argument for the increasing case.) Because the terms of the sequence satisfy $a_1 \leq a_2 \leq a_3 \leq \cdots$, we know that the sequence is bounded from below by a_1 and that the graph of the

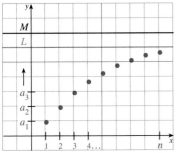

a. If $a_n < M$ for $n = 1, 2, \ldots$, the graph of the points (n, a_n) will approach a horizontal "barrier" line $y = L$.

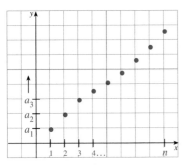

b. If $\{a_n\}$ is not bounded from above, the graph rises indefinitely.

Figure 8.10 Graphical possibilities for the BMCT theorem

corresponding points (n, a_n) will be rising in the plane. Two cases can occur, as shown in Figure 8.10. Suppose the sequence $\{a_n\}$ is also bounded from above by a number M, so that $a_1 \leq a_n \leq M$ for $n = 1, 2, \ldots$. Then the graph of the points (n, a_n) must continually rise (because the sequence is monotonic) and yet it must stay below the line $y = M$. The only way this can happen is for the graph to approach a "barrier" line $y = L$ (where $L \leq M$), and we have $\lim\limits_{n \to \infty} a_n = L$, as shown in Figure 8.10a. However, if the sequence is not bounded from above, the graph will rise indefinitely (Figure 8.10b), and the terms in the sequence $\{a_n\}$ cannot approach any finite number L. ■

EXAMPLE 7   Convergence using the BMCT

Show that the sequence $\left\{\dfrac{1 \cdot 3 \cdot 5 \cdots (2n-1)}{2 \cdot 4 \cdot 6 \cdots (2n)}\right\}$ converges.

Solution   The first few terms of this sequence are

$$a_1 = \frac{1}{2} \qquad a_2 = \frac{1 \cdot 3}{2 \cdot 4} = \frac{3}{8} \qquad a_3 = \frac{1 \cdot 3 \cdot 5}{2 \cdot 4 \cdot 6} = \frac{5}{16}$$

Because $\frac{1}{2} > \frac{3}{8} > \frac{5}{16}$, it appears that the sequence is decreasing (that is, it is monotonic). We can prove this by showing that $a_{n+1} < a_n$, or equivalently, $\dfrac{a_{n+1}}{a_n} < 1$. (Note that $a_n \neq 0$ for all n.)

$$\frac{a_{n+1}}{a_n} = \frac{\dfrac{1 \cdot 3 \cdot 5 \cdots [2(n+1)-1]}{2 \cdot 4 \cdot 6 \cdots [2(n+1)]}}{\dfrac{1 \cdot 3 \cdot 5 \cdots (2n-1)}{2 \cdot 4 \cdot 6 \cdots (2n)}}$$

$$= \frac{1 \cdot 3 \cdot 5 \cdots (2n+1)}{2 \cdot 4 \cdot 6 \cdots (2n+2)} \cdot \frac{2 \cdot 4 \cdot 6 \cdots (2n)}{1 \cdot 3 \cdot 5 \cdots (2n-1)} = \frac{2n+1}{2n+2} < 1$$

for any $n > 0$. Hence, $a_{n+1} < a_n$ for all n, and $\{a_n\}$ is a decreasing sequence. Because $a_n > 0$ for all n, it follows that $\{a_n\}$ is bounded below by 0. Applying the BMCT, we see that $\{a_n\}$ converges, but the BMCT tells us nothing about the limit. ▬

COMMENT: Technically, the sequence $\{a_n\}$ is monotonic only when its terms are either always nonincreasing or always nondecreasing, but the BMCT also applies to sequences whose terms are *eventually* monotonic. That is, it can be shown that the sequence $\{a_n\}$ converges if it is bounded and there exists an integer N such that $\{a_n\}$ is monotonic for all $n > N$. This modified form of the BMCT is illustrated in the following example.

EXAMPLE 8   Convergence of a sequence that is eventually monotonic

Show that the sequence $\left\{\dfrac{\ln n}{\sqrt{n}}\right\}$ converges.

Solution   We will apply the BMCT. Some initial values are shown in Figure 8.11. The succession of numbers suggests that the sequence increases at first and then gradually begins to decrease. To verify this behavior, we let

$$f(x) = \frac{\ln x}{\sqrt{x}}$$

and find that $f'(x) = \dfrac{\sqrt{x}\left(\frac{1}{x}\right) - (\ln x)\left(\frac{1}{2}x^{-1/2}\right)}{x} = \dfrac{2\sqrt{x} - \sqrt{x}\ln x}{2x^2}$

Figure 8.11 $a_n = \dfrac{\ln n}{\sqrt{n}}$

Find the critical values:

$$\frac{2\sqrt{x} - \sqrt{x} \ln x}{2x^2} = 0$$

$$2\sqrt{x} = \sqrt{x} \ln x$$

$$\ln x = 2$$

$$e^2 = x$$

Thus, $x = e^2$ is the only critical value, and you can show that $f'(x) > 0$ for $x < e^2$ and $f'(x) < 0$ for $x > e^2$. This means that f is a decreasing function for $x > e^2$. Thus, the sequence $\left\{\frac{\ln n}{\sqrt{n}}\right\}$ must be decreasing for $n > 8$ (because e^2 is between 7 and 8). We see that the sequence $\left\{\frac{\ln n}{\sqrt{n}}\right\}$ is bounded from below because

$$0 < \frac{\ln n}{\sqrt{n}} \qquad \text{for all } n > 1$$

Therefore, the given sequence is bounded from below and is eventually decreasing, so it must converge.   ▬

The BMCT is an extremely valuable theoretical tool. For example, in Chapter 5, we defined the number e by the limit

$$\lim_{n \to \infty} \left(1 + \tfrac{1}{n}\right)^n = e$$

but to do so we assumed that this limit exists. We can now show this assumption is warranted, because it turns out that the sequence $\left\{\left(1 + \tfrac{1}{n}\right)^n\right\}$ is increasing and bounded from above by 3 (the details are outlined in Problem 53). Thus, the BMCT assures us that the sequence converges, and this in turn guarantees the existence of the limit. We end this section with a result that will be useful in our subsequent work. The proof makes use of the formal definition of limit.

THEOREM 8.5   Convergence of a power sequence

If r is a number such that $|r| < 1$, then $\lim_{n \to \infty} r^n = 0$.

Proof: The case where $r = 0$ is trivial. We shall prove the theorem for the case $0 < r < 1$ and leave the case $-1 < r < 0$ as an exercise. Because $0 < r < 1$, we can write r as

$$r = \frac{1}{1 + h}$$

for some $h > 0$, so

$$r^n = \frac{1}{(1 + h)^n}$$

Because (for all fixed n)

$$(1 + h)^n = 1 + nh + \frac{n(n-1)}{2!}h^2 + \cdots + h^n \qquad \textit{Binomial theorem}$$

$$> nh \qquad\qquad\qquad \textit{Because } h > 0$$

we see

$$r^n = \frac{1}{(1 + h)^n} < \frac{1}{nh} \qquad\qquad \textit{If } a > b, \text{ then } \tfrac{1}{a} < \tfrac{1}{b}.$$

We now use the definition of limit. Given $\varepsilon > 0$, we see that if $n > \frac{1}{\varepsilon h}$, then $\frac{1}{nh} < \varepsilon$ because both n and ε are greater than zero. We can then choose $N = \frac{1}{\varepsilon h}$, and if $n > N$, then $r^n < \varepsilon$ and by the definition of limit we conclude $\lim_{n \to \infty} r^n = 0$.   ▪

PROBLEM SET 8.1

Ⓐ 1. ■ What Does This Say? What do we mean by the limit of a sequence?

2. ■ What Does This Say? What does the bounded, monotonic, convergence theorem say?

Write out the first five terms (beginning with n = 1) of the sequences given in Problems 3–11.

3. $\{1 + (-1)^n\}$

4. $\left\{\left(\dfrac{-1}{2}\right)^{n+2}\right\}$

5. $\left\{\dfrac{\cos 2n\pi}{n}\right\}$

6. $\left\{n \sin \dfrac{n\pi}{2}\right\}$

7. $\left\{\dfrac{3n + 1}{n + 2}\right\}$

8. $\left\{\dfrac{n^2 - n}{n^2 + n}\right\}$

9. $\{a_n\}$ where $a_1 = 256$ and $a_n = \sqrt{a_{n-1}}$ for $n \geq 2$

10. $\{a_n\}$ where $a_1 = -1$ and $a_n = n + a_{n-1}$ for $n \geq 2$

11. $\{a_n\}$ where $a_1 = 1$ and $a_n = (a_{n-1})^2 + a_{n-1} + 1$ for $n \geq 2$

Compute the limit of the convergent sequences in Problems 12–35.

12. $\left\{\dfrac{5n + 8}{n}\right\}$

13. $\left\{\dfrac{5n}{n + 7}\right\}$

14. $\left\{\dfrac{2n + 1}{3n - 4}\right\}$

15. $\left\{\dfrac{4 - 7n}{8 + n}\right\}$

16. $\left\{\dfrac{8n^2 + 800n + 5{,}000}{2n^2 - 1{,}000n + 2}\right\}$

17. $\left\{\dfrac{100n + 7{,}000}{n^2 - n - 1}\right\}$

18. $\left\{\dfrac{8n^2 + 6n + 4{,}000}{n^3 + 1}\right\}$

19. $\left\{\dfrac{n^3 - 6n^2 + 85}{2n^3 - 5n + 170}\right\}$

20. $\left\{\dfrac{2n}{n + 7\sqrt{n}}\right\}$

21. $\left\{\dfrac{8n - 500\sqrt{n}}{2n + 800\sqrt{n}}\right\}$

22. $\left\{\dfrac{3\sqrt{n}}{5\sqrt{n} + \sqrt[4]{n}}\right\}$

23. $\left\{\dfrac{\ln n}{n^2}\right\}$

24. $\{2^{5/n}\}$

25. $\{n^{3/n}\}$

26. $\left\{\left(1 + \dfrac{3}{n}\right)^n\right\}$

27. $\{(n + 4)^{1/n}\}$

28. $\{n^{1/(n+2)}\}$

29. $\{(\ln n)^{1/n}\}$

30. $\left\{\displaystyle\int_0^{\infty} e^{-nx}\, dx\right\}$

31. $\left\{\sqrt{n^2 + n} - n\right\}$

32. $\left\{\sqrt{n + 5\sqrt{n}} - \sqrt{n}\right\}$

33. $\{\sqrt[n]{n}\}$

34. $\{(an + b)^{1/n}\}$, a and b positive constants

35. $\{\ln n - \ln(n + 1)\}$

Ⓑ *Show that each sequence given in Problems 36–41 converges either by showing it is increasing with an upper bound or decreasing with a lower bound.*

36. $\left\{\dfrac{n}{2^n}\right\}$

37. $\left\{\ln\left(\dfrac{n + 1}{n}\right)\right\}$

38. $\left\{\dfrac{3n - 2}{n}\right\}$

39. $\left\{\dfrac{4n + 5}{n}\right\}$

40. $\left\{\dfrac{3n - 7}{2^n}\right\}$

41. $\{\sqrt[n]{n}\}$

Explain why each sequence in Problems 42–45 diverges.

42. $\{1 + (-1)^n\}$

43. $\{\cos n\pi\}$

44. $\left\{\dfrac{n^3 - 7n + 5}{100n^2 + 219}\right\}$

45. $\{\sqrt{n}\}$

46. Suppose a particle of mass m moves back and forth along a line segment of length $|a|$. In classical mechanics, the particle can move at any speed, and thus, its energy can be any positive number. However, quantum mechanics replaces this continuous model of the particle's behavior with one in which the particle's energy level can have only certain discrete values, say, $E_1, E_2, \ldots$. Specifically, it can be shown that the nth term in this quantum sequence has the value

$$E_n = \frac{n^2 h^2}{8ma^2} \quad n = 0, 1, 2, \ldots$$

where h is a physical constant known as *Planck's constant* ($h \approx 6.63 \times 10^{-27}$ erg/s). List the first five values of E_n for a particle with mass 8 mg moving along a segment of length 100 cm.

47. A drug is administered into the body. At the end of each hour, the amount of drug present is half what it was at the end of the previous hour. What percent of the drug is present at the end of 4 hr? At the end of n hours?

48. The Fibonacci rabbit problem The general term in a sequence can be defined in a number of ways. In this problem, we consider a sequence whose nth term is defined by a *recursion formula*; that is, a formula in which the nth term is given in terms of previous terms in the sequence. The problem was originally examined by Leonardo Pisano (also called Fibonacci) in the 13th century. The so-called *Fibonacci sequence* has applications in many areas, including biology and botany.

Suppose rabbits breed in such a way that each pair of adult rabbits produces a pair of baby rabbits each month. The first month after birth, the rabbits are adolescents and produce no offspring. However, beginning with the

Number of Months	Number of Pairs	Pairs of Rabbits (the pink rabbits are ready to reproduce)
Start	1	
1	1	
2	2	
3	3	
4	5	
5	8	
⋮	⋮	Same pair (rabbits never die)

second month, the rabbits are adults and each pair produces a pair of offspring every month. Let a_n denote the number of adult pairs of rabbits in her "colony" at the end of n months.

a. Explain why $a_1 = 1$, $a_2 = 1$, $a_3 = 2$, $a_4 = 3$, and in general

$$a_{n+1} = a_{n-1} + a_n \qquad \text{for } n = 2, 3, 4, \ldots$$

b. The *growth rate* of the colony during the $(n + 1)$th month is

$$r_n = \frac{a_{n+1}}{a_n}$$

Compute r_n for $n = 1, 2, 3, \ldots, 10$.

c. Assume that the growth rate sequence $\{r_n\}$ defined in part **b** converges, and let

$$L = \lim_{n \to \infty} r_n$$

Use the recursion formula in part **a** to show that

$$\frac{a_{n+1}}{a_n} = 1 + \frac{a_{n-1}}{a_n}$$

and conclude that L must satisfy the equation

$$L = 1 + \frac{1}{L}$$

Use this information to compute L.

C *In Problems 49–52, use the fact that $\lim\limits_{n \to \infty} a_n = L$ means $|a_n - L|$ is arbitrarily small when n is sufficiently large.*

49. If $\lim\limits_{n \to \infty} \dfrac{n}{n + 1} = 1$, find N so that $\left|\dfrac{n}{n + 1} - 1\right| < 0.01$ if $n > N$.

50. If $\lim\limits_{n \to \infty} \dfrac{2n + 1}{n + 3} = 2$, find N so that $\left|\dfrac{2n + 1}{n + 3} - 2\right| < 0.01$ if $n > N$.

51. If $\lim\limits_{n \to \infty} \dfrac{n^2 + 1}{n^3} = 0$, find N so that $\left|\dfrac{n^2 + 1}{n^3}\right| < 0.001$ if $n > N$.

52. If $\lim\limits_{n \to \infty} e^{-n} = 0$, find N so that $\dfrac{1}{e^n} < 0.001$ if $n > N$.

53. Convergence of the sequence $\left\{\left(1 + \frac{1}{n}\right)^n\right\}$

a. Suppose n is a positive integer. Use the binomial theorem to show that

$$\left(1 + \frac{1}{n}\right)^n = 1 + 1 + \frac{1}{2!}\left(1 - \frac{1}{n}\right) + \frac{1}{3!}\left(1 - \frac{1}{n}\right)\left(1 - \frac{2}{n}\right)$$
$$+ \cdots + \frac{1}{n!}\left(1 - \frac{1}{n}\right)\left(1 - \frac{2}{n}\right) \cdots \left(1 - \frac{n - 1}{n}\right)$$

b. Use part **a** to show that $\left(1 + \frac{1}{n}\right)^n < 3$ for all n.

c. Use part **a** to show that $\left\{\left(1 + \frac{1}{n}\right)^n\right\}$ is an increasing sequence. Then use the BMCT to show that this sequence converges.

54. Proof of the BMCT Suppose there exists a number M and a positive integer N so that $a_n \leq a_{n+1} \leq M$ for all $n > N$.

a. It is a fundamental property of numbers that a sequence with an upper bound must have a *least* upper bound; that is, there must be a number A with the property that $a_n \leq A$ for all n but if c is a number such that $c < A$, then $a_m > c$ for at least one m. Use this property to show that if $\varepsilon > 0$ is given, there exists a positive integer N such that

$$A - \varepsilon < a_N < A$$

b. If N is the integer that satisfies the condition in part **a**, show that

$$A - \varepsilon < a_n < A$$

for all $n > N$.

c. Show that $|a_n - A| < \varepsilon$ for all $n > N$ and conclude that $\lim\limits_{n \to \infty} a_n = A$.

8.2 INTRODUCTION TO INFINITE SERIES: GEOMETRIC SERIES

IN THIS SECTION Definition of infinite series, general properties of infinite series, geometric series, applications of geometric series

We define an infinite series (sum) as the limit of a special type of sequence. We then study a few basic properties of infinite series and examine *geometric series*, a special kind of series with numerous applications.

■ DEFINITION OF INFINITE SERIES

One way to sum a list of numbers is to form subtotals until the end of the list is reached. Similarly, to give meaning to the infinite sum

$$S = a_1 + a_2 + a_3 + a_4 + \cdots$$

it is natural to examine the "partial sums"

$$a_1, \qquad a_1 + a_2, \qquad a_1 + a_2 + a_3, \qquad a_1 + a_2 + a_3 + a_4, \ldots$$

If it is possible to attach a numerical value to the infinite sum, we would expect the partial sums $S_n = a_1 + a_2 + \cdots + a_n$ to approach that value as n increases without bound. These ideas lead us to the following definition.

Infinite Series

Historical Note

The mathematician Brahmagupta was the most prominent of the Hindu mathematicians of the 7th century. He did some early work on arithmetic series and the sum of the squares of natural numbers. He wrote an astronomical work that contained several chapters on mathematics. He was an exceptionally clear expositor, and before each example he worked, he stated a rule that was appropriate to the problem.

Source: Chandra Sharma, University of Manchester Institute of Science and Technology.

An **infinite series** is an expression of the form
$$a_1 + a_2 + a_3 + \cdots = \sum_{k=1}^{\infty} a_k$$
and the **nth partial sum** of the series is
$$S_n = a_1 + a_2 + \cdots + a_n = \sum_{k=1}^{n} a_k$$
The series is said to **converge with sum S** if the sequence of partial sums $\{S_n\}$ converges to S. In this case, we write
$$\sum_{k=1}^{\infty} a_k = \lim_{n \to \infty} S_n = S$$
If the sequence $\{S_n\}$ does not converge, the series
$$\sum_{k=1}^{\infty} a_k$$
diverges.

■ *What this says*: An infinite series converges if its sequence of partial sums converges and diverges otherwise. If it converges, its sum is defined to be the limit of the sequence of partial sums.

REMARK: We shall use the symbol $\displaystyle\sum_{k=1}^{\infty} a_k$ to denote the series $a_1 + a_2 + a_3 + \cdots$ regardless of whether this series converges or diverges. If the sequence of partial sums $\{S_n\}$ converges, then

$$\sum_{k=1}^{\infty} a_k = \lim_{n \to \infty} \left(\sum_{k=1}^{n} a_k \right)$$

and the symbol $\displaystyle\sum_{k=1}^{\infty} a_k$ is used to represent *both* the series and its sum.

Also, we shall consider certain series in which the starting point is not 1; for example, the series

$$\frac{1}{3} + \frac{1}{4} + \frac{1}{5} + \cdots \quad \text{can be denoted by} \quad \sum_{k=3}^{\infty} \frac{1}{k} \quad \text{or} \quad \sum_{k=2}^{\infty} \frac{1}{k+1}$$

EXAMPLE 1   Convergent series

Show that the series $\displaystyle\sum_{k=1}^{\infty} \frac{1}{2^k}$ converges.

Solution   This series has the following partial sums.

$$S_1 = \tfrac{1}{2}$$

$$S_2 = \tfrac{1}{2} + \tfrac{1}{4} = \tfrac{3}{4}$$

$$S_3 = \tfrac{1}{2} + \tfrac{1}{4} + \tfrac{1}{8} = \tfrac{7}{8}$$

$$\vdots$$

$$S_n = \tfrac{1}{2} + \tfrac{1}{4} + \cdots + \tfrac{1}{2^n}$$

The sequence of partial sums is $\tfrac{1}{2}, \tfrac{3}{4}, \tfrac{7}{8}, \tfrac{15}{16}, \tfrac{31}{32}, \tfrac{63}{64}, \tfrac{127}{128}, \ldots$, and in general,

$$S_n = 1 - \frac{1}{2^n} = \frac{2^n - 1}{2^n}$$

Because $\lim\limits_{n \to \infty} \dfrac{2^n - 1}{2^n} = \lim\limits_{n \to \infty}\left(1 - \dfrac{1}{2^n}\right) = 1$, we conclude that the series converges and its sum is 1.   ▬

EXAMPLE 2   Divergent series

Show that the series $\sum\limits_{k=1}^{\infty} (-1)^k$ diverges.

Solution   The series can be **expanded** (written out) as

$$\sum_{k=1}^{\infty} (-1)^k = -1 + 1 - 1 + 1 - 1 + 1 - \cdots$$

and we see that the nth partial sum is

$$S_n = \begin{cases} -1 & \text{if } n \text{ is odd} \\ \ \ 0 & \text{if } n \text{ is even} \end{cases}$$

Because the sequence $\{S_n\}$ has no limit, the given series must diverge.   ▬

A series is called a **telescoping series** (or collapsing series) if there is internal cancellation in the partial sums, as illustrated by the following example.

EXAMPLE 3   A telescoping series

Show that the series $\sum\limits_{k=1}^{\infty} \dfrac{1}{k^2 + k}$ converges and find its sum.

Solution   Using partial fractions we find that

$$\frac{1}{k^2 + k} = \frac{1}{k(k + 1)} = \frac{1}{k} + \frac{-1}{k + 1}$$

Thus, the nth partial sum of the given series can be represented as follows:

$$S_n = \sum_{k=1}^{n} \frac{1}{k^2 + k} = \sum_{k=1}^{n} \left[\frac{1}{k} - \frac{1}{k + 1}\right]$$

$$= \left(1 - \tfrac{1}{2}\right) + \left(\tfrac{1}{2} - \tfrac{1}{3}\right) + \left(\tfrac{1}{3} - \tfrac{1}{4}\right) + \cdots + \left(\tfrac{1}{n} - \tfrac{1}{n + 1}\right)$$

$$= 1 + \left(-\tfrac{1}{2} + \tfrac{1}{2}\right) + \left(-\tfrac{1}{3} + \tfrac{1}{3}\right) + \cdots + \left(-\tfrac{1}{n} + \tfrac{1}{n}\right) - \tfrac{1}{n + 1}$$

$$= 1 - \frac{1}{n + 1}$$

The limit of the sequence of partial sums is

$$\lim_{n \to \infty} S_n = \lim_{n \to \infty} \left[1 - \frac{1}{n+1} \right] = 1$$

Thus, the series converges, with sum $S = 1$. ▬

■ GENERAL PROPERTIES OF INFINITE SERIES

Next, we shall examine two general properties of infinite series. Here and elsewhere, *when the starting point of a series is not important, we may denote the series by writing*

$$\Sigma a_k \quad \text{instead of} \quad \sum_{k=1}^{\infty} a_k$$

THEOREM 8.6 Linearity of infinite series

If Σa_k and Σb_k are convergent series, then so is $\Sigma(ca_k + db_k)$ for constants c, d, and

$$\Sigma(ca_k + db_k) = c \, \Sigma a_k + d \, \Sigma b_k$$

Proof: Compare this with the linearity property in Theorem 4.1. In Chapter 4 the limit properties are for finite sums, and this theorem is for infinite sums. The proof of this theorem is similar to the proof of Theorem 4.1, but in this case it follows from the linearity rule for sequences (Theorem 8.1). The details are left as a problem. ■

EXAMPLE 4 Linearity used to establish convergence

Show that the series $\sum_{k=1}^{\infty} \left[\frac{4}{k^2 + k} - \frac{6}{2^k} \right]$ converges, and find its sum.

Solution Because we know that $\sum_{k=1}^{\infty} \frac{1}{k^2 + k}$ and $\sum_{k=1}^{\infty} \frac{1}{2^k}$ both converge, the linearity property allows us to write the given series as

$$4 \sum_{k=1}^{\infty} \frac{1}{k^2 + k} - 6 \sum_{k=1}^{\infty} \frac{1}{2^k}$$

We can now use Examples 1 and 3 to conclude that the series converges and that the sum is

$$4 \sum_{k=1}^{\infty} \frac{1}{k^2 + k} - 6 \sum_{k=1}^{\infty} \frac{1}{2^k} = 4(1) - 6(1) = -2$$ ▬

The linearity property also provides useful information about a series of the form $\Sigma(ca_k + db_k)$ when either Σa_k or Σb_k diverges and the other converges.

THEOREM 8.7 Divergence of the sum of a convergent and a divergent series

If either Σa_k or Σb_k diverges and the other converges, then the series $\Sigma(a_k + b_k)$ must diverge.

Proof: Suppose Σa_k diverges and Σb_k converges. Then if the series $\Sigma(a_k + b_k)$ also converges, the linearity property tells us that the series

$$\Sigma[(a_k + b_k) - b_k] = \Sigma a_k$$

must converge, contrary to hypotheses. It follows that the series $\Sigma(a_k + b_k)$ diverges. ∎

This theorem tells us, for example, that $\sum_{k=1}^{\infty}\left[\dfrac{1}{k^2 + k} + (-1)^k\right]$ must diverge because even though $\sum_{k=1}^{\infty}\dfrac{1}{k^2 + k}$ converges (Example 3), $\sum_{k=1}^{\infty}(-1)^k$ diverges (Example 2).

■ GEOMETRIC SERIES

We are still very limited in the available techniques for determining whether a given series is convergent or divergent. In fact, the purpose of a great part of this chapter is to develop efficient techniques for making this determination. We begin this quest by considering an important special kind of series.

Geometric Series

> A **geometric series** is an infinite series in which the ratio of successive terms is constant. If this constant ratio is r, then the series has the form
> $$\sum_{k=0}^{\infty} ar^k = a + ar + ar^2 + ar^3 + \cdots + ar^n + \cdots \qquad a \neq 0$$

For example, $3 + \dfrac{3}{2} + \dfrac{3}{4} + \dfrac{3}{8} + \ldots$ is a geometric series because each term is one-half the preceding term. The ratio of a geometric series may be positive or negative. For example,

$$\sum_{k=0}^{\infty}\dfrac{2}{(-3)^k} = 2 - \dfrac{2}{3} + \dfrac{2}{9} - \dfrac{2}{27} + \cdots$$

is a geometric series with $r = -\dfrac{1}{3}$. The following theorem tells us how to determine whether a given geometric series converges or diverges and, if it does converge, what its sum must be.

THEOREM 8.8   Geometric series theorem

The geometric series $\sum_{k=0}^{\infty} ar^k$ with $a \neq 0$ diverges if $|r| \geq 1$ and converges if $|r| < 1$ with sum

$$\sum_{k=0}^{\infty} ar^k = \dfrac{a}{1 - r}$$

Proof: Note that the nth partial sum of the geometric series is

$$S_n = a + ar + ar^2 + \cdots + ar^{n-1}$$
$$rS_n = ar + ar^2 + ar^3 + \cdots + ar^n \quad \textit{Multiply both sides by } r.$$
$$rS_n - S_n = (ar + ar^2 + ar^3 + \cdots + ar^n) - (a + ar + ar^2 + \cdots + ar^{n-1})$$
$$(r - 1)S_n = ar^n - a$$
$$S_n = \dfrac{a(r^n - 1)}{(r - 1)}$$

If $|r| > 1$, the sequence of partial sums $\{S_n\}$ has no limit, so the geometric series must diverge. However, if $|r| < 1$, Theorem 8.5 tells us that $r^n \to 0$ as $n \to \infty$, and we have

$$\sum_{k=0}^{\infty} ar^k = \lim_{n \to \infty} S_n = \lim_{n \to \infty} a\left(\dfrac{r^n - 1}{r - 1}\right) = \dfrac{a(0 - 1)}{r - 1} = \dfrac{a}{1 - r}$$

To complete the proof, it must be shown that the geometric series diverges when $|r| = 1$, and we leave this final step as a problem.   ■

EXAMPLE 5   Convergence or divergence for a geometric series

Determine whether each of the following geometric series converges or diverges. If the series converges, find its sum.

a. $\displaystyle\sum_{k=0}^{\infty} \tfrac{1}{7}\left(\tfrac{3}{2}\right)^k$ **b.** $\displaystyle\sum_{k=2}^{\infty} 3\left(-\tfrac{1}{5}\right)^k$

Solution   **a.** Because $r = \tfrac{3}{2}$ satisfies $|r| \geq 1$, the series diverges.

b. We have $r = -\tfrac{1}{5}$ so $|r| < 1$, and the geometric series converges. We see that the first term (for $k = 2$) is $a = 3\left(-\tfrac{1}{5}\right)^2 = \tfrac{3}{25}$, so

$$\sum_{k=2}^{\infty} 3\left(-\tfrac{1}{5}\right)^k = \frac{a}{1-r} = \frac{\tfrac{3}{25}}{1 - \left(-\tfrac{1}{5}\right)} = \frac{1}{10}$$

■

■ APPLICATIONS OF GEOMETRIC SERIES

Geometric series can be used in many different ways. Our next three examples illustrate several applications involving geometric series.

Recall that a rational number r is one that can be written as $r = p/q$ for integer p and nonzero integer q. It can be shown that any such number has a decimal representation in which a pattern of numbers repeats. For instance,

$$\frac{5}{10} = 0.5 = 0.5\overline{0} \qquad \frac{5}{11} = 0.454\,545 \ldots = 0.\overline{45}$$

where the bar indicates that the pattern repeats indefinitely. The next example shows how geometric series can be used to reverse this process by writing a given repeating decimal as a rational number.

EXAMPLE 6   Repeating decimals

Write $15.4\overline{23}$ as a rational number $\dfrac{p}{q}$.

Solution   The bar over the 23 indicates that this block of digits is to be repeated; that is $15.423232323\cdots$. The repeating part of the decimal can be written as a geometric series as follows.

$$15.4\overline{23} = 15 + \tfrac{4}{10} + \tfrac{23}{10^3} + \tfrac{23}{10^5} + \tfrac{23}{10^7} + \cdots$$

$$= 15 + \tfrac{4}{10} + \tfrac{23}{10^3}\left[1 + \tfrac{1}{10^2} + \tfrac{1}{10^4} + \cdots\right]$$

$$= 15 + \tfrac{4}{10} + \tfrac{23}{10^3}\left[\frac{1}{1 - \tfrac{1}{100}}\right] \qquad \textit{Sum of a geometric series with } a = 1 \textit{ and } r = 1/100$$

$$= 15 + \tfrac{4}{10} + \tfrac{23}{10^3}\left[\frac{100}{99}\right]$$

$$= 15 + \tfrac{4}{10} + \tfrac{23}{990}$$

$$= \frac{15{,}269}{990}$$

■

A tax rebate that returns a certain amount of money to taxpayers can result in spending that is many times this amount. This phenomenon is known in economics as the *multiplier effect*. It occurs because the portion of the rebate that is spent by one individual becomes income for one or more others who, in turn, spend some of it again, creating income for yet other individuals to spend. If the fraction of income that is saved remains constant as this process continues indefinitely, the total amount spent as a result of the rebate is the sum of a geometric series.

EXAMPLE 7   Multiplier effect in economics

Suppose that nationwide, approximately 90% of all income is spent and 10% is saved. How much additional spending will be generated by a $40 billion tax rebate if savings habits do not change?

Solution   The amount (in billions) spent by original recipients of the rebate is $0.9(40)$. This becomes new income, of which 90%, or $0.9^2(40)$, is spent. This, in turn, generates additional spending of $0.9^3(40)$, and so on. The total amount spent if this process continues indefinitely is

$$0.9(40) + 0.9^2(40) + 0.9^3(40) + \cdots = 0.9(40)[1 + 0.9 + 0.9^2 + \cdots]$$

$$= 36 \sum_{k=0}^{\infty} 0.9^k \qquad \textit{Geometric series} \\ \textit{with } a = 1, r = 0.9$$

$$= 36 \left(\frac{1}{1 - 0.9} \right)$$

$$= 360 \quad \text{(billion)}$$

EXAMPLE 8   Accumulation of medication in a body

A patient is given an injection of 10 units of a certain drug every 24 hr. The drug is eliminated exponentially so that the fraction that remains in the patient's body after t days is $f(t) = e^{-t/5}$. If the treatment is continued indefinitely, approximately how many units of the drug will eventually be in the patient's body just prior to an injection?

Solution   Of the original dose of 10 units, only $10e^{-1/5}$ are left in the patient's body after the first day (just prior to the second injection). That is

$$S_1 = 10e^{-1/5}$$

The medication in the patient's body after 2 days consists of what remains from the first two doses. Of the original dose, only $10e^{-2/5}$ units are left (because 2 days have elapsed), and of the second dose, $10e^{-1/5}$ units remain:

$$S_2 = 10e^{-1/5} + 10e^{-2/5}$$

Similarly, for n days,

$$S_n = 10e^{-1/5} + 10e^{-2/5} + \cdots + 10e^{-n/5}$$

The amount S of medication in the patient's body in the long run is the limit of S_n as $n \to \infty$. That is,

$$S = \lim_{n \to \infty} S_n$$

$$= \sum_{k=1}^{\infty} 10e^{-k/5} \qquad \textit{Geometric series with} \\ a = 10e^{-1/5} \textit{ and } r = e^{-1/5}$$

$$= \frac{10e^{-1/5}}{1 - e^{-1/5}}$$

$$\approx 45.166\,556$$

We see that about 45 units remain in the patient's body.   ▬

⊘ As a final note, remember that a sequence is a mere succession of terms, while series is a sum of such terms. Do not confuse the two concepts. For example, a sequence of terms may converge, but the series of the same terms may diverge:

$$\left\{ 1 + \frac{1}{2^n} \right\} \text{ is the } \textit{sequence } \frac{3}{2}, \frac{5}{4}, \frac{9}{8}, \frac{17}{16}, \dots, \text{ which converges to } 1.$$

$$\sum_{k=1}^{\infty} \left(1 + \frac{1}{2^k} \right) \text{ is the } \textit{series } \frac{3}{2} + \frac{5}{4} + \frac{9}{8} + \dots, \text{ which diverges.} \quad ⊘$$

PROBLEM SET 8.2

A 1. ■ **What Does This Say?** Explain the difference between sequences and series.

2. ■ **What Does This Say?** What is a geometric series? Include a derivation of the formula for the sum of a geometric series.

Determine whether the geometric series given in Problems 3–22 converges or diverges, and find the sum of each convergent series.

3. $\displaystyle\sum_{k=0}^{\infty} \left(\frac{4}{5} \right)^k$

4. $\displaystyle\sum_{k=0}^{\infty} \left(-\frac{4}{5} \right)^k$

5. $\displaystyle\sum_{k=0}^{\infty} \frac{2}{3^k}$

6. $\displaystyle\sum_{k=0}^{\infty} \frac{2}{(-3)^k}$

7. $\displaystyle\sum_{k=1}^{\infty} \left(\frac{3}{2} \right)^k$

8. $\displaystyle\sum_{k=1}^{\infty} \frac{3}{2^k}$

9. $\displaystyle\sum_{k=2}^{\infty} \frac{3}{(-4)^k}$

10. $\displaystyle\sum_{k=1}^{\infty} 5(0.9)^k$

11. $\displaystyle\sum_{k=1}^{\infty} e^{-0.2k}$

12. $\displaystyle\sum_{k=1}^{\infty} \frac{3^k}{4^{k+2}}$

13. $\displaystyle\sum_{k=2}^{\infty} \frac{(-2)^{k-1}}{3^{k+1}}$

14. $\displaystyle\sum_{k=2}^{\infty} (-1)^k \frac{2^{k+1}}{3^{k-3}}$

15. $\dfrac{1}{2} - \dfrac{1}{2^2} + \dfrac{1}{2^3} - \dfrac{1}{2^4} + \cdots$

16. $1 + \pi + \pi^2 + \pi^3 + \cdots$

17. $\dfrac{1}{4} + \left(\dfrac{1}{4} \right)^4 + \left(\dfrac{1}{4} \right)^7 + \left(\dfrac{1}{4} \right)^{10} + \cdots$

18. $\dfrac{2}{3} - \left(\dfrac{2}{3} \right)^3 + \left(\dfrac{2}{3} \right)^5 - \left(\dfrac{2}{3} \right)^7 + \cdots$

19. $2 + \sqrt{2} + 1 + \dfrac{1}{\sqrt{2}} + \dfrac{1}{2} + \cdots$

20. $3 + \sqrt{3} + 1 + \dfrac{1}{\sqrt{3}} + \dfrac{1}{3} + \cdots$

21. $(1 + \sqrt{2}) + 1 + (-1 + \sqrt{2}) + \cdots$

22. $(\sqrt{2} - 1) + 1 + (\sqrt{2} + 1) + \cdots$

In Problems 23–30, each series telescopes. In each case, express the nth partial sum S_n in terms of n and determine whether the series converges or diverges by examining $\lim\limits_{n \to \infty} S_n$.

23. $\displaystyle\sum_{k=1}^{\infty} \left[\frac{1}{k^{0.1}} - \frac{1}{(k+1)^{0.1}} \right]$

24. $\displaystyle\sum_{k=2}^{\infty} \left[\frac{1}{\sqrt{k}} - \frac{1}{\sqrt{k+1}} \right]$

25. $\displaystyle\sum_{k=0}^{\infty} \frac{1}{(k+1)(k+2)}$

26. $\displaystyle\sum_{k=0}^{\infty} \frac{1}{(k+2)(k+3)}$

27. $\displaystyle\sum_{k=1}^{\infty} \ln\left(1 + \frac{1}{k} \right)$

28. $\displaystyle\sum_{k=1}^{\infty} \frac{1}{(2k-1)(2k+1)}$

29. $\displaystyle\sum_{k=1}^{\infty} \frac{2k+1}{k^2(k+1)^2}$ *Hint*: Use partial-fraction decomposition.

30. $\displaystyle\sum_{k=1}^{\infty} \frac{\sqrt{k+1} - \sqrt{k}}{\sqrt{k^2 + k}}$ *Hint*: Note that $\sqrt{k^2 + k} = \sqrt{k}\sqrt{k+1}$.

Express each decimal given in Problems 31–34 as a common (reduced) fraction.

31. $0.\overline{01}$

32. $2.23\overline{1}$

33. $1.405\,\overline{405}$

34. $41.201\,\overline{001\,0}$

B 35. **a.** Find numbers A and B such that

$$\frac{k-1}{2^{k+1}} = \frac{Ak}{2^k} - \frac{Bk+1}{2^{k+1}}$$

b. Evaluate $\displaystyle\sum_{k=1}^{\infty} \frac{k-1}{2^{k+1}}$.

36. Evaluate $\displaystyle\sum_{k=1}^{\infty} \frac{2k-1}{3^{k+1}}$.

Hint: Follow the procedure in Problem 35.

37. Evaluate $\displaystyle\sum_{n=1}^{\infty} \frac{\ln\left(\dfrac{n^{n+1}}{(n+1)^n} \right)}{n(n+1)}$.

Hint: Use the properties of logarithms to show that the series telescopes.

38. Evaluate $\sum\limits_{n=1}^{\infty} \dfrac{n}{(n+1)!}$.   *Hint:* Express as a telescoping series.

39. Find $\sum\limits_{k=0}^{\infty} (2a_k + 2^{-k})$ given that $\sum\limits_{k=0}^{\infty} a_k = 3.57$.

40. Find $\sum\limits_{k=0}^{\infty} \dfrac{b_k - 3^{-k}}{2}$ given that $\sum\limits_{k=0}^{\infty} b_k = 0.54$.

41. Evaluate $\sum\limits_{k=0}^{\infty} \left(\dfrac{1}{2^k} + \dfrac{1}{3^k}\right)^2$.

42. Evaluate $\sum\limits_{k=0}^{\infty} \left[\left(\dfrac{2}{3}\right)^k + \left(\dfrac{3}{4}\right)^k\right]^2$.

43. Show that $\sum\limits_{k=0}^{\infty} \dfrac{1}{(a+k)(a+k+1)} = \dfrac{1}{a}$ if $a > 0$.

44. Evaluate $\sum\limits_{k=0}^{\infty} \dfrac{1}{(2+k)^2 + 2 + k}$.

45. If $\sum\limits_{k=0}^{\infty} a_k^{\,2} = \sum\limits_{k=0}^{\infty} b_k^{\,2} = 4$ and $\sum\limits_{k=0}^{\infty} a_k b_k = 3$, what is $\sum\limits_{k=0}^{\infty} (a_k - b_k)^2$?

46. A pendulum is swung through an arc of length 20 cm from a vertical position and allowed to swing free until it eventually comes to rest. Each subsequent swing of the bob of the pendulum is 90% as far as the preceding swing. How far will the bob travel before coming to rest?

47. A rotating flywheel is allowed to slow to a stop from a speed of 500 rpm. That is, it revolves 500 revolutions in the first minute, and after the first minute it rotates two-thirds as many times as in the preceding minute. How many revolutions will the flywheel make before coming to rest?

48. A ball is dropped from a height of 10 ft. Each time the ball bounces, it rises 0.6 the distance it had previously fallen. What is the total distance traveled by the ball?

49. Suppose the ball in Problem 48 is dropped from a height of h feet and each time rises 75% of the distance it had previously fallen. If it travels a total distance of 21 ft, what is h?

50. Suppose that nationwide, approximately 92% of all income is spent and 8% is saved. How much additional spending will be generated by a $50 billion dollar tax cut if savings habits do not change?

51. Suppose that a piece of machinery costing $10,000 depreciates 20% of its present value each year. That is, the first year $10,000(0.20) = $2,000 is depreciated. The second year's depreciation is $8,000(0.20) = $1,600, because the value for the second year is $10,000 - $2,000 = $8,000. If the depreciation is calculated this way indefinitely, what is the total depreciation?

52. Winnie Winner wins $100 in a pie-baking contest run by the Hi-Do Pie Co. The company gives Winnie the $100. However, the tax collector wants 20% of the $100. Winnie pays the tax. But then she realizes that she didn't really win a $100 prize and tells her story to the Hi-Do Co. The friendly Hi-Do Co. gives Winnie the $20 she paid in taxes. Unfortunately, the tax collector now wants 20% of the $20. She pays the tax again and then goes back to the Hi-Do Co. with her story. Assume that this can go on indefinitely. How much money does the Hi-Do Co. have to give Winnie so that she will really win $100? How much does she pay in taxes?

53. A patient is given an injection of 20 units of a certain drug every 24 hr. The drug is eliminated exponentially, so the fraction that remains in the patient's body after t days is $f(t) = e^{-t/2}$. If the treatment is continued indefinitely, approximately how many units of the drug will eventually be in the patient's body just prior to an injection?

54. A certain drug is injected into a body. It is known that the amount of drug in the body at the end of a given hour is $\frac{1}{4}$ the amount that was present at the end of the previous hour. One gram is injected initially, and to keep the concentration up, an additional gram is injected at the end of each subsequent hour. What is the highest possible amount of the drug that can ever be present in the body?

55. Each January 1, the administration of a certain private college adds 6 new members to its board of trustees. If the fraction of trustees who remain active for at least t years is $f(x) = e^{-0.2t}$, approximately how many active trustees will the college have on December 31, in the long run? Assume that there were 6 members on the board on January 1 of the present year.

56. How much should you invest today at an annual interest rate of 15% compounded continuously so that, starting next year, you can make annual withdrawals of $2,000 forever?

57. **Racecourse paradox** The Greek philosopher Zeno of Elea (495–435 B.C.) presented a number of paradoxes that caused a great deal of concern to the mathematicians of his period (see Section 1.1, for example). Perhaps the most famous is the *racecourse paradox*, which can be stated as follows:

A runner can never reach the end of a race: As he runs the track, he must first run $\frac{1}{2}$ the length of the track, then $\frac{1}{2}$ the remaining distance, so that at this point he has run $\frac{1}{2} + \frac{1}{4} = \frac{3}{4}$ of the length of the track, and $\frac{1}{4}$ remains to be run. After running half this distance, he finds he still has $\frac{1}{8}$ of the track to run, and so on, indefinitely.

Suppose the runner runs at a constant pace and that it takes him T minutes to run the first half of the track. Set up an infinite series that gives the *total* time required to run the track, and verify that the total time is $2T$, as intuition would lead us to expect.

58. SPY PROBLEM The spy just barely survived the gas in the Closet of Doom (Problem 46, Chapter 7 review), but in the process was rendered unconscious and taken prisoner. He is questioned every 3 hours and if he doesn't talk, a new dose of a drug is administered. His sadistic captors use the same small dose of drug each time, to prolong the spy's agony and their fun. The spy knows from previous experience with this drug that each time a dose is given it results in a concentration of 0.04% in his bloodstream and that t hours after a dose is given, the concentration in his bloodstream from that particular dose is given by $0.04e^{-0.322t}$. The spy has a high tolerance for the drug but estimates he will crack when the cumulative concentration of drug in his bloodstream is 80% of the ultimate concentration (as $n \to \infty$). How much time does he have to escape?

C 59. a. Let $\sum_{k=1}^{n} a_k = S_n$ be the nth partial sum of an infinite series. Show that $S_n - S_{n-1} = a_n$.

b. Use part **a** to find the nth term of the infinite series whose nth partial sum is

$$S_n = \frac{n}{2n + 3}$$

60. Prove that if $\Sigma a_k = A$ and $\Sigma b_k = B$, then $\Sigma(a_k + b_k) = A + B$.

61. Show that if Σa_k converges and Σb_k diverges, then $\Sigma(a_k - b_k)$ diverges. *Hint*: Note that $b_k = a_k - (a_k - b_k)$.

62. Find two divergent series Σa_k and Σb_k such that:

a. $\Sigma(a_k + b_k)$ is also divergent.

b. $\Sigma(a_k + b_k)$ is convergent.

63. Show that $\sum_{k=0}^{\infty} ar^k$ diverges if $|r| \geq 1$.

64. a. Show that $\sum_{k=1}^{n} (a_k - a_{k+2}) = (a_1 + a_2) - (a_{n+1} + a_{n+2})$.

b. Use part **a** to show that if $\lim_{k \to \infty} a_k = A$, then

$$\sum_{k=1}^{\infty} (a_k - a_{k+2}) = a_1 + a_2 - 2A$$

c. Use part **b** to evaluate

$$\sum_{k=1}^{\infty} \left[k^{1/k} - (k + 2)^{1/(k+2)} \right]$$

d. Evaluate $\sum_{k=2}^{\infty} \frac{1}{k^2 - 1}$.

65. Square $ABCD$ has sides of length 1. Square $EFGH$ is formed by connecting the midpoints of the sides of the first square, as shown in Figure 8.12. Assume that the pattern of shaded regions in the square is continued indefinitely. What is the total area of the shaded regions?

Figure 8.12 Find the area of the shaded regions.

66. Repeat Problem 65 for a square whose sides have length a.

8.3 THE INTEGRAL TEST: p-SERIES

IN THIS SECTION Divergence test; series of nonnegative numbers, integral test; p-series

In Sections 8.3–8.6, we shall develop "tests" for determining the convergence of a given series. These tests have the advantage that they do not require knowledge of an explicit formula (such as the one we found for a geometric series) for the nth partial sum S_n and the disadvantage that they usually cannot be used to find the actual sum of a convergent series.

The convergence or divergence of an infinite series is determined by the behavior of its nth partial sum S_n. In Section 8.2, we saw how algebraic methods can sometimes be used to find formulas for the nth partial sum of series. Unfortunately, it is often difficult or even impossible to find a compact formula for the nth partial sum S_n of a series, and other techniques must be used to determine convergence or divergence.

■ DIVERGENCE TEST

When investigating the infinite series Σa_k, it is easy to confuse the sequence of *general terms* $\{a_k\}$ with the sequence of *partial sums* $\{S_n\}$, where

$$S_n = \sum_{k=1}^{n} a_k$$

Because the sequence $\{a_k\}$ is usually more accessible than $\{S_n\}$, it would be convenient if the convergence of $\{S_n\}$ could be settled by examining

$$\lim_{k \to \infty} a_k$$

Even though we do not have one simple, definitive test for convergence, we do have a first test that tells us that if certain conditions are met, then the series diverges.

THEOREM 8.9   The divergence test

If the series Σa_k converges, then the sequence $\{a_n\}$ converges, and then $\lim_{k \to \infty} a_k = 0$. Thus, if $\lim_{k \to \infty} a_k \neq 0$, then the series Σa_k must diverge.

Proof: Suppose the sequence of partial sums $\{S_n\}$ converges with sum L, so that $\lim_{n \to \infty} S_n = L$. Then we also have

$$\lim_{n \to \infty} S_{n-1} = L$$

Because $S_k - S_{k-1} = a_k$, it follows that

$$\lim_{k \to \infty} a_k = \lim_{k \to \infty} (S_k - S_{k-1}) = \lim_{k \to \infty} S_k - \lim_{k \to \infty} S_{k-1} = L - L = 0 \qquad ■$$

⊘ Theorem 8.9 gives a necessary but not a sufficient condition for convergence, in the sense that clouds are necessary for rain, but clouds are not sufficient to guarantee rain. ⊘

EXAMPLE 1   Divergence test to show divergence

Show that the series $\sum_{n=0}^{\infty} \dfrac{n - 300}{4n + 750}$ diverges.

Solution   Taking the limit of the kth term as $k \to \infty$, we find

$$\lim_{k \to \infty} \frac{k - 300}{4k + 750} = \frac{1}{4}$$

Because this limit is not 0, the divergence test tells us that the series must diverge.   ▬

⊘   The divergence test is often misinterpreted as saying that Σa_k converges if $\lim_{k \to \infty} a_k = 0$, but this is not necessarily true. For example, we will show in Example 2 that the series $\Sigma \frac{1}{k}$ diverges even though $\lim_{k \to \infty} \frac{1}{k} = 0$.   ⊘

■ *What this says:* The divergence test cannot be used to show convergence. It can only tell us the series diverges if $\lim_{n \to \infty} a_n \neq 0$.

■ SERIES OF NONNEGATIVE NUMBERS; THE INTEGRAL TEST

Series whose terms are all nonnegative numbers play an important role in the general theory of infinite series and in applications. Our next goal is to develop convergence tests for nonnegative term series, and we begin by establishing the following general principle.

THEOREM 8.10   Convergence criterion for series with nonnegative terms

---

A series Σa_k with $a_k \geq 0$ for all k converges if its sequence of partial sums is bounded from above and diverges otherwise.

Proof: Suppose Σa_k is a series of nonnegative terms, and let S_n denote its nth partial sum; that is

$$S_n = \sum_{k=1}^{n} a_k = a_1 + a_2 + \cdots + a_n$$

Because $S_{n+1} = S_n + a_{n+1}$ and because $a_k \geq 0$ for all k, it follows that

$$S_{n+1} \geq S_n$$

for all n, so that $\{S_n\}$ is a nondecreasing sequence. According to the BMCT, the nondecreasing sequence $\{S_n\}$ converges if it is bounded from above and diverges otherwise. Hence, because the series Σa_k represents the limit of the sequence $\{S_n\}$, the series Σa_k converges if the sequence $\{S_n\}$ is bounded from above and diverges if it is unbounded. ■

This convergence criterion is often difficult to apply because it is not easy to determine whether or not the sequence of partial sums $\{S_n\}$ is bounded from above. Our next goal in this section and in Sections 8.4–8.6 is to examine various tests for convergence. These are procedures that allow us to determine indirectly whether a given series converges or diverges without actually having to compute the limit of the partial sums. We begin with a convergence test that relates the convergence of a series to that of an improper integral.

THEOREM 8.11   The integral test

If $a_k = f(k)$ for $k = 1, 2, \ldots$, where f is a positive, continuous, and decreasing function of x for $x \geq 1$, then

$$\sum_{k=1}^{\infty} a_k \quad \text{and} \quad \int_{1}^{\infty} f(x)\, dx$$

either both converge or both diverge.

Proof: We shall use a geometric argument to show that the sequence of partial sums $\{S_n\}$ of the series $\sum_{k=0}^{\infty} a_k$ is bounded from above if the improper integral $\int_{1}^{\infty} f(x)\, dx$ converges and that it is unbounded if the integral diverges. Accordingly, Figures 8.13a and 8.13b show the graph of a continuous decreasing function f that satisfies $f(n) = a_n$ for $n = 1, 2, 3, \ldots$. Rectangles have been constructed at unit

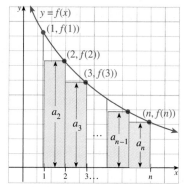

a. The kth rectangle has height
$f(k + 1) = a_{k+1}$.

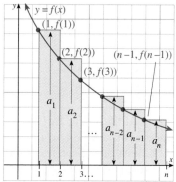

b. The kth rectangle has height
$f(k) = a_k$.

Figure 8.13 Integral test

intervals in both figures, but in Figure 8.13a the kth rectangle has height $f(k + 1) = a_{k+1}$, whereas in Figure 8.13b, the comparable rectangle has height $f(k) = a_k$. *Notice that in Figure 8.13a, the rectangles are inscribed so that*

AREA OF THE FIRST $n - 1$ RECTANGLES $<$ AREA UNDER $y = f(x)$ OVER $[1, n]$

$$a_2 + a_3 + \cdots + a_n < \int_1^n f(x)\, dx$$

$$a_1 + a_2 + a_3 + \cdots + a_n < a_1 + \int_1^n f(x)\, dx \quad \textit{Add } a_1 \textit{ to both sides.}$$

Similarly, in Figure 8.13b, the rectangles are circumscribed so that

AREA UNDER $y = f(x)$ OVER $[1, n + 1]$ $<$ AREA OF THE FIRST n RECTANGLES

$$\int_1^{n+1} f(x)\, dx < a_1 + a_2 + a_3 + \cdots + a_n$$

Let $S_n = a_1 + a_2 + a_3 + \cdots + a_n$ be the nth partial sum of the series so that

$$\int_1^{n+1} f(x)\, dx < S_n < a_1 + \int_1^n f(x)\, dx$$

Now, suppose the improper integral $\int_1^\infty f(x)\, dx$ converges and has the value I; that is, $\int_1^\infty f(x)\, dx = I$. Then

$$S_n < a_1 + \int_1^n f(x)\, dx < a_1 + \int_1^\infty f(x)\, dx = a_1 + I$$

It follows that the sequence of partial sums is bounded from above (by $a_1 + I$), and the convergence criterion for nonnegative term series tells us that the series $\sum_{k=1}^\infty a_k$ must converge.

On the other hand, if the improper integral $\int_1^\infty f(x)\, dx$ diverges, then

$$\lim_{n \to \infty} \int_1^{n+1} f(x)\, dx = \infty$$

It follows that $\lim_{n \to \infty} S_n = \infty$ also because $\int_1^{n+1} f(x)\, dx < S_n$; this means that the series must diverge. Thus, the series and the improper integral either both converge or both diverge, as claimed.   ∎

⊘   When applying the integral test, the function f need not be decreasing for all $x \geq 1$, only for all $x \geq N$ for some number N. That is, f must be decreasing in "the long run."   ⊘

An important series is $\sum_{k=1}^\infty \frac{1}{k}$, which is called the **harmonic series.** In our next example, we use the integral test to show that this series diverges.

EXAMPLE 2   Harmonic series diverges

Test the series $\sum_{k=1}^\infty \frac{1}{k}$ for convergence.

Solution   Because $f(x) = \frac{1}{x}$ is positive, continuous, and decreasing for $x \geq 1$, the conditions of the integral test are satisfied.

$$\int_1^\infty \frac{1}{x}\, dx = \lim_{b\to\infty} \int_1^b \frac{1}{x}\, dx = \lim_{b\to\infty} [\ln b - \ln 1] = \infty$$

The integral diverges, so the series diverges.

EXAMPLE 3   Integral test for convergence

Test the series $\sum_{k=1}^\infty \frac{k}{e^{k/5}}$ for convergence.

Solution   The function $f(x) = \frac{x}{e^{x/5}} = xe^{-x/5}$ is positive and continuous for all $x > 0$. We find that

$$f'(x) = x\left(-\frac{1}{5}\, e^{-x/5}\right) + e^{-x/5} = \left(1 - \frac{x}{5}\right)e^{-x/5}$$

The critical number is found when $f'(x) = 0$, so we solve

$$\left(1 - \frac{x}{5}\right)e^{-x/5} = 0$$

$$1 - \frac{x}{5} = 0 \quad \text{\textit{Set each factor equal to} 0, \textit{but note that}}$$
$$\qquad\qquad e^{-x/5} \neq 0.$$

$$x = 5$$

We see that $f'(x) < 0$ for $x > 5$, so it follows that f is decreasing for $x > 5$. Thus, the conditions for the integral test have been established, and the given series and the improper integral either both converge or both diverge. Computing the improper integral, we find

$$\int_5^\infty xe^{-x/5}\, dx = \lim_{b\to\infty} \int_5^b xe^{-x/5}\, dx$$

$$\text{Let } u = x \qquad dv = e^{-x/5}dx$$
$$\qquad du = dx \qquad v = -5e^{-x/5}$$

$$= \lim_{b\to\infty}\left[-5xe^{-x/5}\Big|_5^b - \int_5^b (-5e^{-x/5})\, dx\right]$$

$$= \lim_{b\to\infty}\left[-5xe^{-x/5} - 25e^{-x/5}\right]\Big|_5^b$$

$$= \lim_{b\to\infty}\left[-5be^{-b/5} - 25e^{-b/5} + 25e^{-1} + 25e^{-1}\right]$$

$$= -5\lim_{b\to\infty}\frac{b+5}{e^{b/5}} + \lim_{b\to\infty} 50e^{-1}$$

$$= -5\lim_{b\to\infty}\frac{1}{\left(\frac{1}{5}\right)e^{b/5}} + 50e^{-1} \quad \textit{l'Hôpital's rule} \lim_{b\to\infty}\frac{5}{e^{b/5}} = 0$$

$$= 50e^{-1}$$

Thus, the improper integral converges, which in turn assures the convergence of the given series.

■ *p*-SERIES

The harmonic series $\sum\frac{1}{k}$ is a special case of a more general series form called a *p*-series.

Computational Window

If you have a graphing calculator, you can easily see that the conditions for the integral test are met.

Y₁◘X/e^(X/5)

Xmin=0   Ymin=0
Xmax=10   Ymax=3
Xscl=1   Yscl=1

Although this graph suggests that the conditions for the integral test are met, you still must use calculus to evaluate the integral.

⊘ Note that the series converges because the integral converges, but this does not mean that the series $\sum_{k=1}^\infty \frac{k}{e^{k/5}}$ equals $50e^{-1}$. ⊘

p-Series

A series of the form

$$\sum_{k=1}^{\infty} \frac{1}{k^p} = \frac{1}{1^p} + \frac{1}{2^p} + \frac{1}{3^p} + \cdots$$

where p is a positive constant is called a **p-series**. If $p = 1$, then the p-series is the *harmonic series*.

The convergence of the p-series is dependent on the value of p. Remember, we have already seen (in Example 2) that the series diverges if $p = 1$.

THEOREM 8.12   The p-series test

The p-series $\displaystyle\sum_{k=1}^{\infty} \frac{1}{k^p}$ converges if $p > 1$ and diverges if $p \leq 1$.

Proof: We leave it for the reader to verify that $f(x) = \dfrac{1}{x^p}$ is continuous, positive, and decreasing for $x \geq 1$ and $p > 1$. We know the harmonic series ($p = 1$) diverges, and for $p > 0$, $p \neq 1$, we have

$$\int_1^{\infty} \frac{dx}{x^p} = \lim_{b \to \infty} \int_1^b x^{-p}\, dx = \lim_{b \to \infty} \frac{b^{1-p} - 1}{1 - p} = \begin{cases} \dfrac{1}{p-1} & \text{if } p > 1 \\ \infty & \text{if } 0 < p < 1 \end{cases}$$

That is, this improper integral converges if $p > 1$ and diverges if $0 < p < 1$. For $p = 0$, the series becomes

$$\sum_{k=1}^{\infty} \frac{1}{k^0} = \frac{1}{1} + \frac{1}{1} + \frac{1}{1} + \cdots$$

and if $p < 0$, we have $\displaystyle\lim_{k \to \infty} \frac{1}{k^p} = \infty$, so the series diverges by the divergence test (Theorem 8.9). Thus, a p-series converges only when $p > 1$. ∎

■ **What this says:** The statement that the series converges if $p > 1$ and diverges if $p \leq 1$ is clear enough. A more subtle question, however, is why? The curves $y = 1/x^p$ ($p > 0$) all decrease as x increases. This also seems clear enough. The answer we seek, namely *why*, lies in looking at the *rate* of decrease for the curves $y = 1/x^p$. If $p > 1$, the curve decreases fast enough that the shaded area in Figure 8.14a is bounded by a fixed number, no matter how large the value b. On the other hand, if the curve decreases slowly enough, then the shaded area in Figure 8.14b increases without bound as $b \to \infty$.

Figure 8.14 Graphs for the p-series test

EXAMPLE 4   *p*-series test

Test each of the following series for convergence.

a. $\sum_{k=1}^{\infty} \frac{1}{\sqrt{k^3}}$ **b.** $\sum_{k=1}^{\infty} \left(\frac{1}{e^k} - \frac{1}{\sqrt{k}} \right)$

Solution   **a.** Here $\sqrt{k^3} = k^{3/2}$, so $p = \frac{3}{2} > 1$ and the series converges.

b. $\sum_{k=1}^{\infty} \left(\frac{1}{e^k} - \frac{1}{\sqrt{k}} \right)$; We note that

$\sum_{k=1}^{\infty} \frac{1}{e^k}$ converges, because it is geometric with $|r| < \left| \frac{1}{e} \right| < 1$,

and $\sum_{k=1}^{\infty} \frac{1}{\sqrt{k}}$ diverges, because it is a *p*-series with $p = \frac{1}{2} < 1$.

Because one series in the difference converges and the other diverges, the given series must diverge (Theorem 8.7).   ▬

PROBLEM SET 8.3

Ⓐ   **1.** ■ **What Does This Say?**   What is a *p*-series?
2. ■ **What Does This Say?**   What is the integral test?

For the p-series given in Problems 3–6, specify the value of p and tell whether the series converges or diverges.

3. $\sum_{k=1}^{\infty} \frac{1}{k^3}$ **4.** $\sum_{k=1}^{\infty} \frac{100}{\sqrt{k}}$ **5.** $\sum_{k=1}^{\infty} \frac{1}{\sqrt[3]{k}}$ **6.** $\sum_{k=1}^{\infty} \frac{1}{2k\sqrt{k}}$

Test the series in Problems 7–28 for convergence.

7. $\sum_{k=1}^{\infty} \frac{\ln k}{k^2}$ **8.** $\sum_{k=1}^{\infty} \frac{\ln k}{k}$ **9.** $\sum_{k=1}^{\infty} \left(2 + \frac{3}{k} \right)^k$

10. $\sum_{k=1}^{\infty} \left(1 + \frac{2}{k} \right)^k$ **11.** $\sum_{k=1}^{\infty} \frac{1}{k^4}$ **12.** $\sum_{k=1}^{\infty} \frac{5}{\sqrt{k}}$

13. $\sum_{k=1}^{\infty} k^{-3/4}$ **14.** $\sum_{k=1}^{\infty} k^{-4/3}$ **15.** $\sum_{k=1}^{\infty} \frac{k}{k^2 + 1}$

16. $\sum_{k=1}^{\infty} \frac{k^2}{(k^3 + 2)^2}$ **17.** $\sum_{k=1}^{\infty} \frac{k^2}{\sqrt{k^3 + 2}}$ **18.** $\sum_{k=1}^{\infty} ke^{-k^2}$

19. $\sum_{k=1}^{\infty} \frac{1}{(0.25)^k}$ **20.** $\sum_{k=1}^{\infty} \frac{1}{4^k}$ **21.** $\sum_{k=2}^{\infty} \frac{1}{k(\ln k)^2}$

22. $\sum_{k=2}^{\infty} \frac{1}{k\sqrt{\ln k}}$ **23.** $\sum_{k=1}^{\infty} \frac{k}{e^k}$ **24.** $\sum_{k=1}^{\infty} \frac{k^2}{e^k}$

25. $\sum_{k=1}^{\infty} \frac{\tan^{-1} k}{1 + k^2}$ **26.** $\sum_{k=1}^{\infty} \cot^{-1} k$ **27.** $\sum_{k=1}^{\infty} \frac{1}{e^k + e^{-k}}$

28. $\sum_{k=1}^{\infty} 3e^{-2k}$

Use the divergence test and the p-series test to determine which of the series in Problems 29–40 converge. Write "inconclusive" if there is not yet enough information to settle convergence.

29. $\sum_{k=1}^{\infty} \frac{k}{k + 1}$ **30.** $\sum_{k=1}^{\infty} \frac{k^2 + 1}{k + 5}$ **31.** $\sum_{k=1}^{\infty} \frac{k^2 + 1}{k^3}$

32. $\sum_{k=1}^{\infty} \frac{2k^4 + 3}{k^5}$ **33.** $\sum_{k=1}^{\infty} \frac{1}{k^2}$ **34.** $\sum_{k=1}^{\infty} \frac{-k^5 + k^2 + 1}{k^5 + 2}$

35. $\sum_{n=1}^{\infty} \frac{n^{\sqrt{3}} + 1}{n^{2.7321}}$ **36.** $\sum_{n=1}^{\infty} \frac{n^{\sqrt{5}} + 1}{n^{2.236}}$

37. $\sum_{k=1}^{\infty} \left[\frac{1}{k} + \frac{k + 1}{k + 2} \right]$ **38.** $\sum_{k=1}^{\infty} \left[\frac{1}{2k} + \left(\frac{3}{2} \right)^k \right]$

39. $\sum_{k=1}^{\infty} \left[\frac{1}{2^k} + \frac{2k + 3}{3k + 4} \right]$ **40.** $\sum_{k=1}^{\infty} \left[\frac{1}{2^k} - \frac{1}{k} \right]$

Show that the function f determined by the nth term of each series given in Problems 41–46 satisfies the hypotheses of the integral test. Then use the integral test to determine whether the series converges or diverges.

41. $\sum_{k=1}^{\infty} \frac{1}{(2 + 3k)^2}$ **42.** $\sum_{k=1}^{\infty} (2 + k)^{-3/2}$ **43.** $\sum_{k=2}^{\infty} \frac{\ln k}{k}$

44. $\sum_{k=2}^{\infty} \frac{1}{k(\ln k)^2}$ **45.** $\sum_{k=1}^{\infty} \frac{(\tan^{-1} k)^2}{1 + k^2}$ **46.** $\sum_{k=1}^{\infty} ke^{-k^2}$

Ⓑ   *Find all values of p for which the series given in Problems 47–52 converges.*

47. $\sum_{k=2}^{\infty} \frac{k}{(k^2 - 1)^p}$ **48.** $\sum_{k=1}^{\infty} \frac{k^2}{(k^2 + 4)^p}$

49. $\sum_{k=2}^{\infty} \frac{1}{k^p \ln k}$ **50.** $\sum_{k=2}^{\infty} \frac{\ln k}{k^p}$

51. $\sum_{k=3}^{\infty} \frac{1}{k \ln k [\ln(\ln k)]^p}$ **52.** $\sum_{k=2}^{\infty} \frac{1}{k(\ln k)^p}$

In these problems we explore some of the numerical implications of the integral test for series of the form

$$\sum_{k=1}^{\infty} \frac{1}{k^p}$$

53. **a.** Argue that the "tail" of the series (the error after taking N terms) is bound by

$$\sum_{k=N+1}^{\infty} \frac{1}{k^p} \leq \int_{N}^{\infty} \frac{dx}{x^p}$$

b. Suppose you want to approximate the sum with $p = 2$ by the partial sum S_N, so that the error is no bigger than 0.01. Use part **a** to decide how many terms are needed; that is, find N.

c. It can be shown that

$$\sum_{k=1}^{\infty} \frac{1}{k^2} = \frac{\pi^2}{6}$$

Using the N found in part **b**, compute S_N and compare with this answer. How good was your estimate of N in part **b**?

54. It is a bit surprising that sums $\sum_{k=1}^{\infty} \frac{1}{k^p}$ can be computed

exactly if p is an even integer. On the other hand, this sum is unknown for $p = 3$.

a. Use the work of Problem 53a to find N sufficient to give an approximation to the sum with $p = 3$ with an error no greater than 0.0005.

b. Since we do not have an exact answer to compare with, the following idea is often used. Compute S_N for your N found in part **a**; then compute S_{2N}. Compare the results and comment on the confidence you have in your work. Was the calculation of S_{2N} necessary to give you this confidence?

Ⓒ 55. THINK TANK PROBLEM   Find two sequences $\{a_k\}$ and $\{b_k\}$ for which $\lim_{k \to \infty} a_k = 0$, $\lim_{k \to \infty} b_k = 0$, $\Sigma a_k b_k$ converges, and Σa_k converges but Σb_k diverges.

56. THINK TANK PROBLEM   Find two sequences $\{a_k\}$ and $\{b_k\}$ for which $\lim_{k \to \infty} a_k = 0$, $\lim_{k \to \infty} b_k = 0$, $\Sigma a_k b_k$ converges, and Σa_k and Σb_k both diverge.

57. Show that if the series $\sum_{k=1}^{\infty} a_k$ converges, then

$$\int_{1}^{\infty} f(x) \, dx \leq \sum_{k=1}^{\infty} a_k \leq a_1 + \int_{0}^{\infty} f(x) \, dx$$

8.4   COMPARISON TESTS

IN THIS SECTION   Direct comparison test, limit comparison tests

Often a given series will have the same general appearance as another series whose convergence properties are known. In such cases, it is convenient to use the properties of the known series to determine those of the given series. The goal of this section is to examine three comparison tests for making such determinations.

■ DIRECT COMPARISON TEST

THEOREM 8.13   Direct comparison test

Let $0 \leq a_k \leq c_k$ for all $k \geq N$ for some N.

If $\sum_{k=1}^{\infty} c_k$ converges, then $\sum_{k=1}^{\infty} a_k$ also converges.

Let $0 \leq d_k \leq a_k$ for all k.

If $\sum_{k=1}^{\infty} d_k$ diverges, then $\sum_{k=1}^{\infty} a_k$ also diverges.

Proof: Suppose Σa_k is a given nonnegative term series that is **dominated by** a convergent series Σc_k in the sense that for sufficiently large k, $0 \leq a_k \leq c_k$ for all k. Then, because the series Σc_k converges, its sequence of partial sums is bounded from above (say, by M), and we have

$$\sum_{k=1}^{n} a_k \leq \sum_{k=1}^{n} c_k < M \qquad \text{for all } n$$

Thus, the sequence of partial sums of the dominated series Σa_k is also bounded from above by M, and it, too, must converge.

On the other hand, suppose the given series Σa_k **dominates** a divergent series Σd_k so that $0 \le d_k \le a_k$. Then because the sequence of partial sums of Σd_k is unbounded, the same must be true for the partial sums of the dominating series Σa_k, and Σa_k must also diverge.   ■

> ■ *What this says*: Let Σa_k and Σd_k be series with positive terms. The series Σa_k *converges* if it is "smaller" than (dominated by) a known convergent series Σc_k and *diverges* if it is "larger" than (dominates) a known divergent series Σd_k. That is, "smaller than small is small," and "bigger than big is big."

EXAMPLE 1   Convergence using the direct comparison test

Test the series $\displaystyle\sum_{k=1}^{\infty} \frac{1}{3^k + 1}$ for convergence.

Solution   For $k \ge 0$, we have $3^k + 1 > 3^k > 0$, and $0 < \dfrac{1}{3^k + 1} < \dfrac{1}{3^k}$. Thus, the given series is *dominated by* the convergent geometric series $\displaystyle\sum_{k=1}^{\infty} \frac{1}{3^k}$ (convergent because $r = \frac{1}{3}$). Direct comparison test tells us the given series must converge. ▬

EXAMPLE 2   Divergence using the direct comparison test

Test the series $\displaystyle\sum_{k=1}^{\infty} \frac{1}{\sqrt{k} - 5}$ for convergence.

Solution   For $k > 25$, we have $\dfrac{1}{\sqrt{k} - 5} > \dfrac{1}{\sqrt{k}} > 0$, so the given series *dominates* the divergent p-series $\displaystyle\sum_{k=1}^{\infty} \frac{1}{k^{1/2}}$ (divergent because $p = \frac{1}{2} < 1$). The direct comparison test tells us the given series must diverge. ▬

Computational Window

It is sometimes possible to program your calculator or computer to give the partial sums of the given series. If the series does not converge or diverge too slowly, you may be able to come to a conclusion about the series convergence or divergence. However, you must keep in mind that such conclusions are fallible. Consider the partial sums for Examples 1 and 2.

Example 1: $\displaystyle\sum_{k=1}^{\infty} \frac{1}{3^k + 1}$

N	F(1) + ... + F(N)
1	.25
2	.35
3	.3857143
4	.3979094
5	.4020078
6	.4033776
7	.4038347
8	.4039871
9	.4040379
10	.4040548
11	.4040605
12	.4040623
13	.404063
14	.4040632
15	.4040632

The partial sums seem to converge in Example 1.

Example 2: $\displaystyle\sum_{k=1}^{\infty} \frac{1}{\sqrt{k} - 5}$

N	F(1) + ... + F(N)
1	−.25
2	−.5288789
3	−.8348812
4	−1.168214
5	−1.530018
6	−1.922096
7	−2.34686
8	−2.807356
9	−3.307356
10	−3.851508
100	20.10886
200	34.38251 ←
1018	80.66898
10018	229.6481

Also, notice how you can be misled by a computer. The series in Example 2 does not exist when $k = 25$, so we cannot sum beyond $k = 25$.

The partial sums do not seem to converge in Example 2.

EXAMPLE 3 Direct comparison test

Test the series $\sum\limits_{k=1}^{\infty} \frac{1}{k!}$ for convergence.

Solution We shall compare the given series with a geometric series. Specifically, note that if $k \geq 2$, then $1/k! > 0$ and

$$k! = k(k-1)(k-2) \cdots 3 \cdot 2 \cdot 1 \geq \underbrace{2 \cdot 2 \cdot 2 \cdots 2 \cdot 2}_{k-1 \text{ terms}} \cdot 1 = 2^{k-1}$$

Therefore, we have $0 < \frac{1}{k!} \leq \frac{1}{2^{k-1}}$, and because the given series is *dominated by* the convergent geometric series $\sum\limits_{k=1}^{\infty} \frac{1}{2^{k-1}}$ $\left(\text{with } r = \frac{1}{2}\right)$, it must also converge. ▬

■ LIMIT COMPARISON TEST

It is not always easy or even possible to make a suitable direct comparison between two similar series. For example, we would expect the series $\Sigma 1/(2^k - 5)$ to converge because it is so much like the convergent geometric series $\Sigma 1/2^k$. To compare the series, we must first note that $\frac{1}{2^k - 5}$ is negative for $k = 1$ and $k = 2$ and positive for $k \geq 3$. Thus, if $k \geq 3$,

$$0 \leq \frac{1}{2^k} < \frac{1}{2^k - 5}$$

That is, $\Sigma 1/(2^k - 5)$ *dominates* the convergent series $\Sigma 1/2^k$, which means the direct comparison test cannot be used to determine the convergence of $\Sigma 1/(2^k - 5)$ by comparing with $\Sigma 1/2^k$. In such situations the following test is often useful.

THEOREM 8.14 Limit comparison test

Suppose $a_k > 0$ and $b_k > 0$ for all sufficiently large k and that

$$\lim_{k \to \infty} \frac{a_k}{b_k} = L$$

where L is finite and positive ($0 < L < \infty$). Then

Σa_k and Σb_k either both converge or both diverge.

Proof: The proof of this theorem is given in Appendix B. ■

■ *What this says*: We have the following procedure for testing the convergence of Σa_k.

Step 1: Find a series Σb_k whose convergence properties are known and whose general term b_k is "essentially the same" as a_k.

Step 2: Verify that $\lim\limits_{k \to \infty} \frac{a_k}{b_k}$ exists and is positive.

Step 3: Determine whether Σb_k converges or diverges. Then the limit comparison test tells us that Σa_k does the same.

EXAMPLE 4   Convergence using the limit comparison test

Test the series $\sum\limits_{k=1}^{\infty} \dfrac{1}{2^k - 5}$ for convergence.

Solution   Because the given series has the same general appearance as the convergent geometric series $\Sigma 1/2^k$, compute the limit

$$\lim_{k \to \infty} \frac{\dfrac{1}{2^k - 5}}{\dfrac{1}{2^k}} = \lim_{k \to \infty} \frac{2^k}{2^k - 5} = 1$$

This limit is finite and positive, so the limit comparison test tells us that the given series will have the same convergence properties as $\Sigma 1/2^k$. Thus, the given series converges.   ▬

EXAMPLE 5   Divergence using the limit comparison test

Test the series $\sum\limits_{k=1}^{\infty} \dfrac{3k + 2}{\sqrt{k}(3k - 5)}$ for convergence.

Solution   For large values of k, the general term of the given series

$$a_k = \frac{3k + 2}{\sqrt{k}(3k - 5)}$$

seems to be similar to

$$b_k = \frac{3k}{\sqrt{k}(3k)} = \frac{1}{\sqrt{k}}$$

To apply the limit comparison test, we compute the limit

$$\lim_{k \to \infty} \frac{a_k}{b_k} = \lim_{k \to \infty} \frac{\dfrac{3k + 2}{\sqrt{k}(3k - 5)}}{\dfrac{1}{\sqrt{k}}} = \lim_{k \to \infty} \frac{3k + 2}{3k - 5} = 1$$

Because the limit is finite and positive, it follows that the given series behaves like the series $\Sigma 1/\sqrt{k}$, which is a divergent p-series $\left(p = \frac{1}{2}\right)$. We conclude that the given series diverges.   ▬

EXAMPLE 6   Limit comparison test

Test the series $\sum\limits_{k=1}^{\infty} \dfrac{7k + 100}{e^{k/5} - 70}$ for convergence.

Solution   For large k,

$$a_k = \frac{7k + 100}{e^{k/5} - 70} \quad \text{seems to behave like} \quad b_k = \frac{k}{e^{k/5}}$$

and indeed, we find that

$$\lim_{k \to \infty} \frac{\dfrac{7k + 100}{e^{k/5} - 70}}{\dfrac{k}{e^{k/5}}} = \lim_{k \to \infty} \frac{e^{k/5}(7k + 100)}{k(e^{k/5} - 70)} = 7$$

In Example 3, Section 8.3, we showed that the series $\Sigma k/e^{k/5}$ converges, and therefore the limit comparison test tells us that the given series also converges. ▬

Occasionally, two series Σa_k and Σb_k appear to have similar convergence properties, but it turns out that

$$\lim_{k \to \infty} \frac{a_k}{b_k}$$

is either 0 or ∞, and the limit comparison test therefore does not apply. In such cases, it is often useful to have the following generalization of the limit comparison test.

THEOREM 8.15   The zero-infinity limit comparison test

Suppose $a_k > 0$ and $b_k > 0$ for all sufficiently large k. Then,

If $\lim\limits_{k \to \infty} \dfrac{a_k}{b_k} = 0$ and Σb_k converges, the series Σa_k converges.

If $\lim\limits_{k \to \infty} \dfrac{a_k}{b_k} = \infty$ and Σb_k diverges, the series Σa_k diverges.

Proof: The first part of the proof is outlined in Problem 62; the second part follows similarly. ∎

EXAMPLE 7   Convergence of the log-power quotient series

Show that the series $\displaystyle\sum_{k=1}^{\infty} \frac{\ln k}{k^q}$ converges if $q > 1$ and diverges if $q \le 1$. We call this the **log-power quotient series.**

Solution We will carry out this proof in three parts:

Case I: $(q > 1)$
   Let p be a number that satisfies $q > p > 1$, and let

$$a_k = \frac{\ln k}{k^q} \quad \text{and} \quad b_k = \frac{1}{k^p}$$

Then

$$\lim_{k \to \infty} \frac{a_k}{b_k} = \lim_{k \to \infty} \frac{\dfrac{\ln k}{k^q}}{\dfrac{1}{k^p}}$$

$$= \lim_{k \to \infty} \frac{\ln k}{k^{q-p}} \qquad \textit{This is the indeterminate form} \\ \textit{∞/∞ because $q - p > 0$.}$$

$$= \lim_{k \to \infty} \frac{\dfrac{1}{k}}{(q - p)k^{q-p-1}} \qquad \textit{l'Hôpital's rule}$$

$$= \lim_{k \to \infty} \frac{1}{(q - p)k^{q-p}} = 0 \qquad \textit{Because $q - p > 0$}$$

Because $\Sigma 1/k^p$ converges (p-series with $p > 1$), the series converges by the zero-infinity comparison test.

Case II: $(q < 1)$

Now, let p satisfy $q < p < 1$. Then with a_k and b_k defined as in case I, we have

$$\lim_{k\to\infty}\frac{a_k}{b_k} = \lim_{k\to\infty}\frac{\ln k}{k^{q-p}} = \lim_{k\to\infty}[(\ln k)k^{p-q}] = \infty \qquad \textit{Because } p - p > 0$$

Because $\sum_{k=1}^{\infty} b_k = \sum_{k=1}^{\infty}\frac{1}{k^p}$ diverges (we know $p < 1$), it follows from the zero-infinity limit comparison test that $\sum_{k=1}^{\infty}\frac{\ln k}{k^q}$ diverges when $q < 1$.

Case III: $(q = 1)$

Here, the series is $\sum_{k=1}^{\infty}\frac{\ln k}{k}$, which diverges by the integral test:

$$\int_1^{\infty}\frac{\ln x}{x}\,dx = \lim_{b\to\infty}\left[\frac{\ln^2 x}{2}\right]\Big|_1^b = \infty$$

Let $u = \ln x$;
$du = \frac{1}{x}\,dx.$

PROBLEM SET 8.4

A *The most common series used for comparison are given in Problems 1 and 2. Tell when each converges and when it diverges.*

1. geometric series: $\sum_{k=0}^{\infty} r^k$

2. p-series: $\sum_{k=1}^{\infty}\frac{1}{k^p}$

Each series in Problems 3–12 can be compared to the geometric series, or p-series given in Problems 1–2. State which, and then determine whether it converges or diverges.

3. $\sum_{k=1}^{\infty}\cos\frac{\pi}{6}$ **4.** $\sum_{k=0}^{\infty} 0.5^k$

5. $\sum_{k=0}^{\infty} 1.5^k$ **6.** $\sum_{k=0}^{\infty} 2^{k/2}$

7. $\sum_{k=1}^{\infty}\frac{1}{k}$ **8.** $\sum_{k=1}^{\infty}\frac{1}{k^{0.5}}$

9. $\sum_{k=1}^{\infty}\frac{1}{k^{3/2}}$ **10.** $\sum_{k=1}^{\infty}\sqrt{\frac{2}{k}}$

11. $\sum_{k=0}^{\infty} 1$ **12.** $\sum_{k=1}^{\infty} e^k$

Test the series in Problems 13–44 for convergence.

13. $\sum_{k=1}^{\infty}\frac{1}{k^2+k}$ **14.** $\sum_{k=1}^{\infty}\frac{1}{k^2+3k+2}$

15. $\sum_{k=1}^{\infty}\frac{1}{\sqrt{k}}$ **16.** $\sum_{k=1}^{\infty}\frac{1}{k\sqrt{k}}$

17. $\sum_{k=1}^{\infty}\frac{1}{\sqrt{2k+3}}$ **18.** $\sum_{k=1}^{\infty}\frac{1}{\sqrt{k(k+1)}}$

19. $\sum_{k=1}^{\infty}\frac{1}{\sqrt{k^3+2}}$ **20.** $\sum_{k=1}^{\infty}\frac{1}{\sqrt{k^2+1}}$

21. $\sum_{k=1}^{\infty}\frac{2k^2}{k^4-4}$ **22.** $\sum_{k=1}^{\infty}\frac{k+1}{k^2+1}$

23. $\sum_{k=1}^{\infty}\frac{(k+2)(k+3)}{k^{7/2}}$ **24.** $\sum_{k=1}^{\infty}\frac{(k+1)^3}{k^{9/2}}$

25. $\sum_{k=1}^{\infty}\frac{2k+3}{k^2+3k+2}$ **26.** $\sum_{k=1}^{\infty}\frac{3k^2+2}{k^2+3k+2}$

27. $\sum_{k=1}^{\infty}\frac{k}{(k+2)2^k}$ **28.** $\sum_{k=1}^{\infty}\frac{5}{4^k+3}$

29. $\sum_{k=1}^{\infty}\frac{1}{k(k+2)}$ **30.** $\sum_{k=1}^{\infty}\frac{1}{(k+2)(k+3)}$

31. $\sum_{k=1}^{\infty}\frac{1}{\sqrt{k}\,2^k}$ **32.** $\sum_{k=1}^{\infty}\frac{1,000}{\sqrt{k}3^k}$

33. $\sum_{k=1}^{\infty}\frac{|\sin(k!)|}{k^2}$ **34.** $\sum_{k=1}^{\infty}\frac{|\cos k^3|}{\sqrt{k}}$

35. $\sum_{k=1}^{\infty}\frac{2k^3+k+1}{k^3+k^2+1}$ **36.** $\sum_{k=1}^{\infty}\frac{6k^3-k-4}{k^3-k^2-3}$

37. $\sum_{k=1}^{\infty}\frac{k}{4k^3-5}$ **38.** $\sum_{k=1}^{\infty}\frac{\ln k}{\sqrt{2k+3}}$

39. $\sum_{k=1}^{\infty}\frac{k^2+1}{(k^2+2)k^2}$ **40.** $\sum_{k=1}^{\infty}\sin\frac{1}{k}$

41. $\sum_{k=1}^{\infty}\frac{6k^2+2k+1}{k^{1.1}(4k^2+k+4)}$ **42.** $\sum_{k=1}^{\infty}\frac{6k^2+2k+1}{k^{0.9}(4k^2+k+4)}$

43. $\sum_{k=1}^{\infty} \frac{\sqrt[6]{k}}{\sqrt[4]{k^3 + 2\sqrt[8]{k}}}$

44. $\sum_{k=1}^{\infty} \frac{\sqrt{k}}{\sqrt[3]{k^3 + 1}\sqrt[6]{k^5}}$

Ⓑ *Test the series given in Problems 45–52 for convergence.*

45. $\sum_{k=1}^{\infty} \frac{1}{k^3 + 4}$

46. $\sum_{k=1}^{\infty} \frac{\ln k}{k - 1}$

47. $\sum_{k=1}^{\infty} \frac{\ln(k + 1)}{(k + 1)^3}$

48. $\sum_{k=1}^{\infty} \frac{\ln k}{k^2}$

49. $\sum_{k=2}^{\infty} \frac{1}{(k + 3)(\ln k)^{1.1}}$

50. $\sum_{k=2}^{\infty} \frac{1}{(k + 3)(\ln k)^{0.9}}$

51. $\sum_{k=1}^{\infty} k^{(1 - k)/k}$

52. $\sum_{k=1}^{\infty} k^{(1 + k)/k}$

53. Show that the series

$$\sum_{k=1}^{\infty} \frac{k + 3}{(k + 3)!} = \frac{4}{4!} + \frac{5}{5!} + \frac{6}{6!} + \cdots$$

converges by using the limit comparison test.

54. Show that the series

$$1 + \frac{1}{1 \cdot 3} + \frac{1}{1 \cdot 3 \cdot 5} + \frac{1}{1 \cdot 3 \cdot 5 \cdot 7} + \cdots + \frac{1}{(2k + 1)!}$$

converges. *Hint*: Compare with the convergent series $\Sigma 1/k!$.

55. Use a comparison test to show that

$$\sum_{k=2}^{\infty} \frac{1}{(\ln k)^{\ln k}}$$

converges. *Hint*: Use the fact that $\ln k > e^2$ for sufficiently large k.

56. For what values of p and q does the series

$$\sum_{k=2}^{\infty} \frac{(\ln k)^p}{k^q}$$

converge?

Ⓒ 57. a. Let $\{a_n\}$ be a positive sequence such that

$$\lim_{k \to \infty} k^p a_k$$

exists. Use the limit comparison test to show that Σa_k converges if $p > 1$.

b. Show that Σe^{-k^2} converges. *Hint*: Show that $\lim_{k \to \infty} k^2 e^{-k^2}$ exists and use part **a**.

58. Let Σa_k be a series of positive terms and let $\{b_n\}$ be a sequence of positive numbers that converge to a positive number. Show that Σa_k converges if and only if $\Sigma a_k b_k$ converges. *Hint*: Use the limit comparison test.

59. Suppose $0 \leq a_k \leq A$ and $b_k \geq k^2$ for some number A. Show that $\Sigma \frac{a_k}{b_k}$ converges.

60. Suppose $a_k > 0$ for all k and that Σa_k converges. Show that $\Sigma \frac{1}{a_k}$ diverges.

61. Suppose $0 < a_k < 1$ for every k, and suppose that Σa_k converges. Use a comparison test to show that Σa_k^2 converges.

62. Show that if $a_k > 0$, and $b_k > 0$, and

$$\lim_{k \to \infty} \frac{a_k}{b_k} = 0$$

then Σa_k converges whenever Σb_k converges. *Hint*: Show that for any $\varepsilon > 0$ there is an integer N for which

$$\left| \frac{a_k}{b_k} - 0 \right| = \frac{a_k}{b_k} < \varepsilon \quad \text{if } k \geq N$$

Then show that $a_k < \varepsilon b_k$ and complete the proof using the limit comparison test.

8.5 THE RATIO TEST AND THE ROOT TEST

IN THIS SECTION Ratio test, root test, summary of convergence tests for positive-term and nonnegative-term series

Comparison tests can be applied to a given series Σa_k only if Σa_k strongly resembles a "known" series Σb_k. Otherwise it is usually necessary to apply a convergence test that uses only the properties of Σa_k itself. We have already seen how the divergence test and the integral test can be used for this purpose, and in this section we shall develop two additional tests, the *ratio test* and the *root test*.

■ RATIO TEST

Intuitively, a series of positive terms Σa_k converges if and only if the sequence $\{a_k\}$ decreases rapidly toward 0. One way to measure the rate at which the sequence $\{a_k\}$ is decreasing is to examine the ratio a_{k+1}/a_k as k grows large. This approach leads to the following result.

THEOREM 8.16   The ratio test

Given the series Σa_k with $a_k > 0$, suppose that

$$\lim_{k \to \infty} \frac{a_{k+1}}{a_k} = L$$

The **ratio test** states the following:

If $L < 1$, then Σa_k converges.
If $L > 1$ or if L is infinite, then Σa_k diverges.
If $L = 1$, the test is inconclusive.

Proof: In a sense, the ratio test is a limit comparison test in which Σa_k is compared to itself. We shall use the direct comparison test to show that Σa_k converges if $L < 1$. Choose R such that $0 < L < R < 1$. By the definition of the limit of a sequence, there exists some $N > 0$ such that

$$\frac{a_{k+1}}{a_k} < L < R \qquad \text{for all } k > N$$

Therefore, for $k \geq N$,

$$a_{N+1} < a_N R$$
$$a_{N+2} < a_{N+1} R < a_N R^2$$
$$a_{N+3} < a_{N+2} R < a_{N+1} R^2 < a_N R^3$$
$$\vdots$$

We now form two series, the geometric series

$$\sum_{k=1}^{\infty} a_N R^k = a_N R + a_N R^2 + \cdots + a_N R^k + \cdots$$

which converges because $R < 1$, and the series

$$\sum_{k=1}^{\infty} a_{N+k} = a_{N+1} + a_{N+2} + \cdots + a_{N+k} + \cdots$$

which also converges by the direct comparison test (because each term is less than the corresponding term of $a_N R^k$). Thus, Σa_k converges, because we can discard a finite number of terms ($k \leq N - 1$).

The proof of the second part is similar, except that we choose R such that

$$\lim_{k \to \infty} \frac{a_{k+1}}{a_k} = L > R > 1$$

and show that there exists some $M > 0$ so that $a_{M+k} > a_M R^k$.

To prove that the ratio test is inconclusive if $L = 1$, it is enough to note that the harmonic series

$$\sum_{k=1}^{\infty} \frac{1}{k} \quad \text{diverges} \quad \text{with } \lim_{k \to \infty} \frac{a_{k+1}}{a_k} = \lim_{k \to \infty} \frac{\dfrac{1}{k+1}}{\dfrac{1}{k}} = 1$$

and the *p*-series

$$\sum_{k=1}^{\infty} \frac{1}{k^2} \quad \text{converges} \quad \text{with } \lim_{k \to \infty} \frac{a_{k+1}}{a_k} = \lim_{k \to \infty} \frac{\dfrac{1}{(k+1)^2}}{\dfrac{1}{k^2}} = 1$$

∎

You will find the ratio test most useful with series involving factorials or exponentials.

EXAMPLE 1   Convergence using the ratio test

Test the series $\sum_{k=1}^{\infty} \dfrac{2^k}{k!}$ for convergence.

Solution   Let $a_k = \dfrac{2^k}{k!}$ and note that

$$L = \lim_{k \to \infty} \frac{a_{k+1}}{a_k} = \lim_{k \to \infty} \frac{\dfrac{2^{k+1}}{(k+1)!}}{\dfrac{2^k}{k!}} = \lim_{k \to \infty} \frac{k!2^{k+1}}{(k+1)!2^k} = \lim_{k \to \infty} \frac{2}{k+1} = 0$$

Thus $L < 1$, and the ratio test tells us that the given series converges.   ▬

EXAMPLE 2   Divergence using the ratio test

Test the series $\sum_{k=1}^{\infty} \dfrac{k^k}{k!}$ for convergence.

Solution   Let $a_k = \dfrac{k^k}{k!}$ and note that

$$L = \lim_{k \to \infty} \frac{a_{k+1}}{a_k} = \lim_{k \to \infty} \frac{\dfrac{(k+1)^{k+1}}{(k+1)!}}{\dfrac{k^k}{k!}} = \lim_{k \to \infty} \frac{k!(k+1)^{k+1}}{k^k(k+1)!} = \lim_{k \to \infty} \frac{(k+1)^k}{k^k} = \lim_{k \to \infty} \left(1 + \frac{1}{k}\right)^k = e$$

Because $L > 1$, the given series diverges.   ▬

Computational Window

It is instructive to compare and contrast two different ways you can use technology to help you with problems like Example 2. First, as you have seen, you can use a calculator or a computer to calculate the partial sums directly. This table is shown here on the left.

$$\sum_{k=1}^{\infty} \frac{k^k}{k!}$$

N	F(1) + . . . + F(N)
1	1
2	3
3	7.5
4	18.16667
5	44.20833
6	109.0083
7	272.4097
8	688.5113
9	1756.138
10	4511.87
11	11659.53
12	30273.46
13	78912.3
14	206375.3
15	541239.9

The partials sums seem to diverge.

A second procedure is to use the ratio test. In this case, we are interested in $\lim_{k \to \infty} \left(1 + \dfrac{1}{k}\right)^k$. We can look at terms of the sequence $a_k = \left(1 + \dfrac{1}{k}\right)^k$ to see if this limit is greater than, less than, or equal to 1. This is shown below.

$$\lim_{k \to \infty} \left(1 + \frac{1}{k}\right)^k$$

We see that the limit of the ratio of consecutive terms of $(a_k + 1)/a^k$ is greater than 1.

EXAMPLE 3   Ratio test fails

Test the series $\sum_{k=2}^{\infty} \dfrac{1}{2k-3}$ for convergence.

Solution   Let $a_k = \dfrac{1}{2k-3}$ and find

$$L = \lim_{k\to\infty} \frac{\dfrac{1}{2(k+1)-3}}{\dfrac{1}{2k-3}} = \lim_{k\to\infty} \frac{2k-3}{2k-1} = 1$$

The ratio test fails. We can use the integral test or the limit comparison test to test convergence. Note that

$$\sum_{k=2}^{\infty} \frac{1}{2k-3} \quad \text{is similar to the known divergent series} \quad \sum_{k=2}^{\infty} \frac{1}{2k}$$

so we suspect the given series is divergent.   ▬

EXAMPLE 4   Convergence of a series of power functions

Find all $x > 0$ for which the series $\sum_{k=1}^{\infty} k^3 x^k$ converges.

Solution   Applying the ratio test,

$$\frac{(k+1)^3 x^{k+1}}{k^3 x^k} = \frac{(k+1)^3}{k^3} x$$

The series converges when $\lim_{k\to\infty} \dfrac{(k+1)^3}{k^3} x < 1$, which is true whenever $x < 1$, because $\lim_{k\to\infty} \dfrac{(k+1)^3}{k^3} = 1$.   ▬

COMMENT: There are more-refined versions of the ratio test that can be used to handle certain series where $L = 1$. A consideration of such tests is delayed until advanced calculus.

■ ROOT TEST

Of all the tests we have developed, the divergence test is perhaps the easiest to apply, because it involves simply computing $\lim_{k\to\infty} a_k$ and observing whether or not that limit is zero. Unfortunately, most "interesting" series have $\lim_{k\to\infty} a_k = 0$, so the divergence test cannot be used to determine whether they converge or diverge. However, the following result shows that it may be possible to say more about the convergence of Σa_k by examining what happens to $\sqrt[k]{a_k}$ as $k \to \infty$. This test will prove particularly useful with a series involving a kth power.

THEOREM 8.17   The root test

Given the series Σa_k with $a_k \geq 0$, suppose that $\lim_{k\to\infty} \sqrt[k]{a_k} = L$. The **root test** states the following:

If $L < 1$, then Σa_k converges.
If $L > 1$ or if L is infinite, then Σa_k diverges.
If $L = 1$, the root test is inconclusive.

Proof: The proof of this theorem is similar to that of the ratio test. ∎

EXAMPLE 5   Convergence with the root test

Test the series $\sum\limits_{k=1}^{\infty} \dfrac{1}{(\ln k)^k}$ for convergence.

Solution   Let $a_k = \dfrac{1}{(\ln k)^k}$ and note that

$$L = \lim_{k \to \infty} \sqrt[k]{a_k} = \lim_{k \to \infty} \sqrt[k]{(\ln k)^{-k}} = \lim_{k \to \infty} \frac{1}{\ln k} = 0$$

Because $L < 1$, the root test tells us that the given series converges. ∎

EXAMPLE 6   Failure of the root test

Test the *p*-series $\sum\limits_{k=1}^{\infty} \dfrac{1}{k^p}$ for convergence.

Solution   We know that the *p*-series converges for $p > 1$ and diverges for $p \leq 1$. The point of this example is to show that the root test gives $L = 1$ for all *p*-series. This confirms the statement that the root test is inconclusive for $L = 1$. Let $a_k = 1/k^p$ so that

$$L = \lim_{k \to \infty} \sqrt[k]{\frac{1}{k^p}} = \lim_{k \to \infty} k^{-p/k}$$

To find this limit, use logarithms:

$$\ln L = \ln \lim_{k \to \infty} k^{-p/k} = \lim_{k \to \infty} \ln k^{-p/k} = \lim_{k \to \infty} \frac{-p \ln k}{k}$$

This is of the form ∞/∞, and we apply l'Hôpital's rule.

$$\ln L = \lim_{k \to \infty} \frac{-p \ln k}{k} = \lim_{k \to \infty} \frac{-p\left(\frac{1}{k}\right)}{1} = 0 \ \text{ so that } L = e^0 = 1$$

Thus, $L = 1$ for any *p*-series, yet those with $p > 1$ converge, whereas those with $p \leq 1$ diverge. ∎

■ SUMMARY OF CONVERGENCE TESTS FOR POSITIVE-TERM AND NONNEGATIVE-TERM SERIES

This concludes our study of basic convergence tests for series of positive terms. There are no firm rules for deciding how to test the convergence of a given series Σa_k, but we can offer a few observations.

In situations where the ratio test and the root test both apply, it is often easier to use the ratio test. However, the root test turns out to be more discriminating in the sense that any series whose convergence can be determined by the ratio test can also be handled by the root test, but the root test can be used to determine the convergence of certain series for which the ratio test is inconclusive (see Problem 56). For this reason we suggest that you try the ratio test first, and if that fails then try the root test. All tests (except for the ratio test) can also be applied for nonnegative terms, as well as for positive terms. These procedures are summarized in Table 8.1.

TABLE 8.1

Guidelines for Determining Convergence of the Series Σa_k for $a_k > 0$

Series with known convergence properties

Geometric series, $\displaystyle\sum_{k=1}^{\infty} ar^k$	diverges if $|r| \geq 1$ and converges if $|r| < 1$, with sum $S = \dfrac{a}{1-r}$
p-series, $\displaystyle\sum_{k=1}^{\infty} \dfrac{1}{k^p}$	converges if $p > 1$ and diverges if $p \leq 1$
(special case $p = 1$) Harmonic series, $\displaystyle\sum_{k=1}^{\infty} \dfrac{1}{k}$	diverges (special case, $p = 1$, of a p-series)
Telescoping series, $\displaystyle\sum_{k=1}^{\infty} (b_k - b_{k+1})$ $- L$	converges if $\displaystyle\lim_{k \to \infty} b_{k+1} = L$ with sum $S = b_1$
Log-power quotient series, $\displaystyle\sum_{k=1}^{\infty} \dfrac{\ln k}{k^q}$	converges if $q > 1$ and diverges if $q \leq 1$

Review of Convergence Tests, Presented in a Suggested Order for Checking

1. Divergence test	Compute $\displaystyle\lim_{k \to \infty} a_k$. If this limit is not 0, the series diverges.
2. Limit comparison test	Check to see whether Σa_k is similar in appearance to a series Σb_k whose convergence properties are known, and apply the limit comparison test. If $\displaystyle\lim_{k \to \infty} a_k/b_k = L$ where L is finite and positive, then Σa_k and Σb_k either both converge or both diverge.
3. Ratio test	If a_k involves $k!$, k^p, or a^k, try the ratio test, $\displaystyle\lim_{k \to \infty} \frac{a_{k+1}}{a_k} = L$. Converges if $L < 1$, diverges if $L > 1$, fails if $L = 1$.
4. Root test	If it is easy to find $\displaystyle\lim_{k \to \infty} \sqrt[k]{a_k} = L$, try the root test. Converges if $L < 1$, diverges if $L > 1$, fails if $L = 1$.
5. Integral test	If f is continuous, positive, and decreasing, and $a_k = f(k)$ for all k, then $\displaystyle\sum_{k=1}^{\infty} a_k$ and the improper integral $\displaystyle\int_1^{\infty} f(x)\, xd$ both converge or diverge. Think of using this test if f is easy to integrate or if a_k involves a logarithm, a trigonometric function, or an inverse trigonometric function.
6. Direct comparison test	If $0 \leq a_k \leq c_k$ and $\displaystyle\sum_{k=1}^{\infty} c_k$ converges, then $\displaystyle\sum_{k=1}^{\infty} a_k$ converges. If $0 \leq d_k \leq a_k$ and $\displaystyle\sum_{k=1}^{\infty} d_k$ diverges, then $\displaystyle\sum_{k=1}^{\infty} a_k$ diverges.
7. Zero-infinity limit comparison test	If $\displaystyle\lim_{k \to \infty} \frac{a_k}{b_k} = 0$ and Σb_k converges, then the series Σa_k converges. If $\displaystyle\lim_{k \to \infty} \frac{a_k}{b_k} = \infty$ and Σb_k diverges, then the series Σa_k diverges.

If a test is inconclusive, do not quit; try another test.

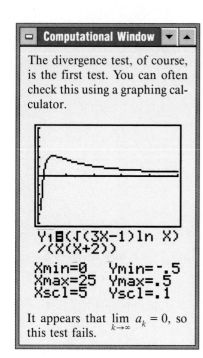

EXAMPLE 7 Testing for convergence

Test the series $\sum\limits_{k=1}^{\infty} \dfrac{\sqrt{3k-1}\,\ln k}{k(k+2)}$.

Solution We would expect the given series to behave like the series

$$\sum_{k=1}^{\infty} \frac{\sqrt{k}\,\ln k}{k^2} = \sum_{k=1}^{\infty} \frac{\ln k}{k^{3/2}}$$

We apply the limit comparison test by considering the following limit:

$$\lim_{k\to\infty}\frac{a_k}{b_k} = \lim_{k\to\infty} \frac{\dfrac{\sqrt{3k-1}\,\ln k}{k(k+2)}}{\dfrac{\ln k}{k^{3/2}}} = \lim_{k\to\infty} \frac{k^{3/2}\sqrt{3k-1}}{k(k+2)}$$

$$= \lim_{k\to\infty} \frac{\sqrt{k}\,\sqrt{3k-1}}{k+2}\cdot\frac{\frac{1}{k}}{\frac{1}{k}} = \lim_{k\to\infty}\frac{\sqrt{3-\frac{1}{k}}}{1+\frac{2}{k}} = \sqrt{3}$$

Thus, by the limit comparison test we see that both series either converge or diverge (because $\sqrt{3}$ is finite and positive). Because the comparison series $\Sigma(\ln k)/k^{3/2}$ is a log-power quotient series with $q = 3/2$, it must converge (because $q > 1$), and thus the given series also converges. ▬

EXAMPLE 8 Testing for convergence

Test the series $\sum\limits_{k=1}^{\infty}\dfrac{k!}{1\cdot4\cdot7\cdots(3k+1)} = 1 + \dfrac{1!}{1\cdot4} + \dfrac{2!}{1\cdot4\cdot7} + \dfrac{3!}{1\cdot4\cdot7\cdot10} + \cdots$ for convergence.

Solution Let $a_k = \dfrac{k!}{1\cdot4\cdot7\cdots(3k+1)}$. Because a_k involves $k!$, we try the ratio test.

$$\frac{a_{k+1}}{a_k} = \frac{\dfrac{(k+1)!}{1\cdot4\cdot7\cdots[3(k+1)+1]}}{\dfrac{k!}{1\cdot4\cdot7\cdots(3k+1)}} = \frac{(k+1)!\cdot1\cdot4\cdot7\cdots(3k+1)}{k!\cdot1\cdot4\cdot7\cdots(3k+4)} = \frac{k+1}{3k+4}$$

Thus,

$$L = \lim_{k\to\infty}\frac{a_{k+1}}{a_k} = \lim_{n\to\infty}\frac{k+1}{3k+4} = \frac{1}{3}$$

and since $L < 1$, the given series converges. ▬

PROBLEM SET 8.5

Ⓐ 1. ■ **What Does This Say?** Compare and contrast the ratio test and root test.

2. ■ **What Does This Say?** Outline a procedure for determining the convergence of Σa_k for $a_k > 0$.

Use either the ratio test or the root test to test for convergence of the series given in Problems 3–26.

3. $\sum\limits_{k=1}^{\infty}\dfrac{1}{k!}$

4. $\sum\limits_{k=1}^{\infty}\dfrac{k!}{2^k}$

5. $\sum\limits_{k=1}^{\infty}\dfrac{k!}{2^{3k}}$

6. $\sum\limits_{k=1}^{\infty}\dfrac{3^k}{k!}$

7. $\sum\limits_{k=1}^{\infty}\dfrac{k}{2^k}$

8. $\sum\limits_{k=1}^{\infty}\dfrac{2^k}{k^2}$

9. $\sum\limits_{k=1}^{\infty}\dfrac{k^{100}}{e^k}$

10. $\sum\limits_{k=1}^{\infty} e^{-k}$

11. $\sum\limits_{k=1}^{\infty} k\left(\dfrac{4}{3}\right)^k$

12. $\sum\limits_{k=1}^{\infty} k\left(\dfrac{3}{4}\right)^k$

13. $\sum\limits_{k=1}^{\infty}\left(\dfrac{2}{k}\right)^k$

14. $\sum\limits_{k=1}^{\infty}\dfrac{k^{10}2^k}{k!}$

15. $\sum\limits_{k=1}^{\infty}\dfrac{k^5}{10^k}$

16. $\sum\limits_{k=1}^{\infty}\dfrac{2^k}{k^2}$

17. $\sum\limits_{k=1}^{\infty}\left(\dfrac{k}{3k+1}\right)^k$

18. $\sum_{k=1}^{\infty} \dfrac{3k+1}{2^k}$ **19.** $\sum_{k=1}^{\infty} \dfrac{k!}{(k+2)^4}$ **20.** $\sum_{k=1}^{\infty} \dfrac{k^5+100}{k!}$

21. $\sum_{k=1}^{\infty} \dfrac{(k!)^2}{(2k)!}$ **22.** $\sum_{k=1}^{\infty} k^2 2^{-k}$ **23.** $\sum_{k=1}^{\infty} \dfrac{(k!)^2}{[(2k)!]^2}$

24. $\sum_{k=1}^{\infty} k^4 3^{-k}$ **25.** $\sum_{k=1}^{\infty} \dfrac{(k^2)!}{[(2k)^2]!}$ **26.** $\sum_{k=1}^{\infty} \left(\dfrac{k}{2k+1}\right)^k$

Test the series in Problems 27–44 for convergence. Justify your answers (that is, state explicitly which test you are using).

27. $\sum_{k=1}^{\infty} \dfrac{1,000}{k}$ **28.** $\sum_{k=1}^{\infty} \dfrac{5,000}{k\sqrt{k}}$ **29.** $\sum_{k=1}^{\infty} \dfrac{5k+2}{k2^k}$

30. $\sum_{k=1}^{\infty} \dfrac{(k!)^2}{k^k}$ **31.** $\sum_{k=1}^{\infty} \dfrac{\sqrt{k!}}{2^k}$ **32.** $\sum_{k=1}^{\infty} \dfrac{3k+5}{k3^k}$

33. $\sum_{k=1}^{\infty} \dfrac{2^k k!}{k^k}$ **34.** $\sum_{k=1}^{\infty} \dfrac{2^{2k} k!}{k^k}$ **35.** $\sum_{k=1}^{\infty} \dfrac{\sqrt{k+1}}{k^{k+0.5}}$

36. $\sum_{k=1}^{\infty} \dfrac{1}{k^k}$ **37.** $\sum_{k=1}^{\infty} \dfrac{k!}{(k+1)!}$ **38.** $\sum_{k=1}^{\infty} \dfrac{2^{1,000k}}{k^{k/2}}$

39. $\sum_{k=1}^{\infty} \left(1+\dfrac{1}{k}\right)^{-k^2}$ **40.** $\sum_{k=1}^{\infty} \left(\dfrac{k+2}{k}\right)^{-k^2}$ **41.** $\sum_{k=1}^{\infty} \left|\dfrac{\cos k}{2^k}\right|$

42. $\sum_{k=1}^{\infty} \left|\dfrac{\sin k}{3^k}\right|$ **43.** $\sum_{k=2}^{\infty} \left(\dfrac{\ln k}{k}\right)^k$ **44.** $\sum_{k=2}^{\infty} \dfrac{1}{(\ln k)^k}$

B *Find all $x > 0$ for which each series in Problems 45–52 converges.*

45. $\sum_{k=1}^{\infty} k^2 x^k$ **46.** $\sum_{k=1}^{\infty} kx^k$

47. $\sum_{k=1}^{\infty} \dfrac{(x+0.5)^k}{k\sqrt{x}}$ **48.** $\sum_{k=1}^{\infty} \dfrac{(3x+0.4)^k}{k^2}$

49. $\sum_{k=1}^{\infty} \dfrac{x^k}{k!}$ **50.** $\sum_{k=1}^{\infty} \dfrac{x^{2k}}{k}$

51. $\sum_{k=1}^{\infty} (ax)^k$ for $a > 0$ **52.** $\sum_{k=1}^{\infty} kx^{2k}$

C **53.** Use the root test to show that $\Sigma k^p e^{-k}$ converges for any fixed positive real number p. What does this imply about the improper integral
$$\int_1^{\infty} x^p e^{-x}\, dx ?$$

54. Consider the series $\sum_{k=1}^{\infty} 2^{-k+(-1)^k}$. What can you conclude about the convergence of this series if you use each of the following?
a. the ratio test   **b.** the root test

55. Let $\{a_k\}$ be a sequence of positive numbers and suppose that $\lim\limits_{k\to\infty} \dfrac{a_{k+1}}{a_k} = L$, where $0 < L < 1$.
a. Show that $\lim\limits_{k\to\infty} a_k = 0$. *Hint*: Note that Σa_k converges.
b. Show that $\lim\limits_{k\to\infty} \dfrac{x^k}{k!} = 0$ for any $x > 0$.

56. Consider the series
$$1 + \tfrac{1}{2} + \tfrac{1}{2} + \tfrac{1}{4} + \tfrac{1}{4} + \tfrac{1}{8} + \tfrac{1}{8} + \tfrac{1}{8} + \cdots$$
a. Show that the ratio test fails.
b. What is the result of applying the root test?

8.6 ALTERNATING SERIES; ABSOLUTE AND CONDITIONAL CONVERGENCE

IN THIS SECTION Leibniz's alternating series test, error estimates for alternating series, absolute and conditional convergence, rearrangement of terms in an absolutely convergent series
We now turn our attention from nonnegative term-series to series with both positive and negative terms. We begin by examining series whose terms alternate in sign. We shall examine conditions that guarantee the convergence of such alternating series and then discuss the speed of convergence. Finally, we make a few general observations about series whose terms are neither all nonnegative nor strictly alternating in sign. This leads to a consideration of absolute and conditional convergence.

There are two classes of series for which the successive terms alternate in sign, and each of these series is appropriately called an **alternating series**:

odd terms are negative: $\sum_{k=1}^{\infty} (-1)^k a_k = -a_1 + a_2 - a_3 + \cdots$

even terms are negative: $\sum_{k=1}^{\infty} (-1)^{k+1} a_k = a_1 - a_2 + a_3 - \cdots$

where in both cases $a_k > 0$.

■ LEIBNIZ'S ALTERNATING SERIES TEST

In general, just knowing that $\lim\limits_{k \to \infty} a_k = 0$ tells us very little about the convergence properties of the series Σa_k, but it turns out that an alternating series must converge if the absolute value of its terms decreases monotonically toward zero. This fact was first proved in the 17th century by Leibniz and may be stated as in the following theorem.

THEOREM 8.18 **Alternating series test**

If $a_k > 0$, then an alternating series

$$\sum_{k=1}^{\infty} (-1)^k a_k \quad \text{or} \quad \sum_{k=1}^{\infty} (-1)^{k+1} a_k$$

converges if both of the following two conditions are satisfied:

1. $\lim\limits_{k \to \infty} a_k = 0$
2. $\{a_k\}$ is a decreasing sequence; that is, $a_{k+1} < a_k$ for all k.

Proof: We will show that when an alternating series of the form

$$\sum_{k=1}^{\infty} (-1)^{k+1} a_k$$

satisfies the two required properties, it converges. The steps for the other type of alternating series are similar. For this proof we are given that

$$\lim\limits_{k \to \infty} a_k = 0 \quad \text{and} \quad a_{k+1} < a_k \quad \text{for all } k$$

We need to prove that the sequence of partial sums $\{S_n\}$ converges, where

$$S_n = \sum_{k=1}^{n} (-1)^{k+1} a_k = a_1 - a_2 + a_3 - a_4 + \cdots + (-1)^{n+1} a_n$$

Our strategy will be to show first that the sequence of *even* partial sums $\{S_{2n}\}$ is *increasing* and converges to a certain limit L. Then we shall show that the sequence of odd partial sums $\{S_{2n-1}\}$ also converges to L.

To understand why we would think to break up S_n to look at the even and odd partial sums, consider Figure 8.15. Start at the origin; and because $a_1 > 0$, S_1 will be somewhere to the right of 0 as shown in Figure 8.15a. We know that $a_2 < a_1$ (decreasing sequence) so S_2 is to the left of S_1 but to the right of 0 as shown in Figure 8.15b. As you continue this process you can see that the partial sums oscillate back and forth. Because $a_n \to 0$, the successive steps are getting smaller and smaller, as shown in Figure 8.15c.

Note that the even partial sums of the alternating series satisfy

$$S_2 = a_1 - a_2$$
$$S_4 = (a_1 - a_2) + (a_3 - a_4)$$
$$\vdots$$
$$S_{2n} = (a_1 - a_2) + (a_3 - a_4) + \cdots + (a_{2n-1} - a_{2n})$$

Because $\{a_k\}$ is a decreasing sequence, each of the quantities in parentheses $(a_{2j-1} - a_{2j})$ is positive, and it follows that $\{S_{2n}\}$ is an increasing sequence:

$$S_2 < S_4 < S_6 < \cdots$$

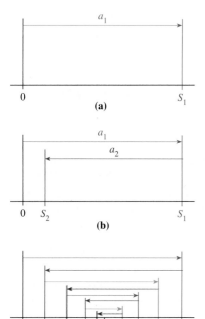

Sequence of even partial sums $\{S_{2n}\}$ is increasing $\quad$ Sequence of odd partial sums $\{S_{2n-1}\}$ is decreasing

(c)

Figure 8.15 Alternating series test

Moreover, because

$$S_2 = a_1 - a_2 < a_1$$
$$S_4 = a_1 - (a_2 - a_3) - a_4 < a_1$$
$$\vdots$$
$$S_{2n} = a_1 - (a_2 - a_3) - (a_4 - a_5) - \cdots - (a_{2n-2} - a_{2n-1}) - a_{2n} < a_1$$

the sequence of even partial sums $\{S_{2n}\}$ is bounded above by a_1 (see Figure 8.15c), and because it is also an increasing sequence, the BMCT tells us that the sequence must converge, say, to L; that is,

$$\lim_{n \to \infty} S_{2n} = L$$

Next, consider $\{S_{2n-1}\}$, the sequence of odd partial sums. Because $S_{2n} - S_{2n-1} = a_n$ and $\lim_{n \to \infty} a_n = 0$, it follows that $S_{2n-1} = S_{2n} - a_n$ and

$$\lim_{n \to \infty} S_{2n-1} = \lim_{n \to \infty} S_{2n} - \lim_{n \to \infty} a_n = L - 0 = L$$

Since the sequence of even partial sums and the sequence of odd partial sums both converge to L, it follows that $\{S_n\}$ converges to L, and the alternating series must converge. ∎

REMARK: When you are testing the alternating series $\Sigma(-1)^{k+1}a_k$ for convergence, it is wise to begin by computing $\lim_{k \to \infty} a_k$. If this limit is 0, you can show that the alternating series converges by verifying that $\{a_k\}$ is a decreasing sequence. However, if $\lim_{k \to \infty} a_k \neq 0$ you know immediately that the series diverges and no further computation is necessary.

EXAMPLE 1 Convergence using the alternating series test

Test the series $\displaystyle\sum_{k=1}^{\infty} \frac{(-1)^k}{k}$ for convergence. This series is called the **alternating harmonic series.**

Solution The series can be expressed as $\Sigma(-1)^k a_k$, where $a_k = \frac{1}{k}$. We have $\lim_{k \to \infty} \frac{1}{k} = 0$ and because

$$\frac{1}{(k+1)} < \frac{1}{k}$$

for all $k > 0$, the sequence $\{a_k\}$ is decreasing. Thus, the alternating series test tells us that the given series must converge. ▬

EXAMPLE 2 Using l'Hôpital's rule with the alternating series test

Test the series $\displaystyle\sum_{k=1}^{\infty} \frac{(-1)^{k+1} \ln k}{k}$ for convergence.

Solution Express the series in the form $\Sigma(-1)^{k+1}a_k$, where $a_k = \frac{\ln k}{k}$. We begin with the divergence test. (Notice that the graph in Figure 8.16 shows that the limit of the kth term as $k \to \infty$ seems to be 0.) For $a_k > 0$ where $k > 1$ and by applying l'Hôpital's rule, we find that

$$\lim_{k \to \infty} \frac{\ln k}{k} = \lim_{k \to \infty} \frac{\frac{1}{k}}{1} = 0$$

Figure 8.16 Graph of $y = \dfrac{\ln k}{k}$

It remains to show that the sequence $\{a_k\}$ is decreasing. We can do this by setting $f(x) = \dfrac{\ln x}{x}$ and noting that the derivative

$$f'(x) = \frac{1 - \ln x}{x^2}$$

satisfies $f'(x) < 0$ for all $x > e$. Thus, the sequence $\{a_k\}$ is decreasing for all $k > 3 > e$. The conditions of the alternating series test are satisfied, and the given alternating series must converge. ▬

EXAMPLE 3 **Divergence using the alternating series test**

Test the series $\displaystyle\sum_{k=1}^{\infty} \frac{(-1)^{k+1}}{\tan^{-1} k}$ for convergence.

Solution The series can be expressed as $\Sigma(-1)^{k+1}a_k$, where $a_k = \dfrac{1}{\tan^{-1} k}$. The graph of $y = \dfrac{1}{\tan^{-1} k}$ is shown in Figure 8.17. It seems that the limit as $x \to \infty$ is not 0, so we suspect the series diverges. We can show this as follows:

$$\lim_{k \to \infty} a_k = \lim_{k \to \infty} \left(\frac{1}{\tan^{-1} k} \right) = \frac{1}{\frac{\pi}{2}} = \frac{2}{\pi} \neq 0$$

Figure 8.17 Graph of $y = \dfrac{1}{\tan^{-1} k}$

Thus, the series diverges by the divergence test. ▬

Alternating p-Series

The series $\displaystyle\sum_{k=1}^{\infty} \frac{(-1)^{k+1}}{k^p}$ is called the **alternating p-series**.

The following example shows that the alternating p-series converges for all $p > 0$.

EXAMPLE 4 **Alternating p-series**

Prove that the alternating p-series $\displaystyle\sum_{k=1}^{\infty} \frac{(-1)^{k+1}}{k^p}$ converges for $p > 0$.

Solution Let $a_k = \dfrac{1}{k^p}$ and note that $\displaystyle\lim_{k \to \infty} a_k = 0$ for $p > 0$. To show that the sequence $\{a_k\}$ is decreasing, we find that

$$\frac{a_{k+1}}{a_k} = \frac{\dfrac{1}{(k+1)^p}}{\dfrac{1}{k^p}} = \frac{k^p}{(k+1)^p} < 1$$

so $a_k > a_{k+1}$. Thus, the alternating p-series converges for all p. ▬

■ ERROR ESTIMATES FOR ALTERNATING SERIES

For any convergent series with sum L, the nth partial sum is an approximation to L that we expect to improve as n increases. In general, it is difficult to know how large an n to pick in order to ensure that the approximation will have a desired degree of accuracy. However, if the series in question satisfies the conditions of the alternating series test, the absolute value of the error incurred by using the sum for the first n terms to estimate the entire sum turns out to be no greater than the $(n + 1)$th excluded term. More formally, we have the following theorem.

THEOREM 8.19 **The error estimate for an alternating series**

Suppose an alternating series

$$\sum_{k=1}^{\infty} (-1)^k a_k \quad \text{or} \quad \sum_{k=1}^{\infty} (-1)^{k+1} a_k$$

satisfies the conditions of the alternating series test; namely,

$$\lim_{k \to \infty} a_k = 0 \quad \text{and} \quad \{a_k\} \text{ is a decreasing sequence } (a_{k+1} < a_k)$$

If the series has sum S, then

$$|S - S_n| < a_{n+1}$$

where S_n is the nth partial sum of the series.

Proof: We will prove the result for the second form of the alternating series and leave the first form for the reader. That is, let

$$S = \sum_{k=1}^{\infty} (-1)^{k+1} a_k \quad \text{and} \quad S_n = \sum_{k=1}^{n} (-1)^{k+1} a_k$$

Begin with $S - S_n$:

$$S - S_n = \sum_{k=1}^{\infty} (-1)^{k+1} a_k - \sum_{k=1}^{n} (-1)^{k+1} a_k = \sum_{k=n+1}^{\infty} (-1)^{k+1} a_k$$

$$= (-1)^{n+2} a_{n+1} + (-1)^{n+3} a_{n+2} + (-1)^{n+4} a_{n+3} + \cdots$$

$$= (-1)^n (-1)^2 a_{n+1} + (-1)^n (-1)^3 a_{n+2} + (-1)^n (-1)^4 a_{n+3} + \cdots$$

$$= (-1)^n [a_{n+1} - a_{n+2} + a_{n+3} - a_{n+4} + \cdots]$$

$$= (-1)^n [a_{n+1} - (a_{n+2} - a_{n+3}) - (a_{n+4} - a_{n+5}) - \cdots]$$

Because the sequence $\{a_n\}$ is decreasing, we have $a_k - a_{k+1} \geq 0$ for all k, and it follows that

$$|S - S_n| = |a_{n+1} - (a_{n+2} - a_{n+3}) - (a_{n+4} - a_{n+5}) - \cdots| \leq a_{n+1}$$

because every quantity in parentheses is positive. ∎

■ *What this says:* If an alternating series satisfies the conditions of the alternating series test, you can approximate the sum of the series by using the nth partial sum (S_n), and your error will have an absolute value no greater than the first term left off (namely, a_{n+1}).

EXAMPLE 5 **Error estimate for an alternating series**

Consider the convergent series $\sum_{k=1}^{\infty} \dfrac{(-1)^{k+1}}{k^4}$.

a. Estimate the sum of the series by taking the sum of the first four terms. How accurate is this estimate?

b. Estimate the sum of the series with three-decimal-place accuracy.

Solution

a. Let $a_k = \dfrac{1}{k^4}$ and let S denote the actual sum of the series. The error estimate tells us that

$$|S - S_4| \le a_5$$

where S_4 is the sum of the first four terms of the series. Using a calculator, we find

$$S_4 = \frac{1}{1^4} - \frac{1}{2^4} + \frac{1}{3^4} - \frac{1}{4^4} \approx 0.945\,939\,4$$

and $a_5 = \dfrac{1}{5^4} = 0.001\,6$. Thus, if we estimate S by $S_4 \approx 0.945\,9$, we incur an error of about $0.001\,6$, which means that

$$|S - S_4| \le 0.001\,6$$
$$0.945\,939\,4 - 0.001\,6 \le S \le 0.945\,939\,4 + 0.001\,6$$
$$0.944\,339\,4 \le S \le 0.947\,539\,4$$

So, we have S, correct to two decimal places, as 0.94.

b. Because we want to approximate S by a partial sum S_n with three-decimal-place accuracy, we can allow an error of no more than 0.0005. The error is measured by

$$a_{n+1} = \frac{1}{(n+1)^4}$$

Thus, we wish to find n so that

$$\frac{1}{(n+1)^4} \le 0.000\,5$$
$$\frac{1}{0.000\,5} \le (n+1)^4$$
$$\sqrt[4]{2,000} \le n + 1$$
$$6.687\,403 - 1 \le n$$

This says that n must be an integer greater than $5.687\,403$; that is, $n \ge 6$.   ▬

⊘ Estimating the remainder is pointless if you are not careful in rounding. ⊘

■ ABSOLUTE AND CONDITIONAL CONVERGENCE

The convergence tests we have developed cannot be applied to a series that has mixed terms or does not strictly alternate. In such cases, it is often useful to apply the following result.

THEOREM 8.20   The absolute convergence test

A series of real numbers Σa_k must converge if the related absolute value series $\Sigma |a_k|$ converges.

Proof: Assume $\Sigma |a_k|$ converges and let $b_k = a_k + |a_k|$ for all k. Note that

$$b_k = \begin{cases} 2|a_k| & \text{if } a_k > 0 \\ 0 & \text{if } a_k \le 0 \end{cases}$$

Thus, we have $0 \le b_k < 2|a_k|$ for all k. Because the series $\Sigma|a_k|$ converges and both Σb_k and $\Sigma|a_k|$ are series of nonnegative terms, the direct comparison test tells us that the dominated series Σb_k also converges. Finally, because

$$a_k = b_k - |a_k|$$

and both Σb_k and $\Sigma|a_k|$ converge, it follows that Σa_k must also converge. ■

EXAMPLE 6   Convergence using the absolute convergence test

Test the series $1 + \frac{1}{4} + \frac{1}{9} - \frac{1}{16} - \frac{1}{25} + \frac{1}{36} + \frac{1}{49} + \frac{1}{64} - \frac{1}{81} - \frac{1}{100} \cdots$ for convergence. This is the series in which the absolute value of the general term is $\frac{1}{k^2}$ and the pattern of the signs is $+++--+++--\cdots$.

Solution   This is not a series of nonnegative terms, nor is it strictly alternating. However, we find that the corresponding series of absolute values is the convergent p-series

$$1 + \frac{1}{4} + \frac{1}{9} + \frac{1}{16} + \cdots = \sum_{k=1}^{\infty} \frac{1}{k^2}$$

Because the absolute value series converges, the absolute convergence test assures us that the given series also converges. ▬

EXAMPLE 7   Convergence of a trigonometric series

Test the series $\displaystyle\sum_{k=1}^{\infty} \frac{\sin k}{2^k}$ for convergence.

Solution   Because $\sin k$ takes on both positive and negative values, the series cannot be analyzed by methods that apply only to series of nonnegative terms. Moreover, the series is not strictly alternating.

The corresponding series of absolute values is

$$\sum_{k=1}^{\infty} \left| \frac{\sin k}{2^k} \right|$$

which is dominated by the convergent geometric series $\Sigma 1/2^k$ because $|\sin k| \le 1$ for all k; that is,

$$0 \le \left| \frac{\sin k}{2^k} \right| \le \frac{1}{2^k} \quad \text{for all } k$$

Therefore, the absolute convergence test assures us that the given series converges. The graph of the related continuous function $f(x) = (\sin x)/2^x$ is shown in Figure 8.18. ▬

Figure 8.18 Graph of $y = \dfrac{\sin x}{2^x}$

If Σa_k converges, then $\Sigma|a_k|$ may either converge or diverge. The two cases that can occur are given the following special names.

Absolutely Convergent Series
Conditionally Convergent Series

> The series Σa_k is **absolutely convergent** if the related series $\Sigma|a_k|$ converges. The series Σa_k is **conditionally convergent** if it converges but $\Sigma|a_k|$ diverges.

For example, the series in Examples 6 and 7 are both absolutely convergent, but the alternating harmonic series

$$\sum_{k=1}^{\infty} \frac{(-1)^{k+1}}{k}$$

is conditionally convergent because it converges (see Example 4), whereas the related series of absolute value terms $\Sigma\frac{1}{k}$ (the harmonic series) diverges.

The ratio test and the root test for nonnegative-term series can be generalized to apply to arbitrary series. The following is a statement and proof of the generalized ratio test. The proof of the generalized root test is left to the problems (see Problem 60).

THEOREM 8.21 **The generalized ratio test**

For the series Σa_k, suppose $a_k \neq 0$ for $k \geq 1$ and that

$$\lim_{k\to\infty}\left|\frac{a_{k+1}}{a_k}\right| = L$$

where L is a real number or ∞. Then:

If $L < 1$, the series Σa_k converges absolutely and hence converges.
If $L > 1$ or if L is infinite, the series Σa_k diverges.
If $L = 1$, the test fails.

Proof: Assume $L < 1$; then the positive series $\Sigma|a_k|$ converges by the ratio test, and hence Σa_k converges absolutely.

Assume $L > 1$; then the sequence $\{|a_k|\}$ is eventually increasing, which means that $\{a_k\}$ cannot converge to 0 as $k \to \infty$. Thus Σa_k diverges by the divergence test.

Assume $L = 1$. See Problem 61 for this part of the proof. ∎

EXAMPLE 8 **Convergence and divergence using the generalized ratio test**

Find all values of x for which the series Σkx^k converges and all x for which it diverges.

Solution Let $a_k = kx^k$.

$$\lim_{k\to\infty}\left|\frac{a_{k+1}}{a_k}\right| = \lim_{k\to\infty}\left|\frac{(k+1)x^{k+1}}{kx^k}\right| = \lim_{k\to\infty}\left(\frac{k+1}{k}\right)\left|\frac{x^{k+1}}{x^k}\right| = \lim_{k\to\infty}\left(1+\frac{1}{k}\right)|x| = |x|$$

Thus, by the generalized ratio test we see for $|x| = L$ that the series converges for $|x| < 1$ and diverges if $|x| > 1$. If $x = 1$, the series is $\Sigma k(1)^k$, which clearly diverges by the divergence test. Similarly, if $x = -1$, $\Sigma k(-1)^k$ diverges by the divergence test. Thus, the series converges for $|x| < 1$ and diverges for $|x| \geq 1$.

Additional Guidelines for Determining Convergence of Series

1. **Test for absolute convergence** Take the absolute value of each term and proceed to test for convergence of positive series, as summarized in Table 8.1.
    1. If $\Sigma|a_k|$ *converges*, then the alternating series will converge.
    2. If $\Sigma|a_k|$ diverges, then the series is *not absolutely convergent*, but the alternating series might still converge conditionally.
2. **Alternating series test** For $a_k > 0$, the series converges if $|a_{k+1}| < |a_k|$ for all k and $\lim_{k\to\infty} a_k = 0$.

■ REARRANGEMENT OF TERMS IN AN ABSOLUTELY CONVERGENT SERIES

You may be surprised to learn that if the terms in a conditionally convergent series are rearranged (that is, the order of the summands is changed), the new series may not converge or it may converge to a different sum from that of the original series! For example, we know that the alternating harmonic series

$$\sum_{k=1}^{\infty} \frac{(-1)^{k+1}}{k}$$

converges conditionally, and it can be shown (see Problem 52)

$$1 - \tfrac{1}{2} + \tfrac{1}{3} - \tfrac{1}{4} + \tfrac{1}{5} - \tfrac{1}{6} + \tfrac{1}{7} - \tfrac{1}{8} + \tfrac{1}{9} - \cdots = \ln 2$$

If we rearrange this series by placing two of the subtracted terms after each added term, we obtain

$$1 - \tfrac{1}{2} - \tfrac{1}{4} + \tfrac{1}{3} - \tfrac{1}{6} - \tfrac{1}{8} + \tfrac{1}{5} - \cdots = \left(1 - \tfrac{1}{2}\right) - \tfrac{1}{4} + \left(\tfrac{1}{3} - \tfrac{1}{6}\right) - \tfrac{1}{8} + \cdots$$

$$= \tfrac{1}{2} - \tfrac{1}{4} + \tfrac{1}{6} - \tfrac{1}{8} + \cdots$$

$$= \tfrac{1}{2}\left(1 - \tfrac{1}{2} + \tfrac{1}{3} - \tfrac{1}{4} + \cdots\right)$$

$$= \tfrac{1}{2} \ln 2$$

In general, it can be shown that if Σa_k is conditionally convergent, there is a rearrangement of the terms of Σa_k so that the sum is equal to *any* given finite number. In Problem 53, for example, you are asked to rearrange the terms of the series

$$\sum_{k=1}^{\infty} \frac{(-1)^{k+1}}{k}$$

so that the sum is $\tfrac{3}{2}\ln 2$.

This information may be somewhat unsettling, because it is reasonable to expect a sum to be unaffected by the order in which the summands are taken. Absolutely convergent series behave more in the way we would expect. In fact, *if the series Σa_k converges absolutely with sum S, then **any** rearrangement of the terms also converges absolutely to S.* A detailed discussion of rearrangement of series requires the techniques of advanced calculus.

PROBLEM SET 8.6

 1. ■ **What Does This Say?** Discuss absolute versus conditional convergence.

2. ■ **What Does This Say?** Discuss the convergence of the alternating *p*-series.

3. ■ **What Does This Say?** Look at Problems 4–31 and notice that most starting values are $k = 1$, but some have starting values $k = 2$. Why do you think we did not use $k = 1$ for all these problems?

Determine if each series in Problems 4–31 converges absolutely, converges conditionally, or diverges.

4. $\sum_{k=1}^{\infty} \frac{(-1)^{k+1}k}{k^2 + 1}$

5. $\sum_{k=1}^{\infty} \frac{(-1)^{k+1}k^2}{k^3 + 1}$

6. $\sum_{k=1}^{\infty} \frac{(-1)^{k+1}k}{2k + 1}$

7. $\sum_{k=1}^{\infty} \frac{(-1)^{k+1}k^2}{k^2 + 1}$

8. $\sum_{k=1}^{\infty} \frac{(-1)^{k+1}}{k^{3/2}}$

9. $\sum_{k=1}^{\infty} \frac{(-1)^{k+1}k}{2^k}$

10. $\sum_{k=1}^{\infty} (-1)^{k+1}\frac{k^2}{e^k}$

11. $\sum_{k=1}^{\infty} \frac{(-1)^k}{\sqrt{k}}$

12. $\sum_{k=1}^{\infty} (-1)^k\frac{(1 + k^2)}{k^3}$

13. $\sum_{k=1}^{\infty} \frac{(-1)^{k+1}k!}{k^k}$

14. $\sum_{k=2}^{\infty} (-1)^k\frac{k!}{\ln k}$

15. $\sum_{k=1}^{\infty} (-1)^k\frac{k!}{k^k}$

16. $\displaystyle\sum_{k=1}^{\infty} (-1)^{k+1} \frac{2^k}{k!}$

17. $\displaystyle\sum_{k=1}^{\infty} \frac{(-2)^k}{k!}$

18. $\displaystyle\sum_{k=1}^{\infty} (-1)^{k+1} \frac{2^{2k+1}}{k!}$

19. $\displaystyle\sum_{k=2}^{\infty} \frac{(-1)^{k+1}}{\ln k}$

20. $\displaystyle\sum_{k=1}^{\infty} \frac{(-1)^{k+1}k}{(k+1)(k+2)}$

21. $\displaystyle\sum_{k=2}^{\infty} \frac{(-1)^{k+1}}{(\ln k)^4}$

22. $\displaystyle\sum_{k=2}^{\infty} \frac{(-1)^{k+1}}{\ln(\ln k)}$

23. $\displaystyle\sum_{k=2}^{\infty} \frac{(-1)^{k+1}}{k \ln k}$

24. $\displaystyle\sum_{k=1}^{\infty} \frac{(-1)^{k+1}\ln k}{k}$

25. $\displaystyle\sum_{k=2}^{\infty} \frac{(-1)^{k+1}k}{\ln k}$

26. $\displaystyle\sum_{k=1}^{\infty} (-1)^{k+1} \frac{\ln k}{k^2}$

27. $\displaystyle\sum_{k=1}^{\infty} \frac{(-1)^{k+1}k}{(k+2)^2}$

28. $\displaystyle\sum_{k=1}^{\infty} (-1)^{k+1}\left(\frac{k}{k+1}\right)^k$

29. $\displaystyle\sum_{k=2}^{\infty} (-1)^{k+1} \frac{\ln(\ln k)}{k \ln k}$

30. $\displaystyle\sum_{k=1}^{\infty} (-1)^{k+1}\left(\frac{1}{k}\right)^{1/k}$

31. $\displaystyle\sum_{k=1}^{\infty} (-1)^{k+1} \frac{k^5 \, 5^{k+2}}{2^{3k}}$

B *Given the series in Problems 32–37,*

a. *Estimate the sum of the series by taking the sum of the first four terms. How accurate is this estimate?*

b. *Estimate the sum of the series with three-decimal-place accuracy.*

32. $\displaystyle\sum_{k=1}^{\infty} \frac{(-1)^{k+1}}{2^{2k-2}}$

33. $\displaystyle\sum_{k=1}^{\infty} \frac{(-1)^{k+1}}{k!}$

34. $\displaystyle\sum_{k=1}^{\infty} \frac{(-1)^k}{k^2}$

35. $\displaystyle\sum_{k=1}^{\infty} \left(\frac{-1}{3}\right)^{k+1}$

36. $\displaystyle\sum_{k=1}^{\infty} \frac{(-1)^{k+1}}{k^3}$

37. $\displaystyle\sum_{k=1}^{\infty} \left(\frac{-1}{5}\right)^k$

Use the generalized ratio test in Problems 38–43 to find all numbers x for which the given series converges.

38. $\displaystyle\sum_{k=1}^{\infty} \frac{x^k}{k}$

39. $\displaystyle\sum_{k=1}^{\infty} \frac{x^k}{\sqrt{k}}$

40. $\displaystyle\sum_{k=1}^{\infty} \frac{2^k x^k}{k!}$

41. $\displaystyle\sum_{k=1}^{\infty} \frac{(k+2)x^k}{k^2(k+3)}$

42. $\displaystyle\sum_{k=1}^{\infty} (-1)^{k+1}\left(\frac{x}{k}\right)^k$

43. $\displaystyle\sum_{k=1}^{\infty} k^p(-1)^k x^k$ for $p > 0$

44. THINK TANK PROBLEM   Find an upper bound for the error if the alternating series $\displaystyle\sum_{k=1}^{\infty} \frac{(-1)^{k+1}}{k}$ is approximated by the partial sum

$$S_5 = 1 - \frac{1}{2} + \frac{1}{3} - \frac{1}{4} + \frac{1}{5}$$

45. THINK TANK PROBLEM   Find an upper bound for the error if the alternating series $\displaystyle\sum_{k=1}^{\infty} \frac{(-1)^{k+1}}{k^2}$ is approximated by the partial sum

$$S_5 = 1 - \frac{1}{2^2} + \frac{1}{3^2} - \frac{1}{4^2} + \frac{1}{5^2}$$

46. THINK TANK PROBLEM   Find an upper bound for the error if the alternating series $\displaystyle\sum_{k=2}^{\infty} \frac{(-1)^k}{\ln k}$ is approximated by the partial sum

$$S_7 = \frac{1}{\ln 2} - \frac{1}{\ln 3} + \frac{1}{\ln 4} - \frac{1}{\ln 5} + \frac{1}{\ln 6} - \frac{1}{\ln 7}$$

47. THINK TANK PROBLEM   Find an upper bound for the error if the alternating series $\displaystyle\sum_{k=1}^{\infty} \frac{(-1)^{k+1}k}{2^k}$ is approximated by the partial sum

$$S_6 = \frac{1}{2} - \frac{2}{2^2} + \frac{3}{2^3} - \frac{4}{2^4} + \frac{5}{2^5} - \frac{6}{2^6}$$

48. For what numbers p does the alternating series $\displaystyle\sum_{k=2}^{\infty} \frac{(-1)^{k+1}}{k(\ln k)^p}$ converge? For what numbers p does it converge absolutely?

49. Test the series $\displaystyle\sum_{k=1}^{\infty} \frac{\sin\sqrt[k]{2}}{k^2}$ for convergence.

50. Use series methods to evaluate $\displaystyle\lim_{k\to\infty} \frac{x^k}{k!}$ where x is a real number.

C 51. Show that

$$\lim_{n\to\infty} \left(\frac{1}{1} + \frac{1}{2} + \frac{1}{3} + \cdots + \frac{1}{n} - \ln n\right)$$

converges.

52. Show that $\displaystyle\sum_{k=1}^{\infty} \frac{(-1)^{k+1}}{k} = \ln 2$ by completing the following steps:

a. Let $S_m = \displaystyle\sum_{k=1}^{m} \frac{(-1)^{k+1}}{k}$ and let $H_m = \displaystyle\sum_{k=1}^{m} \frac{1}{k}$. Show that $S_{2m} = H_{2m} - H_m$.

b. It can be shown (see Problem 51) that

$$\lim_{m\to\infty} \left(1 + \frac{1}{2} + \cdots + \frac{1}{m} - \ln m\right) = \gamma$$

where γ is a number called **Euler's constant** ($\gamma = 0.57722$). Use this fact, along with the relationship in part **a** to show that $\displaystyle\lim_{h\to\infty} S_n = \ln 2$. *Hint:* Note that

$$S_{2m} = H_{2m} - H_m$$
$$= [H_{2m} - \ln(2m)] - [H_m - \ln m] + \ln(2m) - \ln m$$

53. Consider the following rearrangement of the conditionally convergent harmonic series $\displaystyle\sum_{k=1}^{\infty} \frac{(-1)^{k+1}}{k}$:

$$1 + \frac{1}{3} - \frac{1}{2} + \frac{1}{5} + \frac{1}{7} - \frac{1}{4} + \frac{1}{9} + \frac{1}{11} - \frac{1}{6} + \cdots$$

a. Let S_n and H_n denote the nth partial sum of the given rearranged series and the harmonic series $\displaystyle\sum_{k=1}^{\infty} \frac{1}{k}$, respectively. Show that if n is a multiple of $n = 3m$, then $S_{3m} = H_{4m} - \frac{1}{2}H_{2m} - \frac{1}{2}H_m$.

b. Show that $\lim\limits_{n\to\infty} S_n = \frac{3}{2} \ln 2$. *Hint:* You may find it helpful to use

$$\lim_{n\to\infty}\left(1 + \tfrac{1}{2} + \cdots + \tfrac{1}{n} - \ln n\right) = \gamma$$

given in part **b** of Problem 52.

54. THINK TANK PROBLEM   What (if anything) is wrong with the following computation?

$$1 - \tfrac{1}{2} + \tfrac{1}{3} - \tfrac{1}{4} + \tfrac{1}{5} - \tfrac{1}{6} + \cdots$$

$$= 1 + \left(\tfrac{1}{2} - 1\right) + \tfrac{1}{3} + \left(\tfrac{1}{4} - \tfrac{1}{2}\right) + \tfrac{1}{5} + \left(\tfrac{1}{6} - \tfrac{1}{3}\right) + \cdots$$

$$= \left(1 + \tfrac{1}{2} + \tfrac{1}{3} + \tfrac{1}{4}\ldots\right) - 1 - \tfrac{1}{2} - \tfrac{1}{3} - \tfrac{1}{4} - \cdots$$

$$= \left(1 + \tfrac{1}{2} + \tfrac{1}{3} + \cdots\right) - \left(1 + \tfrac{1}{2} + \tfrac{1}{3} + \cdots\right) = 0$$

55. Test the given series for convergence.
  a. $2 - 2^{1/2} + 2^{1/3} - 2^{1/4} + \cdots$
  b. $(1 - 2^{1/1}) - (1 - 2^{1/2}) + (1 - 2^{1/3}) - \cdots$

56. Suppose $\{a_k\}$ is a sequence with the property that $|a_n| < A^n$ for some positive number A and all positive integers n. Show that the series $\Sigma a_k x^k$ converges absolutely for $|x| \le 1/A$.

57. THINK TANK PROBLEM   Give an example of a sequence $\{a_k\}$ with the property that Σa_k^2 converges but Σa_k diverges.

58. THINK TANK PROBLEM   Give an example of a sequence $\{a_k\}$ with the property that Σa_k^2 converges and Σa_k also converges.

59. Show that if $\sum\limits_{k=1}^{\infty} a_k$ converges then $\sum\limits_{k=0}^{\infty} a_k^2$ must also converge.

60. Prove the generalized root test, which may be stated as follows: Suppose $a_k \ne 0$ for $k \ge 1$ and that

$$\lim_{k\to\infty} \sqrt[k]{|a_k|} = L$$

Then:
If $L < 1$, the series Σa_k converges absolutely.
If $L > 1$, the series Σa_k diverges.
If $L = 1$, the test fails.

61. Show that if

$$L = \lim_{k\to\infty}\left|\frac{a_{k+1}}{a_k}\right| = 1$$

the series Σa_k can either converge or diverge. *Hint:* Find a convergent series with $L = 1$ and a divergent series that satisfies the same condition.

62. Let $\Sigma(-1)^{k+1}a_k$ be an alternating series such that $\{a_k\}$ is decreasing and

$$\lim_{k\to\infty} a_k = 0$$

Show that the sequence of odd partial sums S_{2n-1} is decreasing.

8.7 POWER SERIES

> **IN THIS SECTION** Convergence of a power series, power series in $x - c$, term-by-term differentiation, and integration of power series
> A *power series* is a series whose terms are power functions of the form $a_k(x - c)^k$. We shall examine the properties of such series and shall find that under reasonable conditions, they can be differentiated and integrated term by term.

An infinite series of the form

$$\sum_{k=0}^{\infty} a_k(x - c)^k = a_0 + a_1(x - c) + a_2(x - c)^2 + \cdots$$

is called a **power series** in $(x - c)$. The numbers $a_0, a_1, a_2, \ldots$ are the *coefficients* of the power series, and we will be concerned only with the case where these coefficients, as well as x and c, are real numbers. If $c = 0$, the series has the form

$$\sum_{k=0}^{\infty} a_k x^k = a_0 + a_1 x + a_2 x^2 + a_3 x^3 + \cdots$$

■ CONVERGENCE OF A POWER SERIES

How can we determine the set of all numbers x for which a given power series converges? This question is answered by the following fundamental result on convergence. We begin by considering the case where $c = 0$.

THEOREM 8.22   Convergence of a power series

For a power series $\sum\limits_{k=1}^{\infty} a_k x^k$, exactly one of the following is true:

1. The series converges for all x.
2. The series converges only for $x = 0$.
3. The series **converges absolutely** for all x in an open interval $(-R, R)$ and **diverges** for $|x| > R$.
   Note: The series should be checked separately at the endpoints, because it could converge absolutely, or converge conditionally, or diverge at $x = R$ and $x = -R$.

Proof: The proof is found in most advanced calculus textbooks.   ∎

The following three examples show each of these possibilities.

EXAMPLE 1   When the convergence set is the entire x-axis

Show that the power series $\sum\limits_{k=1}^{\infty} \dfrac{x^k}{k!}$ converges for all x.

Solution   If $x = 0$, then the series is trivial and converges. For $x \neq 0$, we use the generalized ratio test to find

$$L = \lim_{k \to \infty} \left| \frac{\dfrac{x^{k+1}}{(k+1)!}}{\dfrac{x^k}{k!}} \right| = \lim_{k \to \infty} \left| \frac{x^{k+1} k!}{(k+1)! x^k} \right| = \lim_{k \to \infty} \frac{|x|}{k+1} = 0$$

Because $L = 0$ satisfies $L < 1$, the series converges for all x.   ▬

EXAMPLE 2   Convergence only at the point x = 0

Show that the power series $\sum\limits_{k=1}^{\infty} k! x^k$ converges only when $x = 0$.

Solution   We use the generalized ratio test to find

$$L = \lim_{k \to \infty} \left| \frac{(k+1)! x^{k+1}}{k! x^k} \right| = \lim_{k \to \infty} (k+1)|x|$$

For $x = 0$, the limit is 0, but for $x \neq 0$, the limit is ∞. Hence, the power series converges only for $x = 0$.   ▬

EXAMPLE 3   When the convergence set is bounded

Find the convergence set for the geometric series
$$\sum_{k=0}^{\infty} x^k = 1 + x + x^2 + x^3 + \cdots$$

Solution   Because this is a geometric series, we know it converges for $|x| < 1$. This is the same as saying it converges on the open interval $(-1, 1)$ and diverges elsewhere.   ▬

The generalized ratio test can be used to show that the convergence set of a power series has one of the three forms described by the following theorem.

THEOREM 8.23   **The convergence set of a power series**

Let $\Sigma a_k u^k$ be a power series, and let

$$L = \lim_{k \to \infty} \left| \frac{a_{k+1}}{a_k} \right|$$

Then:

If $L = \infty$, the power series converges only at $u = 0$.

If $L = 0$, the power series converges for all real u.

If $0 < L < \infty$, let $R = 1/L$. Then the power series **converges absolutely** for $|u| < R$ (or $-R < u < R$) and **diverges** for $|u| > R$. It may either converge or diverge at the endpoints $u = -R$ and $u = R$.

Proof: We shall use the generalized ratio test. First, in the case where

$$L = \lim_{k \to \infty} \left| \frac{a_{k+1}}{a_k} \right| \quad \text{exists, consider the limit}$$

$$M = \lim_{k \to \infty} \left| \frac{a_{k+1} u^{k+1}}{a_k u^k} \right| = \lim_{k \to \infty} \left| \frac{a_{k+1}}{a_k} \right| |u| = L|u|$$

The generalized ratio test tells us that $\Sigma a_k u^k$ converges absolutely if $M < 1$ and diverges if $M > 1$.

If L is infinite, the series $\Sigma a_k u^k$ converges only at $u = 0$ (because this is the only value of u such that $L|u| < 1$). If $L = 0$, then $L|u| < 1$ is always satisfied, and the series converges absolutely for all u. Suppose L is finite and $L \neq 0$. Then the series converges absolutely for all u such that

$$|u| < \frac{1}{L} = \frac{1}{\frac{1}{R}} = R \quad \textit{Because } R = \frac{1}{L}$$

Thus,

$$-R < u < R \quad \textit{Because } |u| < R$$

We see the series diverges for $|u| > R$, and we can have either convergence or divergence at $u = R$ and $u = -R$. ∎

The number R that appears in Theorem 8.23 is called the **radius of convergence** of the power series $\Sigma a_k u^k$, and the interval

$-R < u < R$ is the **interval of absolute convergence.**

Thus, the interval of convergence of a power series consists of the interval of absolute convergence $-R < u < R$, and possibly one or both endpoints $u = -R$ and $u = R$, as shown in Figure 8.19. If the convergence set is all real numbers, we write $R = \infty$.

Figure 8.19 The interval of convergence of a power series

In Example 1, we found that $\Sigma x^k/k!$ converges for all x, so R is infinite and the interval of convergence is the entire real line. In Example 2, we found that the power series $\Sigma k! x^k$ has radius of convergence 0. In Example 3, we found that Σx^k converges on $(-1, 1)$, so $R = 1$.

We now turn our attention to finding R for an example that is not a geometric series.

EXAMPLE 4   Finding an interval of absolute convergence

Find the interval of absolute convergence for $\sum\limits_{k=1}^{\infty} \dfrac{2^k x^k}{k}$.

Solution   We note that $a_k = \dfrac{2^k}{k}$ and $u = x$.

$$L = \lim_{k \to \infty} \left| \frac{\frac{2^{k+1}}{k+1}}{\frac{2^k}{k}} \right| = \lim_{k \to \infty} \left| \frac{2k}{k+1} \right| = 2$$

Thus, the interval of absolute convergence $\left(R = \frac{1}{L} \right)$ is $-\frac{1}{2} < x < \frac{1}{2}$.

EXAMPLE 5   Finding an interval of convergence

Find the radius of convergence and the interval of convergence for the power series

$$\sum_{k=1}^{\infty} \frac{x^k}{k}$$

Solution   We find that $a_k = \dfrac{1}{k}$ and $u = x$.

$$L = \lim_{k \to \infty} \left| \frac{\frac{1}{k+1}}{\frac{1}{k}} \right| = \lim_{k \to \infty} \frac{k}{k+1} = 1$$

so that $R = \frac{1}{L} = 1$. The series converges absolutely for $|x| < 1$. The interval of absolute convergence is $(-1, 1)$, and the radius of convergence is 1.

Next, check the endpoints -1 and 1 for convergence. When $x = -1$, the power series

⊘ Do not forget to check the endpoints. ⊘

$$\sum_{k=1}^{\infty} \frac{(-1)^k}{k}$$

is the convergent alternating harmonic series. If $x = 1$, the power series becomes

$$\sum_{k=1}^{\infty} \frac{1}{k}$$

which is the divergent harmonic series. This means that the endpoint corresponding to $x = 1$ is not included in the interval of convergence. Thus, the interval of convergence is $[-1, 1)$.

Theorem 8.23 uses the ratio test for finding the radius of convergence. However, sometimes it is more convenient to use the root test. The next theorem is a companion to Theorem 8.23, which simply replaces the ratio test with the root test.

THEOREM 8.24   Root test for the radius of convergence

Let $\Sigma a_k u^k$ be a power series, and let

$$L = \lim_{k \to \infty} \sqrt[k]{|a_k|}$$

Then:

If $L = \infty$, the power series converges only at $u = 0$.

If $L = 0$, the power series converges for all real u.

If $0 < L < \infty$, let $R = 1/L$. Then the power series converges absolutely for $|u| < R$ and diverges for $|u| > R$. It may either converge or diverge at the endpoints $u = -R$ and $u = R$.

Proof: The proof is similar to the proof of Theorem 8.23 and is omitted. ∎

EXAMPLE 6   Radius of convergence using the root test

Find the radius of convergence of the power series $\sum_{k=1}^{\infty} \left(\frac{k+1}{k} \right)^{k^2} x^k$.

Solution   Setting $a_k = \left(\frac{k+1}{k} \right)^{k^2}$ and $u = x$, we have

$$L = \lim_{k \to \infty} \sqrt[k]{|a_k|} = \lim_{k \to \infty} \left[\left(\frac{k+1}{k} \right)^{k^2} \right]^{1/k} = \lim_{k \to \infty} \left(1 + \frac{1}{k} \right)^k = e$$

Thus, the radius of convergence of the power series is $R = \frac{1}{L} = \frac{1}{e}$ and the series converges absolutely for $|x| < e^{-1}$ and diverges for $|x| > e^{-1}$. ▬

■ POWER SERIES IN $(x - c)$

In some applications, we will encounter power series of the form

$$\sum_{k=0}^{\infty} a_k(x - c)^k = a_0 + a_1(x - c) + a_2(x - c)^2 + \cdots$$

in which each term is a constant times a power of $x - c$. The intervals of convergence are intervals of the form $-R < x - c < R$, including possibly one or both of the endpoints $x = c - R$ and $x = c + R$. You can easily show this by letting $u = x - c$ in Theorems 8.23 and 8.24.

EXAMPLE 7   Power series in $(x - c)$

Find the interval of absolute convergence of the power series

$$\sum_{k=1}^{\infty} \frac{(x+1)^k}{3^k}$$

Solution   We find that $a_k = \frac{1}{3^k}$ and $c = -1$:

$$L = \lim_{k \to \infty} \left| \frac{\frac{1}{3^{k+1}}}{\frac{1}{3^k}} \right| = \lim_{k \to \infty} \left| \frac{3^k}{3^{k+1}} \right| = \lim_{k \to \infty} \left| \frac{1}{3} \right| = \frac{1}{3}$$

Thus, $R = 3$, so the interval of absolute convergence is

$$-3 < x + 1 < 3$$
$$-4 < \quad x \quad < 2$$

that is, the interval of absolute convergence is $(-4, 2)$. ▬

■ TERM-BY-TERM DIFFERENTIATION AND INTEGRATION OF POWER SERIES

Consider the power series of the form

$$\sum_{k=0}^{\infty} a_k x^k = a_0 + a_1 x + a_2 x^2 + a_3 x^3 + \cdots$$

where x is a variable and all a_n are constants (often called the *coefficients* of the series). For each fixed x, the power series may converge or diverge. In other words, let f be a function defined by $f(x) = a_0 + a_1 x + a_2 x^2 + a_3 x^3 + \cdots$ whose domain is the set of all values of x for which the series converges. The function f looks like a polynomial function, except it has infinitely many terms. For example, consider the function defined by

$$f(x) = \frac{1}{1-x} = 1 + x + x^2 + x^3 + \cdots \quad \textit{By long division (see margin)}$$

$$
\begin{array}{r}
1 + x + x^2 + \cdots \\
1 - x{\overline{\smash{\big)}\,1 + 0x + 0x^2 + 0x^3 + \cdots}} \\
\underline{1 - x} \\
x + 0x^2 \\
\underline{x - x^2} \\
x^2 + 0x^3 \\
\underline{x^2 - x^3} \\
x^3 + \cdots
\end{array}
$$

We recognize this as a geometric series, which has an interval of convergence of $(-1, 1)$, as shown in Example 3. In Figure 8.20 we show the graphs of f as well as some of the graphs of n terms of the corresponding geometric series, as follows:

$$f(x) = \frac{1}{1-x} = 1 + x + x^2 + x^3 + \cdots + x^n + \cdots$$
$$\text{interval of convergence } (-1, 1)$$

$$n = 1: \quad \frac{1}{1-x} \approx 1$$

$$n = 2: \quad \frac{1}{1-x} \approx 1 + x$$

$$n = 3: \quad \frac{1}{1-x} \approx 1 + x + x^2$$

$$n = 4: \quad \frac{1}{1-x} \approx 1 + x + x^2 + x^3$$

a. Polynomial approximations

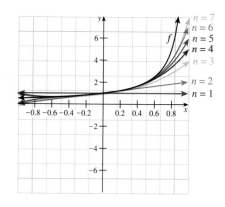

b. Detail showing interval of convergence

Figure 8.20 The graphs of $y = \frac{1}{1-x}$ and the polynomials from the first terms of the associated power series

Notice from Figure 8.20 that the larger the n, the closer the series approximation is to the graph of f.

If we regard a power series as an "infinite polynomial," we would expect to be able to differentiate and integrate it term by term. The following theorem shows that this procedure is legitimate on the interval of absolute convergence.

THEOREM 8.25 Term-by-term differentiation and integration of a power series

A power series $\sum_{k=0}^{\infty} a_k u^k$ with radius of convergence $R > 0$ can be differentiated or integrated term by term on its interval of absolute convergence. More specifically, if $f(u) = \sum_{k=0}^{\infty} a_k u^k$ for $|u| < R$, then for $|u| < R$ we have

$$f'(u) = \sum_{k=1}^{\infty} k a_k u^{k-1} = a_1 + 2a_2 u + 3a_3 u^2 + 4a_4 u^3 + \cdots$$

$$\int f(u)\, du = \int \left(\sum_{k=0}^{\infty} a_k u^k \right) du = \sum_{k=0}^{\infty} \left(\int a_k u^k\, du \right) = \sum_{k=0}^{\infty} \frac{a_k}{k+1} x^{k+1} + C$$

Proof: The proof of this result is outside the scope of this text, but details can be found in practically any advanced calculus text. ▄

> ■ *What this says*: In many ways, a function defined by a power series behaves like a polynomial. It is continuous in its interval of absolute convergence, and its derivative and integral can be determined by differentiating and integrating term by term, respectively.

EXAMPLE 8 Term-by-term differentiation of a power series

Let f be a function defined by the power series

$$f(x) = \sum_{k=0}^{\infty} \frac{x^k}{k!} \qquad \text{for all } x$$

Show that $f'(x) = f(x)$ for all x, and deduce that $f(x) = e^x$.

Solution The given power series converges for all x (by the generalized ratio test—see Example 1), and Theorem 8.25 tells us that it is differentiable for all x. Differentiating term by term, we find

$$f'(x) = \frac{d}{dx}\left[1 + x + \frac{x^2}{2!} + \frac{x^3}{3!} + \frac{x^4}{4!} + \cdots \right]$$

$$= 0 + 1 + \frac{2x}{2!} + \frac{3x^2}{3!} + \frac{4x^3}{4!} + \cdots$$

$$= 1 + x + \frac{x^2}{2!} + \frac{x^3}{3!} + \cdots = f(x)$$

In Chapter 6, we found that the differential equation $f'(x) = f(x)$ has the general solution $f(x) = Ce^x$. Substituting $x = 0$ into the power series for $f(x)$, we obtain

$$f(0) = 1 + 0 + \frac{0^2}{2!} + \frac{0^3}{3!} + \cdots = 1$$

and by solving the equation $1 = Ce^0$ for C, we find $C = 1$; therefore, $f(x) = e^x$. ▄

A power series can be differentiated term by term—not just once, but infinitely often in its interval of absolute convergence. The key to this fact lies in showing that if f satisfies

$$f(x) = \sum_{k=0}^{\infty} a_k x^k$$

and R is the radius of convergence of the power series on the right, then the derivative series

$$f'(x) = \sum_{k=1}^{\infty} ka_k x^{k-1}$$

also has the radius of convergence R. (You are asked to show this in Problem 44). Therefore, Theorem 8.25 can be applied to the derivative series to obtain the second derivative

$$f''(x) = \sum_{k=2}^{\infty} k(k-1)a_k x^{k-2}$$

for $|x| < R$. Continuing in this fashion, we can apply Theorem 8.25 to $f'''(x), f^{(4)}$, and all other higher derivatives of f.

For example, we know that the geometric series

$$\sum_{k=0}^{\infty} x^k \text{ converges absolutely to } f(x) = \frac{1}{1-x} \text{ for } |x| < 1$$

Thus, the term-by-term derivative

$$\frac{d}{dx}\left[\sum_{k=0}^{\infty} x^k\right] = \sum_{k=1}^{\infty} kx^{k-1} = 1 + 2x + 3x^2 + \cdots$$

converges to $f'(x) = \dfrac{1}{(1-x)^2}$ for $|x| < 1$, and the term-by-term *second derivative*

$$\frac{d^2}{dx^2}\left[\sum_{k=0}^{\infty} x^k\right] = \frac{d}{dx}\left[\sum_{k=1}^{\infty} kx^{k-1}\right] = \sum_{k=2}^{\infty} k(k-1)x^{k-2}$$

converges to $f''(x) = \dfrac{2}{(1-x)^3}$ and so on. These ideas are illustrated in our next example.

EXAMPLE 9   Second derivative of a power series

Let f be the function defined by the power series

$$f(x) = \sum_{k=0}^{\infty} \frac{(-1)^k x^{2k}}{(2k)!} \qquad \oslash \text{ Do not forget, } 0! = 1. \oslash$$

for all x. Show that $f''(x) = -f(x)$ for all x.

Solution   First, we use the ratio test to verify that the given power series converges absolutely for all x.

$$L = \lim_{k \to \infty} \left| \frac{\dfrac{x^{2(k+1)}}{[2(k+1)]!}}{\dfrac{x^{2k}}{(2k)!}} \right| = \lim_{k \to \infty} \left| \frac{x^{2k+2}}{[2(k+1)]!} \cdot \frac{(2k)!}{x^{2k}} \right| = \lim_{k \to \infty} \frac{x^2}{(2k+2)(2k+1)} = 0$$

Because $L < 1$, the series converges for all x. Next, differentiate the series, term by term:

$$f'(x) = \frac{d}{dx}\left[1 - \frac{x^2}{2!} + \frac{x^4}{4!} - \frac{x^6}{6!} + \cdots\right] = -\frac{2x}{2!} + \frac{4x^3}{4!} - \frac{6x^5}{6!} + \cdots$$

$$= -\frac{x}{1!} + \frac{x^3}{3!} - \frac{x^5}{5!} + \cdots$$

Finally, by differentiating term by term again, we obtain

$$f''(x) = \frac{d}{dx}\left[-\frac{x}{1!} + \frac{x^3}{3!} - \frac{x^5}{5!} + \cdots\right] = -1 + \frac{3x^2}{3!} - \frac{5x^4}{5!} + \cdots$$

$$= -\left[1 - \frac{x^2}{2!} + \frac{x^4}{4!} + \cdots\right] = -f(x)$$

EXAMPLE 10   Term-by-term integration of a power series

By integrating an appropriate geometric series term by term, show that

$$\sum_{k=0}^{\infty} \frac{x^{k+1}}{k+1} = -\ln(1-x) \quad \text{for } -1 < x < 1$$

Solution   Integrating the geometric series $\sum_{k=0}^{\infty} u^k = \dfrac{1}{1-u}$ term by term in the interval $-1 < u < 1$, we obtain

$$\int_0^x \frac{1}{1-u}\,du = \int_0^x \left[\sum_{k=0}^{\infty} u^k\right] du = \int_0^x [1 + u + u^2 + u^3 + \cdots]\,du$$

$$= x + \frac{x^2}{2} + \frac{x^3}{3} + \cdots = \sum_{k=0}^{\infty} \frac{x^{k+1}}{k+1} \quad \text{for } -1 < x < 1$$

We also know that $\displaystyle\int_0^x \frac{du}{1-u} = -\ln(1-x)$.

Thus, $-\ln(1-x) = \displaystyle\int_0^x \frac{du}{1-u} = \sum_{k=0}^{\infty} \frac{x^{k+1}}{k+1}$ for $-1 < x < 1$

PROBLEM SET 8.7

A *Find the radius of convergence and interval of convergence for the power series given in Problems 1–28.*

1. $\sum_{k=1}^{\infty} \frac{kx^k}{k+1}$

2. $\sum_{k=1}^{\infty} \frac{k^2 x^k}{k+1}$

3. $\sum_{k=1}^{\infty} \frac{k(k+1)x^k}{k+2}$

4. $\sum_{k=1}^{\infty} \sqrt{k-1}\, x^k$

5. $\sum_{k=1}^{\infty} k^2 3^k (x-3)^k$

6. $\sum_{k=1}^{\infty} \frac{k^2(x-2)^k}{3^k}$

7. $\sum_{k=1}^{\infty} \frac{3^k(x+3)^k}{4^k}$

8. $\sum_{k=1}^{\infty} \frac{4^k(x+1)^k}{3^k}$

9. $\sum_{k=1}^{\infty} \frac{k!(x-1)^k}{5^k}$

10. $\sum_{k=1}^{\infty} \frac{(x-15)^k}{\ln(k+1)}$

11. $\sum_{k=1}^{\infty} \frac{k^2}{2^k}(x-1)^k$

12. $\sum_{k=1}^{\infty} \frac{2^k(x-3)^k}{k(k+1)}$

13. $\sum_{k=1}^{\infty} \frac{k(3x-4)^k}{(k+1)^2}$

14. $\sum_{k=1}^{\infty} \frac{(2x+3)^k}{4^k}$

15. $\sum_{k=1}^{\infty} \frac{kx^k}{7^k}$

16. $\sum_{k=1}^{\infty} \frac{(2k)!x^k}{(3k)!}$

17. $\sum_{k=1}^{\infty} \frac{(k!)^2 x^k}{k^k}$

18. $\sum_{k=1}^{\infty} \frac{(-1)^k kx^k}{\ln(k+2)}$

19. $\sum_{k=2}^{\infty} \frac{(-1)^k x^k}{k(\ln k)^2}$

20. $\sum_{k=1}^{\infty} \frac{(3x)^k}{2^{k+1}}$

21. $\sum_{k=1}^{\infty} \frac{(2x)^{2k}}{k!}$

22. $\sum_{k=1}^{\infty} \frac{(x+2)^{2k}}{3^k}$

23. $\sum_{k=1}^{\infty} \frac{k!}{2^k}(3x)^{3k}$

24. $\sum_{k=1}^{\infty} \frac{(3x)^{3k}}{x^k}$

25. $\sum_{k=1}^{\infty} \frac{2^k}{k!}(2x-1)^{2k}$

26. $\sum_{k=1}^{\infty} 2^k(3x)^{3k}$

27. $\sum_{k=1}^{\infty} 3^k(5x)^{4k}$

28. $\sum_{k=1}^{\infty} k!(x+1)^{3k}$

B *Find the interval of convergence in Problems 29–34.*

29. $\sum_{k=1}^{\infty} k^2(x+1)^{2k+1}$

30. $\sum_{k=1}^{\infty} \frac{1}{k^{\sqrt{k}}} x^k$

31. $\sum_{k=1}^{\infty} 2^{\sqrt{k}}(x-1)^k$

32. $\sum_{k=1}^{\infty} k^{\sqrt{k}} x^k$

33. $\sum_{k=1}^{\infty} k(ax)^k$ for constant a 34. $\sum_{k=1}^{\infty} (a^2 x)^k$ for constant a

In Problems 35–38, find the derivative $f'(x)$ by differentiating as a power series.

35. $f(x) = \sum_{k=0}^{\infty} \left(\frac{x}{2}\right)^k$

36. $f(x) = \sum_{k=1}^{\infty} \frac{x^k}{k}$

37. $f(x) = \sum_{k=0}^{\infty} (k+2)x^k$

38. $f(x) = \sum_{k=0}^{\infty} kx^k$

In Problems 39–42, find $\int_0^x f(u)\,du$ by integrating a power series.

39. $f(x) = \sum_{k=0}^{\infty} \left(\frac{x}{2}\right)^k$

40. $f(x) = \sum_{k=1}^{\infty} \frac{x^k}{k}$

41. $f(x) = \sum_{k=0}^{\infty} (k+2)x^k$

42. $f(x) = \sum_{k=0}^{\infty} kx^k$

43. **THINK TANK PROBLEM**   Show that the series

$$\sum_{k=1}^{\infty} \frac{\sin(k!x)}{k^2}$$

converges for all x. Differentiate term by term to obtain the series

$$\sum_{k=1}^{\infty} \frac{k!\cos(k!\,x)}{k^2}$$

Show that this series diverges for all x.

Ⓒ 44. Suppose $\{a_k\}$ is a sequence for which

$$\lim_{k \to \infty} \sqrt[k]{|a_k|} = \frac{1}{R}$$

Show that the power series

$$\sum_{k=1}^{\infty} k a_k x^{k-1}$$

has radius of convergence R.

45. Show that if $f(x) = \sum_{k=1}^{\infty} a_k x^k$ has radius of convergence $R > 0$, then the series

$$\sum_{k=1}^{\infty} a_k x^{kp}$$

where p is a positive integer, has radius of convergence $R^{1/p}$.

46. For what values of x does the series

$$\sum_{k=1}^{\infty} \frac{x}{k+x} \text{ converge?}$$

Note: This is not a power series.

47. For what values of x does the series

$$\sum_{k=1}^{\infty} \frac{k}{x^k} \text{ converge?}$$

Note: This is not a power series.

48. For what values of x does the series

$$\sum_{k=1}^{\infty} \frac{1}{kx^k} \text{ converge?}$$

Note: This is not a power series.

49. Find the radius of absolute convergence for

$$\sum_{k=1}^{\infty} \frac{(k+3)! x^k}{k!(k+4)!}$$

50. Find the radius of absolute convergence for

$$\sum_{k=1}^{\infty} \frac{1 \cdot 2 \cdot 3 \cdots k(-x)^{2k-1}}{1 \cdot 3 \cdot 5 \cdots (2k-1)}$$

51. Let f be the function defined by the power series

$$f(x) = \sum_{k=0}^{\infty} \frac{(-1)^k x^{2k+1}}{(2k+1)!}$$

for all x. Show that $f''(x) = -f(x)$ for all x.

52. Let f be the function defined by the power series

$$f(x) = \sum_{k=1}^{\infty} \frac{x^{2k}}{(2k)!}$$

for all x. Show that $f''(x) = f(x)$.

8.8 TAYLOR AND MACLAURIN SERIES

IN THIS SECTION Taylor and Maclaurin polynomials, Taylor's theorem, Taylor and Maclaurin series, operations with Maclaurin and Taylor series
In this section, we seek to represent a function as an infinite series in such a way that the value of the given function at $x = c$ and the value of the series differ by no more than some specified tolerance. To do this, we introduce an entire new class of power series. We will then conclude by considering operations with power series.

■ TAYLOR AND MACLAURIN POLYNOMIALS

Figure 8.21 Graph of $f(x) = e^x$ and approximating polynomials $M_1(x)$ and $M_2(x)$

Consider a function f that can be differentiated n times on some interval I. Our goal is to find a polynomial function that approximates f at a number c in its domain. For simplicity, we begin by considering an important special case where $c = 0$. For example, consider the function $f(x) = e^x$ at the point $x = 0$, as shown in Figure 8.21. In order to approximate f by a polynomial function $M(x)$, we begin by making sure that both the polynomial function and f pass through the point $x = 0$. That is, $M(0) = f(0)$. We say that the polynomial is **expanded about $c = 0$** or that it is **centered at 0**.

There are many polynomial functions that we could choose to approximate f at $x = 0$, and we proceed by making sure that both f and M have the same slope at $x = 0$. That is,

$$M'(0) = f'(0)$$

BROOK TAYLOR (1685–1731)

The two mathematicians most closely associated with power series are Brook Taylor and Colin Maclaurin (1698–1746). The result stated in this section, called Taylor's theorem, was published by Taylor in 1712, but the result itself was discovered by the Scottish mathematician James Gregory (1638–1675) in 1670 and was published by Gregory in 1688. Taylor wrote extensively on a variety of subjects in addition to mathematics, ranging from physics to music and philosophy. He became secretary of the Royal Society, but his writing style prevented him from receiving full credit for all his achievements, and his personal life was marked with great tragedy.

The graph in Figure 8.21 shows that we have $f(x) = e^x$, so $f'(x) = e^x$ and $f(0) = f'(0) = 1$. To find M_1, we let

$$M_1(x) = a_0 + a_1 x \qquad M_1'(x) = a_1$$

and require $M_1(0) = 1$ and $M_1'(0) = 1$.

Because $M_1'(0) = a_1 = 1$ and $M_1(0) = a_0 = 1$, we find that

$$M_1(x) = 1 + x$$

We see from Figure 8.21 that close to $x = c$ the approximation of f by M_1 is good, but as we move away from $(0, 1)$, M_1 no longer serves as a good approximation. To improve the approximation, we impose the requirement that the values of the second derivatives of M and f agree at $x = 0$. Using this criterion, we find

$$M_2(x) = a_0 + a_1 x + a_2 x^2$$

so that

$$M_2'(x) = a_1 + 2a_2 x \quad \text{and} \quad M_2''(x) = 2a_2$$

Because $f''(x) = e^x$ and $f''(0) = 1$ we want

$$2a_2 = 1 \quad \text{or} \quad a_2 = \tfrac{1}{2}$$

Thus,

$$M_2(x) = 1 + x + \tfrac{1}{2}x^2$$

To improve the approximation even further, we can require that the values of the approximating polynomials $M_3, M_4, \ldots, M_n$ at $x = 0$ have derivatives that match those of f at $x = 0$. We find that

$$M_3(x) = 1 + x + \tfrac{1}{2}x^2 + \tfrac{1}{6}x^3$$

$$M_4(x) = 1 + x + \tfrac{1}{2}x^2 + \tfrac{1}{6}x^3 + \tfrac{1}{24}x^4$$

$$M_5(x) = 1 + x + \tfrac{1}{2}x^2 + \tfrac{1}{6}x^3 + \tfrac{1}{24}x^4 + \tfrac{1}{120}x^5$$

$$\vdots$$

$$M_n(x) = 1 + \frac{x}{1!} + \frac{x^2}{2!} + \frac{x^3}{3!} + \cdots + \frac{x^n}{n!}$$

This nth degree polynomial approximation of f at $x = 0$ is called a **Maclaurin polynomial.** If we repeat the steps for $x = c$ rather than for $x = 0$, we find

$$M_n(x) = e^c + \frac{(x - c)}{1!} + \frac{(x - c)^2}{2!} + \frac{(x - c)^3}{3!} + \cdots + \frac{(x - c)^n}{n!}$$

which is called the **nth degree Taylor polynomial** of the function $f(x) = e^x$ at $x = c$.

■ TAYLOR'S THEOREM

Instead of stopping at the nth term, we will now approximate a function f by an infinite series. A function f is said to be represented by the power series

$$\sum_{k=0}^{\infty} a_k (x - c)^k$$

on an interval I if

$$f(x) = \sum_{k=0}^{\infty} a_k (x - c)^k$$

for all x in I. Power series representation of functions is extremely useful, but before we can deal effectively with such representations, we must answer two questions.

1. **Existence:** Under what conditions does a given function have a power series representation?
2. **Uniqueness:** When f can be represented by a power series, is there only one such series, and if so, what is it?

The uniqueness issue is addressed in the following theorem.

THEOREM 8.26   **The uniqueness theorem for power series representation**

Suppose an infinitely differentiable function f is known to have the power series representation

$$f(x) = \sum_{k=0}^{\infty} a_k(x - c)^k$$

for $-R < x - c < R$. Then there is exactly one such representation, and the coefficients a_k must satisfy

$$a_k = \frac{f^{(k)}(c)}{k!}$$

for $k = 0, 1, 2, \ldots$.

Proof: The uniqueness theorem may be established by differentiating the given power series term by term and evaluating successive derivatives at c. We start with

$$f(x) = \sum_{k=0}^{\infty} a_k(x - c)^k$$

and substitute $x = c$ to obtain

$$f(c) = a_0 + a_1(c - c) + a_2(c - c)^2 + \cdots = a_0$$

Next, differentiate the original series, term by term,

$$f'(x) = a_1 + 2a_2(x - c) + 3a_3(x - c)^2 + \cdots$$

and thus,

$$f'(c) = a_1 + 2a_2(0) + 3a_3(0)^2 + \cdots = a_1$$

Differentiating once again and substituting $x = c$ we find

$$f''(c) = 2a_2 \quad \text{so that} \quad a_2 = \frac{f''(c)}{2}$$

In general, the kth derivative of f at $x = c$ is given by

$$f^{(k)}(x) = k!a_k \quad \text{so that} \quad a_k = \frac{f^{(k)}(c)}{k!} \qquad \blacksquare$$

The question of existence—that is, under what conditions a given function has a power series representation—is answered by considering what is called the **Taylor remainder function:**

$$R_n(x) = f(x) - T_n(x)$$

We see that f exists as a series if and only if

$$\lim_{n \to \infty} R_n(x) = 0 \qquad \text{for all } x \text{ in } I$$

This relationship among f, its Taylor polynomial $T_n(x)$, and the Taylor remainder function $R_n(x)$, is summarized in the following theorem.

THEOREM 8.27   Taylor's theorem

If f and all its derivatives exist in an open interval I containing c, then for each x in I

$$f(x) = f(c) + \frac{f'(c)}{1!}(x - c) + \frac{f''(c)}{2!}(x - c)^2 + \cdots + \frac{f^{(n)}(c)}{n!}(x - c)^n + R_n(x)$$

where the remainder function $R_n(x)$ is given by

$$R_n(x) = \frac{f^{(n+1)}(z_n)}{(n + 1)!}(x - c)^{n+1}$$

for some z_n that depends on x and lies between c and x.

Proof: The proof of this theorem is given in Appendix B.   ■

The formula for $R_n(x)$ is called the *Lagrange form* of the Taylor remainder function, after the French/Italian mathematician Joseph Lagrange (1736–1813).

When applying Taylor's theorem, we do not expect to be able to find the exact value of z_n. Indeed, if we could find that value then an approximation would not have been necessary. However, we can often determine an upper bound for $|R_n(x)|$ in an open interval. We will illustrate this situation later in this section.

■ TAYLOR AND MACLAURIN SERIES

The uniqueness theorem tells us that if f has a power series representation at c, it must be the series

$$f(c) + \frac{f'(c)}{1!}(x - c) + \frac{f''(c)}{2!}(x - c)^2 + \frac{f'''(c)}{3!}(x - c)^3 + \cdots$$

Taylor Series

Suppose there is an open interval I containing c throughout which the function f and all its derivatives exist. Then the power series

$$f(c) + \frac{f'(c)}{1!}(x - c) + \frac{f''(c)}{2!}(x - c)^2 + \frac{f'''(c)}{3!}(x - c)^3 + \cdots$$

is called the **Taylor series of f at c.** The special case where $c = 0$ is called the **Maclaurin series of f:**

Maclaurin Series

$$f(0) + \frac{f'(0)}{1!}x + \frac{f''(0)}{2!}x^2 + \frac{f'''(0)}{3!}x^3 + \cdots$$

⊘   The uniqueness theorem may be summarized by saying that the Taylor series of f at c is the *only* power series of the form $\Sigma a_k(x - c)^k$ that can possibly represent f on I. But you must be careful. All we really know is that *if* f has a power series representation, then its representation must have the Taylor form.   ⊘

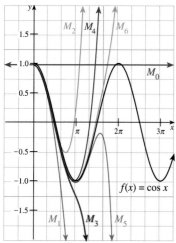

a. $M_0(x) = 1$, $M_1(x) = 1 - \frac{x^2}{2!}$,

$M_2(x) = 1 - \frac{x^2}{2!} + \frac{x^4}{4!}$,

$M_3(x) = 1 - \frac{x^2}{2!} + \frac{x^4}{4!} - \frac{x^6}{6!}$

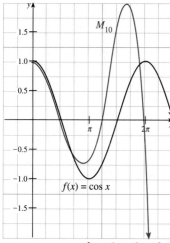

b. $M_{10}(x) = 1 - \frac{x^2}{2!} + \frac{x^4}{4!} - \frac{x^6}{6!} + \frac{x^8}{8!}$
$- \frac{x^{10}}{10!} + \frac{x^{12}}{12!} - \frac{x^{14}}{14!} + \frac{x^{16}}{16!} - \frac{x^{18}}{18!}$
$+ \frac{x^{20}}{20!}$

Figure 8.22 Comparison of a function and its Maclaurin polynomials

EXAMPLE 1   Maclaurin series

Find the Maclaurin series for $f(x) = \cos x$.

Solution   First, note that f is infinitely differentiable at $x = 0$. We find

$$f(x) = \cos x \qquad f(0) = 1$$
$$f'(x) = -\sin x \qquad f'(0) = 0$$
$$f''(x) = -\cos x \qquad f''(0) = -1$$
$$f'''(x) = \sin x \qquad f'''(0) = 0$$
$$f^{(4)}(x) = \cos x \qquad f^{(4)}(0) = 1$$
$$\vdots \qquad\qquad \vdots$$

Thus, by using the definition of a Maclaurin series, we have

$$\cos x = 1 - \frac{x^2}{2!} + \frac{x^4}{4!} - \frac{x^6}{6!} + \cdots = \sum_{k=0}^{\infty} \frac{(-1)^k x^{2k}}{(2k)!}$$

You might ask about the relationship between a Maclaurin series and a Maclaurin polynomial. Figure 8.22 shows the function $f(x) = \cos x$ from Example 1 along with some successive Maclaurin polynomials. We use the notation $M_n(x)$ to represent the first $n + 1$ terms of the corresponding Maclaurin polynomial. Note that the polynomials are quite close to the function near $x = 0$, but that they become very different as x moves away from the origin.

EXAMPLE 2   Maximum error when approximating a function with a Maclaurin polynomial

Find the Maclaurin polynomial $M_5(x)$ for the function $f(x) = e^x$ and use this polynomial to approximate e. Use Taylor's theorem to determine the accuracy of this approximation.

Solution   First find the Maclaurin series for $f(x) = e^x$.

$$f(x) = e^x \qquad f(0) = 1$$
$$f'(x) = e^x \qquad f'(0) = 1$$
$$\vdots \qquad\qquad \vdots$$

The Maclaurin series for e^x is

$$e^x = 1 + \frac{1}{1!}x + \frac{1}{2!}x^2 + \frac{1}{3!}x^3 + \cdots = \sum_{k=0}^{\infty} \frac{x^k}{k!}$$

Then find $M_5(x)$:

$$M_5(x) = 1 + x + \frac{x^2}{2} + \frac{x^3}{6} + \frac{x^4}{24} + \frac{x^5}{120} \approx e^x$$

A comparison of f and $M_5(x)$ is shown in Figure 8.23a. Notice from the graphs of these functions that the error seems to increase as x moves away from the origin. Suppose we draw the graphs on the interval [0, 1], as in Figure 8.23b.

To determine the accuracy we use Taylor's theorem

$$e \approx 1 + 1 + \tfrac{1}{2} + \tfrac{1}{6} + \tfrac{1}{24} + \tfrac{1}{120} + R_5(1)$$

$$= 2.71\overline{6} + R_5(1)$$

a. Comparison of f and M_5 **b.** Comparison on $[0, 1]$ **c.** Error at $x = 1$

Figure 8.23 Comparison of $f(x) = e^x$ and $M_5(x) = 1 + x + \dfrac{x^2}{2} + \dfrac{x^3}{6} + \dfrac{x^4}{24} + \dfrac{x^5}{120}$

⊘ Be careful with rounding. ⊘

The remainder term is given by $R_n(x) = \dfrac{f^{(n+1)}(z_n)}{(n+1)!} x^{n+1}$ for some number z_n between 0 and x. In particular,

$$R_5(1) = \frac{e^{z_5}}{(5+1)!}(1)^{5+1}$$

for some z_5 between 0 and 1. Because $0 < z_5 < 1$, we have $e^{z_5} < e$ and

$$R_5(1) < \frac{e}{6!} < \frac{3}{6!} \approx 0.0041667 \quad \text{because} \quad e < 3$$

Thus, e is between $2.716\,666\,7 + 0.004\,166\,7$ and $2.716\,666\,7 - 0.004\,166\,7$; that is,

$$2.712\,500 < e < 2.720\,834$$

You might wonder about using a bound on e ($e < 3$) to find another bound on e. This is not a new idea (remember the Newton-Raphson method). If we had picked 2.73 instead of 3 as a first choice, we would obtain an even better bound for e. Figure 8.23c shows a representation of the actual error at $x = 1$. ▬

EXAMPLE 3 Taylor series

Find the Taylor series for $f(x) = \ln x$ at $c = 1$.

Solution   Note that f is infinitely differentiable at $x = 1$. We find

$$f(x) = \ln x \qquad\qquad f(1) = 0$$

$$f'(x) = \frac{1}{x} \qquad\qquad f'(1) = 1$$

$$f''(x) = \frac{-1}{x^2} \qquad\qquad f''(1) = -1$$

$$f'''(x) = \frac{2}{x^3} \qquad\qquad f'''(1) = 2$$

$$f^{(4)}(x) = \frac{-6}{x^4} \qquad\qquad f^{(4)}(1) = -6$$

$$\vdots \qquad\qquad\qquad \vdots$$

$$f^{(k)}(x) = \frac{(-1)^{k+1}(k-1)!}{x^k} \qquad f^{(k)}(1) = (-1)^{k+1}(k-1)!$$

Then, use the definition of a Taylor series to write

$$\ln x = 0 + \frac{1}{1!}(x-1) - \frac{1}{2!}(x-1)^2 + \frac{2}{3!}(x-1)^3 - \frac{6}{4!}(x-1)^4 + \cdots$$

$$= (x-1) - \frac{1}{2}(x-1)^2 + \frac{1}{3}(x-1)^3 - \frac{1}{4}(x-1)^4 + \cdots$$

$$= \sum_{k=1}^{\infty} \frac{(-1)^{k+1}(x-1)^k}{k}$$

___

Computational Window

The computer format of the Taylor series expansion for a function may vary considerably from that shown in the text. For example, the Taylor series expansion for 4 terms of ln x expanded about $c = 1$ may be

$$-\frac{x^4}{4} + \frac{4x^3}{3} - 3x^2 + 4x - \frac{25}{12}$$

You notice this is equivalent to the expansion shown in Example 3.

Suppose f is a function that is infinitely differentiable at c. Now we have two mathematical quantities, f and its Taylor series. There are several possibilities:

1. The Taylor series of f may converge to f on the interval of absolute convergence, $-R < x - c < R$ (or $|x - c| < R$).
2. The Taylor series may only converge at $x = c$, in which case it certainly does not represent f on any interval containing c.
3. The Taylor series of f may have a positive radius of convergence (even $R = \infty$), but it may converge to a function g that does not equal f on the interval $|x - c| < R$.

EXAMPLE 4   A function that is defined at points where its Taylor series does not converge

Show that the function ln x is defined at points for which its Taylor series at $c = 1$ does not converge.

Solution   We know that ln x is defined for all $x > 0$. From the previous example, we know the Taylor series for ln x at $c = 1$ is

$$\sum_{k=1}^{\infty} \frac{(-1)^{k-1}(x-1)^k}{k}$$

We find the interval of convergence for this series centered at $c = 1$ by computing

$$\lim_{k \to \infty} \left| \frac{\frac{(-1)^k}{k+1}}{\frac{(-1)^{k-1}}{k}} \right| = \lim_{k \to \infty} \left(\frac{k}{k+1} \right) = 1$$

This means that the interval of absolute convergence is

$$|x - 1| < 1$$

$$-1 + 1 < x < 1 + 1$$

$$0 < x < 2$$

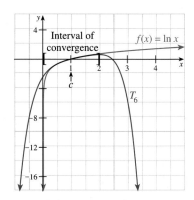

Figure 8.24 Graphs of $f(x) = \ln x$ and $T_6(x)$

Test the endpoints:

$$x = 0: \quad \sum_{k=1}^{\infty} \frac{(-1)^{k-1}(0-1)^k}{k} = \sum_{k=1}^{\infty} \frac{-1}{k}$$

which is known to diverge (harmonic series), and

$$x = 2: \quad \sum_{k=1}^{\infty} \frac{(-1)^{k-1}(2-1)^k}{k}$$

which converges (alternating harmonic series). Thus, the series converges only on $(0, 2]$, but the function itself is defined for all $x > 0$. The function is compared with the sixth-degree Taylor approximation in Figure 8.24.

$$T_6(x) = (x-1) - \frac{(x-1)^2}{2} + \frac{(x-1)^3}{3} - \frac{(x-1)^4}{4} + \frac{(x-1)^5}{5} - \frac{(x-1)^6}{6} \quad \blacksquare$$

The next example illustrates a function whose Maclaurin series does not represent that function on *any* interval.

EXAMPLE 5   A Maclaurin series that represents a function only at a single point

Let f be the function defined by $\begin{cases} e^{-1/x^2} & \text{if } x \neq 0 \\ 0 & \text{if } x = 0 \end{cases}$

Show that f has a Maclaurin series that represents it only at $x = 0$.

Solution   It can be shown that f is infinitely differentiable at 0 and that $f^{(k)}(0) = 0$ for all k, so that f has the Maclaurin series

$$0 + \frac{0}{1!}x + \frac{0}{2!}x^2 + \frac{0}{3!}x^3 + \cdots = 0$$

This series converges to the function $f(x) = 0$ for all x and thus represents $f(x)$ only at $x = 0$. The graph of f and the Maclaurin series is shown in Figure 8.25. $\blacksquare$

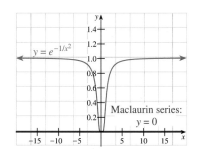

Figure 8.25 Graph of f and its Maclaurin series $y = 0$

■ OPERATIONS WITH MACLAURIN AND TAYLOR SERIES

According to the uniqueness theorem, the Taylor series for f at c is the only power series in $x - c$ that can satisfy

$$f(x) = \sum_{k=0}^{\infty} a_k(x - c)^k$$

for all x in some interval containing c. The coefficients in this series can always be found by substituting into the formula

$$a_k = \frac{f^{(k)}(c)}{k!}$$

but occasionally they can also be found by algebraic manipulation.

EXAMPLE 6   Maclaurin series using substitution

Find the Maclaurin series for $\dfrac{1}{1 + x^2}$.

Solution   We want a series of the form $\sum_{k=0}^{\infty} a_k u^k$ that represents $\dfrac{1}{1 + x^2}$ on an interval containing 0. We could proceed directly using the definition of a Maclaurin series. We could also carry out long division of $1 + x^2$ into 1, but instead we will modify a known series. We know that if $|u| < 1$ we can write

$$\frac{1}{1 - u} = 1 + u + u^2 + \cdots$$

so by substitution ($u = -x^2$) we have

$$\frac{1}{1 + x^2} = \frac{1}{1 - (-x^2)} = 1 - x^2 + x^4 - x^6 + \cdots$$

provided $|-x^2| < 1$; that is, $-1 < x < 1$. Hence, by the uniqueness theorem, the desired representation is

$$\frac{1}{1 + x^2} = \sum_{k=0}^{\infty} (-1)^k x^{2k} \qquad \text{for } -1 < x < 1$$

EXAMPLE 7   Maclaurin series using substitution and subtraction

Find the Maclaurin series for $f(x) = \ln\left(\frac{1 + x}{1 - x}\right)$ and use this series to compute $\ln 2$ correct to five decimal places.

Solution   For this function, we first use a property of logarithms:

$$f(x) = \ln\left(\frac{1 + x}{1 - x}\right) = \ln(1 + x) - \ln(1 - x)$$

From Example 3, we know

$$\ln x = (x - 1) - \tfrac{1}{2}(x - 1)^2 + \tfrac{1}{3}(x - 1)^3 - \cdots$$

so that

$$\ln(1 + x) = [1 + x - 1] - \tfrac{1}{2}[1 + x - 1]^2 + \tfrac{1}{3}[1 + x - 1]^3 - \cdots$$

$$= x - \frac{x^2}{2} + \frac{x^3}{3} - \frac{x^4}{4} + \cdots$$

$$\ln(1 - x) = [1 - x - 1] - \tfrac{1}{2}[1 - x - 1]^2 + \tfrac{1}{3}[1 - x - 1]^3 - \cdots$$

$$= (-x) - \frac{(-x)^2}{2} + \frac{(-x)^3}{3} - \frac{(-x)^4}{4} + \cdots$$

$$= -x - \frac{x^2}{2} - \frac{x^3}{3} - \frac{x^4}{4} - \cdots$$

By subtracting series we find

$$f(x) = \ln(1 + x) - \ln(1 - x)$$

$$= \left[x - \frac{x^2}{2} + \frac{x^3}{3} - \frac{x^4}{4} + \cdots\right] - \left[-x - \frac{x^2}{2} - \frac{x^3}{3} - \frac{x^4}{4} - \cdots\right]$$

$$= 2\left[x + \frac{x^3}{3} + \frac{x^5}{5} + \cdots\right]$$

Next, by solving the equation $\frac{1 + x}{1 - x} = 2$, we find $x = \frac{1}{3}$, so we are looking for $\ln\left(\frac{1 + x}{1 - x}\right)$ where $x = \frac{1}{3}$. It follows that

$$\ln 2 = 2\left[\frac{1}{3} + \frac{\left(\frac{1}{3}\right)^3}{3} + \frac{\left(\frac{1}{3}\right)^5}{5} + \cdots\right] = 2\left[\frac{1}{3} + \frac{1}{3}\left(\frac{1}{3}\right)^3 + \frac{1}{5}\left(\frac{1}{3}\right)^5 + \cdots\right]$$

If we approximate this by a Taylor polynomial we find

$$\ln 2 = \frac{2}{3} + \frac{2}{3}\left(\frac{1}{3}\right)^3 + \frac{2}{5}\left(\frac{1}{3}\right)^5 + \cdots + \frac{2}{2n+1}\left(\frac{1}{3}\right)^{2n+1} + R_n\left(\frac{1}{3}\right)$$

where $R_n\left(\frac{1}{3}\right)$ is the remainder term. To estimate the remainder, we note that $R_n\left(\frac{1}{3}\right)$ is the tail of the infinite series for $\ln 2$. Thus,

$$\left|R_n\left(\tfrac{1}{3}\right)\right| = \frac{2}{2n+3}\left(\frac{1}{3}\right)^{2n+3} + \frac{2}{2n+5}\left(\frac{1}{3}\right)^{2n+5} + \cdots$$

$$< \frac{2}{2n+3}\left(\frac{1}{3}\right)^{2n+3} + \frac{2}{2n+3}\left(\frac{1}{9}\right)\left(\frac{1}{3}\right)^{2n+3} + \cdots$$

$$= \frac{2}{2n+3}\left(\frac{1}{3}\right)^{2n+3}\left[1 + \frac{1}{9} + \frac{1}{81} + \cdots\right]$$

Because the geometric series in brackets converges to $\dfrac{1}{1-\frac{1}{9}} = \dfrac{9}{8}$, we find that

$$R_n\left(\frac{1}{3}\right) < \frac{2}{2n+3}\left(\frac{9}{8}\right)\left(\frac{1}{3}\right)^{2n+3}$$

In particular, to achieve five-place accuracy we must make sure the term on the right is less than 0.000005 (six places to account for round-off error). With a calculator we can see that if $n = 4$, we have

$$\frac{2}{2(4)+3}\left(\frac{9}{8}\right)\left(\frac{1}{3}\right)^{11} \approx 0.000\,001\,2$$

Thus, we approximate $\ln 2$ with $n = 4$:

$$\ln 2 \approx T_4(x) = \frac{2}{3} + \frac{2}{3}\left(\frac{1}{3}\right)^3 + \frac{2}{5}\left(\frac{1}{3}\right)^5 + \frac{2}{7}\left(\frac{1}{3}\right)^7 + \frac{2}{9}\left(\frac{1}{3}\right)^9 \approx 0.693\,146\,0$$

which is correct with an error of no more than 0.000 001 2; therefore

$$0.693\,146\,0 - 0.000\,001\,2 < \ln 2 < 0.693\,146 + 0.000\,001\,2$$

$$0.693\,144\,8 < \ln 2 < 0.693\,147\,3$$

Rounded to five-place accuracy, $\ln 2 = 0.693\,15$.
We can check with calculator accuracy: $\ln 2 \approx 0.693\,147\,180$. ▬

You might wonder "why bother with the accuracy part of Example 7? I can just press ln 2 and obtain better accuracy anyway." The answer to this might be that the accuracy in the design of calculators and computers and programs is of utmost importance. Indeed, the way that engineers ensure accuracy in the design is to use series and arguments similar to the one shown in Example 7. Calculators and computers have not changed the need for accuracy consideration, but have simply pushed out the limits of these accuracy arguments. It is only for convenience that we ask for limits of accuracy that are less than what we can obtain with a calculator (or any available machine), but the method is just as valid if we ask for 100- or 1,000-place accuracy.

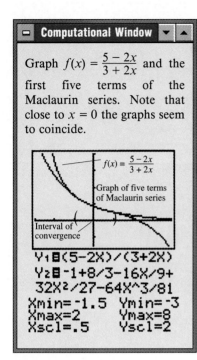

Computational Window ▼ ▲

Graph $f(x) = \dfrac{5 - 2x}{3 + 2x}$ and the first five terms of the Maclaurin series. Note that close to $x = 0$ the graphs seem to coincide.

$f(x) = \dfrac{5 - 2x}{3 + 2x}$

Graph of five terms of Maclaurin series

Interval of convergence

Y₁⊟(5−2X)/(3+2X)
Y₂⊟−1+8/3−16X/9+
32X²/27−64X^3/81
Xmin=−1.5 Ymin=−3
Xmax=2   Ymax=8
Xscl=.5 Yscl=2

EXAMPLE 8   Maclaurin series by rewriting given function in terms of a geometric series

Find the Maclaurin series for $f(x) = \dfrac{5 - 2x}{3 + 2x}$.

Solution   The direct approach, namely, finding the successive derivatives of f, is not a very pleasant prospect. Instead, we recall that a geometric series

$$\sum_{k=0}^{\infty} ar^k \quad \text{converges to the sum} \quad \frac{a}{1 - r} \quad \text{if} \quad |r| < 1$$

Our approach with this example is to rewrite f in the form $\dfrac{a}{1 - r}$ so that we can refer to the geometric series.

$$\frac{5 - 2x}{3 + 2x} = -1 + \frac{8}{3 + 2x} = -1 + \frac{\frac{8}{3}}{1 - \left(-\frac{2}{3}x\right)}$$

The related series converges for

$$\left|\frac{2}{3}x\right| < 1 \quad \text{or} \quad -\frac{3}{2} < x < \frac{3}{2}$$

Thus, for an interval of convergence $\left(-\frac{3}{2}, \frac{3}{2}\right)$ the geometric series is

$$\sum_{k=0}^{\infty} ar^k = \frac{a}{1 - r} \quad \text{where} \quad a = \frac{8}{3} \quad \text{and} \quad r = -\frac{2}{3}x$$

Thus,

$$\frac{5 - 2x}{3 + 2x} = -1 + \sum_{k=0}^{\infty} \frac{8}{3}\left[-\frac{2}{3}x\right]^k = -1 + \frac{8}{3} - \frac{16}{9}x + \frac{32}{27}x^2 - \frac{64}{81}x^3 + \cdots$$

EXAMPLE 9   Using a trigonometric identity with a known series

Find the Maclaurin series for **a.** $\cos x^2$ **b.** $\cos^2 x$

Solution   a. In Example 1, we found that

$$\cos u = 1 - \frac{u^2}{2!} + \frac{u^4}{4!} - \frac{u^6}{6!} + \cdots \quad \text{for all } u$$

Therefore, by substituting $u = x^2$, we obtain

$$\cos x^2 = 1 - \frac{(x^2)^2}{2!} + \frac{(x^2)^4}{4!} - \frac{(x^2)^6}{6!} + \cdots$$

$$= 1 - \frac{x^4}{2!} + \frac{x^8}{4!} - \frac{x^{12}}{6!} + \cdots \quad \text{for all } x$$

b. For $\cos^2 x$ we could use the definition of a Maclaurin series, but instead we will use a double angle trigonometric identity.

$$\cos^2 x = \frac{1}{2} + \frac{1}{2}\cos 2x$$

$$= \frac{1}{2} + \frac{1}{2}\left[1 - \frac{(2x)^2}{2!} + \frac{(2x)^4}{4!} - \frac{(2x)^6}{6!} + \cdots\right] \quad \textit{Let } u = 2x.$$

$$= \frac{1}{2} + \frac{1}{2} - \frac{2x^2}{2!} + \frac{2^3 x^4}{4!} - \frac{2^5 x^6}{6!} + \cdots$$

$$= 1 - x^2 + \frac{1}{3}x^4 - \frac{2}{45}x^6 + \cdots \quad \text{for all } x$$

EXAMPLE 10   Maclaurin series by adding two power series

Find the Maclaurin series for $\dfrac{5 + x}{2 - x - x^2}$.

Solution   Using partial fractions, we can obtain the decomposition (without showing the steps):

$$\frac{5 + x}{2 - x - x^2} = \frac{2}{1 - x} + \frac{1}{2 + x}$$

Both of the terms on the right can be expressed as the sum of a geometric series:

$$\frac{2}{1 - x} = 2\left[\frac{1}{1 - x}\right] = 2[1 + x + x^2 + x^3 + \cdots] = 2\sum_{k=0}^{\infty} x^k \quad \text{on } (-1, 1)$$

$$\frac{1}{2 + x} = \frac{1}{2}\left[\frac{1}{1 - \left(-\frac{x}{2}\right)}\right] = \frac{1}{2}\left[1 + \left(-\frac{x}{2}\right) + \left(-\frac{x}{2}\right)^2 + \left(-\frac{x}{2}\right)^3 + \cdots\right]$$

$$= \frac{1}{2}\sum_{k=0}^{\infty}(-1)^k\left(\frac{x}{2}\right)^k \quad \text{on } (-2, 2)$$

Because we are dealing with two power series, we need to be careful about finding the interval of convergence. It is the intersection of the individual intervals of convergence, so we note that

$$(-1, 1) \cap (-2, 2) = (-1, 1)$$

Thus,

$$\frac{5 + x}{2 - x - x^2} = \underbrace{2\sum_{k=0}^{\infty} x^k}_{} + \underbrace{\frac{1}{2}\sum_{k=0}^{\infty}(-1)^k\left(\frac{x}{2}\right)^k}_{} = \underbrace{\sum_{k=0}^{\infty}\left[2x^k + (-1)^k\frac{1}{2}\left(\frac{x}{2}\right)^k\right]}_{}$$

Interval of convergence: $\underbrace{(-1, 1)}_{} \cap \underbrace{(-2, 2)}_{} = \underbrace{(-1, 1)}_{}$

$$= \sum_{k=0}^{\infty}\left(2 + \frac{(-1)^k}{2^{k+1}}\right)x^k = \left(2 + \tfrac{1}{2}\right) + \left(2 - \tfrac{1}{4}\right)x + \left(2 + \tfrac{1}{8}\right)x^2 + \left(2 - \tfrac{1}{16}\right)x^3 + \cdots$$

$$= \tfrac{5}{2} + \tfrac{7}{4}x + \tfrac{17}{8}x^2 + \tfrac{31}{16}x^3 + \cdots \quad \text{converges on } (-1, 1) \quad \blacksquare$$

EXAMPLE 11   Maclaurin series by integration

Find the Maclaurin series for $\tan^{-1} x$.

Solution   We shall use the fact that $\tan^{-1} x = \displaystyle\int_0^x \frac{dt}{1 + t^2}$. From Example 6,

$$\frac{1}{1 + t^2} = 1 - t^2 + t^4 - t^6 + \cdots = \sum_{k=0}^{\infty}(-1)^k t^{2k}$$

Thus,

$$\tan^{-1} x = \int_0^x \frac{1}{1 + t^2}\, dt$$

$$= \int_0^x [1 - t^2 + t^4 - t^6 + \cdots]\, dt = \sum_{k=0}^{\infty}\int_0^x (-1)^k t^{2k}\, dt$$

$$= x - \frac{x^3}{3} + \frac{x^5}{5} - \frac{x^7}{7} + \cdots = \sum_{k=0}^{\infty}\frac{(-1)^k x^{2k+1}}{2k + 1} \quad \text{for } |x| \le 1 \quad \blacksquare$$

| No. of | Gregory's Series | |
terms	term	partial sum
0	4	
1	−1.3333333333333	2.666666667
2	0.8	3.466666667
3	−0.57142857142857	2.895238095
4	0.44444444444444	3.33968254
5	−0.36363636363636	2.976046176
6	0.30769230769231	3.283738484
7	−0.26666666666667	3.017071817
8	0.23529411764706	3.252365935
9	−0.21052631578947	3.041839619
10	0.19047619047619	3.232315809
11	−0.17391304347826	3.058402766
12	0.16	3.218402766
13	−0.14814814814815	3.070254618
14	0.13793103448276	3.208185652
15	−0.12903225806452	3.079153394
16	0.12121212121212	3.200365515
17	−0.11428571428571	3.086079801
18	0.10810810810811	3.194187909
19	−0.1025641025641	3.091623807
20	0.097560975609756	3.189184782
21	−0.09302325581395	3.096161526
22	0.088888888888889	3.185050415
23	−0.08510638297872	3.099944032
24	0.081632653061224	3.181576685
25	−0.07843137254902	3.103145313
26	0.075471698113208	3.178617011
27	−0.07272727272727	3.105889738
28	0.070175438596491	3.176065177
29	−0.06779661016949	3.108268567
30	0.065573770491803	3.173842337
31	−0.06349206349206	3.110350274
32	0.061538461538462	3.171888735
33	−0.05970149253731	3.112187243
34	0.057971014492754	3.170158257
35	−0.05633802816901	3.113820229
36	0.054794520547945	3.16861475
37	−0.05333333333333	3.115281416
38	0.051948051948052	3.167229468
39	−0.05063291139241	3.116596557
40	0.049382716049383	3.165979273
41	−0.04819277108434	3.117786502
42	0.047058823529412	3.164845325
43	−0.04597701149425	3.118868314
44	0.044943820224719	3.163812134
45	−0.04395604395604	3.11985609
46	0.043010752688172	3.162866843
47	−0.04210526315789	3.12076158
48	0.041237113402062	3.161998693
49	−0.04040404040404	3.121594653
50	0.03960396039604	3.161198613

Approximation of π using Gregory's series

(s^{M}H)

This series for $\tan^{-1} x$ is called **Gregory's series** after the British mathematician James Gregory (1638–1675), who developed it in 1671. It can be shown that the Maclaurin series for $\tan^{-1} x$ found in Example 11 also represents $\tan^{-1} x$ at $x = 1$ and $x = -1$. In particular, at $x = 1$, we have

$$\frac{\pi}{4} = \tan^{-1} 1 = 1 - \frac{1}{3} + \frac{1}{5} - \frac{1}{7} + \frac{1}{9} - \cdots$$

$$\pi = 4\left(1 - \frac{1}{3} + \frac{1}{5} - \frac{1}{7} + \frac{1}{9} - \cdots\right)$$

The convergence of this series is very slow (see the computer output in the margin) in the sense that it takes a relatively large number of terms to achieve a reasonable approximation for π. Look at the partial sums for the 49th and 50th terms, and note that these are not very close to the limit (which is π).

The mathematician Srinivasa Ramanujan (1887–1920) discovered another series that converges much faster. Ramanujan was a very clever mathematician and used the trigonometric identity

(s^{M}H) $\tan(\alpha + \beta) = \dfrac{\tan \alpha + \tan \beta}{1 - \tan \alpha \tan \beta}$

to show that

$$\tan^{-1} 1 = 4 \tan^{-1} \frac{1}{5} - \tan^{-1} \frac{1}{239}$$

Using this identity, we find another series for π.

$$\pi = 16\left[\frac{1}{5} - \frac{1}{3}\left(\frac{1}{5}\right)^3 + \frac{1}{5}\left(\frac{1}{5}\right)^5 - \cdots\right] - 4\left[\frac{1}{239} - \frac{1}{3}\left(\frac{1}{239}\right)^3 + \frac{1}{5}\left(\frac{1}{239}\right)^5 - \cdots\right]$$

| No. of | Ramanujan's Series | |
terms	term	partial sum
0	3.1832635983264	
1	−0.0426665690003	3.140597029
2	0.001023999998974	3.141621029
3	−2.9257142857E-05	3.141591772
4	9.10222222222E-07	3.141592682
5	−2.9789090909E-08	3.141592653
6	1.00824615385E-09	3.141592654
7	−3.4952533333E-11	3.141592654

You can compare the convergence of this spreadsheet approximation with the first one and see that it approximates π much more quickly. (Note that the seventh term is fairly close to the limit π.)

Some of the more common power series that we have derived are given in Table 8.2. For a more complete list see *Student Mathematics Handbook*. Before we present this list, there is one last result we should consider. It is a generalization of the binomial theorem that was discovered by Isaac Newton while he was still a student at Cambridge University.

THEOREM 8.28   Binomial series theorem

The binomial function $(1 + x)^p$ is represented by its Maclaurin series

$$(1 + x)^p = 1 + px + \frac{p(p-1)}{2!}x^2 + \frac{p(p-1)(p-2)}{3!}x^3 + \cdots$$

$$+ \frac{p(p-1) \cdots (p-k+1)}{k!} x^k + \cdots$$

for all x if p is a nonnegative integer; for $-1 < x < 1$ if $p \le -1$; $-1 \le x \le 1$ if $p > 0$ and p is not an integer; and for $-1 < x \le 1$ if $-1 < p < 0$.

TABLE 8.2 Power Series for Elementary Functions

Name	Series	Interval of Convergence
	Taylor series at $x = c$ follows the Maclaurin series for each function.	
Exponential series	$e^u = 1 + u + \dfrac{u^2}{2!} + \dfrac{u^3}{3!} + \dfrac{u^4}{4!} + \cdots + \dfrac{u^k}{k!} + \cdots$	$(-\infty, \infty)$
	$e^x = e^c + e^c(x - c) + \dfrac{e^c(x - c)^2}{2!} + \dfrac{e^c(x - c)^3}{3!} + \cdots + \dfrac{e^c(x - c)^k}{k!} + \cdots$	$(-\infty, \infty)$
Cosine series	$\cos u = 1 - \dfrac{u^2}{2!} + \dfrac{u^4}{4!} - \dfrac{u^6}{6!} + \cdots + \dfrac{(-1)^k u^{2k}}{(2k)!} + \cdots$	$(-\infty, \infty)$
	$\cos x = \cos c - (x - c)\sin c - \dfrac{(x - c)^2}{2!}\cos c + \dfrac{(x - c)^3}{3!}\sin c + \cdots$	$(-\infty, \infty)$
Sine series	$\sin u = u - \dfrac{u^3}{3!} + \dfrac{u^5}{5!} - \dfrac{u^7}{7!} + \cdots + \dfrac{(-1)^k u^{2k+1}}{(2k + 1)!} + \cdots$	$(-\infty, \infty)$
	$\sin x = \sin c + (x - c)\cos c - \dfrac{(x - c)^2}{2!}\sin c - \dfrac{(x - c)^3}{3!}\cos c + \cdots$	$(-\infty, \infty)$
Geometric series	$\dfrac{1}{1 - u} = 1 + u^2 + u^3 + \cdots + u^k + \cdots$	$(-1, 1)$
Reciprocal series	$\dfrac{1}{u} = 1 - (u - 1) + (u - 1)^2 - (u - 1)^3 + (u - 1)^4 - \cdots$	$(0, 2)$
Logarithmic series	$\ln u = (u - 1) - \dfrac{(u - 1)^2}{2} + \dfrac{(u - 1)^3}{3} - \cdots + \dfrac{(-1)^{k-1}(u - 1)^k}{k} + \cdots$	$(0, 2]$
	$\ln(1 + x) = x - \dfrac{1}{2}x^2 + \dfrac{1}{3}x^3 - \dfrac{1}{4}x^4 + \cdots + \dfrac{(-1)^n x^{n+1}}{n + 1} + \cdots$	$(-1, 1]$
	$\ln x = \ln c + \dfrac{x - c}{c} - \dfrac{(x - c)^2}{2c^2} + \dfrac{(x - c)^3}{3c^3} - \cdots + \dfrac{(-1)^{k-1}(x - c)^k}{kc^k} + \cdots$	$(0, 2c]$
Inverse tangent series	$\tan^{-1} u = u - \dfrac{u^3}{3} + \dfrac{u^5}{5} - \dfrac{u^7}{7} + \cdots + \dfrac{(-1)^k u^{2k+1}}{2k + 1} + \cdots$	$[-1, 1]$
Inverse sine series	$\sin^{-1} u = u + \dfrac{u^3}{2 \cdot 3} + \dfrac{1 \cdot 3 u^5}{2 \cdot 4 \cdot 5} + \dfrac{1 \cdot 3 \cdot 5 \cdot u^7}{2 \cdot 4 \cdot 6 \cdot 7} + \cdots + \dfrac{1 \cdot 3 \cdot 5 \cdots (2k - 3)u^{2k-1}}{2 \cdot 4 \cdot 6 \cdots (2k - 2)(2k - 1)} + \cdots$	$[-1, 1]$
Binomial series	$(1 + u)^p = 1 + pu + \dfrac{p(p - 1)}{2!}u^2 + \dfrac{p(p - 1)(p - 2)}{3!}u^3 + \cdots + \dfrac{p(p - 1) \cdots (p - k + 1)}{k!}u^k + \cdots$	$(-1, 1)$

Proof: We begin by showing how the Maclaurin series is found. Let $f(x) = (1 + x)^p$.

$$f(x) = (1 + x)^p \qquad\qquad f(0) = 1$$

$$f'(x) = p(1 + x)^{p-1} \qquad\qquad f'(0) = p$$

$$f''(x) = p(p - 1)(1 + x)^{p-2} \qquad f''(0) = p(p - 1)$$

$$f'''(x) = p(p - 1)(p - 2)(1 + x)^{p-3} \quad f'''(0) = p(p - 1)(p - 2)$$

$$\vdots \qquad\qquad\qquad\qquad \vdots$$

$$f^{(n)}(x) = p(p - 1) \cdots (p - n + 1)(1 + x)^{p-n}$$

and

$$f^{(n)}(0) = p(p - 1) \cdots (p - n + 1)$$

which produces the Maclaurin series. We could use the ratio test to show that this series converges to *some function* on the interval $(-1, 1)$, but to show that it converges to $(1 + x)^p$ requires solving a differential equation. We leave this proof to a course on advanced calculus. ∎

EXAMPLE 12   Using the binomial series theorem to obtain a Maclaurin series expansion

Find the Maclaurin series for $f(x) = \sqrt{9 + x}$ and find its radius of convergence.

Solution   Write $f(x) = \sqrt{9 + x} = (9 + x)^{1/2} = 3\left(1 + \dfrac{x}{9}\right)^{1/2}$. Thus,

$$\sqrt{9 + x} = 3\left(1 + \frac{x}{9}\right)^{1/2}$$

$$= 3\left[1 + \frac{1}{2}\left(\frac{x}{9}\right) + \frac{\frac{1}{2}(\frac{1}{2} - 1)}{2!}\left(\frac{x}{9}\right)^2 + \frac{\frac{1}{2}(\frac{1}{2} - 1)(\frac{1}{2} - 2)}{3!}\left(\frac{x}{9}\right)^3 + \cdots\right]$$

$$= 3\left[1 + \frac{1}{18}x - \frac{1}{648}x^2 + \frac{1}{11,664}x^3 - \cdots\right] = 3 + \frac{1}{6}x - \frac{1}{216}x^2 + \frac{1}{3,888}x^3 - \cdots$$

We know from Theorem 8.28 that the series converges when $\left|\dfrac{x}{9}\right| < 1$; that is, $|x| < 9$, so the radius of convergence is $R = 9$. ▬

PROBLEM SET 8.8

Ⓐ **1.** ■ **What Does This Say?** Compare and contrast Maclaurin and Taylor series.

2. ■ **What Does This Say?** Discuss the binomial series theorem.

Find the Maclaurin series for the functions given in Problems 3–30. Assume that a is any constant.

3. e^{2x} **4.** e^{-x} **5.** e^{x^2} **6.** e^{ax}

7. $\sin x^2$ **8.** $\sin^2 x$ **9.** $\sin ax$ **10.** $\cos ax$

11. $\cos 2x^2$ **12.** $\cos x^3$ **13.** $x^2\cos x$ **14.** $\sin\dfrac{x}{2}$

15. $x^2 + 2x + 1$ **16.** $x^3 - 2x^2 + x - 5$

17. xe^x **18.** $e^{-x} + e^{2x}$

19. $e^x + \sin x$

20. $\sin x + \cos x$

21. $\dfrac{1}{1 + 4x}$

22. $\dfrac{1}{1 - ax}$, $a \neq 0$

23. $\dfrac{1}{a + x}$, $a \neq 0$

24. $\dfrac{1}{a^2 + x^2}$, $a \neq 0$

25. $\ln(3 + x)$

26. $\log(1 + x)$

27. $\tan^{-1}(2x)$

28. $\sqrt{x}$

29. $f(x) = \begin{cases} e^{-x^2} & \text{if } x \neq 0 \\ 1 & \text{if } x = 0 \end{cases}$

30. $f(x) = \begin{cases} \dfrac{\sin x}{x} & \text{if } x \neq 0 \\ 1 & \text{if } x = 0 \end{cases}$

Find the first four terms of the Taylor series of the functions in Problems 31–42 at the given value of c.

31. $f(x) = e^x$ at $c = 1$

32. $f(x) = \ln x$ at $c = 3$

33. $f(x) = \cos x$ at $c = \frac{\pi}{3}$

34. $f(x) = \sin x$ at $c = \frac{\pi}{4}$

35. $f(x) = \tan x$ at $c = 0$

36. $f(x) = x^2 + 2x + 1$ at $c = 200$

37. $f(x) = x^3 - 2x^2 + x - 5$ at $c = 2$

38. $f(x) = \sqrt{x}$ at $c = 9$

39. $f(x) = \dfrac{1}{2 - x}$ at $c = 5$

40. $f(x) = \dfrac{1}{4 - x}$ at $c = -2$

41. $f(x) = \dfrac{3}{2x - 1}$ at $c = 2$

42. $f(x) = \dfrac{5}{3x + 2}$ at $c = 2$

Expand each function in Problems 43–48 as a binomial series. Give the interval of absolute convergence of the series.

43. $f(x) = \sqrt{1 + x}$

44. $f(x) = \dfrac{1}{\sqrt{1 + x^2}}$

45. $f(x) = (1 + x)^{2/3}$

46. $f(x) = (4 + x)^{-1/3}$

47. $f(x) = \dfrac{x}{\sqrt{1 - x^2}}$

48. $f(x) = \sqrt[4]{2 - x}$

Ⓑ 49. Use term-by-term integration to show that

$$\ln(1 + x) = \sum_{k=1}^{\infty} \frac{(-1)^{k-1}x^k}{k} \text{ for } |x| < 1$$

50. Use the Maclaurin series for e^x and e^{-x} to find the Maclaurin series for

$$\cosh x = \frac{e^x + e^{-x}}{2}$$

51. Use the Maclaurin series for e^x and e^{-x} to find the Maclaurin series for

$$\sinh x = \frac{e^x - e^{-x}}{2}$$

52. How many terms of a Maclaurin series expansion of e are necessary to approximate $\sqrt{e}$ to three-decimal-place accuracy?

53. How many terms of a Maclaurin series expansion of e are necessary to approximate $\sqrt[3]{e}$ to three-decimal-place accuracy?

Use partial fractions to find the Maclaurin series for the functions given in Problems 54–60.

54. $f(x) = \dfrac{2x}{x^2 - 1}$

55. $f(x) = \dfrac{6 - x}{4 - x^2}$

56. $f(x) = \dfrac{3(1 - x)}{9 - x^2}$

57. $f(x) = \dfrac{1}{x^2 - 3x + 2}$

58. $f(x) = \dfrac{2x - 3}{x^2 - 3x + 2}$

59. $f(x) = \dfrac{x^2}{(x + 2)(x^2 - 1)}$

60. $f(x) = \dfrac{x^2 - 6x + 7}{(1 - x)(2 - x)(3 - x)}$

61. Use an appropriate identity to find the Maclaurin series for $f(x) = \sin x \cos x$.

62. a. It can be shown that

$$\cos 3x = 4 \cos^3 x - 3 \cos x$$

Use this identity to find the Maclaurin series for $\cos^3 x$.

b. Find the Maclaurin series for $\sin^3 x$.

63. Use the identity

$$\cos x + \cos y = 2\left[\cos \tfrac{1}{2}(x + y)\right]\left[\cos \tfrac{1}{2}(x - y)\right]$$

to find the Maclaurin series for

$$f(x) = \left(\cos \frac{3x}{2}\right)\left(\cos \frac{x}{2}\right)$$

64. Find the Maclaurin series for

$$\ln[(1 + 2x)(1 + 3x)]$$

65. Find the Maclaurin series for

$$\ln\left[\frac{1 + 2x}{1 - 3x + 2x^2}\right]$$

66. Find the Maclaurin series for

$$f(x) = \frac{x + \sin x}{x}$$

and then use this series to find $\lim_{x \to 0} f(x)$.

67. Find the Maclaurin series for

$$g(x) = \frac{e^x - 1}{x}$$

and then use this series to find $\lim_{x \to 0} g(x)$.

In Problems 68–70, the Maclaurin series of a function appears with its remainder. Verify that the remainder satisfies the given inequality.

68. $\sin x = \displaystyle\sum_{k=1}^{n} \frac{(-1)^{k-1}x^{2k-1}}{(2k - 1)!} + R_{2n}(x); \ |R_{2n}(x)| \le \dfrac{|x|^{2n+1}}{(2n + 1)!}$

69. $\cos x = \displaystyle\sum_{k=0}^{n} \frac{(-1)^k x^{2k}}{(2k)!} + R_{2n+1}(x); \ |R_{2n+1}(x)| \le \dfrac{|x|^{2n+2}}{(2n + 2)!}$

70. $\tan^{-1} x = \displaystyle\sum_{k=0}^{n-1} \frac{(-1)^k x^{2k+1}}{2k + 1} + R_{2n}(x);$

$$|R_{2n}(x)| \le \frac{x^{2n+1}}{2n + 1} \text{ for } 0 \le x \le 1$$

Computational Window

In the following two problems we will always be expanding about $x = c = 0$, but will refer to the Taylor (rather than the Maclaurin) expansion. Also, let $P_n(x)$ denote the Taylor polynomial of degree n approximating $f(x)$.

71. Consider the Taylor approximations to
$$f(x) = x \cos 2x.$$

   a. An easy way to get an expansion for f is the following: You know the expansion for $\cos x$; so simply replace x by $2x$ to obtain several terms of $\cos 2x$. Then multiply by x to obtain an expression for $f(x)$.

   b. Suppose you want to approximate $f(x)$ by $P_5(x)$ on $\left[-\frac{1}{2}, \frac{1}{2}\right]$ and you are concerned about accuracy. Rather than compute the remainder terms $R_5(x)$, which is not pleasant, consider the following. Look at the *next* Taylor term (involving x^7), and see how large this term could be on the interval $\left[-\frac{1}{2}, \frac{1}{2}\right]$. Although not fool-proof, this is usually a good estimate of the error in $P_5(x)$. Use this to estimate the error, $f(x) - P_5(x)$.

   c. As a check on your work in part **b**, use a computer to compute the Taylor $P_5(x)$.

   d. Now, plot the difference $f(x) - P(x)$ on $\left[-\frac{1}{2}, \frac{1}{2}\right]$ and see how the actual error compares with the estimate you found in part **b**.

72. The idea in this problem is to use power series to solve a simple-looking, but difficult, differential equation. We want a solution on $[-1, 1]$:
$$y'' = g(x) = e^{-x^2} \sin x$$

with initial conditions
$$y(0) = 0.3, \quad y'(0) = -0.1$$

If you attempt a direct solution, you will have trouble integrating y'' to obtain y'. Instead, we seek an approximation to the solution, as follows.

   a. Try to integrate $g(x)$ using your computer. Describe what happens.

   b. Approximate $g(x)$ by a Taylor $P_n(x)$ until it looks good on $[-1, 1]$. If possible, provide a graph.

   c. Now integrate P_n twice, applying the initial conditions, thus obtaining our desired solution. Provide a graph of the resulting y. *Note*: Make sure your y satisfies $y(0) = 0.3$, $y'(0) = -0.1$.

C 73. Use term-by-term differentiation of a geometric series to find the Maclaurin series of the function
$$f(x) = \frac{1}{(1 - x)^3}$$

74. Find the Maclaurin series expansion for the function defined by the integral
$$F(x) = \int_0^x e^{-t^2} \, dt$$

75. Express $\int_0^1 x^{0.2} e^x \, dx$ as an infinite series.

76. The functions $J_0(x)$ and $J_1(x)$ are defined as the following power series:
$$J_0(x) = \sum_{k=0}^{\infty} \frac{(-1)^k x^{2k}}{(k!)^2 2^{2k}}$$

and
$$J_1(x) = \sum_{k=0}^{\infty} \frac{(-1)^k x^{2k}}{k!(k + 1)! 2^{2k}}$$

   a. Show that $J_0(x)$ and $J_1(x)$ both converge for all x.

   b. Show that $J_0'(x) = -\frac{x}{2} J_1(x)$.

These functions are called **Bessel functions of the first kind**. Bessel functions first were used in analyzing Kepler's laws of planetary motion. These functions play an important role in physics and engineering.

77. Show that J_0, the Bessel function of the first kind defined in Problem 76, satisfies the differential equation
$$x^2 J_0''(x) + x J_0'(x) + x^2 J_0(x) = 0$$

78. For x in the open interval $(-1, 1)$, let
$$f(x) = x + \frac{x^2}{2} + \frac{x^3}{3} + \cdots + \frac{x^k}{k} + \cdots$$

Show that f is a logarithmic function. *Hint:* Find f' and then retrieve f by integrating f'.

CHAPTER 8 REVIEW

> **IN THIS REVIEW** Proficiency examination; supplementary problems
> Problems 1–30 of the proficiency examination test your knowledge of the concepts of this chapter, and Problems 31–40 test your understanding of those concepts by asking you to work sample practice problems. The supplementary problems present questions relating to the material of this chapter in a wide variety of settings.

PROFICIENCY EXAMINATION

Concept Problems

1. What is a sequence?
2. What is meant by the limit of a sequence?
3. Define the convergence and divergence of a sequence.
4. Explain each of the following terms:
   a. bounded sequence
   b. monotonic sequence
   c. strictly monotonic sequence
   d. nonincreasing sequence
5. State the BMCT.
6. What is an infinite series?
7. Compare or contrast the convergence and divergence of sequences and series.
8. What is a telescoping series?
9. Describe the harmonic series. Does it converge or diverge?
10. Define a geometric series and give its sum.
11. State the divergence test.
12. State the integral test.
13. What is a *p*-series? Tell when it converges and when it diverges.
14. State the direct comparison test.
15. State the limit comparison test.
16. State the zero-infinity limit comparison test.
17. State the ratio test.
18. State the root test.
19. What is the alternating series test?
20. How do you make an error estimate for an alternating series?
21. State the absolute convergence test.
22. What is meant by absolute and conditional convergence?
23. What is the generalized ratio test?
24. What is a power series?
25. How do you test the convergence of a power series?
26. What are the radius of convergence and interval of convergence for a power series?
27. What is a Taylor polynomial?
28. State Taylor's theorem.
29. What are Taylor series and Maclaurin series?
30. State the binomial series theorem.

Practice Problems

In Problems 31–33, either find the limit of the given sequence or show that the sequence diverges.

31. $\left\{\dfrac{e^n}{n!}\right\}$ 32. $\left\{\dfrac{3n^2 - n + 1}{(1 - 2n)n}\right\}$ 33. $\left\{\left(1 + \dfrac{1}{n}\right)^n\right\}$

In Problems 34–37, test the given series for convergence.

34. $\displaystyle\sum_{k=1}^{\infty} \frac{e^k}{k!}$ 35. $\displaystyle\sum_{k=1}^{n} \frac{3k^2 - k + 1}{(1 - 2k)k}$ 36. $\displaystyle\sum_{k=2}^{\infty} \frac{1}{k \ln k}$

37. $1 - \dfrac{1}{4} + \dfrac{1}{9} - \dfrac{1}{16} + \dfrac{1}{25} - \dfrac{1}{36} + \dfrac{1}{49} - \dfrac{1}{64} + \cdots + \dfrac{(-1)^{n+1}}{n^2} + \cdots$

38. Find the interval of convergence for the series
$$1 - 2x + 3x^2 - 4x^3 + \cdots$$

39. Find the Maclaurin series for $f(x) = \sin 2x$.

40. Find the Taylor series for $f(x) = \dfrac{1}{x - 3}$ at $c = \dfrac{1}{2}$.

SUPPLEMENTARY PROBLEMS

Determine whether each sequence in Problems 1–17 converges or diverges. If it converges, find its limit.

1. $\left\{\dfrac{(-2)^n}{n^2+1}\right\}$

2. $\left\{\dfrac{(\ln n)^2}{\sqrt{n}}\right\}$

3. $\left\{\left(1-\dfrac{2}{n}\right)^n\right\}$

4. $\left\{\dfrac{e^{0.1n}}{n^5-3n+1}\right\}$

5. $\left\{\dfrac{n+(-1)^n}{n}\right\}$

6. $\left\{\dfrac{3^n}{3^n+2^n}\right\}$

7. $\left\{\dfrac{5n^4-n^2-700}{3n^4-10n^2+1}\right\}$

8. $\left\{\left(1+\dfrac{e}{n}\right)^{2n}\right\}$

9. $\left\{\sqrt{n+1}-\sqrt{n}\right\}$

10. $\left\{\sqrt{n^4+2n^2}-n^2\right\}$

11. $\left\{\dfrac{\ln n}{n}\right\}$

12. $\{1+(-1)^n\}$

13. $\left\{\left(1+\dfrac{4}{n}\right)^n\right\}$

14. $\{5^{2/n}\}$

15. $\left\{\dfrac{n^{3/4}\sin n^2}{n+4}\right\}$

16. $\left\{\displaystyle\sum_{k=1}^{n}\dfrac{n}{n^2+k^2}\right\}$

   Hint: This sequence is related to an integral.

17. $\displaystyle\sum_{k=-123,456,788}^{123,456,789}\dfrac{k}{370,370,367}$

Find the sum of the given convergent geometric or telescoping series in Problems 18–27.

18. $\displaystyle\sum_{k=1}^{\infty}4\left(\dfrac{2}{3}\right)^k$

19. $\displaystyle\sum_{k=1}^{\infty}\left(\dfrac{e}{3}\right)^k$

20. $\displaystyle\sum_{k=2}^{\infty}\dfrac{1}{k^2-1}$

21. $\displaystyle\sum_{k=0}^{\infty}\left[\left(\dfrac{-3}{8}\right)^k+\left(\dfrac{3}{4}\right)^{2k}\right]$

22. $\displaystyle\sum_{k=1}^{\infty}\dfrac{1}{4k^2-1}$

23. $\displaystyle\sum_{k=0}^{\infty}\dfrac{e^k+3^{k-1}}{6^{k+1}}$

24. $\displaystyle\sum_{k=1}^{\infty}(-1)^{k+1}\left(\dfrac{1}{k}+\dfrac{1}{k+1}\right)$

25. $\displaystyle\sum_{k=2}^{\infty}\left[\dfrac{1}{\ln(k+1)}-\dfrac{1}{\ln k}\right]$

26. $\displaystyle\sum_{k=0}^{\infty}\left[3\left(\dfrac{2}{3}\right)^{2k}-\left(\dfrac{-1}{3}\right)^{4k}\right]$

27. $\displaystyle\sum_{k=1}^{\infty}\dfrac{k}{(k+1)(k+2)(k+3)}$

Test the series in Problems 28–48 for convergence.

28. $\displaystyle\sum_{k=1}^{\infty}\dfrac{5^k k!}{k^k}$

29. $\displaystyle\sum_{k=1}^{\infty}\dfrac{1}{\sqrt{k^2+4}}$

30. $\displaystyle\sum_{k=0}^{\infty}\dfrac{k!}{2^k}$

31. $\displaystyle\sum_{k=0}^{\infty}\dfrac{1}{2k-1}$

32. $\displaystyle\sum_{k=0}^{\infty}ke^{-k}$

33. $\displaystyle\sum_{k=0}^{\infty}\dfrac{k^3}{k!}$

34. $\displaystyle\sum_{k=1}^{\infty}\dfrac{7^k}{k^2}$

35. $\displaystyle\sum_{k=1}^{\infty}\dfrac{k}{(2k-1)!}$

36. $\displaystyle\sum_{k=0}^{\infty}\dfrac{k^2}{(k^3+1)^2}$

37. $\displaystyle\sum_{k=0}^{\infty}\dfrac{k^2}{3^k}$

38. $\displaystyle\sum_{k=2}^{\infty}\dfrac{1}{k(\ln k)^{1.1}}$

39. $\displaystyle\sum_{k=2}^{\infty}\dfrac{1}{k(\ln k)^2}$

40. $\displaystyle\sum_{k=1}^{\infty}\dfrac{3^k k!}{k^k}$

41. $\displaystyle\sum_{k=2}^{\infty}\dfrac{1}{(\ln k)^{1/k}}$

42. $\displaystyle\sum_{k=1}^{\infty}e^{-k^2}$

43. $\displaystyle\sum_{k=0}^{\infty}(\sqrt{k^3+1}-\sqrt{k^3})$

44. $\displaystyle\sum_{k=1}^{\infty}\dfrac{1}{\sqrt{k(k+1)}}$

45. $\displaystyle\sum_{k=1}^{\infty}\dfrac{k-1}{k2^k}$

46. $\displaystyle\sum_{k=0}^{\infty}\dfrac{k!}{k^2(k+1)^2}$

47. $\displaystyle\sum_{k=0}^{\infty}\dfrac{1}{1+\sqrt{k}}$

48. $\displaystyle\sum_{k=1}^{\infty}\dfrac{k^2 3^k}{k!}$

Determine whether each series given in Problems 49–58 converges conditionally, converges absolutely, or diverges.

49. $\dfrac{1}{1\cdot 2}-\dfrac{1}{3\cdot 2}+\dfrac{1}{5\cdot 2}-\dfrac{1}{7\cdot 2}+\cdots$

50. $\dfrac{1}{1\cdot 2}-\dfrac{1}{2\cdot 3}+\dfrac{1}{3\cdot 4}-\dfrac{1}{4\cdot 5}+\cdots$

51. $\dfrac{3}{2}-\dfrac{4}{3}+\dfrac{5}{4}-\dfrac{6}{5}+\cdots$

52. $1-\dfrac{1}{3}+\dfrac{1}{9}-\dfrac{1}{27}+\dfrac{1}{81}-\cdots$

53. $1-\dfrac{1}{2}+\dfrac{1}{3}-\dfrac{1}{4}+\cdots$

54. $-1+\dfrac{1}{\sqrt{2}}-\dfrac{1}{\sqrt[3]{3}}+\dfrac{1}{\sqrt[4]{4}}-\cdots$

55. $\displaystyle\sum_{k=1}^{\infty}\dfrac{(-1)^k}{k\,[\ln(k+1)]^2}$

56. $\displaystyle\sum_{k=1}^{\infty}(-1)^k\left(\dfrac{3k+85}{4k+1}\right)^k$

57. $\displaystyle\sum_{k=1}^{\infty}(-1)^k\tan^{-1}\left(\dfrac{1}{2k+1}\right)$

58. $\displaystyle\sum_{k=1}^{\infty}\dfrac{(-1)^{k(k+1)/2}}{2^k}$

Find the interval of convergence for each power series in Problems 59–70.

59. $\displaystyle\sum_{k=1}^{\infty}\dfrac{kx^k}{3^k}$

60. $\displaystyle\sum_{k=1}^{\infty}k(x-1)^k$

61. $\displaystyle\sum_{k=1}^{\infty}\dfrac{x^k}{k(k+1)}$

62. $\displaystyle\sum_{k=1}^{\infty}\dfrac{\ln k(x^2)^k}{\sqrt{k}}$

63. $\displaystyle\sum_{k=1}^{\infty}\dfrac{k^2(x+1)^{2k}}{2^k}$

64. $\displaystyle\sum_{k=1}^{\infty}\dfrac{(-1)^k x^k}{\sqrt[k]{k}}$

65. $\displaystyle\sum_{k=1}^{\infty}\dfrac{(-1)^k(2x-1)^k}{k^2}$

66. $\displaystyle\sum_{k=1}^{\infty}\dfrac{(x+2)^k}{k\ln(k+1)}$

67. $\displaystyle\sum_{k=1}^{\infty}\dfrac{k(x-3)^k}{(k+3)!}$

68. $\displaystyle\sum_{n=1}^{\infty}\dfrac{(3n)!}{n!}x^n$

69. $\displaystyle\sum_{n=1}^{\infty}\dfrac{(-1)^n x^n}{9n^2-1}$

70. $x-\dfrac{x^3}{3!}+\dfrac{x^5}{5!}-\dfrac{x^7}{7!}+\cdots+\dfrac{(-1)^{k+1}x^{2k-1}}{(2k-1)!}+\cdots$

Find the Maclaurin series for each function given in Problems 71–76.

71. $f(x) = x^2 e^{-3x}$

72. $f(x) = x^3 \cos x$

73. $f(x) = 3^x$

74. $f(x) = \cos^3 x$

75. $f(x) = \dfrac{5 + 7x}{1 + 2x - 3x^2}$

76. $f(x) = \dfrac{11x - 1}{2 + x - 3x^2}$

77. Compute the sum of the series

$$1 - \frac{1}{2} + \frac{1}{2!}\left(\frac{1}{2}\right)^2 - \frac{1}{3!}\left(\frac{1}{2}\right)^3 + \cdots$$

correct to three decimal places.

78. Find a bound on the error incurred by approximating the sum of the series

$$1 - \frac{1}{2!} + \frac{2}{3!} - \frac{3}{4!} + \cdots$$

by the sum of the first eight terms.

79. Use geometric series to write $12.342\overline{132}$ as a rational number.

80. A ball is dropped from a height of A feet. Each time it drops h feet, it rebounds $0.8h$ feet. If it travels a total distance of 20 feet before coming to a stop, what is A?

81. Use the Maclaurin series for $\tan x$ and then use term-by-term integration to find the first three terms of the Maclaurin series for $\ln(\cos x)$

82. Show that

$$\cos x = \cos c - (\sin c)(x - c) - (\cos c)\frac{(x - c)^2}{2!}$$
$$+ (\sin c)\frac{(x - c)^3}{3!} + \cdots$$

83. Show that

$$e^x = e^c + e^c(x - c) + e^c\frac{(x - c)^2}{2!} + \cdots + e^c\frac{(x - c)^k}{k!} + \cdots$$

84. Express the integral $\displaystyle\int \sqrt{x^3 + 1}\, dx$ as an infinite series.

Hint: Use the binomial theorem and then integrate term by term.

85. Estimate the value of the integral

$$\int_0^{0.4} \frac{dx}{\sqrt{1 + x^3}}$$

with an error no greater than 0.000001.

86. Show that if $a > 0$, $a \neq 1$,

$$a^x = \sum_{k=0}^{\infty} \frac{(\ln a)^k}{k!} x^k \quad \text{for all } x$$

87. Show that for $0 < x < 2c$,

$$\frac{1}{x} = \frac{1}{c} - \frac{1}{c^2}(x - c) + \frac{1}{c^3}(x - c)^2 - \frac{1}{c^4}(x - c)^3 + \cdots$$

88. Use series to find $\sin 0.2$ correct to five decimal places.

89. Use series to find $\ln 1.05$ correct to five decimal places.

90. Use a Maclaurin series to find a cubic polynomial that approximates e^{2x} for $|x| < 0.001$. Find an upper bound for the error in this approximation.

91. In the expansion

$$\ln(1 - x) = -x - \frac{x^2}{2} - \frac{x^3}{3} - \cdots - \frac{x^k}{k} + \cdots$$

show that the remainder term satisfies

$$|R_n| < \frac{x^{n+1}}{n + 1} \quad \text{when } 0 < x < 1 \text{ and}$$

$$|R_n| < \frac{|x^{n+1}|}{(n + 1)(1 + x)^{n+1}} \quad \text{when } -1 \leq x < 0$$

How many terms of the expansion are sufficient to compute $\ln 1.2$ correct to six decimal places? Estimate the error incurred by computing $\ln 1.2$ as the sum of the first three terms in the series.

92. For what values of x can $\sin x$ be replaced by $x - \dfrac{x^3}{6}$ if the allowable error is 0.0005?

93. For what values of x can $\cos x$ be replaced by $1 - \dfrac{x^2}{2}$ if the allowable error is 0.00005?

94. Find the Maclaurin series for $f(x) = \dfrac{2 \tan x}{1 + \tan^2 x}$.

95. a. Find a formula for the sum of the first n terms of an arithmetic progression that has a for its first term and d for its common difference.

b. Find a formula for the sum of the first n terms of a geometric progression that has a for its first term and r for its common ratio.

c. If $|r| < 1$, show that $\displaystyle\sum_{n=0}^{\infty} ar^n = \frac{a}{1 - r}$

96. Putnam Examination Problem   Express

$$\sum_{k=1}^{\infty} \frac{6^k}{(3^{n+1} - 2^{k+1})(3^k - 2^k)}$$

as a rational number.

97. Putnam Examination Problem   For $0 < x < 1$, express

$$\sum_{k=1}^{\infty} \frac{x^{2^n}}{1 - x^{2^{n+1}}}$$

as a rational function of x.

98. Putnam Examination Problem   For positive real x, let

$$B_n(x) = 1^x + 2^x + 3^x + \cdots + n^x$$

Test for convergence for the series

$$\sum_{k=2}^{\infty} \frac{B_k(\log_k 2)}{(k \log_2 k)^2}$$

"Elastic Tightrope Project"

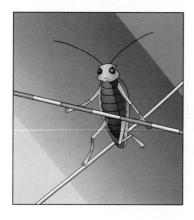

This project is to be done in groups of three or four students. Each group will submit a single written report.

Suppose a cockroach starts at one end of a 1,000-m tightrope and runs toward the other end at a speed of 1 m/s. At the end of every second, the tightrope stretches uniformly and instantaneously, increasing its length by 1,000 meters each time.

Does the roach ever reach the other end? If so, how long does it take?

Your paper is not limited to the following questions but should include these concerns. Suppose it is you standing on the elastic rope b meters from the left end and c meters from the right end. Then suppose the entire rope stretches uniformly, increasing its length by d meters. How far are you from each end? You might also try to generalize the roach problem.

The infinite! No other question has ever moved so profoundly the spirit of man; no other idea has so fruitfully stimulated his intellect; yet no other concept stands in greater need of clarification than that of the infinite.

David Hilbert
To Infinity and Beyond by Eli Maor
(Burkhäuser, 1987), p. vii

There is nothing now which ever gives me any thought or care in algebra except divergent series, which I cannot follow the French in rejecting.

Augustus De Morgan
Graves' Life of W. R. Hamilton
(New York: 1882–1889), p. 249

*This group project was obtained courtesy of David Pengelley, New Mexico State University. You might also check "The Beetle and the Rubber Band," by Alexander A. Pukhov, *Quantum*, March/April 1994, pp. 42–45.

9

Polar Coordinates and the Conic Sections

PREVIEW

We begin this chapter by investigating an alternative coordinate system involving polar coordinates. Much of our work will involve representation of graphs, but we shall also investigate tangent lines, area, arc length, and other issues involving differentiation and integration. We close the chapter by examining the *conic sections*: parabolas, ellipses, and hyperbolas.

PERSPECTIVE

In the rectangular coordinate system of representation, points in the plane are located by specifying their position in relation to a fixed pair of perpendicular lines. However, this is by no means the only way of locating points, and in this chapter, we shall study several alternative forms of representation.

Another topic, the *conic sections*, has been studied extensively since ancient times and has many important applications. For instance, in the early 17th century, Johannes Kepler observed that the planets travel in elliptical paths, and Galileo discovered that in a vacuum, a projectile follows a parabolic path. At the end of the 17th century, Newton used the fact that planets follow elliptical paths as the basis for the inverse-square law of gravitational attraction. In more modern times, conic sections have been used in architecture, in the design of lenses and mirrors, and to study the paths of atomic particles. We shall examine some of these applications in our study of conic sections. (See Sections 9.5 and 9.6.)

9.1 THE POLAR COORDINATE SYSTEM

IN THIS SECTION Plotting points in polar coordinates, primary representations of a point, relationship between polar and rectangular coordinates, points on a polar curve

Up to now, the only coordinate system we have used is a Cartesian coordinate system. In this section, we introduce the *polar coordinate system*, in which points are located by specifying their distance from a fixed point and their direction in relation to a fixed line.

We use the term **rectangular** coordinates to refer to Cartesian coordinates to help you remember that Cartesian coordinates are plotted in a rectangular fashion.

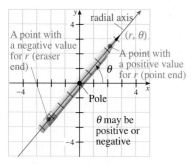

Figure 9.1 Polar-form points

■ PLOTTING POINTS IN POLAR COORDINATES

In a **polar coordinate system** we fix a point O, called the **pole,** and draw a ray (half-line), called the **radial axis,** from the point O. Then we represent each point in the plane by an ordered pair $P(r, \theta)$, where θ (the **polar angle**) measures the angle from the radial axis and r (the **radial distance**) measures the directed distance from the pole to the point P. Both r and θ can be any real numbers. When plotting points rotate the radial axis through an angle θ, as shown in Figure 9.1. You might find it helpful to rotate your pencil as the axis—the tip points in the positive direction and the eraser, in the negative direction. If θ is measured in a counterclockwise direction, it is positive, and if θ is measured in a clockwise direction, it is negative. Next, plot r on the radial axis (the pencil). Notice that any real number can be plotted on this real number line in the direction of the tip if the number is positive and in the direction of the eraser if it is negative. Plotting points seems easy, but it is necessary that you completely understand this process. Study each part of Example 1 and make sure you understand how each point is plotted. We assume an orientation provided by an x-axis and a y-axis with the pole at the origin, and the rotation of the radial axis is measured from the positive x-axis. We consider that points can be plotted using either rectangular or polar coordinates, and that the system we are using in a particular example must be either specified or obvious from the context.

EXAMPLE 1   Plotting polar-form points

Plot each of the following polar-form points: $A\left(4, \frac{\pi}{3}\right)$, $B\left(-4, \frac{\pi}{3}\right)$, $C\left(3, -\frac{\pi}{6}\right)$, $D\left(-3, -\frac{\pi}{6}\right)$, $E(-3, 3)$, $F(-3, -3)$, $G(-4, -2)$, $H\left(5, \frac{3\pi}{2}\right)$, $I\left(-5, \frac{\pi}{2}\right)$, $J\left(5, -\frac{\pi}{2}\right)$.

Solution   Points A, B, C, and D illustrate the basic ideas of plotting polar-form points.

Plot $A\left(4, \frac{\pi}{3}\right)$; positive θ.

Plot $B\left(-4, \frac{\pi}{3}\right)$; positive θ.

Plot $C\left(3, -\frac{\pi}{6}\right)$; negative θ.

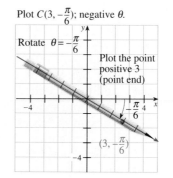

Plot $D\left(-3, -\frac{\pi}{6}\right)$; negative θ.

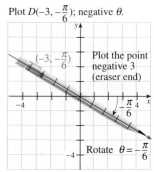

Points E, F, G, H, I, and J illustrate common situations that can sometimes be confusing. Make sure you take time with each example.

Plot $E(-3, 3)$.

Plot $F(-3, -3)$.

Plot $G(-4, -2)$.

Plot $H(5, \frac{3\pi}{2})$.

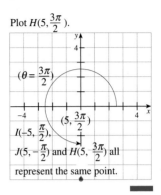

Note that the point $(-r, \theta)$ can be obtained by *reflecting* (r, θ) through the origin, whereas the point $(r, -\theta)$ can be obtained by reflecting (r, θ) in the x-axis. These features of the polar coordinate system are illustrated in Figure 9.2.

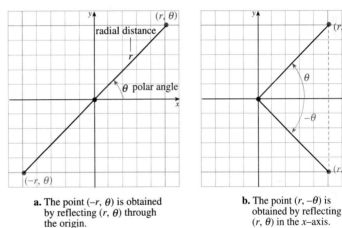

a. The point $(-r, \theta)$ is obtained by reflecting (r, θ) through the origin.

b. The point $(r, -\theta)$ is obtained by reflecting (r, θ) in the x–axis.

Figure 9.2 Plotting points using reflections

■ PRIMARY REPRESENTATIONS OF A POINT

Notice from Example 1 that ordered pairs in polar form are not associated in a one-to-one fashion with points in the plane. Indeed, given any point in the plane, there are infinitely many ordered pairs of polar coordinates associated with that point. If you are given a point $P(r, \theta)$ other than the pole in polar coordinates, then $(-r, \theta + \pi)$ also represents P. In addition, there are infinitely many other polar representations of P; namely, $(r, \theta + n\pi)$ for n an integer. We call (r, θ) and $(-r, \theta + \pi)$ the *primary representations of the point* if the angles θ and $\theta + \pi$ are between 0 and 2π.

⊘ Remember to simplify so the second component represents a nonnegative angle less than one revolution. ⊘

Primary Representations of a Point in Polar Form

Every nonzero point in polar form has two **primary representations:**

$$(r, \theta) \qquad \text{where } 0 \le \theta < 2\pi \quad \text{and}$$
$$(-r, \pi + \theta) \qquad \text{where } 0 \le \pi + \theta < 2\pi$$

EXAMPLE 2   Primary representations of a point

Give both primary representations of the points

a. $\left(3, \frac{\pi}{4}\right)$ **b.** $\left(5, \frac{5\pi}{4}\right)$ **c.** $\left(-6, -\frac{2\pi}{3}\right)$ **d.** $(9, 5)$ **e.** $(9, 7)$

Solution   **a.** $\left(3, \frac{\pi}{4}\right)$ is primary; the other is $\underbrace{\left(-3, \frac{5\pi}{4}\right)}$

Change the sign of r and add π to θ; $\frac{\pi}{4} + \pi$.

b. $\left(5, \frac{5\pi}{4}\right)$ is primary; the other is $\left(-5, \frac{\pi}{4}\right)$.

$\frac{5\pi}{4} + \pi = \frac{9\pi}{4}$, but $\left(-5, \frac{9\pi}{4}\right)$ is not a primary representation because $\frac{9\pi}{4} > 2\pi$.

c. $\left(-6, -\frac{2\pi}{3}\right)$ has primary representations $\left(-6, \frac{4\pi}{3}\right)$ and $\left(6, \frac{\pi}{3}\right)$.

d. $(9, 5)$ has primary representations $(9, 5)$ and $(-9, 5 - \pi)$; a point like $(-9, 5 - \pi)$ may be approximated by $(-9, 1.86)$.

e. $(9, 7)$ has primary representations $(9, 7 - 2\pi)$, or $(9, 0.72)$, and $(-9, 7 - \pi)$, or $(-9, 3.86)$.

■ RELATIONSHIP BETWEEN POLAR AND RECTANGULAR COORDINATES

$\boxed{\text{s}^{\text{M}}\text{H}}$

The relationship between polar and rectangular coordinates can be found by using the definition of trigonometric functions (see Figure 9.3).

Relationship Between Rectangular and Polar Coordinates

1. To change *from polar to rectangular*:
$$x = r \cos\theta \qquad y = r \sin\theta$$

2. To change *from rectangular to polar*:
$$r = \sqrt{x^2 + y^2} \qquad \bar{\theta} = \tan^{-1}\left|\frac{y}{x}\right|, \; x \neq 0$$

where $\bar{\theta}$ is the reference angle* for θ. Place θ in the proper quadrant by noting the signs of x and y. If $x = 0$, then $\bar{\theta} = \frac{\pi}{2}$.

EXAMPLE 3   Converting from polar to rectangular coordinates

Change the polar coordinates $\left(-3, \frac{5\pi}{4}\right)$ to rectangular coordinates.

Solution $x = -3 \cos\frac{5\pi}{4} = -3\left(-\frac{\sqrt{2}}{2}\right) = \frac{3\sqrt{2}}{2}$

$y = -3 \sin\frac{5\pi}{4} = -3\left(-\frac{\sqrt{2}}{2}\right) = \frac{3\sqrt{2}}{2}$

The rectangular coordinates are $\left(\frac{3\sqrt{2}}{2}, \frac{3\sqrt{2}}{2}\right)$.

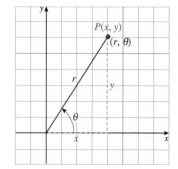

Figure 9.3 Relationship between rectangular and polar coordinates

EXAMPLE 4   Converting from rectangular coordinates to polar coordinates

Write both primary representations of the polar-form coordinates for the point with rectangular coordinates $\left(\frac{5\sqrt{3}}{2}, -\frac{5}{2}\right)$.

*The reference angle $\bar{\theta}$ for a standard position angle θ is defined to be the smallest positive angle that the angle θ makes with the x-axis. Reference angles are discussed in trigonometry and are reviewed in the *Student Mathematics Handbook for CALCULUS*.

□ **Computational Window** ▼ ▲

Check the owner's manual for your calculator. Many have keys for converting between polar and rectangular coordinates.

Solution
$$r = \sqrt{\left(\frac{5\sqrt{3}}{2}\right)^2 + \left(-\frac{5}{2}\right)^2} = \sqrt{\frac{75}{4} + \frac{25}{4}} = 5$$

Note that θ is in Quadrant IV because x is positive and y is negative.

$$\bar{\theta} = \tan^{-1}\left|\frac{-\frac{5}{2}}{\frac{5\sqrt{3}}{2}}\right| = \tan^{-1}\left(\frac{1}{\sqrt{3}}\right) = \frac{\pi}{6}; \quad \text{thus, } \theta = \frac{11\pi}{6} \quad \text{(Quadrant IV)}$$

The polar-form coordinates are $\left(5, \frac{11\pi}{6}\right)$ and $\left(-5, \frac{5\pi}{6}\right)$. ▬

■ POINTS ON A POLAR CURVE

The **graph** of an equation in polar coordinates is the set of all points P whose polar coordinates (r, θ) satisfy the given equation. Circles, lines through the origin, and rays emanating from the origin have particularly simple equations in polar coordinates.

EXAMPLE 5 Graphing circles, lines, and rays

Graph: **a.** $r = 6$; **b.** $\theta = \frac{\pi}{6}$, $r \geq 0$; and **c.** $\theta = \frac{\pi}{6}$.

Solution

    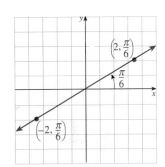

a. The graph is the set of all points (r, θ) such that the first component is 6 for any angle θ. This is a circle with radius 6 centered at the origin.

b. The graph is the closed half-line (ray) that emanates from the origin and makes an angle of $\frac{\pi}{6}$ with the positive x-axis.

c. This is the line through the origin that makes an angle of $\frac{\pi}{6}$ with the positive x-axis. ▬

As with other equations, we begin graphing polar-form curves by plotting some points. However, you must first be able to recognize whether a point in polar form satisfies a given equation.

EXAMPLE 6 Verifying that polar coordinates satisfy an equation

Show that each of the given points lies on the polar graph whose equation is

$$r = \frac{2}{1 - \cos\theta}$$

a. $\left(2, \frac{\pi}{2}\right)$ **b.** $\left(-2, \frac{3\pi}{2}\right)$ **c.** $(-1, 2\pi)$

Solution Begin by substituting the given coordinates into the equation.

a. $2 \stackrel{?}{=} \dfrac{2}{1 - \cos \frac{\pi}{2}} = \dfrac{2}{1 - 0} = 2$;

$\left(2, \frac{\pi}{2}\right)$ is on the curve, because it satisfies the equation.

b. $-2 \stackrel{?}{=} \dfrac{2}{1 - \cos \frac{3\pi}{2}} = \dfrac{2}{1 - 0} = 2$ *This equation is **not** true.*

Although the equation is not satisfied, we *cannot* say that the point is not on the curve. Indeed, we see from part **a** that it is on the curve, because $\left(-2, \frac{3\pi}{2}\right)$ and $\left(2, \frac{\pi}{2}\right)$ name the same point! So even if one primary representation of a point does not satisfy the equation, we must still check the other primary representation of the point. An ordered pair representing a polar-form point (other than the pole) satisfies an equation involving a function of $n\theta$ (for an integer n) if at least one of its primary representations satisfies the given equation.

c. $-1 \stackrel{?}{=} \dfrac{2}{1 - \cos 2\pi} = \dfrac{2}{1 - 1}$, which is undefined.

Check the other representation of the same point—namely, $(1, \pi)$:

$$1 \stackrel{?}{=} \dfrac{2}{1 - \cos \pi} = \dfrac{2}{1 - (-1)} = 1$$

Thus, the point is on the curve.   ▬

We will discuss the graphing of polar-form curves in the next section, but some polar-form equations can be graphed by changing them to rectangular form.

EXAMPLE 7   Polar-form graphing by changing to rectangular form

Graph the given polar-form curves by changing to rectangular form.

a. $r = 3 \cos \theta$ b. $r \cos \theta = 4$ c. $r = \dfrac{6}{2 \sin \theta + \cos \theta}$

Solution   a.

$$r = 3 \cos \theta \qquad \textit{Given equation}$$
$$r^2 = 3r \cos \theta \qquad \textit{Multiply by } r.$$
$$x^2 + y^2 = 3x \qquad \textit{Because } x = r \cos \theta \textit{ and } r^2 = x^2 + y^2$$
$$\left[x^2 - 3x + \left(\tfrac{3}{2}\right)^2\right] + y^2 = \tfrac{9}{4} \qquad \textit{Complete the square.}$$
$$\left(x - \tfrac{3}{2}\right)^2 + y^2 = \tfrac{9}{4}$$

We see this is a circle with center at $\left(\frac{3}{2}, 0\right)$ and radius $\frac{3}{2}$. The graph is shown in Figure 9.4a.

b. Because $x = r \cos \theta$, we see that the given equation can be written $x = 4$, which is a vertical line (Figure 9.4b).

c.
$$r = \dfrac{6}{2 \sin \theta + \cos \theta} \qquad \textit{Given equation}$$
$$2r \sin \theta + r \cos \theta = 6$$
$$2y + x = 6$$

We see that this is a line with y-intercept 3 and slope $-\frac{1}{2}$ (Figure 9.4c).

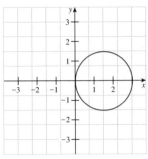

a. Graph of $r = 3 \cos \theta$

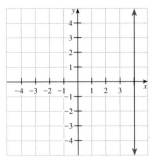

b. Graph of $r \cos \theta = 4$

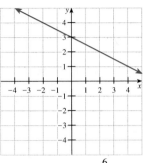

c. Graph of $r = \dfrac{6}{2 \sin \theta + \cos \theta}$

Figure 9.4 Polar-form graphs

PROBLEM SET 9.1

A 1. ■ **What Does This Say?** Illustrate the procedure for plotting points in polar form.

2. ■ **What Does This Say?** Show the derivation of the polar-rectangular-form conversion equations.

In Problems 3–11, plot each of the given polar-form points. Give both primary representations and the rectangular coordinates of the point.

3. $\left(4, \frac{\pi}{4}\right)$ **4.** $\left(6, \frac{\pi}{3}\right)$ **5.** $\left(5, \frac{2\pi}{3}\right)$

6. $\left(3, -\frac{\pi}{6}\right)$ **7.** $\left(\frac{3}{2}, -\frac{5\pi}{6}\right)$ **8.** $(-4, 4)$

9. $(1, 3\pi)$ **10.** $\left(-2, -\frac{3\pi}{2}\right)$ **11.** $(0, -3)$

Plot the rectangular-form points in Problems 12–20 and give both primary representations in polar form.

12. $(5, 5)$ **13.** $(-1, \sqrt{3})$ **14.** $(2, -2\sqrt{3})$

15. $(-2, -2)$ **16.** $(3, -3)$ **17.** $(3, 7)$

18. $(3, -3\sqrt{3})$ **19.** $(\sqrt{3}, -1)$ **20.** $(-3, 0)$

21. Name the country or island in Figure 9.5 in which each of the named points is located.

  a. $(5.5, 260°)$ **b.** $(7.5, 78°)$ **c.** $(-2, 140°)$ **d.** $(-4, 80°)$

22. Name possible coordinates for each of the following cities (see Figure 9.5).

  a. Miami, Florida
  b. Los Angeles, California
  c. Mexico City, Mexico
  d. London, England

Figure 9.5

B *Write each equation given in Problems 23–30 in rectangular coordinates.*

23. $r = 4 \sin \theta$ **24.** $r = 16$

25. $r = 1 - \sin \theta$ **26.** $r = 2 \cos \theta$

27. $r = \sec \theta$ **28.** $r = 4 \tan \theta$

29. $r^2 = \dfrac{2}{1 + \sin^2 \theta}$ **30.** $r^2 = \dfrac{2}{3 \cos^2 \theta - 1}$

Sketch the graph of each equation given in Problems 31–38.

31. $r = \frac{3}{2}$ **32.** $r = \frac{3}{2}, 0 \le \theta < 2$

33. $r = \sqrt{2}, 0 \le \theta < 2$ **34.** $r = 4$

35. $\theta = 1$ **36.** $\theta = 1, r \ge 0$

37. $\theta = \frac{\pi}{6}, r < 0$ **38.** $\theta = \frac{\pi}{2}$

In Problems 39–44, tell whether each of the given points lies on the curve

$$r = \frac{5}{1 - \sin \theta}$$

39. $\left(10, \frac{\pi}{6}\right)$ **40.** $\left(5, \frac{\pi}{2}\right)$ **41.** $\left(-10, \frac{5\pi}{6}\right)$

42. $\left(-\frac{10}{3}, \frac{5\pi}{6}\right)$ **43.** $\left(20 + 10\sqrt{3}, \frac{\pi}{3}\right)$ **44.** $\left(-10, \frac{\pi}{3}\right)$

In Problems 45–52, tell whether each of the given points lies on the curve $r = 2(1 - \cos \theta)$.

45. $\left(1, \frac{\pi}{3}\right)$ **46.** $\left(1, -\frac{\pi}{3}\right)$

47. $\left(-1, \frac{\pi}{3}\right)$ **48.** $\left(-2, \frac{\pi}{2}\right)$

49. $\left(2 + \sqrt{2}, \frac{\pi}{4}\right)$ **50.** $\left(-2 - \sqrt{2}, \frac{\pi}{4}\right)$

51. $\left(0, \frac{\pi}{4}\right)$ **52.** $\left(0, -\frac{2\pi}{3}\right)$

Find three distinct ordered pairs satisfying each of the equations in Problems 53–60. Give both primary representations for each point.

53. $r^2 = 9 \cos \theta$ **54.** $r^2 = 9 \cos 2\theta$

55. $r = 3\theta$ **56.** $r = 5\theta$

57. $r = 2 - 3 \sin \theta$ **58.** $r = 2(1 + \cos \theta)$

59. $\dfrac{r}{1 - \sin \theta} = 2$ **60.** $r = \dfrac{8}{1 - 2 \cos \theta}$

C **61. a.** What is the distance between the polar-form points $\left(3, \frac{\pi}{3}\right)$ and $\left(7, \frac{\pi}{4}\right)$? Explain why you cannot use the distance formula for these ordered pairs.

b. What is the distance between the polar-form points (r_1, θ_1) and (r_2, θ_2)?

62. Use the result of Problem 61b to find an equation for a circle of radius a and polar-form center (R, α).

63. Show that the graph of the polar equation $r = a \sin \theta + b \cos \theta$ is a circle. Find its center and radius.

9.2 GRAPHING IN POLAR COORDINATES

> **IN THIS SECTION** Graphing by plotting points, cardioids, symmetry and rotations, limaçons, rose curves, lemniscates, summary of polar-form curves
> In the last section we found that the graph of the polar equation $r = a$ is a circle centered at the origin with radius a, and $\theta = a$ is a line passing through the origin. In this section we discuss techniques for graphing polar-form equations and categorize several important types of polar-form curves.

■ GRAPHING BY PLOTTING POINTS

We have examined polar forms for lines and circles, and in this section we shall examine curves that are more easily represented in polar coordinates than in rectangular coordinates. We begin with a simple spiral.

EXAMPLE 1   A spiral by plotting points

Graph $r = \theta$ for $\theta \geq 0$.

Solution   Set up a table of values.

θ	r
0	0
1	1
2	2
3	3
4	4
5	5
6	6

Choose a θ, and then find a corresponding r so that (r, θ) satisfies the equation. Plot each of these points and connect them, as shown in Figure 9.6.*

Figure 9.6 Graph of $r = \theta$

Notice that as θ increases, r must also increase.   ▬

In Example 1, the polar equation $r = \theta$, we see that there is exactly one value of r for each value of θ. Thus, the relationship given by $r = \theta$ is a function of θ, and we can write the polar form $r = f(\theta)$, where $f(\theta) = \theta$. A function of the form $r = f(\theta)$, where θ is a polar angle and r is the corresponding radial distance, is called a **polar function**.

---

* Many books use what is called **polar graph paper**, but such paper is not really necessary. It also obscures the fact that polar curves and rectangular curves are both plotted on a Cartesian coordinate system, only with a different meaning attached to the ordered pairs. You can estimate the angles as necessary without polar graph paper. Remember, just as when graphing rectangular curves, the key is not in plotting many points but in recognizing the type of curve and then plotting a few key points.

Check your owner's manual. Some graphing calculators will draw polar-form graphs.

r₁≣2(1-cos θ)
θmin=0
θmax=6.2831853…
θstep=.1308996…
Xmin=⁻6
Xmax=2
Xscl=1
Ymin=⁻3
Ymax=3
Yscl=1

■ CARDIOIDS

Next, we examine a class of polar curves called **cardioids** because of their heartlike shape.

EXAMPLE 2   A cardioid by plotting points

Graph $r = 2(1 - \cos \theta)$.

Solution   Construct a table of values by choosing values for θ and approximating the corresponding values for r.

θ	r
0	0
1	0.919 395
2	2.832 294
3	3.979 985
4	3.307 287
5	1.432 676
6	0.079 659

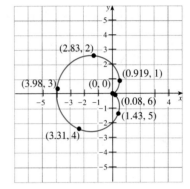

Figure 9.7 Graph of $r = 2(1 - \cos \theta)$ ■

The points are connected as shown in Figure 9.7.

The general form for a cardioid in standard position is given in the following box.

Standard-Position Cardioid

$$r = a(1 - \cos \theta)$$

In general, a cardioid in standard position can be completely determined by plotting four particular points:

θ	$r = a(1 - \cos \theta)$
0	$r = a(1 - \cos 0) = a(1 - 1) = 0$
$\frac{\pi}{2}$	$r = a\left(1 - \cos \frac{\pi}{2}\right) = a(1 - 0) = a$
π	$r = a(1 - \cos \pi) = a(1 + 1) = 2a$
$\frac{3\pi}{2}$	$r = a\left(1 - \cos \frac{3\pi}{2}\right) = a(1 - 0) = a$

These reference points are all you need when graphing other standard-position cardioids, because they will all have the same shape as the one shown in Figure 9.7.

■ SYMMETRY AND ROTATIONS

When sketching a polar graph, it is often useful to determine whether the graph has been rotated or if it has any symmetry.

If an angle α is subtracted from θ in a polar-form equation, it has the effect of rotating the curve (see Problem 73). As before, we note that

Rotation of Polar-Form Graphs

> The polar graph of $r = f(\theta - \alpha)$ is the same as the polar graph of $r = f(\theta)$ only rotated through an angle α. If α is positive, the rotation is counterclockwise, and if α is negative, then the rotation is clockwise.

EXAMPLE 3   Rotated cardioid

Graph $r = 3 - 3\cos\left(\theta - \frac{\pi}{6}\right)$.

Solution   Recognize this as a cardioid with $a = 3$ and a rotation of $\frac{\pi}{6}$. Plot the four points shown in Figure 9.8 and draw the cardioid.   ▬

If the rotation is 180°, the equation simplifies considerably. Consider

$$r = 3 - 3\cos(\theta - \pi) \qquad \textit{Cardioid with } 180° \textit{ rotation}$$
$$= 3 - 3[\cos\theta\cos\pi + \sin\theta\sin\pi] \quad \cos(\alpha - \beta) = \cos\alpha\cos\beta + \sin\alpha\sin\beta$$
$$= 3 - 3[\cos\theta\,(-1) + \sin\theta\,(0)]$$
$$= 3 - 3(-1)\cos\theta$$
$$= 3 + 3\cos\theta$$

Figure 9.8 Graph of
$r = 3 - 3\cos\left(\theta - \frac{\pi}{6}\right)$

Compare this with Example 3 and you will see that the only difference is a 180° rotation instead of a 30° rotation. This means that, whenever you graph an equation of the form

$$r = a(1 + \cos\theta) \qquad \textit{Note the plus sign.}$$

instead of $r = a(1 - \cos\theta)$, it is a standard-form cardioid with a 180° rotation. Similarly,

$r = a(1 - \sin\theta)$ is a standard-form cardioid with a 90° rotation.
$r = a(1 + \sin\theta)$ is a standard-form cardioid with a 270° rotation.

These curves, along with other polar-form curves, are graphed and summarized in Table 9.1 on page 583.

The cardioid is only one of the polar-form curves we will consider. Before sketching other curves, we will consider symmetry. There are three important kinds of polar symmetry, which are described in the following box and are demonstrated in Figure 9.9.

Symmetry in the Graph of the Polar Function $r = f(\theta)$

A polar-form graph $r = f(\theta)$ is symmetric with respect to . . .	. . . if the equation $r = f(\theta)$ is unchanged when (r, θ) is replaced by . . .
x-axis	$(r, -\theta)$
y-axis	$(r, \pi - \theta)$
origin	$(-r, \theta)$

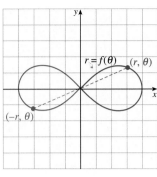

a. Symmetry with respect to the x-axis

b. Symmetry with respect to the y-axis

c. Symmetry with respect to the origin

Figure 9.9 Symmetry in polar form

■ LIMAÇONS

We will illustrate symmetry in polar-form curves by graphing a curve called a *limaçon*.

EXAMPLE 4 Graphing a limaçon using symmetry

Graph $r = 3 + 2\cos\theta$.

Solution Let $f(\theta) = 3 + 2\cos\theta$.

Symmetry with respect to the x-axis:

$f(-\theta) = 3 + 2\cos(-\theta) = 3 + 2\cos\theta = f(\theta)$
Yes; it is symmetric, so it is enough to graph f for θ between 0 and π.

Symmetry with respect to the y-axis:

$$f(\pi - \theta) = 3 + 2\cos(\pi - \theta)$$
$$= 3 + 2[\cos\pi\cos\theta + \sin\pi\sin\theta]$$
$$= 3 - 2\cos\theta$$

After checking the other primary representation, we find that it is not symmetric with respect to the y-axis.

Symmetry with respect to the origin:

$-r \neq f(\theta)$ and $r \neq f(\theta + \pi)$, so the graph is **not symmetric** with respect to the origin.

The graph is shown in Figure 9.10; note that we sketch the top half of the graph (for $0 \leq \theta \leq \pi$) by plotting points and then complete the sketch by reflecting the graph in the x-axis. Because $\cos\theta$ steadily decreases from its largest value of 1 at $\theta = 0$ to its smallest value -1 at $\theta = \pi$, the radial distance $r = 3 + 2\cos\theta$ will also steadily decrease as θ increases from 0 to π. The largest value of r is $r = 3 + 2(1) = 5$ at $\theta = 0$, and its smallest value is $r = 3 + 2(-1) = 1$ at $\theta = \pi$. ■

The graph of any polar equation of the general form

$$r = b \pm a\cos\theta \quad \text{or} \quad r = b \pm a\sin\theta$$

Top half is sketched by plotting points.

(3.14, 1.5) (4.08, 1)

(2.17, 2) (4.76, 0.5)

(1.02, 3) (5, 0)

Bottom half is sketched using x-axis symmetry.

Figure 9.10 Graph of $r = 3 + 2\cos\theta$

is called a **limaçon** (derived from the Latin word "limax," which means "slug"). The special case where $a = b$ is the *cardioid*. Figure 9.11 shows four different kinds of limaçons. Note how the appearance of the graph depends on the ratio a/b. We have discussed cases II and III in Examples 2 and 4. Case I (the "inner loop" case) and case IV (the "convex" case) are examined in the problem set.

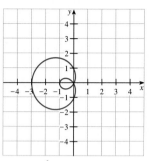

a. $\dfrac{b}{a} < 1$; inner loop
Case I
$(r = 1 - 2 \cos \theta)$

b. $\dfrac{b}{a} = 1$; cardioid
Case II
$(r = 2 - 2 \cos \theta)$

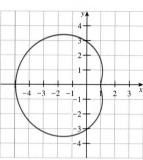

c. $1 < \dfrac{b}{a} < 2$; dimple
Case III
$(r = 3 - 2 \cos \theta)$

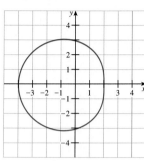

d. $\dfrac{b}{a} \geq 2$; convex
Case IV
$(r = 3 - \cos \theta)$

Figure 9.11 Limaçons: $r = b \pm a \cos \theta$ or $r = b \pm a \sin \theta$

Just as with the cardioid, we designate a standard-form limaçon and consider the others as rotations:

$r = b - a \cos \theta$	**Standard form**
$r = b - a \sin \theta$	90° rotation
$r = b + a \cos \theta$	180° rotation
$r = b + a \sin \theta$	270° rotation

Standard-Position Limaçon

$$r = b - a \cos \theta$$

■ ROSE CURVES

There are several polar-form curves known as **rose curves,** which consist of several loops, called **leaves** or **petals.**

EXAMPLE 5   Graphing a four-leaved rose

Graph $r = 4 \cos 2\theta$.

Solution   Let $f(\theta) = 4 \cos 2\theta$.

Symmetry with respect to the *x*-axis:
$f(-\theta) = 4 \cos 2(-\theta) = 4 \cos 2\theta = f(\theta)$; **Yes,** symmetric

Symmetry with respect to the *y*-axis:
$f(\pi - \theta) = 4 \cos 2(\pi - \theta) = 4 \cos (2\pi - 2\theta) = 4 \cos (-2\theta) = 4 \cos 2\theta = f(\theta)$;
Yes, symmetric

Because of this symmetry, we shall sketch the graph of $r = f(\theta)$ for θ between 0 and $\frac{\pi}{2}$, and then use symmetry to complete the graph.

θ	$f(\theta)$
0	4
0.2	3.684244
0.4	2.786827
0.6	1.449431
0.8	−0.116798
1	−1.664587
1.2	−2.949575
1.4	−3.768889

Keep plotting points until you are satisfied that you have a reasonable representation for the graph. After working through Example 6, you will be able to do other rose curves more easily.

When $\theta = 0$, $r = 4$, and as θ increases from 0 to $\frac{\pi}{4}$, the radial distance r decreases from 4 to 0. Then, as θ increases from $\frac{\pi}{4}$ to $\frac{\pi}{2}$, r becomes negative and decreases from 0 to −4. A table of values is given in the margin.

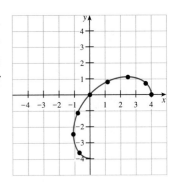

The next part of the graph is obtained by first reflecting in the *y*-axis.

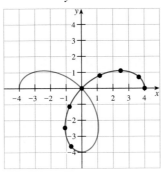

The last part of the graph is found by reflecting in the *x*-axis.

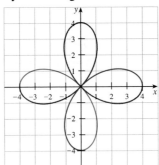

In general, $r = a \cos n\theta$ is the equation of a rose curve in which each petal has length a. If n is an even number, the rose has $2n$ petals; if n is odd, the number of petals is n. The tips of the petals are equally spaced on a circle of radius of a. Equations of the form $r = a \sin n\theta$ are handled as rotations.

Standard-Position Rose Curve

$$r = a \cos n\theta$$

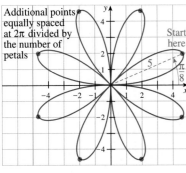

Figure 9.12 Graph of $r = 5 \sin 4\theta$

EXAMPLE 6   Graphing a rose curve with 8 petals and a rotation

Graph $r = 5 \sin 4\theta$.

Solution   We begin by finding the amount of rotation.

$$r = 5 \sin 4\theta$$

$$= 5 \cos\left(\tfrac{\pi}{2} - 4\theta\right) \quad \textit{Cofunctions of complementary angles}$$

$$= 5 \cos\left(4\theta - \tfrac{\pi}{2}\right) \quad \textit{Remember, } \cos(-\theta) = \cos\theta.$$

$$= 5 \cos 4\left(\theta - \tfrac{\pi}{8}\right)$$

Recognize this as a rose curve rotated $\frac{\pi}{8}$. There are $2(4) = 8$ petals of length 5. The petals are a distance of $\frac{\pi}{4}$ (one revolution = 2π divided by the number of petals) apart. The graph is shown in Figure 9.12.

■ LEMNISCATES

The last general type of polar-form curve we will consider is called a **lemniscate**.

Standard-Position Lemniscate

$$r^2 = a^2\cos 2\theta$$

EXAMPLE 7   Graphing a lemniscate

Graph $r^2 = 9\cos 2\theta$.

Solution   As before, when graphing a curve for the first time, begin by checking symmetry and plotting points. For this example, note that you obtain two values for r when solving this quadratic equation. For example, if $\theta = 0$, then $\cos 2\theta = 1$ and $r^2 = 9$, so $r = 3$ or -3.

Symmetry with respect to the x-axis:
$9\cos[2(-\theta)] = 9\cos 2\theta$, so $r^2 = 9\cos 2\theta$ is not affected when θ is replaced by $-\theta$; **yes,** symmetric with respect to the x-axis.

Symmetry with respect to the y-axis:
$9\cos[2(\pi - \theta)] = 9\cos(2\pi - 2\theta) = 9\cos(-2\theta) = 9\cos 2\theta$;   **yes;**   symmetric with respect to the y-axis.

Symmetry with respect to the origin:
$(-r)^2 = r^2$, so $r^2 = 9\cos 2\theta$ is not affected when r is replaced by $-r$; **yes;** symmetric with respect to the origin.

Note that because $r^2 \geq 0$, the function $\cos 2\theta$ is defined only for those values of θ for which $\cos 2\theta \geq 0$; that is

$$-\frac{\pi}{4} \leq \theta \leq \frac{\pi}{4}; \qquad \frac{3\pi}{4} \leq \theta \leq \frac{5\pi}{4}; \ldots$$

We begin by restricting our attention to the interval $0 \leq \theta \leq \frac{\pi}{4}$. Note that $\cos 2\theta$ decreases steadily from 3 to 0 as θ varies from 0 to $\frac{\pi}{4}$.

A second step is to use symmetry to reflect the curve in the x-axis.

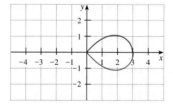

Finally, obtain the rest of the graph by reflecting the curve in the y-axis.

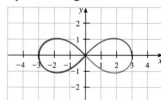

■ SUMMARY OF POLAR-FORM CURVES

We conclude this section by summarizing the special types of polar-form curves we have examined. There are many others, some of which are represented in the problems; others are found in Chapter 5 of *Student Mathematics Handbook*.

TABLE 9.1 Directory of Polar-Form Curves

LIMAÇONS $r = b \pm a \cos \theta$ or $r = b \pm a \sin \theta$

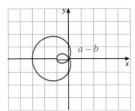

$r = b - a \cos \theta, \dfrac{b}{a} < 1$
standard form
with inner loop

$r = b - a \cos \theta, 1 < \dfrac{b}{a} < 2$
standard form
with a dimple

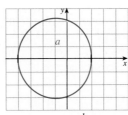

$r = b - a \cos \theta, \dfrac{b}{a} \geq 2$
standard form,
convex

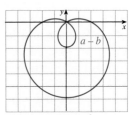

$r = b - a \sin \theta, \dfrac{b}{a} < 1$
$\dfrac{\pi}{2}$ rotation
with inner loop

CARDIOIDS $r = a(1 \pm \cos \theta)$ and $r = a(1 \pm \sin \theta)$
Limaçons in which $a = b$

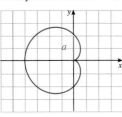

$r = a - a \cos \theta$
standard form

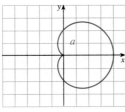

$r = a + a \cos \theta$
π rotation

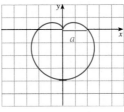

$r = a - a \sin \theta,$
$\dfrac{\pi}{2}$ rotation

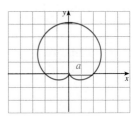

$r = a + a \sin \theta,$
$\dfrac{3\pi}{2}$ rotation

ROSE CURVES
$r = a \cos n\theta$ or $r = a \sin n\theta$
If n is odd, the rose has n petals;
if n is even it has $2n$ petals.

$r = a \cos \theta$
standard form
one (circular) petal

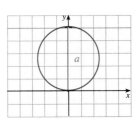

$r = a \sin \theta$
$\dfrac{\pi}{2}$ rotation,
one (circular) petal

LEMNISCATES
$r^2 = a^2 \cos 2\theta$ or $r^2 = a^2 \sin 2\theta$
Two loops

$r^2 = a^2 \cos 2\theta$
standard form

$r^2 = a^2 \sin 2\theta$
$\dfrac{\pi}{4}$ rotation

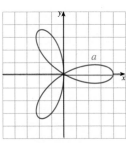

$r = a \cos 3\theta$
standard form,
three petals

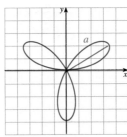

$r = a \sin 3\theta$
$\dfrac{\pi}{6}$ rotation,
three petals

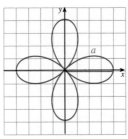

$r = a \cos 2\theta$
standard form,
four petals

$r = a \sin 2\theta$
$\dfrac{\pi}{4}$ rotation,
four petals

PROBLEM SET 9.2

A 1. ■ **What Does This Say?** Describe a procedure for graphing polar-form curves.

2. ■ **What Does This Say?** Discuss symmetry in the graph of a polar-form function.

3. ■ **What Does This Say?** Compare and contrast the forms of the equation for limaçons, cardioids, rose curves, and lemniscates.

4. Identify each of the curves as a cardioid, rose curve (state number of petals), lemniscate, limaçon, circle, line, or none of the above.

a. $r^2 = 9 \cos 2\theta$ b. $r = 2 \sin \frac{\pi}{6}$

c. $r = 3 \sin 3\theta$ d. $r = 3\theta$

e. $r = 2 - 2 \cos \theta$ f. $\theta = \frac{\pi}{6}$

g. $r^2 = \sin 2\theta$ h. $r - 2 = 4 \cos \theta$

5. Identify each of the curves as a cardioid, rose curve (state number of petals), lemniscate, limaçon, circle, line, or none of the above.

a. $r = 2 \sin 2\theta$ b. $r^2 = 2 \cos 2\theta$

c. $r = 5 \cos 60°$ d. $r = 5 \sin 8\theta$

e. $r\theta = 3$ f. $r^2 = 9 \cos\left(2\theta - \frac{\pi}{4}\right)$

g. $r = \sin 3\left(\theta + \frac{\pi}{6}\right)$ h. $\cos \theta = 1 - r$

6. Identify each of the curves as a cardioid, rose curve (state number of petals), lemniscate, limaçon, circle, line, or none of the above.

a. $r = 2 \cos 2\theta$ b. $r = 4 \sin 30°$

c. $r + 2 = 3 \sin \theta$ d. $r + 3 = 3 \sin \theta$

e. $\theta = 4$ f. $\theta = \tan \frac{\pi}{4}$

g. $r = 3 \cos 5\theta$ h. $r \cos \theta = 2$

Graph the polar-form curves given in Problems 7–38.

7. $r = 3, 0 \le \theta \le \frac{\pi}{2}$ 8. $r = -1, 0 \le \theta \le \pi$

9. $\theta = -\frac{\pi}{2}, 0 \le r \le 3$ 10. $\theta = \frac{\pi}{4}, 1 \le r \le 2$

11. $r = \theta + 1, 0 \le \theta \le \pi$ 12. $r = \theta - 1, 0 \le \theta \le \pi$

13. $r = 2\theta, \theta \ge 0$ 14. $r = \frac{\theta}{2}, \theta \ge 0$

15. $r = 2 \cos 2\theta$ 16. $r = 3 \cos 3\theta$

17. $r = 5 \sin 3\theta$ 18. $r^2 = 9 \cos 2\theta$

19. $r^2 = 16 \cos 2\theta$ 20. $r^2 = 9 \sin 2\theta$

21. $r = 3 \cos 3\left(\theta - \frac{\pi}{3}\right)$ 22. $r = 2 \cos 2\left(\theta + \frac{\pi}{3}\right)$

23. $r = 5 \cos 3\left(\theta - \frac{\pi}{4}\right)$ 24. $r = \sin 3\left(\theta + \frac{\pi}{6}\right)$

25. $r = \sin\left(2\theta + \frac{\pi}{3}\right)$ 26. $r = \cos\left(2\theta + \frac{\pi}{3}\right)$

27. $r^2 = 16 \cos 2\left(\theta - \frac{\pi}{6}\right)$ 28. $r^2 = 9 \cos\left(2\theta - \frac{\pi}{3}\right)$

29. $r = 2 + \cos \theta$ 30. $r = 3 + \sin \theta$

31. $r = 1 + \sin \theta$ 32. $r = 1 + \cos \theta$

33. $r \cos \theta = 2$ 34. $r \sin \theta = 3$

35. $r = 1 + 3 \cos \theta$ 36. $r = 1 + 2 \sin \theta$

37. $r = -2 \sin \theta$ 38. $r^2 = -\cos 2\theta$

B *Sketch the graph of the polar function given in Problems 39–44.*

39. $f(\theta) = \sin 2\theta, 0 \le \theta \le \frac{\pi}{2}$; rose petal

40. $f(\theta) = |\sin 2\theta|, 0 \le \theta \le 2\pi$; four-leaf rose

41. $f(\theta) = 2|\cos \theta|, 0 \le \theta \le 2\pi$

42. $f(\theta) = 4|\sin \theta|, 0 \le \theta \le 2\pi$

43. $f(\theta) = \sqrt{|\cos \theta|}, 0 \le \theta \le 2\pi$; lazy eight

44. $f(\theta) = \sqrt{\cos 2\theta}, 0 \le \theta \le 2\pi$; lemniscate

Graph the set of points (r, θ) so that the inequalities in Problems 45–54 are satisfied.

45. $0 \le r \le 1, 0 \le \theta < 2\pi$

46. $2 \le r \le 3, 0 \le \theta < 2\pi$

47. $0 \le r < 4, 0 \le \theta \le \frac{\pi}{2}$

48. $0 \le r \le 4, 0 \le \theta \le \pi$

49. $r > 1, 0 \le \theta < 2\pi$

50. $r \ge 2, \frac{\pi}{2} \le \theta \le \pi$

51. $0 \le \theta \le \frac{\pi}{4}, r \ge 0$

52. $-\pi \le \theta < \pi, r \ge 0$

53. $0 \le \theta \le \frac{\pi}{4}, 1 \le r \le 2$

54. $0 \le \theta \le \frac{\pi}{4}, r > 1$

55. Show that the polar equations

$$r = \cos \theta + 1 \quad \text{and} \quad r = \cos \theta - 1$$

have the same graph in the *xy*-plane.

56. **Spirals** are interesting mathematical curves. There are three special types of spirals:

a. A **spiral of Archimedes** has the form $r = a\theta$; graph $r = 2\theta$.

b. A **hyperbolic spiral** has the form $r\theta = a$; graph $r\theta = 2$.

c. A **logarithmic spiral** has the form $r = a^{k\theta}$; graph $r = 2^\theta$.

57. The **strophoid** is a curve of the form

$$r = a \cos 2\theta \sec \theta$$

Graph this curve where $a = 2$.

58. The **bifolium** has the form

$$r = a \sin \theta \cos^2 \theta$$

Graph this curve where $a = 1$.

59. The **folium of Descartes** has the form

$$r = \frac{3a \sin \theta \cos \theta}{\sin^3 \theta + \cos^3 \theta}$$

Graph the curve where $a = 2$.

60. The **oval of Cassini** has the form

$$r^4 + b^4 - 2b^2r^2 \cos 2\theta = k^4$$

Graph the curve where $b = 2, k = 3$.

In Problems 61–66, graph the given pair of curves on the same coordinate axes. The first equation uses (x, y) as rectangular coordinates and the second uses (r, θ) as polar coordinates.

61. $y = \cos x$ and $r = \cos \theta$

62. $y = \sin x$ and $r = \sin \theta$

63. $y = \tan x$ and $r = \tan \theta$

64. $y = \sec x$ and $r = \sec \theta$

65. $y = \csc x$ and $r = \csc \theta$
66. $y = \cot x$ and $r = \cot \theta$

▭ Computational Window   ▼   ▲

Exploring the periodicity of polar plots *It is surprisingly difficult to predict the periodic behavior of polar plots. For example, here you are to investigate the behavior of the graphs of the form*

$$r = f(\theta) = \sin m\theta$$

for m *a positive integer.*

67. Consider $r = f(\theta) = \sin 2\theta$.

   a. Since $\sin 2\theta$ has period π, one would think that surely the graph repeats itself for $\theta > \pi$. Graphically show that this is *not* the case. Verify that it is necessary for $0 < \theta < 2\pi$ to obtain the entire graph. Describe the graph.

   b. Explain *why* the interval $0 < \theta < \pi$ is not enough.

   c. Now, systematically study $r = f(\theta) = \sin mx$ for m a positive integer. In particular, describe *why m* being even or odd makes a fundamental difference. Summarize the number of leaves on the roses relative to m.

68. Continuing the theme of Problem 67, consider

$$r = f(\theta) = \sin\left(\frac{m\theta}{n}\right)$$

   where m and n are positive integers (and relatively prime). Let P denote the period of the sine.

   a. First set $m = 1$ and study the behavior of the graphs for $n = 1, 2, 3, \ldots$. Clearly, the period of the sine function is $P = 2n\pi$. But what θ interval is

required to get the entire graph? Attempt to explain this. Hand in your favorite graph.

   b. Now do a study for $m = 1, 2, \ldots$ and $n = 1, 2, \ldots$ and attempt to generalize the situation regarding the period of the sine functions, the necessary θ interval, and the number of loops in the graphs. Hand in your favorite graph.

   c. A challenge Attempt to carefully explain the necessary θ interval in part **b**.

Ⓒ 69. Show that the curve $r = f(\theta)$ is symmetric with respect to the x-axis if the equation is unaffected when r is replaced by $-r$ and θ is replaced by $\pi - \theta$.

70. Show that the curve $r = f(\theta)$ is symmetric with respect to the y-axis if the equation is unaffected when r is replaced by $-r$ and θ is replaced by $-\theta$.

71. Show that the curve $r = f(\theta)$ is symmetric in the line $y = x$ if the equation is unaffected when θ is replaced by $\frac{\pi}{2} - \theta$.

72. State and prove a theorem regarding the relationship of the graph of $r = f(\theta)$ to that of $r = f(\theta - \theta_0)$ for $0 < \theta_0 < \frac{\pi}{2}$.

73. **a.** Show that if the polar curve $r = f(\theta)$ is rotated about the pole through an angle α, the equation for the new curve is $r = f(\theta - \alpha)$.

   b. Use a rotation to sketch

$$r = 2\sec\left(\theta - \frac{\pi}{3}\right)$$

74. Sketch the graph of

$$r = \frac{\theta}{\cos\theta} \qquad \text{for } 0 \le \theta \le \frac{\pi}{2}$$

   In particular, show that the graph has a vertical asymptote at $\theta = \frac{\pi}{2}$.

9.3 AREA AND TANGENT LINES IN POLAR COORDINATES

IN THIS SECTION **Intersections of polar-form curves, area bounded by polar graphs, tangent lines**
We have introduced the common polar curves and have considered symmetry and rotations as aids to graphing. In this section we consider the intersection of polar-form curves and the area of the region bounded by polar curves. We conclude by considering tangent lines to polar curves.

■ INTERSECTION OF POLAR-FORM CURVES

In order to find the points of intersection of graphs in rectangular form, you need only find the simultaneous solution of the equations that define those graphs. It is not even necessary to draw the graphs, because there is a one-to-one correspondence between ordered pairs satisfying an equation and points on its graph. However, in polar form, this one-to-one property is lost, so that without drawing the graphs you may fail to find all the points of intersection. For this reason, our method for finding the intersection of polar-form curves will include sketching the graphs.

EXAMPLE 1   Finding the intersection of two polar-form curves

Find the points of intersection of the circles $r = 2 \cos \theta$ and $r = 2 \sin \theta$ for $0 \le \theta < 2\pi$.

Solution   First, consider the simultaneous solution of the system of equations.

$$2 \cos \theta = 2 \sin \theta$$

$$1 = \frac{2 \sin \theta}{2 \cos \theta}$$

$$1 = \tan \theta$$

$$\theta = \frac{\pi}{4}, \frac{5\pi}{4}$$

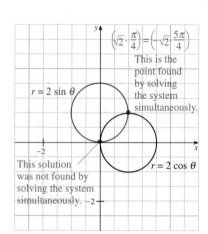

Figure 9.13 Graphs of $r = 2 \cos \theta$ and $r = 2 \sin \theta$

Then find r using either of the two given equations:

$$r = 2 \cos \frac{\pi}{4} = \sqrt{2} \quad \text{and} \quad r = 2 \cos \frac{5\pi}{4} = -\sqrt{2}$$

This gives the points $\left(\sqrt{2}, \frac{\pi}{4}\right)$ and $\left(-\sqrt{2}, \frac{5\pi}{4}\right)$. We see that these ordered pairs are primary representations of the same point. Thus, the simultaneous solution yields one point of intersection.

Next, consider the graphs of these circles, shown in Figure 9.13. It looks as though $(0, 0)$ is also a point of intersection. Check this point in each of the given equations:

If $r = 0$ in $r = 2 \cos \theta$, then $\theta = \frac{\pi}{2}$.

If $r = 0$ in $r = 2 \sin \theta$, then $\theta = \pi$.

At first it does not seem that the pole satisfies the equation, because $r = 0$ gives $\left(0, \frac{\pi}{2}\right)$ and $(0, \pi)$, respectively. Notice that these coordinates are different and do not satisfy the equations simultaneously. But, if you plot the point with the coordinates, you will see that $\left(0, \frac{\pi}{2}\right)$, $(0, \pi)$, and $(0, 0)$ are all the same point. It's as if two ants were crawling along the curves and came to the origin at different times—they would pass each other without colliding.   ▬

The pole is often a solution for a system of polar equations, even though it may not satisfy the equations simultaneously. This is because when $r = 0$, all values of θ will yield the same point—namely, the pole. For this reason, it is necessary to check separately to see if the pole lies on the given graph.

Graphical Solution of the Intersection of Polar Curves

Step 1. Find the simultaneous solution of the given system of equations.
Step 2. Determine whether the pole lies on the two graphs.
Step 3. Graph the curves to look for other points of intersection.

EXAMPLE 2   Intersection of polar form curves

Find the points of intersection of the curves $r = \frac{3}{2} - \cos \theta$ and $\theta = \frac{2\pi}{3}$.

Solution   Step 1: Solve the system by substitution:

$$r = \frac{3}{2} - \cos \frac{2\pi}{3} = \frac{3}{2} - \left(-\frac{1}{2}\right) = 2$$

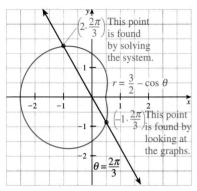

Figure 9.14 Graphs of $r = \frac{3}{2} - \cos\theta$ and $\theta = \frac{2\pi}{3}$

The solution is $\left(2, \frac{2\pi}{3}\right)$.

Step 2: If $r = 0$, the first equation has no solutions because

$$0 = \tfrac{3}{2} - \cos\theta \quad \text{or} \quad \cos\theta = \tfrac{3}{2}$$

and a cosine cannot be larger than 1.

Step 3: Now look at the graphs, as shown in Figure 9.14. From the graphs we see that $\left(-1, \frac{2\pi}{3}\right)$ may also be a point of intersection. It satisfies the equation $\theta = \frac{2\pi}{3}$, but what about $r = \frac{3}{2} - \cos\theta$? Check $\left(-1, \frac{2\pi}{3}\right)$:

$$-1 \overset{?}{=} \tfrac{3}{2} - \cos\left(\tfrac{2\pi}{3}\right)$$
$$= \tfrac{3}{2} - \left(-\tfrac{1}{2}\right)$$
$$= 2 \qquad \textit{Not satisfied}$$

However, if you check the alternative representation $\left(-1, \frac{2\pi}{3}\right) = \left(1, \frac{5\pi}{3}\right)$:

$$1 \overset{?}{=} \tfrac{3}{2} - \cos\left(\tfrac{5\pi}{3}\right)$$
$$= \tfrac{3}{2} - \tfrac{1}{2}$$
$$= 1 \qquad \textit{Satisfied}$$

Be sure to check for points of intersection that you may have missed. ▬

■ AREA BOUNDED BY POLAR GRAPHS

In order to find the area of a region bounded by a polar graph, we use Riemann sums in much the same way as when we developed the integral formula for the area of a region described in rectangular form. However, instead of using rectangles as the basic unit being summed in polar form, we sum the area of *sectors* of a circle. Recall from trigonometry the formula for the area of such a sector.

Area of a Sector

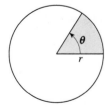

The area of a circular sector of radius r is given by

$$A = \tfrac{1}{2}r^2\theta$$

where θ is the central angle of the sector measured in radians.

This formula gives the following proportions:

Angle	Area	Figure
2π	πr^2	
1	$\frac{1}{2}r^2(1) = \frac{r^2}{2}$	
α	$\frac{1}{2}r^2(\alpha) = \frac{\alpha r^2}{2}$	

Using this formula for the area of a sector, we now state a theorem that gives us a formula for finding the area enclosed by a polar curve.

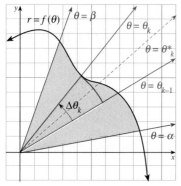

a. The region bounded by the polar curve $r = f(\theta)$ and the rays $\theta = \alpha$ and $\theta = \beta$

b. The area A can be estimated by adding the area of "small" (pink) circular sectors.

Figure 9.15 Area in polar form

THEOREM 9.1   Area in polar coordinates

Let $r = f(\theta)$ define a polar curve, where f is continuous and $f(\theta) \geq 0$ on the closed interval $\alpha \leq \theta \leq \beta$. Then the region bounded by the curve $r = f(\theta)$ and the rays $\theta = \alpha$ and $\theta = \beta$ has area

$$A = \frac{1}{2}\int_{\alpha}^{\beta} r^2\, d\theta = \frac{1}{2}\int_{\alpha}^{\beta} [f(\theta)]^2\, d\theta$$

Proof: The region is shown in Figure 9.15. To find the area bounded by the graphs of the polar functions, partition the region between $\theta = \alpha$ and $\theta = \beta$ by a collection of rays, say $\theta_0, \theta_1, \ldots, \theta_n$. Let $\alpha = \theta_0$ and $\beta = \theta_n$.

Pick any ray $\theta = \theta_k^*$, with $\theta_{k-1} \leq \theta_k^* \leq \theta_k$. Then the area ΔA_k of the circular sector is approximately the same as the area of the region bounded by the graph of f and the lines $\theta = \theta_{k-1}$ and $\theta = \theta_k$. Because this circular sector has radius $f(\theta_k^*)$ and central angle $\Delta\theta_k$, its area is

$$\Delta A_k = \tfrac{1}{2}(\text{radius})^2(\text{central angle}) = \tfrac{1}{2}[f(\theta_k^*)]^2 \Delta\theta_k$$

The sum $\sum\limits_{k=1}^{n} \Delta A_k$ is an approximation to the total area A bounded by the polar curve, and by taking the limit as $n \to \infty$, we obtain

$$A = \lim_{n\to\infty} \sum_{k=1}^{n} \Delta A_k = \frac{1}{2}\lim_{n\to\infty} \sum_{k=1}^{n} [f(\theta_k^*)]^2 \Delta\theta_k = \frac{1}{2}\int_{\alpha}^{\beta} [f(\theta)]^2\, d\theta \quad\blacksquare$$

The process is familiar, and you will find that the most difficult part of the problem is deciding on the limits of integration. A decent sketch of the region will help you do this.

EXAMPLE 3   Finding area enclosed by part of a cardioid

Find the area under the top half ($0 \leq \theta \leq \pi$) of the cardioid $r = 1 + \cos\theta$.

Solution   The cardioid is shown in Figure 9.16. Note that the top half of the graph lies between the rays $\theta = 0$ and $\theta = \pi$. Hence the required area is given by

$$A = \frac{1}{2}\int_0^{\pi} (1 + \cos\theta)^2\, d\theta = \frac{1}{2}\int_0^{\pi} (1 + 2\cos\theta + \cos^2\theta)\, d\theta$$

$$= \frac{1}{2}\left[\theta + 2\sin\theta + \frac{\theta}{2} + \frac{\sin 2\theta}{4}\right]\Big|_0^{\pi} \qquad \text{\textit{Integration table, formula 317}}$$

$$= \frac{1}{2}\left[\pi + 2(0) + \frac{\pi}{2} + \frac{0}{4} - 0\right] = \frac{3\pi}{4}$$

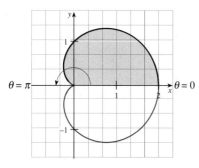

Figure 9.16 Area under the top half of the cardioid $r = 1 + \cos\theta$

EXAMPLE 4   Finding area enclosed by a four-leaved rose

Find the area enclosed by the four-leaved rose $r = \cos 2\theta$.

Solution   The rose curve is shown in Figure 9.17. We will find the area of the top half of the right loop (shaded portion) in order to make sure $f(\theta) \geq 0$. We see this corresponds to angles with measures from $\theta = 0$ to $\theta = \frac{\pi}{4}$. By symmetry,

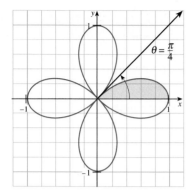

Figure 9.17 Area enclosed by the four-leaved rose $r = \cos 2\theta$

the entire area enclosed by the four-leaved rose is 8 times the shaded region. Thus, the required area is given by

$$A = 8\left[\frac{1}{2}\int_0^{\pi/4}\cos^2 2\theta\, d\theta\right]$$

$$= 4\left[\frac{\theta}{2} + \frac{\sin 4\theta}{8}\right]\Bigg|_0^{\pi/4} \qquad \textit{Integration table, formula 317}$$

$$= 4\left[\frac{\pi}{8} + 0 - 0\right]$$

$$= \frac{\pi}{2}$$

EXAMPLE 5 **Finding the area of a region defined by two polar curves**

Find the area of the region common to the circles $r = a\cos\theta$ and $r = a\sin\theta$.

Solution The circles are shown in Figure 9.18. Note that they intersect at $\theta = \frac{\pi}{4}$ and at the pole (both by inspection). In order to set up the integrals properly, remember to think in terms of polar coordinates and not in terms of rectangular coordinates. Specifically, we must **scan radially**. This means that we need to find the area of intersection by finding the sum of the areas of the regions marked R_1 and R_2. Region R_1 is bounded by the circle $r = a\sin\theta$ and the rays $\theta = 0$, $\theta = \frac{\pi}{4}$. Region R_2 is bounded by the circle $r = a\cos\theta$ and $\theta = \frac{\pi}{4}$, $\theta = \frac{\pi}{2}$. Note that the rays $\theta = 0$ and $\theta = \frac{\pi}{2}$ are not necessary as geometric boundaries for R_1 and R_2, but they are necessary to describe which part of each circle is being defined.

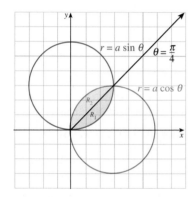

Figure 9.18 Area enclosed by $r = a\cos\theta$ and $r = a\sin\theta$

$$A = \text{AREA OF } R_1 + \text{AREA OF } R_2$$

$$= \frac{1}{2}\int_0^{\pi/4} a^2\sin^2\theta\, d\theta + \frac{1}{2}\int_{\pi/4}^{\pi/2} a^2\cos^2\theta\, d\theta$$

$$= \frac{a^2}{2}\left[\frac{\theta}{2} - \frac{\sin 2\theta}{4}\right]\Bigg|_0^{\pi/4} + \frac{a^2}{2}\left[\frac{\theta}{2} + \frac{\sin 2\theta}{4}\right]\Bigg|_{\pi/4}^{\pi/2} \quad \textit{Integration table, formulas 348 and 317.}$$

$$= \frac{a^2}{2}\left[\frac{\pi}{8} - \frac{1}{4} - 0\right] + \frac{a^2}{2}\left[\frac{\pi}{4} + 0 - \frac{\pi}{8} - \frac{1}{4}\right] = \frac{a^2}{2}\left[\frac{\pi}{4} - \frac{1}{2}\right]$$

$$= \frac{1}{8}a^2(\pi - 2)$$

EXAMPLE 6 **Finding the area between a circle and a limaçon**

Find the area between the circle $r = 5\cos\theta$ and the limaçon $r = 2 + \cos\theta$. Round your answer to the nearest hundredth of a square unit.

Solution As usual, begin by drawing the graphs, as shown in Figure 9.19. We see that because both the limaçon and circle are symmetric with respect to the x-axis, we can find the area in the first quadrant and multiply by 2.

Next, we need to find the points of intersection. We see that the curves do not intersect at the pole. Now solve

$$5\cos\theta = 2 + \cos\theta$$

$$\cos\theta = \frac{1}{2}$$

$$\theta = \frac{\pi}{3} \qquad \textit{Solution in the first quadrant}$$

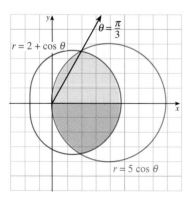

Figure 9.19 Area between $r = 5\cos\theta$ and $r = 2 + \cos\theta$

In order to find the area, divide the region into two parts, along the ray $\theta = \frac{\pi}{3}$. The right part (shaded red) is bounded by the limaçon $r = 2 + \cos\theta$ and the rays $\theta = 0$ and $\theta = \frac{\pi}{3}$. The left part (shaded blue) is bounded by the circle $r = 5\cos\theta$ and the rays $\theta = \frac{\pi}{3}$ and $\theta = \frac{\pi}{2}$. Using this preliminary information we can now set up and evaluate the required integral.

$$A = 2[\text{AREA OF RIGHT PART} + \text{AREA OF LEFT PART}]$$

$$= 2\left[\frac{1}{2}\int_0^{\pi/3}(2 + \cos\theta)^2\,d\theta + \frac{1}{2}\int_{\pi/3}^{\pi/2}(5\cos\theta)^2\,d\theta\right]$$

$$= \int_0^{\pi/3}(4 + 4\cos\theta + \cos^2\theta)\,d\theta + \int_{\pi/3}^{\pi/2}25\cos^2\theta\,d\theta$$

$$= \left[4\theta + 4\sin\theta + \frac{\theta}{2} + \frac{\sin 2\theta}{4}\right]\Bigg|_0^{\pi/3} + 25\left[\frac{\theta}{2} + \frac{\sin 2\theta}{4}\right]\Bigg|_{\pi/3}^{\pi/2}$$

$$= \left[\frac{4\pi}{3} + \frac{4\sqrt{3}}{2} + \frac{\pi}{6} + \frac{\sqrt{3}}{8} - 0\right] + 25\left[\frac{\pi}{4} + 0 - \frac{\pi}{6} - \frac{\sqrt{3}}{8}\right]$$

$$= \frac{9\pi}{6} + \frac{17\sqrt{3}}{8} + \frac{25\pi}{12} - \frac{25\sqrt{3}}{8} = \frac{43\pi}{12} - \sqrt{3} \approx 9.53$$

■

■ TANGENT LINES

⊘ The slope at (r, θ) of $r = f(\theta)$ is NOT $f'(\theta)$. ⊘

In rectangular coordinates, the slope of the tangent line to a graph of $y = g(x)$ at $x = x_0$ is $g'(x_0)$, and we might expect the slope of the tangent line to the graph of $r = f(\theta)$ at $\theta = \theta_0$ to be $f'(\theta_0)$. A simple counterexample shows that this is false. The graph of the polar function $r = c$ ($c > 0$, a constant) is a circle centered at the origin. Because f is a constant, we have $f'(\theta) = 0$ for all θ, so that if $f'(\theta)$ were the slope of the tangent line to this circle, every tangent line would be horizontal, which is clearly false. It turns out that the slope of the tangent line to a polar curve is given by the following more complicated formula.

THEOREM 9.2 **Slope of polar curves**

If $f(\theta)$ is a differentiable function of θ, then the slope of the tangent line to the polar curve $r = f(\theta)$ at the point $P(r_0, \theta_0)$ is given by

$$m = \frac{f(\theta_0)\cos\theta_0 + f'(\theta_0)\sin\theta_0}{-f(\theta_0)\sin\theta_0 + f'(\theta_0)\cos\theta_0}$$

whenever the denominator is not zero.

Proof: Because $r = f(\theta)$ and $x = r\cos\theta$, $y = r\sin\theta$, we have

$$x = f(\theta)\cos\theta \quad \text{and} \quad y = f(\theta)\sin\theta$$

Using the chain rule, we find that $\frac{dy}{d\theta} = \left(\frac{dy}{dx}\right)\left(\frac{dx}{d\theta}\right)$ or, equivalently,

$$\frac{dy}{dx} = \frac{\dfrac{dy}{d\theta}}{\dfrac{dx}{d\theta}}$$

Because $x = f(\theta)\cos\theta$ and $y = f(\theta)\sin\theta$, it follows that

$$\frac{dx}{d\theta} = f(\theta)\frac{d}{d\theta}(\cos\theta) + \cos\theta\frac{df}{d\theta} \qquad \frac{dy}{d\theta} = f(\theta)\frac{d}{d\theta}(\sin\theta) + \sin\theta\frac{df}{d\theta}$$

$$= -f(\theta)\sin\theta + f'(\theta)\cos\theta \qquad\qquad = f(\theta)\cos\theta + f'(\theta)\sin\theta$$

and the slope of the tangent line is given by:

$$m = \frac{dy}{dx} = \frac{\dfrac{dy}{d\theta}}{\dfrac{dx}{d\theta}} = \frac{f(\theta)\cos\theta + f'(\theta)\sin\theta}{-f(\theta)\sin\theta + f'(\theta)\cos\theta}$$

■

The theorem for slope in polar form is not easy to remember, and it may be easier for you to remember

$$\frac{dy}{dx} = \frac{\dfrac{dy}{d\theta}}{\dfrac{dx}{d\theta}}$$

where $x = f(\theta)\cos\theta$ and $y = f(\theta)\sin\theta$. With this form, notice that **horizontal tangents** ($dy/dx = 0$) occur when $\frac{dy}{d\theta} = 0$ and $\frac{dx}{d\theta} \neq 0$, and **vertical tangents** occur when $\frac{dx}{d\theta} = 0$ and $\frac{dy}{d\theta} \neq 0$. If $\frac{dx}{d\theta} = \frac{dy}{d\theta} = 0$, then no conclusions can be drawn without further analysis.

EXAMPLE 7   Computing the slope of a cardioid at a given point

Find the slope of the tangent line to the cardioid $r = 1 + \cos\theta$ at the point $\left(1 + \frac{\sqrt{3}}{2}, \frac{\pi}{6}\right)$.

Solution   First find x and y as functions of θ:

$$x = f(\theta)\cos\theta = (1 + \cos\theta)\cos\theta = \cos\theta + \cos^2\theta$$

$$y = f(\theta)\sin\theta = (1 + \cos\theta)\sin\theta = \sin\theta + \cos\theta\sin\theta = \sin\theta + \tfrac{1}{2}\sin 2\theta$$

Then find the derivatives $\frac{dx}{d\theta}$ and $\frac{dy}{d\theta}$:

$$\frac{dx}{d\theta} = -\sin\theta - 2\cos\theta\sin\theta \qquad \frac{dy}{d\theta} = \cos\theta + \cos 2\theta$$

$$= -\sin\theta - \sin 2\theta$$

At $\theta = \frac{\pi}{6}$, we have

$$\frac{dx}{d\theta} = -\sin\frac{\pi}{6} - \sin\frac{\pi}{3} = -\frac{1}{2} - \frac{\sqrt{3}}{2} = \frac{-1 - \sqrt{3}}{2}$$

$$\frac{dy}{d\theta} = \cos\frac{\pi}{6} + \cos\frac{\pi}{3} = \frac{\sqrt{3}}{2} + \frac{1}{2} = \frac{\sqrt{3} + 1}{2}$$

so the slope is

$$m = \frac{dy}{dx} = \frac{\dfrac{dy}{d\theta}}{\dfrac{dx}{d\theta}} = \frac{\frac{\sqrt{3} + 1}{2}}{\frac{-1 - \sqrt{3}}{2}} = -1$$

The graph of the cardioid, and the tangent line at $\theta = \frac{\pi}{6}$ are shown in Figure 9.20.   ▬

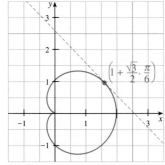

Figure 9.20 Graph of $r = 1 + \cos\theta$ and line passing through $\left(1 + \frac{\sqrt{3}}{2}, \frac{\pi}{6}\right)$ with slope -1

EXAMPLE 8   Finding tangents to a spiral

Find all numbers θ with $0 \le \theta \le \pi$ so that the tangent line to the spiral $r = \theta$ is horizontal.

Solution   We first look at the graph (see Figure 9.21) so that we know what to expect. We now carry out the analytic work:

$$x = f(\theta)\cos\theta = \theta\cos\theta \quad \text{and} \quad y = f(\theta)\sin\theta = \theta\sin\theta, \qquad \text{so that}$$

$$\frac{dx}{d\theta} = -\theta\sin\theta + \cos\theta \qquad \text{and} \qquad \frac{dy}{d\theta} = \theta\cos\theta + \sin\theta$$

Thus,

$$m = \frac{\dfrac{dy}{d\theta}}{\dfrac{dx}{d\theta}} = \frac{\theta\cos\theta + \sin\theta}{-\theta\sin\theta + \cos\theta}$$

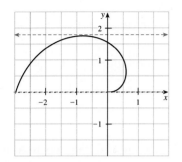

Figure 9.21 By drawing a spiral with $0 \le \theta \le \pi$, it looks like there is a horizontal tangent at the pole and at one other point.

The tangent line is horizontal when $m = 0$, which is equivalent to

$$\theta\cos\theta + \sin\theta = 0$$
$$\theta\cos\theta = -\sin\theta$$
$$\theta = -\frac{\sin\theta}{\cos\theta}, \qquad \cos\theta \ne 0$$
$$\theta = -\tan\theta$$
$$-\theta = \tan\theta$$

This is not an equation we are used to solving, so we can turn to methods of approximation. Either Newton's method (Section 2.9) or a graphical solution is possible, as shown in Figure 9.22.

Figure 9.23 Graph of $r = \theta \ge 0$ and the two horizontal tangents for $0 \le \theta \le \pi$

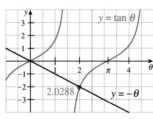

a. Newton's method for finding the solution of the equation $-\theta = \tan\theta$; the approximate solution is $\theta = 2.0288$.

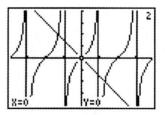

b. On a graphing calculator, graph $y = \tan\theta$ and $y = -\theta$; use TRACE to approximate the solutions: $\theta = 2.0503026$ and 0.

Figure 9.22 Approximating the roots of $-\theta = \tan\theta$

We now find the points on the spiral corresponding to the solution shown in Figure 9.22, namely, $\theta = 0$ and approximately $\theta = 2.03$, as shown in Figure 9.23.

PROBLEM SET 9.3

A

1. ■ **What Does This Say?**   Discuss a procedure for finding the intersection of polar-form curves.

2. ■ **What Does This Say?**   Discuss a procedure for finding the area enclosed by a polar curve.

3. ■ **What Does This Say?**   Discuss why the slope of the tangent line of the polar function $f(\theta)$ is not $f'(\theta)$.

Find the points of intersection of the curves given in Problems 4–29. You need to give only one primary representation for each point of intersection (give the one with a positive r and with $0 \le \theta < 2\pi$).

4. $\begin{cases} r = 4\cos\theta \\ r = 4\sin\theta \end{cases}$

5. $\begin{cases} r = 8\cos\theta \\ r = 8\sin\theta \end{cases}$

6. $\begin{cases} r = 2\cos\theta \\ r = 1 \end{cases}$

7. $\begin{cases} r = 4\sin\theta \\ r = 2 \end{cases}$

8. $\begin{cases} r^2 = 9\cos 2\theta \\ r = 3 \end{cases}$

9. $\begin{cases} r^2 = 4\sin 2\theta \\ r = 2 \end{cases}$

10. $\begin{cases} r = 2(1 + \cos\theta) \\ r = 2(1 - \cos\theta) \end{cases}$

11. $\begin{cases} r = 2(1 + \sin\theta) \\ r = 2(1 - \sin\theta) \end{cases}$

12. $\begin{cases} r^2 = 9\sin 2\theta \\ r = 3 \end{cases}$

13. $\begin{cases} r^2 = 4\sin 2\theta \\ r = 2\sqrt{2}\cos\theta \end{cases}$

14. $\begin{cases} r^2 = 9\cos 2\theta \\ r = 3\sqrt{2}\sin\theta \end{cases}$

15. $\begin{cases} r^2 = 4\cos 2\theta \\ r = 2 \end{cases}$

16. $\begin{cases} r = 3\theta \\ \theta = \frac{\pi}{3} \end{cases}$

17. $\begin{cases} r^2 = \cos 2\theta \\ r = \sqrt{2}\sin\theta \end{cases}$

18. $\begin{cases} r = 2(1 - \cos\theta) \\ r = 4\sin\theta \end{cases}$

19. $\begin{cases} r = 2(1 + \cos\theta) \\ r = -4\sin\theta \end{cases}$

20. $\begin{cases} r = 2(1 - \sin\theta) \\ r = 4\cos\theta \end{cases}$

21. $\begin{cases} r = 2\cos\theta + 1 \\ r = \sin\theta \end{cases}$

22. $\begin{cases} r = 2\sin\theta + 1 \\ r = \cos\theta \end{cases}$

23. $\begin{cases} r = \dfrac{5}{3 - \cos\theta} \\ r = 2 \end{cases}$

24. $\begin{cases} r = \dfrac{2}{1 + \cos\theta} \\ r = 2 \end{cases}$

25. $\begin{cases} r = \dfrac{4}{1 - \cos\theta} \\ r = 2\cos\theta \end{cases}$

26. $\begin{cases} r = \dfrac{1}{1 + \cos\theta} \\ r = 2(1 - \cos\theta) \end{cases}$

27. $\begin{cases} r = 2\cos\theta \\ r = \sec\theta \end{cases}$

28. $\begin{cases} r = 2\sin\theta \\ r = 2\csc\theta \end{cases}$

29. $\begin{cases} r\sin\theta = 1 \\ r = 4\sin\theta \end{cases}$

Find the area of each polar region enclosed by $f(\theta)$, $\theta = a$, $\theta = b$ for $a \le \theta \le b$ in Problems 30–37.

30. $f(\theta) = \sin\theta$, $0 \le \theta \le \frac{\pi}{6}$

31. $f(\theta) = \cos\theta$, $0 \le \theta \le \frac{\pi}{6}$

32. $f(\theta) = \sec\theta$, $-\frac{\pi}{4} \le \theta \le \frac{\pi}{4}$

33. $f(\theta) = \sqrt{\sin\theta}$, $\frac{\pi}{6} \le \theta \le \frac{\pi}{2}$

34. $f(\theta) = e^{\theta/2}$, $0 \le \theta \le 2\pi$

35. $f(\theta) = \sin\theta + \cos\theta$, $0 \le \theta \le \frac{\pi}{4}$

36. $f(\theta) = \dfrac{\theta}{\pi}$, $0 \le \theta \le 2\pi$

37. $f(\theta) = \dfrac{\theta^2}{\pi}$, $0 \le \theta \le 2\pi$

In Problems 38–47, find the slope of the tangent line to the graph of the polar function curves at the given point.

38. $f(\theta) = 1 - \cos\theta$ at $\left(\dfrac{2 - \sqrt{2}}{2}, \dfrac{\pi}{4}\right)$

39. $f(\theta) = 4\cos\theta + 2$ at the pole

40. $f(\theta) = \sqrt{\cos 2\theta}$ at the pole

41. $f(\theta) = 2$ at $\left(2, \frac{\pi}{3}\right)$

42. $r = 2\sec\theta$, where $\theta = \frac{\pi}{4}$

43. $r = \theta$, where $\theta = \frac{\pi}{2}$

44. $r = \dfrac{4}{3\sin\theta - 2\cos\theta}$, where $\theta = \pi$

45. $r = \dfrac{3}{2\cos\theta + 3\sin\theta}$, where $\theta = \pi$

46. $r = 4\sin\theta\cos^2\theta$, where $\theta = \frac{\pi}{3}$

47. $r = 2\cos\theta\sin^2\theta$, where $\theta = \frac{\pi}{6}$

B

48. Find all points on the cardioid $r = 1 + \sin\theta$ where the tangent line is horizontal.

49. Find all points on the cardioid $r = a(1 + \cos\theta)$ where the tangent line is horizontal.

50. Find all points on the cardioid $r = a(1 - \cos\theta)$ where the tangent line is vertical.

51. Find all points on the circle $r = 2\sin\theta$ where the tangent line is parallel to the ray $\theta = \frac{\pi}{4}$.

52. Find the area of one loop of the four-leaved rose $r = 2\cos 2\theta$.

53. Find the area enclosed by the three-leaved rose $r = a\sin 3\theta$.

54. Find the area of the region that is inside the circle $r = 4\cos\theta$ and outside the circle $r = 2$.

55. Find the area of the region that is inside the circle $r = a$ and outside the cardioid $r = a(1 - \cos\theta)$.

56. Find the area of the region that is inside the circle $r = \sin\theta$ and outside the cardioid $r = 1 - \cos\theta$.

57. Find the area of the region that lies inside the circle $r = 6\cos\theta$ and outside the cardioid $r = 2(1 + \cos\theta)$.

58. Find the area of the portion of the lemniscate $r^2 = 8\cos 2\theta$ that lies in the region $r \ge 2$.

59. Find the area between the inner and outer loops of the limaçon $r = 2 - 4\sin\theta$.

C

60. Find an equation in θ for all polar-form points (r, θ) on the spiral $r = \theta^2$ where the tangent line is horizontal. What happens at the origin?

61. Let a and b be any nonzero numbers. Show that the tangent lines to the graphs of the cardioids

$$r_1 = a(1 + \sin\theta) \quad \text{and} \quad r_2 = b(1 - \sin\theta)$$

are perpendicular to each other at all points where they intersect.

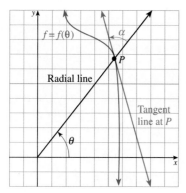

Figure 9.24 Problem 62

62. Because the formula for the slope in polar-form is complicated, it is often more convenient to measure the inclination of the tangent line to a polar curve in terms of the angle α extending from the radial line to the tangent line, as shown in Figure 9.24.

Let P be a point on the polar curve $r = f(\theta)$, and let α be the angle extending from the radial line to the tangent line, as shown in Figure 9.24. Assuming that $f'(\theta) \neq 0$, show that $\tan \alpha = \dfrac{f(\theta)}{f'(\theta)}$

63. Use the formula in Problem 62 to find $\tan \alpha$ for each of the following:

   a. the circle $r = a \cos \theta$

   b. the cardioid $r = 2(1 - \cos \theta)$

   c. the logarithmic spiral $r = 2e^{3\theta}$

9.4 PARAMETRIC REPRESENTATION OF CURVES

> **IN THIS SECTION** Parametric equations, derivatives, arc length, area
> Up to now, each curve we have discussed has been represented by a single equation. In this section we see how we can consider both x and y as functions of some other variable called a *parameter*. After we consider graphing curves with a parameter, we use calculus to find derivatives, arc length, and area for curves defined with a parameter.

■ PARAMETRIC EQUATIONS

Computational Window ▼ ▲

Most graphing calculators will sketch curves in parametric form. Check your owner's manual, but the usual procedure is to change the **MODE** from function format to parametric form.

It is sometimes useful to define the variables x and y in the ordered pair (x, y) so that they are *each* functions of some other variable, say t. That is, let

$$x = g(t) \quad \text{and} \quad y = h(t)$$

for functions g and h, where the domain of these functions is some interval I. The variable t is called a **parameter** and $x = g(t)$ and $y = h(t)$ are **parametric equations**.

Parametric Representation for a Curve

> Let f and g be continuous functions of t on an interval I; then the equations
> $$x = f(t) \quad \text{and} \quad y = g(t)$$
> are called **parametric equations** for the curve C generated by the set of ordered pairs $(x(t), y(t))$.

EXAMPLE 1   Graphing a curve from parametric equations

Graph the curve defined by the functions $x = 2 \cos \theta$, $y = 2 \sin \theta$ for $0 \leq \theta < 2\pi$.

Solution   We could begin by letting θ be the parameter to determine x and y values. When we draw the graph, the parameter is not shown because we still graph the ordered pairs (x, y) in the usual fashion (see Figure 9.25).

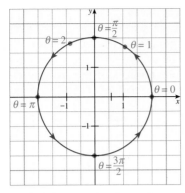

Figure 9.25 Graph of $x = 2 \cos \theta$, $y = 2 \sin \theta$

θ	x	y
0	2	0
1	1.08	1.68
$\frac{\pi}{2}$	0	2
2	-0.83	1.82
π	-2	0
$\frac{3\pi}{2}$	0	-2

If you are using a computer or a graphing calculator, plotting points can be an efficient way of obtaining the graph, but sometimes it is more efficient to **eliminate the parameter**.

$$x^2 = 4 \cos^2 \theta$$

$$y^2 = 4 \sin^2 \theta$$

Add: $\qquad x^2 + y^2 = 4 \cos^2 \theta + 4 \sin^2 \theta = 4(\cos^2 \theta + \sin^2 \theta) = 4$

We recognize this as the equation of a circle centered at $(0, 0)$ with radius 2. ▬

If we start with the parametric equations $x = 2 \cos \theta$, $y = 2 \sin \theta$, we see from Example 1 that after eliminating the parameter we obtain $x^2 + y^2 = 4$. On the other hand, we say that the $x = 2 \cos \theta$, $y = 2 \sin \theta$ is a **parametrization** of the curve $x^2 + y^2 = 4$.

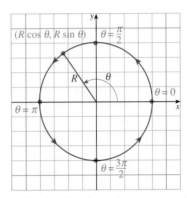

Figure 9.26 Graph of $x = R \cos \theta$, $y = R \sin \theta$

Notice that the curve in Example 1 is not the graph of a function, but it is defined parametrically using functions. This points out one of the advantages of parametric equations—they can be used to represent graphs that are more general than graphs of functions.

In practical applications it is often possible to obtain useful information about a parametrized curve by seeing how it is traced out as the parameter varies from one value to another. For Example 1 we can generalize to say that the parametric equations

$$x = R \cos \theta \qquad y = R \sin \theta \qquad R > 0 \text{ constant}$$

trace out a circle of radius R and center $(0, 0)$ as θ varies from 0 to 2π. We can describe this trace by starting at $\theta = 0$, the point $(R, 0)$, and ending at $\theta = 2\pi$, as shown by the arrows in Figure 9.26. We shall refer to this trace (oriented curve) as the **path** of $x = f(t)$, $y = g(t)$ for $a \le t \le b$ from the point $(f(a), g(a))$ to $(f(b), g(b))$.

EXAMPLE 2   Sketching the path of a parametric curve

Sketch the path of the curve $x = t^2 - 9$, $y = \frac{1}{3}t$ for $-3 \leq t \leq 2$.

Solution   Values of x and y corresponding to various choices of the parameter t are shown in the following table:

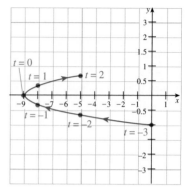

t	x	y	
-3	0	-1	(Starting point)
-2	-5	$-\frac{2}{3}$	
-1	-8	$-\frac{1}{3}$	
0	-9	0	
1	-8	$\frac{1}{3}$	
2	-5	$\frac{2}{3}$	(Ending point)

The graph is shown in Figure 9.27.

Figure 9.27 Graph of $x = t^2 - 9$, $y = \frac{1}{3}t$, for $-3 \leq t \leq 2$. Notice the arrows show the orientation as t increases from -3 to 2. ∎

The parametrization of an equation is not unique. For example, the set of parametric equations

$$x = 9(9t^2 - 1), \qquad y = 3t \qquad \text{for } -\tfrac{1}{3} \leq t \leq \tfrac{2}{9}$$

has the same graph as the one given in Example 2. If we consider t as measuring time, we see that the curve is traced out much more rapidly with this set of equations than the ones given in Example 2. When a parameter is used to describe motion, we call the path a **trajectory**. In many applications we use a parameter to represent different *speeds* at which objects can travel along a given path.

Sometimes a curve defined by parametric equations can be analyzed by the algebraic process of *eliminating the parameter*.

EXAMPLE 3   Sketching the path of a parametric curve by eliminating the parameter

Describe the path $x = \sin \pi t$, $y = \cos 2\pi t$ for $0 \leq t \leq 0.5$.

Solution   Using a double-angle identity, we find

$$\cos 2\pi t = 1 - 2 \sin^2 \pi t$$

so that

$$y = 1 - 2x^2$$

We recognize this as the Cartesian equation for a parabola. Because $y' = -4x$, we can find the critical value $x = 0$, which locates the vertex of the parabola at $(0, 1)$. The parabola is the dashed curve shown in Figure 9.28. Because t is restricted to the interval $0 \leq t \leq 0.5$, the parametric representation involves only part of the right side of the parabola $y = 1 - 2x^2$. The curve is oriented from the point $(0, 1)$, where $t = 0$, to the point $(1, -1)$, where $t = 0.5$. ∎

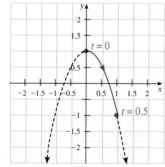

Figure 9.28 The parabolic arc $x = \sin \pi t$, $y = \cos 2\pi t$ for $0 \leq t \leq 0.5$.

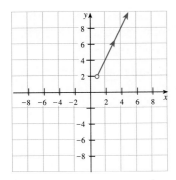

Figure 9.29 Graph of $x = 2^t$, $y = 2^{t+1}$

EXAMPLE 4 Adjusting the domain after eliminating a parameter

Sketch the graph of $x = 2^t$, $y = 2^{t+1}$ for $t > 0$.

Solution Eliminating the parameter, we obtain

$$\frac{y}{x} = \frac{2^{t+1}}{2^t} = 2^{t+1-t} = 2 \quad \text{so that} \quad y = 2x$$

⊘ This answer is not complete until we examine the domain of t. ⊘

For the given parametric equations we see that the domain for t must be positive numbers, because 2^t is not defined in our example for $t \le 0$. However, the equation $y = 2x$ is defined for all values of x and y, so we must adjust the domain of this equation. If $t > 0$, then $x > 1$ and the equation is $y = 2x$, $x > 1$. The graph is shown in Figure 9.29. ▬

When it is difficult to eliminate the parameter from a given parametric representation, we can sometimes get a good picture of the parametric curve by plotting points.

EXAMPLE 5 Describing a spiraling path with a decreasing amplitude

Discuss the path of this curve described by the parametric equations

$$x = e^{-t}\cos t, \qquad y = e^{-t}\sin t \qquad \text{for } t \ge 0$$

Solution We have no convenient way of eliminating the parameter so we write out a table of values (x, y) that correspond to various values of t. The curve is obtained by plotting these points in a Cartesian plane and passing a smooth curve through the plotted points, as shown in Figure 9.30.

t	x	y
0	1	0
$\frac{\pi}{4}$	0.32	0.32
1	0.20	0.31
$\frac{\pi}{2}$	0	0.21
2	−0.06	0.12
π	−0.04	0
$\frac{3\pi}{2}$	0	−0.01
2π	0.00	0

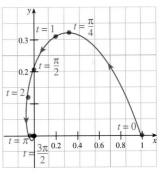

Figure 9.30 Graph of $x = e^{-t}\cos t$, $y = e^{-t}\sin t$ for $t \ge 0$

Note that for each value of t, the distance from $P(x, y)$ on the curve to the origin is

$$\sqrt{x^2 + y^2} = \sqrt{(e^{-t}\cos t)^2 + (e^{-t}\sin t)^2} = \sqrt{e^{-2t}(1)} = e^{-t}$$

Because e^{-t} decreases as t increases, it follows that P gets closer and closer to the origin as t increases. However, because $\cos t$ and $\sin t$ vary between -1 and $+1$, the approach is not direct but takes place along a spiral. ▬

EXAMPLE 6 Finding parametric equations for a trochoid

A bicycle wheel has radius a and a reflector is attached at a point P on the spoke of a bicycle wheel at a fixed distance d from the center of the wheel, which has radius *a*. Find parametric equations for the curve described by *P* as the wheel rolls along a straight line without slipping. Such a curve is called a **trochoid**.

Solution   Assume that the wheel rolls along the *x*-axis and that the center *C* of the wheel begins at (0, *a*) on the *y*-axis. Further assume that *P* also starts on the *y*-axis, *d* units below *C*. Figure 9.31 shows the initial position of the wheel and its position after turning through an angle *θ*.

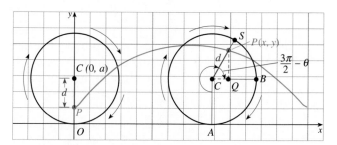

Figure 9.31 The path of a reflector on a bicycle

We begin by labeling some points: The point *A* is on the *x*-axis directly beneath *C*, whereas *B* is the point where the horizontal line through *C* meets the rim of the wheel. Finally, *Q* is the point on *BC* directly beneath *P*, and *S* is the point where the line through *C* and *P* intersects the rim. Let *P* have coordinates (*x*, *y*).

We need to find representations (in terms of *a*, *d*, and *θ*) for *x* and *y*.

$$x = |\overline{OA}| + |\overline{CQ}|$$

$$= a\theta + |\overline{CQ}| \qquad \textit{Because the wheel rolls along the x-axis}$$
without slipping, $|\overline{OA}|$ is the same as the arc length from A to S, so $|\overline{OA}| = a\theta$.

$$y = |\overline{AC}| + |\overline{QP}|$$

$$= a + |\overline{QP}|$$

To complete our evaluation of *x* and *y*, we need to compute $|\overline{CQ}|$ and $|\overline{QP}|$. These are sides of $\triangle PCQ$. Note that $\angle PCQ = \frac{3\pi}{2} - \theta$; therefore, by the definition of cosine and sine, we have

$$\cos\left(\tfrac{3\pi}{2} - \theta\right) = \frac{|\overline{CQ}|}{d} \quad \text{so} \quad |\overline{CQ}| = d\cos\left(\tfrac{3\pi}{2} - \theta\right) = -d\sin\theta$$

Similarly, $|\overline{QP}| = d\sin\left(\frac{3\pi}{2} - \theta\right) = -d\cos\theta$.

We can now substitute these values for $|\overline{CQ}|$ and $|\overline{QP}|$ into the equations we derived for *x* and *y*.

$$x = a\theta + |\overline{CQ}| = a\theta - d\sin\theta$$
$$y = a + |\overline{QP}| = a - d\cos\theta$$

The special case where *P* is on the rim of the wheel in Example 6 (when *d* = *a*) is a curve called a **cycloid**. There are several problems involving these and similar curves in the problem set.

Computational Window

Two variations in the cycloid path discussed in Example 6 may be described as paths traced out by a fixed point P on a circle. If it rolls *inside* a larger circle, the trace is called a **hypocycloid**, and as it rolls around the *outside* of a fixed circle, the trace is called an **epicycloid**. Even though it is not too difficult to derive their parametric equations (see Problems 62 and 63), it is difficult to graph variations of these curves without the assistance of a computer or a graphing calculator. However, if you have access to a computer you might look at an article by Florence and Sheldon Gordon, "Mathematics Discovery via Computer Graphics: Hypocycloids and Epicycloids" in *The Two-Year College Mathematics Journal*, November 1984, p. 441. If a is the radius of the fixed circle and R is the radius of the rolling circle, then the parametric equations are as follows.

Hypocycloid: $\quad x = (a - R)\cos t + R \cos\left(\dfrac{a - R}{R}\right)t, \qquad y = (a - R)\sin t - R \sin\left(\dfrac{a - R}{R}\right)t$

Epicycloid: $\quad x = (a + R)\cos t - R \cos\left(\dfrac{a + R}{R}\right)t, \qquad y = (a + R)\sin t - R \sin\left(\dfrac{a + R}{R}\right)t$

Some variations of these curves, which were drawn by computer, are shown below.

Hypocycloid

$a = 5; R = 1$
$(0 \le t \le 2\pi)$

$a = 7; R = 2$
$(0 \le t \le 4\pi)$

$a = 28; R = 13$
$(0 \le t \le 26\pi)$

Epicycloid

$a = 7; R = 1$
$(0 \le t \le 2\pi)$

$a = 8; R = 3$
$(0 \le t \le 6\pi)$

$a = 28; R = 13$
$(0 \le t \le 26\pi)$

■ DERIVATIVES

We begin by finding the derivative of equations of curves defined by parametric equations.

THEOREM 9.3 Parametric form of the derivative

If a curve is described parametrically by the equations $x = x(t)$, $y = y(t)$, where x and y are differentiable functions of t, then the derivative $\dfrac{dy}{dx}$ can be expressed in terms of $\dfrac{dx}{dt}$ and $\dfrac{dy}{dt}$ by the equation

$$\frac{dy}{dx} = \frac{\dfrac{dy}{dt}}{\dfrac{dx}{dt}} = \frac{y'(t)}{x'(t)} \qquad \text{whenever } \frac{dx}{dt} \ne 0$$

Proof: This formula follows directly from the chain rule, $\dfrac{dy}{dt} = \dfrac{dy}{dx}\dfrac{dx}{dt}$. ■

The curve has a *horizontal tangent* when $\dfrac{dy}{dt} = 0$ and $\dfrac{dx}{dt} \neq 0$, and it has a *vertical tangent* where $\dfrac{dx}{dt} = 0$ and $\dfrac{dy}{dt} \neq 0$. If $\dfrac{dy}{dt} = 0$ and $\dfrac{dx}{dt} = 0$ at the same point, further analysis is required.

EXAMPLE 7   Finding the derivative of a function in parametric form

A curve C is described parametrically by $x = 7t + 2$, $y = t^3 - 12t$ for all t. Find $\dfrac{dy}{dx}$ at the point where $t = 3$, and then find all points of C where the tangent line is horizontal.

Solution   We have $\dfrac{dx}{dt} = 7$ and $\dfrac{dy}{dt} = 3t^2 - 12$, and thus

$$\frac{dy}{dx} = \frac{dy/dt}{dx/dt} = \frac{3t^2 - 12}{7}$$

When $t = 3$, we have

$$\frac{dy}{dx}\bigg|_{t=3} = \frac{3(3)^2 - 12}{7} = \frac{15}{7}$$

The curve and the line tangent at the point where $t = 3$, are shown in Figure 9.32. The tangent line is horizontal when $\dfrac{dy}{dt} = 0$;

$$3t^2 - 12 = 0 \quad \text{when} \quad t = \pm 2$$

At $t = 2$, $x = 7(2) + 2 = 16$ and $y = 2^3 - 12(2) = -16$, and at $t = -2$, $x = 7(-2) + 2 = -12$ and $y = (-2)^3 - 12(-2) = 16$, so that the tangent line is horizontal at the points $(16, -16)$ and $(-12, 16)$. Figure 9.32 also shows the horizontal tangents. ▬

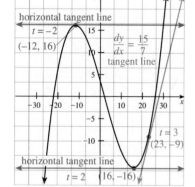

Figure 9.32 Graph of $x = 7t + 2$, $y = t^3 - 12t$ with tangent at $t = 3$

To find the second derivative of a function defined parametrically, we set $y' = \dfrac{dy}{dx}$ and substitute into the derivative formula for parametric equations:

$$\frac{d^2y}{dx^2} = \frac{d}{dx}\left(\frac{dy}{dx}\right) = \frac{d}{dx}(y') = \frac{dy'}{dx} = \frac{\dfrac{dy'}{dt}}{\dfrac{dx}{dt}}$$

For instance, in Example 7, we found $y' = \dfrac{dy}{dx} = \dfrac{3t^2 - 12}{7}$ so that

$$\frac{d^2y}{dx^2} = \frac{\frac{3}{7}(2t)}{7} = \frac{6t}{49}$$

■ ARC LENGTH

Parametric equations can be used to specify a curve, the speed of an object at a given time, or the distance an object has traveled. Finding the distance a point moves along a curve defined by parametric equations requires that we find the arc length.

THEOREM 9.4 Arc length of a curve described parametrically

Let C be the curve described parametrically by the equations $x = x(t)$ and $y = y(t)$ on an interval $[a, b]$, where $\frac{dx}{dt}$ and $\frac{dy}{dt}$ are continuous. Suppose C does not intersect itself (such a C is called a *simple curve*). Then C has arc length given by

$$L = \int_a^b \sqrt{\left(\frac{dx}{dt}\right)^2 + \left(\frac{dy}{dt}\right)^2}\, dt$$

Proof: Recall that the formula for the arc length of a curve C given by $y = f(x)$ over an interval $[a, b]$ is

$$s = \int_a^b \sqrt{1 + [f'(x)]^2}\, dx$$

Use this formula to derive the desired equation. The details are left for the problem set (Problem 62). ∎

EXAMPLE 8 Finding the arc length of a curve defined by parametric equations

Let C be the curve defined by $x = e^t \sin t$, $y = e^t \cos t$ for $0 \le t \le \pi$. Find the length of C on the interval $[0, \pi]$.

Solution We find that

$$\frac{dx}{dt} = e^t \cos t + e^t \sin t = e^t(\cos t + \sin t)$$
$$\frac{dy}{dt} = e^t(-\sin t) + e^t \cos t = e^t(\cos t - \sin t)$$

To obtain the length of the curve we first compute

$$\left(\frac{dx}{dt}\right)^2 + \left(\frac{dy}{dt}\right)^2 = e^{2t}(\cos t + \sin t)^2 + e^{2t}(\cos t - \sin t)^2$$
$$= e^{2t}(\cos^2 t + 2\cos t \sin t + \sin^2 t + \cos^2 t - 2\cos t \sin t + \sin^2 t)$$
$$= 2e^{2t}$$

Thus,

$$s = \int_0^\pi \sqrt{\left(\frac{dx}{dt}\right)^2 + \left(\frac{dy}{dt}\right)^2}\, dt = \int_0^\pi \sqrt{2e^{2t}}\, dt$$
$$= \int_0^\pi \sqrt{2}\, e^t\, dt = \sqrt{2}(e^\pi - 1)$$ ▬

■ AREA

We close this section with a theorem and an example that show how to find the area under a curve when the curve is defined by parametric equations.

▢ **Computational Window** ▼ ▲

X₁ₜ◙e^Tsin T
Y₁ₜ◙e^Tcos T

Tmin=0
Tmax=π
Tstep=.0308996…
Xmin=⁻15
Xmax=25
Xscl=5
Ymin=⁻25
Ymax=5
Yscl=5

You can use the graph to make an estimate of the arc length. Imagine that you are standing on the curve at the point marked $t = 0$ and you walk to the point marked $t = \pi$; how far did you walk? The answer is 8 units to the right, 8 units to the left, and 20 down. This is about 36 units; compare this with the calculated answer:

$$\sqrt{2}(e^\pi - 1) \approx 31.3116678$$

Computational Window

$X_{1T} = e^{\wedge}T$
$Y_{1T} = 2e^{\wedge}T+1$
Tmin=0   Xscl=1
Tmax=1   Ymin=0
Tstep=.04   Ymax=10
Xmin=0   Yscl=10
Xmax=5

After drawing the graph of the parametric equations, we see that the graph is linear, so calculate the area with a single trapezoid:

$$A_T = (1.7182813)\left(\frac{3+6.4365637}{2}\right)$$

$$\approx 8.107\,337\,83$$

Compare with

$$e^2 + e - 2 \approx 8.107337927$$

The reason for the discrepancy is round-off error imposed by calculator evaluation.

THEOREM 9.5   Formula for the area under a curve defined parametrically

Suppose y is a monotonic, continuous function of x on the closed interval $[a, b]$ and that x and y are both functions of a parameter t, for $t_1 \le t \le t_2$. Then if $x'(t)$ is continuous on $[t_1, t_2]$, the area under the curve described parametrically by $x = x(t)$, $y = y(t)$ over $[t_1, t_2]$ is given by

$$A = \int_a^b y\,dx = \int_{t_1}^{t_2} y(t)\,x'(t)\,dt$$

Proof: This proof is straightforward.   ■

EXAMPLE 9   Finding the area under a curve defined parametrically

Find the area under the curve described by

$$x = e^t, \quad y = 2e^t + 1 \qquad \text{over the interval } 0 \le t \le 1$$

Solution   Note that x and y are both continuous and that $y(t) \ge 0$ on $[0, 1]$.

$$A = \int_1^e y(x)\,dx = \int_0^1 y(t)\,x'(t)\,dt$$

$$= \int_0^1 (2e^t + 1)\,e^t\,dt$$

$$= \int_0^1 (2e^{2t} + e^t)\,dt$$

$$= (e^{2t} + e^t)\Big|_0^1 = e^2 + e - 2 \qquad \rule{1em}{0.6em}$$

PROBLEM SET 9.4

 1. ■ **What Does This Say?**   What is a parameter?
2. ■ **What Does This Say?**   Describe the process of finding the derivative in parametric form.

Find an explicit relationship between x and y in Problems 3–24 by eliminating the parameter. In each case, sketch the path described by the parametric equations over the prescribed interval.

3. $x = t + 1$, $y = t - 1$, $0 \le t \le 2$
4. $x = -t$, $y = 3 - 2t$, $0 \le t \le 1$
5. $x = 60t$, $y = 80t - 16t^2$, $0 \le t \le 3$
6. $x = 30t$, $y = 60t - 9t^2$, $-1 \le t \le 2$
7. $x = t$, $y = 2 + \frac{2}{3}(t - 1)$, $2 \le t \le 5$
8. $x = t$, $y = 3 - \frac{3}{5}(t + 2)$, $-1 \le t \le 3$
9. $x = t^2 + 1$, $y = t^2 - 1$, $-1 \le t \le \sqrt{2}$
10. $x = 2t^2$, $y = t^2 + 2$, $-1 \le t \le \sqrt{2}$
11. $x = t^3$, $y = t^2$, $t \ge 0$
12. $x = t^4$, $y = t^2$, $-1 \le t \le \sqrt{2}$
13. $x = 3 \cos\theta$, $y = 3 \sin\theta$, $0 \le \theta < 2\pi$
14. $x = 2 \cos\theta$, $y = 2 \sin\theta$, $0 \le \theta < 2\pi$
15. $x = 1 + \sin t$, $y = -2 + \cos t$, $0 \le t < 2\pi$
16. $x = 1 + \sin^2 t$, $y = -2 + \cos t$, $0 \le t < 2\pi$
17. $x = 4 \tan 2t$, $y = 3 \sec 2t$, $0 \le t < \pi$
18. $x = 4 \sec 2t$, $y = 2 \tan 2t$, $0 \le t < \pi$
19. $x = 3^t$, $y = 3^{t+1}$, $t \ge 0$
20. $x = 2^t$, $y = 2^{1-t}$, $t \ge 0$
21. $x = e^t$, $y = e^{t+1}$, $t \ge 0$
22. $x = e^t$, $y = e^{1-t}$, $t \ge 0$
23. $x = t^3$, $y = 3 \ln t$, $t > 0$
24. $x = e^t$, $y = e^{-t}$, $(-\infty, \infty)$

Find $\dfrac{dy}{dx}$ and $\dfrac{d^2y}{dx^2}$ in Problems 25–30 without eliminating the parameter.

25. $x = t^2$, $y = t^4 + 1$ 26. $x = t^2 + 1$, $y = t^4$
27. $x = e^{4t}$, $y = \sin 2t$ 28. $x = e^t$, $y = t^2 e^t$
29. $x = a \cos t$, $y = b \sin t$ 30. $x = a \cosh t$, $y = b \sinh t$

Find $\dfrac{dy}{dx}$ in Problems 31–34 and then eliminate the parameter to express your answer in terms of x and y.

31. $x = t^2 + 1$, $y = t^4 + 1$
32. $x = 2a \cos t$, $y = a \sin^2 t$; $a > 0$
33. $x = 1 - e^{-t}$, $y = 1 + e^t$ 34. $x = t^2$, $y = \ln t$

Find the area under the curves given in Problems 35–40.

35. $x = t^4 + 1$, $y = t^2$, $0 \le t \le 1$
36. $x = t^4 + t^2 + 1$, $y = (t + 2)^2$, $0 \le t \le 1$

37. $x = \theta - \sin\theta$, $y = 1 + \cos\theta$, $0 \le \theta \le \frac{\pi}{4}$
38. $x = \tan\theta$, $y = \sec^2\theta$, $0 \le \theta \le \frac{\pi}{6}$
39. $x = \tan^{-1}u$, $y = u^3$, $0 \le u \le 1$
40. $x = \sin^{-1}u$, $y = u$, $0 \le u \le \frac{1}{2}$

Find the length of each curve in Problems 41–45.
41. $x = \sqrt{t}$, $y = t^{3/4}$ for $0 \le t \le 4$
42. $x = 2t^2$, $y = t^3$ for $1 \le t \le 2$
43. $x = \frac{1}{2}\ln(t^2 - 1)$, $y = \sqrt{t^2 - 1}$ for $3 \le t \le 7$
44. $x = t\sin t + \cos t$, $y = \sin t - t\cos t$ for $0 \le t \le \frac{\pi}{2}$
45. $x = 2\sin^{-1}t$, $y = \ln(1 - t^2)$ for $0 \le t \le \frac{\sqrt{3}}{2}$

Ⓑ 46. Describe the path of curve defined by $x = \sin\pi t$, $y = \cos 2\pi t$ for $0 \le t < 1$.

47. Let $x = 4a\sin t$, $y = b\cos^2 t$. Express y as a function of x.

48. Find the area under one arch of the cycloid $x = 2(\theta - \sin\theta)$, $y = 2(1 - \cos\theta)$.

49. Find the length of the curve given by $x = 2\cos^3 t$, $y = 2\sin^3 t$, $0 \le t \le 2\pi$. This curve is called an **asteroid**.

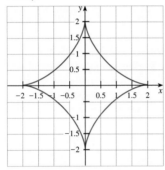

Use the formula $L = \int_a^b \sqrt{[f(\theta)]^2 + [f'(\theta)]^2}\, d\theta$

which is derived in Problem 65 to find the arc length of the polar form curves given in Problems 50–53.
50. the spiral $r = e^\theta$, for $0 \le \theta \le \frac{\pi}{2}$
51. the circle $r = 2\cos\theta$, for $0 \le \theta \le \frac{\pi}{3}$
52. the cardioid $r = 2(1 - \cos\theta)$ on $[0, \pi]$
53. the spiral $r = e^{-\theta}$ for $\theta \ge 0$

▭ Computational Window ▼ ▲

54. Write a paper showing the graphs of several hypocycloids, along with an analysis of what you did to graph them. Make some generalizations based on your graphs.
55. Write a paper describing what happens if the radius of the inner rolling circle is larger than the radius of the outer fixed circle.
56. Write a paper showing the graphs of several epicycloids, along with an analysis of what you did to graph them. Make some generalizations based on your graphs.
57. Write a paper describing what happens if the radius of the outer rolling circle is larger than the radius of the inner fixed circle.

Problems 58 and 59 explore the work required to move a mass or particle along a planar curve which is described parametrically. Let C be the set of points (x, y), where

$$x = x(t), \quad y = y(t), \quad a \le t \le b$$

Suppose a force F = F(t) is applied to the mass in the direction of the curve (that is, the force is applied in the direction of the tangent to C).

58. **a.** Argue that on the interval $[t, t + dt]$, dt very small, the work done is approximately

$$dW = F(t)\, ds = F(t)\sqrt{[x'(t)]^2 + [y'(t)]^2}\, dt$$

   b. Form an appropriate Riemann sum, take a limit and get the formula for the work done on C:

$$W = \int_a^b F(t)\sqrt{[x'(t)]^2 + [y'(x)]^2}\, dt$$

   c. Suppose that $F(t) = 2e^t$ and $x(t) = 6\cosh t$, $y(t) = 6t$ for $0 \le t \le 1$. Compute the work involved on the entire curve C. *Note*: You may use a computer, but a computer is not *needed* to answer this question.

59. As we have seen, arc length intervals are often impossible to do without a computer. The same is true of work integrals. For example, suppose a particle is moving on an elliptical path described by

$$x(t) = \cos t, \, y(t) = 3\sin t,$$

$$0 \le t < 2\pi$$

The force applied is $F(t) = 5|y'(t)|$, hence proportional to the vertical component of velocity.

   a. Compute the arc length of the ellipse to 3-decimal-place accuracy. This is a surprisingly tough integral; so make a common-sense check to make sure your answer is reasonable. Explain your check.

   b. Set up the integral and compute the work involved in one orbit of the particle to 3-place accuracy.

   c. Suppose a constant force $F = 5$ is applied to the spiral path (gravity is working): For $t \ge 0$,

$$x(t) = 2e^{-t/10}\cos t,$$

$$y(t) = 3e^{-t/10}\sin t$$

You are to compute the work (so that the relative error is less than 0.0005). But in order to obtain a rough check on your answer and to determine how far to integrate, you may wish to solve (without a computer) first a problem with an easier path —for example (for $t \ge 0$)

$$x(t) = 2.5e^{-t/10}\cos t,$$

$$y(t) = 2.5e^{-t/10}\sin t$$

60. SPY PROBLEM   Using a special meditation technique, the spy convinces his captors that their truth drug has killed him (Problem 58, Section 8.2). As soon as they start to drag his body away, he revives and dispatches all but one of his tormentors, and with a little persuasion, the survivor tells him that Boldfinger has left the castle through an underground water passage in his private submarine. The spy races from the castle to a nearby naval base and commandeers a destroyer. Since Boldfinger suspects no danger, his submarine is running on the surface, and the spy's destroyer is able to get within 3 miles of the submarine before it submerges. The spy assumes Boldfinger will try to escape by traveling at maximum speed in one direction, but, of course, he does not know which direction his adversary will take. If the destroyer's best speed is twice that of the submarine, what path should the spy order his destroyer to travel in order to guarantee that it will eventually pass over the submarine? *Hint*: The spy may need the formula for polar arc length given in Problem 65.

61. Find parametric equations for the polar curve $r = f(\theta)$ in terms of the parameter θ.

62. A circle of radius R rolls without slipping on the outside of a fixed circle of radius a. Find parametric equations for the curve traced out by a point P on the circumference of the rolling circle of radius R. Assume the fixed circle is centered at the origin and that the moving point begins at $(a, 0)$. Use the angle t measured from the positive x-axis to the ray from the origin to the center of the rolling circle.

Show that this *epicycloid* has parametric equations

$$x = (a + R)\cos t - R \cos\left(\frac{a + R}{R}\right)t,$$

$$y = (a + R)\sin t - R \sin\left(\frac{a + R}{R}\right)t$$

63. A circle of radius R rolls without slipping on the inside of a fixed circle of radius a. Find parametric equations for the curve traced out by a point P on the circumference of the rolling circle of radius R. Let t be the angle measured from the positive x-axis to the ray that passes through the center of the rolling circle, and assume that the point P begins on the x-axis (that is, P has coordinates $(a, 0)$ when $t = 0$. Show that this *hypocycloid* has parametric equations

$$x = (a - R)\cos t + R \cos\left(\frac{a - R}{R}\right)t,$$

$$y = (a - R)\sin t - R \sin\left(\frac{a - R}{R}\right)t$$

64. Prove Theorem 9.4.

65. Arc Length in Polar Coordinates Suppose the polar function $r = f(\theta)$ and its derivative $f'(\theta)$ are continuous on the closed interval $a \le \theta \le b$, $(b \le a + 2\pi)$. Show that the arc length of the graph of f from $\theta = a$ to $\theta = b$ is given by

$$L = \int_a^b \sqrt{[f(\theta)]^2 + [f'(\theta)]^2} \, d\theta$$

9.5   CONIC SECTIONS: THE PARABOLA

> **IN THIS SECTION   Standard-position parabolas, translation of parabolas, representation of a parabola in polar coordinates, parabolic reflectors**
> A second topic in this chapter involves the so-called *conic sections*: *ellipses, parabolas, and hyperbolas*. All of these curves can be obtained by intersecting a plane with a right circular cone, as shown in Figure 9.33. In this section we look at one of these conic sections, the parabola.

We first encountered parabolas in our study of quadratic functions in Chapter 1. At that time, we found that the graph of an equation of the general form $y = ax^2 + bx + c$ (with $a \ne 0$) is a parabola that opens upward if $a > 0$ and downward if $a < 0$. The graph of this quadratic equation is a parabola, but not all parabolas can be represented by this equation, because not all parabolas are graphs of functions. Consider the general second-degree equation

$$Ax^2 + Bxy + Cy^2 + Dx + Ey + F = 0$$

for any constants A, B, C, D, E, and F. If $A = B = C = 0$, the equation is not quadratic but linear (first degree); but if at least one of A, B, or C is not zero, then the equation is quadratic. Historically, second-degree equations in two variables were first considered in a geometric context and were called **conic sections** because the curves they represent can be described as the intersections of a double-napped right circular cone and a plane.

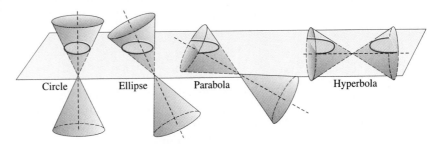

Figure 9.33 Conic sections

Circle   Ellipse   Parabola   Hyperbola

Historical Note

HYPATIA (370–415)

Work with conic sections was done by Apollonius (260?–200? B.C.), but his work was not popularized until 600 years later, when Hypatia wrote several mathematical commentaries, including "On the Conic Sections." Hypatia was a daughter of a professor at the University of Alexandria, where she also became a professor of mathematics, philosophy, and astronomy. See the suggested book review *Hypatia's Heritage* after the guest essay in Chapter 11.

■ STANDARD-POSITION PARABOLAS

We shall use the following definition for a parabola.

Parabola

A **parabola** is the set of all points in the plane that are equidistant from a fixed point (called the **focus**) and a fixed line (called the **directrix**).

The line through the focus perpendicular to the directrix is called the **principal axis** of the parabola, and the point where the axis intersects the parabola is called the **vertex**. The line segment that passes through the focus perpendicular to the axis and with endpoints on the parabola is called the **focal chord**. This terminology is shown in Figure 9.34.

Figure 9.34 Parabola

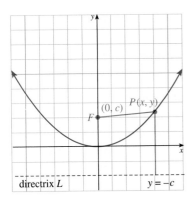

Figure 9.35 Graph of the parabola $x^2 = 4cy$

To obtain the equation of a parabola, first consider a special case: a parabola with focus $F(0, c)$ and directrix $y = -c$, where c is any positive number. This parabola must have its vertex at the origin (the vertex is halfway between the focus and the directrix) and must open upward, as shown in Figure 9.35.

Let (x, y) be any point on the parabola. Then, from the definition of a parabola,

DISTANCE FROM (x, y) to $(0, c)$ = DISTANCE FROM (x, y) TO DIRECTRIX

$$\sqrt{(x - 0)^2 + (y - c)^2} = y + c$$

$$x^2 + y^2 - 2cy + c^2 = y^2 + 2cy + c^2 \quad \textit{Square both sides.}$$

$$x^2 = 4cy$$

This is the equation of the parabola with vertex $(0, 0)$ and directrix $y = -c$.

You can repeat this argument (see Problems 56–58) for parabolas that have their vertex at the origin and open downward, to the left, and to the right to obtain the results summarized next.

Standard-Form Equations for Parabolas

Parabola	Focus	Directrix	Vertex
Upward: $x^2 = 4cy$	$(0, c)$	$y = -c$	$(0, 0)$
Downward: $x^2 = -4cy$	$(0, -c)$	$y = c$	$(0, 0)$
Right: $y^2 = 4cx$	$(c, 0)$	$x = -c$	$(0, 0)$
Left: $y^2 = -4cx$	$(-c, 0)$	$x = c$	$(0, 0)$

The length of the *focal chord* is the coefficient $4c$.

In Chapters 1 and 3 we used calculus to graph parabolas. In this chapter we will find and plot the vertex, determine c (usually by inspection), and count out c units from the vertex *in the appropriate direction* as determined by the form of the equation. Finally, it is shown in the problem set that the length of the focal chord is $4c$, and we use this number to determine the width of the parabola, as shown in the following example.

EXAMPLE 1 **Graphing a standard-form parabola**

Graph $2y^2 - 5x = 0$.

Solution First, algebraically change the equation so that it is in standard form by solving for the second-degree term:

$$y^2 = \tfrac{5}{2}x$$

The vertex is $(0, 0)$ and

$$4c = \tfrac{5}{2} \quad \text{so} \quad c = \tfrac{5}{8}$$

Thus, the parabola opens to the right, the focus is $\left(\tfrac{5}{8}, 0\right)$, and the length of the focal chord is $4c = \tfrac{5}{2}$, as shown in Figure 9.36. ▬

There are two basic types of problems in analytic geometry:

1. Given the equation, draw the graph; this is what we did in Example 1.

2. Given the graph (or information about the graph), write the equation. The next example is of this type.

EXAMPLE 2 **Writing the equation of a parabola**

Find an equation of a parabola with focus $F(0, -2)$ and directrix $y = 2$.

Figure 9.36 Graph of the parabola $2y^2 - 5x = 0$

Solution   This is the curve drawn in Figure 9.37. We see this is a parabola that opens downward with vertex at the origin. By inspection, the value of c is $c = 2$. The form of the equation is $x^2 = -4cy$, so the desired equation is

$$x^2 = -8y$$

Figure 9.37 Graph of the parabola with focus $(0, -2)$ and directrix $y = 2$

■ TRANSLATION OF PARABOLAS

If a parabola is not in standard position but its axis is parallel to one of the coordinate axes, it can be put into standard form by a change of variable of the form $X = x - h$, $Y = y - k$. Such a change in variable is called a **translation**, and it has the general effect shown in Figure 9.38. Suppose $(h, k) = (4, 5)$; then the coordinates of P are $(x, y) = (6, 9)$ and $(X, Y) = (2, 4)$; check

$$X = x - h = 6 - 4 = 2$$
$$Y = y - k = 9 - 5 = 4$$

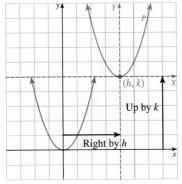

Figure 9.38 Translation of a parabola; vertex is at (h, k).

Effect of a Translation

> Replacing $x - h$ by X and $y - k$ by Y in an equation has the effect of translating the graph of an equation
>
> h units horizontally (**right** if $h > 0$ and **left** if $h < 0$);
> k units vertically (**up** if $k > 0$ and **down** if $k < 0$).

This means that the equations for parabolas with **vertex** (h, k) are

$$(x - h)^2 = 4c(y - k), \qquad X^2 = 4cY; \quad (y - k)^2 = 4c(x - h), \qquad Y^2 = 4cX$$
$$(x - h)^2 = -4c(y - k), \quad X^2 = -4cY; \quad (y - k)^2 = -4c(x - h), \quad Y^2 = -4cX$$

EXAMPLE 3   Graphing a parabola using a translation

Sketch the parabola $y = x^2 + 2x + 3$. Find the vertex, c, and the length of the focal chord. Also, find the focus and the equation of the directrix.

Solution   First, complete the square to obtain $y - 2 = (x + 1)^2$. Next, plot the vertex $(-1, 2)$. If we replace $y - 2$ by Y and $x + 1$ by X, we have $Y = X^2$, which tells us the parabola opens upward, $4c = 1$, and $c = \frac{1}{4}$. Thus, plot the focus by counting up $\frac{1}{4}$ unit, and then draw the focal chord with length 1. Because these points are fairly close on the scale we have chosen, we plot an additional point, say the y-intercept: If $x = 0$, then $y = 0^2 + 2(0) + 3 = 3$. See Figure 9.39.

Notice that we do not need to know the coordinates of the focus or the directrix to draw the graph. We needed to know only the vertex, the distance c,

Figure 9.39 Graph of $y = x^2 + 2x + 3$

and the length of the focal chord $4c$. If c is small relative to the vertex, it may be necessary to plot an additional point.

However, we may need to know the coordinates of the focus and directrix for further analysis. To find these numbers, we can use the reverse translation $x = X + h$, $y = Y + k$.

	XY-coordinates	xy-coordinates
Vertex	$(0, 0)$	$(-1, 2)$
Focus	$\left(0, \frac{1}{4}\right)$	$\left(-1, \frac{9}{4}\right)$
Directrix	$Y = -\frac{1}{4}$	$y = \frac{7}{4}$

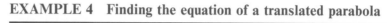

EXAMPLE 4   Finding the equation of a translated parabola

Find an equation for the parabola with focus $(4, -3)$ and directrix the line $x + 2 = 0$.

Solution   Sketch the information as shown in Figure 9.40. The vertex is $(1, -3)$, because it must be equidistant from F and the directrix. Note that $c = 3$. Thus, substitute into the equation of a parabola that opens to the right—namely $y^2 = 4cx$—and then translate to the point (h, k) to obtain the equation

$$(y - k)^2 = 4c(x - h)$$

The desired equation, because $(h, k) = (1, -3)$, is

$$(y + 3)^2 = 12(x - 1)$$

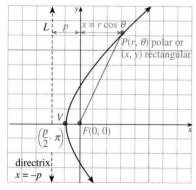

Figure 9.40 Graph of a parabola with focus $(4, -3)$ and directrix $x + 2 = 0$

■ REPRESENTATION OF A PARABOLA IN POLAR COORDINATES

Next, we shall see how a parabola can be represented in polar coordinates. Let a parabola be given in the plane. Then place the x-axis along the principal axis of the parabola, and place the pole at the focus, as shown in Figure 9.41. We refer to this as a **standard polar position** for the parabola. Assume the parabola opens to the right and that the directrix L is the vertical line $x = -p$, where $p > 0$ is the distance from the focus to the directrix.

If P is a point on the parabola with rectangular coordinates (x, y) and polar coordinates (r, θ), we must have

DISTANCE P TO F = DISTANCE P TO L

$$|r| = |p + r \cos \theta|$$

$$r = \pm(p + r \cos \theta)$$

$$r = \frac{p}{1 - \cos \theta} \qquad -r = \frac{p}{1 + \cos \theta}$$

Figure 9.41 A standard polar position for a parabola

It can be shown (see Problem 60) that these two equations represent the same graph, so we shall use the one on the left to represent the given parabola. We can similarly derive equations for parabolas that open downward, left, or to the right. These graphs are shown in Figure 9.42.

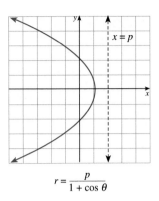

$$r = \frac{p}{1 - \sin \theta} \qquad\qquad r = \frac{p}{1 + \sin \theta} \qquad\qquad r = \frac{p}{1 - \cos \theta} \qquad\qquad r = \frac{p}{1 + \cos \theta}$$

Figure 9.42 Standard-position polar-form parabolas $(0 < p < 1)$

Standard Polar Equations for Parabolas

	Parabola	Focus	Directrix (rectangular-form*)	Polar-form Vertex
Upward:	$r = \dfrac{p}{1 - \sin \theta}$	$(0, 0)$	$y = -p$	$\left(\dfrac{p}{2}, \dfrac{3\pi}{2}\right)$
Downward:	$r = \dfrac{p}{1 + \sin \theta}$	$(0, 0)$	$y = p$	$\left(\dfrac{p}{2}, \dfrac{\pi}{2}\right)$
Right:	$r = \dfrac{p}{1 - \cos \theta}$	$(0, 0)$	$x = -p$	$\left(\dfrac{p}{2}, \pi\right)$
Left:	$r = \dfrac{p}{1 + \cos \theta}$	$(0, 0)$	$x = p$	$\left(\dfrac{p}{2}, 0\right)$

EXAMPLE 5   Graphing a polar-form parabola

Describe and sketch the graph of the equation

$$r = \frac{4}{3 - 3 \cos \theta}$$

Solution

$$r = \frac{4}{3 - 3 \cos \theta} \cdot \frac{\frac{1}{3}}{\frac{1}{3}} = \frac{\frac{4}{3}}{1 - \cos \theta}$$

By inspection, you can now see (Figure 9.43) that the parabola opens to the right and that $p = \frac{4}{3}$. Thus the vertex is

$$\left(\frac{p}{2}, \pi\right) = \left(\frac{2}{3}, \pi\right)$$

Plot the vertex and the line $x = -\frac{4}{3}$, as shown in the margin. You can plot other points that are easy to calculate, such as the points where $\theta = \frac{\pi}{2}$ and $\theta = \pi$ or $\theta = \frac{3\pi}{2}$.   ▬

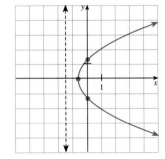

Figure 9.43 Graph of $r = \dfrac{4}{3 - 3 \cos \theta}$

EXAMPLE 6   Finding a polar-form equation of a parabola

Find a polar-form equation for the parabola with focus at the origin and vertex at the polar-form point $(3, \pi)$.

*We could, of course, state these equations of lines in polar form. For example, $y = -p$ is $r \sin \theta = -p$, but we prefer writing the equation of the directrix in rectangular form.

Solution   The vertex $(3, \pi)$ is on the x-axis and to the left of the focus (the pole). Thus, the parabola opens to the right and has a polar-form equation

$$r = \frac{p}{1 - \cos \theta}$$

where p is the distance from the focus to the directrix. Because the vertex $(3, \pi)$ is halfway between the focus and the directrix, we must have $p = 6$, so that the required equation is

$$r = \frac{6}{1 - \cos \theta}$$

■ PARABOLIC REFLECTORS*

Parabolic curves are used in the design of lighting systems, telescopes, and radar antennas, mainly because of the property illustrated in Figure 9.44 and described more formally in Theorem 9.6.

THEOREM 9.6   Reflection property of parabolas

Let P be a point on a parabola in the plane, and let T be the tangent line to the parabola at P. Then the angle between T and the line through P parallel to the principal axis of the parabola equals the angle between T and the line connecting P to the focus.

Proof: A proof is outlined in Problem 65.   ■

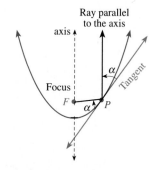

Figure 9.44 The reflection property of parabolas

As an illustration of how this property is used, let us examine its application to reflecting telescopes. The eyepiece of such a telescope is placed at the focus of a parabolic mirror. Light enters the telescope in rays that are parallel to the axis of the paraboloid. It is a principle of physics that when light is reflected, the angle of incidence equals the angle of reflection. Hence, the parallel rays of light strike the parabolic mirror so that they all reflect through the focus, which means that the parallel rays are concentrated at the eyepiece located at the focus.

Flashlights and automobile headlights simply reverse the process: A light source is placed at the focus of a parabolic mirror, the light rays strike the mirror with angle of incidence equal to the angle of reflection, and each ray is reflected along a path parallel to the axis, thus emitting a light beam of parallel rays.

Radar utilizes both of these properties. First, a pulse is transmitted from the focus to a parabolic surface. As with a reflecting telescope, parallel pulses are transmitted in this way. The reflected pulses then strike the parabolic surface and are sent back to be received at the focus.

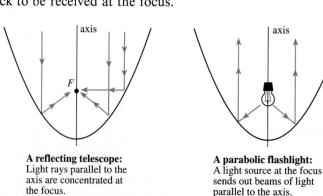

A reflecting telescope:
Light rays parallel to the
axis are concentrated at
the focus.

A parabolic flashlight:
A light source at the focus
sends out beams of light
parallel to the axis.

*Since these reflectors are three-dimensional, the precise word is paraboloidal, but the most common usage is to look at a cross section that is parabolic.

PROBLEM SET 9.5

A 1. ■ **What Does This Say?** Discuss a procedure for graphing a parabola in rectangular form.

2. ■ **What Does This Say?** Discuss a procedure for graphing a parabola in polar form.

Sketch the curves in Problems 3–24. Label the focus F and the vertex V.

3. $y^2 = 8x$ 4. $y^2 = -12x$

5. $y^2 = -20x$ 6. $4x^2 = 10y$

7. $3x^2 = -12y$ 8. $2x^2 = -4y$

9. $2x^2 + 5y = 0$ 10. $5y^2 + 15x = 0$

11. $3y^2 - 15x = 0$ 12. $4y^2 + 3x = 12$

13. $5x^2 + 4y = 20$ 14. $4x^2 + 3y = 12$

15. $(y - 1)^2 = 2(x + 2)$ 16. $(y + 3)^2 = 3(x - 1)$

17. $(x + 2)^2 = 2(y - 1)$ 18. $(x - 1)^2 = 3(y + 3)$

19. $y^2 + 4x - 3y + 1 = 0$ 20. $y^2 - 4x + 10y + 13 = 0$

21. $y^2 + 4y - 10x + 74 = 0$ 22. $x^2 + 9y - 6x + 18 = 0$

23. $9x^2 + 6x + 18y - 23 = 0$ 24. $9x^2 + 6y + 18x - 23 = 0$

Find an equation for each curve in Problems 25–32.

25. Directrix $x = 0$; focus at $(5, 0)$

26. Directrix $y = 0$; focus at $(0, -3)$

27. Directrix $x - 3 = 0$; vertex at $(-1, 2)$

28. Directrix $y + 4 = 0$; vertex at $(4, -1)$

29. Vertex $(-2, -3)$; focus at $(-2, 3)$

30. Vertex $(-3, 4)$; focus at $(1, 4)$

31. Vertex $(-3, 2)$ and passing through $(-2, -1)$; axis parallel to the y-axis

32. Vertex $(4, 2)$ and passing through $(-3, -4)$; axis parallel to the x-axis

B *Sketch the graph of the polar-form parabola in Problems 33–38. Check your work by finding a Cartesian equation.*

33. $r = \dfrac{6}{1 + \cos\theta}$ 34. $r = \dfrac{4}{1 - \sin\theta}$ 35. $r = \dfrac{-9}{1 + \sin\theta}$

36. $r = \dfrac{-2}{1 - \cos\theta}$ 37. $r = \dfrac{8}{2 - 2\cos\theta}$ 38. $r = \dfrac{9}{3 + 3\cos\theta}$

Find a polar equation for a parabola with its focus at the pole and with the property given in Problems 39–42.

39. vertex at the polar-form point $(4, 0)$

40. vertex at the polar-form point $(2, \pi)$

41. directrix at $y = -4$ 42. directrix at $x = 3$

Find a polar equation for the parabola with the Cartesian equation given in Problems 43–46.

43. $y^2 = 4x$ 44. $x^2 = -2y$

45. $4x^2 = y - 3$ 46. $x + 1 = 2(y - 3)^2$

47. Find the point(s) on the parabola $y^2 = 9x$ that is (are) closest to $(2, 0)$.

48. Find the point(s) on the parabola $x^2 = 4cy$ that is (are) closest to the focus.

49. Find the equation for the tangent line and the line perpendicular to the parabola $y^2 = 4x$ at the point $(1, -2)$.

50. Find the equation of the set of all points with distances from $(4, 3)$ that equal their distances from $(0, 3)$.

51. Find the equation of the set of all points with distances from $(4, 3)$ that equal their distances from $(-2, 1)$.

52. Find an equation for a parabola whose focal chord has length 6, if it is known that the parabola has focus $(4, -2)$ and its directrix is parallel to the y-axis.

53. A parabolic archway has the dimensions shown in Figure 9.45. Find the equation of the parabolic portion.

Figure 9.45 A parabolic archway

54. Beams of light parallel to the axis of the parabolic mirror shown in Figure 9.46 strike the mirror and are reflected. Find the distance from the vertex to the point where the beams concentrate.

Figure 9.46 A parabolic mirror

55. A radar antenna is constructed so that a cross section along its axis is a parabola with the receiver at the focus. Find the focus if the antenna is 12 m across and its depth is 4 m. See Figure 9.47.

Figure 9.47 Dimensions for a radar antenna

ⓒ 56. Derive the equation of a parabola with $F(0, -c)$, where c is a positive number and the directrix is the line $y = c$.

57. Derive the equation of a parabola with $F(c, 0)$, where c is a positive number and the directrix is the line $x = -c$.

58. Derive the equation of a parabola with $F(-c, 0)$, where c is a positive number and the directrix is the line $x = c$.

59. Show that the length of the focal chord for the parabola $y^2 = 4cx$ is $4c$ ($c > 0$).

60. Show that the polar equations

$$r = \frac{p}{1 - \cos\theta} \quad \text{and} \quad r = \frac{-p}{1 + \cos\theta}$$

represent the same graph.

61. Show that the vertex is the point on a parabola that is closest to the focus.

62. Show that the tangent to a parabola at the two ends of the focal chord intersect on the directrix.

63. Find the area of the triangle formed by the focal chord and the two tangent lines at the end of the focal chord of the parabola $x^2 = 4cy$.

64. Suppose a circle intersects the parabola $x^2 = 4cy$ in four distinct points (x_1, y_1), (x_2, y_2), (x_3, y_3), and (x_4, y_4). Show that $x_1 + x_2 + x_3 + x_4 = 0$.

65. Reflection property of the parabola   Assume that a parabola is given by the equation

$$y = \frac{x^2}{4c}$$

Use Figure 9.48 to prove the reflection property of the parabola by carrying out the indicated steps.

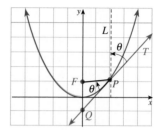

Figure 9.48 Reflection property

a. Find an equation for the tangent line T to the parabola at $P(x_0, y_0)$.

b. Find the coordinates of the point Q where T crosses the y-axis.

c. If F is the focus of the parabola, show that $|\overline{FP}| = |\overline{FQ}|$. Conclude that $\triangle QFP$ is isosceles.

d. Let L be a line parallel to the y-axis. Show that the angle between L and T is $\theta = \angle FPQ$.

9.6 CONIC SECTIONS: THE ELLIPSE AND THE HYPERBOLA

IN THIS SECTION Ellipses, hyperbolas, eccentricity and polar coordinates, geometric properties
In the last section we introduced the geometric definition of the parabola, and in this section, we shall examine two more conic sections, the *ellipse* and the *hyperbola*.

■ ELLIPSES

Ellipse   An **ellipse** is the set of all points in the plane the sum of whose distances from two fixed points is a constant.

The fixed points are called the **foci** (plural of **focus**). To see what an ellipse looks like, we will use the special type of graph paper shown in Figure 9.49a, where F_1 and F_2 are the foci.

Let the constant distance be 12. Plot all the points in the plane so that the sum of their distances from the foci is 12. If a point is 8 units from F_1, for example, then it is 4 units from F_2, and you can plot the points P_1 and P_2. The completed graph of this ellipse is shown in Figure 9.49b.

The line passing through F_1 and F_2 is called the **major axis**. The **center** is the midpoint of the segment $\overline{F_1 F_2}$. The **semimajor axis** is the distance from the center to a point of intersection of the ellipse with its major axis. The line passing through the center perpendicular to the major axis is called the **minor axis**. The **semiminor axis** is the distance from the center to a point of intersection of the

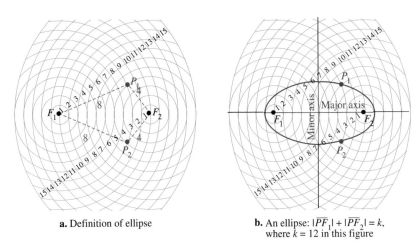

a. Definition of ellipse

b. An ellipse: $|\overline{PF_1}| + |\overline{PF_2}| = k$,
where $k = 12$ in this figure

Figure 9.49

minor axis with the ellipse. The ellipse is symmetric with respect to the major and minor axes. The intercepts on the major axis are called the **vertices** of the ellipse.

To find the equation of an ellipse, first consider a special case where the center is at the origin. Let the distance from the center to a focus be the positive number c; that is, let $F_1(-c, 0)$ and $F_2(c, 0)$ be the foci and let the constant sum of distances be $2a$, as shown in Figure 9.50.

If $P(x, y)$ is any point on the ellipse, then by definition,

$$|\overline{PF_1}| + |\overline{PF_2}| = 2a$$

$$\sqrt{(x + c)^2 + (y - 0)^2} + \sqrt{(x - c)^2 + (y - 0)^2} = 2a$$

Simplifying (the details are not shown), we obtain

$$\frac{x^2}{a^2} + \frac{y^2}{a^2 - c^2} = 1$$

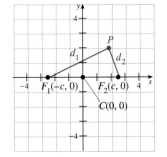

Figure 9.50 Developing the equation of an ellipse by using the definition

Let $b^2 = a^2 - c^2$ to obtain $\dfrac{x^2}{a^2} + \dfrac{y^2}{b^2} = 1$. The graph of this equation is shown in Figure 9.51. Notice that foci are on the major axis, and the intercepts on the minor axis are $(0, b)$ and $(0, -b)$. Also note that $a > c$ and $a > b$.

A similar derivation applies to the ellipse in standard position with foci on the y-axis.

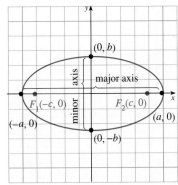

a. Foci on the x-axis

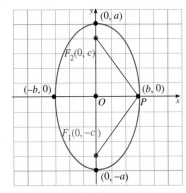

a. Foci on the y-axis

Figure 9.51 Standard-form ellipses

Standard-Form Equations for Ellipses

Orientation	Equation	Foci	Constant	Center
Horizontal	$\dfrac{x^2}{a^2} + \dfrac{y^2}{b^2} = 1$	$(-c, 0), (c, 0)$	$2a$	$(0, 0)$
Vertical	$\dfrac{y^2}{a^2} + \dfrac{x^2}{b^2} = 1$	$(0, c), (0, -c)$	$2a$	$(0, 0)$

where $b^2 = a^2 - c^2$ or $c^2 = a^2 - b^2$ with $a > b > 0$

In order to sketch an ellipse, plot the center, the intercepts $\pm a$ on the major axis, and $\pm b$ on the minor axis.

■ **What This Says:** Write the equation in standard form, so that there is a 1 on the right and the numerator coefficients of the square terms are also 1. The center is $(0, 0)$; plot the intercepts on the x- and y-axes. For the x-intercepts, plot $\pm$ the square root of the number under the x^2-term; for the y-intercepts, plot $\pm$ the square root of the number under the y^2-term. Finally, draw the ellipse using these intercepts. The longer axis is called the major axis; if this larger axis is horizontal, then the ellipse called horizontal, and if the major axis is vertical, the ellipse is called vertical.

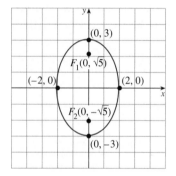

Figure 9.52 Graph of $9x^2 + 4y^2 = 36$

EXAMPLE 1   Graphing an ellipse centered at the origin

Sketch $9x^2 + 4y^2 = 36$. Find the foci.

Solution   First, rewrite the equation in standard form by dividing both sides by 36:

$$\frac{x^2}{4} + \frac{y^2}{9} = 1$$

Because $a^2 = 9$, $b^2 = 4$, the foci are found by calculating c as follows: $c^2 = a^2 - b^2 = 9 - 4 = 5$. Thus, the foci are $(0, -\sqrt{5})$, $(0, \sqrt{5})$. The graph is shown in Figure 9.52. ■

Computational Window

Notice that an ellipse cannot be represented as a single function. In order to graph the ellipse in Example 1 using your graphing calculator, solve for y and define two functions:

$$Y1 = \sqrt{(9(1 - X^2/4))} \quad \text{and} \quad Y2 = -\sqrt{(9(1 - X^2/4))}$$

When using a computer or a graphing calculator, you should take special care with interpreting the scale. Note the graphs of this ellipse using the equations from Example 1. Note that only the last one looks similar to the one shown in Figure 9.52.

As with the parabola, it is easier to use your calculator to graph an ellipse by parameterizing the equation. This is illustrated in the following example.

EXAMPLE 2   Parameterize the equation of an ellipse

Graph $2x^2 + 5y^2 = 10$ by using a parameterization.

Solution   One way to parameterize an ellipse is to recall the identity

$$\cos^2 \theta + \sin^2 \theta = 1.$$

We begin by dividing both sides of the given equation by 10:

$$2x^2 + 5y^2 = 10$$

$$\frac{2x^2}{10} + \frac{5y^2}{10} = 1$$

$$\frac{x^2}{5} + \frac{y^2}{2} = 1$$

$$\left(\frac{x}{\sqrt{5}}\right)^2 + \left(\frac{y}{\sqrt{2}}\right)^2 = 1$$

We know that if $\cos \theta = \dfrac{x}{\sqrt{5}}$ and $\sin \theta = \dfrac{y}{\sqrt{2}}$, then $\cos^2 \theta + \sin^2 \theta = 1$. There are, of course, other choices we could make, but this observation leads us to let $x = \sqrt{5} \cos \theta$ and $y = \sqrt{2} \sin \theta$. You can set up a table of values or use a calculator to obtain the graph shown in Figure 9.53. If you use a table of values, you need only consider values of θ between 0 and $\frac{\pi}{2}$, because we know the ellipse is symmetric with respect to both the major and minor axes.

X₁ₜ ◼√5cos T
Y₁ₜ ◼√2sin T

Tmin=0
Tmax=6.2831853...
Tstep=.1256637...
Xmin=-3
Xmax=3
Xscl=.5
Ymin=-3
Ymax=3
Yscl=.5

θ	x	y
0°; 0	2.24	0
15°; $\frac{\pi}{12}$	2.16	0.37
30°; $\frac{\pi}{6}$	1.94	0.71
45°; $\frac{\pi}{4}$	1.58	1
60°; $\frac{\pi}{3}$	1.12	1.22
75°; $\frac{5\pi}{12}$	0.58	1.37
90°; $\frac{\pi}{2}$	0	1.41

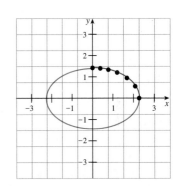

Figure 9.53 Graph of $x = \sqrt{5} \cos \theta$, $y = \sqrt{2} \sin \theta$

The parameterization we obtained for the ellipse in Example 2 is not unique. For example, $x = \sqrt{5} \sin \theta$, $y = \sqrt{2} \cos \theta$ is the same ellipse, but if you sketch these parametric equations, you will note that even though the ellipse is the same, the orientation has reversed.

EXAMPLE 3   Finding the equation of a given ellipse

Find an equation for the ellipse with foci $(-1, 0)$ and $(1, 0)$ and vertices $(-2, 0)$ and $(2, 0)$.

Solution   By inspection, the center of the ellipse is $(0, 0)$ and the distance to a vertex is 2, so $a = 2$; the distance to a focus is 1, so $c = 1$. Therefore, we find $b^2 = a^2 - c^2 = 3$. An equation is

$$\frac{x^2}{4} + \frac{y^2}{3} = 1$$

If an ellipse is not in standard position, but its axes are parallel to the coordinate axes, complete the square to determine the translation. Here is an example of this procedure.

EXAMPLE 4   Graphing an ellipse by completing the square

Sketch the graph of the equation $9x^2 + 4y^2 - 18x + 16y - 11 = 0$.

Solution   Complete the square in both x and y:

$$9x^2 + 4y^2 - 18x + 16y - 11 = 0$$

$$9(x^2 - 2x \quad) + 4(y^2 + 4y \quad) = 11$$

$$9(x^2 - 2x + 1^2) + 4(y^2 + 4y + 2^2) = 11 + 9 \cdot 1^2 + 4 \cdot 2^2$$

$$9(x - 1)^2 + 4(y + 2)^2 = 36$$

$$\frac{(x - 1)^2}{4} + \frac{(y + 2)^2}{9} = 1$$

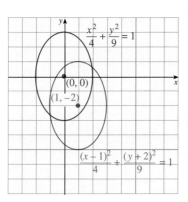

Figure 9.54 Graph of
$9x^2 + 4y^2 - 18x + 16y - 11 = 0$

Thus, the graph may be obtained by translating the graph of the ellipse $\frac{x^2}{4} + \frac{y^2}{9} = 1$ by 1 unit to the right and 2 units down. This process is shown in Figure 9.54. First, plot the center $(h, k) = (1, -2)$; then, from that point, count out a distance of $a = \pm 3$ (the vertices) on the major axis and label those vertices. Finally, from the center, count out the distance $b = \pm 2$ on the minor axis. Using those four points on the ellipse, you can sketch the graph.   ▬

■ HYPERBOLAS

The last of the conic sections to be considered has a definition similar to that of the ellipse.

Hyperbola | A **hyperbola** is the set of all points in the plane such that, for each point on the hyperbola, the difference of its distances from two fixed points is a constant.

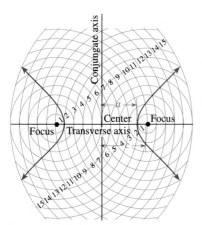

Figure 9.55 Graph of a hyperbola
from the definition

The fixed points are called the **foci**. A hyperbola with foci at F_1 and F_2, where the given constant distance is 8 is shown in Figure 9.55.

The line passing through the foci is called the **transverse axis**. The **center** is the midpoint of the segment connecting the foci. The line passing through the center perpendicular to the transverse axis is called the **conjugate axis**. The transverse axis intersects the hyperbola at points called the **vertices**, and the conjugate axis does not intersect the hyperbola. The hyperbola is symmetric with respect to both the transverse and conjugate axes.

If you use the definition, you can derive the equation for a hyperbola with foci at $(-c, 0)$ and $(c, 0)$ and constant difference $2a$ (both c and a are positive). If (x, y) is any point on the curve, then

$$\left| \sqrt{(x + c)^2 + (y - 0)^2} - \sqrt{(x - c)^2 + (y - 0)^2} \right| = 2a$$

The procedure for simplifying this expression is left as a problem. After several steps you should obtain

$$\frac{x^2}{a^2} - \frac{y^2}{c^2 - a^2} = 1$$

If $b^2 = c^2 - a^2$, then

$$\frac{x^2}{a^2} - \frac{y^2}{b^2} = 1$$

which is the standard-form equation. Notice that $c^2 = a^2 - b^2$ for the ellipse and that $c^2 = a^2 + b^2$ for the hyperbola. For the ellipse it is necessary that $a^2 > b^2$, but for the hyperbola there is no restriction on the relative sizes for a and b (but c is still less than a for the hyperbola).

Repeat the argument for a hyperbola with foci $F_1(0, c)$ and $F_2(0, -c)$, and you will obtain the other standard-form equation for a hyperbola with a vertical transverse axis.

Standard-Form Equations for Hyperbolas

Orientation	Foci	Constant	Center
Horizontal: $\dfrac{x^2}{a^2} - \dfrac{y^2}{b^2} = 1$	$(-c, 0), (c, 0)$	$2a$	$(0, 0)$
Vertical: $\dfrac{y^2}{a^2} - \dfrac{x^2}{b^2} = 1$	$(0, c), (0, -c)$	$2a$	$(0, 0)$

where $b^2 = c^2 - a^2$ or $c^2 = a^2 + b^2$

As with the other conics, we shall sketch a hyperbola by determining some information about the curve directly from the equation by inspection. The vertices are located $\pm a$ units from the center. The number $2a$ is the **length of the transverse axis**. The hyperbola does not intersect the conjugate axis, but if you plot the points located $\pm b$ units from the center, you determine a segment on the conjugate axis with length $2b$ called the **length of the conjugate axis**. The endpoints of this segment are useful in determining the shape of the hyperbola.

EXAMPLE 5   Sketching a hyperbola in standard form

Sketch $\dfrac{x^2}{4} - \dfrac{y^2}{9} = 1$.

Solution   The center of the hyperbola is $(0, 0)$; $a = 2$ and $b = 3$. Plot the vertices at $x = \pm 2$, as shown in the margin. From the form we see that the transverse axis is along the x-axis and the conjugate axis is along the y-axis. Plot the length of the conjugate axis by plotting ± 3 units from the origin. We call these points the **pseudovertices**, because the curve does not actually pass through these points.

Next, form a rectangle by drawing lines through the vertices and pseudovertices parallel to the axes of the hyperbola. This rectangle is called the **central rectangle**. The diagonal lines passing through the corners of the central rectangle are **oblique asymptotes** for the hyperbola, as shown in Figure 9.56; they aid in sketching the hyperbola.   ▬

For the general hyperbola given by the equation

$$\frac{x^2}{a^2} - \frac{y^2}{b^2} = 1$$

the equations of the oblique asymptotes described are found by replacing the constant term 1 by 0 and then factoring and solving:

$$y = \frac{b}{a}x \quad \text{and} \quad y = -\frac{b}{a}x$$

To justify this result, you are asked in Problem 66 to show that the branches of the hyperbola approach $y = \pm \dfrac{b}{a}x$ as $|x| \to \infty$.

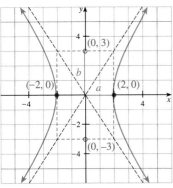

Figure 9.56 Graph of $\dfrac{x^2}{4} - \dfrac{y^2}{9} = 1$

Computational Window

To use a graphing calculator to sketch a hyperbola, either you will need to solve the equation for y and graph the two resulting functions or else you will need to represent the equation parametrically. To solve for y in Example 5, we find

$$\frac{x^2}{4} - \frac{y^2}{9} = 1$$

$$\frac{y^2}{9} = \frac{x^2}{4} - 1$$

$$y^2 = 9\left(\frac{x^2}{4} - 1\right)$$

$$y^2 = \frac{9}{4}(x^2 - 4)$$

$$y = \pm\frac{3}{2}\sqrt{x^2 - 4}$$

Using a calculator, we set $Y1 = 1.5\sqrt{(X^2 - 4)}$ and $Y2 = -1.5\sqrt{(X^2 - 4)}$. The second method of graphing a hyperbola with a calculator, which is preferable (because it is easier), is to use its parameterization. We can parameterize a hyperbola by using the identity $1 + \tan^2\theta = \sec^2\theta$:

Because $\sec^2\theta - \tan^2\theta = 1$ and because $\sec\theta = \frac{x}{a}$ and $\tan\theta = \frac{y}{b}$, we can let $x = a\sec\theta$ and $y = b\tan\theta$. For Example 5, we see the parameterization is

$$x = 2\sec\theta \quad \text{and} \quad y = 3\tan\theta$$

for $0 \le \theta < 2\pi$. The calculator graph is shown at the right.

EXAMPLE 6   Completing the square to sketch a hyperbola

Sketch $16x^2 - 9y^2 - 128x - 18y + 103 = 0$.

Solution   Complete the square in both x and y.

$$16x^2 - 9y^2 - 128x - 18y + 103 = 0$$

$$16(x^2 - 8x \quad) - 9(y^2 + 2y \quad) = -103$$

$$16(x^2 - 8x + 4^2) - 9(y^2 + 2y + 1^2) = -103 + 16 \cdot 4^2 - 9 \cdot 1^2$$

$$16(x - 4)^2 - 9(y + 1)^2 = 144$$

$$\frac{(x - 4)^2}{9} - \frac{(y + 1)^2}{16} = 1$$

The graph is shown in Figure 9.57.

⊘ Watch the signs on the second parentheses. ⊘

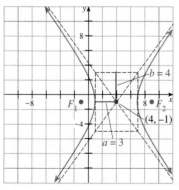

Figure 9.57 Sketch of $16x^2 - 9y^2 - 128x - 18y + 103 = 0$

We conclude our discussion of hyperbolas by considering an example in which information about the graph is given and we are asked to find the equation of the hyperbola.

EXAMPLE 7   Equation of a hyperbola given information about the graph

Find the set of points such that, for any point, the difference of its distances from $(6, 2)$ and $(6, -5)$ is always 3.

Computational Window

To use a graphing calculator, for Example 6 we will parameterize the equation $\dfrac{x-4}{3} = \sec\theta$ so that

$$x = 3\sec\theta + 4$$

Also, $\dfrac{y+1}{4} = \tan\theta$, so that

$$y = 4\tan\theta - 1$$

The graph is shown.

Solution From the definition, we see this is a hyperbola with center $\left(6, -\frac{3}{2}\right)$ and $c = \frac{7}{2}$. Also, $2a = 3$, so $a = \frac{3}{2}$. Because $c^2 = a^2 + b^2$, we have

$$\frac{49}{4} = \frac{9}{4} + b^2 \quad \text{so that} \quad b^2 = 10$$

The desired equation is

$$\frac{\left(y + \frac{3}{2}\right)^2}{\frac{9}{4}} - \frac{(x-6)^2}{10} = 1 \quad \text{or} \quad \frac{4\left(y + \frac{3}{2}\right)^2}{9} - \frac{(x-6)^2}{10} = 1$$

■ ECCENTRICITY AND POLAR COORDINATES

We defined the parabola as the set of all points P equidistant from a given point F (the focus) and a given line L (the directrix). In other words, for a parabola

$$\frac{\text{DISTANCE FROM } P \text{ TO } F}{\text{DISTANCE FROM } P \text{ TO } L} = 1$$

This form of the definition of a parabola is part of the following characterization of conic sections.

> **Eccentricity** Let F be a point in the plane and let L be a line in the same plane. Then the set of all points P in the plane that satisfy
>
> $$\frac{\text{DISTANCE FROM } P \text{ TO } F}{\text{DISTANCE FROM } P \text{ TO } L} = \varepsilon$$
>
> is a conic section, and ε is a fixed number for each conic called the **eccentricity** of the conic. The conic is
>
> An *ellipse* if $\varepsilon < 1$;
> A *parabola* if $\varepsilon = 1$;
> A *hyperbola* if $\varepsilon > 1$.

These criteria for a conic are illustrated in Figure 9.58.

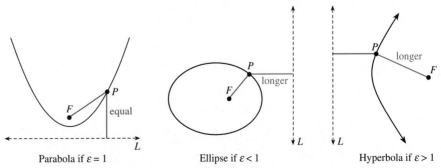

Parabola if $\varepsilon = 1$ Ellipse if $\varepsilon < 1$ Hyperbola if $\varepsilon > 1$

Figure 9.58 Eccentricity characterization of a conic section

Next, we shall examine polar characterizations for the ellipse and the hyperbola that involve the eccentricity ε. Consider an ellipse with one focus F at the origin of a polar coordinate plane. Assume that the corresponding directrix L

is the vertical line $x = p$ ($p > 0$; or in polar form, $r \cos \theta = p$) and that the ellipse has eccentricity ε. Then, if $P(r, \theta)$ is a polar-form point on the ellipse, we have

$$\varepsilon = \frac{\text{DISTANCE FROM } P \text{ TO } F}{\text{DISTANCE FROM } P \text{ TO } L} = \frac{r}{p - r \cos \theta}$$

This relationship is shown in Figure 9.59.

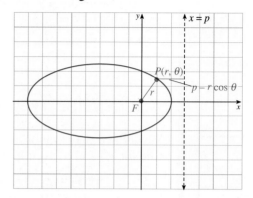

Figure 9.59 Polar representation of an ellipse

Solving for r, we find the ellipse has the polar equation

$$r = \frac{\varepsilon p}{1 + \varepsilon \cos \theta} \quad \textit{Because } 0 \le \varepsilon < 1 \textit{ we have } \varepsilon \cos \theta \ne -1.$$

Similarly, if the directrix is $x = -p$, the equation is $r = \dfrac{\varepsilon p}{1 - \varepsilon \cos \theta}$, and if the directrix is $y = p$ or $y = -p$, the corresponding equations are, respectively,

$$r = \frac{\varepsilon p}{1 + \varepsilon \sin \theta} \quad \text{and} \quad r = \frac{\varepsilon p}{1 - \varepsilon \sin \theta}$$

These four possibilities are summarized in Figure 9.60.

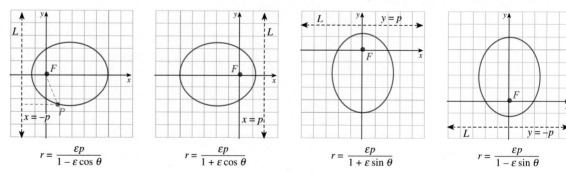

$$r = \frac{\varepsilon p}{1 - \varepsilon \cos \theta} \qquad r = \frac{\varepsilon p}{1 + \varepsilon \cos \theta} \qquad r = \frac{\varepsilon p}{1 + \varepsilon \sin \theta} \qquad r = \frac{\varepsilon p}{1 - \varepsilon \sin \theta}$$

Figure 9.60 Forms for the equation of an ellipse ($\varepsilon < 1$) in standard polar form

EXAMPLE 8   Describing the graph of an equation in polar form

Discuss the graph of the polar-form equation $r = \dfrac{2}{2 - \cos \theta}$.

Solution   Begin by writing the equation in standard form: $r = \dfrac{1}{1 - \frac{1}{2} \cos \theta}$.

This form involves a cosine and has $\varepsilon = \frac{1}{2} < 1$, so by comparing with the forms in Figure 9.60, we see that the graph must be a horizontal ellipse. The

Coordinates in blue are polar.

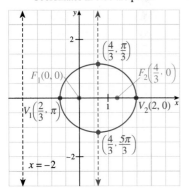

Figure 9.61 Graph of
$r = \dfrac{2}{2 - \cos \theta}$

form also tells us that $\varepsilon p = 1$, so $p = 2$ and the directrix is $x = -2$. The focus F_1 closer to the directrix is at the pole, and the vertices occur where $\theta = 0$ and $\theta = \pi$. For $\theta = 0$, we obtain $r = 2$, and for $\theta = \pi$, $r = \frac{2}{3}$, so the vertices are the polar points $V_1\left(\frac{2}{3}, \pi\right)$ and $V_2(2, 0)$. Since the focus $F_1(0, 0)$ is $\frac{2}{3}$ unit to the left of $V_1(2, 0)$, F_2 is the polar point $\left(\frac{4}{3}, 0\right)$. The center of the ellipse is midway between the foci, at $\left(\frac{2}{3}, 0\right)$, so the minor axis is the vertical line passing through this point. This is the line $x = \frac{2}{3}$ or, in polar form,

$$r \cos \theta = \frac{2}{3} \quad \text{or} \quad r = \frac{\frac{2}{3}}{\cos \theta}$$

To find the endpoints of the minor axis, we need to solve simultaneously the equations for the axis with the equation of the ellipse; namely,

$$\frac{2}{2 - \cos \theta} = \frac{\frac{2}{3}}{\cos \theta}$$

$$2 \cos \theta = \tfrac{2}{3}(2 - \cos \theta)$$

$$\tfrac{8}{3} \cos \theta = \tfrac{4}{3}$$

$$\cos \theta = \tfrac{1}{2}$$

so that $\theta = \frac{\pi}{3}$ and $\frac{5\pi}{3}$. Solving for r, we find $r = \frac{4}{3}$, which gives the vertices $\left(\frac{4}{3}, \frac{\pi}{3}\right)$ and $\left(\frac{4}{3}, \frac{5\pi}{3}\right)$. The graph is shown in Figure 9.61.

Formulas for hyperbolas in polar coordinates are obtained in essentially the same way as polar formulas for ellipses. The four different cases that can occur for hyperbolas in standard form are summarized in Figure 9.62.

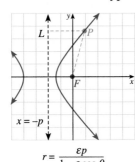

$$r = \frac{\varepsilon p}{1 - \varepsilon \cos \theta}$$

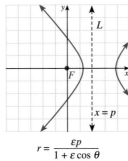

$$r = \frac{\varepsilon p}{1 + \varepsilon \cos \theta}$$

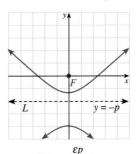

$$r = \frac{\varepsilon p}{1 - \varepsilon \sin \theta}$$

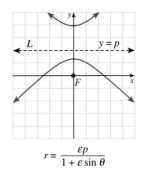

$$r = \frac{\varepsilon p}{1 + \varepsilon \sin \theta}$$

Figure 9.62 Forms for the equation of a hyperbola ($\varepsilon > 1$) in standard polar form

EXAMPLE 9   Describing the graph of a hyperbola in polar form

Discuss the graph of the polar equation $r = \dfrac{5}{3 + 4 \sin \theta}$.

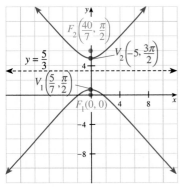

Figure 9.63 Graph of $r = \dfrac{5}{3 + 4 \sin \theta}$

Solution   The standard form of the equation is $r = \dfrac{\frac{5}{3}}{1 + \frac{4}{3} \sin \theta}$. The form tells us that the eccentricity is $\varepsilon = \frac{4}{3}$, and because $\varepsilon > 1$, the graph is a hyperbola. We also see that the transverse axis is the y-axis and that because $\varepsilon p = \frac{5}{3}$ we have $p = \frac{5}{4}$. Thus, the graph has one focus F_1 at the pole and directrix $y = p = \frac{5}{4}$.

The corresponding vertex occurs when $\theta = \frac{\pi}{2}$:

$$r = \frac{5}{3 + 4 \sin \frac{\pi}{2}} = \frac{5}{7}$$

so the polar coordinates of this vertex V_1 are $\left(\frac{5}{7}, \frac{\pi}{2}\right)$. The opposite vertex occurs where $\theta = \frac{3\pi}{2}$ and

$$r = \frac{5}{3 + 4 \sin \frac{3\pi}{2}} = -5$$

so the point is $V_2 \left(-5, \frac{3\pi}{2}\right)$. Because the vertex V_1 is located $\frac{5}{7}$ unit above $F_1(0, 0)$, the other focus F_2 will be located 5 units above the vertex V_1. Thus, F_2 is the polar point $\left(\frac{40}{7}, \frac{\pi}{2}\right)$. The graph is shown in Figure 9.63. ▬

■ GEOMETRIC PROPERTIES

Like the parabola, the ellipse has some useful reflection properties. Let P be any point on an ellipse with foci F_1 and F_2, and let T be the tangent line to the ellipse at P, as shown in Figure 9.64.

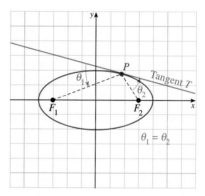

Figure 9.64 Reflection property of an ellipse

Then the line segments $\overline{F_1 P}$ and $\overline{F_2 P}$ (called the **focal radii**) make equal angles with the tangent line T at P (see Problem 69). The reflection property of an ellipse has the following physical interpretation.

Reflective Property of an Ellipse

> An elliptic mirror has the property that waves emanating from one focus are reflected toward the other focus.

The "whispering room" phenomenon found in many science museums and in famous buildings such as the old U.S. Capitol in Washington, D.C., is an application of this principle. Two people stand at each focus of an elliptic dome. If one person whispers, the other will clearly hear what is said, but anyone *not* near a focus will hear nothing. This is especially impressive if the foci are far apart.

The elliptic reflection principle is also used in a procedure for disintegrating kidney stones. A patient is placed in a tub of water with the shape of an ellipsoid (a three-dimensional elliptic figure) in such a way that the kidney stone is at one

Whispering room: Only a person standing at focus F_2 clearly hears a sound at focus F_1.

Pulse emanating from focus F_1 is concentrated on the kidney stone at focus F_2.

Figure 9.65 LORAN measures the differences in the time of arrival of signals from two sets of stations. The plane's position at the intersection lines is charted on a special map based on a hyperbolic coordinate system.

focus of the ellipsoid. A pulse generated at the other focus is then concentrated at the kidney stone.

There is also a useful reflection property of hyperbolas. Suppose an aircraft has crashed somewhere in the desert. A device in the wreckage emits a beep at regular intervals. Two observers, located at listening posts a known distance apart, time a beep. It turns out that the time difference between the two listening posts multiplied by the velocity of sound gives the value $2a$ for a hyperbola on which the airplane is located. A third listening post will determine two more hyperbolas in a similar fashion, and the airplane must be at the intersection of these hyperbolas. (See Problem 61.)

PROBLEM SET 9.6

Ⓐ **1.** ■ What Does This Say? Discuss a procedure for graphing an ellipse.

2. ■ What Does This Say? Discuss a procedure for graphing a hyperbola.

3. ■ What Does This Say? Outline a procedure for recognizing a conic section by looking at its rectangular-form equation.

4. ■ What Does This Say? Outline a procedure for recognizing a conic section by looking at its polar-form equation.

For each equation in Problems 5–24, sketch each curve.

5. $\dfrac{x^2}{4} + \dfrac{y^2}{16} = 1$

6. $\dfrac{x^2}{16} + \dfrac{y^2}{4} = 1$

7. $\dfrac{x^2}{25} - \dfrac{y^2}{9} = 1$

8. $\dfrac{x^2}{9} - \dfrac{y^2}{4} = 1$

9. $y^2 - x^2 = 1$

10. $x^2 - y^2 = 8$

11. $(x-1)^2 + 4y^2 = 64$

12. $2x^2 + 3y^2 = 12$

13. $x^2 - 2y^2 + 2 = 0$

14. $5x^2 - 3y^2 + 15 = 0$

15. $\dfrac{(x-1)^2}{4} + \dfrac{(y+3)^2}{16} = 1$

16. $\dfrac{(x-1)^2}{16} + \dfrac{(y+3)^2}{4} = 1$

17. $4(x-3)^2 - 9(y+1)^2 = 36$

18. $9(x+1)^2 - 4(y-3)^2 = 36$

19. $4x^2 - 9y^2 - 8x + 54y - 41 = 0$

20. $x^2 - 4y^2 + 2x + 8y - 7 = 0$

21. $4x^2 + y^2 + 8x - 2y + 4 = 0$

22. $x^2 + 4y^2 + 2x - 8y + 4 = 0$

23. $9x^2 + 4y^2 - 8y = 32$

24. $4x^2 + 9y^2 - 8x = 32$

Find the standard-form equation for the given information in Problems 25–38.

25. an ellipse with vertices at $(0, 8)$ and $(0, 2)$ and $c = \sqrt{5}$

26. an ellipse centered at the origin with focus at $(0, 3)$; semimajor axis with length 4

27. an ellipse centered at the origin with focus at $(-2, 0)$; minor axis with length 4

28. a hyperbola with foci at $(0, 3)$ and $(0, -3)$ and one vertex at $(0, -2)$

29. a hyperbola with foci at $(\sqrt{2}, 0)$ and $(-\sqrt{2}, 0)$ and one vertex at $(1, 0)$

30. a hyperbola with vertices at $(5, 0)$ and $(-5, 0)$ and one focus at $(-7, 0)$

31. a conic with major axis $-4 \le x \le 4$ and minor axis $-3 \le y \le 3$

32. a conic with transverse axis $-3 \le x \le 3$ and conjugate axis $-4 \le y \le 4$

33. an ellipse with center at $(2, 1)$, semiminor axis with length 3, and vertices at $(2, 6)$ and $(2, -4)$

34. a conic with foci at $(-1, 0)$ and $(1, 0)$ with major axis with length 12

35. a conic with foci at $(0, 6)$ and $(0, -6)$ with transverse axis with length 12

36. the set of points such that for any point, the sum of its distances from $(4, -3)$ and $(-4, -3)$ is 12

37. the set of points such that, for any point, the difference of its distances from $(4, -3)$ and $(-4, -3)$ is 6

38. a hyperbola with vertices $(3, 0)$, $(-3, 0)$ and asymptotes $y = 3x$ and $y = -3x$

Ⓑ *Sketch the graph of each polar-form equation in Problems 39–42.*

39. $r = \dfrac{4}{6 + \cos \theta}$

40. $r = \dfrac{4}{2 + 3 \cos \theta}$

41. $r = \dfrac{5}{1 - 2 \sin \theta}$

42. $r = \dfrac{-3}{2 - \sin \theta}$

43. Find an equation for the tangent line to the ellipse $5x^2 + 4y^2 = 56$ at the point $(-2, 3)$.

44. Find an equation of an ellipse that is tangent to the coordinate axes and the line $y = 6$. Is there only one such ellipse?

45. Find two points on the ellipse $\dfrac{x^2}{4} + y^2 = 1$ where the tangent line also passes through the point $(0, -2)$.

46. Find the smallest distance from the point $(2, 0)$ to the ellipse $3x^2 + 2y^2 + 6x - 3 = 0$

47. Find the volume of the solid generated by revolving the top half $(y \geq 0)$ of the ellipse

$$\dfrac{x^2}{a^2} + \dfrac{y^2}{b^2} = 1$$

about the x-axis.

48. Find the volume of the solid generated by revolving the right half $(x \geq 0)$ of the ellipse

$$\dfrac{x^2}{a^2} + \dfrac{y^2}{b^2} = 1$$

about the y-axis.

49. Let R denote the region of the plane that lies inside the ellipse

$$\dfrac{x^2}{4} + \dfrac{y^2}{1} = 1$$

Find the volume of the solid generated by revolving R about the line $y = -2$.

50. Find an equation for the hyperbola with vertices $(3, -1)$, $(-1, -1)$, and asymptotes $y = \frac{9}{4}x - \frac{13}{4}$ and $y = -\frac{9}{4}x + \frac{5}{4}$.

51. Find an equation for the hyperbola with vertices $(9, 0)$, $(-9, 0)$ whose asymptotes are perpendicular to each other.

52. Find an equation for a hyperbola in standard position that contains the points $(3, \sqrt{5}/2)$ and $(-2, 0)$.

53. Show that $x = x_0 + a \cosh t$, $y = y_0 + b \sinh t$ are parametric equations for one branch of a hyperbola. Find a

Cartesian equation for this hyperbola. *Note:* This is the reason sinh t and cosh t are called "hyperbolic functions."

54. Show that the equations $x = x_0 + a \sinh/t$ and $y = y_0 + b \cosh t$ are parametric equations for one branch of a hyperbola. How does this hyperbola differ from the one in Problem 53?

55. Find the area of the region bounded by the hyperbola $9x^2 - 4y^2 = 36$ and the vertical line $x = 4$.

56. An **equilateral hyperbola** is one with an equation of the general form $y^2 - x^2 = a^2$. Show that a hyperbola in standard form is equilateral if and only if its asymptotes are perpendicular to each other.

57. Let R be the region bounded by the x-axis, the line $x = 4$, and the portion of the hyperbola $9x^2 - 4y^2 = 36$, with $y \geq 0$. Find the volume of the solid generated by revolving R about
    a. the x-axis
    b. the y-axis

58. The orbit of a planet is an ellipse whose major axis and minor axis are, respectively, 100 million and 81 million miles long. Find an equation for the ellipse. How far apart are its foci?

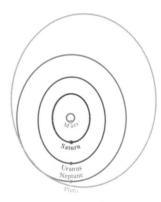

Figure 9.66 Planetary orbits

59. The orbit of the earth around the sun is elliptical with the sun at one focus. The semimajor axis of this orbit is 9.3×10^7 mi and the eccentricity is about 0.017. Determine the greatest and least distance of the earth from the sun (correct to two significant digits). *Hint:* Use polar coordinates.

Ⓒ 60. Consider a person A who fires a rifle at a distant gong B. Assuming that the ground is flat, where must you stand to hear the sound of the gun and the sound of the gong simultaneously? *Hint:* To answer this question, let x be the distance that sound travels in the length of time it takes the bullet to travel from the gun to the gong. Show that the person who hears the sounds simultaneously must stand on a branch of a hyperbola (the one nearest the target), so the difference of the distances from A to B is x.

61. Three LORAN stations are located at $(4, 0)$, $(0, 0)$, and $\left(4, \frac{\pi}{4}\right)$ in a polar coordinate system. Radio signals are sent out from all three stations simultaneously. An airplane

receiving the signals notes that the signals from the second and third stations arrive $2/c$ seconds later than the signal from the first, where c is the velocity of a radio signal. What is the location (in polar coordinates) of the airplane?

62. Derive the equation for the ellipse with foci $F_1(-c, 0)$ and $F_2(c, 0)$ for $c > 0$ and constant distance $2a$.

63. Derive the equation for the hyperbola with foci $F_1(-c, 0)$ and $F_2(c, 0)$ for $c > 0$ and constant distance $2a$.

64. Find conditions on the coefficients of the equation

$$Ax^2 + Cy^2 + Dx + Ey + F = 0$$

with $AC > 0$ that guarantee the graph of the equation will be

a. a line
b. an ellipse
c. a circle
d. a point
e. a hyperbola
f. no graph

65. a. Show that the tangent line to the ellipse

$$\frac{x^2}{a^2} + \frac{y^2}{b^2} = 1$$

at the point (x_0, y_0) has the equation

$$\frac{x_0 x}{a^2} + \frac{y_0 y}{b^2} = 1$$

b. Use part a to show that a tangent line to a vertex of an ellipse in standard form is either vertical or horizontal.

66. Prove that the lines $y = \frac{b}{a}x$ and $y = -\frac{b}{a}x$ are asymptotes of the hyperbola

$$\frac{x^2}{a^2} - \frac{y^2}{b^2} = 1$$

Hint: Show that the vertical distance $D(x)$ between $y = \frac{b}{a}\sqrt{x^2 - a^2}$ and the line $y = \frac{b}{a}x$ tends to 0 as $x \to \infty$, as shown in Figure 9.67.

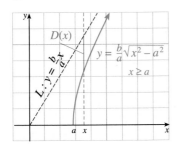

Figure 9.67 Problem 66

67. Note that a hyperbola never intersects its asymptotes. Show that any line parallel to an asymptote will intersect the hyperbola exactly once.

68. As with the parabola, a **focal chord** of an ellipse or hyperbola is a chord through a focus perpendicular to the principal axis.

a. Show that the focal chords of the ellipse and the hyperbola

$$\frac{x^2}{a^2} + \frac{y^2}{b^2} = 1 \quad \text{and} \quad \frac{x^2}{a^2} - \frac{y^2}{b^2} = 1$$

each have length $\frac{2b^2}{a}$.

b. Show that the tangents at the endpoints of the focal chord of an ellipse or hyperbola intersect on the directrix.

c. Find the length of the focal chord of the graph of the polar equation

$$r = \frac{\varepsilon p}{1 - \varepsilon \cos \theta}$$

69. Show that at each point $P(x_0, y_0)$ on the ellipse

$$\frac{x^2}{a^2} + \frac{y^2}{b^2} = 1$$

the focal radii $F_1 P$ and $F_2 P$ make equal angles with the tangent line. *Hint:* Use the result in Problem 40, Section 1.3, to show that

$$\tan \theta_1 = \tan \theta_2 = \frac{b^2}{y_0 c}$$

where $c = \sqrt{a^2 - b^2}$. See Figure 9.68.

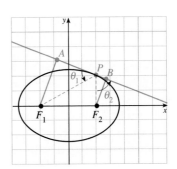

Figure 9.68 Problem 69

Chapter 9 Review

> **IN THIS REVIEW** **Proficiency examination; supplementary problems**
> Problems 1–26 of the proficiency examination test your knowledge of the concepts of this chapter, and Problems 27–34 test your understanding of those concepts by asking you to work sample practice problems. The supplementary problems present questions relating to the material of this chapter in a wide variety of settings.

PROFICIENCY EXAMINATION

Concept Problems

1. What are the primary representations of a point in polar form?

2. What are the formulas for changing from polar to rectangular form?

3. What are the formulas for changing from rectangular to polar form?

4. What does a cardioid look like, and what are the standard-form equations for cardioids?

5. What is the formula for the rotation of a polar-form equation?

6. How do you check for symmetry with a polar-form graph?

7. What does a limaçon look like, and what are the standard-form equations for limaçons?

8. What is a rose curve? What are the standard-form equations for rose curves, and how do you determine the number of leaves?

9. What does a lemniscate look like, and what are the standard-form equations for lemniscates?

10. State the formula for finding the slope of a polar-form curve.

11. What is the procedure for finding the intersection of polar-form curves?

12. What is the polar-form formula for the area of a sector?

13. Outline a procedure for finding the area bounded by a polar graph.

14. What do we mean by parametric equations for a curve?

15. What are a trochoid and a cycloid?

16. How do you find the derivative with parametric equations?

17. What is the parametric formula for arc length?

18. State a formula for finding area under a parametrically defined curve.

19. Give a geometric definition of a parabola, and state the standard-form equations.

20. What is the reflection property of parabolas?

21. Give a geometric definition of an ellipse, and state the standard-form equations.

22. Give a geometric definition of a hyperbola, and state the standard-form equations.

23. What is the reflective property of ellipses?

24. How do you find a focus for an ellipse? A hyperbola?

25. Explain or illustrate the meanings of the following terms: conic sections; eccentricity; principal axis; major axis; minor axis; transverse axis; conjugate axis.

26. What is the polar-form equation for the conic sections? How do you recognize each type of conic section from this general form?

Practice Problems

27. Identify each of the curves whose equations are given.
    a. $3x - 2y^2 - 4y + 7 = 0$ b. $y^2 = x^2 - 1$
    c. $x^2 + y^2 + x - y = 3$ d. $r = 2 \sin \frac{\pi}{2}$
    e. $\frac{x}{4} + \frac{y}{9} = 1$ f. $\frac{x^2}{4} - \frac{y}{9} = 1$
    g. $r = 3 \sin 2\theta$ h. $r - 5 = 5 \cos \theta$

Identify and then sketch the curves whose equations are given in Problems 28–33.

28. $(y - 2)^2 = 16(x - 3)$

29. $r = 2 \cos \theta$

30. $2x^2 + 3y^2 - 4x + 12y = -8$

31. $9x^2 - y^2 + 12y - 18x = 36$

32. $r^2 = \cos 2\theta$

33. $r = 4 - 2 \cos \theta$

34. Find the area of the intersection of the circles $r = 2a \cos \theta$ and $r = 2a \sin \theta$, where $a > 0$ is constant.

SUPPLEMENTARY PROBLEMS

Name and sketch the graph of the curves whose equations are given in Problems 1–22.

1. $r = 2 \sin \theta - 3 \cos \theta$ **2.** $r = -2\theta,\ \theta \geq 0$

3. $r = -4 \cos 2\theta$ **4.** $r = 2 \cos \theta \sin \theta$

5. $x^2 + 8y - 6 = 0$

6. $9y^2 - 25x^2 - 90y - 50x - 25 = 0$

7. $x^2 + 2x - 2y + 2 = 0$ **8.** $9y^2 + 4x^2 - 54y + 45 = 0$

9. $r = -\csc \theta$ **10.** $r = \sin 2\theta$ **11.** $r = \cos\left(\theta - \frac{\pi}{3}\right)$

12. $r = \sin\left(\frac{\pi}{3} + \theta\right)$ **13.** $r = 3 \cos 2\theta$ **14.** $r^2 = \cos \theta$

15. $r = \dfrac{4}{1 - \cos \theta}$ **16.** $r = \dfrac{6}{4(1 + \sin \theta)}$

17. $r = \dfrac{5}{2 + 3 \sin \theta}$ **18.** $r = \dfrac{-4}{2 + \cos \theta}$

19. $r = 9 \cos \theta \sin^2 \theta$ **20.** $r = 5 \sin 2\theta \csc \theta$

21. $r = 2 \sec \theta - 4$ **22.** $r = 3 \sin (2\theta - 1)$

Sketch the curves in Problems 23–26 and find all points where the tangent line is horizontal.

23. $r = 1 - 2 \cos \theta$ **24.** $r = 2 + 4 \sin \theta$

25. $r = \dfrac{4}{1 - \sin \theta}$ **26.** $r = \dfrac{3}{4 - 3 \cos \theta}$

In Problems 27–38, convert each polar equation to Cartesian form and each Cartesian equation to polar form.

27. $2x + 3y = 4$ **28.** $r = -2 \sin \theta$

29. $x^2 + y^2 - 3x = 5$ **30.** $r = \cos 2\theta$

31. $x^2 + y^2 = \tan^{-1}\left(\frac{y}{x}\right)$ **32.** $r = 1 + \cot \theta$

33. $y = mx$ **34.** $x^2 + y^2 + ax = a\sqrt{x^2 + y^2}$

35. $(x - a)^2 + y^2 = a^2$ **36.** $(x^2 + y^2)^2 = a^2(x^2 - y^2)$

37. $r^2 = \dfrac{36}{13 \cos^2 \theta - 4}$ **38.** $r^2 = \dfrac{36}{5 \cos^2 \theta + 4}$

Find a Cartesian-form equation for each curve described in Problems 39–48.

39. the parabola with focus $(0, -5)$ and directrix $y = 5$

40. the ellipse with vertices $(0, 8)$, $(0, -8)$ and foci $(0, 4)$, $(0, -4)$

41. the hyperbola with foci $(8, 0)$, $(-8, 0)$, and vertices $(4, 0)$, $(-4, 0)$

42. the ellipse with center $(2, 1)$, focus $(1, 1)$, and semimajor axis 2

43. the set of points such that, for each point, the difference of the distances from $(3, 0)$ and $(9, 0)$ is always 4

44. the parabola whose vertex is $(4, 3)$ and directrix is $x = 1$

45. the set of points such that, for each point, the difference of distances from $(-3, 4)$ and $(-7, 4)$ is equal to 2

46. the set of points such that, for each point, the sum of the distances from $(-3, 4)$ and $(-7, 4)$ is 12

47. the ellipse with foci $(2, 3)$ and $(-1, 3)$ and eccentricity $\frac{3}{5}$

48. the hyperbola with vertices $(0, -3)$ and $(0, 3)$ and eccentricity $\frac{5}{3}$

Find the points of intersection of the polar-form curves in Problems 49–58.

49. $\begin{cases} r = 2 \cos \theta \\ r = 1 + \cos \theta \end{cases}$ **50.** $\begin{cases} r = 1 + \cos \theta \\ r = 1 - \cos \theta \end{cases}$

51. $\begin{cases} r = 1 + \sin \theta \\ r = 1 + \cos \theta \end{cases}$ **52.** $\begin{cases} r^2 = \cos 2\left(\theta - \frac{\pi}{2}\right) \\ r^2 = \cos 2\theta \end{cases}$

53. $\begin{cases} r \cos \theta + 2r \sin \theta = 4 \\ r = 2 \sec \theta \end{cases}$ **54.** $\begin{cases} r = 2 - 2 \cos \theta \\ r = 2 \cos \theta \end{cases}$

55. $\begin{cases} r = 2 \sin 2\theta \\ r = 1 \text{ for } 0 \leq \theta \leq \frac{\pi}{2} \end{cases}$ **56.** $\begin{cases} r = a(1 + \cos \theta) \\ r = a(1 - \sin \theta) \end{cases}$

57. $\begin{cases} r = a(1 + \sin \theta) \\ r = a(1 - \sin \theta) \end{cases} a > 0$ **58.** $\begin{cases} r = 2\theta \\ \theta = \frac{\pi}{6} \end{cases}$

Find the area of the regions described in Problems 59–65.

59. the region bounded by the polar curve $r = 4 \cos 2\theta$

60. the region inside both the circles $r = 1$ and $r = 2 \sin \theta$

61. the region inside one loop of the lemniscate $r^2 = \cos 2\theta$

62. the region inside the rose petal $r = \sin 2\theta$ for $0 \leq \theta \leq \frac{\pi}{2}$

63. the region inside the circle $r = 2a \sin \theta$ and outside the circle $r = a$

64. the region under the curve given parametrically by

$$x = -\cos^4 \theta, \qquad y = \sin \theta \qquad \text{for } 0 \leq \theta \leq \frac{\pi}{4}$$

65. the region bounded by the spiral $r = e^{2\theta}$ and the x-axis for $0 \leq \theta < \pi$

66. Find the slope of the tangent line to the spiral $r = 2\theta$ at the point where $\theta = \frac{\pi}{3}$. Find an equation (in either polar or Cartesian coordinates) for this tangent line.

67. Find the length of the curve given by $x = 1 + \cos 2t$, $y = \sin 2t$ for $-\frac{\pi}{4} \leq t \leq \frac{\pi}{4}$.

68. Find the length of the curve given by $x = \dfrac{\cos 2t}{4}$, $y = \sin t$ for $0 \leq t \leq \frac{\pi}{2}$.

69. Find the arc length of the spiral given by $x = \dfrac{1}{t}$, $y = \dfrac{1}{t^2}$ for $1 \leq t \leq 2$.

70. A tangent line to the hyperbola $9x^2 - y^2 = 36$ intersects the y-axis at $(0, 6)$. Find all possible points of tangency.

71. Let C be given by $x = a \cot \theta$, $y = a \sin^2 \theta$. Show that the Cartesian form of the curve C is $y = a^3/(a^2 + x^2)$ and sketch C. This curve is called the **witch of Agnesi**.

72. a. Find an equation for the tangent line to the curve C given by $x = 4 \cos t$, $y = 3 \sin t$, at the point where $t = \pi/6$.

    b. Find an equation for the line perpendicular to the curve C in part **a** at the point where $t = \pi/4$.

73. Find the equation of the tangent line to the cycloid $x = a(\theta - \sin \theta)$, $y = a(1 - \cos \theta)$ at the point where

    a. $\theta = \frac{\pi}{2}$ **b.** $\theta = \pi$ **c.** $\theta = 2\pi$

74. a. Show that the tangent line to the cycloid

$$x = a(\theta - \sin \theta), \quad y = a(1 - \cos \theta)$$

has slope $\cot \dfrac{\theta_0}{2}$ at the point where $\theta = \theta_0$.

    b. For what values of θ is the tangent line to the cycloid horizontal?

    c. For what values of θ is the tangent vertical?

75. A curve C is given parametrically by $x = 2t^2 + 1$, $y = t - 1$ for all t. Find all points on C where the tangent line passes through the point $(7, 1)$.

76. Find a polar equation for the line through (r_1, θ_1) and (r_2, θ_2).

77. Find the area under one arch of the cycloid $x = a(\theta - \sin\theta)$, $y = a(1 - \cos\theta)$ where $a > 0$ is a constant. *Hint*: One arch corresponds to the arc obtained when the point on the rim of the wheel begins on the ground and returns to the ground.

78. Find the length of one arch of the cycloid $x = 9(\theta - \sin\theta)$, $y = 9(1 - \cos\theta)$.

79. Show that the parametric equations
$$x = \frac{1 - t^2}{1 + t^2}, \qquad y = \frac{2t}{1 + t^2}$$
describe the unit circle $x^2 + y^2 = 1$.

80. Find all points on the curve C defined by $x = 3 - 4\sin t$, $y = 4 + 3\cos t$ where the tangent line is horizontal.

81. Let $x = \sin t + \cos t$, $y = \cos t - \sin t$.
   a. Show that $dy/dx = -x/y$.
   b. Find a relationship between x and y.

82. Suppose $x = x(t)$, $y = y(t)$ for $a < t < b$. Show that
$$\frac{d^2y}{dx^2} = \left(\frac{d^2y}{dt^2}\frac{dx}{dt} - \frac{d^2x}{dt^2}\frac{dy}{dt}\right) \Big/ \left(\frac{dx}{dt}\right)^3$$

83. Find the slope of the tangent line to the polar curve $r = a\tan\frac{\theta}{2}$ at the point where $\theta = \frac{\pi}{2}$.

84. A particle moves along the circle $r = 4\cos\theta$. If $\frac{d\theta}{dt} = 2$, find the rate at which r is changing with respect to t when $\theta = \frac{\pi}{4}$.

85. A particle moves along the parabola $r = \dfrac{4}{1 + \cos\theta}$. At a certain instant, $\frac{dr}{dt} = -3$ cm/s, and $\theta = \frac{\pi}{4}$. Find $\frac{d\theta}{dt}$ at this instant.

86. Sketch the curve $r = \sec\theta - 2\cos\theta$ for $-\frac{\pi}{2} < \theta < \frac{\pi}{2}$ and find the area enclosed by its loop. This curve is called a **strophoid**.

87. The circle $r = 1$ of radius 1 centered at the origin has the property that any "diameter" (line through the origin) intersects the circle in a segment of length 2.
   a. Show that the cardioid $r = 1 + \sin\theta$ has the same property.
   b. Show that the region bounded by the cardioid and the circle has different areas. Thus, the area of a region cannot be determined in terms of its diameters alone.

88. The major and minor axes of an ellipse have lengths 10 and 5, respectively. Find the volume obtained by revolving the elliptic region on one side of the major axis about its major axis.

89. A straight rod of fixed length L moves in such a way that its top always touches the y-axis and its bottom touches the x-axis. Let $P(x, y)$ be the point on the rod that is $\frac{3}{4}$ the distance from the bottom to the top of the rod. Describe the path that P traces out as the rod slides down the y-axis.

90. An **epitrochoid** is a curve with the parametric equations
$$x = a\cos\theta + b\cos k\theta, \qquad y = a\sin\theta + b\sin k\theta$$

Sketch the graph of an epitrochoid for $a = 4$, $b = 3$, and $k = 5$.

91. Find the length of the hypocycloid
$$x = (a - b)\cos\theta + b\cos\left(\frac{a - b}{b}\right)\theta$$
$$y = (a - b)\sin\theta - b\sin\left(\frac{a - b}{b}\right)\theta$$
for $0 \le \theta \le \frac{b}{a}\pi$ (assume $a > b > 0$).

92. Two LORAN stations A and B are 100 mi apart. An airplane is flying a level course 70 mi parallel to the line between A and B. Signals are sent from A and B at the same time, and the signal from A reaches the plane 400 μs before the one from B. Assuming the signals travel at 0.187 mi/μs, locate the position of the plane in relation to A and B. *Hint*: It may help to set up a coordinate system with A at the origin, B at the point $(100, 0)$, and the plane flying along the line $y = 70$.

93. Points in a certain city are given coordinates such that store A is at the origin $(0, 0)$ and store B is at $(10, 0)$, where the units are in miles. Suppose hamburger costs $3.00 per pound at store A and $2.75 per pound at store B and that the cost of traveling anywhere in the town is 30¢ per mile. Let $P(x, y)$ be a point in the city where it costs the same to buy one pound of hamburger by traveling to store A as it does to travel and buy at store B. Find an equation for the coordinates of P. In other words, find a curve C on which it doesn't matter where you shop. This is sometimes called an *indifference curve*.

94. PUTNAM EXAMINATION PROBLEM   Consider the two mutually tangent parabolas $y = x^2$ and $y = -x^2$. The upper parabola rolls without slipping around the fixed lower parabola. Find the locus (set of possible points) of the focus of the moving parabola, as shown in Figure 9.69.

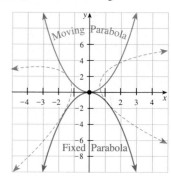

Figure 9.69 Problem 94

95. PUTNAM EXAMINATION PROBLEM   For a point P on an ellipse, let d be the distance from the center of the ellipse to the line tangent to the ellipse at P. Prove that
$$|\overline{PF_1}||\overline{PF_2}|\,d^2$$
is constant as P varies on the ellipse, where $|\overline{PF_1}|$ and $|\overline{PF_2}|$ are the distances from P to the foci F_1 and F_2 of the ellipse.

96. PUTNAM EXAMINATION PROBLEM   Find the minimum value of
$$(u - v)^2 + \left(\sqrt{2 - u^2} - \frac{9}{v}\right)^2$$
for $0 < u < \sqrt{2}$ and $v > 0$.

"Security System Project"

Everything that the greatest minds of all times have accomplished toward the comprehension of forms by means of concepts is gathered into one great science: mathematics.

J. F. Herbart

This project is to be done in groups of three or four students. Each group will submit a single written report.

You are designing a security system for a hospital. You must decide how to program a detector that will be used to watch a 40-ft-long hallway with a door in the middle. The detector runs on a track and points a beam of light straight ahead on the opposite wall. The beam reaches from the floor to the ceiling. Design a security system that will detect an intruder.

You should make the following assumptions:

a. Think of the hallway as a coordinate line with the middle of the door at the origin and the hallway to be watched on the interval $[-20, 20]$. You need to decide what $x(t)$ is for t, in seconds, where $x(t)$ represents the position of the beam at time t. For example, $x(5) = -15$ means that the beam is pointing at the part of the wall 15 ft to the left of the door 5 sec after the detector starts.

b. Assume that t ranges from 0 to 30 min.

c. The door is 3 ft wide, and as long as the beam is hitting any part of the door, it is under surveillance.

d. The beam must stay on an object for at least 0.1 sec in order to detect that object.

Your paper is not limited to the following questions but should include these concerns. Draw a graph of x versus time for what you think is a good choice for $x(t)$. You should mention restrictions on this function, if any, and include the *longest* time interval that the door will not be under surveillance. Could an intruder get to the door by walking down the hallway without being detected by your system? Explain how the intruder could do it and how likely you think it is.

*The group project is courtesy of Steve Hilbert, Ithaca College, Ithaca, New York.

10

Vectors in the Plane and in Space

CONTENTS

PREVIEW

In this chapter, we focus on various algebraic and geometric aspects of vector representations. Then in Chapter 11, we see how vectors can be combined with calculus to study motion in space and other applications.

PERSPECTIVE

Suppose a child is pulling a sled by a rope across a flat field. Intuitively, we would expect quite different results if the child pulls the rope straight up than if the same effort is applied at an angle of $\pi/4$, for instance. In other words, to describe the force exerted by the child on the sled, we must specify not only a magnitude but also a direction. In general, a *scalar* quantity is one that can be described in terms of magnitude alone, whereas a *vector* quantity requires both magnitude and direction. Force, velocity, and acceleration are common vector quantities, and an important goal of this chapter is to develop methods for dealing with such quantities.

10.1 VECTORS IN THE PLANE

IN THIS SECTION   Introduction to vectors, standard representation of vectors in the plane
Many applications of mathematics involve quantities that have both magnitude and direction, such as force, velocity, acceleration, and momentum. Vectors are an important tool in mathematics, and in this section we introduce you to the terminology and notation for vector representation.

■ INTRODUCTION TO VECTORS

A **vector** in a plane can be thought of as a directed line segment, an "arrow" with **initial point** P and **terminal point** Q. The direction of the vector is that of the arrow, and its magnitude is represented by the arrow's length, as shown in Figure 10.1. We shall indicate such a vector by writing **PQ** in boldface print, but in your work you may write an arrow over the designated points: $\overrightarrow{PQ}$. The order of letters you write down is important: **PQ** means that the vector is from P to Q, but **QP** means that the vector is from Q to P. The first letter is always the initial point and the second letter is the terminal point. We shall denote the magnitude (length) of a vector by $\|\mathbf{PQ}\|$. Two vectors are regarded as **equal** (or **equivalent**) if they have the same magnitude and the same direction, even if they do not coincide.

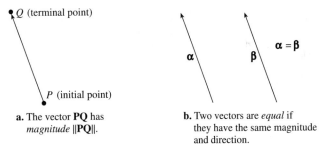

a. The vector **PQ** has *magnitude* $\|\mathbf{PQ}\|$.

b. Two vectors are *equal* if they have the same magnitude and direction.

Figure 10.1   Vectors in a plane

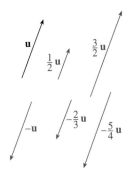

Figure 10.2   Some multiples of the vector **u**

A vector with magnitude 0 is called a **zero** (or **null**) **vector** and is denoted by **0**. The **0** vector has no specific direction, and we shall adopt the convention of assigning it any direction that may be convenient in a particular problem.

If **v** is a vector other than **0**, then any vector **w** that is parallel to **v** is called a **scalar multiple** of **v** and satisfies $\mathbf{w} = s\mathbf{v}$ for some nonzero number s. A **scalar** quantity is one that has only magnitude and in the context of vectors is used to describe a real number. The scalar multiple $s\mathbf{v}$ has length $|s|$ times that of **v**; it points in the same direction as **v** if $s > 0$ and the opposite direction if $s < 0$ (see Figure 10.2). Notice that for any distinct points P and Q, $\mathbf{PQ} = -\mathbf{QP}$. For the zero vector **0**, we define $s\mathbf{0} = \mathbf{0}$ for any scalar s.

Physical experiments indicate that force and velocity vectors can be added (or

resolved) according to a **triangular rule** displayed in Figure 10.3a, and we use this rule as our definition of vector addition. In particular, to add the vector **v** to the vector **u**, we place the end (initial point) of **v** at the tip (terminal point) of **u** and define the sum, also called the **resultant u + v**, to be the vector that extends from the initial point of **u** to the terminal point of **v**.

Equivalently, **u + v** is the diagonal of the parallelogram formed with sides **u** and **v**, as shown in Figure 10.3b. The **difference u − v** is just the vector **w** that satisfies **v + w = u**, and it may be found by placing the initial points of **u** and **v** together and extending a vector from the terminal point of **v** to the terminal point of **u** (see Figure 10.3c).

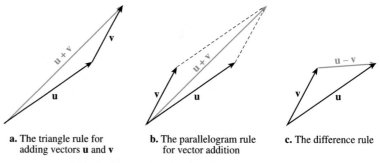

a. The triangle rule for adding vectors **u** and **v**

b. The parallelogram rule for vector addition

c. The difference rule

Figure 10.3   Vector addition and subtraction

A vector **OQ** with initial point at the origin O of a coordinate plane can be uniquely represented by specifying the coordinates of its terminal point Q. If Q has coordinates (a, b), we denote the vector **OQ** by $\langle a, b \rangle$, where the pointed brackets $\langle\ \rangle$ are used to distinguish the *vector* **OQ** $= \langle a, b \rangle$ from the *point* (a, b).

The vector **PQ** with initial point $P(c, d)$ and terminal point $Q(a, b)$ can be denoted in a similar fashion. Using analytic geometry (see Problem 56), it can be shown that **PQ** equals vector **OR** with initial point at the origin $(0, 0)$ and terminal point $R(a - c, b - d)$, as shown in Figure 10.4. Notice that **PQ** $= \langle a - c, b - d \rangle$.

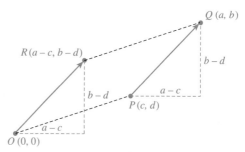

Figure 10.4   Given $P(c, d)$ and $Q(a, b)$, the vector **PQ** is $\langle a - c, b - d \rangle$.

Vector operations are easily represented when vectors are given in component form. In particular, we have

$$\langle a_1, b_1 \rangle = \langle a_2, b_2 \rangle \qquad \text{if and only if } a_1 = a_2 \text{ and } b_1 = b_2$$
$$k\langle a, b \rangle = \langle ka, kb \rangle \qquad \text{for constant } k$$
$$\langle a, b \rangle + \langle c, d \rangle = \langle a + c, b + d \rangle$$
$$\langle a, b \rangle - \langle c, d \rangle = \langle a - c, b - d \rangle$$

These formulas may be verified by analytic geometry. For instance, the rule for multiplication by a scalar may be obtained by using the relationships in Figure 10.5a, and Figure 10.5b can be used to obtain the rule for vector addition.

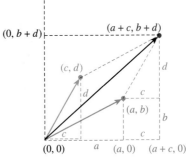

a. Multiplication by a scalar:
$k\langle a, b \rangle = \langle ka, kb \rangle$

b. Vector addition
$\langle a, b \rangle + \langle c, d \rangle = \langle a + c, b + d \rangle$

Figure 10.5 Vector operations

EXAMPLE 1 Vector operations

For the vectors $\mathbf{u} = \langle 2, -3 \rangle$ and $\mathbf{v} = \langle -1, 7 \rangle$ find:

a. $\mathbf{u} + \mathbf{v}$ **b.** $\frac{3}{4}\mathbf{u}$ **c.** $3\mathbf{u} - \frac{1}{2}\mathbf{v}$

Solution   **a.** $\mathbf{u} + \mathbf{v} = \langle 2, -3 \rangle + \langle -1, 7 \rangle = \langle 2 + (-1), -3 + 7 \rangle = \langle 1, 4 \rangle$

b. $\frac{3}{4}\mathbf{u} = \frac{3}{4}\langle 2, -3 \rangle = \langle \frac{3}{4}(2), \frac{3}{4}(-3) \rangle = \langle \frac{3}{2}, \frac{-9}{4} \rangle$

c. $3\mathbf{u} - \frac{1}{2}\mathbf{v} = 3\langle 2, -3 \rangle - \frac{1}{2}\langle -1, 7 \rangle$

$\qquad\qquad = \langle 6, -9 \rangle + \langle \frac{1}{2}, -\frac{7}{2} \rangle$ *Scalar multiplication*

$\qquad\qquad = \langle 6 + \frac{1}{2}, -9 - \frac{7}{2} \rangle$ *Add vectors.*

$\qquad\qquad = \langle \frac{13}{2}, -\frac{25}{2} \rangle$ *Simplify.*   ▬

In general, an expression of the form $a\mathbf{u} + b\mathbf{v}$ is called a **linear combination** of the vectors $\mathbf{u}$ and $\mathbf{v}$. Note that if $\mathbf{u} = \langle u_1, u_2 \rangle$ and $\mathbf{v} = \langle v_1, v_2 \rangle$, then

$$a\mathbf{u} + b\mathbf{v} = a\langle u_1, u_2 \rangle + b\langle v_1, v_2 \rangle = \langle au_1 + bv_1, au_2 + bv_2 \rangle$$

Vector addition and multiplication of a vector by a scalar behave very much like ordinary addition and multiplication. The following theorem lists several useful properties of these operations.

THEOREM 10.1 Properties of vector operations

For any vectors $\mathbf{u}$, $\mathbf{v}$, and $\mathbf{w}$ in the plane and scalars s and t.

Commutativity of vector addition	$\mathbf{u} + \mathbf{v} = \mathbf{v} + \mathbf{u}$
Associativity of vector addition	$(\mathbf{u} + \mathbf{v}) + \mathbf{w} = \mathbf{u} + (\mathbf{v} + \mathbf{w})$
Associativity of scalar multiplication	$(st)\mathbf{u} = s(t\mathbf{u})$
Identity for addition	$\mathbf{u} + \mathbf{0} = \mathbf{u}$
Inverse property for addition	$\mathbf{u} + (-\mathbf{u}) = \mathbf{0}$
Vector distributivity	$(s + t)\mathbf{u} = s\mathbf{u} + t\mathbf{u}$
Scalar distributivity	$s(\mathbf{u} + \mathbf{v}) = s\mathbf{u} + s\mathbf{v}$

Proof: Each vector property can be established by using a corresponding property of real numbers. For example, to prove associativity of vector addition, let $\mathbf{u} = \langle u_1, u_2 \rangle$, $\mathbf{v} = \langle v_1, v_2 \rangle$ and $\mathbf{w} = \langle w_1, w_2 \rangle$. Then

$$(\mathbf{u} + \mathbf{v}) + \mathbf{w} = (\langle u_1, u_2 \rangle + \langle v_1, v_2 \rangle) + \langle w_1, w_2 \rangle$$

$$= \langle u_1 + v_1, u_2 + v_2 \rangle + \langle w_1, w_2 \rangle$$

$$= \langle (u_1 + v_1) + w_1, (u_2 + v_2) + w_2 \rangle$$

$$= \langle u_1 + (v_1 + w_1), u_2 + (v_2 + w_2) \rangle \quad \textit{Associativity of addition for the real numbers}$$

$$= \langle u_1, u_2 \rangle + (\langle v_1, v_2 \rangle + \langle w_1, w_2 \rangle)$$

$$= \mathbf{u} + (\mathbf{v} + \mathbf{w})$$

You are asked to prove the other six properties in the problem set. ■

EXAMPLE 2 Vector proof of a geometric property

Show that the line segment joining the midpoints of two sides of a triangle is parallel to the third side and has half its length.

Solution Consider $\triangle ABC$ and let P and Q be the midpoints of sides $\overline{AC}$ and $\overline{BC}$, respectively, as shown in Figure 10.6.

Given: $\mathbf{AP} = \frac{1}{2}\mathbf{AC}$ and $\mathbf{BQ} = \frac{1}{2}\mathbf{BC}$.

Prove: $\mathbf{PQ}$ is parallel to $\mathbf{AB}$ and $\|\mathbf{PQ}\| = \frac{1}{2}\|\mathbf{AB}\|$, which means that we must establish the vector equation $\mathbf{PQ} = \frac{1}{2}\mathbf{AB}$. Toward this end, we begin by noting that $\mathbf{AB}$ can be expressed as the following vector sum

$$\mathbf{AB} = \mathbf{AP} + \mathbf{PQ} + \mathbf{QB}$$

$$= \tfrac{1}{2}\mathbf{AC} + \mathbf{PQ} - \mathbf{BQ} \qquad \mathbf{AP} = \tfrac{1}{2}\mathbf{AC} \text{ and } \mathbf{QB} = -\mathbf{BQ}$$

$$= \tfrac{1}{2}(\mathbf{AB} + \mathbf{BC}) + \mathbf{PQ} - \tfrac{1}{2}\mathbf{BC} \qquad \mathbf{AC} = (\mathbf{AB} + \mathbf{BC}) \text{ and } \mathbf{BQ} = \tfrac{1}{2}\mathbf{BC}$$

$$= \tfrac{1}{2}\mathbf{AB} + \tfrac{1}{2}\mathbf{BC} + \mathbf{PQ} - \tfrac{1}{2}\mathbf{BC}$$

$$= \tfrac{1}{2}\mathbf{AB} + \mathbf{PQ}$$

$$\tfrac{1}{2}\mathbf{AB} = \mathbf{PQ} \qquad\qquad \textit{Subtract } \tfrac{1}{2}\mathbf{AB} \textit{ from both sides.}$$

Therefore, the theorem is proved. ▬

When a vector $\mathbf{u}$ is represented in component form $\mathbf{u} = \langle u_1, u_2 \rangle$, its length is given by the formula

$$\|\mathbf{u}\| = \sqrt{u_1^2 + u_2^2}$$

This is a simple application of the Pythagorean theorem, as shown in Figure 10.7a. Another important relationship involving the length of vectors is the *triangle inequality*

$$\|\mathbf{u} + \mathbf{v}\| \leq \|\mathbf{u}\| + \|\mathbf{v}\|$$

for any vectors $\mathbf{u}$ and $\mathbf{v}$. Equality will occur precisely when $\mathbf{u}$ and $\mathbf{v}$ are multiples of one another (that is, when $\mathbf{u}$ and $\mathbf{v}$ have the same direction). To establish the inequality, we observe that $\mathbf{u}$ and $\mathbf{v}$ are two sides of a triangle in the plane, the third side has length $\|\mathbf{u} + \mathbf{v}\|$ and is "shorter" than the sum $\|\mathbf{u}\| + \|\mathbf{v}\|$ of the lengths of the other two sides, as shown in Figure 10.7.

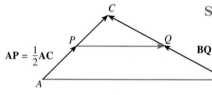

$\mathbf{AP} = \frac{1}{2}\mathbf{AC}$ $\mathbf{BQ} = \frac{1}{2}\mathbf{BC}$

Figure 10.6 Vector proof of a geometric property

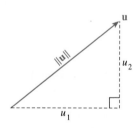

a. The vector $\mathbf{u} = \langle u_1, u_2 \rangle$ has length $\|\mathbf{u}\| = \sqrt{u_1^2 + u_2^2}$

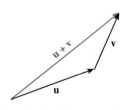

b. The triangle inequality $\|\mathbf{u} + \mathbf{v}\| \leq \|\mathbf{u}\| + \|\mathbf{v}\|$

Figure 10.7 Geometric representation of two vector properties

EXAMPLE 3   Using vectors in a velocity problem

A river 4 mi wide flows south with a current of 5 mi/hr. What speed and heading should a motorboat assume in order to travel directly across the river from east to west in 20 min?

Solution   Begin by drawing a diagram, as shown in Figure 10.8.

Let **B** be the velocity vector of the boat in the direction of the angle θ. If the river's current has velocity **C**, the given information tells us that $\|\mathbf{C}\| = 5$ mi/h and that **C** points directly south. Moreover, because the boat is to cross the river from east to west in 20 min (that is, $\frac{1}{3}$ hr), its *effective velocity* after compensating for the current is a vector **V** that points west and has magnitude

$$\|\mathbf{V}\| = \frac{\text{WIDTH OF THE RIVER}}{\text{TIME OF CROSSING}} = \frac{4 \text{ mi}}{\frac{1}{3} \text{ hr}} = 12 \text{ mi/hr}$$

The effective velocity **V** is the resultant of **B** and **C**; that is, $\mathbf{V} = \mathbf{B} + \mathbf{C}$. Because **V** and **C** act in perpendicular directions, we can determine **B** by referring to the right triangle with sides $\|\mathbf{V}\| = 12$ and $\|\mathbf{C}\| = 5$ with hypotenuse $\|\mathbf{B}\|$. We find that

$$\|\mathbf{B}\| = \sqrt{\|\mathbf{V}\|^2 + \|\mathbf{C}\|^2} = \sqrt{12^2 + 5^2} = 13$$

The direction of the velocity vector **V** is given by the angle θ in Figure 10.8, and we find that

$$\tan\theta = \tfrac{5}{12} \quad \text{so that} \quad \theta = \tan^{-1}\left(\tfrac{5}{12}\right) \approx 0.3948$$

Thus, the boat should travel at 13 mi/hr in a direction of approximately 0.3948 radian. In navigation, it is common to specify direction in degrees rather than radians; this is 22.6° north of west.   ▬

A **unit vector** is just a vector with length 1, and a **direction vector** for a given vector **v** is a unit vector **u** that points in the same direction as **v**. Such a vector can be found by simply dividing **v** by its length $\|\mathbf{v}\|$; that is,

$$\mathbf{u} = \frac{\mathbf{v}}{\|\mathbf{v}\|}$$

EXAMPLE 4   Finding a direction vector

Find a direction vector for the vector $\mathbf{v} = \langle 2, -3 \rangle$.

Solution   The vector **v** has length (magnitude) $\|\mathbf{v}\| = \sqrt{2^2 + (-3)^2} = \sqrt{13}$. Thus, the required direction vector is the unit vector

$$\mathbf{u} = \frac{\mathbf{v}}{\|\mathbf{v}\|} = \frac{\langle 2, -3 \rangle}{\sqrt{13}} = \frac{1}{\sqrt{13}}\langle 2, -3 \rangle = \left\langle \tfrac{2}{\sqrt{13}}, \tfrac{-3}{\sqrt{13}} \right\rangle \qquad ▬$$

■ STANDARD REPRESENTATION OF VECTORS IN THE PLANE

The unit vectors $\mathbf{i} = \langle 1, 0 \rangle$ and $\mathbf{j} = \langle 0, 1 \rangle$ point in the directions of the positive x- and y-axes, respectively, and are called **standard basis vectors**. Any vector $\mathbf{v} = \langle v_1, v_2 \rangle$ in the plane can be expressed as a linear combination of the vectors **i** and **j**, because

$$\mathbf{v} = \langle v_1, v_2 \rangle = v_1\langle 1, 0 \rangle + v_2\langle 0, 1 \rangle = v_1\mathbf{i} + v_2\mathbf{j}$$

This is called the **standard representation** of the vector **v**, and it can be shown that the representation is unique in the sense that if $\mathbf{v} = a\mathbf{i} + b\mathbf{j}$, then $a = v_1$ and $b = v_2$.

Figure 10.8 A velocity problem

In this context, the scalars v_1 and v_2 are called the **horizontal and vertical components** of **v**, respectively. See Figure 10.9.

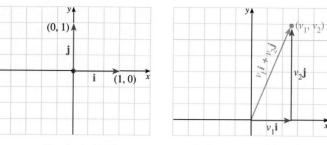

a. The standard basis vectors **i** and **j**

b. Any vector $\mathbf{v} = \langle v_1, v_2 \rangle$ can be expressed uniquely as $\mathbf{v} = v_1\mathbf{i} + v_2\mathbf{j}$

Figure 10.9 Standard representation of vectors in the plane

EXAMPLE 5   Finding the standard representation of a vector

If $\mathbf{u} = 3\mathbf{i} + 2\mathbf{j}$, $\mathbf{v} = -2\mathbf{i} + 5\mathbf{j}$, and $\mathbf{w} = \mathbf{i} - 4\mathbf{j}$, what is the standard representation of the vector $2\mathbf{u} + 5\mathbf{v} - \mathbf{w}$?

Solution   Using Theorem 10.1, we find that

$$2\mathbf{u} + 5\mathbf{v} - \mathbf{w} = 2(3\mathbf{i} + 2\mathbf{j}) + 5(-2\mathbf{i} + 5\mathbf{j}) - (\mathbf{i} - 4\mathbf{j})$$
$$= [2(3) + 5(-2) - 1]\mathbf{i} + [2(2) + 5(5) - (-4)]\mathbf{j}$$
$$= -5\mathbf{i} + 33\mathbf{j}$$

EXAMPLE 6   Finding standard representation of a vector connecting two points

Find the standard representation of the vector **PQ** for the points $P(3, -4)$ and $Q(-2, 6)$.

Solution   The component form of **PQ** is

$$\mathbf{PQ} = \langle (-2) - 3, 6 - (-4) \rangle = \langle -5, 10 \rangle$$

which means that **PQ** has the standard representation $\mathbf{PQ} = -5\mathbf{i} + 10\mathbf{j}$.

EXAMPLE 7   Computing a resultant force

Two forces $\mathbf{F}_1$ and $\mathbf{F}_2$ act on the same body. It is known that $\mathbf{F}_1$ has magnitude 3 newtons and acts in the direction of $-\mathbf{i}$, whereas $\mathbf{F}_2$ has magnitude 2 newtons and acts in the direction of the unit vector

$$\mathbf{u} = \tfrac{3}{5}\mathbf{i} - \tfrac{4}{5}\mathbf{j}$$

What additional force $\mathbf{F}_3$ must be applied in order to keep the body at rest?

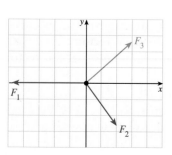

Solution   According to the given information, we have

$$\mathbf{F}_1 = 3(-\mathbf{i}) = -3\mathbf{i} \quad \text{and} \quad \mathbf{F}_2 = 2\left(\tfrac{3}{5}\mathbf{i} - \tfrac{4}{5}\mathbf{j}\right) = \tfrac{6}{5}\mathbf{i} - \tfrac{8}{5}\mathbf{j}$$

and we want to find $\mathbf{F}_3 = a\mathbf{i} + b\mathbf{j}$ so that $\mathbf{F}_1 + \mathbf{F}_2 + \mathbf{F}_3 = \mathbf{0}$. Substituting into this vector equation, we obtain

$$(-3\mathbf{i}) + \left(\tfrac{6}{5}\mathbf{i} - \tfrac{8}{5}\mathbf{j}\right) + (a\mathbf{i} + b\mathbf{j}) = 0\mathbf{i} + 0\mathbf{j}$$

By combining terms on the left, we find that

$$\left(-3 + \tfrac{6}{5} + a\right)\mathbf{i} + \left(-\tfrac{8}{5} + b\right)\mathbf{j} = 0\mathbf{i} + 0\mathbf{j}$$

Because the standard representation is unique, we must have

$$-3 + \tfrac{6}{5} + a = 0 \quad \text{and} \quad -\tfrac{8}{5} + b = 0$$

$$a = \tfrac{9}{5} \qquad\qquad b = \tfrac{8}{5}$$

The required force is $\mathbf{F}_3 = \tfrac{9}{5}\mathbf{i} + \tfrac{8}{5}\mathbf{j}$. This is a force of magnitude

$$\|\mathbf{F}_3\| = \sqrt{\left(\tfrac{9}{5}\right)^2 + \left(\tfrac{8}{5}\right)^2} = \tfrac{1}{5}\sqrt{145} \text{ newtons}$$

which acts in the direction of the unit vector

$$\mathbf{v} = \frac{\mathbf{F}_3}{\|\mathbf{F}_3\|} = \frac{5}{\sqrt{145}}\left(\tfrac{9}{5}\mathbf{i} + \tfrac{8}{5}\mathbf{j}\right) = \frac{9}{\sqrt{145}}\,\mathbf{i} + \frac{8}{\sqrt{145}}\,\mathbf{j}$$

PROBLEM SET 10.1

A *Sketch each vector given in Problems 1–4 assuming that its initial point is at the origin.*

1. $3\mathbf{i} - 4\mathbf{j}$ **2.** $-2\mathbf{i} - 3\mathbf{j}$ **3.** $-\tfrac{1}{2}\mathbf{i} + \tfrac{5}{2}\mathbf{j}$ **4.** $-2(-\mathbf{i} + 2\mathbf{j})$

The initial point P and terminal point Q of a vector are given in Problems 5–8. Sketch each vector and then write it in component form.

5. $P(3, -1)$, $Q(7, 2)$ **6.** $P(5, -2)$, $Q(5, 8)$

7. $P(3, 4)$, $Q(-2, 4)$ **8.** $P\left(\tfrac{1}{2}, 6\right)$, $Q(-3, -2)$

*Express each vector **PQ** in Problems 9–12 in standard form and also find its length.*

9. $P(-1, -2)$, $Q(1, -2)$ **10.** $P(5, 7)$, $Q(6, 8)$
11. $P(-4, -3)$, $Q(0, -1)$ **12.** $P(3, -5)$, $Q(2, 8)$

Find a unit vector that points in the direction of each of the vectors given in Problems 13–16.

13. $\mathbf{i} + \mathbf{j}$ **14.** $\tfrac{1}{2}\mathbf{i} + \tfrac{1}{4}\mathbf{j}$

15. $3\mathbf{i} - 4\mathbf{j}$ **16.** $-4\mathbf{i} + 7\mathbf{j}$

Let $\mathbf{u} = \langle -3, 4 \rangle$ and $\mathbf{v} = \langle 1, -1 \rangle$. Find s and t so that $s\mathbf{u} + t\mathbf{v} = \mathbf{w}$ for the given vector in Problems 17–20.

17. $\mathbf{w} = \langle 6, 0 \rangle$ **18.** $\mathbf{w} = \langle 0, -3 \rangle$
19. $\mathbf{w} = \langle -2, 1 \rangle$ **20.** $\mathbf{w} = \langle 8, 11 \rangle$

Suppose $\mathbf{u} = 3\mathbf{i} - 4\mathbf{j}$, $\mathbf{v} = 4\mathbf{i} - 3\mathbf{j}$, and $\mathbf{w} = \mathbf{i} + \mathbf{j}$. Express each of the expressions in Problems 21–24 in standard form.

21. $2\mathbf{u} + 3\mathbf{v} - \mathbf{w}$ **22.** $\tfrac{1}{2}(\mathbf{u} + \mathbf{v}) - \tfrac{1}{4}\mathbf{w}$

23. $\|\mathbf{v}\|\mathbf{u} + \|\mathbf{u}\|\mathbf{v}$ **24.** $\|\mathbf{u}\|\,\|\mathbf{v}\|\mathbf{w}$

Find all real numbers x and y that satisfy the vector equations given in Problems 25–28.

25. $(x - y - 1)\mathbf{i} + (2x + 3y - 12)\mathbf{j} = \mathbf{0}$
26. $x\mathbf{i} - 4y^2\mathbf{j} = (5 - 3y)\mathbf{i} + (10 - 7x)\mathbf{j}$
27. $(x^2 + y^2)\mathbf{i} + y\mathbf{j} = 16\mathbf{i} + (x + 2)\mathbf{j}$

28. $(y - 1)\mathbf{i} + y\mathbf{j} = (\log x)\mathbf{i} + [\log 2 + \log(x + 4)]\mathbf{j}$

*In Problems 29–32, find a unit vector **u** with the given characteristics.*

29. **u** makes an angle of 30° with the positive x-axis.
30. **u** has the same direction as the vector $2\mathbf{i} - 3\mathbf{j}$.
31. **u** has the direction opposite that of $-4\mathbf{i} + \mathbf{j}$.
32. **u** has the direction of the vector from $P(-1, 5)$ to $Q(7, -3)$.

In Problems 33–36, let $\mathbf{u} = 4\mathbf{i} - \mathbf{j}$, $\mathbf{v} = \mathbf{i} + 2\mathbf{j}$, and $\mathbf{w} = -3\mathbf{i} + 4\mathbf{j}$.

33. Find a unit vector in the same direction as $\mathbf{u} + \mathbf{v}$.
34. Find a vector of length 3 with the same direction as $\mathbf{u} - 2\mathbf{v} + 2\mathbf{w}$.
35. Find the terminal point of the vector $5\mathbf{i} + 7\mathbf{j}$ if the initial point is $(-2, 3)$.
36. Find the initial point of the vector $-\mathbf{i} + 2\mathbf{j}$ if the terminal point is $(-1, -2)$.

B **37.** Use vectors to find the coordinates of the midpoint of the line segment joining the points $P(-3, -8)$ and $Q(9, -2)$. What point is located $\tfrac{5}{6}$ of the distance from P to Q?

38. If $\|\mathbf{v}\| = 3$ and $-3 \le r \le 1$, what are the possible values of $\|r\mathbf{v}\|$?

39. Show that $\mathbf{v} = (\cos\theta)\mathbf{i} + (\sin\theta)\mathbf{j}$ is a unit vector for any angle θ.

40. If **u** and **v** are nonzero vectors and

$$r = \frac{\|\mathbf{u}\|}{\|\mathbf{v}\|}$$

what is $\|r\mathbf{v}\|$?

41. If **u** and **v** are nonzero vectors with $\|\mathbf{u}\| = \|\mathbf{v}\|$, does it follow that $\mathbf{u} = \mathbf{v}$? Explain.

42. If $\mathbf{u} = 2\mathbf{i} - 3\mathbf{j}$ and $\mathbf{v} = x\mathbf{i} + y\mathbf{j}$, describe the set of points in the plane whose coordinates (x, y) satisfy $\|\mathbf{v} - \mathbf{u}\| \le 2$.

43. Let $\mathbf{u}_0 = x_0\mathbf{i} + y_0\mathbf{j}$ for constants x_0 and y_0, and let $\mathbf{u} = x\mathbf{i} + y\mathbf{j}$. Describe the set of all points in the plane whose coordinates satisfy
  a. $\|\mathbf{u} - \mathbf{u}_0\| = 1$ **b.** $\|\mathbf{u} - \mathbf{u}_0\| \leq 2$

44. Let $\mathbf{u} = 3\mathbf{i} - \mathbf{j}$ and $\mathbf{v} = -6\mathbf{i} + 2\mathbf{j}$. Show that there are no numbers a, b for which $a\mathbf{u} + b\mathbf{v} = 2\mathbf{i} + 5\mathbf{j}$.

45. Suppose $\mathbf{u}$ and $\mathbf{v}$ are a pair of nonzero, nonparallel vectors. Find numbers a, b, c such that
$$a\mathbf{u} + b(\mathbf{u} - \mathbf{v}) + c(\mathbf{u} + \mathbf{v}) = 0.$$

46. Suppose $\mathbf{u}$ and $\mathbf{v}$ are perpendicular vectors, with $\|\mathbf{u}\| = 2$ and $\|\mathbf{v}\| = 4$. Sketch the vector $c\mathbf{u} + (1 - c)\mathbf{v}$ for the cases where $c = 0$, $c = \frac{1}{4}$, $c = \frac{1}{2}$, $c = \frac{3}{4}$, and $c = 1$. In general, if the initial point of a vector $c\mathbf{u} + (1 - c)\mathbf{v}$ with $0 \leq c \leq 1$ is at the origin, where is its terminal point?

47. Two forces $\mathbf{F}_1 = 3\mathbf{i} + 4\mathbf{j}$ and $\mathbf{F}_2 = 3\mathbf{i} - 7\mathbf{j}$ act on an object. What additional force should be applied to keep the body at rest?

48. Three forces $\mathbf{F}_1 = \mathbf{i} - 2\mathbf{j}$, $\mathbf{F}_2 = 3\mathbf{i} - 7\mathbf{j}$, and $\mathbf{F}_3 = \mathbf{i} + \mathbf{j}$ act on an object. What additional force $\mathbf{F}_4$ should be applied to keep the body at rest?

49. A rock is thrown into the air at an angle of $40°$ with the horizontal and with an initial velocity of 60 ft/s. Find the vertical and horizontal components of the velocity vector.

50. A river 2.1 mi wide flows south with a current of 3.1 mi/hr. What speed and heading should a motorboat assume to travel across the river from east to west in 30 min?

C 51. Four forces act on an object: $\mathbf{F}_1$ has magnitude 10 lb and acts at an angle of $\frac{\pi}{6}$ measured counterclockwise from the positive x-axis; $\mathbf{F}_2$ has magnitude 8 lb and acts in the direction of the vector $\mathbf{j}$; $\mathbf{F}_3$ has magnitude 5 lb and acts at an angle of $4\pi/3$ measured counterclockwise from the positive x-axis. What must the fourth force $\mathbf{F}_4$ be to keep the object at rest?

52. Use vector methods to show that the diagonals of a parallelogram bisect each other.

53. In a triangle, let $\mathbf{u}$, $\mathbf{v}$, and $\mathbf{w}$ be the vectors from each vertex to the midpoint of the opposite side. Use vector methods to show that $\mathbf{u} + \mathbf{v} + \mathbf{w} = 0$.

54. Two nonzero vectors $\mathbf{u}$ and $\mathbf{v}$ are said to be **linearly independent** in the plane if they are not parallel.
  a. If $\mathbf{u}$ and $\mathbf{v}$ have this property and $a\mathbf{u} = b\mathbf{v}$ for constants a, b, show that $a = b = 0$.
  b. Show that the standard representation of a vector is unique. That is, if the vector $\mathbf{u}$ has the representation $\mathbf{u} = a_1\mathbf{i} + b_1\mathbf{j}$ and $\mathbf{u} = a_2\mathbf{i} + b_2\mathbf{j}$ is another such representation, then $a_1 = a_2$ and $b_1 = b_2$.

55. Prove that the medians of a triangle intersect at a single point by completing the following argument.

  a. Let M and N be the midpoints of sides $\overline{AC}$ and $\overline{AB}$, respectively. Show that
$$\mathbf{CN} = \tfrac{1}{2}\mathbf{AB} - \mathbf{AC} \quad \text{and}$$
$$\mathbf{BM} = \tfrac{1}{2}\mathbf{AC} - \mathbf{AB}$$

  b. Let P be the point where medians $\overline{BM}$ and $\overline{CN}$ intersect. Show that there are constants r and s such that
$$\mathbf{CP} = r\left(\tfrac{1}{2}\mathbf{AB} - \mathbf{AC}\right) \quad \text{and}$$
$$\mathbf{BP} = s\left(\tfrac{1}{2}\mathbf{AC} - \mathbf{AB}\right)$$

  Note that $\mathbf{CP} + \mathbf{PB} = \mathbf{CB}$. Use this relationship to prove that $r = s = \frac{2}{3}$. Explain why this shows that any pair of medians meet at a point located $\frac{2}{3}$ the distance from each vertex to the midpoint of the opposite side. Why does this show that *all three* medians meet at a single point?

  c. The *centroid* of a triangle is the point where the medians meet. Show that if a triangle has vertices (x_1, y_1), (x_2, y_2), (x_3, y_3), then the centroid has coordinates
$$\left(\frac{x_1 + x_2 + x_3}{3}, \frac{y_1 + y_2 + y_3}{3}\right)$$

56. Show that the vector with the initial point $P(c, d)$ and the terminal point $Q(a, b)$ has the component form $\mathbf{PQ} = \langle a - c, b - d \rangle$. See Figure 10.4.

57. Prove the following parts of Theorem 10.1.
  a. commutativity   **b.** identity
  c. vector distributivity   **d.** associativity of scalar multiplication
  e. inverse property of addition   **f.** scalar distributivity

10.2 QUADRIC SURFACES AND GRAPHING IN THREE DIMENSIONS

IN THIS SECTION **Three-dimensional coordinate system, graphs in $\mathbb{R}^3$ (planes, spheres, cylinders, quadric surfaces)**
Because we live in a three-dimensional world, it is essential that we be able to visualize surfaces in three dimensions. To that end we consider ordered triplets and their representation in three-dimensional space, as well as develop some knowledge of simple three-dimensional surfaces, namely, the quadric surfaces. In the next section we will consider vectors in three dimensions in order to describe motion in space efficiently.

■ THREE-DIMENSIONAL COORDINATE SYSTEM

Our next goal is to see how analytic geometry and vector methods can be applied in space. We have already considered ordered pairs and a two-dimensional coordinate system. We shall denote this two-dimensional system by $\mathbb{R}^2$. Because we exist in a three-dimensional world, it is also important to consider a three-dimensional system. We call this *three-space* and denote it by $\mathbb{R}^3$. We introduce a coordinate system to three-space by choosing three mutually perpendicular axes to serve as a frame of reference. The orientation of our reference system will be *right-handed* in the sense that if you stand at the origin with your arms stretched out in the direction of the positive x-axis and y-axis, your right arm will be the one along the x-axis and your left arm will be stretched straight ahead along the y-axis, as shown in Figure 10.10. Your head will then point in the direction of the positive z-axis.

In order to orient yourself to a three-dimensional coordinate system, think of the x-axis and y-axis as lying in the plane of the floor and the z-axis as a line perpendicular to the floor. All the graphs we have drawn in the first nine chapters of this book would now be drawn on the floor. If you orient yourself in a room (your classroom, for example) as shown in Figure 10.11, you may notice some important planes. Assume the room is 25 ft × 30 ft × 8 ft and fix the origin at a front corner (where the board hangs).

Figure 10.10 A "right-handed" rectangular coordinate system for $\mathbb{R}^3$

Figure 10.11 A typical classroom; assume the dimensions are 25 by 30 ft with an 8-ft ceiling

Floor:	**xy-plane**; equation is $z = 0$.	
Ceiling:	Plane parallel to the xy-plane; equation is $z = 8$.	
Front wall:	**yz-plane**; equation is $x = 0$.	
Back wall:	Plane parallel to the yz-plane; equation is $x = 30$.	
Left wall:	**xz-plane**; equation is $y = 0$.	
Right wall:	Plane parallel to the xz-plane; equation is $y = 25$.	

The xy-, xz-, and yz-planes are called the **coordinate planes.** Points in $\mathbb{R}^3$ are located by their position in relation to the three coordinate planes and are given appropriate coordinates. Specifically, the point P is assigned coordinates (a, b, c) to indicate that it is a, b, and c units, respectively, from the yz-, xz-, and xy-planes. Name the coordinates of several objects in your classroom (or in Figure 10.11).

DRAWING LESSON 2A: PLOTTING POINTS

ASSIGNMENT:
Plot $P(3, 4, -5)$.

a. Sketch x-axis and y-axis, adding tick-marks. Outline the xy-plane.

b. Sketch z-axis, adding tickmarks. Use dashed segments for hidden parts.

c. Plot x-distance and y-distance; darken segments from each along gridlines. Colored pencil or highlighter may help you visualize the figure.

d. Plot z-distance, using the unit size from the z-axis. Lightly sketch a grid on the xy-plane, using tickmarks as guides.

DRAWING LESSON 2B: DRAWING VERTICAL PLANES

ASSIGNMENT:
Add planes $x = 2$ and $y = 0$ to the first sketch.

a. Draw a segment of the line $x = 2$ on the xy-plane. Through each endpoint, draw a segment parallel to the z-axis. Then connect the endpoints.

b. Shade the plane $x = 2$ where it is not hidden by the xy-plane. Erase hidden parts of both planes, and use your eraser to dash hidden parts of the axes.

c. Follow the same procedure to draw and shade the plane $y = 0$. Draw the intersection of the two planes.

d. Use colored pencils or highlighters to distinguish individual planes.

EXAMPLE 1   Points in three dimensions

Graph the following ordered triplets:

a. (10, 20, 10)   **b.** (−12, 6, 12)
c. (−12, −18, 6)   **d.** (20, −10, 18)

Solution

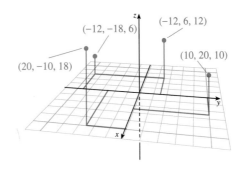

In Example 1, we measured distances in the x-, y-, and z-directions. We will, however, also need to measure distances between points in $\mathbb{R}^3$. The formula for distance in $\mathbb{R}^2$ easily extends to $\mathbb{R}^3$.

Distance Formula

The distance $|P_1P_2|$ between $P_1(x_1, y_1, z_1)$ and $P_2(x_2, y_2, z_2)$ is

$$|P_1P_2| = \sqrt{(x_2 - x_1)^2 + (y_2 - y_1)^2 + (z_2 - z_1)^2}$$

This formula will be derived in Section 10.3. The distance between (10, 20, 10) and (−12, 6, 12) is

$$d = \sqrt{(-12 - 10)^2 + (6 - 20)^2 + (12 - 10)^2} = \sqrt{684} = 6\sqrt{19}$$

■ GRAPHS IN $\mathbb{R}^3$

The **graph of an equation** in $\mathbb{R}^3$ is the collection of all points (x, y, z) whose coordinates satisfy a given equation. This graph is called a **surface**. You are not expected to spend a great deal of time graphing three-dimensional surfaces, but the drawing lessons in this section should help. You may also have access to a computer program to help you look at graphs in three dimensions. We will discuss lines and planes in Section 10.5, but it is worthwhile to begin with a brief introduction to certain surfaces in $\mathbb{R}^3$.

Planes. We shall obtain equations for planes in space after we discuss vectors in space. However, in beginning to visualize objects in $\mathbb{R}^3$, we do not want to ignore planes, because they are so common (for example, the walls, ceiling, and floor in Figure 10.11). In Section 10.5, we will show that the graph of $ax + by + cz = d$ is a **plane** if a, b, c, and d, are real numbers (not all zero).

EXAMPLE 2   Graphing planes

Graph the planes defined by the given equations.

a. $x + 3y + 2z = 6$ **b.** $y + z = 5$ **c.** $x = 4$

Solution   To graph a plane, find some ordered triplets satisfying the equation. The best ones to use are often those that fall on a coordinate axis (the intercepts).

a. Let $x = 0$ and $y = 0$; then $z = 3$; plot the point $(0, 0, 3)$.
  Let $x = 0$ and $z = 0$; then $y = 2$; plot the point $(0, 2, 0)$.
  Let $y = 0$ and $z = 0$; then $x = 6$; plot the point $(6, 0, 0)$.
  Use these points to draw the intersection lines (called **trace lines**) of the plane you are graphing with each of the coordinate planes. The result is shown in Figure 10.12a.

b. When one of the variables is missing from the equation of a plane, then that plane is parallel to the axis corresponding to the missing variable; in this case it is parallel to the x-axis. Draw the line $y + z = 5$ on the yz-plane and then complete the plane, as shown in Figure 10.12b.

c. When two variables are missing, then the plane is parallel to one of the coordinate planes, as shown in Figure 10.12c.

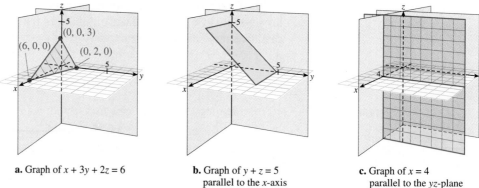

a. Graph of $x + 3y + 2z = 6$ **b.** Graph of $y + z = 5$ parallel to the x-axis   **c.** Graph of $x = 4$ parallel to the yz-plane

Figure 10.12 Graphs of planes

Spheres. A **sphere** is defined as the collection of all points located a fixed distance (the **radius**) from a fixed point (the **center**). See Figure 10.13. In particular, if $P(x, y, z)$ is a point on the sphere with radius r and center $C(a, b, c)$, then the distance from C to P is r. Thus,

$$r = \sqrt{(x - a)^2 + (y - b)^2 + (z - c)^2}$$

If you square both sides of this equation you can see that it is equivalent to the equation of a sphere displayed in the following box. Conversely, if the point (x, y, z) satisfies an equation of this form, it must lie on a sphere with center (a, b, c) and radius r.

Figure 10.13 Graph of a sphere with center (a, b, c), radius r

Equation of a Sphere

The graph of the equation

$$(x - a)^2 + (y - b)^2 + (z - c)^2 = r^2$$

is a sphere with center (a, b, c) and radius r, and any sphere has an equation of this form. This is called the **standard form of the equation of a sphere** (or simply *standard-form sphere*).

EXAMPLE 3   Center and radius of a sphere from a given equation

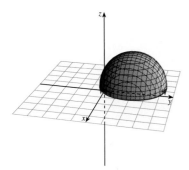

Show that the graph of the equation $x^2 + y^2 + z^2 + 4x - 6y - 3 = 0$ is a sphere, and find its center and radius.

Solution   By completing the square in both variables x and y, we have

$$(x^2 + 4x) + (y^2 - 6y) + z^2 = 3$$

$$(x^2 + 4x + 2^2) + [y^2 - 6y + (-3)^2] + z^2 = 3 + 4 + 9$$

$$(x + 2)^2 + (y - 3)^2 + z^2 = 16$$

Comparing this equation with the standard form, we see that it is the equation of a sphere with center $(-2, 3, 0)$ and radius 4. ∎

Generatrix
L

Principal cross
section curve C
(directrix)

Cylinder

Figure 10.14 A cylinder with directrix C and generatrix L

Cylinders. A **cross section** of a surface in space is a curve obtained by intersecting the surface with a plane. If parallel planes intersect a given surface in congruent cross-sectional curves, the surface is called a **cylinder**. We define a cylinder with **principal cross sections C and generating line L** to be the surface obtained by moving lines parallel to L along the boundary of the curve C, as shown in Figure 10.14. In this context, the curve C is called a **directrix** of the cylinder, and L is the **generatrix**.

We shall deal primarily with cylinders in which the directrix is a conic section and the generatrix L is one of the coordinate axes. Such a cylinder is often named for the type of conic section in its principal cross sections and is described by an equation involving only two of the variables x, y, z. In this case, the generating line L is parallel to the coordinate axis of the missing variable. Thus,

$x^2 + y^2 = 5$ is a **circular cylinder** with L parallel to the z-axis.

$y^2 - z^2 = 9$ is a **hyperbolic cylinder** with L parallel to the x-axis.

$x^2 + 2z^2 = 25$ is an **elliptic cylinder** with L parallel to the y-axis.

The graphs of these cylinders are shown in Figure 10.15.

a. A circular cylinder
$x^2 + y^2 = 5$

b. A hyperbolic cylinder
$y^2 - z^2 = 9$

c. An elliptic cylinder
$x^2 + 2z^2 = 25$

Figure 10.15 Cylinders

Quadric Surfaces. Spheres and elliptic, parabolic, and hyperbolic cylinders are examples of **quadric surfaces**. In general, such a surface is the graph of an equation of the form

$$Ax^2 + By^2 + Cz^2 + Dxy + Exz + Fyz + Gx + Hy + Iz + J = 0$$

Quadric surfaces may be thought of as the generalizations of the conic sections in

$\mathbb{R}^3$. The **trace** of a curve is found by setting one of the variables equal to a constant and then graphing the resulting curve. If $x = k$ (k a constant), the resulting curve is drawn in the plane $x = k$, which is parallel to the yz-plane; and if $z = k$, the curve is drawn in the plane $z = k$, parallel to the xy-plane. Table 10.1 shows the quadric surfaces.

DRAWING LESSON 3: SKETCHING A SURFACE

ASSIGNMENT:

Graph $y = \dfrac{1}{1 + x^2 + y^2}$

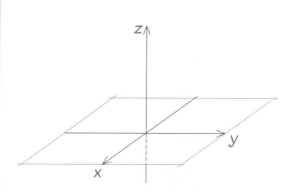

a. Draw the xy-plane in three dimensions, adding the z-axis.

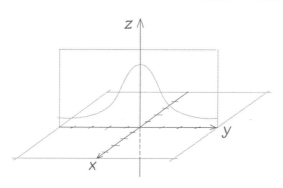

b. Draw a trace in one of the coordinate planes(in this case, the plane $x = 0$). If necessary, adjust the z-scale to show the trace more clearly.

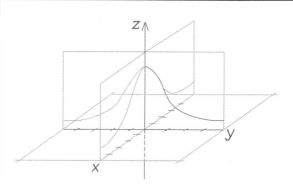

c. Draw a trace in another coordinate plane (in this case, the plane $y = 0$).

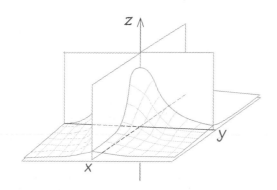

d. Erase all hidden lines. Draw several additonal trace curves to reveal the contours of the surface.

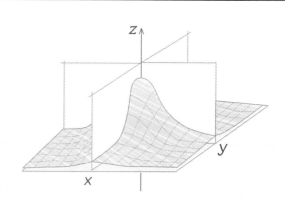

e. Erase all hidden lines. Use highlighters or pen - cils to color the surface and the xy-plane.

TABLE 10.1 Quadric Surfaces

Surface	Description	Surface	Description
Elliptic cone	The trace in the *xy*-plane is a point; in planes parallel to the *xy*-plane it is an ellipse. Traces in the *xz*- and *yz*-planes are intersecting lines; in planes parallel to these they are hyperbolas: $$z^2 = \frac{x^2}{a^2} + \frac{y^2}{b^2}$$	*Elliptic paraboloid*	The trace in the *xy*-plane is a point; in planes parallel to the *xy*-plane it is an ellipse. Traces in the *xz*- and *yz*-planes are parabolas. $$z = \frac{x^2}{a^2} + \frac{y^2}{b^2}$$
Hyperboloid of one sheet	The trace in the *xy*-plane is an ellipse; in the *xz*- and *yz*-planes the traces are hyperbolas. $$\frac{x^2}{a^2} + \frac{y^2}{b^2} - \frac{z^2}{c^2} = 1$$	*Hyperboloid of two sheets.*	There is no trace in the *xy*-plane. In planes parallel to the *xy*-plane, which intersect the surface, the traces are ellipses. Traces in the *xz*- and *yz*-planes are hyperbolas. $$\frac{x^2}{a^2} + \frac{y^2}{b^2} - \frac{z^2}{c^2} = -1$$
Ellipsoid	The traces in the coordinate planes are ellipses. $$\frac{x^2}{a^2} + \frac{y^2}{b^2} + \frac{z^2}{c^2} = 1$$	*Hyperbolic paraboloid* (also called a *saddle*)	The trace in the *xy*-plane is two intersecting lines; in the plane parallel to the *xy*-plane, the traces are hyperbolas. Traces in the *xz*- and *yz*-planes are parabolas. $$z = \frac{y^2}{b^2} - \frac{x^2}{a^2}$$
Sphere	The sphere is a special kind of ellipsoid for which $a = b = c = r$. $$x^2 + y^2 + z^2 = r^2$$		

EXAMPLE 4   Identifying and sketching a quadric surface

Identify and sketch the surface with equation $9x^2 - 16y^2 + 144z = 0$.

Solution   Look at Table 10.1 on page 645 and note that the equation is second degree in x and y but first degree in z. This means it is an elliptic paraboloid or a hyperbolic paraboloid. Solve the equation for z:

$$9x^2 - 16y^2 + 144z = 0$$

$$144z = 16y^2 - 9x^2$$

$$z = \frac{y^2}{9} - \frac{x^2}{16}$$

We recognize this as a hyperbolic paraboloid.

Next, we take cross sections of $9x^2 - 16y^2 + 144z = 0$.

Cross Section	Chosen Value	Equation	Description
xy-plane	$z = 0$	$\frac{y^2}{9} - \frac{x^2}{16} = 0$	Two intersecting lines
Parallel to the xy-plane	$z = 4$	$\frac{y^2}{36} - \frac{x^2}{64} = 1$	Hyperbola
xz-plane	$y = 0$	$z = -\frac{x^2}{16}$	Parabola opens down
Parallel to the xz-plane	$y = 10$	$z - \frac{100}{9} = -\frac{x^2}{16}$	Parabola opens down
yz-plane	$x = 0$	$z = \frac{y^2}{9}$	Parabola opens up
Parallel to the yz-plane	$x = 5$	$z + \frac{25}{16} = \frac{y^2}{9}$	Parabola opens up

These traces are also shown in Figure 10.16.

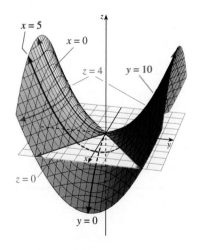

Figure 10.16 Graph of $9x^2 - 16y^2 + 144z = 0$

PROBLEM SET 10.2

Ⓐ *In Problems 1–4, plot the points P and Q in $\mathbb{R}^3$, and find the distance $|\overrightarrow{PQ}|$.*

1. $P(3, -4, 5)$, $Q(1, 5, -3)$
2. $P(0, 3, 0)$, $Q(-2, 5, -7)$
3. $P(-3, -5, 8)$, $Q(3, 6, -7)$
4. $P(0, 5, -3)$, $Q(2, -1, 0)$

In Problems 5–8, find the standard form equation of the sphere with the given center C and radius r.

5. $C(0, 0, 0)$, $r = 1$
6. $C(-3, 5, 7)$, $r = 2$
7. $C(0, 4, -5)$, $r = 3$
8. $C(-2, 3, -1)$, $r = \sqrt{5}$

Find the center and radius of each sphere whose equation is given in Problems 9–12.

9. $x^2 + y^2 + z^2 - 2y + 2z - 2 = 0$
10. $x^2 + y^2 + z^2 + 4x - 2z - 8 = 0$
11. $x^2 + y^2 + z^2 - 6x + 2y - 2z + 10 = 0$
12. $x^2 + y^2 + z^2 - 2x - 4y + 8z + 17 = 0$

In Problems 13–22, match the equation with its graph (A–L).

13. $x^2 = z^2 + y^2$
14. $z^2 = \dfrac{x^2}{4} + \dfrac{y^2}{9}$
15. $\dfrac{x^2}{2} - \dfrac{y^2}{4} + \dfrac{z^2}{9} = 1$
16. $\dfrac{x^2}{9} + \dfrac{y^2}{16} - \dfrac{z^2}{4} = 1$
17. $x^2 + y^2 + z^2 = 9$
18. $y = x^2 + z^2$
19. $x = \dfrac{y^2}{25} + \dfrac{z^2}{16}$
20. $y = \dfrac{z^2}{4} - \dfrac{x^2}{9}$
21. $y^2 + z^2 - x^2 = -1$
22. $\dfrac{x^2}{4} - \dfrac{y^2}{9} + \dfrac{z^2}{9} = -1$

A.

B.

C.

D.

E.

F.

G.

H.

I.

J.

K.

L.

Ⓑ *The vertices A, B, and C of a triangle in space are given in Problems 23–26. Find the lengths of the sides of the triangle and determine whether it is a right triangle, an isosceles triangle, or neither.*

23. $A(3, -1, 0)$, $B(7, 1, 4)$, $C(1, 3, 4)$
24. $A(1, 1, 1)$, $B(3, 3, 2)$, $C(3, -3, 5)$
25. $A(1, 2, 3)$, $B(-3, 2, 4)$, $C(1, -4, 3)$
26. $A(2, 4, 3)$, $B(-3, 2, -4)$, $C(-6, 8, -10)$
27. ■ What Does This Say? Describe a procedure for sketching a quadric surface.
28. ■ What Does This Say? Describe a procedure for identifying a quadric surface by looking at its equation.

In Problems 29–40, sketch the graph of each equation in $\mathbb{R}^3$.

29. $2x + y + 3z = 6$ **30.** $x = 4$

31. $x + 2y + 5z = 10$ **32.** $x + y + z = 1$

33. $3x - 2y - z = 12$ **34.** $y = z^2$

35. $x = -1$ **36.** $y^2 + z^2 = 1$

37. $z = e^y$ **38.** $y = \ln x$

39. $x + z = 1$ **40.** $z = y^{-1}$

In Problems 41–48, identify the quadric surface and describe the traces. Sketch the graph.

41. $9x^2 + 4y^2 + z^2 = 1$ **42.** $\dfrac{x^2}{4} + y^2 + \dfrac{z^2}{9} = 1$

43. $\dfrac{x^2}{4} + \dfrac{y^2}{9} - z^2 = 1$ **44.** $\dfrac{x^2}{9} - y^2 - z^2 = 1$

45. $z = x^2 + \dfrac{y^2}{4}$ **46.** $z = \dfrac{x^2}{9} - \dfrac{y^2}{16}$

47. $x^2 + 2y^2 = 9z^2$ **48.** $z^2 = 1 + \dfrac{x^2}{9} + \dfrac{y^2}{4}$

49. Find an equation for a sphere, given that the endpoints of a diameter of the sphere are $(1, 2, -3)$ and $(-2, 3, 3)$.

© 50. Let $P(3, 2, -1)$, $Q(-2, 1, c)$, and $R(c, 1, 0)$ be points in $\mathbb{R}^3$. For what values of c (if any) is PQR a right triangle?

51. Find the point P that lies $\frac{2}{3}$ of the distance from the point $A(-1, 3, 9)$ to the midpoint of the line segment joining points $B(-2, 3, 7)$ and $C(4, 1, -3)$.

10.3 THE DOT PRODUCT

IN THIS SECTION Vectors in $\mathbb{R}^3$, definition of dot product, angle between vectors, projections, work as a dot product

In this section, we extend our development of vectors from $\mathbb{R}^2$ to $\mathbb{R}^3$ by finding the magnitude of a vector and the distance between points in three dimensions. We then introduce a product of vectors that yields a scalar and use it to find the angle between three-dimensional vectors.

■ VECTORS IN $\mathbb{R}^3$

A vector in $\mathbb{R}^3$ may be thought of as a directed line segment (an "arrow") in space. The vector $\mathbf{P_1P_2}$ with initial point $P_1(x_1, y_1, z_1)$ and terminal point $P_2(x_2, y_2, z_2)$ has the component form

$$\mathbf{P_1P_2} = \langle x_2 - x_1, \, y_2 - y_1, \, z_2 - z_1 \rangle$$

Vector addition and multiplication of a vector by a scalar are defined for vectors in $\mathbb{R}^3$ in essentially the same way as these operations were defined for vectors in $\mathbb{R}^2$. In addition, the properties of vector algebra listed in Theorem 10.1 of Section 10.1 apply to vectors in $\mathbb{R}^3$ as well as to those in $\mathbb{R}^2$.

For example, we observed that each vector in $\mathbb{R}^2$ can be expressed as a unique linear combination of the standard basis vectors $\mathbf{i}$ and $\mathbf{j}$. This representation can be extended to vectors in $\mathbb{R}^3$ by adding a component $\mathbf{k}$ defined to be the unit vector in the direction of the positive z-axis. In component form, we have in $\mathbb{R}^3$,

$$\mathbf{i} = \langle 1, 0, 0 \rangle \qquad \mathbf{j} = \langle 0, 1, 0 \rangle \qquad \mathbf{k} = \langle 0, 0, 1 \rangle$$

We call these the **standard basis vectors in $\mathbb{R}^3$**. The **standard representation** of the vector with initial point at the origin O and terminal point $Q(a_1, a_2, a_3)$ is $\mathbf{OQ} = a_1\mathbf{i} + a_2\mathbf{j} + a_3\mathbf{k}$, as shown in Figure 10.17b.

The vector $\mathbf{PQ}$ with initial point $P(x_0, y_0, z_0)$ and terminal point $Q(x_1, y_1, z_1)$ has the standard representation

$$\mathbf{PQ} = (x_1 - x_0)\mathbf{i} + (y_1 - y_0)\mathbf{j} + (z_1 - z_0)\mathbf{k}$$

EXAMPLE 1   Standard representation of a vector in $\mathbb{R}^3$

Find the standard representation of the vector $\mathbf{PQ}$ with initial point $P(-1, 2, 2)$ and terminal point $Q(3, -2, 4)$.

Solution   We have

$$\mathbf{PQ} = [3 - (-1)]\mathbf{i} + [-2 - 2]\mathbf{j} + [4 - 2]\mathbf{k} = 4\mathbf{i} - 4\mathbf{j} + 2\mathbf{k}$$

a. The standard basis vectors in $\mathbb{R}^3$

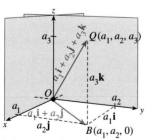

b. The vector from O to $Q(a_1, a_2, a_3)$ is $\mathbf{OQ} = a_1\mathbf{i} + a_2\mathbf{j} + a_3\mathbf{k}$.

Figure 10.17 Standard representation of vectors in $\mathbb{R}^3$

By referring to Figure 10.17b, we can also derive a formula for the length of a vector, which in turn can be used to prove the distance formula (stated in the previous section) between any two points in $\mathbb{R}^3$. Specifically, note that $\triangle OBQ$ in Figure 10.17b is a right triangle with hypotenuse $\|\mathbf{OQ}\|$ and legs $\|\mathbf{BQ}\| = |a_3|$ and $\|\mathbf{OB}\| = \sqrt{a_1^2 + a_2^2}$; by applying the Pythagorean theorem, we conclude that the vector $\mathbf{OQ} = a_1\mathbf{i} + a_2\mathbf{j} + a_3\mathbf{k}$ has length

$$\|\mathbf{OQ}\| = \sqrt{\|\mathbf{OB}\|^2 + \|\mathbf{BQ}\|^2} = \sqrt{(a_1^2 + a_2^2) + a_3^2} = \sqrt{a_1^2 + a_2^2 + a_3^2}$$

Moreover, if $A(a_1, a_2, a_3)$ and $B(b_1, b_2, b_3)$ are any two points in $\mathbb{R}^3$, the distance between them is the length of the vector $\mathbf{AB}$. We find

$$\mathbf{AB} = \mathbf{OB} - \mathbf{OA} = (b_1 - a_1)\mathbf{i} + (b_2 - a_2)\mathbf{j} + (b_3 - a_3)\mathbf{k}$$

so that the distance between A and B is given by

$$\|\mathbf{AB}\| = \sqrt{(b_1 - a_1)^2 + (b_2 - a_2)^2 + (b_3 - a_3)^2}$$

Magnitude of a Vector

> The **magnitude,** or length, of the vector $\mathbf{v} = a_1\mathbf{i} + a_2\mathbf{j} + a_3\mathbf{k}$ is
> $$\|\mathbf{v}\| = \sqrt{a_1^2 + a_2^2 + a_3^2}$$

EXAMPLE 2   Magnitude of a vector

Find the magnitude of the vector $\mathbf{v} = 2\mathbf{i} - 3\mathbf{j} + 5\mathbf{k}$ and the distance between the points $A(1, -1, -4)$ and $B(-2, 3, 8)$.

Solution
$$\|\mathbf{v}\| = \sqrt{2^2 + (-3)^2 + 5^2} = \sqrt{38} \quad \text{and}$$
$$\|\overline{AB}\| = \sqrt{(-2 - 1)^2 + [3 - (-1)]^2 + [8 - (-4)]^2} = 13$$

As in $\mathbb{R}^2$, if $\mathbf{v}$ is a given nonzero vector in $\mathbb{R}^3$, then a unit vector $\mathbf{u}$ that points in the same direction as $\mathbf{v}$ is
$$\mathbf{u} = \frac{\mathbf{v}}{\|\mathbf{v}\|}$$

EXAMPLE 3   Unit vector in a given direction

Find a unit vector that points in the direction of the vector $\mathbf{PQ}$ from $P(-1, 2, 5)$ to $Q(0, -3, 7)$.

Solution
$$\mathbf{PQ} = [0 - (-1)]\mathbf{i} + [-3 - 2]\mathbf{j} + [7 - 5]\mathbf{k} = \mathbf{i} - 5\mathbf{j} + 2\mathbf{k}$$
$$\|\mathbf{PQ}\| = \sqrt{1^2 + (-5)^2 + 2^2} = \sqrt{30}$$

Thus,

$$\mathbf{u} = \frac{\mathbf{PQ}}{\|\mathbf{PQ}\|} = \frac{\mathbf{i} - 5\mathbf{j} + 2\mathbf{k}}{\sqrt{30}} = \frac{1}{\sqrt{30}}\mathbf{i} - \frac{5}{\sqrt{30}}\mathbf{j} + \frac{2}{\sqrt{30}}\mathbf{k}$$

As in $\mathbb{R}^2$, two vectors in $\mathbb{R}^3$ are **parallel** if they are multiples of one another, because parallel vectors point either in the same direction or in opposite directions. That is, nonzero vectors

$\mathbf{u}$ and $\mathbf{v}$ are parallel if and only if $\mathbf{u} = s\mathbf{v}$ for some scalar s

EXAMPLE 4 **Parallel vectors**

A vector **PQ** has initial point $P(1, 0, -3)$ and length 3. Find Q so that **PQ** is parallel to $\mathbf{v} = 2\mathbf{i} - 3\mathbf{j} + 6\mathbf{k}$.

Solution Let Q have coordinates (a_1, a_2, a_3). Then,

$$\mathbf{PQ} = [a_1 - 1]\mathbf{i} + [a_2 - 0]\mathbf{j} + [a_3 - (-3)]\mathbf{k} = (a_1 - 1)\mathbf{i} + a_2\mathbf{j} + (a_3 + 3)\mathbf{k}$$

Because **PQ** is parallel to **v**, we have $\mathbf{PQ} = s\mathbf{v}$ for some scalar s; that is,

$$(a_1 - 1)\mathbf{i} + a_2\mathbf{j} + (a_3 + 3)\mathbf{k} = s(2\mathbf{i} - 3\mathbf{j} + 6\mathbf{k})$$

This implies

$$a_1 - 1 = 2s \qquad a_2 = -3s \qquad a_3 + 3 = 6s$$
$$a_1 = 2s + 1 \qquad\qquad\qquad a_3 = 6s - 3$$

Because **PQ** has length 3 we have

$$3 = \sqrt{(a_1 - 1)^2 + a_2^2 + (a_3 + 3)^2}$$
$$= \sqrt{[(2s + 1) - 1]^2 + (-3s)^2 + [(6s - 3) + 3]^2}$$
$$= \sqrt{4s^2 + 9s^2 + 36s^2} = \sqrt{49s^2} = 7|s|$$

Thus, $s = \pm\frac{3}{7}$ and so

$$a_1 = 2\left(\pm\tfrac{3}{7}\right) + 1 \qquad a_2 = -3\left(\pm\tfrac{3}{7}\right) \qquad a_3 = 6\left(\pm\tfrac{3}{7}\right) - 3$$
$$= \tfrac{13}{7}, \tfrac{1}{7} \qquad\qquad = -\tfrac{9}{7}, \tfrac{9}{7} \qquad\qquad = -\tfrac{3}{7}, -\tfrac{39}{7}$$

There are two points that satisfy the conditions for the required terminal point Q: $\left(\tfrac{13}{7}, -\tfrac{9}{7}, -\tfrac{3}{7}\right)$ and $\left(\tfrac{1}{7}, \tfrac{9}{7}, -\tfrac{39}{7}\right)$. ▬

■ DEFINITION OF DOT PRODUCT

The **dot (scalar) product** and the **cross (vector) product** are two important vector operations. We shall examine the cross product in the next section. The dot product is also known as a scalar product because it is a product of vectors that gives a scalar (that is, real number) as a result. Sometimes the dot product is called the **inner product**.

Dot Product

The **dot product** of vectors $\mathbf{v} = a_1\mathbf{i} + a_2\mathbf{j} + a_3\mathbf{k}$ and $\mathbf{w} = b_1\mathbf{i} + b_2\mathbf{j} + b_3\mathbf{k}$ is the scalar denoted by $\mathbf{v} \cdot \mathbf{w}$ and given by

$$\mathbf{v} \cdot \mathbf{w} = a_1 b_1 + a_2 b_2 + a_3 b_3$$

The dot product of two vectors $\mathbf{v} = a_1\mathbf{i} + a_2\mathbf{j}$ and $\mathbf{w} = b_1\mathbf{i} + b_2\mathbf{j}$ in a plane is given by a similar formula with $a_3 = b_3 = 0$: $\mathbf{v} \cdot \mathbf{w} = a_1 b_1 + a_2 b_2$.

EXAMPLE 5 **Dot product**

Find the dot product of $\mathbf{v} = -3\mathbf{i} + 2\mathbf{j} + \mathbf{k}$ and $\mathbf{w} = 4\mathbf{i} - \mathbf{j} + 2\mathbf{k}$.

Solution $\qquad\qquad \mathbf{v} \cdot \mathbf{w} = -3(4) + 2(-1) + 1(2) = -12$ ▬

EXAMPLE 6 Dot product in component form

If $\mathbf{v} = \langle 4, -1, 3 \rangle$ and $\mathbf{w} = \langle -1, -2, 5 \rangle$, find the dot product, $\mathbf{v} \cdot \mathbf{w}$.

Solution
$$\mathbf{v} \cdot \mathbf{w} = 4(-1) + (-1)(-2) + 3(5) = 13$$

Before we can apply the dot product to geometric and physical problems, we need to know how it behaves algebraically. A number of important general properties of the dot product are listed in the following theorem.

THEOREM 10.2 Properties of the dot product

If $\mathbf{u}$, $\mathbf{v}$, and $\mathbf{w}$ are vectors in $\mathbb{R}^2$ or $\mathbb{R}^3$ and c is a scalar, then:

Magnitude of a vector	$\mathbf{v} \cdot \mathbf{v} = \|\mathbf{v}\|^2$
Zero product	$\mathbf{0} \cdot \mathbf{v} = 0$
Commutativity	$\mathbf{v} \cdot \mathbf{w} = \mathbf{w} \cdot \mathbf{v}$
Scalar multiple	$c(\mathbf{v} \cdot \mathbf{w}) = (c\mathbf{v}) \cdot \mathbf{w} = \mathbf{u} \cdot (c\mathbf{w})$
Distributivity	$\mathbf{u} \cdot (\mathbf{v} + \mathbf{w}) = \mathbf{u} \cdot \mathbf{v} + \mathbf{u} \cdot \mathbf{w}$

Proof: Let $\mathbf{u} = a_1\mathbf{i} + a_2\mathbf{j} + a_3\mathbf{k}$, $\mathbf{v} = b_1\mathbf{i} + b_2\mathbf{j} + b_3\mathbf{k}$, and $\mathbf{w} = c_1\mathbf{i} + c_2\mathbf{j} + c_3\mathbf{k}$.
Magnitude of a vector
$$\|\mathbf{v}\|^2 = \left(\sqrt{a_1^2 + a_2^2 + a_3^2}\right)^2 = a_1^2 + a_2^2 + a_3^2 = \mathbf{v} \cdot \mathbf{v}$$

Zero product, **commutativity**, and **scalar multiple** can be established in a similar fashion.

Distributivity

$$\begin{aligned}
\mathbf{u} \cdot (\mathbf{v} + \mathbf{w}) &= (a_1\mathbf{i} + a_2\mathbf{j} + a_3\mathbf{k}) \cdot [(b_1 + c_1)\mathbf{i} + (b_2 + c_2)\mathbf{j} + (b_3 + c_3)\mathbf{k}] \\
&= a_1(b_1 + c_1) + a_2(b_2 + c_2) + a_3(b_3 + c_3) \\
&= a_1b_1 + a_1c_1 + a_2b_2 + a_2c_2 + a_3b_3 + a_3c_3
\end{aligned}$$

Also,

$$\begin{aligned}
\mathbf{u} \cdot \mathbf{v} + \mathbf{u} \cdot \mathbf{w} &= (a_1b_1 + a_2b_2 + a_3b_3) + (a_1c_1 + a_2c_2 + a_3c_3) \\
&= a_1b_1 + a_1c_1 + a_2b_2 + a_2c_2 + a_3b_3 + a_3c_3
\end{aligned}$$

Thus, $\mathbf{u} \cdot (\mathbf{v} + \mathbf{w}) = \mathbf{u} \cdot \mathbf{v} + \mathbf{u} \cdot \mathbf{w}$. ∎

◼ ANGLE BETWEEN VECTORS

The angle between two nonzero vectors $\mathbf{v}$ and $\mathbf{w}$ is defined to be the angle θ with $0 \leq \theta \leq \pi$ that is formed when the vectors are in standard position (initial points at the origin), as shown in Figure 10.18.

The angle between vectors plays an important role in certain applications and may be computed by using the following formula involving the dot product.

THEOREM 10.3 Angle between two vectors

If θ is the angle between the nonzero vectors $\mathbf{v}$ and $\mathbf{w}$, then

$$\cos \theta = \frac{\mathbf{v} \cdot \mathbf{w}}{\|\mathbf{v}\| \, \|\mathbf{w}\|}$$

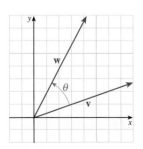

Figure 10.18 The angle between two vectors

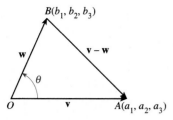

Figure 10.19 Finding an angle between two vectors

Proof: Suppose $\mathbf{v} = a_1\mathbf{i} + a_2\mathbf{j} + a_3\mathbf{k}$ and $\mathbf{w} = b_1\mathbf{i} + b_2\mathbf{j} + b_3\mathbf{k}$, and consider $\triangle AOB$ with vertices at the origin O and the points $A(a_1, a_2, a_3)$ and $B(b_1, b_2, b_3)$, as shown in Figure 10.19. Note that sides $\overline{OA}$ and $\overline{OB}$ have lengths

$$\|\mathbf{v}\| = \sqrt{a_1^2 + a_2^2 + a_3^3} \quad \text{and} \quad \|\mathbf{w}\| = \sqrt{b_1^2 + b_2^2 + b_3^2}$$

respectively, and that side $\overline{AB}$ has length

$$\|\mathbf{v} - \mathbf{w}\| = \sqrt{(a_1 - b_1)^2 + (a_2 - b_2)^2 + (a_3 - b_3)^2}$$

Next, we use the law of cosines.

$$a^2 = b^2 + c^2 - 2bc\cos\theta \qquad \textit{Law of cosines}$$

$$\|\mathbf{v} - \mathbf{w}\|^2 = \|\mathbf{v}\|^2 + \|\mathbf{w}\|^2 - 2\|\mathbf{v}\|\,\|\mathbf{w}\|\cos\theta \qquad \textit{See Figure 10.19.}$$

$$\cos\theta = \frac{\|\mathbf{v}\|^2 + \|\mathbf{w}\|^2 - \|\mathbf{v} - \mathbf{w}\|^2}{2\|\mathbf{v}\|\,\|\mathbf{w}\|} \qquad \textit{Solve for }\cos\theta.$$

$$= \frac{a_1^2 + a_2^2 + a_3^2 + b_1^2 + b_2^2 + b_3^2 - [(a_1 - b_1)^2 + (a_2 - b_2)^2 + (a_3 - b_3)^2]}{2\|\mathbf{v}\|\,\|\mathbf{w}\|}$$

$$= \frac{2a_1b_1 + 2a_2b_2 + 2a_3b_3}{2\|\mathbf{v}\|\,\|\mathbf{w}\|} = \frac{\mathbf{v}\cdot\mathbf{w}}{\|\mathbf{v}\|\,\|\mathbf{w}\|} \qquad \blacksquare$$

EXAMPLE 7   Angle between two given vectors

Let $\triangle ABC$ be the triangle with vertices $A(1, 1, 8)$, $B(4, -3, -4)$, and $C(-3, 1, 5)$. Find the angle formed at A.

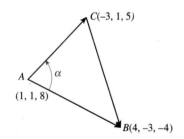

Figure 10.20 Find an angle of a triangle

Solution   Draw $\triangle ABC$ and label the angle formed at A as α as shown in Figure 10.20. The angle α is the angle between vectors $\mathbf{AB}$ and $\mathbf{AC}$, where

$$\mathbf{AB} = (4 - 1)\mathbf{i} + (-3 - 1)\mathbf{j} + (-4 - 8)\mathbf{k} = 3\mathbf{i} - 4\mathbf{j} - 12\mathbf{k}$$

$$\mathbf{AC} = (-3 - 1)\mathbf{i} + (1 - 1)\mathbf{j} + (5 - 8)\mathbf{k} = -4\mathbf{i} - 3\mathbf{k}$$

Thus,

$$\cos\alpha = \frac{\mathbf{AB}\cdot\mathbf{AC}}{\|\mathbf{AB}\|\,\|\mathbf{AC}\|} = \frac{3(-4) + (-4)(0) + (-12)(-3)}{\sqrt{3^2 + (-4)^2 + (-12)^2}\sqrt{(-4)^2 + (-3)^2}}$$

$$= \frac{24}{\sqrt{169}\sqrt{25}} = \frac{24}{65}$$

and the required angle is $\alpha = \cos^{-1}\left(\frac{24}{65}\right) \approx 1.19$.

The formula for the angle between vectors is often used in conjunction with the dot product. If we multiply both sides of the formula by $\|\mathbf{v}\|\,\|\mathbf{w}\|$, we obtain the following alternative form for the dot product formula.

Dot Product (Alternative Form)

$$\mathbf{v}\cdot\mathbf{w} = \|\mathbf{v}\|\,\|\mathbf{w}\|\cos\theta$$

where θ is the angle ($0 \le \theta \le \pi$) between any two vectors $\mathbf{v}$ and $\mathbf{w}$.

Two vectors are said to be **perpendicular**, or **orthogonal**, if the angle between them is $\theta = \pi/2$. The following theorem provides a useful criterion for orthogonality.

THEOREM 10.4   Orthogonal vectors

Nonzero vectors **v** and **w** are **orthogonal** if and only if

$$\mathbf{v} \cdot \mathbf{w} = 0$$

Proof: If the vectors are orthogonal, then the angle between them is $\frac{\pi}{2}$; therefore,

$$\mathbf{v} \cdot \mathbf{w} = \|\mathbf{v}\| \, \|\mathbf{w}\| \cos \tfrac{\pi}{2} = 0$$

Conversely, if $\mathbf{v} \cdot \mathbf{w} = 0$, and **v** and **w** are nonzero vectors, then $\cos \theta = 0$, so that $\theta = \frac{\pi}{2}$ and the vectors are orthogonal. ∎

Determine which (if any) of the following vectors are orthogonal:
$$\mathbf{u} = 3\mathbf{i} + 7\mathbf{j} - 2\mathbf{k} \qquad \mathbf{v} = 5\mathbf{i} - 3\mathbf{j} - 3\mathbf{k} \qquad \mathbf{w} = \mathbf{j} - \mathbf{k}$$

$\mathbf{u} \cdot \mathbf{v} = 3(5) + 7(-3) + (-2)(-3) = 0$; orthogonal vectors.
$\mathbf{u} \cdot \mathbf{w} = 3(0) + 7(1) + (-2)(-1) = 9$; not orthogonal vectors.
$\mathbf{v} \cdot \mathbf{w} = 5(0) + (-3)(1) + (-3)(-1) = 0$; orthogonal vectors.

■ PROJECTIONS

Let **v** and **w** be two vectors in $\mathbb{R}^2$ drawn so that they have a common initial point, as shown in Figure 10.21.* If we drop a perpendicular from the tip of **v** to the line determined by **w**, we determine a vector called the **vector projection of v onto w**, which we have labeled **u** in Figure 10.21.

The **scalar projection of v onto w** (also called the **component of v along w**) is the length of the vector projection, so it is denoted by $\|\mathbf{u}\|$. Let θ be the acute angle between **v** and **w**. Then, by definition of cosine we have

$$\|\mathbf{u}\| = \|\mathbf{v}\| \cos \theta = \|\mathbf{v}\|\left(\frac{\mathbf{v} \cdot \mathbf{w}}{\|\mathbf{v}\| \, \|\mathbf{w}\|}\right) = \frac{\mathbf{v} \cdot \mathbf{w}}{\|\mathbf{w}\|} \quad \textit{Cosine is positive because } \theta \textit{ is acute.}$$

If θ is obtuse, its cosine is negative and $\|\mathbf{u}\| = -\|\mathbf{v}\|\cos \theta$.

In order to find a formula for the vector projection, we note that it is the scalar component of **v** in the direction of **w**. If θ is acute, then the vector projection has length $\|\mathbf{v}\| \cos \theta$ and has direction $\mathbf{w}/\|\mathbf{w}\|$ (the unit vector of **w**). If the angle is obtuse, the vector projection has length $-\|\mathbf{v}\|\cos \theta$ and has direction $-\mathbf{w}/\|\mathbf{w}\|$. In either case,

$$\mathbf{u} = (\|\mathbf{v}\| \cos \theta)\frac{\mathbf{w}}{\|\mathbf{w}\|} = \frac{\mathbf{v} \cdot \mathbf{w}}{\|\mathbf{w}\|}\left(\frac{\mathbf{w}}{\|\mathbf{w}\|}\right) = \frac{\mathbf{v} \cdot \mathbf{w}}{\|\mathbf{w}\|^2}\,\mathbf{w} = \left(\frac{\mathbf{v} \cdot \mathbf{w}}{\mathbf{w} \cdot \mathbf{w}}\right)\mathbf{w}$$

Scalar projection of **v** onto **w** (a number): $\left|\dfrac{\mathbf{v} \cdot \mathbf{w}}{\|\mathbf{w}\|}\right|$

Vector projection of **v** in the direction of **w** (a vector): $\left(\dfrac{\mathbf{v} \cdot \mathbf{w}}{\mathbf{w} \cdot \mathbf{w}}\right)\mathbf{w}$

In $\mathbb{R}^3$ it is important to note that the **i**, **j**, and **k** components of any vector **v** are the projections of **v** onto the basis vector, as shown in Figure 10.22.

Find the scalar and vector projections of $\mathbf{v} = 2\mathbf{i} - 3\mathbf{j} + 5\mathbf{k}$ onto

$$\mathbf{w} = 2\mathbf{i} - 2\mathbf{j} + \mathbf{k}$$

*Even though Figure 10.21 is drawn in $\mathbb{R}^2$, the projection formula applies to $\mathbb{R}^3$ as well.

Figure 10.21 Projection of **v** onto **w**

⊘ Note that $\left(\dfrac{\mathbf{v} \cdot \mathbf{w}}{\mathbf{w} \cdot \mathbf{w}}\right)\mathbf{w}$ is not the same as $\left(\dfrac{\mathbf{v}}{\mathbf{w}}\right)\mathbf{w}$, and you cannot "cancel" the vector **w**. Remember, $\mathbf{v} \cdot \mathbf{w}$ and $\mathbf{w} \cdot \mathbf{w}$ are numbers, whereas $\mathbf{v}/\mathbf{w}$ is not defined. ⊘

Scalar and Vector Projections of v onto w

Figure 10.22 The **i**, **j**, and **k** components of $\mathbf{v} = a\mathbf{i} + b\mathbf{j} + c\mathbf{k}$ are projections of **v** onto **i**, **j**, and **k**.

Solution   We first find the vector projection:

$$\text{Vector projection of } \mathbf{v} \text{ onto } \mathbf{w} = \left(\frac{\mathbf{v} \cdot \mathbf{w}}{\mathbf{w} \cdot \mathbf{w}}\right)\mathbf{w}$$

$$= \left(\frac{2(2) + (-3)(-2) + 5(1)}{2^2 + (-2)^2 + 1^2}\right)(2\mathbf{i} - 2\mathbf{j} + \mathbf{k})$$

$$= \frac{15}{9}(2\mathbf{i} - 2\mathbf{j} + \mathbf{k}) = \frac{10}{3}\mathbf{i} - \frac{10}{3}\mathbf{j} + \frac{5}{3}\mathbf{k}$$

To find the scalar projection, we can find the length of the vector projection or we can use the scalar projection formula (which is usually easier than finding the length directly):

$$\text{Scalar projection of } \mathbf{v} \text{ onto } \mathbf{w} = \left|\frac{\mathbf{v} \cdot \mathbf{w}}{\|\mathbf{w}\|}\right| = \left|\frac{15}{3}\right| = 5$$

a. If the force **F** acts along the line of motion then $W = \|\mathbf{F}\|\,\|\mathbf{PQ}\|$.

b. If **F** acts at a nonzero angle with the line of motion, then $W = \|\text{proj. of } \mathbf{F} \text{ onto } \mathbf{PQ}\|\,\|\mathbf{PQ}\|$.

Figure 10.23 Work W as a dot product

■ WORK AS A DOT PRODUCT

One important application of the dot product and projections occurs in physics when calculating the amount of work done by a constant force. In Section 6.3, we defined the work, W, done by a constant force directed along the line of the motion of the object to be $W = Fd$ (Figure 10.23a). We now consider a force acting in some other direction (Figure 10.23b).

Physics experiments indicate that when a force **F** moves an object along the line from point P to point Q, the work performed is given by the product

$$W = [\text{SCALAR COMPONENT OF } \mathbf{F} \text{ ALONG } \mathbf{PQ}][\text{DISTANCE MOVED BY THE OBJECT}]$$

The distance moved by the object is the length of the *displacement vector* **PQ**, and we find that

$$W = \underbrace{\frac{\overbrace{\mathbf{F} \cdot \mathbf{PQ}}^{\text{Scalar component of } \mathbf{F} \text{ along } \mathbf{PQ}}}{\|\mathbf{PQ}\|} \underbrace{\|\mathbf{PQ}\|}_{\text{Distance moved by the object}}} = \mathbf{F} \cdot \mathbf{PQ}$$

Work As a Dot Product

> An object that moves along a line with displacement **PQ** against a constant force **F** performs
>
> $$W = \mathbf{F} \cdot \mathbf{PQ}$$
>
> units of work.

EXAMPLE 10   Work performed by a constant force

Suppose that the wind is blowing with a force **F** with magnitude 500 lb in the direction of N30°E over a boat's sail. How much work does the wind perform in moving the boat in a northerly direction a distance of 100 ft? Give your answer in foot-pounds.

Solution   We see that $\|\mathbf{F}\| = 500$ lb and is in the direction of N30°E, as shown in Figure 10.24. The displacement direction is $\mathbf{PQ} = 100\mathbf{j}$, so $\|\mathbf{PQ}\| = 100$ ft. Thus, $\mathbf{F} = 500\cos 60°\mathbf{i} + 500\sin 60°\mathbf{j} = 250\mathbf{i} + 250\sqrt{3}\mathbf{j}$. Thus, the work performed is

$$W = \mathbf{F} \cdot \mathbf{PQ} = 100(250\sqrt{3}) = 25,000\sqrt{3}$$

Thus, the work is approximately 43,300 ft-lb.

Side View   Top View

Figure 10.24 Work performed

PROBLEM SET 10.3

Ⓐ 1. ■ **What Does This Say?** Discuss how to find a dot product, and describe an application of dot product.

2. ■ **What Does This Say?** Describe and contrast scalar and vector projections.

Find the standard representation of the vector **PQ**, *and then find* $\|\mathbf{PQ}\|$ *in Problems 3–6.*

3. $P(1, -1, 3)$, $Q(-1, 1, 4)$ 4. $P(0, 2, 3)$, $Q(2, 3, 0)$
5. $P(1, 1, 1)$, $Q(-3, -3, -3)$ 6. $P(3, 0, -4)$, $Q(0, -4, 3)$

Find the dot product $\mathbf{v} \cdot \mathbf{w}$ *in Problems 7–10.*

7. $\mathbf{v} = \langle 3, -2, 4 \rangle$; $\mathbf{w} = \langle 2, -1, -6 \rangle$
8. $\mathbf{v} = \langle 2, -6, 0 \rangle$; $\mathbf{w} = \langle 0, -3, 7 \rangle$
9. $\mathbf{v} = 2\mathbf{i} + 3\mathbf{j} - \mathbf{k}$; $\mathbf{w} = -3\mathbf{i} + 5\mathbf{j} + 4\mathbf{k}$
10. $\mathbf{v} = 3\mathbf{i} - \mathbf{j}$; $\mathbf{w} = 2\mathbf{i} + 5\mathbf{j}$

State whether the given pairs of vectors in Problems 11–14 are orthogonal.

11. $\mathbf{v} = \mathbf{i}$; $\mathbf{w} = \mathbf{k}$ 12. $\mathbf{v} = \mathbf{j}$; $\mathbf{w} = -\mathbf{k}$
13. $\mathbf{v} = 3\mathbf{i} - 2\mathbf{j}$; $\mathbf{w} = 6\mathbf{i} + 9\mathbf{j}$
14. $\mathbf{v} = 4\mathbf{i} - 5\mathbf{j} + \mathbf{k}$; $\mathbf{w} = 8\mathbf{i} + 10\mathbf{j} - 2\mathbf{k}$

Evaluate the expressions given in Problems 15–18.

15. $\|\mathbf{i} + \mathbf{j} + \mathbf{k}\|$ 16. $\|\mathbf{i} - \mathbf{j} + \mathbf{k}\|$
17. $\|2\mathbf{i} + \mathbf{j} - 3\mathbf{k}\|^2$ 18. $\|2(\mathbf{i} - \mathbf{j} + \mathbf{k}) - 3(2\mathbf{i} + \mathbf{j} - \mathbf{k})\|^2$

Let $\mathbf{v} = \mathbf{i} - 2\mathbf{j} + 2\mathbf{k}$ *and* $\mathbf{w} = 2\mathbf{i} + 4\mathbf{j} - \mathbf{k}$; *and find the vector or scalar requested in Problems 19–22.*

19. $2\mathbf{v} - 3\mathbf{w}$ 20. $\|\mathbf{v}\|\mathbf{w}$
21. $\|2\mathbf{v} - 3\mathbf{w}\|$ 22. $\|\mathbf{v} - \mathbf{w}\|(\mathbf{v} + \mathbf{w})$

Determine whether each vector in Problems 23–26 is parallel to $2\mathbf{i} - 3\mathbf{j} + 5\mathbf{k}$.

23. $\mathbf{u} = \langle 4, 0, 10 \rangle$ 24. $\mathbf{v} = \langle -4, 6, -10 \rangle$
25. $\mathbf{w} = \langle 1, -\frac{3}{2}, 2 \rangle$ 26. $\mathbf{v} = \langle -\frac{1}{2}, \frac{3}{2}, 2 \rangle$

Let $\mathbf{v} = 3\mathbf{i} - 2\mathbf{j} + \mathbf{k}$ *and* $\mathbf{w} = \mathbf{i} + \mathbf{j} - \mathbf{k}$. *Evaluate the expressions in Problems 27–30.*

27. $(\mathbf{v} + \mathbf{w}) \cdot (\mathbf{v} - \mathbf{w})$ 28. $(\mathbf{v} \cdot \mathbf{w})\mathbf{w}$
29. $(\|\mathbf{v}\|\mathbf{w}) \cdot (\|\mathbf{w}\|\mathbf{v})$ 30. $\dfrac{2\mathbf{v} + 3\mathbf{w}}{\|3\mathbf{v} + 2\mathbf{w}\|}$

Find the angle between the vectors given in Problems 31–34. Round to the nearest degree.

31. $\mathbf{v} = \mathbf{i} + \mathbf{j} + \mathbf{k}$; $\mathbf{w} = \mathbf{i} - \mathbf{j} + \mathbf{k}$
32. $\mathbf{v} = 2\mathbf{i} + \mathbf{k}$; $\mathbf{w} = \mathbf{j} - 3\mathbf{k}$
33. $\mathbf{v} = 2\mathbf{j} + \mathbf{k}$; $\mathbf{w} = \mathbf{i} - 2\mathbf{k}$
34. $\mathbf{v} = 4\mathbf{i} - \mathbf{j} + \mathbf{k}$; $\mathbf{w} = 2\mathbf{i} + 3\mathbf{j} + 5\mathbf{k}$

Find the vector and scalar projections of **v** *onto* **w** *in Problems 35–38.*

35. $\mathbf{v} = \mathbf{i} + \mathbf{j} + \mathbf{k}$; $\mathbf{w} = 2\mathbf{k}$ 36. $\mathbf{v} = \mathbf{i} + 2\mathbf{k}$; $\mathbf{w} = -3\mathbf{j}$
37. $\mathbf{v} = 2\mathbf{i} - 3\mathbf{j}$; $\mathbf{w} = 2\mathbf{j} - 3\mathbf{k}$ 38. $\mathbf{v} = \mathbf{i} + \mathbf{j} - 2\mathbf{k}$; $\mathbf{w} = \mathbf{i} + \mathbf{j} + \mathbf{k}$

Ⓑ *Find two distinct unit vectors that are orthogonal to each pair of vectors given in Problems 39–42. We will do this type of problem with cross product in the next section.*

39. $\mathbf{v} = \mathbf{i} + \mathbf{k}$; $\mathbf{w} = \mathbf{i} - 2\mathbf{k}$
40. $\mathbf{v} = \mathbf{i} + \mathbf{j} - \mathbf{k}$; $\mathbf{w} = -\mathbf{i} + \mathbf{j} + \mathbf{k}$
41. $\mathbf{v} = 2\mathbf{i} + \mathbf{j} + 2\mathbf{k}$; $\mathbf{w} = -\mathbf{i} + 2\mathbf{j} - \mathbf{k}$
42. $\mathbf{v} = 2\mathbf{j} + 3\mathbf{k}$; $\mathbf{w} = \mathbf{i} + \mathbf{j} + \mathbf{k}$

43. Find a vector that points in the direction opposite to $\mathbf{v} = 2\mathbf{i} + 3\mathbf{j} - 2\mathbf{k}$.

44. Find a vector that points in the same direction as $\mathbf{v} = \mathbf{i} + 2\mathbf{j} - \mathbf{k}$ and has one-third its length.

45. Find x, y, and z that solve
$x(\mathbf{i} + \mathbf{j} + \mathbf{k}) + y(\mathbf{i} - \mathbf{j} + 2\mathbf{k}) + z(\mathbf{i} + \mathbf{k}) = 2\mathbf{i} + \mathbf{k}$

46. Find x, y, and z that solve
$x(\mathbf{i} - \mathbf{k}) + y(\mathbf{j} + \mathbf{k}) + z(\mathbf{i} - \mathbf{j}) = 5\mathbf{i} - \mathbf{k}$

47. Find a number a that guarantees that the vectors $3\mathbf{i} - 2\mathbf{j} + \mathbf{k}$ and $2\mathbf{i} + a\mathbf{j} - 2a\mathbf{k}$ will be orthogonal.

48. Find x if the vectors $\mathbf{v} = 3\mathbf{i} - x\mathbf{j} + 2\mathbf{k}$ and $\mathbf{w} = x\mathbf{i} + \mathbf{j} - 2\mathbf{k}$ are to be orthogonal.

49. Find the angles between the vector $2\mathbf{i} + \mathbf{j} - \mathbf{k}$ and each of the coordinate axes. The cosines of these angles (to the nearest degree) are known as the **direction cosines**.

50. Find the cosine of the angle between the vectors $\mathbf{v} = \mathbf{i} - \mathbf{j} + 2\mathbf{k}$ and $\mathbf{w} = 2\mathbf{i} + \mathbf{j} - \mathbf{k}$. Then find the vector projection of **v** onto **w**.

51. Let $\mathbf{v} = 4\mathbf{i} - \mathbf{j} + \mathbf{k}$ and $\mathbf{w} = 2\mathbf{i} + 3\mathbf{j} - \mathbf{k}$. Find:
   a. $\mathbf{v} \cdot \mathbf{w}$
   b. $\cos \theta$, where θ is the angle between **v** and **w**
   c. a scalar s such that **v** is orthogonal to $\mathbf{v} - s\mathbf{w}$
   d. a scalar s such that $s\mathbf{v} + \mathbf{w}$ is orthogonal to **w**

52. Let $\mathbf{v} = 2\mathbf{i} - 3\mathbf{j} + 6\mathbf{k}$ and $\mathbf{w} = 4\mathbf{i} + 3\mathbf{k}$. Find:
   a. $\mathbf{v} \cdot \mathbf{w}$
   b. $\cos \theta$, where θ is the angle between **v** and **w**
   c. a scalar s such that **v** is orthogonal to $\mathbf{v} - s\mathbf{w}$
   d. a scalar t such that $\mathbf{v} + t\mathbf{w}$ is orthogonal to **w**

53. Find the scalar component of the force $\mathbf{F} = 4\mathbf{i} - 2\mathbf{j} + 3\mathbf{k}$ in the direction of the vector $\mathbf{v} = \mathbf{i} - \mathbf{j} + 2\mathbf{k}$.

54. Find the work done by the constant force $\mathbf{F} = 2\mathbf{i} + 3\mathbf{j} + \mathbf{k}$ when it moves a particle along the line from $P(1, 0, -1)$ to $Q(3, 1, 2)$.

55. Find the work performed when a force $\mathbf{F} = \frac{6}{7}\mathbf{i} - \frac{2}{7}\mathbf{j} + \frac{6}{7}\mathbf{k}$ is applied to an object moving along the line from $P(-3, -5, 4)$ to $Q(4, 9, 11)$.

56. Fred and his son Sam are pulling a heavy log along flat horizontal ground by ropes attached to the front of the log. The ropes are 8 ft long. Fred holds his rope 2 ft above the log and 1 ft to the side, and Sam holds his end 1 ft above the log and 1 ft to the opposite side, as shown in Figure 10.25.

Side View   Top View

Figure 10.25 Problem 56

If Fred exerts a force of 20 lb and Sam exerts a force of 30 lb, what is the resultant force on the log?

57. Find the force required to keep a 5,000-lb van from rolling downhill if it is parked on a 10° slope.

58. A block of ice is dragged 20 ft across a floor, using a force of 50 lb. Find the work done if the direction of the force is inclined θ to the horizontal, where

   a. $\theta = \frac{\pi}{6}$ **b.** $\theta = \frac{\pi}{4}$

59. Suppose that the wind is blowing with a 1,000-lb magnitude force **F** in the direction of N60°W over a boat's sail. How much work does the wind perform in moving the boat in a northerly direction a distance of 50 ft? Give your answer in foot-pounds.

Computational Window ▼ ▲

Orthogonality of Functions. *One of the big discoveries in modern mathematics was that it is very fruitful to extend some of the geometric notions of this chapter to functions. For example, taking the dot product of two functions or asking if two functions are orthogonal, or attempting to project a function onto a second function (or onto a "plane" of functions). You are introduced to this important concepts in Problems 60 and 61.*

60. We say that two functions f and g are **orthogonal** on $[a, b]$ if

$$\int_b^a f(x)g(x)\, dx = 0$$

   a. Show that the two functions x^2 and $x^3 - 5x$ are orthogonal on $[-b, b]$ for any positive b.

   b. For positive integers k and $n \neq k$, show that $\sin kx$ and $\sin nx$ are orthogonal on the interval $[-\pi, \pi]$. You may need the product-to-sum identity. (Identity 38 from the *Student Mathematics Handbook*):

$$2 \sin \alpha \sin \beta = \cos(\alpha - \beta) - \cos(\alpha + \beta)$$

   That is, the *family* of functions $\sin x$, $\sin 2x$, $\sin 3x$, ... are *mutually orthogonal* on $[-\pi, \pi]$.

   c. Make a careful sketch of $\sin x$ and $\sin 2x$ on $[-\pi, \pi]$ and explain why the integral of their product is 0.

---

61. In about 1807 the French mathematician J. B. J. Fourier made the remarkable observation that most important odd functions [that is, $f(-x) = -f(x)$] can be approximated by

$$f(x) \approx b_1 \sin x + b_2 \sin 2x + \cdots + b_n \sin nx = S_n(x)$$

   This formula reminds us of the Taylor approximations; in fact, some call $S_n(x)$ a *trigonometric polynomial*. However, this expansion is physically more meaningful, since it breaks $f(x)$ down into frequency components, where these components can represent things like pitch in sound or colors or chemical elements.

   a. Assume for now that $f(x)$ is actually *equal* to $S_n(x)$. To find the coefficients b_k, for $k = 1, 2, \ldots, n$, multiply the above trigonometric polynomial by $\sin kx$ and then integrate over $[-\pi, \pi]$. Use the orthogonality of the sines and the trigonometric identity $2 \sin^2 \alpha = 1 - \cos 2\alpha$ to show that

$$\int_{-\pi}^{\pi} \sin^2 kx\, dx = \pi$$

$$b_k = \frac{1}{\pi} \int_{-\pi}^{\pi} f(x) \sin kx\, dx$$

$$= \frac{2}{\pi} \int_0^{\pi} f(x) \sin kx\, dx$$

   b. Why, in the evaluation of b_k, is it only necessary to integrate over $[0, \pi]$?

   c. Now let us do a sine (Fourier) expansion of the simple function $f(x) = x$. Using the work from part **a**, show that

$$x \approx 2 \sin x - \sin 2x + \cdots - 2\frac{(-1)^n}{n} \sin nx$$

   d. For $f(x) = x(\pi - x)(\pi + x)$ compute the sine expansion of the above trigonometric polynomial. Starting with a small n, (that is, w or 3) increase n until the sine approximation agrees with $f(x)$ at the graphical level. If possible, turn in a meaningful graph. Then increase n until the difference

$$|f(x) - (b_1 \sin x + b_2 \sin 2x + \cdots + b_n \sin nx)| < 0.02$$

   Note: If the function is not odd, then similar cosine terms are needed; we have ignored this possibility for simplicity.

ⓒ 62. Let $\mathbf{u}_0 = a\mathbf{i} + b\mathbf{j} + c\mathbf{k}$ and let $\mathbf{u} = x\mathbf{i} + y\mathbf{j} + z\mathbf{k}$. Describe the set of points in $\mathbb{R}^3$ defined by

$$\|\mathbf{u}_0 - \mathbf{u}\| < r$$

   where $r > 0$ and a, b, c are constants.

63. Suppose the vectors $\mathbf{v}$ and $\mathbf{w}$ are sides of an equilateral triangle with area $25\sqrt{3}$. Find $\mathbf{v} \cdot \mathbf{w}$.

64. Find the angle (to the nearest hundredth radian) between the diagonal of a cube and a diagonal of one of its faces.

65. If $\mathbf{v} \cdot \mathbf{v} = 0$ and $\mathbf{v} \cdot \mathbf{w} = 0$, what can you conclude about $\mathbf{v}$ and $\mathbf{w}$?

66. **a.** Show that $(\mathbf{v} + \mathbf{w}) \cdot (\mathbf{v} + \mathbf{w}) = \|\mathbf{v}\|^2 + \|\mathbf{w}\|^2 + 2(\mathbf{v} \cdot \mathbf{w})$.

   b. Use part a to prove the triangle inequality:

$$\|\mathbf{v} + \mathbf{w}\| \leq \|\mathbf{v}\| + \|\mathbf{w}\|$$

Hint: Note that

$$\|\mathbf{v} + \mathbf{w}\|^2 = (\mathbf{v} + \mathbf{w}) \cdot (\mathbf{v} + \mathbf{w})$$

67. The **Cauchy–Schwarz** inequality in $\mathbb{R}^3$ states that for any vectors $\mathbf{v}$ and $\mathbf{w}$

$$|\mathbf{v} \cdot \mathbf{w}| \leq \|\mathbf{v}\| \, \|\mathbf{w}\|$$

a. Prove the Cauchy–Schwarz inequality. *Hint*: Use the formula for the angle between vectors.

b. Show that equality in the Cauchy–Schwarz inequality occurs if and only if $\mathbf{v} = t\mathbf{w}$ for some scalar t.

c. Use the Cauchy–Schwarz inequality to prove the **triangle inequality**:

$$\|\mathbf{v} + \mathbf{w}\| \leq \|\mathbf{v}\| + \|\mathbf{w}\|$$

10.4 THE CROSS PRODUCT

> **IN THIS SECTION** Definition of cross product, geometric interpretation of cross product, properties of cross product, triple scalar product and volume, torque
>
> We introduce a second type of vector multiplication called *cross product*, which turns out to be a vector. We shall find that the cross product is a vector orthogonal to each of the given vectors. This geometric property will be particularly useful in the next section.

■ DEFINITION OF CROSS PRODUCT

The cross product is sometimes called the **vector product** because the result is a vector. In other applications it is called the **outer product**. The definition requires a basis of $\mathbf{i}$, $\mathbf{j}$, and $\mathbf{k}$ and therefore, is a definition that makes sense only in $\mathbb{R}^3$.

Cross Product   If $\mathbf{v} = a_1\mathbf{i} + a_2\mathbf{j} + a_3\mathbf{k}$ and $\mathbf{w} = b_1\mathbf{i} + b_2\mathbf{j} + b_3\mathbf{k}$, the **cross product**, written $\mathbf{v} \times \mathbf{w}$, is the vector

$$\mathbf{v} \times \mathbf{w} = (a_2b_3 - a_3b_2)\mathbf{i} + (a_3b_1 - a_1b_3)\mathbf{j} + (a_1b_2 - a_2b_1)\mathbf{k}$$

These terms can be obtained by using a determinant

$$\mathbf{v} \times \mathbf{w} = \begin{vmatrix} \mathbf{i} & \mathbf{j} & \mathbf{k} \\ a_1 & a_2 & a_3 \\ b_1 & b_2 & b_3 \end{vmatrix}$$

(SMH) A brief discussion of the basic properties of determinants is included in *Student Mathematics Handbook*. To verify the determinant formula for the cross product, we will expand this determinant about the first row:

$$\mathbf{v} \times \mathbf{w} = \begin{vmatrix} \mathbf{i} & \mathbf{j} & \mathbf{k} \\ a_1 & a_2 & a_3 \\ b_1 & b_2 & b_3 \end{vmatrix} = \begin{vmatrix} a_2 & a_3 \\ b_2 & b_3 \end{vmatrix} \mathbf{i} - \begin{vmatrix} a_1 & a_3 \\ b_1 & b_3 \end{vmatrix} \mathbf{j} + \begin{vmatrix} a_1 & a_2 \\ b_1 & b_2 \end{vmatrix} \mathbf{k}$$

↑

j is in row 1, column 2, so do not forget negative sign here.

$$= (a_2b_3 - a_3b_2)\mathbf{i} - (a_1b_3 - a_3b_1)\mathbf{j} + (a_1b_2 - a_2b_1)\mathbf{k}$$

$$= (a_2b_3 - a_3b_2)\mathbf{i} + (a_3b_1 - a_1b_3)\mathbf{j} + (a_1b_2 - a_2b_1)\mathbf{k}$$

EXAMPLE 1   Cross product

Find $\mathbf{v} \times \mathbf{w}$, where $\mathbf{v} = 2\mathbf{i} - \mathbf{j} + 3\mathbf{k}$ and $\mathbf{w} = 7\mathbf{j} - 4\mathbf{k}$

Solution

$$\mathbf{v} \times \mathbf{w} = \begin{vmatrix} \mathbf{i} & \mathbf{j} & \mathbf{k} \\ 2 & -1 & 3 \\ 0 & 7 & -4 \end{vmatrix} \qquad \text{Do not forget minus here (}\mathbf{j}\text{ is negative position).}$$

$$= [(-1)(-4) - 3(7)]\mathbf{i} - [2(-4) - 0(3)]\mathbf{j} + [2(7) - 0(-1)]\mathbf{k}$$

$$= -17\mathbf{i} + 8\mathbf{j} + 14\mathbf{k}$$

Properties of determinants can also be used to establish properties of the cross product. For instance, the following computation shows that the cross product is *not* commutative. This property is sometimes called **anticommutativity**.

$$\mathbf{v} \times \mathbf{w} = \begin{vmatrix} \mathbf{i} & \mathbf{j} & \mathbf{k} \\ a_1 & a_2 & a_3 \\ b_1 & b_2 & b_3 \end{vmatrix} = - \begin{vmatrix} \mathbf{i} & \mathbf{j} & \mathbf{k} \\ b_1 & b_2 & b_3 \\ a_1 & a_2 & a_3 \end{vmatrix} = -(\mathbf{w} \times \mathbf{v})$$

THEOREM 10.5   Properties of cross product

If $\mathbf{u}$, $\mathbf{v}$, and $\mathbf{w}$ are vectors in $\mathbb{R}^3$ and s and t are scalars, then

Scalar distributivity	$(s\mathbf{v}) \times (t\mathbf{w}) = st(\mathbf{v} \times \mathbf{w})$
Vector distributivity*	$\mathbf{u} \times (\mathbf{v} + \mathbf{w}) = (\mathbf{u} \times \mathbf{v}) + (\mathbf{u} \times \mathbf{w})$
	$(\mathbf{u} + \mathbf{v}) \times \mathbf{w} = (\mathbf{u} \times \mathbf{w}) + (\mathbf{v} \times \mathbf{w})$
Anticommutativity	$\mathbf{v} \times \mathbf{w} = -(\mathbf{w} \times \mathbf{v})$
Parallel vectors	$\mathbf{v} \times \mathbf{v} = \mathbf{0}$; in particular, if $\mathbf{w} = s\mathbf{v}$, then $\mathbf{v} \times \mathbf{w} = \mathbf{0}$
Zero product	$\mathbf{v} \times \mathbf{0} = \mathbf{0} \times \mathbf{v} = \mathbf{0}$

Proof: Let $\mathbf{u} = a_1\mathbf{i} + a_2\mathbf{j} + a_3\mathbf{k}$, $\mathbf{v} = b_1\mathbf{i} + b_2\mathbf{j} + b_3\mathbf{k}$, and $\mathbf{w} = c_1\mathbf{i} + c_2\mathbf{j} + c_3\mathbf{k}$.

Scalar distributivity and **vector distributivity** are proved by using the definition of cross product and the corresponding properties of real numbers.

Zero factors:

$$\mathbf{v} \times \mathbf{v} = \begin{vmatrix} \mathbf{i} & \mathbf{j} & \mathbf{k} \\ b_1 & b_2 & b_3 \\ b_1 & b_2 & b_3 \end{vmatrix} = \mathbf{0} \qquad \textit{Property of determinants (two rows the same)}$$

$$\mathbf{v} \times \mathbf{w} = \mathbf{v} \times c\mathbf{v} = c(\mathbf{v} \times \mathbf{v}) = \mathbf{0}$$

Zero product is obvious.

---

*Properly, it is the distributive property of vectors for cross product over addition, which, for convenience, we shorten to vector distributivity.

Figure 10.26 Vector product of two vectors

■ GEOMETRIC INTERPRETATION OF CROSS PRODUCT

We will show with the following theorem that the vector ($\mathbf{v} \times \mathbf{w}$) is orthogonal to both the vectors $\mathbf{v}$ and $\mathbf{w}$. The only way this can occur is in a three-dimensional setting. Any two distinct nonzero vectors in $\mathbb{R}^3$ that are not parallel (that is, not scalar multiples of one another) can be arranged to determine a plane. Then, according to the geometric property of cross product (Theorem 10.6) the vector product *must* be orthogonal to this plane, as shown in Figure 10.26.

THEOREM 10.6   Geometric property of cross product

If $\mathbf{v}$ and $\mathbf{w}$ are nonzero vectors in $\mathbb{R}^3$ that are not multiples of one another, then $\mathbf{v} \times \mathbf{w}$ is orthogonal to both $\mathbf{v}$ and $\mathbf{w}$.

Proof: We will show ($\mathbf{v} \times \mathbf{w}$) is orthogonal to $\mathbf{v}$ and leave the proof that $\mathbf{v} \times \mathbf{w}$ is orthogonal to $\mathbf{w}$ as an exercise. Let $\mathbf{v} = a_1\mathbf{i} + a_2\mathbf{j} + a_3\mathbf{k}$ and $\mathbf{w} = b_1\mathbf{i} + b_2\mathbf{j} + b_3\mathbf{k}$. Then,

$$\mathbf{v} \times \mathbf{w} = \begin{vmatrix} \mathbf{i} & \mathbf{j} & \mathbf{k} \\ a_1 & a_2 & a_3 \\ b_1 & b_2 & b_3 \end{vmatrix} = (a_2b_3 - a_3b_2)\mathbf{i} - (a_1b_3 - a_3b_1)\mathbf{j} + (a_1b_2 - a_2b_1)\mathbf{k}$$

To show this vector is orthogonal to $\mathbf{v}$, we find $\mathbf{v} \cdot (\mathbf{v} \times \mathbf{w})$:

$$\mathbf{v} \cdot (\mathbf{v} \times \mathbf{w}) = a_1(a_2b_3 - a_3b_2) - a_2(a_1b_3 - a_3b_1) + a_3(a_1b_2 - a_2b_1)$$
$$= a_1a_2b_3 - a_1a_3b_2 - a_1a_2b_3 + a_2a_3b_1 + a_1a_3b_2 - a_2a_3b_1$$
$$= 0 \qquad ■$$

EXAMPLE 2   A vector orthogonal to two given vectors

Find a nonzero vector that is orthogonal to both $\mathbf{v} = -2\mathbf{i} + 3\mathbf{j} - 7\mathbf{k}$ and $\mathbf{w} = 5\mathbf{i} + 9\mathbf{k}$.

Solution   The cross product $\mathbf{v} \times \mathbf{w}$ is orthogonal to both $\mathbf{v}$ and $\mathbf{w}$.

$$\mathbf{v} \times \mathbf{w} = \begin{vmatrix} \mathbf{i} & \mathbf{j} & \mathbf{k} \\ -2 & 3 & -7 \\ 5 & 0 & 9 \end{vmatrix} = (27 + 0)\mathbf{i} - (-18 + 35)\mathbf{j} + (0 - 15)\mathbf{k}$$
$$= 27\mathbf{i} - 17\mathbf{j} - 15\mathbf{k} \qquad ▬$$

Because both $\mathbf{v} \times \mathbf{w}$ and $\mathbf{w} \times \mathbf{v}$ are orthogonal to the plane determined by $\mathbf{v}$ and $\mathbf{w}$, and because ($\mathbf{v} \times \mathbf{w}$) = $-(\mathbf{w} \times \mathbf{v})$, we see that one points up from the given plane and the other points down. In order to see which is which, we state the **right-hand rule**, which is described in Figure 10.27.

Figure 10.27 The right-hand rule: If you place the palm of your right hand along $\mathbf{v}$ with your fingers pointing in the direction of $\mathbf{v}$, and you curl your fingers toward $\mathbf{w}$, then your thumb points in the direction of $\mathbf{v} \times \mathbf{w}$.

EXAMPLE 3   Right-hand rule

Use the right-hand rule to verify each of the following cross products.

$$\mathbf{i} \times \mathbf{j} = \mathbf{k} \qquad \mathbf{j} \times \mathbf{i} = -\mathbf{k} \qquad \mathbf{i} \times \mathbf{i} = 0 \qquad \mathbf{i} \times \mathbf{k} = -\mathbf{j} \qquad \mathbf{k} \times \mathbf{i} = \mathbf{j}$$

$$\mathbf{j} \times \mathbf{j} = 0 \qquad \mathbf{j} \times \mathbf{k} = \mathbf{i} \qquad \mathbf{k} \times \mathbf{j} = -\mathbf{i} \qquad \mathbf{k} \times \mathbf{k} = 0$$

Solution

i × j   Place the palm of your right hand along **i**, pointing in the direction of **i**, and curl your fingers toward **j**. The answer is **k**.

j × i   Place the palm of your right hand along **j**, pointing in the direction of **j**, and curl your fingers toward **i**. The answer is −**k**.

$$\mathbf{i} \times \mathbf{i} = \begin{vmatrix} \mathbf{i} & \mathbf{j} & \mathbf{k} \\ 1 & 0 & 0 \\ 1 & 0 & 0 \end{vmatrix} = \mathbf{0}$$

The other parts are left for you to verify.

■ PROPERTIES OF CROSS PRODUCT

Next, we will find the magnitude of the cross product of two vectors.

THEOREM 10.7   Magnitude of a cross product

If **v** and **w** are nonzero vectors in $\mathbb{R}^3$ with θ the angle between **v** and **w** ($0 \le \theta \le \pi$), then

$$\|\mathbf{v} \times \mathbf{w}\| = \|\mathbf{v}\| \, \|\mathbf{w}\| \sin \theta$$

Proof: Let $\mathbf{v} = a_1\mathbf{i} + a_2\mathbf{j} + a_3\mathbf{k}$ and $\mathbf{w} = b_1\mathbf{i} + b_2\mathbf{j} + b_3\mathbf{k}$.

$$\|\mathbf{v}\| \, \|\mathbf{w}\| \sin \theta = \|\mathbf{v}\| \, \|\mathbf{w}\| \sqrt{1 - \cos^2 \theta}$$

$$= \|\mathbf{v}\| \, \|\mathbf{w}\| \sqrt{1 - \left[\frac{\mathbf{v} \cdot \mathbf{w}}{\|\mathbf{v}\| \, \|\mathbf{w}\|}\right]^2}$$

$$= \|\mathbf{v}\| \, \|\mathbf{w}\| \frac{\sqrt{\|\mathbf{v}\|^2\|\mathbf{w}\|^2 - (\mathbf{v} \cdot \mathbf{w})^2}}{\|\mathbf{v}\| \, \|\mathbf{w}\|}$$

$$= \sqrt{(a_1{}^2 + a_2{}^2 + a_3{}^2)(b_1{}^2 + b_2{}^2 + b_3{}^2) - (a_1b_1 + a_2b_2 + a_3b_3)^2}$$

$$= \sqrt{(a_2b_3 - a_3b_2)^2 + (a_3b_1 - a_1b_3)^2 + (a_1b_2 - a_2b_1)^2}$$

$$= \|\mathbf{v} \times \mathbf{w}\|$$

There is another interpretation for Theorem 10.7—namely, $\|\mathbf{v} \times \mathbf{w}\|$ is equal to the area of a parallelogram having **v** and **w** as adjacent sides, as shown in Figure 10.28. To see this, note that because $h = \|\mathbf{w}\| \sin \theta$, we have

$$\text{AREA} = (\text{BASE})(\text{HEIGHT}) = \|\mathbf{v}\| \, (\|\mathbf{w}\| \sin \theta) = \|\mathbf{v} \times \mathbf{w}\|$$

Figure 10.28 A geometric interpretation of $\|\mathbf{v} \times \mathbf{w}\|$

Here is an example that uses this formula. You might also note that even though $\mathbf{v} \times \mathbf{w} \ne \mathbf{w} \times \mathbf{v}$, it is true that $\|\mathbf{v} \times \mathbf{w}\| = \|\mathbf{w} \times \mathbf{v}\|$

Find the area of the triangle with vertices $P(-2, 4, 5)$, $Q(0, 7, -4)$, and $R(-1, 5, 0)$.

Draw this triangle as shown in Figure 10.29. Then $\triangle PQR$ has half the area of the parallelogram determined by the vectors $\mathbf{PQ}$ and $\mathbf{PR}$; that is, the triangle has area

$$A = \tfrac{1}{2}\|\mathbf{PQ} \times \mathbf{PR}\|$$

First find

$$\mathbf{PQ} = (0 + 2)\mathbf{i} + (7 - 4)\mathbf{j} + (-4 - 5)\mathbf{k} = 2\mathbf{i} + 3\mathbf{j} - 9\mathbf{k}$$

$$\mathbf{PR} = (-1 + 2)\mathbf{i} + (5 - 4)\mathbf{j} + (0 - 5)\mathbf{k} = \mathbf{i} + \mathbf{j} - 5\mathbf{k}$$

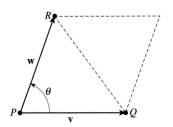

Figure 10.29 Area of a triangle by cross product $A = \tfrac{1}{2}\|\mathbf{v} \times \mathbf{w}\|$

and compute the cross product:

$$\mathbf{PQ} \times \mathbf{PR} = \begin{vmatrix} \mathbf{i} & \mathbf{j} & \mathbf{k} \\ 2 & 3 & -9 \\ 1 & 1 & -5 \end{vmatrix}$$

$$= (-15 + 9)\mathbf{i} - (-10 + 9)\mathbf{j} + (2 - 3)\mathbf{k}$$

$$= -6\mathbf{i} + \mathbf{j} - \mathbf{k}$$

Thus, the triangle has area

$$A = \tfrac{1}{2}\|\mathbf{PQ} \times \mathbf{PR}\|$$

$$= \tfrac{1}{2}\sqrt{(-6)^2 + 1^2 + (-1)^2}$$

$$= \tfrac{1}{2}\sqrt{38}$$

■ TRIPLE SCALAR PRODUCT; VOLUME

The cross product can also be used to compute the volume of a parallelepiped in $\mathbb{R}^3$. Consider the parallelepiped determined by three nonzero vectors $\mathbf{u}$, $\mathbf{v}$, and $\mathbf{w}$ that do not all lie in the same plane, as shown in Figure 10.30.

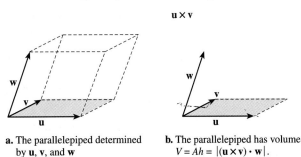

a. The parallelepiped determined by $\mathbf{u}$, $\mathbf{v}$, and $\mathbf{w}$

b. The parallelepiped has volume $V = Ah = |(\mathbf{u} \times \mathbf{v}) \cdot \mathbf{w}|$.

Figure 10.30 Computing volume with the triple scalar product

It is known from solid geometry that this parallelepiped has volume $V = Ah$, where A is the area of the face determined by $\mathbf{u}$ and $\mathbf{v}$ and h is the altitude from the tip of $\mathbf{w}$ to this face (see Figure 10.30b).

The face determined by $\mathbf{u}$ and $\mathbf{v}$ is a parallelogram with area $A = \|\mathbf{u} \times \mathbf{v}\|$, and we know that the cross-product vector $\mathbf{u} \times \mathbf{v}$ is perpendicular to both $\mathbf{u}$ and $\mathbf{v}$ and hence to the face determined by $\mathbf{u}$ and $\mathbf{v}$. From the alternative form of the dot product, we have

$$(\mathbf{u} \times \mathbf{v}) \cdot \mathbf{w} = \|\mathbf{u} \times \mathbf{v}\| \, \|\mathbf{w}\| \cos \theta$$

where θ is the angle between $\mathbf{u} \times \mathbf{v}$ and $\mathbf{w}$. Thus, the parallelepiped has altitude

$$h = \|\mathbf{w}\| \cos \theta = \left| \frac{(\mathbf{u} \times \mathbf{v}) \cdot \mathbf{w}}{\|\mathbf{u} \times \mathbf{v}\|} \right|$$

and the volume is given as

$$V = Ah = \|\mathbf{u} \times \mathbf{v}\| \left| \frac{(\mathbf{u} \times \mathbf{v}) \cdot \mathbf{w}}{\|\mathbf{u} \times \mathbf{v}\|} \right| = |(\mathbf{u} \times \mathbf{v}) \cdot \mathbf{w}|$$

The combined operation $(\mathbf{u} \times \mathbf{v}) \cdot \mathbf{w}$ is called the **triple scalar product** of $\mathbf{u}$, $\mathbf{v}$, and $\mathbf{w}$. These observations are summarized in the following box.

Volume Interpretation of the Triple Scalar Product

Let $\mathbf{u}$, $\mathbf{v}$, and $\mathbf{w}$ be nonzero vectors that do not all lie in the same plane. Then the parallelepiped determined by these vectors has volume

$$V = |(\mathbf{u} \times \mathbf{v}) \cdot \mathbf{w}|$$

EXAMPLE 5   Volume of a parallelepiped

Find the volume of the parallelepiped determined by the vectors

$$\mathbf{u} = \mathbf{i} - 2\mathbf{j} + 3\mathbf{k} \qquad \mathbf{v} = -4\mathbf{i} + 7\mathbf{j} - 11\mathbf{k} \qquad \mathbf{w} = 5\mathbf{i} + 9\mathbf{j} - \mathbf{k}$$

Solution   We first find the cross product.

$$\mathbf{u} \times \mathbf{v} = \begin{vmatrix} \mathbf{i} & \mathbf{j} & \mathbf{k} \\ 1 & -2 & 3 \\ -4 & 7 & -11 \end{vmatrix} = (22 - 21)\mathbf{i} - (-11 + 12)\mathbf{j} + (7 - 8)\mathbf{k}$$

$$= \mathbf{i} - \mathbf{j} - \mathbf{k}$$

Thus,

$$V = |(\mathbf{u} \times \mathbf{v}) \cdot \mathbf{w}| = |(\mathbf{i} - \mathbf{j} - \mathbf{k}) \cdot (5\mathbf{i} + 9\mathbf{j} - \mathbf{k})| = |5 - 9 + 1| = 3$$

The volume of the parallelepiped is 3 cubic units.   ▬

THEOREM 10.8   Determinant form for a triple scalar product: volume of a parallelepiped

If $\mathbf{u} = a_1\mathbf{i} + a_2\mathbf{j} + a_3\mathbf{k}$, $\mathbf{v} = b_1\mathbf{i} + b_2\mathbf{j} + b_3\mathbf{k}$, and $\mathbf{w} = c_1\mathbf{i} + c_2\mathbf{j} + c_3\mathbf{k}$, then the triple scalar product can be found by evaluating the determinant

$$(\mathbf{u} \times \mathbf{v}) \cdot \mathbf{w} = \begin{vmatrix} a_1 & a_2 & a_3 \\ b_1 & b_2 & b_3 \\ c_1 & c_2 & c_3 \end{vmatrix}$$

Proof: The proof follows by expanding the determinant (see Problem 49).   ■

We can use Theorem 10.8 to rework Example 5.

$$(\mathbf{u} \times \mathbf{v}) \cdot \mathbf{w} = \begin{vmatrix} 1 & -2 & 3 \\ -4 & 7 & -11 \\ 5 & 9 & -1 \end{vmatrix} = -3$$

Thus, the volume is $|-3| = 3$.

In the problem set we have included several exercises involving the triple scalar product and the triple vector product $\mathbf{u} \times \mathbf{v} \times \mathbf{w}$. In case you wonder why we neglect the product $(\mathbf{u} \cdot \mathbf{v}) \times \mathbf{w}$, notice that such a product makes no sense, because $\mathbf{u} \cdot \mathbf{v}$ is a *scalar* and the cross product is an operation involving only vectors. Thus, the product $\mathbf{u} \cdot \mathbf{v} \times \mathbf{w}$ must mean $\mathbf{u} \cdot (\mathbf{v} \times \mathbf{w})$.

■ TORQUE

$$T = PQ \times F$$

Figure 10.31 Torque given by a cross product

A useful physical application of the cross product involves **torque**. Suppose the force **F** is applied to the point Q. Then the torque of **F** around P is defined as the cross product of the "arm" vector **PQ** with the force **F**, as shown in Figure 10.31. Thus, the torque, **T**, of **F** at Q about P is

$$\mathbf{T} = \mathbf{PQ} \times \mathbf{F}$$

The magnitude of the torque, $\|\mathbf{T}\|$, provides a measure of the tendency of the vector arm **PQ** to rotate counterclockwise about an axis perpendicular to the plane determined by **PQ** and **F** (see Figure 10.31).

EXAMPLE 6   Torque on the hinge of a door

Figure 10.32 shows a half-open door that is 3 ft wide. A horizontal force of 30 lb is applied at the edge of the door. Find the torque of the force about the hinge on the door.

Figure 10.32 The torque of a force applied at the edge of a door about the hinges

Solution We represent the force by $\mathbf{F} = -30\mathbf{i}$ (see Figure 10.32). Because the door is half open, it makes an angle of $\frac{\pi}{4}$ with the horizontal, and we can represent the "arm" **PQ** by the vector

$$\mathbf{PQ} = 3\left(\cos\frac{\pi}{4}\,\mathbf{i} + \sin\frac{\pi}{4}\,\mathbf{j}\right) = 3\left(\frac{\sqrt{2}}{2}\,\mathbf{i} + \frac{\sqrt{2}}{2}\,\mathbf{j}\right) = \frac{3\sqrt{2}}{2}\,\mathbf{i} + \frac{3\sqrt{2}}{2}\,\mathbf{j}$$

The torque can now be found:

$$\mathbf{T} = \mathbf{PQ} \times \mathbf{F} = \begin{vmatrix} \mathbf{i} & \mathbf{j} & \mathbf{k} \\ \frac{3\sqrt{2}}{2} & \frac{3\sqrt{2}}{2} & 0 \\ -30 & 0 & 0 \end{vmatrix} = 45\sqrt{2}\,\mathbf{k}$$

The magnitude of the torque ($45\sqrt{2}$ ft-lb) is a measure of the tendency of the door to rotate about its hinges. ■

PROBLEM SET 10.4

Ⓐ *Find* **v** × **w** *for the vectors given in Problems 1–10.*

1. **v** = **i**; **w** = **j**
2. **v** = **k**; **w** = **k**
3. **v** = 3**i** + 2**k**; **w** = 2**i** + **j**
4. **v** = **i** − 3**j**; **w** = **i** + 5**k**
5. **v** = 3**i** − 2**j** + 4**k**; **w** = **i** + 4**j** − 7**k**
6. **v** = 5**i** − **j** + 2**k**; **w** = 2**i** + **j** − 3**k**
7. **v** = 3**i** − **j** + 2**k**; **w** = 2**i** + 3**j** − 4**k**
8. **v** = −**j** + 4**k**; **w** = 5**i** + 6**k**
9. **v** = **i** − 6**j** + 10**k**; **w** = −**i** + 5**j** − 6**k**
10. **v** = cos θ **i** + sin θ**j**; **w** = −sin θ **i** + cos θ **j**

Find sin θ *where* θ *is the angle between* **v** *and* **w** *in Problems 11–16.*

11. **v** = **i** + **k**; **w** = **i** + **j**
12. **v** = **i** + **j**; **w** = **i** + **j** + **k**
13. **v** = **j** + **k**; **w** = **i** + **k**
14. **v** = **i** + **j**; **w** = **j** + **k**
15. **v** = **i** + 2**j** + 3**k**; **w** = 4**i** + 5**j** + 6**k**
16. **v** = cos θ **i** − sin θ **j**; **w** = sin θ **i** − cos θ **j**

Find a unit vector that is orthogonal to both **v** *and* **w** *in Problems 17–20.*

17. **v** = 2**i** + **k**; **w** = **i** − **j** − **k**
18. **v** = **j** − 3**k**; **w** = −**i** + **j** + **k**

19. **v** = **i** + **j** + **k**; **w** = 3**i** + 12**j** − 4**k**
20. **v** = 2**i** − 2**j** + **k**; **w** = 4**i** + 2**j** − 3**k**

Find the area of the parallelogram determined by the vectors in Problems 21–24.

21. 3**i** + 4**j** and **i** + **j** − **k**
22. 2**i** − **j** + 2**k** and 4**i** − 3**j**
23. 4**i** − **j** + **k** and 2**i** + 3**j** − **k**
24. 2**i** + 3**k** and 2**j** − 3**k**

Find the area of △*PQR in Problems 25–28.*

25. $P(0, 1, 1), Q(1, 1, 0), R(1, 0, 1)$
26. $P(1, 0, 0), Q(2, 1, −1), R(0, 1, −2)$
27. $P(1, 2, 3), Q(2, 3, 1), R(3, 1, 2)$
28. $P(−1, −1, −1), Q(1, −1, −1), R(−1, 1, −1)$

Determine whether each product in Problems 29–31 is a scalar or a vector or does not exist. Explain your reasoning.

29. **a.** **u** × (**v** · **w**)   **b.** **u** · (**v** × **w**)
30. **a.** **u** × (**v** × **w**)   **b.** **u** · (**v** · **w**)
31. **a.** (**u** × **v**) · (**u** × **w**)   **b.** (**u** × **v**) × (**u** × **w**)

In Problems 32–35, find the volume of the parallelepiped determined by vectors **u**, **v**, *and* **w**.

32. $\mathbf{u} = \mathbf{i} + \mathbf{j}$; $\mathbf{v} = \mathbf{j} + 2\mathbf{k}$; $\mathbf{w} = 3\mathbf{k}$

33. $\mathbf{u} = \mathbf{j} + \mathbf{k}$; $\mathbf{v} = 2\mathbf{i} + \mathbf{j} + 2\mathbf{k}$; $\mathbf{w} = 5\mathbf{i}$

34. $\mathbf{u} = \mathbf{i} + \mathbf{j} + \mathbf{k}$; $\mathbf{v} = \mathbf{i} - \mathbf{j} - \mathbf{k}$; $\mathbf{w} = 2\mathbf{i} + 3\mathbf{k}$

35. $\mathbf{u} = 2\mathbf{i} + \mathbf{j} - \mathbf{k}$; $\mathbf{v} = 3\mathbf{i} + \mathbf{k}$; $\mathbf{w} = \mathbf{j} + \mathbf{k}$

Ⓑ 36. ■ **What Does This Say?** Contrast dot and cross products of vectors, including a discussion of some of their properties.

37. ■ **What Does This Say?** What is the right-hand rule?

38. ■ **What Does This Say?** Describe the meaning of $|(\mathbf{u} \times \mathbf{v}) \cdot \mathbf{w}|$.

39. THINK TANK PROBLEM

    a. If $\mathbf{u} \times \mathbf{w} = \mathbf{v} \times \mathbf{w}$, does it follow that $\mathbf{u} = \mathbf{v}$?

    b. If $\mathbf{u} \cdot \mathbf{w} = \mathbf{v} \cdot \mathbf{w}$, does it follow that $\mathbf{u} = \mathbf{v}$?

    c. If both $\mathbf{u} \times \mathbf{w} = \mathbf{v} \times \mathbf{w}$ and $\mathbf{u} \cdot \mathbf{w} = \mathbf{v} \cdot \mathbf{w}$, does it follow that $\mathbf{u} = \mathbf{v}$?

40. Find a number s that guarantees that the vectors $\mathbf{i}$, $\mathbf{i} + \mathbf{j} + \mathbf{k}$, and $\mathbf{i} + 2\mathbf{j} + s\mathbf{k}$ will be parallel to the same plane.

41. Find a number t that guarantees the vectors $\mathbf{i} + \mathbf{j}$, $2\mathbf{i} - \mathbf{j} + \mathbf{k}$, and $\mathbf{i} + \mathbf{j} + t\mathbf{k}$ will be parallel to the same plane.

42. Find the angle between the vector $2\mathbf{i} - \mathbf{j} + \mathbf{k}$ and the plane determined by the points $P(1, -2, 3)$, $Q(-1, 2, 3)$, and $R(1, 2, -3)$

43. Let $\mathbf{u} = \mathbf{i} + \mathbf{j}$, $\mathbf{v} = 2\mathbf{i} - \mathbf{j} + \mathbf{k}$, and $\mathbf{w} = 3\mathbf{i}$. Compute $(\mathbf{u} \times \mathbf{v}) \times \mathbf{w}$ and $\mathbf{u} \times (\mathbf{v} \times \mathbf{w})$. What does this say about the associativity of cross product?

44. Show that $(a\mathbf{u}) \times (b\mathbf{v}) = ab(\mathbf{u} \times \mathbf{v})$ and scalars a and b.

45. For a given vector $\mathbf{v}$ in $\mathbb{R}^3$, find all vectors $\mathbf{w}$ such that $\mathbf{v} \times \mathbf{w} = \mathbf{w}$.

46. What can be said about vectors $\mathbf{v}$, $\mathbf{w}$ if $\mathbf{v} \cdot \mathbf{w} = \mathbf{0}$? What can be said if $\mathbf{w} \times \mathbf{v} = \mathbf{0}$?

47. One end of a 2-ft lever pivots about the origin in the yz-plane, as shown in Figure 10.33.

Figure 10.33 Finding the torque

If a vertical force of 40 lb is applied at the end of the lever, what is the torque of the lever about the pivot point (the origin) when the lever makes an angle of 30° with the xy-plane?

48. A 3-lb weight hangs from a rope at the end of Q of a 5-ft stick PQ that is held at an angle of 60° to the horizontal, as shown in Figure 10.34. What is the torque about the point P due to the weight?

Figure 10.34 Finding the torque

49. Prove the determinant formula for evaluating a triple scalar product.

50. **a.** Show that the vectors $\mathbf{u}$, $\mathbf{v}$, and $\mathbf{w}$ are coplanar (all in the same plane) if

$$\mathbf{u} \cdot (\mathbf{v} \times \mathbf{w}) = 0 \quad \text{or} \quad (\mathbf{u} \times \mathbf{v}) \cdot \mathbf{w} = 0$$

    b. Verify that the vectors $\mathbf{u} = \mathbf{i} + 3\mathbf{j} + \mathbf{k}$, $\mathbf{v} = 2\mathbf{i} - \mathbf{j} - \mathbf{k}$, and $\mathbf{w} = 7\mathbf{j} + 3\mathbf{k}$ are coplanar.

51. Show that the triangle with vertices (x_1, y_1), (x_2, y_2), (x_3, y_3) has area $A = \frac{1}{2}D$, where

$$D = \begin{vmatrix} x_1 & y_1 & 1 \\ x_2 & y_2 & 1 \\ x_3 & y_3 & 1 \end{vmatrix}$$

52. Using the properties of determinants, show that

$$\mathbf{u} \cdot (\mathbf{v} \times \mathbf{w}) = (\mathbf{u} \times \mathbf{v}) \cdot \mathbf{w}$$

for any vectors $\mathbf{u}$, $\mathbf{v}$, and $\mathbf{w}$.

Ⓒ 53. Let A, B, C, and D be four points that do not lie in the same plane. It can be shown that the volume of the tetrahedron with vertices A, B, C, and D satisfies

$$\begin{bmatrix} \text{VOLUME OF} \\ \text{TETRAHEDRON } ABCD \end{bmatrix} = \frac{1}{3}\begin{pmatrix} \text{AREA OF} \\ \triangle ABC \end{pmatrix}\begin{pmatrix} \text{ALTITUDE FROM} \\ D \text{ TO } \triangle ABC \end{pmatrix}$$

Show that the volume is given by

$$V = \frac{1}{6}|(\mathbf{AB} \times \mathbf{AC}) \cdot \mathbf{AD}|$$

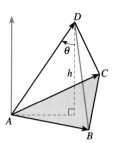

54. Show that if $\mathbf{u}$, $\mathbf{v}$, and $\mathbf{w}$ are vectors in $\mathbb{R}^3$ with $\mathbf{u} + \mathbf{v} + \mathbf{w} = \mathbf{0}$, then

$$\mathbf{u} \times \mathbf{v} = \mathbf{v} \times \mathbf{w} = \mathbf{w} \times \mathbf{u}$$

55. Suppose $\mathbf{u}$, $\mathbf{v}$, and $\mathbf{w}$ are nonzero vectors in $\mathbb{R}^3$ with $\mathbf{u} \times \mathbf{v} = \mathbf{w}$ and $\mathbf{u} \cdot \mathbf{v} = 0$. Show that

$$\mathbf{v} = s(\mathbf{w} \times \mathbf{u}) \quad \text{and} \quad \mathbf{u} = t(\mathbf{v} \times \mathbf{w})$$

for scalars s and t.

56. Show that $(c\mathbf{u}) \times (d\mathbf{v}) = cd(\mathbf{u} \times \mathbf{v})$.

57. Show that
$$\tan\theta = \frac{\|\mathbf{v} \times \mathbf{w}\|}{\mathbf{v} \cdot \mathbf{w}}$$
where $\theta \left(0 \le \theta \le \frac{\pi}{2}\right)$ is the angle between $\mathbf{v}$ and $\mathbf{w}$.

58. Show that if all three vertices of a triangle have integer coordinates, the area of the triangle is at least 0.5.

59. Let $\mathbf{u}$, $\mathbf{v}$, and $\mathbf{w}$ be nonzero vectors in $\mathbb{R}^3$, no two of which lie in the same plane. Show that
$$|\mathbf{u} \cdot (\mathbf{v} \times \mathbf{w})| = |\mathbf{v} \cdot (\mathbf{u} \times \mathbf{w})|$$

What other triple scalar products involving $\mathbf{u}$, $\mathbf{v}$, and $\mathbf{w}$ have the same absolute values?

60. Let $\mathbf{a}$, $\mathbf{b}$, and $\mathbf{c}$ be vectors in space. Show
$$\mathbf{a} \times (\mathbf{b} \times \mathbf{c}) = (\mathbf{c} \cdot \mathbf{a})\mathbf{b} - (\mathbf{b} \cdot \mathbf{a})\mathbf{c}$$
This is called the "cab − bac" formula.

Establish the validity of the equations in Problems 61–64 for arbitrary vectors $\mathbf{u}$, $\mathbf{v}$, $\mathbf{w}$, and $\mathbf{z}$ in $\mathbb{R}^3$.

61. $(\mathbf{u} \times \mathbf{v}) \times (\mathbf{w} \times \mathbf{z}) = (\mathbf{u} \cdot \mathbf{w} \times \mathbf{z})\mathbf{v} - (\mathbf{v} \cdot \mathbf{w} \times \mathbf{z})\mathbf{u}$

62. $\mathbf{u} \times (\mathbf{v} \times \mathbf{w}) + \mathbf{v} \times (\mathbf{w} \times \mathbf{u}) + \mathbf{w} \times (\mathbf{u} \times \mathbf{v}) = 0$

63. $\mathbf{u} \times \mathbf{v} = (\mathbf{u} \cdot \mathbf{v} \times \mathbf{i})\mathbf{i} + (\mathbf{u} \cdot \mathbf{v} \times \mathbf{j})\mathbf{j} + (\mathbf{u} \cdot \mathbf{v} \times \mathbf{k})\mathbf{k}$

64. $\mathbf{u} \times [\mathbf{u} \times (\mathbf{u} \times \mathbf{v})] \cdot \mathbf{w} = -\|\mathbf{u}\|^2\mathbf{u} \cdot \mathbf{v} \times \mathbf{w}$

10.5 LINES AND PLANES IN SPACE

> **IN THIS SECTION** **Lines in $\mathbb{R}^3$, direction cosines, planes in $\mathbb{R}^3$**
> We represent lines in either parametric or symmetric forms and then turn our attention to planes in $\mathbb{R}^3$.

■ LINES IN $\mathbb{R}^3$

Figure 10.35 If L is aligned with $\mathbf{v}$ and contains Q, then P is on L whenever $\mathbf{QP} = t\mathbf{v}$.

As in the plane, a line in space is completely determined once we know one of its points and its direction. We used the concept of slope to measure the direction of a line in the plane, but in space, it is more convenient to specify direction with vectors.

Suppose L is a line in space that contains $Q(x_0, y_0, z_0)$ and is parallel to the vector $\mathbf{v} = A\mathbf{i} + B\mathbf{j} + C\mathbf{k}$. We say that L is **aligned with v**, as shown in Figure 10.35. We also say that the line has **direction numbers** A, B, and C and denote these direction numbers by $[A, B, C]$. If $P(x, y, z)$ is any point on L, then the vector $\mathbf{QP}$ is parallel to $\mathbf{v}$ and must satisfy the vector equation $\mathbf{QP} = t\mathbf{v}$ for some number t. If we introduce coordinates and use the standard representation, we can rewrite this vector equation as
$$(x - x_0)\mathbf{i} + (y - y_0)\mathbf{j} + (z - z_0)\mathbf{k} = t[A\mathbf{i} + B\mathbf{j} + C\mathbf{k}]$$

By equating components on both sides of this equation, we find that the coordinates of P must satisfy the linear system
$$x - x_0 = tA \qquad y - y_0 = tB \qquad z - z_0 = tC$$
where t is a real number.

Parametric Form of a Line in $\mathbb{R}^3$

> If L is a line that contains the point (x_0, y_0, z_0) and is aligned with the vector $\mathbf{v} = A\mathbf{i} + B\mathbf{j} + C\mathbf{k}$, then the point (x, y, z) is on L if and only if its coordinates satisfy
> $$x = x_0 + tA \qquad y = y_0 + tB \qquad z = z_0 + tC$$
> for some number t.

⊘ t will be a different value for each point (x, y, z). ⊘

Turning things around, if we are given the equation of a line with direction numbers $[A, B, C]$, then $\mathbf{v} = A\mathbf{i} + B\mathbf{j} + C\mathbf{k}$ is the **vector** aligned with L.

DRAWING LESSON 4: DRAWING A LINE IN SPACE

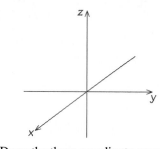

a. Draw the three coordinate axes.

b. Draw the three coordinate planes.

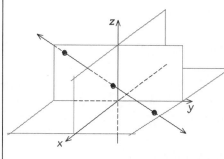

c. Plot points where the line intersects each coordinate plane. Used dashed lines for hidden parts.

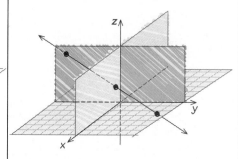

d. Use highlighters or pencils to color the planes in order to add depth to the figure.

EXAMPLE 1   Parametric equations of a line in space

Find the parametric equations for the line that contains the point (3, 1, 4) and is aligned with the vector $\mathbf{v} = -\mathbf{i} + \mathbf{j} - 2\mathbf{k}$. Find where this line passes through the coordinate planes and sketch the line.

Solution   The direction numbers are $[-1, 1, -2]$ and $x_0 = 3$, $y_0 = 1$, $z_0 = 4$, so the line has the parametric form

$$x = 3 - t \qquad y = 1 + t \qquad z = 4 - 2t$$

This line will intersect the xy-plane when $z = 0$;

$$0 = 4 - 2t \quad \text{implies} \quad t = 2$$

If $t = 2$, then $x = 3 - 2 = 1$ and $y = 1 + 2 = 3$. This is the point (1, 3, 0). Similarly, the line intersects the xz-plane at (4, 0, 6) and the yz-plane at (0, 4, −2). Plot these points and draw the line, as shown in Figure 10.36. ▄

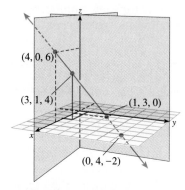

Figure 10.36 Graph of the line $x = 3 - t$, $y = 1 + t$, $z = 4 - 2t$

In the special case where none of the direction numbers A, B, or C is 0, we can solve each of the parametric-form equations for t to obtain the following **symmetric equations** for a line.

Symmetric Form of a Line in $\mathbb{R}^3$

If L is a line that contains the point (x_0, y_0, z_0) and is aligned with the vector $\mathbf{v} = A\mathbf{i} + B\mathbf{j} + C\mathbf{k}$ (A, B, and C nonzero numbers), then the point (x, y, z) is on L if and only if its coordinates satisfy

$$\frac{x - x_0}{A} = \frac{y - y_0}{B} = \frac{z - z_0}{C}$$

EXAMPLE 2 Symmetric form of the equation of a line in space

Find symmetric equations for the line L through the points $P(-1, 3, 7)$ and $Q(4, 2, -1)$. Find the points of intersection with the coordinate planes and sketch the line.

Solution The required line passes through P and is aligned with the vector

$$\mathbf{PQ} = [4 - (-1)]\mathbf{i} + [2 - 3]\mathbf{j} + [-1 - 7]\mathbf{k} = 5\mathbf{i} - \mathbf{j} - 8\mathbf{k}$$

Thus, the direction numbers of the line are $[5, -1, -8]$, and we can choose either P or Q as (x_0, y_0, z_0). Choosing P, we obtain

$$\frac{x + 1}{5} = \frac{y - 3}{-1} = \frac{z - 7}{-8}$$

Next, we find points of intersection with the coordinate planes:

xy-plane: $z = 0$, so $\frac{x + 1}{5} = \frac{7}{8}$ implies $x = \frac{27}{8}$ and $\frac{y - 3}{-1} = \frac{7}{8}$ implies $y = \frac{17}{8}$.

The point of intersection of line with the xy-plane is $\left(\frac{27}{8}, \frac{17}{8}, 0\right)$. Similarly, the other intersections are

$$xz\text{-plane:} \quad (14, 0, -17)$$
$$yz\text{-plane:} \quad \left(0, \frac{14}{5}, \frac{27}{5}\right)$$

The graph is shown in Figure 10.37.

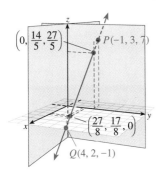

Figure 10.37 Graph of $\frac{x + 1}{5} = \frac{y - 3}{-1} = \frac{z - 7}{-8}$

You might remember that two lines in $\mathbb{R}^2$ must intersect if their slopes are different (because they cannot be parallel), but two lines in space may have different direction numbers and still not intersect. In this case, the lines are said to be **skew**. The reason why the situation in $\mathbb{R}^3$ is different from that in $\mathbb{R}^2$ is that even though lines with different direction numbers cannot be parallel, there is still enough "room" in space for the lines to lie in parallel planes and be aligned with vectors that are not parallel. This situation is shown in Figure 10.38.

a. Intersecting lines   **b.** Parallel lines   **c.** Skew lines

Figure 10.38 Lines in space may intersect, be parallel, or skew.

EXAMPLE 3 Skew lines in space

Determine whether the following pair of lines intersect, are parallel, or are skew.

$$L_1: \quad \frac{x - 1}{2} = \frac{y + 1}{1} = \frac{z - 2}{4} \quad \text{and} \quad L_2: \quad \frac{x + 2}{4} = \frac{y}{-3} = \frac{z + 1}{1}$$

Graph of L_1 and L_2

Note that $S(1, -1, 2)$ lies on L_1 and $T(-2, 0, -1)$ lies on L_2.

Solution   Note that L_1 has direction numbers [2, 1, 4] (that is, L is aligned with $2\mathbf{i} + \mathbf{j} + 4\mathbf{k}$) and L_2 has direction numbers [4, -3, 1]. If we solve

$$\langle 2, 1, 4 \rangle = t \langle 4, -3, 1 \rangle$$

for t, we find no possible solution for any value of t. This implies that the lines are not parallel.

Next we determine if the lines intersect or are skew. The lines intersect if and only if there is a point P that lies on both lines. To determine this, we write the equations of the lines in parametric form. We use a different parameter for each line so that points on one line do not depend on the value of the parameter of the other line:

$$L_1: \quad x = 1 + 2s \qquad y = -1 + s \qquad z = 2 + 4s$$
$$L_2: \quad x = -2 + 4t \qquad y = -3t \qquad z = -1 + t$$

The lines intersect if there are numbers s and t for which

$$x = 1 + 2s = -2 + 4t \quad \text{or} \quad 2s - 4t = -3$$
$$y = -1 + s = -3t \quad \text{or} \quad s + 3t = 1$$
$$z = 2 + 4s = -1 + t \quad \text{or} \quad 4s - t = -3$$

This is equivalent to the system of linear equations

$$\begin{cases} 2s - 4t = -3 \\ s + 3t = 1 \\ 4s - t = -3 \end{cases}$$

Any solution of this system must correspond to a point of intersection of L_1 and L_2, and if no solution exists, then L_1 and L_2 are skew. Because this is a system of three equations with two unknowns, we first solve the first two equations simultaneously to find $s = -\frac{1}{2}$, $t = \frac{1}{2}$. Because $s = -\frac{1}{2}$ and $t = \frac{1}{2}$ do not satisfy the third equation, it follows that L_1 and L_2 do not intersect, so they must be skew.   ■

EXAMPLE 4   Intersecting lines

Show that the lines

$$L_1: \quad \frac{x-1}{2} = \frac{y+1}{1} = \frac{z-2}{4} \quad \text{and} \quad L_2: \quad \frac{x+2}{4} = \frac{y}{-3} = \frac{z - \frac{1}{2}}{-1}$$

intersect and find the point of intersection.

Solution L_1 has direction numbers [2, 1, 4] and L_2 has direction numbers [4, -3, -1]. Because there is no t for which [2, 1, 4] = t[4, -3, -1], the lines are not parallel. Express the lines in parametric form:

$$L_1: \quad x = 1 + 2s \qquad y = -1 + s \qquad z = 2 + 4s$$
$$L_2: \quad x = -2 + 4t \qquad y = -3t \qquad z = \frac{1}{2} - t$$

At an intersection point we must have

$$1 + 2s = -2 + 4t \quad \text{or} \quad 2s - 4t = -3$$
$$-1 + s = -3t \quad \text{or} \quad s + 3t = 1$$
$$2 + 4s = \frac{1}{2} - t \quad \text{or} \quad 4s + t = -\frac{3}{2}$$

$\left(0, -\frac{3}{2}, 0\right)$

Graph of L_1 and L_2

Solving the first two equations simultaneously, we find $s = -\frac{1}{2}$, $t = \frac{1}{2}$. This solution satisfies the third equation, namely,

$$4\left(-\frac{1}{2}\right) + \frac{1}{2} = -\frac{3}{2}$$

To find the coordinates of the point of intersection, substitute $s = -\frac{1}{2}$ into the parametric-form equations for L_1 (or substitute $t = \frac{1}{2}$ into L_2) to obtain

$$x_0 = 1 + 2\left(-\frac{1}{2}\right) = 0$$

$$y_0 = -1 + \left(-\frac{1}{2}\right) = -\frac{3}{2}$$

$$z_0 = 2 + 4\left(-\frac{1}{2}\right) = 0$$

Thus, the lines intersect at $P\left(0, -\frac{3}{2}, 0\right)$.

■ DIRECTION COSINES

α determines blue plane.
β determines pink cone.
γ determines red vector.

Figure 10.39 Direction cosines of the vector **v**

Besides using direction numbers, the direction of a nonzero vector

$$\mathbf{v} = a_1\mathbf{i} + a_2\mathbf{j} + a_3\mathbf{k}$$

can be measured in terms of angles α, β, and γ between v and the coordinate axes, as shown in Figure 10.39. These angles are called the **direction angles** of **v** and their cosines are known as the **direction cosines** of **v**.

Note that because **i** is a unit vector represented by $\langle 1, 0, 0 \rangle$, we have

$$\mathbf{v} \cdot \mathbf{i} = (a_1 \cdot 1) + (a_2 \cdot 0) + (a_3 \cdot 0) = a_1$$

Therefore,

$$a_1 = \mathbf{v} \cdot \mathbf{i} = \|\mathbf{v}\| \|\mathbf{i}\| \cos \alpha \quad \text{so that} \quad \cos \alpha = \frac{a_1}{\|\mathbf{v}\|}$$

Similar formulas hold for the other direction cosines. If **u** is a unit vector in the same direction as **v,** we have

$$\mathbf{u} = \frac{\mathbf{v}}{\|\mathbf{v}\|} = \frac{a_1}{\|\mathbf{v}\|}\mathbf{i} + \frac{a_2}{\|\mathbf{v}\|}\mathbf{j} + \frac{a_3}{\|\mathbf{v}\|}\mathbf{k} = \cos \alpha\, \mathbf{i} + \cos \beta\, \mathbf{j} + \cos \gamma\, \mathbf{k}$$

$$\|\mathbf{u}\|^2 = \left(\frac{a_1}{\|\mathbf{v}\|}\right)^2 + \left(\frac{a_2}{\|\mathbf{v}\|}\right)^2 + \left(\frac{a_3}{\|\mathbf{v}\|}\right)^2 = \cos^2 \alpha + \cos^2 \beta + \cos^2 \gamma = 1$$

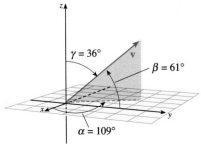

$\gamma = 36°$

$\beta = 61°$

$\alpha = 109°$

Graph of $\mathbf{v} = -2\mathbf{i} + 3\mathbf{j} + 5\mathbf{k}$

Find the direction cosines and direction angles (to the nearest degree) of the vector $\mathbf{v} = -2\mathbf{i} + 3\mathbf{j} + 5\mathbf{k}$, and verify the formula $\cos^2 \alpha + \cos^2 \beta + \cos^2 \gamma = 1$.

We find $\|\mathbf{v}\| = \sqrt{(-2)^2 + 3^2 + 5^2} = \sqrt{38}$. Therefore,

$$\cos \alpha = \frac{a_1}{\|\mathbf{v}\|} = \frac{-2}{\sqrt{38}} \approx -0.3244428 \qquad \alpha \approx \cos^{-1}(-0.324428) \approx 109°$$

$$\cos \beta = \frac{a_2}{\|\mathbf{v}\|} = \frac{3}{\sqrt{38}} \approx 0.4866642 \qquad \beta \approx \cos^{-1}(0.4866642) \approx 61°$$

$$\cos \gamma = \frac{a_3}{\|\mathbf{v}\|} = \frac{5}{\sqrt{38}} \approx 0.8111071 \qquad \gamma \approx \cos^{-1}(0.8111071) \approx 36°$$

and $\cos^2 \alpha + \cos^2 \beta + \cos^2 \gamma \approx (-0.3244)^2 + (0.4867)^2 + (0.8111)^2 \approx 1$.

Figure 10.40 A plane may be described by specifying one of its points and a normal vector **N**.

■ PLANES IN ℝ³

Planes in space can also be characterized by vector methods. In particular, any plane is completely determined once we know one of its points and its orientation; that is, the "direction" it faces. A common way to specify the direction of a plane is by means of a vector **N** that is orthogonal to every vector in the plane, as shown in Figure 10.40. Such a vector is called a **normal** to the plane.

EXAMPLE 6   Obtain the equation for a plane

Find an equation for the plane that contains the point $Q(3, -7, 2)$ and is normal to the vector $\mathbf{N} = 2\mathbf{i} + \mathbf{j} - 3\mathbf{k}$.

Solution   The normal vector **N** is orthogonal to every vector in the plane. In particular, if $P(x, y, z)$ is any point in the plane, then **N** must be orthogonal to the vector

$$\mathbf{QP} = (x - 3)\mathbf{i} + (y + 7)\mathbf{j} + (z - 2)\mathbf{k}$$

Because the dot (or scalar) product of two orthogonal vectors is 0, we have

$$\mathbf{N} \cdot \mathbf{QP} = 2(x - 3) + (1)(y + 7) + (-3)(z - 2) = 0$$
$$2x - 6 + y + 7 - 3z + 6 = 0$$
$$2x + y - 3z + 7 = 0$$

Therefore, $2x + y - 3z + 7 = 0$ is the equation of the plane.   ▬

Graph of plane in Example 6

By generalizing the approach illustrated in Example 6, we can show that the plane that contains the point (x_0, y_0, z_0) and has normal vector $\mathbf{N} = A\mathbf{i} + B\mathbf{j} + C\mathbf{k}$ must have the Cartesian equation

$$A(x - x_0) + B(y - y_0) + C(z - z_0) = 0$$

This is called the **point-normal form** of the equation of a plane. By rearranging terms, we can rewrite this equation in the form $Ax + By + Cz + D = 0$. This is called the **standard form** of the equation of a plane. The numbers $[A, B, C]$ are called the **attitude numbers** of the plane (see Figure 10.41).

Notice from Figure 10.41 that the *attitude numbers of a plane are the same as the direction numbers of the normal line.* This means that you can find normal vectors to a plane by *inspecting the equation of the plane.*

Figure 10.41 The graph of a plane with attitude numbers $[A, B, C]$

EXAMPLE 7   Relationship between normal vectors and planes

Find normal vectors to the planes

    a. $5x + 7y - 3z = 0$;   **b.** $x - 5y + \sqrt{2}z = 6$;   **c.** $3x - 7z = 10$

Solution   **a.** A normal to the plane $5x + 7y - 3z = 0$ is $\mathbf{N} = 5\mathbf{i} + 7\mathbf{j} - 3\mathbf{k}$.
    b. For $x - 5y + \sqrt{2}z = 6$ the normal is $\mathbf{N} = \mathbf{i} - 5\mathbf{j} + \sqrt{2}\mathbf{k}$.
    c. For $3x - 7z = 10$ it is $\mathbf{N} = 3\mathbf{i} - 7\mathbf{k}$.   ▬

Forms for the Equation of a Plane

> A plane with normal $\mathbf{N} = A\mathbf{i} + B\mathbf{j} + C\mathbf{k}$ that contains the point (x_0, y_0, z_0) has the following equations:
>
>   **Point-normal form:** $A(x - x_0) + B(y - y_0) + C(z - z_0) = 0$
>
>   **Standard form:** $Ax + By + Cz + D = 0$
>
> where A, B, C, and D are constants.

THEOREM 10.9   Existence of a plane

Let A, B, C, and D be constants with A, B, and C not all zero. Then the graph of the equation

$$Ax + By + Cz + D = 0$$

is the equation of a plane with normal vector $\mathbf{N} = A\mathbf{i} + B\mathbf{j} + C\mathbf{k}$.

Proof: Suppose $A \neq 0$. Then the equation $Ax + By + Cz + D = 0$ can be written as

$$A\left[x + \frac{D}{A}\right] + By + Cz = 0$$

which is the point-normal form of the plane that passes through the point $(-D/A, 0, 0)$ with a normal $\mathbf{N} = A\mathbf{i} + B\mathbf{j} + C\mathbf{k}$. A similar argument applies if $A = 0$ and either B or C is not zero.   ∎

EXAMPLE 8   Equation of a line orthogonal to a given plane

Find an equation of the line that passes through the point $Q(2, -1, 3)$ and is orthogonal to the plane $3x - 7y + 5z + 55 = 0$. Where does the line intersect the plane?

Solution   *By inspection* of the equation of the plane we see that $\mathbf{N} = 3\mathbf{i} - 7\mathbf{j} + 5\mathbf{k}$ is a normal vector to the plane. Because the required line is also orthogonal to the plane, it must be parallel to $\mathbf{N}$. Thus, the line contains the point $Q(2, -1, 3)$ and has direction numbers $[3, -7, 5]$, so that its equation is

$$\frac{x - 2}{3} = \frac{y + 1}{-7} = \frac{z - 3}{5}$$

To find the point where this line intersects the plane, we rewrite it in parametric form:

$$x = 2 + 3t, \qquad y = -1 - 7t, \quad \text{and} \quad z = 3 + 5t$$

Now, substitute into the equation of the plane:

$$3(2 + 3t) - 7(-1 - 7t) + 5(3 + 5t) = -55$$
$$6 + 9t + 7 + 49t + 15 + 25t = -55$$
$$83t = -83$$
$$t = -1$$

Thus, the point of intersection is found by substituting $t = -1$ for x, y, and z:

$$x = 2 + 3(-1) = -1$$
$$y = -1 - 7(-1) = 6$$
$$z = 3 + 5(-1) = -2$$

The point of intersection is $(-1, 6, -2)$.   ▬

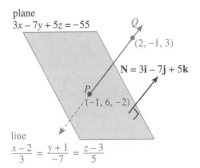

plane
$3x - 7y + 5z = -55$

Q

$(2, -1, 3)$

$\mathbf{N} = 3\mathbf{i} - 7\mathbf{j} + 5\mathbf{k}$

P

$(-1, 6, -2)$

line
$\dfrac{x - 2}{3} = \dfrac{y + 1}{-7} = \dfrac{z - 3}{5}$

EXAMPLE 9   Equation of a plane containing three given points

Find the standard form equation of a plane containing $P(-1, 2, 1)$, $Q(0, -3, 2)$, and $R(1, 1, -4)$.

Solution Because the normal **N** to the required plane is orthogonal to the vectors **PQ** and **PR**, we find **N** by computing the cross product $\mathbf{N} = \mathbf{PQ} \times \mathbf{PR}$.

$$\mathbf{PQ} = (0 + 1)\mathbf{i} + (-3 - 2)\mathbf{j} + (2 - 1)\mathbf{k} = \mathbf{i} - 5\mathbf{j} + \mathbf{k}$$
$$\mathbf{PR} = (1 + 1)\mathbf{i} + (1 - 2)\mathbf{j} + (-4 - 1)\mathbf{k} = 2\mathbf{i} - \mathbf{j} - 5\mathbf{k}$$

$$\mathbf{N} = \mathbf{PQ} \times \mathbf{PR} = \begin{vmatrix} \mathbf{i} & \mathbf{j} & \mathbf{k} \\ 1 & -5 & 1 \\ 2 & -1 & -5 \end{vmatrix}$$

$$= (25 + 1)\mathbf{i} - (-5 - 2)\mathbf{j} + (-1 + 10)\mathbf{k}$$

$$= 26\mathbf{i} + 7\mathbf{j} + 9\mathbf{k}$$

We can now find the equation of the plane using this normal vector and any point in the plane. We will use the point P:

Attitude numbers of the plane — from $\mathbf{N} = 26\mathbf{i} + 7\mathbf{j} + 9\mathbf{k}$

$$2\,6\,(x + 1) + 7\,(y - 2) + 9\,(z - 1) = 0$$

Point on the plane; we are using P(−1, 2, 1).

Thus, the equation of the plane is

$$26x + 26 + 7y - 14 + 9z - 9 = 0$$

$$26x + 7y + 9z + 3 = 0$$

EXAMPLE 10   Equation of the line parallel to the intersection of two given planes

Find the equation of a line passing through $(-1, 2, 3)$ that is parallel to the line of intersection of the planes $3x - 2y + z = 4$ and $x + 2y + 3z = 5$.

Solution By inspection, we see that the normals to the given planes are $\mathbf{N}_1 = 3\mathbf{i} - 2\mathbf{j} + \mathbf{k}$ and $\mathbf{N}_2 = \mathbf{i} + 2\mathbf{j} + 3\mathbf{k}$. The desired line is perpendicular to both of these normals, so the aligned vector is found by computing the cross product:

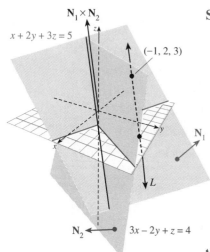

$$\mathbf{N}_1 \times \mathbf{N}_2 = \begin{vmatrix} \mathbf{i} & \mathbf{j} & \mathbf{k} \\ 3 & -2 & 1 \\ 1 & 2 & 3 \end{vmatrix} = (-6 - 2)\mathbf{i} - (9 - 1)\mathbf{j} + (6 + 2)\mathbf{k}$$

$$= -8\mathbf{i} - 8\mathbf{j} + 8\mathbf{k}$$

The direction of this vector is $\langle -8, -8, 8 \rangle = -8\langle 1, 1, -1 \rangle$. The equation of the desired line is

$$\frac{x + 1}{1} = \frac{y - 2}{1} = \frac{z - 3}{-1}$$

Example 10 can also be used to find the equation of the line of intersection of the two planes. Instead of using the given point $(-1, 2, 3)$, you will first need to find a point in the intersection and then proceed, using the steps of Example 10. We conclude this section by finding the equation of a plane containing two given (nonparallel) lines.

EXAMPLE 11   Equation of a plane containing two intersecting lines

Find the standard-form equation of the plane determined by the intersecting lines

$$\frac{x - 2}{3} = \frac{y + 5}{-2} = \frac{z + 1}{4} \quad \text{and} \quad \frac{x + 1}{2} = \frac{y}{-1} = \frac{z - 16}{5}$$

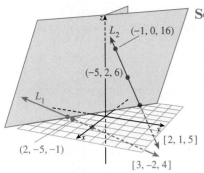

Solution Proceding as in Example 4, we find that the lines intersect at $(-19, 9, -29)$. The aligned vectors for these two lines are $\mathbf{v}_1 = 3\mathbf{i} - 2\mathbf{j} + 4\mathbf{k}$ and $\mathbf{v}_2 = 2\mathbf{i} - \mathbf{j} + 5\mathbf{k}$ and the normal to the desired plane is orthogonal to both $\mathbf{v}_1$ and $\mathbf{v}_2$. Thus, we take the normal to be the cross product:

$$\mathbf{N} = \mathbf{v}_1 \times \mathbf{v}_2 = \begin{vmatrix} \mathbf{i} & \mathbf{j} & \mathbf{k} \\ 3 & -2 & 4 \\ 2 & -1 & 5 \end{vmatrix} = (-10 + 4)\mathbf{i} - (15 - 8)\mathbf{j} + (-3 + 4)\mathbf{k}$$

$$= -6\mathbf{i} - 7\mathbf{j} + \mathbf{k}$$

The point of intersection $P(-19, 9, -29)$ is certainly in the plane, so we can use $(2, -5, -1)$, $(-1, 0, 16)$, or $(-19, 9, -29)$ to obtain the equation of the plane is

$$-6(x - 2) - 7(y + 5) + 1(z + 1) = 0$$

$$-6x + 12 - 7y - 35 + z + 1 = 0$$

$$6x + 7y - z + 22 = 0$$

PROBLEM SET 10.5

A

1. ■ **What Does This Say?** Contrast the parametric and symmetric forms of the equation of a line. How do these forms compare with the equation of a plane?

2. ■ **What Does This Say?** Describe the relationship between normal vectors and planes.

Write each equation for a plane given in Problems 3–6 in standard form.

3. $4(x + 1) - 2(y + 1) + 6(z - 2) = 0$

4. $5(x - 2) - 3(y + 2) + 4(z + 3) = 0$

5. $-3(x - 4) + 2(y + 1) - 2(z + 1) = 0$

6. $-2(x + 1) + 4(y - 3) - 8z = 0$

Find the parametric and symmetric equations for the line(s) passing through the given points with the properties described in Problems 7–16.

7. $(1, -1, -2)$; parallel to $3\mathbf{i} - 2\mathbf{j} + 5\mathbf{k}$

8. $(1, 0, -1)$; parallel to $3\mathbf{i} + 4\mathbf{j}$

9. $(1, -1, 2)$; through $(2, 1, 3)$

10. $(2, 2, 3)$; through $(1, 3, -1)$

11. $(1, -3, 6)$; parallel to $\dfrac{x - 5}{1} = \dfrac{y + 2}{-3} = \dfrac{z}{-5}$

12. $(1, -1, 2)$; parallel to $\dfrac{x + 3}{4} = \dfrac{y - 2}{5} = \dfrac{z + 5}{1}$

13. $(0, 4, -3)$; parallel to $\dfrac{2x - 1}{22} = \dfrac{y + 2}{-6} = \dfrac{z - 1}{10}$

14. $(1, 0, -4)$; parallel to $x = -2 + 3t, y = 4 + t, z = 2 + 2t$

15. $(3, -1, 2)$; parallel to the xy-plane and the yz-plane

16. $(-1, 1, 6)$; perpendicular to $3x + y - 2z = 5$

Find the points of intersection of each line in Problems 17–20 with each of the coordinate planes.

17. $\dfrac{x - 4}{4} = \dfrac{y + 3}{3} = \dfrac{z + 2}{1}$ **18.** $\dfrac{x + 1}{1} = \dfrac{y + 2}{2} = \dfrac{z - 6}{3}$

19. $x = 6 - 2t, y = 1 + t, z = 3t$

20. $x = 6 + 3t, y = 2 - t, z = 2t$

In Problems 21–26, tell whether the two lines intersect, are parallel, are skew, or coincide. If they intersect, give the point of intersection.

21. $\dfrac{x - 4}{2} = \dfrac{y - 6}{-3} = \dfrac{z + 2}{5}, \dfrac{x}{4} = \dfrac{y + 2}{-6} = \dfrac{z - 3}{10}$

22. $x = 4 - 2t; y = 6t; z = 7 - 4t;$
$x = 5 + t; y = 1 - 3t; z = -3 + 2t$

23. $x = 3 + 3t, y = 1 - 4t; z = -4 - 7t;$
$x = 2 + 3t, y = 5 - 4t, z = 3 - 7t$

24. $x = 2 - 4t, y = 1 + t, z = \dfrac{1}{2} + 5t;$
$x = 3t, y = -2 - t, z = 4 - 2t$

25. $\dfrac{x - 3}{2} = \dfrac{y - 1}{-1} = \dfrac{z - 4}{1}; \qquad \dfrac{x + 2}{3} = \dfrac{y - 3}{-1} = \dfrac{z - 2}{1}$

26. $\dfrac{x + 1}{2} = \dfrac{y - 3}{-1} = \dfrac{z - 2}{1}; \qquad \dfrac{x + 1}{2} = \dfrac{y + 1}{3} = \dfrac{z - 3}{-4}$

Find the direction cosines and the direction angles for the vectors given in Problems 27–32.

27. $\mathbf{v} = 2\mathbf{i} - 3\mathbf{j} - 5\mathbf{k}$ **28.** $\mathbf{v} = 3\mathbf{i} - 2\mathbf{k}$

29. $\mathbf{v} = 5\mathbf{i} - 4\mathbf{j} + 3\mathbf{k}$ **30.** $\mathbf{v} = \mathbf{j} - 5\mathbf{k}$

31. $\mathbf{v} = \mathbf{i} - 3\mathbf{j} + 9\mathbf{k}$ **32.** $\mathbf{v} = \mathbf{i} - \mathbf{j} + 3\mathbf{k}$

Find an equation for the plane that contains the point P and has the normal vector N given in Problems 33–38.

33. $P(-1, 3, 5)$; $\mathbf{N} = 2\mathbf{i} + 4\mathbf{j} - 3\mathbf{k}$

34. $P(0, -7, 1)$; $\mathbf{N} = -\mathbf{i} + \mathbf{k}$

35. $P(0, -3, 0)$; $\mathbf{N} = -2\mathbf{j} + 3\mathbf{k}$

36. $P(1, 1, -1)$; $\mathbf{N} = -\mathbf{i} - 2\mathbf{j} + 3\mathbf{k}$

37. $P(0, 0, 0)$; $\mathbf{N} = \mathbf{k}$

38. $P(0, 0, 0)$; $\mathbf{N} = \mathbf{i}$

39. Find two unit vectors parallel to the line

$$\frac{x - 3}{4} = \frac{y - 1}{2} = \frac{z + 1}{1}$$

40. Find two unit vectors parallel to the line

$$\frac{x - 1}{2} = \frac{y + 2}{4} = \frac{z + 5}{1}$$

41. Find two unit vectors that are perpendicular to the plane $2x + 4y - 3z = 4$.

42. Find two unit vectors that are perpendicular to the plane $5x - 3y + 2z = 15$.

Ⓑ 43. Show that the vector $3\mathbf{i} - 4\mathbf{j} + \mathbf{k}$ is orthogonal to the line that passes through the points $(0, 0, 1)$ and $(2, 1, -1)$.

44. Show that the vector $7\mathbf{i} + 4\mathbf{j} + 3\mathbf{k}$ is orthogonal to the line passing through the points $(-2, 2, 7)$ and $(3, -3, 2)$.

45. Find two unit vectors that are parallel to the line of intersection of the planes $x + y = 1$ and $x - 2z = 3$.

46. Find two unit vectors that are parallel to the line of intersection of the planes $x + y + z = 3$ and $x - y + z = 1$.

47. Find an equation for the line of intersection of the planes $x + y - z = 4$ and $2x - y + 3z = 1$.

48. Find an equation for the line of intersection of the planes $x + 2y + z = 3$ and $x + y - 2z = 4$.

49. Find an equation for the plane that passes through $P(1, -1, 2)$ and is normal to $\mathbf{PQ}$ where $Q(2, 1, 3)$.

50. Find an equation for the line that passes through the point $(1, -5, 3)$ and is orthogonal to the plane $2x - 3y + z = 1$.

51. Find an equation for the plane that contains the point $(2, 1, -1)$ and is orthogonal to the line

$$\frac{x - 3}{3} = \frac{y + 1}{5} = \frac{z}{2}$$

52. Find a plane that passes through the point $(1, 2, -1)$ and is parallel to the plane $2x - y + 3z = 1$.

53. Show that the line

$$\frac{x - 1}{2} = \frac{y + 1}{3} = \frac{z - 2}{4}$$

is parallel to the plane $x - 2y + z = 6$.

54. Find the point where the line

$$\frac{x - 1}{2} = \frac{y + 1}{-1} = \frac{z}{3}$$

intersects the plane $3x + 2y - z = 5$.

55. The *angle* between two planes is defined to be the acute angle between their normal vectors. Find the angle between the planes $2x + y - 4z = 3$ and $x - y + z = 2$, rounded to nearest degree.

56. Find the equation of the line that passes through the point $P(2, 3, 1)$ and is parallel to the line of intersection of the planes $x + 2y - 3z = 4$ and $x - 2y + z = 0$.

57. Find the equation of the line that passes through the point $P(0, 1, -1)$ and is parallel to the line of intersection of the planes $2x + y - 2z = 5$ and $3x - 6y - 2z = 7$.

58. Find a vector that is parallel to the line of intersection of the planes $2x + 3y = 0$ and $3x - y + z = 1$.

59. Find the equation of the line of intersection of the planes $3x + y - z = 5$ and $x - 6y - 2z = 10$.

60. Find the equation of the line of intersection of the planes $2x - y + z = 8$ and $x + y - z = 5$.

61. Let $\mathbf{v} = 2\mathbf{i} + \mathbf{j}$ and $\mathbf{w} = 2\mathbf{i} - \mathbf{j} + 3\mathbf{k}$. Find the direction cosines and the direction angles of $\mathbf{v} \times \mathbf{w}$.

62. Find the direction cosines of a vector determined by the intersection of the planes $x + y + z = 3$ and $2x + 3y - z = 4$.

Ⓒ 63. What can be said about the lines

$$\frac{x - x_0}{a_1} = \frac{y - y_0}{b_1} = \frac{z - z_0}{c_1}$$

and

$$\frac{x - x_0}{a_2} = \frac{y - y_0}{b_2} = \frac{z - z_0}{c_2}$$

in the case where $a_1 a_2 + b_1 b_2 + c_1 c_2 = 0$?

64. In Figure 10.42, $\mathbf{N}$ is normal to the plane p and L is a line that intersects p. Assume $\mathbf{N} = a\mathbf{i} + b\mathbf{j} + c\mathbf{k}$ and that L is given by

$$x = x_0 + At, \quad y = y_0 + Bt, \quad z = z_0 + Ct$$

a. Find the angle θ between L and the plane p.

b. Find the angle between the plane $x + y + z = 10$ and the line

$$\frac{x - 1}{2} = \frac{y + 3}{3} = \frac{z - 2}{-1}$$

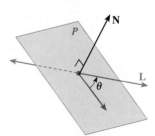

Figure 10.42 Problem 64

65. Show that a plane with x-intercept a, y-intercept b, and z-intercept c has the equation

$$\frac{x}{a} + \frac{y}{b} + \frac{z}{c} = 1$$

assuming a, b, and c, are all nonzero.

66. Suppose planes p_1 and p_2 intersect. If $\mathbf{v}_1$ and $\mathbf{w}_1$ are vectors on p_1 and $\mathbf{v}_2$ and $\mathbf{w}_2$ are on plane p_2, then show that

$$(\mathbf{v}_1 \times \mathbf{w}_1) \times (\mathbf{v}_2 \times \mathbf{w}_2)$$

is aligned with the line of intersection of the planes.

10.6 VECTOR METHODS FOR MEASURING DISTANCE IN $\mathbb{R}^3$

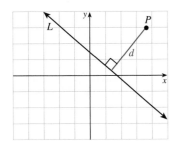

Figure 10.43 Distance from P to L

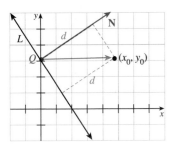

Figure 10.44 Procedure for finding the distance from a point to a line

> **IN THIS SECTION** Distance from a point to a plane, distance from a point to a line
> We shall see how the dot product and cross product can be used to measure distances between points, lines, and planes.

■ DISTANCE FROM A POINT TO A PLANE

To prepare for deriving a formula for the distance from a point to a plane, we will consider a simpler case, namely, the distance from a point to a line in $\mathbb{R}^2$. Let L be any given line and P any given point not on L. We wish to find the distance from P to L—that is, the perpendicular distance d, as shown in Figure 10.43.

If L is a vertical line, then the distance from P to L is easy to find (why?). If L is not vertical, then we let Q be any point on the line and $\mathbf{N}$ be normal to L at Q. Because Q can be any point on the line, we choose a convenient point, say the y-intercept (see Figure 10.44).

The distance we seek is seen to be the scalar projection of the vector $\mathbf{QP}$ onto $\mathbf{N}$. Thus,

$$d = \left| \frac{\mathbf{QP} \cdot \mathbf{N}}{\|\mathbf{N}\|} \right| = \frac{|\mathbf{QP} \cdot \mathbf{N}|}{\|\mathbf{N}\|}$$

In particular, we will now apply this formula to find the distance from the point $P(x_0, y_0)$ to the line

$$Ax + By + C = 0$$

Because Q is any point on the line, we choose Q to be the y-intercept. That is, choose $x = 0$. Then $y = -C/B$ (because L is not vertical, $B \neq 0$) so that

$$\mathbf{QP} = (x_0 - 0)\mathbf{i} + (y_0 + C/B)\mathbf{j}$$

It can be shown that the normal to the line $Ax + By + C = 0$ is $\mathbf{N} = A\mathbf{i} + B\mathbf{j}$ so

$$d = \left| \frac{\mathbf{QP} \cdot \mathbf{N}}{\|\mathbf{N}\|} \right| = \left| \frac{Ax_0 + By_0 + C}{\sqrt{A^2 + B^2}} \right|$$

EXAMPLE 1 Distance from a point to a line in $\mathbb{R}^2$

Find the distance from the point $(5, -3)$ to the line $4x + 3y - 15 = 0$ using the following methods: **a.** as a scalar projection; **b.** by using the formula.

Solution **a.** Let P be the point $(5, -3)$ and Q be the y-intercept $(0, 5)$ of the line. Then

$$\mathbf{QP} = 5\mathbf{i} - 8\mathbf{j} \quad \text{and} \quad \mathbf{N} = 4\mathbf{i} + 3\mathbf{j}$$

$$d = \left| \frac{\mathbf{QP} \cdot \mathbf{N}}{\|\mathbf{N}\|} \right| = \left| \frac{20 - 24}{\sqrt{16 + 9}} \right| = \left| \frac{-4}{5} \right| = \frac{4}{5}$$

b. Note $A = 4$, $B = 3$, $C = -15$, $x_0 = 5$, and $y_0 = -3$ so that

$$d = \left| \frac{Ax_0 + By_0 + C}{\sqrt{A^2 + B^2}} \right| = \left| \frac{4(5) + 3(-3) - 15}{\sqrt{4^2 + 3^2}} \right| = \left| \frac{-4}{5} \right| = \frac{4}{5}$$

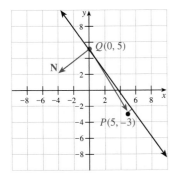

We also use a projection to find the shortest distance from a point to a plane, as described by the following theorem.

THEOREM 10.10   Distance from a point to a plane in $\mathbb{R}^3$

The distance from the point (x_0, y_0, z_0) to the plane $Ax + By + Cz + D = 0$ is given by

$$d = \left| \frac{Ax_0 + By_0 + Cz_0 + D}{\sqrt{A^2 + B^2 + C^2}} \right|$$

Proof: If Q is any point in the given plane, the required distance is found by projecting the vector **QP** onto a normal **N** for the plane. Thus, the distance from the point to the plane is given by

$$d = \|\mathbf{QP}\| \, |\cos \theta| = \frac{\|\mathbf{QP}\| \, \|\mathbf{N}\| \, |\cos \theta|}{\|\mathbf{N}\|} = \frac{|\mathbf{QP} \cdot \mathbf{N}|}{\|\mathbf{N}\|}$$

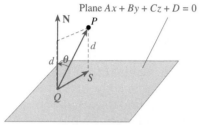

Plane $Ax + By + Cz + D = 0$

Figure 10.45 The distance from a point to a plane in $\mathbb{R}^3$

where θ is the (acute) angle between **QP** and **N** (see Figure 10.45).

Suppose P has coordinates (x_0, y_0, z_0) and the given plane has the standard form $Ax + By + Cz + D = 0$. Then $\mathbf{N} = A\mathbf{i} + B\mathbf{j} + C\mathbf{k}$ is a normal to this plane, and if $Q(x_1, y_1, z_1)$ is any particular point in the plane, we have $Ax_1 + By_1 + Cz_1 + D = 0$ and

$$\mathbf{QP} = (x_0 - x_1)\mathbf{i} + (y_0 - y_1)\mathbf{j} + (z_0 - z)\mathbf{k}$$

The dot product of **QP** with **N** is given by

$$\begin{aligned}
\mathbf{QP} \cdot \mathbf{N} &= (x_0 - x_1)A + (y_0 - y_1)B + (z_0 - z_1)C \\
&= (Ax_0 + By_0 + Cz_0) - (Ax_1 + By_1 + Cz_1) \\
&= Ax_0 + By_0 + Cz_0 + D
\end{aligned}$$

Because the normal vector has length $\|\mathbf{N}\| = \sqrt{A^2 + B^2 + C^2}$, we can substitute into the formula

$$d = \left| \frac{\mathbf{QP} \cdot \mathbf{N}}{\|\mathbf{N}\|} \right| = \left| \frac{Ax_0 + By_0 + Cz_0 + D}{\sqrt{A^2 + B^2 + C^2}} \right| \qquad \blacksquare$$

EXAMPLE 2   Equation of a sphere given a tangent plane

Find an equation for the sphere with center $C(-3, 1, 5)$ that is tangent to the plane $6x - 2y + 3z = 9$.

Solution   The radius r of the sphere is the distance from the center C to the given tangent plane, as shown in Figure 10.46.

$$r = \left| \frac{6(-3) + (-2)(1) + 3(5) - 9}{\sqrt{6^2 + (-2)^2 + 3^2}} \right| = \left| \frac{-14}{7} \right| = 2$$

Therefore, an equation of the sphere is

$$(x + 3)^2 + (y - 1)^2 + (z - 5)^2 = 2^2 \qquad \rule[0.3ex]{1.5em}{0.4ex}$$

Plane $6x - 2y + 3z = 9$

$r = 2$

$C(-3, 1, 5)$

Figure 10.46 The sphere with center $C(-3, 1, 5)$ and radius 2 is tangent to the plane $6x - 2y + 3z = 9$.

■ DISTANCE FROM A POINT TO A LINE

Next, we shall derive a formula for the shortest distance from a point P to a line L in $\mathbb{R}^3$. Let Q be a point on L and let **v** be a vector aligned with L. Then, as shown in Figure 10.47, the distance from P to L is given by

$$d = \|\mathbf{QP}\| \, |\sin \theta|$$

where θ is the acute angle between **v** and the vector **QP**.

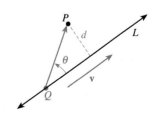

Figure 10.47 The distance from a point to a line in $\mathbb{R}^3$

This reminds us of the cross product $\mathbf{v} \times \mathbf{QP}$, and because

$$\|\mathbf{v} \times \mathbf{QP}\| = \|\mathbf{v}\| \, \|\mathbf{QP}\| \, |\sin \theta|$$

we have

$$d = \|\mathbf{QP}\| \, |\sin \theta| = \frac{\|\mathbf{v} \times \mathbf{QP}\|}{\|\mathbf{v}\|}$$

THEOREM 10.11   Distance from a point to a line

The shortest distance from the point P to the line L is given by the formula

$$d = \frac{\|\mathbf{v} \times \mathbf{QP}\|}{\|\mathbf{v}\|}$$

where $\mathbf{v}$ is a vector aligned with L and Q is any point on L.

Proof: A sketch of the proof precedes the statement of the theorem.   ∎

Find the distance from the point $P(3, -8, 1)$ to the line

$$\frac{x - 3}{3} = \frac{y + 7}{-1} = \frac{z + 2}{5}$$

We need to find a point Q on the line. We see that $Q(3, -7, -2)$ is on the line and that

$$\mathbf{QP} = -\mathbf{j} + 3\mathbf{k}$$

The vector $\mathbf{v}$ aligned with L is $\mathbf{v} = 3\mathbf{i} - \mathbf{j} + 5\mathbf{k}$. We now find

$$\mathbf{v} \times \mathbf{QP} = \begin{vmatrix} \mathbf{i} & \mathbf{j} & \mathbf{k} \\ 3 & -1 & 5 \\ 0 & -1 & 3 \end{vmatrix} = (-3 + 5)\mathbf{i} - (9 - 0)\mathbf{j} + (-3 + 0)\mathbf{k}$$

$$= 2\mathbf{i} - 9\mathbf{j} - 3\mathbf{k}$$

Finally,

$$d = \frac{\|\mathbf{v} \times \mathbf{QP}\|}{\|\mathbf{v}\|} = \frac{\sqrt{2^2 + (-9)^2 + (-3)^2}}{\sqrt{3^2 + (-1)^2 + (5)^2}} = \sqrt{\frac{94}{35}} \approx 1.64$$

PROBLEM SET 10.6

Ⓐ *Find the distance between the point and the line in Problems 1–6.*

1. $(4, 5)$; $3x - 4y + 8 = 0$
2. $(9, -3)$; $3x - 4y + 8 = 0$
3. $(4, -3)$; $12x + 5y - 2 = 0$
4. $(1, -6)$; $x - 3y + 15 = 0$
5. $(8, 14)$; $x - 3y + 15 = 0$
6. $(4, 5)$; $2x - 5y = 0$

Find the distance between the point and the plane given in Problems 7–12.

7. $P(1, 0, -1)$; $x + y - z = 1$
8. $P(0, 0, 0)$; $2x - 3y + 5z = 10$
9. $P(1, 1, -1)$; $x - y + 2z = 4$
10. $P(2, 1, -2)$; $3x - 4y + z = -1$
11. $P(a, -a, 2a)$; $2ax - y + az = 4a$, $a \neq 0$
12. $P(a, 2a, 3a)$; $3x - 2y + z = -1/a$, $a \neq 0$

Find the distance from the point $(-1, 2, 1)$ to each plane given in Problems 13–16.

13. the plane through the points $(0, 0, 0)$, $(1, 2, 4)$, and $(-2, -1, 1)$
14. the plane through the point $(1, 0, 1)$ with normal vector $2\mathbf{i} - \mathbf{j} + 2\mathbf{k}$
15. the plane through the point $(-3, 5, 1)$ with normal vector $3\mathbf{i} + \mathbf{j} + 5\mathbf{k}$

16. the plane through the points $(-1, 1, 1)$, $(4, 3, 7)$, and $(3, -1, 0)$

Find the distance from the point P to the line L in Problems 17–22.

17. $P(1, 0, -1)$; $\dfrac{x-2}{3} = \dfrac{y+1}{1} = \dfrac{z-1}{2}$

18. $P(1, 0, 1)$; $\dfrac{x}{3} = \dfrac{y-1}{2} = \dfrac{z}{1}$

19. $P(1, -2, 2)$; $\dfrac{x}{1} = \dfrac{2y}{1} = \dfrac{z}{-1}$

20. $P(0, 1, -1)$; $\dfrac{2x-1}{2} = \dfrac{y}{2} = \dfrac{z}{-1}$

21. $P(a, 0, -a)$; $\dfrac{x+a}{2} = \dfrac{y-a}{1} = \dfrac{z-a}{2}$; $a \neq 0$

22. $P\left(0, a, \dfrac{a}{2}\right)$; $\dfrac{x-a}{1} = \dfrac{y}{1} = \dfrac{z+4a}{1}$

23. Find the equation of the sphere with center $C(-2, 3, 7)$ that is tangent to the plane $2x + 3y - 6z = 5$.

Ⓑ 24. **a.** Show that the line

$$\frac{x-1}{3} = \frac{y}{-2} = \frac{z+1}{1}$$

and the plane $x + 2y + z = 1$ are parallel.

   b. Find the distance from the line to the plane in part **a.**

25. Three of the four vertices of a parallelogram in $\mathbb{R}^3$ are $Q(-1, 3, 5)$, $R(6, -3, 2)$, and $S(2, 4, -3)$. What is the area of the parallelogram?

26. Find an equation for the set of all points $P(x, y, z)$ such that the distance from P to the point $P_0(-1, 2, 4)$ is the same as the distance from P to the plane $2x - 5y + 3z = 7$. (Do not expand binomials.)

27. Find an equation for the set of all points $P(x, y, z)$ such that the distance from P to the line

$$\frac{x-1}{4} = \frac{y+1}{-1} = \frac{z}{3}$$

is 5. (Do not expand trinomials.)

Find the (perpendicular) distance between the lines given in Problems 28–31. See Problem 32 for a formula.

28. $\dfrac{x+1}{3} = \dfrac{y-2}{-2} = \dfrac{z-1}{1}$ and $\dfrac{x-2}{5} = \dfrac{y+1}{1} = \dfrac{z}{3}$

29. $x = 2 - t$, $y = 5 + 2t$, $z = 3t$ and $x = 2t$, $y = -1 - t$, $z = 1 + 2t$

30. $\dfrac{x+1}{1} = \dfrac{y-3}{2} = \dfrac{z+2}{3}$ and the line passing through $(1, 3, -2)$ and $(0, 1, -1)$

31. $x = -1 + t$, $y = -2t$, $z = 3$ and the line passing through $(0, -1, 2)$ and $(1, -2, 3)$

Ⓒ 32. Vector methods can also be used to derive a formula for the distance between two skew lines L_1 and L_2 in $\mathbb{R}^3$. Assume that L_1 contains the point P_1 and is aligned with vector $\mathbf{v}_1$, whereas L_2 contains P_2 and is aligned with $\mathbf{v}_2$. Then, the distance d between L_1 and L_2 (see Figure 10.48) is the same as the distance between two parallel planes containing the lines. Because $\mathbf{N} = \mathbf{v}_1 \times \mathbf{v}_2$ is normal to both planes, it follows that the required distance d is a scalar multiple of $\mathbf{v}_1 \times \mathbf{v}_2$. These geometric observations are used in the following theorem.

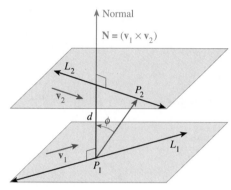

Figure 10.48 Distance between lines

Assume L_1 and L_2 contain the points P_1 and P_2 and are aligned with the vectors $\mathbf{v}_1$ and $\mathbf{v}_2$, respectively. Then the distance between the lines is

$$d = \left| \frac{(\mathbf{v}_1 \times \mathbf{v}_2) \cdot \mathbf{P}_1\mathbf{P}_2}{\|\mathbf{v}_1 \times \mathbf{v}_2\|} \right| = \left| \frac{\mathbf{N} \cdot \mathbf{P}_1\mathbf{P}_2}{\|\mathbf{N}\|} \right|$$

Prove this result.

33. **a.** Is the distance between two parallel planes $Ax + By + Cz = D_1$ and $Ax + By + Cz = D_2$ given by the formula $d = |D_1 - D_2|$? If not, what is the correct formula?

   b. Find the distance between the parallel planes

$$x + y + 2z = 2 \quad \text{and} \quad x + y + 2z = 4$$

Chapter 10 Review

IN THIS REVIEW   **Proficiency examination; supplementary problems**
Problems 1–33 of the proficiency examination test your knowledge of the concepts of this chapter, and Problems 34–49 test your understanding of those concepts by asking you to work sample practice problems. The supplementary problems present questions relating to the material of this chapter in a wide variety of settings.

PROFICIENCY EXAMINATION

Concept Problems

1. What is a vector and what is a scalar?
2. Give both an algebraic and a geometric interpretation of scalar multiplication of a vector by a scalar.
3. What is the triangular rule for vector sums?
4. What is the parallelogram rule for vector sums?
5. State each of the following properties of vector operations:
   a. commutativity of vector addition
   b. associativity of vector addition
   c. associativity of scalar multiplication
   d. identity for vector addition
   e. inverse property for vector addition
   f. vector distributivity
   g. scalar distributivity for vectors
   h. magnitude of a vector
   i. parallel vectors
   j. commutativity for dot product
   k. scalar multiple for dot product
   l. distributivity for dot product over addition
   m. scalar distributivity for cross product
   n. zero product for cross product
   o. anticommutativity for cross product
   p. vector distributivity
   r. parallel vectors property for cross product
6. How do you find the length of a vector?
7. State the triangle inequality.
8. What are the standard basis vectors in $\mathbb{R}^3$?
9. What is the standard-form equation of a sphere?
10. What is a cylinder?
11. What is the distance between two points in $\mathbb{R}^3$?
12. How do you find a unit vector in a given direction?
13. How do you determine if two vectors are parallel?
14. Define dot product.
15. What is the formula for the angle between two vectors?
16. What is meant by *orthogonal* vectors? What is the algebraic condition for finding orthogonal vectors?
17. What is a vector projection? Give a formula for finding the vector projection of **v** onto **w**.
18. What is a scalar projection? Give a formula for finding the scalar projection of **v** onto **w**.
19. What is the vector formula for work?
20. Define cross product.
21. What is the right-hand rule?
22. Give a geometric interpretation of cross product.
23. What is the formula for the magnitude of a cross product?
24. What is the determinant form for the triple scalar product?
25. How do you find the volume of a parallelepiped?
26. What is the parametric form of a line in $\mathbb{R}^3$?
27. What is the symmetric form of a line in $\mathbb{R}^3$?
28. What are the direction cosines of a vector in $\mathbb{R}^3$?
29. What is the normal vector of a plane in $\mathbb{R}^3$?
30. What is the point-normal form of a plane in $\mathbb{R}^3$?
31. What is the standard form of a plane in $\mathbb{R}^3$?
32. What is the formula for the distance from a point to a plane?
33. What is the formula for the distance from a point to a line?

Practice Problems

34. Given $\mathbf{v} = 2\mathbf{i} - 3\mathbf{j} + \mathbf{k}$, $\mathbf{w} = 3\mathbf{i} - 2\mathbf{j}$. Find each of the following vectors.
    a. $2\mathbf{v} + 3\mathbf{w}$
    b. $\|\mathbf{v}\|^2 - \|\mathbf{w}\|^2$
    c. vector projection of **v** onto **w**
    d. scalar projection of **w** onto **v**
35. For $\mathbf{v} = 2\mathbf{i} - 5\mathbf{j} + \mathbf{k}$ and $\mathbf{w} = \mathbf{j} - 3\mathbf{k}$, find
    a. $\mathbf{v} \cdot \mathbf{w}$ b. $\mathbf{v} \times \mathbf{w}$
36. Given $\mathbf{u} = 2\mathbf{i} - 3\mathbf{j} + \mathbf{k}$, $\mathbf{v} = \mathbf{i} + \mathbf{j} - 2\mathbf{k}$, and $\mathbf{w} = 3\mathbf{i} + 5\mathbf{k}$. In each of the following cases, either perform the indicated computation or explain why it cannot be computed.
    a. $(\mathbf{u} \times \mathbf{v}) \cdot \mathbf{w}$ b. $(\mathbf{u} \cdot \mathbf{v}) \times \mathbf{w}$
    c. $(\mathbf{u} \times \mathbf{v}) \times \mathbf{w}$ d. $(\mathbf{u} \cdot \mathbf{v}) \cdot \mathbf{w}$

Find the equations for the lines and planes in Problems 37–41.

37. The line through the points $P(-1, \ 4, \ -3)$ and $Q(0, -2, 1)$
38. The plane that contains the point $P(1, \ 1, \ 3)$ and is normal to the vector $\mathbf{v} = 2\mathbf{i} + 3\mathbf{k}$
39. The line of intersection of the planes $2x + 3y + z = 2$ and $y - 3z = 5$
40. The plane that contains the points $P(0, \ 2, \ -1)$, $Q(1, -3, 5)$, and $R(3, 0, -2)$
41. The line that contains the points $(1, \ 2, -1)$ and $(3, -1, 2)$
42. Find the direction cosines and the direction angles of the vector $\mathbf{u} = -2\mathbf{i} + 3\mathbf{j} + \mathbf{k}$. Round to the nearest degree.
43. In each case, determine whether the lines intersect, are parallel, or are skew. If they intersect, find the point of intersection.
    a. $x = 2t - 3$, $y = 4 - t$, $z = 2t$ and
       $\dfrac{x + 2}{3} = \dfrac{y - 3}{5}; z = 3$
    b. $\dfrac{x - 7}{5} = \dfrac{y - 6}{4} = \dfrac{z - 8}{5}$ and $\dfrac{x - 8}{6} = \dfrac{y - 6}{4} = \dfrac{z - 9}{6}$

44. Let $\mathbf{u} = 2\mathbf{i} + \mathbf{j}$, $\mathbf{v} = \mathbf{i} - \mathbf{j} - \mathbf{k}$, and $\mathbf{w} = 3\mathbf{i} + \mathbf{k}$.

  a. Find the volume of the parallelepiped determined by these vectors.

  b. Find a positive number A that guarantees that the tetrahedron determined by $A\mathbf{u}$, $A\mathbf{v}$, and $\mathbf{w}$ has a volume which is twice the volume of the original tetrahedron.

45. Find the distance from $P(-1, 1, 4)$ to $2x + 5y - z = 3$.

46. Find the distance from the line $x = t, y = 2t, z = 3t - 1$ to the line $x = 1 - t, y = t + 2, z = t$.

47. Find the distance from the point $P(4, 5, 0)$ to the line

$$\frac{x-2}{3} = \frac{y}{5} = \frac{z+1}{-1}$$

48. An airplane flies at 200 mph parallel to the ground at an altitude of 10,000 ft. If the plane flies due south and the wind is blowing toward the northeast at 50 mph, what is the ground speed of the plane (that is, effective speed)?

49. A girl pulls a sled 50 ft on level ground with a rope inclined at an angle of 30° with the horizontal (the ground). If she applies 3 lb of tension to the rope, how much work is performed on the sled?

SUPPLEMENTARY PROBLEMS

A triangle in $\mathbb{R}^3$ *has vertices* $A(0, 2, -1)$, $B(1, 1, 3)$, *and* $C(1, 0, -4)$. *Use this information for Problems 1–4.*
1. Find the perimeter of the triangle.
2. Find the area of the triangle.
3. Find the three vertex angles of the triangle. (Round to the nearest degree.)
4. Find a number p such that the points A, B, C, and $D(p, p, 0)$ form a tetrahedron of volume $V = 100$ cubic units.

Find the equations, in both parametric and symmetric forms, of the lines described in Problems 5–8. Find two additional points on each line.
5. passing through $A(1, -2, 3)$, $B(4, -1, 2)$
6. passing through $A(1, 0, -3)$, $B(-4, 3, -2)$
7. passing through $P(1, 4, 0)$ with direction numbers $[2, 0, 1]$
8. passing through $P(1, 2, -5)$ with direction numbers $\left[\frac{1}{2}, \frac{5}{2}, -\frac{7}{2}\right]$

Find the equation of the line passing through P and parallel to the line of intersection of the planes given in Problems 9–12.
9. $P(3, 4, -1)$; $x + 2y + 2z + 5 = 0$; $2x + y - 3z - 6 = 0$
10. $P(-1, 0, -2)$; $x + 3y - z + 4 = 0$; $3x - y - z + 5 = 0$
11. $P(2, 3, -1)$; $2x + 3y - 4z - 3 = 0$; $x - 5y + 2z + 1 = 0$
12. $P(5, 1, -3)$; $x - y - z + 5 = 0$; $2x + 3y - z - 3 = 0$

Find the equation of the plane satisfying the conditions given in Problems 13–20.
13. the xy-plane
14. the plane parallel to the xy-plane passing through $(4, 3, 7)$
15. the plane through $(1, -3, 4)$ with attitude numbers $\langle 3, 4, -1 \rangle$
16. the plane through $(-1, 4, 5)$ and perpendicular to a line with direction numbers $\langle 4, 4, -3 \rangle$
17. the plane through $(4, -3, 2)$ and parallel to the plane $5x - 2y + 3z - 10 = 0$
18. the plane containing
$$\frac{x-3}{4} = \frac{z-1}{2}; \quad y = -2; \quad \text{and} \quad \frac{x-3}{3} = \frac{y+2}{1} = \frac{z-1}{-2}$$

19. the plane passing through $(4, 1, 3)$, $(-4, 2, 1)$ and $(1, 0, 2)$
20. the plane passing through $(4, -1, 2)$ and parallel to
$$\frac{x+2}{3} = \frac{y-2}{-1} = \frac{z+1}{2} \quad \text{and} \quad \frac{x-2}{1} = \frac{y-3}{2} = \frac{z-4}{3}$$

For the vectors given in Problems 21–24, find $\|\mathbf{v}\|$, $\mathbf{v} - \mathbf{w}$, *and* $2\mathbf{v} + 3\mathbf{w}$.
21. $\mathbf{v} = 3\mathbf{i} - 2\mathbf{j} + \mathbf{k}$, $\mathbf{w} = 4\mathbf{i} + \mathbf{j} - 3\mathbf{k}$
22. $\mathbf{v} = \mathbf{i}$, $\mathbf{w} = \mathbf{j}$
23. $\mathbf{v} = 5\mathbf{i} - 3\mathbf{j} + 2\mathbf{k}$, $\mathbf{w} = -\mathbf{i} + 2\mathbf{j} - 3\mathbf{k}$
24. $\mathbf{v} = 5\mathbf{i} + 4\mathbf{k}$, $\mathbf{w} = \mathbf{j} + 3\mathbf{k}$

For the vectors given in Problems 25–30, find $\mathbf{v} \cdot \mathbf{w}$ *and* $\mathbf{v} \times \mathbf{w}$.
25. $\mathbf{v} = \mathbf{i}$, $\mathbf{w} = \mathbf{j}$
26. $\mathbf{v} = \mathbf{k}$, $\mathbf{w} = \mathbf{k}$
27. $\mathbf{v} = 3\mathbf{i} + 2\mathbf{k}$, $\mathbf{w} = 2\mathbf{i} + \mathbf{j}$
28. $\mathbf{v} = \mathbf{i} - 3\mathbf{j}$, $\mathbf{w} = \mathbf{i} + 5\mathbf{k}$
29. $\mathbf{v} = 2\mathbf{i} + 3\mathbf{k}$, $\mathbf{w} = \mathbf{i} - 2\mathbf{j}$
30. $\mathbf{v} = \mathbf{i} - \mathbf{j} + \mathbf{k}$, $\mathbf{w} = \mathbf{i} + \mathbf{j} - \mathbf{k}$
31. Given the vectors $\mathbf{v} = 4\mathbf{i} + 2\mathbf{j} + \mathbf{k}$, $\mathbf{w} = 2\mathbf{i} + \mathbf{j} - 5\mathbf{k}$. Find
  a. $5\mathbf{v} - 3\mathbf{w}$ **b.** $\|2\mathbf{v} - \mathbf{w}\|$
  c. vector projection of $\mathbf{v}$ onto $\mathbf{w}$
  d. scalar projection of $\mathbf{w}$ onto $\mathbf{v}$
32. Find the dot and cross product for $\mathbf{v} = 2\mathbf{i} + 5\mathbf{j}$ and $\mathbf{w} = 3\mathbf{i} + 2\mathbf{j} - 4\mathbf{k}$.
33. Find the direction cosines for $\mathbf{v} = (2\mathbf{i} + \mathbf{j}) \times (\mathbf{i} + \mathbf{j} - 3\mathbf{k})$.
34. Find the direction angles of $\mathbf{w} = -5\mathbf{i} + 4\mathbf{j} - 3\mathbf{k}$. Round to the nearest degree.
35. Find two unit vectors that are parallel to the line
$$\frac{x}{6} = \frac{y}{2} = \frac{z-1}{6}$$
36. Find the (acute) angle, rounded to the nearest degree, between the intersecting lines
$$\frac{x-1}{3} = \frac{y-3}{-1} = \frac{z+5}{2} \quad \text{and} \quad \frac{x-1}{2} = \frac{y-3}{-1} = \frac{z+5}{-2}$$
37. Find the area of the parallelogram determined by $3\mathbf{i} - 4\mathbf{j}$ and $-\mathbf{i} - \mathbf{j} + \mathbf{k}$.
38. Find the center and the radius of the sphere
$$4x^2 + 4y^2 + 4z^2 + 12y - 4z + 1 = 0$$

39. Find the points of intersection of the line $x = 6 + 3t$, $y = 10 - 2t$, $z = 5t$ with each of the coordinate planes.

40. Find the points of intersection of the line
$$\frac{x+1}{3} = \frac{y-2}{4} = \frac{z+4}{8}$$
with each of the coordinate planes.

41. Find the point of intersection of the planes $3x - y + 4z = 15$, $2x + y - 3z - 1 = 0$, and $x + 3y + 5z - 2 = 0$

42. Find the point of intersection of the planes $x + 2y - 3z + 8 = 0$, $5x - 4y + 5z + 2 = 0$, and $3x + 3y - 2z + 5 = 0$

43. Find the equation of the plane determined by
$$\frac{x+3}{3} = \frac{y}{-2} = \frac{z-7}{6} \quad \text{and} \quad \frac{x+6}{1} = \frac{y+5}{-3} = \frac{z-1}{2}$$

44. Find the distance from the point $(1, -1, 2)$ to the plane $2x + y - z = 4$.

45. Find the distance from the point $(1, -1, 2)$ to the line
$$\frac{x+2}{2} = \frac{y-1}{1} = \frac{z}{4}$$

46. Find the work done by the constant force $\mathbf{F} = 5\mathbf{i} + 4\mathbf{j} + \mathbf{k}$ when it moves a particle along the line from $P(2, 1, -1)$ to $Q(4, 1, 2)$.

47. How much work does it take to move a container 25 m along a horizontal loading platform onto a truck using a constant force of 100 newtons at an angle of $\frac{\pi}{6}$ from the horizontal?

48. SPY PROBLEM The spy successfully computes the intercept path in Problem 60, Section 9.4, but the wily Boldfinger escapes by varying his speed and direction instead of traveling at top speed in a fixed direction. Two days later, the submarine is observed landing offshore from a desert area, and Boldfinger takes off in a helicopter. Suppose the desert is coordinatized (units of thousands of feet) and that two observation posts are at points $A(7, 0, 0)$ and $B(0, 4, 0)$. At noon, Boldfinger's helicopter is observed from A in the direction of the vector $-4\mathbf{i} + 2\mathbf{j} + 5\mathbf{k}$ and simultaneously from B in the direction of $3\mathbf{i} - 2\mathbf{j} + 5\mathbf{k}$. One minute later, it is observed from A in the direction $6\mathbf{i} + 7\mathbf{j} + 5.005\mathbf{k}$ and from B in the direction $13\mathbf{i} + 3\mathbf{j} + 5.005\mathbf{k}$. The spy is notified and at 12:10 P.M. is flying at the point $Q(0, 0, 1)$ — that is, 1,000 ft above the origin O — in an attack helicopter traveling at 150 mph. Assuming that Boldfinger travels in a fixed direction at a fixed rate this time, in which direction should the spy fly (from Q) in order to intercept Boldfinger?

49. Suppose $\mathbf{v}$ and $\mathbf{w}$ are nonzero vectors. Show that $\|\mathbf{v}\|\mathbf{w} + \|\mathbf{w}\|\mathbf{v}$ and $\|\mathbf{v}\|\mathbf{w} - \|\mathbf{w}\|\mathbf{v}$ are orthogonal vectors.

50. Let $\mathbf{v} = \cos\theta\,\mathbf{i} + \sin\theta\,\mathbf{j}$ and $\mathbf{w} = \cos\phi\,\mathbf{i} + \sin\phi\,\mathbf{j}$. Find $\mathbf{v} \times \mathbf{w}$. Interpret this cross product geometrically, and use it to derive a well-known trigonometric identity.

51. Find the three vertex angles (rounded to the nearest degree) of the triangle whose vertices are $(1, -2, 3)$, $(-1, 2, -3)$ and $(2, 1, -3)$.

52. Find a relationship between the numbers a_1, b_1, and c_1 so that the angle between the vectors $\mathbf{v} = a_1\mathbf{i} + b_1\mathbf{j} + c_1\mathbf{k}$ and

$\mathbf{i} - 2\mathbf{j}$ is the same as the angle between $\mathbf{v}$ and $2\mathbf{i} + \mathbf{k}$.

53. Find an equation of a plane that passes through $(a, 0, 0)$, $(0, a, 0)$, and $(a, 0, a)$.

54. Find an equation of a plane that passes through $(b, -b, 0)$, $(0, b, -b)$, and $(-b, 0, b)$.

55. Find the area of a triangle with vertices $(0, -1, 2)$, $(1, 2, -1)$, and $(3, -1, 2)$.

56. Find an equation for the set of all points whose distances from the point $(0, 0, 6)$ are equal to their distance from the xy-plane.

57. Find the area of the triangle in which the vectors $\mathbf{v} = \mathbf{i} - \mathbf{j} + \mathbf{k}$ and $\mathbf{w} = 2\mathbf{i} + \mathbf{j} - 2\mathbf{k}$ form two sides of the triangle.

58. Find an equation for the plane that passes through the origin and is parallel to the vectors $\mathbf{i} - 2\mathbf{j} - 3\mathbf{k}$ and $-\mathbf{i} + \mathbf{j} + 2\mathbf{k}$.

59. Find an equation for the plane that passes through the origin and whose normal vector is parallel to the line of intersection of the planes $2x - y + z = 4$ and $x + 3y - z = 2$.

60. Find a number A such that the planes $2Ax + 3y + z = 1$ and $x - Ay + 3z = 5$ are orthogonal.

61. The lines L_1 and L_2 are aligned with the vectors $\mathbf{i} - \mathbf{j}$ and $\mathbf{i} - \mathbf{j} + 2\mathbf{k}$, respectively. Find an equation for the line L that passes through the point $(-1, 2, 0)$ and is orthogonal to both L_1 and L_2.

62. A parallelepiped is determined by the vectors $\mathbf{u} = \mathbf{i} - \mathbf{j} + \mathbf{k}$, $\mathbf{v} = \mathbf{i} + 2\mathbf{j} - \mathbf{k}$, and $\mathbf{w} = 2\mathbf{i} + \mathbf{j} + \mathbf{k}$. Find the altitude from the tip of $\mathbf{w}$ to the side determined by $\mathbf{u}$ and $\mathbf{v}$.

63. In Chapter 11, we show that $\mathbf{T} = \mathbf{i} + 2x\mathbf{j}$ is a vector in the direction of the tangent line at each point $P(x, x^2)$ on the parabola $y = x^2$. Find a unit vector normal to the parabola at the point $(3, 9)$.

64. For any nonzero vectors $\mathbf{u}$, $\mathbf{v}$, and $\mathbf{w}$ show that the vector $(\mathbf{u} \times \mathbf{v}) \times (\mathbf{u} \times \mathbf{w})$ is parallel to $\mathbf{u}$.

65. Let $\mathbf{v} = a\mathbf{i} + b\mathbf{j} + c\mathbf{k}$ and $\mathbf{w} = A\mathbf{i} + B\mathbf{j} + C\mathbf{k}$, where a, b, c, A, B, and C are constants. Describe the set of vectors $\mathbf{v} + \mathbf{w}t$, where t is any scalar.

66. Using vectors, show that if the diagonals of a rectangle intersect at right angles, then the rectangle is a square.

67. Use vectors to show that the sum of the squares of the lengths of the sides of a parallelogram equals the sum of the squares of the lengths of the diagonals.

68. Use vector methods to show that any angle inscribed in a semicircle is a right angle.

69. Let $\mathbf{v}$ and $\mathbf{w}$ be nonzero vectors. Show that the vector
$$\mathbf{B} = \|\mathbf{w}\|\mathbf{v} + \|\mathbf{v}\|\mathbf{w}$$
bisects the angle between $\mathbf{v}$ and $\mathbf{w}$.

70. The vectors $\mathbf{u}$, $\mathbf{v}$, and $\mathbf{w}$ are said to be *linearly independent* in $\mathbb{R}^3$ if the only solution to the equation $a\mathbf{u} + b\mathbf{v} + c\mathbf{w} = \mathbf{0}$ is $a = b = c = 0$. Otherwise, the vectors are *linearly dependent*. Determine whether the vectors $\mathbf{u} = -\mathbf{i} + 2\mathbf{k}$, $\mathbf{v} = 2\mathbf{i} - \mathbf{j} + 3\mathbf{k}$, $\mathbf{w} = \mathbf{i} + 3\mathbf{j} - 2\mathbf{k}$ are linearly independent or dependent.

71. Figure 10.49 shows a parallelogram $ABCD$. If M is the midpoint of side $\overline{AB}$, show that line $\overline{CM}$ intersects diagonal $\overline{BD}$ at a point P located one-third of the distance from B to D by completing the following steps.

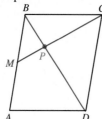

Figure 10.49 Parallelogram $ABCD$

a. Let a and b be scalars such that $\mathbf{MP} = a\mathbf{MC}$ and $\mathbf{BP} = b\mathbf{BD}$. Show that

$$\tfrac{1}{2}\mathbf{AB} + b[\mathbf{AD} - \mathbf{AB}] = a\left[\tfrac{1}{2}\mathbf{AB} + \mathbf{AD}\right]$$

b. Use the fact that $\mathbf{AB}$ and $\mathbf{AD}$ are linearly independent (see Problem 70) to show that

$$\tfrac{1}{2} - b - \tfrac{1}{2}a = 0 \text{ and } a - b = 0$$

Solve this system of equations to show that P has the required location.

72. Show that $\mathbf{u} = a_1\mathbf{i} + a_2\mathbf{j} + a_3\mathbf{k}$, $\mathbf{v} = b_1\mathbf{i} + b_2\mathbf{j} + b_3\mathbf{k}$, and $\mathbf{w} = c_1\mathbf{i} + c_2\mathbf{j} + c_3\mathbf{k}$ are linearly dependent (see Problem 70) if and only if

$$\begin{vmatrix} a_1 & a_2 & a_3 \\ b_1 & b_2 & b_3 \\ c_1 & c_2 & c_3 \end{vmatrix} = 0$$

73. Show that the vectors $\mathbf{u}$, $\mathbf{v}$, and $\mathbf{w}$ lie in the same plane if and only if $\mathbf{u} \times \mathbf{w} \cdot \mathbf{w} = 0$.

74. Show that

$$\begin{vmatrix} \mathbf{u}_1 \cdot \mathbf{v}_1 & \mathbf{u}_1 \cdot \mathbf{v}_2 \\ \mathbf{u}_2 \cdot \mathbf{v}_1 & \mathbf{u}_2 \cdot \mathbf{v}_2 \end{vmatrix} = (\mathbf{u}_1 \times \mathbf{u}_2) \cdot (\mathbf{v}_1 \times \mathbf{v}_2)$$

Hint: First examine the case where $\mathbf{u}_1$ and $\mathbf{u}_2$ are chosen from the vectors $\mathbf{i}$, $\mathbf{j}$, and $\mathbf{k}$.

75. Prove the **Lagrange identity:** $\|\mathbf{u} \times \mathbf{v}\|^2 = \|\mathbf{u}\|^2\|\mathbf{v}\|^2 - (\mathbf{u} \cdot \mathbf{v})^2$.

76. Let $A(-2, 3, 7)$, $B(1, 5, -3)$, $C(2, 8, -1)$ be the vertices of a triangle in $\mathbb{R}^3$. What are the coordinates of the point M where the medians of the triangle meet (the centroid)?

77. The medians of a triangle meet at a point (the centroid) located two-thirds of the distance from each vertex to the midpoint of the opposite side. Generalize this result by showing that the four lines that join each vertex of a tetrahedron to the centroid of the opposite face meet at a point located three-fourths of the distance from the vertex to the centroid.

78. A triangle in $\mathbb{R}^3$ is determined by the vectors $\mathbf{v}$ and $\mathbf{w}$, as shown in Figure 10.50. Show that the triangle has area

$$A = \tfrac{1}{2}\sqrt{\|\mathbf{v}\|^2\|\mathbf{w}\|^2 - (\mathbf{v} \cdot \mathbf{w})^2}$$

Figure 10.50 Area of a triangle

79. THINK TANK PROBLEM   In Figure 10.51, $\triangle ABC$ is equilateral and the points M, N, and O are located so that

$$\mathbf{AM} = \tfrac{1}{3}\mathbf{AB} \qquad \mathbf{BN} = \tfrac{1}{3}\mathbf{BC} \qquad \mathbf{CO} = \tfrac{1}{3}\mathbf{CA}$$

It can be shown that $\triangle PQR$ is also equilateral, and

$$\|\mathbf{PM}\| = \|\mathbf{QN}\| = \|\mathbf{RO}\| \text{ and}$$
$$\|\mathbf{AP}\| = \|\mathbf{BQ}\| = \|\mathbf{CR}\|.$$

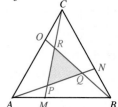

Figure 10.51 Problem 79

a. Show that $\mathbf{PQ} = \tfrac{3}{7}\mathbf{AN}$, then show that $\|\mathbf{AN}\|^2 = \tfrac{7}{9}\|\mathbf{AB}\|^2$. *Hint:* Use the law of cosines.

b. Show that $\triangle PQR$ has area 1/7 that of $\triangle ABC$.

c. Do you think the same result would hold if $\triangle ABC$ were not equilateral? Investigate your conjecture.

80. Gram-Schmidt orthogonalization process Let $\mathbf{u}$, $\mathbf{v}$, and $\mathbf{w}$ be nonzero vectors in $\mathbb{R}^3$ that do not lie on the same plane. Define vectors $\boldsymbol{\alpha}$ and $\boldsymbol{\beta}$ as follows:

$$\boldsymbol{\alpha} = \mathbf{v} - \left[\frac{\mathbf{v} \cdot \mathbf{u}}{\|\mathbf{u}\|^2}\right]\mathbf{u} \quad \text{and} \quad \boldsymbol{\beta} = \mathbf{w} - \left[\frac{\mathbf{w} \cdot \mathbf{u}}{\|\mathbf{u}\|^2}\right]\mathbf{u} - \left[\frac{\mathbf{w} \cdot \boldsymbol{\alpha}}{\|\boldsymbol{\alpha}\|^2}\right]\boldsymbol{\alpha}$$

a. Show that $\mathbf{u}$, $\boldsymbol{\alpha}$, $\boldsymbol{\beta}$ are mutually orthogonal (any pair are orthogonal).

b. If $\boldsymbol{\gamma}$ is any vector in $\mathbb{R}^3$, show that

$$\boldsymbol{\gamma} = \left[\frac{\boldsymbol{\gamma} \cdot \mathbf{u}}{\|\mathbf{u}\|^2}\right]\mathbf{u} + \left[\frac{\boldsymbol{\gamma} \cdot \boldsymbol{\alpha}}{\|\boldsymbol{\alpha}\|^2}\right]\boldsymbol{\alpha} + \left[\frac{\boldsymbol{\gamma} \cdot \boldsymbol{\beta}}{\|\boldsymbol{\beta}\|^2}\right]\boldsymbol{\beta}$$

81. PUTNAM EXAMINATION PROBLEM   Find the equations of two straight lines, each of which cuts all four of the following lines:

$$L_1: \ x = 1, y = 0 \qquad L_2: \ y = 1, z = 0$$
$$L_3: \ z = 1, x = 0 \qquad L_4: \ x = y = -6z$$

82. PUTNAM EXAMINATION PROBLEM   Find the equation of the smallest sphere that is tangent to both the lines

$$L_1: \ x = t + 1, y = 2t + 4, z = -3t + 5 \quad \text{and}$$
$$L_2: \ x = 4t - 12, y = t + 8, z = t + 17$$

83. PUTNAM EXAMINATION PROBLEM   The hands of an accurate clock have lengths 3 cm and 4 cm. Find the distance between the tips of the hands when the distance is increasing most rapidly.

"Star Trek Project"

This project is to be done in groups of three or four students. Each group will submit a single written report.

The starship *Enterprise* has been captured by the evil Romulans and is being held in orbit by a Romulan tractor beam. The orbit is elliptical with the planet Romulus at one focus of the ellipse. Repeated efforts to escape have been futile and have almost exhausted the fuel supplies. Morale is low and the food replicator is failing.

In searching the ship's log, Lieutenant Commander Data discovers that the Enterprise had been captured long ago by a Romulan tractor beam and had escaped. The key to that escape was to fire the ship's thrusters at exactly the right position in the orbit. Captain Picard gives the command to feed the required information into the computer to find that position. But, alas, a Romulan virus has rendered the computer all but useless for this task. Everyone turns to you and asks for your help in solving the problem.

Here is what Data discovered: If F represents the focus of the ellipse and P is the position of the ship on the ellipse, then the vector **V** from F to P can be written as a sum **T** + **N,** where **T** is tangent to the ellipse and **N** is normal to the ellipse. The thrusters must be fired when the ratio $\|\mathbf{T}\|/\|\mathbf{N}\|$ is equal to the eccentricity of the ellipse.

Your mission is to save the starship from the evil Romulans.

Time is said to have only one **dimension,** and space to have **three dimensions** . . . The mathematical **quaternion** partakes of **both** of these elements; in technical language it may be said to be "time plus space," or "space plus time:" and in the sense it has, or at least involves a reference to, **four dimensions** . . .

W. R. Hamilton
Graves' Life of Hamilton (New York, 1882–1889), Vol. 3, p. 635.

MAA Notes 17 (1991). "Priming the Calculus Pump: Innovations and Resources," by Marcus S. Cohen, Edward D. Gaughan, R. Arthur Knoebel, Douglas S. Kurtz, and David J. Pengelley.

11

Vector Calculus

PREVIEW

The marriage of calculus and vector methods forms what is called *vector calculus*. The key to using vector calculus is the concept of a *vector-valued function*. In this chapter we introduce such functions and examine some of their properties. We shall see that vector-valued functions behave very much like the *scalar-valued functions* studied earlier in this text.

PERSPECTIVE

A car travels down a curved road at a constant speed of 55 mi/hr. What additional information do we need about the car to determine whether it will stay on the road or skid off as it rounds a particular curve? Can we modify the road (say, by banking) so an average-sized car can travel at moderate speeds without skidding? How does a highway department decide what warning sign to install on a particular curve? A soldier fires a howitzer whose muzzle velocity and angle of elevation are known. If the shell overshoots its target by 40 yd, how should the angle of elevation be changed to ensure a hit on the next shot? If a satellite is 200 mi above the earth, how fast must it travel to remain stationary about a particular point on the earth's surface? These and other similar questions can be answered using vector calculus.

11.1 INTRODUCTION TO VECTOR FUNCTIONS

> **IN THIS SECTION** Vector-valued functions, operations with vector functions, limits and continuity
> Vector-valued functions are defined and are used to study curves in the plane and in space. We shall also study limits and continuity of vector-valued functions.

■ VECTOR-VALUED FUNCTIONS

In Section 9.4 we described a *plane curve* using parametric equations

$$x = f(t) \text{ and } y = g(t)$$

where f and g are continuous functions of t on some interval. We extend this definition to three dimensions. A **space curve** is the set of all ordered triples $f_1(t)$, $f_2(t), f_3(t)$ satisfying the parametric equations $x = f_1(t)$, $y = f_2(t)$, $z = f_3(t)$, where f_1, f_2, and f_3 are continuous functions of t on some domain D.

The concept of a vector-valued function is fundamental to the ideas we plan to explore. Here is a definition of this concept.

Vector-Valued Function

> A **vector-valued function** (or, simply, a **vector function**) $\mathbf{F}$ with *domain D* assigns a unique vector $\mathbf{F}(t)$ to each scalar t in the set D. The set of all vectors $\mathbf{v}$ of the form $\mathbf{v} = \mathbf{F}(t)$ for t in D is the *range* of $\mathbf{F}$. In this text, we shall be concerned with vector functions whose range is in $\mathbb{R}^2$ or $\mathbb{R}^3$. That is,
>
> $$\mathbf{F}(t) = f_1(t)\mathbf{i} + f_2(t)\mathbf{j} \qquad \text{in } \mathbb{R}^2 \text{ (plane)}$$
>
> $$\mathbf{F}(t) = f_1(t)\mathbf{i} + f_2(t)\mathbf{j} + f_3(t)\mathbf{k} \qquad \text{in } \mathbb{R}^3 \text{ (space)}$$
>
> where f_1, f_2, and f_3 are real-valued (**scalar-valued**) functions of the real number t defined on the domain set D. In this context f_1, f_2, and f_3 are called the **components** of $\mathbf{F}$.

Let $\mathbf{F}$ be a vector function, and suppose the initial point of the vector $\mathbf{F}(t)$ is at the origin. The graph of $\mathbf{F}$ is the curve traced out by the terminal point of the vector $\mathbf{F}(t)$ as t varies over the domain set D, as shown in Figure 11.1.

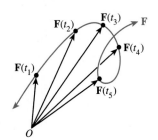

Figure 11.1 The graph of the vector function $\mathbf{F}(t)$ is traced out by the terminal point of $\mathbf{F}(t)$ as t varies over D.

EXAMPLE 1   Graph of a vector function

Sketch the graph of the vector function

$$\mathbf{F}(t) = (3 - t)\mathbf{i} + (2t)\mathbf{j} + (3t - 4)\mathbf{k}$$

for all t.

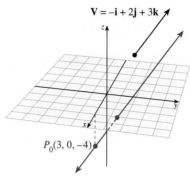

Figure 11.2 The graph of
$\mathbf{F}(t) = (3 - t)\mathbf{i} + (2t)\mathbf{j} + (3t - 4)\mathbf{k}$

Solution The graph is the collection of all points (x, y, z) with

$$x = 3 - t \qquad y = 2t \qquad z = 3t - 4$$

for all t. We recognize these as the parametric equations for the line in $\mathbb{R}^3$ that contains the point $P(3, 0, -4)$ and is aligned with the vector

$$\mathbf{v} = -\mathbf{i} + 2\mathbf{j} + 3\mathbf{k}$$

as shown in Figure 11.2. ▬

EXAMPLE 2   Graph of a circular helix

Sketch the graph of the vector function

$$\mathbf{F}(t) = (2 \sin t)\mathbf{i} - (2 \cos t)\mathbf{j} + (3t)\mathbf{k}$$

Solution The graph of $\mathbf{F}$ is the collection of all points (x, y, z) in $\mathbb{R}^3$ whose coordinates satisfy

$$x = 2 \sin t \qquad y = -2 \cos t \qquad z = 3t \qquad \text{for all } t$$

The first two components satisfy

$$x^2 + y^2 = (2 \sin t)^2 + (-2 \cos t)^2 = 4(\sin^2 t + \cos^2 t) = 4$$

which means that the graph lies on the surface of the right circular cylinder with radius 2, whose axis of symmetry is the z-axis, as shown in Figure 11.3. We also know that as t increases, the z-coordinate of the point $P(x, y, z)$ on the graph of $\mathbf{F}$ increases according to the formula $z = 3t$, which means that the point (x, y, z) on the graph rises in a spiral on the surface of the cylinder $x^2 + y^2 = 4$. The point on the graph of $\mathbf{F}$ that corresponds to $t = 0$ is $(0, -2, 0)$, and the points that correspond to $t = \frac{\pi}{2}$ and $t = \pi$ are $\left(2, 0, \frac{3\pi}{2}\right)$ and $(0, 2, 3\pi)$, respectively. Thus, the graph spirals upward counterclockwise (as viewed from above). The graph, which is known as a **right circular helix**, is shown in Figure 11.3. ▬

Figure 11.3 The graph of
$\mathbf{F}(t) = (2 \sin t)\mathbf{i} - (2 \cos t)\mathbf{j} + (3t)\mathbf{k}$

A well-known application of a helix is the DNA (deoxyribonucleic acid) molecule, which has a structure consisting of two intertwined helixes, as shown in Figure 11.4. Some other computer-generated helixes are also shown.

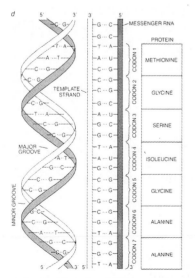

a. The double helix of DNA was discovered in 1953 by James Watson and Francis Crick.

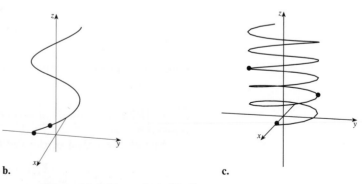

Figure 11.4 Examples of helixes

Examples 1 and 2 illustrate how the graph of a vector function

$$\mathbf{F}(t) = f_1(t)\mathbf{i} + f_2(t)\mathbf{j} + f_3(t)\mathbf{k}$$

can be obtained by examining the parametric equations

$$x = f_1(t) \qquad y = f_2(t) \qquad z = f_3(t)$$

In Example 3, we turn things around and find a vector function whose graph is a given curve.

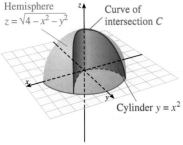

Hemisphere $z = \sqrt{4 - x^2 - y^2}$

Curve of intersection C

Cylinder $y = x^2$

Figure 11.5 The intersection curve of the hemisphere and the cylinder

EXAMPLE 3 Find a vector function

Find a vector function $\mathbf{F}$ whose graph is the curve of intersection of the hemisphere $z = \sqrt{4 - x^2 - y^2}$ and the parabolic cylinder $y = x^2$, as shown in Figure 11.5.

Solution   Finding the parametric representation is sometimes called **parametrizing the curve**. There are several ways this can be done, but the natural choice is to let $x = t$. Then $y = t^2$ (from the equation of the parabola), and by substituting into the equation for the hemisphere, we find

$$z = \sqrt{4 - x^2 - y^2} = \sqrt{4 - (t)^2 - (t^2)^2} = \sqrt{4 - t^2 - t^4}$$

We can now state a formula for a vector function of the given graph:

$$\mathbf{F}(t) = t\mathbf{i} + t^2\mathbf{j} + \sqrt{4 - t^2 - t^4}\,\mathbf{k}$$

■ OPERATIONS WITH VECTOR FUNCTIONS

It follows from the definition of vector operations that vector functions can be added, subtracted, multiplied by a scalar function, and multiplied together. We summarize these operations in the following box.

Vector Function Operations

Let $\mathbf{F}$ and $\mathbf{G}$ be vector functions of the real variable t, and let $f(t)$ be a scalar function. Then, $\mathbf{F} + \mathbf{G}$, $\mathbf{F} - \mathbf{G}$, $f\mathbf{F}$, and $\mathbf{F} \times \mathbf{G}$ are vector functions, and $\mathbf{F} \cdot \mathbf{G}$ is a scalar function. These operations are summarized as follows:

Vector functions:

$$(\mathbf{F} + \mathbf{G})(t) = \mathbf{F}(t) + \mathbf{G}(t) \qquad (\mathbf{F} - \mathbf{G})(t) = \mathbf{F}(t) - \mathbf{G}(t)$$

$$(f\mathbf{F})(t) = f(t)\mathbf{F}(t) \qquad (\mathbf{F} \times \mathbf{G})(t) = \mathbf{F}(t) \times \mathbf{G}(t)$$

Scalar function: $(\mathbf{F} \cdot \mathbf{G})(t) = \mathbf{F}(t) \cdot \mathbf{G}(t)$

EXAMPLE 4   Vector function operations

Let $\mathbf{F}(t) = t^2\mathbf{i} + t\mathbf{j} - (\sin t)\mathbf{k}$ and $\mathbf{G}(t) = t\mathbf{i} + \frac{1}{t}\mathbf{j} + 5\mathbf{k}$. Find

a. $(\mathbf{F} + \mathbf{G})(t)$ **b.** $(e^t\mathbf{F})(t)$
c. $(\mathbf{F} \times \mathbf{G})(t)$ **d.** $(\mathbf{F} \cdot \mathbf{G})(t)$

Solution **a.** $(\mathbf{F} + \mathbf{G})(t) = \mathbf{F}(t) + \mathbf{G}(t)$

$$= [t^2\mathbf{i} + t\mathbf{j} - (\sin t)\mathbf{k}] + [t\mathbf{i} + \frac{1}{t}\mathbf{j} + 5\mathbf{k}]$$

$$= (t^2 + t)\mathbf{i} + (t + t^{-1})\mathbf{j} + (5 - \sin t)\mathbf{k}$$

b. $(e^t\mathbf{F})(t) = e^t\mathbf{F}(t) = e^t t^2\mathbf{i} + e^t t\mathbf{j} - (e^t\sin t)\mathbf{k}$

c. $(\mathbf{F} \times \mathbf{G})(t) = \mathbf{F}(t) \times \mathbf{G}(t)$

$$= [t^2\mathbf{i} + t\mathbf{j} - (\sin t)\mathbf{k}] \times [t\mathbf{i} + \frac{1}{t}\mathbf{j} + 5\mathbf{k}]$$

$$= \begin{vmatrix} \mathbf{i} & \mathbf{j} & \mathbf{k} \\ t^2 & t & -\sin t \\ t & \frac{1}{t} & 5 \end{vmatrix}$$

$$= \left[5t + \frac{\sin t}{t} \right]\mathbf{i} - [5t^2 + t\sin t]\mathbf{j} + [t - t^2]\mathbf{k}$$

d. $(\mathbf{F} \cdot \mathbf{G})(t) = \mathbf{F}(t) \cdot \mathbf{G}(t)$

$$= [t^2\mathbf{i} + t\mathbf{j} - (\sin t)\mathbf{k}] \cdot \left[t\mathbf{i} + \frac{1}{t}\mathbf{j} + 5\mathbf{k} \right]$$

$$= t^3 + 1 - 5\sin t$$

■ LIMITS AND CONTINUITY

Limit of a Vector Function

Suppose the components f_1, f_2, f_3 of the vector function

$$\mathbf{F}(t) = f_1(t)\mathbf{i} + f_2(t)\mathbf{j} + f_3(t)\mathbf{k}$$

all have finite limits as $t \to t_0$, where t_0 is any number or $\pm \infty$. Then the **limit** of $\mathbf{F}(t)$ as $t \to t_0$ is the vector

$$\lim_{t \to t_0} \mathbf{F}(t) = \left[\lim_{t \to t_0} f_1(t) \right]\mathbf{i} + \left[\lim_{t \to t_0} f_2(t) \right]\mathbf{j} + \left[\lim_{t \to t_0} f_3(t) \right]\mathbf{k}$$

EXAMPLE 5 **Limit of a vector function**

Find $\lim\limits_{t \to 2} \mathbf{F}(t)$, where $\mathbf{F}(t) = (t^2 - 3)\mathbf{i} + e^t\mathbf{i} + (\sin \pi t)\mathbf{k}$.

Solution $\lim\limits_{t \to 2} \mathbf{F}(t) = \left[\lim\limits_{t \to 2} (t^2 - 3) \right]\mathbf{i} + \left[\lim\limits_{t \to 2} (e^t) \right]\mathbf{j} + \left[\lim\limits_{t \to 2} (\sin \pi t) \right]\mathbf{k}$

$$= 1\mathbf{i} + e^2\mathbf{j} + (\sin 2\pi)\mathbf{k}$$

$$= \mathbf{i} + e^2\mathbf{j}$$

For the most part, vector limits behave like scalar limits. The following theorem contains some useful general properties of such limits.

THEOREM 11.1 **Rules for vector limits**

If the vector functions $\mathbf{F}$ and $\mathbf{G}$ are functions of a real variable t and $h(t)$ is a scalar function such that all three functions have finite limits as $t \to t_0$, then

Limit of a sum	$\lim\limits_{t \to t_0} [\mathbf{F}(t) + \mathbf{G}(t)] = \lim\limits_{t \to t_0} \mathbf{F}(t) + \lim\limits_{t \to t_0} \mathbf{G}(t)$
Limit of a difference	$\lim\limits_{t \to t_0} [\mathbf{F}(t) - \mathbf{G}(t)] = \lim\limits_{t \to t_0} \mathbf{F}(t) - \lim\limits_{t \to t_0} \mathbf{G}(t)$
Limit of a scalar multiple	$\lim\limits_{t \to t_0} [h(t)\mathbf{F}(t)] = \left[\lim\limits_{t \to t_0} h(t) \right]\left[\lim\limits_{t \to t_0} \mathbf{F}(t) \right]$

Limit of a dot product $\displaystyle\lim_{t \to t_0} [\mathbf{F}(t) \cdot \mathbf{G}(t)] = \left[\lim_{t \to t_0} \mathbf{F}(t)\right] \cdot \left[\lim_{t \to t_0} \mathbf{G}(t)\right]$

Limit of a cross product $\displaystyle\lim_{t \to t_0} [\mathbf{F}(t) \times \mathbf{G}(t)] = \left[\lim_{t \to t_0} \mathbf{F}(t)\right] \times \left[\lim_{t \to t_0} \mathbf{G}(t)\right]$

These limit formulas are also valid as $t \to +\infty$ or as $t \to -\infty$, assuming all limits exist.

Proof: We shall establish the formula for the limit of a dot product and leave the rest of the proof as an exercise. Let

$$\mathbf{F}(t) = f_1(t)\mathbf{i} + f_2(t)\mathbf{j} + f_3(t)\mathbf{k} \quad \text{and} \quad \mathbf{G}(t) = g_1(t)\mathbf{i} + g_2(t)\mathbf{j} + g_3(t)\mathbf{k}$$

Apply the limit of vector function along with the sum rule and product rule for scalar limits to write

$$\lim_{t \to t_0} [\mathbf{F}(t) \cdot \mathbf{G}(t)] = \lim_{t \to t_0} [f_1(t)g_1(t) + f_2(t)g_2(t) + f_3(t)g_3(t)]$$

$$= \left[\lim_{t \to t_0} f_1(t)\right]\left[\lim_{t \to t_0} g_1(t)\right] + \left[\lim_{t \to t_0} f_2(t)\right]\left[\lim_{t \to t_0} g_2(t)\right] + \left[\lim_{t \to t_0} f_3(t)\right]\left[\lim_{t \to t_0} g_3(t)\right]$$

$$= \left(\left[\lim_{t \to t_0} f_1(t)\right]\mathbf{i} + \left[\lim_{t \to t_0} f_2(t)\right]\mathbf{j} + \left[\lim_{t \to t_0} f_3(t)\right]\mathbf{k}\right) \cdot \left(\left[\lim_{t \to t_0} g_1(t)\right]\mathbf{i} + \left[\lim_{t \to t_0} g_2(t)\right]\mathbf{j} + \left[\lim_{t \to t_0} g_3(t)\right]\mathbf{k}\right)$$

$$= \left[\lim_{t \to t_0} \mathbf{F}(t)\right] \cdot \left[\lim_{t \to t_0} \mathbf{G}(t)\right]$$

EXAMPLE 6 Limit of a cross product of vector functions

Verify that $\displaystyle\lim_{t \to 1} [\mathbf{F}(t) \times \mathbf{G}(t)] = \left[\lim_{t \to 1} \mathbf{F}(t)\right] \times \left[\lim_{t \to 1} \mathbf{G}(t)\right]$ for the vector functions
$$\mathbf{F}(t) = t\mathbf{i} + (1 - t)\mathbf{j} + t^2\mathbf{k} \quad \text{and} \quad \mathbf{G}(t) = e^t\mathbf{i} - (3 + e^t)\mathbf{k}$$

Solution

$$\mathbf{F}(t) \times \mathbf{G}(t) = \begin{vmatrix} \mathbf{i} & \mathbf{j} & \mathbf{k} \\ t & 1 - t & t^2 \\ e^t & 0 & -(3 + e^t) \end{vmatrix}$$

$$= [(1 - t)(-3 - e^t) - 0]\mathbf{i} - [-t(3 + e^t) - t^2 e^t]\mathbf{j} + [0 - e^t(1 - t)]\mathbf{k}$$

$$= (te^t + 3t - e^t - 3)\mathbf{i} + (t^2 e^t + te^t + 3t)\mathbf{j} + (te^t - e^t)\mathbf{k}$$

Thus, the limit of the cross product is

$$\lim_{t \to 1} [\mathbf{F}(t) \times \mathbf{G}(t)] = \lim_{t \to 1} [te^t + 3t - e^t - 3]\mathbf{i} + \lim_{t \to 1} [t^2 e^t + te^t + 3t]\mathbf{j} + \lim_{t \to 1} [te^t - e^t]\mathbf{k}$$

$$= (e + 3 - e - 3)\mathbf{i} + (e + e + 3)\mathbf{j} + (e - e)\mathbf{k} = (2e + 3)\mathbf{j}$$

Now we find the cross product of the limits.

$$\lim_{t \to 1} \mathbf{F}(t) = \left[\lim_{t \to 1} t\right]\mathbf{i} + \left[\lim_{t \to 1} (1 - t)\right]\mathbf{j} + \left[\lim_{t \to 1} t^2\right]\mathbf{k} = \mathbf{i} + \mathbf{k}$$

$$\lim_{t \to 1} \mathbf{G}(t) = \left[\lim_{t \to 1} e^t\right]\mathbf{i} + \left[\lim_{t \to 1} (-3 - e^t)\right]\mathbf{k} = e\mathbf{i} + (-3 - e)\mathbf{k}$$

Thus,

$$\left[\lim_{t \to 1} \mathbf{F}(t)\right] \times \left[\lim_{t \to 1} \mathbf{G}(t)\right] = \begin{vmatrix} \mathbf{i} & \mathbf{j} & \mathbf{k} \\ 1 & 0 & 1 \\ e & 0 & -3 - e \end{vmatrix}$$

$$= (0 - 0)\mathbf{i} - (-3 - e - e)\mathbf{j} + (0 - 0)\mathbf{k} = (3 + 2e)\mathbf{j}$$

We see $\displaystyle\lim_{t \to 1} [\mathbf{F}(t) \times \mathbf{G}(t)] = \left[\lim_{t \to 1} \mathbf{F}(t)\right] \times \left[\lim_{t \to 1} \mathbf{G}(t)\right]$. ▬

Continuity of a Vector Function

A vector function $\mathbf{F}(t)$ is said to be **continuous** at t_0 if t_0 is in the domain of $\mathbf{F}$ and $\lim\limits_{t \to t_0} \mathbf{F}(t) = \mathbf{F}(t_0)$.

▌ *What this says*: This is the same as requiring each component of $\mathbf{F}(t)$ to be continuous at t_0. That is,

$$\mathbf{F}(t) = f_1(t)\mathbf{i} + f_2(t)\mathbf{j} + f_3(t)\mathbf{k}$$

is continuous at t_0 when t_0 is in the domain of the component functions $f_1(t)$, $f_2(t)$, and $f_3(t)$ and

$$\lim_{t \to t_0} f_1(t) = f_1(t_0) \qquad \lim_{t \to t_0} f_2(t) = f_2(t_0) \qquad \lim_{t \to t_0} f_3(t) = f_3(t_0)$$

The rules for vector limits listed in Theorem 11.1 can be used to derive general properties of vector continuity.

EXAMPLE 7   Continuity of a vector function

For what values of t is $\mathbf{F}(t) = (\sin t)\mathbf{i} + (1 - t)^{-1}\mathbf{j} + (\ln t)\mathbf{k}$ continuous?

Solution   The vector function $\mathbf{F}$ is continuous where its component functions

$$f_1(t) = \sin t \qquad f_2(t) = (1 - t)^{-1} \qquad f_3(t) = \ln t$$

are continuous. The function f_1 is continuous for all t; f_2 is continuous where $1 - t \neq 0$ (that is, where $t \neq 1$); f_3 is continuous for $t > 0$. Thus, $\mathbf{F}$ is continuous when t is a positive number other than 1— that is, $t > 0$, $t \neq 1$.   ▬

PROBLEM SET 11.1

Ⓐ *Find the domain for the vector functions given in Problems 1–8.*

1. $\mathbf{F}(t) = 2t\mathbf{i} - 3t\mathbf{j} + \dfrac{1}{t}\mathbf{k}$

2. $\mathbf{F}(t) = (1 - t)\mathbf{i} + \sqrt{t}\,\mathbf{j} - \dfrac{1}{t - 2}\mathbf{k}$

3. $\mathbf{F}(t) = (\sin t)\mathbf{i} + (\cos t)\mathbf{j} + (\tan t)\mathbf{k}$

4. $\mathbf{F}(t) = (\cos t)\mathbf{i} - (\cot t)\mathbf{j} + (\csc t)\mathbf{k}$

5. $h(t)\mathbf{F}(t)$ where $h(t) = \sin t$ and
$$\mathbf{F}(t) = \frac{1}{\cos t}\mathbf{i} + \frac{1}{\sin t}\mathbf{j} + \frac{1}{\tan t}\mathbf{k}$$

6. $\mathbf{F}(t) + \mathbf{G}(t)$, where
$$\mathbf{F}(t) = 3t\mathbf{j} + t^{-1}\mathbf{k}$$
and
$$\mathbf{G}(t) = 5t\mathbf{i} + \sqrt{10 - t}\,\mathbf{j}$$

7. $\mathbf{F}(t) - \mathbf{G}(t)$, where
$$\mathbf{F}(t) = (\ln t)\mathbf{i} + 3t\mathbf{j} - t^2\mathbf{k}$$
and
$$\mathbf{G}(t) = \mathbf{i} + 5t\mathbf{j} - t^2\mathbf{k}$$

8. $\mathbf{F}(t) \times \mathbf{G}(t)$, where
$$\mathbf{F}(t) = t^2\mathbf{i} - t\mathbf{j} + 2t\mathbf{k}$$
and
$$\mathbf{G}(t) = \frac{1}{t + 2}\mathbf{i} + (t + 4)\mathbf{j} - \sqrt{-t}\,\mathbf{k}$$

Sketch the graph in $\mathbb{R}^3$ of the vector functions given in Problems 9–20.

9. $\mathbf{F}(t) = 2t\mathbf{i} + t^2\mathbf{j}$

10. $\mathbf{G}(t) = (1 - t)\mathbf{i} + \dfrac{1}{t}\mathbf{j}$

11. $\mathbf{G}(t) = (\sin t)\mathbf{i} - (\cos t)\mathbf{j}$

12. $\mathbf{F}(t) = (2 \cos t)\mathbf{i} + (\sin t)\mathbf{j}$

13. $\mathbf{F}(t) = t\mathbf{i} - 4\mathbf{k}$

14. $\mathbf{G}(t) = e^t\mathbf{j} + t\mathbf{k}$

15. $\mathbf{F}(t) = (\cos t)\mathbf{i} + (\sin t)\mathbf{j} + t\mathbf{k}$

16. $\mathbf{F}(t) = e^t\mathbf{i} + e^t\mathbf{j} + e^{-t}\mathbf{k}$

17. $\mathbf{G}(t) = (1 - t)\mathbf{i} + t^2\mathbf{j} + t\mathbf{k}$

18. $\mathbf{F}(t) = (\frac{\sqrt{2}}{2} \sin t)\mathbf{i} + (\frac{\sqrt{2}}{2} \sin t)\mathbf{j} + (\cos^2 t)\mathbf{k}$

19. $\mathbf{F}(t) = t\mathbf{i} + (t^2 + 1)\mathbf{j} + t^2\mathbf{k}$

20. $\mathbf{G}(t) = (2 \sin t)\mathbf{i} + (2 \cos t)\mathbf{j} + 3\mathbf{k}$

Ⓑ 21. ■ **What Does This Say?**   Discuss the concept of a vector-valued function.

22. ■ **What Does This Say?**   Discuss the concept of the limit of a vector-valued function.

23. Show that the curve given by
$$\mathbf{R}(t) = (2 \sin t)\mathbf{i} + (2 \sin t)\mathbf{j} + (\sqrt{8} \cos t)\mathbf{k}$$
lies on a sphere centered at the origin.

24. Sketch the graph of the curve given by
$$\mathbf{R}(t) = (2 \cos t)\mathbf{i} + (\sin t)\mathbf{j} - 2t\mathbf{k}$$

Find a vector function F *whose graph is the curve given in Problems 25–30.*

25. $y = x^2$; $z = 2$

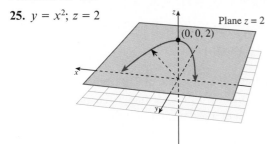

Plane $z = 2$
(0, 0, 2)

26. $x^2 + y^2 = 4$; $z = -1$

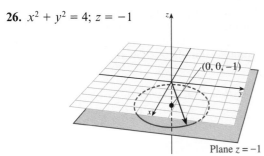

(0, 0, −1)

Plane $z = -1$

27. $x = 2t$, $y = 1 - t$, $z = \sin t$

28. $\dfrac{x - 2}{3} = \dfrac{y - 1}{2} = \dfrac{z}{4}$

(2, 1, 0)

29. The curve of intersection of the hemisphere $z = \sqrt{9 - x^2 - y^2}$ and the parabolic cylinder $x = y^2$

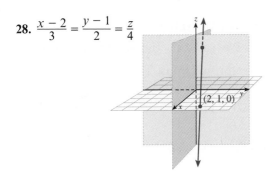

$x = y^2$

$z = \sqrt{9 - x^2 - y^2}$

30. The line of intersection of the planes $2x + y + 3z = 6$ and $x - y - z = 1$

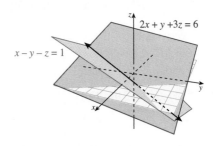

$2x + y + 3z = 6$

$x - y - z = 1$

Perform the operations indicated in Problems 31–42 with

$$\mathbf{F}(t) = 2t\mathbf{i} - 5\mathbf{j} + t^2\mathbf{k}, \quad \mathbf{G}(t) = (1 - t)\mathbf{i} + \frac{1}{t}\mathbf{k},$$

$$\mathbf{H}(t) = (\sin t)\mathbf{i} + e^t\mathbf{j}$$

31. $2\mathbf{F}(t) - 3\mathbf{G}(t)$ **32.** $t^2\mathbf{F}(t) - 3\mathbf{H}(t)$

33. $\mathbf{F}(t) \cdot \mathbf{G}(t)$ **34.** $\mathbf{F}(t) \cdot \mathbf{H}(t)$

35. $\mathbf{G}(t) \cdot \mathbf{H}(t)$ **36.** $\mathbf{F}(t) \times \mathbf{G}(t)$

37. $\mathbf{F}(t) \times \mathbf{H}(t)$ **38.** $\mathbf{G}(t) \times \mathbf{H}(t)$

39. $2e^t\mathbf{F}(t) + t\mathbf{G}(t) + 10\mathbf{H}(t)$

40. $\mathbf{F}(t) \cdot [\mathbf{H}(t) \times \mathbf{G}(t)]$

41. $\mathbf{G}(t) \cdot [\mathbf{H}(t) \times \mathbf{F}(t)]$

42. $\mathbf{H}(t) \cdot [\mathbf{G}(t) \times \mathbf{F}(t)]$

Find each limit indicated in Problems 43–50.

43. $\lim\limits_{t \to 1} [3t\mathbf{i} + e^{2t}\mathbf{j} + (\sin \pi t)\mathbf{k}]$

44. $\lim\limits_{t \to 0} \left[\dfrac{(\sin t)\mathbf{i} - t\mathbf{k}}{t^2 + t - 1} \right]$

45. $\lim\limits_{t \to 1} \left[\dfrac{t^3 - 1}{t - 1}\mathbf{i} + \dfrac{t^2 - 3t + 2}{t^2 + t - 2}\mathbf{j} + (t^2 + 1)e^{t-1}\mathbf{k} \right]$

46. $\lim\limits_{t \to 0} \left[\dfrac{te^t}{1 - e^t}\mathbf{i} + \dfrac{e^{t-1}}{\cos t}\mathbf{j} \right]$

47. $\lim\limits_{t \to 0} \left[\dfrac{\sin t}{t}\mathbf{i} + \dfrac{1 - \cos t}{t}\mathbf{j} + e^{1-t}\mathbf{k} \right]$

48. $\lim\limits_{t \to 0^+} \left[\dfrac{\sin 3t}{\sin 2t}\mathbf{i} + \dfrac{\ln(\sin t)}{\ln(\tan t)}\mathbf{j} + t^t\mathbf{k} \right]$

49. $\lim\limits_{t \to 1} [2t\mathbf{i} - 3\mathbf{j} + e^t\mathbf{k}]$

50. $\lim\limits_{t \to 2} [(2\mathbf{i} - t\mathbf{j} + e^t\mathbf{k}) \times (t^2\mathbf{i} + 4 \sin t \, \mathbf{j})]$

Determine all values of t for which the vector function given in Problems 51–56 is continuous.

51. $\mathbf{F}(t) = t\mathbf{i} + 3\mathbf{j} - (1 - t)\mathbf{k}$

52. $\mathbf{G}(t) = t\mathbf{i} - \dfrac{1}{t}\mathbf{k}$

53. $\mathbf{G}(t) = \dfrac{\mathbf{i} + 2\mathbf{j}}{t^2 + t}$

54. $\mathbf{F}(t) = (e^t\sin t)\mathbf{i} + (e^t\cos t)\mathbf{k}$

55. $\mathbf{F}(t) = e^t[t\mathbf{i} + \dfrac{1}{t}\mathbf{j} + 3\mathbf{k}]$

56. $\mathbf{G}(t) = \dfrac{\mathbf{u}}{\|\mathbf{u}\|}$, where $\mathbf{u} = t\mathbf{i} + \sqrt{t}\mathbf{j}$

57. Given the vector functions

$$\mathbf{F}(t) = t\mathbf{i} + t^2\mathbf{j} + t^3\mathbf{k} \quad \text{and} \quad \mathbf{G}(t) = \frac{1}{t}\mathbf{i} - e^t\mathbf{j}$$

directly verify each of the following limit formulas (that is, without using Theorem 11.1).

a. $\displaystyle\lim_{t\to 0} e^t\mathbf{F}(t) = \left[\lim_{t\to 0} e^t\right]\left[\lim_{t\to 0} \mathbf{F}(t)\right]$

b. $\displaystyle\lim_{t\to 1} \mathbf{F}(t) \cdot \mathbf{G}(t) = \left[\lim_{t\to 1} \mathbf{F}(t)\right] \cdot \left[\lim_{t\to 1} \mathbf{G}(t)\right]$

c. $\displaystyle\lim_{t\to 1} [\mathbf{F}(t) \times \mathbf{G}(t)] = \left[\lim_{t\to 1} \mathbf{F}(t)\right] \times \left[\lim_{t\to 1} \mathbf{G}(t)\right]$

Ⓒ 58. If $\mathbf{H}(t)$ is a vector function, we define the **difference operator** $\Delta\mathbf{H}$ by the formula

$$\Delta\mathbf{H} = \mathbf{H}(t + \Delta t) - \mathbf{H}(t)$$

where Δt is a change in the parameter t. (*Note:* Usually, Δt is a small number.) If $\mathbf{F}(t)$ and $\mathbf{G}(t)$ are vector functions, show that

$$\Delta(\mathbf{F} \times \mathbf{G})(t) = \mathbf{F}(t + \Delta t) \times \Delta\mathbf{G}(t) + \Delta\mathbf{F}(t) \times \mathbf{G}(t)$$

Hint: Note that

$$\Delta(\mathbf{F} \times \mathbf{G})(t) = \mathbf{F}(t + \Delta t) \times \mathbf{G}(t + \Delta t)$$
$$- \mathbf{F}(t + \Delta t) \times \mathbf{G}(t) + \mathbf{F}(t + \Delta t) \times \mathbf{G}(t)$$
$$- \mathbf{F}(t) \times \mathbf{G}(t)$$

59. Prove the limit of a sum rule of Theorem 11.1.

60. Prove the limit of a difference rule of Theorem 11.1.

61. Prove the limit of a scalar multiple rule of Theorem 11.1.

62. Prove the limit of a cross product rule of Theorem 11.1.

63. THINK TANK PROBLEM Let $\mathbf{F}(t)$ and $\mathbf{G}(t)$ be vector functions that are continuous at t_0, and let $h(t)$ be a scalar function continuous at t_0. In each of the following cases, either show that the given function is continuous at t_0 or provide a counterexample to show that it is not continuous.

a. $3\mathbf{F}(t) + 5\mathbf{G}(t)$ **b.** $\mathbf{F}(t) \cdot \mathbf{G}(t)$

c. $h(t)\mathbf{F}(t)$ **d.** $\mathbf{F}(t) \times \mathbf{G}(t)$

11.2 DIFFERENTIATION AND INTEGRATION OF VECTOR FUNCTIONS

> **IN THIS SECTION** Vector derivatives, tangent vectors, properties of vector derivatives, the motion of an object in space, vector integrals
>
> Our next objective is to introduce the derivative and integral of a vector function, along with some of their basic properties and applications.

■ VECTOR DERIVATIVES

In Chapter 2, we defined the derivative of the (scalar) function f to be the limit as $\Delta x \to 0$ of the difference quotient $\dfrac{\Delta f}{\Delta x}$. We call this the **scalar derivative** to distinguish it from derivatives involving vector functions. The **difference quotient of a vector function** $\mathbf{F}$ is the vector expression

$$\frac{\Delta\mathbf{F}}{\Delta t} = \frac{\mathbf{F}(t + \Delta t) - \mathbf{F}(t)}{\Delta t}$$

and we define the derivative of $\mathbf{F}$ as follows.

Derivative of a Vector Function

> The **derivative** of the vector function $\mathbf{F}$ is the vector function $\mathbf{F}'$ determined by the limit
>
> $$\mathbf{F}'(t) = \lim_{\Delta t \to 0} \frac{\Delta\mathbf{F}}{\Delta t} = \lim_{\Delta t \to 0} \frac{\mathbf{F}(t + \Delta t) - \mathbf{F}(t)}{\Delta t}$$
>
> wherever this limit exists. In the Leibniz notation, the derivative of $\mathbf{F}(t)$ is denoted by $\dfrac{d\mathbf{F}}{dt}$.

We say that the vector function $\mathbf{F}$ is **differentiable** at $t = t_0$ if $\mathbf{F}'(t)$ is defined at t_0.

The following theorem establishes a convenient method for computing the derivative of a vector function.

THEOREM 11.2 Derivative of a vector function

The vector function $\mathbf{F}(t) = f_1(t)\mathbf{i} + f_2(t)\mathbf{j} + f_3(t)\mathbf{k}$ is differentiable whenever the component functions $f_1, f_2,$ and f_3 are all differentiable, and in this case

$$\mathbf{F}'(t) = f_1'(t)\mathbf{i} + f_2'(t)\mathbf{j} + f_3'(t)\mathbf{k}$$

Proof: We use the definition of the derivative, along with rules of vector limits (Theorem 11.1), and the fact that the scalar derivatives $f_1'(t)$, $f_2'(t)$, and $f_3'(t)$ all exist.

$$\mathbf{F}'(t) = \lim_{\Delta t \to 0} \frac{\mathbf{F}(t + \Delta t) - \mathbf{F}(t)}{\Delta t}$$

$$= \lim_{\Delta t \to 0} \frac{[f_1(t + \Delta t)\mathbf{i} + f_2(t + \Delta t)\mathbf{j} + f_3(t + \Delta t)]\mathbf{k} - [f_1(t)\mathbf{i} + f_2(t)\mathbf{j} + f_3(t)\mathbf{k}]}{\Delta t}$$

$$= \left[\lim_{\Delta t \to 0} \frac{f_1(t + \Delta t) - f_1(t)}{\Delta t}\right]\mathbf{i} + \left[\lim_{\Delta t \to 0} \frac{f_2(t + \Delta t) - f_2(t)}{\Delta t}\right]\mathbf{j} + \left[\lim_{\Delta t \to 0} \frac{f_3(t + \Delta t) - f_3(t)}{\Delta t}\right]\mathbf{k}$$

$$= f_1'(t)\mathbf{i} + f_2'(t)\mathbf{j} + f_3'(t)\mathbf{k} \qquad \blacksquare$$

EXAMPLE 1 Differentiability of a vector function

For what values of t is $\mathbf{G}(t) = |t|\mathbf{i} + (\cos t)\mathbf{j} + (t - 5)\mathbf{k}$ differentiable?

Solution The component functions $\cos t$ and $t - 5$ are differentiable for all t, but $|t|$ is not differentiable at $t = 0$. Thus, the vector function $\mathbf{G}$ is differentiable for all $t \neq 0$. ▬

EXAMPLE 2 Derivative of a vector function

Find the derivative of the vector function

$$\mathbf{F}(t) = e^t\mathbf{i} + (\sin t)\mathbf{j} + (t^3 + 5t)\mathbf{k}$$

Solution $\mathbf{F}'(t) = (e^t)'\mathbf{i} + (\sin t)'\mathbf{j} + (t^3 + 5t)'\mathbf{k} = e^t\mathbf{i} + (\cos t)\mathbf{j} + (3t^2 + 5)\mathbf{k}$ ▬

■ TANGENT VECTORS

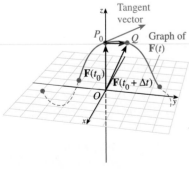

Figure 11.6 The difference quotient is a multiple of the secant line vector.

Recall that the scalar derivative $f'(x_0)$ gives the slope of the tangent line to the graph of f at the point where $x = x_0$ and thus provides a measure of the graph's direction at that point. Our first goal is to extend this interpretation by showing how the vector derivative can be used to find tangent vectors to curves in space.

Let t be a number in the domain of the vector function $\mathbf{F}(t)$, and let P_0 be the point on the graph of $\mathbf{F}$ that corresponds to t_0, as shown in Figure 11.6. Then, for any positive number Δt, the difference quotient

$$\frac{\Delta \mathbf{F}}{\Delta t} = \frac{\mathbf{F}(t_0 + \Delta t) - \mathbf{F}(t_0)}{\Delta t}$$

is a vector that points in the same direction as the secant vector

$$\mathbf{P_0 Q} = \mathbf{F}(t_0 + \Delta t) - \mathbf{F}(t_0)$$

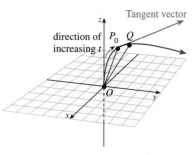

Tangent vector

direction of P_0 Q
increasing t

O

Figure 11.7 As $\Delta t \to 0$, the vector **PQ**—and hence the difference quotient $\Delta\mathbf{F}/\Delta t$—approaches the tangent vector at P_0.

where Q is the point on the graph of **F** that corresponds to $t = t_0 + \Delta t$ (see Figure 11.6). If we choose $\Delta t < 0$, the difference quotient $\Delta\mathbf{F}/\Delta t$ points in the *opposite* direction to that of the secant vector $\mathbf{P_0Q}$.

Suppose the difference quotient $\Delta\mathbf{F}/\Delta t$ has a limit as $\Delta t \to 0$ and that

$$\lim_{\Delta t \to 0} \frac{\Delta\mathbf{F}}{\Delta t} \neq \mathbf{0}$$

Then, as $\Delta t \to 0$, the direction of the secant $\mathbf{P_0Q}$—and hence that of the difference quotient $\Delta\mathbf{F}/\Delta t$—will approach the direction of the tangent vector at P_0, as shown in Figure 11.7. Thus, we expect the tangent vector at P_0 to be the limit vector

$$\lim_{\Delta t \to 0} \frac{\Delta\mathbf{F}}{\Delta t}$$

which we recognize as the vector derivative $\mathbf{F}'(t_0)$. These observations lead to the following definition.

Tangent Vector

> Suppose $\mathbf{F}(t)$ is differentiable at t_0 and that $\mathbf{F}'(t_0) \neq \mathbf{0}$. Then $\mathbf{F}'(t_0)$ is defined to be a **tangent vector** to the graph of $\mathbf{F}(t)$ at the point where $t = t_0$.

EXAMPLE 3   Finding a tangent vector

Find a tangent vector at the point where $t = 3$ on the graph of the vector function

$$\mathbf{F}(t) = e^{2t}\mathbf{i} + (t^2 - t)\mathbf{j} + (\ln t)\mathbf{k}$$

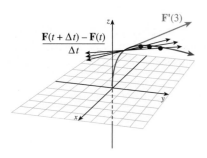

$\dfrac{\mathbf{F}(t + \Delta t) - \mathbf{F}(t)}{\Delta t}$ $\mathbf{F}'(3)$

Solution   Because $\mathbf{F}(3) = e^6\mathbf{i} + 6\mathbf{j} + (\ln 3)\mathbf{k}$, the point of tangency P_0 has coordinates $(e^6, 6, \ln 3)$. The derivative of **F** is

$$\mathbf{F}'(t) = 2e^{2t}\mathbf{i} + (2t - 1)\mathbf{j} + t^{-1}\mathbf{k}$$

The required tangent vector is found by evaluating $\mathbf{F}'(t)$ at $t = 3$:

$$\mathbf{F}'(3) = 2e^6\mathbf{i} + 5\mathbf{j} + \tfrac{1}{3}\mathbf{k}$$

■

Once we have the point of tangency and a tangent vector, we can find an equation for the tangent line to a graph by using the parametric form for a line. For instance, the tangent line in Example 3 contains the point $P_0(e^6, 6, \ln 3)$ and is aligned with the tangent vector $\mathbf{v} = 2e^6\mathbf{i} + 5\mathbf{j} + \tfrac{1}{3}\mathbf{k}$, so that the tangent line at P_0 has the parametric form

$$x = e^6 + 2e^6 t \qquad y = 6 + 5t \qquad z = \ln 3 + \tfrac{1}{3}t$$

where t is a real number (scalar).

We have seen that the graph of **F** will have a tangent vector $\mathbf{F}'(t_0)$ at the point P_0, where $t = t_0$ if $\mathbf{F}'(t_0)$ exists and **F** is not the zero vector. If we also require the derivative $\mathbf{F}'$ to be continuous at t_0, then the tangent vector at each point of the graph of **F** near P_0 will be close to the tangent vector at P_0. In this case, the graph has a *continuously turning tangent* at P_0, and we say that it is *smooth* there.

Smooth Curve

> The graph of the vector function defined by $\mathbf{F}(t)$ is said to be **smooth** on any interval of t where $\mathbf{F}'$ is continuous and $\mathbf{F}'(t) \neq \mathbf{0}$. The graph is **piecewise smooth** on an interval that can be subdivided into a finite number of subintervals on which **F** is smooth.

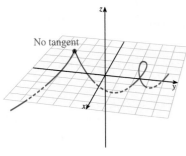

a. A curve that is smooth has a continuously turning tangent.

b. A curve that is not smooth can have "sharp" points. Note that this graph is piecewise smooth.

Figure 11.8 Smooth and piecewise smooth curves

As indicated in Figure 11.8, a smooth graph will have no sharply angled points (cusps). For this reason, vector functions with smooth graphs are "nicely behaved" and play an especially important role in vector calculus.

■ PROPERTIES OF VECTOR DERIVATIVES

Higher derivatives of a vector function $\mathbf{F}$ are obtained by successively differentiating the components of $\mathbf{F}(t) = f_1(t)\mathbf{i} + f_2(t)\mathbf{j} + f_3(t)\mathbf{k}$. For instance, the **second derivative** of $\mathbf{F}$ is the vector function

$$\mathbf{F}''(t) = [\mathbf{F}'(t)]' = f_1''(t)\mathbf{i} + f_2''(t)\mathbf{j} + f_3''(t)\mathbf{k}$$

whereas the **third derivative** $\mathbf{F}'''(t)$ is the derivative of $\mathbf{F}''(t)$, and so forth. In the Leibniz notation, the second vector derivative of $\mathbf{F}$ with respect to t is denoted by $\dfrac{d^2\mathbf{F}}{dt^2}$, and the third derivative by $\dfrac{d^3\mathbf{F}}{dt^3}$.

EXAMPLE 4   Higher derivatives of a vector function

Find the second and third derivatives of the vector function

$$\mathbf{F}(t) = e^{2t}\mathbf{i} + (1 - t^2)\mathbf{j} + (\cos 2t)\mathbf{k}$$

Solution $\mathbf{F}'(t) = 2e^{2t}\mathbf{i} + (-2t)\mathbf{j} + (-2\sin 2t)\mathbf{k}$

$\mathbf{F}''(t) = 4e^{2t}\mathbf{i} - 2\mathbf{j} - (4\cos 2t)\mathbf{k}$

$\mathbf{F}'''(t) = 8e^{2t}\mathbf{i} + (8\sin 2t)\mathbf{k}$ ▬

Several rules for computing derivatives of vector functions are listed in the following theorem, which can be proved by applying rules for limits of vector functions to appropriate theorems for scalar derivatives (or even for difference quotients).

THEOREM 11.3   Rules for differentiating vector functions

If the vector functions $\mathbf{F}$ and $\mathbf{G}$ and the scalar function h are differentiable at t, then so are $a\mathbf{F} + b\mathbf{G}$, $h\mathbf{F}$, $\mathbf{F} \cdot \mathbf{G}$, and $\mathbf{F} \times \mathbf{G}$, and

Linearity rule	$(a\mathbf{F} + b\mathbf{G})'(t) = a\mathbf{F}'(t) + b\mathbf{G}'(t)$	for constants a, b
Scalar multiple	$(h\mathbf{F})'(t) = h'(t)\mathbf{F}(t) + h(t)\mathbf{F}'(t)$	
Dot product rule	$(\mathbf{F} \cdot \mathbf{G})'(t) = (\mathbf{F}' \cdot \mathbf{G})(t) + (\mathbf{F} \cdot \mathbf{G}')(t)$	
Cross-product rule*	$(\mathbf{F} \times \mathbf{G})'(t) = (\mathbf{F}' \times \mathbf{G})(t) + (\mathbf{F} \times \mathbf{G}')(t)$	
Chain rule	$[\mathbf{F}(h(t))]' = h'(t)\mathbf{F}'(h(t))$	

Proof: We shall prove the linearity rule and leave the rest of the proof as an exercise. Note that if $\mathbf{F}$ and $\mathbf{G}$ are vector functions differentiable at t and a, b are constants, then the linear combination $a\mathbf{F} + b\mathbf{G}$ has the difference quotient

$$\frac{\Delta(a\mathbf{F} + b\mathbf{G})}{\Delta t} = \frac{a\Delta\mathbf{F}}{\Delta t} + \frac{b\Delta\mathbf{G}}{\Delta t}$$

*The order is important in the cross-product rule, because the cross product of vectors is not commutative.

We can now find the derivative:

$$(a\mathbf{F} + b\mathbf{G})'(t) = \lim_{\Delta t \to 0}\left[\frac{\Delta(a\mathbf{F} + b\mathbf{G})}{\Delta t}\right] = \lim_{\Delta t \to 0}\left[\frac{a\Delta\mathbf{F}}{\Delta t} + \frac{b\Delta\mathbf{G}}{\Delta t}\right]$$

$$= a\lim_{\Delta t \to 0}\frac{\Delta\mathbf{F}}{\Delta t} + b\lim_{\Delta t \to 0}\frac{\Delta\mathbf{G}}{\Delta t} = a\mathbf{F}'(t) + b\mathbf{G}'(t)$$ ▪

EXAMPLE 5   Derivative of a cross product

Let $\mathbf{F}(t) = \mathbf{i} + t\mathbf{j} + t^2\mathbf{k}$ and $\mathbf{G}(t) = t\mathbf{i} + e^t\mathbf{j} + 3\mathbf{k}$. Verify that

$$(\mathbf{F} \times \mathbf{G})'(t) = (\mathbf{F}' \times \mathbf{G})(t) + (\mathbf{F} \times \mathbf{G}')(t)$$

Solution   First find the derivative of the cross product:

$$(\mathbf{F} \times \mathbf{G})(t) = \begin{vmatrix} \mathbf{i} & \mathbf{j} & \mathbf{k} \\ 1 & t & t^2 \\ t & e^t & 3 \end{vmatrix} = (3t - t^2e^t)\mathbf{i} - (3 - t^3)\mathbf{j} + (e^t - t^2)\mathbf{k}$$

so that $(\mathbf{F} \times \mathbf{G})'(t) = (3 - 2te^t - t^2e^t)\mathbf{i} + (3t^2)\mathbf{j} + (e^t - 2t)\mathbf{k}$.

Next, find $(\mathbf{F}' \times \mathbf{G})(t) + (\mathbf{F} \times \mathbf{G}')(t)$ by first finding the derivatives of $\mathbf{F}$ and $\mathbf{G}$ and then the appropriate cross products.

$$\mathbf{F}'(t) = \mathbf{j} + 2t\mathbf{k} \quad \text{and} \quad \mathbf{G}'(t) = \mathbf{i} + e^t\mathbf{j}$$

$$\mathbf{F}' \times \mathbf{G} = \begin{vmatrix} \mathbf{i} & \mathbf{j} & \mathbf{k} \\ 0 & 1 & 2t \\ t & e^t & 3 \end{vmatrix} = (3 - 2te^t)\mathbf{i} - (-2t^2)\mathbf{j} + (-t)\mathbf{k}$$

$$\mathbf{F} \times \mathbf{G}' = \begin{vmatrix} \mathbf{i} & \mathbf{j} & \mathbf{k} \\ 1 & t & t^2 \\ 1 & e^t & 0 \end{vmatrix} = (-t^2e^t)\mathbf{i} - (-t^2)\mathbf{j} + (e^t - t)\mathbf{k}$$

Finally, add these vector functions:

$$(\mathbf{F}' \times \mathbf{G}) + (\mathbf{F} \times \mathbf{G}') = [(3 - 2te^t) - t^2e^t]\mathbf{i} + [2t^2 + t^2]\mathbf{j} + [-t + e^t - t]\mathbf{k}$$

$$= (3 - 2te^t - t^2e^t)\mathbf{i} + (3t^2)\mathbf{j} + (e^t - 2t)\mathbf{k}$$

Thus, $(\mathbf{F} \times \mathbf{G})' = (\mathbf{F}' \times \mathbf{G}) + (\mathbf{F} \times \mathbf{G}')$.   ▬

EXAMPLE 6   Derivatives of vector function expressions

Let $\mathbf{F}(t) = \mathbf{i} + e^t\mathbf{j} + t^2\mathbf{k}$ and $\mathbf{G}(t) = 3t^2\mathbf{i} + e^{-t}\mathbf{j} - 2t\mathbf{k}$. Find

a. $\dfrac{d}{dt}[2\mathbf{F}(t) + t^3\mathbf{G}(t)]$ **b.** $\dfrac{d}{dt}[\mathbf{F}(t) \cdot \mathbf{G}(t)]$

Solution   Begin by finding $\dfrac{d\mathbf{F}}{dt}$ and $\dfrac{d\mathbf{G}}{dt}$.

$$\frac{d\mathbf{F}}{dt} = e^t\mathbf{j} + 2t\mathbf{k} \quad \text{and} \quad \frac{d\mathbf{G}}{dt} = 6t\mathbf{i} - e^{-t}\mathbf{j} - 2\mathbf{k}$$

a. $\dfrac{d}{dt}[2\mathbf{F}(t) + t^3\mathbf{G}(t)] = 2\dfrac{d\mathbf{F}}{dt} + \left[t^3\dfrac{d\mathbf{G}}{dt} + \dfrac{d}{dt}(t^3)\,\mathbf{G}(t)\right]$

$= 2(e^t\mathbf{j} + 2t\mathbf{k}) + t^3(6t\mathbf{i} - e^{-t}\mathbf{j} - 2\mathbf{k}) + 3t^2(3t^2\mathbf{i} + e^{-t}\mathbf{j} - 2t\mathbf{k})$

$= (6t^4 + 9t^4)\mathbf{i} + (2e^t - t^3e^{-t} + 3t^2e^{-t})\mathbf{j} + (4t - 2t^3 - 6t^3)\mathbf{k}$

$= 15t^4\mathbf{i} + [2e^t + e^{-t}t^2(3 - t)]\mathbf{j} - 4t(2t^2 - 1)\mathbf{k}$

b. $\frac{d}{dt}[\mathbf{F}(t) \cdot \mathbf{G}(t)] = \frac{d\mathbf{F}}{dt} \cdot \mathbf{G}(t) + \mathbf{F}(t) \cdot \frac{d\mathbf{G}}{dt}$

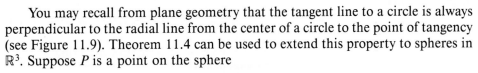

$= (e^t\mathbf{j} + 2t\mathbf{k}) \cdot (3t^2\mathbf{i} + e^{-t}\mathbf{j} - 2t\mathbf{k}) + (\mathbf{i} + e^t\mathbf{j} + t^2\mathbf{k}) \cdot (6t\mathbf{i} - e^{-t}\mathbf{j} - 2\mathbf{k})$

$= [0(3t^2) + e^t(e^{-t}) + 2t(-2t)] + [1(6t) + e^t(-e^{-t}) + t^2(-2)]$

$= (1 - 4t^2) + (6t - 1 - 2t^2)$

$= -6t^2 + 6t$

We shall use Theorem 11.3 in both applied and theoretical problems. In the following theorem, we establish an important geometric property of vector functions.

THEOREM 11.4 Orthogonality of a derivative

If the nonzero vector function $\mathbf{F}(t)$ is differentiable and has constant length, then $\mathbf{F}(t)$ is orthogonal to the derivative vector $\mathbf{F}'(t)$

Proof: We are given that $\|\mathbf{F}(t)\| = r$ for some constant r and all t. To prove that $\mathbf{F}$ and $\mathbf{F}'$ are orthogonal, we shall show that $\mathbf{F}(t) \cdot \mathbf{F}'(t) = 0$ for all t. First, note that

$$r^2 = \|\mathbf{F}(t)\|^2 = \mathbf{F}(t) \cdot \mathbf{F}(t)$$

for all t. We take the derivative of both sides (remember the derivative of r^2 is zero because it is a constant):

$$[r^2]' = [\mathbf{F}(t) \cdot \mathbf{F}(t)]'$$
$$0 = \mathbf{F}'(t) \cdot \mathbf{F}(t) + \mathbf{F}(t) \cdot \mathbf{F}'(t)$$
$$0 = 2\mathbf{F}(t) \cdot \mathbf{F}'(t)$$
$$0 = \mathbf{F}(t) \cdot \mathbf{F}'(t)$$

Thus, $\mathbf{F}$ and $\mathbf{F}'$ are orthogonal. ■

You may recall from plane geometry that the tangent line to a circle is always perpendicular to the radial line from the center of a circle to the point of tangency (see Figure 11.9). Theorem 11.4 can be used to extend this property to spheres in $\mathbb{R}^3$. Suppose P is a point on the sphere

$$x^2 + y^2 + z^2 = r^2$$

Let $\mathbf{R}(t) = x(t)\mathbf{i} + y(t)\mathbf{j} + z(t)\mathbf{k}$ be a vector function whose graph lies entirely on the surface of the sphere and contains the point P_0. Suppose P_0 corresponds to $t = t_0$. Then $\mathbf{R}(t_0)$ is the vector from the center of the sphere to P_0, and $\mathbf{R}'(t_0)$ is a tangent vector to the graph of $\mathbf{R}(t)$ at P_0, which means that $\mathbf{R}'(t_0)$ is also tangent to the sphere at P_0. Because $\mathbf{R}(t)$ has constant length,

$$\|\mathbf{R}(t)\| = \sqrt{x^2(t) + y^2(t) + z^2(t)} = r \qquad \text{for all } t$$

it follows from Theorem 11.4 that $\mathbf{R}$ is orthogonal to $\mathbf{R}'$. Thus, the tangent vector $\mathbf{R}'(t_0)$ at P_0 is orthogonal to the vector $\mathbf{R}(t_0)$ from the center of the sphere to the point of tangency.

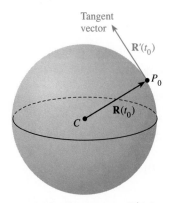

Figure 11.9 The tangent $\mathbf{R}'(t_0)$ at P_0 is orthogonal to the radius vector $\mathbf{R}(t_0)$ from the center of the sphere to P_0.

■ THE MOTION OF AN OBJECT IN SPACE

Recall from Chapter 2 that the derivative of an object's position is the velocity, and the derivative of the velocity is the acceleration. We frequently know the acceleration and can use integration to find the velocity and the position. We will now express these concepts in terms of vector functions.

An object that moves in such a way that its position at time t is given by the vector function $\mathbf{R}(t)$ is said to have

Position Vector   **Position vector** (or **displacement**) $\mathbf{R}(t)$ and

Velocity   **Velocity** $\mathbf{V} = \dfrac{d\mathbf{R}}{dt} = \mathbf{R}'(t)$

and

Acceleration   **Acceleration** $\mathbf{A} = \dfrac{d\mathbf{V}}{dt} = \dfrac{d^2\mathbf{R}}{dt^2}$

At any time t,
the **speed** is $\|\mathbf{V}\|$, the magnitude of velocity, and

the **direction of motion** is $\dfrac{\mathbf{V}}{\|\mathbf{V}\|}$.

The graph of the position vector $\mathbf{R}(t)$ is called the **trajectory** of the object's motion. According to the results obtained earlier in this section, the velocity $\mathbf{V}(t) = \mathbf{R}'(t)$ is a tangent vector to the trajectory at any point where $\mathbf{V}(t)$ exists and $\mathbf{V}(t) \neq \mathbf{0}$ (see Figure 11.10). Appropriately, whenever $\mathbf{V}(t) = \mathbf{0}$, the object is said to be **stationary**.

In practice, the position vector is often represented in the form

$$\mathbf{R}(t) = f_1(t)\mathbf{i} + f_2(t)\mathbf{j} + f_3(t)\mathbf{k}$$

and in this case, the velocity and the acceleration vectors are given by

$$\mathbf{V}(t) = \mathbf{R}'(t) = f_1'(t)\mathbf{i} + f_2'(t)\mathbf{j} + f_3'(t)\mathbf{k}$$

and

$$\mathbf{A}(t) = \mathbf{V}'(t) = \mathbf{R}''(t) = f_1''(t)\mathbf{i} + f_2''(t)\mathbf{j} + f_3''(t)\mathbf{k}$$

Figure 11.10 The velocity vector is tangent to the trajectory of the object's motion.

EXAMPLE 7   Speed and direction of a particle

A particle's position at time t is determined by the vector

$$\mathbf{R}(t) = (\cos t)\mathbf{i} + (\sin t)\mathbf{j} + t^3\mathbf{k}$$

Analyze the particle's motion. In particular, find the particle's velocity, speed, direction, and acceleration at $t = 2$.

Solution

$$\mathbf{V} = \frac{d\mathbf{R}}{dt} = (-\sin t)\mathbf{i} + (\cos t)\mathbf{j} + 3t^2\mathbf{k}$$

$$\mathbf{A} = \frac{d\mathbf{V}}{dt} = (-\cos t)\mathbf{i} - (\sin t)\mathbf{j} + 6t\mathbf{k}$$

The velocity at time $t = 2$ is

$$(-\sin 2)\mathbf{i} + (\cos 2)\mathbf{j} + 3(2)^2\mathbf{k} \approx -0.91\mathbf{i} - 0.42\mathbf{j} + 12\mathbf{k}$$

The acceleration at $t = 2$ is

$$(-\cos 2)\mathbf{i} - (\sin 2)\mathbf{j} + 6(2)\mathbf{k} \approx 0.42\mathbf{i} - 0.91\mathbf{j} + 12\mathbf{k}$$

The speed is $\|\mathbf{V}\| = \sqrt{(-\sin t)^2 + (\cos t)^2 + (3t^2)^2}$

$$= \sqrt{1 + 9t^4}$$

At time $t = 2$, the speed is $\sqrt{1 + 144} \approx 12.04$

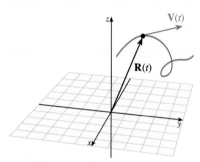

$\oslash$ Notice $\mathbf{V} = \|\mathbf{V}\| \cdot \dfrac{\mathbf{V}}{\|\mathbf{V}\|}$

$= (\text{SPEED}) \cdot (\text{DIRECTION}). \oslash$

The direction of motion is $\dfrac{\mathbf{V}}{\|\mathbf{V}\|} = \dfrac{1}{\sqrt{145}}\,[(-\sin t)\mathbf{i} + (\cos t)\mathbf{j} + 3t^2\mathbf{k}]$

At time $t = 2$, the direction is

$$\frac{1}{\sqrt{145}}[(-\sin 2)\mathbf{i} + (\cos 2)\mathbf{j} + 12\mathbf{k}] \approx -0.08\mathbf{i} - 0.03\mathbf{j} + \mathbf{k}$$

■ VECTOR INTEGRALS

Suppose we know the velocity of a particle and wish to know its position. We need to integrate the velocity vector to obtain its displacement. This can be accomplished by using the following definition.

Indefinite Integral

Definite Integral

> Let $\mathbf{F}(t) = f_1(t)\mathbf{i} + f_2(t)\mathbf{j} + f_3(t)\mathbf{k}$, where f_1, f_2, and f_3 are continuous on the closed interval $a \le t \le b$. Then the **indefinite integral** of $\mathbf{F}(t)$ is the vector function
>
> $$\int \mathbf{F}(t)\,dt = \left[\int f_1(t)\,dt\right]\mathbf{i} + \left[\int f_2(t)\,dt\right]\mathbf{j} + \left[\int f_3(t)\,dt\right]\mathbf{k}$$
>
> The **definite integral** of $\mathbf{F}(t)$ on $a \le t \le b$ is the vector
>
> $$\int_a^b \mathbf{F}(t)\,dt = \left[\int_a^b f_1(t)\,dt\right]\mathbf{i} + \left[\int_a^b f_2(t)\,dt\right]\mathbf{j} + \left[\int_a^b f_3(t)\,dt\right]\mathbf{k}$$

EXAMPLE 8   Integrals of vector functions

Find $\displaystyle\int_0^\pi [t\mathbf{i} + 3\mathbf{j} - (\sin t)\mathbf{k}]\,dt$.

Solution $\displaystyle\int_0^\pi [t\mathbf{i} + 3\mathbf{j} - (\sin t)\mathbf{k}]\,dt = \left[\int_0^\pi t\,dt\right]\mathbf{i} + \left[\int_0^\pi 3\,dt\right]\mathbf{j} - \left[\int_0^\pi \sin t\,dt\right]\mathbf{k}$

$$= \left(\frac{t^2}{2}\right)\Big|_0^\pi \mathbf{i} + (3t)\big|_0^\pi \mathbf{j} - (-\cos t)\big|_0^\pi \mathbf{k}$$

$$= \tfrac{1}{2}\pi^2\mathbf{i} + 3\pi\mathbf{j} + (\cos\pi - \cos 0)]\mathbf{k}$$

$$= \tfrac{1}{2}\pi^2\mathbf{i} + 3\pi\mathbf{j} - 2\mathbf{k}$$

EXAMPLE 9   Position of a particle given its velocity

The velocity of a particle moving in space is

$$\mathbf{V}(t) = e^t\mathbf{i} + t^2\mathbf{j} + (\cos 2t)\mathbf{k}$$

Find the particle's position as a function of t if $\mathbf{R}(0) = 2\mathbf{i} + \mathbf{j} - \mathbf{k}$.

Solution   We need to solve the initial value problem that consists of:

the differential equation $\mathbf{V}(t) = \dfrac{d\mathbf{R}}{dt} = e^t\mathbf{i} + t^2\mathbf{j} + (\cos 2t)\mathbf{k}$

the initial condition $\mathbf{R} = 2\mathbf{i} + \mathbf{j} - \mathbf{k}$

We integrate both sides of the differential equation with respect to t:

$$\int d\mathbf{R} = \left[\int e^t \, dt\right]\mathbf{i} + \left[\int t^2 \, dt\right]\mathbf{j} + \left[\int \cos 2t \, dt\right]\mathbf{k}$$

$$\mathbf{R}(t) = (e^t + C_1)\mathbf{i} + \left(\tfrac{1}{3}t^3 + C_2\right)\mathbf{j} + \left(\tfrac{1}{2}\sin 2t + C_3\right)\mathbf{k}$$

$$= e^t\mathbf{i} + \tfrac{1}{3}t^3\mathbf{j} + \left(\tfrac{1}{2}\sin 2t\right)\mathbf{k} + \underbrace{C_1\mathbf{i} + C_2\mathbf{j} + C_3\mathbf{k}}_{\mathbf{C}}$$

Now use the initial condition to find $\mathbf{C}$:

$$\underbrace{2\mathbf{i} + \mathbf{j} - \mathbf{k}}_{\mathbf{R}(0)} = e^0\mathbf{i} + \tfrac{1}{3}(0)^3\mathbf{j} + \left(\tfrac{1}{2}\sin 0\right)\mathbf{k} + \mathbf{C} = \mathbf{i} + \mathbf{C}$$

so that

$$\mathbf{i} + \mathbf{j} - \mathbf{k} = \mathbf{C}$$

Thus, the particle's position at any time t is

$$\mathbf{R}(t) = e^t\mathbf{i} + \tfrac{1}{3}t^3\mathbf{j} + \left(\tfrac{1}{2}\sin 2t\right)\mathbf{k} + \mathbf{i} + \mathbf{j} - \mathbf{k}$$

$$= (e^t + 1)\mathbf{i} + \left(\tfrac{1}{3}t^3 + 1\right)\mathbf{j} + \left(\tfrac{1}{2}\sin 2t - 1\right)\mathbf{k}$$

PROBLEM SET 11.2

Ⓐ *Find the vector derivative* $\mathbf{F}'$ *in Problems 1–4.*
  1. $\mathbf{F}(t) = t\mathbf{i} + t^2\mathbf{j} + (t + t^3)\mathbf{k}$
  2. $\mathbf{F}(s) = (s\mathbf{i} + s^2\mathbf{j} + s^2\mathbf{k}) + (2s^2\mathbf{i} - s\mathbf{j} + 3\mathbf{k})$
  3. $\mathbf{F}(s) = \ln s[s\mathbf{i} + 5\mathbf{j} - e^s\mathbf{k}]$
  4. $\mathbf{F}(\theta) = \cos\theta[\mathbf{i} + (\tan\theta)\mathbf{j} + 3\mathbf{k}]$

Find $\mathbf{F}'$ *and* $\mathbf{F}''$ *for the vector functions given in Problems 5–8.*
  5. $\mathbf{F}(t) = t^2\mathbf{i} + t^{-1}\mathbf{j} + e^{2t}\mathbf{k}$
  6. $\mathbf{F}(s) = (1 - 2s^2)\mathbf{i} + (s\cos s)\mathbf{j} - s\mathbf{k}$
  7. $\mathbf{F}(s) = (\sin s)\mathbf{i} + (\cos s)\mathbf{j} + s^2\mathbf{k}$
  8. $\mathbf{F}(\theta) = (\sin^2\theta)\mathbf{i} + (\cos 2\theta)\mathbf{j} + \theta^2\mathbf{k}$

Differentiate the scalar functions in Problems 9–12.
  9. $f(x) = [x\mathbf{i} + (x + 1)\mathbf{j}] \cdot [(2x)\mathbf{i} - (3x^2)\mathbf{j}]$
  10. $f(x) = [(\cos x)\mathbf{i} + x\mathbf{j} - x\mathbf{k}] \cdot [(\sec x)\mathbf{i} - x^2\mathbf{j} + 2x\mathbf{k}]$
  11. $g(x) = \|(\sin x)\mathbf{i} - 2x\mathbf{j} + (\cos x)\mathbf{k}\|$
  12. $f(x) = \|[x\mathbf{i} + x^2\mathbf{j} - 2\mathbf{k}] + [(1 - x)\mathbf{i} - e^x\mathbf{j}]\|$

In Problems 13–18, $\mathbf{R}$ *is the position vector for a particle in space at time* t. *Find the particle's velocity and acceleration vector and then find the speed and direction of motion for the given value of* t.

  13. $\mathbf{R}(t) = t\mathbf{i} + t^2\mathbf{j} + 2t\mathbf{k}$ at $t = 1$
  14. $\mathbf{R}(t) = (1 - 2t)\mathbf{i} - t^2\mathbf{j} + e^t\mathbf{k}$ at $t = 0$
  15. $\mathbf{R}(t) = (\cos t)\mathbf{i} + (\sin t)\mathbf{j} + 3t\mathbf{k}$ at $t = \frac{\pi}{4}$
  16. $\mathbf{R}(t) = (2\cos t)\mathbf{i} + t^2\mathbf{j} + (2\sin t)\mathbf{k}$ at $t = \frac{\pi}{2}$
  17. $\mathbf{R}(t) = e^t\mathbf{i} + e^{-t}\mathbf{j} + e^{2t}\mathbf{k}$ at $t = \ln 2$
  18. $\mathbf{R}(t) = (\ln t)\mathbf{i} + \frac{1}{2}t^3\mathbf{j} - t\mathbf{k}$ at $t = 1$

Find the tangent vector to the graph of the given vector function $\mathbf{F}$ *at the points indicated in Problems 19–24.*
  19. $\mathbf{F}(t) = t^2\mathbf{i} + 2t\mathbf{j} + (t^3 + t^2)\mathbf{k}$; $t = 0$, $t = 1$, $t = -1$
  20. $\mathbf{F}(t) = t^{-3}\mathbf{i} + t^{-2}\mathbf{j} + t^{-1}\mathbf{k}$; $t = 1$, $t = -1$
  21. $\mathbf{F}(t) = \dfrac{t\mathbf{i} + t^2\mathbf{j} + t^3\mathbf{k}}{1 + 2t}$; $t = 0$, $t = 2$
  22. $\mathbf{F}(t) = t^2\mathbf{i} + (\cos t)\mathbf{j} + (t^2\cos t)\mathbf{k}$; $t = 0$, $t = \frac{\pi}{2}$
  23. $\mathbf{F}(t) = (\sin t)\mathbf{i} + (\cos t)\mathbf{j} + at\mathbf{k}$; $t = \frac{\pi}{2}$, $t = \pi$
  24. $\mathbf{F}(t) = (e^t\sin \pi t)\mathbf{i} + (e^t\cos \pi t)\mathbf{j} + (\sin \pi t + \cos \pi t)\mathbf{k}$; $t = 0$, $t = 1$, $t = 2$

Find the indefinite vector integrals in Problems 25–30.
  25. $\int [t\mathbf{i} - e^{3t}\mathbf{j} + 3\mathbf{k}] \, dt$
  26. $\int [(\cos t)\mathbf{i} + (\sin t)\mathbf{j} - (2t)\mathbf{k}] \, dt$
  27. $\int [(\ln t)(\mathbf{i} - t\mathbf{j} + 3\mathbf{k})] \, dt$
  28. $\int e^{-t}[3\mathbf{i} + t\mathbf{j} + (\sin t)\mathbf{k}] \, dt$
  29. $\int [(t \ln t)\mathbf{i} - \sin(1 - t)\mathbf{j} + t\mathbf{k}] \, dt$
  30. $\int [(\sinh t)\mathbf{i} - 3\mathbf{j} + (\cosh t)\mathbf{k}] \, dt$

Ⓑ 31. ■ **What Does This Say?** Describe the concept of a smooth curve.

  32. ■ **What Does This Say?** Compare or contrast the notions of speed and acceleration of a vector function.

Let $\mathbf{v} = 2\mathbf{i} - \mathbf{j} + 5\mathbf{k}$ *and* $\mathbf{w} = \mathbf{i} + 2\mathbf{j} - 3\mathbf{k}$. *Find the derivatives in Problems 33–36.*

  33. $\dfrac{d}{dt}(\mathbf{v} + t\mathbf{w})$ 34. $\dfrac{d^2}{dt^2}(\mathbf{v} \cdot t^4\mathbf{w})$

35. $\dfrac{d^2}{dt^2}(t\|\mathbf{v}\| + t^2\|\mathbf{w}\|)$ **36.** $\dfrac{d}{dt}(t\mathbf{v} \times t^2\mathbf{w})$

In Problems 37–38, verify the indicated equation for the vector functions.

$$\mathbf{F}(t) = (3 + t^2)\mathbf{i} - (\cos 3t)\mathbf{j} + t^{-1}\mathbf{k}$$

and

$$\mathbf{G}(t) = \sin(2 - t)\mathbf{i} - e^{2t}\mathbf{k}$$

37. $(3\mathbf{F} - 2\mathbf{G})'(t) = 3\mathbf{F}'(t) - 2\mathbf{G}'(t)$

38. $(\mathbf{F} \cdot \mathbf{G})'(t) = (\mathbf{F}' \cdot \mathbf{G})(t) + (\mathbf{F} \cdot \mathbf{G}')(t)$

39. The velocity of a particle moving in space is

$$\mathbf{V}(t) = \dfrac{d\mathbf{R}(t)}{dt} = e^t\mathbf{i} + t^2\mathbf{j}$$

Find the particle's position as a function of t if $\mathbf{R}(0) = \mathbf{i} - \mathbf{j}$.

40. The acceleration of a particle moving in space is

$$\mathbf{A}(t) = \dfrac{d\mathbf{V}}{dt} = \dfrac{d^2\mathbf{R}}{dt^2} = 24t^2\mathbf{i} + 4\mathbf{j}$$

Find the particle's position as a function of t if $\mathbf{R}(0) = \mathbf{i} + 2\mathbf{j}$ and $\mathbf{V}(0) = \mathbf{0}$.

41. Find $\displaystyle\int_0^1 \mathbf{F}(t)\, dt$, where

$$\mathbf{F}(t) = (t\sqrt{1 + t^2})\,\mathbf{i} + \left(\dfrac{1}{1 + t^2}\right)\mathbf{j}$$

42. Find $\displaystyle\int_0^{\pi/2} \mathbf{F}(t)\, dt$, where

$$\mathbf{F}(t) = (\cos t)\mathbf{i} + (\sin t)\mathbf{j} + (\sin t \cos t)\mathbf{k}$$

In Problems 43–44, show that $\mathbf{F}(t)$ and $\mathbf{F}''(t)$ are parallel for all t with constant k.

43. $\mathbf{F}(t) = e^{kt}\mathbf{i} + e^{-kt}\mathbf{j}$ **44.** $\mathbf{F}(t) = (\cos kt)\mathbf{i} + (\sin kt)\mathbf{j}$

Ⓒ 45. Let $\mathbf{F}(t) = u(t)\mathbf{i} + v(t)\mathbf{j} + w(t)\mathbf{k}$, where u, v, and w are differentiable scalar functions of t. Show that

$$\mathbf{F}(t) \cdot \mathbf{F}'(t) = \|\mathbf{F}(t)\| \left(\|\mathbf{F}(t)\|\right)'$$

46. Let $\mathbf{F}(t)$ be a differentiable vector function and let $h(t)$ be a differentiable scalar function of t. Show that

$$[h(t)\mathbf{F}(t)]' = h(t)\mathbf{F}'(t) + h'(t)\mathbf{F}(t)$$

47. If $\mathbf{F}$ and $\mathbf{G}$ are differentiable vector functions of t, prove

$$(\mathbf{F} \cdot \mathbf{G})'(t) = (\mathbf{F}' \cdot \mathbf{G})(t) + (\mathbf{F} \cdot \mathbf{G}')(t)$$

48. If $\mathbf{F}$ and $\mathbf{G}$ are differentiable vector functions of t, prove

$$(\mathbf{F} \times \mathbf{G})'(t) = (\mathbf{F}' \times \mathbf{G})(t) + (\mathbf{F} \times \mathbf{G}')(t)$$

49. If $\mathbf{F}$ is a differentiable vector function such that $\mathbf{F}(t) \neq \mathbf{0}$, show that

$$\dfrac{d}{dt}\dfrac{\mathbf{F}(t)}{\|\mathbf{F}(t)\|} = \dfrac{\mathbf{F}'(t)}{\|\mathbf{F}(t)\|} - \dfrac{[\mathbf{F}(t) \cdot \mathbf{F}'(t)]\mathbf{F}(t)}{\|\mathbf{F}(t)\|^3}$$

11.3 MODELING BALLISTICS AND PLANETARY MOTION

IN THIS SECTION The motion of a projectile in a vacuum, Kepler's second law

Historically, the study of projectile planes and planetary motion were two of the earliest applications of calculus. In this section, we explore these applications using the methods of vector calculus.

■ THE MOTION OF A PROJECTILE IN A VACUUM

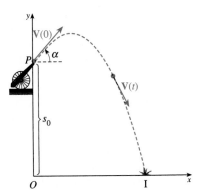

Figure 11.11 The motion of a projectile

In general, it can be quite difficult to analyze the motion of a projectile, but the problem becomes manageable if we assume that the acceleration due to gravity is constant and that the projectile travels in a vacuum (that is, there is no air resistance). A model of the motion in the real world (with air resistance, etc.) based on these assumptions is fairly realistic as long as the projectile is reasonably heavy, travels at relatively low speed, and stays close to the surface of the earth.

Figure 11.11 shows a projectile that is fired from a point P and travels in a vertical plane coordinatized so that P is directly above the origin O and the impact point I is on the x-axis at ground level. We let s_0 be the height of P above O, v_0 be the initial speed of the projectile (the **muzzle velocity**), and α be the angle of elevation of the "gun" that fires the projectile.

Because our projectile is to travel in a vacuum, we shall assume that the only force acting on the projectile at any given time is the force due to gravity. This force **F** is directed downward. The magnitude of this force is the projectile's weight. If m is the mass of the projectile and g is the "free-fall" acceleration due to gravity (g is approximately 32 ft/s² or 9.8 m/s²), then the magnitude of **F** is mg. Thus, **F** $= (-mg)$**j**. Also, according to **Newton's second law of motion**, the sum of all the forces acting on the projectile must equal $m\mathbf{A}(t)$, where $\mathbf{A}(t)$ is the acceleration of the projectile at time t. Because **F** $= -mg\mathbf{j}$ is the only force acting on the projectile, it follows that

$$-mg\mathbf{j} = \mathbf{F} = m\mathbf{A}(t)$$

$$\mathbf{A}(t) = -g\mathbf{j} \qquad \text{for all } t \geq 0$$

The velocity $\mathbf{V}(t)$ of the projectile can now be obtained by integrating $\mathbf{A}(t)$. Specifically, we have

$$\mathbf{V}(t) = \int \mathbf{A}(t)\, dt = \int (-g\mathbf{j})\, dt = -gt\mathbf{j} + \mathbf{C}_1$$

where $\mathbf{C}_1 = \mathbf{V}(0)$ is the velocity when $t = 0$ (that is, the *initial velocity*). Because the projectile is fired with initial speed v_0 at an angle of elevation α, the initial velocity must be

$$\mathbf{C}_1 = \mathbf{V}(0) = (v_0\cos\alpha)\mathbf{i} + (v_0\sin\alpha)\mathbf{j}$$

(as shown in the detail of Figure 11.11), and by substitution we find

$$\mathbf{V}(t) = -gt\mathbf{j} + (v_0\cos\alpha)\mathbf{i} + (v_0\sin\alpha)\mathbf{j}$$

$$= (v_0\cos\alpha)\mathbf{i} + (v_0\sin\alpha - gt)\mathbf{j}$$

Next, by integrating **V** with respect to t, we find that the projectile has displacement

$$\mathbf{R}(t) = \int \mathbf{V}(t)\, dt = \int [(v_0\cos\alpha)\mathbf{i} + (v_0\sin\alpha - gt)\mathbf{j}]\, dt$$

$$= (v_0\cos\alpha)t\mathbf{i} + \left[(v_0\sin\alpha)t - \tfrac{1}{2}gt^2\right]\mathbf{j} + \mathbf{C}_2$$

where $\mathbf{C}_2 = \mathbf{R}(0)$ is the displacement at time $t = 0$. Because the projectile begins its flight at P, the initial displacement is $\mathbf{R}(0) = s_0\mathbf{j}$, and by substituting this expression for $\mathbf{C}_2$, we find that the displacement at time t is

$$\mathbf{R}(t) = [(v_0\cos\alpha)t]\mathbf{i} + \left[(v_0\sin\alpha)t - \tfrac{1}{2}gt^2 + s_0\right]\mathbf{j}$$

This vector gives the position of the projectile at any time t after it is fired and before it hits the ground. If we let $x(t)$ and $y(t)$ denote the horizontal and vertical components of $\mathbf{R}(t)$, respectively, we can make the following statement.

V(0)

$v_0 \sin\alpha$

α

$v_0 \cos\alpha$

Detail of Figure 11.11

Motion of a Projectile in a Vacuum

Consider a projectile that travels in a vacuum in a coordinate plane, with the x-axis along level ground. If the projectile is fired from a height of s_0 with initial speed v_0 and angle of elevation α, then at time t ($t \geq 0$) it will be at the point $(x(t), y(t))$, where

$$x(t) = (v_0\cos\alpha)t \quad \text{and} \quad y(t) = -\tfrac{1}{2}gt^2 + (v_0\sin\alpha)t + s_0$$

The parametric equations for the motion of a projectile in a vacuum provide useful general information about a projectile's motion. For instance, note that if $\alpha \neq 90°$, we can eliminate the parameter t by solving the first equation, obtaining

$$t = \frac{x}{v_0\cos\alpha}$$

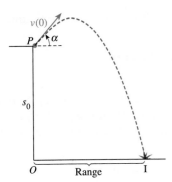

Figure 11.12 The motion of a projectile. The trajectory is part of a parabolic arc.

By substituting into the second equation, we find

$$y = -\frac{1}{2}g\left[\frac{x}{v_0\cos\alpha}\right]^2 + (v_0\sin\alpha)\left[\frac{x}{v_0\cos\alpha}\right] + s_0$$

$$= \left[\frac{-g}{2(v_0\cos\alpha)^2}\right]x^2 + (\tan\alpha)x + s_0$$

This is the Cartesian equation for the trajectory of the projectile, and because the equation has the general form $y = ax^2 + bx + c$, with $a < 0$, the trajectory must be part of a downward-opening parabola. That is, *if a projectile is not fired vertically (so that $\tan\alpha$ is defined), its trajectory will be part of a downward-opening parabolic arc*, as shown in Figure 11.12. The *time of flight* T_f of a projectile is the elapsed time between launch and impact, and the *range* is the total horizontal distance R traveled by the projectile during its flight. Because $y = 0$ at impact, it follows that T_f must satisfy the quadratic equation

$$-\frac{1}{2}gT_f^2 + (v_0\sin\alpha)T_f + s_0 = 0$$

Then, because the flight begins at $x = 0$ when $t = 0$ and ends at $x = R$ when $t = T_f$, the range R can be computed by evaluating $x(t)$ at $t = T_f$.

EXAMPLE 1   Path of a projectile

A boy standing at the edge of a cliff throws a ball upward at a 30° angle with an initial speed of 64 ft/s. Suppose that when the ball leaves the boy's hand, it is 48 ft above the ground at the base of the cliff.

a. What are the time of flight of the ball and its range?
b. What are the velocity of the ball and its speed at impact?
c. What is the highest point reached by the ball during its flight?

Solution: We know that $g = 32$ ft/s², and we are given $s_0 = 48$ ft, $v_0 = 64$ ft/s, and $\alpha = 30°$. We can now write the parametric equations for the parabola:

$$x(t) = (v_0\cos\alpha)t = (64\cos 30°)t = 32\sqrt{3}\,t$$
$$y(t) = -\frac{1}{2}gt^2 + (v_0\sin\alpha)t + s_0$$
$$= -\frac{1}{2}(32)t^2 + (64\sin 30°)t + 48$$
$$= -16t^2 + 32t + 48$$

a. The ball hits the ground when $y = 0$, and by solving the equation $-16t^2 + 32t + 48 = 0$ for $t \geq 0$, we find that $t = 3$, so the time of flight is $T_f = 3$ sec. The range is
$$x(3) = 32\sqrt{3}(3) \approx 166.27688$$

That is, the ball hits the ground about 166 ft from the base of the cliff.

b. We find that $x'(t) = 32\sqrt{3}$ and $y'(t) = -32t + 32$, so the velocity at time t is

$$\mathbf{V}(t) = 32\sqrt{3}\,\mathbf{i} + (-32t + 32)\mathbf{j}$$

Computational Window

Graph the curve in Example 1.

$X_{1T} \boxminus (32\sqrt{3})T$
$Y_{1T} \boxminus -16T^2 + 32T + 48$

Ymin=0   Tmin=0
Ymax=100 Tmax=5
Yscl=10   Tstep=.1
          Xmin=0
          Xmax=200
          Xscl=10

Use TRACE to find the highest point as well as the range and time of flight.

Thus, at impact (when $t = 3$), the velocity is $\mathbf{V}(3) = 32\sqrt{3}\ \mathbf{i} - 64\mathbf{j}$, and its speed is

$$\|\mathbf{V}(3)\| = \sqrt{(32\sqrt{3})^2 + (-64)^2} \approx 84.664042$$

That is, the speed at impact is about 85 ft/s.

c. The ball attains its maximum height when the upward (vertical) component of its velocity $\mathbf{V}(t)$ is 0—that is, when $y'(t) = 0$. Solving the equation $-32t + 32 = 0$, we find that this occurs when $t = 1$; therefore, the maximum height attained by the ball is

$$y_m = y(1) = -16(1)^2 + 32(1) + 48 = 64$$
$$x_m = x(1) = 32\sqrt{3}(1) \approx 55.425626$$

Thus, the highest point reached by the ball has coordinates (rounded to the nearest unit) of (55, 64).

We shall now carry out the steps illustrated by Example 1 in a general way to derive a formula. If the projectile is fired from ground level, then $s_0 = 0$. In this case, the time of flight satisfies

$$-\tfrac{1}{2}gT_f^2 + (v_0\sin\alpha)T_f = 0$$

and we obtain (solving for T_f and rejecting the solution $T_f = 0$):

$$T_f = \frac{2}{g}v_0\sin\alpha$$

By substituting $t = T_f$ in the equation for x, we can find the range:

$$R = x(T_f) = (v_0\cos\alpha)\left(\frac{2v_0\sin\alpha}{g}\right) = \frac{v_0^2}{g}(2\sin\alpha\cos\alpha) = \frac{v_0^2}{g}\sin 2\alpha$$

Notice that for a given initial speed v_0, the range assumes its largest value $R_m = \frac{1}{g}v_0^2$ when $\sin 2\alpha = 1$—that is, when $\alpha = 45° = \frac{\pi}{4}$.

Time of Flight and Range

A projectile fired from ground level has **time of flight** T_f and **range** R given by the equations

$$T_f = \frac{2}{g}v_0\sin\alpha \quad\text{and}\quad R = \frac{v_0^2}{g}\sin 2\alpha$$

The maximal range is $R_m = \frac{v_0^2}{g}$, and it occurs when $\alpha = \frac{\pi}{4}$.

EXAMPLE 2   Flight time and range for the flight of a projectile

A projectile is fired from ground level at an angle of 40° with muzzle velocity of 110 ft/s. Find the time of flight and the range.

Solution   With $g = 32$ ft/s^2, we see that the flight time T_f is

$$T_f = \frac{2}{g}v_0\sin\alpha = \frac{2}{32}(110)(\sin 40°) \approx 4.4191648$$

The range R is

$$R = \frac{v_0^2}{g}\sin 2\alpha = \frac{(110)^2}{32}(\sin 80°) \approx 372.38043$$

That is, the projectile travels about 372 ft horizontally before it hits the ground, and it takes a little more than 4 sec. ▬

■ KEPLER'S SECOND LAW

In the 17th century, the German astronomer Johannes Kepler (1571–1630) formulated three useful laws for describing planetary motion. The guest essay at the end of this chapter discusses the discovery of these laws.

Kepler's Laws

1. The planets move about the sun in elliptical orbits, with the sun at one focus.
2. The radius vector joining a planet to the sun sweeps over equal areas in equal intervals of time.
3. The square of the time of one complete revolution of a planet about its orbit is proportional to the cube of the orbit's semimajor axis.

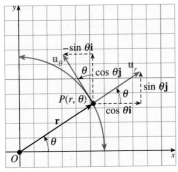

Figure 11.13 Describing the motion of a particle along a curve

We will show how to use vector methods to prove Kepler's second law, and the other two can be established in a similar fashion. However, before we begin we need to prove a result about the velocity and acceleration of a planet.

We shall describe the motion of the planet by means of a polar coordinate system with the sun at the origin. The position, velocity, and acceleration can be expressed in terms of the moving unit vectors

$$\mathbf{u}_r = (\cos \theta)\mathbf{i} + (\sin \theta)\mathbf{j} \quad \text{and} \quad \mathbf{u}_\theta = (-\sin \theta)\mathbf{i} + (\cos \theta)\mathbf{j}$$

which are shown in Figure 11.13. The "particle" might be a planet in orbit around the sun, a satellite moving around a planet, or a comet revolving about a star. The vector $\mathbf{u}_r$ has unit length and points in the direction of **OP**. The vector $\mathbf{u}_\theta$ has unit length, points in the direction of increasing θ, and is perpendicular to $\mathbf{u}_r$. Notice that because $\mathbf{u}_r = (\cos \theta)\mathbf{i} + (\sin \theta)\mathbf{j}$, we have

$$\frac{d\mathbf{u}_r}{d\theta} = (-\sin \theta)\mathbf{i} + (\cos \theta)\mathbf{j} = \mathbf{u}_\theta$$

Similarly, you can show that $\dfrac{d\mathbf{u}_\theta}{d\theta} = -\mathbf{u}_r$.

We now find the velocity:

$$\mathbf{V}(t) = \frac{d\mathbf{R}}{dt} \qquad \textit{Definition of velocity}$$

$$= (r\mathbf{u}_r)' \qquad \begin{array}{l}\mathbf{R}(t) = r\mathbf{u}_r \textit{ for } r = \|\mathbf{R}(t)\| \textit{ because } \mathbf{u}_r \\ \textit{and } \mathbf{OP} \textit{ point in the same direction.}\end{array}$$

$$= \frac{dr}{dt}\mathbf{u}_r + r\frac{d\mathbf{u}_r}{dt} \qquad \textit{Scalar multiple (Theorem 11.3)}$$

$$= \frac{dr}{dt}\mathbf{u}_r + r\frac{d\mathbf{u}_r}{d\theta}\frac{d\theta}{dt} \qquad \textit{Chain rule}$$

$$= \frac{dr}{dt}\mathbf{u}_r + r\frac{d\theta}{dt}\mathbf{u}_\theta$$

To date, there are more than 4,000 earth satellites.

You can find a similar formula for acceleration (see Problem 34). We summarize these formulas in the following box.

Polar Formulas for Velocity and Acceleration

$$\mathbf{V}(t) = \frac{dr}{dt}\mathbf{u}_r + r\frac{d\theta}{dt}\mathbf{u}_\theta$$

$$\mathbf{A}(t) = \frac{d\mathbf{V}(t)}{dt} = \frac{d^2\mathbf{R}}{dt^2} = \left[\frac{d^2r}{dt^2} - r\left(\frac{d\theta}{dt}\right)^2\right]\mathbf{u}_r + \left[r\frac{d^2\theta}{dt^2} + 2\frac{dr}{dt}\frac{d\theta}{dt}\right]\mathbf{u}_\theta$$

EXAMPLE 3   Find the velocity of a moving body

The displacement of a moving body is $\mathbf{R}(t) = 2t\mathbf{i} - t^2\mathbf{j}$ for $t \geq 0$. Express $\mathbf{R}$ and the velocity vector $\mathbf{V}(t)$ in terms of $\mathbf{u}_r$ and $\mathbf{u}_\theta$.

Solution   We note that on the trajectory, $x = 2t$, $y = -t^2$, and the displacement $\mathbf{R}$ has length

$$r = \|\mathbf{R}(t)\| = \sqrt{(2t)^2 + (-t^2)^2} = \sqrt{4t^2 + t^4} = t\sqrt{t^2 + 4}$$

We see $\mathbf{R} = r\mathbf{u}_r = t\sqrt{t^2 + 4}\,\mathbf{u}_r$. Because

$$\mathbf{V}(t) = \frac{dr}{dt}\mathbf{u}_r + r\frac{d\theta}{dt}\mathbf{u}_\theta, \quad \text{we find} \quad \frac{dr}{dt} \quad \text{and} \quad \frac{d\theta}{dt}$$

$$\frac{dr}{dt} = \sqrt{t^2 + 4} + t\left(\tfrac{1}{2}\right)(t^2 + 4)^{-1/2}(2t) = \frac{2t^2 + 4}{\sqrt{t^2 + 4}}$$

Because the polar angle satisfies $\theta = \tan^{-1}(y/x)$ for all points (x, y) on the curve (except where $x = 0$), we have $\theta = \tan^{-1}\left(\frac{-t^2}{2t}\right) = \tan^{-1}\left(-\frac{t}{2}\right)$

$$\frac{d\theta}{dt} = \frac{1}{1 + \left(-\frac{t}{2}\right)^2}\left(-\frac{1}{2}\right) = \frac{-2}{t^2 + 4} \qquad \textit{Theorem 5.18, page 367}$$

Thus,

$$\mathbf{V}(t) = \frac{2t^2 + 4}{\sqrt{t^2 + 4}}\mathbf{u}_r + t\sqrt{t^2 + 4}\left(\frac{-2}{t^2 + 4}\right)\mathbf{u}_\theta = \frac{(2t^2 + 4)\mathbf{u}_r - 2t\mathbf{u}_\theta}{\sqrt{t^2 + 4}}$$

We now have the tools we need to establish Kepler's second law.

THEOREM 11.5   Kepler's second law

The radius vector from the sun to a planet in its orbit sweeps over equal areas in equal intervals of time.

Proof: The situation described by Kepler's second law is illustrated in Figure 11.14. We shall assume that the only force acting on a planet is the gravitational attraction of the sun. According to the universal law of gravitation, the force of attraction is given by

$$\mathbf{F} = -G\frac{mM}{r^2}\mathbf{u}_r$$

where G is a physical constant and m and M are the masses of the planet and the sun, respectively. Because this is the only force acting on the planet, Newton's second law of motion tells us that $\mathbf{F} = m\mathbf{A}$, where $\mathbf{A}$ is the acceleration of the planet in its orbit. By equating these two expressions for the force $\mathbf{F}$, we find

$$m\mathbf{A} = -G\frac{mM}{r^2}\mathbf{u}_r$$

$$\mathbf{A} = \frac{-GM}{r^2}\mathbf{u}_r$$

Figure 11.14 The radial line sweeps out equal area in equal time

This says that *the acceleration of a planet in its orbit has only a radial component.* Note how this conclusion depends on our assumption that the only force on the planet is the sun's gravitational attraction, which acts along radial lines from the sun to the planet.

This means that the $\mathbf{u}_\theta$ component of the planet's acceleration is 0, and by examining the formula for acceleration we see that this condition is equivalent to the differential equation

$$\left[r\frac{d^2\theta}{dt^2} + 2\frac{dr}{dt}\frac{d\theta}{dt} \right] = 0$$

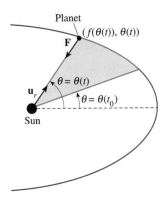

Planet

$(f(\theta(t)), \theta(t))$

F

$\theta = \theta(t)$

$\mathbf{u}_r$

$\theta = \theta(t_0)$

Sun

Figure 11.15 The radial line sweeps out area at the rate $\frac{dA}{dt} = \frac{1}{2}r^2\frac{d\theta}{dt}$.

If we set $z = \dfrac{d\theta}{dt}$, we obtain $\dfrac{d^2\theta}{dt^2} = \dfrac{dz}{dt}$, so that

$$r\frac{dz}{dt} + 2z\frac{dr}{dt} = 0$$

$$z^{-1}\frac{dz}{dt} = -2r^{-1}\frac{dr}{dt}$$

$$\int z^{-1}dz = \int (-2r^{-1})dr$$

$$\ln|z| + C_1 = -2\ln|r| + C_2$$

$$\ln z = \ln(Cr^{-2}) \qquad \text{since } r > 0 \text{ and } z > 0$$

$$z = Cr^{-2}$$

$$\frac{d\theta}{dt} = Cr^{-2}$$

$$r^2\frac{d\theta}{dt} = C$$

This formula is equivalent to Kepler's second law by the following argument. Let S be the area swept out by the line from the sun to the planet as time varies from t_0 to t, as shown in Figure 11.15. Then from Theorem 9.1 (area in polar form),

$$S(t) = \frac{1}{2}\int_{\theta(t_0)}^{\theta(t)} r^2\,d\theta \quad \text{so that} \quad \frac{dS}{dt} = \frac{1}{2}r^2\frac{d\theta}{dt} = \frac{1}{2}C$$

Integrating, we find that $S = \frac{1}{2}Ct + K$. In Problem 38 you are asked to show that because the area $S(t)$ swept out between times t_0 and t is a linear function of t, it follows that equal area is swept out in equal time. This verifies Kepler's second law. ∎

An object is said to move in a **central force field** if it is subject to a force that is always directed toward a single point. Our derivation of Kepler's second law is based on the assumption that planetary motion occurs in a central force field. In particular, the formula

$$\mathbf{A} = \frac{-GM}{r^2}\mathbf{u}_r$$

shows that a planet's acceleration has only a radial component, and this turns out to be true for an object moving in a plane in any central force field.

Much of what we know about the bodies in our solar system is a result of the mathematics associated with Kepler's laws. Table 11.1 provides some of these data.

TABLE 11.1 Data on Planetary Orbits

Planet	Mean Orbit (in millions of miles)	Eccentricity	Period (in days)	Comparative Mass (earth = 1.00)
Mercury	36.0	0.205635	88.0	0.06
Venus	67.3	0.006761	224.7	0.81
Earth	**93.0**	**0.016678**	**365.265**	**1**
			Actual mass: **5.975 × 10²⁴ kg**	
Mars	141.7	0.093455	687.0	0.12
Jupiter	484.0	0.048207	4,332.1	317.83
Saturn	887.0	0.055328	10,825.9	95.16
Uranus	1,787.0	0.047694	30,676.1	14.5
Neptune	2,797.0	0.010034	59,911.1	17.2
Pluto	3,675.0	0.248646	90,824.2	0.0025

PROBLEM SET 11.3

Ⓐ *In Problems 1–8, find the time of flight T_f (to the nearest tenth second) and the range R (to the nearest unit) of a projectile fired at the given angle α with the indicated initial speed v_0. Assume that $g = 32$ ft/s² or $g = 9.8$ m/s².*

1. $\alpha = 35°$, $v_0 = 128$ ft/s
2. $\alpha = 45°$, $v_0 = 80$ ft/s
3. $\alpha = 48.5°$, $v_0 = 850$ m/s
4. $\alpha = 43.5°$, $v_0 = 185$ m/s
5. $\alpha = 23.74°$, $v_0 = 23.3$ m/s
6. $\alpha = 31.04°$, $v_0 = 38.14$ m/s
7. $\alpha = 14.11°$, $v_0 = 100$ ft/s
8. $\alpha = 78.09°$, $v_0 = 88$ ft/s

In Problems 9–14, an object moves along the given curve in the plane (described in either polar or parametric form). Find its velocity and acceleration in terms of the unit polar vectors $\mathbf{u}_r$ and $\mathbf{u}_\theta$.

9. $x = 2t$, $y = t$
10. $x = \sin t$, $y = \cos t$
11. $r = \sin \theta$, $\theta = 2t$
12. $r = e^{-\theta}$, $\theta = 1 - t$
13. $r = 5(1 + \cos \theta)$, $\theta = 2t + 1$
14. $r = \dfrac{1}{1 - \cos \theta}$, $\theta = t$

Ⓑ **15.** A shell fired from ground level at an angle of 45° hits the ground 2000 m away. What is the muzzle velocity of the shell? *Note*: $g \approx 9.8$ m/s².

16. A gun at ground level has muzzle velocity of 300 ft/s. What angle of elevation (to the nearest degree) should be used to hit an object 1500 ft away?

17. At what angle (to the nearest tenth of a degree) should a projectile be fired from ground level if its muzzle velocity is 167.1 ft/s and the desired range is 600 ft?

18. A shell is fired at ground level with a muzzle velocity of 280 ft/s and at an elevation of 45° from ground level.

    a. Find the maximum height attained by the shell.

    b. Find the time of flight and the range of the shell.

    c. Find the speed of the shell at impact.

19. Jeff Bagwell hit a baseball at a 30° angle with a speed of 90 ft/sec. If the ball is 4 ft above ground level when it is hit, what is the maximum height reached by the ball? How far will it travel from home plate before it lands? If it just barely clears a five-foot wall in the outfield, how far (to the nearest foot) is the wall from home plate?

20. A baseball hit in the Astrodome at a 24° angle from 3 ft above the ground just goes over the 9-ft fence 400 ft from home plate. About how fast was the ball traveling, and how long did it take the ball to reach the wall?

21. One of the shortest possible home runs in major league baseball is over the right field fence at the Kingdome in Seattle. If the distance is 312 ft and if the fence is 8 ft high, how long will it take for a ball to leave the playing field at that point if it is struck $3\frac{1}{2}$ ft above the ground at a 32° angle and we assume that the ball just barely clears the fence?

22. Steve Young, a quarterback for the San Francisco '49ers, throws a pass at a 45° angle with a speed of 50 ft/s. A receiver, Jerry Rice, running at a constant speed of 32 ft/s, catches the ball at a height of 6 ft. If Steve and Jerry both line up on the 50-yard line at the start of the play, how far does Steve fade back from the line of scrimmage before he releases the ball?

23. A golf ball is hit from the tee to a green with an initial speed of 125 ft/s at an angle of elevation of 45°. How long will it take the ball to hit the green?

24. Basketball player Shaquille O'Neal could hit a shot while standing 20 ft from the basket. If "The Shaq" shot from a height of 7 ft and the ball reached a maximum height of 12 ft before passing through the 10-ft-high basket, what was the initial speed of the ball?

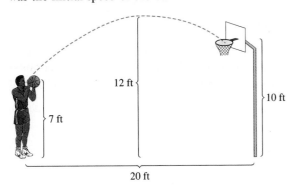

25. If a shotputter throws a shot from a height of 5 ft with an angle of 46° and initial speed of 25 ft/s, what is the horizontal distance of the throw?

26. In 1974 Evel Knievel attempted a skycycle ride across the Snake River, and at the time there was a great deal of hype about "will he make it?" If the angle of the launching ramp was 45° and if the horizontal distance the skycycle needed to travel was 4,700 ft, at what speed did Evel have to leave the ramp in order to make it across the Snake River Canyon?

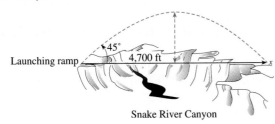

Snake River Canyon

Hint: Assume that the opposite edges of the canyon are at the same height.

27. A particle moves along the polar path (r, θ), where $r(t) = 3 + 2 \sin t$, $\theta(t) = t^3$. Find $\mathbf{V}(t)$ and $\mathbf{A}(t)$ in terms of $\mathbf{u}_r$ and $\mathbf{u}_\theta$.

In Problems 28–31, consider a particle moving on a circular path of radius a described by the equation

$$\mathbf{r}(t) = (a \cos \omega t)\mathbf{i} + (a \sin \omega t)\mathbf{j}$$

where $\omega = d\theta/dt$ *is the constant angular velocity.*

28. Find the velocity vector and show that it is orthogonal to $\mathbf{r}(t)$.

29. Find the speed of the particle.

30. Find the acceleration vector and show that its direction is always toward the center of the circle.

31. Find the magnitude of the acceleration vector.

32. A 3-oz paddleball attached to a string is swung in a circular path with a 1-ft radius. If the string will break under a force of 2 lb, find the maximum velocity the ball can attain without breaking the string. *Hint:* Note that the ball is 3 oz, and this is $\frac{3}{16}$ lb. Thus, use $\mathbf{F} = m\mathbf{A}$, where $m = \left(\frac{3}{16}\right)/32 = 3/2^9$.

33. A child, running along level ground at the top of a 30-ft-high vertical cliff at a speed of 15 ft/s throws a rock over the cliff into the sea below. Suppose the child's arm is 3 ft above the ground and her arm speed is 25 ft/s. If the rock is released 10 ft from the edge of the cliff at an angle of 30°, how long does it take for the rock to hit the water? How far from the base of the cliff does it hit? You may assume that the effective initial speed of the rock is $v_0 = 15 + 25 = 40$ ft/s.

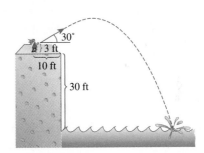

● 34. Use the formula

$$\mathbf{V}(t) = \frac{dr}{dt}\mathbf{u}_r + r\frac{d\theta}{dt}\mathbf{u}_\theta$$

to verify the acceleration formula

$$\mathbf{A}(t) = \frac{d\mathbf{V}(t)}{dt} = \frac{d^2\mathbf{R}}{dt}$$

$$= \left[\frac{d^2r}{dt^2} - r\left(\frac{d\theta}{dt}\right)^2\right]\mathbf{u}_r + \left[r\frac{d^2\theta}{dt^2} + 2\frac{dr}{dt}\frac{d\theta}{dt}\right]\mathbf{u}_\theta$$

Hint: Use the product rule to find $\mathbf{A}(t) = \mathbf{V}'(t)$. In the computation of $\mathbf{A}(t)$, use the chain rule to show that

$$\frac{d\mathbf{u}_r}{dt} = \frac{d\mathbf{u}_r}{d\theta}\frac{d\theta}{dt} = \mathbf{u}_\theta\frac{d\theta}{dt}$$

and

$$\frac{d\mathbf{u}_\theta}{dt} = \frac{d\mathbf{u}_\theta}{d\theta}\frac{d\theta}{dt} = -\mathbf{u}_r\frac{d\theta}{dt}$$

35. Using the acceleration formula given in Problem 34, show that the force **F** on an object is given by

$$\mathbf{F}(t) = m\mathbf{A}(t) = \mathbf{F}_r\mathbf{u}_r + \mathbf{F}_\theta\mathbf{u}_\theta$$

where

$$\mathbf{F}_r(t) = m\frac{d^2r}{dt^2} - mr\left(\frac{d\theta}{dt}\right)^2$$

and

$$\mathbf{F}_\theta(t) = mr\frac{d^2\theta}{dt^2} + 2m\frac{dr}{dt}\frac{d\theta}{dt}$$

36. Using Problem 35, show that

$$r\mathbf{F}_\theta(t) = \frac{d}{dt}\left(mr^2\frac{d\theta}{dt}\right)$$

37. Use Problem 36 to show that if $\mathbf{F}_\theta(t) = 0$, then

$$mr^2\frac{d\theta}{dt}$$

is constant.

38. Use Problem 37 to show that in a central force field, the radius vector $\mathbf{R}(t)$ sweeps out area at a constant rate. *Hint:* Note that the rate at which **R** sweeps out area is

$$\frac{1}{2}r^2\frac{d\theta}{dt}$$

11.4 UNIT TANGENT AND NORMAL VECTORS; CURVATURE

> **IN THIS SECTION** Unit tangent and principal unit normal vectors, arc length as a parameter, curvature
> In physical problems, it is often useful to describe the motion of an object in terms of unit vectors that are tangent and normal at each point on the trajectory. In this section, we see how unit tangent and normal vectors can be computed; then in the next section, we examine physical applications of such vectors. We also introduce the idea of curvature, which measures the amount of bend in a curve.

■ UNIT TANGENT AND PRINCIPAL UNIT NORMAL VECTORS

From Section 11.2, we know that if $\mathbf{R}(t)$ is a vector function with a smooth graph, then the derivative $\mathbf{R}'(t)$ is a tangent vector to the graph at the point corresponding to $\mathbf{R}(t)$. Because the graph is smooth, we have $\mathbf{R}'(t) \neq \mathbf{0}$, and a unit tangent vector $\mathbf{T}(t)$ can be obtained by dividing $\mathbf{R}'(t)$ by its length; that is,

$$\mathbf{T}(t) = \frac{\mathbf{R}'(t)}{\|\mathbf{R}'(t)\|}$$

A unit tangent vector at a point P of a curve is shown in Figure 11.16.

Based on our experience with normal lines to curves in the plane, we would expect a normal vector to be orthogonal to the tangent vector $\mathbf{T}(t)$ at each point on the graph of **R**. To obtain such a vector, we recall (Theorem 11.4) that any vector function with constant length is always orthogonal to its derivative $\mathbf{R}'(t)$. Therefore, because $\mathbf{T}(t)$ has length 1 for all t, it follows that $\mathbf{T}(t)$ is orthogonal to $\mathbf{T}'(t)$ for all t, so that

$$\mathbf{N}(t) = \frac{\mathbf{T}'(t)}{\|\mathbf{T}'(t)\|}$$

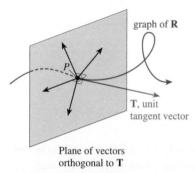

Figure 11.16 Unit tangent vector and vectors orthogonal to a tangent vector on a given curve

is a unit normal vector. Actually, there are infinitely many vectors orthogonal to $\mathbf{T}(t)$—see Figure 11.16—and we shall refer to $\mathbf{N}(t)$ as the **principal unit normal** whenever it is necessary to distinguish it from other normal vectors.

Unit Tangent Vector

If $\mathbf{R}(t)$ is a vector function that defines a smooth graph, then at each point a unit tangent is

$$\mathbf{T}(t) = \frac{\mathbf{R}'(t)}{\|\mathbf{R}'(t)\|}$$

Principal Unit Normal Vector

and the principal unit normal vector is

$$\mathbf{N}(t) = \frac{\mathbf{T}'(t)}{\|\mathbf{T}'(t)\|}$$

■ *What this says:* For each number t_0 in the domain of $\mathbf{R}(t)$, we have constructed a pair of unit vectors, $\mathbf{T}(t_0)$ and $\mathbf{N}(t_0)$, with $\mathbf{T}$ tangent to the graph of $\mathbf{R}$ at $t = t_0$ and with $\mathbf{N}$ orthogonal to $\mathbf{T}$ at $t = t_0$.

EXAMPLE 1   Unit tangent and principal unit normal

Find the unit tangent vector $\mathbf{T}(t)$ and the principal unit normal vector $\mathbf{N}(t)$ at each point on the graph of the vector function

$$\mathbf{R}(t) = e^t\mathbf{i} + e^{-t}\mathbf{j} + \sqrt{2}t\,\mathbf{k}$$

In particular, find $\mathbf{T}(1)$ and $\mathbf{N}(1)$.

Solution   The derivative of $\mathbf{R}(t)$ with respect to t is the vector function $\mathbf{R}'(t) = e^t\mathbf{i} - e^{-t}\mathbf{j} + \sqrt{2}\,\mathbf{k}$, which has length

$$\|\mathbf{R}'(t)\| = \sqrt{(e^t)^2 + (-e^{-t})^2 + (\sqrt{2})^2}$$
$$= \sqrt{e^{2t} + e^{-2t} + 2} = \sqrt{(e^t + e^{-t})^2} = e^t + e^{-t}$$

Thus,

$$\mathbf{T}(t) = \frac{\mathbf{R}'(t)}{\|\mathbf{R}'(t)\|} = \frac{e^t\mathbf{i} - e^{-t}\mathbf{j} + \sqrt{2}\,\mathbf{k}}{e^t + e^{-t}}$$
$$= \left(\frac{e^t}{e^t + e^{-t}}\right)\mathbf{i} + \left(\frac{-e^{-t}}{e^t + e^{-t}}\right)\mathbf{j} + \left(\frac{\sqrt{2}}{e^t + e^{-t}}\right)\mathbf{k}$$

So

$$\mathbf{T}(1) = \frac{e\mathbf{i} - e^{-1}\mathbf{j} + \sqrt{2}\,\mathbf{k}}{e + e^{-1}} \approx 0.88\mathbf{i} - 0.12\mathbf{j} + 0.46\mathbf{k}$$

To compute the principal unit normal $\mathbf{N}$, we first find $\mathbf{T}'(t)$:

$$\mathbf{T}'(t) = \frac{(e^t + e^{-t})e^t - e^t(e^t - e^{-t})}{(e^t + e^{-t})^2}\,\mathbf{i}$$
$$+ \frac{(e^t + e^{-t})(e^{-t}) + e^{-t}(e^t - e^{-t})}{(e^t + e^{-t})^2}\,\mathbf{j}$$
$$- \sqrt{2}(e^t + e^{-t})^{-2}(e^t - e^{-t})\mathbf{k}$$
$$= \frac{1}{(e^t + e^{-t})^2}\left[(e^{2t} + 1 - e^{2t} + 1)\mathbf{i} + 2\mathbf{j} - \sqrt{2}(e^t - e^{-t})\mathbf{k}\right]$$
$$= \frac{2\mathbf{i} + 2\mathbf{j} - \sqrt{2}(e^t - e^{-t})\mathbf{k}}{(e^t + e^{-t})^2}$$

and

$$\|\mathbf{T}'(t)\| = \frac{\sqrt{2^2 + 2^2 + 2(e^t - e^{-t})^2}}{(e^t + e^{-t})^2} = \frac{\sqrt{2e^{2t} + 4 + 2e^{-2t}}}{(e^t + e^{-t})^2} = \frac{\sqrt{2(e^t + e^{-t})^2}}{(e^t + e^{-t})^2} = \frac{\sqrt{2}}{e^t + e^{-t}}$$

So, the unit normal is

$$\mathbf{N}(t) = \frac{\mathbf{T}'(t)}{\|\mathbf{T}'(t)\|} = \frac{\dfrac{2\mathbf{i} + 2\mathbf{j} - \sqrt{2}(e^t - e^{-t})\mathbf{k}}{(e^t + e^{-t})^2}}{\dfrac{\sqrt{2}}{e^t + e^{-t}}}$$

$$= \frac{2\mathbf{i} + 2\mathbf{j} - \sqrt{2}(e^t - e^{-t})\mathbf{k}}{\sqrt{2}(e^t + e^{-t})} = \frac{\sqrt{2}\mathbf{i} + \sqrt{2}\mathbf{j} - (e^t - e^{-t})\mathbf{k}}{e^t + e^{-t}}$$

In particular,

$$\mathbf{N}(1) = \frac{2\mathbf{i} + 2\mathbf{j} - \sqrt{2}(e - e^{-1})\mathbf{k}}{\sqrt{2}(e + e^{-1})} \approx 0.46\mathbf{i} + 0.46\mathbf{j} - 0.76\mathbf{k}$$

Remember, because $\mathbf{T}$ and $\mathbf{N}$ are to be orthogonal, we can check our work by noting that

$$\mathbf{T} \cdot \mathbf{N} = (0.88\mathbf{i} - 0.12\mathbf{j} + 0.46\mathbf{k}) \cdot (0.46\mathbf{i} + 0.46\mathbf{j} - 0.76\mathbf{k}) = 0$$

Computational Window

We continue to remind you that if you use some software packages, your answers may take on slightly different, but yet equivalent, forms. For Example 1 we obtain

$$\mathbf{T}'(t) = \frac{2e^{2t}}{(e^{2t} + 1)^2}\mathbf{i} + \frac{2e^{2t}}{(e^{2t} + 1)^2}\mathbf{j} + \frac{\sqrt{2}e^t(1 - e^t)(e^t + 1)}{(e^{2t} + 1)^2}\mathbf{k}$$

Continuing with the software program, we find

$$\|\mathbf{T}'(t)\| = \frac{\sqrt{2}e^t}{e^{2t} + 1}$$

Finally,

$$\mathbf{N}(t) = \frac{\mathbf{T}'(t)}{\|\mathbf{T}'(t)\|} = \frac{\sqrt{2}e^t}{e^{2t} + 1}\mathbf{i} + \frac{\sqrt{2}e^t}{e^{2t} + 1}\mathbf{j} + \left(\frac{1 - e^{2t}}{e^{2t} + 1}\right)\mathbf{k}$$

$$\mathbf{N}(1) = 0.458243571484\mathbf{i} + 0.458243571484\mathbf{j} - 0.761594155955\mathbf{k}$$

Checking $\mathbf{T} \cdot \mathbf{N}$ for $t = 1$, we obtain $-1.49398426240 \; 10^{-6}$, which is scientific notation for a number very close (but not equal to) zero. Note that the rounded check in Example 1 showed that this was exactly 0, but that result was, by coincidence, due to rounding. The best you can do with most approximate results is to show that they are approximately equal.

■ ARC LENGTH AS A PARAMETER

In Section 11.2, we found that time t is the most natural parameter for studying motion along a curve. However, if we are primarily interested in the geometric features of a curve, it may be more convenient to use arc length s as a parameter, because arc length is a natural feature of the curve and is independent of coordinate systems. The arc length parameter is defined in terms of the following integral function.

Arc Length Function

> Let $\mathbf{R}(t)$ be a vector function whose graph is a smooth curve C on the closed interval $[a, b]$. Then the **arc length function** on $[a, b]$ is defined by
> $$s(t) = \int_a^t \|\mathbf{R}'(u)\| \, du \qquad a \le t \le b$$

Notice that $s(t)$ increases in the direction of increasing t. That is, arc length s increases in the same direction as the parameter t along the curve C (see Figure 11.17).

In the case where $\mathbf{R}(t) = x(t)\mathbf{i} + y(t)\mathbf{j} + z(t)\mathbf{k}$, we have

$$\mathbf{R}'(u) = x'(u)\mathbf{i} + y'(u)\mathbf{j} + z'(u)\mathbf{k}$$

and

$$\|\mathbf{R}'(u)\| = \sqrt{[x'(u)]^2 + [y'(u)]^2 + [z'(u)]^2}$$

Thus, on the interval $[a, b]$, the trajectory of $\mathbf{R}(t)$ has arc length

$$L = s(b) = \int_a^b \|\mathbf{R}'(u)\| \, du = \int_a^b \sqrt{[x'(u)]^2 + [y'(u)]^2 + [z'(u)]^2} \, du$$

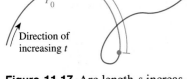

Figure 11.17 Arc length s increases in the same direction as t along the graph of $\mathbf{R}$.

This gives a formula for the arc length of a curve in space that is a direct generalization of the formula obtained for the arc length of a planar curve in Chapter 9 (Theorem 9.4).

THEOREM 11.6   Arc length of a space curve

If C is a smooth curve defined by $\mathbf{R}(t) = x(t)\mathbf{i} + y(t)\mathbf{j} + z(t)\mathbf{k}$ on an interval $[a, b]$, then the arc length of C is given by

$$s = \int_a^b \|\mathbf{R}'(t)\| \, dt = \int_a^b \sqrt{[x'(t)]^2 + [y'(t)]^2 + [z'(t)]^2} \, dt$$

Proof: $s = \int_a^b ds = \int_a^b \frac{ds}{dt} \, dt = \int_a^b \|\mathbf{R}'(t)\| \, dt = \int_a^b \sqrt{[x'(t)]^2 + [y'(t)]^2 + [z'(t)]^2} \, dt$

Note that s is also the length of the trajectory between times $t = a$ and $t = b$. ∎

EXAMPLE 2   Finding the arc length of a space curve

Find the arc length of the curve defined by

$$\mathbf{R}(t) = 12t\mathbf{i} + (5 \cos t)\mathbf{j} + (3 - 5 \sin t)\mathbf{k}$$

from $t = 0$ to $t = 2$.

Solution We have $x(t) = 12t$, $y(t) = 5 \cos t$, and $z(t) = 3 - 5 \sin t$, so that $x'(t) = 12$, $y'(t) = -5 \sin t$, and $z'(t) = -5 \cos t$. We now use Theorem 11.6.

$$s = \int_a^b \sqrt{[x'(t)]^2 + [y'(t)]^2 + [z'(t)]^2} \, dt$$

$$= \int_0^2 \sqrt{12^2 + (-5 \sin t)^2 + (-5 \cos t)^2} \, dt = \int_0^2 13 \, dt = 26 \qquad \blacksquare$$

By applying the second fundamental theorem of calculus, we can differentiate the arc length function on $[a, b]$ to obtain

$$\frac{ds}{dt} = \|\mathbf{R}'(t)\|$$

Recall from Section 11.2 that the *speed* of an object moving on its trajectory is given by $\|\mathbf{V}(t)\| = \|\mathbf{R}'(t)\|$, where $\mathbf{V}(t)$ is the velocity vector of the object. Thus, the speed, in terms of arc length, is

$$\|\mathbf{V}(t)\| = \|\mathbf{R}'(t)\| = \frac{ds}{dt}$$

For future reference, we summarize this result in the following theorem.

THEOREM 11.7   Speed in terms of arc length

Suppose an object moves with displacement $\mathbf{R}(t)$, where $\mathbf{R}'(t)$ is continuous on the interval $[a, b]$. Then the object has speed

$$\|\mathbf{V}(t)\| = \|\mathbf{R}'(t)\| = \frac{ds}{dt} \qquad \text{for } a \leq t \leq b$$

Proof: An outline of the proof precedes the statement of the theorem. ■

EXAMPLE 3   Speed and distance traveled by an object moving in space

An object moves with displacement

$$\mathbf{R}(t) = e^t\mathbf{i} + (\sqrt{2}\, t + 3)\mathbf{j} + e^{-t}\mathbf{k}$$

Find the speed of the object at time t and compute the distance the object travels between times $t = 0$ and $t = 1$.

Solution   By differentiating $\mathbf{R}(t)$ with respect to t, we find the velocity:

$$\mathbf{V}(t) = \mathbf{R}'(t) = e^t\mathbf{i} + \sqrt{2}\,\mathbf{j} - e^{-t}\mathbf{k}$$

Therefore, the speed at time t is

$$\frac{ds}{dt} = \|\mathbf{R}'(t)\| = \sqrt{(e^t)^2 + (\sqrt{2})^2 + (-e^{-t})^2}$$
$$= \sqrt{e^{2t} + 2 + e^{-2t}} = \sqrt{(e^t + e^{-t})^2} = e^t + e^{-t}$$

The distance traveled by the object between times $t = 0$ and $t = 1$ is the arc length and is given by

$$s = \int_0^1 (e^t + e^{-t})\, dt = [e^t - e^{-t}]_0^1 = e - e^{-1} - 1 + 1 \approx 2.350\,402\,4$$ ▬

COMMENT: Incidentally, notice that the object is at the point $P(1, 3, 1)$ when $t = 0$ and is at $Q(e, \sqrt{2} + 3, e^{-1})$ when $t = 1$. The straight-line distance between P and Q is

$$d = \sqrt{(e - 1)^2 + (\sqrt{2} + 3 - 3)^2 + (e^{-1} - 1)^2} \approx 2.313\,453\,9$$

which, as might be expected, is slightly less than the distance measured from P to Q along the trajectory.

When $\mathbf{R}$ is represented as $\mathbf{R}(s)$ in terms of the arc length parameter s, the unit tangent vector $\mathbf{T}$ can be represented as $\mathbf{T} = d\mathbf{R}/ds$. To see why this is true, recall from Theorem 11.7 that $\|\mathbf{R}'(t)\| = ds/dt$, and because

$$\mathbf{R}'(t) = \frac{d\mathbf{R}}{dt}$$

it follows that

$$\mathbf{T} = \frac{\mathbf{R}'(t)}{\|\mathbf{R}'(t)\|} = \frac{\frac{d\mathbf{R}}{dt}}{\frac{ds}{dt}} = \frac{d\mathbf{R}}{ds}$$

Note that because s increases with t, we have $\frac{ds}{dt} > 0$, so the unit tangent vector $\mathbf{T} = \frac{d\mathbf{R}}{ds}$ must point in the direction of increasing s.

Next, to obtain a formula for the principal unit normal vector

$$\mathbf{N} = \frac{\mathbf{T}'(t)}{\|\mathbf{T}'(t)\|}$$

in terms of the arc length parameter s, we first note that

$$\mathbf{T}'(t) = \frac{d\mathbf{T}}{dt} = \frac{d\mathbf{T}}{ds}\frac{ds}{dt}$$

Because $\frac{ds}{dt} > 0$, it follows that the vector derivatives $\frac{d\mathbf{T}}{dt}$ and $\frac{d\mathbf{T}}{ds}$ point in the same direction, and $\mathbf{N}$ can be computed by finding $\frac{d\mathbf{T}}{ds}$ and dividing by its length. The scalar function $\kappa = \left\|\frac{d\mathbf{T}}{ds}\right\|$ is called the **curvature** of the graph (defined below). Thus, we have

$$\mathbf{N} = \frac{\frac{d\mathbf{T}}{ds}}{\left\|\frac{d\mathbf{T}}{ds}\right\|} = \frac{1}{\kappa}\frac{d\mathbf{T}}{ds}$$

We summarize these observations in the following box.

Formulas for Unit Tangent and Principal Unit Normal in Terms of the Arc Length Parameter

If $\mathbf{R}(t)$ has a smooth graph and is represented as $\mathbf{R}(s)$ in terms of the arc length parameter s, then the unit tangent $\mathbf{T}$ and the principal normal $\mathbf{N}$ at each point satisfy

$$\mathbf{T} = \frac{d\mathbf{R}}{ds} \quad \text{and} \quad \mathbf{N} = \frac{1}{\kappa}\frac{d\mathbf{T}}{ds}$$

where $\kappa = \left\|\frac{d\mathbf{T}}{ds}\right\|$ is the curvature of the graph.

We also note that

$$\frac{d\mathbf{T}}{ds} = (\text{CURVATURE})(\text{PRINCIPAL UNIT NORMAL}) = \kappa\mathbf{N}$$

■ CURVATURE

Curvature plays an important role in certain applications, some of which we shall explore in the next section. For a plane curve, the **curvature** is the absolute value of the rate of change of the angle of inclination of the tangent line with respect to the distance along the curve.

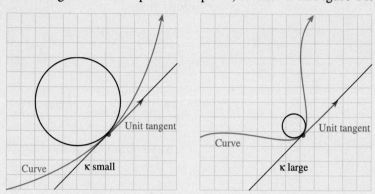

■ **What this says:** The curvature κ measures the rate at which the curve bends away from the tangent line at a particular point, as shown in Figure 11.18.

Figure 11.18 Curves with large and small curvature κ

Thus, curvature of the graph of $\mathbf{R}(t)$ may be computed by finding $\mathbf{T}$ and then substituting into the formula

$$\kappa = \left\| \frac{d\mathbf{T}}{ds} \right\| = \frac{\left\| \dfrac{d\mathbf{T}}{dt} \right\|}{\dfrac{ds}{dt}}$$

For instance, in Example 1 we found that $\mathbf{R}(t) = e^t\mathbf{i} + e^{-t}\mathbf{j} + \sqrt{2}t\mathbf{k}$, and $\mathbf{T}(t) = \dfrac{e^t\mathbf{i} - e^{-t}\mathbf{j} + \sqrt{2}\mathbf{k}}{e^t + e^{-t}}$, so that

$$\frac{ds}{dt} = \|\mathbf{R}'(t)\| = e^t + e^{-t} \quad \text{and} \quad \left\| \frac{d\mathbf{T}}{dt} \right\| = \frac{\sqrt{2}}{e^t + e^{-t}}$$

Thus, the curvature in this case is the scalar function

$$\kappa = \frac{\left\| \dfrac{d\mathbf{T}}{dt} \right\|}{\dfrac{ds}{dt}} = \frac{\dfrac{\sqrt{2}}{e^t + e^{-t}}}{e^t + e^{-t}} = \frac{\sqrt{2}}{(e^t + e^{-t})^2}$$

Curvature for $\mathbf{R}(t) = e^t\mathbf{i} + e^{-t}\mathbf{j} + \sqrt{2}t\,\mathbf{k}$	
t	κ
0.0	0.353 553 390 59
0.5	0.278 051 262 51
1.0	0.148 483 352 44
1.5	0.063 889 444 89
2.0	0.024 978 838 68
2.5	0.009 401 771 91
3.0	0.003 488 170 89
3.5	0.001 287 247 14
4.0	0.000 474 097 66
4.5	0.000 174 484 75
5.0	0.000 064 199 37

It can be shown (see Problem 27) that a line has curvature 0. Because the curvature is nonnegative, smaller curvature indicates a gentler curve. For Example 1, we see that if $t = 0$, the curvature is about 0.35, whereas if $t = 5$ the curvature is 0.0000642 (almost flat). Some curvature calculations for this curve are shown by the table in the margin (which was done using a spreadsheet program).

In the case where the graph of $\mathbf{R}(t)$ lies entirely in a plane, the curvature $\kappa(t)$ has a nice geometric interpretation. Note that in this case, the unit tangent vector $\mathbf{T}$ at a point P can be expressed as

$$\mathbf{T} = (\cos \phi)\mathbf{i} + (\sin \phi)\mathbf{j}$$

where ϕ is the angle of inclination of the tangent line at P, as shown in Figure 11.19. Then, differentiating both sides of the equation for $\mathbf{T}$, we have

$$\frac{d\mathbf{T}}{ds} = \left(-\sin \phi \, \frac{d\phi}{ds}\right)\mathbf{i} + \left(\cos \phi \, \frac{d\phi}{ds}\right)\mathbf{j}$$

and because the curvature is the length of this vector, we find

$$\kappa = \left\| \frac{d\mathbf{T}}{ds} \right\| = \left| \frac{d\phi}{ds} \right| \sqrt{(-\sin \phi)^2 + (\cos \phi)^2} = \left| \frac{d\phi}{ds} \right|$$

This curvature is interpreted geometrically in Figure 11.19b.

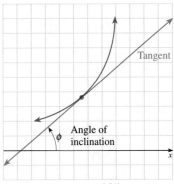

Figure 11.19 The curvature of a graph

a. In a plane, the unit tangent vector is $\mathbf{T} = (\cos \phi)\mathbf{i} + (\sin \phi)\mathbf{j}$.

b. The curvature $\kappa = \left| \frac{d\phi}{ds} \right|$ measures the rate at which the curve bends away from the tangent.

By looking at the formula $\kappa = \left| \frac{d\phi}{ds} \right|$, we see that at each point P on a planar curve, the curvature κ measures the rate at which the curve bends away from the tangent line.

The preceding curvature formula is not particularly easy to use, and because the graph C of the vector function is frequently defined by $\mathbf{R}(t)$, it is often useful to have the following formula for κ in terms of $\mathbf{R}$:

Curvature Formula

The curvature of a graph C defined by a vector function $\mathbf{R}(t)$ can be found by

$$\kappa = \frac{\|\mathbf{R}' \times \mathbf{R}''\|}{\|\mathbf{R}'\|^3}$$

This formula is derived in Problem 51 and is illustrated in Example 4.

EXAMPLE 4 Curvature of a helix

Given $\mathbf{R}(t) = (a \cos t)\mathbf{i} + (a \sin t)\mathbf{j} + bt\mathbf{k}$ with a and b both nonnegative, express the curvature of $\mathbf{R}(t)$ in terms of a and b ($a > 0$).

Solution We begin by finding $\mathbf{V}$ and $\mathbf{A}$ and the cross product $\mathbf{V} \times \mathbf{A}$:

$$\mathbf{R}'(t) = (-a \sin t)\mathbf{i} + (a \cos t)\mathbf{j} + b\mathbf{k}$$

$$\mathbf{R}''(t) = (-a \cos t)\mathbf{i} + (-a \sin t)\mathbf{j}$$

$$\mathbf{R}' \times \mathbf{R}'' = \begin{vmatrix} \mathbf{i} & \mathbf{j} & \mathbf{k} \\ -a \sin t & a \cos t & b \\ -a \cos t & -a \sin t & 0 \end{vmatrix} = (ab \sin t)\mathbf{i} - (ab \cos t)\mathbf{j} + a^2\mathbf{k}$$

We now need to find the magnitude of this vector, as well as that of **V**:

$$\|\mathbf{R}' \times \mathbf{R}''\| = \sqrt{(ab \sin t)^2 + (ab \cos t)^2 + a^4}$$

$$= \sqrt{a^2 b^2 (\sin^2 t + \cos^2 t) + a^4}$$

$$= \sqrt{a^2 b^2 + a^4}$$

and

$$\|\mathbf{R}'\| = \sqrt{a^2 \sin^2 t + a^2 \cos^2 t + b^2} = \sqrt{a^2 + b^2}$$

Then we have

$$\kappa = \frac{\|\mathbf{R}' \times \mathbf{R}''\|}{\|\mathbf{R}'\|^3} = \frac{\sqrt{a^2 b^2 + a^4}}{(\sqrt{a^2 + b^2})^3} = \frac{a\sqrt{a^2 + b^2}}{(a^2 + b^2)\sqrt{a^2 + b^2}} = \frac{a}{a^2 + b^2}$$

If we increase b, then for a fixed a the curvature decreases. If $b = 0$, the helix reduces to a circle of radius a. If $a = 0$, the helix flattens out along the z-axis.   ▄▄▄

In the plane, where a curve is given by $\mathbf{R}(t) = x(t)\mathbf{i} + y(t)\mathbf{j}$, the curvature may be computed by the formula

$$\kappa = \frac{|x'y'' - y'x''|}{[(x')^2 + (y')^2]^{3/2}}$$

A derivation of this formula is outlined in Problem 52. We will use this formula to show that a circle has constant curvature.

EXAMPLE 5   Curvature of a circle

Show that a circle of radius r has curvature $\kappa = \dfrac{1}{r}$ at each point.

Solution   Suppose a circle has radius r and center (h, k). Then its Cartesian equation is $(x - h)^2 + (y - k)^2 = r^2$, and we can obtain a parametrization of the circle by setting

$$x - h = r \cos t \quad \text{and} \quad y - k = r \sin t$$

In other words, the circle is the graph of the vector function $\mathbf{R}(t) = x(t)\mathbf{i} + y(t)\mathbf{j}$, where

$$x(t) = h + r \cos t \quad \text{and} \quad y(t) = k + r \sin t$$

Differentiating with respect to t, we obtain

$$x'(t) = -r \sin t \qquad y'(t) = r \cos t$$
$$x''(t) = -r \cos t \qquad y''(t) = -r \sin t$$

and by substituting these into the curvature formula, we find:

$$\kappa = \frac{|x'y'' - y'x''|}{[(x')^2 + (y')^2]^{3/2}} = \frac{(-r \sin t)(-r \sin t) - (r \cos t)(-r \cos t)}{[(-r \sin t)^2 + (r \cos t)^2]^{3/2}}$$

$$= \frac{r^2 \sin^2 t + r^2 \cos^2 t}{[r^2(\sin^2 t + \cos^2 t)]^{3/2}} = \frac{r^2}{r^3} = \frac{1}{r}$$ ▄▄▄

If $\kappa \neq 0$ at the point P on the graph of $\mathbf{R}(t)$, the reciprocal $\rho = \dfrac{1}{\kappa}$ is called the **radius of curvature** at P. The **osculating** (*kissing*) **circle** at P is the circle in the plane of **T** and **N** whose shape best approximates that of the graph of $\mathbf{R}(t)$ in the vicinity of P (see Figure 11.20). This follows from the definition, which says that the osculating circle is the circle that is tangent to the graph at P and whose radius is the radius of curvature $\rho = 1/\kappa$.

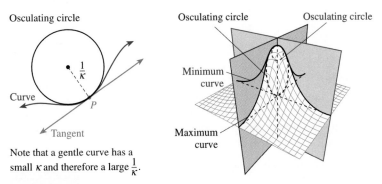

Note that a gentle curve has a small κ and therefore a large $\frac{1}{\kappa}$.

Figure 11.20 The osculating circle best fits the shape of the curve at P.

In the special case where the graph of $\mathbf{R}(t)$ is a circle C, the radius of curvature is the radius of C, and the osculating circle coincides with C.

We conclude this section by providing a summary of the various curvature formulas (Table 11.2).

TABLE 11.2 Curvature Formulas

Type	Given Information	Formula to Use	Where Derived
Arc length parameter	$\mathbf{R}(s)$	$\left\Vert \dfrac{d\mathbf{T}}{ds} \right\Vert$	Page 715
Vector derivative form	$\mathbf{R}(t)$	$\dfrac{\Vert \mathbf{R}' \times \mathbf{R}'' \Vert}{\Vert \mathbf{R}' \Vert^3}$	Page 717
Velocity/acceleration form	position $\mathbf{R}(t)$	$\dfrac{\Vert \mathbf{V} \times \mathbf{A} \Vert}{\Vert \mathbf{V} \Vert^3}$	Problem 51
Parametric equation form	$x = x(t),\ y = y(t)$	$\dfrac{\vert x'y'' - y'x'' \vert}{[(x')^2 + (y')^2]^{3/2}}$	Problem 52
Functional form	$y = f(x)$	$\dfrac{\vert y'' \vert}{(1 + y'^2)^{3/2}}$	Problem 53
Polar form	$r = f(\theta)$	$\dfrac{\vert r^2 + 2r'^2 - rr'' \vert}{(r^2 + r'^2)^{3/2}}$	Problem 54

PROBLEM SET 11.4

Ⓐ *In Problems 1–8, find the unit tangent vector $\mathbf{T}(t)$ and the principal unit normal vector $\mathbf{N}(t)$ for the curve given by $\mathbf{R}(t)$.*

1. $\mathbf{R}(t) = t^2\mathbf{i} + t^3\mathbf{j},\ t \neq 0$

2. $\mathbf{R}(t) = t^2\mathbf{i} + \sqrt{t}\,\mathbf{j},\ t > 0$

3. $\mathbf{R}(t) = (e^t\cos t)\mathbf{i} + (e^t\sin t)\mathbf{j}$

4. $\mathbf{R}(t) = (t\cos t)\mathbf{i} + (t\sin t)\mathbf{j}$

5. $\mathbf{R}(t) = (\cos t)\mathbf{i} + (\sin t)\mathbf{j} + t\mathbf{k}$

6. $\mathbf{R}(t) = (\sin t)\mathbf{i} + (\cos t)\mathbf{j} + t\mathbf{k}$

7. $\mathbf{R}(t) = (\ln t)\mathbf{i} + t^2\mathbf{k}$

8. $\mathbf{R}(t) = (e^{-t}\sin t)\mathbf{i} + e^{-t}\mathbf{j} + (e^{-t}\cos t)\mathbf{k}$

In Problems 9–14, sketch the given curve and find its length over the given interval.

9. $\mathbf{R}(t) = 2t\mathbf{i} + t\mathbf{j}$, over $[0, 4]$

10. $\mathbf{R}(t) = t\mathbf{i} + 3t\mathbf{j}$, over $[0, 4]$

11. $\mathbf{R}(t) = 3t\mathbf{i} + 3\cos t\,\mathbf{j} + 3\sin t\,\mathbf{k}$, over $\left[0, \frac{\pi}{2}\right]$

12. $\mathbf{R}(t) = t\mathbf{i} + 2t\mathbf{j} + 3t\mathbf{k}$, over $[0, 2]$

13. $\mathbf{R}(t) = 4\cos t\mathbf{i} + 4\sin t\,\mathbf{j} + 5t\mathbf{k}$, over $[0, \pi]$

14. $\mathbf{R}(t) = \cos^3 t\,\mathbf{i} + \cos^2 t\,\mathbf{k}$, over $[0, 2\pi]$

Find the curvature of the plane curves at the points indicated in Problems 15–26.

15. $y = 4x - 2$ at $x = 2$

16. $y = mx + b$ at $x = a$

17. $y = x - \frac{1}{9}x^2$, at $x = 3$

18. $y = 2x^2 + 1$, at $x = 1$

19. $y = ax^2 + bx$, at $x = c$

20. $y = x + x^{-1}$, at $x = 1$

21. $y = \sqrt{4 - x^2}$, at $x = 1$

22. $y = \sqrt{r^2 - x^2}$, at $x = 0$

23. $y = \sin x$, at $x = \frac{\pi}{2}$

24. $y = \cos x$, at $x = \frac{\pi}{4}$

25. $y = \ln x$, at $x = 1$

26. $y = e^x$, at $x = 0$

Ⓑ 27. Let **u** and **v** be constant, nonzero vectors. Show that the line given by $\mathbf{R}(t) = \mathbf{u} + \mathbf{v}t$ has curvature 0 at each point.

28. Find the unit tangent **T** and principal normal **N** for $\mathbf{R}(t) = (\cosh t)\mathbf{i} + (\sinh t)\mathbf{j}$ at the point where $t = 0$.

29. Find the unit tangent **T** and principal normal **N** for $\mathbf{R}(t) = [\ln(\sin t)]\mathbf{i} + [\ln(\cos t)]\mathbf{j}$ at the point where $t = \frac{\pi}{3}$.

30. A curve C in the plane is given parametrically by $x = 32t$, $y = 16t^2 - 4$.

  a. Sketch the graph of the curve.

  b. Find the unit tangent vector when $t = 3$.

  c. Find the radius of curvature of the point P on C where $t = 3$.

31. For the curve given by
$$\mathbf{R}(t) = (\sin t)\mathbf{i} + (\cos t)\mathbf{j} + t\mathbf{k}$$

  a. Find a unit tangent vector **T** at the point on the curve where $t = \pi$.

  b. Find the curvature when $t = \pi$.

  c. Find the length of the curve from $t = 0$ to $t = \pi$.

32. Let C be the curve given by
$$\mathbf{R}(t) = (t - \sin t)\mathbf{i} + (1 - \cos t)\mathbf{j} + \left(4 \sin \frac{t}{2}\right)\mathbf{k}$$

  a. Find the unit tangent vector $\mathbf{T}(t)$ to C.

  b. Find $\dfrac{d\mathbf{T}}{ds}$ and the curvature $\kappa(t)$.

33. Find the point (or points) where the ellipse $9x^2 + 4y^2 = 36$ has maximum curvature.

34. Find the point (or points) where the curve $y = e^{2x}$ has maximum curvature.

35. Find the radius of curvature at each relative extremum of the graph of $y = x^6 - 3x^2$.

36. Find the curvature of the curve given by $x = t - \sin t$, $y = 1 - \cos t$. Sketch the curve on $0 \le t \le 2\pi$ and sketch the osculating circle at the point where $t = \frac{\pi}{2}$.

37. The tangent line at a point P on a curve C in space is the line that passes through P and is aligned with the tangent vector **T** to C at P. Find parametric equations for the tangent line to $\mathbf{R}(t) = 2t\mathbf{i} - t\mathbf{j} + t^2\mathbf{k}$ at $P(2, -1, 1)$.

38. The tangent line at a point P on a curve C in space is the line that passes through P and is aligned with the tangent vector **T** to C at P. Find parametric equations for the tangent line to $\mathbf{R}(t) = e^t\mathbf{i} - 3\mathbf{j} + (1 - t)\mathbf{k}$ at $P(1, -3, 1)$.

There are many different formulas for finding curvature, as summarized in Table 11.2. In Problems 39–46, find the curvature of each of the given curves using the indicated formula.

39. $\mathbf{R}(t) = t\mathbf{i} + t^2\mathbf{j} + t^3\mathbf{k}$ (velocity/acceleration form)

40. $\mathbf{R}(t) = (t - \cos t)\mathbf{i} + (\sin t)\mathbf{j} + 3\mathbf{k}$ (velocity/acceleration form)

41. $y = x^2$ (functional form)

42. $y = x^3$ (functional form)

43. $y = x^{-1}$, $x > 0$ (functional form)

44. $y = \sin x$ (functional form)

45. The spiral $r = e^\theta$ (polar form)

46. The cardioid $r = 1 + \cos \theta$, for $0 \le \theta \le 2\pi$ (polar form)

47. ■ **What Does This Say?** Describe what is meant by using arc length as a parameter.

48. ■ **What Does This Say?** Discuss the various curvature formulas given in Table 11.2.

  Computational Window

49. Projections onto a plane in $\mathbb{R}^3$

A very important notion in applied mathematics is that of projecting a vector onto a subspace of some kind, for example, a plane. Later in your career, the "vectors" can also be functions in which a difficult function is approximated by "nice" functions. In this problem, our work is limited to $\mathbb{R}^3$.

  a. Suppose that **u** and **v** are unit vectors and that they are orthogonal. Show that the "linear combination" $a\mathbf{u} + b\mathbf{v}$ generate a plane, through $(0, 0, 0)$, as a and b take on all real values.

  b. Let **w** be a third vector, not the plane described in part **a**. We want to project **w** onto the plane, so we write $\mathbf{w} = \mathbf{p} + \mathbf{n} = (a\mathbf{u} + b\mathbf{v}) + \mathbf{n}$, where **p** is the desired projection and **n** is the normal component of **w**. To find a, take the dot product of **w** and **u** and show that **p** is orthogonal to **n** (hence **p** is the orthogonal projection).

  c. For the three following vectors, find the orthogonal projection of **w** onto the plane generated by **u** and **v**:
$$\mathbf{u} = \frac{1}{\sqrt{3}}(\mathbf{i} + \mathbf{j} + \mathbf{k})$$
$$\mathbf{v} = \frac{1}{\sqrt{6}}(2\mathbf{i} - \mathbf{j} - \mathbf{k})$$
$$\mathbf{w} = \mathbf{j} + 2\mathbf{k}$$

  d. A projection is especially simple if we have $\mathbf{u} = \mathbf{i}$ and $\mathbf{v} = \mathbf{j}$. Explain the situation here for an arbitrary vector $\mathbf{w} = a\mathbf{i} + b\mathbf{j} + c\mathbf{k}$.

  e. Show that for a given vector $\mathbf{w} = a\mathbf{i} + b\mathbf{j} + c\mathbf{k}$, its slope relative to the xy-plane is $m = \dfrac{c}{\sqrt{a^2 + b^2}}$.

50. This problem will make some use of Problem 49 and addresses the arc length of a curve in $\mathbb{R}^3$ and the work involved in moving along its path. Suppose that a mining company has built a road up a hill that roughly satisfies the following parametric definition $(0 \le t \le 2\pi)$.

$$x(t) = e^{-t/3} \cos 3t$$
$$y(t) = e^{-t/3} \sin 3t$$
$$z(t) = \frac{13t}{t^2 + 40}$$

a. Generate a rough graph of this curve; then somehow (use your imagination!) get a decent estimate of its length, say within 10%.
b. Use your computer to compute its length; then check with your previous estimate.
c. Let $\mathbf{T}(t)$ denote the tangent to the curve at that point and assume the force

$$F(t) = \frac{8z'(t)}{\sqrt{[x'(t)]^2 + [y'(t)]^2}}$$

Compute the work required to move a cart from the bottom to the top of the hill. (Recall, work = $\int F\,ds$).

C **51.** One of the most fundamental forms for curvature is the velocity/acceleration form. Let C be the trajectory of an object, where position is given by the vector function $\mathbf{R}(t)$. Show that the curvature of C is given by

$$\kappa = \frac{\|\mathbf{V} \times \mathbf{A}\|}{\|\mathbf{V}\|^3}$$

Hint: $\mathbf{V} = \dfrac{ds}{dt}\mathbf{T}$ and $\mathbf{A} = \dfrac{ds}{dt}\dfrac{d\mathbf{T}}{dt} + \mathbf{T}\dfrac{d^2 s}{dt^2}$

52. Use the formula in Problem 51 to verify the formula

$$\kappa = \frac{|x'y'' - y'x''|}{[(x')^2 + (y')^2]^{3/2}}$$

Hint: Let $\mathbf{R}(t) = x(t)\mathbf{i} + y(t)\mathbf{j}$.

53. A curve in the plane is given by $y = f(x)$. Show that the functional form for curvature is given by

$$\frac{|f''(x)|}{\{1 + [f'(x)]^2\}^{3/2}}$$

Hint: Use the formula given in Problem 51, with $\mathbf{R}(x) = x\mathbf{i} + f(x)\mathbf{j}$.

54. Let f be a twice differentiable function. Show that, in polar coordinates, the curvature of the curve given by $r = f(\theta)$ satisfies

$$\kappa(\theta) = \frac{|r^2 + 2r'^2 - rr''|}{(r^2 + r'^2)^{3/2}}$$

Hint: Use the formula in Problem 51 with $x = f(\theta)\cos\theta$, $y = f(\theta)\sin\theta$.

55. Use the formula in Problem 51 to show that the curve C given by $\mathbf{R}(t)$ has curvature

$$\kappa = \frac{[\|\mathbf{V}\|^2\|\mathbf{A}\|^2 - \mathbf{V} \cdot \mathbf{A}]^{1/2}}{\|\mathbf{V}\|^3}$$

56. Let $P(a, b)$ be a point on the graph C of the vector function $\mathbf{R}(t)$.

a. Describe a general procedure for finding an equation for the osculating circle to C at P.
b. Find an equation for the osculating circle at the point $P(32, 12)$ on the curve C defined by

$$x = 32t, \quad y = 16t^2 - 4$$

57. If $\mathbf{T}$ and $\mathbf{N}$ are the unit tangent and normal vectors, respectively, on the trajectory of a moving body, then the cross-product vector $\mathbf{B} = \mathbf{T} \times \mathbf{N}$ is called the unit **binormal** of the trajectory. Three planes determined by $\mathbf{T}$, $\mathbf{N}$, and $\mathbf{B}$ are shown in Figure 11.21.

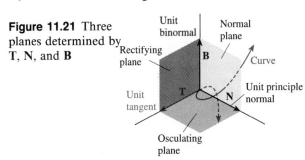

Figure 11.21 Three planes determined by $\mathbf{T}$, $\mathbf{N}$, and $\mathbf{B}$

a. Show that $\mathbf{T}$ is orthogonal to $\dfrac{d\mathbf{B}}{ds}$.
Hint: Differentiate $\mathbf{B} \cdot \mathbf{T}$.

b. Show that $\mathbf{B}$ is orthogonal to $\dfrac{d\mathbf{B}}{ds}$.
Hint: Differentiate $\mathbf{B} \cdot \mathbf{B}$.

c. Show that $\dfrac{d\mathbf{B}}{ds} = -\tau\mathbf{N}$ for some constant τ. *Note*: τ is called the **torsion** of the trajectory. It provides a measure of the amount of twisting at each point on the trajectory.

11.5 TANGENTIAL AND NORMAL COMPONENTS OF ACCELERATION

IN THIS SECTION Components of acceleration, applications
We see how the velocity and acceleration vectors of a moving body can be decomposed into tangential and normal components. Then we examine a few applications in which this decomposition is especially useful.

■ COMPONENTS OF ACCELERATION

When a body is caused to accelerate or brakes are applied, it is of interest to know how much of the acceleration acts in the direction of the body's motion, as indicated by the unit tangent vector **T**. This question is answered by the following theorem.

THEOREM 11.8   Tangential and normal components of acceleration

---

An object moving along a smooth curve (with $\mathbf{T}' \neq \mathbf{0}$) has velocity **V** and acceleration **A**, where

$$\mathbf{V} = \left(\frac{ds}{dt}\right)\mathbf{T} \quad \text{and} \quad \mathbf{A} = \left(\frac{d^2s}{dt^2}\right)\mathbf{T} + \kappa\left(\frac{ds}{dt}\right)^2\mathbf{N}$$

and s is the arc length along the trajectory.

Proof: An object moving with displacement **R** has unit tangent $\mathbf{T} = \dfrac{d\mathbf{R}}{ds}$ and unit normal $\mathbf{N} = \dfrac{1}{\kappa}\dfrac{d\mathbf{T}}{ds}$. We use the chain rule to write the velocity vector **V** as follows:

$$\mathbf{V} = \frac{d\mathbf{R}}{dt} = \frac{d\mathbf{R}}{ds}\frac{ds}{dt} = \mathbf{T}\frac{ds}{dt}$$

Differentiate both sides of this equation with respect to t and substitute $\dfrac{d\mathbf{T}}{ds} = \kappa\mathbf{N}$:

$$\mathbf{A} = \frac{d\mathbf{V}}{dt} \qquad\qquad \textit{Definition of } \mathbf{A}$$

$$= \frac{d}{dt}\left[\mathbf{T}\frac{ds}{dt}\right] \qquad\qquad \mathbf{V} = \left(\frac{ds}{dt}\right)\mathbf{T}$$

$$= \frac{d^2s}{dt^2}\mathbf{T} + \frac{ds}{dt}\frac{d\mathbf{T}}{dt} \qquad\qquad \textit{Product rule}$$

$$= \frac{d^2s}{dt^2}\mathbf{T} + \frac{ds}{dt}\left[\frac{d\mathbf{T}}{ds}\frac{ds}{dt}\right] \qquad \textit{Chain rule}$$

$$= \frac{d^2s}{dt^2}\mathbf{T} + \left(\frac{ds}{dt}\right)^2\frac{d\mathbf{T}}{ds}$$

$$= \frac{d^2s}{dt^2}\mathbf{T} + \left(\frac{ds}{dt}\right)^2(\kappa\mathbf{N}) \qquad \textit{Since } \kappa\mathbf{N} = \frac{d\mathbf{T}}{ds} \qquad\blacksquare$$

■ *What this says*: At each point on the trajectory of a moving object, the velocity **V** points in the direction of the unit tangent **T**, but the acceleration **A** has both a tangential and normal component. The trajectory may twist and turn, but the acceleration is always in the plane determined by **T** and the unit normal **N**.

The two components of acceleration have special names.

Tangential and Normal Components of Acceleration

The acceleration $\mathbf{A}$ of a moving object can be written as

$$\mathbf{A} = A_T\mathbf{T} + A_N\mathbf{N}$$

where

$$A_T = \frac{d^2s}{dt^2} \qquad \text{is the \textbf{tangential component}.}$$

$$A_N = \kappa\left(\frac{ds}{dt}\right)^2 \qquad \text{is the \textbf{normal component}.}$$

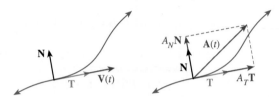

Figure 11.22 Components of velocity and acceleration

It is usually fairly easy to find A_T, but it may be more difficult to find A_N, because computing the curvature κ is often a messy process. Fortunately, there is a way to compute A_N without first finding κ. We expand the dot product of $\mathbf{A} = A_T\mathbf{T} + A_N\mathbf{N}$ with itself and use the fact that $\mathbf{T}$ and $\mathbf{N}$ are orthogonal unit vectors:

$$\|\mathbf{A}\|^2 = \mathbf{A} \cdot \mathbf{A} \qquad\qquad \textit{Theorem 11.8 } \mathbf{A} = A_T\mathbf{T} + \mathbf{A}_N\mathbf{N}$$

$$= (A_T\mathbf{T} + A_N\mathbf{N}) \cdot (A_T\mathbf{T} + A_N\mathbf{N})$$

$$= A_T^2(\mathbf{T} \cdot \mathbf{T}) + 2A_TA_N(\mathbf{N} \cdot \mathbf{T}) + A_N^2(\mathbf{N} \cdot \mathbf{N})$$

$$= A_T^2(1) + 2A_TA_N(0) + A_N^2(1) \qquad \mathbf{T} \cdot \mathbf{T} = 1, \mathbf{N} \cdot \mathbf{T} = 0, \textit{ and } \mathbf{N} \cdot \mathbf{N} = 1$$

$$= A_T^2 + A_N^2$$

Thus, once we know $\mathbf{A}$ and A_T, we can compute A_N by applying the following formula.

Computation of Normal Component

The normal component A_N can be found using the formula

$$A_N = \sqrt{\|\mathbf{A}\|^2 - A_T^2}$$

EXAMPLE 1 **Finding tangential and normal components of acceleration**

Find the tangential and normal components of an object that moves with displacement

$$\mathbf{R}(t) = t^3\mathbf{i} + t^2\mathbf{j} + t\mathbf{k}$$

Solution $\mathbf{V} = \dfrac{d\mathbf{R}}{dt} = 3t^2\mathbf{i} + 2t\mathbf{j} + \mathbf{k}$ and $\mathbf{A} = \dfrac{d\mathbf{V}}{dt} = 6t\mathbf{i} + 2\mathbf{j}$

$$\frac{ds}{dt} = \|\mathbf{V}\| = \sqrt{(3t^2)^2 + (2t)^2 + (1)^2} = \sqrt{9t^4 + 4t^2 + 1}$$

$$A_T = \frac{d^2s}{dt^2} = \frac{1}{2}(9t^4 + 4t^2 + 1)^{-1/2}(36t^3 + 8t) = \frac{18t^3 + 4t}{\sqrt{9t^4 + 4t^2 + 1}}$$

This is the tangential component of acceleration.

$$A_N = \sqrt{\|\mathbf{A}\|^2 - A_T^2} = \sqrt{\left[\sqrt{36t^2 + 4}\right]^2 - \left[\frac{18t^3 + 4t}{\sqrt{9t^4 + 4t^2 + 1}}\right]^2}$$

$$= \sqrt{4(9t^2 + 1) - \frac{4t^2(9t^2 + 2)^2}{9t^4 + 4t^2 + 1}}$$

$$= \sqrt{\frac{36t^4 + 36t^2 + 4}{9t^4 + 4t^2 + 1}} \quad \textit{There are several simplification steps that are not shown.}$$

$$= 2\sqrt{\frac{9t^4 + 9t^2 + 1}{9t^4 + 4t^2 + 1}}$$

This is the normal component of acceleration.   ▬

EXAMPLE 2   Finding tangential and normal components on a helix

An object moves along the helix with position vector

$$\mathbf{R}(t) = (\cos t)\mathbf{i} + (\sin t)\mathbf{j} + t\mathbf{k}$$

Find the tangential and normal components of acceleration.

Solution $\mathbf{V} = \dfrac{d\mathbf{R}}{dt} = (-\sin t)\mathbf{i} + (\cos t)\mathbf{j} + \mathbf{k}$ and $\mathbf{A} = \dfrac{d\mathbf{V}}{dt} = (-\cos t)\mathbf{i} + (-\sin t)\mathbf{j}$

$$\frac{ds}{dt} = \|\mathbf{V}\| = \sqrt{\sin^2 t + \cos^2 t + 1} = \sqrt{2} \quad \text{and} \quad A_T = \frac{d^2 s}{dt^2} = 0$$

$$A_N = \sqrt{\|\mathbf{A}\|^2 - A_T^2} = \sqrt{(\sqrt{\cos^2 t + \sin^2 t})^2 - 0^2} = 1$$

The tangential and normal components of acceleration are 0 and 1, respectively. This means that the acceleration satisfies

$$\mathbf{A} = A_T\mathbf{T} + A_N\mathbf{N} = (0)\mathbf{T} + (1)\mathbf{N} = \mathbf{N}$$

That is, the acceleration vector is the principal unit normal **N**, and the acceleration is always normal to the trajectory of the helix.   ▬

■ APPLICATIONS

Now that we know how to compute the tangential and normal components of acceleration, A_T and A_N, we shall examine some applications. First, according to Newton's second law of motion, the total force acting on a moving object of mass m satisfies $\mathbf{F} = m\mathbf{A}$, where $\mathbf{A}$ is the acceleration of the object. Because $\mathbf{A} = A_T\mathbf{T} + A_N\mathbf{N}$, we have

$$\mathbf{F} = m\mathbf{A} = (mA_T)\mathbf{T} + (mA_N)\mathbf{N} = F_T\mathbf{T} + F_N\mathbf{N}$$

where

$$F_T = m\frac{d^2 s}{dt^2} \quad \text{and} \quad F_N = m\kappa\left(\frac{ds}{dt}\right)^2$$

For instance, experience leads us to expect a car to skid if it makes a sharp turn at moderate speed or even a gradual turn at high speed. Mathematically, a "sharp turn" occurs when the radius of curvature $\rho = 1/\kappa$ is small (that is, when κ is large), and "high speed" means that ds/dt is large. In either case,

$$F_N = m\kappa\left(\frac{ds}{dt}\right)^2$$

Figure 11.23 Tendency to skid

will be relatively large, and the car will stay on the road (its trajectory) only if there is a correspondingly large frictional force between the tires of the car and the surface of the road (see Figure 11.23).

When forces, masses, and accelerations are involved, it is customary to express the mass m in slugs of an object whose weight W has been given in pounds.* From the definition of weight,

$$m = \frac{W}{g}$$

where g is the acceleration of gravity ($g \approx 32.2$ ft/s²)

EXAMPLE 3   Tendency of a vehicle to skid

A car weighing 2,700 lb makes a turn on a flat road while traveling at 56 ft/s (about 38 mi/hr). If the radius of the turn is 21 ft, how much frictional force is required to keep the car from skidding?

Solution   The required frictional force is $F_N = m\kappa\left(\dfrac{ds}{dt}\right)^2$, where m is the mass of the car and κ is the curvature of the road. We know that

$$\frac{ds}{dt} = 56 \text{ ft/s}$$

and because the car weighs $W = 2{,}700$ lb, its mass is $m = \dfrac{W}{g} = \dfrac{2{,}700}{32.2} \approx 83.85$

slugs. Because the turn radius is 21 ft, we have $\kappa = \dfrac{1}{21}$, so that

$$F_N = \left(\frac{2{,}700}{32.2} \text{ slug}\right)\left(\frac{1}{21 \text{ ft}}\right)\left(56 \frac{\text{ft}}{\text{s}}\right)^2 \approx 12{,}522 \frac{\text{lb} \cdot \text{s}^2}{\text{ft}} \frac{1}{\text{ft}} \frac{\text{ft}^2}{\text{s}^2} = 12{,}522 \text{ lb}$$

There are certain important applications in which an object moves along its trajectory with constant speed ds/dt, and when this occurs, the acceleration $\mathbf{A}$ can have only a normal component, because $d^2s/dt^2 = 0$.

THEOREM 11.9   Acceleration of an object with constant speed

The acceleration of an object moving with constant speed is always orthogonal to the direction of motion.

Proof: Notice that we really do not need to know anything about components of acceleration to prove this result. Saying that the object has constant speed means that $\|\mathbf{R}'(t)\|$ is constant, and by the orthogonality of a derivative theorem (Theorem 11.4), we conclude that $\mathbf{R}'(t)$ is orthogonal to its derivative $\mathbf{R}''(t) = \mathbf{A}(t)$. But $\mathbf{R}'(t)$ points in the direction of the object's motion along its trajectory, which means that the acceleration $\mathbf{A}$ is orthogonal to the direction of motion.   ∎

As an application of this result, note that when an object moves with constant speed v_0 along a circular path of radius R (so that $\kappa = 1/R$), its acceleration is directed toward the center of the path and has magnitude

$$A_N = \kappa\left(\frac{ds}{dt}\right)^2 = \frac{1}{R}v_0^2$$

(See Figure 11.24).

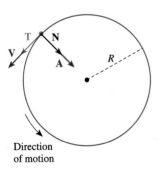

T N
V
A   R

Direction
of motion

If the speed is v_0 and the path has radius R, the acceleration is

$$\mathbf{A} = \frac{v_0^2}{R}\mathbf{N}$$

Figure 11.24 An object moving with constant speed on a circular path

*A slug is a unit of measurement defined as the unit of mass that receives an acceleration of 1 ft/s² when a force of 1 lb is applied to it. That is,

$$1 \text{ slug} = \frac{1 \text{ lb}}{1 \text{ ft/s}^2} = \frac{\text{lb} \cdot \text{s}^2}{\text{ft}}$$

EXAMPLE 4   Time for a satellite to orbit

An artificial satellite travels at constant speed in a stable circular orbit 20,000 km above the earth's surface. How long does it take for the satellite to make one complete circuit of the earth?

Solution   Let m denote the satellite's mass and v denote its speed. We shall assume that the earth is a sphere of radius 6,440 km, so the curvature of the path is $\kappa = 1/R$, where

$$R = \underbrace{6,440}_{\text{Radius of earth}} + \overbrace{20,000}^{\text{Height}} = 26,440 \text{ km}$$

is the distance of the satellite from the center of the earth. The **centripetal** (*center-seeking*) force $\mathbf{F}_g$ on the object satisfies $\|\mathbf{F}_g\| = mA_N = mv^2/R$. This force is balanced by a **centrifugal** (*center-fleeing*) force $\mathbf{F}_c$, and according to Newton's law of universal gravitation, $|\mathbf{F}_c| = GmM/R^2$, where M is the mass of the earth and G is the gravitational constant. It can be shown that the product GM is approximately equal to

$$GM = 398,600 \text{ km}^3/\text{s}^2$$

Since the centrifugal and centripetal forces on the object must be equal for it to maintain its stable orbit, we have

$$\|\mathbf{F}_g\| = \frac{mv^2}{R} = \frac{GmM}{R^2} = \|\mathbf{F}_c\|$$

Solving for v, we obtain

$$v = \sqrt{\frac{GM}{R}} = \sqrt{\frac{398,600}{26,440}} \approx 3.88273653$$

Finally, suppose that T is the time required for the satellite to make one complete circuit of the earth (called the **period** of the satellite). In each period, the satellite travels a distance equal to the circumference of a circle of radius $R = 26,440$ km, and because it travels at v km/s, we must have $vT = 2\pi R$, so that

$$T = \frac{2\pi R}{v} = \frac{2\pi(26,440 \text{ km})}{3.882\,736\,53} \approx 42,786.168\,52$$

or approximately 713 minutes (11 hr 53 min).   ▬

Figure 11.25 A satellite in a stable orbit; centrifugal force $\mathbf{F}_C$ equals the force $\mathbf{F}_g$ due to gravity.

PROBLEM SET 11.5

Ⓐ *In Problems 1–8, an object moves with displacement $\mathbf{R}(t)$. Find the tangential and normal components of the object's acceleration.*

1. $\mathbf{R}(t) = t\mathbf{i} + t^2\mathbf{j}$
2. $\mathbf{R}(t) = t\mathbf{i} + e^t\mathbf{j}$
3. $\mathbf{R}(t) = (t \sin t)\mathbf{i} + (t \cos t)\mathbf{j}$
4. $\mathbf{R}(t) = (3 \cos t)\mathbf{i} + (2 \sin t)\mathbf{j}$
5. $\mathbf{R}(t) = t\mathbf{i} + t^2\mathbf{j} + t\mathbf{k}$
6. $\mathbf{R}(t) = (\sin t)\mathbf{i} + (\cos t)\mathbf{j} + (\sin t)\mathbf{k}$
7. $\mathbf{R}(t) = (4 \cos t)\mathbf{i} + (\sin t)\mathbf{k}$
8. $\mathbf{R}(t) = \left(\frac{5}{13} \cos t\right)\mathbf{i} + \frac{12}{13}(1 - \cos t)\mathbf{j} + \sin t\mathbf{k}$

Ⓑ 9. The position of an object at time t is (x, y), where $x = 1 + \cos 2t$, $y = \sin 2t$. Find the velocity, the accelera-

tion, and the normal and tangential components of acceleration of the object at time t.

10. An object moves with constant angular velocity ω around the circle $x^2 + y^2 = r^2$ in the xy-plane. The displacement vector is

$$\mathbf{R}(t) = (r \cos \omega t)\mathbf{i} + (r \sin \omega t)\mathbf{j}$$

   a. Find the tangential and normal components of acceleration.

   b. Show that the curvature is $\kappa = 1/r$ at each point on the circle.

11. Find the tangential and normal components of the acceleration of an object that moves along the parabolic path $y = 4x^2$ at the instant the speed is $ds/dt = 20$.

12. A pail attached to a rope 1 yd long is twirled at the rate of 1 rev/s. Find the tangential and normal components of the pail's acceleration. *Hint:* Assume the rope is twirled from a position that only rotates.

13. A boy holds onto a pail of water weighing 3 lb and swings it in a vertical circle with a radius of 2 ft (the length of his arm). If the pail travels at ω rpm, what is the pressure of the water on the bottom of the pail when it is at its highest point? What is the *smallest* value of ω required to keep the water from spilling from the pail? Assume the pail is held by a handle so that its bottom is straight up when it is at its highest point.

14. A car weighing 2,700 lb ≈ 1.35 tons moves along the elliptic path $9x^2 + 4y^2 = 36$ (units in kilometers). If the car travels at the constant speed 100 km/h, how much frictional force is required to keep it from skidding as it turns the "corner" at $(2, 0)$? What about the corner $(0, 3)$?

15. A curve on a road should be banked so that there is no lateral friction force exerted on the tires as the vehicle rounds the curve. Suppose the road is a level curve that is a circle of radius 200 ft, and the average speed on this curve is 55 mi/hr. Also assume that the vehicle weighs 3,500 lb.

a. Find the force between the tires and the road so that the car stays on the circular path and does not skid. *Hint:* Use $\mathbf{F} = m\mathbf{A}$, where $m = 3500/32.2$. Also, 1 mi = 5,280 ft.

b. Find the angle the roadway should be banked so that no lateral friction force is exerted on the tires of the car.

16. What is the smallest radius that should be used for a circular highway curve if the normal component of the acceleration of a car traveling at 45 mi/h is not to exceed 2.4 ft/s²?

17. A Ferris wheel with radius 15 ft rotates in a vertical plane at ω revolutions per minute. What is the maximum value of ω for a Ferris wheel carrying a person of weight W?

Use the formula in Problem 24 to find A_T and A_N for the given position vector $\mathbf{R}(t)$ in Problems 18–21.

18. $\mathbf{R}(t) = t^3\mathbf{i} + t^2\mathbf{j} + t\mathbf{k}$

19. $\mathbf{R}(t) = t\mathbf{i} + 2t\mathbf{j} + t^2\mathbf{k}$

20. $\mathbf{R}(t) = (\cos t)\mathbf{i} + (\sin t)\mathbf{j} + \mathbf{k}$

21. $\mathbf{R}(t) = (e^t \cos t)\mathbf{i} + (e^t \sin t)\mathbf{j} + e^t\mathbf{k}$

Ⓒ 22. Let $\mathbf{T}$ be the unit tangent vector, $\mathbf{N}$ be the principal unit normal, and $\mathbf{B}$ be the unit binormal vector (see Problem 57, Section 11.4) to a given curve C. Show

$$\frac{d\mathbf{B}}{ds} = \mathbf{T} \times \frac{d\mathbf{N}}{ds}$$

23. An amusement park ride consists of a large (25-ft radius), flat wheel on which volunteers pay to sit while it is at rest. The wheel then begins to rotate until all the passengers are thrown from the wheel. The purpose of this problem is to discover how fast the wheel can rotate without losing its passengers.

a. Suppose the wheel rotates at ω revolutions per minute and that a volunteer weighing W pounds stands at the rim, 15 feet from the center of the wheel. Find the frictional force mA_N required to keep the volunteer from sliding off, where $m = W/g$ is the volunteer's mass.

b. If the frictional force of the volunteer in part **a** needed to stay on the wheel is $0.12W$, find the largest value of ω that will allow the volunteer to stay in place. *Hint:* Set $0.12W$ equal to your answer in part **a** and solve for ω; also note that the weight of the volunteer is irrelevant.

24. Suppose the position vector of a moving object is $\mathbf{R}(t)$. Show that the tangential and normal components of the object's acceleration may be computed by the formulas

$$A_T = \frac{\mathbf{R}' \cdot \mathbf{R}''}{\|\mathbf{R}'\|} \quad \text{and} \quad A_N = \frac{\|\mathbf{R}' \times \mathbf{R}''\|}{\|\mathbf{R}'\|}$$

25. Suppose an object moves in the plane along the curve $y = f(x)$. Use the formulas obtained in Theorem 11.8 to show that

$$A_T = \frac{f'(x)f''(x)}{\sqrt{1 + [f'(x)]^2}}; \quad A_N = \frac{|f''(x)|}{\sqrt{1 + [f'(x)]^2}}$$

26. If the graph of the function of f has an inflection point at $x = a$ and $f''(a)$ exists, show that the graph of f has curvature 0 at $(a, f(a))$.

27. A projectile is fired from ground level with an angle of elevation α and muzzle velocity v_0. Find formulas for the tangential and normal components of the projectile's acceleration at time t. What are A_T and A_N at the time the projectile is at its maximum height?

28. An object connected to a string of length r is spun counterclockwise in a circular path in a horizontal plane. Let ω be the constant angular velocity of the object.

   a. Show that the displacement vector of the object is

$$\mathbf{R}(t) = (r \cos \omega t)\mathbf{i} + (r \sin \omega t)\mathbf{j}$$

   b. Find the normal component of the object's acceleration.

   c. If the angular velocity ω is doubled, what is the effect on the normal component of acceleration? What is the effect on $\mathbf{A}$ if ω is unchanged but the length of the string is doubled? What happens to A_N if ω is doubled and r is halved?

29. An artificial satellite travels at constant speed in a stable circular orbit R km above the earth's surface (as in Example 4).

   a. Show that the satellite's period is given by the formula

$$T = 2\pi \frac{(R + R_e)^{3/2}}{\sqrt{GM}}$$

   where R_e is the radius of the earth.

   b. A satellite is said to be in **geosynchronous orbit** if it completes one orbit every sidereal day (23 hr, 56 min). How high above the earth should the satellite be in order to achieve such an orbit? Assume the radius of the earth is approximately 6,440 km.

30. SPY PROBLEM   After finally disposing of Boldfinger (Problem 48, Chapter 10 Supplementary Problems), the spy finds himself in hot pursuit of a gang of international terrorists who are holding his superior's innocent daughter prisoner. The terrorists are hiding in a bunker on the side of a hill inclined at an angle of 15° to the horizontal. The spy flies toward the bunker in a helicopter traveling at 200 ft/s at an altitude of 10,000 ft. Just as the helicopter flies over the base of the hill, the spy sights a ventilation hole in the top of the bunker at an angle of 20°. He decides to drop a canister of knockout gas into the bunker. How long should he wait before releasing the canister?

CHAPTER 11 REVIEW

IN THIS REVIEW Proficiency examination; supplementary problems
Problems 1–23 of the proficiency examination test your knowledge of the concepts of this chapter, and Problems 24–30 test your understanding of those concepts by asking you to work sample practice problems. The supplementary problems present questions relating to the material of this chapter in a wide variety of settings.

TABLE 11.3 Summary of Velocity, Acceleration, and Curvature

	CURVES
Position vector	$\mathbb{R}^2$ (plane) $\mathbf{R}(t) = x(t)\mathbf{i} + y(t)\mathbf{j}$ $\mathbb{R}^3$ (space) $\mathbf{R}(t) = x(t)\mathbf{i} + y(t)\mathbf{j} + z(t)\mathbf{k}$ The graph is called the **trajectory** of the object's motion.
Velocity vector	$\mathbf{V}(t) = \dfrac{d\mathbf{R}}{dt} = \mathbf{R}'(t)$ $\|\mathbf{V}\| = \dfrac{ds}{dt}$ This is called the **speed**. $\dfrac{\mathbf{V}}{\|\mathbf{V}\|}$ This is the direction of $\mathbf{V}$ or *direction of motion*.
Acceleration vector	$\mathbf{A}(t) = \dfrac{d^2\mathbf{R}}{dt^2} = \dfrac{d\mathbf{V}}{dt} = A_T\mathbf{T} + A_N\mathbf{N}$ where $A_T = \dfrac{d^2s}{dt^2} = \mathbf{A} \cdot \mathbf{T} = \dfrac{\mathbf{V} \cdot \mathbf{A}}{\|\mathbf{V}\|}$ This is the **tangential component**. $A_N = \kappa\left(\dfrac{ds}{dt}\right)^2 = \mathbf{A} \cdot \mathbf{N} = \sqrt{\|\mathbf{A}\|^2 - A_T{}^2}$ This is the **normal component**.
Unit tangent and normal vectors	$\mathbf{T} = \dfrac{\mathbf{V}}{\|\mathbf{V}\|} = \dfrac{\mathbf{R}'(t)}{\|\mathbf{R}'(t)\|} = \dfrac{d\mathbf{R}}{ds}$ This is the **unit tangent vector** in the *direction of motion*. $\mathbf{N} = \dfrac{\mathbf{T}'(t)}{\|\mathbf{T}'(t)\|} = \dfrac{1}{\kappa}\dfrac{d\mathbf{T}}{ds}$ This is the **unit normal vector**.
Curvature	$\kappa = \left\|\dfrac{d\mathbf{T}}{ds}\right\| = \dfrac{\left\|\dfrac{d\mathbf{T}}{dt}\right\|}{\dfrac{ds}{dt}} = \dfrac{\|\mathbf{V} \times \mathbf{A}\|}{\|\mathbf{V}\|^3}$; if $y = y(x)$, then $\kappa = \dfrac{|x'y'' - y'x''|}{[(x')^2 + (y')^2]^{3/2}}$
Torsion	$\tau = \left\|\dfrac{d\mathbf{B}}{ds}\right\|$

PROFICIENCY EXAMINATION

Concept Problems

1. What is a vector-valued function?
2. What are the components of a vector function?
3. Describe what is meant by the graph of a vector function.
4. Define the limit of a vector function.
5. Define the derivative of a vector function.
6. Define the integral of a vector function.
7. What is a smooth curve?
8. Complete the following rules for differentiating vector functions:
   a. Linearity rule
   b. Scalar rule
   c. Dot product rule
   d. Cross-product rule
   e. Chain rule

9. State the orthogonality of a derivative theorem.
10. What are the displacement, velocity, and acceleration vectors?
11. What is the speed of a particle moving on a curve C?
12. What are the formulas for the motion of a projectile in a vacuum?
13. What are the formulas for time of flight and range of a projectile?
14. State Kepler's laws.
15. What are the unit polar vectors, $\mathbf{u}_r$ and $\mathbf{u}_\theta$?
16. What are the unit tangent and normal vectors?
17. What is speed in terms of arc length?
18. What is the arc length of a space curve?
19. What is the curvature of a graph?
20. What is the formula for curvature in terms of the velocity and acceleration vectors?

21. What are the formulas for unit tangent and principal unit normal in terms of the arc length parameter?

22. What is the radius of curvature?

23. What are the tangential and normal components of acceleration?

Practice Problems

24. Sketch the graph of $\mathbf{R}(t) = (3 \cos t)\mathbf{i} + (3 \sin t)\mathbf{j} + t\mathbf{k}$ and find the length of this curve from $t = 0$ to $t = 2\pi$.

25. If $\mathbf{F}(t) = \left(\dfrac{t}{1 + t}\right)\mathbf{i} + \left(\dfrac{\sin t}{t}\right)\mathbf{j} + (\cos t)\mathbf{k}$, find $\mathbf{F}'(t)$ and $\mathbf{F}''(t)$.

26. Evaluate $\displaystyle\int_1^2 [3t\mathbf{i} + 3\mathbf{k}] \times [(\ln t)\mathbf{j} - t^2\mathbf{k}]\, dt$.

27. Find a vector function $\mathbf{F}$ such that $\mathbf{F}''(t) = e^t\mathbf{i} - t^2\mathbf{j} + 3\mathbf{k}$ and $\mathbf{F}(0) = \mathbf{i} - 2\mathbf{j}$, $\mathbf{F}'(0) = 3\mathbf{k}$.

28. Find the velocity $\mathbf{V}$, the speed ds/dt, and the acceleration $\mathbf{A}$ for the body with displacement vector $\mathbf{R}(t) = t\mathbf{i} + 2t\mathbf{j} + te^t\mathbf{k}$.

29. Find $\mathbf{T}$, $\mathbf{N}$, the tangential and normal components of acceleration A_T, and A_N), and κ (curvature) for an object with displacement $\mathbf{R}(t) = t^2\mathbf{i} + 3t\mathbf{j} - 3t\mathbf{k}$.

30. A projectile is fired from ground level with initial velocity 50 ft/s at an angle of elevation of α.
    a. If $\alpha = 30°$, what is the maximum height reached by the projectile?
    b. If $\alpha = 30°$, what is the time of flight and the range?

SUPPLEMENTARY PROBLEMS

Find the vector limits in Problems 1–6.

1. $\displaystyle\lim_{t \to 0} \left[t^2\mathbf{i} - 3te^t\mathbf{j} + \dfrac{\sin 2t}{t}\mathbf{k} \right]$ 2. $\displaystyle\lim_{t \to 0} \left[\dfrac{\mathbf{i} + t\mathbf{j} - e^{-t}\mathbf{k}}{1 - t} \right]$

3. $\displaystyle\lim_{t \to 0} [t\mathbf{i} + 5\mathbf{k}] \cdot [(\sin t)\mathbf{i} + 3t\mathbf{j} - (1 - t)\mathbf{k}]$

4. $\displaystyle\lim_{t \to 0} [(1 + t)\mathbf{i} - 3\mathbf{j}] \times [t^2\mathbf{j} + (\cos \pi t)\mathbf{k}]$

5. $\displaystyle\lim_{t \to 0} \left[\left(1 + \dfrac{1}{t}\right)^t \mathbf{i} - \left(\dfrac{\sin t}{t}\right)\mathbf{j} - t\mathbf{k} \right]$

6. $\displaystyle\lim_{t \to 0} \left[\left(\dfrac{1 - \cos t}{t}\right)\mathbf{i} + 4\mathbf{j} + \left(1 + \dfrac{3}{t}\right)^t\mathbf{k} \right]$

Find $\mathbf{F}'(t)$ and $\mathbf{F}''(t)$ for the vector functions in Problems 7–12.

7. $\mathbf{F}(t) = te^t\mathbf{i} + t^2\mathbf{j}$ 8. $\mathbf{F}(t) = (t \ln 2t)\mathbf{i} + t^{3/2}\mathbf{k}$

9. $\mathbf{F}(t) = 2t^{-1}\mathbf{i} - 2t\mathbf{j} + te^{-t}\mathbf{k}$

10. $\mathbf{F}(t) = [t\mathbf{i} - (1 - t)\mathbf{j}] \times [t^2\mathbf{j} + e^{-t}\mathbf{k}]$

11. $\mathbf{F}(t) = (t^2 + e^{at})\mathbf{i} + (te^{-at})\mathbf{j} + (e^{at+1})\mathbf{k}$, a a constant

12. $\mathbf{F}(t) = (1 - t)^{-1}\mathbf{i} + (\sin 2t)\mathbf{j} + (\cos^2 t)\mathbf{k}$

Sketch the graph of the vector functions in Problems 13–18.

13. $\mathbf{F}(t) = te^t\mathbf{i} + t^2\mathbf{j}$ 14. $\mathbf{F}(t) = t^2\mathbf{i} - 3t\mathbf{j}$

15. $\mathbf{F}(t) = 2t\mathbf{i} + (1 - t)\mathbf{j} + t^2\mathbf{k}$

16. $\mathbf{F}(t) = (1 - \cos t)\mathbf{i} + (\sin t)\mathbf{k}$

17. $\mathbf{F}(t) = (3 \cos t)\mathbf{i} + (3 \sin t)\mathbf{j} + t\mathbf{k}$

18. $\mathbf{F}(t) = (2 \sin t)\mathbf{i} + (2 \cos t)\mathbf{j} + 5t\mathbf{k}$

Let $\mathbf{F}(t) = f_1(t)\mathbf{i} + f_2(t)\mathbf{j} + f_3(t)\mathbf{k}$ and find the indicated derivative in terms of $\mathbf{F}'$ in Problems 19–24.

19. $\dfrac{d}{dt}\|\mathbf{F}(t)\|$ 20. $\dfrac{d}{dt}\left[\|\mathbf{F}(t)\|\mathbf{F}(t)\right]$

21. $\dfrac{d}{dt}\left[\dfrac{\mathbf{F}(t)}{\|\mathbf{F}(t)\|}\right]$ 22. $\dfrac{d}{dt}\left[\mathbf{F}(t) \cdot \mathbf{F}(t)\right]$

23. $\dfrac{d}{dt}\left[\mathbf{F}(t) \times \mathbf{F}(t)\right]$ 24. $\dfrac{d}{dt}\mathbf{F}(e^t)$

Evaluate the definite and indefinite vector integrals in Problems 25–30.

25. $\displaystyle\int_{-1}^1 (e^{-t}\mathbf{i} + t^3\mathbf{j} + 3\mathbf{k})\, dt$ 26. $\displaystyle\int_1^2 [(1 - t)\mathbf{i} - t^{-1}\mathbf{j} + e^t\mathbf{k}]\, dt$

27. $\displaystyle\int [te^t\mathbf{i} - (\sin 2t)\mathbf{j} + t^2\mathbf{k}]\, dt$

28. $\displaystyle\int e^{2t}[2\mathbf{i} - t\mathbf{j} + (\sin t)\mathbf{k}]\, dt$

29. $\displaystyle\int t[e^t\mathbf{i} + (\ln t)\mathbf{j} + 3\mathbf{k}]\, dt$

30. $\displaystyle\int [e^t\mathbf{i} + 2\mathbf{j} - t\mathbf{k}] \cdot [e^{-t}\mathbf{i} - t\mathbf{j}]\, dt$

In Problems 31–34, $\mathbf{R}$ is the displacement vector of a moving body. Find the velocity $\mathbf{V}$, the speed ds/dt, and the acceleration $\mathbf{A}$.

31. $\mathbf{R}(t) = t\mathbf{i} + (3 - t)\mathbf{j} + 2\mathbf{k}$

32. $\mathbf{R}(t) = (\sin 2t)\mathbf{i} + 2\mathbf{j} - (\cos 2t)\mathbf{k}$

33. $\mathbf{R}(t) = (t \sin t)\mathbf{i} + (te^{-t})\mathbf{j} - (1 - t)\mathbf{k}$

34. $\mathbf{R}(t) = (\ln t)\mathbf{i} + e^t\mathbf{j} - (\tan t)\mathbf{k}$

Find $\mathbf{T}$ and $\mathbf{N}$ for the vector functions given in Problems 35–38.

35. $\mathbf{R}(t) = t\mathbf{i} - t\mathbf{j}$

36. $\mathbf{R}(t) = (3 \cos t)\mathbf{i} - (3 \sin t)\mathbf{j}$

37. $\mathbf{R}(t) = (4 \cos t)\mathbf{i} - 3t\mathbf{j} + (4 \sin t)\mathbf{k}$

38. $\mathbf{R}(t) = (e^t \sin t)\mathbf{i} + e^t\mathbf{j} + (e^t \cos t)\mathbf{k}$

In Problems 39–42, find the tangential and normal components of acceleration, and the curvature of a moving object with displacement $\mathbf{R}(t)$.

39. $\mathbf{R}(t) = t^2\mathbf{i} + 2t\mathbf{j} + e^t\mathbf{k}$

40. $\mathbf{R}(t) = t^2\mathbf{i} - 2t\mathbf{j} + (t^2 - t)\mathbf{k}$

41. $\mathbf{R}(t) = (4 \sin t)\mathbf{i} + (4 \cos t)\mathbf{j} + 4t\mathbf{k}$

42. $\mathbf{R}(t) = (a \sin 3t)\mathbf{i} + (a + a \cos 3t)\mathbf{j} + (3a \sin t)\mathbf{k}$, for constant $a \neq 0$

A polar curve C is given by $r = f(\theta)$. If $f''(\theta)$ exists (see Problem 54, Section 11.4), then the curvature can be found by the formula

$$\kappa = \dfrac{|[f(\theta)]^2 + 2[f'(\theta)]^2 - f(\theta)f''(\theta)|}{\{[f(\theta)]^2 + [f'(\theta)]^2\}^{3/2}}$$

Find the curvature at the given point on each of the polar curves given in Problems 43–48.

43. $r = 4 \cos \theta$, where $\theta = \frac{\pi}{3}$ **44.** $r = \theta^2$, where $\theta = 2$

45. $r = e^{-\theta}$, where $\theta = 1$ **46.** $r = 1 + \cos \theta$, where $\theta = \frac{\pi}{2}$

47. $r = 4 \cos 3\theta$, where $\theta = \frac{\pi}{6}$

48. $r = 1 - 2 \sin \theta$, where $\theta = \frac{\pi}{4}$

49. For what values of t is the following vector function continuous?

$$\mathbf{F}(t) = (2t - 1)\mathbf{i} + \left(\frac{t^2 - 1}{t - 1}\right)\mathbf{j} + 4\mathbf{k}$$

50. Find the length of the graph of the vector function

$$\mathbf{R}(t) = \left(\frac{t^2 - 2}{2}\right)\mathbf{i} + \frac{(2t + 1)^{3/2}}{3}\mathbf{j}$$

from $t = 0$ to $t = 6$.

51. Find a vector function $\mathbf{F}$ such that $\mathbf{F}(0) = \mathbf{F}'(0) = \mathbf{i}$, $\mathbf{F}''(0) = 2\mathbf{j} + \mathbf{k}$, and

$$\mathbf{F}'''(t) = (\cos t)\mathbf{i} + (\sin t)\mathbf{j} + \frac{t}{\pi}\mathbf{k}$$

52. An object moves in space with acceleration

$$\mathbf{A}(t) = (-t)\mathbf{i} + 2\mathbf{j} + (2 - t)\mathbf{k}$$

When $t = 0$, it is known that the object is at the point $(1, 0, 0)$ and that it has velocity $\mathbf{V}(0) = 2\mathbf{i} - 4\mathbf{j}$.

a. Find the velocity $\mathbf{V}(t)$ and the position $\mathbf{R}(t)$.

b. What is the speed and location of the object when $t = 1$?

c. When is the object stationary and what is its displacement at that time?

53. The position vector for a curve is given in terms of arc length s by

$$\mathbf{R}(s) = \left(a \cos \frac{s}{a}\right)\mathbf{i} + \left(a \sin \frac{s}{a}\right)\mathbf{j} + 2s\mathbf{k}$$

for $0 \le s \le 2\pi a$ and $a > 0$. Find the unit tangent vector $\mathbf{T}(s)$, and the principal unit normal $\mathbf{N}(s)$.

54. Find the radius of curvature of the curve given by $y = 1 + \sin x$ at the points where x is

a. $\frac{\pi}{6}$ **b.** $\frac{\pi}{4}$ **c.** $\frac{3\pi}{2}$

55. Find the radius of curvature of the ellipse given by

$$\mathbf{R}(t) = (a \cos t)\mathbf{i} + (b \sin t)\mathbf{j}$$

where $a > 0$, $b > 0$, $a \ne b$, and $0 \le t \le 2\pi$ at the points where $t = 0$ and $\pi/2$.

56. A stunt pilot flying at an altitude of 4,000 ft with a speed of 180 mi/hr drops a weighted marker, attempting to hit a target on the ground below, as shown in the figure in the margin. How far away from the target (measured horizontally) should the pilot be when he releases the marker? You may neglect air resistance.

4000 ft

57. The position of an object moving in space is given by

$$\mathbf{R}(t) = (e^{-t}\cos t)\mathbf{i} + (e^{-t}\sin t)\mathbf{j} + e^{-t}\mathbf{k}$$

a. Find the velocity, speed, and acceleration of the object at arbitrary time t.

b. Determine the curvature of the trajectory at time t.

58. Find the point or points on the curve $y = e^{ax}$ ($a > 0$) where the radius of curvature is maximized.

59. The position vector of an object in space is

$$\mathbf{R}(t) = (a \cos \omega t)\mathbf{i} + (a \sin \omega t)\mathbf{j} + \omega^2 t\mathbf{k}$$

Find the object's tangential and normal components of acceleration.

60. A particle moves along a path given in polar coordinates (r, θ), where $r(t) = 1 + \cos at$ and $\theta(t) = e^{-at}$ (for positive constant a). Find the velocity and acceleration of the particle in terms of the unit polar vectors $\mathbf{u}_r$ and $\mathbf{u}_\theta$.

61. A car weighing 3,000 lb travels at a constant speed of 60 mi/hr on a flat road and then makes a circular turn on an interchange. If the radius of the turn is 40 ft, what frictional force is needed to keep the car from skidding?

62. A nozzle discharges a stream of water with an initial velocity of v_0 of 50 ft/s into the end of a horizontal pipe of inside diameter $d = 5$ ft. What is the largest distance that the stream can reach?

63. Recall that the tangent line at a point P on a curve in space is the line that passes through P and is aligned with the tangent vector $\mathbf{T}$ at P. Find parametric equations for the tangent line to the curve given by

$$\mathbf{R}(t) = \left(\frac{3t}{1+t^3}\right)\mathbf{i} + \left(\frac{3t^2}{1+t^3}\right)\mathbf{j}$$

at the point $P(0, 0)$. Sketch the curve. This curve is called the *folium of Descartes*.

Computational Window

64. A fire nozzle discharges water with an initial velocity v_0 at an angle of 62° with the horizontal. Use a spreadsheet or a computer program to determine where the stream of water strikes the ground or building for values of v_0 from 4 m/s to 16 m/s at 1-m/s intervals.

65. A bicycle travels at the constant speed of 10 m/s. Find the maximum velocity of a point on the bicycle tire located 25 cm from the axle. Assume the radius of the tire is greater than 25 cm.

66. A DNA molecule has the shape of a double helix (see Figure 11.4). The radius of each helix is about 10^{-8} cm. Each helix rises about 3×10^{-8} cm during each complete turn and there are about 3×10^8 complete turns. Estimate the length of each helix.

67. Show that the tangential component of acceleration of a moving object is 0 if the object has constant speed. Is the converse statement also true? That is, if $A_T = 0$, can we conclude that the speed is constant?

68. The path of a particle P is an Archimedean spiral. The motion of the particle is described by the polar coordinates $r = 10t$ and $\theta = 2\pi t$, where r is expressed in inches and t is in seconds. Determine the velocity of the particle (in terms of $\mathbf{u}_r$ and $\mathbf{u}_\theta$) when
  a. $t = 0$ **b.** $t = 0.25$ sec

In Problems 69–70, find $\mathbf{F}'(x)$.

69. $\mathbf{F}(x) = \displaystyle\int_1^x [(\sin t)\mathbf{i} - (\cos 2t)\mathbf{j} + e^{-t}\mathbf{k}]\, dt$

70. $\mathbf{F}(x) = \displaystyle\int_1^x [t^2\mathbf{i} + (\sec e^{-t})\mathbf{j} - (\tan e^{2t})\mathbf{k}]\, dt$

In Problems 71–74, solve the initial value problems for $\mathbf{F}$ as a vector function of t.

71. Differential equation: $\mathbf{F}'(t) = t\mathbf{i} + t\mathbf{j} - t\mathbf{k}$;
  initial condition: $\mathbf{F}(0) = \mathbf{i} + 2\mathbf{j} - 3\mathbf{k}$

72. Differential equation:

$$\mathbf{F}'(t) = \tfrac{3}{2}\sqrt{t+1}\,\mathbf{i} + (t+1)^{-1}\mathbf{j} + e^t\mathbf{k}$$

  initial condition: $\mathbf{F}(0) = \mathbf{j} + 2\mathbf{k}$

73. Differential equation:

$$\mathbf{F}'(t) = (\sin 2t)\mathbf{i} + (e^t\cos t)\mathbf{j} - \left(\frac{3}{t+1}\right)\mathbf{k}$$

  initial condition: $\mathbf{F}(0) = \mathbf{i} - 3\mathbf{k}$

74. Differential equation:

$$\frac{d^2\mathbf{F}}{dt^2} = -32\mathbf{j}$$

  initial conditions:

$$\mathbf{F} = 50\mathbf{j} \text{ and } \frac{d\mathbf{F}}{dt} = 5\mathbf{i} + 5\mathbf{k} \text{ at } t = 0$$

75. PUTNAM EXAMINATION PROBLEM   A shell strikes an airplane flying at a height h above the ground. It is known that the shell was fired from a gun on the ground with muzzle velocity v_0, but the position of the gun and its angle of elevation are both unknown. Deduce that the gun is situated within a circle whose center lies directly below the airplane and whose radius is

$$\frac{v_0}{g}\sqrt{v_0{}^2 - 2gh}$$

Neglect resistance of the atmosphere.

76. PUTNAM EXAMINATION PROBLEM   A coast artillery gun can fire at any angle of elevation between 0° and 90° in a fixed vertical plane. If air resistance is neglected and the muzzle velocity is constant ($v = v_0$), determine the set H of points in the plane that can be hit. Consider only those points above the horizontal.

77. PUTNAM EXAMINATION PROBLEM   A particle moves on a circle with center O, starting from rest at a point P and coming to rest again at a point Q, without coming to rest at any intermediate point. Prove that the acceleration vector of the particle does not vanish at any point between P and Q and that, at some point R between P and Q, the acceleration vector points in along the radius $\overline{RO}$.

For Further Study—The Simulation of Science by Howard Eves

Howard Eves was born in Paterson, New Jersey, in 1911 and is professor emeritus of mathematics at the University of Maine. This guest essay first appeared in Great Moments in Mathematics Before 1650. *Professor Eves reminds us, "It must be remembered that a moment in history is sometimes an inspired flash and sometimes an evolution extending over a long period of time." Howard Eves' lectures (from which this guest essay was taken) are so renowned that each college and university at which he taught awarded him, at one time or another, every available honor for distinguished teaching. Howard Eves is a prolific and successful textbook author with a real love for the history of mathematics. He now lives with his wife at a retirement retreat in Lubec, Maine.*

The die is cast; I have written my book; it will be read either in the present age or by posterity, it matters not which; it may well await a reader, since God has waited six thousand years for an interpreter of his words.

Johannes Kepler
From James R. Newman, *The World of Mathematics, Volume I* (New York: Simon and Schuster, 1952), p. 220.

The mighty Antaeus was the giant son of Neptune (god of the sea) and Ge (goddess of the earth), and his strength was invincible so long as he remained in contact with his Mother Earth. Strangers who came to his country were forced to wrestle to the death with him, and so it chanced one day that Hercules and Antaeus came to grips with one another. But Hercules, aware of the source of Antaeus' great strength, lifted and held the giant from the earth and crushed him in the air.

There is a parable here for mathematicians. For just as Antaeus was born of and nurtured by his Mother Earth, history has shown us that all significant and lasting mathematics is born of and nurtured by the real world. As in the case of Antaeus, so long as mathematics maintains its contact with the real world, it will remain powerful. But should it be lifted too long from the solid ground of its birth into the filmy air of pure abstraction, it runs the risk of weakening. It must of necessity return, at least occasionally, to the real world for renewed strength.

Such a rejuvenation of mathematics occurred in the seventeenth century, following discoveries made by two eminent mathematician-scientists—Galileo Galilei (1564–1642) and Johannes Kepler (1571–1630). Galileo, through a sequence of experiments started before his 25th birthday, discovered a number of basic facts concerning the motion of bodies in the earth's gravitational field, and Kepler, by 1619, had induced all three of his famous laws of planetary motion. These achievements proved to be so influential on the development of so much of subsequent mathematics that they must be ranked as two of the GREAT MOMENTS IN MATHEMATICS. Galileo's discoveries led to the creation of the modern science of dynamics and Kepler's, to the creation of modern celestial mechanics; and each of these studies, in turn, required, for their development, the creation of a new mathematical tool—the calculus—capable of dealing with change, flux, and motion.

Galileo was born in Pisa in 1564 as the son of an impoverished Florentine nobleman. After a disinterested start as a medical student, Galileo obtained parental permission to change his studies to science and mathematics, fields in which he possessed a strong natural talent. While still a medical student at the University of Pisa, he made his historically famous observation that the great pendulous lamp in the cathedral there oscillated to and fro with a period independent of the size of the arc of oscillation.* Later, he showed that the period of a pendulum is also independent of the weight of the pendulum's bob. When he was 25, he accepted an appointment as professor of mathematics at the University of Pisa. It was during this appointment that he is alleged to have performed experiments from the leaning tower of Pisa, showing that, contrary to the teaching

*This is only approximately true, the approximation being very close in the case of small amplitudes of oscillation.

Historical Note

JOHANNES KEPLER
(1571–1630)

Copernicus revolutionized the world with his heliocentric theory, and Galileo confirmed this theory with his telescope, but Johannes Kepler is remembered not only for his work in astronomy, but also for his mathematical discoveries.

Kepler has been described as "number-intoxicated." He was looking for mathematical harmonies in the physical universe. He is quoted in *The World of Mathematics*: "Nothing holds me; I will indulge my sacred fury; I will triumph over mankind by the honest confession that I have stolen the golden vases of the Egyptians to build up a tabernacle for my God far away from the confines of Egypt."

The three laws of Kepler described in this chapter forever changed the history of science.

of Aristotle, heavy bodies do not fall faster than light ones. By rolling balls down inclined planes, he arrived at the law that the distance a body falls is proportional to the square of the time of falling, in accordance with the now-familiar formula $s = \frac{1}{2}gt^2$.

Unpleasant local controversies caused Galileo to resign his chair at Pisa in 1591, and the following year he accepted a professorship in mathematics at the University of Padua, where there reigned an atmosphere more friendly to scientific pursuits. Here at Padua, for nearly 18 years, Galileo continued his experiments and his teaching, achieving a widespread fame. While at Padua, he heard of the discovery, in about 1607, of the telescope by the Dutch lens-grinder Johann Lipersheim, and he set about making instruments of his own, producing a telescope with a magnifying power of more than 30 diameters. With this telescope he observed sunspots (contradicting Aristotle's assertion that the sun is without blemish), saw mountains on the moon, and noticed the phases of Venus, Saturn's rings, and the four bright satellites of Jupiter (all three of these lending credence to the Copernican theory of the solar system). Galileo's discoveries roused the opposition of the Church, and finally, in the year 1633, he was summoned to appear before the Inquisition and there forced to recant his scientific findings. Not many years later the great scientist became blind. He died, a prisoner in his own home, in 1642, the year Isaac Newton was born.

Johannes Kepler was born near Stuttgart, Germany in 1571 and commenced his studies at the University of Tübingen with the intention of becoming a Lutheran minister. Like Galileo, he found his first choice of an occupation far less congenial than his deep interest in science, particularly astronomy, and he accordingly changed his plans. In 1594, when in his early twenties, he accepted a lectureship at the University of Gratz in Austria. Five years later he became assistant to the famous Danish-Swedish astronomer Tycho Brahe, who had moved to Prague to serve as the court astronomer to Kaiser Rudolph II. Shortly after, in 1601, Brahe suddenly died, and Kepler inherited both his master's position and his vast collection of very accurate data on the positions of the planets as they moved about the sky. With amazing perseverance, Kepler set out to find, from Brahe's enormous mass of observational data, just how the planets move in space.

It has often been remarked that almost any problem can be solved if one but continuously worries over it and works at it a sufficiently long time. As Thomas Edison said, genius is 1% inspiration and 99% perspiration. Perhaps nowhere in the history of science is this more clearly demonstrated than in Kepler's incredible pertinacity in solving the problem of the motion of the planets about the sun. Thoroughly convinced of the Copernican theory that the planets revolve in orbits about the central sun, Kepler strenuously sought to determine the nature and position of those orbits and the manner in which the planets travel in their orbits. With Brahe's great set of observational recordings at hand, the problem became this: to obtain a pattern of motion of the planets that would exactly agree with Brahe's observations. So dependable were Brahe's recordings that any solution that should differ from Brahe's observed positions by even as little as a quarter of the moon's apparent diameter must be discarded as incorrect. Kepler had, then, first to guess with his *imagination* some plausible solution and then, with painful *perseverance*, to endure the mountain of tedious calculations needed to confirm or reject his guess. He made hundreds of fruitless attempts and performed reams and reams of calculations, laboring with undiminished zeal and patience for many years. Finally he solved his problem, in the form of his three famous laws of planetary motion, the first two around 1609 and the third one 10 years later in 1619:

I. The planets move about the sun in elliptical orbits with the sun at one focus.
II. The radius vector joining a planet to the sun sweeps over equal areas in equal intervals of time.
III. The square of the time of one complete revolution of a planet about its orbit is proportional to the cube of the orbit's semimajor axis.

The empirical discovery of these laws from Brahe's mass of data constitutes one of the most remarkable inductions ever made in science. With justifiable pride, Kepler prefaced his *Harmony of the Worlds* of 1619 with the following outburst:

I am writing a book for my contemporaries or—it does not matter—for posterity. It may be that my book will wait for a hundred years for a reader. Has not God waited 6000 years for an observer?

Kepler's laws of planetary motion are landmarks in the history of astronomy and mathematics, for in the effort to justify them Isaac Newton was let to create modern celestial mechanics. It is very interesting that 1800 years after the Greeks had developed the properties of the conic sections, there should occur such an illuminating practical application of them. *One never knows when a piece of pure mathematics may receive an unexpected application.*

In order to compute the areas involved in his second law, Kepler had to resort to a crude form of the integral calculus, making him one of the precursors of that calculus. Also, in his *Stereometria doliorum vinorum* (*Solid Geometry of Wine Barrels*, 1615), he applied crude integration procedures to the finding of the volumes of 93 different solids obtained by revolving arcs of conic sections about axes in their planes. Among these solids were the torus and two that he called *the apple* and *the lemon*, these latter being obtained by revolving a major and a minor arc, respectively, of a circle about the arc's chord as an axis. Kepler's interest in these matters arose when he observed some of the poor methods in use by the wine gaugers of the time.

It was Kepler who introduced the word *focus* (Latin for "hearth") into the geometry of conic sections. He approximated the perimeter of an ellipse of semiaxes a and b by the formula $\pi(a + b)$. He also laid down a so-called principle of continuity, which postulates the existence in a plane of certain ideal points and an ideal line having many of the properties of ordinary points and lines, lying at infinity. Thus he explained that a straight line can be considered as closed at infinity and that a parabola may be regarded as the limiting case of either an ellipse or a hyperbola in which one of the foci has retreated to infinity. The ideas were extended by later geometers.

Kepler was a confirmed Pythagorean, with the result that his work is often a blend of the fancifully mystical and the carefully scientific. It is sad that his personal life was made almost unendurable by a multiplicity of worldly misfortunes. An infection from smallpox when he was four years old left his eyesight much impaired. In addition to his general lifelong weakness, he spent a joyless youth; his marriage was a constant source of unhappiness; his favorite child died of smallpox; his wife went mad and died; he was expelled from his lectureship at the University of Graz when the city fell to the Catholics; his mother was charged and imprisoned for witchcraft, and for almost a year he desperately tried to save her from the torture chamber; he himself very narrowly escaped condemnation for heterodoxy; and his stipend was always in arrears. One report says that his second marriage was even less fortunate than his first, although he took the precaution to analyze carefully the merits and demerits of 11 women before choosing the wrong one. He was forced to augment his income by casting horoscopes, and he died of a fever in 1630 at the age of 59 while on a journey to try to collect some of his long overdue salary.

MATHEMATICAL ESSAYS

1. Write a 500-word essay on the life and mathematics of Galileo Galilei.

2. Write a 500-word essay on the life and mathematics of Johannes Kepler.

3. Explain the remark in Galileo's *The Two New Sciences* of 1638 that "neither is the number of squares less than the totality of all numbers, nor the latter greater than the former."

4. Explain the following geometric paradox considered by Galileo in his *The Two New Sciences*:

Suppose the larger circle of Figure 11.26 has made one revolution in rolling along the straight line from A to B, so that $|\overline{AB}|$ is equal to the circumference of the large circle. Then the small circle, fixed to the large one, has also made one revolution, so that $|\overline{CD}|$ is equal to the circumference of the small circle. It follows that the *two circles have equal circumferences*.

Figure 11.26 Aristotle's wheel

This paradox had been earlier described by Aristotle and is therefore sometimes referred to as *Aristotle's wheel*.

5. Prove Kepler's first law. You may search the literature for help with this proof.

6. Prove Kepler's third law. You may search the literature for help with this proof.

7. Where is a planet in its orbit when its speed is the greatest? Support your response.

8. Two hypothetical planets are moving about the sun in elliptical orbits having equal major axes. The minor axis of one, however, is half that of the other. How do the periods of the two planets compare? Support your response.

9. **a.** Kepler divided a circle of radius r and circumference C into a large number of very thin sectors. By regarding each sector as a thin isosceles triangle of altitude r and base equal to the arc of the sector, he heuristically arrived at the formula $A = \frac{1}{2}rC$ for the area of a circle. Show how this was done.

b. Use Kepler's type of reasoning to obtain a volume V of a sphere of radius r and surface area S as $V = \frac{1}{3}rS$.

c. Use Kepler's type of reasoning to obtain the area A of the ellipse of semimajor axis a and semiminor axis b as $A = \pi ab$.

10. **Book report**   "Science is that body of knowledge that describes, defines, and where possible, explains the universe . . . we think of the history of science as a history of men. . . . [History] is the story of thousands of people who contributed to the knowledge and theories that constituted the science of their eras and made the 'great leaps' possible. Many of these people were women." So begins a history of women in science entitled *Hypatia's Heritage* by Margaret Alic (Boston: Beacon Press, 1986). Read this book and write a book report.

11. Make up a word problem involving the calculus of vector-valued functions. Send your problem to:

Mathematics Editor,
RE: Bradley and Smith
Calculus
Prentice Hall
113 Sylvan Ave., Route 9W
Englewood Cliffs, NJ 07632

The best ones submitted will appear in the next edition (along with credit to the problem poser).

CUMULATIVE REVIEW FOR CHAPTERS 7–11

1. ■ **What Does This Say?**   In your own words, outline a procedure for integrating a given function.

2. ■ **What Does This Say?**   In your own words, outline a procedure for deciding if a given series converges or diverges.

3. ■ **What Does This Say?**   What is a quadric surface? In your own words, discuss classifying and sketching quadric surfaces.

4. ■ **What Does This Say?**   What is a vector? What is a vector function? In your own words, discuss what is

meant by vector calculus.

5. If $y = x \cosh^{-1} x$, find y'.

6. If $x \sinh^{-1} y + y \tanh^{-1} x = 0$, find $\dfrac{dy}{dx}$.

Find the integrals in Problems 7–15.

7. $\displaystyle\int x \ln \sqrt[3]{x}\, dx$ **8.** $\displaystyle\int \sin^2 x \cos^3 x\, dx$

9. $\displaystyle\int \tan^2 x \sec x\, dx$ **10.** $\displaystyle\int x\sqrt{16 - x}\, dx$

11. $\displaystyle\int \dfrac{\cosh x\, dx}{1 + \sinh^2 x}$ **12.** $\displaystyle\int \dfrac{dx}{1 + \cos x}$

13. $\displaystyle\int \dfrac{dx}{x^2(x^2 + 5)}$ **14.** $\displaystyle\int \dfrac{dx}{\sqrt{x} - \sqrt[3]{x}}$ **15.** $\displaystyle\int \dfrac{dx}{\sqrt{2x - x^2}}$

Find the equation of the line or plane satisfying the conditions given in Problems 16–18.

16. The line through $(-1, 2, 5)$ and perpendicular to the plane $2x - 3y + z = 11$.

17. The plane passing through $(5, 1, 2)$, $(3, 1, -2)$, and $(3, 2, 5)$.

18. The plane that passes through $(-2, -1, 4)$ and perpendicular to the line
$$\frac{x}{2} = \frac{y + 1}{5} = \frac{3 - z}{2}$$

Test the series in Problems 19–25 for convergence.

19. $\displaystyle\sum_{k=0}^{\infty} \dfrac{k^3}{k^4 + 2}$ **20.** $\displaystyle\sum_{k=1}^{\infty} \dfrac{1}{k \cdot 4^k}$

21. $\displaystyle\sum_{k=2}^{\infty} \dfrac{1}{k \ln k}$ **22.** $\displaystyle\sum_{k=0}^{\infty} \dfrac{3k^2 - 7k + 2}{(2k - 1)(k + 3)}$

23. $\displaystyle\sum_{k=1}^{\infty} \dfrac{k!}{2^k \cdot k}$ **24.** $\displaystyle\sum_{k=0}^{\infty} \dfrac{(-1)^{k+1} k}{k^2 + k - 1}$

25. $1 + \frac{1}{8} - \frac{1}{27} - \frac{1}{64} + \frac{1}{125} + \frac{1}{216} - - + + \cdots$

26. In each case, find the sum of the convergent series

   a. $\displaystyle\sum_{k=1}^{\infty} \dfrac{2^{k-1}}{5^{k+3}}$ **b.** $\displaystyle\sum_{k=1}^{\infty} \dfrac{1}{(3k - 1)(3k + 2)}$

27. In each case, determine whether the given improper integral converges, and if it does, find its value.

   a. $\displaystyle\int_{1}^{\infty} x^2 e^{-x}\, dx$ **b.** $\displaystyle\int_{0}^{2} \dfrac{dx}{\sqrt{4 - x^2}}$

28. Find $\mathbf{v} \cdot \mathbf{w}$ and $\mathbf{v} \times \mathbf{w}$ for the vectors $\mathbf{v} = 3\mathbf{i} - 2\mathbf{j} + 5\mathbf{k}$ and $\mathbf{w} = \mathbf{i} - 3\mathbf{j} - \mathbf{k}$.

29. Find $\mathbf{F}'$ and $\mathbf{F}''$ for $\mathbf{F}(t) = 2t\mathbf{i} + e^{-3t}\mathbf{j} + t^4\mathbf{k}$.

30. Find $\displaystyle\int [e^t\mathbf{i} - \mathbf{j} - t\mathbf{k}] \cdot [e^{-t}\mathbf{i} + t\mathbf{j} - \mathbf{k}]\, dt$.

31. Find $\mathbf{T}$ and $\mathbf{N}$ for
$\mathbf{R}(t) = 2(\sin 2t)\mathbf{i} + (2 + 2\cos 2t)\mathbf{j} + 6t\mathbf{k}$.

32. Show that the alternating series
$$S = \sum_{k=1}^{\infty} \frac{(-1)^{k+1}}{\sqrt{k}}$$
converges and determine what N must be to guarantee

that the partial sum
$$S_N = \sum_{k=1}^{N} \frac{(-1)^{k+1}}{\sqrt{k}}$$
approximates the entire sum S with 4-decimal-place accuracy.

33. a. Find the Maclaurin series representation for $f(x) = x^2 e^{-x^2}$.

   b. Use the representation in **a** to approximate
$$\int_0^1 x^2 e^{-x^2}\, dx$$
with 3-decimal-place accuracy.

34. Solve the first-order linear differential equation
$$\frac{dy}{dx} + 2y = x^2$$
subject to the condition $y = 2$ when $x = 0$.

35. Sketch the given polar curves.

   a. $2r = 2 - \sin \theta$ **b.** $r = \dfrac{9}{2 + 2\cos \theta}$

36. Find the area of the region inside the circle $r = 4$ and to the right of the line $r = 2 \sec \theta$.

37. Find an equation in terms of x and y for the line tangent to the curve given by
$$x = t^2 - 2t - 1, \; y = t^4 - 4t^2 + 2$$
at the point $(-1, 2)$.

38. A particle moves in space with position vector
$$\mathbf{R}(t) = (\sin t)\mathbf{i} - (\cos t)\mathbf{j} + \mathbf{k}$$

   a. Find the velocity and acceleration vectors for the particle and find its speed.

   b. Find the Cartesian equation for the particle's trajectory.

   c. Find the curvature κ and the tangential and normal components of acceleration for the particle's motion.

39. At what speed must a satellite travel in order to maintain a circular orbit 1,000 mi above the surface of the earth? Assume earth is a sphere of radius 4,000 mi and that GM in Newton's law of universal gravitation is approximately 9.56×10^4 mi³/s².

40. A calculus textbook (other than the one you are presently reading) is hurled downward from the top of a 120-ft-high building at an angle of 30° with the horizontal. Assuming the initial speed of the book is 8 ft/s, how far from the base of the building will the textbook land?

12

Partial Differentiation

PREVIEW

The goal of this chapter is to extend the methods of single-variable differential calculus to functions of several variables. The vector methods developed in Chapters 10 and 11 play an important role in our work. Indeed, we shall find that the closest analog of the single variable derivative in higher dimensions is the vector function called the *gradient*, which will be used, among other things, to find tangent planes to surfaces in space. We conclude this chapter by solving rate and optimization problems involving functions of several variables.

PERSPECTIVE

In many practical situations, the value of one quantity may depend on the values of two or more others. For example, the amount of water in a reservoir may depend on the amount of rainfall and on the amount of water consumed by local residents. The current in an electrical circuit may vary with the electromotive force, the capacitance, the resistance, and the impedance in the circuit. The flow of blood from an artery into a small capillary may depend on the diameter of the capillary and the pressure in both the artery and the capillary. The output of a factory may depend on the amount of capital invested in the plant and on the size of the labor force. We will analyze such situations using functions of several variables. Graphs will play an especially important role in our work. For instance, the computer graphics of Mt. St. Helens shown here was created by considering a function of two variables.

Mount St. Helens, Washington

Before May 18, 1980

After May 18, 1980

12.1 FUNCTIONS OF SEVERAL VARIABLES

> **IN THIS SECTION** Basic concepts, level curves and surfaces, the graph of a function of two variables
> The basic terminology for functions of several variables is introduced, along with the notion of level curves and surfaces. We also examine various methods for sketching graphs of functions of two variables.

In the real world, physical quantities often depend on two or more variables (see the Perspective box at the beginning of this chapter). For example, we might be concerned with the temperature on a metal plate at various points at time t. Locations on the plate are designated as ordered pairs (x, y), so that the temperature T can be considered as a function of two location variables, x and y, as well as a time variable, t. Extending the notation for a function of a single variable, we might write this as $T(x, y, t)$. We begin our study of functions of several variables by examining this notation and a few other basic concepts.

■ BASIC CONCEPTS

We begin our investigation of functions of several variables by introducing notation and terminology and examining a few basic concepts.

Function of Two Variables

> A **function of two variables** is a rule that assigns to each ordered pair (x, y) in a set D a unique number $f(x, y)$. The set D is called the **domain** of the function, and the corresponding values of $f(x, y)$ constitute the **range** of f.

Functions of three or more variables can be defined in a similar fashion. For simplicity, we shall focus most of our attention on functions of two or three variables.

When dealing with a function of two variables f, we may write $z = f(x, y)$ and refer to x and y as the **independent variables** and to z as the **dependent variable**. Often, the functional "rule" will be given as a formula, and unless otherwise stated, *we shall assume that the domain is the largest set of points in the plane (or in space) for which the functional formula is defined.* These definitions and conventions are illustrated in Example 1 for a function of two variables.

⊘ Note the convention in this book for the domain of a function of two variables. ⊘

EXAMPLE 1 Evaluating a function of two variables and finding the domain and range

Let $f(x, y) = \sqrt{1 - x + y}$.

a. Evaluate $f(2, 1)$, $f(-4, 3)$, and $f(2t, t^2)$.

b. Describe the domain and range of f.

Solution **a.** $f(2, 1) = \sqrt{1 - 2 + 1} = 0$
$$f(-4, 3) = \sqrt{1 - (-4) + 3} = \sqrt{8} = 2\sqrt{2}$$
$$f(2t, t^2) = \sqrt{1 - (2t) + (t^2)} = \sqrt{(t - 1)^2} = |t - 1|$$

b. The domain of f is the set of all ordered pairs (x, y) for which $\sqrt{1 - x + y}$ is defined. We must have $1 - x + y \geq 0$, or, equivalently, $y \geq x - 1$, in order for the square root to be defined. Thus, the domain of f is the shaded set shown in Figure 12.1.

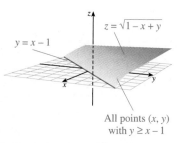

a. Graph of domain in $\mathbb{R}^2$. This is the way the graph looks in two dimensions.

b. Graph of domain in $\mathbb{R}^3$. Notice that the xy-plane is now a horizontal plane.

Figure 12.1 The domain of $f(x, y) = \sqrt{1 - x + y}$

Because $z = f(x, y) = \sqrt{1 - x + y}$, we see that z must be nonnegative, and the range of f is all $z \geq 0$ (because square roots are nonnegative). ▬

Functions of several variables can be combined just like functions of a single variable.

Operations with Functions of Two Variables

If $f(x, y)$ and $g(x, y)$ are functions of two variables with domain D, then

Sum	$(f + g)(x, y) = f(x, y) + g(x, y)$
Difference	$(f - g)(x, y) = f(x, y) - g(x, y)$
Product	$(fg)(x, y) = f(x, y)g(x, y)$
Quotient	$\left(\dfrac{f}{g}\right)(x, y) = \dfrac{f(x, y)}{g(x, y)} \qquad g(x, y) \neq 0$

A **polynomial function in x and y** is the sum of functions of the form

$$Cx^m y^n$$

with nonnegative integers m and n; for instance,

$$3x^5 y^3 - 7x^2 y + 2x - 3y + 11$$

is a polynomial in x and y. A **rational function** is a quotient of two polynomial functions. Similar notation and terminology apply to functions of three or more variables.

■ LEVEL CURVES AND SURFACES

By analogy with the single-variable case, we define the **graph of the function $f(x, y)$** to be the collection of all 3-tuples (ordered triplets) (x, y, z) such that (x, y) is in the domain of f and $z = f(x, y)$. The graph of $f(x, y)$ is a surface in $\mathbb{R}^3$ whose projection onto the xy-plane is the domain D.

It is usually not easy to sketch the graph of a function of two variables. One way to proceed is illustrated in Figure 12.2.

Figure 12.2 Graph of a function of two variables. Computer programs for three-dimensional sketching are common; see the *Technology Manual*.

Notice that when the plane $z = C$ intersects the surface $z = f(x, y)$, the result is the space curve with the equation $f(x, y) = C$. Such an intersection is called the **trace** of the graph of f in the plane $z = C$. The set of points (x, y) in the xy-plane that satisfy $f(x, y) = C$ is called the **level curve** of f at C, and an entire family of level curves (or **contour curves**) is generated as C varies over the range of f. We can think of a level curve as a "slice" of the surface at a particular location. By sketching members of this family on the xy-plane, we obtain a useful topographical map of the surface $z = f(x, y)$.

For instance, imagine that the surface $z = f(x, y)$ is a "mountain," and further assume that we wish to draw a two-dimensional "graph" of the mountain. To draw such a graph, we indicate the paths of constant elevation by sketching the family of level curves in the plane and pinning a "flag" to each curve to show the elevation to which it corresponds, as shown in Figure 12.3b. Notice that regions in the map

a. The surface $z = f(x, y)$ as a mountain

b. Level curves yield a topographic map of $z = f(x, y)$.

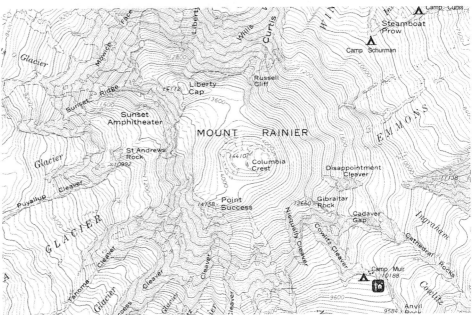

c.

Figure 12.3 Level curves of a surface

where paths are crowded together correspond to the steeper portions of the mountain. An actual topographic map of Mount Rainier is shown in Figure 12.3c.

You probably have seen level curves on the weather report in the newspaper or on the evening news, where level curves of equal temperature are called **isotherms.** Other common uses of level curves involve curves of equal pressure (called **isobars**) or curves of equal electric potential (called **equipotential lines**). See Figure 12.4.

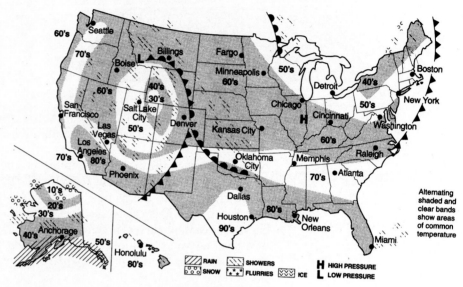

Figure 12.4 Isotherms

EXAMPLE 2   Level curves

Sketch some level curves of the function $f(x, y) = xy$.

Solution   The level curves have the form $xy = C$ for constant C. For $C \neq 0$, these curves are hyperbolas of the form $y = C/x$, and for $C = 0$ the level curves are the coordinate axes, as shown in Figure 12.5.

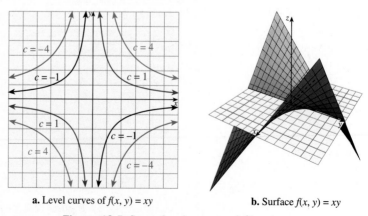

a. Level curves of $f(x, y) = xy$ **b.** Surface $f(x, y) = xy$

Figure 12.5 Some level curves of $f(x, y) = xy$

■ THE GRAPH OF A FUNCTION OF TWO VARIABLES

The level curves of a function $f(x, y)$ provide information about the cross sections of the surface $z = f(x, y)$ perpendicular to the z-axis. However, a more complete picture of the surface can often be obtained by examining the cross sections in other directions as well. This procedure is used to graph a function in Example 3.

EXAMPLE 3   Level curves

Discuss the level curves of the function $f(x, y) = x^2 + y^2$ and sketch the graph of f.

Solution   If C is a real number, the level curve $f(x, y) = C$ has the equation $x^2 + y^2 = C$, and it follows that $C \geq 0$, because $x^2 + y^2 \geq 0$ for all x and y. The level curve $x^2 + y^2 = 0$ (that is, $C = 0$) is the point $(0, 0)$, and for $C > 0$, the level curve $x^2 + y^2 = C$ is the circle with center $(0, 0)$ and radius $\sqrt{C}$ (Figure 12.6a).

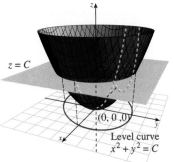

a. Level curves of $f(x, y) = x^2 + y^2$ are circles of the form $x^2 + y^2 = C$.

b. The surface $z = x^2 + y^2$. Cross sections perpendicular to the x- and y-axes shown in green are parabolas.

Figure 12.6 The graph of the function $f(x, y) = x^2 + y^2$

We can gain additional information about the appearance of the surface by examining cross sections perpendicular to the other two principal directions. Cross-sectional planes perpendicular to the x-axis have the form $x = A$ and intersect the surface $z = x^2 + y^2$ in parabolas of the form $z = A^2 + y^2$, $x = A$. Similarly, cross-sectional planes perpendicular to the y-axis have the form $y = B$ and intersect the surface in parabolas of the form $z = x^2 + B^2$, $y = B$.

To summarize, the surface $z = x^2 + y^2$ has cross sections that are circular in planes perpendicular to the z-axis and parabolic in the other two principal directions. For this reason, the surface is called a **circular paraboloid** or a **paraboloid of revolution**. The graph of the surface is shown in Figure 12.6b. ■

The concept of level curve can be generalized to apply to functions of more than two variables. In particular, if f is a function of the n variables $x_1, x_2, \ldots, x_n$ and C is a number in the range of f, then the solution set of the equation $f(x_1, x_2, \ldots, x_n) = C$ is a region of n-space called the **level surface** of f at C. The level surfaces of a function of three variables are surfaces in $\mathbb{R}^3$ and can provide some insight into the nature of the function, but level surfaces of functions of four or more variables are very difficult to visualize.

DRAWING LESSON 5: SKETCHING SURFACES WITH LEVEL CURVES

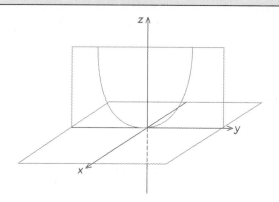

a. Draw the three coordinate axes and the *xy*-plane. Draw a trace of the surface in the *yz*-plane.

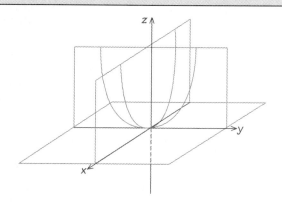

b. Draw a trace of the surface in the *xz*-plane.

c. Draw a trace in the plane *z* = constant. Drop dashed segment from the intercepts of this trace down to the *xy*-plane. Then draw the level curve in the *xy*-plane. Finish outlining the surface.

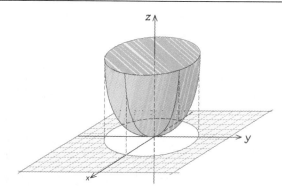

d. Lightly erase all planes except the *xy*-plane. Use highlighters or colored pencils to shade the surface.

EXAMPLE 4   Isothermal surface

Suppose a region of R is heated so that its temperature T at each point (x, y, z) is given by $T(x, y, z) = 100 - x^2 - y^2 - z^2$ degrees Celsius. Describe the isothermal surfaces for $T > 0$.

Solution   The isothermal surfaces are given by $T(x, y, z) = k$ for constant k, $k > 0$; that is, $x^2 + y^2 + z^2 = 100 - k$. If $100 - k > 0$, the graph of

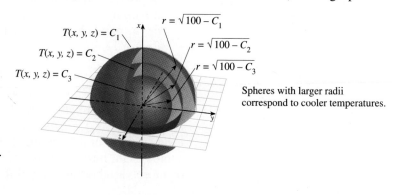

Spheres with larger radii correspond to cooler temperatures.

Figure 12.7 Isothermal surfaces for $T(x, y, z) = 100 - x^2 - y^2 - z^2$

$x^2 + y^2 + z^2 = 100 - k$ is a sphere of radius $\sqrt{100 - k}$ and center $(0, 0, 0)$. When $k = 100$, the graph is a single point (the origin), and $T(0, 0, 0) = 100°C$. As the temperature drops, the constant k gets smaller, and the radius $\sqrt{100 - k}$ of the sphere gets larger. Hence, the isothermal surfaces are spheres, and the larger the radius, the cooler the surface. This situation is illustrated in Figure 12.7. ▬

As you can see by the examples in this section, you will need to recall the graphs of quadric surfaces. It will also help if you can recognize the surface by looking at its equation. What you will need to remember is summarized in Table 10.1, page 644.

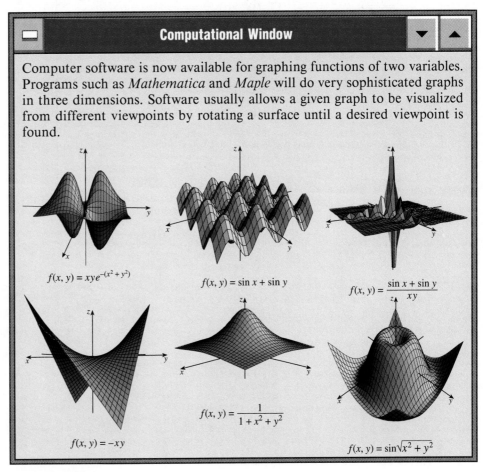

Computational Window

Computer software is now available for graphing functions of two variables. Programs such as *Mathematica* and *Maple* will do very sophisticated graphs in three dimensions. Software usually allows a given graph to be visualized from different viewpoints by rotating a surface until a desired viewpoint is found.

$f(x, y) = xye^{-(x^2 + y^2)}$

$f(x, y) = \sin x + \sin y$

$f(x, y) = \dfrac{\sin x + \sin y}{xy}$

$f(x, y) = -xy$

$f(x, y) = \dfrac{1}{1 + x^2 + y^2}$

$f(x, y) = \sin\sqrt{x^2 + y^2}$

PROBLEM SET 12.1

Ⓐ 1. Let $f(x, y) = x^2y + xy^2$. If t is a real number, find:
   a. $f(0, 0)$ **b.** $f(-1, 0)$ **c.** $f(0, -1)$ **d.** $f(1, 1)$
   e. $f(2, 4)$ **f.** $f(t, t)$ **g.** $f(t, t^2)$ **h.** $f(1 - t, t)$

2. Let $f(x, y) = \left(1 - \dfrac{x}{y}\right)^2$. If t is a nonzero real number, find:

   a. $f(0, 1)$ **b.** $f(5, 5)$ **c.** $f(6, 1)$ **d.** $f(1, 2)$
   e. $f(t, t)$ **f.** $f(5t, t)$ **g.** $f(t, 2t)$ **h.** $f(1 + t, t)$

3. Let $f(x, y, z) = x^2ye^{2x} + (x + y - z)^2$. Find:
   a. $f(0, 0, 0)$ **b.** $f(1, -1, 1)$ **c.** $f(-1, 1, -1)$

   d. $\dfrac{d}{dx} f(x, x, x)$ **e.** $\dfrac{d}{dy} f(1, y, 1)$ **f.** $\dfrac{d}{dz} f(1, 1, z^2)$

4. Let $f(x, y, z) = x \sin y + y \cos z$. Find
   a. $f(0, 0, 0)$ **b.** $f\left(1, \dfrac{\pi}{2}, \pi\right)$ **c.** $f\left(1, \pi, \dfrac{\pi}{2}\right)$
   d. $\dfrac{d}{dx} f(x, x, x)$ **e.** $\dfrac{d}{dx} f(x, 2x, 3x)$ **f.** $\dfrac{d}{dy} f(y, y, 0)$

5. ■ **What Does This Say?** Discuss the notion of a function of two variables. Your discussion should include additional examples of a function of two variables.

6. ■ **What Does This Say?** How do you think that a function of three variables differs from a function of two variables?

7. ■ **What Does This Say?** Discuss level curves and amplify with some examples (different from those in this text).

Find the domain and range for each function given in Problems 8–17.

8. $f(x, y) = \sqrt{x - y}$

9. $f(x, y) = \dfrac{1}{\sqrt{x - y}}$

10. $f(u, v) = \sqrt{uv}$

11. $f(x, y) = \sqrt{\dfrac{y}{x}}$

12. $f(x, y) = \ln(y - x)$

13. $f(u, v) = \sqrt{u} \sin v$

14. $f(x, y) = \sqrt{(x + 3)^2 + (y - 1)^2}$

15. $f(x, y) = e^{(x+1)/(y-2)}$

16. $f(x, y) = \dfrac{1}{\sqrt{x^2 - y^2}}$

17. $f(x, y) = \dfrac{1}{\sqrt{9 - x^2 - y^2}}$

Sketch the level curves of the functions given in Problems 18–23.

18. $f(x, y) = 2x - 3y$

19. $f(x, y) = x^2 - y^2$

20. $f(x, y) = x^3 - y$

21. $g(x, y) = x^2 - y$

22. $h(u, v) = u^2 + \dfrac{v^2}{4}$

23. $f(x, t) = \dfrac{x}{t}$

In Problems 24–29, sketch the level surface f(x, y, z) = C for the given value of C.

24. $f(x, y, z) = y^2 + z^2$ for $C = 1$

25. $f(x, y, z) = x^2 + z^2$ for $C = 1$

26. $f(x, y, z) = x + y - z$ for $C = 1$

27. $f(x, y, z) = x + y - z$ for $C = 0$

28. $f(x, y, z) = (x + 1)^2 + (y - 2)^2 + (z - 3)^2$ for $C = 4$

29. $f(x, y, z) = 2x^2 + 2y^2 - z$ for $C = 1$

In Problems 30–37, describe the traces of the given quadric surface. You might wish to review Section 10.2 (page 644). Sketch the graph of the quadric and identify it.

30. $9x^2 + 4y^2 + z^2 = 1$

31. $\dfrac{x^2}{4} + y^2 + \dfrac{z^2}{9} = 1$

32. $\dfrac{x^2}{4} + \dfrac{y^2}{9} - z^2 = 1$

33. $\dfrac{x^2}{9} - y^2 - z^2 = 1$

34. $z = x^2 + \dfrac{y^2}{4}$

35. $z = \dfrac{x^2}{9} - \dfrac{y^2}{16}$

36. $x^2 + 2y^2 = 9z^2$

37. $z^2 = 1 + \dfrac{x^2}{9} + \dfrac{y^2}{4}$

Match each level curve given in Problems 38–43 with one of the surfaces labeled A–F.

38. $f(x, y) = x^2 - y^2$

39. $f(x, y) = e^{1 - x^2 - y^2}$

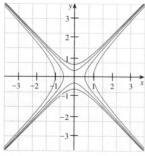

40. $f(x, y) = \dfrac{1}{x^2 + y^2}$

41. $f(x, y) = \sin\left(\dfrac{x^2 + y^2}{2}\right)$

42. $f(x, y) = \dfrac{\cos xy}{x^2 + y^2}$

43. $f(x, y) = \sin\sqrt{x^2 + y^2}$

A.

B.

C.

D.

E.

F.

B *Sketch the graph of each function given in Problems 44–55.*

44. $f(x, y) = -4$

45. $f(x, y) = x$

46. $f(x, y) = y^2 + 1$

47. $f(x, y) = x^3 - 1$

48. $f(x, y) = 2x - 3y$

49. $f(x, y) = x^2 - y$

50. $f(x, y) = 2x^2 + y^2$

51. $f(x, y) = x^2 - y^2$

52. $f(x, y) = \dfrac{x}{y}$

53. $f(x, y) = \sqrt{x + y}$

54. $f(x, y) = x^2 + y^2 + 2$

55. $f(x, y) = \sqrt{1 - x^2 - y^2}$

56. In physics, the *lens equation* states

$$\frac{1}{d_0} + \frac{1}{d_i} = \frac{1}{L}$$

where d_0 is the distance of an object from a thin, spherical lens, d_i is the distance of its image on the other side of the lens, and L is the *focal length* of the lens. Describe the level curves for the constant focal length.

57. The EZGRO agricultural company estimates that when $100x$ worker-hours of labor are employed on y acres of land, the number of bushels of wheat produced is $f(x, y) = Ax^a y^b$, where A, a, and b are nonnegative constants. Suppose the company decides to double the production factors x and y. Determine how this decision affects the production of wheat in each of these cases:

a. $a + b > 1$ **b.** $a + b < 1$ **c.** $a + b = 1$

58. Suppose that when x machines and y worker-hours are used each day, a certain factory will produce $Q(x, y) = 10xy$ mobile phones. Describe the relationship between the "inputs" x and y that result in an "output" of 1,000 phones each day. *Note*: You are finding a level curve of the production function Q.

59. At a certain factory, the daily output is $Q = CK^r L^{1-r}$ units, where K denotes capital investment, L is the size of the labor force, and C and r are constants, with $0 < r < 1$ (this is called a *Cobb-Douglas production function*). What happens to Q if K and L are both doubled? What if both are tripled?

60. Sketch the graph of $f(x, y) = xy$ in the first octant (x, y, and z are all positive).

61. The ideal gas law says that $PV = kT$, where P is the pressure of a confined gas, V is its volume, T is its temperature (Kelvin), and k is a constant. Express P as a function of V and T and describe the level curves of this function.

62. A publishing house has found that in a certain city each of its salespeople will sell approximately

$$\frac{r^2}{2,000p} + \frac{s^2}{100} - s$$

units per month, where s denotes the total number of salespeople employed, p is the price per unit, and r is the amount of money spent each month on local advertising. Express the total revenue P as a function of p, r, and s.

63. A manufacturer with exclusive rights to a sophisticated new industrial machine is planning to sell a limited number of the machines to both foreign and domestic firms. The price the manufacturer can expect to receive for the machines will depend on the number of machines made available. It is estimated that if the manufacturer supplies x machines to the domestic market and y machines to the foreign market, the machines will sell for

$$60 - \frac{x}{5} + \frac{y}{20}$$

thousand dollars apiece at home and

$$50 - \frac{x}{10} + \frac{y}{20}$$

thousand dollars apiece abroad. Express the revenue P as a function of x and y.

12.2 LIMITS AND CONTINUITY

IN THIS SECTION Limit of a function of two variables, properties of limits, continuity, formal definition of limit

As in the single-variable case, the concept of limit plays a fundamental role in the calculus of functions of several variables. In this section we define the limit of a function of two variables and examine some of its properties. We shall also consider what it means for such a function to be continuous. Our focus will be on functions of two variables, but the notions discussed also apply to functions of three or more variables. We will include some functions of three or more variables in some of the exercises.

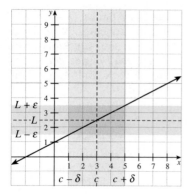

Figure 12.8 $\lim_{x \to 3}\left(\frac{1}{2}x + 1\right)$, where $\varepsilon = 1$

Find a δ-interval such that $\frac{1}{2}x + 1$ is close to $L = 2.5$ whenever x is in the δ-interval.

a. A punctured disk

Circle with radius δ and with deleted center (x_0, y_0)

b. $\lim_{(x, y)\to(x_0, y_0)} f(x, y) = L$

Figure 12.9 Limit of a function of two variables

■ LIMIT OF A FUNCTION OF TWO VARIABLES

For functions of a single variable (in two dimensions) we first discussed the intuitive notion of a limit and *then* stated the formal definition of a limit. We will do the same in this section.

Recall from Chapter 1 that the limit of a function of a single variable requires that we find a δ-interval on the x-axis ($\delta > 0$) that forces the function to be within an ε-interval of some value, called the limit. In particular, the limit statement

$$\lim_{x \to c} f(x) = L$$

means that the functional values of $f(x)$ can be made arbitrarily close to L by choosing x sufficiently close to c but not equal to c. That is, to force f to be within an ε-interval of L on the y-axis, we must choose x within some δ-interval on the x-axis (see Figure 12.8).

For a function of two variables, the situation is similar but the domain has two dimensions. Instead of a δ-interval around c on the x-axis we consider a **δ-neighborhood** about a point (x_0, y_0) in the plane. This neighborhood is the interior of a circle centered at (x_0, y_0) with radius $\delta > 0$; that is,

All points (x, y) satisfying $\sqrt{(x - x_0)^2 + (y - y_0)^2} < \delta$

This neighborhood (the circle and its interior) is **open** if we use $<$ and **closed** if we use $\leq$. The neighborhood is called a **disk**. A **punctured disk** is a disk whose center (x_0, y_0) has been excluded. This disk in the xy-plane is shown in Figure 12.9a. We will now give an informal definition of a limit of a function of two variables.

Limit of a Function of Two Variables (Informal Definition)

The notation

$$\lim_{(x, y)\to(x_0, y_0)} f(x, y) = L$$

means that the functional values $f(x, y)$ can be made arbitrarily close to L by choosing a point (x, y) sufficiently close (but not equal) to the point (x_0, y_0).

We need to determine what we mean by "arbitrarily close." Given some $\varepsilon > 0$, we wish to find a $\delta > 0$ so that for any point (x, y) in the punctured disk of radius δ centered at (x_0, y_0), the functional value $f(x, y)$ lies between $L + \varepsilon$ and $L - \varepsilon$. This is illustrated in Figure 12.9b.

When considering the limit of a function of a single variable we need to examine (or test) the approach of x to c from two directions (the left- and right-hand limits). However, for a function of two variables, we write $(x, y) \to (x_0, y_0)$ to mean that the point (x, y) is allowed to approach (x_0, y_0) along any curve that passes through (x_0, y_0). If the value of

$$\lim_{(x, y) \to (x_0, y_0)} f(x, y)$$

is not the same for *all* approaches, or **paths,** then *the limit does not exist.*

EXAMPLE 1   Limit of a function of two variables

a. Show

$$\lim_{(x, y)\to(0, 0)} \frac{2xy}{x^2 + y^2}$$

does not exist by evaluating this limit along the x-axis ($y = 0$), the y-axis ($x = 0$), and along the line $y = x$ and noting that these values are not the same.

b. Evaluate

$$\lim_{(x,\,y)\to(1,\,2)} 2xy$$

along the paths $y = 2$, $x = 1$, and $y = 2x$, and show that these values are all the same.

Solution **a.** First note that the denominator is zero at $(0, 0)$ so $f(0, 0)$ is not defined. If we approach the origin along the x-axis (where $y = 0$) we find that

$$\frac{2xy}{x^2 + y^2} \to \frac{2x(0)}{x^2 + 0^2} = 0 \quad \text{as} \quad (x, y) \to (0, 0) \qquad \text{along } y = 0 \text{ (and } x \neq 0)$$

We find a similar result if we approach the origin along the y-axis (where $x = 0$); see Figure 12.10. However, along the line $y = x$, the functional values are

$$f(x, y) = f(x, x) = \frac{2x^2}{x^2 + x^2} = 1 \qquad \text{for } x \neq 0$$

so that $\dfrac{2xy}{x^2 + y^2} \to 1 \quad \text{as} \quad (x, y) \to (0, 0) \qquad \text{along } y = x$

Because $f(x, y)$ tends toward different numbers as $(x, y) \to (0, 0)$ from different directions, it follows that f has no limit at the origin.

b. If we approach the point $(1, 2)$ along the line $y = 2$ (see Figure 12.11a), we have

$$2xy = 4x \to 4 \quad \text{as} \quad (x, y) \to (1, 2) \qquad \text{along } y = 2$$

Similarly, along the line $x = 1$ (Figure 12.11b)

$$2xy = 2y \to 4 \quad \text{as} \quad (x, y) \to (1, 2) \qquad \text{along } x = 1$$

Finally, along the line $y = 2x$ (Figure 12.11c)

$$2xy = 2x(2x) = 4x^2 \to 4 \quad \text{as} \quad (x, y) \to (1, 2) \qquad \text{along } y = 2x$$

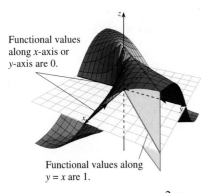

Functional values along x-axis or y-axis are 0.

Functional values along $y = x$ are 1.

Figure 12.10 Graph of $y = \dfrac{2xy}{x^2 + y^2}$ and limits as $(x, y) \to (0, 0)$

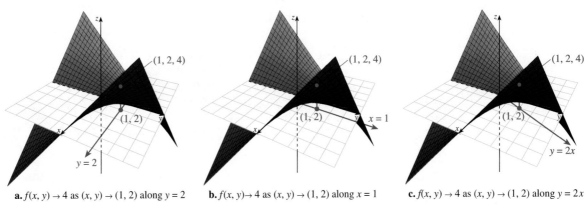

a. $f(x, y) \to 4$ as $(x, y) \to (1, 2)$ along $y = 2$ **b.** $f(x, y) \to 4$ as $(x, y) \to (1, 2)$ along $x = 1$ **c.** $f(x, y) \to 4$ as $(x, y) \to (1, 2)$ along $y = 2x$

Figure 12.11 Graph of $y = 2xy$

⊘ As in Example 1a, the two-path procedure is enough to show that a *limit does NOT exist*. However, just showing that the limits along different paths in Example 1b are the same is not enough to conclude that a limit *DOES exist*, because we have not evaluated the limit along *every* pathway. ⊘

■ PROPERTIES OF LIMITS

The various rules for manipulating limits of a function of one variable all have counterparts for limits of two variables.

Basic Formulas and Rules for Limits of a Function of Two Variables

Suppose that $\lim\limits_{(x,\,y)\to(x_0,\,y_0)} f(x,\,y) = L$ and $\lim\limits_{(x,\,y)\to(x_0,\,y_0)} g(x,\,y) = M$, Then

Scalar multiple rule

$$\lim\limits_{(x,\,y)\to(x_0,\,y_0)} [af](x,\,y) = aL \text{ for constant } a$$

Sum rule

$$\lim\limits_{(x,\,y)\to(x_0,\,y_0)} [f+g](x,\,y) = \left[\lim\limits_{(x,\,y)\to(x_0,\,y_0)} f(x,\,y)\right] + \left[\lim\limits_{(x,\,y)\to(x_0,\,y_0)} g(x,\,y)\right] = L + M$$

Product rule

$$\lim\limits_{(x,\,y)\to(x_0,\,y_0)} [fg](x,\,y) = \left[\lim\limits_{(x,\,y)\to(x_0,\,y_0)} f(x,\,y)\right]\left[\lim\limits_{(x,\,y)\to(x_0,\,y_0)} g(x,\,y)\right] = LM$$

Quotient rule

$$\lim\limits_{(x,\,y)\to(x_0,\,y_0)} \left[\frac{f}{g}\right](x,\,y) = \frac{\lim\limits_{(x,\,y)\to(x_0,\,y_0)} f(x,\,y)}{\lim\limits_{(x,\,y)\to(x_0,\,y_0)} g(x,\,y)} = \frac{L}{M} \quad \text{if } M \neq 0$$

EXAMPLE 2   Finding limits using properties of limits

Assuming each limit exists, evaluate:

a. $\lim\limits_{(x,\,y)\to(3,\,-4)} (x^2 + xy + y^2)$ **b.** $\lim\limits_{(x,\,y)\to(1,\,2)} \dfrac{2xy}{x^2 + y^2}$

Solution   a. $\lim\limits_{(x,\,y)\to(3,\,-4)} (x^2 + xy + y^2) = (3)^2 + (3)(-4) + (-4)^2 = 13$

A graph is shown in Figure 12.12a.

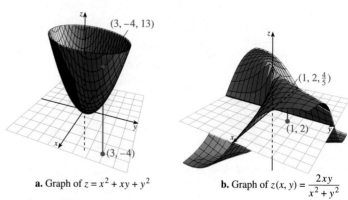

a. Graph of $z = x^2 + xy + y^2$ **b.** Graph of $z(x,\,y) = \dfrac{2xy}{x^2 + y^2}$

Figure 12.12 Graphs showing limits

b. $\lim\limits_{(x,\,y)\to(1,\,2)} \dfrac{2xy}{x^2 + y^2} = \dfrac{\lim\limits_{(x,\,y)\to(1,\,2)} 2xy}{\lim\limits_{(x,\,y)\to(1,\,2)} (x^2 + y^2)} = \dfrac{2(1)(2)}{1^2 + 2^2} = \dfrac{4}{5}$

The graph is shown in Figure 12.12b.

Historical Note

MARY FAIRFAX SOMERVILLE
(1780–1872)

Mary Somerville's life was devoted to popularizing science and mathematics, and during her long life she wrote several textbooks. Somerville College was named after her in recognition of her contributions to science. She did not study mathematics seriously until she was 27, and she purchased her first mathematics books when she was 30. The reason for her late start was due to the early influence of males in her life. She received no education and taught herself reading, writing, arithmetic, and Latin. At the age of fourteen she saw an algebra problem in a fashion magazine and asked her brother's tutor to let her see an algebra book. Her father, however, opposed this study and refused her the opportunity. Likewise, she married a man who also opposed the education of women, and it was not until her husband's death in 1807 that she became financially independent and able to begin her study of mathematics. She went on to a distinguished career and received a Victoria gold medal in 1869. Also, she was one of the first two women elected honorary members of the Royal Astronomical Society.

■ CONTINUITY

Recall the definition of continuity for a function of a single variable: f is continuous at $x = c$ if

1. $f(c)$ is defined   **2.** $\lim\limits_{x \to c} f(x)$ exists   **3.** $\lim\limits_{x \to c} f(x) = f(c)$.

Using the definition of the limit of a function of two variables, we can now define the continuity of a function of two variables in an analogous fashion.

Continuity of a Function of Two Variables

The function $f(x, y)$ is **continuous** at the point (x_0, y_0) if and only if

1. $f(x_0, y_0)$ is defined

2. $\lim\limits_{(x, y) \to (x_0, y_0)} f(x, y)$ exists

3. $\lim\limits_{(x, y) \to (x_0, y_0)} f(x, y) = f(x_0, y_0)$.

Also, f is **continuous on a set** S in its domain if it is continuous at each point in S.

■ *What this says:* The function f is continuous at (x_0, y_0) if the functional value of $f(x, y)$ is close to $f(x_0, y_0)$ whenever (x, y) is sufficiently close to (x_0, y_0). Geometrically, this means that f is continuous if the surface $z = f(x, y)$ has no "gaps" or "holes."

a. $f(x, y) = \dfrac{x - y}{x^2 + y^2}$
is discontinuous at $(0, 0)$; a hole

b. $f(x, y) = \dfrac{1}{y - x^2}$
is discontinuous on the parabola $y = x^2$; a gap

EXAMPLE 3 Testing for continuity

Test the continuity of the functions whose graphs are shown here, namely,

a. $f(x, y) = \dfrac{x - y}{x^2 + y^2}$ **b.** $f(x, y) = \dfrac{1}{y - x^2}$

Solution **a.** Because $x - y$ and $x^2 + y^2$ are both polynomial functions in x and y, f is a rational function and the only place where it might not be continuous is when the denominator is zero. Because $x^2 + y^2 = 0$ only when both x and y are 0, the only possible point of discontinuity is at $(0, 0)$. Because $f(0, 0)$ is not defined, we see f is discontinuous at $(0, 0)$.

b. Once again we need to check when the denominator is 0:

$$y - x^2 = 0 \quad \text{when} \quad y = x^2$$

We can, therefore, conclude that the function is continuous at all points except those lying on the parabola $y = x^2$. ▬

The basic properties of limits can be used to show that if f and g are both continuous on the set S, then so are the sum $f + g$, the multiple af, the product fg, the quotient f/g (whenever $g \neq 0$), and the root $\sqrt[n]{f}$ wherever it is defined. Also, if F is a continuous function of two variables at (x_0, y_0) and G is a function of one variable that is continuous at $F(x_0, y_0)$, it can be shown that the composite function $G \circ F$ is continuous at (x_0, y_0).

Many common functions of two variables are continuous wherever they are defined. For instance, a polynomial in two variables, such as $x^3 y^2 + 3xy^3 - 7x + 2$, is continuous throughout the plane, and a rational function in two variables is continuous wherever the denominator polynomial is not zero. In this text all of the "standard" functions of two or more variables are continuous over their domains.

a. P_0 is an interior point.

■ FORMAL DEFINITION OF LIMIT*

Next, we examine a formal ε-δ definition of limit. The informal definition of limit we have given is sufficient for our purposes in this course, but many advanced applications require precise definitions.

A point $P_0(x_0, y_0)$ is said to be an **interior point** of a set S in the plane if some open disk centered at P_0 is contained entirely within S, as shown in Figure 12.13a. If S is the empty set or if every point of S is an interior point, then S is an **open set.** The point P_0 is called a **boundary point** of S if every open disk centered at P_0 contains both points that belong to S and points that do not (see Figure 12.13b.) The collection of all boundary points of S is called the **boundary of S.** Finally, the set S is said to be **closed** if it contains its boundary—that is, if every boundary point of S is also a point in S (see Figure 12.14). If S has no boundary points, then it automatically contains "all of them" (because there aren't any) and is therefore closed. Finally, a two-dimensional set S is said to be **bounded** if it can be enclosed in a circle (or a rectangle), as shown in Figure 12.13c.

b. P_0 is a boundary point.

c. S is bounded.

Figure 12.13 Topology of the plane

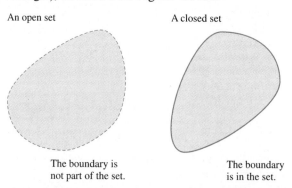

An open set   A closed set

The boundary is   The boundary
not part of the set.   is in the set.

Figure 12.14 Open and closed sets in the plane

We now turn to a formal definition of limit of a function of two variables.

*The material of this section is not required for subsequent topics.

Limit of a Function of Two Variables (Formal Definition)

Suppose $f(x, y)$ is a function defined everywhere on an open disk centered at the point $P_0(x_0, y_0)$ except possibly at P_0 itself. Then the number L is the **limit of f at P** if for every $\varepsilon > 0$ there exists a $\delta > 0$ such that

$$|f(x, y) - L| < \varepsilon \quad \text{whenever} \quad 0 < \sqrt{(x - x_0)^2 + (y - y_0)^2} < \delta$$

In this case, we write

$$\lim_{(x, y) \to (x_0, y_0)} f(x, y) = L$$

■ *What this says:* If L is the limit of f at $P_0(x_0, y_0)$, then for each point $P(x, y)$ in the punctured disk of radius δ centered at P_0, the number $f(x, y)$ lies between $L - \varepsilon$ and $L + \varepsilon$.

EXAMPLE 4   Continuity using the limit definition

Show that f is continuous at $(0, 0)$, where

$$f(x, y) = \begin{cases} y \sin \dfrac{1}{x} & x \neq 0 \\ 0 & x = 0 \end{cases}$$

Solution   The graph is shown in Figure 12.15. It appears to be continuous. In order to prove this, we must show that for any $\varepsilon > 0$, there exists a $\delta > 0$ such that

$$|f(x, y) - 0| = \left| y \sin \tfrac{1}{x} \right| < \varepsilon \quad \text{whenever} \quad 0 < x^2 + y^2 < \delta^2$$

(We use $x^2 + y^2$ and δ^2 here instead of $\sqrt{x^2 + y^2}$ and δ for convenience.) Note that $\left| y \sin \tfrac{1}{x} \right| \leq |y|$ for all $x \neq 0$, because $\left| \sin \tfrac{1}{x} \right| \leq 1$ for $x \neq 0$. Let $\delta = \varepsilon$. Then if (x, y) satisfies $x^2 + y^2 < \delta^2 = \varepsilon^2$, we have $|y| < \varepsilon$ so that

$$|f(x, y) - 0| \leq |y| < \delta = \varepsilon \quad \text{whenever} \quad |y| < \delta$$

Front view　　　　　　Side view

Figure 12.15 Graph of the function f in Example 4

PROBLEM SET 12.2

Ⓐ 1. ■ **What Does This Say?**   Describe the notion of a limit of function of two variables.

2. ■ **What Does This Say?**   Describe the basic formulas and rules for limits of a function of two variables.

In Problems 3–20, find the given limit, assuming it exists.

3. $\lim\limits_{(x,\,y)\to(-1,\,0)} (xy^2 + x^3y + 5)$

4. $\lim\limits_{(x,\,y)\to(0,\,0)} (5x^2 - 2xy + y^2 + 3)$

5. $\lim\limits_{(x,\,y)\to(1,\,3)} \dfrac{x+y}{x-y}$

6. $\lim\limits_{(x,\,y)\to(3,\,4)} \dfrac{x-y}{\sqrt{x^2+y^2}}$

7. $\lim\limits_{(x,\,y)\to(1,\,0)} e^{xy}$

8. $\lim\limits_{(x,\,y)\to(1,\,0)} (x+y)e^{xy}$

9. $\lim\limits_{(x,\,y)\to(0,\,1)} [e^{x^2+x}\ln(ey^2)]$

10. $\lim\limits_{(x,\,y)\to(e,\,0)} \ln(x^2+y^2)$

11. $\lim\limits_{(x,\,y)\to(0,\,0)} \dfrac{x^2-2xy+y^2}{x-y}$

12. $\lim\limits_{(x,\,y)\to(1,\,2)} \dfrac{(x^2-1)(y^2-4)}{(x-1)(y-2)}$

13. $\lim\limits_{(x,\,y)\to(0,\,0)} \dfrac{e^x\tan^{-1}y}{y}$

14. $\lim\limits_{(x,\,y)\to(0,\,0)} \dfrac{e^x\tan^{-1}y}{x}$

15. $\lim\limits_{(x,\,y)\to(0,\,0)} \dfrac{\sin(x+y)}{x+y}$

16. $\lim\limits_{(x,\,y)\to(0,\,0)} (\sin x + \cos y)$

17. $\lim\limits_{(x,\,y)\to(5,\,5)} \dfrac{x^4-y^4}{x^2-y^2}$

18. $\lim\limits_{(x,\,y)\to(a,\,a)} \dfrac{x^4-y^4}{x^2-y^2}$; a is a constant.

19. $\lim\limits_{(x,\,y)\to(2,\,1)} \dfrac{x^2-4y^2}{x-2y}$

20. $\lim\limits_{(x,\,y)\to(0,\,0)} \dfrac{x^2+y^2}{\sqrt{x^2+y^2+4}-2}$

In Problems 21–29, evaluate the indicated limit, if it exists.

21. $\lim\limits_{(x,\,y)\to(2,\,1)} (xy^2 + x^3y)$

22. $\lim\limits_{(x,\,y)\to(1,\,2)} (5x^2 - 2xy + y^2)$

23. $\lim\limits_{(x,\,y)\to(0,\,0)} \dfrac{x+y}{x-y}$

24. $\lim\limits_{(x,\,y)\to(0,\,0)} \dfrac{x-y}{\sqrt{x^2+y^2}}$

25. $\lim\limits_{(x,\,y)\to(0,\,0)} e^{xy}$

26. $\lim\limits_{(x,\,y)\to(1,\,1)} (x+y)e^{xy}$

27. $\lim\limits_{(x,\,y)\to(0,\,0)} (\sin x - \cos y)$

28. $\lim\limits_{(x,\,y)\to(0,\,0)} \left[1 - \dfrac{\sin(x^2+y^2)}{x^2+y^2}\right]$

29. $\lim\limits_{(x,\,y)\to(0,\,0)} \dfrac{\sin(x^2+y^2)}{x^2+y^2}$

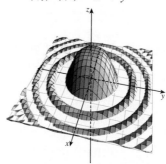

Ⓑ *In Problems 30–33, show that* $\lim\limits_{(x,\,y)\to(0,\,0)} f(x,y)$ *does not exist.*

30. $f(x,y) = \dfrac{x^4y^4}{(x^2+y^4)^3}$

31. $f(x,y) = \dfrac{x-y^2}{x^2+y^2}$

32. $f(x, y) = \dfrac{x^2 + y}{x^2 + y^2}$

33. $f(x, y) = \dfrac{x^2 y^2}{x^4 + y^4}$

34. Let f be the functions defined by

$$f(x, y) = \begin{cases} \dfrac{xy^2}{x^2 + y^4} & \text{for } (x, y) \neq (0, 0) \\ 0 & \text{for } (x, y) = (0, 0) \end{cases}$$

  a. Show that $f(x, y) \to 0$ as $(x, y) \to (0, 0)$ along any straight line path of the form $y = kx$ or along either coordinate axis.
  b. Show that $f(x, y)$ is not continuous at the origin. *Hint:* Consider the limit as $(x, y) \to (0, 0)$ along the parabolic path $y^2 = x$.

35. Let f be the functions defined by

$$f(x, y) = \begin{cases} \dfrac{xy^3}{x^2 + y^6} & \text{for } (x, y) \neq (0, 0) \\ 0 & \text{for } (0, 0) \end{cases}$$

  a. Show that $f(x, y) \to 0$ as $(x, y) \to (0, 0)$ along any straight line path of the form $y = kx$ or along either coordinate axis.
  b. Show that $f(x, y)$ is not continuous at the origin. *Hint:* Consider the limit as $(x, y) \to (0, 0)$ along the path $y^3 = x$.

36. Let f be the function defined by

$$f(x, y) = \dfrac{x^2 - y^2}{x^2 + y^2} \quad \text{for } (x, y) \neq (0, 0)$$

  a. Find $\displaystyle\lim_{(x, y) \to (2, 1)} f(x, y)$.
  b. Prove that f has no limit at $(0, 0)$ by showing that $f(x, y)$ tends toward different numbers as $(x, y) \to (0, 0)$ along each coordinate axis.

37. Let f be the function defined by

$$f(x, y) = \dfrac{x^2 + 2y^2}{x^2 + y^2} \quad \text{for } (x, y) \neq (0, 0)$$

  a. Find $\displaystyle\lim_{(x, y) \to (3, 1)} f(x, y)$.
  b. Prove that f has no limit at $(0, 0)$ by showing that $f(x, y)$ tends toward different numbers as $(x, y) \to (0, 0)$ along each coordinate axis.

38. Find the constant A for which the function

$$f(x, y) = \begin{cases} \dfrac{x^3 + y^3}{x^2 + y^2} & \text{for } (x, y) \neq (0, 0) \\ A & \text{for } (x, y) = (0, 0) \end{cases}$$

is continuous at the origin.

39. Find the constant B for which the function

$$f(x, y) = \begin{cases} \dfrac{3x^3 - 3y^3}{x^2 - y^2} & \text{for } (x, y) \neq (0, 0) \\ B & \text{for } (x, y) = (0, 0) \end{cases}$$

is continuous at the origin.

40. Let

$$f(x, y) = \begin{cases} \dfrac{x^2 y^2}{x^2 + y^2} & \text{for } (x, y) \neq (0, 0) \\ 0 & \text{for } (0, 0) \end{cases}$$

Is f continuous at $(0, 0)$? Explain.

41. Assuming that the limit exists, show that

$$\lim_{(x, y, z) \to (0, 0, 0)} \dfrac{xyz}{x^2 + y^2 + z^2} = 0$$

Ⓒ *Use the definition of limit to verify the limit statements given in Problems 42–45.*

42. $\displaystyle\lim_{(x, y) \to (0, 0)} (2x^2 + 3y^2) = 0$

43. $\displaystyle\lim_{(x, y) \to (0, 0)} (x + y^2) = 0$

44. $\displaystyle\lim_{(x, y) \to (0, 0)} \dfrac{x^2 - y^2}{x + y} = 0$

45. $\displaystyle\lim_{(x, y) \to (1, -1)} \dfrac{x^2 - y^2}{x + y} = 2$

46. Prove that if f is continuous and $f(a, b) > 0$, then there exists a δ-neighborhood about (a, b) such that $f(x, y) > 0$ for every point (x, y) in the neighborhood.

47. Prove the scalar multiple rule:

$$\lim_{(x, y) \to (x_0, y_0)} [af](x, y) = a \lim_{(x, y) \to (x_0, y_0)} f(x, y) = aL$$

48. Prove the sum rule:

$$\lim_{(x, y) \to (x_0, y_0)} [f + g](x, y) = L + M$$

where

$$L = \lim_{(x, y) \to (x_0, y_0)} f(x, y) \quad \text{and} \quad M = \lim_{(x, y) \to (x_0, y_0)} g(x, y).$$

49. A function of two variables $f(x, y)$ may be continuous in each separate variable at $x = x_0$ and $y = y_0$ without being itself continuous at (x_0, y_0). Let $f(x, y)$ be defined by

$$f(x, y) = \begin{cases} \dfrac{x^2 y}{x^2 + y^2} & \text{for } (x, y) \neq (0, 0) \\ 0 & \text{for } (0, 0) \end{cases}$$

Let $g(x) = f(x, 0)$ and $h(y) = f(0, y)$. Show that both $g(x)$ and $h(y)$ are continuous at 0, but that $f(x, y)$ is not continuous at $(0, 0)$.

12.3 PARTIAL DERIVATIVES

IN THIS SECTION Partial differentiation, geometric interpretation, partial derivative as a rate, higher partial derivatives

In many problems involving functions of several variables, the goal is to find the derivative of the function with respect to one of its variables when all the others are held constant. In this section we consider this concept and shall see how it can be used to find slopes and rates of change.

■ PARTIAL DIFFERENTIATION

The process of differentiating a function of several variables with respect to one of its variables while keeping the other variable(s) fixed is called **partial differentiation**, and the resulting derivative is a **partial derivative** of the function.

Recall that the derivative of a function of a single variable f is defined to be the limit of a difference quotient, namely,

$$f'(x) = \lim_{\Delta x \to 0} \frac{f(x + \Delta x) - f(x)}{\Delta x}$$

Partial derivatives with respect to x or y are defined similarly.

Partial Derivative of a Function of Two Variables

If $z = f(x, y)$, then the **(first) partial derivatives** of f with respect to x and y are the functions f_x and f_y respectively, defined by

$$f_x(x, y) = \lim_{\Delta x \to 0} \frac{f(x + \Delta x, y) - f(x, y)}{\Delta x}$$

$$f_y(x, y) = \lim_{\Delta y \to 0} \frac{f(x, y + \Delta y) - f(x, y)}{\Delta y}$$

provided the limits exist.

■ *What this says*: For the partial differentiation of a function of two variables, $z = f(x, y)$, we find the partial derivative with respect to x by regarding y as constant while differentiating the function with respect to x. Similarly, the partial derivative with respect to y is found by regarding x as constant while differentiating with respect to y.

EXAMPLE 1   Partial derivatives

If $f(x, y) = x^3y + xy^2$, find **a.** f_x and **b.** f_y.

Solution   **a.** For f_x, hold y constant and find the derivative with respect to x:

$$f_x(x, y) = 3x^2y + y^2$$

b. For f_y, hold x constant and find the derivative with respect to y:

$$f_y(x, y) = x^3 + 2xy$$ ▬

Several different symbols are used to denote partial derivatives, as indicated in the following box.

Alternative Notation for First Partial Derivatives

For $z = f(x, y)$, the partial derivatives f_x and f_y are denoted by

$$f_x(x, y) = \frac{\partial f}{\partial x} = \frac{\partial z}{\partial x} = \frac{\partial}{\partial x} f(x, y) = z_x = D_x(f)$$

and

$$f_y(x, y) = \frac{\partial f}{\partial y} = \frac{\partial z}{\partial y} = \frac{\partial}{\partial y} f(x, y) = z_y = D_y(f)$$

The values of the partial derivatives of $f(x, y)$ at the point (a, b) are denoted by

$$\left.\frac{\partial f}{\partial x}\right|_{(a,b)} = f_x(a, b) \quad \text{and} \quad \left.\frac{\partial f}{\partial y}\right|_{(a,b)} = f_y(a, b)$$

EXAMPLE 2 Finding and evaluating a partial derivative

Let $z = x^2 \sin(3x + y^3)$.

a. Evaluate $\frac{\partial z}{\partial x}$ at $\left(\frac{\pi}{3}, 0\right)$.   **b.** Evaluate $\frac{\partial z}{\partial y}$ at $\left(\frac{\pi}{3}, 0\right)$.

Solution   **a.** $\frac{\partial z}{\partial x} = 2x \sin(3x + y^3) + x^2 \cos(3x + y^3) \cdot (3)$

$$= 2x \sin(3x + y^3) + 3x^2 \cos(3x + y^3)$$

Thus,

$$\left.\frac{\partial z}{\partial x}\right|_{\left(\frac{\pi}{3}, 0\right)} = 2\left(\frac{\pi}{3}\right)\sin\pi + 3\left(\frac{\pi}{3}\right)^2 \cos\pi = \frac{2\pi}{3}(0) + \frac{\pi^2}{3}(-1) = -\frac{\pi^2}{3}$$

b. $\frac{\partial z}{\partial y} = x^2 \cos(3x + y^3) \cdot (3y^2) = 3x^2 y^2 \cos(3x + y^3)$, so that

$$\left.\frac{\partial z}{\partial y}\right|_{\left(\frac{\pi}{3}, 0\right)} = 3\left(\frac{\pi}{3}\right)^2 (0)^2 \cos\pi = 0$$
▬

EXAMPLE 3 Partial derivative of a function of three variables

Let $f(x, y, z) = x^2 + 2xy^2 + yz^3$; find: **a.** f_x **b.** f_y **c.** f_z

Solution   **a.** For f_x, think of f as a function of x alone with y and z treated as constants: $f_x(x, y, z) = 2x + 2y^2$.
b. $f_y(x, y, z) = 4xy + z^3$ **c.** $f_z(x, y, z) = 3yz^2$
▬

EXAMPLE 4 Partial derivative of an implicitly defined function

Let z be defined implicitly as a function of x and y by the equation

$$x^2 + 5xy^2 + z^3 = 1$$

Find **a.** $\frac{\partial z}{\partial x}$,   **b.** $\frac{\partial z}{\partial y}$.

Solution   **a.** Differentiate implicitly with respect to x, treating y as a constant:

$$2x + 5y^2 + 3z^2 \frac{\partial z}{\partial x} = 0 \quad \text{so that} \quad \frac{\partial z}{\partial x} = \frac{-2x - 5y^2}{3z^2}$$

b. For this part, differentiate implicitly with respect to y.

$$10xy + 3z^2 \frac{\partial z}{\partial y} = 0 \quad \text{so that} \quad \frac{\partial z}{\partial y} = \frac{-10xy}{3z^2}$$
▬

The following example uses implicit differentiation to find the slope of the tangent line to a level curve at a particular point.

EXAMPLE 5   Slope of a level curve

A certain level curve of the surface $z = x^2 + 3xy + y^2$ contains the point P, where $x = 1$ and $y = 1$. Find the slope of the tangent line to this curve at P.

Solution   The required level curve has the form $F(x, y) = C$, where

$$F(x, y) = x^2 + 3xy + y^2$$

We find the slope, $\dfrac{dy}{dx}$, implicitly:

$$x^2 + 3xy + y^2 = C$$

$$\frac{d}{dx}(x^2 + 3xy + y^2) = \frac{d}{dx}(C)$$

$$2x + 3y + 3x\frac{dy}{dx} + 2y\frac{dy}{dx} = 0$$

$$(3x + 2y)\frac{dy}{dx} = -2x - 3y$$

$$\frac{dy}{dx} = \frac{-(2x + 3y)}{3x + 2y}$$

This provides the slope at each point on the level curve where $3x + 2y \neq 0$. In particular, at the point where $x = 1$ and $y = 1$, we have

$$\left.\frac{dy}{dx}\right|_{(1,\,1)} = \frac{-[2(1) + 3(1)]}{3(1) + 2(1)} = \frac{-5}{5} = -1$$

so that the required line has slope -1.   ■

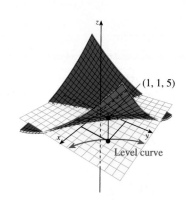

The slope of the line tangent to a level curve of a surface

■ GEOMETRIC INTERPRETATION

A useful geometric interpretation of partial derivatives is indicated in Figure 12.16. In Figure 12.16a, the plane $y = y_0$ intersects the surface $z = f(x, y)$ in a curve C parallel to the xz-plane. That is, C is the trace of the surface in the plane $y = y_0$. An equation for this curve is $z = f(x, y_0)$, and because y_0 is fixed, the function depends only on x. Because C lies in the plane $y = y_0$, we can compute the slope of the tangent line to C at the point $P(x_0, y_0, z_0)$ in the plane $y = y_0$ by differentiating $f(x, y_0)$ with respect to x and evaluating the derivative at $x = x_0$. That is, the slope is $f_x(x_0, y_0)$, the value of the partial derivative f_x at (x_0, y_0). There is a similar interpretation for $f_y(x_0, y_0)$, as shown in Figure 12.16b.

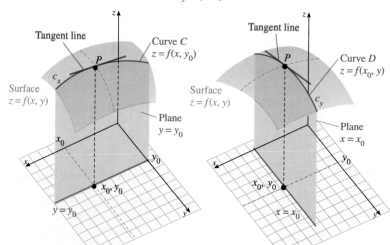

a. The tangent line in the plane $y = y_0$ to the curve C at the point P has slope $f_x(x_0, y_0)$.

b. The tangent line in the plane $x = x_0$ to the curve D at the point P has slope $f_y(x_0, y_0)$.

Figure 12.16 Slope interpretation of the partial derivative

Partial Derivative as the Slope of a Tangent Line

The line parallel to the xz-plane and tangent to the surface $z = f(x, y)$ at the point $P_0(x_0, y_0, z_0)$ has slope $f_x(x_0, y_0)$. Likewise, the tangent line to the surface at P_0 that is parallel to the yz-plane has slope $f_y(x_0, y_0)$.

EXAMPLE 6   Slope of a line parallel to the xz-plane

Find the slope of the line that is parallel to the xz-plane and tangent to the surface $z = x\sqrt{x + y}$ at the point $P(1, 3, 2)$.

Solution   If $f(x, y) = x\sqrt{x + y} = x(x + y)^{1/2}$, then the required slope is $f_x(1, 3)$. We find that

$$f_x(x, y) = x\left(\tfrac{1}{2}\right)(x + y)^{-1/2}(1 + 0) + (1)(x + y)^{1/2} = \frac{x}{2\sqrt{x + y}} + \sqrt{x + y}$$

Thus,

$$f_x(1, 3) = \frac{1}{2\sqrt{1 + 3}} + \sqrt{1 + 3} = \frac{9}{4}$$

■ PARTIAL DERIVATIVE AS A RATE

The derivative of a function of one variable can be interpreted as a rate of change, and the analogous interpretation of partial derivative can be described as follows.

Partial Derivatives as Rates of Change

As the point (x, y) moves from the fixed point $P_0(x_0, y_0)$, the function $f(x, y)$ changes at a rate given by $f_x(x_0, y_0)$ in the direction of the positive x-axis and by $f_y(x_0, y_0)$ in the direction of the positive y-axis.

EXAMPLE 7   Partial derivatives as a rate of change

In an electrical circuit with electromotive force (EMF) of E volts and resistance R ohms, the current is $I = E/R$ amperes. Find the partial derivatives $\frac{\partial I}{\partial E}$ and $\frac{\partial I}{\partial R}$ at the instant when $E = 120$ and $R = 15$ and interpret these derivatives as rates.

Solution   We find that because $I = ER^{-1}$

$$\frac{\partial I}{\partial E} = R^{-1} \quad \text{and} \quad \frac{\partial I}{\partial R} = -ER^{-2}$$

and thus, when $E = 120$ and $R = 15$, we have

$$\frac{\partial I}{\partial E} = 15^{-1} \approx 0.0667 \quad \text{and} \quad \frac{\partial I}{\partial R} = -(120)(15)^{-2} \approx -0.5333$$

This means that if the resistance is fixed at 15 ohms, the current is increasing (because the slope is positive) with respect to voltage at the rate of 0.0667 amperes per volt when the EMF is 120 volts. It also means that if the EMF is fixed at 120 volts, the current is decreasing (because the slope is negative) with respect to resistance at the rate of 0.5333 amperes per ohm when the resistance is 15 ohms.

■ HIGHER PARTIAL DERIVATIVES

The partial derivative of a function is a function, and often it is possible to take the partial derivative of a partial derivative. This is very much like taking the second derivative of a function of one variable if we take two consecutive partial derivatives with respect to the same variable, and the resulting derivative is called the **second partial derivative** with respect to that variable. However, we can also take the partial derivative with respect to one variable and then take another partial derivative with respect to a different variable; in this case, the derivative is called a **mixed partial derivative**. The higher partial derivatives for a function of two variables $f(x, y)$ are denoted as indicated in the following box.

Higher Partial Derivatives

Given $z = f(x, y)$.
Second partial derivatives

$$\frac{\partial^2 f}{\partial x^2} = \frac{\partial^2 z}{\partial x^2} = \frac{\partial}{\partial x}\left(\frac{\partial z}{\partial x}\right) = (f_x)_x = f_{xx}$$

$$\frac{\partial^2 f}{\partial y^2} = \frac{\partial^2 z}{\partial y^2} = \frac{\partial}{\partial y}\left(\frac{\partial z}{\partial y}\right) = (f_y)_y = f_{yy}$$

Mixed partial derivatives

$$\frac{\partial^2 f}{\partial x \partial y} = \frac{\partial^2 z}{\partial x \partial y} = \frac{\partial}{\partial x}\left(\frac{\partial z}{\partial y}\right) = (f_y)_x = f_{yx}$$

$$\frac{\partial^2 f}{\partial y \partial x} = \frac{\partial^2 z}{\partial y \partial x} = \frac{\partial}{\partial y}\left(\frac{\partial z}{\partial x}\right) = (f_x)_y = f_{xy}$$

EXAMPLE 8   Higher partial derivatives of a function of two variables

For $z = f(x, y) = 5x^2 - 2xy + 3y^3$, find the requested higher partial derivatives.

a. $\dfrac{\partial^2 z}{\partial x \partial y}$ **b.** $\dfrac{\partial^2 z}{\partial y \partial x}$ **c.** $\dfrac{\partial^2 z}{\partial x^2}$ **d.** $f_{xy}(3, 2)$

Solution   Part of what this example is illustrating is the variety of notation that can be used for higher partial derivatives.

a. $\dfrac{\partial z}{\partial y} = -2x + 9y^2$ *First differentiate with respect to y; then differentiate with respect to x.*

$$\frac{\partial^2 z}{\partial x \partial y} = \frac{\partial}{\partial x}\left(\frac{\partial z}{\partial y}\right) = \frac{\partial}{\partial x}(-2x + 9y^2) = -2$$

b. Differentiate first with respect to x and then with respect to y:

$$\frac{\partial^2 z}{\partial y \partial x} = \frac{\partial}{\partial y}\left(\frac{\partial z}{\partial x}\right) = \frac{\partial}{\partial y}(10x - 2y) = -2$$

c. Differentiate with respect to x twice:

$$\frac{\partial^2 z}{\partial x^2} = \frac{\partial}{\partial x}\left(\frac{\partial z}{\partial x}\right) = \frac{\partial}{\partial x}(10x - 2y) = 10$$

d. Differentiate first with respect to x and then with respect to y (part **b**), and evaluate at the point $(3, 2)$: $f_{xy}(3, 2) = -2$.   ■

Notice from parts **a** and **b** that $\frac{\partial^2 z}{\partial x \partial y} = \frac{\partial^2 z}{\partial y \partial x}$. This equality of mixed partials does not hold for all functions, but for most functions we shall encounter, it will be true. The following theorem provides sufficient conditions for this equality to occur.

THEOREM 12.1 Equality of mixed partials

If $f(x, y)$ has mixed partial derivatives at (x_0, y_0) and the mixed partials are continuous in an open set containing (x_0, y_0), then

$$f_{yx}(x_0, y_0) = f_{xy}(x_0, y_0)$$

Proof: This proof requires methods of advanced calculus and is omitted in this text. ∎

EXAMPLE 9 Partial derivatives of functions of two variables

Find f_{xy}, f_{yx}, f_{xx}, and f_{xxy}, where $f(x, y) = x^2 y e^y$.

Solution We have the first partial derivatives

$$f_x = 2xye^y \qquad f_y = x^2 e^y + x^2 y e^y$$

The mixed partial derivatives (which must be the same by the previous theorem) are

$$f_{xy} = (f_x)_y = 2xe^y + 2xye^y \qquad f_{yx} = (f_y)_x = 2xe^y + 2xye^y$$

Finally, we compute the second and higher partial derivatives:

$$f_{xx} = (f_x)_x = 2ye^y \quad \text{and} \quad f_{xxy} = (f_{xx})_y = 2e^y + 2ye^y \qquad \blacksquare$$

The **heat equation** $\frac{\partial T}{\partial t} = c^2 \frac{\partial^2 T}{\partial x^2}$ describes the heat in an insulated rod. The constant c depends on the material in the rod.

EXAMPLE 10 Verifying that a function satisfies the heat equation

Verify that $T(x, t) = e^{-t} \cos \frac{x}{c}$ satisfies the heat equation.

Solution $\frac{\partial T}{\partial t} = -e^{-t}\cos\frac{x}{c}$ and $\frac{\partial^2 T}{\partial x^2} = \frac{\partial}{\partial x}\left(-\frac{1}{c}e^{-t}\sin\frac{x}{c}\right) = -\frac{1}{c^2}e^{-t}\cos\frac{x}{c}$

Thus, T satisfies the heat equation $\frac{\partial T}{\partial t} = c^2 \frac{\partial^2 T}{\partial x^2}$. $\blacksquare$

Analogous definitions can be made for functions of more than two variables. For example,

$$f_{zzz} = \frac{\partial^3 f}{\partial z^3} = \frac{\partial}{\partial z}\left[\frac{\partial}{\partial z}\left(\frac{\partial f}{\partial z}\right)\right] \quad \text{or} \quad f_{xyz} = \frac{\partial^3 f}{\partial z \partial y \partial x} = \frac{\partial}{\partial z}\left[\frac{\partial}{\partial y}\left(\frac{\partial f}{\partial x}\right)\right]$$

EXAMPLE 11 Higher partial derivatives of a function of several variables

By direct calculation, show that $f_{xyz} = f_{yzx} = f_{zyx}$ for the function $f(x, y, z) = xyz + x^2 y^3 z^4$.

Solution   Find the first partials:

$$f_x(x, y, z) = yz + 2xy^3z^4; \quad f_y(x, y, z) = xz + 3x^2y^2z^4; \quad f_z(x, y, z) = xy + 4x^2y^3z^3$$

Next, find the required second mixed partials:

$$f_{xy}(x, y, z) = (yz + 2xy^3z^4)_y = z + 6xy^2z^4$$

$$f_{yz}(x, y, z) = (xz + 3x^2y^2z^4)_z = x + 12x^2y^2z^3$$

$$f_{zy}(x, y, z) = (xy + 4x^2y^3z^3)_y = x + 12x^2y^2z^3$$

Finally, find the third mixed partials:

$$f_{xyz}(x, y, z) = (z + 6xy^2z^4)_z = 1 + 24xy^2z^3$$

$$f_{yzx}(x, y, z) = (x + 12x^2y^2z^3)_x = 1 + 24xy^2z^3$$

$$f_{zyx}(x, y, z) = (x + 12x^2y^2z^3)_x = 1 + 24xy^2z^3$$

—

PROBLEM SET 12.3

Ⓐ 1. ■ **What Does This Say?**   What is a partial derivative?
2. ■ **What Does This Say?**   Describe the algebraic process for finding the partial derivative of a function of three variables.

Find f_x, f_y, f_{xx}, and f_{yx} in Problems 3–8.
3. $f(x, y) = x^3 + x^2y + xy^2 + y^3$
4. $f(x, y) = (x + xy + y)^3$

5. $f(x, y) = \dfrac{x}{y}$
6. $f(x, y) = xe^{xy}$

7. $f(x, y) = \ln(2x + 3y)$
8. $f(x, y) = \sin x^2y$

Find f_x and f_y in Problems 9–16.
9. **a.** $f(x, y) = (\sin x^2)\cos y$
   b. $f(x, y) = \sin(x^2\cos y)$
10. **a.** $f(x, y) = (\sin \sqrt{x})\ln y^2$
    b. $f(x, y) = \sin(\sqrt{x} \ln y^2)$
11. $f(x, y) = \sqrt{3x^2 + y^4}$
12. $f(x, y) = xy^2\ln(x + y)$
13. $f(x, y) = x^2e^{x+y}\cos y$
14. $f(x, y) = xy^3\tan^{-1} y$
15. $f(x, y) = \sin^{-1} xy$
16. $f(x, y) = \cos^{-1} xy$

Find f_x, f_y, and f_z in Problems 17–22.
17. $f(x, y, z) = xy^2 + yz^3 + xyz$
18. $f(x, y, z) = xye^z$
19. $f(x, y, z) = \dfrac{x + y^2}{z}$
20. $f(x, y, z) = \dfrac{xy + yz}{xz}$
21. $f(x, y, z) = \ln(x + y^2 + z^3)$
22. $f(x, y, z) = \sin(xy + z)$

In Problems 23–28, find $\dfrac{\partial z}{\partial x}$ and $\dfrac{\partial z}{\partial y}$ by differentiating implicitly.
23. $\dfrac{x^2}{9} - \dfrac{y^2}{4} + \dfrac{z^2}{2} = 1$
24. $3x^2 + 4y^2 + 2z^2 = 5$
25. $3x^2y + y^3z - z^2 = 1$
26. $x^3 - xy^2 + yz^2 - z^3 = 4$
27. $\sqrt{x} + y^2 + \sin xz = 2$
28. $\ln(xy + yz + xz) = 5$
    $(x > 0, y > 0, z > 0)$

Ⓑ 29. Find f_x and f_y for

$$f(x, y) = \int_x^y (t^2 + 2t + 1)\, dt$$

Hint: Review the second fundamental theorem.

30. Find f_x and f_y for

$$f(x, y) = \int_x^y (e^t + 3t)\, dt$$

Hint: Review the second fundamental theorem.

31. Find the slope of the tangent line to the level curve at the point $P(1, 1, 3)$ on the surface $z = x^2 + xy^2 + y^3$.

32. Find the slope of the tangent line to the level curve at the point $P(\sqrt{\pi}/2, \sqrt{\pi}/2, \pi/4)$ on the surface

$$z = xy + \cos(x^2 + y^2)$$

*A function f(x, y) is said to be **harmonic** on the set S (1) if it is continuously differentiable, (2) if it satisfies the **Laplace equation***

$$f_{xx} + f_{yy} = 0$$

throughout S, and (3) if its second derivatives are continuous. Show that the functions given in Problems 33–36 are harmonic on the prescribed set. You may assume that the functions are continuously differentiable and that the second derivatives are continuous.

33. $f(x, y) = 3x^2 y - y^3$; S is the entire plane.

34. $f(x, y) = \ln(x^2 + y^2)$; S is the plane with the point $(0, 0)$ removed.

35. $f(x, y) = e^x \sin y$; S is the entire plane.

36. $f(x, y) = \sin x \cosh y$; S is the entire plane.

37. Let $f(x, y) = xy^3 + x^3 y$. Find the slope of the tangent line to the graph of f at $P(1, -1, -2)$ in the direction of
  a. the x-axis.   **b.** the y-axis.

38. Find the slope of the tangent line at the point $P(1, -1, -2)$ on the graph of

$$f(x, y) = \frac{x^2 + y^2}{xy}$$

  in the direction
  a. parallel to the xz-plane.
  b. parallel to the yz-plane.

39. For $f(x, y) = \cos xy^2$, show $f_{xy} = f_{yx}$.

40. For $f(x, y) = (\sin^2 x)(\sin y)$, show $f_{xy} = f_{yx}$.

41. Find $f_{xzy} - f_{yzz}$, where

$$f(x, y, z) = x^2 + y^2 - 2xy \cos z$$

42. It has been determined that the flow (in cm^3/s) of blood from an artery into a small capillary is given by

$$F(x, y, z) = \frac{c\pi x^2}{4} \sqrt{y - z}$$

  for constant $c > 0$, where x is the diameter of the capillary, y is the pressure in the artery, and z is the pressure in the capillary. What is the rate of change of the flow of blood with respect to
  a. the diameter of the capillary?
  b. the arterial pressure?
  c. the capillary pressure?

43. Biologists have studied the oxygen consumption of certain furry mammals. They have found that if the mammal's body temperature is T degrees Celsius, fur temperature is t degrees Celsius, and the mammal does not sweat, than its relative oxygen consumption is approximated by

$$C(m, t, T) \approx \sigma(T - t)m^{-0.67}$$

  (kg/h) where m is the mammal's mass (in kg) and σ is a physical constant. Find the rate (rounded to two decimal places) at which the oxygen consumption changes with respect to:

a. the mass m.

b. the body temperature T.

c. the fur temperature t.

44. A gas that gathers on a surface in a condensed layer is said to be *adsorbed* in the surface, and the surface is called an *adsorbing surface*. It has been determined that the amount of gas adsorbed per unit area on an adsorbing surface is given by a formula of the form

$$S(p, T, h) = ape^{h/(bT)}$$

  where p is the gas pressure, T is the temperature of the gas, h is the heat of the adsorbed layer of gas, and a and b are physical constants. Find the rate of change of S with respect to
  a. p **b.** h **c.** T

45. The ideal gas law says that $PV = kT$, where P is the pressure of a confined gas, V is the volume, T is the temperature, and k is a physical constant.

  a. Find $\dfrac{\partial V}{\partial T}$.   **b.** Find $\dfrac{\partial V}{\partial P}$.

  c. Show that $\dfrac{\partial P}{\partial V} \cdot \dfrac{\partial V}{\partial T} \cdot \dfrac{\partial T}{\partial P} = -1$.

46. At a certain factory, output is given by $Q = 120K^{2/3} L^{2/5}$, where K denotes the capital investment (in units of \$1,000) and L measures the size of the labor force (in worker-hours).

  a. Find the *marginal productivity of capital*, $\partial Q/\partial K$, and the *marginal productivity of labor*, $\partial Q/\partial L$.

  b. Determine the signs of the second partial derivatives $\partial^2 Q/\partial L^2$ and $\partial^2 Q/\partial K^2$ and give an economic interpretation.

  Note: Q is an example of a Cobb-Douglas production function.

47. The temperature at a point (x, y) on a given metal plate in the xy plane is determined according to the formula $T(x, y) = x^3 + 2xy^2 + y$ degrees. Find the rate at which the temperature changes with distance if we start at $(2, 1)$ and move:

  a. up (parallel to the y-axis).

  b. to the right (parallel to the x-axis).

48. In physics, the **wave equation** is

$$\frac{\partial^2 z}{\partial t^2} = c^2 \frac{\partial^2 z}{\partial x^2}$$

  and the **heat equation** is

$$\frac{\partial z}{\partial t} = c^2 \frac{\partial^2 z}{\partial x^2}$$

  In each of the following cases, determine whether z satisfies the wave equation, the heat equation, or neither.
  a. $z = e^{-t}\left(\sin\frac{x}{c} + \cos\frac{x}{c}\right)$
  b. $z = \sin 3\, ct \sin 3x$
  c. $z = \sin 5\, ct \cos 5x$

⊙ 49. THINK TANK PROBLEM   Let

$$f(x, y) = \begin{cases} xy\left(\dfrac{x^2 - y^2}{x^2 + y^2}\right) & \text{if } (x, y) \neq (0, 0) \\ 0 & \text{if } (x, y) = (0, 0) \end{cases}$$

Show that $f_x(0, y) = -y$ and $f_y(x, 0) = x$, for all x and y. Then show that $f_{xy}(0, 0) = -1$ and $f_{yx}(0, 0) = 1$. Why does this not violate the equality of the mixed partials theorem?

50. Show that $f_x(0, 0) = 0$ but $f_y(0, 0)$ does not exist, where

$$f(x, y) = \begin{cases} (x^2 + y)\sin\left(\dfrac{1}{x^2 + y^2}\right) & \text{if } (x, y) \neq (0, 0) \\ 0 & \text{if } (x, y) = (0, 0) \end{cases}$$

51. Suppose a substance is injected into a tube containing a liquid solvent. Suppose the tube is placed so that its axis is parallel to the x-axis as shown in Figure 12.17.

Figure 12.17 Problem 52

Assume that the concentration of the substance varies only in the x-direction and let $C(x, t)$ denote the concen-

tration at position x and time t. Because the number of molecules in this substance is very large, it is reasonable to assume that C is a continuous function whose partial derivatives exist. One model for the flow yields the **diffusion equation in one dimension**; namely,

$$\frac{\partial C}{\partial t} = \delta \frac{\partial^2 C}{\partial x^2}$$

where δ is the **diffusion constant**.

a. What relationship must exist among a, b, and δ for a function of the form

$$C(x, t) = e^{ax + bt}$$

(a and b are constants) to satisfy the diffusion equation?

b. Verify that

$$C(x, t) = t^{-1/2}e^{-x^2 t/(4\delta)}$$

satisfies the diffusion equation?

52. The area of a triangle is $A = \frac{1}{2}ab \sin \gamma$, where γ is the angle between sides of length a and b.

a. Find $\dfrac{\partial A}{\partial a}$, $\dfrac{\partial A}{\partial b}$, and $\dfrac{\partial A}{\partial \gamma}$.

b. Suppose a is given as a function of b, A, and γ. What is $\dfrac{\partial a}{\partial b}$?

12.4 TANGENT PLANES, APPROXIMATIONS, AND DIFFERENTIABILITY

> **IN THIS SECTION** Tangent planes, incremental approximations, the total differential, differentiability
> We now find the equation of a plane tangent to a surface at a given point on the surface and then use this tangent plane as an approximation for the value of a corresponding nearby point on the surface. This leads us to introduce the increment of a function of two variables and to show how this concept can be used to define differentiability.

■ TANGENT PLANES

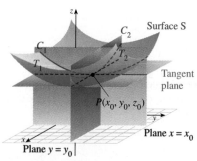

Figure 12.18 Tangent plane

Suppose S is a surface with the equation $z = f(x, y)$, where f has continuous first partial derivatives, and let $P(x_0, y_0, z_0)$ be a point on S. Let C_1 be the trace on S of the intersection of S and the plane $x = x_0$ and C_2 be the trace on S of the intersection of S and the plane $y = y_0$, as shown in Figure 12.18. Note that C_1 and C_2 must intersect at P. Consider the tangent lines T_1 and T_2 to the curves C_1 and C_2, respectively, at the point P. Then, if a tangent plane to the surface S exists at P, it is reasonable to expect it to contain the tangent lines T_1 and T_2 to the curves C_1 and C_2, respectively.

In Section 12.6, we will see that if C is any other curve that lies on the surface S and passes through the point P, then its tangent line will also lie in the tangent plane at P. Thus, the tangent plane to S at P consists of all possible tangent lines at P to curves that lie on S and pass through P. The tangent plane at P is the plane that most closely approximates the surface S near the point P.

In order to find the equation of this tangent plane, recall that the equation of a plane is

$$A(x - x_0) + B(y - y_0) + C(z - z_0) = 0$$

If $C \neq 0$, divide both sides by C and let $a = -\dfrac{A}{C}$, and $b = -\dfrac{B}{C}$ to obtain

$$z - z_0 = a(x - x_0) + b(y - y_0)$$

Note that the intersection of this plane and the plane $x = x_0$ is the tangent line T_1. Setting $x = x_0$, we obtain

$$z - z_0 = b(y - y_0)$$

which we recognize as the equation (in point-slope form) of a line with slope b. Therefore, $b = f_y(x_0, y_0)$. Similarly, putting $y = y_0$, we obtain

$$z - z_0 = a(x - x_0)$$

which represents the tangent line T_2, so that $a = f_x(x_0, y_0)$.

Equation of the Tangent Plane

> Suppose S is a surface with the equation $z = f(x, y)$ and let $P_0(x_0, y_0, z_0)$ be a point on S at which a tangent plane exists. Then the **equation of the tangent plane** to S at P_0 is
>
> $$z - z_0 = f_x(x_0, y_0)(x - x_0) + f_y(x_0, y_0)(y - y_0)$$

EXAMPLE 1   Equation of a tangent plane for a surface defined by $z = f(x, y)$

Find an equation for the tangent plane to the surface $z = \tan^{-1}\dfrac{y}{x}$ at the point $P_0\left(1, \sqrt{3}, \frac{\pi}{3}\right)$.

Solution
$$f_x(x, y) = \frac{-yx^{-2}}{1 + \left(\frac{y}{x}\right)^2} = \frac{-y}{x^2 + y^2}; \qquad f_x(1, \sqrt{3}) = \frac{-\sqrt{3}}{1 + 3} = \frac{-\sqrt{3}}{4}$$

$$f_y(x, y) = \frac{x^{-1}}{1 + \left(\frac{y}{x}\right)^2} = \frac{x}{x^2 + y^2}; \qquad f_y(1, \sqrt{3}) = \frac{1}{1 + 3} = \frac{1}{4}$$

The equation of the tangent plane is

$$z - \frac{\pi}{3} = \left(\frac{-\sqrt{3}}{4}\right)(x - 1) + \frac{1}{4}(y - \sqrt{3})$$

or

$$3\sqrt{3}x - 3y + 12z = 4\pi$$

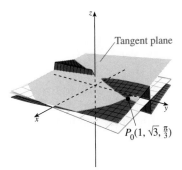

Tangent plane for the surface defined by $z = \tan^{-1}(y/x)$

■ INCREMENTAL APPROXIMATIONS

In Chapter 2, we noted that if f is differentiable at x_0 and Δx is sufficiently small, then the increment $\Delta f = f(x_0 + \Delta x) - f(x_0)$ can be closely approximated by $f'(x_0)\Delta x$ or, equivalently,

$$f(x_0 + \Delta x) \approx f(x_0) + f'(x_0)\Delta x$$

The analogous approximation formula for a function of two variables is called the **incremental** or **(linear)** approximation and may be stated as follows:

**Incremental Approximation
of a Function of Two Variables**

If $f(x, y)$ and its partial derivatives f_x and f_y are defined in an open region R containing the point $P(x_0, y_0)$ and f_x and f_y are continuous at P, then

$$\Delta f = f(x_0 + \Delta x, y_0 + \Delta y) - f(x_0, y_0) \approx f_x(x_0, y_0)\Delta x + f_y(x_0, y_0)\Delta y$$

so that

$$f(x_0 + \Delta x, y_0 + \Delta y) \approx f(x_0, y_0) + f_x(x_0, y_0)\Delta x + f_y(x_0, y_0)\Delta y$$

A graphical interpretation of this incremental approximation formula is shown in Figure 12.19.

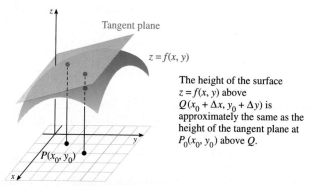

The height of the surface $z = f(x, y)$ above $Q(x_0 + \Delta x, y_0 + \Delta y)$ is approximately the same as the height of the tangent plane at $P_0(x_0, y_0)$ above Q.

Figure 12.19 Incremental approximation to a function of two variables

The tangent plane to the surface $z = f(x, y)$ has the equation

$$z - f(x_0, y_0) = f_x(x_0, y_0)\Delta x + f_y(x_0, y_0)\Delta y$$

As long as we are near (x_0, y_0), the height of the tangent plane is approximately the same as the height of the surface. Thus, if Δx and Δy are small, the point $(x_0 + \Delta x, y_0 + \Delta y)$ will be near (x_0, y_0) and we have

$$\underbrace{f(x_0 + \Delta x, y_0 + \Delta y)}_{\substack{\text{Height of } z = f(x, y) \\ \text{above } Q(x_0 + \Delta x, y_0 + \Delta y)}} \approx \underbrace{f(x_0, y_0) + f_x(x_0, y_0)\Delta x + f_y(x_0, y_0)\Delta y}_{\text{Height of the tangent plane above } Q}$$

Increments of a function of three variables $f(x, y, z)$ can be defined in a similar fashion. Suppose f has continuous partial derivatives f_x, f_y, f_z at and near the point (x_0, y_0, z_0). Then if the numbers $\Delta x, \Delta y, \Delta z$ are all sufficiently small, we have

$$\Delta f = f(x_0 + \Delta x, y_0 + \Delta y, z_0 + \Delta z) - f(x_0, y_0, z_0)$$

$$\approx f_x(x_0, y_0, z_0)\Delta x + f_y(x_0, y_0, z_0)\Delta y + f_z(x_0, y_0, z_0)\Delta z$$

EXAMPLE 2   Using increments to estimate the change of a function

An open box has length 3 ft, width 1 ft, and height 2 ft, and is constructed from material that costs $\$2/\text{ft}^2$ for the sides and $\$3/\text{ft}^2$ for the bottom. Compute the cost of constructing the box and then use increments to estimate the change in cost if the length and width are each increased by 3 in. and the height is decreased by 4 in.

Solution   An open (no top) box with length x, width y, and height z has an area

$$S = \underbrace{xy}_{\text{Bottom}} + \underbrace{2xz + 2yz}_{\text{Four sides}}$$

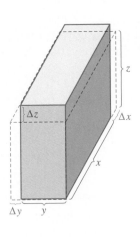

Because the sides cost \$2/ft^2 and the bottom \$3/ft^2, the total cost is

$$C(x, y, z) = 3xy + 2(2xz + 2yz)$$

The partial derivatives of C are

$$C_x = 3y + 4z \quad C_y = 3x + 4z \quad C_z = 4x + 4y$$

and the dimensions of the box change by

$$\Delta x = \tfrac{3}{12} = 0.25 \text{ ft} \quad \Delta y = \tfrac{3}{12} = 0.25 \text{ ft} \quad \Delta z = \tfrac{-4}{12} \text{ ft}$$

Thus, the change in the total cost is approximated by

$$\Delta C \approx C_x(3, 1, 2)\Delta x + C_y(3, 1, 2)\Delta y + C_z(3, 1, 2)\Delta z$$

$$= [3(1) + 4(2)](0.25) + [3(3) + 4(2)](0.25) + [4(3) + 4(1)]\left(-\tfrac{4}{12}\right) \approx 1.67$$

That is, the cost increases by approximately \$1.67. ▬

EXAMPLE 3 Maximum percentage error using differentials

The radius and height of a right circular cone are measured with errors of at most 3% and 2%, respectively. Use increments to approximate the maximum possible percentage error in computing the volume of the cone using these measurements and the formula $V = \tfrac{1}{3}\pi R^2 H$.

Solution We are given that

$$\left|\frac{\Delta R}{R}\right| \le 0.03 \quad \text{and} \quad \left|\frac{\Delta H}{H}\right| \le 0.02$$

The partial derivatives of V are

$$V_R = \tfrac{2}{3}\pi RH \quad \text{and} \quad V_H = \tfrac{1}{3}\pi R^2$$

so the change in V is approximated by

$$\Delta V \approx \left(\tfrac{2}{3}\pi RH\right)\Delta R + \left(\tfrac{1}{3}\pi R^2\right)\Delta H$$

Dividing by the volume $V = \tfrac{1}{3}\pi R^2 H$, we obtain

$$\frac{\Delta V}{V} \approx \frac{\tfrac{2}{3}\pi RH\,\Delta R + \tfrac{1}{3}\pi R^2\,\Delta H}{\tfrac{1}{3}\pi R^2 H} = 2\left(\frac{\Delta R}{R}\right) + \left(\frac{\Delta H}{H}\right)$$

so that

$$\left|\frac{\Delta V}{V}\right| \le 2\left|\frac{\Delta R}{R}\right| + \left|\frac{\Delta H}{H}\right| = 2(0.03) + (0.02) = 0.08$$

Thus, the maximum percentage error in computing the volume V is approximately 8%. ▬

■ THE TOTAL DIFFERENTIAL

For a function of one variable, $y = f(x)$, we defined the differential dy to be $dy = f'(x)\,dx$. For the two-variable case, we make the following analogous definition.

Total Differential

If $z = f(x, y)$ and Δx and Δy are increments of x and y, respectively, and if we let $dx = \Delta x$ and $dy = \Delta y$ be differentials for x and y, respectively, then the **total differential** of $f(x, y)$ is

$$df = \frac{\partial f}{\partial x}\, dx + \frac{\partial f}{\partial y}\, dy = f_x(x, y)\, dx + f_y(x, y)\, dy$$

Similarly, for a function of three variables $z = f(x, y, z)$, with $dz = \Delta z$, the **total differential** is

$$df = \frac{\partial f}{\partial x}\, dx + \frac{\partial f}{\partial y}\, dy + \frac{\partial f}{\partial z}\, dz$$

COMMENT: The total differential is useful because it is relatively easy to calculate, and approximates the increment Δf, which generally is not easy to compute.

EXAMPLE 4   Total differential

Find the total differential of the given functions:

a. $f(x, y, z) = 2x^3 + 5y^4 - 6z$ **b.** $f(x, y) = x^2 \ln(3y^2 - 2x)$

Solution   **a.** $df = \dfrac{\partial f}{\partial x}\, dx + \dfrac{\partial f}{\partial y}\, dy + \dfrac{\partial f}{\partial z}\, dz$

$\qquad = 6x^2\, dx + 20y^3\, dy - 6\, dz$

b. $df = \dfrac{\partial f}{\partial x}\, dx + \dfrac{\partial f}{\partial y}\, dy$

$\qquad = \left[2x \ln(3y^2 - 2x) + x^2\, \dfrac{-2}{3y^2 - 2x} \right] dx + \left[x^2\, \dfrac{6y}{3y^2 - 2x} \right] dy$

$\qquad = \left[2x \ln(3y^2 - 2x) - \dfrac{2x^2}{3y^2 - 2x} \right] dx + \dfrac{6x^2 y}{3y^2 - 2x}\, dy$

EXAMPLE 5   Application of the total differential

At a certain factory, the daily output is $Q = 60K^{1/2}L^{1/3}$ units, where K denotes the capital investment (in units of \$1,000) and L, the size of the labor force (in worker-hours). The current capital investment is \$900,000, and 1,000 worker-hours of labor are used each day. Estimate the change in output that will result if capital investment is increased by \$1,000 and labor is decreased by 2 worker-hours.

Solution   The change in output is estimated by the total differential dQ. We have $K = 900$, $L = 1,000$, $dK = \Delta K = 1$, and $dL = \Delta L = -2$. The total differential of $Q(x, y)$ is

$$dQ = \frac{\partial Q}{\partial K}\, dK + \frac{\partial Q}{\partial L}\, dL$$

$$= 60\left(\tfrac{1}{2}\right)K^{-1/2}L^{1/3}\, dK + 60\left(\tfrac{1}{3}\right)K^{1/2}L^{-2/3}\, dL$$

$$= 30K^{-1/2}L^{1/3}\, dK + 20K^{1/2}L^{-2/3}\, dL$$

Substituting for K, L, dK, and dL, we obtain

$$dQ = 30(900)^{-1/2}(1,000)^{1/3}(1) + 20(900)^{1/2}(1,000)^{-2/3}(-2) = -2$$

Thus, the output decreases by approximately 2 units when the capital investment is increased by \$1,000 and labor is decreased by 2 worker-hours.

EXAMPLE 6   Maximum percentage error in an electrical circuit
---

When two resistances R_1 and R_2 are connected in parallel, the total resistance R is given by

$$R = \frac{R_1 R_2}{R_1 + R_2}$$

If R_1 is measured as 300 ohms with a maximum error of 2% and R_2 is measured as 500 Ω with a maximum error of 3%, what is the maximum percentage error in R?

Solution   We are given that

$$\left|\frac{dR_1}{R_1}\right| \leq 0.02 \quad \text{and} \quad \left|\frac{dR_2}{R_2}\right| \leq 0.03$$

and we wish to find the maximum value of $\left|\frac{dR}{R}\right|$. Because

$$\frac{\partial R}{\partial R_1} = \frac{R_2{}^2}{(R_1 + R_2)^2} \quad \text{and} \quad \frac{\partial R}{\partial R_2} = \frac{R_1{}^2}{(R_1 + R_2)^2} \qquad \textit{Quotient rule}$$

it follows that the total differential of R is

$$dR = \frac{\partial R}{\partial R_1}\, dR_1 + \frac{\partial R}{\partial R_2}\, dR_2$$

$$= \frac{R_2{}^2}{(R_1 + R_2)^2}\, dR_1 + \frac{R_1{}^2}{(R_1 + R_2)^2}\, dR_2$$

We now find $\frac{dR}{R}$ by dividing both sides by R; however, because $R = \frac{R_1 R_2}{R_1 + R_2}$, we note that $\frac{1}{R} = \frac{R_1 + R_2}{R_1 R_2}$

$$dR \cdot \frac{1}{R} = \left[\frac{R_2{}^2}{(R_1 + R_2)^2}\, dR_1 + \frac{R_1{}^2}{(R_1 + R_2)^2}\, dR_2\right] \cdot \frac{R_1 + R_2}{R_1 R_2}$$

$$\frac{dR}{R} = \frac{R_2}{R_1 + R_2} \cdot \frac{dR_1}{R_1} + \frac{R_1}{R_1 + R_2} \cdot \frac{dR_2}{R_2}$$

Finally, apply the triangle inequality (Table 1.1, p. 00) to this relationship:

$$\left|\frac{dR}{R}\right| \leq \left|\frac{R_2}{R_1 + R_2}\right| \left|\frac{dR_1}{R_1}\right| + \left|\frac{R_1}{R_1 + R_2}\right| \left|\frac{dR_2}{R_2}\right|$$

$$\leq \frac{500}{300 + 500}(0.02) + \frac{300}{300 + 500}(0.03) = 0.02375$$

The maximum percentage is approximately 2.4%.   ▬

$$\Delta f = f(x_0 + \Delta x) - f(x_0) = f'(x_0)\, \Delta x + \underbrace{\varepsilon \Delta x}$$

Error when using df to estimate Δf

▪ DIFFERENTIABILITY

Recall from Chapter 2 that if $f(x)$ is differentiable at x_0, its *increment* is

$$\Delta f = f(x_0 + \Delta x) - f(x_0) = f'(x_0)\, \Delta x + \varepsilon \Delta x$$

where $\varepsilon \to 0$ as $\Delta x \to 0$ and $\varepsilon = 0$ when $\Delta x = 0$. For a function of two variables, the increment of x is an independent variable denoted by Δx, the increment of y is an independent variable denoted by Δy, and the increment of f at (x_0, y_0) is defined as

$$\Delta f = f(x_0 + \Delta x, y_0 + \Delta y) - f(x_0, y_0)$$

We use this increment representation to define differentiability as follows.

Definition of Differentiability

Suppose $f(x, y)$ is defined at each point in a circular disk that is centered at (x_0, y_0) and contains the point $(x_0 + \Delta x, y_0 + \Delta y)$. Then f is said to be **differentiable** at (x_0, y_0) if the increment of f can be expressed as

$$\Delta f = f_x(x_0, y_0)\Delta x + f_y(x_0, y_0)\Delta y + \varepsilon_1 \Delta x + \varepsilon_2 \Delta y$$

where $\varepsilon_1 \to 0$ and $\varepsilon_2 \to 0$ as both $\Delta x \to 0$ and $\Delta y \to 0$ (and $\varepsilon_1 = \varepsilon_2 = 0$ when $\Delta x = \Delta y = 0$). Also, $f(x, y)$ is said to be **differentiable on the region R** of the plane if f is differentiable at each point in R.

In Section 2.1, we showed that a function of one variable is continuous wherever it is differentiable. The following theorem establishes the same result for a function of two variables.

THEOREM 12.2   Differentiability implies continuity

If $f(x, y)$ is differentiable at (x_0, y_0), it is also continuous there.

Proof: We wish to show that $f(x, y) \to f(x_0, y_0)$ as $(x, y) \to (x_0, y_0)$, or, equivalently, that

$$\lim_{(x, y) \to (x_0, y_0)} [f(x, y) - f(x_0, y_0)] = 0$$

If we set $\Delta x = x - x_0$ and $\Delta y = y - y_0$ and let Δf denote the increment of f at (x_0, y_0), we have (by substitution)

$$f(x, y) - f(x_0, y_0) = f(x_0 + \Delta x, y_0 + \Delta y) - f(x_0, y_0) = \Delta f$$

Then, because $(\Delta x, \Delta y) \to (0, 0)$ as $(x, y) \to (x_0, y_0)$, we wish to prove that

$$\lim_{(\Delta x, \Delta y) \to (0,0)} \Delta f = 0$$

Because f is differentiable at (x_0, y_0), we have

$$\Delta f = f_x(x_0, y_0)\Delta x + f_y(x_0, y_0)\Delta y + \varepsilon_1 \Delta x + \varepsilon_2 \Delta y$$

where $\varepsilon_1 \to 0$ and $\varepsilon_2 \to 0$ as $(\Delta x, \Delta y) \to (0, 0)$. It follows that

$$\lim_{(\Delta x, \Delta y) \to (0,0)} \Delta f = \lim_{(\Delta x, \Delta y) \to (0,0)} [f_x(x_0, y_0)\Delta x + f_y(x_0, y_0)\Delta y + \varepsilon_1 \Delta x + \varepsilon_2 \Delta y]$$

$$= [f_x(x_0, y_0)] \cdot 0 + [f_y(x_0, y_0)] \cdot 0 + 0 + 0 = 0$$

as required. ∎

⊘ Be careful about how you use the word *differentiable*. In a single variable case, a function is differentiable at a point if its derivative exists there. However, the word is used differently for a function of two variables. In particular, the existence of the partial derivatives f_x and f_y does not guarantee that the function is differentiable. ⊘

EXAMPLE 7   Think Tank example: Possible existence of partial derivatives with a nondifferentiable function

Let

$$f(x, y) = \begin{cases} 1 & \text{if } x > 0 \text{ and } y > 0 \\ 0 & \text{otherwise} \end{cases}$$

That is, the function f has the value 1 when (x, y) is in the first quadrant and 0 elsewhere. Show that the partial derivatives f_x and f_y exist at the origin, but f is not differentiable there.

Solution We first note that at the origin, the function has the value 0; that is, $f(0, 0) = 0$. The key to showing that f_x exists at $(0, 0)$ depends on the fact that

$$\frac{f(0 + \Delta x, 0) - f(0, 0)}{\Delta x} = 0$$

which is true because $f(x, y) = 0$ along the x-axis (not just at the origin). This means that $f_x(0, 0) = 0$. Similarly, $f_y(0, 0) = 0$, which verifies that the partial derivatives exist at the origin.

Next, we need to show that $f(x, y)$ is not differentiable at the origin. We recall that differentiability implies continuity (Theorem 12.2), so if we can show that f is not continuous at $(0, 0)$, we can conclude that it is not differentiable at this point.

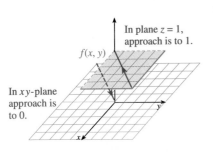

In plane $z = 1$, approach is to 1.

$f(x, y)$

In xy-plane approach is to 0.

1. $f(0, 0) = 0$, so $f(0, 0)$ is defined.
2. $\displaystyle\lim_{(x,y) \to (0, 0)} f(x, y) = 1$ along the line $y = x$ in the first quadrant.

Thus, f is not continuous at $(0, 0)$ because

$$\lim_{(x,y) \to (0,0)} f(x, y) \neq f(0, 0)$$

even if f exists at $(0, 0)$. Therefore, f is not differentiable at $(0, 0)$. ▄

Although the existence of partial derivatives at $P(x_0, y_0)$ is not enough to guarantee that $f(x, y)$ is differentiable at P, we do have the following sufficient condition for differentiability.

THEOREM 12.3   Sufficient condition for differentiability

If f is function of x and y and f, f_x, and f_y are continuous in a disk D centered at (x_0, y_0), then f is differentiable at (x_0, y_0).

Proof: The proof is found in advanced calculus. ■

EXAMPLE 8   Establish differentiability

Show that $f(x, y) = x^2y + xy^3$ is differentiable for all (x, y).

Solution   We shall apply the sufficient condition for differentiability. First, compute the partial derivatives

$$f_x(x, y) = \frac{\partial}{\partial x}(x^2 y + xy^3) = 2xy + y^3$$

$$f_y(x, y) = \frac{\partial}{\partial y}(x^2 y + xy^3) = x^2 + 3xy^2$$

Because f, f_x, and f_y are all polynomials in x and y, they are continuous throughout the plane. Therefore, the sufficient condition for the differentiability theorem assures us that f must be differentiable throughout the entire plane.   ▬

PROBLEM SET 12.4

Ⓐ *In Problems 1–6, find standard-form equations for the tangent plane to the given surface at the prescribed point P_0 on the surface.*

1. $z = \sqrt{x^2 + y^2}$
     at $P_0(3, 1, \sqrt{10})$

2. $z = 10 - x^2 - y^2$
     at $P_0(2, 2, 2)$

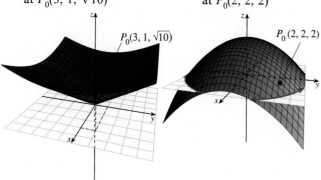

$P_0(3, 1, \sqrt{10})$

$P_0(2, 2, 2)$

3. $f(x, y) = x^2 + y^2 + \sin xy$ at
     $P_0 = (0, 2, 4)$

4. $f(x, y) = e^{-x}\sin y$ at
     $P_0\left(0, \frac{\pi}{2}, 1\right)$

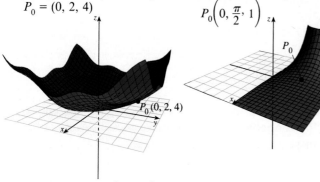

$P_0(0, 2, 4)$

P_0

5. $z = \tan^{-1}\frac{y}{x}$ at $P_0\left(2, 2, \frac{\pi}{4}\right)$

6. $z = \ln|x + y^2|$ at $P_0(-3, 2, 0)$

Find the total differential of the functions given in Problems 7–18.

7. $f(x, y) = 5x^2 y^3$

8. $f(x, y) = 8x^3 y^2 - x^4 y^5$

9. $f(x, y) = \sin xy$

10. $f(x, y) = \cos x^2 y$

11. $f(x, y) = \frac{y}{x}$

12. $f(x, y) = \frac{x^2}{y}$

13. $f(x, y) = ye^x$

14. $f(x, y) = e^{x^2} + y$

15. $f(x, y, z) = 3x^3 - 2y^4 + 5z$

16. $f(x, y, z) = \sin x + \sin y + \cos z$

17. $f(x, y, z) = z^2\sin(2x - 3y)$

18. $f(x, y, z) = 3y^2 z \cos x$

Show that functions in Problems 19–22 are differentiable for all (x, y).

19. $f(x, y) = xy^3 + 3xy^2$

20. $f(x, y) = x^2 + 4x - y^2$

21. $f(x, y) = x^3 y^2$

22. $f(x, y) = x + 4y - y^2$

Ⓑ *Use an incremental approximation to estimate the functions at the values given in Problems 23–28. Check by using a calculator and direct calculation.*

23. $f(1.01, 2.03)$, where $f(x, y) = 3x^4 + 2y^4$

24. $f(0.98, 1.03)$, where $f(x, y) = x^5 - 2y^3$

25. $f\left(\frac{\pi}{2} + 0.01, \frac{\pi}{2} - 0.01\right)$, where $f(x, y) = \sin(x + y)$

26. $f\left(\sqrt{\frac{\pi}{2}} + 0.01, \sqrt{\frac{\pi}{2}} - 0.01\right)$, where $f(x, y) = \sin(xy)$

27. $f(1.01, 0.98)$, where $f(x, y) = e^{xy}$

28. $f(1.01, 0.98)$, where $f(x, y) = e^{x^2 y^2}$

29. Find an equation for each horizontal tangent plane to the surface

$$z = 5 - x^2 - y^2 + 4y$$

30. Find an equation for each horizontal tangent plane to the surface

$$z = 4(x - 1)^2 + 3(y + 1)^2$$

31. a. Show that if x and y are sufficiently close to zero and f is differentiable at $(0, 0)$, then

$$f(x, y) \approx f(0, 0) + xf_x(0, 0) + yf_y(0, 0)$$

b. Use the approximation formula in part **a** to show that

$$\frac{1}{1 + x - y} \approx 1 - x + y$$

for small x and y.

c. If x and y are sufficiently close to zero, what is the approximate value of the following expression?

$$\frac{1}{(x + 1)^2 + (y + 1)^2}$$

32. If an electrical circuit with two resistors connected in parallel has a total resistance of R ohms, then

$$\frac{1}{R} = \frac{1}{P} + \frac{1}{Q}$$

where P and Q are the resistances (in ohms) of the resistors. Suppose P and Q are measured at 6 and 10 ohms, respectively, and that each measurement is accurate to within 0.01 ohms. What is the maximum percentage error involved in the computation?

33. A closed box is found to have length 2 ft, width 4 ft, and height 3 ft, where the measurement of each dimension is made with a maximum possible error of ± 0.02 ft. The top of the box is made from material that costs $2/ft^2, and each square foot of the sides and bottom costs only $1.50/ft^2. What is the maximum possible error involved in the computation?

34. A cylindrical tank is 4 ft high and has a diameter of 2 ft. The walls of the tank are 0.2 in. thick. Approximate ΔV assuming the tank has a top and a bottom that are both also 0.2 in. thick.

35. The Higrade Company sells two brands, X and Y, of a commercial soap in thousand-pound units. If x units of brand X and y units of brand Y are sold, the unit price for brand X is

$$p(x) = 4,000 - 500x$$

and that of brand Y is

$$q(y) = 3,000 - 450y$$

a. Find an expression for the total revenue $R(x, y)$ obtained by selling x units of brand X and y units of brand Y.

b. Suppose brand X sells for $500 per unit and brand Y sells for $750 per unit. Estimate the change in total revenue if the unit prices are increased by $20 for brand X and $18 for brand Y. *Hint*: Find the change in x and the change in y that correspond to $p(x)$ increasing from 500 to 520 and $q(y)$ increasing from 750 to 768.

36. The output at a certain factory is

$$Q = 150K^{2/3} L^{1/3}$$

where K is the capital investment in units of $1,000 and L is the size of the labor force, measured in worker-hours. The current capital investment is $500,000 and 1,500 worker-hours of labor are used.

a. Estimate the change in output that results when capital investment is increased by $700 and labor is increased by 6 worker-hours.

b. What if capital investment is increased by $500 and labor is decreased by 4 worker-hours?

37. According to Poiseuille's law, the resistance to the flow of blood offered by a cylindrical blood vessel of radius r and length x is

$$R(r, x) = \frac{cx}{r^4}$$

for a constant $c > 0$. Estimate the percentage change in R that results when x increases by 3% and r is decreased by 2%.

38. In one mole of an ideal gas, the volume V, pressure P, and absolute temperature T are related by the equation $PV = RT$, where R is a certain fixed constant that depends on the gas. Suppose we know that if $T = 400°$ (*absolute*) and $P = 3,000$ lb/ft^2, then $V = 14$ ft^3. Approximate the change in pressure if the temperature and volume are increased to $403°$ and 14.1 ft^3, respectively.

39. If x gram-moles of sulfuric acid are mixed with y gram-moles of water, the heat liberated is given by

$$F(x, y) = \frac{1.786\, xy}{1.798x + y} \text{ cal}$$

Approximately how much additional heat is generated if a mixture of 5 gram-moles of acid and 4 gram-moles of water is changed to a mixture of 5.1 gram-moles of acid and 4.04 gram-moles of water?

40. An editor estimates that if x thousand dollars are spent on development and y thousand dollars, on promotion, approximately

$$Q(x, y) = 20x^{3/2}y$$

copies of a new book will be sold. Current plans call for the expenditure of $36,000 on development and $25,000 on promotion. Use the total differential of Q to estimate the change in sales that will result if the amount spent on development is increased by $500 and the amount spent on promotion is decreased by $500.

41. A grocer's weekly profit from the sale of two brands of orange juice is

$$P(x, y) = (x - 30)(70 - 5x + 4y) \\ + (y - 40)(80 + 6x - 7y)$$

dollars, where x is the price per can in cents of the first brand and y is the price per can in cents of the second. Currently, the first brand sells for 50¢ per can and the second, for 52¢ per can. Use the total differential to estimate the change in the weekly profit that will result if the grocer raises the price of the first brand by 1¢ per can and raises the price of the second brand by 2¢ per can.

42. A juice can is 12 cm tall and has a radius of 3 cm. A manufacturer is planning to reduce the height of the can by 0.2 cm and the radius by 0.3 cm. Use a total differential to estimate how much less the volume will be in each can after the new cans are introduced.

43. It is known that the period T of a simple pendulum with small oscillations is given by

$$T = 2\pi\sqrt{\frac{L}{g}}$$

where L is the length of the pendulum and g is the acceleration due to gravity. For a certain pendulum, it is known that $L = 4.03$ ft. It is also known that $g = 32.2$ ft/s^2. What is the approximate error in calculating T by using $L = 4$ and $g = 32$?

44. If the weight of an object in the air is x pounds and its weight in water is y pounds, then the specific gravity of the object is

$$S = \frac{x}{x - y}$$

For a certain object, x and y are measured to be 1.2 lb and 0.5 lb, respectively. It is known that the measuring instrument will not register less than the true weights, but it could register more than the true weights by as much as 0.01 lb. What is the maximum possible error in the computation of the specific gravity?

Ⓒ **45.** Show that the following function is not differentiable at $(0, 0)$:

$$f(x, y) = \begin{cases} \dfrac{xy}{x^2 + y^2} & \text{if } (x, y) \neq (0, 0) \\ 0 & \text{if } (x, y) = (0, 0) \end{cases}$$

46. Compute the total differentials

$$d\left(\frac{x}{x - y}\right) \quad \text{and} \quad d\left(\frac{y}{x - y}\right)$$

Why are these differentials alike?

47. Let A be the area of a triangle with sides a and b separated by an angle θ, as shown in Figure 12.20.

Figure 12.20 Problem 47

Suppose $\theta = \frac{\pi}{6}$ and a is increased by 4% while b is decreased by 3%. Use differentials to estimate the percentage change in A.

48. In Problem 47, suppose that θ also changes by no more than 2%. What is the maximum percentage change in A?

12.5 CHAIN RULES

IN THIS SECTION Chain rule for one parameter, chain rule for two parameters

Functional composition is as important in several-variable calculus as in the single-variable case, and now because more than one variable are available, it is possible to form a "function of a function" in a variety of ways. We shall examine several derivatives and partial derivatives in each case.

■ CHAIN RULE FOR ONE PARAMETER

We begin with a differentiable function of two variables $f(x, y)$. If $x = x(t)$ and $y = y(t)$ are, in turn, functions of a single variable t, then $z = f[x(t), y(t)]$ is a composite function of a parameter t. In this case, the chain rule for finding the derivative with respect to one independent variable can now be stated.

THEOREM 12.4   The chain rule for one independent parameter

Let $f(x, y)$ be a differentiable function of x and y, and let $x = x(t)$ and $y = y(t)$ be differentiable functions of t. Then $z = f(x, y)$ is a differentiable function of t, and

$$\frac{dz}{dt} = \frac{\partial z}{\partial x}\frac{dx}{dt} + \frac{\partial z}{\partial y}\frac{dy}{dt}$$

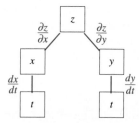

Chains from the chain rule represented schematically

■ **What this says:** Recall the chain rule for a single variable:

$$\frac{dy}{dx} = \frac{dy}{du}\frac{du}{dx}$$

The corresponding rule for two variables is *essentially* the same, except the formula involves *both* variables.

Proof: Recall that because $z = f(x, y)$ is differentiable, we can write the increment Δz in the following form:

$$\Delta z = \frac{\partial z}{\partial x}\Delta x + \frac{\partial z}{\partial y}\Delta y + \varepsilon_1\,\Delta x + \varepsilon_2\,\Delta y$$

where $\varepsilon_1 \to 0$ and $\varepsilon_2 \to 0$ as both $\Delta x \to 0$ and $\Delta y \to 0$ and $\varepsilon_1 = \varepsilon_2 = 0$ when $\Delta x = \Delta y = 0$. Dividing by $\Delta t \neq 0$, we obtain

$$\frac{\Delta z}{\Delta t} = \frac{\partial z}{\partial x}\frac{\Delta x}{\Delta t} + \frac{\partial z}{\partial y}\frac{\Delta y}{\Delta t} + \varepsilon_1\frac{\Delta x}{\Delta t} + \varepsilon_2\frac{\Delta y}{\Delta t}$$

Because x and y are functions of t, we can write their increments as

$$\Delta x = x(t + \Delta t) - x(t) \quad\text{and}\quad \Delta y = y(t + \Delta t) - y(t)$$

We know that x and y both vary continuously with t (remember, they are differentiable), and it follows that $\Delta x \to 0$ and $\Delta y \to 0$ as $\Delta t \to 0$, so that $\varepsilon_1 \to 0$ and $\varepsilon_2 \to 0$ as $\Delta t \to 0$. Therefore, we have

$$\frac{dz}{dt} = \lim_{\Delta t \to 0}\frac{\Delta z}{\Delta t} = \lim_{\Delta t \to 0}\left[\frac{\partial z}{\partial x}\frac{\Delta x}{\Delta t} + \frac{\partial z}{\partial y}\frac{\Delta y}{\Delta t} + \varepsilon_1\frac{\Delta x}{\Delta t} + \varepsilon_2\frac{\Delta y}{\Delta t}\right]$$

$$= \frac{\partial z}{\partial x}\frac{dx}{dt} + \frac{\partial z}{\partial y}\frac{dy}{dt} + 0\frac{dx}{dt} + 0\frac{dy}{dt} \qquad\blacksquare$$

EXAMPLE 1   Verifying the chain rule explicitly

Let $z = x^2 + y^2$, where $x = \frac{1}{t}$ and $y = t^2$. Find $\frac{dz}{dt}$ in two ways:

a. by first expressing z explicitly in terms of t.
b. by using the chain rule.

Solution   **a.** By substituting $x = \frac{1}{t}$ and $y = t^2$, we find that

$$z = x^2 + y^2 = \left(\frac{1}{t}\right)^2 + (t^2)^2 = t^{-2} + t^4 \qquad\text{for } t \neq 0$$

Thus, $\frac{dz}{dt} = -2t^{-3} + 4t^3$.

b. Because $z = x^2 + y^2$ and $x = t^{-1}$, $y = t^2$, so

$$\frac{\partial z}{\partial x} = 2x; \qquad \frac{\partial z}{\partial y} = 2y; \qquad \frac{dx}{dt} = -t^{-2}; \qquad \frac{dy}{dt} = 2t$$

Use the chain rule for one independent parameter:

$$\frac{dz}{dt} = \frac{\partial z}{\partial x}\frac{dx}{dt} + \frac{\partial z}{\partial y}\frac{dy}{dt}$$

$$= (2x)(-t^{-2}) + 2y(2t) \qquad\text{\textit{Chain rule}}$$

$$= 2(t^{-1})(-t^{-2}) + 2(t^2)(2t) \quad\text{\textit{Substitute.}}$$

$$= -2t^{-3} + 4t^3 \qquad\qquad\qquad\blacksquare$$

EXAMPLE 2   Chain rule for one independent parameter

Let $z = \sqrt{x^2 + 2xy}$, where $x = \cos\theta$ and $y = \sin\theta$. Find $\frac{dz}{d\theta}$.

Solution $\dfrac{\partial z}{\partial x} = \dfrac{1}{2}(x^2 + 2xy)^{-1/2}(2x + 2y)$ and $\dfrac{\partial z}{\partial y} = \dfrac{1}{2}(x^2 + 2xy)^{-1/2}(2x)$

Also, $\dfrac{dx}{d\theta} = -\sin\theta$ and $\dfrac{dy}{d\theta} = \cos\theta$. Use the chain rule for one independent parameter to find

$$\dfrac{dz}{d\theta} = \dfrac{\partial z}{\partial x}\dfrac{dx}{d\theta} + \dfrac{\partial z}{\partial y}\dfrac{dy}{d\theta}$$

$$= \tfrac{1}{2}(x^2 + 2xy)^{-1/2}(2x + 2y)(-\sin\theta) + \tfrac{1}{2}(x^2 + 2xy)^{-1/2}(2x)(\cos\theta)$$

$$= (x^2 + 2xy)^{-1/2}(x\cos\theta - x\sin\theta - y\sin\theta)$$

—

EXAMPLE 3   Related rate application using the chain rule

A right circular cylinder is changing in such a way that its radius r is increasing at the rate of 3 in./min and its height h is decreasing at the rate of 5 in./min. At what rate is the volume of the cylinder changing when the radius is 10 in. and the height is 8 in.?

Solution   The volume of the cylinder is $V = \pi r^2 h$, and we are given $\dfrac{dr}{dt} = 3$ and $\dfrac{dh}{dt} = -5$. We find that

$$\dfrac{\partial V}{\partial r} = \pi(2r)h \quad\text{and}\quad \dfrac{\partial V}{\partial h} = \pi r^2(1)$$

By the chain rule for one parameter:

$$\dfrac{dV}{dt} = \dfrac{\partial V}{\partial r}\dfrac{dr}{dt} + \dfrac{\partial V}{\partial h}\dfrac{dh}{dt} = 2\pi rh\dfrac{dr}{dt} + \pi r^2\dfrac{dh}{dt}$$

Thus, at the instant when $r = 10$ and $h = 8$, we have

$$\dfrac{dV}{dt} = 2\pi(10)(8)(3) + \pi(10)^2(-5) = -20\pi \approx -62.83185307$$

The volume is decreasing at the rate of about 62.8 in.^{3}/min.

—

EXAMPLE 4   Second derivative of a function of two variables

Let $z = f(x, y)$, where $x = at$ and $y = bt$ for constants a and b. Assuming all necessary differentiability, find d^2z/dt^2 in terms of the partial derivatives of z.

Solution   We note that $\dfrac{dx}{dt} = a$ and $\dfrac{dy}{dt} = b$, so that

$$\dfrac{dz}{dt} = \dfrac{\partial z}{\partial x}\dfrac{dx}{dt} + \dfrac{\partial z}{\partial y}\dfrac{dy}{dt} \qquad \textit{Chain rule}$$

Differentiate both sides with respect to t:

$$\frac{d^2z}{dt^2} = \frac{\partial z}{\partial x}\frac{d^2x}{dt^2} + \frac{dx}{dt}\left[\frac{\partial^2 z}{\partial x^2}\frac{dx}{dt} + \frac{\partial^2 z}{\partial x \partial y}\frac{dy}{dt}\right] + \frac{\partial z}{\partial y}\frac{d^2y}{dt^2} + \frac{dy}{dt}\left[\frac{\partial^2 z}{\partial y \partial x}\frac{dx}{dt} + \frac{\partial^2 z}{\partial y^2}\frac{dy}{dt}\right]$$

Apply the chain rule again.

$$= \frac{\partial z}{\partial x}(0) + a\left[\frac{\partial^2 z}{\partial x^2}a + \frac{\partial^2 z}{\partial x \partial y}b\right] + \frac{\partial z}{\partial y}(0) + b\left[\frac{\partial^2 z}{\partial y \partial x}a + \frac{\partial^2 z}{\partial y^2}b\right]$$

$$= a^2\frac{\partial^2 z}{\partial x^2} + 2ab\frac{\partial^2 z}{\partial x \partial y} + b^2\frac{\partial^2 z}{\partial y^2} \qquad Note \quad \frac{\partial^2 z}{\partial x \partial y} = \frac{\partial^2 z}{\partial y \partial x}.$$

■ CHAIN RULE FOR TWO PARAMETERS

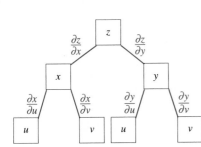

Next, we shall consider the kind of composite function that occurs when x and y are both functions of *two* variables. Specifically, let $z = F(x, y)$, where $x = x(u, v)$ and $y = y(u, v)$ are both functions of two independent parameters u and v. Then $z = F[x(u, v), y(u, v)]$ is a composite function of u and v, and with suitable assumptions regarding differentiability, we can find the partial derivatives $\partial z/\partial u$ and $\partial z/\partial v$ by applying the chain rule obtained in the following theorem.

THEOREM 12.5 **The chain rule for two independent parameters**

Suppose $z = f(x, y)$ is differentiable at (x, y) and that the partial derivatives of $x = x(u, v)$ and $y = y(u, v)$ exist at (u, v). Then the composite function $z = f[x(u, v), y(u, v)]$ is differentiable at (u, v) with

$$\frac{\partial z}{\partial u} = \frac{\partial z}{\partial x}\frac{\partial x}{\partial u} + \frac{\partial z}{\partial y}\frac{\partial y}{\partial u} \quad \text{and} \quad \frac{\partial z}{\partial v} = \frac{\partial z}{\partial x}\frac{\partial x}{\partial v} + \frac{\partial z}{\partial y}\frac{\partial y}{\partial v}$$

Proof: This version of the chain rule follows immediately from the chain rule for one independent parameter. For example, if v is fixed, the composite function $z = f[x(u, v), y(u, v)]$ really depends on u alone, and we have the situation described in the chain rule of one independent variable. We apply this chain rule with a partial derivative instead of an "ordinary" derivative (because x and y are functions of more than one variable):

$$\frac{\partial z}{\partial u} = \frac{\partial z}{\partial x}\frac{\partial x}{\partial u} + \frac{\partial z}{\partial y}\frac{\partial y}{\partial u}$$

The formula for $\frac{\partial z}{\partial v}$ can be established in a similar fashion. ∎

EXAMPLE 5 **Chain rule for two independent parameters**

Let $z = 4x - y^2$, where $x = uv^2$ and $y = u^3v$. Find $\frac{\partial z}{\partial u}$ and $\frac{\partial z}{\partial v}$.

Solution First find the partial derivatives:

$$\frac{\partial z}{\partial x} = \frac{\partial}{\partial x}(4x - y^2) = 4 \qquad \frac{\partial z}{\partial y} = \frac{\partial}{\partial y}(4x - y^2) = -2y$$

and

$$\frac{\partial x}{\partial u} = \frac{\partial}{\partial u}(uv^2) = v^2 \qquad \frac{\partial y}{\partial u} = \frac{\partial}{\partial u}(u^3v) = 3u^2v$$

$$\frac{\partial x}{\partial v} = \frac{\partial}{\partial v}(uv^2) = 2uv \qquad \frac{\partial y}{\partial v} = \frac{\partial}{\partial v}(u^3v) = u^3$$

Therefore, the chain rule for two independent parameters gives

$$\frac{\partial z}{\partial u} = \frac{\partial z}{\partial x}\frac{\partial x}{\partial u} + \frac{\partial z}{\partial y}\frac{\partial y}{\partial u}$$

$$= (4)(v^2) + (-2y)(3u^2v) = 4v^2 - 2(u^3v)(3u^2v) = 4v^2 - 6u^5v^2$$

and

$$\frac{\partial z}{\partial v} = \frac{\partial z}{\partial x}\frac{\partial x}{\partial v} + \frac{\partial z}{\partial y}\frac{\partial y}{\partial v}$$

$$= (4)(2uv) + (-2y)(u^3) = 8uv - 2(u^3v)u^3 = 8uv - 2u^6v \quad \rule[0.5ex]{1.5em}{0.6ex}$$

The chain rules can be extended to functions of three or more variables. For instance, if $w = f(x, y, z)$ is a differentiable function of three variables and $x = x(t)$, $y = y(t)$, $z = z(t)$ are each differentiable functions of t, then w is a differentiable composite function of t and

$$\frac{dw}{dt} = \frac{\partial w}{\partial x}\frac{dx}{dt} + \frac{\partial w}{\partial y}\frac{dy}{dt} + \frac{\partial w}{\partial z}\frac{dz}{dt}$$

In general, if $w = f(x_1, x_2, \ldots, x_n)$ is a differential function of the n variables x_1, $x_2, \ldots, x_n$, which in turn are differentiable functions of m variables $t_1, t_2, \ldots, t_m$, then

$$\frac{\partial w}{\partial t_1} = \frac{\partial w}{\partial x_1}\frac{\partial x_1}{\partial t_1} + \frac{\partial w}{\partial x_2}\frac{\partial x_2}{\partial t_1} + \cdots + \frac{\partial w}{\partial x_n}\frac{\partial x_n}{\partial t_1}$$

$$\vdots$$

$$\frac{\partial w}{\partial t_m} = \frac{\partial w}{\partial x_1}\frac{\partial x_1}{\partial t_m} + \frac{\partial w}{\partial x_2}\frac{\partial x_2}{\partial t_m} + \cdots + \frac{\partial w}{\partial x_n}\frac{\partial x_n}{\partial t_m}$$

EXAMPLE 6   Chain rule for a function of several variables

Find $\dfrac{\partial w}{\partial s}$ if $w = 4x + y^2 + z^3$ where $x = e^{rs^2}$, $y = \ln\dfrac{r+s}{t}$, and $z = rst^2$

Solution

$$\frac{\partial w}{\partial s} = \frac{\partial w}{\partial x}\frac{\partial x}{\partial s} + \frac{\partial w}{\partial y}\frac{\partial y}{\partial s} + \frac{\partial w}{\partial z}\frac{\partial z}{\partial s}$$

$$= \left[\frac{\partial}{\partial x}(4x + y^2 + z^3)\right]\left[\frac{\partial}{\partial s}\left(e^{rs^2}\right)\right] + \left[\frac{\partial}{\partial y}(4x + y^2 + z^3)\right]\left[\frac{\partial}{\partial s}\left(\ln\frac{r+s}{t}\right)\right]$$

$$+ \left[\frac{\partial}{\partial z}(4x + y^2 + z^3)\right]\left[\frac{\partial}{\partial s}(rst^2)\right]$$

$$= 4\left[e^{rs^2}(2rs)\right] + 2y\left(\frac{1}{\frac{r+s}{t}}\right)\left(\frac{1}{t}\right) + 3z^2(rt^2)$$

$$= 8rse^{rs^2} + \frac{2y}{r+s} + 3rt^2z^2$$

In terms of r, s, and t, the partial derivative is

$$\frac{\partial w}{\partial s} = 8rse^{rs^2} + \frac{2}{r+s} \ln \frac{r+s}{t} + 3r^3s^2t^6$$

▬

PROBLEM SET 12.5

Ⓐ **1.** ■ **What Does This Say?** Discuss the various chain rules and the need for such chain rules.

2. ■ **What Does This Say?** Discuss the usefulness of the schematic representation for the chain rules.

3. ■ **What Does This Say?** Write out a chain rule for three independent parameters and two intermediate variables.

In Problems 4–7, the function f(x, y) depends on x and y, which in turn are both functions of t. In each case, find dz/dt two different ways:

a. *Express z explicitly in terms of t.*

b. *By using the chain rule for one parameter.*

4. $f(x, y) = 2xy + y^2$, where $x = -3t^2$ and $y = 1 + t^3$

5. $f(x, y) = (4 + y^2)x$, where $x = e^{2t}$ and $y = e^{3t}$

6. $f(x, y) = (1 + x^2 + y^2)^{1/2}$, where $x = \cos 5t$ and $y = \sin 5t$

7. $f(x, y) = xy^2$, where $x = \cos 3t$ and $y = \tan t$

In Problems 8–11, the function F(x, y) depends on x and y. Let x = x(u, v) and y = y(u, v) be given functions of u and v. Let z = F[x(u, v), y(u, v)] and find the partial derivatives ∂z/∂u and ∂z/∂v in these two ways:

a. *Express z explicitly in terms of u and v.*

b. *Apply the chain rule for two independent parameters.*

8. $F(x, y) = x + y^2$, where $x = u + v$ and $y = u - v$

9. $F(x, y) = x^2 + y^2$, where $x = u \sin v$ and $y = u - 2v$

10. $F(x, y) = e^{xy}$, where $x = u - v$ and $y = u + v$

11. $F(x, y) = \ln xy$, where $x = e^{uv^2}$, $y = e^{uv}$

Write out the chain rule for the functions given in Problems 12–15.

12. $z = f(x, y)$, where $x = x(s, t)$, $y = y(s, t)$

13. $w = f(x, y, z)$, where $x = x(s, t)$, $y = y(s, t)$, $z = z(s, t)$

14. $w = f(u, v)$, where $u = u(x, y, z, w)$, $v = v(x, y, z, w)$

15. $w = f(x, y, z)$, where $x = x(s, t, u)$, $y = y(s, t, u)$, $z = z(s, t, u)$

Find the indicated derivatives or partial derivatives in Problems 16–21. Leave your answers in mixed form (x, y, z, t, u, v).

16. Find $\frac{dw}{dt}$, where $w = \ln(x + 2y - z^2)$ and $x = 2t - 1$, $y = \frac{1}{t}$, $z = \sqrt{t}$.

17. Find $\frac{dw}{dt}$, where $w = \sin xyz$ and $x = 1 - 3t$, $y = e^{1-t}$, $z = 4t$.

18. Find $\frac{dw}{dt}$, where $w = ze^{xy^2}$ and $x = \sin t$, $y = \cos t$, $z = \tan 2t$.

19. Find $\frac{dw}{dt}$, where $w = e^{x^3} + yz$ and $x = \frac{2}{t}$, $y = \ln(2t - 3)$, $z = t^2$.

20. Find $\frac{\partial w}{\partial r}$, where $w = e^{2x - y + 3z^2}$ and $x = r + s - t$, $y = 2r - 3s$, $z = \cos rst$.

21. Find $\frac{\partial w}{\partial r}$ and $\frac{\partial w}{\partial t}$, where $w = \frac{x+y}{2-z}$ and $x = 2rs$, $y = \sin rt$, $z = st^2$.

Ⓑ *Find the following higher partial derivatives in Problems 22–27.*

a. $\frac{\partial^2 z}{\partial x \partial y}$ **b.** $\frac{\partial^2 z}{\partial x^2}$ **c.** $\frac{\partial^2 z}{\partial y^2}$

22. $x^3 + y^2 + z^2 = 5$ **23.** $xyz = 2$

24. $\ln(x + y) = y^2 + 1$ **25.** $x^{-1} + y^{-1} + z^{-1} = 3$

26. $x \cos y = y + z$ **27.** $z^2 + \sin x = \tan y$

28. Let $f(x, y)$ be a differentiable function of x and y, and let $x = r \cos \theta$, $y = r \sin \theta$ for $r > 0$ and $0 < \theta < 2\pi$.

a. If $z = f[x(r, \theta), y(r, \theta)]$, find $\frac{\partial z}{\partial r}$ and $\frac{\partial z}{\partial \theta}$

b. Show that

$$\left(\frac{\partial z}{\partial r}\right)^2 + \frac{1}{r^2}\left(\frac{\partial z}{\partial \theta}\right)^2 = \left(\frac{\partial z}{\partial x}\right)^2 + \left(\frac{\partial z}{\partial y}\right)^2$$

29. Let $z = f(x, y)$, where $x = au$ and $y = bv$, with a, b constants. Express $\partial^2 z/\partial u^2$ and $\partial^2 z/\partial v^2$ in terms of the partial derivatives of z with respect to x and y. Assume the existence and continuity of all necessary first and second partial derivatives.

30. Let (x, y, z) lie on the ellipsoid

$$\frac{x^2}{a^2} + \frac{y^2}{b^2} + \frac{z^2}{c^2} = 1$$

Without solving for z explicitly in terms of x and y, compute the higher partial derivatives

$$\frac{\partial^2 z}{\partial x^2} \quad \text{and} \quad \frac{\partial^2 z}{\partial x \partial y}$$

31. The dimensions of a rectangular box are changing in such a way that the length $\ell(t)$, width $w(t)$, and height $h(t)$ are linear functions of time t. If the length and width are increasing at 2 in./sec and the height is decreasing at 3 in./sec, find the rates at which the volume V and the surface area S are changing with respect to time. If $\ell(0) = 10$, $w(0) = 8$, and $h(0) = 20$, is V increasing or decreasing when $t = 5$ sec? What about S when $t = 5$?

32. Using x hours of skilled labor and y hours of unskilled labor, a manufacturer can produce $f(x, y) = 10xy^{1/2}$ units. Currently, the manufacturer has used 30 hr of skilled labor and 36 h of unskilled labor and is planning to use

1 additional hour of skilled labor. Use calculus to estimate the corresponding change that the manufacturer should make in the level of unskilled labor so that the total output will remain the same.

In Problems 33–39, assume that all functions have whatever derivatives or partial derivatives are necessary for the problem to be meaningful.

33. If $z = f(uv^2)$, show that

$$2u \frac{\partial z}{\partial u} - v \frac{\partial z}{\partial v} = 0$$

Hint: Let $w = uv^2$ and apply the chain rule.

34. If $z = u + f(u^2 v^2)$, show that

$$u \frac{\partial z}{\partial u} - v \frac{\partial z}{\partial v} = u$$

Hint: Let $w = u^2 v^2$ and apply the chain rule.

35. If $z = f(u - v, v - u)$, show that

$$\frac{\partial z}{\partial u} + \frac{\partial z}{\partial v} = 0$$

36. If $z = u + f(uv)$, show that $u \frac{\partial z}{\partial u} - v \frac{\partial z}{\partial v} = u$.

37. If $w = f\left(\frac{r - s}{s}\right)$, show that $r \frac{\partial w}{\partial r} + s \frac{\partial w}{\partial s} = 0$.

38. If $z = f(x^2 - y^2)$, evaluate $y \frac{\partial z}{\partial x} + x \frac{\partial z}{\partial y}$.

39. If $z = xy + f(x^2 + y^2)$, show that

$$y \frac{\partial z}{\partial x} - x \frac{\partial z}{\partial y} = y^2 - x^2$$

40. Let $w = f(t)$ be a differentiable function of t, where $t = (x^2 + y^2 + z^2)^{1/2}$. Show that

$$\left(\frac{dw}{dt}\right)^2 = \left(\frac{\partial w}{\partial x}\right)^2 + \left(\frac{\partial w}{\partial y}\right)^2 + \left(\frac{\partial w}{\partial z}\right)^2$$

41. Suppose f is a twice differentiable function of one variable, and let $z = f(x^2 + y^2)$. Find

   a. $\frac{\partial^2 z}{\partial x^2}$ b. $\frac{\partial^2 z}{\partial y^2}$ c. $\frac{\partial^2 z}{\partial x \partial y}$

42. Find $\frac{d^2 z}{d\theta^2}$ where f is a twice differentiable function of one variable and $z = f(\cos \theta, \sin \theta)$. *Hint*: Let $x = \cos \theta$ and $y = \sin \theta$. Leave your answer in terms of x and y.

43. Let f and g be twice differentiable functions of one variable, and let

$$u(x, t) = f(x + ct) + g(x - ct)$$

for a constant c. Show that $\frac{\partial^2 u}{\partial t^2} = c^2 \frac{\partial^2 u}{\partial x^2}$

Hint: Let $u = x + ct$; $v = x - ct$

44. Suppose $z = f(x, y)$ has continuous second-order partial derivatives. If $x = e^r \cos \theta$ and $y = e^r \sin \theta$, show that

$$\frac{\partial^2 z}{\partial x^2} + \frac{\partial^2 z}{\partial y^2} = e^{-2r}\left[\frac{\partial^2 z}{\partial r^2} + \frac{\partial^2 z}{\partial \theta^2}\right]$$

Ⓒ 45. Suppose F is a differentiable function of x and y and that $F(x, y) = C$ for some constant C in an open set S where $y = y(x)$ is a differentiable function of x. Show that

$$\frac{dy}{dx} = \frac{-F_x}{F_y}, \quad F_y \neq 0$$

46. Let $F(x, y, z)$ be a function of three variables with continuous partial derivatives F_x, F_y, F_z in a certain region where $F(x, y, z) = C$ for some constant C. Use the chain rule for two parameters and $\partial y/\partial x = 0$ to show that

$$\frac{\partial z}{\partial x} = \frac{-\dfrac{\partial F}{\partial x}}{\dfrac{\partial F}{\partial z}} = \frac{-F_x}{F_z}$$

47. Suppose the system

$$\begin{cases} xu + yv - uv = 0 \\ yu - xv + uv = 0 \end{cases}$$

can be solved for u and v in terms of x and y, so that $u = u(x, y)$ and $v = v(x, y)$. Use implicit differentiation to find the partial derivatives $\partial u/\partial x$ and $\partial v/\partial x$.

48. Repeat Problem 47 for the system

$$\begin{cases} xu + yv - uv = 0 \\ yu - xv + uv = 0 \end{cases}$$

for $\partial u/\partial y$ and $\partial v/\partial y$.

49. Suppose that F and G are functions of three variables and that it is possible to solve the equations $F(x, y, z) = 0$ and $G(x, y, z) = 0$ for y and z in terms of x, so that $y = y(x)$ and $z = z(x)$. Use the chain rule to express dy/dx and dz/dx in terms of the partial derivatives of F and G. Assume these partials are continuous and that

$$\frac{\partial F}{\partial y}\frac{\partial G}{\partial z} \neq \frac{\partial F}{\partial z}\frac{\partial G}{\partial y}$$

12.6 DIRECTIONAL DERIVATIVES AND THE GRADIENT

IN THIS SECTION The directional derivative, the gradient, normal property of the gradient, tangent planes and normal lines

In Section 12.3, we observed that if P_0 is a point on a surface, then the slopes of the tangent lines through P_0 on the surface parallel to the *xz*- or *yz*-plane are given by f_x or f_y, respectively, as shown in the illustration.

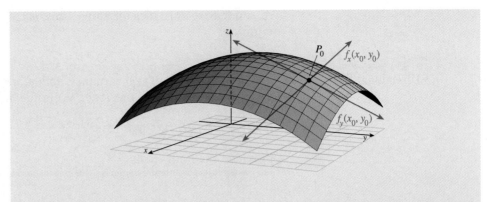

In this section, we seek to find a derivative in other directions, called the *directional derivative*. After we find the directional derivative, we will express it in terms of a vector function called a *gradient*. We conclude by looking at some applications of the gradient.

■ THE DIRECTIONAL DERIVATIVE

In Chapter 1 we defined the *slope of a curve* at a point to be the ratio of the change in the dependent variable with respect to the change in the independent variable at the given point. In order to determine the slope of the tangent line at a point $P_0(x_0, y_0)$ on a surface defined by $z = f(x, y)$, we need to specify the *direction* in which we wish to measure. We do this by using vectors. In Section 12.3 we found the slope parallel to the xz-plane to be the partial derivative $f_x(x_0, y_0)$. We could have specified this direction in terms of the vector $\mathbf{i}$ (x-direction). Similarly, $f_y(x, y)$ could have been specified in terms of the $\mathbf{j}$ vector. Finally, to measure the slope of the tangent line in an *arbitrary* direction, we use a unit vector $\mathbf{u} = u_1\mathbf{i} + u_2\mathbf{j}$ in that direction.

⊘ **u** must have unit length. ⊘

To find the desired slope, we look at the intersection of the surface with the vertical plane passing through the point P_0 parallel to the vector $\mathbf{u}$, as shown in Figure 12.21. This vertical plane intersects the surface to form a curve C, and we define the slope of the surface at P_0 in the direction of $\mathbf{u}$ to be the slope of the tangent line to the curve C defined by $\mathbf{u}$ at that point.

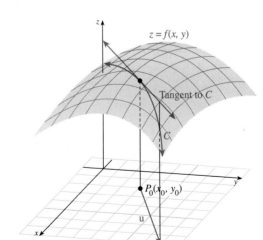

Figure 12.21 The directional derivative $D_u f(x_0, y_0)$ is the slope of the tangent line to the curve on the surface $z = f(x, y)$ in the direction of the unit vector $\mathbf{u}$ at $P_0(x_0, y_0)$.

We summarize this idea of slope *in a particular direction* with the following definition.

Directional Derivative

Let f be a function of two variables, and let $\mathbf{u} = u_1\mathbf{i} + u_2\mathbf{j}$ be a unit vector. The **directional derivative of f at $P_0(x_0, y_0)$ in the direction of u** is given by

$$D_u f(x_0, y_0) = \lim_{h \to 0} \frac{f(x_0 + hu_1, y_0 + hu_2) - f(x_0, y_0)}{h}$$

provided the limit exists.

EXAMPLE 1   Computing partial derivatives as directional derivatives

Use the definition of directional derivative to show that the directional derivative of $f(x, y)$ in the directions of the positive x- and y-axes are f_x and f_y respectively.

Solution   In the direction of the positive x-axis, $\mathbf{u} = \mathbf{i}$, so that $u_1 = 1$ and $u_2 = 0$.

$$D_i f(x_0, y_0) = \lim_{h \to 0} \frac{f(x_0 + h, y_0) - f(x_0, y_0)}{h} \qquad \begin{array}{l}\textit{Definition of directional} \\ \textit{derivative, where } u_1 = 1 \\ \textit{and } u_2 = 0\end{array}$$

$$= f_x(x_0, y_0) \qquad \textit{Definition of } f_x$$

In the direction of the positive y-axis, $\mathbf{u} = \mathbf{j}$, so that $u_1 = 0$ and $u_2 = 1$.

$$D_j f(x_0, y_0) = \lim_{h \to 0} \frac{f(x_0, y_0 + h) - f(x_0, y_0)}{h} \qquad \begin{array}{l}\textit{Definition of directional} \\ \textit{derivative, where } u_1 = 0 \\ \textit{and } u_2 = 1\end{array}$$

$$= f_y(x_0, y_0) \qquad \textit{Definition of } f_y \qquad \blacksquare$$

The definition of directional derivative is similar to the definition of the derivative of a function of a single variable. Just as with a single variable, it is difficult to apply the definition directly. Fortunately, the following theorem allows us to find directional derivatives more efficiently than by using the definition.

THEOREM 12.6   Directional derivatives using partials

Let $f(x, y)$ be a function that is differentiable at $P_0(x_0, y_0)$. Then f has a directional derivative in the direction of any unit vector $\mathbf{u} = u_1\mathbf{i} + u_2\mathbf{j}$. That directional derivative is given by

$$D_u f(x_0, y_0) = f_x(x_0, y_0)u_1 + f_y(x_0, y_0)u_2$$

Proof: We define a function F of a single variable h by $F(h) = f(x_0 + hu_1, y_0 + hu_2)$, so that

$$D_u f(x_0, y_0) = \lim_{h \to 0} \frac{f(x_0 + hu_1, y_0 + hu_2) - f(x_0, y_0)}{h}$$

$$= \lim_{h \to 0} \frac{F(h) - F(0)}{h} = F'(0)$$

Apply the chain rule with $x = x_0 + hu_1$ and $y = y_0 + hu_2$,

$$F'(h) = \frac{dF}{dh} = \frac{\partial f}{\partial x}\frac{dx}{dh} + \frac{\partial f}{\partial y}\frac{dy}{dh} = f_x(x, y)u_1 + f_y(x, y)u_2$$

When $h = 0$, we have $x = x_0$ and $y = y_0$, so that

$$D_u f(x_0, y_0) = F'(0) = \frac{\partial f}{\partial x}u_1 + \frac{\partial f}{\partial y}u_2 = f_x(x_0, y_0)\,u_1 + f_y(x_0, y_0)\,u_2 \qquad \blacksquare$$

EXAMPLE 2   Finding a directional derivative using partials

Find the directional derivative of $f(x, y) = 3 - 2x^2 + y^3$ at the point $P(1, 2)$ in the direction of the unit vector $\mathbf{u} = \frac{1}{2}\mathbf{i} - \frac{\sqrt{3}}{2}\mathbf{j}$.

Solution   First find the partial derivatives $f_x(x, y) = -4x$ and $f_y(x, y) = 3y^2$. Notice that $u_1 = \frac{1}{2}$ and $u_2 = -\sqrt{3}/2$, so

$$D_u f(1, 2) = f_x(1, 2)\left(\tfrac{1}{2}\right) + f_y(1, 2)\left(-\tfrac{\sqrt{3}}{2}\right)$$

$$= -4(1)\left(\tfrac{1}{2}\right) + 3(2)^2\left(-\tfrac{\sqrt{3}}{2}\right) = -2 - 6\sqrt{3} \approx -12.4 \qquad \rule[0.3em]{1.5em}{0.12em}$$

Notice that the directional derivative is a number. This number can be interpreted as the slope of a tangent line to $z = f(x, y)$ or as a rate of change of the function $z = f(x, y)$.

Directional derivative as a slope. Geometrically, we look at the surface defined by $z = 3 - 2x^2 + y^3$, as shown in Figure 12.22. The intersection of this surface with a plane aligned with the vector $\mathbf{u} = \frac{1}{2}\mathbf{i} - \frac{\sqrt{3}}{2}\mathbf{j}$ is a curve labeled C, and the directional derivative is the slope of the tangent line to C at the point on the surface above $P(1, 2)$. This directional derivative is shown in Figure 12.22.

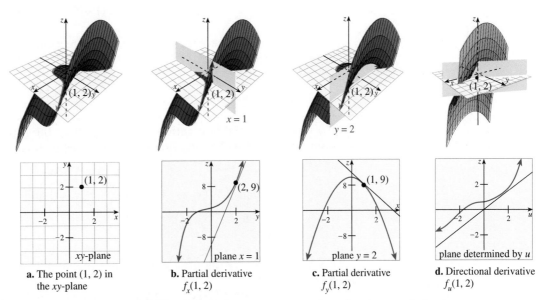

a. The point $(1, 2)$ in the xy-plane

b. Partial derivative $f_x(1, 2)$

c. Partial derivative $f_y(1, 2)$

d. Directional derivative $f_u(1, 2)$

Figure 12.22 Graph of $z = 3 - 2x^2 + y^3$ and some derivatives

Directional derivative as a rate. The directional derivative $D_u f(x_0, y_0)$ can also be interpreted as the rate at which the function $z = f(x, y)$ changes as a point moves from $P_0(x_0, y_0)$ in the direction of the unit vector **u**. Thus, in Example 2, we say that the function $f(x, y) = 3 - 2x^2 + y^3$ changes at the rate of $-2 - 6\sqrt{3}$ as we move from $P(1, 2)$ in the direction of the unit vector $\mathbf{u} = \frac{1}{2}\mathbf{i} - \frac{\sqrt{3}}{2}\mathbf{j}$.

■ THE GRADIENT

The directional derivative $D_u f(x, y)$ can be expressed concisely in terms of a vector function called the *gradient*, which has many important uses in mathematics. The gradient of a function of two variables may be defined as follows.

Gradient

Let f be a differentiable function at (x, y) and let $f(x, y)$ have partial derivatives $f_x(x, y)$ and $f_y(x, y)$. Then the **gradient** of f, denoted by ∇f (pronounced "del eff"), is a vector given by

$$\nabla f(x, y) = f_x(x, y)\mathbf{i} + f_y(x, y)\mathbf{j}$$

⊘ Think of the symbol ∇ as an "operator" on a function that produces a vector. Another notation for ∇f is **grad** $f(x, y)$. ⊘

EXAMPLE 3   Finding the gradient of a given function

Find $\nabla f(x, y)$ for $f(x, y) = x^2 y + y^3$.

Solution   Begin with the partial derivatives:

$$f_x(x, y) = \frac{\partial}{\partial x}(x^2 y + y^3) = 2xy \quad \text{and} \quad f_y(x, y) = \frac{\partial}{\partial y}(x^2 y + y^3) = x^2 + 3y^2$$

Then,

$$\nabla f(x, y) = 2xy\mathbf{i} + (x^2 + 3y^2)\mathbf{j}$$

The following theorem shows how the directional derivative can be expressed in terms of the gradient.

THEOREM 12.7   The gradient formula for the directional derivative

If f is a differentiable function of x and y, then the directional derivative at the point $P_0(x_0, y_0)$ in the direction of the unit vector **u** is

$$D_u f(x, y) = \nabla f \cdot \mathbf{u}$$

Proof: Because $\nabla f(x, y) = f_x(x, y)\mathbf{i} + f_y(x, y)\mathbf{j}$ and $\mathbf{u} = u_1\mathbf{i} + u_2\mathbf{j}$, then

$$\nabla f_0 \cdot \mathbf{u} = f_x(x_0, y_0)u_1 + f_y(x_0, y_0)u_2 = D_u f(x_0, y_0) \quad \textit{Dot product} \qquad ∎$$

EXAMPLE 4   Using gradient formula to compute a directional derivative

Find the directional derivative of $f(x, y) = \ln(x^2 + y^3)$ at $P_0(1, -3)$ in the direction of $\mathbf{v} = 2\mathbf{i} - 3\mathbf{j}$.

Solution
$$f_x(x, y) = \frac{2x}{x^2 + y^3}, \quad \text{so} \quad f_x(1, -3) = -\frac{1}{13}$$

$$f_y(x, y) = \frac{3y^2}{x^2 + y^3}, \quad \text{so} \quad f_y(1, -3) = -\frac{27}{26}$$

$$\nabla f_0(1, -3) = -\frac{2}{26}\mathbf{i} - \frac{27}{26}\mathbf{j}$$

A unit vector in the direction of **v** is

$$\mathbf{u} = \frac{\mathbf{v}}{\|\mathbf{v}\|} = \frac{2\mathbf{i} - 3\mathbf{j}}{\sqrt{2^2 + (-3)^2}} = \frac{1}{\sqrt{13}}(2\mathbf{i} - 3\mathbf{j})$$

Thus,

$$D_u(1, -3) = \nabla f_0 \cdot \mathbf{u} = \left(-\frac{2}{26}\right)\left(\frac{2}{\sqrt{13}}\right) + \left(-\frac{27}{26}\right)\left(-\frac{3}{\sqrt{13}}\right) = \frac{77\sqrt{13}}{338} \approx 0.82 \quad \blacksquare$$

We know that a differentiable function of one variable $f(x)$ has exactly one derivative $f'(x)$, but a differentiable function of two variables $F(x, y)$ has two partial derivatives and a multitude of directional derivatives. Is there any single mathematical entity for functions of several variables that is the analog of the derivative of a function of a single variable? The answer is that the gradient is perhaps the best analog, as may be seen by comparing the properties listed in the following theorem with the properties of the derivative.

THEOREM 12.8   Basic properties of the gradient

Let f and g be differentiable functions. Then

Constant rule	$\nabla c = \mathbf{0}$ for any constant c
Linearity rule	$\nabla(af + bg) = a\nabla f + b\nabla g$ for constants a and b
Product rule	$\nabla(fg) = f\nabla g + g\nabla f$
Quotient rule	$\nabla\left(\dfrac{f}{g}\right) = \dfrac{g\nabla f - f\nabla g}{g^2}$ $g \neq 0$
Power rule	$\nabla(f^n) = nf^{(n-1)}\nabla f$

Proof: Linearity rule:

$$\nabla(af + bg) = (af + bg)_x\mathbf{i} + (af + bg)_y\mathbf{j} = (af_x + bg_x)\mathbf{i} + (af_y + bg_y)\mathbf{j}$$
$$= af_x\mathbf{i} + bg_x\mathbf{i} + af_y\mathbf{j} + bg_y\mathbf{j} = a(f_x\mathbf{i} + f_y\mathbf{j}) + b(g_x\mathbf{i} + g_y\mathbf{j})$$
$$= a\nabla f + b\nabla g$$

Power rule:

$$\nabla f^n = [f^n]_x\,\mathbf{i} + [f^n]_y\,\mathbf{j} = nf^{n-1}f_x\mathbf{i} + nf^{n-1}f_y\mathbf{j}$$
$$= nf^{n-1}[f_x\mathbf{i} + f_y\mathbf{j}] = nf^{n-1}\nabla f$$

The other rules are left for the problem set (Problems 58 and 59).   ∎

In applications, it is often useful to compute the greatest rate of increase (or decrease) of a given function at a specified point. The direction in which this occurs is called the direction of **steepest ascent** (or **steepest descent**), as shown in Figure 12.23a.

For example, imagine a person skiing down a mountain. The function $z = f(x, y)$ gives the altitude of the skier on the slope, and we want to state a theorem that will give the skier the *compass direction* of the path of steepest descent. We emphasize the words "compass direction" because the gradient gives direction in the xy-plane and does not itself point up or down the mountain.

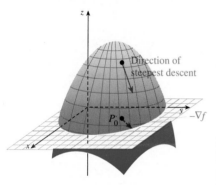

"Steepest" tangent vector has magnitude $|\nabla f_0|$.

$z = f(x, y)$

"Least steep" tangent vector has magnitude $-|\nabla f_0|$.

∇f_0

P_0

The optimal direction property of the gradient

Figure 12.23 Steepest ascent or steepest descent

Direction of steepest descent

P_0

$-\nabla f$

The gradient of f is a vector ∇f_0 in the xy-plane. This vector points in the direction of steepest ascent or descent at a given point.

THEOREM 12.9   Optimal direction property of the gradient

Suppose f is differentiable and let ∇f_0 denote the gradient at P_0. Then if $\nabla f_0 \neq \mathbf{0}$:

a. The largest value of the directional derivative of $D_u f$ is $\|\nabla f_0\|$ and occurs when the unit vector $\mathbf{u}$ points in the direction of ∇f_0.

b. The smallest value of $D_u f$ is $-\|\nabla f_0\|$ and occurs when $\mathbf{u}$ points in the direction of $-\nabla f_0$.

Proof: If $\mathbf{u}$ is any unit vector, then

$$D_u f = \nabla f_0 \cdot \mathbf{u} = \|\nabla f_0\|(\|\mathbf{u}\| \cos \theta) = \|\nabla f_0\| \cos \theta \quad \textit{Dot product (alternative form)}$$

where θ is the angle between ∇f_0 and $\mathbf{u}$. But $\cos \theta$ assumes its largest value 1 at $\theta = 0$; that is, when $\mathbf{u}$ points in the direction ∇f_0. Thus, the largest possible value of $D_u f$ is

$$D_u f = \|\nabla f_0\|(1) = \|\nabla f_0\|$$

Statement **b** may be established in a similar fashion by noting that $\cos \theta$ assumes its smallest value -1 when $\theta = \pi$. This value occurs when $\mathbf{u}$ points toward $-\nabla f_0$, and in this direction $D_u f = \|\nabla f_0\|(-1) = -\|\nabla f_0\|$. ∎

> ■ ***What this says:*** The theorem states that at P_0, the function f increases most rapidly in the direction of the gradient ∇f_0 and decreases most rapidly in the opposite direction.

EXAMPLE 5   Optimal rate of increase and decrease

In what direction is the function defined by $f(x, y) = xe^{2y-x}$ increasing most rapidly at the point $P_0(2, 1)$, and what is the optimal rate of increase? In what direction is f decreasing most rapidly?

Solution   We begin by finding the gradient of f:

$$\nabla f = f_x \mathbf{i} + f_y \mathbf{j} = [e^{2y-x} + xe^{2y-x}(-1)]\mathbf{i} + [xe^{2y-x}(2)]\mathbf{j}$$
$$= e^{2y-x}[(1 - x)\mathbf{i} + 2x\mathbf{j}]$$

At $(2, 1)$, $\nabla f_0 = e^{2(1)-2}[(1 - 2)\mathbf{i} + 2(2)\mathbf{j}] = -\mathbf{i} + 4\mathbf{j}$. The most rapid rate of increase is $\|\nabla f_0\| = \sqrt{(-1)^2 + (4)^2} = \sqrt{17}$ and it occurs in the direction of $-\mathbf{i} + 4\mathbf{j}$. The most rapid rate of decrease occurs in the direction of $-\nabla f_0 = \mathbf{i} - 4\mathbf{j}$. ▬

The directional derivative and gradient concepts can easily be extended to functions of three or more variables. For a function of three variables, $f(x, y, z)$, the gradient ∇f is defined by

$$\nabla f_0 = f_x \mathbf{i} + f_y \mathbf{j} + f_z \mathbf{k}$$

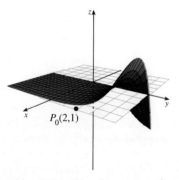

$P_0(2,1)$

Surface defined by $f(x, y) = xe^{2y-x}$

and the directional derivative $D_u f$ of $f(x, y, z)$ at $P_0(x_0, y_0, z_0)$ in the direction of the unit vector **u** is given by $\qquad D_u f = \nabla f_0 \cdot \mathbf{u}$

where, as before, ∇f_0 is the gradient ∇f evaluated at P_0. The basic properties of the gradient (Theorem 12.8) are still valid, as are the optimization properties in Theorem 12.9. Similar definitions and properties are valid for functions of more than three variables.

EXAMPLE 6   Directional derivative of a function of three variables

Let $f(x, y, z) = xy \sin xz$. Find ∇f_0 at the point $P_0(1, -2, \pi)$ and then compute the directional derivative of f at P_0 in the direction of the vector
$\mathbf{v} = -2\mathbf{i} + 3\mathbf{j} - 5\mathbf{k}$.

Solution   Begin with the partial derivatives:

$$f_x = y \sin xz + xy(z \cos xz); \qquad f_x(1, -2, \pi) = -2 \sin \pi - 2\pi \cos \pi = 2\pi$$

$$f_y = x \sin xz; \qquad f_y(1, -2, \pi) = 1 \sin \pi = 0$$

$$f_z = xy(x \cos xz); \qquad f_z(1, -2, \pi) = (1)(-2)(1)\cos \pi = 2$$

Thus, the gradient of f at P_0 is

$$\nabla f_0 = 2\pi \mathbf{i} + 2\mathbf{k}$$

To find $D_u f$ we need **u**, the unit vector in the direction of **v**:

$$\mathbf{u} = \frac{\mathbf{v}}{\|\mathbf{v}\|} = \frac{-2\mathbf{i} + 3\mathbf{j} - 5\mathbf{k}}{\sqrt{(-2)^2 + (3)^2 + (-5)^2}} = \frac{1}{\sqrt{38}}(-2\mathbf{i} + 3\mathbf{j} - 5\mathbf{k})$$

Finally,

$$D_u f(1, -2, \pi) = \nabla f_0 \cdot \mathbf{u} = \frac{1}{\sqrt{38}}(-4\pi - 10) \approx -3.66$$

■ NORMAL PROPERTY OF THE GRADIENT

Suppose S is a level surface of the function defined by $f(x, y, z)$; that is, $f(x, y, z) = K$ for some constant K. Then if $P_0(x_0, y_0, z_0)$ is a point on S, it can be shown that the gradient ∇f_0 at P_0 is a vector that is **normal** (that is, perpendicular) to the tangent vector of every smooth curve on S that passes through P_0 (see Figure 12.24).

Figure 12.24 The normal property of the gradient

THEOREM 12.10   The normal property of the gradient

Suppose the function f is differentiable at the point P_0 and that the gradient at P_0 satisfies $\nabla f_0 \neq \mathbf{0}$. Then ∇f_0 is orthogonal to the level surface $f(x, y, z) = K$ at P_0.

Proof: Let C be any smooth curve on the level surface $f(x, y, z) = K$ that passes through $P_0(x_0, y_0, z_0)$, and describe the curve C by the vector function $\mathbf{R}(t) = x(t)\mathbf{i} + y(t)\mathbf{j} + z(t)\mathbf{k}$ for all t in some interval I. We shall show that the gradient ∇f_0 is orthogonal to the tangent vector $d\mathbf{R}/dt$ at P_0.

Because C lies on the level surface, any point $P(x(t), y(t), z(t))$ on C must satisfy

$$f[x(t), y(t), z(t)] = K$$

and by applying the chain rule, we obtain

$$\frac{d}{dt}[f(x(t), y(t), z(t))] = f_x(x, y, z)\frac{dx}{dt} + f_y(x, y, z)\frac{dy}{dt} + f_z(x, y, z)\frac{dz}{dt}$$

Suppose $t = t_0$ at P_0. Then

$$\frac{d}{dt}[f(x(t), y(t), z(t))]\Big|_{t=t_0}$$

$$= f_x(x(t_0), y(t_0), z(t_0))\frac{dx}{dt} + f_y(x(t_0), y(t_0), z(t_0))\frac{dy}{dt} + f_z(x(t_0), y(t_0), z(t_0))\frac{dz}{dt}$$

$$= \nabla f_0 \cdot \frac{d\mathbf{R}}{dt}$$

Remember that $\dfrac{d\mathbf{R}}{dt} = \dfrac{dx}{dt}\mathbf{i} + \dfrac{dy}{dt}\mathbf{j} + \dfrac{dz}{dt}\mathbf{k}$. We also know that $f(x(t), y(t), z(t)) = K$ for all t in I (because the curve C lies on the level surface $f(x, y, z) = K$). Thus, we have

$$\frac{d}{dt}\{f[x(t), y(t), z(t)]\} = \frac{d}{dt}(K) = 0$$

and it follows that $\nabla f_0 \cdot \dfrac{d\mathbf{R}}{dt} = 0$. We are given that $\nabla f_0 \neq \mathbf{0}$, and $d\mathbf{R}/dt \neq \mathbf{0}$ because the curve C is smooth. Thus, ∇f_0 is orthogonal to $d\mathbf{R}/dt$, as required. ∎

> ■ *What this says:* The gradient ∇f_0 at each point P_0 on the level surface $F(x, y, z) = K$ is normal to the surface at P_0. That is, ∇f_0 is orthogonal to all tangent lines to curves on $F(x, y, z) = k$ through P_0.

Here is an example in which f involves only two variables, so $f(x, y) = K$ is a level curve in the plane instead of a level surface in space.

EXAMPLE 7   Finding a vector normal to a level curve

Sketch the level curve corresponding to $C = 1$ for the function $f(x, y) = x^2 - y^2$ and find a normal vector at the point $P_0(2, \sqrt{3})$.

Solution   The level curve for $C = 1$ is a hyperbola given by $x^2 - y^2 = 1$, as shown in Figure 12.25 (along with the surface defined by $f(x, y) = x^2 - y^2$).

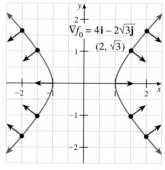

Plane $z = 1$

Figure 12.25 The surface $f(x, y) = x^2 - y^2$ and the level curve for which $C = 1$

The gradient vector is perpendicular to the level curve, so we have

$$\nabla f = f_x \mathbf{i} + f_y \mathbf{j} = 2x\mathbf{i} - 2y\mathbf{j}$$

At the point $(2, \sqrt{3})$, $\nabla f_0 = 4\mathbf{i} - 2\sqrt{3}\mathbf{j}$ is the required normal. This normal vector and a few others are shown in Figure 12.25. ▬

EXAMPLE 8 Finding a vector that is normal to a level surface

Find a vector that is normal to the level surface $x^2 + 2xy - yz + 3z^2 = 7$ at the point $P_0(1, 1, -1)$.

Solution The gradient vector is perpendicular to the level surface:

$$\nabla f = f_x \mathbf{i} + f_y \mathbf{j} + f_z \mathbf{k} = (2x + 2y)\mathbf{i} + (2x - z)\mathbf{j} + (6z - y)\mathbf{k}$$

At the point $(1, 1, -1)$, $\nabla f_0 = 4\mathbf{i} + 3\mathbf{j} - 7\mathbf{k}$ is the required normal. ▬

EXAMPLE 9 Heat flow application

The set of points (x, y) with $0 \le x \le 5$ and $0 \le y \le 5$ is a square in the first quadrant of the xy plane. Suppose this square is heated in such a way that $T(x, y) = x^2 + y^2$ is the temperature at the point $P(x, y)$. In what direction will heat flow from the point $P_0(3, 4)$?

Solution The flow of heat in the region is given by a vector function $\mathbf{H}(x, y)$, whose value at each point (x, y) depends on x and y. From physics it is known that $\mathbf{H}(x, y)$ will be perpendicular to the isothermal curves $T(x, y) = C$ for C constant. The gradient ∇T and all its multiples point in such a direction. Therefore, we can express the heat flow as $\mathbf{H} = -k\nabla T$, where k is a positive constant (called the **thermal conductivity**) and the negative sign is introduced to account for the fact that heat flows "downhill" (that is, toward a decreasing temperature).

Because $T(3, 4) = 25$, the point $P_0(3, 4)$ lies on the isotherm $T(x, y) = 25$, which is part of the circle $x^2 + y^2 = 25$, as shown in Figure 12.26. We know that the heat flow $\mathbf{H}_0$ at P_0 will satisfy $\mathbf{H}_0 = -k\nabla T_0$, where ∇T_0 is the gradient at P_0. Because $\nabla T = 2x\mathbf{i} + 2y\mathbf{j}$, we see that $\nabla T_0 = 6\mathbf{i} + 8\mathbf{j}$. Thus, the heat flow at P_0 satisfies

$$\mathbf{H}_0 = -k\nabla T_0 = -k(6\mathbf{i} + 8\mathbf{j})$$

Because the thermal conductivity k is positive, we can say that heat flows from P_0 in the direction of the unit vector $\mathbf{u}$ given by

$$\mathbf{u} = \frac{-(6\mathbf{i} + 8\mathbf{j})}{\sqrt{(-6)^2 + (-8)^2}} = -\frac{3}{5}\mathbf{i} - \frac{4}{5}\mathbf{j}$$ ▬

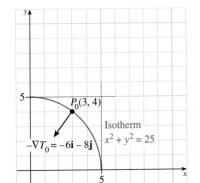

Figure 12.26 The heat flow P_0 is in the direction of $-\nabla T_0 = -6\mathbf{i} - 8\mathbf{j}$

Figure 12.27 Tangent plane and normal line

■ TANGENT PLANES AND NORMAL LINES

Tangent planes and normal lines to a surface are the natural extensions to $\mathbb{R}^3$ of the tangent and normal lines we examined in $\mathbb{R}^2$. Suppose S is a surface and $\mathbf{N}$ is a vector normal to S at the point P_0. We would intuitively expect the normal line and the tangent plane to S at P_0 to be, respectively, the line through P_0 with the direction of $\mathbf{N}$ and the plane perpendicular to the line at P_0 (see Figure 12.27.)

These observations lead us to the following definition.

Normal Line Tangent Plane

Suppose the surface S has a nonzero normal vector $\mathbf{N}$ at the point P_0. Then the line through P_0 parallel to $\mathbf{N}$ is called the **normal line** to S at P_0, and the plane through P_0 with normal vector $\mathbf{N}$ is the tangent plane to S at P_0.

By analogy with the single-variable case, we would expect a surface S to have a tangent plane precisely where it can be represented by a differentiable function. In particular, if S has an equation of the form $F(x, y, z) = C$, where C is a constant and F is a function differentiable at P_0, the normal property of a gradient tells us that the gradient ∇F_0 at P_0 is normal to S (if $\nabla F_0 \neq \mathbf{0}$) and that S must therefore have a tangent plane at P_0.

EXAMPLE 10   **Finding the tangent plane and normal line to a given surface**

Find equations for the tangent plane and the normal line at the point $P_0(1, -1, 2)$ on the surface S given by $x^2y + y^2z + z^2x = 5$.

Solution   We need to rewrite this problem so that the normal property of the gradient theorem applies. Let $F(x, y, z) = x^2y + y^2z + z^2x$, and consider S to be the level surface $F(x, y, z) = 5$. The gradient ∇F is normal to S.

$$\nabla F(x, y, z) = (2xy + z^2)\mathbf{i} + (x^2 + 2yz)\mathbf{j} + (y^2 + 2xz)\mathbf{k}$$

Evaluate ∇F at $P_0(1, -1, 2)$ to obtain the normal to the surface at P_0:

$$\mathbf{N} = \nabla F_0 = \nabla F(1, -1, 2) = 2\mathbf{i} - 3\mathbf{j} + 5\mathbf{k}$$

Hence, the required tangent plane is

$$2(x - 1) - 3(y + 1) + 5(z - 2) = 0 \quad \text{or} \quad 2x - 3y + 5z = 15$$

The normal line to the surface at P_0 is

$$x = 1 + 2t, \qquad y = -1 - 3t, \qquad z = 2 + 5t \qquad \blacksquare$$

By generalizing the procedure illustrated in the preceding example, we are led to the following formulas for the tangent plane and normal line.

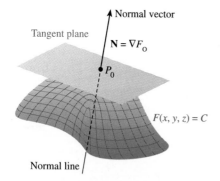

Figure 12.28 The tangent plane and normal line to a surface

Formulas for the Tangent Plane and Normal Line to a Surface

Suppose S is a surface with the equation $F(x, y, z) = C$ and let $P_0(x_0, y_0, z_0)$ be a point on S where F is differentiable. Then the **equation of the tangent plane** to S at P_0 is

$$F_x(x_0, y_0, z_0)(x - x_0) + F_y(x_0, y_0, z_0)(y - y_0) + F_z(x_0, y_0, z_0)(z - z_0) = 0$$

and the **equation of the normal line** to S at P_0 is

$$x = x_0 + F_x(x_0, y_0, z_0)t$$
$$y = y_0 + F_y(x_0, y_0, z_0)t$$
$$z = z_0 + F_z(x_0, y_0, z_0)t$$

provided that F_x, F_y, and F_z are not all zero.

EXAMPLE 11   **Equations of the tangent plane and the normal line**

Find the equations for the tangent plane and the normal line to the cone $z^2 = x^2 + y^2$ at the point where $x = 3$, $y = 4$, and $z > 0$.

Tangent plane and normal line to the cone $z^2 = x^2 + y^2$ at $(3, 4, 5)$

Solution If $P_0(x_0, y_0, z_0)$ is the point of tangency and $x_0 = 3$, $y_0 = 4$, and $z_0 > 0$, then

$$z_0 = \sqrt{x_0{}^2 + y_0{}^2} = \sqrt{9 + 16} = 5$$

If we consider $F(x, y, z) = x^2 + y^2 - z^2$, then the cone can be regarded as the level surface $F(x, y, z) = 0$. The partial derivatives of F are

$$F_x = 2x \qquad F_y = 2y \qquad F_z = -2z$$

so at $P_0(3, 4, 5)$,

$$F_x(3, 4, 5) = 6, \qquad F_y(3, 4, 5) = 8, \qquad F_z(3, 4, 5) = -10$$

Thus the tangent plane is

$$6(x - 3) + 8(y - 4) - 10(z - 5) = 0$$

or $3x + 4y - 5z = 0$, and the normal line is

$$x = 3 + 6t, \qquad y = 4 + 8t, \qquad z = 5 - 10t$$

PROBLEM SET 12.6

Ⓐ *Find the gradient of the functions given in Problems 1–10.*

1. $f(x, y) = x^2 - 2xy$ **2.** $f(x, y) = 3x + 4y^2$

3. $f(x, y) = \dfrac{y}{x} + \dfrac{x}{y}$ **4.** $f(x, y) = \ln(x^2 + y^2)$

5. $f(u, v) = ue^{3-v}$ **6.** $f(u, v) = e^{u+v}$

7. $f(x, y) = \sin(x + 2y)$ **8.** $f(x, y, z) = xyz^2$

9. $g(x, y, z) = xe^{y+3z}$ **10.** $f(x, y, z) = \dfrac{xy - 1}{z + x}$

Compute the directional derivative of the functions given in Problems 11–16 at the point P_0 in the direction of the given vector $\mathbf{v}$.

Function	Point P_0	Vector $\mathbf{v}$
11. $f(x, y) = x^2 + xy$	$(1, -2)$	$\mathbf{i} + \mathbf{j}$
12. $f(x, y) = e^{-x}y^{-1}$	$(2, -1)$	$-\mathbf{i} + \mathbf{j}$
13. $f(x, y) = \ln(x^2 + 3y)$	$(1, 1)$	$\mathbf{i} + \mathbf{j}$
14. $f(x, y) = \ln(3x + y^2)$	$(0, 1)$	$\mathbf{i} - \mathbf{j}$
15. $f(x, y) = \sec(xy - y^3)$	$(2, 0)$	$-\mathbf{i} - 3\mathbf{j}$
16. $f(x, y) = \sin xy$	$(\sqrt{\pi}, \sqrt{\pi})$	$3\pi\mathbf{i} - \pi\mathbf{j}$

Find a unit vector (if possible) that is normal to each surface given in Problems 17–24 at the prescribed point. Also find the equation of the tangent plane at that point.

17. $x^2 + y^2 + z^2 = 3$ at $(1, -1, 1)$

18. $x^4 + y^4 + z^4 = 3$ at $(1, -1, -1)$

19. $\cos z = \sin(x + y)$ at $\left(\frac{\pi}{2}, \frac{\pi}{2}, \frac{\pi}{2}\right)$

20. $\sin(x + y) + \tan(y + z) = 1$ at $\left(\frac{\pi}{4}, \frac{\pi}{4}, -\frac{\pi}{4}\right)$

21. $\ln\left(\dfrac{x}{y - z}\right) = 0$ at $(2, 5, 3)$

22. $\ln\left(\dfrac{x - y}{y + z}\right) = x - z$ at $(1, 0, 1)$

23. $ze^{x+2y} = 3$ at $(2, -1, 3)$ **24.** $ze^{x^2-y^2} = 3$ at $(1, 1, 3)$

Find the direction from P_0 in which the given function f increases most rapidly and compute the magnitude of the greatest rate of increase in Problems 25–34.

25. $f(x, y) = 3x + 2y - 1$
  a. $P_0(1, -1)$ **b.** $P_0(1, 1)$

26. $f(x, y) = 1 - x^2 - y^2$
  a. $P_0(1, 2)$ **b.** $P_0(0, 0)$

27. $f(x, y) = x^3 + y^3$
  a. $P_0(3, -3)$ **b.** $P_0(-3, 3)$

28. $f(x, y) = ax + by + c$; $P_0(a, b)$

29. $f(x, y, z) = ax^2 + by^2 + cz^2$; $P_0(a, b, c)$
  Assume $a^4 + b^4 + c^4 \neq 0$.

30. $f(x, y) = ax^3 + by^3$; $P_0(a, b)$

31. $f(x, y) = \ln\sqrt{x^2 + y^2}$; $P_0(1, 2)$

32. $f(x, y) = \sin xy$; $P_0\left(\frac{\sqrt{\pi}}{3}, \frac{\sqrt{\pi}}{2}\right)$

33. $f(x, y, z) = (x + y)^2 + (y + z)^2 + (z + x)^2$; $P_0(2, -1, 2)$

34. $f(x, y, z) = z \ln\left(\frac{y}{x}\right)$; $P_0(1, e, -1)$

Ⓑ *In Problems 35–38, find a unit vector that is normal to the given curve or line at the point $P_0(x_0, y_0)$ on the line or curves. Assume that a, b, and c are constants.*

35. The line $ax + by = c$ **36.** The circle $x^2 + y^2 = a^2$

37. The ellipse $\dfrac{x^2}{a^2} + \dfrac{y^2}{b^2} = 1$ **38.** The hyperbola $\dfrac{x^2}{a^2} - \dfrac{y^2}{b^2} = 1$

39. Find the directional derivative of $f(x, y) = x^2 + y^2$ at the point $P_0(1, 1)$ in the direction of the unit vector $\mathbf{u}$ shown in Figure 12.29.

Figure 12.29 Problem 39

40. Find the directional derivative of $f(x, y) = x^2 + xy + y^2$ at $P_0(1, -1)$ in the direction toward the origin.

41. Find the directional derivative of $f(x, y) = e^{x^2}y^2$ at $P_0(1, -1)$ in the direction toward $Q(2, 3)$.

42. Let $f(x, y, z) = 2x^2 - y^2 + 3z^2 - 8x - 4y + 201$, and let P_0 be the point $\left(2, -\frac{3}{2}, \frac{1}{2}\right)$
   a. Find ∇f_0.
   b. Find $\cos\theta$, where θ is the angle between ∇f_0 and the vector from the origin to P_0.

43. Let $f(x, y, z) = xyz$, and let **u** be a unit vector perpendicular to both $\mathbf{v} = \mathbf{i} - 2\mathbf{j} + 3\mathbf{k}$ and $\mathbf{w} = 2\mathbf{i} + \mathbf{j} - \mathbf{k}$. Find the directional derivative of f at $P_0(1, -1, 2)$ in the direction of **u**.

44. Let $f(x, y, z) = ye^{x+z} + ze^{y-x}$. At the point $P(2, 2, -2)$, find the unit vector pointing in the direction of most rapid increase of f.

45. Suppose a box in space given by $0 \le x \le 2, 0 \le y \le 2, 0 \le z \le 2$ is temperature-controlled so that the temperature at a point $P(x, y, z)$ in the box is
$$T(x, y, z) = xy + yz + xz.$$
A heat-seeking missile is located at $P_0(1, 1, 1)$. In what direction will the missile move in order to increase the temperature as quickly as possible? What is the maximum rate of change of the temperature at the point P_0?

46. A metal plate that is covering the rectangular region $0 \le x \le 6, 0 \le y \le 5$ is charged electrically in such a way that the potential at each point (x, y) is inversely proportional to the square of its distance from the origin. If an object is at the point $(3, 4)$, in which direction should it move in order to increase the potential most rapidly?

47. A hiker is walking on a mountain path when it begins to rain. If the surface of the mountain is given by $z = 1 - 3x^2 - \frac{5}{2}y^2$ (where x, y, and z are in miles) and the rain begins when the hiker is at the point $P_0\left(\frac{1}{4}, -\frac{1}{2}, \frac{3}{16}\right)$, in what direction should she turn in order to descend the mountainside most rapidly?

48. Let f have continuous partial derivatives, and assume the maximal directional derivative of f at $(0, 0)$ is equal to 100. If the maximal value of the directional derivative is attained in the direction of the vector $(0, 0)$ toward $(3, -4)$, find the gradient ∇f at $(0, 0)$.

49. Suppose a certain function $f(x, y)$ has the directional derivative 8 at the point $P_0(-1, 2)$ in the direction of the unit vector
$$u = \frac{3}{5}\mathbf{i} - \frac{4}{5}\mathbf{j}$$
and the directional derivative 1 in the direction from P_0 toward $Q(11, 7)$. What is the directional derivative of f at P_0 in the direction of $\mathbf{v} = 3\mathbf{i} - 5\mathbf{j}$?

50. Suppose $f(x, y)$ has directional derivatives $D_{v_1}f = 2$ at $P_0(1, 5)$ in the direction of $\mathbf{v}_1 = 2\mathbf{i} + 3\mathbf{j}$ and $D_{v_2}f = -5$ in the direction of $\mathbf{v}_2 = 3\mathbf{i} - 5\mathbf{j}$. What is the directional derivative of f at P_0 in the direction of $\mathbf{v}_3 = 2\mathbf{i} - 3\mathbf{j}$?

51. Let f have continuous partial derivatives and suppose the maximal directional derivative of f at $P_0(1, 2)$ has magnitude 50 and is attained in the direction from P_0 toward $Q(3, -4)$. Use this information to find $\nabla f(1, 2)$.

52. Let $T(x, y) = 1 - x^2 - 2y^2$ be the temperature at each point $P(x, y)$ in the plane. A heat-loving bug is placed in the plane at the point $P_0(-1, 1)$. Find the path that the bug should take in order to stay as warm as possible. *Hint:* Assume that at each point on the bug's path, the tangent line will point in the direction for which T increases most rapidly.

53. Repeat Problem 52 for the temperature function $T(x, y) = 1 - ax^2 - by^2$ and starting at the point (x_0, y_0). Assume $a > 0$ and $b > 0$ and $(x_0, y_0) \ne (0, 0)$.

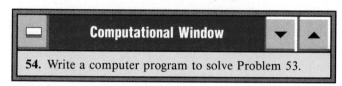

54. Write a computer program to solve Problem 53.

55. SPY PROBLEM   The spy enters the gas filled bunker of the international terrorists (Problem 30, Section 11.5) and finds himself in a trap. The door slams shut behind him and he begins to feel very warm. Too late he realizes the bunker is a large roasting oven. Fortunately, he is wearing his heat-detector ring, which indicates the direction of greatest temperature decrease. Suppose the bunker is coordinatized so that the temperature at each point (x, y) on the floor of the bunker is given by
$$T(x, y) = 3(x - 6)^2 + 1.5(y - 1)^2 + 41$$
degrees Fahrenheit, where x and y are in feet. The spy begins at the point $(1, 5)$ and stumbles across the room at the rate of 4 ft/min, always moving in the direction of maximum temperature decrease. But he can last no more than 2 minutes under these conditions! Assuming that there is an escape hole at the point where the temperature is minimal, does he make it or is the spy toast at last? *Hint:* Hallucinating in the heat, the spy remembers the odd fact that $f(x, y) = x^2 + y^2 + c$ is minimized when $x = 0$ and $y = 0$.

56. Recall from Chapter 9 (Problem 69, Section 9.6) that an ellipse is the set of all points $P(x, y)$ such that the sum of the distances from P to two fixed points (the *foci*) is constant. Let $P(x, y)$ be a point on the ellipse, and let r_1 and r_2 denote the respective distances from P to the two foci, F_1 and F_2, as shown in Figure 12.30.

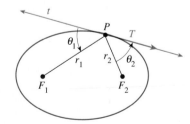

Figure 12.30 Unit tangent to an ellipse

   a. Show that $\mathbf{T} \cdot \nabla(r_1 + r_2) = 0$, where **T** is the unit tangent to the ellipse at P.

b. Use part **a** to show that the tangent line to the ellipse at P makes equal angles with the lines joining P to the foci (that is, $\theta_1 = \theta_2$ in Figure 12.30.)

© 57. A particle P_1 with mass m_1 is located at the origin, and a particle P_2 with mass 1 unit is located at the point (x, y, z). According to Newton's law of gravity, the force P_1 exerts on P_2 is given by

$$\mathbf{F} = \frac{-gm_1(x\mathbf{i} + y\mathbf{j} + z\mathbf{k})}{r^3}$$

The number r is the distance between P_1 and P_2 and g is the gravitational constant.

a. Starting from the fact that $r^2 = x^2 + y^2 + z^2$, show that

$$\frac{\partial}{\partial x}\left(\frac{1}{r}\right) = \frac{-x}{r^3}, \qquad \frac{\partial}{\partial y}\left(\frac{1}{r}\right) = \frac{-y}{r^3}, \qquad \frac{\partial}{\partial z}\left(\frac{1}{r}\right) = \frac{-z}{r^3}$$

b. The function $V = -gm_1/r$ is called the **potential energy** function for the system. Show that $\mathbf{F} = -\nabla V$.

58. Verify each of the following properties for functions of two variables.

a. $\nabla(cf) = c(\nabla f)$ for constant c

b. $\nabla(f + g) = \nabla f + \nabla g$

c. $\nabla(f/g) = \dfrac{g\nabla f - f\nabla g}{g^2}, \quad g \neq 0$

59. Verify the product rule

$$\nabla(fg) = f\nabla g + g\nabla f$$

for functions of three variables.

60. Find a general formula for the directional derivative $D_{\mathbf{u}}f$ of the function $f(x, y)$ at the point $P(x_0, y_0)$ in the direction of the unit vector $\mathbf{u} = (\cos\theta)\mathbf{i} + (\sin\theta)\mathbf{j}$. Apply your formula to obtain the directional derivative of $f(x, y) = xy^2e^{x-2y}$ at $P_0(-1, 3)$ in the direction of the unit vector $\mathbf{u} = \left(\cos\frac{\pi}{6}\right)\mathbf{i} + \left(\sin\frac{\pi}{6}\right)\mathbf{j}$.

61. Suppose that $\mathbf{u}$ and $\mathbf{v}$ are unit vectors and that f has continuous partial derivatives. Show that

$$D_{\mathbf{u}+\mathbf{v}}f = \frac{1}{\|\mathbf{u} + \mathbf{v}\|}(D_{\mathbf{u}}f + D_{\mathbf{v}}f)$$

62. If $\mathbf{a}$ is a constant vector and $\mathbf{R} = x\mathbf{i} + y\mathbf{j} + z\mathbf{k}$, show that $\nabla(\mathbf{a} \cdot \mathbf{R}) = \mathbf{a}$.

63. Let $\mathbf{R} = x\mathbf{i} + y\mathbf{j} + z\mathbf{k}$, and let

$$r = \|\mathbf{R}\| = \sqrt{x^2 + y^2 + z^2}$$

a. Show that ∇r is a unit vector in the direction of $\mathbf{R}$.

b. Show that $\nabla(r^n) = nr^{n-2}\mathbf{R}$, for any positive integer n.

12.7 EXTREMA OF FUNCTIONS OF TWO VARIABLES

> **IN THIS SECTION** Relative extrema, second partials test, extreme value theorem
> In the real world we encounter a variety of problems involving optimization. In Chapter 3 we considered extrema of functions of a single variable, and in this section we extend our work to functions of two variables.

There are many practical situations in which it is necessary or useful to know the largest and smallest values of a function of two variables. For example, if $T(x, y)$ is the temperature at a point (x, y) in a plate, where are the hottest and coldest points in the plate and what are these extreme temperatures? This is an example of a problem in which we are asked to find the extreme (that is, the largest or smallest) values of a function of two variables. We begin our study of extrema with some terminology.

Absolute Extrema

> The function $f(x, y)$ is said to have an **absolute maximum** at (x_0, y_0) if $f(x_0, y_0) \geq f(x, y)$ for all (x, y) in the domain D of f. Similarly, f has an **absolute minimum** at (x_0, y_0) if $f(x_0, y_0) \leq f(x, y)$ for all (x, y) in D. Collectively, absolute maxima and minima are called **absolute extrema**.

In Chapter 3, we located absolute extrema of a function of one variable by first finding *relative extrema*: those values of $f(x)$ that are larger or smaller than those at all "nearby" points. The relative extrema of a function of two variables may be defined as follows.

Relative Extrema

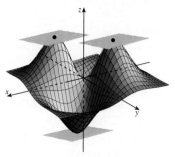

Extrema occur on the boundary or where the tangent plane is horizontal.

Let f be a function defined at (x_0, y_0). Then

$f(x_0, y_0)$ is a **relative maximum** if $f(x, y) \leq f(x_0, y_0)$ for all (x, y) in an open disk containing (x_0, y_0).

$f(x_0, y_0)$ is a **relative minimum** if $f(x, y) \geq f(x_0, y_0)$ for all (x, y) in an open disk containing (x_0, y_0).

Collectively, relative maxima and minima are called **relative extrema**.

We also found in Chapter 3 that an absolute extremum of a function f can occur either at an endpoint of an interval in the domain of f or at an interior critical point where it is a relative extremum—that is, at a point where either $f'(x)$ does not exist or $f'(x) = 0$. In Section 12.6, we observed that the gradient ∇f is the two-variable analog to the derivative in the single-variable case. Thus, it is reasonable to expect extrema of a function of two variables to occur in one of the following situations:

1. either on the boundary of the domain of f, or
2. at points in the interior where the gradient ∇f does not exist, or
3. where $\nabla f = \mathbf{0}$; that is, where $f_x = f_y = 0$.

We begin by considering relative extrema, and then we turn to the more general question of finding absolute extrema.

■ RELATIVE EXTREMA

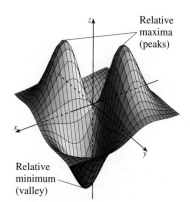

Relative maxima (peaks)

Relative minimum (valley)

Figure 12.31 Relative extrema occur at peaks and valleys.

In Chapter 3, we observed that relative extrema of the function f correspond to "peaks and valleys" on the graph of f, and the same observation can be made about relative extrema in the two-variable case, as seen in Figure 12.31.

For a function f of one variable, we found that the relative extrema occur where $f'(x) = 0$ or $f'(x)$ does not exist. The following theorem shows that the relative extrema of a function of two variables can be located in a similar fashion.

THEOREM 12.11   Partial derivative criteria for relative extrema

If f has a relative extremum (maximum or minimum) at $P_0(x_0, y_0)$ and partial derivatives f_x and f_y both exist at $P_0(x_0, y_0)$, then

$$f_x(x_0, y_0) = f_y(x_0, y_0) = 0$$

Proof: Let $F(x) = f(x, y_0)$. Then $F(x)$ must have a relative extremum at $x = x_0$, so $F'(x_0) = 0$, which means that $f_x(x_0, y_0) = 0$. Similarly, $G(y) = f(x_0, y)$ has a relative extremum at $y = y_0$, so $G'(y_0) = 0$ and $f_y(x_0, y_0) = 0$. Thus, we must have *both* $f_x(x_0, y_0) = 0$ and $f_y(x_0, y_0) = 0$, as claimed. ∎

⊘   If a point is an extreme point and if the first partial derivatives exist, then there is a horizontal tangent plane at that point. This does NOT say that if there is a horizontal tangent plane at a point that point is an extremum. However, such a point IS a *possible* location for a relative extremum.   ⊘

In single variable calculus, we referred to a number x_0, where $f'(x_0)$ does not exist or $f'(x_0) = 0$, as a *critical value*. This terminology is extended to functions of two variables, as follows.

Critical Points

> A **critical point** of a function f defined on an open set S is a point (x_0, y_0) in S where either one of the following is true:
>
> **a.** $f_x(x_0, y_0) = f_y(x_0, y_0) = 0$.
>
> **b.** $f_x(x_0, y_0)$ or $f_y(x_0, y_0)$ does not exist (one or both).

EXAMPLE 1 Distinguishing critical points

Discuss the nature of the critical point $(0, 0)$ for the quadric surfaces

a. $z = x^2 + y^2$ **b.** $z + x^2 + y^2 = 1$ **c.** $z = y^2 - x^2$

Solution   The graphs of these quadric surfaces are shown in Figure 12.32.

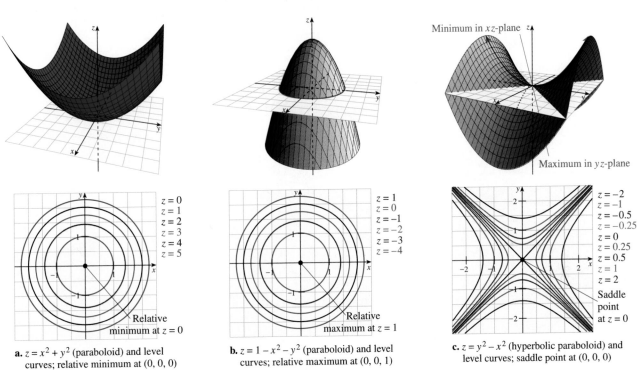

a. $z = x^2 + y^2$ (paraboloid) and level curves; relative minimum at $(0, 0, 0)$

b. $z = 1 - x^2 - y^2$ (paraboloid) and level curves; relative maximum at $(0, 0, 1)$

c. $z = y^2 - x^2$ (hyperbolic paraboloid) and level curves; saddle point at $(0, 0, 0)$

Figure 12.32 Classification of critical points

Let $f(x, y) = x^2 + y^2$, $g(x, y) = 1 - x^2 - y^2$, and $h(x, y) = y^2 - x^2$. We find the critical points:

a. $f_x(x, y) = 2x$, $f_y(x, y) = 2y$; the critical point is $(0, 0)$. The function f has a relative minimum at $(0, 0)$ because x^2 and y^2 are both nonnegative yielding $x^2 + y^2 \geq 0$ for all nonzero x and y.

b. $g_x(x, y) = -2x$, $g_y(x, y) = -2y$; critical point $(0, 0)$. The function f has a relative maximum at $(0, 0)$ because $z = 1 - x^2 - y^2$ and x^2 and y^2 are both nonnegative, so the largest value of z occurs at $(0, 0)$.

c. $h_x(x, y) = -2x$, $h_y(x, y) = 2y$; critical point $(0, 0)$. The function f has neither a relative maximum nor a relative minimum at $(0, 0)$ because when $z = 0$, f is positive on the y-axis (where $x = 0$) and negative on the x-axis (where $y = 0$).

If (x_0, y_0) is a critical point for $f(x, y)$ that is neither a relative maximum nor a relative minimum, it may be a **saddle point**. Such a point is a *maximum* in one direction and a *minimum* is another direction and so has a saddle shape, as shown in Figure 12.32c.

■ SECOND PARTIALS TEST

The cases examined in Example 1 point to the need for some sort of a test to determine the nature of a critical point. In Chapter 3, we developed the second derivative test as a means for classifying a critical point of f as a relative maximum or minimum. According to this test, if $f'(c) = 0$, then at $x = c$, a relative maximum occurs if $f''(c) < 0$ and a relative minimum occurs if $f''(c) > 0$. If $f''(c) = 0$, the test is inconclusive. The analogous result for the two-variable case may be stated as follows.

Second Partials Test

Summary:

Critical Point	D	f_{xx}	Type
(x_1, y_1)	Pos.	Neg.	Rel. max
(x_2, y_2)	Pos.	Pos.	Rel. min
(x_3, y_3)	Neg.		Saddle pt.
(x_4, y_4)	Zero		Inconclusive

Let $f(x, y)$ have a critical point at $P_0(x_0, y_0)$ and assume that f has continuous partial derivatives in a disk centered at (x_0, y_0). Let

$$D = f_{xx}(x_0, y_0)f_{yy}(x_0, y_0) - [f_{xy}(x_0, y_0)]^2$$

Then,

A **relative maximum** occurs at P_0 if

$$D > 0 \quad \text{and} \quad f_{xx}(x_0, y_0) < 0$$

$z = 1 - x^2 - y^2$ (See Ex 1b)

A **relative minimum** occurs at P_0 if

$$D > 0 \quad \text{and} \quad f_{xx}(x_0, y_0) > 0$$

$z = x^2 + y^2$ (See Ex 1a)

A **saddle point** occurs at P_0 if $D < 0$.

If $D = 0$, then the test is **inconclusive**.

$z = y^2 - x^2$ (See Ex 1c)

⊘   The same result holds if $f_{xx}(x_0, y_0)$ is replaced by $f_{yy}(x_0, y_0)$.   ⊘

When $D(x_0, y_0) = 0$, the critical point (x_0, y_0) is said to be **degenerate**; otherwise, it is **nondegenerate**. Note that D can be expressed in *determinant form* as

$$D = \begin{vmatrix} f_{xx} & f_{xy} \\ f_{xy} & f_{yy} \end{vmatrix}$$

where all the partials are evaluated at (x_0, y_0). Some students find this the easiest form of D to remember.

EXAMPLE 2   Second partials test with a relative maximum

Find all critical points on the graph of $f(x, y) = 1 - x^2 - y^2$ and use the second partials test to classify each critical point as a relative extremum or a saddle point.

Solution $f_x(x, y) = -2x, f_y(x, y) = -2y$, so the only critical point is at $(0, 0)$. $f_{xx}(x, y) = -2, f_{xy}(x, y) = 0$, and $f_{yy}(x, y) = -2$, so

$$D = \begin{vmatrix} -2 & 0 \\ 0 & -2 \end{vmatrix} = 4$$

Because $D = 4 > 0$ for all (x, y), and because $f_{xx}(0, 0) = -2 < 0$, the second partials test tells us that a relative maximum occurs at $(0, 0)$.   ▬

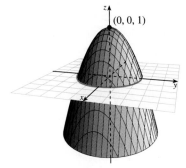

Graph of $f(x, y) = 1 - x^2 - y^2$

EXAMPLE 3   Second partials test with a relative minimum and a saddle point

Find all critical points on the graph of $f(x, y) = 8x^3 - 24xy + y^3$ and use the second partials test to classify each point as a relative extremum or a saddle point.

Solution $f_x(x, y) = 24x^2 - 24y, f_y(x, y) = -24x + 3y^2$

To find the critical points, solve

$$\begin{cases} 24x^2 - 24y = 0 \\ -24x + 3y^2 = 0 \end{cases}$$

From the first equation $y = x^2$; substitute this into the second equation to find

$$-24x + 3(x^2)^2 = 0$$
$$x^4 - 8x = 0$$
$$x(x^3 - 8) = 0$$
$$x(x - 2)(x^2 + 2x + 4) = 0$$
$$x = 0, 2 \quad \text{The solutions of } x^2 + 2x + 4 = 0 \text{ are not real.}$$

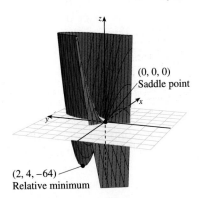

Graph of
$f(x, y) = 8x^3 - 24xy + y^3$ $(2, 4, -64)$
Relative minimum

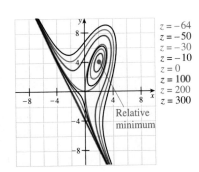

Summary:

Critical Point	D	f_{xx}	Type
(0, 0)	Neg.		Saddle
(2, 4)	Pos.	Pos.	Rel. min.

If $x = 0$, then $y = 0$, and if $x = 2$, then $y = 4$, so the critical points are (0, 0), (2, 4). To obtain D, we first find $f_{xx}(x, y) = 48x$, $f_{xy}(x, y) = -24$, and $f_{yy}(x, y) = 6y$ and then compute

$$D = \begin{vmatrix} f_{xx} & f_{xy} \\ f_{xy} & f_{yy} \end{vmatrix} = \begin{vmatrix} 48x & -24 \\ -24 & 6y \end{vmatrix} = 288xy - 576$$

At (0, 0), $D = -576 < 0$, so there is a saddle point at (0, 0). At (2, 4), $D = 288(2)(4) - 576 = 1,728 > 0$ and $f_{xx}(2, 4) = 96 > 0$, so there is a relative minimum at (2, 4). ■

EXAMPLE 4   Extrema when the second partial test fails

Find all relative extrema and saddle points on the graph of

$$f(x, y) = x^2 y^4$$

Solution $f_x(x, y) = 2xy^4$, $f_y(x, y) = 4x^2 y^3$; we can see the only critical points occur whenever $x = 0$ or $y = 0$; that is, every point on the x- or y-axis is a critical point. Because $f_{xx}(x, y) = 2y^4$, $f_{xy}(x, y) = 8xy^3$, $f_{yy}(x, y) = 12x^2 y^2$, we have

$$D = \begin{vmatrix} f_{xx} & f_{xy} \\ f_{xy} & f_{yy} \end{vmatrix} = \begin{vmatrix} 2y^4 & 8xy^3 \\ 8xy^3 & 12x^2 y^2 \end{vmatrix} = 24x^2 y^6 - 64x^2 y^6 = -40x^2 y^6$$

For any critical point $(x_0, 0)$ or $(0, y_0)$, $D = 0$; so the second partials test fails. But $f(x, y) = 0$ for every critical point (because either $x = 0$ or $y = 0$, or both), and because $f(x, y) = x^2 y^4 > 0$ when $x \neq 0$ and $y \neq 0$, it follows that each critical point must be a relative minimum. ■

Graph of $f(x, y) = x^2 y^4$

The second partials test provides explicit information about the case where f is nondegenerate at $P_0(x_0, y_0)$, but if f is degenerate, practically anything can happen, as shown in Problem 47. In that problem you are asked to show that (0, 0) is a degenerate critical point for each of the following functions:

$$f(x, y) = x^4 - y^4; \qquad g(x, y) = x^2 y^2; \qquad h(x, y) = x^3 + y^3$$

The following conclusions can be made:

$f(x, y)$ has a saddle point at (0, 0).

$g(x, y)$ has a relative minimum at (0, 0).

$h(x, y)$ has neither kind of extremum nor a saddle point at (0, 0).

■ **EXTREME VALUE THEOREM**

In Chapter 3, we noted that a function of one variable $f(x)$ assumes both a maximum and a minimum on any closed, bounded interval where it is continuous, and that all absolute extrema must occur either at one of the endpoints of the interval or at an interior critical value. The following is the analogous result for functions of two variables.

THEOREM 12.12   Extreme value theorem for a function of two variables

A function of two variables $f(x, y)$ assumes an absolute extremum on any closed, bounded set S in the plane where it is continuous. Moreover, all absolute extrema must occur either on the boundary of S or at a critical point in the interior of S.

Proof: The proof of this theorem is beyond the scope of this text and is usually given in an advanced calculus course.   ∎

> ■ *What this says:* Visualize a surface in space $z = f(x, y)$ with f continuous that projects onto a closed, bounded region D in the xy-plane. Then the surface must have a highest point (peak) and a lowest point (valley) over D. These extreme features must occur either on the boundary of D or at a high point (low point) in its interior.

The extreme value theorem for a function of two variables leads to the procedure summarized in the following box.

Procedure for Determining Absolute Extrema

Given a function f that is continuous on a closed, bounded set S:
Step 1: Find all critical points of f in S.
Step 2: Find all points on the boundary of S where absolute extrema can occur (boundary critical points, endpoints, etc.)
Step 3: Compute the value of $f(x_0, y_0)$ for each of the points (x_0, y_0) found in steps 1 and 2.
Evaluation: The absolute maximum of f on S is the largest of the values computed in step 3, and the absolute minimum is the smallest of the computed values.

EXAMPLE 5   Finding absolute extrema

Find the absolute extrema of the function $f(x, y) = e^{x^2-y^2}$ over the disk $x^2 + y^2 \leq 1$.

Solution
  Step 1: $f_x(x, y) = 2xe^{x^2-y^2}$ and $f_y(x, y) = -2ye^{x^2-y^2}$. These partial derivatives are defined for all (x, y). Because $f_x(x, y) = f_y(x, y) = 0$ only when $x = 0$ and $y = 0$, it follows that $(0, 0)$ is the only critical point of f.
  Step 2: Examine the values of f on the boundary curve $x^2 + y^2 = 1$. Because $y^2 = 1 - x^2$ on the boundary, we find that

$$f(x, y) = e^{x^2-(1-x^2)} = e^{2x^2-1}$$

on the boundary $x^2 + y^2 = 1$. Let $F(x) = e^{2x^2-1}$ for $-1 \leq x \leq 1$. We must find the points where the extreme values of $F(x)$ occur. Because this is a function of a single variable, we find

$$F'(x) = 4xe^{2x^2-1}$$

for $-1 \leq x \leq 1$, and $F'(x) = 0$ when

$$4xe^{2x^2-1} = 0$$
$$x = 0 \quad \text{or} \quad e^{2x^2-1} = 0$$

Because the exponential is never 0, we see that $F'(x) = 0$ only when $x = 0$.

At $x = 0$, $y^2 = 1 - 0^2$ which implies $y = \pm 1$;

this gives the points $(0, 1)$ and $(0, -1)$. The endpoints of F are $x = \pm 1$, which implies $y^2 = 1 - 1^2 = 0$; this gives the points $(1, 0)$ and $(-1, 0)$.

Step 3: Compute the value of f for the points found in steps 1 and 2:

Points to check	Compute $f(x_0, y_0) = e^{x_0^2 - y_0^2}$
$(0, 0)$	$f(0, 0) = e^0 = 1$
$(0, 1)$	$f(0, 1) = e^{-1}$; minimum
$(0, -1)$	$f(0, -1) = e^{-1}$; minimum
$(1, 0)$	$f(1, 0) = e$; maximum
$(-1, 0)$	$f(-1, 0) = e$; maximum

Evaluation: As indicated in the preceding table, the absolute maximum value of f on the given disk is e at $(1, 0)$ and $(-1, 0)$, and the absolute minimum value is e^{-1} at $(0, 1)$ and $(0, -1)$.   ▬

EXAMPLE 6   Minimum distance from a point to a plane

Find the shortest distance from the point $(0, 3, 4)$ to the plane $x + 2y + z = 5$.

Solution   The distance from a point (x, y, z) to $(0, 3, 4)$ is

$$d = \sqrt{(x - 0)^2 + (y - 3)^2 + (z - 4)^2}$$

However, because (x, y, z) is on the plane $x + 2y + z = 5$, we know

$$z = 5 - x - 2y$$

so that $d = \sqrt{x^2 + (y - 3)^2 + (5 - x - 2y - 4)^2}$. Instead of minimizing d, we can minimize the simpler expression

$$d^2 = f(x, y) = x^2 + (y - 3)^2 + (1 - x - 2y)^2$$

To find the critical values, we solve

$$f_x = 2x - 2(1 - x - 2y) = 4x + 4y - 2 = 0$$
$$f_y = 2(y - 3) - 4(1 - x - 2y) = 4x + 10y - 10 = 0$$

The only critical point is $\left(-\frac{5}{6}, \frac{4}{3}\right)$. Also, $f_{xx} = 4$, $f_{yy} = 10$, $f_{xy} = 4$, so $D > 0$, which means there is a relative minimum at $\left(-\frac{5}{6}, \frac{4}{3}\right)$. Intuitively, we see that this relative minimum must also be an absolute minimum because there must be exactly one point on the plane that is closest to the given point. We now calculate that distance:

$$d = \sqrt{\left(-\frac{5}{6}\right)^2 + \left(\frac{4}{3} - 3\right)^2 + \left[1 + \frac{5}{6} - 2\left(\frac{4}{3}\right)\right]^2} = \sqrt{\frac{25}{6}} = \frac{5}{\sqrt{6}}$$

Check: You might want to check your work by using the formula for the distance from a point to a plane in $\mathbb{R}^3$ (Theorem 10.10):

$$d = \left|\frac{Ax_0 + By_0 + Cz_0 + D}{\sqrt{A^2 + B^2 + C^2}}\right| = \left|\frac{0 + 2(3) + 4 - 5}{\sqrt{1^2 + 2^2 + 1^2}}\right| = \frac{5}{\sqrt{6}}$$ ▬

The following example uses calculus to justify a formula used in statistics and in many applications in the social and physical sciences.

EXAMPLE 7   Least squares approximation of data

Suppose data consisting of n points $P_1, \ldots, P_n$ are known, and we wish to find a function $y = f(x)$ that fits the data reasonably well. In particular, find a line $y = mx + b$ that "best fits" the data in the sense that the sum of the squares of the vertical distances from each data point to the line is minimized.

Solution We wish to find values of m and b that minimize the sum of the squares of the differences between the y-values on the line $y = mx + b$. This line we seek is called the **regression line**. Suppose that the point P_k has components (x_k, y_k). Now, at this point, the value on the regression line is $y = mx_k + b$ and the value of the data point is y_k. The "error" caused by using the point on the regression line rather than the actual data point is

$$y_k - (mx_k + b)$$

and we wish to minimize the function that represents the sum of the *squares* of all these differences:

$$F(m, b) = \sum_{k=1}^{n} [y_k - (mx_k + b)]^2$$

The situation is illustrated in Figure 12.33.

Next, we find the critical points of $F(m, b)$ by computing F_m and F_b and solving $F_m = F_b = 0$:

$$F_m(m, b) = \sum_{k=1}^{n} 2[y_k - (mx_k + b)](-x_k)$$

$$= 2m \sum_{k=1}^{n} x_k^2 + 2b \sum_{k=1}^{n} x_k - 2 \sum_{k=1}^{n} x_k y_k$$

$$F_b(m, b) = \sum_{k=1}^{n} 2[y_k - (mx_k + b)](-1)$$

$$= 2m \sum_{k=1}^{n} x_k + 2b \sum_{k=1}^{n} 1 - 2 \sum_{k=1}^{n} y_k$$

$$= 2m \sum_{k=1}^{n} x_k + 2bn - 2 \sum_{k=1}^{n} y_k$$

Figure 12.33 Least squares approximation of data

Set each of these partial derivatives equal to 0 to find (after a great deal of algebra) the critical values:

$$m = \frac{n \sum_{k=1}^{n} x_k y_k - \left(\sum_{k=1}^{n} x_k \right) \left(\sum_{k=1}^{n} y_k \right)}{n \sum_{k=1}^{n} x_k^2 - \left(\sum_{k=1}^{n} x_k \right)^2}$$

and

$$b = \frac{\sum_{k=1}^{n} x_k^2 \sum_{k=1}^{n} y_k - \left(\sum_{k=1}^{n} x_k \right) \left(\sum_{k=1}^{n} x_k y_k \right)}{n \sum_{k=1}^{n} x_k^2 - \left(\sum_{k=1}^{n} x_k \right)^2}$$

We leave it to you to verify that these values of m and b yield a minimum. ▬

Most applications of the **least squares formula** stated in Example 7 involve using a calculator or computer software. The following computational window provides an example.

PROBLEM SET 12.7

Ⓐ 1. ■ What Does This Say? Describe what is meant by a critical value.

2. ■ What Does This Say? Describe a procedure for determining absolute extrema.

3. ■ What Does This Say? Describe what is meant by a regression line, as well as describing the procedure for finding such a line.

Find the critical points in Problems 4–19, and classify each as a relative maximum, a relative minimum, or a saddle point.

4.
$f(x, y) = 2x^2 - 4xy + y^3 + 2$

5. $f(x, y) = (x - 2)^2 + (y - 3)^4$

6. $f(x, y) = e^{-x}\sin y$

7.
$f(x, y) = (1 + x^2 + y^2)\, e^{1-x^2-y^2}$

8. $f(x, y) = \dfrac{9x}{x^2 + y^2 + 1}$

9. $f(x, y) = x^2 + xy + y^2$
10. $f(x, y) = xy - x + y$
11. $f(x, y) = -x^3 + 9x - 4y^2$
12. $f(x, y) = e^{-(x^2 + y^2)}$
13. $F(x, y) = (x^2 + 2y^2)e^{1-x^2-y^2}$
14. $f(x, y) = e^{xy}$
15. $f(x, y) = x^{-1} + y^{-1} + 2xy$
16. $f(x, y) = (x - 4)\ln xy$
17. $f(x, y) = x^3 + y^3 + 3x^2 - 18y^2 + 81y + 5$
18. $f(x, y) = 2x^3 + y^3 + 3x^2 - 3y - 12x - 4$
19. $f(x, y) = x^2 + y^2 - 6xy + 9x + 5y + 2$

Ⓑ *Find the absolute extrema of f on the closed bounded set S in the plane as described in Problems 20–25.*

20. $f(x, y) = 2x^2 - y^2$; S is the disk $x^2 + y^2 \leq 1$.

21. $f(x, y) = x^2 + 3y^2 - 4x + 2y - 3$; S is the square with vertices $(0, 0)$, $(3, 0)$, $(3, -3)$, and $(0, -3)$.

22. $f(x, y) = 2\sin x + 5\cos y$; S is the rectangle with vertices $(0, 0)$, $(2, 0)$, $(2, 5)$, and $(0, 5)$.

23. $f(x, y) = e^{x^2+2x+y^2}$; S is the region $x^2 + 2x + y^2 \leq 0$.

24. $f(x, y) = x^2 + xy + y^2$; S is the square region $-1 \leq x \leq 1$, and $-1 \leq y \leq 1$.

25. $f(x, y) = x^2 - 4xy + y^3 + 4y$; S is the square region $0 \leq x \leq 2$, $0 \leq y \leq 2$.

Find the least squares regression line for the data points given in Problems 26–29.

26. $(-2, -3), (-1, -1), (0, 1), (1, 3), (3, 5)$

27. $(0, 1), (1, 1.6), (2.2, 3), (3.1, 3.9), (4, 5)$

28. $(3, 5.72), (4, 5.31), (6.2, 5.12), (7.52, 5.32), (8.03, 5.67)$

29. $(-4, 2), (-3, 1), (0, 0), (1, -3), (2, -1), (3, -2)$

30. A rectangular box with no top is to have a fixed volume. What should its dimensions be if we want to use the least amount of material in its construction?

31. Show that of all triangles with fixed perimeter P, the equilateral triangle has the greatest area.

32. Find the smallest perimeter of an isosceles triangle with fixed area A.

33. A dairy produces whole milk and skim milk in quantities x and y gallons, respectively. Suppose the price of whole milk is $p(x) = 100 - x$ and that of skim milk is $q(y) = 100 - y$; also assume that $C(x, y) = x^2 + xy + y^2$ is the joint-cost function of the commodities. Maximize the profit

$$P(x, y) = px + qy - C(x, y)$$

34. Repeat Problem 33 for the case where $p(x) = 4 - 5x$, $q(y) = 4 - 2y$, and the joint-cost function is $C(x, y) = 2xy + 4$.

35. A particle of mass m in a rectangular box with dimensions x, y, z has ground state energy

$$E(x, y, z) = \frac{k^2}{8m}\left(\frac{1}{x^2} + \frac{1}{y^2} + \frac{1}{z^2}\right)$$

where k is a physical constant. If the volume of the box is fixed (say $V_0 = xyz$), find the values of x, y, and z that minimize the ground state energy.

36. A manufacturer produces two different kinds of graphing calculators, A and B, in quantities x and y (units of 1,000), respectively. If the revenue function (in dollars) is

$$R(x, y) = -x^2 - 2y^2 + 2xy + 8x + 5y$$

find the quantities of A and B that should be produced in order to maximize revenue.

37. Suppose we wish to construct a rectangular box with volume 32 ft^3. Three different materials will be used in the construction. The material for the sides costs $1 per square foot, the material for the bottom costs $3 per square foot, and the material for the top costs $5 per square foot. What are the dimensions of the least expensive such box?

38. A store carries two competing brands of bottled water, one from California and the other from New York. The owner of the store can obtain both at a cost of $2 per bottle and estimates that if the California water is sold for x dollars per bottle and the New York water for y dollars per bottle, consumers will buy approximately $40 - 50x + 40y$ bottles of California water and $20 + 60x - 70y$ bottles of the New York water each day. How should the owner price the bottled water to generate the largest possible profit?

39. The telephone company is planning to introduce two new types of executive communications systems that it hopes to sell to its largest commercial customers. It is estimated that if the first type of system is priced at x hundred dollars per system and the second type at y hundred dollars per system, approximately $40 - 8x + 5y$ consumers will buy the first type and $50 + 9x - 7y$ will buy the second type. If the cost of manufacturing the first type is $1,000 per system and the cost of manufacturing the second type is $3,000 per system, how should the telephone company price the systems to generate maximum profit?

40. A manufacturer with exclusive rights to a sophisticated new industrial machine is planning to sell a limited number of the machines to both foreign and domestic firms. The price the manufacturer can expect to receive for the machines will depend on the number of machines made available. For example, if only a few of the machines are placed on the market, competitive bidding among prospective purchasers will tend to drive the price up. It is estimated that if the manufacturer supplies x machines to the domestic market and y machines to the foreign market, the machines will sell for $60 - 0.2x + 0.05y$ thousand dollars apiece at home and $50 - 0.1y + 0.05x$ thousand dollars apiece abroad. If the manufacturer can produce the machines at the total cost of $10,000 apiece, how many should be supplied to each market to generate the largest possible profit?

41. A college admission officer, Dr. Westfall, has compiled the following data relating students' high-school and college GPAs:

HS GPA	2.0	2.5	3.0	3.0	3.5	3.5	4.0	4.0
College GPA	1.5	2.0	2.5	3.5	2.5	3.0	3.0	3.5

Plot the data points on a graph and find the equation of the least-squares line for this data. Then use the least-squares line to predict the college GPA of a student whose high school GPA is 3.75.

42. It is known that if an ideal spring is displaced a distance y from its natural length by a force (weight) x, then $y = kx$, where k is the so-called spring constant. In order to compute this constant for a particular spring, a scientist obtains the following data:

x	5.2	7.3	8.4	10.12	12.37
y (in.)	11.32	15.56	17.44	21.96	26.17

Based on these data, what is the "best" choice for k?

Computational Window

43. Linearizing nonlinear data

In this problem, we turn to data that do *not* tend to change linearly. Often one can "linearize" the data by taking the logarithm or exponential of the data, then changing it to a linear fit.

a. Suppose we have, or suspect, a relationship $y = kx^m$. Show that by taking the natural logarithm of this equation we obtain a linear relationship:

$$Y = K + mX$$

Explain the new variables and constant K.

b. Below are data relating the periods of revolution t (in days) of the six inner planets and their semimajor axis a (in 10^6 km). Kepler conjectured the relationship $t = ka^m$, which is very accurate for the correct k and a. You are to "transform" the data as in part **a** (obtaining $T_i = \ln t_i, \ldots$); and do a linear fit to the new data, finding k and m.

t-data: (87.97, 224.7, 365.26, 686.98, 4332.59, 10 759.2)
a-data: (58, 108, 149, 228, 778, 1 426)

44. Below are data pertaining to the 1988 Olympic weight-lifting competition. The x-data are the "class data" giving seven weight classes from Featherweight to Heavyweight-2 (given in kg). The w-data are the combined weights lifted by the winners in each class. Theoretically, we would expect a relationship $w = kx^m$, where $m = \frac{2}{3}$. (Can you see why?) Once again, linearize the data as in Problem 43.

a. Linearize the data as in Problem 43 and curve fit to find k and m.

x-data: (56, 60, 67.5, 75, 82.5, 90, 100, 110)
y-data: (292.5, 342.5, 340, 375, 377.5, 412.5, 425, 455)

b. Comment on the 60-km entry. Do you see why this participant (N. Suleymanoglu of Turkey) was referred to as the strongest man in the world?

In Problems 45–46, you will see how the Newton–Raphson method in one independent variable can be extended to more than one variable. Then the Newton–Raphson method will be applied to an extrema problem in $\mathbb{R}^3$. For two functions $z = f(x, y)$ and $z = g(x)$, we are interested in finding the "zeros" — that is, values (x, y) such that $z = 0$ for both functions. Geometrically, this means finding the intersection points of the two level curves in the xy-plane defined by $f(x, y) = 0$ and $g(x, y) = 0$.

45. a. Find the zeros for the functions defined by $f(x, y) = 5x - 3y - 21$ and $g(x, y) = 2x + 6y + 6$. Graph of the level curves and the zero(s) found. In the linear case, could there be more than one point such that both functions are zero? Explain.

b. Now assume that f and g are nonlinear functions.

Suppose you know that f and g both have a zero near (x_0, y_0) and need to find this zero much more accurately. Write down the equations of the tangent planes (in $\mathbb{R}^3$ for f and g at the point (x_0, y_0, z_0)). Then, since you want both planes where they intersect in the xy-plane, derive the following pair of linear equations for the unknown intersection point (x_1, y_1):

$$f_x(x_0, y_0)(x_2 - x_0) + f_y(x_0, y_0)(y_1 - y_0) = -f(x_0, y_0)$$
$$g_x(x_0, y_0)(x_2 - x_0) + g_y(x_0, y_0)(y_1 - y_0) = -g(x_0, y_0)$$

Solve this pair of equations given the first Newton iterate (x_1, y_1). Why is this the analog in $\mathbb{R}^2$ of the Newton method in one variable?

c. Do one Newton iteration to find (x_1, y_1).

$$f(x, y) = x^2 - 2x + 2y^2 + 4y - 4$$

$$g(x, y) = 10 - 15 \sin\left(\frac{x + 2y}{5}\right)$$

Then *set up* to take the second iteration; that is, going from (x_1, y_1) to (x_2, y_2). If convenient, actually compute (x_2, y_2).

d. To test your progress in part **c**, evaluate f and g at (x_0, y_0) and (x_1, y_1). Both functions should be much smaller at (x_1, y_1). Take two or three iterations and discuss the convergence.

46. We now turn to finding the maximum or minimum of a function, say $H(x, y)$. Recall that the primary conditions are $H_x = 0$ and $H_y = 0$. Here you are to apply the Newton method, as developed in Problem 45, to accurately find a zero for H_x and H_y. Consider

$$H(x, y) = \exp\left(9x - x^2 - y^2 - \frac{y}{2}\right)$$

a. By completing the square in H, show that the unique maximum is at $(4.5, -0.25)$.

b. Letting H_x and H_y represent f and g in Problem 45, set up to apply Newton's method to search for the local maximum of H. Derive equations:

$$H_{xx}(x_0, y_0)(x_1 - x_0) + H_{xy}(x_0, y_0)(y_1 - y_0) = -H_x(x_0, y_0)$$
$$H_{xy}(x_0, y_0)(x_1 - x_0) + H_{yy}(x_0, y_0)(y_1 - y_0) = -H_y(x_0, y_0)$$

c. Let $(x_0, y_0) = (4.6, 0)$ and do one Newton iteration on H_x and H_y in searching for the nearby extrema. Check for the accuracy of (x_1, y_1).

d. If your software allows, take another iteration obtaining (x_2, y_2). How accurate is this value?

e. Newton's method is quite sensitive to starting values when there is more than one independent variable; so great care is needed. To see this, use $(5, 0)$ as a starting value and report what happens.

f. Repeat **c** and **d** for this function, starting at $(1, 0)$

$$H(x, y) = \exp(2x - x^2 - y^2) + 0.1(x^2 + y^2 - 2y + 1)$$

© 47. This problem was designed to show, by example, that if f is degenerate at the critical point, then almost anything can happen.

  a. Show that $f(x, y) = x^4 - y^4$ has a saddle point at $(0, 0)$.

  b. Show that $g(x, y) = x^2 y^2$ has a relative minimum at $(0, 0)$.

  c. Show that $h(x, y) = x^3 + y^3$ has no extremum or saddle point at $(0, 0)$.

48. THINK TANK PROBLEM Consider the function $f(x, y) = (y - x^2)(y - 2x^2)$. Discuss the behavior of this function at $(0, 0)$.

49. THINK TANK PROBLEM Sometimes the critical points of a function can be classified by looking at the level curves. In each case shown in Figure 12.34, determine the nature of the critical point(s) of f at $(0, 0)$.

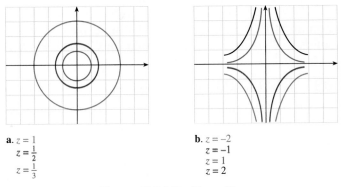

a. $z = 1$
    $z = \frac{1}{2}$
    $z = \frac{1}{3}$

b. $z = -2$
    $z = -1$
    $z = 1$
    $z = 2$

Figure 12.34 Problem 49

50. Prove the second partials test. *Hint:* Compute the second directional derivative of f in the direction of $\mathbf{u} = h\mathbf{i} + k\mathbf{j}$ and complete the square.

51. Verify the formulas for m and b associated with the least squares approximation.

52. This problem involves a generalization of the least-squares procedure, in which a "least-squares plane" is found to produce the best fit for a given set of data. A researcher knows that the quantity y is related to x_1 and x_2 by a formula of the form $y = k_1 x_1 + k_2 x_2$, where k_1 and k_2 are physical constants. To determine these constants, she conducts a series of experiments, the results of which are tabulated as follows:

x_1	1.20	0.86	1.03	1.65	-0.95	-1.07
x_2	0.43	1.92	1.52	-1.03	1.22	-0.06
y	3.21	5.73	2.22	0.92	-1.11	-0.97

Modify the method of least squares to find a "best approximation" for k_1 and k_2.

12.8 LAGRANGE MULTIPLIERS

> **IN THIS SECTION** Method of Lagrange multipliers, constrained optimization problems, Lagrange multipliers with two parameters, a geometric interpretation of Lagrange's theorem
>
> The general problem of optimizing a function *subject to a constraint* is the subject of this section. The procedure we use is called the *method of Lagrange multipliers*, after the French mathematician Joseph Louis Lagrange (see the historical note on page 812).

■ METHOD OF LAGRANGE MULTIPLIERS

In many applied problems, a function of two variables is to be optimized subject to a restriction or **constraint** on the variables. For example, consider a container heated in such a way that the temperature at the point (x, y, z) in the container is given by the function $T(x, y, z)$. Suppose that the surface $z = f(x, y)$ lies in the container, and that we wish to find the point on $z = f(x, y)$ where the temperature is the greatest. In other words, *What is the maximum value of T subject to the constraint $z = f(x, y)$, and where does this maximum value occur?* (See Figure 12.35.)

We will use the following theorem to solve such a problem.

Figure 12.35 Find the maximum value on the surface defined by $f(x, y) = 1 - x^2 - y^2$ subject to the constraint $x + y = 1$ ($x \geq 0$, $y \geq 0$). See Example 1 for a solution.

[Figure labels: Unconstrained maximum; Constrained maximum; $x + y = 1$; $z = 1 - x^2 - y^2$]

THEOREM 12.13   Lagrange's theorem

Assume that f and g have continuous first partial derivatives and that f has an extremum at $P_0(x_0, y_0)$ on the smooth constraint curve $g(x, y) = c$. If $\nabla g(x_0, y_0) \neq \mathbf{0}$, there is a number λ such that

$$\nabla f(x_0, y_0) = \lambda \nabla g(x_0, y_0)$$

Proof: Denote the constraint curve $g(x, y) = c$ by C, and note that C is smooth. We represent this curve by the vector function

$$\mathbf{R}(t) = x(t)\mathbf{i} + y(t)\mathbf{j}$$

for all t in an open interval I, including t_0 corresponding to P_0, where $x'(t)$ and $y'(t)$ exist and are continuous. Let $F(t) = f[x(t), y(t)]$ for all t in I, and apply the chain rule to obtain

$$F'(t) = f_x \frac{dx}{dt} + f_y \frac{dy}{dt} = \nabla f[x(t), y(t)] \cdot \mathbf{R}'(t)$$

Because $f(x, y)$ has an extremum at P_0, we know that $F(t)$ has an extremum at t_0, the value of t that corresponds to P_0 (that is, P_0 is the point on C where $t = t_0$). Therefore, we have $F'(t_0) = 0$ and

$$F'(t_0) = \nabla f[x(t_0), y(t_0)] \cdot \mathbf{R}'(t_0) = 0$$

If $\nabla f[x(t_0), y(t_0)] = 0$, then $\lambda = 0$, and the condition $\nabla f = \lambda \nabla g$ is satisfied (which is trivial with $\lambda = 0$). If $\nabla f[x(t_0), y(t_0)] \neq 0$, then $\nabla f[x(t_0), y(t_0)]$ is orthogonal to $\mathbf{R}'(t_0)$. Because $\mathbf{R}'(t_0)$ is tangent to the constraint curve C, it follows that $\nabla f(x_0, y_0)$ is normal to C. But $\nabla g(x_0, y_0)$ is also normal to C (because C is a level curve of g), and we conclude that ∇f and ∇g must be *parallel* at P_0. Thus, there is a scalar λ such that $\nabla f(x_0, y_0) = \lambda \nabla g(x_0, y_0)$ as required.   ∎

■ CONSTRAINED OPTIMIZATION PROBLEMS

The general procedure for the method of Lagrange multipliers may be described as follows.

Procedure for the Method of Lagrange Multipliers

Suppose f and g satisfy the hypotheses of Lagrange's theorem, and suppose that $f(x)$ has an extremum (minimum and/or a maximum) subject to the constraint $g(x, y) = c$. Then to find the extreme values, proceed as follows:

Step 1: Simultaneously solve the following three equations:

$$f_x(x, y) = \lambda g_x(x, y) \qquad f_y(x, y) = \lambda g_y(x, y) \qquad g(x, y) = c$$

Step 2: Evaluate f at all points found in Step 1. The largest of these values is the maximum value of f and the smallest of these values is the minimum value of f.

EXAMPLE 1   Optimization with Lagrange multiplier

Find the largest and smallest values of $f(x, y) = 1 - x^2 - y^2$ subject to the constraint $x + y = 1$ with $x \geq 0$, $y \geq 0$.

Solution   Because the constraint is $x + y = 1$, let $g(x, y) = x + y - 1$.

$$f_x(x, y) = -2x \qquad f_y(x, y) = -2y \qquad g_x(x, y) = 1 \qquad g_y(x, y) = 1$$

Form the system

$$\begin{cases} -2x = \lambda(1) \\ -2y = \lambda(1) \\ x + y = 1 \end{cases}$$

The only solution is $x = \frac{1}{2}$, $y = \frac{1}{2}$.

$$f\left(\frac{1}{2}, \frac{1}{2}\right) = 1 - \left(\frac{1}{2}\right)^2 - \left(\frac{1}{2}\right)^2 = \frac{1}{2}$$

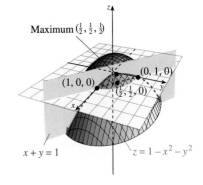

Figure 12.36 The maximum is the high point of the curve of intersection of the surface and the plane.

The endpoints of $x + y = 1$ where $x \geq 0$, $y \geq 0$ are at $(1, 0)$ and $(0, 1)$, and we find that

$$f(1, 0) = 1 - 1^2 - 0^2 = 0$$

$$f(0, 1) = 1 - 0^2 - 1^2 = 0$$

Therefore, the maximum value is $\frac{1}{2}$ at $\left(\frac{1}{2}, \frac{1}{2}\right)$ and the minimum value is 0 at either $(1, 0)$ and $(0, 1)$.   ▬

The method of Lagrange multipliers extends naturally to functions of three or more variables. If a function $f(x, y, z)$ has an extreme value subject to a constraint $g(x, y, z) = c$, then the extremum occurs at a point (x_0, y_0, z_0) such that $g(x_0, y_0, z_0) = c$ and $\nabla f(x_0, y_0, z_0) = \lambda \nabla g(x_0, y_0, z_0)$ for some number λ. Here is an example.

EXAMPLE 2   Hottest and coldest points on a plate

A container in $\mathbb{R}^3$ has the shape of the cube given by $0 \leq x \leq 1$, $0 \leq y \leq 1$, $0 \leq z \leq 1$. A plate is placed in the container in such a way that it occupies that portion of the plane $x + y + z = 1$ that lies in the cubical container. If the container is heated so that the temperature at each point (x, y, z) is given by

$$T(x, y, z) = 4 - 2x^2 - y^2 - z^2$$

in hundreds of degrees Celsius, what are the hottest and coldest points on the plate?

Solution   The cube and plate are shown in Figure 12.37. We shall use Lagrange multipliers to find all critical points in the interior of the plate, and then we shall examine the plate's boundary. To apply the method of Lagrange multipliers, we must solve $\nabla T = \lambda \nabla g$, where $g(x, y, z) = x + y + z - 1$. We obtain the partial derivatives

$$T_x = -4x \qquad T_y = -2y \qquad T_z = -2z \qquad g_x = g_y = g_z = 1$$

We must solve the system

$$\begin{cases} -4x = \lambda \\ -2y = \lambda \\ -2z = \lambda \\ x + y + z = 1 \end{cases}$$

Figure 12.37 Find the hottest and coldest points on the plate inside the cube.

The solution of this system is $x = \frac{1}{5}$, $y = \frac{2}{5}$, $z = \frac{2}{5}$, and $\lambda = -\frac{4}{5}$. The boundary of the plate is a triangle with vertices $A(1, 0, 0)$, $B(0, 1, 0)$, and $C(0, 0, 1)$. The temperature along the edges of this triangle may be found as follows:

Edge AC: $x + z = 1$, $y = 0$ $T_1(x) = 4 - 2x^2 - (0)^2 - (1 - x)^2 = 3 - 3x^2 + 2x$, $0 \le x \le 1$

Edge AB: $x + y = 1$, $z = 0$ $T_2(x) = 4 - 2x^2 - (1 - x)^2 - (0)^2 = 3 - 3x^2 + 2x$, $0 \le x \le 1$

Edge BC: $y + z = 1$, $x = 0$ $T_3(y) = 4 - 2(0)^2 - y^2 - (1 - y)^2 = 3 + 2y - 2y^2$, $0 \le y \le 1$

Edge AC: Differentiating, $T_1{}'(x) = T_2{}'(x) = -6x + 2$, which equals 0 when $x = \frac{1}{3}$. If $x = \frac{1}{3}$, then $z = \frac{2}{3}$ (because $x + z = 1$, $y = 0$ on edge AC), so we have the critical point $\left(\frac{1}{3}, 0, \frac{2}{3}\right)$.

Edge AB: Because $T_2 = T_1$, we see $x = \frac{1}{3}$. If $x = \frac{1}{3}$, then $y = \frac{2}{3}$ (because $x + y = 1$, $z = 0$ on edge BC), so we have another critical point $\left(\frac{1}{3}, \frac{2}{3}, 0\right)$.

Edge BC: Differentiating, $T_3{}'(y) = 2 - 4y$, which equals 0 when $y = \frac{1}{2}$. Because $y + z = 1$ and $x = 0$, we have the critical point $\left(0, \frac{1}{2}, \frac{1}{2}\right)$.

Endpoints of the edges: $(1, 0, 0)$, $(0, 1, 0)$, and $(0, 0, 1)$.

The last step is to evaluate T at the critical points and the endpoints:

$$T\left(\tfrac{1}{5}, \tfrac{2}{5}, \tfrac{2}{5}\right) = 3.6;$$

$$T\left(\tfrac{1}{3}, 0, \tfrac{2}{3}\right) = 3\tfrac{1}{3}; \qquad T\left(\tfrac{1}{3}, \tfrac{2}{3}, 0\right) = 3\tfrac{1}{3}; \qquad T\left(0, \tfrac{1}{2}, \tfrac{1}{2}\right) = 3.5;$$

$$T(1, 0, 0) = 2; \qquad T(0, 1, 0) = 3; \qquad T(0, 0, 1) = 3$$

Comparing these values (remember the temperature is in hundreds of degrees Celsius), we see that the highest temperature is 360 °C at $\left(\frac{1}{5}, \frac{2}{5}, \frac{2}{5}\right)$ and the lowest temperature is 200 °C at $(1, 0, 0)$.   ▬

Notice that, in the end, we do not care about the value of λ. The multiplier is just used as an intermediary device for finding the critical points. However, in some problems, we do care about the value of λ, because of the interpretation given in the following theorem.

THEOREM 12.14   Rate of change of the extreme value

Suppose E is an extreme value (maximum or minimum) of f subject to the constraint $g(x, y) = c$. Then the Lagrange multiplier λ is the rate of change of E with respect to c; that is, $\lambda = dE/dc$.

Proof: Note that at the extreme value (x, y) we have

$$f_x = \lambda g_x, \qquad f_y = \lambda g_y, \quad \text{and} \quad g(x, y) = c$$

The coordinates of the optimal ordered pair (x, y) depend on c (because different constraint levels will generally lead to different optimal combinations of x and y). Thus,

$$E = E(x, y) \qquad \text{where } x \text{ and } y \text{ are functions of } c$$

By the chain rule for partial derivatives:

$$\frac{dE}{dc} = \frac{\partial E}{\partial x}\frac{dx}{dc} + \frac{\partial E}{\partial y}\frac{dy}{dc}$$

$$= f_x \frac{dx}{dc} + f_y \frac{dy}{dc} \qquad \textit{Because } E = f(x, y)$$

$$= \lambda g_x \frac{dx}{dc} + \lambda g_y \frac{dy}{dc} \qquad \textit{Because } f_x = \lambda g_x \textit{ and } f_y = \lambda g_y$$

$$= \lambda \left(g_x \frac{dx}{dc} + g_y \frac{dy}{dc} \right)$$

$$= \lambda \frac{dg}{dc} \qquad\qquad \textit{Chain rule}$$

$$= \lambda \qquad\qquad\qquad \textit{Because } \frac{dg}{dc} = 1 \textit{ (remember } g = c) \quad \blacksquare$$

This theorem can be interpreted as saying that the multiplier gives the change in the extreme value E that results when the constraint c is increased by 1 unit. This interpretation is illustrated in the following example.

EXAMPLE 3   Maximum output for a Cobb-Douglas production function

If x thousand dollars is spent on labor, and y thousand dollars is spent on equipment, it is estimated that the output of a certain factory will be

$$Q(x, y) = 50x^{2/5}y^{3/5}$$

units. If \$150,000 is available, how should this capital be allocated between labor and equipment to generate the largest possible output? How does the maximum output change if the money available for labor and equipment is increased by \$1,000? In economics, an output function of the general form $Q(x, y) = x^{\alpha}y^{1-\alpha}$ is known as a **Cobb-Douglas production function.**

Solution   Because x and y are given in units of \$1,000, the constraint equation is $x + y = 150$. If we set $g(x, y) = x + y - 150$, we wish to maximize Q subject to $g(x, y) = 0$. To apply the method of Lagrange multipliers, we first find

$$Q_x = 20x^{-3/5}y^{3/5} \qquad Q_y = 30x^{2/5}y^{-2/5} \qquad g_x = 1 \qquad g_y = 1$$

Next, solve the system

$$\begin{cases} 20x^{-3/5}y^{3/5} = \lambda \\ 30x^{2/5}y^{-2/5} = \lambda \\ x + y - 150 = 0 \end{cases}$$

From the first two equations we have

$$20x^{-3/5}y^{3/5} = 30x^{2/5}y^{-2/5}$$

$$20y = 30x$$

$$y = 1.5x$$

Substitute $y = 1.5x$ into the equation $x + y = 150$ to find $x = 60$. This leads to the solution $y = 90$, so that the maximum output is

$$Q(60, 90) = 50(60)^{2/5}(90)^{3/5} \approx 3,826.273\,502 \text{ units}$$

We also find that

$$\lambda = 20(60)^{-3/5}(90)^{3/5} \approx 25.508\,490\,01$$

Thus, the maximum output is about 3,826 units and occurs when $60,000 is allocated to labor and $90,000 to equipment. We also note that an increase of $1,000 (1 unit) in the available funds will increase the maximum output by approximately $\lambda \approx 25.5$ units (from 3,826.27 to 3,851.78 units). ■

■ LAGRANGE MULTIPLIERS WITH TWO PARAMETERS

The method of Lagrange multipliers can also be applied in situations with more than one constraint equation. Suppose we wish to locate an extremum of a function defined by $f(x, y, z)$ subject to *two* constraints, $g(x, y, z) = c_1$ and $h(x, y, z) = c_2$. By generalizing Lagrange's theorem, it can be shown that if (x_0, y_0, z_0) is the desired extremum, then there are numbers λ and μ such that $g(x_0, y_0, z_0) = c_1$, $h(x_0, y_0, z_0) = c_2$, and

$$\nabla f(x_0, y_0, z_0) = \lambda \nabla g(x_0, y_0, z_0) + \mu \nabla h(x_0, y_0, z_0)$$

provided that the functions f, g, and h are continuously differentiable and that the extremum occurs in the interior of a region where neither ∇g nor ∇h vanishes. As in the case of one constraint, when searching for the optimum values, we find values that satisfy this equation by solving a system of equations, and then we must also check boundary points and points where the constraint gradients vanish. We close this section with an example that illustrates this procedure.

EXAMPLE 4   Optimization with two constraints

Find the point on the intersection of the plane $x + 2y + z = 10$ and the paraboloid $z = x^2 + y^2$ that is closest to the origin.

Solution   The distance from a point (x, y, z) to the origin is $s = \sqrt{x^2 + y^2 + z^2}$, but instead of minimizing this quantity, it is easier to minimize its square. That is, we shall minimize $f(x, y, z) = x^2 + y^2 + z^2$ subject to the joint constraints

$$g(x, y, z) = x + 2y + z = 10 \quad \text{and} \quad h(x, y, z) = x^2 + y^2 - z = 0$$

Compute the partial derivatives of f, g, and h:

$$
\begin{array}{ccc}
f_x = 2x & f_y = 2y & f_z = 2z \\
g_x = 1 & g_y = 2 & g_z = 1 \\
h_x = 2x & h_y = 2y & h_z = -1
\end{array}
$$

To apply the method of Lagrange multipliers, we use the formula

$$\nabla f(x_0, y_0, z_0) = \lambda \nabla g(x_0, y_0, z_0) + \mu \nabla h(x_0, y_0, z_0)$$

which leads to the following system of equations:

$$
\begin{cases}
2x = \lambda(1) + \mu(2x) \\
2y = \lambda(2) + \mu(2y) \\
2z = \lambda(1) + \mu(-1) \\
x + 2y + z = 10 \\
z = x^2 + y^2
\end{cases}
$$

This is not a linear system, so solving it requires ingenuity.

Intersection curve $z = x^2 + y^2$

Find the point on the intersection curve that is closest to the origin.

$x + 2y + z = 10$

Graphic representation of Example 4

Multiply the first equation by 2 and subtract the second equation to obtain

$$4x - 2y = (4x - 2y)\mu$$

$$(4x - 2y) - (4x - 2y)\mu = 0$$

$$(4x - 2y)(1 - \mu) = 0$$

$$4x - 2y = 0 \quad \text{or} \quad 1 - \mu = 0$$

Case I: If $4x - 2y = 0$, then $y = 2x$. Substitute this into the two constraint equations:

$x + 2y + z = 10$	$x^2 + y^2 - z = 0$
$x + 2(2x) + z = 10$	$x^2 + (2x)^2 - z = 0$
$z = 10 - 5x$	$z = 5x^2$

By substitution we have $5x^2 = 10 - 5x$, which has solutions $x = 1$ and $x = -2$. This implies

$x = 1$	$x = -2$
$y = 2x = 2(1) = 2$	$y = 2x = 2(-2) = -4$
$z = 5x^2 = 5(1)^2 = 5$	$z = 5x^2 = 5(-2)^2 = 20$

Thus, the points $(1, 2, 5)$ and $(-2, -4, 20)$ are candidates for the minimal distance.

Case II:. If $1 - \mu = 0$, then $\mu = 1$, and we look at the system of equations involving x, y, z, λ, and μ.

$$\begin{cases} 2x = \lambda(1) + \mu(2x) \\ 2y = \lambda(2) + \mu(2y) \\ 2z = \lambda(1) + \mu(-1) \\ x + 2y + z = 10 \\ z = x^2 + y^2 \end{cases}$$

The top equation becomes $2x = \lambda + 2x$, so that $\lambda = 0$. We now find z from the third equation:

$$2z = -1, \quad \text{or} \quad z = -\tfrac{1}{2}$$

Now, turn to the constraint equations:

$x + 2y + z = 10$	$x^2 + y^2 - z = 0$
$x + 2y - \tfrac{1}{2} = 10$	$x^2 + y^2 + \tfrac{1}{2} = 0$
$x + 2y = 10 + \tfrac{1}{2}$	$x^2 + y^2 = -\tfrac{1}{2}$

There is no solution because $x^2 + y^2$ cannot equal a negative number.
We check the candidates for the minimal distance:

$$f(x, y, z) = x^2 + y^2 + z^2 \quad \text{so that}$$

$$f(1, 2, 5) = 1^2 + 2^2 + 5^2 = 30$$

$$f(-2, -4, 20) = (-2)^2 + (-4)^2 + 20^2 = 420$$

Because $f(x, y, z)$ represents the square of the distance, the minimal distance is $\sqrt{30}$ and the point on the intersection of the two surfaces nearest to the origin is $(1, 2, 5)$.

■ A GEOMETRIC INTERPRETATION FOR LAGRANGE'S THEOREM

Lagrange's theorem can be interpreted geometrically. Suppose the constraint curve $g(x, y) = c$ and the level curves $f(x, y) = k$ are drawn in the xy-plane, as shown in Figure 12.38.

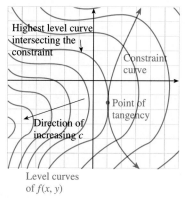

Figure 12.38 Increasing level curves and the constraint curve

To maximize $f(x, y)$ subject to the constraint $g(x, y) = c$, we must find the highest level curve of f that intersects the constraint curve. As the sketch in Figure 12.37 suggests, this critical intersection occurs at a point where the constraint curve is tangent to a level curve—that is, where the slope of the constraint curve $g(x, y) = c$ is equal to the slope of a level curve $f(x, y) = k$. According to the formula derived in Problem 45, Section 12.5,

Slope of constraint curve $g(x, y) = c$ is $\dfrac{-g_x}{g_y}$.

Slope of each level curve is $\dfrac{-f_x}{f_y}$.

The condition that the slopes are equal can be expressed by

$$\frac{-f_x}{f_y} = \frac{-g_x}{g_y}, \quad \text{or, equivalently,} \quad \frac{f_x}{g_x} = \frac{f_y}{g_y}$$

Let λ equal this common ratio,

$$\lambda = \frac{f_x}{g_x} \quad \text{and} \quad \lambda = \frac{f_y}{g_y}$$

so that

$$f_x = \lambda g_x \quad \text{and} \quad f_y = \lambda g_y$$

and $\nabla f = f_x \mathbf{i} + f_y \mathbf{j} = \lambda(g_x \mathbf{i} + g_y \mathbf{j}) = \lambda \nabla g$

Because the point in question must lie on the constraint curve, we also have $g(x, y) = c$. If these equations are satisfied at a certain point (a, b), then f will reach its constrained *maximum* at (a, b) if the *highest* level curve that intersects the constraint curve does so at this highest point. On the other hand, if the *lowest* level curve that intersects the constraint curve does so at (a, b), then f achieves its constrained *minimum* at this point.

PROBLEM SET 12.8

Ⓐ *Use the method of Lagrange multipliers to find the required constrained extrema in Problems 1–12.*

1. Maximize $f(x, y) = xy$ subject to $2x + 2y = 5$.

2. Maximize $f(x, y) = xy$ subject to $x + y = 20$.

3. Maximize $f(x, y) = 16 - x^2 - y^2$ subject to $x + 2y = 6$.

4. Minimize $f(x, y) = x^2 + y^2$ subject to $x + y = 24$.

5. Minimize $f(x, y) = x^2 + y^2$ subject to $xy = 1$.

6. Minimize $f(x, y) = x^2 - xy + 2y^2$ subject to $2x + y = 22$.

7. Minimize $f(x, y) = x^2 - y^2$ subject to $x^2 + y^2 = 4$.

8. Maximize $f(x, y) = x^2 - 2y - y^2$ subject to $x^2 + y^2 = 1$.

9. Maximize $f(x, y) = \cos x + \cos y$ subject to $y = x + \frac{\pi}{4}$.

10. Maximize $f(x, y, z) = xyz$ subject to $3x + 2y + z = 6$.

11. Minimize $f(x, y, z) = x^2 + y^2 + z^2$ subject to $x - 2y + 3z = 4$.

12. Minimize $f(x, y, z) = x^2 + y^2 + z^2$ subject to $4x^2 + 2y^2 + z^2 = 4$.

Ⓑ 13. Find the smallest value of $f(x, y, z) = 2x^2 + 4y^2 + z^2$ subject to $4x - 8y + 2z = 10$. What, if anything, can be said about the largest value of f subject to this constraint?

14. Let $f(x, y, z) = x^2y^2z^2$. Show that the maximum value of f subject to $x^2 + y^2 + z^2 = R^2$ is $R^6/27$.

15. Find the maximum value of $f(x, y, z) = x - y + z$ on the sphere $x^2 + y^2 + z^2 = 100$.

16. Find the minimum value of $f(x, y, z) = x - y + z$ on the sphere $x^2 + y^2 + z^2 = 100$.

17. Use Lagrange multipliers to find the distance from the origin to the plane $Ax + By + Cz = 0$ where at least one of A, B, C is nonzero.

18. Find the maximum and minimum distance from the origin to the ellipse $5x^2 - 6xy + 5y^2 = 4$.

19. Find the point on the plane

$$2x + y + z = 1$$

that is nearest the origin.

20. Find the largest product of positive numbers x, y, and z such that their sum is 24.

21. Write the number 12 as the sum of three numbers x, y, z in such a way that the product xy^2z is a maximum.

22. A rectangular box with no top is to be constructed from 96 ft^2 of material. What should be the dimensions of the box if it is to enclose maximum volume?

23. The temperature T at point (x, y, z) in a region of space is given by the formula $T = 100 - xy - xz - yz$. Find the lowest temperature on the plane $x + y + z = 10$.

24. A farmer wishes to fence off a rectangular pasture along the bank of a river. The area of the pasture is to be 3,200 yd^2, and no fencing is needed along the river bank. Find the dimensions of the pasture that will require the least amount of fencing.

25. There are 320 yd of fencing available to enclose a rectangular field. How should the fencing be used so that the enclosed area is as large as possible?

26. Use the fact that 12 fl oz is approximately 6.89π in.^{3} to find the dimensions of the 12-oz soda can that can be constructed using the least amount of metal. Compare your answer with an actual can of Pepsi.

27. A cylindrical can is to hold 4π in.^{3} of orange juice. The cost per in.^{2} of constructing the metal top and bottom is twice the cost per in.^{2} of constructing the cardboard side. What are the dimensions of the least expensive can?

28. Find the volume of the largest rectangular parallelepiped that can be inscribed in the ellipsoid

$$x^2 + \frac{y^2}{4} + \frac{z^2}{9} = 1$$

29. A manufacturer has $8,000 to spend on the development and promotion of a new product. It is estimated that if x thousand dollars are spent on development and y thousand are spent on promotion, sales will be approximately $f(x, y) = 50x^{1/2}y^{3/2}$ units. How much money should the manufacturer allocate to development and how much to promotion to maximize sales?

30. If x thousand dollars are spent on labor and y thousand dollars are spent on equipment, the output at a certain factory will be $Q(x, y) = 60x^{1/3}y^{2/3}$ units. Assume that $120,000 is available.

   a. How should money be allocated between labor and equipment to generate the largest possible output?

   b. Use the Lagrange multiplier λ to estimate the change in the maximum output of the factory that would result if the money available for labor and equipment is increased by $1,000.

31. A university extension agricultural service concludes that on a particular farm the yield of wheat per acre is a function of water and fertilizer. Let x be the number of acre-feet of water applied and y be the number of pounds of fertilizer applied during the growing season. The agricultural service then concluded that the yield (measured in bushels), represented by f can be defined by the formula $f(x, y) = 500 - x^2 - 2y^2$. Suppose that water costs $20 per acre-foot, fertilizer costs $12 per pound, and the farmer will invest $236 per acre for water and fertilizer. How much water and fertilizer should the farmer buy to maximize the yield?

32. How much would the farmer of Problem 31 maximize the yield if the amount spent is $100 instead of $236?

33. Present post office regulations specify that a box (that is, a package in the form of a rectangular parallelepiped) can be mailed parcel post only if the sum of its length and

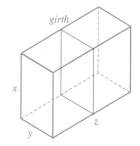
girth

Figure 12.39 Maximum volume for a box mailed by U.S. parcel post

girth does not exceed 108 inches, as shown in Figure 12.39. Find the maximum volume of such a package.

34. If x, y, z are the angles of a triangle, what is the maximum value of the product $P(x, y, z) = \sin x \sin y \sin z$? What about $Q(x, y, z) = \cos x \cos y \cos z$?

Use the method of Lagrange multipliers in Problems 35–38 to find the required extrema for the two given constraints.

35. Find the minimum of $f(x, y, z) = x^2 + y^2 + z^2$ subject to $x + y = 4$ and $y + z = 6$.

36. Find the maximum of $f(x, y, z) = xyz$ subject to $x^2 + y^2 = 3$ and $y = 2z$.

37. Maximize $f(x, y, z) = xy + xz$ subject to $2x + 3z = 5$ and $xy = 4$.

38. Minimize $f(x, y, z) = 2x^2 + 3y^2 + 4z^2$ subject to $x + y + z = 4$ and $x - 2y + 5z = 3$.

39. A manufacturer is planning to sell a new product at the price of $150 per unit and estimates that if x thousand dollars is spent on development and y thousand dollars on promotion, approximately

$$\frac{320y}{y + 2} + \frac{160x}{x + 4}$$

units of the product will be sold. The cost of manufacturing the product is $50 per unit.

a. If the manufacturer has a total of $8,000 to spend on development and promotion, how should this money be allocated to generate the largest possible profit?

b. Suppose the manufacturer decides to spend $8,100 instead of $8,000 on the development and promotion of the new product. Estimate how this change will affect the maximum possible profit.

c. If unlimited funds are available, how much should the manufacturer spend on development and promotion to maximize profit?

d. What is the Lagrange multiplier in part **c**? Your answer should suggest another method for solving part **c**. Solve the problem using this alternative approach.

ⓒ 40. A farmer wants to build a metal silo in the shape of a right circular cylinder with a right circular cone on the top (the bottom of the silo will be a concrete slab). What is the least amount of metal that can be used if the silo is to have a fixed volume?

41. Find the volume of the largest rectangular parallelepiped (box) that can be inscribed in the ellipsoid

$$\frac{x^2}{a^2} + \frac{y^2}{b^2} + \frac{z^2}{c^2} = 1$$

(See Problem 28.)

In Problems 42–45, let $Q = f(x, y)$ be a production function in which x and y represent units of labor and capital, respectively. If p and q represent unit costs of labor and capital, respectively, then $px + qy$ represents the total cost of production.

42. Use Lagrange multipliers to show that subject to a fixed production level c, the total cost is smallest when

$$\frac{f_x}{p} = \frac{f_y}{q} \quad \text{and} \quad Q = f(x, y) = c$$

(provided $\nabla f \neq 0$, and $p \neq 0$, $q \neq 0$). This is often referred to as the **minimum cost problem**, and its solution is called the **least cost combination of inputs**.

43. Show that the inputs x, y that maximize the production level $Q = f(x, y)$ subject to a fixed cost k satisfy

$$\frac{f_x}{p} = \frac{f_y}{q} \quad \text{with } px + qy = k$$

(assume $p \neq 0$, $q \neq 0$). This is called a **fixed-budget problem**.

44. A Cobb–Douglas production function is an output function of the form $Q(x, y) = cx^\alpha y^\beta$, with $\alpha + \beta = 1$. Show that such a function is maximized with respect to the fixed cost $px + qy = k$ when $x = \alpha k/p$ and $y = \beta k/q$. Where does the maximum occur if we drop the condition $\alpha + \beta = 1$? How does the maximum output change if k is increased by 1 unit?

45. Show that the cost function $C(x, y) = px + qy$ is minimized subject to the fixed production level $Ax^\alpha y^\beta = k$, with $\alpha + \beta = 1$ when $x = \dfrac{k}{A}\left(\dfrac{\alpha q}{\beta p}\right)^\beta$ and $y = \dfrac{k}{A}\left(\dfrac{\beta p}{\alpha q}\right)^\alpha$.

CHAPTER 12 REVIEW

IN THIS REVIEW Proficiency examination; supplementary problems
Problems 1–31 of the proficiency examination test your knowledge of the concepts of this chapter, and Problems 32–40 test your understanding of those concepts by asking you to work sample practice problems. The supplementary problems present questions relating to the material of this chapter in a wide variety of settings.

PROFICIENCY EXAMINATION

Concept Problems

1. What is a function of two variables?
2. What is the domain of a function of two variables?
3. What is a level curve of the function defined by $f(x, y)$?
4. What do we mean by the limit of a function of two variables?
5. State the following properties of a limit of functions of two variables.

    a. scalar rule   **b.** sum rule

    c. product rule   **d.** quotient rule

6. Define the continuity of a function defined by $f(x, y)$ at a point (x_0, y_0) in its domain.
7. If $z = f(x, y)$, define the first partial derivatives of f with respect to x and y.
8. What is the slope of a tangent line to the surface defined by $z = f(x, y)$ that is parallel to the xz plane?
9. If $z = f(x, y)$ find the second partial derivatives and the mixed partial derivatives.
10. If $z = f(x, y)$, what are the increments of x, y, and z?
11. What does it mean for a function of two variables to be differentiable at (x_0, y_0)?
12. State the incremental approximation of $f(x, y)$.
13. Define the total differential of $z = f(x, y)$.
14. State the chain rule for one parameter.
15. State the chain rule for two parameters.
16. Define the directional derivative of a function defined by $z = f(x, y)$.
17. Define the gradient $\nabla f(x, y)$.
18. State the following basic properties of the gradient.

    a. constant rule   **b.** linearity rule

    c. product rule   **d.** quotient rule

    e. power rule

19. Express the directional derivative in terms of the gradient.
20. State the optimal direction property of the gradient (that is, the steepest ascent and steepest descent).
21. State the normal property of the gradient.
22. Define a normal line and a tangent plane to a surface S at a point P_0.
23. Define the absolute extrema of a function of two variables.
24. Define the relative extrema of a function of two variables.
25. What is a critical point of a function of two variables?
26. State the second partials test.
27. State the extreme value theorem for a function of two variables.
28. What is the least squares approximation of data, and what is a regression line?
29. State Lagrange's theorem.
30. State the procedure for the method of Lagrange multipliers.
31. State the rate of change of the extreme value theorem.

Practice Problems

32. If $f(x, y) = \sin^{-1} xy$, verify that $f_{xy} = f_{yx}$.
33. Let $w = x^2 y + y^2 z$, where $x = t \sin t$, $y = t \cos t$, and $z = 2t$. Use the chain rule to find dw/dt where $t = \pi$.
34. Let $f(x, y, z) = xy + yz + xz$, and let P_0 denote the point $(1, 2, -1)$.

    a. Find the gradient of f at P_0.

    b. Find the directional derivative of f in the direction from P_0 toward the point $Q(-1, 1, -1)$.

    c. Find the direction from P_0 in which the directional derivative has its largest value. What is the magnitude of the largest directional derivative at P_0?

35. Show that the function defined by

$$f(x, y) = \begin{cases} \dfrac{x^2 y}{x^3 + y^3} & \text{if } (x, y) \neq (0, 0) \\ 0 & \text{if } (x, y) = (0, 0) \end{cases}$$

is not continuous at $(0, 0)$.

36. If $f(x, y) = \ln\left(\dfrac{y}{x}\right)$, find f_x, f_y, f_{yy}, and f_{xy}.
37. Show that if $f(x, y, z) = x^2 y + y^2 z + z^2 x$, then

$$\frac{\partial f}{\partial x} + \frac{\partial f}{\partial y} + \frac{\partial f}{\partial z} = (x + y + z)^2$$

38. Let $f(x, y) = (x^2 + y^2)^2$. Find the directional derivative of f at $(2, -2)$ in the direction that makes an angle of $2\pi/3$ with the positive x-axis.
39. Find all critical points of $f(x, y) = (x^2 + y^2)e^{-(x^2+y^2)}$.

Figure 12.40 Graph of $f(x, y) = (x^2 + y^2)e^{-(x^2+y^2)}$

40. Use the method of Lagrange multipliers to find the maximum and minimum values of the function $f(x, y) = x^2 + 2y^2 + 2x + 3$ subject to the constraint $x^2 + y^2 = 4$.

SUPPLEMENTARY PROBLEMS

Describe the domain of each function given in Problems 1–4.

1. $f(x, y) = \sqrt{16 - x^2 - y^2}$

2. $f(x, y) = \dfrac{x^2 - y^2}{x - y}$

3. $f(x, y) = \sin^{-1} x + \cos^{-1} y$

4. $f(x, y) = e^{x+y}\tan^{-1}\left(\dfrac{y}{x}\right)$

Find the partial derivatives f_x and f_y for the function defined in Problems 5–10.

5. $f(x, y) = \dfrac{x^2 - y^2}{x + y}$

6. $f(x, y) = x^3 e^{3y/2x}$

7. $f(x, y) = x^2 y + \sin\dfrac{y}{x}$

8. $f(x, y) = \ln\left(\dfrac{xy}{x + 2y}\right)$

9. $f(x, y) = 2x^3 y + 3xy^2 + \dfrac{y}{x}$

10. $f(x, y) = xye^{xy}$

For each function given in Problems 11–15, describe the level curve or level surface $f = c$ for the given values of the constant c.

11. $f(x, y) = x^2 - y$; $c = 2$, $c = -2$

12. $f(x, y) = 6x + 2y$; $c = 0$, $c = 1$, $c = 2$

13. $f(x, y) = \begin{cases} \sqrt{x^2 + y^2} & \text{if } x \geq 0 \\ |y| & \text{if } x < 0 \end{cases}$ $c = 2, c = 1, c = -1$

14. $f(x, y, z) = x^2 + y^2 + z^2$; $c = 16$, $c = 0$, $c = -25$

15. $f(x, y, z) = x^2 + \dfrac{y^2}{2} + \dfrac{z^2}{9}$; $c = 1$, $c = 2$

Evaluate the limits in Problems 16–19, assuming they exist.

16. $\displaystyle\lim_{(x,y)\to(1,1)} \dfrac{xy}{x^2 + y^2}$

17. $\displaystyle\lim_{(x,y)\to(1,1)} \dfrac{x^2 - y^2}{x^4 - y^4}$

18. $\displaystyle\lim_{(x,y)\to(0,0)} \dfrac{x^2 - y^2}{x^4 - y^4}$

19. $\displaystyle\lim_{(x,y)\to(0,0)} \dfrac{x + ye^{-x}}{1 + x^2}$

Show that each limit in Problem 20–23 does not exist.

20. $\displaystyle\lim_{(x,y)\to(0,0)} \dfrac{x^3 - y^3}{x^3 + y^3}$

21. $\displaystyle\lim_{(x,y)\to(0,0)} \dfrac{x^4 - y^4}{x^4 + y^4}$

22. $\displaystyle\lim_{(x,y)\to(0,0)} \dfrac{x^2 - 2y^2}{2x^2 + y^2}$

23. $\displaystyle\lim_{(x,y)\to(0,0)} \dfrac{x^2 - y^3}{x^2 + y^3}$

Find the derivatives in Problems 24–27 using the chain rule. You may leave your answers in terms of x, y, t, u, and v.

24. Find $\dfrac{dz}{dt}$ where $z = -xy + y^3$, and $x = -3t^2$, $y = 1 + t^3$.

25. Find $\dfrac{dz}{dt}$ where $z = xy + y^2$, and $x = e^t t^{-1}$, $y = \tan t$.

26. Find $\dfrac{\partial z}{\partial u}$ and $\dfrac{\partial z}{\partial v}$ where $z = x^2 - y^2$, and $x = u + 2v$, $y = u - 2v$.

27. Find $\dfrac{\partial z}{\partial u}$ and $\dfrac{\partial z}{\partial v}$ where $z = x\tan\dfrac{x}{y}$, and $x = uv$, $y = \dfrac{u}{v}$.

Use implicit differentiation to find $\dfrac{\partial z}{\partial x}$ and $\dfrac{\partial z}{\partial y}$ in Problems 28–33.

28. $x^2 + 6y^2 + 2z^2 = 5$

29. $e^x + e^y + e^z = 3$

30. $x^3 + 2xz - yz^2 - z^3 = 1$

31. $\ln(2x - z^2) - (x - y)e^{2z} = 0$

32. $x^3 + y^3 + z^3 = 6$

33. $x + 2y - 3z = \ln z$

In Problems 34–41, find f_x, f_y, f_{xx}, f_{yx}.

34. $f(x, y) = \tan^{-1} xy$

35. $f(x, y) = \sin^{-1} xy$

36. $f(x, y) = x^2 + y^3 - 2xy^2$

37. $f(x, y) = e^{x^2+y^2}$

38. $f(x, y) = x \ln y$

39. $f(x, y, z) = x^3 e^{3y/z^2}$

40. $f(x, y) = \displaystyle\int_x^y \sin(\cos t)\, dt$

41. $f(x, y, z) = x^3 y^2 \sqrt{z} + \sin(x^2 + y \ln z)$

Find equations for the tangent plane and normal line to the surfaces given in Problems 42–44 at the prescribed point.

42. $x^2 y^3 z = 8$ at $P_0(2, -1, -2)$

43. $x^2 + 2xy^2 - 7x^3 + 3y + 1 = 0$ at $P_0(1, 1, 1)$

44. $z = \dfrac{-4}{2 + x^2 + y^2}$ at $P_0(1, 1, -1)$

Find all critical points of $f(x, y)$ in Problems 45–50 and classify each as a relative maximum, a relative minimum, or a saddle point.

45. $f(x, y) = x^2 - 6x + 2y^2 + 4y - 2$

46. $f(x, y) = x^3 + y^3 - 6xy$

47. $f(x, y) = (x - 1)(y - 1)(x + y - 1)$

48. $f(x, y) = x^2 + y^3 + 6xy - 7x - 6y$

49. $f(x, y) = x^3 + y^3 - 3x^2 - 18y^2 + 81y + 7$

50. $f(x, y) = \sin(x + y) + \sin x + \sin y$ for $0 < x < \pi$, $0 < y < \pi$ (See Figure 12.41.)

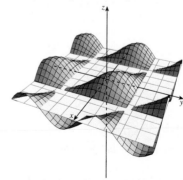

Figure 12.41 Graph of $f(x, y) = \sin(x + y) + \sin x + \sin y$

51. Use the chain rule to find $\frac{dz}{dt}$ if $z = x^2 - 3xy^2$; $x = 2t$, $y = t^2$.

52. Use the chain rule to find $\frac{dz}{dt}$ if $z = x \ln y$; $x = 2t$, $y = e^t$.

53. Let $z = ue^{u^2-v^2}$, where $u = 2x^2 + 3y^2$ and $v = 3x^2 - 2y^2$. Use the chain rule to find $\frac{\partial z}{\partial x}$ and $\frac{\partial z}{\partial y}$.

54. Use implicit differentiation to find $\frac{\partial z}{\partial x}$ and $\frac{\partial z}{\partial y}$, where x, y, and z are related by the equation $x^3 + 2xz - yz^2 - z^3 = 1$.

55. Find the slope at the point $P_0(1, 1)$ on the level curve of $f(x, y) = x^2 + y^2$ that passes through P_0.

56. Find the slope at the point $P_0(2, 0)$ on the level curve of $f(x, y) = xe^y$ that passes through P_0.

57. Find the equations for the tangent plane and normal line to the surface $z = \sin x + e^{xy} + 2y$ at the point $P_0(0, 1, 3)$.

58. The electric potential at each point (x, y) in the disk $x^2 + y^2 < 4$ is $V = 2(4 - x^2 - y^2)^{-1/2}$ volts. Draw the equipotential curves $V = c$ for $c = 8, 6, 4$, and 2.

59. Let $f(x, y, z) = x^3y + y^3z + z^3x$. Find a function $g(x, y, z)$ such that $\frac{\partial f}{\partial x} + \frac{\partial f}{\partial y} + \frac{\partial f}{\partial z} = x^3 + y^3 + z^3 + 3g(x, y, z)$.

60. Let $u = \sin\frac{x}{y} + \ln\frac{y}{x}$. Show that $y\frac{\partial u}{\partial y} + x\frac{\partial u}{\partial x} = 0$.

61. Let $w = \ln(1 + x^2 + y^2) - 2\tan^{-1} y$, where $x = \ln(1 + t^2)$ and $y = e^t$. Use the chain rule to find $\frac{dw}{dt}$.

62. Let $f(x, y) = \tan^{-1}\frac{y}{x}$. Find the directional derivative of f at $(1, 2)$ in the direction that makes an angle of $\frac{\pi}{3}$ with the positive x-axis.

63. Let $f(x, y) = y^x$. Find the directional derivative of f at $(3, 2)$ in the direction toward the point $(1, 1)$.

64. Find the directional derivative of $f(x, y) = (xy)^y$ at the point $(2, 2)$ in the direction of the vector $\mathbf{i} - \mathbf{j}$.

65. Let $f(x, y, z) = z(x - y)^5 + xy^2z^3$.

    a. Find the directional derivative of f at $(2, 1, -1)$ in the direction of the outward normal to the sphere $x^2 + y^2 + z^2 = 6$.

    b. In what direction is the directional derivative at $(2, 1, -1)$ largest?

66. Find positive numbers x and y for which xyz is a maximum, given that $x + y + z = 1$.

67. Maximize $f(x, y, z) = x^2yz$ given that x, y, and z are all positive numbers and $x + y + z = 12$.

68. Find the shortest distance from the origin to the surface $y^2 - z^2 = 10$.

69. Find the shortest distance from the origin to the surface $z^2 = 3 + xy$.

70. A plate is heated in such a way that its temperature at a point (x, y) measured in centimeters on the plate is given in degrees Celsius by

$$T(x, y) = \frac{64}{x^2 + y^2 + 4}$$

    a. Find how fast the temperature is changing at the point $(3, 4)$ in the direction $2\mathbf{i} + \mathbf{j}$.

    b. Find the direction and the magnitude of the greatest rate of change of the temperature at the point $(3, 4)$.

71. The marketing manager for a certain company has compiled the following data relating monthly advertising expenditure and monthly sales (in units of $1,000).

Advertising	3	4	7	9	10
Sales	78	86	138	145	156

    a. Plot the data on a graph and find the least-squares line.

    b. Use the least-squares line to predict monthly sales if the monthly advertising expenditure is $5,000.

72. Find $f_{xx} + f_{xy} + f_{yy}$, where $f(x, y) = x^2y^3 + x^3y^2$.

73. Find f_{xyz}, where $f(x, y, z) = \cos(x^2 + y^3 + z^4)$

74. Let $z = f(x, y)$, where $x = t + \cos t$ and $y = e^t$.

    a. Suppose $f_x(1, 1) = 4$ and $f_y(1, 1) = -3$. Find $\frac{dz}{dt}$ when $t = 0$.

    b. Suppose $f_x(0, 2) = -1$ and $f_y(0, 2) = 3$. Find $\partial z/\partial r$ and $\partial z/\partial \theta$ at the point where $r = 2$, $\theta = \frac{\pi}{2}$, and $x = r\cos\theta$, $y = r\sin\theta$.

75. Suppose f has continuous partial derivatives in some region in the plane that contains another region D, and suppose $f(x, y) = 0$ for all (x, y) in D. If $(1, 2)$ is in D and $f_x(1, 2) = 4$ and $f_y(1, 2) = 6$, find dy/dx when $x = 1$ and $y = 2$.

76. Suppose $\nabla f(x, y, z)$ is parallel to the vector $x\mathbf{i} + y\mathbf{j} + z\mathbf{k}$ for all (x, y, z). Show that $f(0, 0, a) = f(0, 0, -a)$ for any a.

77. Find two unit vectors that are normal to the surface given by $f(x, y) = \sin x + e^{xy} + 2y$ at the point $(0, 1)$.

78. Let $f(x, y) = 3(x - 2)^2 - 5(y + 1)^2$. Find all points on the graph of f where the tangent plane is parallel to the plane $2x + 2y - 1 = 0$.

79. Let z be defined implicitly as a function of x and y by the equation $\cos(x + y) + \cos(x + z) = 1$. Find $\frac{\partial^2 z}{\partial x \partial y}$ in terms of x, y, and z.

80. Suppose F and F' are continuous functions of t and that $F'(t) = 0$. Define f by $f(x, y) = F(x^2 + y^2)$.

    a. Find $\nabla f(x, y)$.

b. Show that the direction of $\nabla f(a, b)$ is the same as the direction of the line joining (a, b) to $(0, 0)$.

81. Let $f(x, y) = 12x^{-1} + 18y^{-1} + xy$, where $x > 0, y > 0$. Find the relative minimum for $x > 0, y > 0$, if one exists.

82. Let $f(x, y) = 3x^4 - 4x^2y + y^2$. Show that f has a minimum at $(0, 0)$ on every line $y = mx$ that passes through the origin, f has a minimum at $(0, 0)$. Then show that f has no relative minimum at $(0, 0)$.

83. Find the minimum of $x^2 + y^2 + z^2$ subject to the constraint $ax + by + cz = 1$ (with $a \neq 0, b \neq 0, c \neq 0$).

84. Suppose $0 < a < 1$ and $x \geq 0, y \geq 0$. Find the minimum of $x^a y^{1-a}$ subject to the constraint

$$ax + (1 - a)y = 1.$$

85. The **geometric mean** of three positive numbers x, y, z is $G = (xyz)^{1/3}$ and the **arithmetic mean** is $A = \frac{1}{3}(x + y + z)$. Use the method of Lagrange multipliers to show that $G(x, y, z) \leq A(x, y, z)$ for all x, y, z. *Hint:* Maximize $G(x, y, z)$ subject to a suitable constraint.

86. Liquid flows through a tube with length L centimeters and internal radius r centimeter. The total volume V of fluid that flows each second is related to the pressure P and the viscosity a of the fluid by the formula $V = \dfrac{\pi P r^4}{8aL}$. What is the maximum error that can occur in using this formula to compute the viscosity a, if errors of $\pm 1\%$ can be made in measuring r and L, $\pm 2\%$ in measuring V, and $\pm 3\%$ in measuring P?

87. Suppose the functions f and g have continuous partial derivatives and satisfy

$$\frac{\partial f}{\partial x} = \frac{\partial g}{\partial y} \quad \text{and} \quad \frac{\partial f}{\partial y} = -\frac{\partial g}{\partial x}$$

This is called the **Cauchy–Riemann condition.**

a. Show that level curves of f and g intersect at right angles provided that $\nabla f \neq 0$ and $\nabla g \neq 0$.

b. Assuming that the second partials of f and g are continuous, show that f and g satisfy Laplace's equations

$$f_{xx} + f_{yy} = 0 \quad \text{and} \quad g_{xx} + g_{yy} = 0.$$

88. Show that if $z = f(r, \theta)$, where r and θ are defined implicitly as functions of x and y by the equations $x = r \cos \theta, y = r \sin \theta$, then the equation

$$\frac{\partial^2 z}{\partial x^2} + \frac{\partial^2 z}{\partial y^2} = 0 \quad \text{becomes} \quad \frac{\partial^2 z}{\partial r^2} + \frac{1}{r^2} \frac{\partial^2 z}{\partial \theta^2} + \frac{1}{r} \frac{\partial z}{\partial r} = 0$$

This is Laplace's equation in polar coordinates.

89. Suppose the angle and radius of a circular sector are allowed to vary. Use Lagrange multipliers to find the angle of the circular sector for which the perimeter of the sector is smallest, assuming the area of the sector is a fixed constant.

90. For the production function given by $Q(x, y) = x^a y^b$, where $a > 0$ and $b > 0$, show that

$$x \frac{\partial Q}{\partial x} + y \frac{\partial Q}{\partial y} = (a + b)Q$$

In particular, if $b = 1 - a$ with $0 < a < 1$,

$$x \frac{\partial Q}{\partial x} + y \frac{\partial Q}{\partial y} = Q$$

91. The diameter of the base and the height of a right circular cylinder are measured, and the measurements are known to have errors of at most 0.5 cm. If the diameter and height are taken to be 4 cm and 8 cm, respectively, find bounds for the propagated error in:

a. the volume V of the cylinder.

b. the surface area S of the cylinder.

92. A right circular cone is measured and is found to have base radius $R = 40$ cm and altitude $h = 20$ cm. If it is known that each measurement is accurate to within 2%, what is the maximum percentage error in the measurement of the volume?

93. An elastic cylindrical container is filled with air so that the radius of the base is 2.02 cm and the height is 6.04 cm. If the container is deflated so that the radius of the base reduces to 2 cm and the height to 6 cm, approximately how much air has been removed? (Ignore the thickness of the container.)

94. Suppose f is a differentiable function of two variables with f_x and f_y also differentiable, and assume that f_{xy} and f_{yx} are continuous. Let $\mathbf{u} = a\mathbf{i} + b\mathbf{j}$ be a unit vector in the xy-plane. The **second directional derivative** $D_{\mathbf{u}} f(x, y)$ of f at the point (a, b), where a and b are the components of u in the direction of the unit vector $\mathbf{u}$, is defined by $D_{\mathbf{u}} f(x, y) = D_{\mathbf{u}}[D_{\mathbf{u}} f(x, y)]$. Show that

$$D_{\mathbf{u}}^2 f(x, y) = a^2 f_{xx}(x, y) + 2ab f_{xy}(x, y) + b^2 f_{yy}(x, y)$$

Hint: Use $P_0 \left(\dfrac{\sqrt{k}}{3}, \dfrac{\sqrt{k}}{3}, \dfrac{\sqrt{k}}{3} \right)$.

95. What can be said about the sum of the intercepts of a tangent plane to the surface $\sqrt{x} + \sqrt{y} + \sqrt{z} = \sqrt{k}$ for a constant k?

96. A pharmaceutical capsule is a cylinder of radius r and length ℓ, capped on each end by a hemisphere. Assume that the capsule dissolves in the stomach at a rate proportional to the ratio $R = S/V$, where V is the volume and S is the surface area of the capsule. Show that

$$\frac{\partial R}{\partial r} < 0 \quad \text{and} \quad \frac{\partial R}{\partial \ell} < 0$$

97. THINK TANK PROBLEM Find the minimum distance from the origin to the paraboloid $z = 4 - x^2 - 4y^2$. The graph is shown in Figure 12.42. The distance from $P(x, y, z)$ to the origin is

$$d = \sqrt{x^2 + y^2 + z^2}$$

This distance will be minimized when d^2 is minimized. Thus, the function to be minimized (after replacing x^2 by $4 - 4y^2 - z$) is

$$D(x, y) = 4 - 4y^2 - z + y^2 + z^2 = 4 - 3y^2 + z^2 - z.$$

Setting the partial derivatives D_y and D_z to 0 gives the critical point $y = 0$, $z = 0.5$. Solving for x on the paraboloid gives the points $Q_1(\sqrt{3.5}, 0, 0.5)$ and $Q_2(-\sqrt{3.5}, 0, 0.5)$. These points are NOT minimal because $(0, 1, 0)$ is closer. Explain what is going on here. Our thanks to Herbert R. Bailey, who presented this problem in *The College Mathematics Journal*, May 1991: "'Hidden' Boundaries in Constrained Max–Min Problems," p. 227.

Figure 12.42

Soap bubbles form minimal surfaces. For an interesting discussion, see "The Geometry of Soap Films and Soap Bubbles," by Frederick J. Almgren, Jr., and Jean E. Taylor, *Scientific American*.

98. A **minimal surface** is a surface that has the least surface area of any surface with a given boundary. It can be shown that if $z = f(x, y)$ is a minimal surface, then

$$(1 + z_y^2)z_{xx} - zz_{xy} + (1 + z_x^2)z_{yy} = 0$$

a.
$$z = \ln\left(\frac{A \cos y}{B \cos x}\right)$$

is a minimal surface, find A and B.

b. Is it possible to find C and D so that
$z = C \ln(\sin x) + D \ln(\sin y)$ is a minimal surface?

99. PUTNAM EXAMINATION PROBLEM Let f be a real-valued function having partial derivatives that is defined for $x^2 + y^2 < 1$ and satisfies $|f(x, y)| \leq 1$. Show that there exists a point (x_0, y_0) in the interior of the unit circle such that $[f_x(x_0, y_0)]^2 + [f_y(x_0, y_0)]^2 \leq 16$.

100. PUTNAM EXAMINATION PROBLEM Find the smallest volume bounded by the coordinate planes and a tangent plane to the ellipsoid

$$\frac{x^2}{a^2} + \frac{y^2}{b^2} + \frac{z^2}{c^2} = 1$$

101. PUTNAM EXAMINATION PROBLEM Find the shortest distance between the plane $Ax + By + Cz + 1 = 0$ and the ellipsoid

$$\frac{x^2}{a^2} + \frac{y^2}{b^2} + \frac{z^2}{c^2} \leq 1$$

GROUP RESEARCH PROJECT*

"Desertification"

This project is to be done in groups of three or four students. Each group will submit a single written report.

A friend of yours named Maria is studying the causes of the continuing expansion of deserts (a process known as *desertification*). She is working on a biological index of vegetation disturbance, which she has defined. By seeing how this index and other factors change through time, she hopes to discover the role played in desertification. She is studying a huge tract of land bounded by a rectangle; this piece of land surrounds a major city but does not include it. She needs to find an economical way to calculate for this piece of land the important vegetation disturbance index $J(x, y)$. The domain for J is all (x, y) in the rectangle but not in the city.

Maria has embarked upon an ingenious approach of combining the results of photographic and radar images taken during flights over the area to calculate the index J. She is assuming that J is a smooth function. Although the flight data does not directly reveal the values of the function J, it gives the rate at which the values of J change as the flights sweep over the landscape surrounding the city. Her staff has conducted numerous flights, and from the data she believes she has been able to find actual formulas for the rates at which J changes in the east-west and north-south directions. She has given these functions the names M and N. Thus, $M(x, y)$ is the rate at which J changes as one sweeps in the positive x-direction and $N(x, y)$ is the corresponding rate in the y-direction. Maria shows you these formulas:

$$M(x, y) = 3.4e^{x(y-7.8)^2} \quad \text{and} \quad N(x, y) = 22 \sin{(75 - 2xy)}$$

Convince her that these two formulas cannot possibly be correct. Do this by showing her that there is a condition that the two functions M and N must satisfy if they are to be the east-west and north-south rates of change of the function J and that her formulas for M and N do not meet this condition. However, show Maria that if she can find formulas for M and N that satisfy the condition that you showed her, it is possible to find a formula for the function J from the formulas for M and N.

Mathematics in its pure form, as arithmetic, algebra, geometry, and the applications of the analytic method, as well as mathematics applied to matter and force, or statics and dynamics, furnishes the peculiar study that gives to us, whether as children or as men, the command of nature in this its quantitative aspect; mathematics furnishes the instrument, the tool of thought, which we wield in this realm.

W. T. Harris
Psychological Foundations of Education (New York, 1898), p. 325.

*Marcus S. Cohen, Edward D. Gaughan, R. Arthur Knoebel, Douglas S. Kurtz, and David J. Pengelley, "Priming the Calculus Pump: Innovations and Resources," *MAA Notes* 17(1991).

13

Multiple Integration

PREVIEW

In this chapter we introduce the concept of multiple integration, which is used in much the same way as single integration. For instance, just as single integrals can be used to compute area, we shall find that double integrals (and triple integrals in a different way) are used to compute volume. In Chapter 4, we found that a single integral can be used to "add" small pieces of a quantity to obtain a definition of the "total" quantity over a given interval.

We are interested in using multiple integrals to define and compute surface area, moments and centroids, and some special quantities in probability theory, business, and economics. In many cases, we shall find it is more natural and computationally easier to use multiple integrals to define and compute a quantity that can also be handled by single integrals.

PERSPECTIVE

We first learned about integration in Chapter 4, and it has played an important role in many subsequent topics in this text. The kind of integral introduced in Chapter 4 has been denoted by

$$\int_a^b f(x)\, dx$$

where the integrand $f(x)$ is continuous on the interval of integration $[a, b]$. From now on, we shall refer to this kind of integral as a **single integral**. In this chapter, we shall introduce a generalization of the single integral called a **multiple integral**. Such an integral is multiple in the sense that the integrand is a function of *several* variables. In particular, a **double** integral is one in which the integrand $f(x, y)$ involves two independent variables, and in a **triple** integral the integrand $f(x, y, z)$ involves three independent variables.

13.1 DOUBLE INTEGRATION OVER RECTANGULAR REGIONS

> **IN THIS SECTION** Definition of double integral, volume interpretation, iterated integration, an informal argument for Fubini's theorem
> We introduce the concept of a **double integral**—that is, an integral with respect to two independent variables. In this and the next section, we see how double integrals can be interpreted geometrically in terms of volume.

■ DEFINITION OF DOUBLE INTEGRAL

We begin by defining the double integral $\iint_R f(x, y) \, dA$, where $f(x, y)$ is continuous over the rectangle R: $a \leq x \leq b$, $c \leq y \leq d$. The definition requires the ideas and notation shown in the following three steps.

Step 1: Partition the interval $a \leq x \leq b$ into m parts and the interval $c \leq y \leq d$ into n parts. Using these subdivisions, we partition the rectangle R into $N = mn$ **cells** (subrectangles), as shown in Figure 13.1. Call this partition P.

Step 2: Choose an arbitrary point (x_k^*, y_k^*) from each cell in the partition of the rectangle. Form the sum

$$\sum_{k=1}^{N} f(x_k^*, y_k^*) \, \Delta A_k$$

where ΔA_k is the area of the kth approximating rectangle. This is called the **Riemann sum** of $f(x, y)$ with respect to the partition P.

Step 3: We define the **norm** $\|P\|$ of the partition to be the length of the longest diagonal of any rectangle in the partition. To **refine** the partition means to add more cells in such a way that the norm decreases. When this process is applied to the Riemann sum and the norm decreases indefinitely, we write

$$\lim_{\|P\| \to 0} \sum_{k=1}^{N} f(x_k^*, y_k^*) \, \Delta A_k$$

We now use this notation and terminology to define a *double integral*.

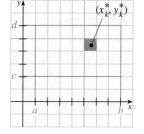

Figure 13.1 A partition of the rectangle R into mn cells

Double Integral

> If f is defined on a closed, bounded region R in the xy-plane, then the **double integral of f over R** is defined by
>
> $$\iint_R f(x, y) \, dA = \lim_{\|P\| \to 0} \sum_{k=1}^{N} f(x_k^*, y_k^*) \, \Delta A_k$$
>
> provided this limit exists. If the limit exists, we say that f is **integrable** over R.

Remarks:

1. The number N of cells depends on the partition P.
2. As $\|P\| \to 0$, it follows that $N \to \infty$.
3. More formally, the phrase "provided this limit exists" means:
    If I is the double integral,

$$I = \iint_R f(x, y) \, dA,$$

then for any $\varepsilon > 0$, there exists a $\delta > 0$ such that

$$\left| I - \sum_{k=1}^{N} f(x_k^*, y_k^*) \Delta A_k \right| < \varepsilon$$

whenever $\sum_{k=1}^{N} f(x_k^*, y_k^*) \Delta A_k$ is a Riemann sum whose norm satisfies $\|P\| < \delta$.

4. It can be shown that if $f(x, y)$ is continuous on R, then it is bounded and integrable on R.

◼ VOLUME INTERPRETATION

We know that the single integral $\int_a^b f(x)\, dx$ can be interpreted as the area under the curve $y = f(x)$ over the interval $[a, b]$, and the double integral $\int\int_R f(x, y)\, dA$ has a similar interpretation in terms of volume. To see this, note that if $f(x, y) \geq 0$ on the region R and we partition R using rectangles, then the product $f(x_k^*, y_k^*)\, \Delta A_k$ is the volume of a parallelepiped (a box) with height $f(x_k^*, y_k^*)$ and base area ΔA_k, as shown in Figure 13.2.

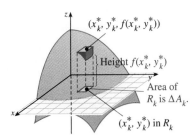

Figure 13.2 The approximating parallelepiped has volume $\Delta V_k = f(x_k^*, y_k^*)\, \Delta A_k$.

Thus, the Riemann sum

$$\sum_{k=1}^{N} f(x_k^*, y_k^*)\, \Delta A_k$$

provides an estimate of the total volume under the surface $z = f(x, y)$ over the rectangular domain R. If f is continuous on R, we expect the approximation to improve if we take a more refined partition of R (that is, more rectangles with smaller norm). Thus, it is natural to define the total volume under the surface as the limit of Riemann sums as the norm tends to 0. That is, the volume under $z = f(x, y)$ over the domain R is given by

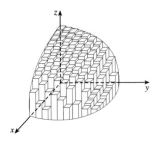

Volume approximated by rectangular parallelepipeds

$$V = \lim_{\|P\| \to 0} \sum_{k=1}^{N} f(x_k^*, y_k^*)\, \Delta A_k = \int\int_R f(x, y)\, dA$$

EXAMPLE 1   **Evaluate a double integral by relating it to a volume**

Evaluate $\int\int_R (2 - y)\, dA$, where R is the rectangle in the xy-plane with vertices $(0, 0)$, $(3, 0)$, $(3, 2)$, and $(0, 2)$.

Solution Because $z = 2 - y$ satisfies $z \geq 0$ for all points in R, the value of the double integral is the same as the volume of the solid bounded above by the plane $z = 2 - y$ and below by the rectangle R. As shown in Figure 13.3, this solid is a wedge whose volume can be found by looking at it sideways—that is, with a triangular base of area B and height $h = 3$. We use the formula $V = Bh$.

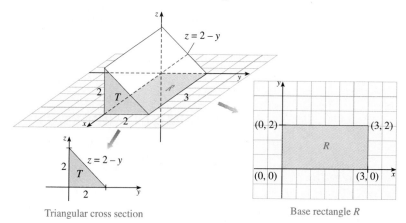

Figure 13.3 Evaluation of $\displaystyle\iint_R (2 - y)\, dA$ as a volume

Because the base is a triangle of side 2 and altitude 2, we have $B = \frac{1}{2}(2)(2) = 2$, and

$$V = Bh = \left[\tfrac{1}{2}(2)(2)\right](3) = 6$$

Therefore, the value of the integral is also 6; that is,

$$\iint_R (2 - y)\, dA = 6$$

■

■ ITERATED INTEGRATION

Just as we did not find derivatives or integrals using their limit definitions, we see that it is not practical to evaluate a double integral even over a simple rectangular region by using the definition. Instead, we shall compute double integrals by a process called **successive partial integration**. To be specific, if we hold the y-variable constant (denoted by $\bar{y}$) and integrate $f(x, y)$ with respect to x, we have a single integral

$$\int f(x, \bar{y})\, dx$$

which we shall refer to as the **partial integral of f with respect to x**. The dx tells us that the integration is with respect to x and that y is to be held constant for the integration, but when the process is complete the result is a function of y. Similarly, the integral

$$\int f(\bar{x}, y)\, dy$$

is the **partial integral of f with respect to y**, which means that x is held constant (denoted by $\bar{x}$) and integration is with respect to y. This integral is a function of x.

In successive partial integration, we evaluate a double integral by integrating first with respect to one variable and then again with respect to the other variable. In partial integration, we work from the inside out, as indicated in the following notation:

$$\int \int f(x, y) \, dx \, dy = \int \left[\int f(x, \bar{y}) \, dx \right] dy \qquad \text{\textit{Integrate with respect to x first, then with respect to y.}}$$

$$\int \int f(x, y) \, dy \, dx = \int \left[\int f(\bar{x}, y) \, dy \right] dx \qquad \text{\textit{Integrate with respect to y first, then with respect to x.}}$$

Integrals of this form are said to be **iterated integrals**. Our next theorem tells us how to evaluate iterated integrals, which in turn enables us to evaluate double integrals. The theorem was first proved by the Italian mathematician Guido Fubini (1879–1943) in 1907.

THEOREM 13.1   Fubini's theorem over a rectangular region

If $f(x, y)$ is continuous over the rectangle R: $a \leq x \leq b$, $c \leq y \leq d$, then the double integral

$$\int_R \int f(x, y) \, dA$$

may be evaluated by either iterated integral; that is,

$$\int_R \int f(x, y) \, dA = \int_c^d \int_a^b f(x, y) \, dx \, dy = \int_a^b \int_c^d f(x, y) \, dy \, dx$$

■ **What this says:** Instead of using the definition of a double integral, consider the region R, namely, $a \leq x \leq b$ and $c \leq y \leq d$, and evaluate *either* of the iterated integrals

Limits of x (outside brackets) $\downarrow$

Limits of x (variable inside brackets) $\downarrow$

$$\int_a^b \left[\int_c^d f(\bar{x}, y) \, dy \right] dx \qquad \text{or} \qquad \int_c^d \left[\int_a^b f(x, \bar{y}) \, dx \right] dy$$

$\uparrow$ Limits of y (variable inside brackets)

$\uparrow$ Limits of y (outside brackets)

Proof: We shall provide an informal, geometric argument at the end of this section. The formal proof may be found in most advanced calculus textbooks. ■

Let us see how Fubini's theorem can be used to evaluate double integrals. We begin by taking another look at Example 1.

EXAMPLE 2   Evaluate a double integral by using Fubini's theorem

Use iterated integrals to compute $\int_R \int (2 - y) \, dA$, where R is the rectangle with vertices $(0, 0)$, $(3, 0)$, $(3, 2)$, and $(0, 2)$.

Solution   The region of integration is the rectangle $0 \le x \le 3, 0 \le y \le 2$ (see Example 1 and Figure 13.3). Thus, by Fubini's theorem, the double integral can be evaluated as an iterated integral:

$$\iint_R (2-y)\, dA = \int_0^3 \int_0^2 (2-y)\, dy\, dx \quad \textit{Integrate inner integral with respect to y.}$$

$$= \int_0^3 \left[2y - \frac{y^2}{2} \right]\Big|_0^2 dx = \int_0^3 \left[4 - \frac{4}{2} - (0) \right] dx = \int_0^3 2\, dx = 2x\Big|_0^3 = 6$$

which is the same as the result obtained geometrically in Example 1.   ▬

EXAMPLE 3   Double integral using an iterated integral

Evaluate $\displaystyle\iint_R x^2 y^5\, dA$, where R is the rectangle $1 \le x \le 2, 0 \le y \le 1$, using

an iterated integral with: **a.** y-integration first   **b.** x-integration first

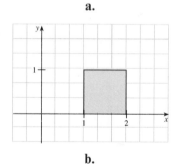

(2, 1)

a.

b.

Figure 13.4 Graph of $z = x^2 y^5$ and defining rectangle

Solution   The graph of the surface $x^2 y^5$ over the rectangle is shown in Figure 13.4a. In your work, you would usually sketch only the rectangle, as shown in Figure 13.4b.

a. $\displaystyle\iint_R x^2 y^5\, dA = \int_1^2 \int_0^1 x^2 y^5\, dy\, dx$ *Read this as* $\displaystyle\int_1^2 \left[\int_0^1 x^2 y^5\, dy \right] dx.$

$$= \int_1^2 \left[x^2 \frac{y^6}{6} \right]\Big|_0^1 dx = \int_1^2 \left[x^2 \left(\frac{1}{6} - \frac{0}{6} \right) \right] dx = \frac{x^3}{18}\Big|_1^2 = \frac{8}{18} - \frac{1}{18} = \frac{7}{18}$$

b. $\displaystyle\iint_R x^2 y^5\, dA = \int_0^1 \int_1^2 x^2 y^5\, dx\, dy = \int_0^1 y^5 \left[\frac{x^3}{3} \right]\Big|_1^2 dy$

$$= \int_0^1 \left[y^5 \left(\frac{8}{3} - \frac{1}{3} \right) \right] dy = \frac{7y^6}{18}\Big|_0^1 = \frac{7}{18} - \frac{0}{18} = \frac{7}{18}$$ ▬

In the preceding examples, the amount of work required to evaluate the integrals was about the same if we integrated first with respect to either x or y. However, this is not always the case, as illustrated by the following example.

EXAMPLE 4   Choosing the order of integration for a double integral

Evaluate $\displaystyle\iint_R x \cos xy\, dA$ for $R: 0 \le x \le \frac{\pi}{2}, 0 \le y \le 1$.

Set up both iterated integrals and decide which would be easier to evaluate.

Limits *of x*   Limits *of y*
↓   ↓

Solution   With respect to y first: $\displaystyle\int_0^{\pi/2} \left[\int_0^1 x \cos xy\, dy \right] dx$

Limits *of y*

Limits *of x*

With respect to x first:

$$\int_0^1 \left[\int_0^{\pi/2} x \cos xy \, dx \right] dy$$

The second of these integrals (with respect to x first) requires integration by parts, but integrating with respect to y first is quite straightforward:

$$\int\int_R x \cos xy \, dA = \int_0^{\pi/2} \left[\int_0^1 x \cos xy \, dy \right] dx = \int_0^{\pi/2} \left[\int_0^x \cos u \, du \right] dx$$

Let $u = xy$; When $y = 0$, $u = 0$
then $du = x \, dy$. $y = 1$, $u = x$

$$= \int_0^{\pi/2} \left[\sin u\right]\Big|_0^x \, dx = \int_0^{\pi/2} (\sin x - \sin 0) \, dx = -\cos x \Big|_0^{\pi/2} = 1 \qquad \blacksquare$$

■ AN INFORMAL ARGUMENT FOR FUBINI'S THEOREM

We can make Fubini's theorem plausible with a geometric argument in the case where $f(x, y) \geq 0$ on R. If $\int\int_R f(x, y) \, dA$ is defined on a rectangle R: $a \leq x \leq b$, $c \leq y \leq d$, it represents the volume of the solid S bounded above by the surface $z = f(x, y)$ and below by the rectangle R. If $A(y_k^*)$ is the cross-sectional area perpendicular to the y-axis at the point y_k^*, then $A(y_k^*)\Delta y_k$ represents the volume of a "slab" that approximates the volume of part of the solid S, as shown in Figure 13.5.

Figure 13.5 Cross-sectional volume parallel to the xz-plane

By using a limit to "add up" all such approximating volumes, we obtain an estimate of the volume of the entire solid S. Thus, if we let V be the exact volume of the solid S, we have

$$\int\int_R f(x, y) \, dA = V = \lim_{\|P\| \to 0} \sum_{k=0}^N A(y_k^*) \, \Delta y_k$$

The limit on the right is just the integral of $A(y)$ over the interval $c \leq y \leq d$, where $A(y)$ is the area of a cross section with fixed y. In Chapter 4, we found that the area $A(y)$ can be computed by the integral

$$A(y) = \int_a^b f(x, y) \, dx \quad \textit{Integration with respect to } x \text{ (} y \text{ a constant)}$$

We can now make this substitution for $A(y)$ to obtain:

$$\iint_R f(x, y)\, dA = V = \lim_{\|P\| \to 0} \sum_{k=0}^{N} A(y_k^*)\, \Delta y_k$$

$$= \int_c^d A(y)\, dy$$

$$= \int_c^d \underbrace{\left[\int_a^b f(x, y)\, dx \right]}_{A(y)} dy \quad \text{Substitution}$$

The fact that

$$\iint_R f(x, y)\, dA = \int_a^b \int_c^d f(x, y)\, dy\, dx$$

can be justified in a similar fashion (you are asked to do this in Problem 42). Thus, we have

$$\int_c^d \left[\int_a^b f(x, y)\, dx \right] dy = \iint_R f(x, y)\, dA = \int_a^b \left[\int_c^d f(x, y)\, dy \right] dx$$

PROBLEM SET 13.1

Ⓐ *Use an appropriate volume formula to evaluate the double integral given in Problems 1–6.*

1. $\displaystyle\iint_R 4\, dA;$

$R: 0 \le x \le 2;\ 0 \le y \le 4$

2. $\displaystyle\iint_R 5\, dA;$

$R: 2 \le x \le 5;\ 1 \le y \le 3$

3. $\displaystyle\iint_R (4 - y)\, dA;$

$R: 0 \le x \le 3;\ 0 \le y \le 4$

4. $\displaystyle\iint_R (4 - 2y)\, dA;$

$R: 0 \le x \le 4;\ 0 \le y \le 2$

5. $\displaystyle\iint_R \frac{y}{2}\, dA;$

$R: 0 \le x \le 6;\ 0 \le y \le 4$

6. $\displaystyle\iint_R \frac{y}{4}\, dA;$

$R: 0 \le x \le 2;\ 0 \le y \le 8$

Use successive partial integration to compute the double integrals in Problems 7–14 over the specified rectangle.

7. $\displaystyle\int\int_R x^2 y\, dA$; R: $1 \le x \le 2$; $0 \le y \le 1$

8. $\displaystyle\int\int_R (x + 2y)\, dA$; R: $2 \le x \le 3$; $-1 \le y \le 1$

9. $\displaystyle\int\int_R 2xe^y\, dA$; R: $-1 \le x \le 0$; $0 \le y \le \ln 2$

10. $\displaystyle\int\int_R x^2 e^{xy}\, dA$; R: $0 \le x \le 1$; $0 \le y \le 1$

11. $\displaystyle\int\int_R \frac{2xy\, dA}{x^2 + 1}$; R: $0 \le x \le 1$; $1 \le y \le 3$

12. $\displaystyle\int\int_R y\sqrt{1 - y^2}\, dA$; R: $1 \le x \le 5$; $0 \le y \le 1$

13. $\displaystyle\int\int_R \sin(x + y)\, dA$; R: $0 \le x \le \frac{\pi}{4}$; $0 \le y \le \frac{\pi}{2}$

14. $\displaystyle\int\int_R x \sin xy\, dA$; R: $0 \le x \le \pi$, $0 \le y \le 1$

Find the volume of the solid bounded below by the rectangle R in the xy-plane and above by the graph of $z = f(x, y)$ in Problems 15–25. Assume that a, b, and c are positive constants.

15. $f(x, y) = 2x + 3y$; R: $0 \le x \le 1$; $0 \le y \le 2$
16. $f(x, y) = 5x + 2y$; R: $0 \le x \le 1$; $0 \le y \le 2$
17. $f(x, y) = ax + by$; R: $0 \le x \le a$; $0 \le y \le b$
18. $f(x, y) = axy$; R: $0 \le x \le b$; $0 \le y \le c$
19. $f(x, y) = \sqrt{xy}$; R: $0 \le x \le 1$; $0 \le y \le 4$
20. $f(x, y) = \sqrt{xy}$; R: $0 \le x \le a$; $0 \le y \le b$
21. $f(x, y) = xe^y$; R: $0 \le x \le 2$; $0 \le y \le \ln 2$
22. $f(x, y) = xe^{xy}$; R: $0 \le x \le 1$; $0 \le y \le \ln 3$
23. $f(x, y) = (x + y)^5$; R: $0 \le x \le 1$; $0 \le y \le 1$
24. $f(x, y) = \sqrt{x + y}$; R: $0 \le x \le 1$; $0 \le y \le 1$
25. $f(x, y) = (x + y)^n$; $n \ne -1$ and $n \ne -2$; R: $0 \le x \le 1$; $0 \le y \le 1$

B 26. ■ *What Does This Say?* Discuss the definition of double integral.

27. ■ *What Does This Say?* Describe the implementation of Fubini's theorem.

28. Suppose R is a region within the boundary of a certain national forest that contains 600,000 trees per square mile. Express the number of trees per square mile in the forest as a double integral. Assume that x and y are measured in miles.

29. Suppose mass is distributed on a rectangular region R in the xy-plane so that the density (mass per unit area) at the point (x, y) is $f(x, y)$. Express the total mass as a double integral.

30. Suppose R is the rectangular region within the boundary of a certain city, and let the city center be at the origin

$(0, 0)$. Assume that the population density r miles from the city center is $12e^{-0.07r}$ thousand people per square mile. Express the total population of the region of the city as a double integral.

31. Suppose R is a rectangular region within the boundary of a certain county, and let $f(x, y)$ denote the housing density (in homes per square mile) at the point (x, y). If the property tax on each home in the county is \$1,400 per year, express the total property tax collected in the region of the county as a double integral.

32. Compute $\displaystyle\int\int_R x\sqrt{1 - x^2}\, e^{3y}\, dA$, where R is the rectangle $0 \le x \le 1$, $0 \le y \le 2$.

33. Compute $\displaystyle\int\int_R \frac{\ln \sqrt{y}}{xy}\, dA$, where R is the rectangle $1 \le x \le 4$, $1 \le y \le e$.

34. Compute $\displaystyle\int\int_R \frac{xy}{x^2 + y^2}\, dA$ (correct to the nearest hundredth), where R is the rectangle $1 \le x \le 3$, $1 \le y \le 2$.

35. Explain why $\displaystyle\int\int_R (4 - x^2 - y^2)\, dA \ge 2$ where R is the rectangular domain in the plane given by $0 \le x \le 1$, $0 \le y \le 1$.

Computational Window

36. Approximate the volume of the solid lying between the surface

$$f(x, y) = 4 - x^2 - y^2$$

and the square region R given by $0 \le x \le 1$, $0 \le y \le 1$. Use a partition made up of squares whose edges have length 0.25.

37. Approximate the volume of the solid lying between the surface

$$f(x, y) = x^2 + y^2 + 1$$

and the square region R given by $0 \le x \le 1$, $0 \le y \le 1$. Use a partition made up of squares whose edges have length 0.25.

38. Evaluate $\displaystyle\int\int_R (3 - \sqrt{x^2 + y^2})\, dA$, where R is the disk $x^2 + y^2 \le 9$ in the xy-plane. *Hint:* Relate the integral to the volume of a simple solid.

39. Evaluate $\displaystyle\int\int_R (1 - \sqrt{x^2 + z^2})\, dA$, where R is the disk $x^2 + z^2 \le 1$ in the xz-plane. *Hint:* Relate the integral to the volume of a simple solid.

40. Evaluate $\displaystyle\iint_R (4 - \sqrt{y^2 + z^2})\, dA$, where R is the disk $y^2 + z^2 \le 16$ in the yz-plane. *Hint:* Relate the integral to the volume of a simple solid.

C 41. Let f be a function with continuous second partial derivatives on a rectangular domain R with vertices (x_1, y_1), (x_2, y_2), (x_1, y_2), and (x_2, y_1), where $x_1 < x_2$ and $y_1 < y_2$. Use the fundamental theorem of calculus to show that

$$\iint_R \frac{\partial^2 f}{\partial y \partial x}\, dA = f(x_1, y_1) - f(x_2, y_1) + f(x_2, y_2) - f(x_1, y_2)$$

42. Let f be a continuous function defined on the rectangle R: $a \le x \le b$, $c \le y \le d$. Use a geometric argument to show that

$$\iint_R f(x, y)\, dA = \int_a^b \int_c^d f(x, y)\, dy\, dx$$

Hint: Modify the argument given in the text by taking cross-sectional areas perpendicular to the x-axis.

13.2 DOUBLE INTEGRATION OVER NONRECTANGULAR REGIONS

> **IN THIS SECTION** Nonrectangular regions, more on areas and volumes, reversing the order of integration in a double integral, properties of double integrals
>
> We show how double integrals can be evaluated over regions that are not rectangles. We conclude by examining some general properties of double integrals.

■ NONRECTANGULAR REGIONS

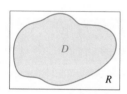

Figure 13.6 The region D is bounded by a rectangle R.

A region is said to be **bounded** if it is contained in a rectangular region R, as shown in Figure 13.6.

Suppose D is a bounded region in the xy-plane that is not a rectangle. Define a function F that coincides with f on D and is 0 elsewhere in R. If F is integrable over R, then f is said to be **integrable over D**, and the **double integral of f over D** is defined as

$$\iint_D f(x, y)\, dA = \iint_R F(x, y)\, dA$$

In the last section, you saw how the double integral $\displaystyle\iint_R f(x, y)\, dA$ could be evaluated by successive partial integration when R is a rectangle. A modification of this procedure allows you to evaluate the double integral in the important case where R is not a rectangle, but is still bounded by vertical (or horizontal) lines on two opposing sides.

Type I Region (Vertical Strip)

A **type I** region contains points (x, y) such that for each fixed x between constants a and b, y varies from $g_1(x)$ to $g_2(x)$, where g_1 and g_2 are continuous functions. Think of a vertical strip.

Type I region: For a fixed x between a and b, y varies from $g_1(x)$ to $g_2(x)$.

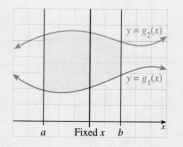

Type II Region (Horizontal Strip)

A **type II** region contains points (x, y) such that for each fixed y between constants c and d, x varies from $h_1(y)$ to $h_2(y)$, where h_1 and h_2 are continuous functions. Think of a horizontal strip.

Type II region: For a fixed y between c and d, x varies from $h_1(y)$ to $h_2(y)$.

By applying Fubini's theorem for rectangular regions, we can derive the following theorem, which shows how to evaluate a double integral over a type I or type II region.

THEOREM 13.2   Fubini's theorem for nonrectangular regions

If D is a type I region, then

TYPE I: (vertical strip): x-fixed, y varies (form $dy\,dx$)

$$\int\!\!\int_D f(x, y)\, dA = \int_a^b \int_{g_1(x)}^{g_2(x)} f(x, y)\, dy\, dx$$

whenever both integrals exist. Similarly, for a type II region,

TYPE II: (horizontal strip): y-fixed, x varies (form $dx\,dy$)

$$\int\!\!\int_D f(x, y)\, dA = \int_c^d \int_{h_1(y)}^{h_2(y)} f(x, y)\, dx\, dy$$

Proof: The proof is omitted. ∎

When using Fubini's theorem for nonrectangular regions, it helps to sketch the region of integration D and to find equations for all boundary curves of D. Such a sketch often provides the information needed to determine whether D is a type I or type II region (or neither) and to set up the limits of integration of an iterated integral.

EXAMPLE 1   Double integral over a triangular region

Let T be the triangular region enclosed by the lines $y = 0$, $y = 2x$, and $x = 1$. Evaluate the double integral

$$\int\!\!\int_T (x + y)\, dA$$

using an iterated integral with:

a. y-integration first   **b.** x-integration first

Figure 13.7 For each fixed x ($0 \le x \le 1$), y varies from $y = 0$ to $y = 2x$.

Solution   a. To set up the limits of integration in the iterated integral, we draw the graph as shown in Figure 13.7 and note that for fixed x, the variable y varies from $y = 0$ (the x-axis) to the line $y = 2x$. These are the limits of integration for the inner integral (with respect to y first). The other limits of integration are the numerical limits of integration for x—that is, x varies between $x = 0$ and $x = 1$.

$$\iint\limits_{T} (x + y)\, dA = \int_0^1 \int_0^{2x} (x + y)\, dy\, dx = \int_0^1 \left[xy + \tfrac{1}{2} y^2 \right]\Big|_{y=0}^{y=2x} dx$$

$$= \int_0^1 \left[x(2x) + \tfrac{1}{2}(2x)^2 - \left(x(0) + \tfrac{1}{2}(0)^2 \right) \right] dx = \int_0^1 4x^2\, dx = \tfrac{4}{3} x^3 \Big|_{x=0}^{x=1} = \tfrac{4}{3}$$

b. Reversing the order of integration, we see from Figure 13.8 that for each y, the variable x varies (left to right) from the line $x = y/2$ to the vertical line $x = 1$. The outer limits of integration are for y as y varies from $y = 0$ to $y = 2$.

$$\iint\limits_{T} (x + y)\, dA = \int_0^2 \int_{y/2}^{1} (x + y)\, dx\, dy$$

$$= \int_0^2 \left[\tfrac{1}{2} x^2 + xy \right]\Big|_{x=y/2}^{x=1} dy = \int_0^2 \left[\tfrac{1}{2} + y - \tfrac{y^2}{8} - \tfrac{y^2}{2} \right] dy$$

$$= \left[\tfrac{y}{2} + \tfrac{y^2}{2} - \tfrac{5y^3}{24} \right]\Big|_{y=0}^{y=2} = \left[1 + 2 - \tfrac{5(8)}{24} \right] - [0] = \tfrac{4}{3}$$

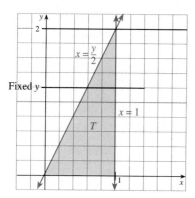

Figure 13.8 For each fixed $y\,(0 \le y \le 2)$, x varies from $y/2$ to 1.

MORE ON AREAS AND VOLUMES

Even though we can find the area between curves with single integrals, it is often easier to compute area using a double integral. If $f(x, y) \ge 0$ over a region D in the xy-plane, then $\iint\limits_{D} f(x, y)\, dA$ gives the **volume of the solid** bounded above by the surface $z = f(x, y)$ and below by the region of D. In the special case where $f(x, y) = 1$, the integral gives the **area** of D.

The Double Integral as Area and Volume

The area of the region D in the xy-plane is given by

$$A = \iint\limits_{D} dA$$

If f is continuous and $f(x, y) \ge 0$ on the region D, the volume of the solid under the surface $z = f(x, y)$ above the region D is given by

$$V = \iint\limits_{D} f(x, y)\, dA$$

EXAMPLE 2   **Area of a region in the xy-plane using a double integral**

Find the area of the region D between $y = \cos x$ and $y = \sin x$ over the interval $0 \le x \le \tfrac{\pi}{4}$ using

a. a single integral   **b.** a double integral

Solution   **a.** The graph is shown in Figure 13.9.

$$\int_0^{\pi/4} (\cos x - \sin x)\, dx = [\sin x + \cos x]\Big|_0^{\pi/4} = \sqrt{2} - 1$$

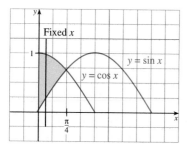

Figure 13.9 The area of the region between $y = \cos x$ and $y = \sin x$

b.

$$A = \iint_D dA = \int_0^{\pi/4} \int_{\sin x}^{\cos x} 1 \, dy \, dx = \int_0^{\pi/4} [y] \Big|_{y=\sin x}^{y=\cos x} dx$$

$$= \int_0^{\pi/4} [\cos x - \sin x] \, dx = \sqrt{2} - 1$$

The area is $\sqrt{2} - 1 \approx 0.41$ square units. ▬

In comparing the single and double integral solutions for area in Example 2, you might ask, "Why bother with the double integral, because it reduced to the single integral case after one step?" The answer is that the double integral will do *most* of the work in *setting up* the proper integral. It is often easier to begin with the double integral

$$A = \iint_D dA$$

and then let the *evaluation* lead to the proper form.

EXAMPLE 3   Volume using a double integral

Find the volume of the solid bounded above by the plane $z = y$ and below in the xy-plane by the part of the disk $x^2 + y^2 \le 1$ with $x \ge 0$, $y \ge 0$.

Solution   The three-dimensional solid is shown in the margin, but for your work you need only be concerned with the projection in the xy-plane, which is shown in Figure 13.10.

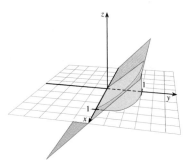

Graph of $z = y$ showing the disk in the xy plane

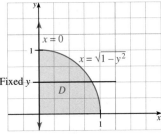

Figure 13.10 The quarter disk $x^2 + y^2 \le 1$, $x \ge 0$, $y \ge 0$

We can regard D as either a type I or type II region, and because we worked with a type I (vertical) region in Example 2, we shall use a type II (horizontal) region for this example. Accordingly, note that for each fixed number y between 0 and 1, x varies between $x = 0$ on the left and $x = \sqrt{1 - y^2}$ on the right. Thus,

$$V = \iint_D f(x, y) \, dA = \int_0^1 \int_0^{\sqrt{1-y^2}} y \, dx \, dy \qquad f(x, y) = y \text{ is given; } dA = dx \, dy.$$

$$= \int_0^1 [yx] \Big|_{x=0}^{x=\sqrt{1-y^2}} dy = \int_0^1 y\sqrt{1 - y^2} \, dy \qquad \text{Let } u = 1 - y^2 \text{ to integrate.}$$

$$= \left[-\tfrac{1}{3}(1 - y^2)^{3/2} \right] \Big|_{y=0}^{y=1} = \frac{1}{3}$$

The volume is $\frac{1}{3}$ cubic unit. ▬

■ REVERSING THE ORDER OF INTEGRATION IN A DOUBLE INTEGRAL

It is often useful to be able to reverse the order of integration in a given iterated integral. This procedure is illustrated in the next two examples.

EXAMPLE 4   Reversing the order of integration

Reverse the order of integration in the iterated integral

$$\int_0^2 \int_1^{e^x} f(x) \, dy \, dx$$

Solution   Begin by drawing the region D by looking at the limits of integration for both x and y in the double integral. For this example, we see that the y-integration comes first, so D is a type I region. The inner limits are

$$y = e^x \quad (\text{top curve}) \quad \text{and} \quad y = 1 \quad (\text{bottom curve})$$

These are shown in Figure 13.11a. Next, draw the appropriate limits of integration for x. *Note*: These limits should be constants:

$$x = 0 \quad (\text{left point}) \quad \text{and} \quad x = 2 \quad (\text{right point})$$

These vertical lines are also drawn in Figure 13.11a.

To reverse the order of integration, we need to regard D as a type II region (Figure 13.11b). Note that the region varies from $y = 1$ to $y = e^2$ (corresponding to where $y = e^x$ intersects $x = 0$ and $x = 2$, respectively). For each fixed y (horizontal strip) between 1 and e^2, the region extends from the curve $x = \ln y$ (that is, $y = e^x$) on the left to the line $x = 2$ on the right. Thus, reversing the order of integration, we find that the given integral becomes

$$\int_1^{e^2} \int_{\ln y}^2 f(x, y) \, dx \, dy$$

The two different ways of representing the integral are illustrated together for easy reference:

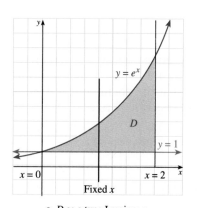

a. D as a type I region; y varies from 1 to e^x

D as a type I region; y varies from 1 to e^x.

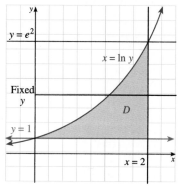

b. D as a type II region; x varies from $\ln y$ to 2

D as a type II region; x varies from $\ln y$ to 2.

Figure 13.11 Type I and Type 2 regions

Type I: x fixed (vertical strip)	Type II: y fixed (horizontal strip)
y-integration first; varies from $y=1$ to $y=e^x$.	x-integration first; varies from $x = \ln y$ to $x = 2$.
$\downarrow$	$\downarrow$
$\displaystyle\int_0^2 \int_1^{e^x} f(x, y) \, dy \, dx \qquad = $	$\displaystyle\int_1^{e^2} \int_{\ln y}^2 f(x, y) \, dx \, dy$
$\uparrow$	$\uparrow$
Constant limits for x; varies from 0 to 2.	Constant limits for y; varies from 1 to e^2.

EXAMPLE 5   Reversing the order that requires a sum of integrals

Reverse the order of integration in the integral

$$\int_{-1}^2 \int_{x^2-2}^x f(x, y) \, dy \, dx$$

a. Type I description

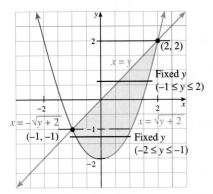

b. Type II description

Figure 13.12

a. y-integration first

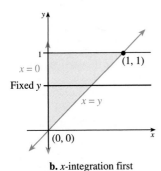

b. x-integration first

Figure 13.13 The region of integration for Example 6

Solution This is a type I form (because the y-integration comes first). To reverse the order of integration we begin by drawing the region D, as shown in Figure 13.12a. We draw the bottom and top curves:

$$y = x^2 - 2 \quad \text{(bottom)} \quad \text{and} \quad y = x \quad \text{(top)}$$

Then we draw the left and right boundaries:

$$x = -1 \quad \text{and} \quad x = 2$$

To change this to a type II form, we shift from a vertical strip (x fixed) to a horizontal strip (y fixed), as shown in Figure 13.12b. We see that for y between -2 and -1 the horizontal line is bounded by the left and right branches of the parabolic arch, whereas for y between -1 and 2 it is bounded on the left by the line $x = y$ and on the right by the parabola. This means that the integral with the order of integration reversed must be expressed as the sum of two integrals.

$$\int_{-1}^{2} \int_{x^2-2}^{x} f(x, y)\, dy\, dx \quad \text{\textit{For a fixed x between -1 and 2,}} \atop \text{\textit{y varies between $y = x^2 - 2$ and $y = x$.}}$$

$$= \underbrace{\int_{-2}^{-1} \int_{-\sqrt{y+2}}^{\sqrt{y+2}} f(x, y)\, dx\, dy}_{\substack{\text{Part between left and right} \\ \text{branches of parabola (red part)}}} + \underbrace{\int_{-1}^{2} \int_{y}^{\sqrt{y+2}} f(x, y)\, dx\, dy}_{\substack{\text{Part between line and} \\ \text{parabola (blue part)}}}$$

For a fixed y between   *For a fixed y between*
-2 and -1, x varies   *-1 and 2, x varies*
between $x = -\sqrt{y+2}$ *between $x = y$ and*
and $x = \sqrt{y+2}$ *$x = \sqrt{y+2}$*

A given iterated integral can often be evaluated in either order, although it may happen that one order is more convenient than the other. For instance, the integral in Example 5 is easier to handle by performing y-integration first, because the reverse order involves two integrations instead of just one. However, there are iterated integrals that can be evaluated *only* after reversing the order of integration. Such an integral is featured in the following example.

EXAMPLE 6   Evaluating a double integral by reversing the order

Evaluate $\displaystyle\int_{0}^{1} \int_{x}^{1} e^{y^2}\, dy\, dx$

Solution We cannot evaluate the integral in the given order (y-integration first) because the integrand e^{y^2} has no elementary antiderivative. We shall evaluate the integral by reversing the order of integration. The region of integration is sketched in Figure 13.13a. Note that for any fixed x between 0 and 1, y varies from x to 1.

To reverse the order of integration, observe that for each fixed y between 0 and 1, x varies from 0 to y, as shown in Figure 13.13b.

$$\int_{0}^{1} \int_{x}^{1} e^{y^2}\, dy\, dx = \int_{0}^{1} \int_{0}^{y} e^{y^2}\, dx\, dy = \int_{0}^{1} x e^{y^2} \Big|_{x=0}^{x=y}\, dy = \int_{0}^{1} y e^{y^2}\, dy \quad \text{\textit{Let $u = y^2$.}}$$

$$= \left[\tfrac{1}{2} e^{y^2}\right]_{0}^{1} = \tfrac{1}{2}(e^1 - e^0) = \tfrac{1}{2}(e - 1)$$

■ PROPERTIES OF DOUBLE INTEGRALS

Double integrals have many of the same properties as single integrals. Three of these properties are contained in the following theorem.

THEOREM 13.3   Properties of double integrals

Assume that all the given integrals exist.

Linearity rule: For constants a and b,

$$\iint_D [af(x, y) + bg(x, y)] \, dA = a \iint_D f(x, y) \, dA + b \iint_D g(x, y) \, dA$$

Dominance rule: If $f(x, y) \geq g(x, y)$ throughout a region D, then

$$\iint_D f(x, y) \, dA \geq \iint_D g(x, y) \, dA$$

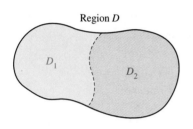

Region D

Subdivision rule: If the region of integration D can be subdivided into two subregions D_1 and D_2, then

$$\iint_D f(x, y) \, dA = \iint_{D_1} f(x, y) \, dA + \iint_{D_2} f(x, y) \, dA$$

Proof: To prove this, you can first show that each is true for rectangular regions of integration. Then, the general case is proved by applying the definition of a double integral, Fubini's theorem, and various theorems for single integrals. ■

PROBLEM SET 13.2

Ⓐ 1. ■ **What Does This Say?** Describe the process for finding volume using a double integral.

2. ■ **What Does This Say?** Describe the process of reversing the order of integration.

Sketch the region of integration in Problems 3–14, and compute the double integral (either in the order of integration given or with the order reversed).

3. $\displaystyle\int_0^4 \int_0^{4-x} xy \, dy \, dx$

4. $\displaystyle\int_0^4 \int_{x^2}^{4x} dy \, dx$

5. $\displaystyle\int_0^1 \int_{-x^2}^{x^2} dy \, dx$

6. $\displaystyle\int_1^e \int_0^{\ln x} xy \, dy \, dx$

7. $\displaystyle\int_0^{2\sqrt{3}} \int_{y^2/4}^{\sqrt{12-y^2}} dx \, dy$

8. $\displaystyle\int_{-2}^1 \int_{y^2+4y}^{3y+2} dx \, dy$

9. $\displaystyle\int_0^3 \int_1^{4-x} (x + y) \, dy \, dx$

10. $\displaystyle\int_0^1 \int_{x^3}^1 (x + y^2) \, dy \, dx$

11. $\displaystyle\int_0^1 \int_0^x (x^2 + 2y^2) \, dy \, dx$

12. $\displaystyle\int_{-1}^1 \int_{-1}^x (3x + 2y) \, dy \, dx$

13. $\displaystyle\int_0^2 \int_0^{\sin x} y \cos x \, dy \, dx$

14. $\displaystyle\int_0^{\pi/2} \int_0^{\sin x} e^y \cos x \, dy \, dx$

Evaluate the double integral given in Problems 15–26 for the specified region of integration D.

15. $\displaystyle\iint_D (x + y) \, dA$; D is the triangle with vertices $(0, 0)$, $(0, 1)$, $(1, 1)$.

16. $\displaystyle\iint_D (x + 2y) \, dA$; D is the triangle with vertices $(0, 0)$, $(1, 0)$, $(0, 2)$.

17. $\displaystyle\iint_D 48xy \, dA$; D is the region bounded by $y = x^3$ and $y = \sqrt{x}$.

18. $\displaystyle\iint_D (2y - x) \, dA$; D is the region bounded by $y = x^2$ and $y = 2x$.

19. $\displaystyle\iint_D y \, dA$; D is the region bounded by $y = \sqrt{x}$, $y = 2 - x$, and $y = 0$.

20. $\displaystyle\iint_D 4x \, dA$; D is the region bounded by $y = 4 - x^2$, $y = 3x$, and $x = 0$.

21. $\displaystyle\iint_D 4x \, dA$; D is the region in the first quadrant bounded by $y = 4 - x^2$, $y = 3x$, and $y = 0$.

22. $\displaystyle\iint_D (2x + 1) \, dA$; D is the triangle with vertices $(-1, 0)$, $(1, 0)$, and $(0, 1)$.

23. $\displaystyle\iint_D 2x \, dA$; D is the region bounded by $x^2 y = 1$, $y = x$, $x = 2$, and $y = 0$.

24. $\displaystyle\iint_D \frac{dA}{y^2 + 1}$; D is the triangle bounded by $x = 2y$, $y = -x$, and $y = 2$.

25. $\displaystyle\iint_D 12x^2 e^{y^2} \, dA$; D is the region in the first quadrant bounded by $y = x^3$ and $y = x$.

26. $\displaystyle\iint_D y \, dA$; D is the region bounded by $y = \ln x$, $y = 0$, and $x = e$.

Sketch the region of integration in Problems 27–34, and then compute the integral in two ways: (a) with the given order of integration and (b) with the order of integration reversed.

27. $\displaystyle\int_0^4 \int_0^{4-x} xy \, dy \, dx$

28. $\displaystyle\int_0^4 \int_{x^2}^{4x} dy \, dx$

29. $\displaystyle\int_0^1 \int_x^{2x} e^{y-x} \, dy \, dx$

30. $\displaystyle\int_0^4 \int_0^{\sqrt{x}} 3x^5 \, dy \, dx$

31. $\displaystyle\int_0^1 \int_{-x^2}^{x^2} dy \, dx$

32. $\displaystyle\int_1^e \int_0^{\ln x} xy \, dy \, dx$

33. $\displaystyle\int_0^{2\sqrt{3}} \int_{y^2/6}^{\sqrt{16-y^2}} dx \, dy$

34. $\displaystyle\int_{-2}^1 \int_{y^2+4y}^{3y+2} dx \, dy$

Sketch the region of integration in Problems 35–42, and write an equivalent integral with the order of integration reversed. Do not evaluate.

35. $\displaystyle\int_0^1 \int_0^{2y} f(x, y) \, dx \, dy$

36. $\displaystyle\int_0^1 \int_{x^2}^{\sqrt{x}} f(x, y) \, dy \, dx$

37. $\displaystyle\int_0^4 \int_{y/2}^{\sqrt{y}} f(x, y) \, dx \, dy$

38. $\displaystyle\int_1^{e^2} \int_{\ln x}^2 f(x, y) \, dy \, dx$

39. $\displaystyle\int_0^3 \int_{y/3}^{\sqrt{4-y}} f(x, y) \, dx \, dy$

40. $\displaystyle\int_0^1 \int_x^{2-x} f(x, y) \, dy \, dx$

41. $\displaystyle\int_{-3}^2 \int_{x^2}^{6-x} f(x, y) \, dy \, dx$

42. $\displaystyle\int_2^3 \int_x^{16/x} f(x, y) \, dy \, dx$

B *Express the area of the region D bounded by the curve given in Problems 43–44 as a double integral in two different ways (with different orders of integration). Evaluate one of these integrals to find the volume.*

43. Let D denote the region in the first quadrant of the xy-plane that is bounded by the curves $y = \dfrac{4}{x^2}$ and $y = 5 - x^2$.

44. Let D denote the region bounded by the ellipse $\dfrac{x^2}{a^2} + \dfrac{y^2}{b^2} = 1$.

45. Find the volume under the surface $z = x + y + 2$ above the region D bounded by the curves $y = x^2$ and $y = 2$.

46. Find the volume under the plane $z = 4x$ above the region D given by $y = x^2$, $y = 0$, and $x = 1$.

47. Evaluate

$$\int_0^1 \int_0^y (x^2 + y^2) \, dx \, dy + \int_1^2 \int_0^{2-y} (x^2 + y^2) \, dx \, dy$$

by reversing the order of integration.

48. Let $f(x, y)$ be a continuous function for all x and y. Reverse the order of integration in

$$\int_1^2 \int_x^{x^3} f(x, y) \, dy \, dx + \int_2^8 \int_x^8 f(x, y) \, dy \, dx$$

49. Evaluate $\displaystyle\iint_D xy \, dA$, where D is the triangular region in the xy-plane with vertices $(0, 0)$, $(1, 0)$, and $(4, 1)$.

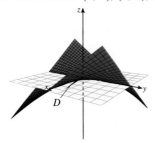

50. Compute $\displaystyle\iint_D (x^2 - xy - 1) \, dA$, where D is the triangular region bounded by the lines $x - 2y + 2 = 0$, $x + 3y - 3 = 0$, and $y = 0$.

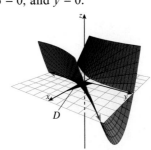

51. Find the volume under the surface $z = x + 2y + 4$ above the region D bounded by the lines $y = 2x$, $y = 3 - x$, and $y = 0$.

52. Find the volume under the plane $3x + y - z = 0$ above the elliptic region bounded by $4x^2 + 9y^2 \leq 36$, with $x \geq 0$ and $y \geq 0$.

53. Find the volume under the surface $z = x^2 + y^2$ above the square region bounded by $|x| \leq 1$ and $|y| \leq 1$.

© 54. Show that if $f(x, y)$ is continuous on a region D and $m \leq f(x, y) \leq M$ for all points (x, y) in D, then

$$m \leq \iint_D f(x, y)\, dA \leq M \quad \text{if} \quad \iint_D dA = 1$$

55. Use the result of Problem 54 to estimate the value of the double integral

$$\iint_D e^{y \sin x}\, dA$$

where D is the triangle with vertices $(-1, 0)$, $(2, 0)$, and $(0, 1)$.

13.3 DOUBLE INTEGRALS IN POLAR COORDINATES

> **IN THIS SECTION** **Change of variables to polar form, improper double integrals in polar coordinates**
> In general, changing variables in a double integral is more complicated than in a single integral. In this section, we focus attention on using polar coordinates in a double integral, and in Section 13.8, we examine changing variables from a more general standpoint.

■ CHANGE OF VARIABLES TO POLAR FORM

Graph of $f(x, y) = x^2 + y^2 + 1$

Polar coordinates are used in double integrals primarily when the integrand or the region of integration (or both) have relatively simple polar descriptions. As a preview of the ideas we plan to explore, let us examine the double integral

$$\iint_D (x^2 + y^2 + 1)\, dA$$

where D is the region (disk) bounded by the circle $x^2 + y^2 = 4$.

Interpreting D as a type I (vertical strip), we see that for each fixed x between -2 and 2, y varies from the lower boundary semicircle with equation $y = -\sqrt{4 - x^2}$ to the upper semicircle $y = \sqrt{4 - x^2}$, as shown in Figure 13.14a.

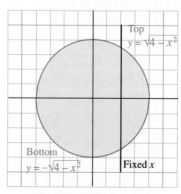

a. Type I description:
For fixed x between -2 and 2
y varies from $y = -\sqrt{4 - x^2}$
to $y = \sqrt{4 - x^2}$

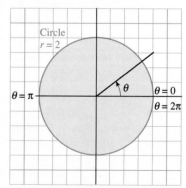

b. Polar description:
For fixed θ between 0 and 2π,
r varies from 0 to 2.

Figure 13.14 Two interpretations of a region D

Using the type I description, we have

$$\iint_D (x^2 + y^2 + 1)\, dA = \int_{-2}^{2} \int_{-\sqrt{4-x^2}}^{\sqrt{4-x^2}} (x^2 + y^2 + 1)\, dy\, dx$$

The iterated integral on the right is clearly difficult to evaluate, but both the integrand and the domain of integration can be represented quite simply in terms of polar coordinates. Specifically, using the polar conversion formulas

$$x = r\cos\theta \qquad y = r\sin\theta \qquad r = \sqrt{x^2 + y^2} \qquad \tan\theta = \frac{y}{x}$$

we find that the integrand $f(x, y) = x^2 + y^2 + 1$ can be rewritten

$$f(r\cos\theta, r\sin\theta) = (r\cos\theta)^2 + (r\sin\theta)^2 + 1 = r^2 + 1$$

and the region of integration D is just the interior of the circle $r = 2$. Thus, D can be described as the set of all points (r, θ) so that for each fixed angle θ between 0 and 2π, r varies from the origin ($r = 0$) to the circle $r = 2$, as shown in Figure 13.14b.

But how is the differential of integration dA changed in polar coordinates? Can we simply substitute "$dr\, d\theta$" for dA and perform the integration with respect to r and θ? The answer is no, and the correct formula for expressing a given double integral in polar form is given in the following theorem.

THEOREM 13.4 Double integral in polar coordinates

If f is continuous in the polar region D described by $a \leq r \leq b$ ($a, b \geq 0$), $\alpha \leq \theta \leq \beta$ ($0 \leq \beta - \alpha < 2\pi$), then

$$\iint_D f(r, \theta)\, dA = \int_{\alpha}^{\beta} \int_{a}^{b} f(r, \theta)\, r\, dr\, d\theta$$

■ *What this says*: The procedure for changing from a Cartesian integral

$$\iint_R f(x, y)\, dA$$

into a polar integral is done in two steps. First, substitute $x = r\cos\theta$ and $y = r\sin\theta$, $dx\, dy = r\, dr\, d\theta$ into the Cartesian integral. Then supply the polar limits for the boundary, where D denotes the region of integration in polar coordinates. Thus,

$$\iint_R f(x, y)\, dA = \iint_D f(r\cos\theta, r\sin\theta)\, r\, dr\, d\theta$$

Proof: A region described by $a \leq r \leq b$, $\alpha \leq \theta \leq \beta$ is called a **polar rectangle**. A typical polar rectangle is shown in Figure 13.15.

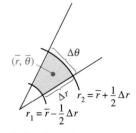

Figure 13.15 A polar rectangle

a. A partition of a region into polar coordinates

b. A typical polar rectangle in the partition

To prove the theorem, we subdivide the region of integration into polar rectangles. Pick an arbitrary polar-form point (r_k^*, θ_k^*) in each polar rectangle in the partition and then take the limit of an appropriate Riemann sum

$$\sum_{k=1}^{N} f(r_k^*, \theta_k^*) \, \Delta A_k$$

where ΔA_k is the area of the kth polar rectangle.

To find the area of a typical polar rectangle, let $(\bar{r}, \bar{\theta})$ be the center of the polar rectangle—that is, the point midway between the arcs and rays that form the polar rectangle, as shown in Figure 13.15b. If the circular arcs that bound the polar rectangle are Δr apart, then the arcs are given by

$$r_1 = \bar{r} - \tfrac{1}{2}\Delta r \quad \text{and} \quad r_2 = \bar{r} + \tfrac{1}{2}\Delta r$$

It can be shown that a circular section of radius r and central angle θ has area $\tfrac{1}{2}r^2\theta$ (see the *Student Mathematics Handbook* for details). Thus, a typical polar rectangle has area

$$\Delta A = \left[\tfrac{1}{2}\underbrace{\left(\bar{r} + \tfrac{1}{2}\Delta r\right)^2}_{\text{Radius of outside arc}} - \tfrac{1}{2}\underbrace{\left(\bar{r} - \tfrac{1}{2}\Delta r\right)^2}_{\text{Radius of inside arc}}\right]\Delta\theta = \bar{r}\,\Delta r\,\Delta\theta$$

Finally, we compute the given double integral in polar form by taking the limit

$$\iint_D f(r, \theta)\, dA = \lim_{\|P\|\to 0}\sum_{k=1}^{N} f(\bar{r}_k, \bar{\theta}_k)\,\Delta A = \lim_{\|P\|\to 0}\sum_{k=1}^{N} f(r, \theta)r\,\Delta r\,\Delta\theta$$

$$= \int_{\alpha}^{\beta}\int_{a}^{b} f(r, \theta)r\,dr\,d\theta \qquad \blacksquare$$

PREVIEW: It can be shown that under reasonable conditions, the change of variable $x = x(u, v)$, $y = y(u, v)$ transforms the integral $\iint f(x, y)\, dA$ into $\iint f(u, v)\,|\,J(u, v)\,|\,du\,dv$, where

$$J(u, v) = \begin{vmatrix} \dfrac{\partial x}{\partial u} & \dfrac{\partial x}{\partial v} \\[2mm] \dfrac{\partial y}{\partial u} & \dfrac{\partial y}{\partial v} \end{vmatrix}$$

This determinant is known as the **Jacobian** of the transformation. In the case of polar coordinates, we have $x = r\cos\theta$ and $y = r\sin\theta$, so that the Jacobian is

$$J(r, \theta) = \begin{vmatrix} \dfrac{\partial}{\partial r}(r\cos\theta) & \dfrac{\partial}{\partial\theta}(r\cos\theta) \\[2mm] \dfrac{\partial}{\partial r}(r\sin\theta) & \dfrac{\partial}{\partial\theta}(r\sin\theta) \end{vmatrix}$$

$$= \begin{vmatrix} \cos\theta & -r\sin\theta \\ \sin\theta & r\cos\theta \end{vmatrix} = r\cos^2\theta + r\sin^2\theta = r$$

This yields the result of Theorem 13.4.

$$\iint_R f(x, y)\, dA = \iint_D f(r, \theta)\, r\, dr\, d\theta = \int_{\alpha}^{\beta}\int_{a}^{b} f(r\cos\theta, r\sin\theta)r\,dr\,d\theta$$

We discuss this more completely in Section 13.8.

If you carefully compare the result in the preview box with the result of Theorem 13.4, you will see that they are not *exactly* the same. The region D in Theorem 13.4 already is in polar coordinates. The more common situation is that we are given f and a region R in rectangular coordinates that we need to change to polar coordinates.

We now present the example we promised in the introduction.

EXAMPLE 1   Double integral in polar form

Evaluate $\iint\limits_D (x^2 + y^2 + 1)\, dA$, where D is the region inside the circle $x^2 + y^2 = 4$.

Solution   In this example, the region D is given in rectangular form. We will describe this as a polar region D^*. Earlier, we observed that in D^*, for each fixed angle θ between 0 and 2π, r varies from $r = 0$ (the pole) to $r = 2$ (the circle). Thus,

$$\iint\limits_D \underbrace{(x^2 + y^2 + 1)}_{f(x,\,y)}\, dA = \int_0^{2\pi}\int_0^2 \underbrace{(r^2 + 1)}_{f(r\cos\theta,\,r\sin\theta)}\ \underbrace{r\, dr\, d\theta}_{dA}$$

$$= \int_0^{2\pi}\int_0^2 (r^3 + r)\, dr\, d\theta = \int_0^{2\pi}\left[\frac{r^4}{4} + \frac{r^2}{2}\right]\Big|_0^2\, d\theta = \int_0^{2\pi} 6\, d\theta = 6\theta\Big|_0^{2\pi} = 12\pi$$

EXAMPLE 2   Double integral in polar form

Evaluate $\iint\limits_D x\, dA$, where D is the region bounded above by the line $y = x$ and below by the circle $x^2 + y^2 - 2y = 0$.

Solution   The circle $x^2 + y^2 - 2y = 0$ and the line $y = x$ are shown in Figure 13.16. We rewrite these equations in polar form:

$$x^2 + y^2 - 2y = (r\cos\theta)^2 + (r\sin\theta)^2 - 2(r\sin\theta) = 0$$

$$r^2 - 2r\sin\theta = 0 \qquad \textit{Because } \cos^2\theta + \sin^2\theta = 1$$

$$r(r - 2\sin\theta) = 0$$

$$r = 0 \quad \text{or} \quad r = 2\sin\theta \qquad \textit{Reject } r = 0.$$

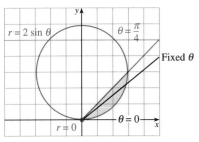

Figure 13.16 The region D

The polar-form equation for the circle is $r = 2\sin\theta$, and the line $y = x$ in polar form is

$$r\sin\theta = r\cos\theta$$

This is true only when $\tan\theta = 1$ (divide both sides by $r\cos\theta$), which implies $\theta = \frac{\pi}{4}$. Thus, the region D may be described by saying that for each fixed angle θ between 0 and $\frac{\pi}{4}$, r varies from 0 (the pole) to $2\sin\theta$ (the circle). Thus,

$$\iint\limits_D x\, dA = \int_0^{\pi/4}\int_0^{2\sin\theta} \underbrace{(r\cos\theta)}_{x}\ \underbrace{r\, dr\, d\theta}_{dA} = \int_0^{\pi/4}\left[\frac{r^3}{3}\cos\theta\right]\Big|_{r=0}^{r=2\sin\theta}\, d\theta$$

$$= \int_0^{\pi/4}\left[\frac{(2\sin\theta)^3}{3}\cos\theta - 0\right]\, d\theta = \int_0^{\pi/4} \frac{8}{3}\sin^3\theta\cos\theta\, d\theta \qquad \text{Let } u = \sin\theta.$$

$$= \left[\frac{8}{3}\cdot\frac{1}{4}\sin^4\theta\right]\Big|_{\theta=0}^{\theta=\pi/4} = \frac{1}{6}$$

EXAMPLE 3   Volume in polar form

Use a polar double integral to show that a sphere of radius a has volume $\frac{4}{3}\pi a^3$.

The top hemisphere is bounded above by the sphere and below by the disk D.

Solution   We compute the required volume by doubling the volume of the solid hemisphere $x^2 + y^2 + z^2 \leq a^2$, with $z > 0$. This hemisphere may be regarded as a solid bounded below by the circular disk $x^2 + y^2 \leq a^2$ and above by the spherical surface.

We need to change the equation of the hemisphere to polar form:

In rectangular form: $z = \sqrt{a^2 - x^2 - y^2}$

In polar form: $z = \sqrt{a^2 - r^2}$ *Because* $r^2 = x^2 + y^2$

Describing the disk D in polar terms, we see that for each fixed θ between 0 and 2π, r varies from the origin to the circle $x^2 + y^2 = a^2$, which has the polar equation $r = a$, as shown in Figure 13.17. Thus, the volume is given by the integral

$$V = 2 \iint_D z \, dA \qquad\qquad \textit{Rectangular form}$$

$$= 2 \int_0^{2\pi} \int_0^a \sqrt{a^2 - r^2} \, r \, dr \, d\theta \qquad \boxed{\begin{array}{l} \text{Let } u = a^2 - r^2; \\ du = -2r \, dr. \end{array}}$$

$$= 2 \int_0^{2\pi} \left[-\frac{1}{3}(a^2 - r^2)^{3/2} \right]\Big|_{r=0}^{r=a} d\theta$$

$$= -\frac{2}{3} \int_0^{2\pi} [(a^2 - a^2)^{3/2} - (a^2 - 0)^{3/2}] \, d\theta$$

$$= \frac{2}{3} \int_0^{2\pi} a^3 \, d\theta = \frac{2}{3} a^3 \theta \Big|_0^{2\pi} = \frac{4}{3}\pi a^3$$

Figure 13.17 The disk D: For θ between 0 and 2π, r varies from 0 to a.

You will need to be familiar with the graphs of many polar-form curves. These can be found in Table 9.1 on page 583 and also in the *Student Mathematics Handbook.*

Example 3 has constant limits for the distance r. However, the extension to variable limits is quite natural.

Area as a Double Integral in Polar Coordinates

> If D is the polar region described by $r_1(\theta) \leq r \leq r_2(\theta)$, and $\alpha \leq \theta \leq \beta$, its area is given by
>
> $$A = \int_\alpha^\beta \int_{r_1(\theta)}^{r_2(\theta)} r \, dr \, d\theta$$

This formula is illustrated in the following examples.

EXAMPLE 4   Area between two curves in polar form

Evaluate $\displaystyle\iint_D \frac{1}{x} \, dA$, where D is the region in the first quadrant that lies inside the circle $r = 3\cos\theta$ and outside the cardioid $r = 1 + \cos\theta$.

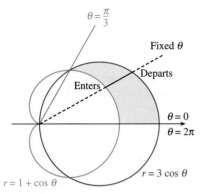

$\theta = \frac{\pi}{3}$

Fixed θ

Departs

Enters

$\theta = 0$
$\theta = 2\pi$

$r = 3 \cos \theta$

$r = 1 + \cos \theta$

Figure 13.18 Region D

Solution Begin by sketching the given curves, as shown in Figure 13.18. Next, find the points of intersection:

$$3 \cos \theta = 1 + \cos \theta$$

$$2 \cos \theta = 1$$

$$\cos \theta = \tfrac{1}{2}$$

$$\theta = \tfrac{\pi}{3}$$

We see that D is the region such that, for each fixed angle θ between 0 and $\pi/3$, r varies from $1 + \cos \theta$ (the cardioid) to $3 \cos \theta$ (the circle). This gives us the limits of integration. Finally, we need to write the integrand in polar form:

$$\underbrace{\frac{1}{x}}_{\text{Rectangular form}} = \underbrace{\frac{1}{r \cos \theta}}_{\text{Polar form}}$$

Thus,

$$\int\int_D \frac{1}{x}\, dA = \int\int_D \frac{1}{r \cos \theta}\, r\, dr\, d\theta$$

$$= \int_0^{\pi/3} \int_{1+\cos\theta}^{3\cos\theta} \frac{1}{\cos \theta}\, dr\, d\theta \qquad \textit{Write } \frac{1}{\cos \theta} = \sec \theta; \textit{ note that} \\ \textit{sec } \theta \textit{ is a constant with} \\ \textit{respect to the variable } r.$$

$$= \int_0^{\pi/3} [r \sec \theta]\Big|_{r=1+\cos\theta}^{r=3\cos\theta}\, d\theta$$

$$= \int_0^{\pi/3} [3 \cos \theta \sec \theta - (1 + \cos \theta)\sec \theta]\, d\theta$$

$$= \int_0^{\pi/3} (2 - \sec \theta)\, d\theta \qquad \textit{Note: } 2\cos\theta\sec\theta = 2 \textit{ be-} \\ \textit{cause cosine and secant are} \\ \textit{reciprocal functions.}$$

$$= \Big[2\theta - \ln|\sec \theta + \tan \theta|\Big]\Big|_0^{\pi/3}$$

$$= \frac{2\pi}{3} - \ln(2 + \sqrt{3})$$

■ IMPROPER DOUBLE INTEGRALS IN POLAR COORDINATES

Improper double integrals play a useful role in probability theory and in certain physical applications. We shall demonstrate the basic approach to this topic by examining the special case of double integrals that are improper because the region of integration is the (unbounded) first quadrant. A general treatment of improper multiple integrals is outside the scope of this text.

Suppose the function $f(x, y)$ is continuous throughout the first quadrant Q; then define the improper integral in terms of rectangular coordinates as follows:

$$\int\int_Q f(x, y)\, dA = \lim_{n\to\infty} \int\int_{S_n} f(x, y)\, dA$$

where S_n is the square described by $0 \le x \le n$, $0 \le y \le n$. In terms of polar coordinates, let C_n denote the quarter circular region described by $r \le n$,

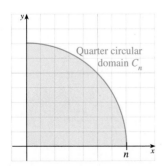

y

Quarter circular domain C_n

n x

Figure 13.19 Quarter circular domain

$0 \leq \theta \leq \pi/2$, as shown in Figure 13.19. We use this quarter circular region to formulate the following definition.

Improper Double Integral in Polar Coordinates

Let Q denote the first quadrant of the Cartesian plane, and let C_n denote the quarter circular region described by $r \leq n$, $0 \leq \theta \leq \frac{\pi}{2}$. Then the improper integral $\iint_Q f(x, y)\, dA$ is defined in polar coordinates as

$$\lim_{n \to \infty} \iint_{C_n} f(r \cos \theta, r \sin \theta) r\, dr\, d\theta = \lim_{n \to \infty} \int_0^{\pi/2} \int_0^n f(r \cos \theta, r \sin \theta) r\, dr\, d\theta$$

If the limit in this definition exists and is equal to L, we say that the improper integral **converges** to L. Otherwise, we say that the improper integral **diverges**.

EXAMPLE 5   Evaluating a convergent improper double integral

Evaluate $\iint_Q e^{-(x^2+y^2)}\, dA$, where Q is the first quadrant of the xy-plane.

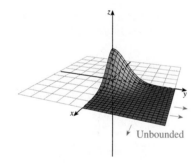
Unbounded

Solution   To evaluate this integral (improper because Q is unbounded), we convert to polar coordinates.

$$\iint_Q e^{-(x^2+y^2)}\, dA = \lim_{n \to \infty} \int_0^{\pi/2} \int_0^n e^{-r^2} r\, dr\, d\theta$$

$$= \lim_{n \to \infty} \int_0^{\pi/2} \left[-\tfrac{1}{2}e^{-r^2} \right]\Big|_{r=0}^{r=n} d\theta = \lim_{n \to \infty} \int_0^{\pi/2} \left[-\tfrac{1}{2}e^{-n^2} + \tfrac{1}{2} \right] d\theta$$

$$= \lim_{n \to \infty} \tfrac{1}{2}(1 - e^{-n^2})[\theta]\Big|_{\theta=0}^{\theta=\pi/2} = \lim_{n \to \infty} \tfrac{\pi}{4}(1 - e^{-n^2}) = \tfrac{\pi}{4}$$

Thus, the improper integral converges to $\frac{\pi}{4}$.

PROBLEM SET 13.3

Ⓐ *Evaluate the double integral* $\iint_D f(x, y)\, dA$ *in Problems 1–8, and sketch the region of integration D.*

1. $\displaystyle\int_0^{\pi/2} \int_0^{2\sin\theta} dr\, d\theta$

2. $\displaystyle\int_0^{\pi} \int_0^{1+\sin\theta} dr\, d\theta$

3. $\displaystyle\int_0^{\pi/2} \int_1^{3} re^{-r^2}\, dr\, d\theta$

4. $\displaystyle\int_0^{\pi/2} \int_1^{2} \sqrt{4 - r^2}\ r\, dr\, d\theta$

5. $\displaystyle\int_0^{\pi} \int_0^{4} r^2 \sin^2\theta\, dr\, d\theta$

6. $\displaystyle\int_0^{\pi/2} \int_1^{3} r^2 \cos^2\theta\, dr\, d\theta$

7. $\displaystyle\int_0^{2\pi} \int_0^{4} 2r^2 \cos\theta\, dr\, d\theta$

8. $\displaystyle\int_0^{2\pi} \int_0^{1-\sin\theta} \cos\theta\, dr\, d\theta$

Use a double integral to find the area of the shaded region in Problems 9–22.

9. $r = 4$

10. $r = 2\cos\theta$

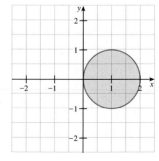

11. $r = 2(1 - \cos\theta)$

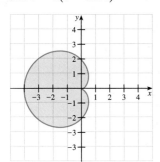

12. $r = 1 + \sin\theta$

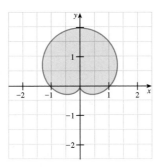

13. $r = 4\cos 3\theta$

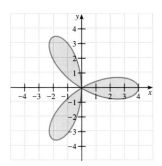

14. $r = 5\sin 2\theta$

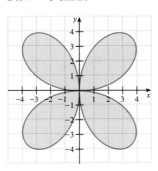

15. $r = \cos 2\theta$

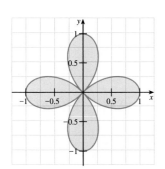

16. $r = 1$ and $r = 2\sin\theta$ *Hint:* consider $0 < \theta < \frac{\pi}{6}$ and $\frac{\pi}{6} < \theta < \frac{\pi}{2}$ separately.

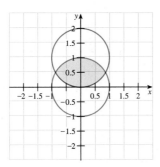

17. $r = 1$ and $r = 2\sin\theta$

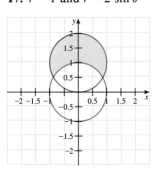

18. $r = 1$ and $r = 1 + \cos\theta$

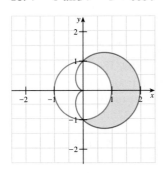

19. $r = 1$ and $r = 1 + \cos\theta$ **20.** $r = 1$ and $r = 1 + \cos\theta$

 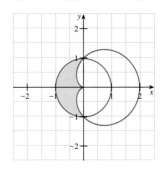

21. $r = 3\cos\theta$ and $r = 1 + \cos\theta$

22. $r = 3\cos\theta$ and $r = 2 - \cos\theta$

 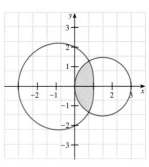

Use polar coordinates in Problems 23–28 to find $\displaystyle\iint_D f(x, y)\, dA$, where D is the circular disk defined by $x^2 + y^2 \le a^2$ for constant $a > 0$.

23. $f(x, y) = y^2$

24. $f(x, y) = x^2 + y^2$

25. $f(x, y) = \dfrac{1}{a^2 + x^2 + y^2}$

26. $f(x, y) = e^{-(x^2+y^2)}$

27. $f(x, y) = \dfrac{1}{a + \sqrt{x^2 + y^2}}$

28. $f(x, y) = \ln(a^2 + x^2 + y^2)$

Use polar coordinates in Problems 29–34 to evaluate the given double integral.

29. $\displaystyle\iint_D y\, dA$, where D is the disk $x^2 + y^2 \le 4$

30. $\displaystyle\iint_D (x^2 + y^2)\, dA$, where D is the region bounded by the x-axis, the line $y = x$, and the circle $x^2 + y^2 = 1$

31. $\displaystyle\iint_D e^{x^2+y^2}\, dA$, where D is the region inside the circle $x^2 + y^2 = 9$

32. $\displaystyle\iint_D \sqrt{x^2 + y^2}\, dA$, where D is the region inside the circle $(x - 1)^2 + y^2 = 1$ in the first quadrant

33. $\displaystyle\iint_D \ln(x^2 + y^2 + 2)\, dA$, where D is the region inside the circle $x^2 + y^2 = 4$ in the first quadrant

34. $\iint\limits_D \sin(x^2 + y^2)\, dA$, where D is the region in the first quadrant bounded by the circles $x^2 + y^2 = 1$ and $x^2 + y^2 = 4$ and the lines $y = 0$ and $x = \sqrt{3}\, y$

35. Find the volume of the solid bounded by the paraboloid $z = x^2 + y^2$ and the plane $z = 4$.

36. Find the volume of the solid bounded above by the cone $z = 6\sqrt{x^2 + y^2}$ and below by the circular region $x^2 + y^2 \leq a^2$ in the xy-plane, where a is a positive constant.

Ⓑ 37. Use polar coordinates to evaluate $\iint\limits_D xy\, dA$, where D is the intersection of the circular disks $r \leq 4\cos\theta$ and $r \leq 4\sin\theta$. Sketch the region of integration.

38. Let D be the region formed by intersecting the regions (in the xy-plane) described by $y \leq x$, $y \geq 0$, and $x \leq 1$.
   a. Express $\iint\limits_D dA$ as an iterated integral in Cartesian coordinates.
   b. Express $\iint\limits_D dA$ in terms of polar coordinates.

39. Example 5 of Section 9.3 used a single integral to find the area of the region common to the circles $r = a\cos\theta$ and $r = a\sin\theta$. Rework this example using double integrals.

40. Example 6 of Section 9.3 used a single integral to find the area between the circle $r = 5\cos\theta$ and the limaçon $r = 2 + \cos\theta$. Use double integrals to find the same area.

41. Use a double integral in polar coordinates to find the volume of the solid that lies inside the sphere $x^2 + y^2 + z^2 = 25$ and outside the cylinder $x^2 + y^2 = 9$.

Evaluate the improper integrals in Problems 42–46 over Q, the first quadrant in the xy-plane.

42. $\iint\limits_Q (x^2 + y^2 + 1)^{-3/2}\, dA$ 43. $\iint\limits_Q \dfrac{dA}{(1 + x^2 + y^2)^2}$

44. $\iint\limits_Q \dfrac{dA}{(1 + x^2 + y^2)^3}$ 45. $\iint\limits_Q e^{-2(x^2 + y^2)}\, dA$

46. $\iint\limits_Q e^{-4(x^2 + y^2)}\, dA$

47. Use polar coordinates to evaluate the double integral $\iint\limits_D (x^2 + y^2)\, dA$ over the shaded region.

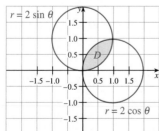

48. Use polar coordinates to evaluate the double integral $\iint\limits_D (x^2 + y^2)\, dA$ over the shaded region.

49. THINK TANK PROBLEM   To evaluate the integral
$$\iint\limits_R r^2\, dr\, d\theta$$
where R is the region in the xy-plane bounded by $r = 2\cos\theta$, we get
$$\int_0^\pi \int_0^{2\cos\theta} r^2\, dr\, d\theta = \int_0^\pi \frac{r^3}{3}\Big|_0^{2\cos\theta}\, d\theta$$
$$= \frac{8}{3}\int_0^\pi \cos^3\theta\, d\theta = \frac{8}{3}\left[\sin\theta - \frac{\sin^3\theta}{3}\right]_0^\pi = 0$$
Alternatively, we can set up the integral as
$$\int_{-\pi/2}^{\pi/2} \int_0^{2\cos\theta} r^2\, dr\, d\theta = \int_{-\pi/(2a)}^{\pi/2} \frac{r^3}{3}\Big|_0^{2\cos\theta}\, d\theta$$
$$= \frac{8}{3}\int_{-\pi/2}^{\pi/2} \cos^3\theta\, d\theta = \frac{8}{3}\left[\sin\theta - \frac{\sin^3\theta}{3}\right]_{-\pi/2}^{\pi/2} = \frac{32}{9}$$

Both of these answers cannot be correct. Which procedure (if either) is correct and why?

Ⓒ 50. In Example 5, we used polar coordinates to show that
$$\iint\limits_Q e^{-(x^2 + y^2)}\, dA = \frac{\pi}{4}$$
where Q is the first quadrant of the xy-plane.
   a. Explain why
   $$\int_0^n \int_0^n e^{-(x^2 + y^2)}\, dy\, dx = \left[\int_0^n e^{-x^2}\, dx\right]\left[\int_0^n e^{-y^2}\, dy\right]$$
   b. Show that
   $$\left[\int_0^\infty e^{-x^2}\, dx\right]\left[\int_0^\infty e^{-y^2}\, dy\right] = \frac{\pi}{4}$$
   c. Explain why $\displaystyle\int_0^\infty e^{-x^2}\, dx = \frac{\sqrt{\pi}}{2}$

51. Evaluate
$$\int_0^\infty e^{-2x^2}\, dx$$
(*Hint:* Use Problem 50.)

52. For constant a where $0 \leq a \leq R$, the plane $z = R - a$ cuts off a "cap" from the sphere
$$x^2 + y^2 + z^2 = R^2$$
Use a double integral in polar coordinates to find the volume of the cap.

13.4 SURFACE AREA

> **IN THIS SECTION** Definition of surface area, surface area projections, area of a surface defined parametrically
>
> In Chapter 6, we found that if f has a continuous derivative on the closed, bounded interval $[a, b]$, then the length L of the portion of the graph of $y = f(x)$ between the points where $x = a$ and $x = b$ may be defined by
>
> $$L = \int_a^b \sqrt{1 + [f'(x)]^2}\, dx$$
>
> The goal of this section is to study an analogous formula for the surface area of the graph of a differentiable function of two variables.

■ DEFINITION OF SURFACE AREA

Consider a surface defined by $z = f(x, y)$ defined over a region R of the xy-plane. We will find the area of this surface by considering a Riemann sum. We begin by enclosing the region R in a rectangle, which is then partitioned by a grid with lines parallel to the coordinate axes, as shown in Figure 13.20a. This creates a number of cells, and we let $R_1, R_2, \ldots, R_n$ denote those that lie entirely within R.

a. The region R is partitioned by a rectangular grid

Figure 13.20 Surface area

b. The surface area above R_m is approximated by the area of the parallelogram on the tangent plane.

For $m = 1, 2, \ldots, n$, let $P_m(x_m^*, y_m^*)$ be a corner of the rectangle R_m, and let T_m be the tangent plane above P_m on the surface of $z = f(x, y)$. Finally, let ΔS_m denote the area of the "patch" of surface that lies directly above R_m.

The rectangle R_m projects onto a parallelogram $ABDC$ in the tangent plane T_m, and if R_m is "small," we would expect the area of this parallelogram to approximate closely the element of surface area ΔS_m (see Figure 13.20b).

If Δx_m and Δy_m are the lengths of the sides of the rectangle R_m, the approximating parallelogram will have sides determined by the vectors

$$\mathbf{AB} = \Delta x_m \mathbf{i} + [f_x(x_m^*, y_m^*)\Delta x_m]\mathbf{k} \qquad \text{and} \qquad \mathbf{AC} = \Delta y_m \mathbf{j} + [f_y(x_m^*, y_m^*)\Delta y_m]\mathbf{k}$$

In Chapter 10, we showed that such a parallelogram with sides $\mathbf{AB}$ and $\mathbf{AC}$ has area

$$\|\mathbf{AB} \times \mathbf{AC}\|$$

This is shown in Figure 13.21.

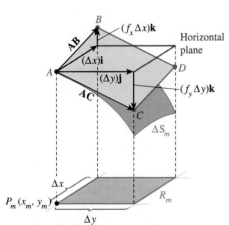

Figure 13.21 An element of surface area has area $\|\mathbf{AB} \times \mathbf{AC}\|$.

If K_m is the area of the approximating parallelogram, we have

$$K_m = \|\mathbf{AB} \times \mathbf{AC}\|$$

First, we calculate the cross product:

$$\mathbf{AB} \times \mathbf{AC} = \begin{vmatrix} \mathbf{i} & \mathbf{j} & \mathbf{k} \\ \Delta x_m & 0 & f_x(x_m^*, y_m^*)\Delta x_m \\ 0 & \Delta y_m & f_y(x_m^*, y_m^*)\Delta y_m \end{vmatrix}$$

$$= -f_x \Delta x \Delta y \mathbf{i} - f_y \Delta x \Delta y \mathbf{j} + \Delta x \Delta y \mathbf{k}$$

Then, we calculate the norm:

$$K_m = \|\mathbf{AB} \times \mathbf{AC}\|$$
$$= \sqrt{[f_x(x_m^*, y_m^*)]^2 \Delta x_m^2 \Delta y_m^2 + [f_y(x_m^*, y_m^*)]^2 \Delta x_m^2 \Delta y_m^2 + \Delta x_m^2 \Delta y_m^2}$$
$$= \sqrt{[f_x(x_m^*, y_m^*)]^2 + [f_y(x_m^*, y_m^*)]^2 + 1} \, \Delta x_m \Delta y_m$$

Finally, summing over the entire partition, we see that the surface area over R may be approximated by the sum

$$\Delta S_n = \sum_{m=1}^{n} \sqrt{[f_x(x_m^*, y_m^*)]^2 + [f_y(x_m^*, y_m^*)]^2 + 1} \, \Delta A_m$$

where $\Delta A_m = \Delta x_m \Delta y_m$. This may be regarded as a Riemann sum, and by taking an appropriate limit (as the partition becomes more and more refined), we find that surface area, S, satisfies

$$S = \lim_{n \to \infty} \sum_{m=1}^{n} \sqrt{[f_x(x_m^*, y_m^*)]^2 + [f_y(x_m^*, y_m^*)]^2 + 1} \, \Delta A_m$$

$$= \iint_R \sqrt{[f_x(x, y)]^2 + [f_y(x, y)]^2 + 1} \, dA$$

Surface Area as a Double Integral

Assume that the function $f(x, y)$ has continuous partial derivatives f_x and f_y in a region R of the xy-plane. Then the portion of the surface $z = f(x, y)$ that lies over R has the **surface area**

$$S = \iint_R \sqrt{[f_x(x, y)]^2 + [f_y(x, y)]^2 + 1} \, dA$$

■ *What this says:* The region R may be regarded as the projection of the surface $z = f(x, y)$ on the xy-plane. If there were a light source with rays perpendicular to the xy-plane, R would be the "shadow" of the surface on the plane. You will notice the shadows drawn in the figures shown in this section. It is also worthwhile to make the following comparisons:

Length on x-axis:	Arc length:
$\displaystyle \int_a^b dx$	$\displaystyle \int_a^b ds = \int_a^b \sqrt{[f'(x)]^2 + 1} \, dx$

Area in xy-plane:	Surface area:
$\displaystyle \iint_R dA$	$\displaystyle \iint_R dS = \iint_R \sqrt{[f_x(x, y)]^2 + [f_y(x, y)]^2 + 1} \, dA$

EXAMPLE 1 Surface area of a plane region

Find the surface area of the portion of the plane $x + y + z = 1$ that lies in the first octant (where $x \geq 0$, $y \geq 0$, $z \geq 0$).

Solution The plane $x + y + z = 1$ and the triangular region T that lies beneath it in the xy-plane are shown in Figure 13.22. We begin by letting $f(x, y) = 1 - x - y$. Then $f_x(x, y) = -1$ and $f_y(x, y) = -1$, and

$$S = \iint_T \sqrt{[f_x(x, y)]^2 + [f_y(x, y)]^2 + 1} \; dA$$

$$= \iint_T \sqrt{(-1)^2 + (-1)^2 + 1} \; dA$$

$$= \iint_T \sqrt{3} \; dA$$

$$= \int_0^1 \int_0^{1-x} \sqrt{3} \; dy \, dx \quad \textit{Look at Figure 13.22 to see the region} \atop \textit{T and the limits for both x and y.}$$

$$= \sqrt{3} \int_0^1 [y] \Big|_0^{1-x} dx$$

$$= \sqrt{3} \int_0^1 (1 - x) \, dx$$

$$= \sqrt{3} \left[x - \frac{x^2}{2} \right] \Big|_0^1 = \frac{\sqrt{3}}{2}$$

The surface area is $\dfrac{\sqrt{3}}{2} \approx 0.866$.

a. The surface of the plane $x + y + z = 1$ in the first octant

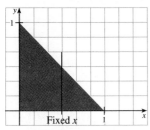

b. The surface projects onto a triangle in the xy-plane.

Figure 13.22 Surface area

EXAMPLE 2 Surface area by changing to polar coordinates

Find the surface area (to the nearest hundredth square unit) of that part of the paraboloid $x^2 + y^2 + z = 5$ that lies above the plane $z = 1$.

Solution Let $f(x, y) = 5 - x^2 - y^2$. Then $f_x(x, y) = -2x$, $f_y(x, y) = -2y$, and

$$S = \iint_D \sqrt{[f_x(x, y)]^2 + [f_y(x, y)]^2 + 1} \; dA = \iint_D \sqrt{4x^2 + 4y^2 + 1} \; dA$$

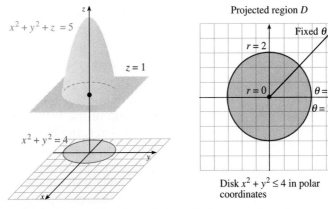

Disk $x^2 + y^2 \leq 4$ in polar coordinates

Figure 13.23 The surface $x^2 + y^2 + z = 5$ above $z = 1$ projects onto a disk.

Now we need to determine the limits for the region D and carry out the integration by using Fubini's theorem. The paraboloid intersects the plane $z = 1$ in the circle $x^2 + y^2 = 4$. Thus, the part of the paraboloid whose surface area we seek projects onto the disk $x^2 + y^2 \leq 4$ in the xy-plane, as shown in Figure 13.23 (note the shadow).

It is easier if we convert to polar coordinates by letting $x = r \cos \theta$, $y = r \sin \theta$. Because the region is bounded by $0 \leq r \leq 2$ and $0 \leq \theta \leq 2\pi$, we have

$$S = \iint_D \sqrt{4x^2 + 4y^2 + 1}\; dA$$

$$= \int_0^{2\pi} \int_0^2 \sqrt{4r^2 + 1}\; r\; dr\; d\theta$$

Let $u = 4r^2 + 1$, so
$du = 8\,r\,dr$.
If $r = 2$, then $u = 17$
and if $r = 0$, $u = 1$.

$$= \int_0^{2\pi} \int_1^{17} u^{1/2} \frac{du}{8}\; d\theta$$

$$= \int_0^{2\pi} \frac{1}{8} \cdot \frac{2}{3} u^{3/2} \Big|_1^{17}\; d\theta$$

$$= \frac{1}{12} \int_0^{2\pi} (17^{3/2} - 1)\; d\theta$$

$$= \frac{1}{12}(17^{3/2} - 1)(2\pi - 0) \approx 36.18$$

The surface area is approximately 36.18 square units.

■ SURFACE AREA PROJECTIONS

We have been projecting the given surface on the xy-plane, but we can easily modify our procedure to handle other cases. For instance, if the surface $y = f(x, z)$ is projected onto the region Q in the xz-plane, the formula for surface area becomes

$$S = \iint_Q \sqrt{[f_x(x, z)]^2 + [f_z(x, z)]^2 + 1}\; dx\; dz$$

An analogous formula for projection onto the region T in the yz-plane would be

$$S = \iint_T \sqrt{[f_y(y, z)]^2 + [f_z(y, z)]^2 + 1}\; dy\; dz$$

EXAMPLE 3   Surface area of a cylinder

Find the lateral surface area of the cylinder $x^2 + y^2 = 4$, $0 \leq z \leq 3$.

Solution   The cylinder is shown in Figure 13.24a. We can find the lateral surface area using the formula for a rectangle by imagining the cylinder "opened up." The length of one side is the height of the cylinder (3 units), and the length of the other side of the rectangle is the circumference of the bottom, namely, $2\pi(2) = 4\pi$. Thus, the lateral surface area is 12π.

We shall illustrate our formula by using it to recompute this surface area. Specifically, we shall compute the surface area of the right half of the cylinder and then double it to obtain the required area. It does no good to project the half-cylinder onto the xy-plane, because if we do we will not be accounting for the height of the cylinder.

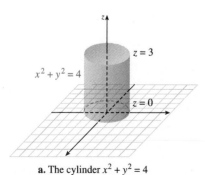

a. The cylinder $x^2 + y^2 = 4$

Figure 13.24 Surface area of a cylinder.

b. The projection of the cylinder on the xz-plane

Figure 13.24 Surface area of a cylinder

Instead, we will project the surface onto the xz-plane to obtain the rectangle Q bounded by $x = 2$, $x = -2$, $z = 0$, and $z = 3$, as shown in Figure 13.24b. Because we are projecting onto the xz-plane, we solve for y to express the surface as $y = f(x, z)$. Because

$$y = f(x, z) = \sqrt{4 - x^2}$$

we have $f_x(x, z) = \dfrac{-x}{\sqrt{4 - x^2}}$ and $f_z(x, z) = 0$, so that

$$[f_x(x, z)]^2 + [f_z(x, z)]^2 + 1 = \frac{x^2}{4 - x^2} + 1 = \frac{4}{4 - x^2}$$

Finally, we note the limits of integration:

$$-2 \leq x \leq 2 \quad \text{and} \quad 0 \leq z \leq 3$$

The surface area can now be calculated:

$$S = \int\int_Q \sqrt{\frac{4}{4 - x^2}}\, dA = \int_{-2}^{2}\int_{0}^{3} \frac{2}{\sqrt{4 - x^2}}\, dz\, dx$$

$$= \int_{-2}^{2} \frac{2z}{\sqrt{4 - x^2}}\Big|_0^3\, dx = \int_{-2}^{2} \frac{6}{\sqrt{4 - x^2}}\, dx$$

$$= \int_{-\pi/2}^{\pi/2} \frac{6(2\cos\theta\, d\theta)}{\sqrt{4 - 4\sin^2\theta}}$$

> Let $x = 2\sin\theta$, so $dx = 2\cos\theta\, d\theta$.
> If $x = 2$, then $\theta = \dfrac{\pi}{2}$ and if $x = -2$, then $\theta = -\dfrac{\pi}{2}$.

$$= 6\int_{-\pi/2}^{\pi/2} d\theta = 6\left[\frac{\pi}{2} - \left(-\frac{\pi}{2}\right)\right] = 6\pi$$

The surface area of the whole cylinder is $2(6\pi) = 12\pi$.

■ AREA OF A SURFACE DEFINED PARAMETRICALLY

Suppose a surface S (see Figure 13.25) is defined parametrically by

$$\mathbf{R}(u, v) = x(u, v)\mathbf{i} + y(u, v)\mathbf{j} + z(u, v)\mathbf{k}$$

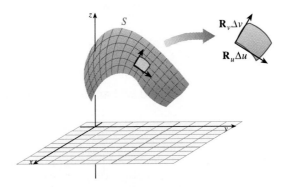

Figure 13.25 Area of a parametrically defined function.

Tangent plane

$\mathbf{R}_v \Delta v$

S_k

S

$\mathbf{R}_u \Delta u$

Δx

D_k

Δy

Figure 13.26 Area of a surface defined by a vector function

for parameters u and v. Let D be a region in the xy-plane on which x, y, and z, as well as their partial derivatives with respect to u and v are continuous. The partial derivatives of $\mathbf{R}(u, v)$ are given by

$$\mathbf{R}_u = \frac{\partial \mathbf{R}}{\partial u} = \frac{\partial x}{\partial u}\mathbf{i} + \frac{\partial y}{\partial u}\mathbf{j} + \frac{\partial z}{\partial u}\mathbf{k} \qquad \mathbf{R}_v = \frac{\partial \mathbf{R}}{\partial v} = \frac{\partial x}{\partial v}\mathbf{i} + \frac{\partial y}{\partial v}\mathbf{j} + \frac{\partial z}{\partial v}\mathbf{k}$$

Suppose the region D is subdivided into cells, as shown in Figure 13.26. Consider a typical rectangle in this partition, with dimensions Δx and Δy, where Δx and Δy are small. If we project a typical parallelogram onto the surface $\mathbf{R}(u, v)$, we obtain a **curvilinear** parallelogram with adjacent sides $\mathbf{R}_u(u, v)\Delta u$ and $\mathbf{R}_v(u, v)\Delta v$. The area of this parallelogram is approximated by

$$\Delta S = \|\mathbf{R}_u(u, v)\Delta u \times \mathbf{R}_v(u, v)\Delta v\| = \|\mathbf{R}_u(u, v) \times \mathbf{R}_v(u, v)\|\Delta u\,\Delta v$$

By taking an appropriate limit, we find the surface area to be a double integral.

Surface Area Defined Parametrically

Let D be a region in the xy-plane on which x, y, z and their partial derivatives with respect to u and v are continuous. Also, let S be a surface defined by a vector function

$$\mathbf{R}(u, v) = x(u, v)\mathbf{i} + y(u, v)\mathbf{j} + z(u, v)\mathbf{k}$$

Then the surface area is defined by

$$S = \int\int_D \|\mathbf{R}_u(u, v) \times \mathbf{R}_v(u, v)\|\, du\, dv$$

We call the quantity $\mathbf{R}_u(u, v) \times \mathbf{R}_v(u, v)$ the **fundamental cross product**.

EXAMPLE 4   Surface area defined by a vector function

Find the surface area (to the nearest square unit) of the surface given parametrically by

$$\mathbf{R}(u, v) = (u \sin v)\mathbf{i} + (u \cos v)\mathbf{j} + u^2\mathbf{k} \qquad \text{for } 0 \le u \le 3, 0 \le v \le 2\pi$$

Solution   We find that $\mathbf{R}_u = \sin v\mathbf{i} + \cos v\mathbf{j} + 2u\mathbf{k}$

$$\mathbf{R}_v = u \cos v\mathbf{i} + (-u \sin v)\mathbf{j}$$

We begin with the fundamental cross product

$$\mathbf{R}_u \times \mathbf{R}_v = \begin{vmatrix} \mathbf{i} & \mathbf{j} & \mathbf{k} \\ \sin v & \cos v & 2u \\ u \cos v & -u \sin v & 0 \end{vmatrix} = (2u^2\sin v)\mathbf{i} + (2u^2\cos v)\mathbf{j} - u\mathbf{k}$$

We find that

$$\|\mathbf{R}_u \times \mathbf{R}_v\| = \sqrt{4u^4\sin^2 v + 4u^4\cos^2 v + u^2} = \sqrt{4u^4 + u^2} = u\sqrt{4u^2 + 1}$$

and we can now compute the surface area:

$$S = \int_0^{2\pi}\int_0^3 u\sqrt{4u^2 + 1}\, du\, dv = \int_0^{2\pi}\left[\frac{1}{12}(4u^2 + 1)^{3/2}\right]\Big|_{u=0}^{u=3} dv$$

$$= \int_0^{2\pi}\left[\frac{1}{12}(37^{3/2} - 1)\right] dv = \frac{37^{3/2} - 1}{12}[2\pi - 0] \approx 117.3187007$$

The surface area is approximately 117 square units.

Notice that in the special case where the surface under consideration has the explicit representation $z = f(x, y)$, it can also be represented in the vector form

$$\mathbf{R}_x = x\mathbf{i} + y\mathbf{j} + f(x, y)\mathbf{k}$$

where x and y are used as parameters ($x = u$ and $y = v$). With this vector representation, we find that

$$\mathbf{R}_x = \mathbf{i} + f_x\mathbf{k} \quad \text{and} \quad \mathbf{R}_y = \mathbf{j} + f_y\mathbf{k}$$

so the fundamental cross product is

$$\mathbf{R}_x \times \mathbf{R}_y = \begin{vmatrix} \mathbf{i} & \mathbf{j} & \mathbf{k} \\ 1 & 0 & f_x \\ 0 & 1 & f_y \end{vmatrix} = -f_x\mathbf{i} - f_y\mathbf{j} + \mathbf{k}$$

Therefore, in the case where $z = f(x, y)$, the surface area over the region D is given by

$$S = \iint_D \|\mathbf{R}_x \times \mathbf{R}_y\| \, dx \, dy$$
$$= \iint_D \sqrt{(-f_x)^2 + (-f_y)^2 + 1^2} \, dx \, dy$$
$$= \iint_D \sqrt{f_x^2 + f_y^2 + 1} \, dx \, dy$$

which is the formula obtained at the beginning of this section.

PROBLEM SET 13.4

A *Find the surface area of each surface given in Problems 1–19.*

1. The portion of the plane $2x + y + 4z = 8$ that lies in the first octant

2. The portion of the plane $4x + y + z = 9$ that lies in the first octant

3. The portion of the paraboloid

$$z = 4 - x^2 - y^2$$

that lies above the *xy*-plane

4. The portion of the paraboloid

$$z = x^2 + y^2 - 9$$

that lies below the *xy*-plane

5. The portion of the plane $3x + 6y + 2z = 12$ that is above the triangular region in the plane with vertices $(0, 0, 0)$, $(1, 0, 0)$, and $(1, 1, 0)$

6. The portion of the plane $2x + 2y - z = 0$ that is above the square region in the plane with vertices $(0, 0, 0)$, $(1, 0, 0)$, $(0, 1, 0)$, $(1, 1, 0)$

7. The portion of the surface $x^2 + z = 9$ above the square region in the plane with vertices $(0, 0, 0)$, $(2, 0, 0)$, $(0, 2, 0)$, $(2, 2, 0)$

8. The portion of the surface $z = x^2$ that lies over the triangular region in the plane with vertices $(0, 0, 0)$, $(0, 1, 0)$, and $(1, 0, 0)$

9. The portion of the surface $z = x^2$ over the square region with vertices $(0, 0, 0)$, $(0, 4, 0)$, $(4, 0, 0)$, $(4, 4, 0)$

10. The portion of the surface $z = 2x + y^2$ over the square region with vertices $(0, 0, 0)$, $(3, 0, 0)$, $(0, 3, 0)$, $(3, 3, 0)$

11. The portion on the paraboloid

$$z = x^2 + y^2$$

that lies below the plane $z = 1$

12. The portion of the sphere $x^2 + y^2 + z^2 = 25$ that lies above the plane $z = 3$

13. The part of the cylinder $x^2 + z^2 = 4$ that is in the first octant and is bounded by the plane $y = 2$

14. The portion of the plane $x + y + z = 4$ that lies inside the cylinder $x^2 + y^2 = 16$

15. The portion of the sphere $x^2 + y^2 + z^2 = 4$ that lies inside the cylinder $x^2 + y^2 = 2y$

16. The portion of the sphere $x^2 + y^2 + z^2 = 8$ that is inside the cone $x^2 + y^2 - z^2 = 0$.

17. The portion of the surface $z = x^2 + y$ above the square $0 \le x \le 2, 0 \le y \le 5$

18. The portion of the surface $z = x^2 - y^2$ that lies inside the cylinder $x^2 + y^2 = 9$

19. The portion of the surface $z = 9 - x^2 - y^2$ that lies above the *xy*-plane

Ⓑ 20. ■ **What Does This Say?** Describe the process for finding a surface area.

21. ■ **What Does This Say?** Describe what is meant by a surface area projection.

22. On a given map a city parking lot is shown by a rectangle that is 300 ft by 400 ft. However, the parking lot slopes in the 400-ft direction. It rises uniformly 1 ft for every 5 ft of horizontal displacement. What is the actual surface area of the parking lot?

23. Find the surface area of the portion of the plane $Ax + By + Cz = D$ (A, B, C, and D all positive) that lies in the first octant.

24. Find the portion of the plane $x + 2y + 3z = 12$ that lies over the triangular region in the *xy*-plane with vertices $(0, 0, 0)$, $(0, a, 0)$, and $(a, a, 0)$.

25. Find the surface area of that portion of the plane

$$x + y + z = a$$

that lies between the concentric cylinders

$$x^2 + y^2 = \frac{a^2}{4} \text{ and } x^2 + y^2 = a^2 \ (a > 0).$$

26. Find the surface area of the portion of the cylinder $x^2 + z^2 = 9$ that lies inside the cylinder $x^2 + y^2 = 9$.

Problem 26

27. Verify that a sphere of radius a has surface area $4\pi a^2$.

28. Verify that a cylinder of radius a and height h has surface area $2\pi ah$.

29. Find a formula for the area of the conical surface $z = \sqrt{x^2 + y^2}$ between the planes $z = 0$ and $z = h$. Express your answer in terms of h and the radius of the base of the cone.

30. Find a formula for the surface area of the frustum of the cone $z = 4\sqrt{x^2 + y^2}$ between the planes $z = h_1$ and $z = h_2, h_1 > h_2$.

31. Find the surface area of that portion of the sphere $x^2 + y^2 + z^2 = 9z$ that lies inside the paraboloid $x^2 + y^2 = 4z$.

32. Find the surface area of that portion of the cylinder $x^2 + z^2 = 4$ that is above the triangle with vertices $(0, 0, 0)$, $(1, 1, 0)$, and $(0, 1, 0)$.

In Problems 33–38, **set up** *(but do not evaluate) the double integral for the surface area of the given portion of surface.*

33. The surface given by $z = e^{-x}\sin y$ over the triangle with vertices $(0, 0, 0)$, $(1, 1, 0)$, $(0, 1, 0)$

34. The surface given by $z = x^3 - xy + y^3$ over the square $(0, 0, 0)$, $(2, 0, 0)$, $(0, 2, 0)$, $(2, 2, 0)$

35. The surface given by $z = \cos(x^2 + y^2)$ over the disk $x^2 + y^2 \le \frac{\pi}{2}$

36. The surface given by $z = e^{-x}\cos y$ over the disk $x^2 + y^2 \le 9$

37. The surface given by $z = x^2 + 5xy + y^2$ over the region in the *xy*-plane bounded by the lines $x = y, x = 3$, and $y = 0$

38. The surface given by $z = x^2 + 3xy + y^2$ over the region in the *xy*-plane bounded by $0 \le x \le 4, 0 \le y \le x$

Compute the magnitude of the fundamental cross product for the surfaces defined parametrically in Problems 39–42.

39. $R(u, v) = (2u \sin v)i + (2u \cos v)j + u^2 k$

40. $R(u, v) = (4 \sin u \cos v)i + (4 \sin u \sin v)j + (5 \cos u)k$

41. $R(u, v) = ui + vj + u^3 k$

42. $R(u, v) = (2u \sin v)i + (2u \cos v)j + (u^2 \sin 2v)k$

43. Find the surface area of the surface given parametrically by the equation

$$R(u, v) = uvi + (u - v)j + (u + v)k$$

for $u^2 + v^2 \le 1$. *Hint*: Use polar coordinates.

44. A *spiral ramp* has the vector parametric equation

$$R(u, v) = (u \cos v)i + (u \sin v)j + vk$$

for $0 \le u \le 1, 0 \le v \le \pi$. Sketch the ramp and find its surface area.

Ⓒ 45. Find the surface area of the torus defined by

$$R(u, v) = (a + b \cos v)\cos u\, i$$
$$+ (a + b \cos v)\sin u\, j + b \sin v\, k$$

for $0 < b < a, 0 \le u \le 2\pi, 0 \le v \le 2\pi$.

46. Suppose a surface is given implicitly by $F(x, y, z) = 0$. If the surface can be projected onto a region D in the xy-plane, show that the surface area is given by

$$A = \int_D \int \frac{\sqrt{F_x^2 + F_y^2 + F_z^2}}{|F_z|}\, dA_{xy}$$

where $F_z \ne 0$. Use this formula to find the surface area of a sphere of radius R.

47. Let S be the surface defined by $f(x, y, z) = C$, and let R be the projection of S on a plane. Show that the surface area of S can be computed by the integral

$$\int_R \int \frac{\|\nabla f\|}{|\nabla f \cdot \mathbf{u}|}\, dA$$

where $\mathbf{u}$ is a unit vector normal to the plane containing R and $\nabla f \cdot \mathbf{u} \ne 0$. This is a practical formula which is sometimes used in calculating the surface area.

13.5 TRIPLE INTEGRALS

> **IN THIS SECTION** Definition of triple integral, iterated integration, volume by triple integrals
>
> Triple integrals are defined and developed in essentially the same way as double integrals. We evaluate triple integrals by iterated integration and interpret them geometrically in terms of volume. Changing the order of integration in a triple integral can be complicated, and we consider several examples of this procedure.

■ DEFINITION OF TRIPLE INTEGRAL

A double integral $\int_R \int f(x, y)\, dA$ is evaluated over a closed, bounded region in the plane, and in essentially the same way, a **triple integral** $\int \int_S \int f(x, y, z)\, dV$ is evaluated over a closed, bounded solid region in $\mathbb{R}^3$. Suppose $f(x, y, z)$ is defined on a closed region S, which in turn is contained in a "box" D in space. Partition D into a finite number of smaller boxes with planes parallel to the coordinate planes, as shown in Figure 13.27.

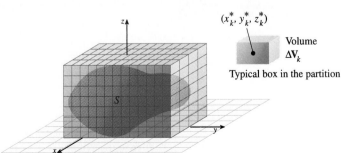

Figure 13.27 The region of integration S is subdivided into smaller boxes.

We exclude from consideration any boxes with points outside S. Let $\Delta V_1, \Delta V_2, \ldots,$ ΔV_n denote the volumes of the boxes that remain, and define the norm $\|P\|$ of the partition to be the length of the longest diagonal of any box in the partition. Next, choose a representative point (x_k^*, y_k^*, z_k^*) from each box in the partition and form the **Riemann sum**

$$\sum_{k=1}^{n} f(x_k^*, y_k^*, z_k^*) \Delta V_k$$

If we repeat the process with more subdivisions, so that the norm approaches zero, we are led to the following definition.

Triple Integral

If f is a function defined over a closed, bounded solid region S, then the **triple integral of f over S** is defined to be the limit

$$\iiint_S f(x, y, z)\, dV = \lim_{\|P\| \to 0} \sum_{k=1}^{n} f(x_k^*, y_k^*, z_k^*)\, \Delta V_k$$

provided this limit exists.

In advanced calculus, it is shown that the triple integral $\iiint_S f(x, y, z)\, dV$

exists if $f(x, y, z)$ is continuous on S and S is **piecewise smooth** in the sense that it consists of a finite number of pieces, each of which has a continuously turning tangent plane (that is, the tangent plane varies continuously from point to point). It can also be shown that triple integrals have the following properties (which are analogous to those of double integrals listed in Theorem 13.3). In each case, assume the indicated integrals exist.

Linearity rule. For constants a and b

$$\iiint_S [af(x, y, z) + bg(x, y, z)]\, dV$$
$$= a \iiint_S f(x, y, z)\, dV + b \iiint_S g(x, y, z)\, dV$$

Dominance rule. If $f(x, y, z) \geq g(x, y, z)$ on S, then

$$\iiint_S f(x, y, z)\, dV \geq \iiint_S g(x, y, z)\, dV$$

Solid S

Subdivision rule. If the solid region of integration S can be subdivided into two solid subregions S_1 and S_2, then

$$\iiint_S f(x, y, z)\, dV = \iiint_{S_1} f(x, y, z)\, dV + \iiint_{S_2} f(x, y, z)\, dV$$

■ ITERATED INTEGRATION

As with double integrals, we evaluate triple integrals by iterated integration. However, it is generally more difficult to set up the limits of integration in a triple integral, because the region of integration S is a solid. The relatively simple case where S is a rectangular solid (box) may be handled by applying the following theorem.

THEOREM 13.5   Fubini's theorem over a parallelepiped in space

If $f(x, y, z)$ is continuous over a rectangular solid R: $a \leq x \leq b$, $c \leq y \leq d$, $r \leq z \leq s$, then the triple integral may be evaluated by the iterated integral

$$\iiint\limits_{R} f(x, y, z) \, dV = \int_r^s \int_c^d \int_a^b f(x, y, z) \, dx \, dy \, dz$$

The iterated integration can be performed in any order (with appropriate adjustments to the limits of integration):

$$
\begin{array}{ccc}
dx \, dy \, dz & dx \, dz \, dy & dz \, dx \, dy \\
dy \, dx \, dz & dy \, dz \, dx & dz \, dy \, dx
\end{array}
$$

Proof: This proof is beyond the scope of this course and is given in many advanced calculus courses. ∎

EXAMPLE 1   Evaluating a triple integral using Fubini's theorem

Evaluate $\displaystyle\iiint\limits_{R} z^2 y e^x \, dV$, where R is the box given by

$$0 \leq x \leq 1, \qquad 1 \leq y \leq 2, \qquad -1 \leq z \leq 1$$

Solution   We shall evaluate the integral in the order $dx \, dy \, dz$.

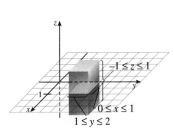

$$\iiint\limits_{R} f(x, y, z) \, dV = \int_{-1}^1 \int_1^2 \int_0^1 z^2 y e^x \, dx \, dy \, dz$$

$$\textit{This means } \int_{-1}^1 \left[\int_1^2 \left[\int_0^1 z^2 y e^x \, dx \right] dy \right] dz.$$

$$= \int_{-1}^1 \int_1^2 z^2 y [e^x] \Big|_{x=0}^{x=1} \, dy \, dz = \int_{-1}^1 \int_1^2 z^2 y [e - 1] \, dy \, dz$$

$$= (e - 1) \int_{-1}^1 z^2 \left[\frac{y^2}{2} \right] \Big|_{y=1}^{y=2} \, dz = \int_{-1}^1 z^2 (e - 1) \left[\frac{2^2}{2} - \frac{1^2}{2} \right] dz$$

$$= \frac{3}{2}(e - 1) \int_{-1}^1 z^2 \, dz = \frac{3}{2}(e - 1) \frac{z^3}{3} \Big|_{z=-1}^{z=1}$$

$$= \frac{3}{2}(e - 1) \left[\frac{1^3}{3} - \frac{(-1)^3}{3} \right] = e - 1$$

It might be instructive for you to verify that the same result is obtained by using any other order of integration—for example,

$$dz \, dy \, dx$$

To evaluate a triple integral over a region that is not a box, suppose we have a solid region S with an "upper" surface $z = u(x, y)$ and a "lower" surface $z = v(x, y)$ defined over a common domain A in the xy-plane. In this case, S may be described as the set of all points (x, y, z) such that for each fixed point (x, y) in A, z varies from v to u, as shown in Figure 13.28.

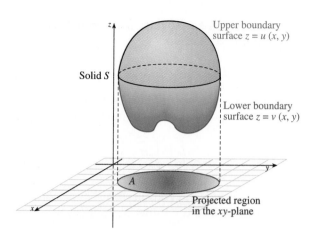

Figure 13.28 A solid region S bounded by the surfaces $z = u(x, y)$ and $z = v(x, y)$

The domain A is then described in a double integral. These observations are summarized in the following theorem.

THEOREM 13.6   Triple integral over a general region

If S is a region in space that is bounded above by the surface $z = u(x, y)$ and below by $z = v(x, y)$ as (x, y) varies over the planar region A, then

$$\iiint_S f(x, y, z)\, dV = \iint_A \int_{v(x,y)}^{u(x,y)} f(x, y, z)\, dz\, dA$$

Proof: This proof is omitted.   ■

If the region of integration S has the form described in Theorem 13.6, the integral may be evaluated by integrating first with respect to z (as z varies from $z = v(x, y)$ to $z = u(x, y)$) and then computing a double integral over the planar region A.

EXAMPLE 2   Evaluating a triple integral over a general region

Evaluate $\displaystyle\iiint_S x\, dV$, where S is the solid in the first octant bounded by the cylinder $x^2 + y^2 = 4$ and the plane $2y + z = 4$.

Solution   The solid is shown in Figure 13.29.

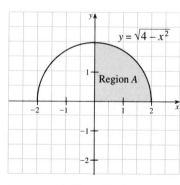

Figure 13.29 The region S bounded by the plane $2y + z = 4$ and the cylinder $x^2 + y^2 = 4$ in the first octant

a. The solid S

b. The region A

The upper boundary surface of S is the plane $z = 4 - 2y$, and the lower boundary surface $z = 0$ is the xy-plane. The projection A of the solid on the xy-plane is the quarter disk $x^2 + y^2 \leq 4$ with $x \geq 0$, $y \geq 0$ (because S lies in the first octant). This projection may be described in type I form as the set of all (x, y) such that for each fixed x between 0 and 2, y varies from 0 to $\sqrt{4 - x^2}$. Thus, we have

$$\iiint_S x\, dV = \iint_A \int_0^{4-2y} x\, dz\, dA = \int_0^2 \int_0^{\sqrt{4-x^2}} \int_0^{4-2y} x\, dz\, dy\, dx$$

$$= \int_0^2 \int_0^{\sqrt{4-x^2}} x[(4 - 2y) - 0]\, dy\, dx = \int_0^2 \int_0^{\sqrt{4-x^2}} (4x - 2xy)\, dy\, dx$$

$$= \int_0^2 [4xy - xy^2]\Big|_{y=0}^{y=\sqrt{4-x^2}}\, dx = \int_0^2 \left[4x\sqrt{4 - x^2} - x(4 - x^2)\right] dx$$

$$= \left[-\tfrac{4}{3}(4 - x^2)^{3/2} - 2x^2 + \tfrac{1}{4}x^4\right]\Big|_0^2 = [0 - 8 + 4 + \tfrac{32}{3} + 0 - 0] = \tfrac{20}{3}$$ ■

■ VOLUME BY TRIPLE INTEGRALS

Just as a double integral can be interpreted as the area of the region of integration, a triple integral may be interpreted as the **volume** of the solid of integration. That is, if V is the volume of the solid region S, then

$$V = \iiint_S dV$$

EXAMPLE 3   Volume of a tetrahedron

Find the volume of the tetrahedron T bounded by the part of the plane $2x + y + 3z = 6$ in the first octant.

Solution   The tetrahedron T is shown in Figure 13.30a.

a. The tetrahedron bounded by the plane $2x + y + 3z = 6$ and the positive coordinate planes.

b. The region projected onto the xy-plane is a triangle.

Figure 13.30 Volume of a tetrahedron

The upper surface of T is the plane $z = \frac{1}{3}(6 - 2x - y)$ and its lower surface is $z = 0$. Note that T projects onto a triangle in the xy-plane, as shown in Figure 13.30b. Described in type I form, this triangle is the set of all (x, y) such that for each fixed x between 0 and 3, y varies from 0 to $6 - 2x$. Thus,

$$V = \iiint_T dV = \iint_A \int_0^{\frac{1}{3}(6-2x-y)} dz \, dA = \int_0^3 \int_0^{6-2x} \int_0^{\frac{1}{3}(6-2x-y)} dz \, dy \, dx$$

$$= \int_0^3 \int_0^{6-2x} \left[\frac{1}{3}(6 - 2x - y) - 0\right] dy \, dx = \int_0^3 \left[2y - \frac{2}{3}xy - \frac{1}{6}y^2\right]\Big|_{y=0}^{y=6-2x} dx$$

$$= \int_0^3 \left[2(6 - 2x) - \frac{2}{3}x(6 - 2x) - \frac{1}{6}(6 - 2x)^2 - 0\right] dx$$

$$= \int_0^3 \frac{1}{6}(6 - 2x)[12 - 4x - (6 - 2x)] \, dx \qquad \text{Common factor}$$

$$= \frac{1}{6}\int_0^3 (6 - 2x)(6 - 2x) \, dx = \frac{1}{6}\int_0^3 (6 - 2x)^2 \, dx = 6$$

The volume of the tetrahedron is 6 cubic units. ▬

Sometimes it is easier to evaluate a triple integral by integrating first with respect to x or y instead of z. For instance, if the solid region of integration S is bounded in the back by $x = x_1(y, z)$ and in the front by $x = x_2(y, z)$, and the boundary surfaces project onto a region A in the yz-plane, as shown in Figure 13.31a, then

$$\iiint_S f(x, y, z) \, dV = \iint_A \int_{x_1}^{x_2} f(x, y, z) \, dx \, dA$$

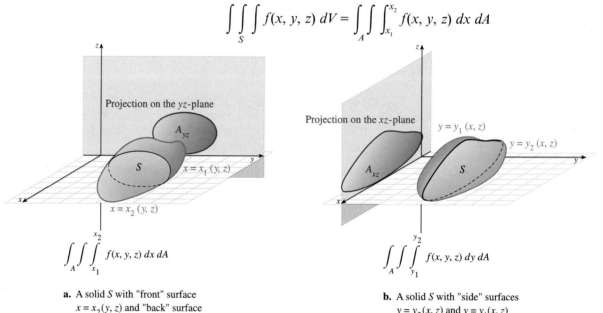

$$\iint_A \int_{x_1}^{x_2} f(x, y, z) \, dx \, dA \qquad\qquad \iint_A \int_{y_1}^{y_2} f(x, y, z) \, dy \, dA$$

a. A solid S with "front" surface $x = x_2(y, z)$ and "back" surface $x = x_1(y, z)$

b. A solid S with "side" surfaces $y = y_2(x, z)$ and $y = y_1(x, z)$

Figure 13.31 Iterated integration with respect to x or y first

On the other hand, if the solid region of integration S is bounded on one side by the surface $y = y_1(x, z)$ and on the other by $y = y_2(x, z)$, and the boundary surfaces project onto a region A in the yz-plane, as shown in Figure 13.31b, then

$$\iiint_S f(x, y, z) \, dV = \iint_A \int_{y_1}^{y_2} f(x, y, z) \, dy \, dA$$

As an illustration, we will now rework Example 3 by projecting the tetrahedron S onto the yz-plane.

EXAMPLE 4   Volume of a tetrahedron by changing the order of integration

Find the volume of the tetrahedron S bounded by the part of the plane $2x + y + 3z = 6$ in the first octant by projecting S onto the yz-plane.

Solution   In Example 3 we projected S onto the xy-plane to find

$$V = \int \int\int_S dV = \int\int_A \int_0^{\frac{1}{3}(6-2x-y)} dz \, dA$$

where A was the projection in the xy-plane and we found the volume to be 6. Now, project onto the yz-plane as shown in Figure 13.32.

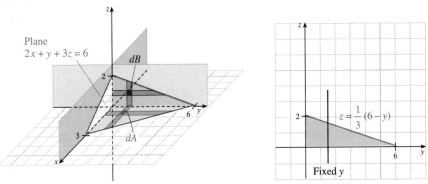

a. The tetrahedron bounded by the plane $2x + y + 3z = 6$ and the positive coordinate planes.

b. The region projected onto the yz-plane is a triangle.

Figure 13.32 Volume of a tetrahedron; alternative projection

First, we note that S is bounded from "behind" by the yz-plane and "in front" by the plane $2x + y + 3z = 6$, which we express this time by solving for x: $x = \frac{1}{2}(6 - y - 3z)$. Thus,

$$V = \int \int\int_S dV = \int\int_{A_{yz}} \int_0^{\frac{1}{2}(6-y-3z)} dx \, dA_{yz}$$

where A_{yz} is the projection onto the yz-plane, as shown in Figure 13.32b. We see that this projection is the triangle B bounded by the lines $z = 0$, $y = 0$, and $z = \frac{1}{3}(6 - y)$. Thus, for each fixed y between 0 and 6, z varies from 0 to $\frac{1}{3}(6 - y)$, and we have

$$V = \int_0^6 \int_0^{\frac{1}{3}(6-y)} \int_0^{\frac{1}{2}(6-y-3z)} dx \, dz \, dy = \int_0^6 \int_0^{\frac{1}{3}(6-y)} \frac{1}{2}(6 - y - 3z) \, dz \, dy$$

$$= \int_0^6 \left[3z - \frac{1}{2}yz - \frac{3}{4}z^2 \right] \Big|_{z=0}^{z=\frac{1}{3}(6-y)} dy$$

$$= \int_0^6 \left[(6 - y) - \frac{1}{6}y(6 - y) - \frac{1}{12}(6 - y)^2 - 0 \right] dy$$

$$= \frac{1}{12} \int_0^6 (6 - y)^2 \, dy = \frac{-1}{36}(6 - y)^3 \Big|_0^6 = 0 + \frac{1}{36}(6)^3 = 6$$

As you would expect, this is the same as the result from projecting on the xy-plane. ▬

EXAMPLE 5   Setting up a triple integral to find a volume

Set up (but do not evaluate) a triple integral for the volume of the solid S that is bounded above by the sphere $x^2 + y^2 + z^2 = 4$ and below by the plane $y + z = 2$.

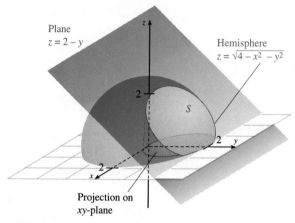

Plane
$z = 2 - y$

Hemisphere
$z = \sqrt{4 - x^2 - y^2}$

S

Projection on
xy-plane

Solution   First, note that the intersection of the plane and the sphere occurs above the xy-plane (where $z \geq 0$), so the sphere can be represented by the equation

$$z = \sqrt{4 - x^2 - y^2}$$

(the upper hemisphere). To find the limits of integration for x and y we consider the projection of S onto the xy-plane. To this end, consider the intersection of the hemisphere and the plane $z = 2 - y$:

$$\sqrt{4 - x^2 - y^2} = 2 - y$$
$$4 - x^2 - y^2 = 4 - 4y + y^2$$
$$x^2 + 2y^2 - 4y = 0$$
$$x^2 + 2(y - 1)^2 = 2$$

Although this intersection occurs in $\mathbb{R}^3$, its equation does not contain z; therefore, the equation serves as a projection on the xy-plane, where $z = 0$. This is an ellipse centered at $(0, 1)$. We sketch this curve in the xy-plane, as shown in Figure 13.33.

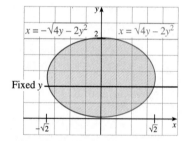

$x = -\sqrt{4y - 2y^2}$ $x = \sqrt{4y - 2y^2}$

Fixed y

Figure 13.33 The projection of S onto the xy-plane

We consider this as a type II region, which means we will integrate first with respect to x, then with respect to y. Because $x^2 + 2(y - 1)^2 = 2$, we see for fixed y between 0 and 2, x varies from $-\sqrt{2 - 2(y - 1)^2} = -\sqrt{4y - 2y^2}$ to $\sqrt{4y - 2y^2}$. However, we can use symmetry to find twice the integral as x varies from 0 to $\sqrt{4y - 2y^2}$. This leads us to set up the following triple integral.

$$V = 2 \int_0^2 \int_0^{\sqrt{4y - 2y^2}} \int_{2-y}^{\sqrt{4 - x^2 - y^2}} dz\, dx\, dy$$
▬

PROBLEM SET 13.5

A 1. ■ **What Does This Say?** Describe Fubini's theorem over a parallelpiped in space.

2. ■ **What Does This Say?** Set up integrals, with appropriate limits of integration, for the six possible orders of integration for $\iiint_S f(x, y, z) \, dV$ where S is the solid described by
$S: \ y^2 \le x \le 4; \quad 0 \le y \le 2; \quad 0 \le z \le 2 - x$

Compute the iterated triple integrals in Problems 3–14.

3. $\int_1^4 \int_{-2}^3 \int_2^5 dx \, dy \, dz$

4. $\int_{-1}^3 \int_0^2 \int_{-2}^2 dy \, dz \, dx$

5. $\int_1^2 \int_0^1 \int_{-1}^2 8x^2yz^3 \, dx \, dy \, dz$

6. $\int_4^7 \int_{-1}^2 \int_0^3 x^2y^2z^2 \, dx \, dy \, dz$

7. $\int_0^2 \int_0^x \int_0^{x+y} xyz \, dz \, dy \, dx$

8. $\int_0^1 \int_{\sqrt{x}}^{\sqrt{1+x}} \int_0^{xy} y^{-1}z \, dz \, dy \, dx$

9. $\int_{-1}^2 \int_0^\pi \int_1^4 yz \cos xy \, dz \, dx \, dy$

10. $\int_0^\pi \int_0^1 \int_0^1 x^2y \cos xyz \, dz \, dy \, dx$

11. $\int_0^1 \int_0^y \int_0^{\ln y} e^{z+2x} \, dz \, dx \, dy$

12. $\int_1^3 \int_0^{2z} \int_0^{\ln y} y \, e^{-x} \, dx \, dy \, dz$

13. $\int_1^4 \int_{-1}^{2z} \int_0^{\sqrt{3}x} \frac{x-y}{x^2+y^2} \, dy \, dx \, dz$

14. $\int_0^1 \int_{x-1}^{x^2} \int_{-x}^y (x+y) \, dz \, dy \, dx$

Evaluate the triple integrals in Problems 15–22.

15. $\iiint_S (x^2y + y^2z) \, dV$, where S is the box $1 \le x \le 3$, $-1 \le y \le 1, 2 \le z \le 4$

16. $\iiint_S (xy + 2yz) \, dV$, where S is the box $2 \le x \le 4$, $1 \le y \le 3, -2 \le z \le 4$

17. $\iiint_S xyz \, dV$, where S is the tetrahedron with vertices $(0, 0, 0), (1, 0, 0), (0, 1, 0)$, and $(0, 0, 1)$

18. $\iiint_S x^2y \, dV$, where S is the tetrahedron with vertices $(0, 0, 0), (3, 0, 0), (0, 2, 0)$, and $(0, 0, 1)$

19. $\iiint_S xyz \, dV$, where S is the region given by $x^2 + y^2 + z^2 \le 1, y \ge 0, z \ge 0$

20. $\iiint_S x \, dV$, where S is bounded by the paraboloid $z = x^2 + y^2$ and the plane $z = 1$

21. $\iiint_S e^z \, dV$,

where S is the region described by the inequalities $0 \le x \le 1, 0 \le y \le x$, and $0 \le z \le x + y$

22. $\iiint_S yz \, dV$,

where S is the solid in the first octant bounded by the hemisphere $x = \sqrt{9 - y^2 - z^2}$ and the coordinate planes

Find the volume V of the solids bounded by the graphs of the equations given in Problems 23–28 by using triple integration.

23. $x + y + z = 1$ and the coordinate planes

24. $y = 9 - x^2, z = 0,$ $z = y$

25. $(x - 1)^2 + (y - 2)^2 + (z - 3)^2 = 1$

26. $z = 4 - 4x^2 - 4y^2, z = 0$

27. $x^2 + 3y^2 = z$ and the cylinder $y^2 + z = 4$

28. $x^2 + y^2 + z^3 = 9, z = 0$

For each given iterated integral there are five other equivalent iterated integrals. Find the one with the requested order in Problems 29–32.

29. $\int_0^1 \int_0^x \int_0^y f(x, y, z) \, dz \, dy \, dx$; change the order to $dz \, dx \, dy$.

30. $\int_1^2 \int_0^{z-1} \int_0^x f(x, y, z) \, dy \, dx \, dz$;

change the order to $dy \, dz \, dx$.

31. $\int_0^2 \int_0^{\sqrt{4-x^2}} \int_0^{\sqrt{4-x^2-y^2}} f(x, y, z) \, dz \, dy \, dx$;

change the order to $dx \, dy \, dz$.

32. $\int_0^2 \int_0^{\sqrt{4-x^2}} \int_{\frac{3}{2}\sqrt{x^2+y^2}}^{} f(x, y, z) \, dz \, dy \, dx$;

change the order to $dx \, dy \, dz$.

B 33. Find the volume of the ellipsoid

$$\frac{x^2}{4} + \frac{y^2}{9} + \frac{z^2}{16} = 1$$

34. Find the volume of the region between the two elliptic paraboloids

$$z = \frac{x^2}{9} + y^2 - 4 \quad \text{and} \quad z = -\frac{x^2}{9} - y^2 + 4$$

35. Find the volume of the region bounded by the paraboloids $z = 16 - x^2 - 2y^2$ and $z = 3x^2 + 2y^2$.

36. Find the volume of the region that is bounded above by the elliptic paraboloid

$$z = \frac{x^2}{9} + y^2$$

on the sides by the cylinder

$$\frac{x^2}{9} + y^2 = 1$$

and below by the xy-plane.

37. Find the volume of the solid region in the first octant that is bounded by the planes $z = 8 + 2x + y$, $y = 3 - 2x$, and $y = x$.

38. Use triple integration to find the volume of the Great Pyramid of Cheops in Egypt, which is approximately 480 ft tall and has a square base of side 755 ft.

C 39. Use triple integration to find the volume of a sphere.

40. Use triple integration to find the volume of a right pyramid with height H and a square base of side s.

41. Use triple integration to find the volume of the ellipsoid

$$\frac{x^2}{a^2} + \frac{y^2}{b^2} + \frac{z^2}{c^2} = 1$$

$(a > 0, b > 0, c > 0)$. Set up, but do not evaluate.

42. Find the volume of the solid region between the paraboloid $z = k(x^2 + y^2)$ and the sphere $x^2 + y^2 + z^2 = 2k^{-1}$, where $k > 0$

43. Let V be the volume of the tetrahedron bounded by the plane

$$\frac{x}{a} + \frac{y}{b} + \frac{z}{c} = 1$$

$(a > 0, b > 0, c > 0)$ in the first octant. Express V as six different iterated triple integrals and evaluate one of these integrals to show that $V = \frac{1}{6} abc$.

44. THINK TANK PROBLEM Let B be the box defined by $a \le x \le b, c \le y \le d, r \le z \le s$. Is it true that

$$\iiint_B f(x)g(y)h(z) \, dV$$

$$= \left[\int_a^b f(x) \, dx \right] \left[\int_c^d g(y) \, dy \right] \left[\int_r^s h(z) \, dz \right]$$

Either show that this equation is generally true, or find a counterexample.

45. Change the order of integration to show that

$$\int_0^x \int_0^v f(u) \, du \, dv = \int_0^x (x - t) f(t) \, dt$$

Also show that

$$\int_0^x \int_0^v \int_0^u f(w) \, dw \, du \, dv = \frac{1}{2} \int_0^x (x - t)^2 f(t) \, dt$$

46. Evaluate the triple integral

$$\iiint_S \sin(\pi - z)^3 \, dz \, dx \, dy$$

where S is the solid region bounded below by the xy-plane, above by the plane $x = z$, and laterally by the planes $x = y$ and $y = \pi$. *Hint:* See Problem 45.

Higher-dimensional multiple integrals can be defined and evaluated in essentially the same way as double and triple integrals. Evaluate the multiple integrals in Problems 47–48.

47. $\iiiint_H xyz^2w^2 \, dx \, dy \, dz \, dw$,

where H is the four-dimensional "hyperbox" defined by $0 \le x \le 1, 0 \le y \le 2, -1 \le z \le 1, 1 \le w \le 2$

48. $\iiiint_H e^{x-2y+z+w} \, dw \, dz \, dy \, dx$,

where H is the four-dimensional region bounded by the hyperplane $x + y + z + w = 4$ and the coordinate spaces $x = 0$, $y = 0$, $z = 0$, and $w = 0$ in the first hyperoctant (where $x \ge 0, y \ge 0, z \ge 0, w \ge 0$)

13.6 MASS, MOMENTS, AND PROBABILITY DENSITY FUNCTIONS

> **IN THIS SECTION** Mass and center of mass, moments of inertia, joint probability density functions
> We investigate applications of double and triple integrals to problems involving center of mass for both homogeneous and nonhomogeneous laminas. We also examine moments of inertia and joint probability density functions.

■ MASS AND CENTER OF MASS

Recall (from Section 6.3) that a solid object that is sufficiently "flat" to be regarded as essentially two-dimensional is called a **lamina.** It is worthwhile to recall some of the formulas from Section 6.3. Consider a region between the graphs of $y = f(x)$ and $y = g(x)$ over the interval $[a, b]$ with density ρ. Then,

The mass of the lamina is $m = \displaystyle\int_a^b \rho[f(x) - g(x)]\, dx$.

The moments are defined as follows:

About the x-axis: $M_x = \displaystyle\int_a^b \frac{\rho}{2}[f(x) + g(x)][f(x) - g(x)]\, dx$

About the y-axis: $M_y = \displaystyle\int_a^b \rho x[f(x) - g(x)]\, dx$

⊘ The moment of an object about an axis is the product of its mass and the signed distance from that axis. ⊘

The center of mass $(\bar{x}, \bar{y})$ is given by $\bar{x} = \dfrac{M_y}{m}$ and $\bar{y} = \dfrac{M_x}{m}$.

Suppose a particular lamina occupies a bounded region R in the xy-plane, and let $\rho(x, y)$ be the density (mass per unit area) of the lamina. A **homogeneous** lamina has constant density $\rho = m/A$, where m is the mass and A is the area of the lamina. If the lamina is **nonhomogeneous**, its density $\rho(x, y)$ varies from point to point. In

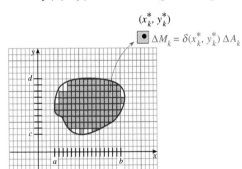

Figure 13.34 Partition of a lamina in the plane

this case, we can partition the region R into a number of rectangles, as shown in Figure 13.34. Choose a representative point (x_k^*, y_k^*) in each rectangle of the partition, and use the formula

$$\Delta m_k = \rho(x_k^*, y_k^*)\, \Delta A_k$$

to approximate the mass of each rectangle. We then approximate the total mass m by the Riemann sum

$$\sum_{k=1}^n \rho(x_k^*, y_k^*)\, \Delta A_k$$

so that

$$m = \lim_{\|P\| \to 0} \sum_{k=1}^{n} \rho(x_k^*, y_k^*) \Delta A_k = \int\int_R \rho(x, y)\, dA$$

We use these observations as the basis for the following definition.

Mass of a Planar Lamina of Variable Density

If ρ is a continuous density function on the lamina corresponding to a plane region R, then the mass m of the lamina is given by

$$m = \int\int_R \rho(x, y)\, dA$$

EXAMPLE 1   Mass of a planar lamina

Find the mass of the lamina of density $\rho(x, y) = x^2$ that occupies the region R bounded by the parabola $y = 2 - x^2$ and the line $y = x$.

Solution   Begin by drawing the parabola and the line, and by finding their points of intersection, as shown in Figure 13.35. By substitution,

$$x = 2 - x^2 \qquad (x + 2)(x - 1) = 0$$
$$x^2 + x - 2 = 0 \qquad\qquad x = -2, 1$$

We see that the region R is the set of all (x, y) such that for each x between -2 and 1, y varies from x to $2 - x^2$.

$$m = \int\int_R x^2\, dA = \int_{-2}^{1} \int_x^{2-x^2} x^2\, dy\, dx = \int_{-2}^{1} x^2(2 - x^2 - x)\, dx$$

$$= \int_{-2}^{1} (2x^2 - x^4 - x^3)\, dx = \left[\frac{2x^3}{3} - \frac{x^5}{5} - \frac{x^4}{4}\right]\Big|_{-2}^{1} = \frac{63}{20} = 3.15$$

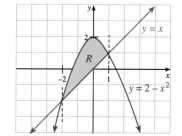

Figure 13.35 A lamina over the region R bounded by $y = 2 - x^2$ and $y = x$

The moment of an object about an axis is the product of its mass and the signed distance from the axis. Thus, by partitioning the region R as before (with mass), we see that the moments M_x and M_y of the lamina about the x-axis and y-axis, respectively, are approximately equal to the Riemann sums

By taking the limit as the norm of the partition tends to 0, we can formulate the following definition.

Moments and Center of Mass of a Variable Density Planar Lamina

If ρ is a continuous density function on a lamina corresponding to a plane region R, then the **moments of mass** with respect to the x- and y-axes, respectively, are

$$M_x = \int\int_R y\, \rho(x, y)\, dA \quad \text{and} \quad M_y = \int\int_R x\, \rho(x, y)\, dA$$

Furthermore, if m is the mass of the lamina, the **center of mass** is $(\bar{x}, \bar{y})$, where

$$\bar{x} = \frac{M_y}{m} \quad \text{and} \quad \bar{y} = \frac{M_x}{m}$$

If the density ρ is constant, the point $(\bar{x}, \bar{y})$ is called the **centroid** of the region.

⊘ M_x has a factor of y and M_y has a factor of x. ⊘

EXAMPLE 2   Finding a center of mass

Find the center of mass of the lamina of density $\rho(x, y) = x^2$ that occupies the region R bounded by the parabola $y = 2 - x^2$ and the line $y = x$. This is the lamina defined in Example 1.

Solution   In Example 1, we found that for each fixed x between -2 and 1, y varies from x to $2 - x^2$ (see Figure 13.35). Thus, we have

$$M_x = \int\int_R y(x^2)\, dA \qquad\qquad M_y = \int\int_R x(x^2)\, dA$$

$$= \int_{-2}^{1}\int_x^{2-x^2} yx^2\, dy\, dx \qquad\qquad = \int_{-2}^{1}\int_x^{2-x^2} x^3\, dy\, dx$$

$$= \int_{-2}^{1} \left[\tfrac{1}{2}x^2 y^2\right]\Big|_{y=x}^{y=2-x^2} dx \qquad\qquad = \int_{-2}^{1} x^3[(2 - x^2) - x]\, dx$$

$$= \tfrac{1}{2}\int_{-2}^{1} x^2(x^4 - 5x^2 + 4)\, dx \qquad\qquad = \int_{-2}^{1} (2x^3 - x^5 - x^4)\, dx$$

$$= \tfrac{1}{2}\left[\tfrac{1}{7}x^7 - x^5 + \tfrac{4}{3}x^3\right]\Big|_{-2}^{1} \qquad\qquad = \left[\frac{2x^4}{4} - \frac{x^6}{6} - \frac{x^5}{5}\right]\Big|_{-2}^{1}$$

$$= -\tfrac{9}{7} \qquad\qquad\qquad\qquad\qquad\quad = -\tfrac{18}{5}$$

From Example 1, $m = \tfrac{63}{20}$, so the center of mass is $(\bar{x}, \bar{y})$, where

$$\bar{x} = \frac{M_y}{m} = \frac{-\tfrac{18}{5}}{\tfrac{63}{20}} = -\frac{8}{7} \approx -1.14 \qquad \bar{y} = \frac{M_x}{m} = \frac{-\tfrac{9}{7}}{\tfrac{63}{20}} = -\frac{20}{49} \approx -0.41$$

In a completely analogous way, we can use the triple integral to find the mass and center of mass of a solid in $\mathbb{R}^3$. The density $\rho(x, y, z)$ at a point in the solid now refers to mass per unit volume, and the mass m, moments M_{yz}, M_{xz}, M_{xy} about the yz-, xz-, and xy-planes, respectively, and coordinates $\bar{x}$, $\bar{y}$, $\bar{z}$ of the center of mass are given by:

Note the distances to the coordinate axes.

Mass $$m = \int\int\int_R \rho(x, y, z)\, dV$$

Moments $$M_{yz} = \int\int\int_R \underset{\substack{\uparrow \\ \text{Distance to the } yz\text{-plane}}}{x}\, \rho(x, y, z)\, dV$$

$$M_{xz} = \int\int\int_R \underset{\substack{\uparrow \\ \text{Distance to the } xz\text{-plane}}}{y}\, \rho(x, y, z)\, dV$$

$$M_{xy} = \int\int\int_R \underset{\substack{\uparrow \\ \text{Distance to the } xy\text{-plane}}}{z}\, \rho(x, y, z)\, dV$$

Center of mass $$(\bar{x}, \bar{y}, \bar{z}) = \left(\frac{M_{yz}}{m}, \frac{M_{xz}}{m}, \frac{M_{xy}}{m}\right)$$

If the density is constant, the center of mass is still called the **centroid**. Example 3 illustrates how this point can be found by multiple integration.

EXAMPLE 3   Centroid of a tetrahedron

A solid tetrahedron has vertices $(0, 0, 0)$, $(1, 0, 0)$, $(0, 1, 0)$, and $(0, 0, 1)$ and constant density $\rho = 6$. Find the centroid. (The density must be constant to talk about the centroid.)

Solution   The tetrahedron may be described as the region in the first octant that lies beneath the plane $x + y + z = 1$, as shown in Figure 13.36a.

a. A tetrahedron   **b**. Projection on the xy-plane

Figure 13.36 The centroid of a tetrahedron

The boundary of the projection of the upper face of the tetrahedron in the xy-plane is found by solving the equations $x + y + z = 1$ and $z = 0$ simultaneously. We find that the projection is the region bounded by the coordinate axes and the line $x + y = 1$, as shown in Figure 13.36b. This means that for each fixed x between 0 and 1, y varies from 0 to $1 - x$.

$$m = \iiint\limits_{R} \rho \, dV = \int_0^1 \int_0^{1-x} \int_0^{1-x-y} 6 \, dz \, dy \, dx$$

$$= \int_0^1 \int_0^{1-x} 6(1 - x - y) \, dy \, dx = \int_0^1 [6y - 6xy - 3y^2]\Big|_{y=0}^{y=1-x} \, dx$$

$$= \int_0^1 3(x - 1)^2 \, dx = [x^3 - 3x^2 + 3x]\Big|_0^1 = 1$$

Similarly, we find that

$$M_{yz} = \iiint\limits_{R} 6x \, dV = \int_0^1 \int_0^{1-x} \int_0^{1-x-y} 6x \, dz \, dy \, dx = \tfrac{1}{4}$$

$$M_{xz} = \iiint\limits_{R} 6y \, dV = \int_0^1 \int_0^{1-x} \int_0^{1-x-y} 6y \, dz \, dy \, dx = \tfrac{1}{4}$$

$$M_{xy} = \iiint\limits_{R} 6z \, dV = \int_0^1 \int_0^{1-x} \int_0^{1-x-y} 6z \, dz \, dy \, dx = \tfrac{1}{4}$$

(Verify the details of these integrations.) Thus,

$$\bar{x} = \frac{M_{yz}}{m} = \frac{\tfrac{1}{4}}{1} = 0.25, \; \bar{y} = \frac{M_{xz}}{m} = \frac{\tfrac{1}{4}}{1} = 0.25, \; \bar{z} = \frac{M_{xy}}{m} = \frac{\tfrac{1}{4}}{1} = 0.25$$

The centroid is $(0.25, 0.25, 0.25)$.

■ MOMENTS OF INERTIA

The moments M_x and M_y of a lamina are sometimes called the **first moments** about the x- and y-axes.

$$M_x = \int\int_R \underbrace{y}_{} \underbrace{\rho(x, y)\, dA}_{\text{Mass}} \qquad \text{and} \qquad M_y = \int\int_R \underbrace{x}_{} \underbrace{\rho(x, y)\, dA}_{\text{Mass}}$$

Distance to x-axis   Distance to y-axis

We now attach meaning to a **second moment**, also known as the **moment of inertia**.

The concept of moment of inertia is closely related to the kinetic energy of a rotating particle. Suppose a particle of mass m rotates in a plane at a distance of r from a fixed axis L that is perpendicular to the plane of motion, as shown in Figure 13.37.

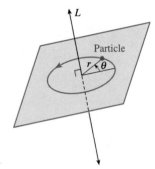

Figure 13.37 The particle has moment of inertia $I = mr^2$ about line L.

If the angular velocity is $\omega = d\theta/dt$, then the kinetic energy of the particle is defined by K.E. $= \frac{1}{2}I\omega^2$, where $I = mr^2$ is defined to be the **moment of inertia** of the particle about the axis L. Likewise, it can be shown that a particle of mass m moving along a straight line with velocity v has kinetic energy $\frac{1}{2}mv^2$, and by comparing the formulas for energy, we see that the moment of inertia I is in some sense the rotational analog of the mass of the particle. Alternatively, the moment of inertia can be thought of as measuring the tendency of matter to resist a change in its rotation.

Suppose we now look at a lamina that occupies the region R in the plane. Consider a small "cell" of the lamina with mass Δm, and assume that the cell is small enough for all the mass to be located at a single point (x, y). Then the cell is y units from the x-axis and x units from the y-axis, and it has moment of inertia $\Delta I_x = \Delta m y^2$ about the x-axis, and $\Delta I_y = \Delta m x^2$ about the y-axis. If the cell has area ΔA and its density is $\rho(x, y)$, then $\Delta m = \rho(x, y)\Delta A$. Finally, by partitioning the lamina into a number of cells and taking the limit as the partition becomes more and more refined, we expect that the moments of inertia of the entire lamina about the x-axis and the y-axis will be given by the following integrals:

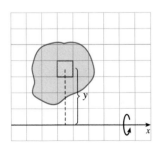

Moments of Inertia

⊘ I_x has a factor of y^2 and I_y has a factor of x^2. ⊘

The **moments of inertia** of a lamina of variable density ρ about the x- and y-axes, respectively, are

$$I_x = \int\int_R \underbrace{y^2}_{} \underbrace{\rho(x, y)\, dA}_{\text{Increment of mass}} \qquad \text{and} \qquad I_y = \int\int_R \underbrace{x^2}_{} \underbrace{\rho(x, y)\, dA}_{\text{Increment of mass}}$$

Moment about   (Distance)²   Moment about   (Distance)²
x-axis   to the x-axis y-axis   to the y-axis

EXAMPLE 4   Finding the moments of inertia

A lamina occupies the region R in the plane that is bounded by the parabola $y = x^2$ and the lines $x = 2$ and $y = 1$. The density of the lamina at each point (x, y) is $\rho(x, y) = x^2 y$. Find the moments of inertia of the lamina about the x-axis and the y-axis.

Solution   The graph of R is shown in Figure 13.38. We see that for each fixed x between 1 and 2, y varies from 1 to x^2.

$$I_x = \iint_R y^2 \, dm = \iint_R y^2 \rho(x, y) \, dA = \iint_R y^2 (x^2 y) \, dA$$

$$= \int_1^2 \int_1^{x^2} x^2 y^3 \, dy \, dx = \frac{1}{4} \int_1^2 x^2 (x^8 - 1) \, dx = \frac{1,516}{33} \approx 45.94$$

$$I_y = \iint_R x^2 \, dm = \iint_R x^2 \rho(x, y) \, dA = \iint_R x^2 (x^2 y) \, dA$$

$$= \int_1^2 \int_1^{x^2} x^4 y \, dy \, dx = \frac{1}{2} \int_1^2 x^4 (x^4 - 1) \, dx = \frac{1,138}{45} \approx 25.29$$

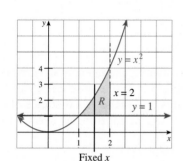

Figure 13.38 Moment of inertia of a lamina

A simple generalization enables us to compute the moment of inertia of a solid figure about an axis L outside the figure. Specifically, suppose the solid occupies a region R and that the density at each point (x, y, z) in R is given by $\rho(x, y, z)$. Because the square of the distance of a typical cell in R from the x-axis is $y^2 + z^2$, the moment of inertia about the x-axis is

$$I_x = \iiint_R \underbrace{(y^2 + z^2)}_{\substack{\uparrow \\ \text{Square of the distance to the } x\text{-axis}}} \underbrace{\rho(x, y, z) \, dV}_{\text{Increment of mass}}$$

Similarly, the moments of inertia of the solid about the y-axis and the z-axis are, respectively,

$$I_y = \iiint_R \underbrace{(x^2 + z^2)}_{\substack{\uparrow \\ \text{Square of the distance to the } y\text{-axis}}} \underbrace{\rho(x, y, z) \, dV}_{\text{Increment of mass}}$$

$$I_z = \iiint_R \underbrace{(x^2 + y^2)}_{\substack{\uparrow \\ \text{Square of the distance to the } z\text{-axis}}} \underbrace{\rho(x, y, z) \, dV}_{\text{Increment of mass}}$$

EXAMPLE 5   Moment of inertia of a solid

Find the moment of inertia about the z-axis of the solid tetrahedron S with vertices $(0, 0, 0)$, $(0, 1, 0)$, $(1, 0, 0)$, $(0, 0, 1)$ and density $\rho(x, y, z) = x$.

Solution   In Example 3, we observed that the solid S can be described as the set of all (x, y, z) such that for each fixed x between 0 and 1, y lies between 0 and $1 - x$, and $0 \le z \le 1 - x - y$. Thus,

$$I_z = \iiint_S (x^2 + y^2) \rho(x, y, z) \, dV = \int_0^1 \int_0^{1-x} \int_0^{1-x-y} x(x^2 + y^2) \, dz \, dy \, dx$$

$$= \int_0^1 \int_0^{1-x} x(x^2 + y^2)(1 - x - y) \, dy \, dx$$

$$= \int_0^1 \left[\frac{x^3(1-x)^2}{2} + \frac{x(1-x)^4}{12} \right] dx = \frac{1}{90}$$

■ JOINT PROBABILITY DENSITY FUNCTIONS

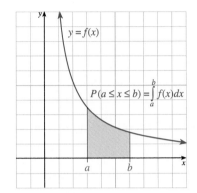

Figure 13.39 Probability as the area under a curve

An important application of integration is the computation of probabilities. A **probability density function** of a single variable x is a function $f(x)$ with $f(x) \geq 0$ and

$$\int_{-\infty}^{\infty} f(x) \, dx = 1$$

Then the probability that x is between a and b is defined by

$$P(a \leq x \leq b) = \int_a^b f(x) \, dx$$

In geometric terms, the probability $P(a \leq x \leq b)$ is the area under the graph of f over the interval $a \leq x \leq b$. (See Figure 13.39.)

To extend this definition to two variables, we define a **joint probability density function** for the variables x and y to be a function $f(x, y)$ such that $f(x, y) \geq 0$ and

$$\int_{-\infty}^{\infty} \int_{-\infty}^{\infty} f(x) \, dx \, dy = 1$$

Then the probability that the point (x, y) lies in the region R is defined by

$$P[(x, y) \text{ in } R] = \int\int_R f(x, y) \, dA$$

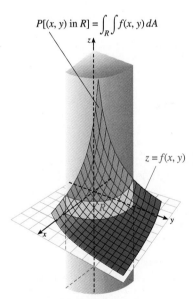

Figure 13.40 Probability that a point lies in a region

See Figure 13.40. The techniques for constructing joint probability density functions from experimental data are outside the scope of this textbook and are discussed in many textbooks on probability and statistics. The use of a double integral to compute a probability with a given joint density function is illustrated in the next example.

EXAMPLE 6   Compute a probability

Suppose x denotes the time (in minutes) that a customer at a particular grocery store spends shopping and y denotes the time the customer spends standing in the checkout line. A study suggests that the joint probability function for x and y is

$$f(x, y) = \begin{cases} \frac{1}{200} e^{-x/10} e^{-y/20} & \text{for } x \geq 0 \text{ and } y \geq 0 \\ 0 & \text{otherwise} \end{cases}$$

Find the probability that the customer's total time in the store will be no greater than 30 min.

Solution   The goal is to find the probability that $x + y \leq 30$. Stated geometrically, we wish to find the probability that a randomly selected point (x, y) lies in the region R in the first quadrant that is bounded by the coordinate axes and

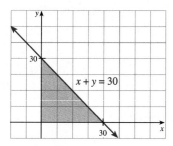

Figure 13.41 Triangle consisting of all points (x, y) such that $x + y \leq 30$, $x \geq 0$, $y \geq 0$

the line $x + y = 30$ (see Figure 13.41). This probability is given by the double integral

$$P[(x, y) \text{ is in } R] = \iint_R f(x, y) \, dA = \int_0^{30} \int_0^{30-x} \frac{1}{200} e^{-x/10} e^{-y/20} \, dy \, dx$$

$$= \frac{1}{200} \int_0^{30} e^{-x/10} \left[\frac{e^{-y/20}}{-1/20} \right] \Big|_0^{30-x} dx$$

$$= \frac{-20}{200} \int_0^{30} e^{-x/10} [e^{-(1/20)(30-x)} - 1] \, dx$$

$$= \frac{-1}{10} \left[\frac{e^{-3/2} e^{-x/20}}{-1/20} - \frac{e^{-x/10}}{-1/10} \right] \Big|_0^{30}$$

$$= e^{-3} - 2e^{-3/2} + 1$$

$$\approx 0.6035$$

Thus, it is about 60% likely that the shopper will spend no more than 30 minutes in the store. ▬

Many times we use a complementary property of probability that states

$$P(E) + P(\overline{E}) = 1$$

where E and $\overline{E}$ together constitute the set of all possible outcomes (that is, they are *complementary* probabilities). For Example 6, since the events $E = \{$the shopper will spend no more than 30 minutes in the store$\}$ and $\overline{E} = \{$the shopper will spend more than 30 minutes in the store$\}$, we can find the probability that the shopper will spend more than 30 minutes in the store by using this complementary property:

$$1 - 0.6035 = 0.3965$$

PROBLEM SET 13.6

Ⓐ
1. ■ **What Does This Say?** Discuss the procedure for finding the center of mass of a lamina.
2. ■ **What Does This Say?** Discuss a procedure for finding moments in three dimensions.
3. ■ **What Does This Say?** Discuss the terms center of mass and centroid.
4. ■ **What Does This Say?** Discuss moments of inertia.

Find the centroid for the regions described in Problems 5–12.
5. A lamina with $\rho = 5$ over the rectangle with vertices $(0, 0)$, $(3, 0)$, $(0, 4)$, $(3, 4)$
6. A lamina with $\rho = 4$ over the region bounded by the curve $y = \sqrt{x}$ and the line $x = 4$ in the first quadrant.
7. A lamina with $\rho = 2$ over the region between the line $y = 2x$ and the parabola $y = x^2$
8. A lamina with $\rho = 4$ over the region bounded by $y = \sin \frac{\pi}{2} x$, $x = 0$, $y = 0$, $x = \frac{1}{2}$
9. A thin homogeneous plate of density $\rho = 1$ with the shape of the region bounded above by the parabola $y = 2 - 3x^2$ and below by the line $3x + 2y = 1$

10. The part of the spherical solid of density $\rho = 2$ described by $x^2 + y^2 + z^2 \leq 9$, $x \geq 0$, $y \geq 0$, $z \geq 0$
11. The solid tetrahedron of density $\rho = 4$ bounded by the plane $x + y + z = 4$ in the first octant
12. The solid bounded by the surface $z = \sin x$, $x = 0$, $x = \pi$, $y = 0$, $z = 0$, and $y + z = 1$, where the density is $\rho = 1$

Use double integration in Problems 13–18 to find the center of mass of a lamina covering the given region in the plane and having the specified density ρ.
13. $\rho(x, y) = x^2 + y^2$ over $x^2 + y^2 \leq 9$, $y \geq 0$
14. $\rho(x, y) = k(x^2 + y^2)$ over $x^2 + y^2 \leq a^2$, $y \geq 0$
15. $\rho(x, y) = 7x$ over the triangle with vertices $(0, 0)$, $(6, 5)$ and $(12, 0)$.
16. $\rho(x, y) = 3x$ over the region bounded by $y = 0$, $y = x^2$, and $x = 6$
17. $\rho(x, y) = x^{-1}$ over the region bounded by $y = \ln x$, $y = 0$, $x = 2$
18. $\rho(x, y) = y$ over the region bounded by $y = e^{-x}$, $x = 0$, $x = 2$, $y = 0$

19. A lamina in the xy-plane has the shape of the semicircular region $x^2 + y^2 \le a^2$, $y \ge 0$. Find the center of mass if the density at any point in the lamina is
   a. directly proportional to the distance of the point from the origin
   b. directly proportional to the polar angle

20. A lamina has the shape of a semicircular region $x^2 + y^2 \le a^2$, $y \ge 0$. Find the center of mass of the lamina if the density at each point is directly proportional to the square of the distance from the point to the origin.

21. Find the center of mass of a lamina that covers the region bounded by the curve $y = \ln x$ and the lines $x = e^2$, and $y = 0$ if the density at each point (x, y) is $\rho = 1$.

22. Find the center of mass of the solid bounded above by the elliptic paraboloid $z = x^2 + y^2$, on the sides by the cylinder $x^2 + y^2 = 9$ and the plane $x = 0$, and below by $z = 0$, where $\rho(x, z) = x^2 + y^2 + z^2$.

23. Find I_x, the moment of inertia about the x-axis, of the lamina that covers the region bounded by the graph of $y = 1 - x^2$ and the x-axis, if the density is $\rho(x, y) = x^2$.

24. Find I_z, the moment of inertia about the z-axis, of the lamina that covers the square in the plane with vertices $(-1, -1)$, $(1, -1)$, $(1, 1)$, and $(-1, 1)$, if the density is $\rho(x, y) = x^2 y^2$.

Ⓑ 25. Find the center of mass of the cardioid $r = 1 + \sin \theta$ if the density at each point (r, θ) is $\rho(r, \theta) = r$.

26. Find the center of mass of the loop of the lemniscate $r^2 = 2 \sin 2\theta$ that lies in the first quadrant, for density $\rho = 1$.

27. Find the center of mass (correct to the nearest hundredth) of the part of the large loop of the limaçon $r = 1 + 2 \cos \theta$ that does not include the small loop. Assume that $\rho = 1$.

28. Find the center of mass of the lamina that covers the triangular region with vertices $(0, 0)$, $(a, 0)$, (a, b), if a and b are both positive and the density at $P(x, y)$ is directly proportional to the distance of P from the y-axis.

29. THINK TANK PROBLEM A solid has the shape of the rectangular parallelepiped given by $-a \le x \le a$, $-b \le y \le b$, $-c \le z \le c$, and its density is $\rho(x, y, z) = x^2 y^2 z^2$.
   a. Guess the location of the center of mass and the moment of inertia about the z-axis.
   b. Check your response to part a by direct calculation.

30. A rectangular lamina has vertices $(0, 0)$, $(a, 0)$, (a, b), $(0, b)$ and its density at any point (x, y) is the product $\rho(x, y) = xy$. Find the center of mass of the plate.

In Problems 31–35, assume that the density in the given lamina is constant. Find the centroid of the plate.

31. The boundary and the interior of the circular region $x^2 + y^2 = ax$ form a homogeneous lamina of density $\rho = 1$. Find the moment of inertia of this circular plate about a diameter passing through the center of the lamina. *Hint*: Use polar coordinates.

32. Show that the lamina that covers the circular region $x^2 + y^2 = a^2$, and has mass m, will have moment of inertia $ma^2/4$ with respect to the x-axis.

33. Show that the lamina that covers the circular region $x^2 + y^2 = a^2$, with mass m, will have moment of inertia $ma^2/4$ with respect to the y-axis.

34. Show that the lamina that covers the circular region $x^2 + y^2 = a^2$, with mass m will have moment of inertia $ma^2/2$ with respect to the z-axis.

35. Show that the lamina that covers the ellipse

$$\frac{x^2}{a^2} + \frac{y^2}{b^2} \le 1$$

with mass m and density $\rho = 1$ has moment of inertia about the x-axis equal to

$$I_x = ab^3 \rho = \tfrac{1}{4} m b^2$$

note: $m = \rho \underbrace{(\pi ab)}_{\text{area of ellipse}}$

36. Find the center of mass of the tetrahedron bounded by the plane

$$\frac{x}{a} + \frac{y}{b} + \frac{z}{c} = 1$$

where a, b, and c are all positive constants in the first octant. Assume the density is $\rho = x$.

37. A solid has the shape of the sphere $x^2 + y^2 + z^2 \le a^2$. Find the centroid of the part of the solid in the first octant $(x \ge 0, y \ge 0, z \ge 0)$. Assume $\rho = 1$.

38. Suppose the joint probability density function for the nonnegative variables x and y is $f(x, y) = 2e^{-2x} e^{-y}$. Find the probability that $x + y \le 1$.

39. Suppose the joint probability density function for the nonnegative variables x and y is $f(x, y) = xe^{-x} e^{-y}$. Find the probability that $x + y \le 1$.

40. Suppose x is the length of time (in days) that a person stays in the hospital after abdominal surgery and y is the length of time (in days) that a person stays in the hospital after orthopedic surgery. On Monday, the patient in bed 107A undergoes an emergency appendectomy (abdominal surgery), and the patient's roommate in bed 107B undergoes orthopedic surgery for the repair of torn knee cartilage. If the joint probability density function for x and y is

$$f(x, y) = \tfrac{1}{6} e^{-x/2} e^{-y/3}$$

find the probability (to the nearest hundredth) that both patients will be discharged from the hospital within 3 days.

41. A certain appliance consisting of two independent electronic components will be usable as long as either one of its components is still operating. The appliance carries a warranty from the manufacturer guaranteeing replacement if the appliance becomes unusable within 1 yr of the date of purchase. Let x denote the life span (in years) of the first component and y the life span (in years) of the second, and suppose that the joint probability density function for x and y is

$$f(x, y) = \tfrac{1}{4} e^{-x/2} e^{-y/2}$$

You purchase one of these appliances, selected at random from the manufacturer's stock. Find the probability that the appliance breaks before the warranty expires.

42. Suppose x denotes the time (in minutes) that a person stands in line at a certain bank and y, the duration (in minutes) of a routine transaction at the teller's window. You arrive at the bank to deposit a check. If the joint probability density function for x and y is

$$f(x, y) = \tfrac{1}{8}e^{-x/2}e^{-y/4}$$

find the probability that you will complete your business at the bank within 8 min.

43. Suppose x denotes the time (in minutes) that a person spends with an insurance agent choosing a life insurance policy and y the time (in minutes) that the agent spends doing the paperwork once the client has decided. You arrange to meet with an insurance agent to buy a life insurance policy. If the joint probability density function for x and y is

$$f(x, y) = \tfrac{1}{300}e^{-x/30}e^{-y/10}$$

find the probability that the entire transaction will take less than half an hour.

*The **average value** of the continuous function f over R is given by*

One variable: $\dfrac{1}{\text{length of segment } R} \displaystyle\int_R f(x)\, dx$

Two variables: $\dfrac{1}{\text{area of region } R} \displaystyle\iint_R f(x, y)\, dA$

Three variables: $\dfrac{1}{\text{volume of solid } R} \displaystyle\iiint_R f(x, y, z)\, dV$

Use these definitions in Problems 44–47.

44. Find the average value of $f(x, y) = e^{x^3}$, where R is the region in the first quadrant bounded by $y = x^2$, $y = 0$, and $x = 1$.

45. Find the average value of

$$f(x, y) = e^x y^{-1/2}$$

where R is the region in the first quadrant bounded by $y = x^2$, $x = 0$, and $y = 1$.

46. Find the average value of the function

$$f(x, y, z) = x + 2y + 3z$$

over the solid region S bounded by the tetrahedron with vertices $(0, 0, 0)$, $(1, 0, 0)$, $(0, 1, 0)$, and $(0, 0, 1)$.

47. Find the average value of the function $f(x, y, z) = xyz$ over the solid sphere $x^2 + y^2 + z^2 \leq 1$.

*The **radius of gyration** for revolving a region R with mass m about an axis of rotation L, with moment of inertia I, is*

$$d = \sqrt{\frac{I}{m}}$$

Note that if the entire mass m of R is located at a distance d from the axis of rotation L, then R would have the same moment of inertia. Use this definition in Problems 48–50.

48. A lamina has the shape of the right triangle in the xy-plane where vertices are $(0, 0)$, $(a, 0)$, and $(0, b)$, $a > 0$, $b > 0$. Find the radius of gyration of the lamina about the z-axis. Assume $\rho = 1$.

49. Find the radius of gyration about the x-axis of the semicircular region $x^2 + y^2 \leq a^2$, $y \geq 0$ given that the density at (x, y) is directly proportional to the distance of the point from the x-axis.

50. Let R be the lamina bounded by the parabola $y = x^2$ and the lines $x = 2$ and $y = 1$, with density $\rho(x, y) = x^2 y$. What is the radius of gyration about the x-axis?

Computational Window

Often the knowledge of the center of mass allows us to greatly simply a problem; but sometimes it can lead us to an incorrect answer. We explore this incongruity in Problems 51–52.

51. Centers of mass in physics

   a. Suppose a volume of liquid (or granular solid) is located so that its center of mass is at the origin. The material is to be lifted to a height of h units above the center of mass. Starting with a small element of volume, ΔV, to be lifted to height, h, derive the formula for the total work done:

   $$\text{Work} = \rho \iiint (h - z)\, dV$$

   where ρ is the weight (density) of the material.

   b. Explain why the integral in part **a** simplifies to the formula

   $$\text{Work} = \rho V h = \text{force} \times \text{distance}$$

   where h is the distance between the center of mass and the level to which the material is lifted.

   c. Picture a cylindrical tank of radius 6 ft and height 10 ft positioned so its center of mass is at the origin. Compute the work required to lift (that is, pump) the contents (of density ρ) to a level of 15 ft above the center of mass. Compute this two ways: by the integral in part **a** (suggestion—do the $dx\, dy$ integral by inspection), and also by simply lifting the center of mass to the required height. The results of these computations should agree.

52. Newton's inverse square law

   Recall that if two masses m and M are each concentrated at (or nearly at) a point and are separated by a distance p, the the attractive force is expressed $F = GmM/p^2$. What physicists and others prefer to do in the case of real-life masses (which occupy some volume) is to use p, the distance between the two centers of mass. The question you are to explore here (and again in Section 13.7 is whether, and when, this simplifying way of computing attracting forces is justified.

a. Suppose one mass, m, is a point mass located at $(0, 0, h)$ and the second M, has its center of mass at $(0, 0, 0)$—both have density ρ. We are interested in the total *resultant* force that M exerts on m, and we assume this to be in the z-direction; hence we will sum the vertical component of the forces acting on m. Consider, in M, a small element of volume ΔV (at x, y, z) and argue that the magnitude of the force exerted on m and its vertical component are

$$\Delta F_{\text{mag}} = \frac{Gm\,\Delta V}{p^2}$$

$$\Delta F = \frac{Gm\,\Delta V(h-3)^2}{p^3}$$

where $p^2 = x^2 + y^2 + (h-z)^2$. Note that the term $(h-z)/p$ projects the force vector onto the z-axis, giving the vertical component. Do you see why?

b. Form the usual Riemann sum and obtain the following force acting between m and M.

$$F = Gm\rho \iiint \frac{(h-x)dV}{p^3}$$

c. Consider a solid (with density $\rho = 5$) positioned at $-2 \leq x \leq 2$, $-4 \leq y \leq 4$, and $-1 \leq z \leq 1$. (Note the center of mass is at the origin.) Then compute the attracting force between this mass and a point mass, m, at $(0, 0, 8)$ using the center of mass formula $F = GmM/p^2$.

d. For the masses in part c, compute F using the integration formula in part b; compare this result

with that of part c.

e. Repeat the last calculation with $h = 200$ and compare with the center of mass approximation. Comment on the role the separating distance p plays.

C 53. Find the moment of inertia of a rectangular lamina with dimensions h and l about an axis L through its center of mass. Assume the lamina has density $\rho = 1$.

54. Prove the following area theorem of Pappus:
Let C be a curve of length L in the plane. Then the surface obtained by rotating C about the axis ℓ in the plane has area $2\pi Lh$, where h is the distance from the centroid of C to the axis of rotation.

55. A torus (doughnut) has the vector parametric form

$$\mathbf{R}(u, v) = (a + b\cos v)\cos u\,\mathbf{i} + (a + b\cos v)\sin u\,\mathbf{j} + b\sin v\,\mathbf{k}$$

for $0 < b < a$, $0 \leq u \leq 2\pi$, $0 \leq v \leq 2\pi$. (see Problem 45, Section 13.4.) Find its surface area by applying Pappus's theorem (see Problem 54).

56. Prove the volume theorem of Pappus: Let R be a lamina in the plane with density $\rho = 1$ and area A, and let L be a line that does not intersect R. If σ is the distance from the center of mass of R to L, then the volume V of the solid formed by revolving R about L is $V = 2\pi\sigma A$. (See Figure 13.42.)

Figure 13.42 Torus

13.7 CYLINDRICAL AND SPHERICAL COORDINATES

IN THIS SECTION Cylindrical coordinates, integration with cylindrical coordinates, spherical coordinates, integration with spherical coordinates
We have seen that certain curves have simpler descriptions in polar coordinates than in rectangular coordinates. In this section, we introduce the *cylindrical and spherical coordinate systems*, which are equally useful for describing certain surfaces and solids in space.

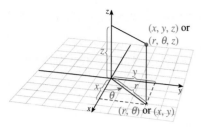

Figure 13.43 The cylindrical coordinate system

CYLINDRICAL COORDINATES

Cylindrical coordinates are a generalization of polar coordinates in $\mathbb{R}^3$. Recall that the point P with Cartesian coordinates (x, y, z) is located z units above the point $Q(x, y)$ in the xy-plane (below if $z < 0$). In cylindrical coordinates we measure the point in the xy-plane in polar coordinates, with the same z-coordinate as in the Cartesian coordinate system. These relationships are shown in Figure 13.43.

Cylindrical coordinates are convenient for representing cylindrical surfaces and surfaces of revolution for which the z-axis is the axis of symmetry. Some examples are shown in Figure 13.44.

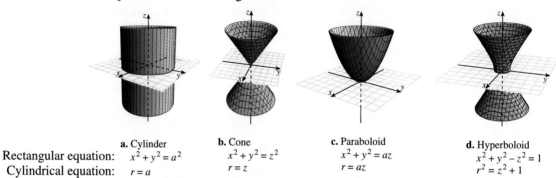

	a. Cylinder	**b.** Cone	**c.** Paraboloid	**d.** Hyperboloid
Rectangular equation:	$x^2 + y^2 = a^2$	$x^2 + y^2 = z^2$	$x^2 + y^2 = az$	$x^2 + y^2 - z^2 = 1$
Cylindrical equation:	$r = a$	$r = z$	$r = az$	$r^2 = z^2 + 1$

Figure 13.44 Surfaces with convenient cylindrical coordinates

We have the following conversion formulas, which follow directly from the rectangular-polar conversions.

Conversion Formulas
Rectangular/Cylindrical
Coordinates

Cylindrical to rectangular:	$x = r\cos\theta$
(r, θ, z) **to** (x, y, z)	$y = r\sin\theta$
	$z = z$
Rectangular to cylindrical:	$r = \sqrt{x^2 + y^2}$
(x, y, z) **to** (r, θ, z)	$\tan\theta = \dfrac{y}{x}$
	$z = z$

If (r, θ, z) with $r > 0$ are cylindrical coordinates for any point Q not on the z-axis, then $(r, \theta + 2n\pi, z)$, for any integer n, will also be cylindrical coordinates for Q. Hence, if $r > 0$, points that are not on the z-axis have multiple labelings (the values of θ differ by a multiple of 2π). To avoid this multiplicity, we require that $0 \le \theta \le 2\pi$. The point $(0, 0, 0)$ is called the **pole**.

EXAMPLE 1   Converting from rectangular to cylindrical coordinates

Find the cylindrical coordinates of the point whose rectangular coordinates are $P(\sqrt{3}, 1, 2)$.

Solution   Because $x = \sqrt{3}$, $y = 1$, and $z = 2$, we have

$$r = \sqrt{3 + 1} = 2, \qquad \tan\theta = \frac{1}{\sqrt{3}}, \quad \text{so} \quad \theta = \frac{\pi}{6}$$

This means that the cylindrical coordinates are $\left(2, \frac{\pi}{6}, 2\right)$. Note in Figure 13.45 that we are considering a *single* point, whether we measure its location in rectangular or cylindrical coordinates.

Figure 13.45 Cylindrical and rectangular coordinates of a point

As might be expected, cylindrical coordinates are especially convenient for describing cylinders.

EXAMPLE 2 Rectangular-form equation converted to cylindrical-form equation

For $a > 0$, express the equation of the cylinder $x^2 + y^2 = a^2$ in terms of cylindrical coordinates.

Solution Because we are working in three dimensions, but the equation does not contain z, we recognize that z is arbitrary, and we draw the cylinder as shown in Figure 13.46. First, obtain the polar coordinates for all points in the xy-plane that lie on the cylinder. Each such point P lies on the circle $x^2 + y^2 = a^2$. Because $r^2 = x^2 + y^2$, we find

$$r^2 = a^2 \quad \text{or} \quad r = a \qquad z \text{ arbitrary}$$

We keep only the positive value because we require $r > 0$. ▬

Figure 13.46 The cylinder $x^2 + y^2 = a^2$ or $r = a$

EXAMPLE 3 Rectangular-form equation converted to cylindrical-form equation

Find an equation in cylindrical coordinates for the elliptical paraboloid $z = x^2 + 3y^2$.

Solution We use the conversion formulas $x = r \cos \theta$ and $y = r \sin \theta$.

$$z = x^2 + 3y^2 = (r \cos \theta)^2 + 3(r \sin \theta)^2$$
$$= r^2(\cos^2 \theta + 3 \sin^2 \theta)$$
$$= r^2[(1 - \sin^2 \theta) + 3 \sin^2 \theta]$$
$$= r^2(1 + 2 \sin^2 \theta)$$ ▬

■ INTEGRATION WITH CYLINDRICAL COORDINATES

In order to do triple integration with cylindrical coordinates, we simply apply our results from Section 13.3 to convert from rectangular to polar form. Even though there are six possible orders of integration, we will focus on the one for which the region is bounded below and above by $u(r, \theta) \leq z \leq v(r, \theta)$. In this case we let D *be the region in the xy-plane described by polar coordinates.* This means that the order of integration we will use is $dz\, dr\, d\theta$. In other words, we will first integrate with respect to z, then with respect to r, and finally with respect to θ. Figure 13.47 illustrates triple integration in polar coordinates. Note that dV is replaced by $r\, dz\, dr\, d\theta$, which follows from Theorem 13.4.

Integrate with respect to z. Integrate with respect to r. Integrate with respect to θ.

Figure 13.47 Integration with polar coordinates

Triple Integral in Cylindrical Coordinates

If f is a continuous function of r, θ, and z on the bounded, solid region R, then in cylindrical coordinates the **triple integral of f over R** is

$$\iiint\limits_{R} f(r,\,\theta,\,z)\,dV = \iint\limits_{D} \int_{u(r,\,\theta)}^{v(r,\,\theta)} f(r,\,\theta,\,z)\,r\,dz\,dr\,d\theta$$

where D is the region in the xy-plane described by polar coordinates.

EXAMPLE 4   Finding volume in cylindrical coordinates

Find the volume of the solid in the first octant that is bounded by the cylinder $x^2 + y^2 = 2y$, the cone $z = \sqrt{x^2 + y^2}$, and the xy-plane.

Solution   Let S be the region occupied by the solid as shown in Figure 13.48. This surface is most easily described in cylindrical coordinates.

$z = r$

$r = 2 \sin \theta$

Solid S

Figure 13.48 The solid bounded by $x^2 + y^2 = 2y$, $z = \sqrt{x^2 + y^2}$, and the xy-plane

Cylinder:

$$x^2 + y^2 = 2y$$
$$r^2 = 2\,r \sin \theta$$
$$r = 2 \sin \theta$$

Cone:

$$z = \sqrt{x^2 + y^2}$$
$$z = r$$

Thus, we see that the region S has the description

$$0 \le z \le r \qquad 0 \le r \le 2 \sin \theta \qquad 0 \le \theta \le \frac{\pi}{2}$$

$$V = \iiint\limits_{R} dV = \iint\limits_{D} \int_{u(r,\theta)}^{v(r,\theta)} r\,dz\,dr\,d\theta = \int_{0}^{\pi/2} \int_{0}^{2 \sin \theta} \int_{0}^{r} r\,dz\,dr\,d\theta$$

$$= \int_{0}^{\pi/2} \int_{0}^{2 \sin \theta} r^2\,dr\,d\theta = \int_{0}^{\pi/2} \frac{r^3}{3}\Big|_{r=0}^{r=2 \sin \theta}\,d\theta = \frac{8}{3} \int_{0}^{\pi/2} \sin^3 \theta\,d\theta$$

$$= \frac{8}{3}\left[-\cos \theta + \frac{\cos^3 \theta}{3}\right]\Bigg|_{0}^{\pi/2} = \frac{16}{9} \qquad \textit{Integration table (formula 350)} \qquad \blacksquare$$

EXAMPLE 5   Centroid in cylindrical coordinates

A homogeneous solid S ($\rho = 1$) is bounded below by the xy-plane, on the sides by the cylinder $x^2 + y^2 = a^2$ ($a > 0$), and above by the surface $z = x^2 + y^2$. Find the centroid of the solid.

Solution   Let S be the described solid as shown in Figure 13.49. Because the solid is bounded by a cylinder, we will carry out the integration in cylindrical coordinates.

$z = r^2$

$r = a$

Figure 13.49 The solid bounded by $x^2 + y^2 = a^2$ and $z = x^2 + y^2$

Cylinder:

$$x^2 + y^2 = a^2$$
$$r^2 = a^2$$
$$r = a \qquad (a > 0)$$

Paraboloid:

$$z = x^2 + y^2$$
$$z = r^2$$

Let $(\overline{x}, \overline{y}, \overline{z})$ denote the centroid. By symmetry, we have $\overline{x} = \overline{y} = 0$. Let m denote the mass of S. Then

$$\overline{z} = \frac{M_{xy}}{m} = \frac{\iiint\limits_{S} z\rho(x, y, z)\, dV}{\iiint\limits_{S} r\rho(x, y, z)\, dz\, dr\, d\theta} = \frac{\iiint\limits_{S} zr\, dz\, dr\, d\theta}{\iiint\limits_{S} r\, dz\, dr\, d\theta}$$

$$= \frac{\int_0^{2\pi} \int_0^a \int_0^{r^2} zr\, dz\, dr\, d\theta}{\int_0^{2\pi} \int_0^a \int_0^{r^2} r\, dz\, dr\, d\theta} = \frac{\frac{\pi}{6}\, a^6}{\frac{\pi}{2}a^4} = \frac{a^2}{3}$$

Verify the details of the integration.

The centroid is $\left(0, 0, \dfrac{a^2}{3}\right)$.

■ SPHERICAL COORDINATES

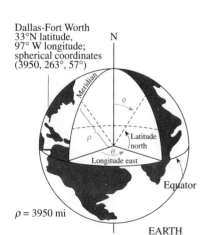

Figure 13.50 The spherical coordinate system

In **spherical coordinates** we label a point P by a triple (ρ, θ, ϕ), where ρ, θ, and ϕ are numbers determined as follows (refer to Figure 13.50):

ρ = the distance from the origin to the point P; we require $\rho \geq 0$.

θ = the polar angle (as in polar coordinates). In spherical coordinates, this is called the **azimuth** of P; we take the principal value of the polar angle to be $0 \leq \theta < 2\pi$.

ϕ = the angle measured down from the positive z-axis to the ray from the origin through P. The angle ϕ is called the **colatitude** of P; we require $0 \leq \phi \leq \pi$.

You might recognize spherical coordinates (as well as the associated terminology) as being related to the latitude-longitude system used to identify points on the surface of the earth. In spherical coordinates, points above the xy-plane satisfy $0 \leq \phi < \pi/2$ and points below satisfy $\pi/2 < \phi \leq \pi$, whereas the equation $\phi = \pi/2$ describes the xy-plane. When this coordinate system is used to measure points on the earth, the number ρ is the distance from the center of the earth to the point with longitude θ from the prime meridian; because latitude is the angle *up* from the equator, it is measured in spherical coordinates as $\pi/2 - \phi$.

Spherical coordinates are desirable when representing spheres, cones, or certain planes. Some examples are shown in Figure 13.51.

Dallas-Fort Worth
33°N latitude,
97° W longitude;
spherical coordinates
(3950, 263°, 57°)

ρ = 3950 mi

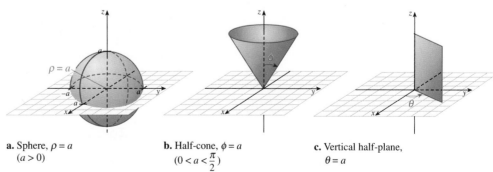

a. Sphere, $\rho = a$
  ($a > 0$)

b. Half-cone, $\phi = a$
  ($0 < a < \dfrac{\pi}{2}$)

c. Vertical half-plane,
  $\theta = a$

Figure 13.51 Surfaces with convenient spherical coordinates

We can use Figure 13.51, as well as the definition of the trigonometric functions, to state the remaining conversion formulas.

Conversion Formulas
**   for Coordinate Systems**

Spherical to rectangular:	$x = \rho \sin \phi \cos \theta$
(ρ, θ, ϕ) to (x, y, z)	$y = \rho \sin \phi \sin \theta$
	$z = \rho \cos \phi$
Rectangular to spherical:	$\rho = \sqrt{x^2 + y^2 + z^2}$
(x, y, z) to (ρ, θ, ϕ)	$\tan \theta = \dfrac{y}{x}$
	$\phi = \cos^{-1}\left(\dfrac{z}{\sqrt{x^2 + y^2 + z^2}}\right)$
Spherical to cylindrical:	$r = \rho \sin \phi$
(ρ, θ, ϕ) to (r, θ, z)	$\theta = \theta$
	$z = \rho \cos \phi$
Cylindrical to spherical:	$\rho = \sqrt{r^2 + z^2}$
(r, θ, z) to (ρ, θ, ϕ)	$\theta = \theta$
	$\phi = \cos^{-1}\left(\dfrac{z}{\sqrt{r^2 + z^2}}\right)$

EXAMPLE 6   Converting rectangular-form equations to spherical-form equations

Rewrite each of the given equations in spherical form.

a. the sphere $x^2 + y^2 + z^2 = a^2$ $(a > 0)$

b. the paraboloid $z = x^2 + 3y^2$ (This is the same elliptic paraboloid we analyzed in Example 3.)

Solution   **a.** Because $\rho = \sqrt{x^2 + y^2 + z^2}$, we see $x^2 + y^2 + z^2 = \rho^2$, so we can write

$$\rho^2 = a^2$$
$$\rho = a \quad \text{Because } \rho \geq 0$$

b. $$z = x^2 + 3y^2$$

$$\rho \cos \phi = (\rho \sin \phi \cos \theta)^2 + 3(\rho \sin \phi \sin \theta)^2$$

$$\rho \cos \phi = \rho^2 \sin^2 \phi \cos^2 \theta + 3\rho^2 \sin^2 \phi \sin^2 \theta$$

$$0 = \rho^2 \sin^2 \phi \cos^2 \theta + 3\rho^2 \sin^2 \phi \sin^2 \theta - \rho \cos \phi$$

$$0 = \rho(\rho \sin^2 \phi \cos^2 \theta + 3\rho \sin^2 \phi \sin^2 \theta - \cos \phi)$$

Thus, $\rho = 0$ or $\rho \sin^2 \phi \cos^2 \theta + 3\rho \sin^2 \phi \sin^2 \theta - \cos \phi = 0$. Solving this second equation for ρ, we obtain

$$\rho = \frac{\cos \phi}{\sin^2 \phi \cos^2 \theta + 3 \sin^2 \phi \sin^2 \theta} = \frac{\cos \phi}{\sin^2 \phi(\cos^2 \theta + 3 \sin^2 \theta)}$$

$$= \frac{\cos \phi}{\sin^2 \phi(1 - \sin^2 \theta + 3 \sin^2 \theta)} = \frac{\cos \phi}{\sin^2 \phi(1 + 2 \sin^2 \theta)} \quad \phi \neq 0 \quad \blacksquare$$

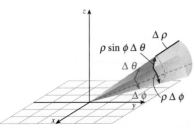

Figure 13.52 A spherical wedge

■ INTEGRATION WITH SPHERICAL COORDINATES

For a solid S in spherical coordinates, the fundamental element of volume is a spherical "wedge" bounded in such a way that

$$\rho_1 \le \rho \le \rho_1 + \Delta\rho \qquad \phi_1 \le \phi \le \phi_1 + \Delta\phi, \qquad \theta_1 \le \theta \le \theta_1 + \Delta\theta$$

This wedge is shown in Figure 13.52. It can be shown that the volume of the wedge is given by

$$dV = \rho^2 \sin\phi \, d\rho \, d\phi \, d\theta$$

Using this formula, we can form partitions and take a limit of a Riemann sum as the partitions are refined.

Triple Integral in Spherical Coordinates

If f is a continuous function of ρ, θ, and ϕ on a bounded, solid region S, the **triple integral of f over S** is, in spherical coordinates,

$$\iiint\limits_S f(\rho, \theta, \phi) \, dV = \iiint\limits_S f(\rho, \theta, \phi) \, \rho^2 \sin\phi \, d\rho \, d\theta \, d\phi$$

EXAMPLE 7   Volume of a sphere

Find the volume of the sphere described by $x^2 + y^2 + z^2 = 9$.

Solution   It seems clear that we should work in spherical coordinates, because in spherical coordinates the equation of the sphere is $\rho = 3$ for $0 \le \theta \le 2\pi$ and $0 \le \phi \le \pi$.

$$V = \iiint\limits_S dV = \int_0^\pi \int_0^{2\pi} \int_0^3 \rho^2 \sin\phi \, d\rho \, d\theta \, d\phi$$

$$= \int_0^\pi \int_0^{2\pi} \frac{\rho^3}{3} \sin\phi \Big|_{\rho=0}^{\rho=3} d\theta \, d\phi = \int_0^\pi \int_0^{2\pi} 9 \sin\phi \, d\theta \, d\phi$$

$$= \int_0^\pi 18\pi \sin\phi \, d\phi = 18\pi(-\cos\phi) \Big|_0^\pi = 36\pi$$

EXAMPLE 8   Moment of inertia using spherical coordinates

A toy top of uniform density is constructed from a portion of a solid hemisphere with a conical base, as shown in Figure 13.53. The center of the spherical cap is at the point where the top spins, and the height of the conical base is equal to its radius. Find the moment of inertia of the top about its axis of symmetry.

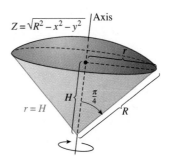

Figure 13.53 Moment of inertia for a spinning top

Solution   We use a Cartesian coordinate system in which the z-axis is the axis of symmetry of the top. Suppose that the cap is part of the hemisphere

$z = \sqrt{R^2 - x^2 - y^2}$. Since the height of the conical base is equal to its radius, the cone makes an angle of $\pi/4$ radians (45°) with the z-axis. Let S denote the solid region occupied by the top. Because the top is constructed from material whose density is uniform, we can assume that the density is constant, say $d = d_0$. Then the moment of inertia I_z with respect to the z-axis is given by

$$I_z = \int\int\int_S (x^2 + y^2)\, dm = \int\int\int_S (x^2 + y^2)d_0\, dV$$

The shape of the top suggests that we convert to spherical coordinates, and we find that S can be described as

$$0 \le \theta \le 2\pi \qquad 0 \le \phi \le \tfrac{\pi}{4} \qquad 0 \le \rho \le R$$

Also,

$$x^2 + y^2 = \rho^2\sin^2\phi\,\cos^2\theta + \rho^2\sin^2\phi\,\sin^2\theta = \rho^2\sin^2\phi$$

We now evaluate the integral using spherical coordinates:

$$I_z = \int\int\int_S (x^2 + y^2)d_0\, dV$$

$$= d_0 \int_0^{\pi/4}\int_0^{2\pi}\int_0^R \underbrace{\rho^2\sin^2\phi}_{x^2 + y^2}\,\underbrace{\rho^2\sin\phi\,d\rho\,d\theta\,d\phi}_{dV} = d_0\int_0^{\pi/4}\int_0^{2\pi}\int_0^R \rho^4\sin^3\phi\,d\rho\,d\theta\,d\phi$$

$$= d_0\int_0^{\pi/4}\int_0^{2\pi} \frac{\rho^5}{5}\sin^3\phi\Big|_{\rho=0}^{\rho=R}\,d\theta\,d\phi = \frac{R^5 d_0}{5}\int_0^{\pi/4}(2\pi - 0)\sin^3\phi\,d\phi$$

$$= \frac{2R^5 d_0\pi}{5}\Big[-\cos\phi + \tfrac{1}{3}\cos^3\phi\Big]\Big|_0^{\pi/4} = \frac{2R^5\,d_0\pi}{5}\Big[-\tfrac{1}{2}\sqrt{2} + \tfrac{1}{12}\sqrt{2} + 1 - \tfrac{1}{3}\Big]$$

$$\approx 0.09728 d_0 R^5$$

PROBLEM SET 13.7

A **1.** ■ **What Does This Say?** Compare and contrast the rectangular, cylindrical, and spherical coordinate systems.

2. ■ **What Does This Say?** Suppose you need to find a particular volume. Discuss some criteria about choosing a coordinate system.

In Problems 3–20, give answers correct to the nearest hundredth.

In Problems 3–8, convert from rectangular coordinates to (a) cylindrical and (b) spherical.

3. $(1, 1, 1)$　　　　**4.** $(0, 4, \sqrt{3})$

5. $(\sqrt{2}, -2, \sqrt{3})$　　**6.** $(-\sqrt{2}, \sqrt{3}, 2)$

7. $(1, 2, 3)$　　　　**8.** (π, π, π)

In Problems 9–14, convert from cylindrical coordinates to (a) rectangular and (b) spherical.

9. $\left(3, \tfrac{2\pi}{3}, -3\right)$　　**10.** $\left(4, \tfrac{\pi}{6}, -2\right)$

11. $\left(2, \tfrac{\pi}{4}, \pi\right)$　　**12.** $\left(-1, \tfrac{\pi}{2}, 3\right)$

13. $(1, 2, 3)$　　　**14.** (π, π, π)

In Problems 15–20, convert from spherical coordinates to (a) rectangular and (b) cylindrical.

15. $\left(2, \tfrac{\pi}{6}, \tfrac{2\pi}{3}\right)$　　**16.** $\left(3, \tfrac{\pi}{4}, \tfrac{\pi}{6}\right)$

17. $\left(1, \tfrac{\pi}{6}, 0\right)$　　**18.** $\left(2, \tfrac{\pi}{3}, \tfrac{\pi}{4}\right)$

19. $(1, 2, 3)$　　**20.** (π, π, π)

Convert each equation in Problems 21–26 to cylindrical coordinates and sketch its graph in $\mathbb{R}^3$.

21. $z = x^2 - y^2$　　　**22.** $x^2 - y^2 = 1$

23. $\dfrac{x^2}{4} - \dfrac{y^2}{9} + z^2 = 0$　　**24.** $z = x^2 + y^2$

25. $y^2 + z^2 = 9, 0 < x < 2$

26. $x^2 + y^2 = 9, 0 < z < 4$

Convert each equation in Problems 27–32 to spherical coordinates and sketch its graph in $\mathbb{R}^3$.

27. $z^2 = x^2 + y^2, z \ge 0$　　**28.** $x^2 + y^2 = 1$

29. $2x^2 + 2y^2 + 2z^2 = 1$　　**30.** $4z = x^2 + 3y^2$

31. $x^2 + y^2 + z^2 = 4$ **32.** $x^2 + y^2 - 4z^2 = 1$

Convert each equation in Problems 33–38 to rectangular coordinates and sketch its graph in $\mathbb{R}^3$.

33. $z = r^2\sin 2\theta$ **34.** $r = \sin\theta$

35. $z = r^2\cos 2\theta$ **36.** $\rho^2\sin^2\phi = 1$

37. $\rho^2\sin\phi\cos\phi\cos\theta = 1$ **38.** $\rho = \sin\phi\cos\theta$

Evaluate the iterated integral in Problems 39–44.

39. $\displaystyle\int_0^\pi \int_0^2 \int_0^{\sqrt{4-r^2}} r\sin\theta\, dz\, dr\, d\theta$

40. $\displaystyle\int_0^{\pi/4} \int_0^1 \int_0^{\sqrt{r}} r^2\sin\theta\, dz\, dr\, d\theta$

41. $\displaystyle\int_0^{\pi/2} \int_0^{2\pi} \int_0^2 \cos\phi\sin\phi\, d\rho\, d\theta\, d\phi$

42. $\displaystyle\int_0^{\pi/2} \int_0^{\pi/4} \int_0^{\cos\phi} \rho^2\sin\phi\, d\rho\, d\theta\, d\phi$

43. $\displaystyle\int_0^{2\pi} \int_0^4 \int_0^1 zr\, dz\, dr\, d\theta$

44. $\displaystyle\int_{-\pi/4}^{\pi/3} \int_0^{\sin\theta} \int_0^{4\cos\theta} r\, dz\, dr\, d\theta$

Ⓑ 45. The point (x, y, z) lies on an ellipsoid if

$$x = ar\sin\phi\cos\theta$$
$$y = br\sin\phi\sin\theta$$
$$z = cr\cos\phi$$

Find an equation for this ellipsoid in rectangular coordinates if r is a constant.

46. Use cylindrical coordinates to compute the integral

$$\iiint\limits_R xy\, dx\, dy\, dz$$

where R is the cylindrical solid $x^2 + y^2 \le 1$ with $0 \le z \le 1$.

47. Use cylindrical coordinates to compute the integral

$$\iiint\limits_R (x^4 + 2x^2y^2 + y^4)\, dx\, dy\, dz$$

where R is the cylindrical solid

$$x^2 + y^2 \le a^2 \quad\text{with}\quad 0 \le z \le \frac{1}{\pi}$$

48. Use cylindrical coordinates to compute the integral

$$\iiint\limits_S z(x^2 + y^2)^{-1/2}\, dx\, dy\, dz$$

where S is the solid bounded above by the plane $z = 2$ and below by the surface $2z = x^2 + y^2$.

49. Find the center of mass of the solid bounded by the surface $z = \sqrt{x^2 + y^2}$ and the plane $z = 9$. Assume $\rho = 1$.

50. Evaluate $\displaystyle\iiint\limits_R \sqrt{x^2 + y^2 + z^2}\, dx\, dy\, dz$, where R is defined by $x^2 + y^2 + z^2 \le 2$.

51. Evaluate $\displaystyle\iiint\limits_R (x^2 + y^2 + z^2)\, dx\, dy\, dz$, where R is defined by $x^2 + y^2 + z^2 \le 2$.

52. Evaluate $\displaystyle\iiint\limits_S z^2\, dx\, dy\, dz$, where S is the hemisphere $x^2 + y^2 + z^2 \le 1, z \ge 0$.

53. Evaluate $\displaystyle\iiint\limits_S \frac{dx\, dy\, dz}{\sqrt{x^2 + y^2 + z^2}}$, where S is the sphere $x^2 + y^2 + z^2 \le 3$.

Find the volume of the solid S given in Problems 54–59 by using integration in any convenient system of coordinates.

54. S is bounded by the surface $z = 1 - 4(x^2 + y^2)$ and the xy-plane.

55. S is bounded above by the paraboloid $z = 4 - (x^2 + y^2)$, below by the plane $z = 0$, and laterally by the cylinder $x^2 + y^2 = 1$.

56. S is the intersection of the solid sphere $x^2 + y^2 + z^2 \le 9$ and the solid cylinder $x^2 + y^2 \le 1$.

57. S is the region bounded laterally by the cylinder $r = 2 \sin \theta$, below by the plane $z = 0$, and above by the paraboloid $z = 4 - r^2$.

58. S is the region that remains in the spherical solid $\rho \le 4$ after the solid cone $\phi \le \frac{\pi}{6}$ has been removed.

59. SPY PROBLEM   The spy crawls through the hole in the floor of the burning bunker (Problem 55, Section 12.6), and finds himself in a small beehive-shaped cave, surrounded by the terrorists. Gasping for breath, he looks at his captors and is shocked to find that their leader is none other than his superior's daughter, Purity. A terrorist raises his gun, but Purity orders, "No! Tie him securely. I want him to think for awhile before he dies. And hurry—Scélérat is waiting for us and he is not a patient man." The spy is tied and the terrorists leave. Purity is the last to go, and just before leaving, pulls a lever by the door, and the cave begins to flood with water. The spy is able to pull himself into a sitting position, so that his nose is 4 ft above the floor. In desperation, the spy does some quick calculations and decides that the beehive shape of the cave can be described as the part of the surface $\rho = 4(1 + \cos \phi)$, where ρ is measured in feet, that lies above the xy-plane. If the spy needs at least 10 min to free himself, and if water is entering at the rate of 25 ft³/min, will he drown or will he survive?

■ COMPUTATIONAL WINDOW ▼ ▲

60. In the last section (Problems 51 and 52), we said that it is not always accurate to compute the attractive force between two masses by simply using the distance between their centers of mass. This approximation was done first in astronomy in which the bodies were typically spherical in shape. As we shall see, in this case the simple calculation is very appropriate. Consider a sphere of radius a with density δ centered at the origin; and a point mass m located at $(x, y, z) = (0, 0, R)$. In this problem, you are to set up the integral to compute the attractive force between the masses; in the next problem, you will do some computing.
   a. Show that the distance p between point $(x, y, z) = (0, 0, R)$ and a point in the sphere, (ρ, θ, ϕ), can be expressed $p^2 = R^2 + \rho^2 - 2R\rho \cos \phi$. *Hint:* Use the law of cosines.
   b. In the sphere, consider a small element of volume ΔV at point (ρ, θ, ϕ). Argue that the magnitude of

the force exerted on m, and the vertical component, are

$$\Delta F_{\text{mag}} = \frac{Gm(\delta\Delta V)}{p^2}$$

$$\Delta F = \frac{Gm(\delta\Delta V)(R - \rho\cos \phi)}{p^3}$$

Note that the term $(R - \rho \cos \phi)/p$ projects the force vector onto the z-axis, giving the vertical component. Do you see why?
   c. Form the Riemann sum involving ΔF and get the following for the force acting between point mass m and the sphere of radius a:

$$F = \iiint \frac{Gm\delta(R - \rho \cos \phi)dV}{p^3}$$
$$= 2\pi Gm\delta \int_0^a \int_0^\pi p^2 \frac{(R - \rho \cos \phi) \sin \phi}{(R^2 + p^2 - 2R\rho \cos \phi)^{3/2}} d\phi \, dp$$

Note: The integrand is independent of θ.

61. a. For an unspecified radius a and $R > a$, compute the attractive force between the masses in the previous problem using the center of mass calculation.
   b. Set a and R to numerical values and compute the attractive force by the integral in part **c** of Problem 60. Try two or three different values of R until you are satisfied that the center of mass "approximation" is exact in this case.
   c. Compare this result with the corresponding calculations of Section 13.6 and conjecture why the center of mass argument is sound in the case of the sphere and not for the rectangular region.

ⓒ 62. Let S be a homogeneous solid with density 1 that has the shape of a right circular cylinder with height h and radius R. Use cylindrical coordinates to find the moment of inertia of S about its axis of symmetry.

63. Find the sum $I_x + I_y + I_z$ of the moments of inertia of the solid ellipsoid

$$x^2 + y^2 + z^2 \le 1$$

about the coordinate axes. Assume the density in 1.

64. How much volume remains from a spherical ball of radius a when a cylindrical hole of radius b ($0 < b < a$) is bored out of its center?

13.8 JACOBIANS: CHANGE OF VARIABLES

> **IN THIS SECTION** Change of variables in a double integral, change of variables in a triple integral
> We have seen how a change of variables to polar coordinates often simplifies the evaluation of a double integral and, likewise, how cylindrical and spherical coordinates can be used in evaluating triple integrals. However, these are not the only substitutions that may be used effectively, and the goal of this section is to examine some general ideas about changing variables in a multiple integral.

■ CHANGE OF VARIABLES IN A DOUBLE INTEGRAL

The German mathematician Carl Gustav Jacobi (see Historical Note, p. 886) was one of the first to work with change of variables. In honor of his early work, we define, in the following theorem, an important tool called a *Jacobian*, which makes it easy for us to change variables when working with multiple integrals.

For a single variable, the change of variables is called *integration by substitution*. When we carry out the process of substitution for a single integral, we see that the change of variable $x = g(u)$ introduces a new factor into the integrand:

$$\int_a^b f(x)\, dx = \int_c^d f[g(u)]g'(u)\, du$$

where the limits of integration change so that $a = g(c)$ and $b = g(d)$.

For a change of variables in a double integral, we could expect to transform (or "map") a region D onto a region D^*, with the goal of having D^* be simpler than D. Because we know that changing variables with a single variable introduces a new factor (namely, $g'(u)$), by analogy we would expect the change of variable with a double integral to also introduce a "mapping factor." The following theorem shows that this is indeed the case.

THEOREM 13.7 Change of variables in a double integral

Let f be a continuous function on a region D, and let T be a one-to-one transformation that maps the region D in the uv-plane onto a region D^* in the xy-plane under the change of variable $x = g(u, v)$, $y = h(u, v)$, where g and h are continuously differentiable on D^*. Then

$$\int\int_{D^*} f(x, y)\, dy\, dx = \int\int_D f[g(u, v), h(u, v)]\, |J(u, v)|\, du\, dv$$

where

$$J(u, v) = \begin{vmatrix} \dfrac{\partial x}{\partial u} & \dfrac{\partial x}{\partial v} \\[2mm] \dfrac{\partial y}{\partial u} & \dfrac{\partial y}{\partial v} \end{vmatrix} = \frac{\partial x}{\partial u}\frac{\partial y}{\partial v} - \frac{\partial y}{\partial u}\frac{\partial x}{\partial v}$$

$J(u, v)$ is a mapping factor called the **Jacobian** for mapping from x, y variables to u, v variables. The Jacobian is also denoted by $\left|\dfrac{\partial(x, y)}{\partial(u, v)}\right|$. We assume $J(u, v) \neq 0$.

Proof: A formal proof is a matter for advanced calculus, but a geometric argument for this theorem is presented in Appendix B. ∎

EXAMPLE 1   Finding the Jacobian

Find the Jacobian for the change of variables from rectangular to polar coordinates, namely, $x = r \cos \theta$ and $y = r \sin \theta$.

Solution   In this example, we are changing rectangular form (x, y) to polar form (r, θ), so we write $\dfrac{\partial(x, y)}{\partial(r, \theta)}$.

$$\frac{\partial(x, y)}{\partial(r, \theta)} = \begin{vmatrix} \dfrac{\partial x}{\partial r} & \dfrac{\partial x}{\partial \theta} \\ \dfrac{\partial y}{\partial r} & \dfrac{\partial y}{\partial \theta} \end{vmatrix} = \begin{vmatrix} \cos \theta & -r \sin \theta \\ \sin \theta & r \cos \theta \end{vmatrix} = r \cos^2 \theta + r \sin^2 \theta = r$$

This result justifies the formula we have previously used:

$$\iint\limits_{D^*} f(x, y)\, dy\, dx = \iint\limits_{D} f(r \cos \theta, r \sin \theta)\, r\, dr\, d\theta$$

where D is the region in the (r, θ) plane that is mapped into D^* in the (x, y) plane of the polar transform $x = r \cos \theta$, $y = r \sin \theta$, as illustrated in Figure 13.53.

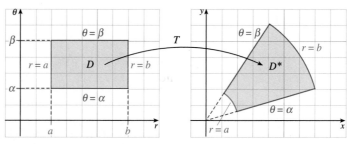

Figure 13.54 Polar transformation of a region D by T: $x = r \cos \theta$, $y = r \sin \theta$

EXAMPLE 2   Calculating a double integral by changing variables

Compute $\displaystyle\iint\limits_{D^*} \left(\frac{x - y}{x + y}\right)^4 dy\, dx$, where D^* is the triangular region bounded by the line $x + y = 1$ and the coordinate axes.

Solution   This is a rather difficult computation if no substitution is made. We wish to make a substitution that simplifies the integrand while leaving the region of integration relatively uncomplicated. Keep in mind that changing the region from D to D^* is the same as changing the limits of integration on a single integral.

Let $u = x - y$ and $v = x + y$, so that the integrand simplifies to $(u/v)^4$. Let D^* be the interior of a triangle in the xy-plane with vertices $(0, 0)$, $(0, 1)$, $(1, 0)$, as shown in Figure 13.55a. To determine the effect of this transformation on the region of integration D^*, we need to solve the system of equations for x and y in terms of u and v:

$$x = \tfrac{1}{2}(u + v) \qquad y = \tfrac{1}{2}(v - u)$$

Now transform *each* boundary of D^* to the variables u and v:

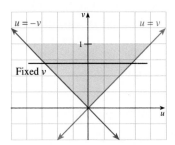

b. The transformed region, D

Figure 13.55 Transformation of D^* to D

Boundary	Substitute	Simplify
$x = 0$	$\frac{1}{2}(u + v) = 0$	$v = -u$
$y = 0$	$\frac{1}{2}(v - u) = 0$	$v = u$
$x + y = 1$	$\frac{1}{2}(u + v) + \frac{1}{2}(v - u) = 1$	$v = 1$

We draw the simplified boundary on a uv-axis, as shown in Figure 13.55b, and then note that D is the triangular region with vertices $(0, 0)$, $(1, 1)$, and $(-1, 1)$ in the uv-plane.

D can be described in type II form (fixed v) as the set of all (u, v) such that for each v between 0 and 1, u varies from the line $u = -v$ to the line $u = v$.

The last step before setting up the integral is to compute the Jacobian of the change of variables (x, y) to (u, v):

$$\frac{\partial(x, y)}{\partial(u, v)} = \begin{vmatrix} \frac{\partial}{\partial u}\left(\frac{u + v}{2}\right) & \frac{\partial}{\partial v}\left(\frac{u + v}{2}\right) \\ \frac{\partial}{\partial u}\left(\frac{v - u}{2}\right) & \frac{\partial}{\partial v}\left(\frac{v - u}{2}\right) \end{vmatrix} = \begin{vmatrix} \frac{1}{2} & \frac{1}{2} \\ -\frac{1}{2} & \frac{1}{2} \end{vmatrix} = \frac{1}{2}$$

Thus,

$$\iint_{D^*} \left(\frac{x - y}{x + y}\right)^4 dy\, dx = \iint_D \left(\frac{u}{v}\right)^4 \left|\frac{1}{2}\right| du\, dv = \frac{1}{2} \int_0^1 \int_{-v}^v u^4 v^{-4} du\, dv$$

$$= \frac{1}{2} \int_0^1 \left[\frac{v^5}{5} - \frac{-v^5}{5}\right] v^{-4} dv = \frac{1}{2} \int_0^1 \frac{2v}{5} dv = \frac{1}{5} \int_0^1 v\, dv = \frac{1}{10}$$

In Example 2, the change of variables was chosen in order to simplify the integrand, but it is also useful to introduce a change of variables that simplifies the region of integration.

EXAMPLE 3 Change of variable to simplify a region

Find the area of the region E bounded by the ellipse $\frac{x^2}{a^2} + \frac{y^2}{b^2} = 1$.

Solution The area is given by the integral

$$A = \iint_E dy\, dx$$

where E is the region shown in Figure 13.56a.

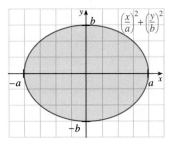

a. The elliptical region E

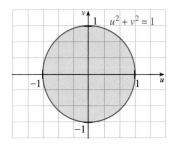

b. The transformed region C is a circular disk.

Figure 13.56 Transformation of the ellipse E to the circle C

We will transform the elliptical region E to one that is circular. Because E can be represented by

$$\left(\frac{x}{a}\right)^2 + \left(\frac{y}{b}\right)^2 \le 1$$

we consider the substitution $u = \frac{x}{a}$ and $v = \frac{y}{b}$, which will map the elliptical region E onto the circular disk C, where

$$C: u^2 + v^2 \le 1$$

as shown in Figure 13.56b. Solving the two equations for x and y, we obtain $x = au$, $y = bv$, the Jacobian gives us the mapping (change of variable) factor:

$$\frac{\partial(x, y)}{\partial(u, v)} = \begin{vmatrix} \dfrac{\partial}{\partial u}(au) & \dfrac{\partial}{\partial v}(au) \\ \dfrac{\partial}{\partial u}(bv) & \dfrac{\partial}{\partial v}(bv) \end{vmatrix} = \begin{vmatrix} a & 0 \\ 0 & b \end{vmatrix} = ab$$

Because $ab > 0$, we have $|ab| = ab$, and the area of E is given by

$$\iint_E dy\, dx = \iint_C ab\, du\, dv = ab \iint_C du\, dv = ab\underbrace{\left[\pi(1)^2\right]}_{\text{Because } C \text{ is a circle of radius 1}} = \pi ab \quad \blacksquare$$

■ CHANGE OF VARIABLES IN A TRIPLE INTEGRAL

The change of variable formula for triple integrals is similar to the one given for double integrals. Let T be a change of variable that maps a region R^* in xyz-space onto a region R in uvw-space, where

$$T: x = x(u, v, w) \qquad y = y(u, v, w) \qquad z = z(u, v, w)$$

Then the Jacobian of T is the determinant

$$\frac{\partial(x, y, z)}{\partial(u, v, w)} = \begin{vmatrix} \dfrac{\partial x}{\partial u} & \dfrac{\partial x}{\partial v} & \dfrac{\partial x}{\partial w} \\ \dfrac{\partial y}{\partial u} & \dfrac{\partial y}{\partial v} & \dfrac{\partial y}{\partial w} \\ \dfrac{\partial z}{\partial u} & \dfrac{\partial z}{\partial v} & \dfrac{\partial z}{\partial w} \end{vmatrix}$$

and the change of variable yields

$$\iiint_{R^*} f(x, y, z)\, dx\, dy\, dz = \iiint_R f[x(u, v, w), y(u, v, w), z(u, v, w)] \left|\frac{\partial(x, y, z)}{\partial(u, v, w)}\right| du\, dv\, dw$$

EXAMPLE 4   Formula for integrating with spherical coordinates

Find the formula for integrating with spherical coordinates.

Solution   The conversion formulas from rectangular coordinates to spherical coordinates are:

$$x = \rho \sin\phi \cos\theta \qquad y = \rho \sin\phi \sin\theta \qquad z = \rho \cos\phi$$

The Jacobian of this transformation is

$$\frac{\partial(x, y, z)}{\partial(\rho, \theta, \phi)} = \begin{vmatrix} \frac{\partial}{\partial\rho}(\rho\sin\phi\cos\theta) & \frac{\partial}{\partial\theta}(\rho\sin\phi\cos\theta) & \frac{\partial}{\partial\phi}(\rho\sin\phi\cos\theta) \\ \frac{\partial}{\partial\rho}(\rho\sin\phi\sin\theta) & \frac{\partial}{\partial\theta}(\rho\sin\phi\sin\theta) & \frac{\partial}{\partial\phi}(\rho\sin\phi\sin\theta) \\ \frac{\partial}{\partial\rho}(\rho\cos\phi) & \frac{\partial}{\partial\theta}(\rho\cos\phi) & \frac{\partial}{\partial\phi}(\rho\cos\phi) \end{vmatrix}$$

$$= \begin{vmatrix} \sin\phi\cos\theta & -\rho\sin\phi\sin\theta & \rho\cos\phi\cos\theta \\ \sin\phi\sin\theta & \rho\sin\phi\cos\theta & \rho\cos\phi\sin\theta \\ \cos\phi & 0 & -\rho\sin\phi \end{vmatrix}$$

After many steps, we can evaluate this determinant as $-\rho^2\sin\phi$. Because $0 \le \phi \le \pi$, we have $\sin\phi \ge 0$ and $\rho^2 \ge 0$ so that $|-\rho^2\sin\phi| = \rho^2\sin\phi$.

$$\iiint_{R^*} f(x, y, z)\, dz\, dx\, dy = \iint_R \int f(\rho\sin\phi\cos\theta, \rho\sin\phi\sin\theta, \rho\cos\phi)\, \rho^2\sin\phi\, d\rho\, d\theta\, d\phi$$

PROBLEM SET 13.8

A *Find the Jacobian of the change of variables given in Problems 1–12.*

1. $x = u + v,\ y = uv$
2. $x = u^2,\ y = u + v$
3. $x = u - v,\ y = u + v$
4. $x = u^2 - v^2,\ y = 2uv$
5. $x = u^2v^2,\ y = v^2 - u^2$
6. $x = u\cos v,\ y = u\sin v$
7. $x = e^{u+v},\ y = e^{u-v}$
8. $x = e^u\sin v,\ y = e^u\cos v$
9. $x = u + v - w;\ y = 2u - v + 3w;\ z = -u + 2v - w$
10. $x = 2u - w,\ y = u + 3v,\ z = v + 2w$
11. $x = u\cos v,\ y = u\sin v,\ z = we^{uv}$
12. $x = \dfrac{u}{v},\ y = \dfrac{v}{w},\ z = \dfrac{w}{u}$

A region R^* is given in Problems 13–16. Sketch the image R in the uv-plane using the given transformations.

13.

$u = x + y,\ v = x - y$

14.

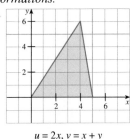

$u = 2x,\ v = x + y$

15.

$u = x^2 - y^2,\ v = 2xy$

16.

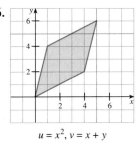

$u = x^2,\ v = x + y$

17. Suppose a uv-plane is mapped onto an xy-plane by the equations $x = u(1 - v),\ y = uv$. Express $dx\, dy$ in terms of $du\, dv$.

18. Suppose a uv-plane is mapped onto an xy-plane by the equations $x = u^2 - v^2,\ y = 2uv$. Express $dx\, dy$ in terms of $du\, dv$.

Let D be the region in the xy-plane that is bounded by the coordinate axes and the line $x + y = 1$. Use the change of variable $u = x - y,\ v = x + y$ to compute the integrals given in Problems 19–22.

19. $\displaystyle\iint_{D^*} \left(\frac{x - y}{x + y}\right)^5 dy\, dx$

20. $\displaystyle\iint_{D^*} \left(\frac{x + y}{x - y}\right)^4 dy\, dx$

21. $\displaystyle\iint_{D^*} (x - y)^5(x + y)^3\, dy\, dx$

22. $\displaystyle\iint_{D^*} (x - y)e^{x^2 + y^2}\, dy\, dx$

B **23.** ■ **What Does This Say?**   Discuss the process of changing variables in a triple integral.

24. ■ **What Does This Say?**   Discuss the necessity of using the Jacobian when changing variables in a double integral.

Under the transformation

$$u = \tfrac{1}{5}(2x + y) \qquad v = \tfrac{1}{5}(x - 2y)$$

the square S in the xy-plane with vertices $(0, 0)$, $(1, -2)$, $(2, 1)$, $(3, -1)$ is mapped onto the square in the uv-plane that is bounded by the positive coordinate axes and the lines $u = 1$ and $v = 1$. Use this information to find the integrals in Problems 25–30.

25. $\displaystyle\iint_S \left(\frac{2x + y}{x - 2y + 5}\right)^2 dy\, dx$

26. $\displaystyle\iint_S (2x + y)(x - 2y)^2\, dy\, dx$

27. $\displaystyle\int\int_S (2x + y)^2(x - 2y)\, dy\, dx$

28. $\displaystyle\int\int_S \sqrt{(2x + y)(x - 2y)}\, dy\, dx$

29. $\displaystyle\int\int_S (2x + y)\tan^{-1}(x - 2y)\, dy\, dx$

30. $\displaystyle\int\int_S \cos(2x + y)\sin(x - 2y)\, dy\, dx$

31. Let R be the region in the xy-plane that is bounded by the parallelogram with vertices $(0, 0)$, $(1, 1)$, $(2, 1)$ and $(1, 0)$. Use the linear transformation $x = u + v$, $y = v$ to compute $\int\int_R (2x - y)\, dy\, dx$.

32. Use a suitable linear transformation $u = ax + by$, $v = rx + sy$ to evaluate the integral

$$\int\int_R \left(\frac{x + y}{2}\right)^2 e^{(y-x)/2}\, dy\, dx$$

where R is the region inside the parallelogram with vertices $(0, 0)$, $(1, 1)$, $(-1, 1)$, and $(0, 2)$.

33. Under the change of variables $x = s^2 - t^2$, $y = 2st$, the quarter circular region in the st-plane given by $s^2 + t^2 \leq 1$, $s \geq 0$, $t \geq 0$ is mapped onto a certain region S of the xy-plane. Evaluate

$$\int\int_S \frac{dy\, dx}{\sqrt{x^2 + y^2}}$$

34. Use $x = ar\cos\theta$, $y = br\sin\theta$ to evaluate

$$\int\int_S \exp\left(-\frac{x^2}{a^2} - \frac{y^2}{b^2}\right)\, dy\, dx$$

where S is the quarter ellipse

$$\frac{x^2}{a^2} + \frac{y^2}{b^2} \leq 1, \qquad x \geq 0, y \geq 0$$

35. A rotation of the xy-plane through the fixed angle θ is given by

$$x = u\cos\theta - v\sin\theta; \ y = u\sin\theta + v\cos\theta$$

Figure 13.57 Rotational transformation

a. Compute the Jacobian $\dfrac{\partial(x, y)}{\partial(u, v)}$.

b. Let E denote the ellipse

$$x^2 + xy + y^2 = 3$$

Use a rotation of $\frac{\pi}{4}$ to obtain an integral that is equivalent to $\int\int_E y\, dy\, dx$. Evaluate the transformed integral.

36. THINK TANK PROBLEM   Let R be the region bounded by the parallelogram with vertices $(0, 0)$, $(2, 0)$, $(1, 1)$, and $(-1, 1)$. Show that under a suitable change of variable of the form $x = au + bv$, $y = cu + dv$, we have

$$\int\int_R f(x, y)\, dy\, dx = \int_0^2 f(t)\, dt$$

where f is continuous on $[0, 2]$.

37. Find the Jacobian of the cylindrical coordinate transformation:

$$x = r\cos\theta, \qquad y = r\sin\theta, \qquad z = z$$

38. Use the change of variable

$$x = au, y = bv, z = cw$$

to find the volume of the ellipsoid

$$\frac{x^2}{a^2} + \frac{y^2}{b^2} + \frac{z^2}{c^2} = 1$$

39. Evaluate $\displaystyle\int\int_R \ln\left(\frac{x - y}{x + y}\right)\, dy\, dx$, where R is the triangular region with vertices $(1, 0)$, $(4, -3)$, and $(4, 1)$.

Ⓒ 40. Show that if $ad - bc \neq 0$, the linear transformation

$$u = ax + by \quad \text{and} \quad v = cx + dy$$

can be solved for x and y to obtain

$$x = \frac{du - bv}{ad - bc} \quad \text{and} \quad y = \frac{av - cu}{ad - bc}$$

41. THINK TANK PROBLEM   Find the volume of the solid under the surface

$$z = \frac{xy}{1 + x^2y^2}$$

over the region bounded by $xy = 1$, $xy = 5$, $x = 1$, and $x = 5$. *Hint*: Use a change of variables of the form $x = u$, $xy = v$. See Figure 13.58.

Figure 13.58 Problem 41

CHAPTER 13 REVIEW

> **IN THIS REVIEW** Proficiency examination; supplementary problems
> Problems 1–22 of the proficiency examination test your knowledge of the concepts of this chapter, and Problems 23–30 test your understanding of those concepts by asking you to work sample practice problems. The supplementary problems present questions relating to the material of this chapter in a wide variety of settings.

PROFICIENCY EXAMINATION

Concept Problems

1. Define a double integral.
2. State Fubini's theorem over a rectangular region.
3. What is a type I region? State Fubini's theorem for a type I region.
4. What is a type II region? State Fubini's theorem for a type II region.
5. State the formula for finding an area using a double integral.
6. State the formula for finding a volume using a double integral.
7. State the following properties of a double integral:
   a. linearity rule   **b.** dominance rule
   c. subdivision rule
8. What is the formula for double integral in polar coordinates?
9. Explain how to evaluate an improper integral in polar coordinates.
10. State the double integral formula for surface area.
11. State the formula for surface area defined by a vector function.
12. State Fubini's theorem over a parallelepiped in space.
13. Give a triple integral formula for volume.
14. Explain how to use a double integral to find the mass of a planar lamina of variable density.
15. How do you find the moment of mass with respect to the x-axis?
16. What are the formulas for the centroid of a region?
17. Define moment of inertia.
18. What is a joint probability density function?
19. Complete the following table for the conversion of coordinates.

	(x, y, z) Rectangular	(r, θ, z) Cylindrical	(ρ, θ, ϕ) Spherical
From	To		
(x, y, z) Rectangular	$x = x$ $y = y$ $z = z$	$r = \underline{\ ?\ }$ $\tan\theta = \underline{\ ?\ }$ $z = \underline{\ ?\ }$	$\rho = \underline{\ ?\ }$ $\tan\theta = \underline{\ ?\ }$ $\phi = \underline{\ ?\ }$
(r, θ, z) Cylindrical	$x = \underline{\ ?\ }$ $y = \underline{\ ?\ }$ $z = \underline{\ ?\ }$	$r = r$ $\theta = \theta$ $z = z$	$\rho = \underline{\ ?\ }$ $\theta = \underline{\ ?\ }$ $\phi = \underline{\ ?\ }$
(ρ, θ, ϕ) Spherical	$x = \underline{\ ?\ }$ $y = \underline{\ ?\ }$ $z = \underline{\ ?\ }$	$r = \underline{\ ?\ }$ $\theta = \underline{\ ?\ }$ $z = \underline{\ ?\ }$	$\rho = \rho$ $\theta = \theta$ $\phi = \phi$

20. **a.** State the formula for triple integral in cylindrical coordinates.
    b. State the formula in spherical coordinates.
21. Define the Jacobian for the change of variables from xy-coordinates to uv-coordinates, where $x = g(u, v)$, $y = h(u, v)$.
22. State the formula for the change of variables in a double integral.

Practice Problems

23. Evaluate $\displaystyle\int_0^{\pi/3}\int_0^{\sin y} e^{-x}\cos y\, dx\, dy$.

24. Evaluate $\displaystyle\int_{-1}^{1}\int_0^{z}\int_y^{y-z}(x + y - z)\, dx\, dy\, dz$.

25. Use a double integral to compute the area of the region R that is bounded by the x-axis and the parabola $y = 9 - x^2$.

26. Use polar coordinates to evaluate
$$\int_0^1\int_0^{\sqrt{1-x^2}}\cos(x^2 + y^2)\, dy\, dx$$

27. Find the surface area of the portion of the sphere $x^2 + y^2 + z^2 = 4$ that lies above the xy-plane.

Figure 13.59 Problem 28, page 892

28. Set up and evaluate a triple integral for the volume of the solid region in the first octant that is bounded above by the plane $z = 4x$ and on the sides by the paraboloid $z = x^2 + 2y^2$. See Figure 13.59, p. 891.

29. A solid S is bounded above by the plane $z = 4$ and below by the surface $z = x^2 + y^2$. Its density $\rho(x, y, z)$ at each point P is equal to the distance of P from the z-axis. Find the total mass of S.

30. Use a linear change of variables to evaluate the double integral

$$\iint_R (x + y)e^{x - 2y} \, dy \, dx$$

where R is the triangular region with vertices $(0, 0)$, $(2, 0)$, $(1, 1)$.

SUPPLEMENTARY PROBLEMS

In Problems 1–10, sketch the region of integration, exchange the order, and evaluate the integral using either order of integration.

1. $\displaystyle\int_0^1 \int_0^{3x} x^2 y^2 \, dy \, dx$

2. $\displaystyle\int_0^4 \int_0^1 \sqrt{\frac{y}{x}} \, dx \, dy$

3. $\displaystyle\int_1^2 \int_0^y \frac{1}{x^2 + y^2} \, dx \, dy$

4. $\displaystyle\int_0^{\pi/2} \int_0^{\pi/2} \cos(x + y) \, dx \, dy$

5. $\displaystyle\int_0^1 \int_0^1 x\sqrt{x^2 + y} \, dx \, dy$

6. $\displaystyle\int_0^{\pi/2} \int_0^{\sqrt{\sin x}} xy \, dy \, dx$

7. $\displaystyle\int_0^1 \int_{-\sqrt{1 - x^2}}^0 y\sqrt{x} \, dy \, dx$

8. $\displaystyle\int_0^1 \int_{\sqrt{y}}^1 \sqrt{1 - x^3} \, dx \, dy$

9. $\displaystyle\int_0^1 \int_{x^2}^1 x^3 \sin y^3 \, dy \, dx$

10. $\displaystyle\int_0^2 \int_0^{\sqrt{4 - x^2}} \sqrt{4 - x^2 - y^2} \, dy \, dx$

Evaluate the integrals given in Problems 11–38.

11. $\displaystyle\int_0^1 \int_{\sqrt{x}}^1 e^{y^3} \, dy \, dx$

12. $\displaystyle\int_0^2 \int_x^2 \frac{y}{(x^2 + y^2)^{3/2}} \, dy \, dx$

13. $\displaystyle\int_0^1 \int_{-1}^4 \int_x^y z \, dz \, dy \, dx$

14. $\displaystyle\int_1^2 \int_0^1 \int_0^{\sqrt{1 - x^2}} e^{\sqrt{x^2 + y^2}} \, dy \, dx \, dz$

15. $\displaystyle\int_0^{\pi/4} \int_0^{2\pi} \int_0^\theta r^2 \sin\phi \, dr \, d\theta \, d\phi$

16. $\displaystyle\int_0^1 \int_0^x \int_0^y x^2 y \, dz \, dy \, dx$

17. $\displaystyle\int_1^2 \int_x^{x^2} \int_0^{\ln x} xe^z \, dz \, dy \, dx$

18. $\displaystyle\int_0^1 \int_{1 - x}^{1 + x} \int_0^{xy} xz \, dz \, dy \, dx$

19. $\displaystyle\int_{-\sqrt{3}}^{\sqrt{3}} \int_{-\sqrt{3 - y^2}}^{\sqrt{3 - y^2}} \int_{(x^2 + y^2)^2}^9 y^2 \, dz \, dx \, dy$

Hint: Change to cylindrical coordinates.

20. $\displaystyle\iint_D x^2 y \, dA$, where D is the circular disk $x^2 + y^2 \leq 4$

21. $\displaystyle\iint_D (x^2 + y^2 + 1) \, dA$, where D is the circular disk $x^2 + y^2 \leq 4$

22. $\displaystyle\iint_D e^{x^2 + y^2} \, dA$, where D is the circular disk $x^2 + y^2 \leq 4$

23. $\displaystyle\iint_D (x^2 + y^2)^n \, dA$, where D is the circular disk $x^2 + y^2 \leq 4$, $n \geq 0$

24. $\displaystyle\iint_D \frac{2y}{x} \, dA$, where D is the region above the line $x + y = 1$ and below the circle $x^2 + y^2 = 1$

25. $\displaystyle\iint_D x^2\sqrt{4 - y} \, dA$, where D is the circular disk $x^2 + y^2 \leq 4$

26. $\displaystyle\iint_D \exp\left(\frac{y - x}{y + x}\right) dy \, dx$, where D is the triangular region with vertices $(0, 0)$, $(2, 0)$, $(0, 2)$ *Hint*: Make a suitable change of variables.

27. $\displaystyle\iint_D x^3 \, dA$, where D is the shaded portion of the figure

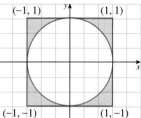

28. $\displaystyle\iint_D xy^2 \, dA$, where D is the shaded portion of the figure

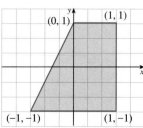

29. $\displaystyle\iint\limits_{P} \frac{dA}{(a^2 + x^2 + y^2)^m}$, $a > 0$, $m > 1$, where P is the entire xy-plane. *Hint*: Note this is an improper double integral.

30. $\displaystyle\iint\limits_{P} e^{-(a|x|+b|y|)}\, dA$, $a > 0$, $b > 0$, where P is the entire xy-plane. *Hint*: Use Cartesian coordinates and note this is an improper double integral.

31. $\displaystyle\iint\limits_{R} \frac{\partial^2 f}{\partial x \partial y}\, dx\, dy$, where R is the rectangle $a \le x \le b$, $c \le y \le d$ and $\dfrac{\partial^2 f}{\partial x \partial y}$ is continuous over R with $f(a, c) = 4$, $f(a, d) = -3$, $f(b, c) = 1$, $f(b, d) = 5$

32. $\displaystyle\iiint\limits_{S} \sqrt{x^2 + y^2 + z^2}\, dV$, where S is the portion of the solid sphere $x^2 + y^2 + z^2 \le 1$ that lies in the first octant

33. $\displaystyle\iiint\limits_{S} (x^2 + y^2 + z^2)\, dV$, where S is the portion of the solid sphere $x^2 + y^2 + z^2 \le 1$ that lies in the first octant

34. $\displaystyle\iiint\limits_{H} z^2\, dV$, where H is the solid hemisphere $x^2 + y^2 + z^2 \le 1$ with $z \ge 0$

35. $\displaystyle\iiint\limits_{H} \frac{dV}{\sqrt{x^2 + y^2 + z^2}}$, where H is the solid hemisphere $x^2 + y^2 + z^2 \le 1$, with $z \ge 0$

36. $\displaystyle\iiint\limits_{S} \frac{dV}{x^2 + y^2 + z^2}$, where S is the solid region bounded on the sides by the paraboloid $2z = x^2 + y^2$, and above by the sphere $x^2 + y^2 + z^2 = 8$

37. $\displaystyle\iiint\limits_{S} z(x^2 + y^2)^{-1/2}\, dV$, where S is the solid bounded by the surface $2z = x^2 + y^2$ and the plane $z = 2$

38. $\displaystyle\iiint\limits_{S} (x^4 + 2x^2 y^2 + y^4)\, dV$, where S is the solid cylinder given by $x^2 + y^2 \le a^2$, $0 \le z \le \dfrac{1}{\pi}$

39. Rewrite the triple integral $\displaystyle\int_0^1 \int_0^x \int_0^{\sqrt{xy}} f(x, y, z)\, dz\, dy\, dx$ as a triple integral in the order $dy\, dx\, dz$.

40. Convert the double integral
$$\int_0^{\pi/2} \int_0^{2a \cos \theta} r \sin 2\theta\, dr\, d\theta$$
to rectangular coordinates and evaluate.

41. Evaluate by reversing the order of integration
$$\int_1^2 \int_{y^2}^{y^5} e^{x/y^2}\, dx\, dy$$

42. Express the integral
$$\int_0^1 \int_0^y f(x, y)\, dx\, dy + \int_1^4 \int_0^{(4-y)/3} f(x, y)\, dx\, dy$$
as a double integral with the order of integration reversed.

43. Express the integral
$$\int_0^1 \int_{-\sqrt{y}}^{\sqrt{y}} f(x, y)\, dx\, dy + \int_1^3 \int_{-1}^{2-y} f(x, y)\, dx\, dy$$
as a double integral with the order of integration reversed.

44. Find numbers a, b, and c so that
$$\int_{-\infty}^{\infty} \int_{-\infty}^{\infty} \exp[-(ax^2 + bxy + cy^2)]\, dA = 1$$
Hint: Use a change of variables of the general form $u = Ax + By$, $v = Cx + Dy$.

45. Find the area inside the circle $r = \cos\theta$ and outside the cardioid $r = 1 - \cos\theta$.

46. Find the area outside the cardioid $r = 1 + \cos\theta$ and inside the cardioid $r = 1 + \sin\theta$.

47. Find the area outside the small loop of $r = 1 + 2\sin\theta$ and inside the large loop.

48. Use a double integral to compute the volume of the tetrahedral region in the first octant that is bounded by the coordinate planes and the plane $3x + y + 2z = 6$.

49. Find the volume of the tetrahedron that is bounded by the coordinate planes and the plane
$$\frac{x}{a} + \frac{y}{b} + \frac{z}{c} = 1$$
with $a > 0$, $b > 0$, $c > 0$.

50. Find the volume of the solid that is bounded above by the paraboloid $z = x^2 + y^2$ and below by the square region $0 \le x \le 1$, $0 \le y \le 1$.

51. Find the volume of the solid that is bounded above by the surface $z = xy$, below by the xy-plane, and on the sides by the part of the circular disk $x^2 + y^2 \le a^2$ $(a > 0)$ that lies in the first quadrant.

52. Find the volume of the solid that is bounded above by the paraboloid $z = 4 - x^2 - y^2$ and below by the plane $z = 4 - 2x$.

53. Find the surface area of that portion of the surface $z = \sqrt{x^2 + y^2}$ that is contained in the cylinder $x^2 + y^2 = 1$.

54. Find the surface area of the portion of the paraboloid $z = x^2 + y^2$ that lies below the plane $z = 9$.

55. Find the surface area of the portion of the cylinder $x^2 + z^2 = 4$ that is bounded by the planes $x = 0$, $x = 1$, $y = 0$, and $y = 2$.

56. Find the volume of the region bounded by the surface $y^2 + z^2 = 2x$ and the plane $x + y = 1$.

57. Find the volume of the region bounded above by the paraboloid $z = 4 - x^2 - y^2$ and below by the plane $z + 2x = 4$.

58. Find the volume of the region bounded by the ellipsoid $z^2 = 4 - 4r^2$ and the cylinder $r = \cos\theta$.

59. Find the volume of the region bounded above by the hemisphere $z = \sqrt{9 - x^2 - y^2}$, below by the xy-plane, and on the sides by the cylinder $x^2 + y^2 = 1$.

60. Show that the solid bounded below by the cone $z = \sqrt{x^2 + y^2}$ and above by the sphere $x^2 + y^2 + z^2 = 2az$ for $a > 0$ has volume $V = \pi a^3$.

61. Find the volume of the solid region bounded above by the sphere given in spherical coordinates by $\rho = a$ $(a > 0)$ and below by the cone $\phi = \phi_0$ where $0 < \phi_0 < \frac{\pi}{2}$.

62. A homogeneous solid S is bounded above by the sphere $\rho = a$ $(a > 0)$ and below by the cone $\phi = \phi_0$, where $9 < \phi_0 < \frac{\pi}{2}$. Find the moment of inertia of S about the z-axis.

63. The region between the circles $x^2 + y^2 = 1$ and $x^2 + y^2 = 4$ with $0 \le z \le 5$ form a "washer." Find the moment of inertia of the washer about the z-axis if the density ρ is given by
    a. $\rho = k$ (k a constant)   b. $\rho(x, y) = x^2 + y^2$
    c. $\rho(x, y) = x^2 y^2$

64. Find $\bar{x}$, the x-coordinate of the center of mass, of a triangular lamina with vertices $(0, 0)$, $(1, 0)$, and $(0, 1)$ if the density is $\rho(x, y) = x^2 + y^2$.

65. Find the mass of a cone of top radius R and height H if the density at each point P is proportional to the distance of P from the tip of the cone.

66. Find the centroid of a homogeneous $(\rho = 1)$ right circular cone with height H and base radius R.

67. Find the Jacobian $\dfrac{\partial(u, v, w)}{\partial(x, y, z)}$ of the change of variables $u = 2x - 3y + z$, $v = 2y - z$, $w = 2z$.

68. Find the Jacobian $\dfrac{\partial(u, v, w)}{\partial(x, y, z)}$ of the change of variables $u = x^2 + y^2 + z^2$, $v = 2y^2 + z^2$, $w = 2z^2$.

69. Let $u = 2x - y$ and $v = x + 2y$. Find the image of the unit square given by $0 \le x \le 1$, $0 \le y \le 1$.

70. Find the image under the linear transformation $u = x - y$, $v = y$ for the lines of the general form $y = Cx + 1$, for constant C.

71. Suppose $u = \frac{1}{2}(x^2 + y^2)$ and $v = \frac{1}{2}(x^2 - y^2)$, with $x > 0$, $y > 0$.
    a. Find the Jacobian $\dfrac{\partial(u, v)}{\partial(x, y)}$.
    b. Solve for x and y in terms of u and v and find the Jacobian
    $$\frac{\partial(x, y)}{\partial(u, v)}$$
    c. Verify that $\dfrac{\partial(u, v)}{\partial(x, y)} \dfrac{\partial(x, y)}{\partial(u, v)} = 1$

72. Let D be the region given by $u \ge 0$, $v \ge 0$, $1 \le u + v \le 2$.
    a. Show that under the transformation $u = x + y$, $v = x - y$, D is mapped onto the region R such that $-x \le y \le x$, $\frac{1}{2} \le x \le 1$.
    b. Find the Jacobian $\dfrac{\partial(u, v)}{\partial(x, y)}$, and compute $\displaystyle\iint_D (u + v)\, du\, dv$.

73. Use a change of variables after a transformation of the form $x = Au$, $y = Bv$, $z = Cw$ to find the volume of the region bounded by the surface $\sqrt{x} + \sqrt{2y} + \sqrt{3z} = 1$ and the coordinate planes.

74. Find the centroid of a homogeneous lamina $(\rho = 1)$ that covers the part of the plane $Ax + By + Cz = 1$, $A > 0$, $B > 0$, $C > 0$ in the first quadrant.

75. A homogeneous plate $(\rho = 1)$ has the shape of the region in the first quadrant of the xy-plane that is bounded by the circle $x^2 + y^2 = 1$ and the lines $y = x$ and $x = 0$. Sketch the region and find $\bar{x}$, the x-coordinate of the centroid.

76. Let R be a lamina covering the region in the xy-plane that is bounded by the parabola $y = 1 - x^2$ and the positive coordinate axes. Assume that the lamina has density $\rho(x, y) = xy$.
    a. Find the center of mass of the lamina.
    b. Find the moment of inertia of the plate about the z-axis.

77. A solid has the shape of the cylinder $x^2 + y^2 \le a$, with $0 \le z \le b$. Assume the solid has density $\rho(x, y, z) = x^2 + y^2$.
    a. Find the mass of the solid.
    b. Find the center of mass of the solid.

78. Use cylindrical coordinates to find the volume of the solid bounded by the circular cylinder $r = 2a \cos \theta$ $(a > 0)$, the cone $z = r$, and the xy-plane.

79. Let u be everywhere continuous in the plane, and define the functions f and g by
$$f(x) = \int_a^x u(x, y)\, dy \qquad g(y) = \int_y^b u(x, y)\, dx$$

Show that
$$\int_a^b f(x)\, dx = \int_a^b g(y)\, dy$$

Hint: Show that both integrals equal $\displaystyle\iint_D u(x, y)\, dA$ for a certain region D.

80. Find the volume of the solid region bounded by the surface
$$x^{2/3} + y^{2/3} + z^{2/3} = a^{2/3}$$
where a is a positive constant.

81. Let f be a probability density function on a closed set R. Recall that a probability density function has the properties:
$$f(x, y) > 0 \qquad \text{for all } (x, y) \text{ in } R$$
$$\int_{-\infty}^{\infty} f(x, y)\, dA = 1$$

Show that the following functions are probability density functions:

a. $f(x, y) = \begin{cases} \dfrac{1}{A(R)} & \text{if } (x, y) \text{ is in } R \text{ and } A(R) \text{ is the} \\ & \text{area of } R \text{ if } (x, y) \text{ is not in } R \\ 0 \end{cases}$

b. $f(x, y) = \lambda\mu \exp(-\lambda x - \mu y)$ for $\lambda > 0$, $\mu > 0$ and (x, y) is in the first quadrant.

82. A cube of side 2 is surmounted by a hemisphere of radius 1, as shown in Figure 13.60. Suppose the center of coordinates is at the center of the hemispherical dome. If the combined solid has density $\rho = 1$, where is the center of mass?

Figure 13.60 Center of mass of a hemisphere dome

83. Set up (but do not evaluate) an integral for the mass of a lamina that covers the region outside the circle $r = \sqrt{2}\, a$ and inside the lemniscate $r^2 = 4a^2 \sin 2\theta$.

84. Set up (but do not evaluate) an integral for the mass of a lamina that covers the region enclosed by the rose $r = \cos 3\theta$.

85. Find the centroid of the solid common to the cylindrical solids $x^2 + z^2 \leq 1$ and $y^2 + z^2 \leq 1$.

86. Show that if $z = f(r, \theta)$ is the equation of a surface S in polar coordinates, the surface area of S is given by

$$\iint_R \sqrt{1 + \left(\frac{\partial z}{\partial r}\right)^2 + \frac{1}{r^2}\left(\frac{\partial z}{\partial \theta}\right)^2}\; r\, dr\, d\theta$$

where R is the projected region in the $r\theta$-plane.

87. Find the center of mass of the solid S that lies inside the sphere $x^2 + y^2 + z^2 = 1$ in the first octant $x \geq 0$, $y \geq 0$, $z \geq 0$ if the density is $\rho(x, y, z) = (x^2 + y^2 + z^2 + 1)^{-1}$.

88. Suppose we drill a square hole of side c through the center of a sphere of radius c, as shown in Figure 13.61. What is the volume of the solid that remains? *Hint*: Use spherical coordinates.

Figure 13.61 Sphere with a square hole drilled out

89. PUTNAM EXAMINATION PROBLEM   A circle of radius a is revolved through $180°$ about a line in its plane, distant b from the center of the circle ($b > a$). For what value of the ratio b/a does the center of gravity of the solid thus generated lie on the surface of the solid?

90. PUTNAM EXAMINATION PROBLEM   For $f(x)$ a positive, monotone, decreasing function defined in $0 \leq x \leq 1$, prove that

$$\frac{\displaystyle\int_0^1 x[f(x)]^2\, dx}{\displaystyle\int_0^1 xf(x)\, dx} \leq \frac{\displaystyle\int_0^1 [f(x)]^2\, dx}{\displaystyle\int_0^1 f(x)\, dx}$$

91. PUTNAM EXAMINATION PROBLEM   Show that the integral equation

$$f(x, y) = 1 + \int_0^x \int_0^y f(u, v)\, du\, dv$$

has at most one solution continuous for $0 \leq x \leq 1$, $0 \leq y \leq 1$.

GROUP RESEARCH PROJECT

"Space-Capsule Design"

This project is to be done in groups of three or four students. Each group will submit a single written report.

Suppose you are transported back in time to be part of a team of engineers designing the Apollo space-capsule. The capsule is composed of two parts:

1. A cone with a height of 4 m and a base of radius 3 m.
2. A reentry shield in the shape of a parabola revolved about the axis of the cone, which is attached to the cone along the edge of the base of the cone. Its vertex is a distance D below the base of the cone. Find values of the design parameters D and ρ so that the capsule will float with the vertex of the cone pointing up and with the waterline 2 m below the top of the cone, in order to keep the exit port $\frac{1}{3}$ m above water.

You can make the following assumptions:

a. The capsule has uniform density ρ.
b. The center of mass of the capsule should be below the center of mass of the displaced water because this will give the capsule better stability in heavy seas.
c. A body floats in a fluid at the level at which the weight of the displaced fluid equals the weight of the body (Archimedes' principle).

The science of mathematics has grown to such vast proportion that probably no living mathematician can claim to have achieved its mastery as a whole.

A. N. Whitehead
An Introduction to Mathematics
(New York, 1911), p. 252

Consider the mathematics discovered from 1911 to 1995! How many times multiplied is the quotation of Whitehead?

Your paper is not limited to the following questions but should include these concerns: Show the project director that the task is impossible; that is, there are no values of D and ρ that satisfy the design specifications. However, you can solve this dilemma by incorporating a flotation collar in the shape of a torus. The collar will be made by taking hollow plastic tubing with a circular cross section of radius 1 m and wrapping it in a circular ring about the capsule, so that it fits snugly. The collar is designed to float just submerged with its top tangent to the surface of the water. Show that this flotation collar makes the capsule plus collar assembly satisfy the design specifications. Find the density ρ needed to make the capsule float at the 2-meter mark. Assume the weight of the tubing is negligible compared to the weight of the capsule, that the design parameter D is equal to 1 meter, and the density of the water is 1.

MAA Notes 17 (1991), "Priming the Calculus Pump: Innovations and Resources," by Marcus S. Cohen, Edward D. Gaughan, R. Arthur Knoebel, Douglas S. Kurtz, and David J. Pengelley.

14

Vector Analysis

PREVIEW

This chapter joins together two important concepts—vectors and integration. The key concepts involve a collection of vectors called a **vector field** and a function called a **vector-valued function**. We use these concepts to define a **line integral**, which can be described informally as integration along a curve in space. We also examine applications of line integrals, such as computing the work performed when an object moves along a curve in a force field. A key result in vector analysis is **Green's theorem** in the plane, which allows us to compute a line integral around a closed planar curve C. We also consider the concept of surface integrals and then close by examining Stokes's theorem and the divergence theorem, which are generalizations of Green's theorem involving surface integrals.

PERSPECTIVE

In Chapter 11, we showed how vectors can be used in conjunction with the methods of calculus to describe and analyze motion in space. At that time, we were primarily interested in applications involving the derivative, and our present goal is to see how vector methods may be applied to integration problems. The topic we shall now study is called **vector analysis**, although "vector integration" might be a more appropriate name for what we plan to explore. The material of this chapter provides the mathematical background necessary for theoretical work in fluid mechanics, electricity, orbital mechanics, and magnetism.

14.1 PROPERTIES OF A VECTOR FIELD: DIVERGENCE AND CURL

IN THIS SECTION Definition of a vector field; divergence; curl; a physical interpretation of curl
In order to model properties of electricity, magnetism, fluid dynamics, and other applications, we use the notion of a *vector field*. After introducing some basic terminology, we consider two concepts, called the *divergence* and the *curl*, which involve vector differentiation. We conclude by considering applications of these concepts in the study of fluid motion.

■ DEFINITION OF A VECTOR FIELD

Figure 14.1 A wind-velocity map of the Indian Ocean

The wind-velocity map in Figure 14.1 shows wind measurements over the Indian Ocean. Notice that vectors are used to show the wind direction and the length (magnitude) and color of the vectors indicate the wind speed. In Chapter 11, we studied vector-valued functions that assign a vector to each number in a *real-number* domain. However, these simple vector-valued functions by themselves cannot describe the variety of motion shown here. To describe the behavior *at every point* in a given space, it is necessary to use a *vector field*, which is a function that assigns a vector to each member of a given set of points in $\mathbb{R}^2$ or $\mathbb{R}^3$. Here is a definition for the $\mathbb{R}^3$ case.

Vector Field

A **vector field** is a collection S of points in space together with a rule that assigns to each point (x, y, z) in S exactly one vector $\mathbf{V}(x, y, z)$.

For instance, we may represent the velocity $\mathbf{V}(x, y, z)$ of a fluid flow by drawing an appropriate vector at each point (x, y, z) in the domain of the flow, and the resulting collection of vectors is called a **velocity field**. In practice, we often express a given vector field $\mathbf{V}$ in the form

$$\mathbf{V}(x, y) = u(x, y)\mathbf{i} + v(x, y)\mathbf{j} \qquad \text{in } \mathbb{R}^2$$

or

$$\mathbf{V}(x, y, z) = u(x, y, z)\mathbf{i} + v(x, y, z)\mathbf{j} + w(x, y, z)\mathbf{k} \qquad \text{in } \mathbb{R}^3$$

The functions u, v, and w are scalar functions called the **components** of $\mathbf{V}$. For example,

$$\mathbf{V} = 2x^2 y\mathbf{i} + e^{yz}\mathbf{j} + \left(\tan\frac{x}{z}\right)\mathbf{k}$$

is a vector field with $\mathbf{i}$-component $2x^2 y$, $\mathbf{j}$-component e^{yz}, and $\mathbf{k}$-component $\tan\frac{x}{z}$.
   To get an idea of what a vector field "looks like," it is often helpful to draw $\mathbf{V}(x, y, z)$ as an "arrow" at selected points in S. We shall refer to such a diagram as the **graph of V**.

EXAMPLE 1   Graph of a vector field

Sketch the graph of the vector field $\mathbf{F}(x, y) = y\mathbf{i} - x\mathbf{j}$.

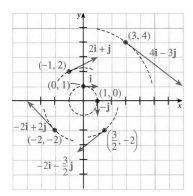

Figure 14.2 The graph of the vector field $\mathbf{F}(x, y) = y\mathbf{i} - x\mathbf{j}$

Solution We shall evaluate $\mathbf{F}$ at various points. For example,

$$\mathbf{F}(3, 4) = 4\mathbf{i} - 3\mathbf{j} \quad \text{and} \quad \mathbf{F}(-1, 2) = 2\mathbf{i} - (-1)\mathbf{j} = 2\mathbf{i} + \mathbf{j}$$

We can generate as many such vector values of $\mathbf{F}$ as we wish. Several such vectors are shown in Figure 14.2.

Computational Window

You may want to use software for graphing vector fields. The examples below show some vector fields obtained using computer software.

The graph of a vector field often yields useful information about the properties of the field. For instance, suppose $\mathbf{F}(x, y)$ represents the velocity of a compressible fluid (like a gas) at a point (x, y) in the plane. Then $\mathbf{F}$ assigns a velocity vector to each point in the plane, and the graph of $\mathbf{F}$ provides a picture of the fluid flow. Thus, the flow in Figure 14.3a is a constant, whereas Figure 14.3b suggests a circular flow.

Gravitational, electrical, and magnetic vector fields play an important role in physical applications. We shall discuss gravitational fields now and electrical and magnetic fields later in this section. Accordingly, we begin with Newton's law of gravitation which says that a point mass (particle) m at the origin exerts on a unit point mass located at the point $P(x, y, z)$ a force $\mathbf{F}(x, y, z)$ given by

$$\mathbf{F}(x, y, z) = \frac{Gm}{x^2 + y^2 + z^2}\, \mathbf{u}(x, y, z)$$

where G is a constant (the universal gravitational constant) and $\mathbf{u}$ is the unit vector extending from the point P toward the origin. The vector field $\mathbf{F}(x, y, z)$ is called the **gravitational field** of the point mass m. Because

$$\mathbf{u}(x, y, z) = \frac{-1}{\sqrt{x^2 + y^2 + z^2}}(x\mathbf{i} + y\mathbf{j} + z\mathbf{k})$$

it follows that

$$\mathbf{F}(x, y, z) = \frac{-Gm}{(x^2 + y^2 + z^2)^{3/2}}(x\mathbf{i} + y\mathbf{j} + z\mathbf{k})$$

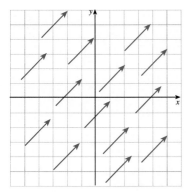

a. A constant fluid flow

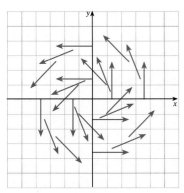

b. A circular flow

Figure 14.3 Flow diagrams

Note that the gravitational field $\mathbf{F}$ always points toward the origin and has the same magnitude for any point m located $r = \sqrt{x^2 + y^2 + z^2}$ units from the origin. Such a vector field is called a **central force field**. This force field is shown in Figure 14.4a. Some other examples of force fields are shown in Figures 14.4b and 14.4c.

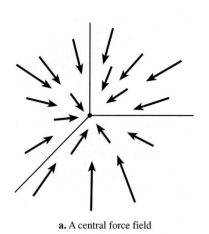

a. A central force field

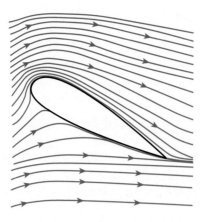

b. Air flow vector field

c. Wind velocity on a map

Figure 14.4 Examples of physical vector fields

■ DIVERGENCE

A vector field **V** can be differentiated in two different ways, one of which produces a derivative that is a scalar and the other, a vector. The scalar derivative may be defined as follows.

Divergence

⊘ The divergence of a vector field is a scalar. ⊘

The **divergence** of a vector field
$$\mathbf{V}(x, y, z) = u(x, y, z)\mathbf{i} + v(x, y, z)\mathbf{j} + w(x, y, z)\mathbf{k}$$
is denoted by div **V** and is defined by
$$\text{div } \mathbf{V} = \frac{\partial u}{\partial x}(x, y, z) + \frac{\partial v}{\partial y}(x, y, z) + \frac{\partial w}{\partial z}(x, y, z)$$

EXAMPLE 2   Finding div V

Find the divergence of each of the following vector fields.

a. $\mathbf{F}(x, y) = x^2 y\mathbf{i} + xy^3\mathbf{j}$ **b.** $\mathbf{G}(x, y, z) = x\mathbf{i} + y^3 z^2\mathbf{j} + xz^3\mathbf{k}$

Solution   **a.** div $\mathbf{F} = \frac{\partial}{\partial x}(x^2 y) + \frac{\partial}{\partial y}(xy^3) = 2xy + 3xy^2$

b. div $\mathbf{G} = \frac{\partial}{\partial x}(x) + \frac{\partial}{\partial y}(y^3 z^2) + \frac{\partial}{\partial z}(xz^3) = 1 + 3y^2 z^2 + 3xz^2$

Suppose the vector field
$$\mathbf{V}(x, y, z) = u(x, y, z)\mathbf{i} + v(x, y, z)\mathbf{j} + w(x, y, z)\mathbf{k}$$
represents the velocity of a compressible fluid (for example, a gas) with density $\rho(x, y, z)$ at a point (x, y, z) in a certain region R in $\mathbb{R}^3$. In general, the position of the fluid will vary with time t, and at each fixed time, the vector field **V** assigns a velocity to every point in R. Because the fluid is compressible, the scalar function ρ varies from one point to another. The vector field $\rho\mathbf{V}$ is called the **flux density**

and is denoted by **D**. We can think of **D** = ρ**V** as measuring the "mass flow" of the liquid.

Assuming there are no external processes acting on the fluid that would tend to create or destroy fluid, it can be shown that div **D** gives the negative time rate change of the density; that is,

$$\text{div } \mathbf{D} = -\frac{\partial \rho}{\partial t}$$

This is often referred to as the **continuity equation** of fluid dynamics. (A derivation is given in Section 14.7.). When div **D** = 0, **D** is said to be **divergence free** or **solenoidal**, and the fluid is said to be **incompressible**. If div **D** > 0 at a point (x_0, y_0, z_0), then the point is called a **source**; if div **D** < 0, the point is called a **sink** (see Figure 14.5). The terms *sink*, *source*, and *incompressible* apply to any vector field **F** and are not reserved only for fluid applications.

Figure 14.5 Flow of a fluid across a plane region, **D**

A useful way to think of the divergence div **V** is in terms of the **del operator** defined by

$$\nabla = \frac{\partial}{\partial x}\mathbf{i} + \frac{\partial}{\partial y}\mathbf{j} + \frac{\partial}{\partial z}\mathbf{k}$$

The del operator *operates* on a differentiable function $f(x, y, z)$ of three variables, and for such a function, we have

$$\nabla f = \frac{\partial f}{\partial x}\mathbf{i} + \frac{\partial f}{\partial y}\mathbf{j} + \frac{\partial f}{\partial z}\mathbf{k}$$

We can also define ∇f in a totally analogous way for functions of one, two, or more than three variables. In particular, for a differentiable function $f(x, y)$ of two variables, we have

$$\nabla f = \frac{\partial f}{\partial x}\mathbf{i} + \frac{\partial f}{\partial y}\mathbf{j}$$

We recognize ∇f as the **gradient** of f, which was introduced in Chapter 12. We can think of div **V** as the dot product of the operator ∇ and the vector field **V** = $u\mathbf{i} + v\mathbf{j} + w\mathbf{k}$; that is,

$$\text{div } \mathbf{V} = \frac{\partial u}{\partial x} + \frac{\partial v}{\partial y} + \frac{\partial w}{\partial z} = \left(\frac{\partial}{\partial x}\mathbf{i} + \frac{\partial}{\partial y}\mathbf{j} + \frac{\partial}{\partial z}\mathbf{k}\right) \cdot (u\mathbf{i} + v\mathbf{j} + w\mathbf{k}) = \nabla \cdot \mathbf{V}$$

■ CURL

The del operator may also be used to describe another derivative operation for vector fields, called the *curl*.

Curl   The **curl** of a vector field

$$\mathbf{V}(x, y, z) = u(x, y, z)\mathbf{i} + v(x, y, z)\mathbf{j} + w(x, y, z)\mathbf{k}$$

is denoted by curl $\mathbf{V}$ and is defined by

$$\text{curl } \mathbf{V} = \left(\frac{\partial w}{\partial y} - \frac{\partial v}{\partial z}\right)\mathbf{i} + \left(\frac{\partial u}{\partial z} - \frac{\partial w}{\partial x}\right)\mathbf{j} + \left(\frac{\partial v}{\partial x} - \frac{\partial u}{\partial y}\right)\mathbf{k}$$

This can be remembered in the following useful form:

$$\text{curl } \mathbf{V} = \begin{vmatrix} \mathbf{i} & \mathbf{j} & \mathbf{k} \\ \frac{\partial}{\partial x} & \frac{\partial}{\partial y} & \frac{\partial}{\partial z} \\ u & v & w \end{vmatrix}$$

We saw that $\nabla \cdot \mathbf{V} = \text{div } \mathbf{V}$, and from this definition of curl, we see that

$$\text{curl } \mathbf{V} = \left(\frac{\partial w}{\partial y} - \frac{\partial v}{\partial z}\right)\mathbf{i} + \left(\frac{\partial u}{\partial z} - \frac{\partial w}{\partial x}\right)\mathbf{j} + \left(\frac{\partial v}{\partial x} - \frac{\partial u}{\partial y}\right)\mathbf{k} = \nabla \times \mathbf{V}$$

This representation for curl and the one for divergence derived earlier are summarized in the following box.

Del Operator Forms for Divergence and Curl

⊘ div is a scalar, and curl is a vector. ⊘

Consider a vector field

$$\mathbf{V}(x, y, z) = u(x, y, z)\mathbf{i} + v(x, y, z)\mathbf{j} + w(x, y, z)\mathbf{k}$$

The divergence and curl of $\mathbf{V}$ are given by

$$\text{div } \mathbf{V} = \nabla \cdot \mathbf{V} \quad \text{and} \quad \text{curl } \mathbf{V} = \nabla \times \mathbf{V}$$

EXAMPLE 3   Curl of a vector field

Find the curl of the vector fields

$$\mathbf{F} = x^2yz\mathbf{i} + xy^2z\mathbf{j} + xyz^2\mathbf{k} \text{ and } \mathbf{G} = (x\cos y)\mathbf{i} + xy^2\mathbf{j}$$

Solution

$$\text{curl } \mathbf{F} = \begin{vmatrix} \mathbf{i} & \mathbf{j} & \mathbf{k} \\ \frac{\partial}{\partial x} & \frac{\partial}{\partial y} & \frac{\partial}{\partial z} \\ x^2yz & xy^2z & xyz^2 \end{vmatrix}$$

$$= \left(\frac{\partial}{\partial y}xyz^2 - \frac{\partial}{\partial z}xy^2z\right)\mathbf{i} - \left(\frac{\partial}{\partial x}xyz^2 - \frac{\partial}{\partial z}x^2yz\right)\mathbf{j} + \left(\frac{\partial}{\partial x}xy^2z - \frac{\partial}{\partial y}x^2yz\right)\mathbf{k}$$

$$= (xz^2 - xy^2)\mathbf{i} + (x^2y - yz^2)\mathbf{j} + (y^2z - x^2z)\mathbf{k}$$

$$\text{curl } \mathbf{G} = \begin{vmatrix} \mathbf{i} & \mathbf{j} & \mathbf{k} \\ \frac{\partial}{\partial x} & \frac{\partial}{\partial y} & \frac{\partial}{\partial z} \\ x\cos y & xy^2 & 0 \end{vmatrix}$$

$$= \left[0 - \frac{\partial}{\partial z}xy^2\right]\mathbf{i} + \left[\frac{\partial}{\partial z}(x\cos y) - 0\right]\mathbf{j} + \left[\frac{\partial}{\partial x}xy^2 - \frac{\partial}{\partial y}(x\cos y)\right]\mathbf{k}$$

$$= (y^2 + x\sin y)\mathbf{k}$$

■

EXAMPLE 4 **A constant vector field has divergence and curl zero**

Let **F** be a constant vector field. Show div **F** = 0 and curl **F** = **0**.

Solution Let **F** = a**i** + b**j** + c**k** for constants a, b, and c. Then

$$\text{div } \mathbf{F} = \frac{\partial}{\partial x}(a) + \frac{\partial}{\partial y}(b) + \frac{\partial}{\partial z}(c) = 0$$

$$\text{curl } \mathbf{F} = \begin{vmatrix} \mathbf{i} & \mathbf{j} & \mathbf{k} \\ \frac{\partial}{\partial x} & \frac{\partial}{\partial y} & \frac{\partial}{\partial z} \\ a & b & c \end{vmatrix} = 0\mathbf{i} - 0\mathbf{j} + 0\mathbf{k} = \mathbf{0}$$

⊘ Example 4 shows that the divergence and curl of a constant vector field are zero, but this does *not* mean that if the divergence or curl vanishes, then the associated vector field is a constant. For instance, if

$$\mathbf{F}(x, y, z) = yz\mathbf{i} + x\mathbf{j} + xy^2\mathbf{k}$$

then div **F** = 0. ⊘

■ A PHYSICAL INTERPRETATION OF CURL

The concepts of the divergence and curl, as well as most of the other terms in this chapter, are motivated by concepts from physics. For example, we can apply the curl to the study of fluid motion. If a fluid is moving about a region in the xy-plane, the curl can be thought of as the circulation of the fluid. A good way to measure the effect (magnitude and direction) of the circulation is to place a small paddle wheel into the fluid. The curl measures the rate of the fluid's rotation at the point P where the paddle wheel is placed in the direction of the paddle wheel's axis. The curl is positive when the rotation is counterclockwise and negative when it is clockwise. Let $\mathbf{V}(x, y, z) = u(x, y, z)\mathbf{i} + v(x, y, z)\mathbf{j} + w(x, y, z)\mathbf{k}$ be the velocity of an incompressible fluid and suppose a paddle wheel is inserted into the fluid in such a way that its axis lies along the z-axis, as shown in Figure 14.6. Disregard the weight of the paddle. The fluid tends to swirl about the z-axis, causing the paddle to rotate, and we can analyze the fluid's swirling motion by studying the motion of the paddle. It turns out that the angular velocity of the liquid

about the x-axis is proportional to $\left(\dfrac{\partial w}{\partial y} - \dfrac{\partial v}{\partial z}\right)$;

about the y-axis is proportional to $\left(\dfrac{\partial u}{\partial z} - \dfrac{\partial w}{\partial x}\right)$;

about the z-axis is proportional to $\left(\dfrac{\partial v}{\partial x} - \dfrac{\partial u}{\partial y}\right)$.

Curl V

Figure 14.6 A physical interpretation of curl **V**

Thus, the tendency of the fluid to swirl is measured by curl **V**. In the special case where curl **V** = **0**, the fluid has no rotational motion and is said to be **irrotational**.

Certain combinations of the gradient, divergence, and curl appear in many applications. In particular, note that if f is a differentiable scalar function, its gradient ∇f is a vector field and we can compute

$$\text{div } \nabla f = \left(\frac{\partial}{\partial x}\mathbf{i} + \frac{\partial}{\partial y}\mathbf{j} + \frac{\partial}{\partial z}\mathbf{k}\right) \cdot \left(\frac{\partial f}{\partial x}\mathbf{i} + \frac{\partial f}{\partial y}\mathbf{j} + \frac{\partial f}{\partial z}\mathbf{k}\right)$$

$$= \frac{\partial^2 f}{\partial x^2} + \frac{\partial^2 f}{\partial y^2} + \frac{\partial^2 f}{\partial z^2}$$

$$= \nabla \cdot \nabla f$$

The notation $\nabla \cdot \nabla f$ is usually abbreviated by writing $\nabla^2 f$, and it is called either "del-squared f" or the **Laplacian of f**, after the French mathematician Pierre Laplace (1749–1827). A function f whose first and second partials are continuous and that satisfies the equation $\nabla^2 f = 0$ is called **harmonic**. We summarize these ideas in the following box.

The Laplacian Operator

Let $f(x, y, z)$ define a function with continuous first and second partial derivatives. Then the **Laplacian of f** is

$$\nabla^2 f = \nabla \cdot \nabla f = \frac{\partial^2 f}{\partial x^2} + \frac{\partial^2 f}{\partial y^2} + \frac{\partial^2 f}{\partial z^2} = f_{xx} + f_{yy} + f_{zz}$$

The equation $\nabla^2 f = 0$ is called **Laplace's equation**, and a function that satisfies such an equation in a region D is said to be **harmonic** in D.

EXAMPLE 5   Showing a function is harmonic

Show that $f(x, y) = e^x \cos y$ is harmonic in the plane.

Solution
$$f_x(x, y) = e^x \cos y \quad \text{and} \quad f_{xx}(x, y) = e^x \cos y$$
$$f_y(x, y) = -e^x \sin y \quad \text{and} \quad f_{yy}(x, y) = -e^x \cos y$$

The Laplacian of f is given by
$$f(x, y) = f_{xx}(x, y) + f_{yy}(x, y) = e^x \cos y - e^x \cos y = 0$$

Thus, f is harmonic.

Historical Note

JAMES CLERK MAXWELL
(1831–1879)

James Maxwell was a Scottish mathematician who published a treatise on electricity and magnetism that provided the framework for modern discoveries in this area. He compiled all the facts about electricity and magnetism that were known at the time. He formulated several equations basic to the theory of electricity and magnetism now known as Maxwell's equations. James Clerk Maxwell was sometimes referred to as *dp/dt* because in thermodynamics *dp/dt* = JCM (a unit of measurement named for James Clerk Maxwell).

In many ways, the study of electricity and magnetism is analogous to that of fluid dynamics, and the curl and divergence play an important role in this study. In electromagnetic theory, it is often convenient to regard interaction between electrical charges as forces somewhat like the gravitational force between masses and then to seek quantitative measure of these forces.

One of the great scientific achievements of the 19th century was the discovery of the laws of electromagnetism by the English scientist James Clerk Maxwell. These laws have an elegant expression in terms of the divergence and curl. It is known empirically that the force acting on a charge due to an electromagnetic field depends on the position, velocity, and amount of the particular charge and not on the number of other charges that may be present or how those other charges are moving. Suppose a charge is located at the point (x, y, z) at time t, and consider the electric intensity field $\mathbf{E}(x, y, z, t)$ and the magnetic intensity field $\mathbf{H}(x, y, z, t)$. Then the behavior of the resulting electromagnetic field is determined by the following equations:

$$\operatorname{div} \mathbf{E} = \frac{Q}{\varepsilon} \qquad \operatorname{curl} \mathbf{E} = -\frac{\partial}{\partial t}(\mu \mathbf{H}) \qquad \operatorname{curl} \mathbf{H} = \mathbf{J}$$

where Q is the *electric charge density* (charge per unit volume), $\mathbf{J}$ is the *electric current density* (rate at which the charge flows through a unit area per second), μ is a constant called the *permeability*, and ε is a constant called the *permittivity*. Furthermore, if σ is a constant called the *conductivity*, then

$$(\nabla \cdot \nabla)\mathbf{E} = \mu \sigma \frac{\partial \mathbf{E}}{\partial t} + \mu \varepsilon \frac{\partial^2 \mathbf{E}}{\partial t^2}$$

Working with these equations and terms is beyond the scope of this course, but if you are interested there are many references you can consult. One of the best (in spite of the fact it is 30 years old) is the classic book written by Nobel laureate Richard Feynman, Robert Leighton, and Matthew Sands, *Feynman Lectures in Physics* (Reading, Mass.: Addison-Wesley, 1963).

PROBLEM SET 14.1

Ⓐ 1. ■ **What Does This Say?** Compare and contrast divergence and curl.

2. ■ **What Does This Say?** Discuss the del operator.

Sketch several representatives of the given vector field in Problems 3–8.

3. $\mathbf{F} = x\mathbf{i} + y\mathbf{j}$

4. $\mathbf{G} = -x\mathbf{i} + y\mathbf{j}$

5. $\mathbf{V} = x^2\mathbf{i} + y\mathbf{j}$

6. $\mathbf{H} = x^2\mathbf{i} + y^2\mathbf{j}$

7. $\mathbf{F}(x, y) = y\mathbf{i} + x\mathbf{j}$

8. $\mathbf{G}(x, y) = xy\mathbf{i} - \mathbf{j}$

In Problems 9–12, find div F and curl F for the given vector function.

9. $\mathbf{F}(x, y) = \dfrac{x}{\sqrt{x^2 + y^2}}\mathbf{i} + \dfrac{y}{\sqrt{x^2 + y^2}}\mathbf{j}$

10. $\mathbf{F}(x, y) = \mathbf{i} + (x^2 + y^2)\mathbf{j}$

11. $\mathbf{F}(x, y, z) = 2y\mathbf{j}$ 12. $\mathbf{F}(x, y, z) = z\mathbf{i} - \mathbf{j} + 2y\mathbf{k}$

In Problems 13–18, find div F and curl F for each vector field F at the given point.

13. $\mathbf{F}(x, y, z) = \mathbf{i} + \mathbf{j} + \mathbf{k}$ at $(2, -1, 3)$

14. $\mathbf{F}(x, y, z) = xz\mathbf{i} + y^2z\mathbf{j} + xz\mathbf{k}$ at $(1, -1, 2)$

15. $\mathbf{F}(x, y, z) = xyz\mathbf{i} + y\mathbf{j} + x\mathbf{k}$ at $(1, 2, 3)$

16. $\mathbf{F}(x, y, z) = (\cos y)\mathbf{i} + (\sin y)\mathbf{j} + \mathbf{k}$ at $\left(\frac{\pi}{4}, \pi, 0\right)$

17. $\mathbf{F}(x, y, z) = e^{-xy}\mathbf{i} + e^{xz}\mathbf{j} + e^{yz}\mathbf{k}$ at $(3, 2, 0)$

18. $\mathbf{F}(x, y, z) = (e^{-x}\sin y)\mathbf{i} + (e^{-x}\cos y)\mathbf{j} + \mathbf{k}$ at $(1, 3, -2)$

Find div F and curl F for each vector field F given in Problems 19–34.

19. $\mathbf{F} = (\sin x)\mathbf{i} + (\cos y)\mathbf{j}$ 20. $\mathbf{F} = (-\cos x)\mathbf{i} + (\sin y)\mathbf{j}$

21. $\mathbf{F} = x\mathbf{i} - y\mathbf{j}$ 22. $\mathbf{F} = -x\mathbf{i} + y\mathbf{j}$

23. $\mathbf{F} = \dfrac{x}{\sqrt{x^2 + y^2}}\mathbf{i} + \dfrac{y}{\sqrt{x^2 + y^2}}\mathbf{j}$

24. $\mathbf{F} = x^2\mathbf{i} - y^2\mathbf{j}$

25. $\mathbf{F} = ax\mathbf{i} + by\mathbf{j} + c\mathbf{k}$ for constants a, b, c

26. $\mathbf{F} = (e^x\sin y)\mathbf{i} + (e^x\cos y)\mathbf{j} + \mathbf{k}$

27. $\mathbf{F} = x^2\mathbf{i} + y^2\mathbf{j} + z^2\mathbf{k}$ 28. $\mathbf{F} = y\mathbf{i} + z\mathbf{j} + x\mathbf{k}$

29. $\mathbf{F} = xy\mathbf{i} + yz\mathbf{j} + xz\mathbf{k}$ 30. $\mathbf{F} = 2xz\mathbf{i} + 2yz^2\mathbf{j} - \mathbf{k}$

31. $\mathbf{F} = xyz\mathbf{i} + x^2y^2z^2\mathbf{j} + y^2z^3\mathbf{k}$

32. $\mathbf{F} = -z^3\mathbf{i} + 3\mathbf{j} + 2y\mathbf{k}$

33. $\mathbf{F} = (x - y)\mathbf{i} + (y - z)\mathbf{j} + (z - x)\mathbf{k}$

34. $\mathbf{F} = \dfrac{x\mathbf{i} + y\mathbf{j} + z\mathbf{k}}{\sqrt{x^2 + y^2 + z^2}}$

Determine whether each scalar function in Problems 35–38 is harmonic.

35. $u(x, y, z) = e^{-x}(\cos y - \sin y)$

36. $v(x, y, z) = (x^2 + y^2 + z^2)^{1/2}$

37. $w(x, y, z) = (x^2 + y^2 + z^2)^{-1/2}$

38. $r(x, y, z) = xyz$

Ⓑ 39. If $\mathbf{F}(x, y, z) = 2\mathbf{i} + 2x\mathbf{j} + 3y\mathbf{k}$ and $\mathbf{G}(x, y, z) = x\mathbf{i} - y\mathbf{j} + z\mathbf{k}$, find curl $(\mathbf{F} \times \mathbf{G})$.

40. If $\mathbf{F}(x, y, z) = xy\mathbf{i} + yz\mathbf{j} + z^2\mathbf{k}$ and $\mathbf{G}(x, y, z) = x\mathbf{i} + y\mathbf{j} - z\mathbf{k}$, find curl $(\mathbf{F} \times \mathbf{G})$.

41. If $\mathbf{F}(x, y, z) = 2\mathbf{i} + 2x\mathbf{j} + 3y\mathbf{k}$ and $\mathbf{G}(x, y, z) = x\mathbf{i} - y\mathbf{j} + z\mathbf{k}$, find div$(\mathbf{F} \times \mathbf{G})$.

42. If $\mathbf{F}(x, y, z) = xy\mathbf{i} + yz\mathbf{j} + z^2\mathbf{k}$ and $\mathbf{G}(x, y, z) = x\mathbf{i} + y\mathbf{j} - z\mathbf{k}$, find div$(\mathbf{F} \times \mathbf{G})$.

43. Find div $\mathbf{F}$, given that $\mathbf{F} = \nabla f$, where $f(x, y, z) = xy^3z^2$.

44. Find div $\mathbf{F}$, given that $\mathbf{F} = \nabla f$, where $f(x, y, z) = x^2yz^3$.

45. A magnetic field that has zero divergence everywhere is said to be **solenoidal** (because such a field can be generated by a solenoid). Show that the field $\mathbf{B} = y^2z\mathbf{i} + xz^3\mathbf{j} + y^2x^2\mathbf{k}$ is solenoidal.

46. A **central force field** $\mathbf{F}$ is one that can be described as $\mathbf{F} = f(r)\mathbf{R}$, where $\mathbf{R} = x\mathbf{i} + y\mathbf{j} + z\mathbf{k}$ and $r = \|\mathbf{R}\| = (x^2 + y^2 + z^2)^{1/2}$. Show that such a field is irrotational everywhere it is defined and differentiable. That is, show curl $\mathbf{F} = \mathbf{0}$.

Ⓒ 47. Let $\mathbf{A}$ be a constant vector and let $\mathbf{R} = x\mathbf{i} + y\mathbf{j} + z\mathbf{k}$. Show that div$(\mathbf{A} \times \mathbf{R}) = 0$.

48. Let $\mathbf{A}$ be a constant vector and let $\mathbf{R} = x\mathbf{i} + y\mathbf{j} + z\mathbf{k}$. Show that curl$(\mathbf{A} \times \mathbf{R}) = 2\mathbf{A}$.

49. If $\mathbf{F}(x, y) = u(x, y)\mathbf{i} + v(x, y)\mathbf{j}$, show that curl $\mathbf{F} = \mathbf{0}$ if and only if

$$\frac{\partial u}{\partial y} = \frac{\partial v}{\partial x}$$

50. If $\mathbf{R} = x\mathbf{i} + y\mathbf{j} + z\mathbf{k}$ and $\mathbf{F} = \dfrac{-\mathbf{R}}{\|\mathbf{R}\|}$, show that curl $\mathbf{F} = \mathbf{0}$.

51. Consider a rigid body that is rotating about the z-axis (counterclockwise from above) with constant angular velocity ω. If P is a point in the body located at $\mathbf{R} = x\mathbf{i} + y\mathbf{j} + z\mathbf{k}$, the velocity at P is given by the vector field $\mathbf{V} = \omega \times \mathbf{R}$.

a. Express $\mathbf{V}$ in terms of $\mathbf{i}$, $\mathbf{j}$, and $\mathbf{k}$ vectors.

b. Find div $\mathbf{V}$ and curl $\mathbf{V}$.

52. THINK TANK PROBLEM Find an expression for curl(curl $\mathbf{F}$) for any vector field $\mathbf{F}$.

53. Which (if any) of the following is the same as div$(\mathbf{F} \times \mathbf{G})$ for any vector fields $\mathbf{F}$ and $\mathbf{G}$?

I. (div $\mathbf{F}$)(div $\mathbf{G}$)

II. (curl $\mathbf{F}$) $\cdot$ $\mathbf{G}$ − $\mathbf{F}$ $\cdot$ (curl $\mathbf{G}$)

III. $\mathbf{F}(\text{div } \mathbf{G}) + (\text{div } \mathbf{F})\mathbf{G}$

IV. $(\text{curl } \mathbf{F}) \cdot \mathbf{G} + \mathbf{F} \cdot (\text{curl } \mathbf{G})$

In Problems 54–64, prove the given property for the vector fields F and G, scalar c, and scalar function f. Assume that the required partial derivatives are continuous.

54. $\text{div}(c\mathbf{F}) = c \text{ div } \mathbf{F}$

55. $\text{div}(\mathbf{F} + \mathbf{G}) = \text{div } \mathbf{F} + \text{div } \mathbf{G}$

56. $\text{curl}(\mathbf{F} + \mathbf{G}) = \text{curl } \mathbf{F} + \text{curl } \mathbf{G}$

57. $\text{curl}(c\mathbf{F}) = c \text{ curl } \mathbf{F}$

58. $\text{div}(\mathbf{F} \times \mathbf{G}) = (\text{curl } \mathbf{F}) \cdot \mathbf{G} - \mathbf{F} \cdot (\text{curl } \mathbf{G})$

59. $\text{curl}(f\mathbf{F}) = f \text{ curl } \mathbf{F} + (\nabla f \times \mathbf{F})$

60. $\text{div}(f\mathbf{F}) = f \text{ div } \mathbf{F} + (\nabla f \cdot \mathbf{F})$

61. $\text{curl}(\nabla f + \text{curl } \mathbf{F}) = \text{curl}(\nabla f) + \text{curl } \mathbf{F}$

62. $\text{div}(f\nabla g) = \nabla \cdot (f\nabla g)$

63. The curl of the gradient of a function is always **0**. That is, $\nabla \times (\nabla f) = \mathbf{0}$.

64. The divergence of the curl of a vector field is 0. That is, $\text{div}(\text{curl } \mathbf{F}) = 0$.

14.2 LINE INTEGRALS

> **IN THIS SECTION** Definition of a line integral, evaluation of line integrals in parametric form, line integrals of vector fields, computing work using line integrals, evaluation of line integrals with respect to arc length
>
> In Section 6.3, we showed that the single Riemann integral can be used to compute the work done when an object moves along a line segment against a given force, but what if the object moves along a curve in space? This is one of many situations that occur in science and engineering in which a more general definition of integration is required. The line integral introduced in this section is the first of many such generalizations of integration you will encounter if you continue your studies in mathematics.

■ DEFINITION OF A LINE INTEGRAL

Figure 14.7 A partitioned smooth curve

In order to model certain physical notions, such as work or potential, it is appropriate to generalize the original concept of integral by considering limits of sums whose summands depend in a certain way on a curve, called the *path of integration*. This leads us to the concept of *line integration*, which is really integration along a curve in space. We begin by defining the line integral of a scalar function f along a curve C with respect to x. The line integral of a scalar function g along C with respect to y or the line integral of h with respect to z may be defined in an analogous fashion.

First, we need to introduce some terminology regarding curves. Recall (Section 11.2) that a curve C with the parametric representation $\mathbf{R}(t) = x(t)\mathbf{i} + y(t)\mathbf{j} + z(t)\mathbf{k}$ is said to be *smooth* on the interval $t_1 < t < t_2$ if the derivatives $x'(t)$, $y'(t)$, and $z'(t)$ are all continuous and not all simultaneously zero at any point t on the interval. More generally, C is **piecewise smooth** if it can be decomposed into a finite number of smooth parts. Also, C is said to be **orientable** if it is possible to describe direction along the curve for increasing t.

Assume C is a piecewise smooth, orientable curve that begins at $P = P_0$ and ends at $Q = P_n$, as shown in Figure 14.7. Let C be partitioned into n pieces by the points $P_0, P_1, \ldots, P_n$, and let (x_k, y_k, z_k) be the coordinates of the point P_k. Finally, for $k = 1, 2, \ldots, n$, let $\hat{P}_k(x_k^*, y_k^*, z_k^*)$ be a point chosen arbitrarily from the arc joining points P_{k-1} and P_k, and let $\Delta x_k = x_k - x_{k-1}$, $\Delta y_k = y_k - y_{k-1}$, and $\Delta z_k = z_k - z_{k-1}$. We shall refer to the largest of the Δx_k as the **x-norm** of the partition and shall denote this norm by $\|\Delta x\|$. Similar definitions hold for the y-norm and the z-norm. For a given scalar function f we form the sum

$$S = \sum_{k=1}^{n} f(\hat{P}_k)\Delta x_k$$

and define the line integral $\int_C f\, dx$ over C with respect to x as follows.

Line Integral

The **line integral** $\int_C f\, dx$ of the scalar function f with respect to x along the curve C is given by

$$\int_C f\, dx = \lim_{\|\Delta x\| \to 0} \sum_{k=1}^{n} f(\hat{P}_k)\, \Delta x_k$$

provided that this limit exists.

The line integrals $\int_C f\, dy$ and $\int_C f\, dz$ are defined similarly.

THEOREM 14.1   Properties of line integrals

Let f be a given scalar function defined with respect to x on a piecewise smooth, orientable curve C. Then, for any constant k:

Constant multiple rule: $\displaystyle\int_C kf\, dx = k\int_C f\, dx$

Sum rule: $\displaystyle\int_C (f_1 + f_2)\,dx = \int_C f_1\, dx + \int_C f_2\, dx$

where f_1 and f_2 are scalar functions defined with respect to x on C.

Opposite direction rule: $\displaystyle\int_{-C} f\, dx = -\int_C f\, dx$

where $-C$ denotes the curve C traversed in the opposite direction.

Subdivision rule: $\displaystyle\int_C f\, dx = \int_{C_1} f\, dx + \int_{C_2} f\, dx$

where C is subdivided into subarcs C_1 and C_2 (with $C = C_1 \cup C_2$ and $C_1 \cap C_2 = \varnothing$). This property generalizes to any finite number of subdivisions.

Similar properties hold for line integrals of the form $\int_C g\, dy$ or $\int_C h\, dz$.

Proof: The proof follows directly from the properties of limits and the definition of a line integral. ∎

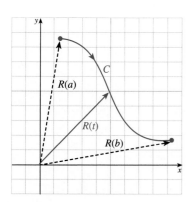

■ EVALUATION OF LINE INTEGRALS IN PARAMETRIC FORM

In practice, the line integral $\int_C f\, dx$ is almost never evaluated using the definition.

Instead, we note that if the integrand $f(x, y, z)$ is continuous on C and if C can be represented parametrically in vector form by $\mathbf{R}(t) = x(t)\mathbf{i} + y(t)\mathbf{j} + z(t)\mathbf{k}$, where the derivative $\mathbf{R}'(t)$ exists and is not zero for $a \le t \le b$, then

$$\int_C f\, dx = \int_a^b f[x(t), y(t), z(t)]\, \frac{dx}{dt}\, dt$$

Similarly, if g and h are continuous on C,

$$\int_C g \, dy = \int_a^b g[x(t), y(t), z(t)] \frac{dy}{dt} \, dt \qquad \int_C h \, dz = \int_a^b h[x(t), y(t), z(t)] \frac{dz}{dt} \, dt$$

These formulas enable us to convert a line integral into "ordinary" Riemann integrals that may be evaluated by the methods developed earlier in this text. The same answer is obtained independent of the parametrization chosen.

EXAMPLE 1   Evaluating a line integral

Let C be the portion of the parabola $y = x^2$ from $(0, 0)$ to $(2, 4)$. Evaluate

a. $\displaystyle\int_C (x^2 + y) \, dx$ **b.** $\displaystyle\int_C (x^2 + y) \, dy$

Solution   First, parametrize the curve (this step is not unique). We let $x = t$ so that $y = t^2$ for $0 \le t \le 2$.

a. Because $\dfrac{dx}{dt} = 1$, we have

$$\int_C (x^2 + y) \, dx = \int_0^2 [(t)^2 + (t^2)] \frac{dx}{dt} \, dt = 2 \int_0^2 t^2 \, dt = \left[\frac{2}{3} t^3\right]_0^2 = \frac{16}{3}$$

b. Now we have $\dfrac{dy}{dt} = 2t$, and we find

$$\int_C (x^2 + y) \, dy = \int_0^2 [(t)^2 + (t^2)] \frac{dy}{dt} \, dt = \int_0^2 2t^2 \cdot 2t \, dt = 4 \int_0^2 t^3 \, dt = \left[t^4\right]_0^2 = 16$$

EXAMPLE 2   Evaluating a line integral

Evaluate $\displaystyle\int_C xe^{yz} \, dz$, where C is the curve described parametrically by $x = t$, $y = t$, and $z = -t$ for $1 \le t \le 2$.

Solution
$$\int_C xe^{yz} \, dz = \int_1^2 te^{-t^2} \frac{dz}{dt} \, dt$$

$$= \int_1^2 (-t)e^{-t^2} \, dt \quad \text{Because } \frac{dz}{dt} = -1$$

$$= \tfrac{1}{2}(e^{-4} - e^{-1})$$

■ LINE INTEGRALS OF VECTOR FIELDS

We shall now discuss what it means to compute the **line integral of a vector field**.

Line Integral of a Vector Field

Let $\mathbf{F}(x, y, z) = f(x, y, z)\mathbf{i} + g(x, y, z)\mathbf{j} + h(x, y, z)\mathbf{k}$ be a vector field, and let C be the curve with parametric representation

$$\mathbf{R}(t) = x(t)\mathbf{i} + y(t)\mathbf{j} + z(t)\mathbf{k} \qquad \text{for } a \le t \le b$$

Using $d\mathbf{R} = dx\,\mathbf{i} + dy\,\mathbf{j} + dz\,\mathbf{k}$, we denote the **line integral of $\mathbf{F}$ over C** by $\displaystyle\int_C \mathbf{F} \cdot d\mathbf{R}$ and define it by

$$\int_C \mathbf{F} \cdot d\mathbf{R} = \int_C f \, dx + g \, dy + h \, dz$$

$$= \int_a^b \left[f[x(t), y(t), z(t)] \frac{dx}{dt} + g[x(t), y(t), z(t)] \frac{dy}{dt} + h[x(t), y(t), z(t)] \frac{dz}{dt} \right] dt$$

EXAMPLE 3   Line integral of a vector function

Evaluate $\int_C \mathbf{F} \cdot d\mathbf{R}$, where $\mathbf{F} = (y^2 - z^2)\mathbf{i} + (2yz)\mathbf{j} - x^2\mathbf{k}$ and C is the curve defined parametrically by $x = t^2$, $y = 2t$, and $z = t$ for $0 \leq t \leq 1$.

Solution   Rewrite $\mathbf{F}$ using the parameter:
$\mathbf{F} = [(2t)^2 - (t)^2]\mathbf{i} + [2(2t)(t)]\mathbf{j} - [(t^2)^2]\mathbf{k} = 3t^2\mathbf{i} + 4t^2\mathbf{j} - t^4\mathbf{k}$. Also, because
$\mathbf{R}(t) = t^2\mathbf{i} + 2t\mathbf{j} + t\mathbf{k}$, we have $d\mathbf{R} = (2t\,dt)\mathbf{i} + (2\,dt)\mathbf{j} + dt\mathbf{k}$, so that
$\mathbf{F} \cdot d\mathbf{R} = (3t^2)(2t\,dt) + (4t^2)(2\,dt) + (-t^4)(dt) = (6t^3 + 8t^2 - t^4)\,dt$.

$$\int_C \mathbf{F} \cdot d\mathbf{R} = \int_0^1 (6t^3 + 8t^2 - t^4)\,dt = \left[\tfrac{3}{2}t^4 + \tfrac{8}{3}t^3 - \tfrac{1}{5}t^5\right]_0^1 = \frac{119}{30}$$

EXAMPLE 4   Line integral of a vector defined function

Compute the line integral $\int_C \mathbf{F} \cdot d\mathbf{R}$, where $\mathbf{F} = y\mathbf{i} + x\mathbf{j}$ and C is the top half of the circle $x^2 + y^2 = 4$ traversed counterclockwise from $(2, 0)$ to $(-2, 0)$.

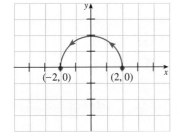

Solution   First, we parametrize the curve by setting $x = 2\cos\theta$, $y = 2\sin\theta$ for $0 \leq \theta \leq \pi$. Thus,

$\mathbf{R}(t) = (2\cos\theta)\mathbf{i} + (2\sin\theta)\mathbf{j}$ so that $d\mathbf{R} = (-2\sin\theta\,d\theta)\mathbf{i} + (2\cos\theta\,d\theta)\mathbf{j}$

$$\int_C \mathbf{F} \cdot d\mathbf{R} = \int_0^\pi [(2\sin\theta)\mathbf{i} + (2\cos\theta)\mathbf{j}] \cdot [(-2\sin\theta)\mathbf{i} + (2\cos\theta)\mathbf{j}]\,d\theta$$

$$= \int_0^\pi (-4\sin^2\theta + 4\cos^2\theta)\,d\theta$$

$$= 4\int_0^\pi (\cos^2\theta - \sin^2\theta)\,d\theta = 4\int_0^\pi \cos 2\theta\,d\theta = \left[2\sin 2\theta\right]_0^\pi = 0$$

EXAMPLE 5   Line integrals along different paths

Let $\mathbf{F} = xy^2\mathbf{i} + x^2y\mathbf{j}$ and evaluate the line integral $\int_C \mathbf{F} \cdot d\mathbf{R}$ between the points $(0, 0)$ and $(2, 4)$ along the following paths:

a. the line segment connecting the points
b. the parabolic arc $y = x^2$ connecting the points

Solution   The two paths we are considering are shown in Figure 14.8.

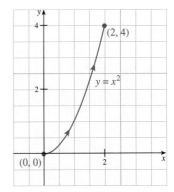

a. The line segment path   **b.** The parabolic path

Figure 14.8 A line integral along different paths

a. The line joining the given points has equation $y = 2x$, which may be parametrized by setting $x = t$, $y = 2t$ for $0 \le t \le 2$. Thus,

$$\mathbf{R}(t) = t\mathbf{i} + 2t\mathbf{j} \quad \text{so that} \quad d\mathbf{R} = dt\,\mathbf{i} + 2dt\,\mathbf{j}$$

In terms of t, we find $\mathbf{F} = 4t^3\mathbf{i} + 2t^3\mathbf{j}$ and

$$\mathbf{F} \cdot d\mathbf{R} = 4t^3\,dt + 4t^3\,dt = 8t^3\,dt$$

$$\int_C \mathbf{F} \cdot d\mathbf{R} = \int_0^2 8t^3\,dt = \left[2t^4\right]_0^2 = 32$$

b. The parabola $y = x^2$ can be parametrized by setting $x = t$, $y = t^2$ for $0 \le t \le 2$. Thus,

$$\mathbf{R}(t) = t\mathbf{i} + t^2\mathbf{j} \quad \text{so that} \quad d\mathbf{R} = dt\,\mathbf{i} + 2t\,dt\,\mathbf{j}$$

In terms of t, $\mathbf{F} = xy^2\mathbf{i} + x^2y\mathbf{j} = (t)(t^2)^2\mathbf{i} + (t)^2(t^2)\mathbf{j} = t^5\mathbf{i} + t^4\mathbf{j}$ and

$$\mathbf{F} \cdot d\mathbf{R} = t^5\,dt + 2t^5\,dt = 3t^5\,dt$$

$$\int_C \mathbf{F} \cdot d\mathbf{R} = \int_0^2 3t^5\,dt = \left[\tfrac{1}{2}t^6\right]_0^2 = 32$$

     In Example 5, we see that the value of the line integral is the same for both paths. Indeed, it can be shown that for the vector field $\mathbf{F} = xy^2\mathbf{i} + x^2y\mathbf{j}$, the line integral $\int_C \mathbf{F} \cdot d\mathbf{R}$ along *any* path C joining $(0, 0)$ to $(2, 4)$ has the same value. This, of course, is not true for every $\mathbf{F}$, but when it is true, we say that the line integral is **independent of path**. Path independence is an important feature of line integration and will be discussed in detail in the next section.

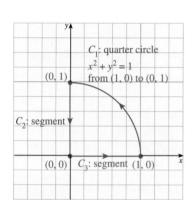

Figure 14.9 A path C composed of three parts

EXAMPLE 6   Line integral over a path consisting of several parts

Evaluate $\displaystyle\int_C (-y\,dx + x\,dy)$, where C is the closed path shown in Figure 14.9.

Solution   Because the given closed path can best be described using three separate equations (C_1, C_2, and C_3 in Figure 14.9), we consider the integration by evaluating the line integrals for each part separately. Let $\mathbf{F} = -y\mathbf{i} + x\mathbf{j}$, so that $\displaystyle\int_C (-y\,dx + x\,dy) = \int_C \mathbf{F} \cdot d\mathbf{R}$. Then

$$\int_C \mathbf{F} \cdot d\mathbf{R} = \int_{C_1} \mathbf{F} \cdot d\mathbf{R} + \int_{C_2} \mathbf{F} \cdot d\mathbf{R} + \int_{C_3} \mathbf{F} \cdot d\mathbf{R}$$

Along C_1, a parametrization is $x = \cos t$, $y = \sin t$ for $0 \le t \le \frac{\pi}{2}$, so $\mathbf{R}(t) = (\cos t)\mathbf{i} + (\sin t)\mathbf{j}$ and $d\mathbf{R} = (-\sin t\,dt)\mathbf{i} + (\cos t\,dt)\mathbf{j}$. In terms of the parameter, $\mathbf{F} = (-\sin t)\mathbf{i} + (\cos t)\mathbf{j}$ and

$$\int_{C_1} \mathbf{F} \cdot d\mathbf{R} = \int_0^{\pi/2} (\sin^2 t\,dt + \cos^2 t\,dt) = \int_0^{\pi/2} dt = \frac{\pi}{2}$$

Along C_2, a parametrization is $x = 0$, $y = 1 - t$ for $0 \le t \le 1$, so $\mathbf{R}(t) = (1 - t)\mathbf{j}$ and $d\mathbf{R} = (-dt)\mathbf{j}$. In terms of the parameter, $\mathbf{F} = (t - 1)\mathbf{i}$ and

$$\int_{C_2} \mathbf{F} \cdot d\mathbf{R} = \int_0^1 0 = 0$$

Along C_3, a parametrization is $x = t$, $y = 0$ for $0 \le t \le 1$. $\mathbf{R}(t) = t\mathbf{i}$, $d\mathbf{R} = dt\mathbf{i}$ and $\mathbf{F} = t\mathbf{j}$. Because $\mathbf{F} \cdot d\mathbf{R} = 0$, we see

$$\int_{C_3} \mathbf{F} \cdot d\mathbf{R} = 0$$

Thus,

$$\int_C \mathbf{F} \cdot d\mathbf{R} = \int_{C_1} \mathbf{F} \cdot d\mathbf{R} + \int_{C_2} \mathbf{F} \cdot d\mathbf{R} + \int_{C_3} \mathbf{F} \cdot d\mathbf{R} = \frac{\pi}{2} + 0 + 0 = \frac{\pi}{2}$$

■ COMPUTING WORK USING LINE INTEGRALS

One of the most important physical applications of the line integral is in computing work. Recall from Section 10.3 that if an object moves along a straight line in a constant force field $\mathbf{F}$ with displacement $\mathbf{R}$, the work done is $\mathbf{F} \cdot \mathbf{R}$.

The case (shown in Figure 14.10) where the force field $\mathbf{F}$ is not constant and the object moves along a smooth curve C (instead of along a straight line) requires additional attention. Assume that C is parametrized by $\mathbf{R}(t)$ and is oriented in the direction of motion. Partition C with subdivision points $P_0, P_1, P_2, \ldots, P_n$, as shown in Figure 14.11.

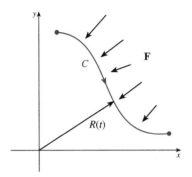

Figure 14.10 If $\mathbf{F}$ and $\mathbf{R}$ are constant, work $= \mathbf{F} \cdot \mathbf{R}$. If they are not, then a line integral is required.

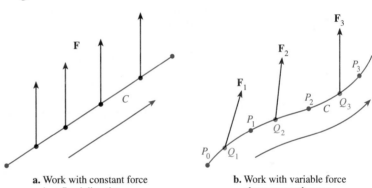

a. Work with constant force in a fixed direction

b. Work with variable force along a smooth curve

Figure 14.11 Computing work

For $k = 1, 2, \ldots, n$, let Q_k be a point chosen arbitrarily from the kth subarc C_k (with endpoints P_{k-1} and P_k), and let $\mathbf{F}_k$ be the value of the force field $\mathbf{F}$ at Q_k. If the length of the subarc C_k is small, $\mathbf{F}$ will be approximately constant with value $\mathbf{F}_k$ over C_k, and the object's displacement along C_k is given approximately by the secant vector $\Delta\mathbf{R}_k$ from P_{k-1} to P_k. Then, the work done by the force as the object moves along C_k may be estimated by

$$\Delta W_k = \left(\mathbf{F}_k \cdot \frac{\Delta\mathbf{R}_k}{\Delta t} \right) \Delta t$$

and by adding the contributions along all n subarcs, we obtain

$$\left(\mathbf{F}_1 \cdot \frac{\Delta\mathbf{R}_1}{\Delta t} \right) \Delta t + \left(\mathbf{F}_2 \cdot \frac{\Delta\mathbf{R}_2}{\Delta t} \right) \Delta t + \cdots + \left(\mathbf{F}_n \cdot \frac{\Delta\mathbf{R}_n}{\Delta t} \right) \Delta t = \sum_{k=1}^{n} \left(\mathbf{F}_k \cdot \frac{\Delta\mathbf{R}_k}{\Delta t} \right) \Delta t$$

as an estimate of the total work done by $\mathbf{F}$ as the object moves along C. As $\Delta t \to 0$. The limiting value of this sum is the line integral of $\mathbf{F} \cdot \dfrac{d\mathbf{R}}{dt}$; that is,

$$W = \lim_{\Delta t \to 0} \sum_{k=1}^{n} \left(\mathbf{F}_k \cdot \frac{\Delta\mathbf{R}_k}{\Delta t} \right) \Delta t = \int_C \mathbf{F} \cdot \frac{d\mathbf{R}}{dt}\, dt = \int_C \mathbf{F} \cdot d\mathbf{R}$$

This leads us to the following definition.

Work as a Line Integral

Let **F** be a continuous force field over a domain D. Then the **work** W done by **F** as an object moves along a smooth curve C in D is given by the line integral

$$W = \int_C \mathbf{F} \cdot d\mathbf{R}$$

EXAMPLE 7   Work as a line integral

An object moves in the force field

$$\mathbf{F} = y^2\mathbf{i} + 2(x + 1)y\mathbf{j}$$

counterclockwise from the point $(2, 0)$ along the elliptical path $x^2 + 4y^2 = 4$ to $(-2, 0)$, and back to the point $(2, 0)$ along the x-axis. How much work is done by the force field on the object?

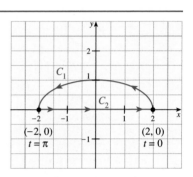

Solution   Let C denote the path of the object. Then the total work W done by **F** on the object as it moves along C is given by the line integral $\int_C \mathbf{F} \cdot d\mathbf{R}$. We divide the curve C into two parts so that $C = C_1 \cup C_2$. The curve C_1 may be parametrized by

$$x = 2\cos t, \quad y = \sin t \text{ for } 0 \le t \le \pi$$

$$\textit{Because } \left(\frac{x}{2}\right)^2 + y^2 = 1$$

$$\mathbf{R}(t) = (2\cos t)\mathbf{i} + (\sin t)\mathbf{j} \qquad \text{and} \qquad d\mathbf{R} = (-2\sin t \, dt)\mathbf{i} + (\cos t \, dt)\mathbf{j}$$

In parametric form,

$$\mathbf{F} = (\sin^2 t)\mathbf{i} + (4\cos t \sin t + 2\sin t)\mathbf{j}$$

and we have

$$W_1 = \int_{C_1} \mathbf{F} \cdot d\mathbf{R}$$

$$= \int_0^\pi (-2\sin^3 t + 4\cos^2 t \sin t + 2\sin t \cos t) \, dt$$

$$= \int_0^\pi (-2\sin^2 t + 4\cos^2 t + 2\cos t) \sin t \, dt$$

$$= \int_0^\pi (6\cos^2 t + 2\cos t - 2)\sin t \, dt \qquad \boxed{\begin{array}{l} \text{Let } u = \cos t; \\ du = -\sin t \, dt. \\ \text{If } t = 0, u = 1, \\ \text{and if } t = \pi, u = -1. \end{array}}$$

$$= -\int_1^{-1} (6u^2 + 2u - 2) \, du = 0$$

The curve C_2 is described by $y = 0$, so $\mathbf{F} = \mathbf{0}$ and, therefore, $W_2 = 0$. Thus,

$$W = W_1 + W_2 = 0.$$

■ EVALUATION OF LINE INTEGRALS WITH RESPECT TO ARC LENGTH

Line integrals of the form $\int_C \mathbf{F} \cdot d\mathbf{R}$ can often be expressed in other forms. For example, recall from Chapter 11 that $\mathbf{T} = d\mathbf{R}/ds$ is a unit tangent vector to the curve C at the point $P(x, y, z)$, where s is the arc length parameter. We have

$$\int_C \mathbf{F} \cdot d\mathbf{R} = \int_C \mathbf{F} \cdot \frac{d\mathbf{R}}{ds}\, ds = \int_C \mathbf{F} \cdot \mathbf{T}\, ds$$

In particular, the work W done by a force field $\mathbf{F}$ on an object moving along a curve C may be expressed as

$$W = \int_C \mathbf{F} \cdot d\mathbf{R} = \int_C \mathbf{F} \cdot \mathbf{T}\, ds$$

This integral is called the **line integral of the tangential component of F** and can also be written as $\int_C f(x, y, z)\, ds$. The integral will exist if f is continuous on the curve C and if C itself is piecewise smooth with finite length. A formula for computing this line integral may be obtained by noting that if $\mathbf{R}(t) = x(t)\mathbf{i} + y(t)\mathbf{j} + z(t)\mathbf{k}$, then

$$\left\| \frac{d\mathbf{R}}{dt} \right\| = \left\| \frac{dx}{dt}\mathbf{i} + \frac{dy}{dt}\mathbf{j} + \frac{dz}{dt}\mathbf{k} \right\|$$

$$= \sqrt{\left(\frac{dx}{dt}\right)^2 + \left(\frac{dy}{dt}\right)^2 + \left(\frac{dz}{dt}\right)^2} = \frac{ds}{dt}$$

so that $\int_C f(x, y, z)\, ds = \int_C f(x, y, z)\, \dfrac{ds}{dt}\, dt$. To summarize:

Evaluation of a Line Integral with Respect to Arc Length

Let f be continuous on a smooth curve C. If C is defined by $\mathbf{R}(t) = x(t)\mathbf{i} + y(t)\mathbf{j} + y(t)\mathbf{k}$, where $a \leq t \leq b$, then

$$\int_C f(x, y, z)\, ds = \int_a^b f[x(t), y(t), z(t)]\sqrt{[x'(t)]^2 + [y'(t)]^2 + [z'(t)]^2}\, dt$$

EXAMPLE 8   Evaluating a line integral with respect to arc length

Find $\displaystyle\int_C (x + y^2 - z)\, ds$, where C is the curve described parametrically by $x = t$, $y = 2t$, $z = t + 1$ for $0 \leq t \leq 1$.

Solution Because $\dfrac{dx}{dt} = 1$, $\dfrac{dy}{dt} = 2$, and $\dfrac{dz}{dt} = 1$, we have

$$\int_C (x + y^2 - z)\, ds = \int_0^1 [t + (2t)^2 - (t + 1)]\sqrt{(1)^2 + (2)^2 + (1)^2}\, dt$$

$$= \sqrt{6} \int_0^1 (4t^2 - 1)\, dt = \tfrac{1}{3}\sqrt{6}$$

$x = t, y = 2t, z = t + 1$
for $0 \leq t \leq 1$

PROBLEM SET 14.2

A 1. ■ **What Does This Say?** Describe a line integral.
2. ■ **What Does This Say?** Discuss the evaluation of a line integral.

Evaluate each line integral given in Problems 3–16.

3. $\int_C (-y\,dx + x\,dy)$

C is the parabolic path
$y = 4x^2$ from $(1, 4)$ to $(0, 0)$.

4. $\int_C (-y\,dx + 3x\,dy)$

C is the parabolic path
$y^2 = x$ from $(1, 1)$ to $(9, 3)$.

5. $\int_C (x\,dy - y\,dx)$

C is the line segment defined
by $2x - 4y = 1$ as x varies
from 4 to 8.

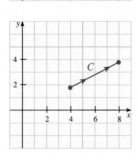

6. $\int_C [(y - x)\,dx + x^2 y\,dy]$

C is the curve defined by
$y^2 = x^3$ from $(1, -1)$ to $(1, 1)$.

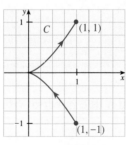

7. $\int_C [(x + y)^2 dx - (x - y)^2 dy]$

C is the curve defined by
$y = |2x|$ from $(-1, 2)$ to $(1, 2)$.

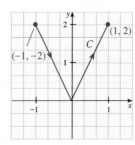

8. $\int_C [(y^2 - x^2)\,dx - x\,dy]$

C is the quarter-circle
$x^2 + y^2 = 4$ from $(0, 2)$ to
$(2, 0)$.

9. $\int_C [(x^2 + y^2)\,dx + 2xy\,dy]$ for these choices of the curve C:

a. C is the quarter-circle $x^2 + y^2 = 1$ traversed counterclockwise from $(1, 0)$ to $(0, 1)$.
b. C is the straight line $y = 1 - x$ from $(1, 0)$ to $(0, 1)$.

10. $\int_C [x^2 y\,dx + (x^2 - y^2)\,dy]$ for these choices of the curve C:

a. C is the arc of the parabola $y = x^2$ from $(0, 0)$ to $(2, 4)$.
b. C is the segment of the line $y = 2x$ for $0 \le x \le 2$.

11. Rework Problem 10 for the path C that consists of the horizontal line segment $(0, 0)$ to $(2, 0)$, followed by the vertical segment from $(2, 0)$ to $(2, 4)$.

12. $\int_C (-xy^2\,dx + x^2\,dy)$

where C is the path defined
by the given figure.

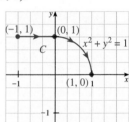

13. $\int_C (-y^2\,dx + x^2\,dy)$

where C is the path defined
by the given figure.

14. $\int_C [(x^2 - y^2)\,dx + x\,dy]$, where C is the closed circular path given by $x = 2\cos\theta$, $y = 2\sin\theta$, $0 \le \theta \le 2\pi$.

15. $\int_C (x^2 y\,dx - xy\,dy)$, where C is the closed path that begins at $(0, 0)$, goes to $(1, 1)$ along the parabola $y = x^2$, and then returns to $(0, 0)$ along the line $y = x$.

16. $\int_C \dfrac{x\,dx - y\,dy}{\sqrt{x^2 + y^2}}$, where C is the quarter-circular path $x^2 + y^2 = a^2$, traversed from $(a, 0)$ to $(0, a)$.

In Problems 17–19, evaluate $\int_C \mathbf{F} \cdot d\mathbf{R}$, where

$\mathbf{F} = (5x + y)\mathbf{i} + x\mathbf{j}$ and C is the specified curve.

17. C is the straight-line segment from $(0, 0)$ to $(2, 1)$.

18. C is the curve given by $\mathbf{R}(t) = 2t\mathbf{i} + t\mathbf{j}$ for $0 \le t \le 1$.

19. C is the vertical line from $(0, 0)$ to $(0, 1)$, followed by the horizontal line from $(0, 1)$ to $(2, 1)$.

Evaluate the line integrals in Problems 20–35.

20. $\int_C (y\, dx - x\, dy + dz)$; C is the helical path given by:

   a. $x = 3\sin t$, $y = 3\cos t$, $z = t$ for $0 \le t \le \frac{\pi}{2}$

   b. $x = a\sin t$, $y = a\cos t$, $z = t$ for constant a and $0 \le t \le \frac{\pi}{2}$

21. $\int_C (x\, dx + y\, dy + z\, dz)$, where C is the following path:

   a. the helix defined by $x = \cos t$, $y = \sin t$, $z = t$ for $0 \le t \le \frac{\pi}{2}$

   b. the straight-line segment from $(1, 0, 0)$ to $\left(0, 1, \frac{\pi}{2}\right)$

22. $\int_C (-y\, dx + x\, dy + xz\, dz)$, where C is the following path:

   a. the helix defined by $x = \cos t$, $y = \sin t$, $z = t$ for $0 \le t \le 2\pi$

   b. the unit circle $x^2 + y^2 = 1$, $z = 0$, traversed once counterclockwise as viewed from above

23. $\int_C (5\, xy\, dx + 10\, yz\, dy + z\, dz)$; C is the following path:

   a. the parabolic arc $x = y^2$ from $(0, 0, 0)$ to $(1, 1, 0)$ followed by the line segment given by $x = 1$, $y = 1$, $0 \le z \le 1$

   b. the straight-line segment from $(0, 0, 0)$ to $(1, 1, 1)$

24. $\int_C \dfrac{dx + dy}{|x| + |y|}$, where C is the square $|x| + |y| = 1$, traversed once counterclockwise

25. $\int_C [(y + z)\, dx + (x + z)\, dy + (x + y)\, dz]$, where C is the circle of radius 1 centered on the z-axis in the plane $z = 2$, traversed once counterclockwise as viewed from above

26. $\int_C \mathbf{F} \cdot d\mathbf{R}$, where $\mathbf{F} = (y - 3)\mathbf{i} + x\mathbf{j}$, and C is the curve given by $\mathbf{R}(t) = (\sin t)\mathbf{i} - (\cos t)\mathbf{j}$ for $0 \le t \le \pi$

27. $\int_C \mathbf{F} \cdot d\mathbf{R}$, where $\mathbf{F} = (y - 2z)\mathbf{i} + x\mathbf{j} - 2xy\mathbf{k}$ and C is the path given by $\mathbf{R}(t) = t\mathbf{i} + t^2\mathbf{j} - \mathbf{k}$ for $1 \le t \le 2$

28. $\int_C \mathbf{F} \cdot d\mathbf{R}$, where $\mathbf{F} = x\mathbf{i} + xy\mathbf{j} + x^2yz\mathbf{k}$, and C is the elliptical path given by $x^2 + 4y^2 - 8y + 3 = 0$ in the xy-plane, traversed once counterclockwise as viewed from above

29. $\int_C \mathbf{F} \cdot d\mathbf{R}$, where $\mathbf{F} = y^2\mathbf{i} + x^2\mathbf{j} - (x + z)\mathbf{k}$ and C is the boundary of the triangle with vertices $(0, 0, 0)$, $(1, 0, 0)$, $(1, 1, 0)$, traversed once clockwise, as viewed from above

30. $\int_C \mathbf{F} \cdot \mathbf{T}\, ds$, where $\mathbf{F} = -3y\mathbf{i} + 3x\mathbf{j} + 3x\mathbf{k}$, and C is the straight-line segment from $(0, 0, 1)$ to $(1, 1, 1)$

31. $\int_C \mathbf{F} \cdot \mathbf{T}\, ds$, where $\mathbf{F} = -x\mathbf{i} + 2\mathbf{k}$, and C is the boundary of the trapezoid with vertices $(0, 0)$, $(1, 0)$, $(2, 1)$, $(0, 1)$, traversed once clockwise as viewed from above

32. $\int_C y\, ds$, where C is the curve given by $\mathbf{R}(t) = t\mathbf{i} + 2t^3\mathbf{j}$, $0 \le t \le 2$

33. $\int_C (x + y)\, ds$, where C is given by $\mathbf{R}(t) = (\cos^2 t)\mathbf{i} + (\sin^2 t)\mathbf{j}$, $-\frac{\pi}{4} \le t \le 0$

34. $\int_C \dfrac{x^2 + xy + y^2}{z^2}\, ds$, where C is the path given by $\mathbf{R}(t) = (\cos t)\mathbf{i} + (\sin t)\mathbf{j} - \mathbf{k}$ for $0 \le t \le 2\pi$

35. Evaluate the line integral

$$\int_C \frac{x\, dy - y\, dx}{x^2 + y^2}$$

where C is the unit circle $x^2 + y^2 = 1$ traversed once counterclockwise.

B 36. How much work is done by a constant force $\mathbf{F} = a\mathbf{i} + \mathbf{j}$ when a particle moves along the line $y = ax$ from $x = a$ to $x = 0$?

37. A force field in the plane is given by $\mathbf{F} = (x^2 - y^2)\mathbf{i} + 2xy\mathbf{j}$. Find the total work done by this force in moving a point mass counterclockwise around the square with vertices $(0, 0)$, $(2, 0)$, $(2, 2)$, $(0, 2)$.

38. Find the work done by the force field $\mathbf{F} = (x^2 + y^2)\mathbf{i} + (x + y)\mathbf{j}$ as an object moves counterclockwise along the circle $x^2 + y^2 = 1$ from $(1, 0)$ to $(-1, 0)$, and then back to $(1, 0)$ along the x-axis.

39. A force acting on a point mass located at (x, y) is given by $\mathbf{F} = y\mathbf{i} + 2x\mathbf{j}$. Find the work done by this force as the point mass moves along a straight line from $(1, 0)$ to $(0, 1)$.

Find the work done by the force $\mathbf{F}(x, y, z)$ on an object moving along the curve C in Problems 40–43.

40. $\mathbf{F} = (y^2 - z^2)\mathbf{i} + 2yz\mathbf{j} - x^2\mathbf{k}$, and C is the path given by $x(t) = t$, $y(t) = t^2$, $z(t) = t^3$, for $0 \le t \le 1$.

41. $\mathbf{F} = 2xy\mathbf{i} + (x^2 + 2)\mathbf{j} + y\mathbf{k}$, and C is the line segment from $(1, 0, 2)$ to $(3, 4, 1)$.

42. $\mathbf{F} = x\mathbf{i} + y\mathbf{j} + (xz - y)\mathbf{k}$, and C is the line segment from $(0, 0, 0)$ to $(2, 1, 2)$.

43. $\mathbf{F} = x\mathbf{i} + y\mathbf{j} + (xz - y)\mathbf{k}$, and C is the path given by $\mathbf{R}(t) = t^2\mathbf{i} + 2t\mathbf{j} + 4t^3\mathbf{k}$ for $0 \le t \le 1$.

44. A person carries a bag of sand up a circular helical staircase on the outside of a tower 150 ft high and 80 ft in diameter. Suppose the person weighs 150 lb, the bag weighs 40 lb, and 50 ft can be climbed in exactly 5 revolutions.

How much work is done by gravity on the person and the bag during the climb to the top?

45. Repeat Problem 44 assuming that the bag leaks 1 lb of sand for every 15 ft of ascent. How much work is done by gravity during the person's climb to the top?

46. A 5000-lb satellite orbits the earth in a circular orbit 5000 mi from the center of the earth. How much work is done on the satellite by gravity during one complete revolution?

47. Suppose a particle with charge Q and mass m moves with velocity $\mathbf{V}$ under the influence of an electric field $\mathbf{E}$ and a magnetic field $\mathbf{B}$. Then the total force on the particle is $\mathbf{F} = Q(\mathbf{E} + \mathbf{V} \times \mathbf{B})$, called the **Lorentz force**. Use Newton's second law of motion, $\mathbf{F} = m\mathbf{A}$, to show that

$$m\frac{d\mathbf{V}}{dt} \cdot \mathbf{V} = Q\mathbf{E} \cdot \frac{d\mathbf{R}}{dt}$$

Then find the work done by the Lorentz force as a particle moves along the curve C parametrized as $\mathbf{R}(t)$, for $t_1 \le t \le t_2$.

48. Suppose a thin wire fits a smooth curve C in $\mathbb{R}^3$, and let $\rho(x, y, z)$ be the density of the wire. Explain why the mass m of the wire is given by the line integral

$$m = \int_C \rho(x, y, z) \, ds$$

Express the center of mass of the wire in terms of line integrals.

14.3 INDEPENDENCE OF PATH

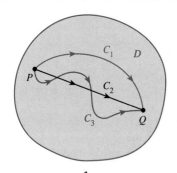

A line integral $\displaystyle\int_C \mathbf{F} \cdot d\mathbf{R}$ that has the same value for any curve C in D with given endpoints is said to be independent of path.

IN THIS SECTION Conservative vector fields, fundamental theorem on line integrals

In general, the value of the line integral $\displaystyle\int_C \mathbf{F} \cdot d\mathbf{R}$ depends on the path of integration C, but in certain cases, the integral will be the same for all paths in a given region D with the same initial point P and terminal point Q. In this case, we say the line integral is **independent of path** in D. In this section, we shall study path independence and characterize the kind of vector field $\mathbf{F}$ for which it occurs.

■ CONSERVATIVE VECTOR FIELDS

The issue of path independence for the line integral $\displaystyle\int_C \mathbf{F} \cdot d\mathbf{R}$ is closely related to determining whether or not $\mathbf{F}$ is the gradient of some scalar function f. It is useful to have the following terminology.

Conservative Vector Field

A vector field $\mathbf{F}$ is said to be **conservative** in a region D if it can be represented in D as the gradient of a continuously differentiable function f, which is then called a **scalar potential** of $\mathbf{F}$. That is,

$$\mathbf{F} = \nabla f \quad \text{for } (x, y) \text{ in } D$$

↑   ↑

Conservative vector field   Scalar potential

EXAMPLE 1   Conservative vector field

Verify that the vector field $\mathbf{F} = 2xy\mathbf{i} + x^2\mathbf{j}$ is conservative, with scalar potential $f = x^2y$.

Solution $\nabla f = 2xy\mathbf{i} + x^2\mathbf{j}$ and this is the same as $\mathbf{F}$, so $\mathbf{F}$ is conservative. ▬

As we work this example, two questions might come to mind:

1. Does there exist an easy test to determine if $\mathbf{F}$ is conservative?
2. Once such a determination has been made, how can a scalar potential function f be found?

We now answer both these questions.

Before developing a simple criterion for determining whether a vector field is conservative, we need to introduce some new terminology. Specifically, a region D is **connected** if any two points in D can be joined by a path that lies entirely within D. If, in addition, every closed curve in D encloses only points that are also in D, then D is **simply connected**. Roughly speaking, a simply connected region is one with no "holes," as shown in Figure 14.12.

a. A simply connected region

b. A region that is *not* simply connected

Figure 14.12 Connected regions

THEOREM 14.2 **Cross-partials test for a conservative vector field in the plane**

Consider the vector field $\mathbf{F}(x, y) = u(x, y)\mathbf{i} + v(x, y)\mathbf{j}$, where u and v have continuous first partials in the open, simply connected region D. Then $\mathbf{F}(x, y)$ is conservative in D if and only if

$$\frac{\partial u}{\partial y} = \frac{\partial v}{\partial x} \qquad \text{throughout } D$$

Proof: The proof is left for Problem Set 14.4, after our discussion of Green's theorem. ∎

In the next two examples, we use this theorem to show that a given vector field $\mathbf{F}$ is conservative. Then we "partially integrate" the components of $\mathbf{F}$ to obtain a scalar potential of $\mathbf{F}$ such that $\nabla f = \mathbf{F}$.

EXAMPLE 2 **Finding a scalar potential function**

Show that the vector field $\mathbf{F} = (e^x\sin y - y)\mathbf{i} + (e^x\cos y - x - 2)\mathbf{j}$ is conservative and then find a scalar potential function f for $\mathbf{F}$.

Solution Let $u(x, y) = e^x\sin y - y$ and $v(x, y) = e^x\cos y - x - 2$. Then

$$\frac{\partial u}{\partial y} = e^x\cos y - 1 \quad \text{and} \quad \frac{\partial v}{\partial x} = e^x\cos y - 1$$

Thus, $\frac{\partial u}{\partial y} = \frac{\partial v}{\partial x}$, and $\mathbf{F}$ is conservative. To find a scalar potential function f such that $\nabla f = \mathbf{F}$, we note that f must satisfy $u(x, y) = f_x(x, y)$ and $v(x, y) = f_y(x, y)$.

$$f(x, y) = \int u(x, y)\, dx = \underbrace{\int (e^x\sin y - y)\, dx}$$

This is the "partial integral" in the sense that y is held constant while the integration is performed with respect to x alone.

$$= e^x\sin y - yx + c(y)$$

Where $c(y)$ is a function of y alone—a "constant" as far as x-integration is concerned

Because f must also satisfy $f_y(x, y) = v(x, y)$, we compute the partial derivative of this result with respect to y:

$$f_y(x, y) = \frac{\partial}{\partial y}[e^x \sin y - yx + c(y)] = e^x \cos y - x + \frac{dc}{dy}$$

Set this equal to $v = e^x \cos y - x - 2$ and solve for $\frac{dc}{dy}$.

$$e^x \cos y - x + \frac{dc}{dy} = e^x \cos y - x - 2$$

$$\frac{dc}{dy} = -2$$

We integrate this to find $c(y) = -2y + C$. We now have found the function $f(x, y) = e^x \sin y - xy - 2y + C$. Any such function is a scalar potential of **F**, and for simplicity, we pick $C = 0$:

$$f(x, y) = e^x \sin y - xy - 2y \qquad \blacksquare$$

In Example 2, we began by using the fact that $f_x = u$. In general, the issue of whether to start with $u = f_x$ or $v = f_y$ is a matter of personal taste and is often determined by which equation leads to the simpler integration.

EXAMPLE 3   Testing for a conservative vector field in the plane

Determine whether or not the vector field $\mathbf{F} = ye^{xy}\mathbf{i} + (xe^{xy} + x)\mathbf{j}$ is conservative; if it is, find a scalar potential.

Solution   We have $u(x) = ye^{xy}$ and $v(x) = xe^{xy} + x$.

$$\frac{\partial u}{\partial y} = xye^{xy} + e^{xy}, \qquad \frac{\partial v}{\partial x} = xye^{xy} + e^{xy} + 1,$$

so $\frac{\partial u}{\partial y} \neq \frac{\partial v}{\partial x}$, and **F** is not conservative. $\blacksquare$

◼ FUNDAMENTAL THEOREM ON LINE INTEGRALS

Recall that according to the fundamental theorem of calculus, if the derivative f' is continuous on $a \leq x \leq b$, then

$$\int_a^b d[f(x)] = \int_a^b f'(x)\,dx = f(b) - f(a)$$

The following is a generalization of this result for line integrals.

THEOREM 14.3   Fundamental theorem on line integrals

Let **F** be a conservative vector field on the region D and let f be a scalar potential function for **F**; that is, $\nabla f = \mathbf{F}$. Then, if C is any piecewise smooth curve lying entirely within D, with initial point P and terminal point Q, we have

$$\int_C \mathbf{F} \cdot d\mathbf{R} = f(Q) - f(P)$$

Thus, the line integral $\int_C \mathbf{F} \cdot d\mathbf{R}$ is independent of path in D.

Proof: We shall prove this theorem for the case where the curve C is smooth in D, leaving the more general case where C is piecewise smooth as an exercise. Suppose C is described by the vector function $\mathbf{R}(t) = x(t)\mathbf{i} + y(t)\mathbf{j}$ where $a \le t \le b$, and $P = \mathbf{R}(a)$, $Q = \mathbf{R}(b)$. Because $\mathbf{F}(x, y) = \nabla f(x, y) = f_x(x, y)\mathbf{i} + f_y(x, y)\mathbf{j}$, we have

$$\int_C \mathbf{F} \cdot d\mathbf{R} = \int_a^b \mathbf{F} \cdot \frac{d\mathbf{R}}{dt}\, dt$$

$$= \int_a^b \left[f_x(x, y) \frac{dx}{dt} + f_y(x, y) \frac{dy}{dt} \right] dt$$

$$= \int_a^b \frac{d}{dt}\{f[x(t), y(t)]\}\, dt \qquad \text{Chain rule (in reverse)}$$

$$= f[x(b), y(b)] - f[x(a), y(a)] \qquad \text{Fundamental theorem of calculus}$$

$$= f[\mathbf{R}(b)] - f[\mathbf{R}(a)]$$

$$= f(Q) - f(P)$$

EXAMPLE 4 Evaluating a line integral using the fundamental theorem on line integrals

Evaluate the line integral $\int_C \mathbf{F} \cdot d\mathbf{R}$, where $\mathbf{F} = (e^x \sin y - y)\mathbf{i} + (e^x \cos y - x - 2)\mathbf{j}$ and C is the path given by $\mathbf{R}(t) = \left[t^3 \sin \frac{\pi t}{2} \right]\mathbf{i} - \left[\frac{\pi}{2} \cos\left(\frac{\pi t}{2} + \frac{\pi}{2}\right) \right]\mathbf{j}$ for $0 \le t \le 1$.

Solution Evaluating this line integral by the parametric method would be both difficult and tedious. However, we showed in Example 2 that the vector field $\mathbf{F}$ is conservative with scalar potential

$$f(x, y) = e^x \sin y - xy - 2y$$

and according to the fundamental theorem on line integrals, the value of the line integral depends only on the value of f at the endpoints of the path C. (You should also verify that the hypotheses of the theorem are satisfied by $\mathbf{F}$ and C.)

At the endpoint where $t = 0$: $\mathbf{R}(0) = 0\mathbf{i} - \left[\frac{\pi}{2} \cos\left(\frac{\pi}{2}\right) \right]\mathbf{j} = 0\mathbf{i} + 0\mathbf{j}$

$$f(0, 0) = e^0 \sin 0 - 0 - 0 = 0$$

At the endpoint where $t = 1$: $\mathbf{R}(1) = \left[\sin \frac{\pi}{2} \right]\mathbf{i} - \left[\frac{\pi}{2} \cos \pi \right] = \mathbf{i} + \frac{\pi}{2}\mathbf{j}$

$$f\left(1, \frac{\pi}{2}\right) = e^1 \sin \frac{\pi}{2} - \frac{\pi}{2} - 2\left(\frac{\pi}{2}\right) = e - \frac{3\pi}{2}$$

We now apply the fundamental theorem for line integrals:

$$\int_C \mathbf{F} \cdot d\mathbf{R} = f(Q) - f(P) = f\left(1, \frac{\pi}{2}\right) - f(0, 0)$$

$$= \left(e - \frac{3\pi}{2}\right) - 0 = e - \frac{3\pi}{2}$$

EXAMPLE 5 Work along a closed path in a conservative force field

Show that no net work is done when an object moves along a closed path back to its starting point in a connected domain where the force field is conservative.

Solution   In such a force field **F**, we have $\nabla f = \mathbf{F}$, where f is a scalar potential of **F**, and because the path of motion is closed, it begins and ends at the same point P. Thus, the work is given by

$$W = \int_C \mathbf{F} \cdot d\mathbf{R} = f(P) - f(P) = 0 \qquad \blacksquare$$

This result appears as part of the proof of the following useful theorem, which ties together several equivalent conditions for path independence.

THEOREM 14.4   Closed curve theorem for a conservative force field

The continuous vector field **F** is conservative in the open connected region D if and only if $\int_C \mathbf{F} \cdot d\mathbf{R} = 0$ for every piecewise smooth closed curve C in D.

Proof: If a line integral $\int_C \mathbf{F} \cdot d\mathbf{R}$ is independent of path in the open, connected region D, then $\int_C \mathbf{F} \cdot d\mathbf{R} = 0$ for any piecewise smooth closed path C in D. Indeed, if P and Q are two points on such a path, and C_T is the path from P to Q along, say, the "top" of C, while C_B is the "bottom" path along C from Q to P (see Figure 14.13), we must have $\int_{C_B} \mathbf{F} \cdot d\mathbf{R} = -\int_{C_T} \mathbf{F} \cdot d\mathbf{R}$ and

$$\int_C \mathbf{F} \cdot d\mathbf{R} = \int_{C_T} \mathbf{F} \cdot d\mathbf{R} + \int_{C_B} \mathbf{F} \cdot d\mathbf{R} = \int_{C_T} \mathbf{F} \cdot d\mathbf{R} - \int_{C_T} \mathbf{F} \cdot d\mathbf{R} = 0$$

Conversely, if $\int_C \mathbf{F} \cdot d\mathbf{R} = 0$ for every closed curve C in a region D, it can be shown (see Problem 47) that **F** must be conservative in D. ∎

We have now stated three equivalent conditions for path independence, which we summarize in the following box.

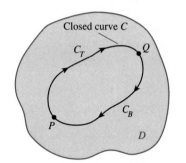

Figure 14.13 A continuous vector field **F** is conservative in the region D if and only if $\int_C \mathbf{F} \cdot d\mathbf{R} = 0$ for every closed curve C in D.

Equivalent Conditions for Path Independence

Let $\mathbf{F}(x, y, z)$ have continuous first partial derivatives in an open connected region D, and let C be a piecewise smooth curve in D. Then the following conditions are equivalent.

a. $\displaystyle\int_C \mathbf{F} \cdot d\mathbf{R}$ is independent of path within D.

b. **F** is conservative; that is, $\mathbf{F} = \nabla f$ for some function f defined on D.

c. $\displaystyle\int_C \mathbf{F} \cdot d\mathbf{R} = 0$ for every closed path C enclosing only points of D.

Here is an example that illustrates how these conditions can be used to evaluate line integrals.

EXAMPLE 6   Using path independence to evaluate a line integral

Show that $\mathbf{F} = (xy^2)\mathbf{i} + (x^2 y)\mathbf{j}$ is conservative and evaluate $\displaystyle\int_C xy^2 \, dx + x^2 y \, dy$ over each of the given curves:

The purpose of this example is to show that the line integral is 0 if **F** is conservative and the path is closed, and if the curve is not closed, then the value of the integral is independent of the indicated paths.

Solution   First, apply the cross-partials test to see if $\mathbf{F}(x, y) = xy^2\mathbf{i} + x^2y\mathbf{j}$ is conservative.

$$\frac{\partial}{\partial y}(xy^2) = 2xy \qquad \frac{\partial}{\partial x}(x^2y) = 2xy$$

Thus, **F** is conservative.

a. Because C is a closed curve and because **F** is conservative,

$$\int_C xy^2\, dx + x^2y\, dy = 0$$

b. Because $y = \sqrt{1 - x^2}$ is the upper portion of the circle $x^2 + y^2 = 1$, we can parametrize C by $x = \cos\theta$, $y = \sin\theta$ for $0 \le \theta \le \frac{\pi}{4}$. We represent the curve as

$$\mathbf{R}(t) = (\cos\theta)\mathbf{i} + (\sin\theta)\mathbf{j}$$

$$d\mathbf{R} = (-\sin\theta\, d\theta)\mathbf{i} + (\cos\theta\, d\theta)\mathbf{j}$$

and find that

$$\mathbf{F} = xy^2\mathbf{i} + x^2y\mathbf{j} = (\cos\theta\sin^2\theta)\mathbf{i} + (\cos^2\theta\sin\theta)\mathbf{j}$$

We have

$$\int_C xy^2\, dx + x^2y\, dy = \int_C \mathbf{F} \cdot d\mathbf{R}$$

$$= \int_0^{\pi/4} \tfrac{1}{2}\sin 2\theta \cos 2\theta\, d\theta$$

$$= \tfrac{1}{8}\sin^2 2\theta\,\Big|_0^{\pi/4} = \tfrac{1}{8}$$

c. Because **F** is conservative, the line integral is independent of path. Thus, the result is the same as part **b.**

$$\int_C xy^2\, dx + x^2y\, dy = \tfrac{1}{8}$$

It might be instructive to illustrate the power of these equivalent conditions by evaluating this same line integral without the benefit of part **b.** ▄▄

In the next section, we develop another criterion for path independence as part of our study of an important result known as Green's theorem.

PROBLEM SET 14.3

 1. ■ **What Does This Say?** Discuss conservative vector fields.

2. ■ **What Does This Say?** Describe the fundamental theorem on line integrals.

3. ■ **What Does This Say?** Compare and contrast the various equivalent conditions for independence of path.

Determine whether or not each vector field in Problems 4–9 is conservative, and if it is, find a scalar potential.

4. $y^2\mathbf{i} + 2xy\mathbf{j}$ **5.** $2xy^3\mathbf{i} + 3y^2x^2\mathbf{j}$

6. $(xe^{xy}\sin y)\mathbf{i} + (e^{xy}\cos y + y)\mathbf{j}$

7. $(-y + e^x\sin y)\mathbf{i} + [(x + 2)e^2\cos y]\mathbf{j}$

8. $(y - x^2)\mathbf{i} + (2x + y^2)\mathbf{j}$ **9.** $(e^{2x}\sin y)\mathbf{i} + (e^{2x}\cos y)\mathbf{j}$

Evaluate the line integrals in Problems 10–13 for each of the given paths.

10. $\displaystyle\int_C (3x + 2y)dx + (2x + 3y)dy$

a.   **b.**

c.

11. $\displaystyle\int_C (3x + 2y)dx - (2x + 3y)dy$

a.   **b.**

c.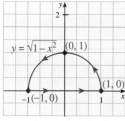

12. $\displaystyle\int_C 2x^2y\,dx + x^3\,dy$

a.   **b.**

c.

13. $\displaystyle\int_C 2xy\,dx + x^2\,dy$

a.   **b.**

c.

Show that the vector field **F** *in Problems 14–19 is conservative, find a scalar potential f for* **F**, *and evaluate the line integral* $\int_C \mathbf{F} \cdot d\mathbf{R}$, *where C is any path connecting* $(0, 0)$ *to* $(1, 1)$.

14. $\mathbf{F}(x, y) = (x + 2y)\mathbf{i} + (2x + y)\mathbf{j}$

15. $\mathbf{F}(x, y) = 2xy\mathbf{i} + x^2\mathbf{j}$

16. $\mathbf{F}(x, y) = (y - x^2)\mathbf{i} + (x + y^2)\mathbf{j}$

17. $\mathbf{F}(x, y) = (2x - y)\mathbf{i} + (y^2 - x)\mathbf{j}$

18. $\mathbf{F}(x, y) = \left[3x^2\cos y + \dfrac{y}{1 + x^2y^2}\right]\mathbf{i} + \left[-x^3\sin y + \dfrac{x}{1 + x^2y^2}\right]\mathbf{j}$

19. $\mathbf{F}(x, y) = [2\cos 2x - e^{-x}(\cos xy + y\sin xy)]\mathbf{i} - [xe^{-x}\sin xy]\mathbf{j}$

B **20.** A force field

$$\mathbf{F}(x, y) = (3x^2 + 6xy^2)\mathbf{i} + (6x^2y + 4y^2)\mathbf{j}$$

acts on an object moving in the plane. Show that $\mathbf{F}$ is conservative, and find a scalar potential for $\mathbf{F}$. How much work is done as the object moves from $(1, 0)$ to $(0, 1)$ along any path connecting these points?

Verify that each line integral in Problems 21–26 is independent of path and then find its value.

21. $\displaystyle\int_C (3x^2 + 2x + y^2)\, dx + (2xy + y^3)\, dy$

where C is any path from $(0, 0)$ to $(1, 1)$

22. $\displaystyle\int_C (xy \cos xy + \sin xy)\, dx + (x^2 \cos xy)\, dy$

where C is any path from $\left(0, \frac{\pi}{18}\right)$ to $\left(1, \frac{\pi}{6}\right)$

23. $\displaystyle\int_C (y - x^2)\, dx + (x + y^2)\, dy$

where C is any path from $(-1, -1)$ to $(0, 3)$

24. $\displaystyle\int_C (3x^2y + y^2)\, dx + (x^3 + 2xy)\, dy$

where C is the path given parametrically by $\mathbf{R}(t) = t\mathbf{i} + (t^2 + t - 2)\mathbf{j}$ for $0 \le t \le 2$

25. $\displaystyle\int_C (\sin y)\, dx + (3 + x \cos y)\, dy$

where C is the path given parametrically by $\mathbf{R}(t) = 2 \sin(\pi t/2) \cos(\pi t)\mathbf{i} + (\sin^{-1} t)\mathbf{j}$ for $0 \le t \le 1$

26. $\displaystyle\int_C (e^x \cos y)\, dx + (-e^x \sin y)\, dy$

where C is the path given parametrically by $\mathbf{R}(t) = (\cos t)\mathbf{i} + (\sin t)\mathbf{j}$ for $0 \le t \le \frac{\pi}{2}$

Evaluate the line integrals given in Problems 27–31 using the fundamental theorem of line integrals.

27. $\displaystyle\int_C (y\mathbf{i} + x\mathbf{j}) \cdot d\mathbf{R}$, where C is any path from $(0, 0)$ to $(2, 4)$

28. $\displaystyle\int_C (xy^2\mathbf{i} + x^2y\mathbf{j}) \cdot d\mathbf{R}$; C is any path from $(4, 1)$ to $(0, 0)$

29. $\displaystyle\int_C (2y\, dx + 2x\, dy)$, where C is the line segment from $(0, 0)$ to $(4, 4)$

30. $\displaystyle\int_C (e^x \sin y\, dx + e^x \cos y\, dy)$, where C is any smooth curve from $(0, 0)$ to $(0, 2\pi)$

31. $\displaystyle\int_C \left[\tan^{-1}\left(\frac{y}{x}\right) - \frac{xy}{x^2 + y^2}\right] dx + \left[\frac{x^2}{x^2 + y^2} + e^{-y}(1 - y)\right] dy$

where C is the curve given by $\mathbf{R}(t) = e^{t(1-t)}(\cos t\, \mathbf{i} - t \sin t\, \mathbf{j})$ for $0 \le t \le 1$

It can be shown that the vector field
$\mathbf{F}(x, y, z) = M(x, y, z)\mathbf{i} + N(x, y, z)\mathbf{j} + P(x, y, z)\mathbf{k}$
is conservative if there exists a scalar function $\phi(x, y, z)$ such that $\mathbf{F} = \nabla\phi$. It can be shown that under reasonable conditions $\mathbf{F}$ is conservative if curl $\mathbf{F} = \mathbf{0}$.

(See also Problem 45.) Use this result to verify that each vector field $\mathbf{F}$ in Problems 32–37 is conservative.

32. $yz^2\mathbf{i} + xz^2\mathbf{j} + 2xyz\mathbf{k}$

33. $e^{xy}yz\mathbf{i} + e^{xy}xz\mathbf{j} + e^{xy}\mathbf{k}$

34. $yz^{-1}\mathbf{i} + xz^{-1}\mathbf{j} - xyz^{-2}\mathbf{k}$

35. $(x^2 + y^2 + z^2)(x\mathbf{i} + y\mathbf{j} + z\mathbf{k})$

36. $(y \sin z)\mathbf{i} + (x \sin z + 2y)\mathbf{j} + (xy \cos z)\mathbf{k}$

37. $(xy^2 + yz)\mathbf{i} + (x^2y + xz + 3y^2z)\mathbf{j} + (xy + y^3)\mathbf{k}$

38. a. Over what region in the xy-plane will the line integral

$$\int_C [(-yx^{-2} + x^{-1})\, dx + x^{-1}\, dy]$$

be independent of path?

b. Evaluate the line integral in **a** if C is defined by

$$\mathbf{R}(t) = (\cos^3 t)\mathbf{i} + (2\sqrt{\sec t})\mathbf{j} \text{ for } 0 \le t \le \frac{\pi}{6}.$$

39. The **gravitational force field** $\mathbf{F}$ between two particles of masses M and m separated by a distance r is given by

$$\mathbf{G}(x, y, z) = -\frac{KmM}{r^3}\mathbf{R}$$

where $\mathbf{R} = x\mathbf{i} + y\mathbf{j} + z\mathbf{k}$ and K is the gravitational constant.

a. Show that $\mathbf{F}$ is conservative and find a scalar potential for $\mathbf{F}$. The scalar potential function f is often called the **Newtonian potential**.

b. Compute the amount of work done against the force field $\mathbf{G}$ in moving an object from the point $P(a_1, b_1, c_1)$ to $Q(a_2, b_2, c_2)$.

40. Let $\mathbf{F}(x, y) = \dfrac{-y\mathbf{i} + x\mathbf{j}}{x^2 + y^2}$.

a. Compute the line integral $\int_C \mathbf{F} \cdot d\mathbf{R}$, where C is the upper semicircle $y = \sqrt{1 - x^2}$ traversed counterclockwise. What is the value of $\int_{C_2} \mathbf{F} \cdot d\mathbf{R}$ if C is the lower semicircle $y = -\sqrt{1 - x^2}$ also traversed counterclockwise?

b. Show that if $\mathbf{F} = M\mathbf{i} + N\mathbf{j}$, then

$$\frac{\partial M}{\partial y} = \frac{\partial N}{\partial x}$$

but $\mathbf{F}$ is not conservative on the unit disk $x^2 + y^2 \le 1$.

41. A person whirls a bucket filled with water in a circle, at the rate of 1 revolution per second. If the bucket and water weigh 30 lb and are whirled horizontally with the center of gravity 3 ft away from the person, how much work is done by the force that keeps the bucket moving in a circular path?

Computational Window

In Problems 42 and 43, experiment with computing work along a path, with and without the benefit of independence of path. Suppose that you are to power a boat from point A = (0, 0) to point B = (2, 1), and the primary consideration is the force of the wind that opposes you. Investigate the effect of taking different paths from A to B.

42. **a.** Suppose that the wind force is $\mathbf{F} = \langle -a, -b \rangle$, for a and b positive. Compute the work involved along the straight-line path between A and B; then along a second path, of your choice. Does the path matter here? Why or why not?

   b. Due to the effect of the harbor you are entering, suppose the wind force is $\langle -a, -ae^{-y} \rangle$. Again, compute the work along two paths as in part **a**. Does the path matter here? Why or why not?

   c. Repeat part **b** for $\langle -a, -ae^{-y+x/9} \rangle$.

43. An important type of problem is, "Can we find the optimal path in order to minimize the work?" You are to explore this issue in regard to the wind force in Problem 42c, $\mathbf{F} = \langle -a, -ae^{-y+x/9} \rangle$.

   a. You should have the work computed for two different paths from the last problem. By studying $\mathbf{F}$ carefully, note that we will be rewarded (or punished) by changing the path slightly from the straight-line path. What do your observations suggest regarding trying to minimize the work?

   b. Attempt to find an (approximate) optimal path, starting with your observations in part **a** and common sense. For example, the path could be described by a parabola (or higher degree polynomial) or by some trigonometric function. Find a "good" path for this purpose.

   c. Explore the following question: "Is there a realistic optimal path from A to B?" Consider two conditions: first, there is no restriction on the path; second, suppose there is a shoreline at $y = 1$ so that one's path cannot exceed this limit. *Hint:* consider all parabolic paths of the form

   $$y = x(b - ax)$$

   where a and b are nonnegative, and $y(2) = 1$. In

this case, you can eliminate b and do a one-parameter study.

   d. Assume that the path in part **c** cannot go above $y = 1$. You may have discovered the optimal path. What is it? If you did the parabolic study suggested in part **c**, what is the optimal path in this case?

C 44. Show that if the vector field
   $\mathbf{F}(x, y, z) = M(x, y, z)\mathbf{i} + N(x, y, z)\mathbf{j} + P(x, y, z)\mathbf{k}$ is conservative, then curl $F = 0$; that is,

   $$\frac{\partial P}{\partial y} = \frac{\partial N}{\partial z} \qquad \frac{\partial M}{\partial z} = \frac{\partial P}{\partial x} \qquad \frac{\partial N}{\partial x} = \frac{\partial M}{\partial y}$$

45. It can be shown that $F = M\mathbf{i} + N\mathbf{j} + P\mathbf{k}$ is conservative if curl $F = 0$ whenever M, N, and P have continuous partial derivatives in a ball, a box, or other "simply connected" regions. (The precise definition of a simply connected region in $\mathbb{R}^3$ is a bit technical and will be omitted.) Show that the vector field defined by
   $\mathbf{F}(x, y, z) = (y^2 - 2xz)\mathbf{i} + (2xy + z)\mathbf{j} + (y - x^2)\mathbf{k}$
   is conservative and complete the following steps to find a scalar potential function $f(x, y, z)$:

   a. Note that if $\nabla f = \mathbf{F}$, we must have
   $$f_x = y^2 - 2xz, f_y = 2xy + z, f_z = y - x^2$$
   Partially integrate f_x with respect to x to express f in terms of x, y, z, and a function $c(y, z)$ that acts as a "constant" with respect to x-integration.

   b. Find f_y and set it equal to $N = 2xy + z$. What can you conclude about the function $c(y, z)$? Partially integrate with respect to y to express f in terms of x, y, z and a function of z alone.

   c. Find the scalar potential f.

46. Let f and g be differentiable functions of one variable. Show that vector field $\mathbf{F} = [f(x) + y]\mathbf{i} + [g(y) + x]\mathbf{j}$ is conservative; find the corresponding potential function.

47. Complete the proof of Theorem 14.4 by showing that if $\int_C \mathbf{F} \cdot d\mathbf{R} = 0$ for every closed curve C in a domain D where $\mathbf{F}$ is continuous, then $\mathbf{F}$ must be conservative in D. *Hint:* Let C_1 and C_2 be two curves in D with the same endpoints P and Q. Define a closed curve C so that

   $$\int_C \mathbf{F} \cdot d\mathbf{R} = \int_{C_1} \mathbf{F} \cdot d\mathbf{R} - \int_{C_2} \mathbf{F} \cdot d\mathbf{R}$$

   and conclude that $\int_C \mathbf{F} \cdot d\mathbf{R}$ is independent of path, so that $\mathbf{F}$ is conservative in D.

14.4   GREEN'S THEOREM

IN THIS SECTION Green's theorem, area as a line integral, alternative forms of Green's theorem

The fundamental theorem of calculus, $\int_a^b \dfrac{dF}{dx} dx = F(b) - F(a)$, can be described

as saying that when the derivative $\dfrac{dF}{dx}$ is integrated over the closed interval

$a \leq x \leq b$, the result is the same as that obtained by evaluating $F(x)$ at the "boundary points" a and b and forming the difference $F(b) - F(a)$. An analogous result for functions of two variables is introduced in this section. It is called **Green's theorem** after George Green (Historical Note, page 925).

■ GREEN'S THEOREM

Green's theorem relates the double integral of a certain differential expression over a region in the plane to a line integral over a closed boundary curve of the region. We begin with some terminology. A **Jordan curve**, named for the French mathematician Camille Jordan (1838–1922), is a closed curve C in the plane that does not intersect itself (see Figure 14.14). We can redefine a simply connected region D in terms of a Jordan curve C. A region is **simply connected** if it is connected and the interior of every Jordan curve C in D also lies in D, as shown in Figure 14.14.

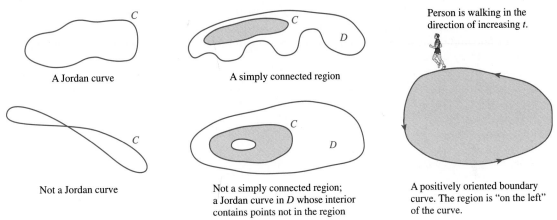

A Jordan curve

A simply connected region

Person is walking in the direction of increasing t.

Not a Jordan curve

Not a simply connected region; a Jordan curve in D whose interior contains points not in the region

A positively oriented boundary curve. The region is "on the left" of the curve.

Figure 14.14 A Jordan curve is a closed curve with no self-intersections. A region is simply connected if every Jordan curve has all its interior points in D.

Picture yourself as a point moving along a curve. If the region D stays on your *left* as you, the point, move along the curve C with increasing t, then C is said to be **positively oriented** (see Figure 14.14.)

THEOREM 14.5   Green's theorem

Let D be a simply connected region with a positively oriented piecewise-smooth boundary C. Then if the vector field $\mathbf{F}(x, y) = M(x, y)\mathbf{i} + N(x, y)\mathbf{j}$ is continuously differentiable on D, we have

$$\int_C (M\, dx + N\, dy) = \int\int_D \left(\frac{\partial N}{\partial x} - \frac{\partial M}{\partial y} \right) dA$$

> ■ *What this says*: This theorem expresses an important relationship between a line integral over a simple closed curve in the plane and a double integral over the region bounded by the curve. It is one of the most important and elegant theorems in calculus. Take special note that D is required to be simply connected with a *positively oriented* boundary C. This condition is so important that sometimes the notation
>
> $$\oint_C (M\, dx + N\, dy) \quad \text{or} \quad \oint_C (M\, dx + N\, dy)$$
>
> is used to indicate the line integral in order to emphasize the positive (or counterclockwise) orientation.

Historical Note

GEORGE GREEN (1793–1841)

George Green was a self-taught 19th-century mathematician whose ideas were far ahead of his time. He graduated from Cambridge in 1837 and, as an undergraduate, wrote a brilliant paper that included many important results in mathematical physics. Perhaps because he was still an undergraduate, the paper was largely unnoticed until it was discovered by Sir William Thompson (later known as Lord Kelvin).

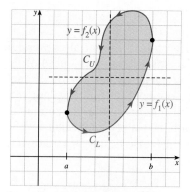

Figure 14.15 Standard region: No vertical or horizontal line intersects the boundary more than twice.

Proof: A **standard region** is one in which no vertical or horizontal line can intersect the boundary curve more than twice (see Figure 14.15). We shall prove Green's theorem for the special case where D is a standard region, and then we shall indicate how to extend the proof to more general regions.

Suppose D is a standard region with boundary curve C. We begin by showing that

$$\iint_D \frac{\partial M}{\partial y}\, dx\, dy = -\int_C M\, dx$$

Because D is a standard region, as shown in Figure 14.15, the boundary curve C is composed of a lower portion C_L and an upper portion C_U, which are the graphs of functions $f_1(x)$ and $f_2(x)$, respectively, on a certain interval $a \le x \le b$. Then we can evaluate the double integral by iterated integration:

$$\iint_D \frac{\partial M}{\partial y}\, dx\, dy = \iint_D \frac{\partial M}{\partial y}\, dy\, dx = \int_a^b \left[\int_{f_1(x)}^{f_2(x)} \frac{\partial M}{\partial y}\, dy \right] dx$$

$$= \int_a^b M[x, f_2(x)]\, dx - \int_a^b M[x, f_1(x)]\, dx = \int_{-C_U} M\, dx - \int_{C_L} M\, dx$$

$$= -\left[\int_{C_U} M\, dx + \int_{C_L} M\, dx \right] = -\int_C M\, dx$$

A similar argument shows that $\iint_D \frac{\partial N}{\partial x}\, dx\, dy = \int_C N\, dy$. Thus,

$$\iint_D \left(\frac{\partial N}{\partial x} - \frac{\partial M}{\partial y} \right) dA = \iint_D \frac{\partial N}{\partial x}\, dx\, dy - \iint_D \frac{\partial M}{\partial y}\, dx\, dy$$

$$= \int_C N\, dy - \int_C (-M)\, dx = \int_C (M\, dx + N\, dy)$$

Figure 14.16 General case: The region is decomposed into a finite number of standard regions by cuts.

This completes the proof for the standard region. If D is not a standard region, it can be decomposed into a number of standard subregions by using horizontal and vertical "cuts," as shown in Figure 14.16. The proof for the standard region is then applied to each of these subregions and the results are added. The line integrals along the cuts cancel in pairs, and after cancellation, the only remaining line integral is the one along the outer boundary C. Thus,

$$\int_C (M\, dx + N\, dy) = \iint_R \left(\frac{\partial N}{\partial x} - \frac{\partial M}{\partial y} \right) dA$$

The case where there is one cut is considered in Problem 38. ∎

EXAMPLE 1 Verifying Green's Theorem

Verify Green's theorem for the line integral $\int_C (-y\, dx + x\, dy)$, where C is the closed path shown.

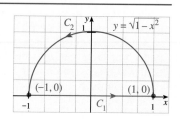

Solution First, evaluate the line integral directly. The curve C consists of the portion of the x-axis from $(-1, 0)$ to $(1, 0)$ followed by the semicircular arc from $(1, 0)$ back to $(-1, 0)$. The line segment is called C_1 and the semicircle is called C_2. We parametrize each of these:

$$C_1: \quad x = t, \qquad y = 0 \qquad -1 \le t \le 1$$
$$dx = dt, \qquad dy = 0$$

$$C_2: \quad x = \cos s, \; y = \sin s \qquad 0 \le s \le \pi$$
$$dx = -\sin s \, ds, \qquad dy = \cos s \, ds$$

$$\int_C (-y \, dx + x \, dy) = \int_{C_1} (-y \, dx + x \, dy) + \int_{C_2} (-y \, dx + x \, dy)$$

$$= \int_{-1}^{1} [-0 \, dt + t \cdot 0] + \int_0^{\pi} [-\sin s(-\sin s \, ds) + \cos s(\cos s \, ds)]$$

$$= \int_0^{\pi} (\sin^2 s + \cos^2 s) \, ds = \pi$$

Next, we use Green's theorem to evaluate this integral. Note that the boundary curve C is simple and $M = -y$, $N = x$ so that $\mathbf{F}(x, y) = -y\mathbf{i} + x\mathbf{j}$ is continuously differentiable. The domain of D is given by $0 \le y \le \sqrt{1 - x^2}$ for $-1 \le x \le 1$. We now apply Green's theorem:

$$\int_C (-y \, dx + x \, dy) = \int\int_D \left(\frac{\partial}{\partial x}(x) - \frac{\partial}{\partial y}(-y) \right) = \int_{-1}^{1} \int_0^{\sqrt{1-x^2}} 2 \, dy \, dx$$

$$= 2(\text{AREA OF SEMICIRCLE}) = 2\left[\tfrac{1}{2}\pi(1)^2\right] = \pi \qquad \blacksquare$$

EXAMPLE 2 Computing work with Green's theorem

A closed path C in the plane is defined by the given figure. Find the work done by the force $\mathbf{F}$ as the object moves along C in the force field

$$\mathbf{F}(x, y) = (x + xy^2)\mathbf{i} + 2(x^2y - y^2 \sin y)\mathbf{j}$$

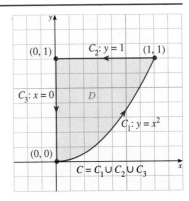

Solution The work done, W, is given by the line integral $\int_C \mathbf{F} \cdot d\mathbf{R}$. Note that $\mathbf{F}$ is continuously differentiable on D and that D is a simply connected region with a positively oriented boundary C; thus, the hypotheses of Green's theorem are satisfied. We find that

$$W = \int_C \mathbf{F} \cdot d\mathbf{R} = \int\int_D \left[\frac{\partial}{\partial x}(2x^2y - 2y^2\sin y) - \frac{\partial}{\partial y}(x + xy^2) \right] dA$$

$$= \int\int_D (4xy - 2xy) \, dA = 2 \int_0^1 \int_{x^2}^1 xy \, dy \, dx = 2 \int_0^1 \tfrac{1}{2}xy^2 \Big|_{y=x^2}^{y=1} dx$$

$$= \int_0^1 (x - x^5) \, dx = \left[\tfrac{1}{2}x^2 - \tfrac{1}{6}x^6\right]_0^1 = \tfrac{1}{3} \qquad \blacksquare$$

■ AREA AS A LINE INTEGRAL

A line integral can be used to compute an area of a region in the plane by applying the following theorem.

THEOREM 14.6   Area as a line integral

Let D be a simply connected region in the plane with piecewise-smooth closed boundary C. Then the area A of region D is given by the line integral

$$A = \frac{1}{2} \int_C (-y\, dx + x\, dy)$$

Proof: Suppose C is a closed curve that encloses a region D, as shown in Figure 14.17.

Let $\mathbf{F}(x, y) = -y\mathbf{i} + x\mathbf{j}$. Then, if $\mathbf{F}$ is continuously differentiable on D, Green's theorem applies. We have

$$\int_C (-y\, dx + x\, dy) = \int\!\!\int_D \left[\frac{\partial}{\partial x}(x) - \frac{\partial}{\partial y}(-y) \right] dA = \int\!\!\int_D 2\, dA = 2A$$

so that $A = \frac{1}{2} \int_C (-y\, dx + x\, dy)$.   ■

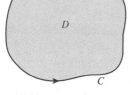

Figure 14.17 Area of region D

⊘   This gives us yet another technique for finding the area of a region, especially when its boundary is specified in parametric form. Do not forget the factor one-half after you finish the integration.   ⊘

EXAMPLE 3   Area enclosed by an ellipse

Show that the ellipse $\dfrac{x^2}{a^2} + \dfrac{y^2}{b^2} = 1$ has area πab.

Solution   The elliptical path E is given parametrically by $x = a\cos\theta$, $y = b\sin\theta$ for $0 \le \theta \le 2\pi$. We find $dx = -a\sin\theta\, d\theta$, $dy = b\cos\theta\, d\theta$. If A is the area of this ellipse, then

$$
\begin{aligned}
A &= \frac{1}{2} \int_C (-y\, dx + x\, dy) \\
&= \frac{1}{2} \int_0^{2\pi} [-(b\sin\theta)(-a\sin\theta\, d\theta) + (a\cos\theta)(b\cos\theta\, d\theta)] \\
&= \frac{1}{2} \int_0^{2\pi} ab(\cos^2\theta + \sin^2\theta)\, d\theta \\
&= \frac{1}{2} \int_0^{2\pi} ab\, d\theta \qquad \text{\textit{Because} } \cos^2\theta + \sin^2\theta = 1 \\
&= \frac{1}{2} ab(2\pi - 0) = \pi ab
\end{aligned}
$$

■ ALTERNATIVE FORMS OF GREEN'S THEOREM

Green's theorem can be expressed in a form that generalizes nicely to $\mathbb{R}^3$. In particular, note that the curl of the vector field $\mathbf{F}(x, y) = M(x, y)\mathbf{i} + N(x, y)\mathbf{j}$ is given by

Historical Note
Green's work significantly influenced the work of later mathematical physicists at Cambridge, including William Thompson (Lord Kelvin), James Clerk Maxwell, and Gabriel Stokes. The theorem known as Green's theorem was proved independently by Thompson and Mikhail Ostrogradsky, a Russian mathematician. Green's work also influenced Karl Gauss in the development of Gauss's theorem, which is also called the divergence theorem.

$$\text{curl } \mathbf{F} = \begin{bmatrix} \mathbf{i} & \mathbf{j} & \mathbf{k} \\ \dfrac{\partial}{\partial x} & \dfrac{\partial}{\partial y} & \dfrac{\partial}{\partial z} \\ M(x,\,y) & N(x,\,y) & 0 \end{bmatrix}$$

$$= \left(-\frac{\partial N}{\partial z} \right)\mathbf{i} + \left(\frac{\partial M}{\partial z} \right)\mathbf{j} + \left[\frac{\partial N}{\partial x} - \frac{\partial M}{\partial y} \right]\mathbf{k} = \left[\frac{\partial N}{\partial x} - \frac{\partial M}{\partial y} \right]\mathbf{k} \qquad \textit{Because M and N are functions of only x and y}$$

Thus, the formula in Green's theorem can be expressed as

$$\int_C \mathbf{F} \cdot d\mathbf{R} = \int\!\!\int_D (\text{curl } \mathbf{F} \cdot \mathbf{k})\, dA$$

In Section 14.6, when we extend this result to surfaces in $\mathbb{R}^3$, it will be called Stokes's theorem.

EXAMPLE 4   Relationship of the double integral of div F to the line integral of $\mathbf{F} \cdot \mathbf{N}$

Suppose $\mathbf{F}(x,\,y) = M(x,\,y)\mathbf{i} + N(x,\,y)\mathbf{j}$ with a piecewise-smooth boundary C. Show

$$\int_C \mathbf{F} \cdot \mathbf{N}\, ds = \int\!\!\int_D \text{div } \mathbf{F}\, dA$$

This is the line integral of $\mathbf{F} \cdot \mathbf{N}$, the normal component of $\mathbf{F}$.

Solution   Let $\mathbf{R}(s) = x(s)\mathbf{i} + y(s)\mathbf{j}$ so that a unit tangent vector $\mathbf{T}$ to the curve C is $\mathbf{T} = \mathbf{R}'(s) = x'(s)\mathbf{i} + y'(s)\mathbf{j}$, which means that an outward normal vector is $\mathbf{N} = y'(s)\mathbf{i} - x'(s)\mathbf{j}$. We now apply Green's theorem to find a representation using div $\mathbf{F}$.

$$\int_C \mathbf{F} \cdot \mathbf{N}\, ds = \int_a^b (M\mathbf{i} + N\mathbf{j}) \cdot [y'(s)\mathbf{i} - x'(s)\mathbf{j}]\, ds$$

$$= \int_a^b \left(M\frac{dy}{ds} - N\frac{dx}{ds} \right) ds = \int_C (-N\, dx + M\, dy)$$

$$= \int\!\!\int_D \left(\frac{\partial M}{\partial x} + \frac{\partial N}{\partial y} \right) dx\, dy = \int\!\!\int_D \text{div } \mathbf{F}\, dA$$

When we extend this result to $\mathbb{R}^3$ in Section 14.7, it will be called the divergence theorem.

We repeat these alternative forms of Green's theorem for easy reference.

Alternative Forms of Green's Theorem

Let D be a simply connected region with a positively oriented boundary C. Then if the vector field $\mathbf{F} = M\mathbf{i} + N\mathbf{j}$ is continuously differentiable on D, we have

$$\int_C \underset{\underset{\text{Tangent component of } \mathbf{F}}{\uparrow}}{\mathbf{F} \cdot d\mathbf{R}} = \int_C (M\, dx + N\, dy) = \int\!\!\int_D \left(\frac{\partial N}{\partial x} - \frac{\partial M}{\partial y} \right) dA = \int\!\!\int_D (\text{curl } \mathbf{F} \cdot \mathbf{k}) dA$$

$$\int_C \underset{\underset{\text{Normal component of } \mathbf{F}}{\uparrow}}{\mathbf{F} \cdot \mathbf{N}}\, ds = \int\!\!\int_D \left(\frac{\partial M}{\partial x} + \frac{\partial N}{\partial y} \right) dA = \int\!\!\int_D \text{div } \mathbf{F}\, dA$$

In physics, some important applications of Green's theorem involve the so-called *normal derivative* of a scalar function f, which is defined as the directional derivative of f in the direction of the outward normal to some curve or surface.

Normal Derivative

The **normal derivative** of f is denoted by $\partial f/\partial n$ and is the directional derivative of f in the direction of the normal pointing to the exterior of the domain of f. The normal derivative of f satisfies the property

$$\frac{\partial f}{\partial n} = \nabla f \cdot \mathbf{N}$$

where $\mathbf{N}$ is an outer unit normal.

The following example illustrates how Green's theorem can be used in connection with the normal derivative. Additional problems are found in the problem set.

EXAMPLE 5   Green's formula for the integral of the Laplacian

Suppose f is a scalar function with continuous first and second partial derivatives in the simply connected region D. If the piecewise-smooth curve C bounds D, show that

$$\iint_D \nabla^2 f\, dx\, dy = \int_C \frac{\partial f}{\partial n}\, ds$$

where $\nabla^2 f = f_{xx} + f_{yy}$ is the Laplacian of f and $\dfrac{\partial f}{\partial n} = \nabla f \cdot \mathbf{N}$ is the normal derivative.

Solution   Let $u = -\dfrac{\partial f}{\partial y}$ and $v = \dfrac{\partial f}{\partial x}$. Then we have

$$\nabla^2 f = f_{xx} + f_{yy} = \frac{\partial v}{\partial x} - \frac{\partial u}{\partial y}$$

$$\iint_D \nabla^2 f\, dx\, dy = \iint_D \left(\frac{\partial v}{\partial x} - \frac{\partial u}{\partial y} \right) dx\, dy = \int_C u\, dx + v\, dy \quad \textit{Green's theorem}$$

$$= \int_C \left(u\, \frac{dx}{ds} + v\, \frac{dy}{ds} \right) ds$$

$$= \int_C \left(-\frac{\partial f}{\partial y}\, \frac{dx}{ds} + \frac{\partial f}{\partial x}\, \frac{dy}{ds} \right) ds$$

$$= \int_C \left(f_x\, \frac{dy}{ds} - f_y\, \frac{dx}{ds} \right) ds$$

$$= \int_C \nabla f \cdot \left(\frac{dy}{ds}\, \mathbf{i} - \frac{dx}{ds}\, \mathbf{j} \right) ds$$

$$= \int_C \nabla f \cdot \mathbf{N}\, ds \quad \textit{Where } \mathbf{N} = \frac{dy}{ds}\, \mathbf{i} - \frac{dx}{ds}\, \mathbf{j} \textit{ is an outward unit normal to } C$$

$$= \int_C \frac{\partial f}{\partial n}\, ds$$

PROBLEM SET 14.4

A *Evaluate the line integrals in Problem 1–6 by applying Green's theorem. Check your answer by direct computation (that is, by parametrizing the curve C).*

1. $\int_C (y^2\, dx + x^2\, dy)$

2. $\int_C (y^3\, dx - x^3\, dy)$

3. $\int_C [(2x^2 + 3y)\, dx - 3y^2\, dy]$

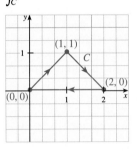

4. $\int_C (y^2\, dx + 3xy^2\, dy)$

5. $\int_C 4xy\, dx$

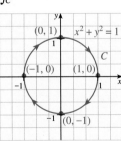

6. $\int_C (4y\, dx - 3x\, dy)$

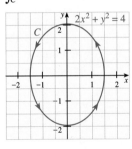

Evaluate the line integral in Problems 7–12 by applying Green's theorem.

7. $\int_C (2y\, dx - x\, dy)$

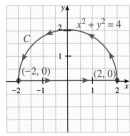

8. $\int_C (e^x\, dx - \sin x\, dy)$

9. $\int_C (x \sin x\, dx - \tan y\, dy)$

10. $\int_C [(x + y)\, dx - (3x - 2y)\, dy]$

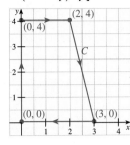

11. $\int_C [(x - y^2)\, dx + 2xy\, dy]$

12. $\int_C (y^2\, dx + x\, dy)$

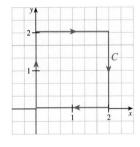

13. Use Green's theorem to find the work done by the force field $\mathbf{F}(x, y) = (3y - 4x)\mathbf{i} + (4x - y)\mathbf{j}$ when an object moves once counterclockwise around the ellipse $4x^2 + y^2 = 4$.

14. Find the work done when an object moves in the force field $\mathbf{F}(x, y) = y^2\mathbf{i} + x^2\mathbf{j}$ counterclockwise along the circular path $x^2 + y^2 = 2$.

Use Theorem 14.6 to find the area enclosed by the regions described in Problems 15–18 and then check by using an appropriate formula.

15. Circle $x^2 + y^2 = 4$

16. Triangle with vertices $(0, 0)$, $(1, 1)$, and $(0, 2)$

17. Trapezoid with vertices $(0, 0)$, $(4, 0)$, $(0, 3)$, and $(1, 3)$

18. Semicircle $x = \sqrt{4 - y^2}$

B **19.** Evaluate the line integral

$$\int_C (x^2 y\, dx - y^2 x\, dy)$$

where C is the boundary of the region between the x-axis and the semicircle $y = \sqrt{a^2 - x^2}$, traversed counterclockwise.

20. Evaluate the line integral

$$\int_C (3y\, dx - 2x\, dy)$$

where C is the cardioid $r = 1 + \sin \theta$, traversed counterclockwise.

21. Show that

$$\int_C (5 - xy - y^2)\, dx - (2xy - x^2)\, dy = 3\overline{x}$$

where C is the square $0 \le x \le 1, 0 \le y \le 1$ traversed counterclockwise and $\overline{x}$ is the x-coordinate of the centroid of the square.

22. Find the work done by the force field

$$\mathbf{F}(x, y) = (x + 2y^2)\mathbf{j}$$

as an object moves once counterclockwise about the circle $(x - 2)^2 + y^2 = 1$.

23. Let D be the region bounded by the Jordan curve C, and let A be the area of D. If $(\overline{x}, \overline{y})$ is the centroid of D, show that

$$A\overline{x} = \frac{1}{2} \int_C x^2\, dy$$

where C is traversed counterclockwise.

24. Use Theorem 14.6 and the polar transformation formulas $x = r \cos\theta, y = r \sin\theta$ to obtain the area formula in polar coordinates, namely,

$$A = \frac{1}{2} \int_{\theta_1}^{\theta_2} r^2\, d\theta = \frac{1}{2} \int_{\theta_1}^{\theta_2} [g(\theta)]^2\, d\theta$$

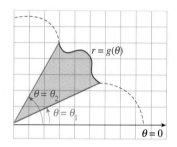

25. Evaluate $\displaystyle\int_C \left[\left(\frac{-y}{x^2} + \frac{1}{x} \right) dx + \frac{1}{x}\, dy \right]$, where C is any Jordan curve that does not touch or cross the y-axis, traversed counterclockwise.

26. Evaluate $\displaystyle\int_C \frac{x\, dx + y\, dy}{x^2 + y^2}$, where C is any Jordan curve whose interior does not contain the origin, traversed counterclockwise.

27. Evaluate $\displaystyle\int_C \frac{-y\, dx + (x - 1)\, dy}{(x - 1)^2 + y^2}$, where C is any Jordan curve whose interior does not contain the point $(1, 0)$, traversed counterclockwise.

28. Evaluate $\displaystyle\int_C \frac{-(y + 2)\, dx + (x - 1)\, dy}{(x - 1)^2 + (y + 2)^2}$, where C is any Jordan curve whose interior does not contain the point $(1, -2)$, traversed counterclockwise.

29. Evaluate $\displaystyle\int_C \frac{\partial z}{\partial n}\, ds$, where $z(x, y) = 2x^2 + 3y^2$ and C is the circular path $x^2 + y^2 = 16$, traversed counterclockwise.

30. Evaluate $\displaystyle\int_C \frac{\partial f}{\partial n}\, ds$, where $f(x, y) = x^2 y - 2xy + y^2$ and C is the boundary of the unit square $0 \le x \le 1, 0 \le y \le 1$, traversed counterclockwise.

31. Evaluate $\displaystyle\int_C x \frac{\partial x}{\partial n}\, ds$, where C is the boundary of the unit square $0 \le x \le 1, 0 \le y \le 1$, traversed counterclockwise.

32. If C is a closed curve, show that

$$\int_C [(x - 3y)\, dx + (2x - y^2)\, dy] = 5A$$

where A is the area of the region D enclosed by C.

33. SPY PROBLEM   After escaping from Purity's watery trap (Problem 59, Section 13.7), the spy takes a deep gulp of fresh air and enters the next room. The door slams shut behind him, and he finds himself looking across a large, rectangular room at Purity and the arch fiend, André Scélérat. The spy takes a step toward his nemesis, but finds his movements restricted by a force field that appears to sap his strength. Scélérat laughs cruelly and says, "I see you have noticed the Death Force my lovely assistant has designed for you. I hope you appreciate her efforts." Scélérat takes Purity's arm and leads her from the room, saying, "Goodbye, old friend, and by the way, it will do you no good to stay still, because the rays given off by the Death Force will eventually kill you even if you never move." One more peal of laughter and the spy is left alone. Quickly, he presses the stem on his wristwatch and sees the equation of the force field appear on the face:

$$\mathbf{F}(x, y) = \left[ye^{xy} + 2xy^3 \right]\mathbf{i} + \left[xe^{xy} + 3x^2 y^2 + \cos y \right]\mathbf{j}$$

Assuming that the spy is at $(0, 0)$ on the wristwatch's coordinate system and that the door (and safety) is at $(5, 4)$, what path should the spy take in order to minimize the work of struggling against the Death Force while crossing the room in the least possible time?

34. Prove the following theoretical application of Green's theorem: Let $\mathbf{F}(x, y) = u(x, y)\mathbf{i} + v(x, y)\mathbf{j}$ be continuously differentiable on the simply connected region D. Then $\mathbf{F}$ is conservative if and only if

$$\frac{\partial v}{\partial x} = \frac{\partial u}{\partial y}$$

throughout D.

35. Recall that a scalar function f with continuous first and second partial derivatives is said to be **harmonic** in a region D if $\nabla^2 f = 0$ (that is, if $f_{xx} + f_{yy} = 0$). If f is such a function, show that

$$\int\int_D (f_x^2 + f_y^2)\, dx\, dy = \int_C f\, \frac{\partial f}{\partial n}\, ds$$

where C is the boundary of D.

36. Derive the following result, known as **Green's first identity**.

$$\int\int_D [f\nabla^2 g - g\,\nabla^2 f]\, dx\, dy = \int_C \left(f\frac{\partial g}{\partial n} - g\frac{\partial f}{\partial n} \right) ds$$

Hint: Start with the line integral.

37. Derive the following result, known as **Green's second identity**.

$$\int\int_D [f\nabla^2 g + \nabla f \cdot \nabla g]\, dx\, dy = \int_C f\frac{\partial g}{\partial n}\, ds$$

Hint: Start with the line integral.

38. Prove Green's theorem in the plane for the region D shown in Figure 14.18.

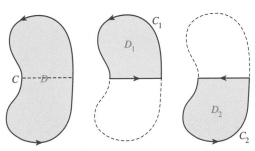

Figure 14.18 Green's theorem

The line L "cuts" the region into two standard subregions D_1 and D_2.

14.5 SURFACE INTEGRALS

> **IN THIS SECTION** Terminology, surface integrals, surface integrals of vector fields, parametrically defined surfaces
>
> A **surface integral** is a generalization of the line integral in which we integrate over regions in space bounded by a surface. The rest of this chapter deals with surface integrals. We introduce the concept in this section, and then in the next two sections we shall use surface integrals to generalize Green's theorem to $\mathbb{R}^3$.

◼ TERMINOLOGY

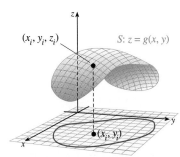

S is a surface defined by $z = g(x, y)$.

Recall that line integrals are defined only along oriented curves that are piecewise smooth and have no self-intersections, and there are similar restrictions on the nature of the surfaces used in the study of surface integrals. First, recall that a surface is *smooth* if it has a unit normal vector $\mathbf{N}(x, y, z)$, that varies continuously as the point (x, y, z) ranges over the surface, and it is *piecewise smooth* if it consists of a finite number of smooth pieces. For instance, a sphere is a smooth surface, and a cube is piecewise smooth because it consists of six smooth faces, with adjacent faces meeting on an edge where it is not smooth.

A surface is **orientable** if it is possible to choose a unit normal $\mathbf{N}$ at each point on the surface S so that $\mathbf{N}$ varies continuously over S. A **closed surface** is one that bounds a solid region. The region enclosed by S is called its *interior* and the region outside S is its *exterior*. The normal N is an *outer normal* of S if it points toward the exterior of S and *inner normal* if it points toward the interior. These terms are illustrated in Figure 14.19. Most common surfaces, such as planes, spheres, ellipses, and paraboloids are orientable.

We are not interested in piecewise-smooth surfaces with only one side, such as the Möbius strip, which is obtained by twisting a strip of paper and then attaching the ends together (see Figure 14.19b). Henceforth, we shall use the word **surface** to mean an **orientable, piecewise smooth surface**.

a. Two-sided (orientable) surface: a football. This is also a closed surface.

b. One-sided (non-orientable) surface: a Möbius strip

Figure 14.19 Surfaces in space

A **boundary point** p of a set of points S in $\mathbb{R}^3$ has the property that any sphere centered at p (no matter how small) contains points in S and also points not in S. The **boundary** of S is the collection of all its boundary points, and S is **closed** if it contains its boundary. For example, the solid spherical region $x^2 + y^2 + z^2 \le r^2$ is closed because it contains its boundary $x^2 + y^2 + z^2 = r^2$. A solid region is **bounded** if it can be contained inside a sphere of finite radius.

Definition of a surface integral

■ SURFACE INTEGRALS

Now we can define the surface integral of a scalar function g. Suppose g is defined and continuous on a surface S. Partition S into n subregions, the kth of which has area ΔS_k, and let P_k^* be a point chosen arbitrarily from the kth subregion, for $k = 1, 2, \ldots, n$. Form the sum

$$\sum_{k=1}^{n} g(P_k^*)\Delta S_k$$

and take the limit as the largest of the ΔS_k tends to 0, just as we did with the surface area in Section 13.4. If this limit exists, it is called the **surface integral of g over S** and is denoted by

$$\iint_S g(x, y, z)\, dS$$

Recall from Section 13.4 that when the surface S projects onto the region R_{xy} in the xy-plane and S has the representation $z = f(x, y)$, then

$$dS = \sqrt{f_x^2 + f_y^2 + 1}\, dA_{xy}$$

where dA_{xy} is either $dx\, dy$ or $dy\, dx$ (or $r\, dr\, d\theta$ if A_{xy} is described in terms of polar coordinates). We can now state the formula for evaluating a surface integral. (*Note:* We write R_{xy} and A_{xy} instead of the usual R and A to help you remember that these are regions in the xy-plane.)

Surface Integral

Let S be a surface defined by $z = f(x, y)$ and R_{xy} its projection on the xy-plane. If f, f_x, and f_y are continuous in R_{xy} and g is continuous on S, then the **surface integral** of g over S is

$$\iint_S g(x, y, z)\, dS = \iint_{R_{xy}} g(x, y, f(x, y))\sqrt{[f_x(x, y)]^2 + [f_y(x, y)]^2 + 1}\, dA_{xy}$$

EXAMPLE 1   Evaluating a surface integral

Evaluate the surface integral

$$\iint_S g \, dS$$

where $g(x, y, z) = xz + 2x^2 - 3xy$ and S is that portion of the plane $2x - 3y + z = 6$ that lies over the unit square.

$$R_{xy}: 0 \le x \le 1, \qquad 0 \le y \le 1$$

Solution   First, note that the equation of the plane can be written as $z = f(x, y)$, where $f(x, y) = 6 - 2x + 3y$. We have $f_x(x, y) = -2$ and $f_y(x, y) = 3$, so that

$$dS = \sqrt{f_x^2 + f_y^2 + 1} \, dA_{xy} = \sqrt{(-2)^2 + (3)^2 + 1} \, dA_{xy} = \sqrt{14} \, dA_{xy}$$

Consequently,

$$
\begin{aligned}
\iint_S g \, dS &= \iint_S (xz + 2x^2 - 3xy)\sqrt{14} \, dA_{xy} \\
&= \iint_R [x(6 - 2x + 3y) + 2x^2 - 3xy]\sqrt{14} \, dy \, dx \\
&= \sqrt{14} \iint_R 6x \, dy \, dx \\
&= 6\sqrt{14} \int_0^1 \int_0^1 x \, dy \, dx = 6\sqrt{14} \int_0^1 x \, dx = 3\sqrt{14}
\end{aligned}
$$

If the function g defined on S is simply $g(x, y, z) = 1$, then the surface integral gives the *surface area* of S.

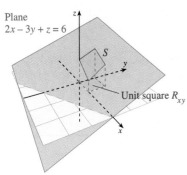

Plane
$2x - 3y + z = 6$

The portion of the plane that lies above the unit square

Surface Area Formula

$$\text{Surface area} = \iint_S dS$$

A useful application of surface integrals is to find the center of mass of a thin curved lamina whose shape is a given surface S, as shown in Figure 14.20.

Thin curved lamina

Surface S

Figure 14.20 A thin lamina whose shape is the surface S

Suppose $\rho(x, y, z)$ is the density (mass per unit area) at a point (x, y, z) on the lamina. Then the *total mass, m, of the lamina* can also be represented by a surface integral.

Mass of a Lamina

$$m = \iint_S \rho(x, y, z) \, dS$$

and the center of mass of the surface is the point $C(\bar{x}, \bar{y}, \bar{z})$ where

$$\bar{x} = \frac{1}{m} \int_S \int x\rho(x, y, z) \, dS, \qquad \bar{y} = \frac{1}{m} \int_S \int y\rho(x, y, z) \, dS, \qquad \bar{z} = \frac{1}{m} \int_S \int z\rho(x, y, z) \, dS$$

These formulas may be derived by essentially the same approach used in our previous work with moments and centroids of solid regions. (See, for example, Sections 6.3 and 10.3.)

EXAMPLE 2   Mass of a curved lamina

Find the mass of a lamina of density $\rho(x, y, z) = z$ in the shape of the hemisphere $z = (a^2 - x^2 - y^2)^{1/2}$.

Solution   We begin by calculating dS.

$$z_x = \tfrac{1}{2}(a^2 - x^2 - y^2)^{-1/2}(-2x) = -x(a^2 - x^2 - y^2)^{-1/2}$$

$$z_y = \tfrac{1}{2}(a^2 - x^2 - y^2)^{-1/2}(-2y) = -y(a^2 - x^2 - y^2)^{-1/2}$$

$$dS = \sqrt{z_x{}^2 + z_y{}^2 + 1} \, dA_{xy} = \sqrt{\frac{x^2}{a^2 - x^2 - y^2} + \frac{y^2}{a^2 - x^2 - y^2} + 1} \, dA_{xy}$$

$$= \sqrt{\frac{a^2}{a^2 - x^2 - y^2}} \, dA_{xy} = a(a^2 - x^2 - y^2)^{-1/2} \, dA_{xy}$$

The mass of the hemisphere S is given by

$$m = \int_S \int \rho(x, y, z) \, dS = \int_S \int z \, dS$$

$$= \int_R \int (a^2 - x^2 - y^2)^{1/2} a(a^2 - x^2 - y^2)^{-1/2} \, dA_{xy} = a \int_R \int dA_{xy} = a(\pi a^2) = \pi a^3$$

Figure 14.21 Note that S projects onto the circle R in the xy-plane with the equation $x^2 + y^2 = a^2$.

■ SURFACE INTEGRALS OF VECTOR FIELDS

Velocity field

Many applications of surface integrals require the integral of the normal component of a given vector field $\mathbf{F}$—that is, an integral of the form $\int_S \int \mathbf{F} \cdot \mathbf{N} \, dS$, where

$\mathbf{N}$ is the outward unit normal to the surface S. Because $\mathbf{F} \cdot \mathbf{N}$ is a scalar function, this type of surface integral is really the same as the kind we have already studied, but it is still useful to examine a few situations that involve surface integrals of this form. Consider the following example.

EXAMPLE 3   Surface integral of a vector field

Compute $\int_S \int \mathbf{F} \cdot \mathbf{N} \, dS$, where

$\mathbf{F} = x\mathbf{i} - 5y\mathbf{j} + 4z\mathbf{k}$, and S is the union of the two squares

$$S_1: \quad x = 0, \qquad 0 \le y \le 1, \qquad 0 \le z \le 1$$

$$S_2: \quad z = 1, \qquad 0 \le x \le 1, \qquad 0 \le y \le 1$$

Note the orientation of the axes.

Solution On S_1, the outward unit normal is $\mathbf{N}_1 = -\mathbf{i}$ and

$$\mathbf{F} \cdot \mathbf{N}_1 = (x\mathbf{i} - 5y\mathbf{j} + 4z\mathbf{k}) \cdot (-\mathbf{i}) = -x = 0$$

(because $x = 0$ on S_1). Thus,

$$\int\int_{S_1} \mathbf{F} \cdot \mathbf{N}_1 \, dS_1 = 0$$

On S_2, $\mathbf{N}_2 = \mathbf{k}$, and $\mathbf{F} \cdot \mathbf{N}_2 = \mathbf{F} \cdot \mathbf{k} = 4z = 4$ (because $z = 1$ on S_2). Thus,

$$\int\int_{S_2} \mathbf{F} \cdot \mathbf{N}_2 \, dS_2 = \int\int_{S_2} 4 \, dS_2 = 4(\text{area of } S_2) = 4$$

Finally,

$$\int\int_S \mathbf{F} \cdot \mathbf{N} \, dS = \int\int_{S_1} \mathbf{F} \cdot \mathbf{N}_1 \, dS_1 + \int\int_{S_2} \mathbf{F} \cdot \mathbf{N}_2 \, dS_2 = 0 + 4 = 4$$

The unit normal of a surface is not always as obvious as it was in Example 3. For an orientable surface S defined by $z = g(x, y)$, we let $G(x, y, z) = z - g(x, y)$. Then, $\mathbf{N}$ can be found as follows (see Section 12.6):

$$\mathbf{N} = \frac{\nabla G(x, y, z)}{\|\nabla G(x, y, z)\|} = \frac{-g_x\mathbf{i} - g_y\mathbf{j} + \mathbf{k}}{\sqrt{g_x^2 + g_y^2 + 1}} \qquad \textbf{Outward unit normal}$$

$$\mathbf{N} = \frac{-\nabla G(x, y, z)}{\|\nabla G(x, y, z)\|} = \frac{g_x\mathbf{i} + g_y\mathbf{j} - \mathbf{k}}{\sqrt{g_x^2 + g_y^2 + 1}} \qquad \textbf{Inward unit normal}$$

EXAMPLE 4 **Surface integral of a vector field**

Compute $\displaystyle\int\int_S \mathbf{F} \cdot \mathbf{N} \, dS$, where

$$\mathbf{F} = xy\mathbf{i} + z\mathbf{j} + (x + y)\mathbf{k}$$

and S is the triangular region cut off from the plane $x + y + z = 1$ by the positive coordinate axes, as shown in Figure 14.22. Assume $\mathbf{N}$ is the unit normal that points away from the origin.

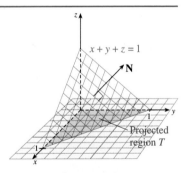

Figure 14.22

Solution Let $g(x, y) = z = 1 - x - y$. Then $g_x = -1$, $g_y = -1$, and an outward unit normal to the plane is

$$\mathbf{N} = \frac{-(-1)\mathbf{i} - (-1)\mathbf{j} + \mathbf{k}}{\sqrt{(-1)^2 + (-1)^2 + 1}} = \frac{1}{\sqrt{3}}(\mathbf{i} + \mathbf{j} + \mathbf{k})$$

so that

$$\mathbf{F} \cdot \mathbf{N} = [xy\mathbf{i} + z\mathbf{j} + (x + y)\mathbf{k}] \cdot \left(\tfrac{1}{\sqrt{3}}\mathbf{i} + \tfrac{1}{\sqrt{3}}\mathbf{j} + \tfrac{1}{\sqrt{3}}\mathbf{k}\right) = \frac{1}{\sqrt{3}}(xy + z + x + y)$$

We can write this as a function of x and y because $z = 1 - x - y$:

$$\mathbf{F} \cdot \mathbf{N} = \frac{1}{\sqrt{3}}(xy + 1 - x - y + x + y) = \frac{1}{\sqrt{3}}(xy + 1)$$

We also find that

$$dS = \sqrt{g_x^2 + g_y^2 + 1} \, dA_{xy} = \sqrt{3} \, dA_{xy}$$

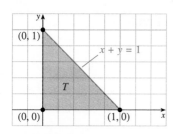

Figure 14.23 Projected region T from Figure 14.22.

The final piece of the puzzle we need before turning to the evaluation of the integral is to find the projection of S onto the xy-plane. We see from Figure 14.23 that this is a triangular region. Let us call this region T, which can be described as the set of all points (x, y) such that for each x between 0 and 1, y varies between $y = 0$ and $y = 1 - x$ (as shown in Figure 14.23). Finally, we find that

$$\iint_S \mathbf{F} \cdot \mathbf{N} \, dS = \iint_T \frac{1}{\sqrt{3}}(xy + 1) \sqrt{3} \, dA_{xy}$$

$$= \int_0^1 \int_0^{1-x} (xy + 1) \, dy \, dx = \int_0^1 \left[\tfrac{1}{2}xy^2 + y \right]_{y=0}^{y=1-x} dx$$

$$= \frac{1}{2} \int_0^1 (x^3 - 2x^2 - x + 2) \, dx = \frac{1}{2}\left[\tfrac{1}{4}x^4 - \tfrac{2}{3}x^3 - \tfrac{1}{2}x^2 + 2x \right]_0^1 = \frac{13}{24}$$ ▬

■ PARAMETRICALLY DEFINED SURFACES

In Section 13.4, we showed that if a surface S is defined parametrically by the vector function

$$\mathbf{R}(u, v) = x(u, v)\mathbf{i} + y(u, v)\mathbf{j} + z(u, v)\mathbf{k}$$

over a region D in the uv-plane, the surface area of S is given by the integral

$$\iint_D \|\mathbf{R}_u \times \mathbf{R}_v\| \, du \, dv$$

Then if f is continuous on D, the surface integral of f over D is given by

$$\iint_S f(x, y, z) \, dS = \iint_D f(\mathbf{R}) \|\mathbf{R}_u \times \mathbf{R}_v\| \, du \, dv$$

EXAMPLE 5   Surface integral for a surface defined parametrically

Evaluate $\displaystyle\iint_S (x + y + z) \, dS$ where S is the surface defined parametrically by

$\mathbf{R}(u, v) = (2u + v)\mathbf{i} + (u - 2v)\mathbf{j} + (u + 3v)\mathbf{k}$ for $0 \le u \le 1, 0 \le v \le 2$.

Solution $$\iint_S (x + y + z) \, dS = \iint_D f(\mathbf{R})\|\mathbf{R}_u \times \mathbf{R}_v\| \, du \, dv$$

Before we go on, we need to find the component parts for the integral on the right. If $\mathbf{R} = x\mathbf{i} + y\mathbf{j} + z\mathbf{k}$, we see for this problem $x = 2u + v$, $y = u - 2v$, and $z = u + 3v$. Because $f(x, y, z) = x + y + z$,

$$f(\mathbf{R}) = f(2u + v, u - 2v, u + 3v)$$

$$= 2u + v + u - 2v + u + 3v = 4u + 2v$$

$\mathbf{R}_u = 2\mathbf{i} + \mathbf{j} + \mathbf{k}$ and $\mathbf{R}_v = \mathbf{i} - 2\mathbf{j} + 3\mathbf{k}$, so

$$\mathbf{R}_u \times \mathbf{R}_v = \begin{vmatrix} \mathbf{i} & \mathbf{j} & \mathbf{k} \\ 2 & 1 & 1 \\ 1 & -2 & 3 \end{vmatrix} = (3 + 2)\mathbf{i} - (6 - 1)\mathbf{j} + (-4 - 1)\mathbf{k} = 5\mathbf{i} - 5\mathbf{j} - 5\mathbf{k}$$

Thus, $\|\mathbf{R}_u \times \mathbf{R}_v\| = \sqrt{5^2 + (-5)^2 + (-5)^2} = 5\sqrt{3}$

We now substitute these values into the surface integral formula:

$$\iint_S (x + y + z)\, dS = \iint_D f(\mathbf{R})\|\mathbf{R}_u \times \mathbf{R}_v\|\, du\, dv$$

$$= \int_0^2 \int_0^1 (4u + 2v)(5\sqrt{3})\, du\, dv = 5\sqrt{3}\int_0^2 \left[2u^2 + 2uv\right]_0^1 dv$$

$$= 5\sqrt{3}\int_0^2 (2 + 2v)\, dv = 5\sqrt{3}\left[2v + v^2\right]_0^2 = 5\sqrt{3}(8) = 40\sqrt{3}$$

PROBLEM SET 14.5

Ⓐ *Let S be the hemisphere $x^2 + y^2 + z^2 = 4$, with $z \geq 0$, in Problems 1–6. Evaluate the surface integral.*

1. $\displaystyle\iint_S z\, dS$ **2.** $\displaystyle\iint_S z^2\, dS$

3. $\displaystyle\iint_S (x - 2y)\, dS$ **4.** $\displaystyle\iint_S (5 - 2x)\, dS$

5. $\displaystyle\iint_S (x^2 + y^2)z\, dS$ **6.** $\displaystyle\iint_S (x^2 + y^2)\, dS$

In Problems 7–10, evaluate $\displaystyle\iint_S xy\, dS$.

7. $S: z = 2 - y, 0 \leq x \leq 2, 0 \leq y \leq 2$
8. $S: z = 4 - x - y, 0 \leq x \leq 4, 0 \leq y \leq 4$
9. $S: z = 5, x^2 + y^2 \leq 1$
10. $S: z = 10, \dfrac{x^2}{4} + \dfrac{y^2}{1} \leq 1$

In Problems 11–14, evaluate $\displaystyle\iint_S (x^2 + y^2)\, dS$.

11. $S: z = 4 - x - 2y, 0 \leq x \leq 4, 0 \leq y \leq 2$
12. $S: z = 4 - x, 0 \leq x \leq 2, 0 \leq y \leq 2$
13. $S: z = 4, x^2 + y^2 \leq 1$
14. $S: z = xy, x^2 + y^2 \leq 4, x \geq 0, y \geq 0$

In Problems 15–18, suppose S is the portion of the paraboloid $z = x^2 + y^2$ for which $z \leq 4$. Evaluate the given surface integral.

15. $\displaystyle\iint_S z\, dS$ **16.** $\displaystyle\iint_S (4 - z)\, dS$

17. $\displaystyle\iint_S \sqrt{1 + 4z}\, dS$ **18.** $\displaystyle\iint_S \dfrac{dS}{\sqrt{1 + 4z}}$

19. Evaluate $\displaystyle\iint_S (x^2 + y^2)\, dS$, where S is the surface bounded above by the hemisphere $z = \sqrt{1 - x^2 - y^2}$, and below by the plane $z = 0$.

20. Evaluate $\displaystyle\iint_S 2x\, dS$, where S is the portion of the plane $x + y + z = 1$ with $x \geq 0, y \geq 0, z \geq 0$.

21. Evaluate $\displaystyle\iint_S (x^2 + y^2 + z^2)\, dS$, where S is the portion of the plane $z = x + 1$ inside the cylinder $x^2 + y^2 = 1$.

Evaluate $\displaystyle\iint_S \mathbf{F} \cdot \mathbf{N}\, dS$ for the vector fields $\mathbf{F}$ and surfaces S given in Problems 22–27. Assume $\mathbf{N}$ is the outer normal.

22. $\mathbf{F} = x\mathbf{i} + 2y\mathbf{j} + z\mathbf{k}$, and S is the triangular region bounded by the intersection of the plane $x + 2y + z = 1$ and the positive coordinate axes.

23. $\mathbf{F} = x\mathbf{i} + 2y\mathbf{j} - 3z\mathbf{k}$, and S is that part of the plane $15x - 12y + 3z = 6$ that lies above the unit square $0 \leq x \leq 1, 0 \leq y \leq 1$.

24. $\mathbf{F} = x\mathbf{i} + y\mathbf{j} + 2z\mathbf{k}$, and S is the surface of the cube bounded by the planes $x = 0, x = 1, y = 0, y = 1, z = 0,$ and $z = 1$.

25. $\mathbf{F} = x\mathbf{i} + y\mathbf{j}$, and S is the hemisphere $z = \sqrt{1 - x^2 - y^2}$.

26. $\mathbf{F} = 2x\mathbf{i} - 3y\mathbf{j}$, and S is the part of the hemisphere given by $x^2 + y^2 + z^2 = 5$, for $z \geq 1$.

27. $\mathbf{F} = x^2\mathbf{i} + y^2\mathbf{j} + z^2\mathbf{k}$, and S is the portion of the plane $z = y + 1$ that lies inside the cylinder $x^2 + y^2 = 1$.

B **28.** Evaluate $\displaystyle\iint_S (3x - y + 2z) \, dS$, where S is the surface determined by $\mathbf{R}(u, \ v) = u\mathbf{i} + u\mathbf{j} - v\mathbf{k}$, $0 \le u \le 1$, $1 \le v \le 2$.

29. Evaluate $\displaystyle\iint_S (x - y^2 + z) \, dS$, where S is the surface defined by $\mathbf{R}(u, v) = u^2\mathbf{i} + v\mathbf{j} + u\mathbf{k}$, $0 \le u \le 1, 0 \le v \le 1$.

30. Evaluate $\displaystyle\iint_S (\tan^{-1}x + y - z^2) \, dS$, where S is the surface defined by $\mathbf{R}(u, v) = u\mathbf{i} + v^2\mathbf{j} - v\mathbf{k}$, $0 \le u \le 1, 0 \le v \le 1$.

31. Evaluate $\displaystyle\iint_S (x^2 + y - z) \, dS$, where S is the surface defined by $\mathbf{R}(u, v) = u\mathbf{i} - u^2\mathbf{j} + v\mathbf{k}$, $0 \le u \le 2, 0 \le v \le 1$.

In Problems 32–37, find the mass of the homogeneous lamina that has the shape of the given surface S. Assume $\rho(x, y, z) = 1$.
32. S is the surface $z = 4 - x - 2y$, with $z \ge 0, x \ge 0$
33. S is the surface $z = 10 - 2x - y$, with $z \ge 0, y \ge 0$
34. S is the surface $z = x^2 + y^2$, with $z \le 1$.
35. S is the surface $z = 1 - x^2 - y^2$, with $z \ge 0$.
36. S is the surface $x^2 + y^2 + z^2 = 5$, with $z \ge 1$.

37. S is the triangular surface with vertices $(1, 0, 0)$, $(0, 1, 0)$, and $(0, 0, 1)$.

C **38.** Let S be the spherical shell centered at the origin with radius a, and let C be the right circular cone whose vertex is at the origin and whose axis of symmetry coincides with the z-axis. (This has the shape of an old-fashioned ice cream cone.) Suppose the vertex angle of the cone is ϕ, with $0 \le \phi < \pi$. Determine the mass of that portion of the sphere that is enclosed in the intersection of S and C. Assume $\rho(x, y, z) = 1$.

39. Use the formula

$$I_z = \iint_S (x^2 + y^2)\rho(x, y, z) \, dS$$

for the moment of inertia about the z- axis. Show that the moment of inertia of a conical shell about its axis is $\frac{1}{2}ma^2$, where m is the mass and a is the radius. Assume that $\rho(x, y, z) = 1$.

40. Use the formula

$$I_z = \iint_S (x^2 + y^2)\rho(x, y, z) \, dS$$

for the moment of inertia about the y-axis. Show that the moment of inertia of a spherical shell of uniform density about its diameter is $\frac{2}{3}ma^2$, where m is the mass and a is the radius. Assume $\rho(x, y, z) = 1$.

41. THINK TANK PROBLEM   Show that a Möbius strip is not orientable.

14.6 STOKES'S THEOREM

> **IN THIS SECTION** Stokes's theorem, physical interpretation of Stokes's theorem
> In Section 14.4, we observed that Green's theorem can be written
> $$\int_C \mathbf{F} \cdot d\mathbf{R} = \iint_A (\text{curl } \mathbf{F} \cdot \mathbf{k}) \, dA$$
> where A is the plane region bounded by the closed curve C. Stokes's theorem is a generalization of this result to surfaces in space and their boundaries.

■ STOKES'S THEOREM

Before stating Stokes's theorem, we need to explain what is meant by a *compatible orientation*. We say that the orientation of a closed path C on the surface S is **compatible with the orientation on S** if the positive direction is *counterclockwise* in relation to the outward normal of the surface (see Figure 14.24). If you point the thumb of your right hand in the direction of the outward unit normal, your fingers will curl in the direction of the compatibly oriented curve C.

GEORGE STOKES (1819–1903)

Stokes's theorem is named for George Gabriel Stokes, an English mathematical physicist who publicized the theorem in 1854. According to Stokes, the result was first obtained by one of his colleagues, William Thompson, who is also known as Lord Kelvin.

Figure 14.24 Compatible orientation: The surface S is on the left of someone walking in a counterclockwise direction around the boundary curve C.

THEOREM 14.7   Stokes's theorem

Let S be an oriented surface with unit normal vector $\mathbf{N}$, and assume that S is bounded by a closed, piecewise-smooth curve C whose orientation is compatible with that of S. If $\mathbf{F}$ is a vector field that is continuously differentiable on S, then

$$\int_C \mathbf{F} \cdot d\mathbf{R} = \iint_S (\text{curl } \mathbf{F} \cdot \mathbf{N}) \, dS$$

Proof: The general proof is beyond the scope of this text. However, a proof where S is the graph of $z = z(x, y)$ and $\mathbf{F}$, S, and C are "well behaved" is given in Appendix B. ∎

Notice that the surface S in the statement of Stokes's theorem is *not* closed.

EXAMPLE 1   Verifying Stokes's theorem for a particular example

Let $\mathbf{F} = -\frac{3}{2}y^2\mathbf{i} - 2xy\mathbf{j} + yz\mathbf{k}$, where S is that part of the surface of the plane $x + y + z = 1$ contained within the triangle C with vertices $(1, 0, 0)$, $(0, 1, 0)$, and $(0, 0, 1)$, traversed counterclockwise as viewed from above. Verify Stokes's theorem.

Solution   The planar surface S and boundary curve C are shown in Figure 14.25. We shall show that the line integral $\int_C \mathbf{F} \cdot d\mathbf{R}$ and the surface integral $\iint_S (\text{curl } \mathbf{F} \cdot \mathbf{N}) \, dS$ have the same value.

I. *Evaluation of* $\displaystyle\int_C \mathbf{F} \cdot d\mathbf{R}$

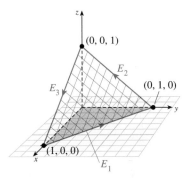

Figure 14.25 The triangle C bounds the part of the plane $x + y + z = 1$ that lies in the first octant.

The three edges of the boundary triangle C are expressed as

$$E_1: \ x + y = 1, z = 0 \qquad E_2: \ y + z = 1, x = 0 \qquad E_3: \ x + z = 1, y = 0$$

We traverse C in a counterclockwise direction (see Figure 14.25).

Edge E_1: Parametrize with $x = 1 - t$, $y = t$, $z = 0$, for $0 \le t \le 1$, so we have $\mathbf{R}(t) = (1 - t)\mathbf{i} + t\mathbf{j}$ and $d\mathbf{R} = -dt\,\mathbf{i} + dt\,\mathbf{j}$. Finally, in terms of the parameter t, we have $\mathbf{F}(t) = -\frac{3}{2}t^2\mathbf{i} - 2(1 - t)t\mathbf{j}$.

$$\int_{E_1} \mathbf{F} \cdot d\mathbf{R} = \int_0^1 \left(\tfrac{3}{2}t^2 - 2t + 2t^2\right) dt = \int_0^1 \left(\tfrac{7}{2}t^2 - 2t\right) dt = \left(\tfrac{7}{6}t^3 - t^2\right)\Big|_0^1 = \tfrac{1}{6}$$

Edge E_2: Parametrize with $x = 0$, $y = 1 - s$, $z = s$, for $0 \le s \le 1$, so $\mathbf{R}(s) = (1 - s)\mathbf{j} + s\mathbf{k}$ and $d\mathbf{R} = -ds\mathbf{j} + ds\mathbf{k}$. In terms of the parameter s, we have $\mathbf{F}(s) = -\frac{3}{2}(1 - s)^2\mathbf{i} + (1 - s)s\mathbf{k}$.

$$\int_{E_2} \mathbf{F} \cdot d\mathbf{R} = \int_0^1 (1 - s)s \, ds = \left(\frac{s^2}{2} - \frac{s^3}{3}\right)\Big|_0^1 = \frac{1}{6}$$

Edge E_3: Parametrize with $x = r$, $y = 0$, $z = 1 - r$, for $0 \le r \le 1$, so $\mathbf{R}(r) = r\mathbf{i} + (1 - r)\mathbf{k}$ and $d\mathbf{R} = dr\mathbf{i} - dr\mathbf{k}$. In terms of the parameter r, we have $\mathbf{F}(r) = \mathbf{0}$.

$$\int_{E_3} \mathbf{F} \cdot d\mathbf{R} = 0$$

Combining these results, we find

$$\int_C \mathbf{F} \cdot d\mathbf{R} = \int_{E_1} \mathbf{F} \cdot d\mathbf{R} + \int_{E_2} \mathbf{F} \cdot d\mathbf{R} + \int_{E_3} \mathbf{F} \cdot d\mathbf{R} = \tfrac{1}{6} + \tfrac{1}{6} + 0 = \tfrac{1}{3}$$

II. *Evaluation of* $\displaystyle\iint_S (\text{curl } \mathbf{F} \cdot \mathbf{N}) \, dS$

$$\text{curl } \mathbf{F} = \begin{vmatrix} \mathbf{i} & \mathbf{j} & \mathbf{k} \\ \dfrac{\partial}{\partial x} & \dfrac{\partial}{\partial y} & \dfrac{\partial}{\partial z} \\ -\dfrac{3}{2}y^2 & -2xy & yz \end{vmatrix} = z\mathbf{i} + y\mathbf{k}$$

The triangular region on the surface of the plane $x + y + z = 1$ has outward unit normal

$$\mathbf{N} = \frac{1}{\sqrt{3}}(\mathbf{i} + \mathbf{j} + \mathbf{k})$$

Because $z = 1 - x - y$, we find

$$\text{curl } \mathbf{F} \cdot \mathbf{N} = (z\mathbf{i} + y\mathbf{k}) \cdot \frac{1}{\sqrt{3}}(\mathbf{i} + \mathbf{j} + \mathbf{k}) = \frac{1}{\sqrt{3}}(z + y)$$

$$= \frac{1}{\sqrt{3}}(\underbrace{1 - x - y}_{z} + y) = \frac{1}{\sqrt{3}}(1 - x)$$

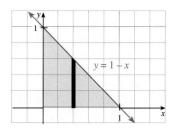

Figure 14.26 The projected region in the xy-plane is a triangle bounded by $y = 1 - x$ and the positive coordinate axes.

Finally,

$$dS = \sqrt{z_x^2 + z_y^2 + 1} \, dA_{xy} = \sqrt{(-1)^2 + (-1)^2 + 1} \, dA_{xy} = \sqrt{3} \, dA_{xy}$$

Combining these results, we get (see Figure 14.26)

$$\iint_S (\text{curl } \mathbf{F} \cdot \mathbf{N}) \, dS = \iint_D \frac{1}{\sqrt{3}}(1 - x)\sqrt{3} \, dA_{xy} = \int_0^1 \int_0^{1-x} (1 - x) \, dy \, dx$$

$$= \int_0^1 (1 - x)[(1 - x) - 0] \, dx = -\frac{(1 - x)^3}{3}\Big|_0^1 = \frac{1}{3}$$

We see that for this example, $\displaystyle\int_C \mathbf{F} \cdot d\mathbf{R} = \tfrac{1}{3} = \iint_S (\text{curl } \mathbf{F} \cdot \mathbf{N}) \, dS$, as claimed by Stokes's theorem.

▬

EXAMPLE 2 Using Stokes's theorem to evaluate a line integral

Evaluate $\int_C \left(\frac{1}{2}y^2\,dx + z\,dy + x\,dz\right)$, where C is the curve of intersection of the plane $x + z = 1$ and the ellipsoid $x^2 + 2y^2 + z^2 = 1$, oriented clockwise as seen from the origin. The curve C is shown in Figure 14.27.

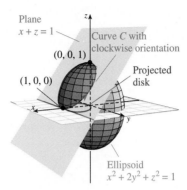

Figure 14.27 The surface bounded by the curve of intersection projects onto a disk in the xy-plane.

Solution Let $\mathbf{F} = \frac{1}{2}y^2\mathbf{i} + z\mathbf{j} + x\mathbf{k}$. From Stokes's theorem, we can evaluate the given integral by computing

$$\iint_S (\text{curl } \mathbf{F} \cdot \mathbf{N})\,dS$$

We choose S to be the part of the plane $x + z = 1$ bounded by C, along with C. Because S is a portion of the plane $x + z = 1$, we have $z = 1 - x$ so that $z_x = -1$, $z_y = 0$. We now find the required parts of the surface integral.

$$\text{curl } \mathbf{F} = \begin{vmatrix} \mathbf{i} & \mathbf{j} & \mathbf{k} \\ \frac{\partial}{\partial x} & \frac{\partial}{\partial y} & \frac{\partial}{\partial z} \\ \frac{1}{2}y^2 & z & x \end{vmatrix} = -\mathbf{i} - \mathbf{j} - y\mathbf{k}$$

The unit normal to the plane $x + z = 1$ is $\mathbf{N} = \frac{1}{\sqrt{2}}(\mathbf{i} + \mathbf{k})$, so that

$$\text{curl } \mathbf{F} \cdot \mathbf{N} = \frac{1}{\sqrt{2}}(-1 - y)$$

We also have

$$dS = \sqrt{z_x{}^2 + z_y{}^2 + 1}\,dA_{xy} = \sqrt{(-1)^2 + (0)^2 + 1}\,dA_{xy} = \sqrt{2}\,dA_{xy}$$

Finally, to describe C we substitute $z = 1 - x$ into the equation for the ellipsoid:

$$x^2 + 2y^2 + z^2 = 1$$
$$x^2 + 2y^2 + (1 - x)^2 = 1$$
$$x^2 - x + y^2 = 0$$
$$\left(x - \tfrac{1}{2}\right)^2 + y^2 = \tfrac{1}{4}$$

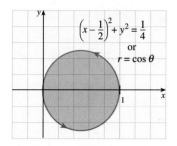

Figure 14.28 This is the projected disk in the xy-plane; call it S_{xy}.

Thus, the projection of this curve on the xy-plane is the circle S_{xy} shown in Figure 14.28. Notice that this circle has the polar equation $r = \cos\theta$. Note also that although C is oriented clockwise as viewed from the origin, the projected curve in the xy-plane is oriented counterclockwise as viewed from above.

We now calculate the desired line integral using Stokes's theorem.

$$\int_C \left(\tfrac{1}{2}y^2\, dx + z\, dy + x\, dz\right) = \int_C \mathbf{F} \cdot d\mathbf{R}$$

$$= \int\!\!\int_S (\text{curl } \mathbf{F} \cdot \mathbf{N})\, dS \quad \textit{Stokes's theorem}$$

$$= \int\!\!\int_{S_{xy}} \frac{1}{\sqrt{2}}(-1-y)\sqrt{2}\, dA_{xy} = -\int\!\!\int_{S_{xy}} (1+y)\, dA_{xy}$$

$$= -\int_{-\pi/2}^{\pi/2}\int_0^{\cos\theta}(1 + r\sin\theta)\, r\, dr\, d\theta \quad \textit{Change to polar coordinates.}$$

$$= -\int_{-\pi/2}^{\pi/2}\left[\tfrac{1}{2}\cos^2\theta + \tfrac{1}{3}\cos^3\theta\sin\theta\right]d\theta = -\frac{\pi}{4}$$

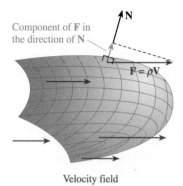

Component of $\mathbf{F}$ in the direction of $\mathbf{N}$

$\mathbf{F} = \rho\mathbf{V}$

Velocity field

Figure 14.29 Flux density is measured by $\mathbf{F} = \rho\mathbf{V}$.

■ PHYSICAL INTERPRETATION OF STOKES'S THEOREM

In Section 14.1, we defined the *flux density* as the vector field $\mathbf{F} = \rho\mathbf{V}$, where $\mathbf{V}(x, y, z)$ is the velocity of a fluid with density $\rho(x, y, z)$. The flux density measures the volume of fluid crossing surface S per unit of time and is also called the **flux of F across S**. Suppose the surface S is located in the region through which the fluid flows. If $\mathbf{N}$ is the unit normal to the surface S, then $\mathbf{F} \cdot \mathbf{N}$ is the component of flux in the direction normal to S, as shown in Figure 14.29. Then the mass of the fluid flowing through S in unit time in the direction normal to the surface is given by a surface integral, which is called a **flux integral**.

Flux Integral

The **flux integral** of a vector field $\mathbf{F}$ across a surface S is given by

$$\int\!\!\int_S \mathbf{F} \cdot \mathbf{N}\, dS$$

$\displaystyle\int\!\!\int_S (\text{curl } \mathbf{V} \cdot \mathbf{N})\, dS$

measures the cumulative rotational tendency of a fluid to "swirl" across the surface S.

If $\mathbf{V}$ is the velocity field of a fluid flow, then curl $\mathbf{V}$ measures the tendency of the fluid to rotate, or swirl. Usually, if the fluid flows across a surface S, the rotational tendency will vary from point to point on the surface, and the surface integral $\int\!\!\int_S (\text{curl } \mathbf{V} \cdot \mathbf{N})\, dS$ provides a measure of the *cumulative* rotational tendency over the entire surface.

Stokes's theorem tells us that this cumulative measure of rotational tendency equals the line integral $\int_C \mathbf{V} \cdot d\mathbf{R}$. To interpret this line integral, recall that it can be written $\int_C \mathbf{V} \cdot \mathbf{T}\, ds$ in terms of the arc length parameter s and the unit tangent $\mathbf{T}$ to the curve. Thus, the line integral sums the *tangential component* of the velocity field $\mathbf{V}$ around the boundary C, and it is reasonable to interpret $\int_C \mathbf{V} \cdot \mathbf{T}\, ds$ as a *measure of the circulation of the fluid flow around C*.

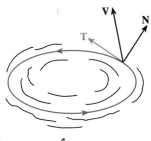

$$\int_C \mathbf{V} \cdot d\mathbf{R} = \int_C \mathbf{V} \cdot \mathbf{T} \, ds$$

measures the tendency of a fluid to "circulate" about the curve C.

■ **What this says:**

$$\underbrace{\int_S\!\!\int (\operatorname{curl} \mathbf{V} \cdot \mathbf{N}) \, dS}_{\substack{\text{The cumulative tendency} \\ \text{of a fluid to swirl across} \\ \text{the surface } S}} = \underbrace{\int_C \mathbf{V} \cdot \mathbf{T} \, ds}_{\substack{\text{The circulation} \\ \text{of a fluid around the} \\ \text{boundary curve } C}}$$

In physics and other applied areas, Stokes's theorem is often used as a device for establishing general properties. For instance, we can use it to prove that a vector field $\mathbf{F}$ is conservative if and only if curl $\mathbf{F} = \mathbf{0}$.

THEOREM 14.8   Test for a vector field to be conservative

If $\mathbf{F}$ and curl $\mathbf{F}$ are continuous in the simply connected region D, then $\mathbf{F}$ is conservative in D if and only if curl $\mathbf{F} = \mathbf{0}$ in D.

Proof: If $\mathbf{F}$ is conservative, let f be a scalar potential function, so that $\nabla f = \mathbf{F}$. Then curl $\mathbf{F} = \nabla \times \mathbf{F} = \nabla \times (\nabla f) = \mathbf{0}$. (See Problem 63, Section 14.1.)

Conversely, if curl $\mathbf{F} = \mathbf{0}$, let C be the boundary curve of the smooth surface S. Then Stokes's theorem gives

$$\int_C \mathbf{F} \cdot d\mathbf{R} = \int_S\!\!\int (\operatorname{curl} \mathbf{F} \cdot \mathbf{N}) \, dS = \int_S\!\!\int 0 \, dS = 0$$

so that $\mathbf{F}$ is independent of path and $\mathbf{F}$ must be conservative.   ■

EXAMPLE 3   Showing that a vector field is conservative

Show that the vector field $\mathbf{F} = yz\mathbf{i} + xz\mathbf{j} + xy\mathbf{k}$ is conservative in $\mathbb{R}^3$.

Solution   We check to see that the region is simply connected.

$$\operatorname{curl} \mathbf{F} = \begin{vmatrix} \mathbf{i} & \mathbf{j} & \mathbf{k} \\ \frac{\partial}{\partial x} & \frac{\partial}{\partial y} & \frac{\partial}{\partial z} \\ yz & xz & xy \end{vmatrix} = (x - x)\mathbf{i} - (y - y)\mathbf{j} + (z - z)\mathbf{k} = \mathbf{0}$$

It follows from Theorem 14.8 that $\mathbf{F}$ is conservative.   ▬

Sometimes it is possible to exchange a particularly difficult surface integration over one surface for a less difficult integration over another surface with the same boundary curve. Suppose two surfaces S_1 and S_2 are bounded by the same curve C and they induce the same orientation on C. Stokes's theorem tells us that

$$\int_{S_1}\!\!\int (\operatorname{curl} \mathbf{F} \cdot \mathbf{N}_1) \, dS_1 = \int_C \mathbf{F} \cdot d\mathbf{R} = \int_{S_2}\!\!\int (\operatorname{curl} \mathbf{F} \cdot \mathbf{N}_2) \, dS_2$$

for any function $\mathbf{F}$ whose components have continuous partial derivatives on both S_1 and S_2. It is also assumed that the unit normals $\mathbf{N}_1$ and $\mathbf{N}_2$ are compatible with C.

EXAMPLE 4   Using Stokes's theorem to evaluate a surface integral

Evaluate $\displaystyle\iint_S (\text{curl } \mathbf{F} \cdot \mathbf{N})\, dS$, where $\mathbf{F} = x\mathbf{i} + y^2\mathbf{j} + ze^{xy}\mathbf{k}$ and S is that part of the surface $z = 1 - x^2 - 2y^2$ with $z \geq 0$.

Solution   By setting $z = 0$ in the equation of the surface, we find that the boundary curve C for S is the ellipse $x^2 + 2y^2 = 1$, and the outward unit normal on S induces a counterclockwise orientation on C, as shown in Figure 14.30.

Let S^* be the elliptical disk defined by $x^2 + 2y^2 \leq 1$. We see that S and S^* have the same boundary, the same orientation, and the same normal $\mathbf{N_1} = \mathbf{k}$. Thus,

$$\iint_S (\text{curl } \mathbf{F} \cdot \mathbf{N})\, dS = \iint_{S^*} (\text{curl } \mathbf{F} \cdot \mathbf{k})\, dS^*$$

and we use this second integral to calculate the required integral. We obtain

$$\text{curl } \mathbf{F} = \begin{vmatrix} \mathbf{i} & \mathbf{j} & \mathbf{k} \\ \dfrac{\partial}{\partial x} & \dfrac{\partial}{\partial y} & \dfrac{\partial}{\partial z} \\ x & y^2 & ze^{xy} \end{vmatrix} = (zxe^{xy})\mathbf{i} - (zye^{xy})\mathbf{j}$$

and because curl $\mathbf{F} \cdot \mathbf{k} = 0$, we conclude

$$\iint_S (\text{curl } \mathbf{F} \cdot \mathbf{N})\, dS = \iint_{S^*} (\text{curl } \mathbf{F} \cdot \mathbf{k})\, dS^* = \iint_{S^*} 0 \, dS^* = 0$$

Figure 14.30 Surface $z = 1 - x^2 - 2y^2$ with $z \geq 0$

Stokes's theorem has important application in the theory of electromagnetism. We will now use Stokes's theorem to derive one of Maxwell's equations, named after James Clerk Maxwell (see Historical Note, page 904).

EXAMPLE 5   Maxwell's current density equation

From physics, Ampere's circuit law states

$$\int_C \mathbf{H} \cdot d\mathbf{R} = I$$

where $\mathbf{H}$ is the magnetic intensity, I is the current crossing any surface S bounded by the closed curve C, and $\mathbf{R} = x\mathbf{i} + y\mathbf{j} + z\mathbf{k}$. Use Ampere's circuit law to derive Maxwell's equation curl $\mathbf{H} = \mathbf{J}$, where $\mathbf{H}$ is the magnetic intensity and $\mathbf{J}$ is the electric current density.

Solution   If $\mathbf{J}$ is the *current density*, the total current flowing across S is given by the surface integral $\iint_S \mathbf{J} \cdot \mathbf{N}\, dS$. When this fact is used in conjunction with Ampere's law, we have

$$\int_C \mathbf{H} \cdot d\mathbf{R} = I = \iint_S \mathbf{J} \cdot \mathbf{N}\, dS$$

By Stokes's theorem, $\displaystyle\int_C \mathbf{H} \cdot d\mathbf{R} = \iint_S (\text{curl } \mathbf{H} \cdot \mathbf{N})\, dS.$

Equating the two surface integrals that equal $\int_C \mathbf{H} \cdot d\mathbf{R}$, we have

$$\iint_S \mathbf{J} \cdot \mathbf{N}\, dS = \iint_S (\text{curl } \mathbf{H} \cdot \mathbf{N})\, dS$$

or, equivalently,

$$\iint_S (\mathbf{J} - \text{curl } \mathbf{H}) \cdot \mathbf{N}\, dS = 0$$

Because this equation holds for *any* surface S bounded by C, it follows that

$$\mathbf{J} - \text{curl } \mathbf{H} = \mathbf{0}$$

$$\mathbf{J} = \text{curl } \mathbf{H} \qquad \blacksquare$$

PROBLEM SET 14.6

Ⓐ *Verify Stokes's theorem for the vector functions and surfaces given in Problems 1–5.*

1. $\mathbf{F} = z\mathbf{i} + 2x\mathbf{j} + 3y\mathbf{k}$, over the hemisphere $x^2 + y^2 + z^2 = 9$ for $z \geq 0$

2. $\mathbf{F} = (y + z)\mathbf{i} + x\mathbf{j} + (z - x)\mathbf{k}$, over the triangular region bounded by the plane $x + 2y + z = 3$ and the coordinate axes

3. $\mathbf{F} = (x + 2z)\mathbf{i} + (y - x)\mathbf{j} + (z - y)\mathbf{k}$, over the triangular region bounded by the plane $x + 2y + z = 3$ and the coordinate axes

4. $\mathbf{F} = 2xy\mathbf{i} + z^2\mathbf{k}$, over the paraboloid $y = x^2 + z^2$, with $y \leq 4$

5. $\mathbf{F} = 2y\mathbf{i} - 6z\mathbf{j} + 3x\mathbf{k}$, over the paraboloid $z = 4 - x^2 - y^2$ and above the xy-plane, with the outward normal

Use Stokes's theorem to evaluate the line integrals given in Problems 6–13.

6. $\int_C (x^3 y^2\, dx + dy + z^2\, dz)$, where C is the circle $x^2 + y^2 = 1$ in the plane $z = 1$ traversed counterclockwise when viewed from the origin.

7. $\int_C (z\, dx + x\, dy + y\, dz)$, where C is the triangle with vertices $(3, 0, 0)$, $(0, 0, 2)$, and $(0, 6, 0)$, traversed in the given order

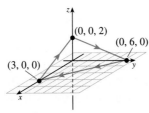

8. $\int_C (y\, dx - 2x\, dy + z\, dz)$, where C is the intersection of the surface $z = x^2 + y^2$ and the plane $x + y + z = 1$ traversed counterclockwise when viewed from the origin

9. $\int_C [2xy^2 z\, dx + 2x^2 yz\, dy + (x^2 y^2 - 2z)\, dz]$, where C is the curve given by $x = \cos t, y = \sin t, z = \sin t, 0 \leq t \leq 2\pi$, traversed in the direction of increasing t

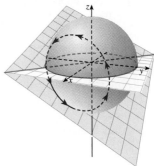

10. $\int_C (y\, dx + z\, dy + y\, dz)$, where C is the intersection of the sphere $x^2 + y^2 + z^2 = 4$ and the plane $x + y + z = 0$, traversed counterclockwise when viewed from above

11. $\int_C (y\, dx + z\, dy + x\, dz)$, where C is the intersection of the plane $x + y = 2$ and the surface $x^2 + y^2 + z^2 = 2(x + y)$, traversed clockwise as viewed from above

12. $\int_C [(z + \cos x)\, dx + (x + y^2)\, dy + (y + e^z)\, dz]$ where C is

the intersection of the sphere $x^2 + y^2 + z^2 = 4$ and the cone $z = \sqrt{x^2 + y^2}$, traversed counterclockwise as viewed from above

13. $\int_C (3y\ dx + 2z\ dy - 5x\ dz)$, where C is the positively oriented boundary of the hemisphere $z = \sqrt{1 - x^2 - y^2}$

B *In Problems 14–19, use Stokes's theorem to evaluate* $\iint_S (\text{curl}\ \mathbf{F} \cdot \mathbf{N})\ dS$ *for the vector fields and surfaces.*

14. $\mathbf{F} = x\mathbf{i} + y^2\mathbf{j} + xyz\mathbf{k}$ and S is the part of the paraboloid $z = 4 - x^2 - y^2$ with $z \geq 0$. Use the upward unit normal.

15. $\mathbf{F} = xy\mathbf{i} - z\mathbf{j}$ and S is the surface of the cube $0 \leq x \leq 1$, $0 \leq y \leq 1$, $0 \leq z \leq 1$ except for the face where $z = 0$. Use the outward unit normal.

16. $\mathbf{F} = y\mathbf{i} + z\mathbf{j} + x\mathbf{k}$, and S is the part of the plane $x + y + z = 1$ that lies in the first quadrant. Use the outward normal.

17. $\mathbf{F} = xy\mathbf{i} + x^2\mathbf{j} + z^2\mathbf{k}$, and C is the intersection of the paraboloid $z = x^2 + y^2$ and the plane $z = y$.

18. $\mathbf{F} = xz\mathbf{i} + y^2\mathbf{j} + x^2\mathbf{k}$, and C is the intersection of the plane $x + y + z = 3$ and the surface

$$x^2 + \frac{y^2}{9} = 1$$

19. $\mathbf{F} = 4y\mathbf{i} + z\mathbf{j} + 2y\mathbf{k}$, and C is the intersection of the sphere $x^2 + y^2 + z^2 = 4$ with the plane $z = 0$.

In Problems 20–22, use Stokes's theorem to evaluate the line integral

$$\int_C [(1 + y)z\ dx + (1 + z)x\ dy + (1 + x)y\ dz]$$

for the given choice for the path C.

20. C is the elliptic path $x = 2\cos\theta$, $y = \sin\theta$, $z = 1$ for $0 \leq \theta \leq 2\pi$.

21. C is the triangle with vertices $(1, 0, 0)$, $(0, 1, 0)$, $(0, 0, 1)$.

22. C is *any* closed path in the plane $2x - 3y + z = 1$.

23. Let $\mathbf{F} = y^2\mathbf{i} + xy\mathbf{j} + xz\mathbf{k}$, and suppose S is the hemisphere $x^2 + y^2 + z^2 = 1$ with $z \geq 0$. Use Stokes's theorem to express

$$\iint_S (\text{curl}\ \mathbf{F} \cdot \mathbf{N})\ dS$$

as a line integral, and then evaluate the surface integral by evaluating this line integral.

24. Let $\mathbf{F} = z\mathbf{i} + x\mathbf{j} + y\mathbf{k}$, and suppose S is a smooth surface in $\mathbb{R}^3$ whose boundary is given by $x = 2\cos\theta$, $y = 3\sin\theta$,

$z = \sin\theta$, $0 < \theta \leq 2\pi$, oriented in the direction of increasing θ. Use Stokes's theorem to evaluate

$$\iint_S (\text{curl}\ \mathbf{F} \cdot \mathbf{N})\ dS$$

C 25. Let S be the ellipsoid $\dfrac{x^2}{4} + \dfrac{y^2}{9} + z^2 = 1$, and let $\mathbf{F}$ be a vector field whose component functions have continuous partial derivatives on S. Use Stokes's theorem to show that

$$\iint_S (\text{curl}\ \mathbf{F} \cdot \mathbf{N})\ dS = 0$$

Does it matter that S is an ellipsoid? State and prove a more general result based on what you have discovered in the first part of this problem.

26. **Faraday's law** of electromagnetism says that if $\mathbf{E}$ is the electric intensity vector in a system, then

$$\int_C \mathbf{E} \cdot d\mathbf{R} = -\frac{\partial \phi}{\partial t}$$

around any closed curve C where t is time and ϕ is the total magnetic flux directed outward through any surface S bounded by C. Given that

$$\phi = \iint_S \mathbf{B} \cdot \mathbf{N}\ dS$$

where $\mathbf{B}$ is the magnetic flux density, show that

$$\text{curl}\ \mathbf{E} = -\frac{\partial \mathbf{B}}{\partial t}$$

Hint: It can be shown that

$$\frac{\partial}{\partial t} \iint_S \mathbf{B} \cdot \mathbf{N}\ dS = \iint_S \frac{\partial \mathbf{B}}{\partial t} \cdot \mathbf{N}\ dS$$

27. According to Ampere's law $\int_C \mathbf{H} \cdot d\mathbf{R} = I$, where $\mathbf{H}$ is the magnetic intensity and I is the total current flowing across a given surface S (in the direction of the outward normal). Given that curl $\mathbf{B} = k\mathbf{J}$, where $\mathbf{J}$ is the current density and k is a physical constant, show that

$$\int_C \mathbf{B} \cdot d\mathbf{R} = kI$$

for any closed curve C. $\mathbf{B}$ is the magnetic flux density (see Problem 26).

14.7 DIVERGENCE THEOREM

IN THIS SECTION   Divergence theorem, applications of the divergence theorem

In this section, we develop the divergence theorem, one of the great theorems of elementary calculus. We shall also see that the divergence theorem can be used to derive theoretical results and to study the properties of fluid dynamics. In particular, in Example 5 we derive the heat equation, which is important in physics and engineering.

■ DIVERGENCE THEOREM

We used Green's theorem to show that $\int_C \mathbf{F} \cdot \mathbf{N}\, ds = \int_D \int \operatorname{div} \mathbf{F}\, dA$, where D is a simple connected domain in the plane with the closed boundary curve C. The *divergence theorem* (also known as **Gauss's theorem**) is a generalization of this form of Green's theorem that relates a closed surface integral to a volume integral.

THEOREM 14.9   The divergence theorem

Let D be a region in space bounded by a smooth, orientable closed surface S. If $\mathbf{F}$ is a continuous vector field whose components have continuous partial derivatives in D, then

$$\int_S \int \mathbf{F} \cdot \mathbf{N}\, dS = \int \int_D \int \operatorname{div} \mathbf{F}\, dV$$

where $\mathbf{N}$ is an outward unit normal to the surface S.

Proof: The general proof of this theorem is beyond the scope of this course, but an important special case is proved in Appendix B.   ■

EXAMPLE 1   Verifying the divergence theorem for a particular example

Let $\mathbf{F} = 2x\mathbf{i} - 3y\mathbf{j} + 5z\mathbf{k}$, and let S be the hemisphere $z = \sqrt{9 - x^2 - y^2}$ together with the disk $x^2 + y^2 \le 9$ in the xy-plane. Verify the divergence theorem.

Solution   The solid is shown in Figure 14.31. We shall show that the surface integral and the triple integral have the same value.

I. *Evaluation of* $\int_S \int \mathbf{F} \cdot \mathbf{N}\, dS$

Figure 14.31 The surface of the hemisphere

S consists of two parts: S_1, the disk on the bottom of the hemisphere, and S_2, the hemisphere. We will consider these separately because

$$\int_S \int \mathbf{F} \cdot \mathbf{N}\, dS = \int_{S_1} \int \mathbf{F} \cdot \mathbf{N_1}\, dS_1 + \int_{S_2} \int \mathbf{F} \cdot \mathbf{N_2}\, dS_2$$

Consider S_1:   Note that the disk $x^2 + y^2 \le 9$ on the bottom of the hemisphere has outward unit normal $\mathbf{N} = -\mathbf{k}$. (Because $\mathbf{k}$ points into the solid, $-\mathbf{k}$ is the outward normal.) We have

$$\int_{S_1} \int \mathbf{F} \cdot \mathbf{N}\, dS_1 = \int_{S_1} \int (2x\mathbf{i} - 3y\mathbf{j} + 5z\mathbf{k}) \cdot (-\mathbf{k})\, dS_1 = \int_{S_1} \int (-5z)\, dS_1 = 0$$

Because $z = 0$ on S_1

Consider S_2:   Regard the hemisphere as the level surface

$$S_2(x, y, z) = 9, \text{ where } S_2(x, y, z) = x^2 + y^2 + z^2 \text{ and } z \geq 0.$$

The outward unit normal (for $z \geq 0$) is given by

$$\mathbf{N} = \frac{\nabla S_2}{\|\nabla S_2\|}$$

$$= \frac{2x\mathbf{i} + 2y\mathbf{j} + 2z\mathbf{k}}{\sqrt{4x^2 + 4y^2 + 4z^2}} \quad \textit{Remember that } \nabla f = \frac{\partial f}{\partial x}\mathbf{i} + \frac{\partial f}{\partial y}\mathbf{j} + \frac{\partial f}{\partial z}\mathbf{k}.$$

$$= \frac{x\mathbf{i} + y\mathbf{j} + z\mathbf{k}}{\sqrt{x^2 + y^2 + z^2}}$$

$$= \frac{x\mathbf{i} + y\mathbf{j} + z\mathbf{k}}{\sqrt{9}} \quad \textit{Because } x^2 + y^2 + z^2 = 9 \text{ on } S_2$$

$$= \tfrac{1}{3}(x\mathbf{i} + y\mathbf{j} + z\mathbf{k})$$

Because $\mathbf{F} = 2x\mathbf{i} - 3y\mathbf{j} + 5z\mathbf{k}$, we find

$$\mathbf{F} \cdot \mathbf{N} = \tfrac{1}{3}(2x^2 - 3y^2 + 5z^2)$$

Finally, to find dS_2 we note that $z_x^2 = x^2(9 - x^2 - y^2)^{-1}$ and $z_y^2 = y^2(9 - x^2 - y^2)^{-1}$, so that

$$dS_2 = \sqrt{z_x^2 + z_y^2 + 1}\, dA_{xy}$$

$$= \sqrt{\frac{x^2}{9 - x^2 - y^2} + \frac{y^2}{9 - x^2 - y^2} + 1}\, dA_{xy}$$

$$= \sqrt{\frac{9}{9 - x^2 - y^2}}\, dA_{xy}$$

$$= \frac{3}{\sqrt{9 - x^2 - y^2}}\, dA_{xy}$$

It follows that

$$\iint_{S_2} \mathbf{F} \cdot \mathbf{N}\, dS_2 = \iint_{S_2} \tfrac{1}{3}(2x^2 - 3y^2 + 5z^2) \frac{3}{\sqrt{9 - x^2 - y^2}}\, dA_{xy}$$

$$= \iint_{S_2} [2x^2 - 3y^2 + 5(9 - x^2 - y^2)]\, [9 - x^2 - y^2]^{-1/2}\, dA_{xy}$$

$$= \iint_{S_2} (45 - 3x^2 - 8y^2)(9 - x^2 - y^2)^{-1/2}\, dA_{xy}$$

$$= \int_0^{2\pi} \int_0^3 \frac{45 - 3(r\cos\theta)^2 - 8(r\sin\theta)^2}{\sqrt{9 - r^2}}\, r\, dr\, d\theta \quad \textit{See Figure 14.32.}$$

$$= \int_0^{2\pi} [135 - 54\cos^2\theta - 144\sin^2\theta]\, d\theta$$

$$= 72\pi$$

We can now state

$$\iint_S \mathbf{F} \cdot \mathbf{N}\, dS = \iint_{S_1} \mathbf{F} \cdot \mathbf{N}\, dS_1 + \iint_{S_2} \mathbf{F} \cdot \mathbf{N}\, dS_2 = 0 + 72\pi = 72\pi$$

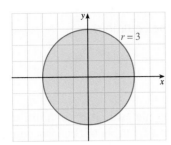

Figure 14.32 The hemisphere with boundary $z^2 = 9 - x^2 - y^2$ projects onto disk $x^2 + y^2 \leq 9$, or, in polar form, $r \leq 3$

II. *Evaluation of* $\displaystyle\int\int\int_D \text{div } \mathbf{F} \, dV$

$$\text{div } \mathbf{F} = \frac{\partial}{\partial x}(2x) + \frac{\partial}{\partial y}(-3y) + \frac{\partial}{\partial z}(5z) = 2 - 3 + 5 = 4$$

Therefore, $\int\int\int \text{div } \mathbf{F} \, dV = \int\int\int 4 \, dV$, but $\int\int\int dV$ is just the volume of the hemisphere $z = \sqrt{9 - x^2 - y^2}$. A sphere of radius $r = 3$ has volume $V = \frac{4}{3}\pi r^3 = \frac{4}{3}\pi(3)^3 = 36\pi$, so a hemisphere of radius 3 has volume $\frac{1}{2}\left[\frac{4}{3}\pi(3)^3\right] = 18\pi$.

$$\int\int\int_D \text{div } \mathbf{F} \, dV = \int\int\int_D 4 \, dV = 4V = 4(18\pi) = 72\pi$$

and we have $\int\int\int \text{div } \mathbf{F} \, dV = \int\int \mathbf{F} \cdot \mathbf{N} \, dS$, as required.   ▬

EXAMPLE 2   Evaluating a surface integral using the divergence theorem

Evaluate $\displaystyle\int\int_S \mathbf{F} \cdot \mathbf{N} \, dS$, where

$\mathbf{F} = x^2\mathbf{i} + xy\mathbf{j} + x^3y^3\mathbf{k}$ and S is the surface of the tetrahedron bounded by the plane $x + y + z = 1$ and the coordinate planes, with outward unit normal $\mathbf{N}$.

Solution   We will use the divergence theorem. Let D be the solid bounded by S and note that

$$\text{div } \mathbf{F} = \frac{\partial}{\partial x}(x^2) + \frac{\partial}{\partial y}(xy) + \frac{\partial}{\partial z}(x^3y^3) = 2x + x + 0 = 3x$$

We choose to describe the solid tetrahedron as the set of all (x, y, z) such that $0 \leq z \leq 1 - x - y$ whenever $0 \leq y \leq 1 - x$ for all $0 \leq x \leq 1$. The projection of S on the xy-plane is shown in the margin. Finally, by applying the divergence theorem, we find that

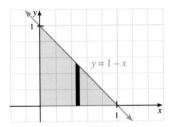

Projected region in the xy-plane

$$\int\int_S \mathbf{F} \cdot \mathbf{N} \, dS = \int\int\int_D \text{div } \mathbf{F} \, dV = \int_0^1 \int_0^{1-x} \int_0^{1-x-y} 3x \, dz \, dy \, dx$$

$$= \int_0^1 \int_0^{1-x} 3x(1 - x - y) \, dy \, dx = 3\int_0^1 \left[x(1-x)y - \frac{1}{2}xy^2\right]_0^{1-x} dx$$

$$= 3\int_0^1 x(1-x)^2 - \frac{1}{2}x(1-x)^2 \, dx = \frac{1}{8}$$ ▬

The divergence theorem applies only to closed surfaces. However, if we wish to evaluate $\int\int_{S_1} \mathbf{F} \cdot \mathbf{N} \, dS$ where S_1 is *not* closed, we may be able to find a closed surface S that is the union of S_1 and some other surface S_2. Then, if the hypotheses of the divergence theorem are satisfied by $\mathbf{F}$ and S, we have

$$\int\int_{S_1} \mathbf{F} \cdot \mathbf{N} \, dS + \int\int_{S_2} \mathbf{F} \cdot \mathbf{N} \, dS = \int\int_S \mathbf{F} \cdot \mathbf{N} \, dS = \int\int\int_D \text{div } \mathbf{F} \, dV$$

where D is the solid region bounded by S. Thus, if we can compute $\int\int\int_D \text{div } \mathbf{F} \, dV$

and $\iint\limits_{S_2} \mathbf{F} \cdot \mathbf{N}\, dS$, we can compute $\iint\limits_{S_1} \mathbf{F} \cdot \mathbf{N}\, dS$ by the equation

$$\iint\limits_{S_1} \mathbf{F} \cdot \mathbf{N}\, dS = \iiint\limits_{D} \operatorname{div} \mathbf{F}\, dV - \iint\limits_{S_2} \mathbf{F} \cdot \mathbf{N}\, dS$$

This equation can also be used as a device for trading the evaluation of a difficult surface integral for that of an easier integral. Here is an example of this procedure.

EXAMPLE 3   Evaluating a surface integral over an open surface

Evaluate $\displaystyle\iint\limits_{S} \mathbf{F} \cdot \mathbf{N}\, dS$, where $\mathbf{F} = xy\mathbf{i} - z^2\mathbf{k}$ and S is the surface of the upper

five faces of the unit cube $0 \le x \le 1,\ 0 \le y \le 1,\ 0 < z \le 1$, as shown in Figure 14.33.

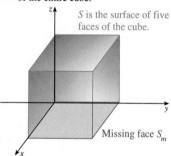

S^* is the closed surface of the entire cube.

S is the surface of five faces of the cube.

Missing face S_m

Figure 14.33 Evaluating a surface integral

Solution   Note that the surface S is not closed, but we can close it by adding the missing face S_m, thus forming a closed surface S^* that satisfies the conditions of the divergence theorem. The strategy is to evaluate the surface integral of S^* and then subtract the surface integral of the added face S_m.

$$\iint\limits_{S^*} \mathbf{F} \cdot \mathbf{N}\, dS = \iiint\limits_{\text{cube}} \operatorname{div} \mathbf{F}\, dV = \int_0^1 \int_0^1 \int_0^1 (y - 2z)\, dx\, dy\, dz$$

$$= \int_0^1 \int_0^1 (y - 2z)\, dy\, dz = \int_0^1 \left(\tfrac{1}{2} - 2z\right) dz = -\tfrac{1}{2}$$

Also, because the unit normal to the added face S_m is $\mathbf{N} = -\mathbf{k}$ and $z = 0$ on this face, it follows that

$$\iint\limits_{S_m} \mathbf{F} \cdot \mathbf{N}\, dS = \iint\limits_{S_m} (xy\mathbf{i} - z^2\mathbf{k}) \cdot (-\mathbf{k})\, dS = \iint\limits_{S_m} z^2\, dS = 0$$

Therefore,

$$\iint\limits_{S} \mathbf{F} \cdot \mathbf{N}\, dS = \iiint\limits_{D} \operatorname{div} \mathbf{F}\, dV - \iint\limits_{S_m} \mathbf{F} \cdot \mathbf{N}\, dS = -\tfrac{1}{2} - 0 = -\tfrac{1}{2}$$

■ APPLICATIONS OF THE DIVERGENCE THEOREM

Like Stokes's theorem, the divergence theorem is often used for theoretical purposes, especially as a tool for deriving general properties in mathematical physics. The key to some of these applications is the fact that because $\mathbf{F}(x, y, z)$ is the rate of flow per unit area, the surface integral $\int \int_S \mathbf{F} \cdot \mathbf{N} \, dS$ represents the net rate of outward flux per unit volume. This is the reason for the name *divergence*, because

$$\underbrace{\int \int_S \mathbf{F} \cdot \mathbf{N} \, dS}_{\text{Flux integral}} = \underbrace{\int \int \int_D \text{div } \mathbf{F} \, dV}_{\text{Flow out of small cubes}}$$

The integral on the left is a flux integral and thus determines the total fluid flow across the surface S per unit of time. On the other hand, the integral on the right measures the same fluid flow by calculating the flow out of small cubes.

Recall from Section 14.1 that a point is called a *source* if div $\mathbf{F} > 0$, a *sink* if div $\mathbf{F} < 0$, and *incompressible* if div $\mathbf{F} = 0$. The next example derives an important property of fluid dynamics.

EXAMPLE 4 Continuity equation of fluid dynamics

Suppose a fluid with density $\rho(x, y, z, t)$ flows in some region of space with velocity $\mathbf{F}(x, y, z, t)$ at the point (x, y, z) and time t. Assuming there are no sources or sinks, show that

$$\text{div } \rho\mathbf{F} = -\frac{\partial \rho}{\partial t}$$

Solution Let D be an arbitrary solid region of space, with closed boundary surface S. In physics, it is shown that the amount of fluid flowing out of D across S in unit time is $\int \int_S \rho\mathbf{F} \cdot \mathbf{N} \, dS$. For example, suppose ρ is measured in pounds per cubic foot so that $\frac{\partial \rho}{\partial t}$ is measured in pounds per cubic foot per second and $\frac{\partial \rho}{\partial t} \, dV$ is measured in pounds per second. Thus, $-\int \int_S \rho\mathbf{F} \cdot \mathbf{N} \, dS$ is the amount of outflow and is equal to the amount of inflow, $\int \int \int_D \frac{\partial \rho}{\partial t} \, dV$, because we are assuming there are no sinks or sources. Setting these two quantities equal, we have

$$\overbrace{-\int \int_S \rho \, \mathbf{F} \cdot \mathbf{N} \, dS}^{\text{OUTFLOW}} = \overbrace{\int \int \int_D \frac{\partial \rho}{\partial t} \, dV}^{\text{INFLOW}}$$

By the divergence theorem, we have $\int \int_S \rho \, \mathbf{F} \cdot \mathbf{N} \, dS = \int \int \int_D \text{div } \rho \, \mathbf{F} \, dV$ so that

$$\int \int \int_D \text{div } \rho\mathbf{F} \, dV + \int \int \int_D \frac{\partial \rho}{\partial t} \, dV = 0$$

$$\int \int \int_D \left[\text{div } \rho\mathbf{F} + \frac{\partial \rho}{\partial t} \right] dV = 0$$

This equation must hold for any region D, no matter how small, which means that the integrand of the integral must be 0. That is,

$$\text{div } \rho\mathbf{F} = -\frac{\partial \rho}{\partial t}$$

In physics it is known that the total heat contained in a body with uniform density ρ and specific heat σ is $\int \int \int_D \sigma \rho T \, dV$ where T is the temperature. Thus, the amount of heat leaving D per unit of time is also given by

$$-\frac{\partial}{\partial t}\left[\int \int \int_D \sigma \rho T \, dV\right] = \int \int \int_D -\sigma \rho \frac{\partial T}{\partial t} \, dV$$

We will use this result in the following example, which is one of the most important results in mathematics and physics.

EXAMPLE 5   Derivation of the heat equation

Let $T(x, y, z, t)$ be the temperature at each point (x, y, z) in a solid body D at time t. Given that the velocity of heat flow in the body is $\mathbf{F} = -k\nabla T$ for a positive constant k (called the **thermal conductivity**) show that

$$\frac{\partial T}{\partial t} = \frac{k}{\sigma \rho}\nabla^2 T$$

where σ is the specific heat of the body and ρ is its density.

Solution   Let S be the closed surface that bounds D. Because $\mathbf{F}$ is the velocity of heat flow, the amount of heat leaving D per unit time is $\int \int_S \mathbf{F} \cdot \mathbf{N} \, dS$, and the divergence theorem applies:

$$\int \int_S \mathbf{F} \cdot \mathbf{N} \, dS = \int \int \int_D \operatorname{div}(-k\nabla T) \, dV = \int \int \int_D (-k \, \nabla \cdot \nabla T) \, dV$$

$$= \int \int \int_D -k \, \nabla^2 T \, dV$$

Because this is the amount of heat leaving D per unit of time, we know this is equal to the heat integral from physics derived just before this example. Thus,

$$\int \int \int_D -k\nabla^2 T \, dV = \int \int \int_D -\sigma \rho \frac{\partial T}{\partial t} \, dV$$

This equation holds not only for the body as a whole, but for every part of the body, no matter how small. Thus, we can shrink the body to a single point, and it then follows that the integrands are equal; that is,

$$-k\nabla^2 T = -\sigma \rho \frac{\partial T}{\partial t}$$

$$\frac{\partial T}{\partial t} = \frac{k}{\sigma \rho}\nabla^2 T$$

For the concluding example, recall that the *normal derivative* $\partial g / \partial n$ of a scalar function g defined on the closed surface S is the directional derivative of f in the direction of the outward unit normal $\mathbf{N}$ to S; that is,

$$\frac{\partial g}{\partial n} = \nabla g \cdot \mathbf{N}$$

We will use this equation in the following example, which is a generalization of a property we first obtained for $\mathbb{R}^2$ (see Section 14.4).

EXAMPLE 6   Derivation of Green's first identity

Show that if f and g are scalar functions such that $\mathbf{F} = f\nabla g$ is continuously differentiable in the solid domain D bounded by the closed surface S, then

$$\iiint_D [f\nabla^2 g + \nabla f \cdot \nabla g]\, dV = \iint_S f\frac{\partial g}{\partial n}\, dS$$

This is called **Green's first identity**.

Solution   We shall apply the divergence theorem to the vector field $\mathbf{F}$ (note that $\mathbf{F}$ is continuously differentiable).

$$\operatorname{div}\mathbf{F} = \operatorname{div}(f\nabla g)$$

$$= \nabla \cdot (f\nabla g) \quad \textit{Property of divergence (Problem 62, Section 14.1)}$$

$$= \left[\frac{\partial}{\partial x}\mathbf{i} + \frac{\partial}{\partial y}\mathbf{j} + \frac{\partial}{\partial z}\mathbf{k}\right] \cdot \left[f\frac{\partial g}{\partial x}\mathbf{i} + f\frac{\partial g}{\partial y}\mathbf{j} + f\frac{\partial g}{\partial z}\mathbf{k}\right]$$

$$= \frac{\partial}{\partial x}\left[f\frac{\partial g}{\partial x}\right] + \frac{\partial}{\partial y}\left[f\frac{\partial g}{\partial y}\right] + \frac{\partial}{\partial z}\left[f\frac{\partial g}{\partial z}\right]$$

$$= \left[\frac{\partial f}{\partial x}\frac{\partial g}{\partial x} + f\frac{\partial^2 g}{\partial x^2}\right] + \left[\frac{\partial f}{\partial y}\frac{\partial g}{\partial y} + f\frac{\partial^2 g}{\partial y^2}\right] + \left[\frac{\partial f}{\partial z}\frac{\partial g}{\partial z} + f\frac{\partial^2 g}{\partial z^2}\right]$$

$$= \left[\frac{\partial f}{\partial x}\frac{\partial g}{\partial x} + \frac{\partial f}{\partial y}\frac{\partial g}{\partial y} + \frac{\partial f}{\partial z}\frac{\partial g}{\partial z}\right] + f\left[\frac{\partial^2 g}{\partial x^2} + \frac{\partial^2 g}{\partial y^2} + \frac{\partial^2 g}{\partial z^2}\right]$$

$$= (\nabla f) \cdot (\nabla g) + f\nabla^2 g$$

This calculation gives us the first step in the following derivation.

$$\iiint_D [f\nabla^2 g + \nabla f \cdot \nabla g]\, dV = \iiint_D \operatorname{div}\mathbf{F}\, dV$$

$$= \iint_S \mathbf{F} \cdot \mathbf{N}\, dS \qquad \textit{Divergence theorem}$$

$$= \iint_S (f\nabla g) \cdot \mathbf{N}\, dS \quad \textit{Because } \mathbf{F} = f\nabla g$$

$$= \iint_S f(\nabla g \cdot \mathbf{N})\, dS$$

$$= \iint_S f\frac{\partial g}{\partial n}\, dS \qquad \textit{Because } \nabla g \cdot \mathbf{N} = \frac{\partial g}{\partial n} \textit{ by}$$
$$\textit{definition}$$

━━

PROBLEM SET 14.7

Ⓐ *Verify the divergence theorem for the vector function* $\mathbf{F}$ *and solid D given in Problems 1–4. Assume* $\mathbf{N}$ *is the unit normal pointing away from the origin.*

1. $\mathbf{F} = xz\mathbf{i} + y^2\mathbf{j} + 2z\mathbf{k}$;
   D is the ball $x^2 + y^2 + z^2 \le 4$.

2. $\mathbf{F} = x\mathbf{i} - 2y\mathbf{j}$; D is the interior of the paraboloid $z = x^2 + y^2$, $0 \le z < 9$.

3. $\mathbf{F} = 2y^2\mathbf{j}$; D is the part of the surface of the plane $x + 4y + z = 8$ that lies in the first octant.

4. $\mathbf{F} = 3x\mathbf{i} + 5y\mathbf{j} + 6z\mathbf{k}$; D is the tetrahedron bounded by the coordinate planes and the plane $2x + y + z = 4$.

Use the divergence theorem in Problems 5–19 to evaluate the surface integral $\iint_S \mathbf{F} \cdot \mathbf{N}\, dS$ *for the given choice of* $\mathbf{F}$ *and the boundary surface S. For each closed surface, assume* $\mathbf{N}$ *is the outward unit normal.*

5. $\mathbf{F} = x\mathbf{i} + y\mathbf{j} + z\mathbf{k}$; S is the surface of the cube $0 \le x \le 1$, $0 \le y \le 1$, $0 \le z \le 1$.

6. $\mathbf{F} = xyz\mathbf{j}$; S is the surface of the cylinder $x^2 + y^2 = 9$, for $0 \le z \le 5$. Note S is the closed can with its top in the plane $z = 5$ and its bottom in the xy-plane.

7. $\mathbf{F} = (\cos yz)\mathbf{i} + e^{xz}\mathbf{j} + 3z^2\mathbf{k}$; S is the surface of the hemisphere $z = \sqrt{4 - x^2 - y^2}$ together with the disk $x^2 + y^2 \le 4$ in the xy-plane.

8. $\mathbf{F} = \text{curl}[e^{xz}\mathbf{i} - 4\mathbf{j} + (\sin xyz)\mathbf{k}]$; S is the surface of the ellipsoid $2x^2 + 3y^2 + 7z^2 = 1$.

9. $\mathbf{F} = (x^2 + y^2 - z^2)\mathbf{i} + x^2y\mathbf{j} + 3z\mathbf{k}$; S is the surface of the five faces of the unit cube $0 \le x \le 1$, $0 \le y \le 1$, $0 < z \le 1$.

10. $\mathbf{F} = 2y\mathbf{i} - z\mathbf{j} + 3x\mathbf{k}$; S is the five faces of the unit cube $0 \le x \le 1$, $0 \le y \le 1$, $0 < z \le 1$.

11. $\mathbf{F} = x\mathbf{i} + y\mathbf{j} + z\mathbf{k}$; S is the surface of the paraboloid $z = x^2 + y^2$ for $0 \le z \le 9$.

12. $\mathbf{F} = \text{curl}(y\mathbf{i} + x\mathbf{j} - z\mathbf{k})$; S is the surface of the hemisphere $z = \sqrt{4 - x^2 - y^2}$.

13. $\mathbf{F} = x^2\mathbf{i} + y^2\mathbf{j} + z^2\mathbf{k}$; S is the surface of the sphere $x^2 + y^2 + z^2 = 4$.

14. $\mathbf{F} = xyz\mathbf{i} + xyz\mathbf{j} + xyz\mathbf{k}$; S is the surface of the box $0 \le x \le 1$, $0 \le y \le 2$, $0 \le z \le 3$.

15. $\mathbf{F} = x\mathbf{i} + y\mathbf{j} + (z^2 - 1)\mathbf{k}$; S is the surface of a solid bounded by the cylinder $x^2 + y^2 = 4$ and the planes $z = 0$ and $z = 1$.

16. $\mathbf{F} = (x^5 + 10xy^2z^2)\mathbf{i} + (y^5 + 10yx^2z^2)\mathbf{j} + (z^5 + 10zx^2y^2)\mathbf{k}$; S is the closed hemispherical surface $z = \sqrt{1 - x^2 - y^2}$ together with the disk $x^2 + y^2 \le 1$ in the xy-plane.

17. $\mathbf{F} = xy^2\mathbf{i} + yz^2\mathbf{j} + 2x^2y^3\mathbf{k}$; S is the surface bounded by the cylinder $y^2 + z^2 = 1$, the xy-plane, and the planes $x = 0$ and $x = 1$.

18. $\mathbf{F} = xy^2\mathbf{i} + yz^2\mathbf{j} + x^2z\mathbf{k}$; S is the surface (in spherical coordinates) with top $\rho = 2$, $0 \le \phi \le \frac{\pi}{4}$, $0 \le \theta \le 2\pi$, and bottom $0 \le \rho \le 2$, $\phi = \frac{\pi}{4}$, $0 \le \theta \le 2\pi$.

19. $\mathbf{F} = x^3\mathbf{i} + y^3\mathbf{j} + 3a^2z\mathbf{k}$ (constant $a > 0$); S is the surface bounded by the cylinder $x^2 + y^2 = a^2$ and the planes $z = 0$ and $z = 1$.

B 20. Suppose that S is a closed surface that encloses a solid region D.

  a. Show that the volume of D is given by

$$V(D) = \frac{1}{3} \int\int_S (x\mathbf{i} + y\mathbf{j} + z\mathbf{k}) \cdot \mathbf{N} \, dS$$

  where $\mathbf{N}$ is an outward unit normal to S.

  b. Use the formula in part **a** to find the volume of the hemisphere $z = \sqrt{R^2 - x^2 - y^2}$.

21. Use the divergence theorem to evaluate

$$\int\int_S \|\mathbf{R}\| \, \mathbf{R} \cdot \mathbf{N} \, dS$$

where $\mathbf{R} = x\mathbf{i} + y\mathbf{j} + z\mathbf{k}$ and S is the sphere $x^2 + y^2 + z^2 = a^2$, with constant $a > 0$.

22. The moment of inertia about the z-axis of a solid T of constant density $\rho = a$ is proportional to the volume integral

$$\int\int\int_T (x^2 + y^2) \, dV$$

Express this integral as a surface integral over the surface S that bounds T.

C 23. Let u be a scalar function with continuous second partial derivatives in a region containing the solid region T, with closed boundary surface S.

  a. Show that $\displaystyle\int\int_S \frac{\partial u}{\partial n} \, dS = \int\int\int_T \nabla^2 u \, dV$.

  b. Let $u = x + y + z$ and $v = \frac{1}{2}(x^2 + y^2 + z^2)$. Use part **a** to evaluate

$$\int\int_S (u\nabla v) \cdot \mathbf{N} \, dS$$

  where S is the boundary of the cube $0 \le x \le 1$, $0 \le y \le 1$, $0 \le z \le 1$.

24. Let f and g be scalar functions such that $\mathbf{F} = f\nabla g$ is continuously differentiable in the region D, which is bounded by the closed surface S. Prove *Green's second identity*:

$$\int\int\int_D (f\nabla^2 g - g\nabla^2 f) \, dV$$

$$= \int\int_S \left(f\frac{\partial g}{\partial n} - g\frac{\partial f}{\partial n} \right) dS$$

25. Show that if g is harmonic in the region D, then

$$\int\int_S \frac{\partial g}{\partial n} \, dS = 0$$

where the closed surface S is the boundary of D.

26. Show that $\displaystyle\int\int_S \mathbf{F} \cdot \mathbf{N} \, dS = 0$ if S is a closed surface and $\mathbf{F} = \text{curl } \mathbf{U}$ throughout the interior of S for some vector field $\mathbf{U}$. A vector field $\mathbf{U}$ with this property is said to be a **vector potential** for $\mathbf{F}$.

27. In our derivation of the heat equation in this section, we assumed that the coefficient of thermal conductivity k is constant (no sinks or sources). If $k = k(x, y, z)$ is a variable, show that the heat equation becomes

$$k\nabla^2 T + \nabla k \cdot \nabla T = \sigma\rho \frac{\partial T}{\partial t}$$

28. An electric charge q located at the origin produces the electric field

$$\mathbf{E} = \frac{q\mathbf{R}}{4\pi\varepsilon\|\mathbf{R}\|^3}$$

where $\mathbf{R} = x\mathbf{i} + y\mathbf{j} + z\mathbf{k}$ and ε is a physical constant, called the **electric permittivity.**

a. Show that

$$\iint_S \mathbf{E} \cdot \mathbf{N} \, dS = 0$$

if the closed surface S does not enclose the origin. This is **Gauss's law.**

b. Show that

$$\iint_S \mathbf{E} \cdot \mathbf{N} \, dS = \frac{q}{\varepsilon}$$

in the case where the closed surface S encloses the origin. Note that the divergence theorem does not apply directly to this case.

29. Gauss's law can be expressed as

$$\iint_S \mathbf{D} \cdot \mathbf{N} \, dS = q$$

where $\mathbf{D} = \varepsilon\mathbf{E}$ is the electric flux density, with electric intensity $\mathbf{E}$, permittivity ε, and q a constant. Show that div $\mathbf{D} = Q$, where Q is the charge density; that is,

$$\iiint_V Q \, dV = q$$

30. Suppose that

$$\text{curl } \mathbf{E} = -\frac{\partial \mathbf{B}}{\partial t} \quad \text{and} \quad \text{curl } \mathbf{H} = \sigma\mathbf{E} + \varepsilon\frac{\partial \mathbf{E}}{\partial t}$$

where $\mathbf{E}$ is electric intensity; $\mathbf{B}$ is magnetic flux density; $\mathbf{H}$ is magnetic intensity; and σ, ε, and μ are positive constants.

a. Show that $\text{curl}(\text{curl } \mathbf{E}) = -\dfrac{\partial}{\partial t}(\text{curl } \mathbf{B})$.

b. Given that $\mathbf{B} = \mu\mathbf{H}$, first show that

$$\text{curl}(\text{curl } \mathbf{E}) = -\mu\frac{\partial}{\partial t}(\text{curl } \mathbf{H})$$

and then derive the formula

$$\nabla(\text{div } \mathbf{E}) - (\nabla \cdot \nabla)\mathbf{E} = -\mu\frac{\partial}{\partial t}\left(\sigma\mathbf{E} + \varepsilon\frac{\partial \mathbf{E}}{\partial t}\right)$$

c. If $Q = 0$, show that div $\mathbf{E} = 0$, and then derive **Maxwell's equation** for the electric intensity $\mathbf{E}$:

$$(\nabla \cdot \nabla)\mathbf{E} = \mu\sigma\frac{\partial \mathbf{E}}{\partial t} + \mu\varepsilon\frac{\partial^2 \mathbf{E}}{\partial t^2}$$

CHAPTER 14 REVIEW

IN THIS REVIEW Chapter checklist, proficiency examination, supplementary problems

The checklist can be used to summarize the theory techniques and notation used in this chapter. Problems 1–22 of the proficiency examination test your knowledge of the concepts of this chapter, and Problems 23–30 test your understanding of those concepts by asking you to work sample practice problems from the chapter. The supplementary problems present questions relating to the material of this chapter in a wide variety of settings.

■ CHAPTER CHECKLIST

In the following statements, assume that all required conditions are satisfied. Main results are collected here (without hypotheses) so that you can compare and contrast various results and conclusions.

Scalar function: $f = f(x, y, z)$

Vector field: $\mathbf{F}(x, y, z) = u(x, y, z)\mathbf{i} + v(x, y, z)\mathbf{j} + w(x, y, z)\mathbf{k}$

Notation:

Del operator: $\nabla = \dfrac{\partial}{\partial x}\mathbf{i} + \dfrac{\partial}{\partial y}\mathbf{j} + \dfrac{\partial}{\partial z}\mathbf{k}$

Gradient: $\nabla f = \dfrac{\partial f}{\partial x}\mathbf{i} + \dfrac{\partial f}{\partial y}\mathbf{j} + \dfrac{\partial f}{\partial z}\mathbf{k}$

Laplacian: $\nabla^2 f = \dfrac{\partial^2 f}{\partial x^2} + \dfrac{\partial^2 f}{\partial y^2} + \dfrac{\partial^2 f}{\partial z^2} = f_{xx} + f_{yy} + f_{zz}$

Normal derivative: $\dfrac{\partial f}{\partial n} = \nabla f \cdot \mathbf{N}$

Derivatives of a vector field:

$$\text{div } \mathbf{F} = \frac{\partial u}{\partial x} + \frac{\partial v}{\partial y} + \frac{\partial w}{\partial z} \quad \textit{This is a scalar derivative.}$$

$$= \nabla \cdot \mathbf{F}$$

If P is a point (x_0, y_0, z_0), then P is a

source if div $\mathbf{F} > 0$

sink if div $\mathbf{F} < 0$

$\mathbf{F}$ is incompressible if div $\mathbf{F} = 0$.

$$\text{curl } \mathbf{F} = \begin{vmatrix} \mathbf{i} & \mathbf{j} & \mathbf{k} \\ \frac{\partial}{\partial x} & \frac{\partial}{\partial y} & \frac{\partial}{\partial z} \\ u & v & w \end{vmatrix} \quad \textit{This is a vector derivative.}$$

$$= \nabla \times \mathbf{F}$$

Conservative vector fields:

a. $\mathbf{F}$ is *conservative* if it is the gradient of some scalar function f called the *scalar potential of* $\mathbf{F}$; that is, $\mathbf{F} = \nabla f$.

b. $\mathbf{F}$ is conservative if and only if $\frac{\partial u}{\partial y} = \frac{\partial v}{\partial x}$, $\frac{\partial u}{\partial z} = \frac{\partial w}{\partial x}$ and $\frac{\partial v}{\partial z} = \frac{\partial w}{\partial y}$.

c. Equivalent conditions:

(i) $\displaystyle\int_C \mathbf{F} \cdot d\mathbf{R}$ is independent of path.

(ii) $\mathbf{F}$ is conservative.

(iii) $\displaystyle\int_C \mathbf{F} \cdot d\mathbf{R} = 0$ for every closed path C.

d. Conservative vector field theorem: $\mathbf{F}$ is conservative in D if and only if curl $\mathbf{F} = \mathbf{0}$.

EVALUATION OF LINE INTEGRALS: $\displaystyle\int_C \mathbf{F} \cdot d\mathbf{R}$

Step 1. Check to see if $\mathbf{F}$ is conservative; if it is, then

$$\int_C \mathbf{F} \cdot d\mathbf{R} = 0 \text{ if } C \text{ is closed}$$

$$\int_C \mathbf{F} \cdot d\mathbf{R} = f(Q) - f(P) \quad \text{Initial point } P, \text{ terminal } Q$$

Step 2. If $\mathbf{F}$ is not conservative and C is a closed curve bounding the surface S, use Stokes's theorem (or Green's theorem in $\mathbb{R}^2$) to equate the given integral to a surface integral, namely,

$$\int_C \mathbf{F} \cdot d\mathbf{R} = \int\int_S (\text{curl } \mathbf{F} \cdot \mathbf{N}) \, dS$$

Step 3. If $\mathbf{F}$ is not conservative and C is an open curve, try to add an arc C_1 so that the curve formed by C and C_1 is closed. Try to choose C_1 so that $\oint_{C_1} \mathbf{F} \cdot d\mathbf{R}$ is relatively easy to evaluate.

$$\int_C \mathbf{F} \cdot d\mathbf{R} = \int\int_S (\text{curl } \mathbf{F} \cdot \mathbf{N}) \, dS - \int_{C_1} \mathbf{F} \cdot d\mathbf{R}$$

Step 4. As a last resort, parametrize **F** and **R**.

Let $\mathbf{R}(t) = x(t)\mathbf{i} + y(t)\mathbf{j} + z(t)\mathbf{k}$ for $a \leq t \leq b$.

$$\int_C f(x, y, z) \, dx = \int_a^b f[x(t), y(t), z(t)] \frac{dx}{dt} \, dt$$

$$\int_C f(x, y, z) \, ds = \int_a^b f[x(t), y(t), z(t)]\sqrt{[x'(t)]^2 + [y'(t)]^2 + 1} \, dt$$

EVALUATION OF FLUX INTEGRALS: $\iint_S \mathbf{F} \cdot \mathbf{N} \, dS$

Step 1. If S is a closed surface bounding the solid region D, use the divergence theorem to write the surface integral as a triple integral.

$$\iint_S \mathbf{F} \cdot \mathbf{N} \, dS = \iiint_D \text{div } \mathbf{F} \, dV$$

Step 2. If the surface S is open, try to find a supplementary surface S_1 such that the surface formed by S and S_1 is closed. Try to choose S_1 so that $\iint_{S_1} \mathbf{F} \cdot \mathbf{N} \, dS$ is easy to evaluate. Then

$$\iint_S \mathbf{F} \cdot \mathbf{N} \, dS = \iiint_D \text{div } \mathbf{F} \, dV - \iint_{S_1} \mathbf{F} \cdot \mathbf{N} \, dS_1$$

Step 3. If neither steps 1 or 2 applies, parametrize **F**, **N**, and dS. This may be quite difficult.

In the special case where $z = f(x,y)$, we have

$$\iint_S g(x, y, z) \, dS = \iint_R g[x, y, f(x, y)]\sqrt{[f_x(x, y)]^2 + [f_y(x, y)]^2 + 1} \, dA_{xy}$$

■ APPLICATIONS

FLUID MECHANICS

Let **V** be the velocity of an incompressible fluid:

div **V** measures the rate of particle flow per unit volume at a point.
curl **V** measures the tendency of a fluid to swirl.

Flux integral: $\iint_S \mathbf{V} \cdot \mathbf{N} \, dS$ measures the rate of flow across the surface S in unit time.

Circulation: $\int_C \mathbf{V} \cdot \mathbf{T} \, ds$ measures the tendency of a fluid to move around C.

Stokes's theorem says that the cumulative tendency of a fluid to swirl across a surface S is equal to the circulation of a fluid around the boundary curve C.

The divergence theorem says that the total flow across a surface S per unit of time is equal to the flow into (or out of) small cubes. If there are no sources or sinks, it follows that

$$\text{div } \rho\mathbf{V} = -\frac{\partial \rho}{\partial t} \quad \text{(continuity equation)}$$

where $\rho(x, y, z, t)$ is the density of the fluid.

TABLE 14.1 Comparison of important integral theorems

Riemann Integral (Section 4.2)	*Line Integral* (Section 14.2)

$$\int_a^b f(x)\, dx$$

$$\int_C f(x, y, z)\, dx$$

Subdivisions on the *x*-axis

Fundamental Theorem of Calculus (Section 4.3)

$$\int_a^b f(x)\, dx = F(b) - F(a)$$

F is an antiderivative of *f*.

Subdivisions on a curve *C* in space

Fundamental Theorem for Line Integrals (Section 14.3)

$$\int_C \mathbf{F} \cdot d\mathbf{R} = f(Q) - f(P)$$

f is a scalar potential of **F** where **F** is conservative; that is, $\nabla f = \mathbf{F}$.

Green's Theorem (Section 14.4); applies to $\mathbb{R}^2$ (two dimensions): $\mathbf{F}(x, y) = M(x, y)\mathbf{i} + N(x, y)\mathbf{j}$

$$\int_C \mathbf{F} \cdot d\mathbf{R} = \int_C (M\, dx + N\, dy) = \iint_D \left(\frac{\partial N}{\partial x} - \frac{\partial M}{\partial y} \right) dA = \iint_D (\text{curl } \mathbf{F} \cdot \mathbf{k})\, dA$$

and

$$\int_C \mathbf{F} \cdot \mathbf{N}\, ds = \iint_D \left(\frac{\partial M}{\partial x} + \frac{\partial N}{\partial y} \right) dA = \iint_D \text{div } \mathbf{F}\, dA$$

Double integral (Section 13.1)	*Surface integral* (Section 14.5)

$$\iint_R f(x, y)\, dA$$

$$\iint_S g(x, y, z)\, dS = \iint_{R_{xy}} g(x, y, z)\sqrt{g_x^2 + g_y^2 + 1}\, dA_{xy}$$

where $z = f(x_1 y)$.

Partition of *R* into *mn* cells in the *xy*-plane

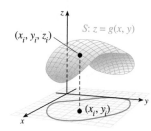

Partition of the surface *S* into *n* subregions

Stokes's Theorem

(Section 14.6; Green's theorem in three dimensions)

$$\int_C \mathbf{F} \cdot d\mathbf{R} = \iint_S (\text{curl } \mathbf{F} \cdot \mathbf{N})\, dS$$

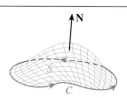

Divergence Theorem (Section 14.7; also known as *Gauss's theorem*; Green's theorem in three dimensions)

$$\iint_S \mathbf{F} \cdot \mathbf{N}\, dS = \iiint_D \text{div } \mathbf{F}\, dV$$

ELECTROMAGNETISM

Let **E** be the electric intensity field and **H** be the magnetic intensity field:

$\text{div } \mathbf{E} = \dfrac{Q}{\varepsilon}$ where Q is the electric charge density and ε is the permittivity.

$\text{curl } \mathbf{E} = -\dfrac{\partial(\mu\mathbf{H})}{\partial t}$ where μ is the permeability and t the time.

$\text{curl } \mathbf{H} = \mathbf{J}$ where **J** is the electric current density.

Maxwell's equation for electric intensity:

$$(\nabla \cdot \nabla)\mathbf{E} = \mu\sigma\frac{\partial \mathbf{E}}{\partial t} + \mu\varepsilon\frac{\partial^2 \mathbf{E}}{\partial t^2}$$ where σ is the conductivity.

Ampere's circuit law: $\displaystyle\int_C \mathbf{H} \cdot d\mathbf{R} = I$, where I is the current crossing any surface S bounded by the closed curve C.

THERMODYNAMICS

The heat equation is: $\dfrac{\partial T}{\partial t} = \dfrac{k}{\sigma\rho}\nabla^2 T$, where $T(x, y, z, t)$ is the temperature at (x, y, z) at time t. The constant k is the thermal conductivity, σ is the specific heat of the body, and ρ is its density.

WORK: $W = \displaystyle\int_C \mathbf{F} \cdot d\mathbf{R}$

MASS: $m = \displaystyle\iint_S \rho(x, y, z)\, dS$

PROFICIENCY EXAMINATION

Concept Problems

1. What is a vector field?
2. What is the divergence of a vector field?
3. What is the curl of a vector field?
4. What is the del operator?
5. What is Laplace's equation?
6. What is the difference between the Riemann integral and a line integral? Discuss.
7. What is the formula for a line integral of a vector field?
8. How do we find work as a line integral?
9. What is the formula for a line integral in terms of arc length parameter?
10. State the fundamental theorem on line integrals.
11. Define a conservative vector field.
12. What is the scalar potential of a conservative vector field?
13. What is a Jordan curve?
14. State Green's theorem.
15. How can you use Green's theorem to find area as a line integral?
16. What is a normal derivative?
17. Define a surface integral.
18. What is the formula for a surface integral of a surface defined parametrically?
19. What is a flux integral?
20. State Stokes's theorem.
21. State the conservative vector field theorem.
22. State the divergence theorem.

Practice Problems

23. Show that $yz\mathbf{i} + xz\mathbf{j} + xy\mathbf{k}$ is conservative and find a scalar potential function.

24. Compute div $\mathbf{F}$ and curl $\mathbf{F}$ for $\mathbf{F} = x^2y\mathbf{i} - e^{yz}\mathbf{j} + \frac{1}{2}x\mathbf{k}$.

25. Use Green's theorem to evaluate the line integral $\int_C \mathbf{F} \cdot d\mathbf{R}$, where $\mathbf{F} = (2x + y)\mathbf{i} + 3y^2\mathbf{j}$ and C is the boundary of the triangle with vertices $(-1, 2)$, $(0, 0)$, $(1, 2)$, traversed in that order.

26. Use Stokes's theorem to evaluate the line integral $\int_C \mathbf{F} \cdot d\mathbf{R}$, where $\mathbf{F} = 2y\mathbf{i} + z\mathbf{j} + y\mathbf{k}$ and C is the intersection of the plane $z = x + 2$ and the sphere $x^2 + y^2 + z^2 = 4z$, traversed counterclockwise as viewed from above.

27. Use the divergence theorem to evaluate the surface integral $\iint_S \mathbf{F} \cdot \mathbf{N}\, dS$, where $\mathbf{F} = x^2\mathbf{i} + (y + z)\mathbf{j} - 2z\mathbf{k}$, and S is the surface of the unit cube $0 \le x \le 1$, $0 \le y \le 1, 0 \le z \le 1$.

28. Evaluate $\int_C \dfrac{x\, dx + y\, dy}{(x^2 + y^2)^2}$, where C is the path shown in Figure 14.34.

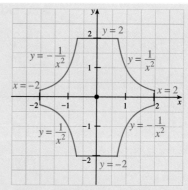

Figure 14.34 Problem 28

29. An object with mass m travels counterclockwise (as viewed from above) in the circular orbit $x^2 + y^2 = 9$, $z = 2$, with angular speed ω. The mass is subject to a centrifugal force $\mathbf{F} = m\omega^2\mathbf{R}$, where $\mathbf{R} = x\mathbf{i} + y\mathbf{j} + z\mathbf{k}$. Show that $\mathbf{F}$ is conservative, and find a scalar potential function for $\mathbf{F}$.

30. Find the work done by $\mathbf{F}$ from Problem 29 as the object makes a half-orbit from $(3, 0, 2)$ to $(-3, 0, 2)$.

SUPPLEMENTARY PROBLEMS

In Problems 1–6, determine whether the given vector field is conservative, and if it is, find a scalar potential function.

1. $\mathbf{F} = 2\mathbf{i} - 3\mathbf{j}$

2. $\mathbf{F} = xy^{-2}\mathbf{i} + x^{-2}y\mathbf{j}$

3. $\mathbf{F} = y^{-3}\mathbf{i} + (-3xy^{-4} + \cos y)\mathbf{j}$

4. $\mathbf{F} = y^2\mathbf{i} + (2xy)\mathbf{j}$

5. $\mathbf{F} = \left(\dfrac{1}{y} + \dfrac{y}{x^2}\right)\mathbf{i} - \left(\dfrac{x}{y^2} - \dfrac{1}{x}\right)\mathbf{j}$

6. $\mathbf{F} = \left[2x \tan^{-1}\left(\dfrac{y}{x}\right) - y\right]\mathbf{i} + \left[2y \tan^{-1}\left(\dfrac{y}{x}\right) + x\right]\mathbf{j}$

In Problems 7–12, find $\int_C \mathbf{F} \cdot d\mathbf{R}$, where C is the curve $\mathbf{R}(t) = t\mathbf{i} + t^2\mathbf{j}$, $1 \le t \le 2$. Note that these are the same as the vector fields in Problems 1–6.

7. $\mathbf{F} = 2\mathbf{i} - 3\mathbf{j}$

8. $\mathbf{F} = xy^{-2}\mathbf{i} + x^{-2}y\mathbf{j}$

9. $\mathbf{F} = y^{-3}\mathbf{i} + (-3xy^{-4} + \cos y)\mathbf{j}$

10. $\mathbf{F} = y^2\mathbf{i} + (2xy)\mathbf{j}$

11. $\mathbf{F} = \left(\dfrac{1}{y} + \dfrac{y}{x^2}\right)\mathbf{i} - \left(\dfrac{x}{y^2} - \dfrac{1}{x}\right)\mathbf{j}$

12. $\mathbf{F} = \left[2x \tan^{-1}\left(\dfrac{y}{x}\right) - y\right]\mathbf{i} + \left[2y \tan^{-1}\left(\dfrac{y}{x}\right) + x\right]\mathbf{j}$

In Problems 13–16, find div $\mathbf{F}$ and curl $\mathbf{F}$.

13. $\mathbf{F} = x\mathbf{i} + y\mathbf{j} + z\mathbf{k}$

14. $\mathbf{F} = \left(\tan^{-1}\dfrac{y}{x}\right)\mathbf{i} - 3\mathbf{j} + z^2\mathbf{k}$

15. $\mathbf{F} = \dfrac{1}{r}(x\mathbf{i} + y\mathbf{j} + z\mathbf{k})$, where $r = \sqrt{x^2 + y^2 + z^2}$, $r \ne 0$

16. $\mathbf{F} = (xy \sin z)\mathbf{i} + (x^2 \cos yz)\mathbf{j} + (z \sin xy)\mathbf{k}$

Evaluate the line integrals in Problems 17–18 by parametrization.

17. $\int_C [(\sin \pi y)\, dx + (\cos \pi x)\, dy]$, where C is the line segment from $(1, 0)$ to $(\pi, 0)$, followed by the line segment from $(\pi, 0)$ to (π, π)

18. $\int_C (z\, dx - x\, dy + dz)$, where C is the arc of the helix $x = 3 \sin t$, $y = 3 \cos t$, $z = t$ for $0 \le t \le \frac{\pi}{4}$.

In each of Problems 19–33, evaluate the line integral or the surface integral. In each case, assume the orientation of C is counterclockwise when viewed from above or that $\mathbf{N}$ is the unit outward normal.

19. $\int_C [yz\, dx + xz\, dy + (xy + 2)]\, dz$
C is the curve $\mathbf{R}(t) = (\tan^{-1}t)\mathbf{i} + t^2\mathbf{j} - 3t\mathbf{k}$, $0 \le t \le 1$.

20. $\int_C [(x^2 + y)\, dx + xz\, dy - (y + z)\, dz]$
C is the curve $\mathbf{R}(t) = t\mathbf{i} + t^2\mathbf{j} + 2\mathbf{k}$, $0 \le t \le 1$.

21. $\iint_S (3x^2 + y - 2z) \, dS$

S is the surface $\mathbf{R}(u, v) = u\mathbf{i} + (u + v)\mathbf{j} + u\mathbf{k}, 0 \le u \le 1,$
$0 \le v \le 1.$

22. $\iint_S \mathbf{F} \cdot \mathbf{N} \, dS$

$\mathbf{F} = 3x\mathbf{i} + z^2\mathbf{j} - 2y\mathbf{k}$ and S is the surface of the hemisphere $z = \sqrt{4 - x^2 - y^2}.$

23. $\int_C (x \, dx + x \, dy - y \, dz)$

C is the curve $\mathbf{R}(t) = t\mathbf{i} + t^2\mathbf{j} + t\mathbf{k}, 0 \le t \le 1.$

24. $\int_C (x^2 \, dx - 3y^2 \, dz)$

C is the line segment from $(0, 1, 1)$ to $(1, 1, 2).$

25. $\int_C (x^2 \, dx + y \, dy)$

C is the curve $\mathbf{R}(t) = (t \sin t)\mathbf{i} + (1 - t \cos t)\mathbf{j},$
$0 \le t \le 2\pi.$

26. $\int_C (xy \, dx - x^2 \, dy)$

C is the square with vertices $(1, 0), (0, 1), (-1, 0), (0, -1)$ traversed counterclockwise.

27. $\int_C (y \, dx + x \, dy - 2 \, dz)$

C is the curve of intersection of the cylinder $x^2 + y^2 = 2x$ and the plane $x = z.$

28. $\int_C [(y + z) \, dx + (x + z) \, dy + (x + y) \, dz]$

C is the curve of intersection of the sphere $x^2 + (y - 3)^2 + z^2 = 9$ and the plane $x + 2y + z = 3.$

29. $\int_C (-2y \, dx + 2x \, dy + dz)$

C is the circle $x^2 + y^2 = 1$ in the plane $z = 3.$

30. $\iint_S (\text{curl } y\mathbf{i}) \cdot \mathbf{N} \, dS$

S is the hemisphere $z = \sqrt{1 - x^2 - y^2}.$

31. $\iint_S (2x^3\mathbf{i} + y^3\mathbf{j} + z^3\mathbf{k}) \cdot \mathbf{N} \, dS$

S is the surface of the ellipsoid $2x^2 + y^2 + z^2 = 1.$

32. $\iint_S (y^2\mathbf{i} + y^2\mathbf{j} + yz\mathbf{k}) \cdot \mathbf{N} \, dS$

S is the surface of the tetrahedron bounded by the plane $2x + 3y + z = 1$ and the coordinate planes, in the first octant.

33. $\iint_S \nabla\phi \cdot \mathbf{N} \, dS,$ where $\phi(x, y) = 2x + 3y$

where S is the portion of the plane $ax + by + cz = 1$ $(a > 0, b > 0, c > 0)$ that lies in the first octant.

In Problems 34–38, find $\iint_S \mathbf{F} \cdot \mathbf{N} \, dS.$

34. $\mathbf{F} = x^2\mathbf{i} + y^2\mathbf{j} + x^2\mathbf{k},$ and S is the surface of the unit cube $0 \le x \le 1, 0 \le y \le 1, 0 \le z \le 1.$

35. $\mathbf{F} = 2yz\mathbf{i} + (\tan^{-1} xz)\mathbf{j} + e^{xy}\mathbf{k},$ and S is the surface of the sphere $x^2 + y^2 + z^2 = 1.$

36. $\mathbf{F} = x\mathbf{i} - 4\mathbf{j} + 3\mathbf{k},$ and S is the paraboloid $y = x^2 + z^2$ with $x^2 + z^2 \le 9.$ The disk $x^2 + y^2 = 9$ is omitted; that is, the paraboloid is open on the right.

37. $\mathbf{F} = xyz\mathbf{i} + xyz\mathbf{j} + xyz\mathbf{k},$ and S is the surface of the five faces of the unit cube $0 \le x \le 1, 0 \le y \le 1,$ $0 < z \le 1.$

38. $\mathbf{F} = xy\mathbf{i} - 2z\mathbf{j},$ and S is the surface defined parametrically by $\mathbf{R}(u, v) = u\mathbf{i} + v\mathbf{j} + u\mathbf{k}$ for $0 \le u \le 1, 0 \le v \le 1.$

Find all real numbers c for which each vector field in Problems 39–41 is conservative.

39. $\mathbf{F}(x, y) = (\sqrt{x} + 3xy)\mathbf{i} + (cx^2 + 4y)\mathbf{j}$

40. $\mathbf{F}(x, y) = \left(\dfrac{cy}{x^2} - \dfrac{y}{x^2}\right)\mathbf{i} + \left(\dfrac{1}{x^2} - \dfrac{1}{x}\right)\mathbf{j}$

41. $\mathbf{F}(x, y, z) = e^{yz/x}\left[\left(\dfrac{cyz}{x^2}\right)\mathbf{i} + \left(\dfrac{z}{x}\right)\mathbf{j} + \left(\dfrac{y}{x}\right)\mathbf{k}\right]$

42. If $\mathbf{F} = (y^2 + x^{-2}ye^{x/y})\mathbf{i} + (2xy + z - x^{-1}e^{x/y})\mathbf{j} + y\mathbf{k},$ either show that $\mathbf{F}$ is not conservative, or show that it is and find a scalar potential.

43. Find the work done when an object moves in the force field $\mathbf{F} = 2x\mathbf{i} - (x + z)\mathbf{j} + (y - x)\mathbf{k}$ along the path given by $\mathbf{R}(t) = t^2\mathbf{i} + (t^2 - t)\mathbf{j} + 3\mathbf{k}, 0 \le t \le 1.$

44. Show that the force field

$$\mathbf{F} = yz^2\mathbf{i} + (xz^2 - 1)\mathbf{j} + (2xyz - 1)\mathbf{k}$$

is conservative and determine the work done when an object moves in the force field from the origin to the point $(1, 0, 1).$

45. Find a region R in the plane where the vector field

$$\mathbf{F} = \dfrac{1}{x + y}(\mathbf{i} + \mathbf{j}) \text{ is conservative. Then evaluate } \int_C \mathbf{F} \cdot d\mathbf{R},$$

where C is any path in R from the point $P_0(a, b)$ to $P_1(c, d).$

46. Solve $(2y \sin x \cos x + y^2 \sin x) \, dx + (\sin^2 x - 2y \cos x) \, dy = 0,$ subject to $y(0) = 1.$

47. Solve $(6xy + 2y^2 - 5) \, dx + (3x^2 + 4xy - 6) \, dy = 0,$ subject to $y(0) = 0.$

48. If u is a scalar function and $\mathbf{F}$ is a continuously differentiable vector field, show that

$$\text{curl}(u\mathbf{F}) = u \text{ curl } \mathbf{F} + (\nabla u \times \mathbf{F})$$

49. Show that $\text{div}(\mathbf{F} \times \mathbf{G}) = \mathbf{G} \cdot \text{curl } \mathbf{F} - \mathbf{F} \cdot \text{curl } \mathbf{G},$ for any continuously differentiable vector fields $\mathbf{F}$ and $\mathbf{G}.$

50. A vector field **F** is **solenoidal** (or **incompressible**) in a region D if div **F** $= 0$ throughout D. If **F** and **G** are both conservative vector fields in D, show that **F** × **G** is solenoidal.

51. If **F** = curl **G**, show that **F** is solenoidal. (See Problem 50.)

52. Suppose **F** $= f(x, y, z)$**A**, where **A** is a constant vector and f is a scalar function. Show that curl **F** is orthogonal to **A** and to ∇f.

53. If **A** is a constant vector and **F** is a continuously differentiable vector field, show that div(**A** × **F**) $= -$**A** · curl **F**.

54. Evaluate the line integral $\displaystyle\int_C \frac{x\,dx - y\,dy}{x^2 - y^2}$, where C is any path in the xy-plane that is interior to the region $x > 0$, $y < x$, $y > -x$ and connects the point $(5, 4)$ to $(2, 0)$.

55. Evaluate $\displaystyle\int_C \left(\frac{-y}{x^2}\,dx + \frac{1}{x}\,dy\right)$, where C is the closed path $(x - 2)^2 + y^2 = 1$, traversed once counterclockwise.

56. THINK TANK PROBLEM Let $u(x, y)$ and $v(x, y)$ be functions of two variables with continuous partial derivatives everywhere in the plane, and suppose that u and v satisfy the equation

$$\frac{\partial u}{\partial y} = \frac{\partial v}{\partial x}$$

for all (x, y). Are u and v necessarily harmonic? Either show that they are or find a counterexample.

57. **a.** Find a region in the plane where the vector field

$$\mathbf{F} = \left(\frac{1 + y^2}{x^3}\right)\mathbf{i} - \left(\frac{y + x^2y}{x^2}\right)\mathbf{j}$$

is conservative, and find a scalar potential for **F**.

b. Evaluate $\displaystyle\int_C \mathbf{F} \cdot d\mathbf{R}$, where C is a path from $(1, 1)$ to $(3, 4)$. Are there any limitations on the path C? Explain.

58. Determine the most general function $u(x, y)$ for which the vector field $\mathbf{F} = u(x, y)\mathbf{i} + (2y\,e^x + y^2 e^{3x})\mathbf{j}$ will be conservative.

59. Consider the line integral $\displaystyle\int_C \left(\frac{dx}{y} + \frac{dy}{x}\right)$, where C is the closed triangular path formed by the lines $y = 2x$, $x + 2y = 5$, and $x = 2$, traversed counterclockwise. First evaluate the line integral directly (by parametrizing C) and then by using Green's theorem.

60. If S is a closed surface in a region R and **F** is a continuously differentiable vector field on R, show that

$$\iint_S (\text{curl } \mathbf{F} \cdot \mathbf{N})\,dS = 0$$

where **N** is the outward unit normal to S.

61. A certain closed path C in the plane $2x + 2y + z = 1$ is known to project onto the unit circle $x^2 + y^2 = 1$ in the xy-plane. Let c be a constant, and let $\mathbf{R} = x\mathbf{i} + y\mathbf{j} + z\mathbf{k}$. Use Stokes's theorem to evaluate

$$\int_C (c\mathbf{k} \times \mathbf{R}) \cdot d\mathbf{R}$$

62. **a.** Show that if the scalar function w is harmonic, then

$$\nabla \cdot (w\,\nabla\,w) = \|\nabla w\|^2$$

b. Let $w = x - y + 2z$, and let S be the surface of the sphere $x^2 + y^2 + z^2 = 9$. Evaluate

$$\iint_S w\,\frac{\partial w}{\partial n}\,dS$$

Hint: See the normal derivative in Section 14.4.

63. A particle moves along a curve C in space that is given parametrically by $\mathbf{R}(t) = x(t)\mathbf{i} + y(t)\mathbf{j} + z(t)\mathbf{k}$ for $a \leq t \leq b$. A force field **F** is applied to the particle in such a way that **F** is always perpendicular to the path C. How much work is performed by the force field **F** when the particle moves from the point where $t = a$ to the point where $t = b$?

64. If **D** is the electric displacement field, then div **D** $= \phi$, where ϕ is the **charge density**. A region of space is said to be **charge-free** if $\phi = 0$ there. Describe the charge-free regions of the electric displacement field $\mathbf{D} = 2x^2\mathbf{i} + 3y^2\mathbf{j} - 2z^2\mathbf{k}$.

65. A satellite weighing 10,000 kg travels in a circular orbit 7,000 km from the center of the earth. How much work is done by gravity on the satellite during half a revolution?

66. If **F** is a conservative force field, the scalar function f such that $\mathbf{F} = -\nabla f$ is called the **potential energy**. Suppose an object with mass 10 g moves in the force field in such a way that its speed decreases from 3 cm/s to 2.5 cm/s. What is the corresponding change in the potential energy of the object?

67. Find the work done by the force field

$$\mathbf{F} = 2xyz\mathbf{i} + \left(x^2 z - \frac{1}{z}\tan^{-1}\frac{y}{z}\right)\mathbf{j} + \left(x^2y + \frac{y}{z^2}\tan^{-1}\frac{y}{z}\right)\mathbf{k}$$

in moving an object along the circular helix

$$\mathbf{R}(t) = (\sin \pi t)\mathbf{i} + (\cos \pi t)\mathbf{j} + (2t + 1)\mathbf{k}$$

for $0 \leq t \leq \frac{1}{2}$.

68. Find the work done when an object moves against the force field $\mathbf{F} = 4xy\mathbf{i} + (3x + y)\mathbf{j}$ from $(1, 0)$ to $(-1, 0)$ along the top half of the ellipse $x^2 + \frac{y^2}{k^2} = 1$. What value of k minimizes the work?

69. One of Maxwell's laws of electromagnetism states that div $\mathbf{E} = \frac{1}{\varepsilon}Q$, where **E** is the electric intensity, ε (a constant) is the permittivity of the medium, and Q is the charge density (charge per unit volume). Show that

$$\iint_S \mathbf{E} \cdot \mathbf{N} \, dS = \frac{1}{\varepsilon} q$$

where q is the total charge in a solid region $\mathbf{R}$ with boundary surface S. This is called **Gauss's law**.

70. Evaluate the line integral

$$\int_C \frac{-y \, dx + x \, dy}{x^2 + y^2}$$

where C is the limaçon given in polar coordinates by $r = 3 + 2 \cos \theta$, $0 \le \theta \le 2\pi$.

71. Suppose f and g are both harmonic in the region R with boundary surface S. Show that

a. $\displaystyle \iint_S f \frac{\partial g}{\partial n} \, dS = \iint_S g \frac{\partial f}{\partial n} \, dS$

b. $\displaystyle \iint_S f \frac{\partial f}{\partial n} \, dS = \iiint_D \|\nabla f\|^2 \, dV$

Hint: $\dfrac{\partial f}{\partial n}$ denotes the normal derivative (see Section 14.4).

72. Show that curl(curl $\mathbf{F}$) = ∇(div $\mathbf{F}$) $- \nabla^2 \mathbf{F}$ if the components of $\mathbf{F}$ have continuous second-order partial derivatives.

73. Evaluate the surface integral

$$\iint_S \frac{\partial f}{\partial n} \, dS$$

where S is the surface of the unit sphere $x^2 + y^2 + z^2 = 1$ and f is a scalar field such that $\|\nabla f\|^2 = 3f$ and div($f \nabla f$) = $7f$. Remember that $\dfrac{\partial f}{\partial n}$ denotes the normal derivative.

74. Evaluate the surface integral $\int \int_S dS$, where S is the torus

$$\mathbf{R}(u, v) = [(a + b \cos v)\cos u]\mathbf{i}$$
$$+ [(a + b \cos v)\sin u]\mathbf{j} + (b \sin v)\mathbf{k}$$

for $0 < b < a$ and $0 \le u \le 2\pi$, $0 \le v \le 2\pi$.

75. Evaluate $\displaystyle \iint_S \mathbf{F} \cdot \mathbf{N} \, dS$, where $\mathbf{F} = x\mathbf{i} + y\mathbf{j} + z\mathbf{k}$ and S is a cubic surface with a corner block removed, as shown in Figure 14.35.

Figure 14.35 Cube with a corner block removed

76. THINK TANK PROBLEM Prove or disprove that it does not matter which corner is removed in Problem 75.

77. Show that a lamina that covers a standard region D in the plane with density $\rho = 1$ has moment of inertia

$$I = \frac{1}{3} \int_C (-y^3 \, dx + x^3 \, dy)$$

with respect to the z-axis, where C is the boundary curve of D.

78. Use vector analysis to find the centroid of the conical surface (shell). $z = \sqrt{x^2 + y^2}$ between $z = 0$ and $z = 3$.

79. Having conserved as much energy as possible after his escape from the Death Force Field (Problem 33, Section 14.4), the spy continues his search for Purity and Scélérat. He rushes into a small room and finds no Scélérat but *two* Purities struggling ferociously on the floor. As he separates them, he notices one is dressed in red and the other in green. The red one cries, "She's my evil twin, Rottona. She escaped from prison and is going to take my place." The green Purity shouts back, "Liar! I'm the real Purity. I've been tied up here all along and just got free." The spy is better at logic than with colors. He thinks for a moment and then says to the Green Purity, "I remember not — *you* are the one who has been trying to kill me. You're going back to prison, but first, I'm going to give you the same kind of chance to escape you gave me. You choose an integer N, and then your sister will pick a number x and you will have

$$S(N, x) = \frac{3\exp[(x + N)^2 + 4N + 22]}{(x + N)^2(e^{40} + e^{8N})}$$

minutes head start before I come after you." The Red Purity laughs and says, "Choose carefully, dear sister, because I plan to minimize your time!" The Green Purity declares, "It's not fair. I'm innocent." Then she blurts out a number. The Red Purity's smile fades and she cries, "Can you believe it! She always was lucky." What number did the Green Purity choose? How much time will she get? What happens next?

80. PUTNAM EXAMINATION PROBLEM A force acts on the element ds of a closed plane curve. The magnitude of this force is $r^{-1} \, ds$, where r is the radius of curvature at the point considered and the direction of the force is perpendicular to the curve; it points to the convex side. Show that the system of such forces acting on all elements of the curve keeps it in equilibrium.

Continuous vs. Discrete Mathematics by William F. Lucas

William F. Lucas is a professor of mathematics and department chairman of the department The Claremont Graduate School. He is an Avery Fellow to Harvey Mudd College and is known for his research in game theory. This modern subject provides a mathematical approach to the study of conflict, cooperation, and fairness. Dr. Lucas has also been active in educational reform efforts with a goal toward introducing recently discovered topics into the mathematics curriculum.

Most human heads have a fixed point, in the form of a whorl, sometimes called a cowlick, from which all the hair radiates. It would be impossible to cover a sphere with hair (or with radiating lines) without at least one such fixed point.

Mathematicians often distinguish between *discrete* and *continuous* mathematics. The latter is illustrated by the calculus and its many descendants, including the subject of differential equations. Continuous mathematics deals with "solid" infinite sets such as the real number line $\mathbb{R}$ and functions defined on $\mathbb{R}$. One of the primary concerns is with the solutions of differential equations, which are typical families of such solid curves or surfaces. The many applications of such differential equations to discoveries in the physical sciences and engineering over the past three centuries has been one of the greatest intellectual success stories of all times.

Prior to the invention of calculus by Newton and Leibniz, most mathematics was of a discrete nature. It dealt with sets that had a finite number of elements and with infinite but "countable" sets such as the natural numbers. These sets often include continuous curves such as the conics, which can be characterized by a small number of conditions. Discrete mathematics also deals with the solutions to algebraic equations, which are usually discrete sets. The twentieth century has witnessed the creation of many additional subjects in the discrete direction. This development was spurred on by the rapidly increasing use of mathematics in the social, behavioral, decisional, and system sciences, where the items under investigation are typically finite in number and not readily approximated by some continuous idealization. Moreover, nearly all aspects of the ongoing revolution in *digital* computers involve discrete considerations.

A metal bar at the minute level is composed of discrete molecules, atoms, and elementary particles. Many of its physical properties, however, can be determined by viewing the bar as a solid continuum and employing the analytical techniques of calculus. One applies the basic laws of physics to express the local (infinitesimal) properties of the bar in terms of differential equations. The solutions of these equations, in turn, provide an excellent description of the observed global behavior of the bar.

One of the greatest mathematical discoveries of the twentieth century in continuous mathematics is the famous fixed-point theorem, published in 1912 by the Dutch mathematician L. E. J. Brouwer (1881–1966). It states that any continuous function f from a set S (with certain desirable properties) into the same set S has at least one *fixed point* x_0, that is, $f(x_0) = x_0$. For example, for any continuous function $y = f(x)$ from the set $S = \{x \; \varepsilon \; \mathbb{R}: 0 \le x \le 1\}$ into S there is some number $x_0 \; \varepsilon \; S$ such that the curve $y = f(x)$ crosses the line $y = x$ at x_0. A head of hair must either have a seam (a parting of the hair, a discontinuity) or else a cowlick (where the hair stands straight up, a fixed point). Fixed points are realized in many physical and social phenomena such as equilibrium states in mechanics or stable prices in economics.

Like many of the outstanding results in continuous mathematics, Brouwer's theorem has an analog in discrete mathematics, known as the labeling lemma of the German mathematician Emanuel Sperner, which appeared in 1928. Given a triangle with vertices 0, 1, and 2 as shown in Figure 14.36, one can partition the interior of this triangle into (nonoverlapping) smaller triangles in any possible way.

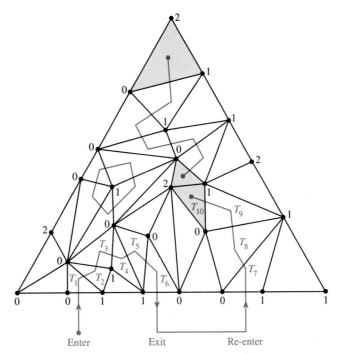

Figure 14.36 Arbitrary partitioning of a triangle

One can then label each of the newly created vertices with any one of the numbers 0, 1, or 2. There is only one stipulation on how the new vertices on the perimeter of the triangle can be labeled: Any vertex on a particular side of $\triangle 012$ cannot be labeled with the number appearing on the *main* vertex opposite (disjoint from) this side. For example, the side 01 of $\triangle 012$ cannot contain a vertex with the label 2. Sperner's lemma states that there must exist at least one elementary triangle inside $\triangle 012$ (or an *odd* number, in general) whose three vertices are "completely labeled" in the sense that they have all three labels 0, 1, and 2. There are three such triangles (shown in color) in Figure 14.36.

There is an elementary constructive proof of Sperner's lemma that uses the idea of a "path-following algorithm" published by Daniel I. A. Cohen in 1967. This proof is illustrated by the dashed line in Figure 14.36. One can enter into $\triangle 012$ from outside via some elementary triangle T_1 whose perimeter edge carries the labels 0 and 1. The third vertex on this elementary triangle T_1 must be either 2 (in which case T_1 is a completely labeled elementary triangle), or else it is 0 or 1. In the latter cases, one can exit T_1 via a second 01 edge. One can continue to enter and exit subsequent elementary triangles T_2, T_3, . . . through successive 01 edges until one finally reaches an elementary triangle T_n that has completely labeled vertices 0, 1, and 2. (If this path were ever to exit $\triangle 012$, then there must be still another 01 edge on the perimeter of $\triangle 012$ where one can reenter the main triangle and continue along the path, as did occur once in Figure 14.36.)

This path-following method also extends to a proof of Sperner's labeling lemma for dimensions higher than two. Furthermore, this approach is used in practical problems to arrive at a "very small" elementary triangle that can serve as an approximation to a fixed point, when it is excessively difficult or impossible to determine the precise location of the fixed point itself. In such cases, the broken path in Figure 14.36 can be viewed as the analog in discrete mathematics of the continuous curves one arrives at when solving differential equations.

Around 1945, the great Hungarian-American mathematician John von Neumann (1903–1957) pointed out the need for approximating paths in a discrete manner when it proves too difficult to arrive at the exact continuous solutions to certain ordinary or partial differential equations. Cohen's constructive proof of Sperner's lemma, and work in the late 1960s by the mathematical economist Herbert Scarf on approximating equilibrium points, have paved the way for one very rich and extensive discrete theory that provides numerical approximations for continuous phenomena when the latter problems cannot be solved directly by the many analytic techniques of continuous mathematics.

MATHEMATICAL ESSAYS

1. If your college offers a course on discrete mathematics, interview an instructor of the course and, using that interview as a basis, write an essay comparing continuous and discrete mathematics.

2. Draw several triangles and attempt to draw a counterexample for Sperner's Labeling Lemma. In each case, show how this lemma is satisfied.

3. Consider two sheets of paper containing the numbers 1 to 120, as shown in the drawing.

If the top sheet is crumpled and dropped on the bottom sheet, the fixed-point theorem tells us that at least one point must still lie directly above its starting point. In the following drawing, it is a point in the region of the number 78. Perform this experiment several times in an attempt to find a counterexample. In each case, show how the fixed-point theorem is satisfied.

4. Write a 500-word essay on William Rowan Hamilton.

5. Write a 500-word essay on Pierre de Fermat.

6. Write a 500-word essay on Archimedes.

7. Write a 500-word essay on the history of Green's theorem, Stokes's theorem, and the divergence theorem.

8. Write a report on four-dimensional geometry.

9. **Book Report** "We often hear that mathematics consists mainly in 'proving theorems.' Is a writer's job mainly that of 'writing sentences'? A mathematician's work is mostly a tangle of guesswork, analogy, wishful thinking, and frustration, and proof, far from being the core of discovery, is more often than not a way of making sure that our minds are not playing tricks. Few people, if any, had dared write this out loud before Davis and Hersh. Theorems are not to mathematics what successful courses are to a meal. The nutritional analogy is misleading. To master mathematics is to master an intangible view . . . ." This quotation comes from the introduction to the book *The Mathematical Experience* by Philip J. Davis and Reuben Hersh (Boston: Houghton Mifflin, 1981). Read this book and prepare a book report.

10. Make up a word problem involving vector fields. Send your problem to:

    Mathematics Editor,
    re: Bradley, Smith: *CALCULUS*
    Prentice Hall
    113 Sylvan Ave., Route 9W
    Englewood Cliffs, NJ 07632

    The best ones submitted will appear in the next edition (along with credit to the problem poser).

CUMULATIVE REVIEW FOR CHAPTERS 12–14

1. ■ **What Does This Say?** Suppose you tell a fellow college student that you are about to finish a calculus course. The student has not had any mathematics beyond high school and asks you, "What is calculus?" Answer this question using your own words.

2. ■ **What Does This Say?** There are three great ideas in calculus: the idea of a limit, the idea of a derivative, and the idea of an integral. In your own words, explain each of these concepts.

3. ■ **What Does This Say?** Chapters 12-14 were concerned with functions of several variables. This is often referred to as **multivariable caculus**. In your own words, discuss what is meant by multivariable calculus.

Find f_x, f_y, and f_{xy} for the functions whose equations are given in Problems 4-9.

4. $f(x, y) = 2x^2 + xy - 5y^3$ **5.** $f(x, y) = x^2 e^{y/x}$

6. $f(x, y) = \dfrac{x^2 - y^2}{x - y}$ **7.** $f(x, y) = y \sin^2 x + \cos xy$

8. $f(x, y) = e^{x+y}$ **9.** $f(x, y) = \dfrac{x^2 + y^2}{x - y}$

Evaluate the integrals in Problems 10-17.

10. $\displaystyle\int_0^1 \int_x^{2x} e^{y-x} \, dy \, dx$ **11.** $\displaystyle\int_0^4 \int_0^{\sqrt{x}} 3x^5 \, dy \, dx$

12. $\displaystyle\int_0^1 \int_0^z \int_y^{y-z} (x + y + z) \, dx \, dy \, dz$

13. $\displaystyle\int_0^{15\pi} \int_0^\pi \int_0^{\sin\phi} \rho^3 \sin\phi \, d\rho \, d\theta \, d\phi$

14. $\displaystyle\int\int_R e^{x+y} \, dA;$ **15.** $\displaystyle\int\int_R y e^{xy} \, dA;$

$R: 0 \le x \le 1; 0 \le y \le 1$ $R: 0 \le x \le 1; 0 \le y \le 2$

16. $\displaystyle\int\int_R \sin(x + y) \, dA;$ **17.** $\displaystyle\int\int_R x \sin xy \, dA;$

$R: 0 \le x \le \frac{\pi}{2}; 0 \le y \le \frac{\pi}{4}$ $R: 0 \le x \le \pi; 0 \le y \le 1$

Evaluate the line integrals in Problems 18-21.

18. $\displaystyle\int_C (y^2 z \, dx + 2xyz \, dy + xy^2 \, dz)$, where C is any path from $(0, 0, 0)$ to $(1, 1, 1)$

19. $\displaystyle\int_C (5 \, xy \, dx + 10 \, yz \, dy + z \, dz)$, where C is given by $x = t^2, y = t, z = 2t^3$ for $0 \le t \le 1$

20. $\displaystyle\int_C \mathbf{F} \cdot d\mathbf{R}$, where $\mathbf{F} = yz\mathbf{i} - x\mathbf{k}$, and C is the boundary of the triangle $(1, 1, 1)$, $(1, 0, 1)$, $(0, 0, 1)$, traversed once counterclockwise as viewed from the origin

21. $\displaystyle\int_C (x^3 + y^3) \, ds$, where C is given by

$\mathbf{R}(t) = (\cos^3 t)\mathbf{i} + (\sin^3 t)\mathbf{j}$, for $0 \le t \le 2\pi$

22. Find the equation for the tangent plane and the normal line to $z = x^2 + y^2 + \sin xy$ at $P = (0, 2, 4)$.

23. What are the dimensions of the rectangular box of fixed volume V_0 that has minimum surface area?

24. Suppose we model a heat-seeking missile by making the following assumptions. Suppose the spherical ball in the nose of the missile with equation $x^2 + y^2 + z^2 \le 100$ is heated so that its temperature (in degrees Celsius) at the point (x, y, z) is given by

$$T(x, y, z) = \frac{1}{10}(x^2 + y + z^3)$$

where x, y, and z are measured in kilometers.

a. Find the rate at which the temperature is changing as (x, y, z) moves from the point $P_0(-2, 9, 1)$ toward $Q(1, -3, 5)$.

b. If a heat-seeking missile is at P_0, in what direction will it travel to maximize the rate of heat increase?

c. What is the maximal rate of increase (in degrees Celsius per kilometer)?

25. Use double polar integration to find the area inside the cardioid $r = 1 - \cos\theta$ and outside the circle $r = 1$.

26. Find the volume of the solid bounded above by the surface $z = x^2 + y^2 + 1$ and below by the circular disk $x^2 + y^2 \le 1$ in the xy-plane.

27. Find the surface area of that portion of the paraboloid $z = x^2 + y^2$ that lies below the plane $z = 16$.

28. Find the center of mass of the lamina whose shape is the region inside the circle $x^2 + y^2 = 4$ in the first quadrant, given that the density at any point (x, y) is $\delta(x, y) = x + y$. *Hint:* Reverse the order of integration.

29. A force field $\mathbf{F}(x, y) = (x - 2y)\mathbf{i} + (y - 2x)\mathbf{j}$ acts on an object moving in the plane. Show that $\mathbf{F}$ is conservative, and find a scalar potential for $\mathbf{F}$. How much work is done as the object moves from $(1, 0)$ to $(0, 1)$ along any path connecting these points?

30. A particle of weight w is acted on only by the constant gravitational force $\mathbf{F} = -w\mathbf{k}$. How much work is done in moving the weight along the helical path given by $x = \cos t, y = \sin t, z = t$ for $0 \le t \le 2\pi$?

APPENDICES

APPENDIX A Theorems by Chapter

CHAPTER 1

THEOREM 1.1 **Distance between two points in the plane**
The distance d between the points $P(x_1, y_1)$ and (x_2, y_2) in the plane is given by

$$d = \sqrt{(\Delta x)^2 + (\Delta y)^2}$$

THEOREM 1.2 **Slope criterion for parallel and perpendicular lines**
If ℓ_1 and ℓ_2 are nonvertical lines with slopes m_1 and m_2, then

ℓ_1 and ℓ_2 are **parallel** if and only if $m_1 = m_2$.

ℓ_1 and ℓ_2 are **perpendicular** if and only if $m_1 m_2 = -1$ or $m_1 = -\dfrac{1}{m_2}$.

THEOREM 1.3 **Limits of trigonometric functions**
If c is any number in the domain of the given trigonometric function, then

$$\lim_{x \to c} \cos x = \cos c \qquad \lim_{x \to c} \sec x = \sec c$$

$$\lim_{x \to c} \sin x = \sin c \qquad \lim_{x \to c} \csc x = \csc c$$

$$\lim_{x \to c} \tan x = \tan c \qquad \lim_{x \to c} \cot x = \cot c$$

THEOREM 1.4 **Continuity theorems**
If f is a polynomial, or a rational function, a power function, or a trigonometric function then, f is continuous at any number $x = c$ for which $f(c)$ is defined.

THEOREM 1.5 **Properties of continuous functions**
If s is a real number (called a *scalar*) and f and g are functions which are continuous at $x = c$, then the following functions are also continuous at $x = c$.

Scalar multiple	sf	
Sum and difference	$f + g$ and $f - g$	
Product	fg	
Quotient	$\dfrac{f}{g}$	provided $g(c) \neq 0$
Composition	$f \circ g$	provided f is continuous at $g(c)$

THEOREM 1.6   **The intermediate value theorem**

If f is a continuous function on the closed interval $[a, b]$ and L is any number between $f(a)$ and $f(b)$, then there exists at least one number c on (a, b) such that $f(c) = L$.

THEOREM 1.7   **Root location theorem**

If f is continuous on the closed interval $[a, b]$ and if $f(a)$ and $f(b)$ have opposite algebraic signs, then $f(c) = 0$ for at least one number c on (a, b).

THEOREM 1.8   **Limit limitation theorem**

Suppose $\lim\limits_{x \to c} f(x)$ exists and $f(x) \geq 0$ throughout an open interval containing the number c, except possibly at c itself. Then

$$\lim_{x \to c} f(x) \geq 0$$

THEOREM 1.9   **The squeeze theorem**

If $g(x) \leq f(x) \leq h(x)$ for all x in an open interval containing c (except possibly at c itself) and if

$$\lim_{x \to c} g(x) = \lim_{x \to c} h(x) = L$$

then $\lim\limits_{x \to c} f(x) = L$.

CHAPTER 2

THEOREM 2.1   **Equation of a line tangent to a curve at a point**

If f is a differentiable function at x_0, the graph of $y = f(x_0)$ has a tangent line at the point $P(x, f(x_0))$ with slope $f'(x)$ and equation

$$y = f'(x_0)(x - x_0) + f(x_0)$$

THEOREM 2.2   **Differentiability implies continuity**

If a function f is differentiable at c, then it is also continuous at $x = c$.

THEOREM 2.3   **Constant rule**

A constant function $f(x) = k$ has a derivative $f'(x) = 0$; that is, in Leibniz notation

$$\frac{d}{dx}(k) = 0$$

THEOREM 2.4   **Power rule**

For any real number n, the power function $f(x) = x^n$ has the derivative $f'(x) = nx^{n-1}$; that is, in Leibniz notation

$$\frac{d}{dx}(x^n) = nx^{n-1}$$

THEOREM 2.5   **Basic rules for combining derivatives—Procedural forms**

If f and g are differentiable functions at x and a, b, and c are any real numbers, then so are the functions cf, $f + g$, fg, and f/g (for $g(x) \neq 0$), and their derivatives satisfy the following formulas:

Name of Rule	Prime Notation	Function Notation	Leibniz Notation
Constant multiple	$(cf)' = cf'$	$[cf(x)]' = cf'(x)$	$\dfrac{d}{dx}(cf) = c\dfrac{df}{dx}$
Sum rule	$(f + g)' = f' + g'$	$[f(x) + g(x)]' = f'(x) + g'(x)$	$\dfrac{d}{dx}(f + g) = \dfrac{df}{dx} + \dfrac{dg}{dx}$
Difference rule	$(f - g)' = f' - g'$	$[f(x) - g(x)]' = f'(x) - g'(x)]$	$\dfrac{d}{dx}(f - g) = \dfrac{df}{dx} - \dfrac{dg}{dx}$

The constant multiple, sum, and difference rules can be combined into a single rule called the *linearity rule.*

Name of Rule	Prime Notation	Function Notation	Leibniz Notation
Linearity rule	$(af + bg)' = af' + bg'$	$[af(x) + bg(x)]' = af'(x) + bg'(x)$	$\dfrac{d}{dx}(af + bg) = a\dfrac{df}{dx} + b\dfrac{dg}{dx}$
Product rule	$(fg)' = fg' + f'g$	$[f(x)g(x)]' = f(x)g'(x) + f'(x)g(x)$	$\dfrac{d}{dx}(fg) = f\dfrac{dg}{dx} + g\dfrac{df}{dx}$
Quotient rule	$\left(\dfrac{f}{g}\right)' = \dfrac{gf' - fg'}{g^2}$	$\left[\dfrac{f(x)}{g(x)}\right]' = \dfrac{g(x)f'(x) - f(x)g'(x)}{[g(x)]^2}$	$\dfrac{d}{dx}\left(\dfrac{f}{g}\right) = \dfrac{g\dfrac{df}{dx} - f\dfrac{dg}{dx}}{g^2}$

Corollary to THEOREM 2.5   **The extended linearity rule**

If $f_1, f_2, \ldots, f_2$ are differentiable functions and $a_1, a_2, \ldots, a_n$ are constants, then

$$\frac{d}{dx}[a_1 f_1 + a_2 f_2 + \cdots + a_n f_n] = a_1 \frac{df_1}{dx} + a_2 \frac{df_2}{dx} + \cdots + a_n \frac{df_n}{dx}$$

THEOREM 2.6   **Special limit theorems for the sine and cosine**

$$\lim_{h \to 0} \frac{\sin h}{h} = 1 \qquad \lim_{h \to 0} \frac{\cos h - 1}{h} = 0$$

THEOREM 2.7   **Derivatives of the cosine and sine functions**

The functions $\cos x$ and $\sin x$ are differentiable for all x and

$$\frac{d}{dx}\sin x = \cos x \qquad \frac{d}{dx}\cos x = -\sin x$$

THEOREM 2.8   **Derivatives of the trigonometric functions**

The six basic trigonometric functions, $\cos x, \sin x, \tan x, \sec x, \csc x,$ and $\cot x$, are all differentiable wherever they are defined and

$$\frac{d}{dx}\sin x = \cos x \qquad \frac{d}{dx}\cos x = -\sin x$$

$$\frac{d}{dx}\tan x = \sec^2 x \qquad \frac{d}{dx}\cot x = -\csc^2 x$$

$$\frac{d}{dx}\sec x = \sec x \tan x \qquad \frac{d}{dx}\csc x = -\csc x \cot x$$

THEOREM 2.9   **Chain rule**

If $y = f(u)$ is a differentiable function of u and $u = g(x)$ is a differentiable function of x, then $y = f[g(x)]$ is a differentiable function of x and

$$\frac{dy}{dx} = \frac{dy}{du}\frac{du}{dx}$$

THEOREM 2.9a   **The chain rule (alternate form)**

If u is differentiable at x and f is differentiable at $u(x)$, then the composite function $f \circ u$ is differentiable at x and

$$(f \circ u)'(x) = f'(u)u'(x) \quad \text{or} \quad \frac{d}{dx} f[u(x)] = f(u)\frac{du}{dx}$$

THEOREM 2.10   **Power rule for rational exponents**

If $n = \dfrac{p}{q}$ is a rational number, then $\dfrac{d}{dx}(x^n) = nx^{n-1}$.

THEOREM 2.11   **The Newton–Raphson method**

To approximate a root of the equation $f(x) = 0$, start with a preliminary estimate x_0 and generate a sequence of increasingly accurate approximations $x_1, x_2, x_3, \ldots$ using the formula

$$x_{n+1} = x_n - \frac{f(x_n)}{f'(x_n)} \qquad f(x_n) \neq 0$$

This sequence of approximations will either approach a limit that is a root of the equation or the sequence does not have a limit.

CHAPTER 3

THEOREM 3.1   **The extreme value theorem**

A continuous function f on a closed, bounded interval $[a, b]$ has an absolute maximum and an absolute minimum.

THEOREM 3.2   **Critical value theorem**

If a continuous function f has a relative extremum at c, then c must be a critical value of f.

THEOREM 3.3   **Rolle's theorem**

Suppose f is continuous on the closed interval $[a, b]$ and differentiable on the open interval (a, b). Then, if $f(a) = f(b)$, there exists a number c between a and b such that $f'(c) = 0$.

THEOREM 3.4   **The mean value theorem (MVT) for derivatives**

If f is continuous on the closed interval $[a, b]$ and differentiable on the open interval (a, b), then there exists at least one number c such that

$$\frac{f(b) - f(a)}{b - a} = f'(c) \qquad \text{for } a < c < b$$

THEOREM 3.5   **Zero derivative theorem**

Suppose f is a continuous function on the closed interval $[a, b]$ and differentiable on the open interval (a, b). Then if $f'(x) = 0$ for all x in (a, b), the function f is constant on $[a, b]$.

THEOREM 3.6   **Constant difference theorem**

Suppose the functions f and g are continuous on the closed interval $[a, b]$ and differentiable on the open interval (a, b). Then if $f'(x) = g'(x)$ on (a, b), there exists a constant C such that $f(x) = g(x) + C$ for all x on $[a, b]$.

THEOREM 3.7   **Increasing and decreasing function theorem**

Let f be differentiable on the open interval (a, b). Then the function f is strictly increasing on (a, b) if

$$f'(x) > 0 \text{ for } a < x < b$$

and, f is strictly decreasing on (a, b) if

$$f'(x) < 0 \text{ for } a < x < b$$

THEOREM 3.8   **Limits to infinity**

If n is a positive rational number, and A is any nonzero real number, then

$$\lim_{x \to +\infty} \frac{A}{x^n} = 0$$

Furthermore, if x^n is defined when $x < 0$, then

$$\lim_{x \to -\infty} \frac{A}{x^n}$$

THEOREM 3.9   **l'Hôpital's rule**

Let f and g be differentiable functions on an open interval containing c (except possibly at c itself). If

$$\lim_{x \to c} \frac{f(x)}{g(x)} \text{ produces an indeterminate form } \frac{0}{0} \text{ or } \frac{\infty}{\infty}, \text{ then}$$

$$\lim_{x \to c} \frac{f(x)}{g(x)} = \lim_{x \to c} \frac{f'(x)}{g'(x)}$$

provided the limit on the right side exists (or is infinite).

THEOREM 3.10   **Antiderivatives differ by a constant**

If F is an antiderivative of the continuous function f, then any other antiderivative of f must have the form

$$G(x) = F(x) + C$$

THEOREM 3.11   **Basic integration rules**

PROCEDURAL RULES	Differentiation Formulas	Integration Formulas
Constant multiple	$\frac{d}{du}(cf) = c\frac{df}{du}$	$\int cf(u)\,du = c\int f(u)\,du$
Sum rule	$\frac{d}{du}(f + g) = \frac{df}{du} + \frac{dg}{du}$	$\int [f(u) + g(u)]\,du = \int f(u)\,du + \int g(u)\,du$
Difference rule	$\frac{d}{du}(f - g) = \frac{df}{du} - \frac{dg}{du}$	$\int [f(u) - g(u)]\,du = \int f(u)\,du - \int g(u)\,du$
Linearity rule	$\frac{d}{du}(af + bg) = a\frac{df}{du} + b\frac{dg}{du}$	$\int [af(u) + bg(u)]\,du = a\int f(u)\,du + b\int g(u)\,du$

Constant rule	$\dfrac{d}{du}(c) = 0$	$\displaystyle\int 0 \, du = c$
Power rule	$\dfrac{d}{du}(u^n) = nu^{n-1}$	$\displaystyle\int u^n \, du = \dfrac{u^{n+1}}{n+1} + C; \quad n \neq -1$
Trigonometric rules	$\dfrac{d}{du}(\cos u) = -\sin u$	$\displaystyle\int \sin u \, du = -\cos u + C$
	$\dfrac{d}{du}(\sin u) = \cos u$	$\displaystyle\int \cos u \, du = \sin u + C$
	$\dfrac{d}{du}(\tan u) = \sec^2 u$	$\displaystyle\int \sec^2 u \, du = \tan u + C$
	$\dfrac{d}{du}(\csc u) = -\csc u \cot u$	$\displaystyle\int \csc u \cot u \, du = -\csc u + C$
	$\dfrac{d}{du}(\cot u) = -\csc^2 u$	$\displaystyle\int \csc^2 u \, du = -\cot u + C$

CHAPTER 4

THEOREM 4.1   **Basic rules and formulas for sums**
For any numbers c and d, and positive integers k, m, and n:

1. **Constant term rule** $\displaystyle\sum_{k=1}^{n} c = \underbrace{c + c + \cdots + c}_{n \text{ terms}} = nc$

2. **Sum rule** $\displaystyle\sum_{k=1}^{n} (a_k + b_k) = \sum_{k=1}^{n} a_k + \sum_{k=1}^{n} b_k$

3. **Scalar multiple rule** $\displaystyle\sum_{k=1}^{n} ca_k = c \sum_{k=1}^{n} a_k$

4. **Linearity rule** $\displaystyle\sum_{k=1}^{n} (ca_k + db_k) = c \sum_{k=1}^{n} a_k + d \sum_{k=1}^{n} b_k$

5. **Subtotal rule**   If $1 < m < n$, then

   $\displaystyle\sum_{k=1}^{n} a_k = \sum_{k=1}^{m} a_k + \sum_{k=m+1}^{n} a_k$

6. **Dominance rule**   If $a_k \leq b_k$ for $k = 1, 2, \ldots, n$, then

   $\displaystyle\sum_{k=1}^{n} a_k \leq \sum_{k=1}^{n} b_k$

THEOREM 4.2   **Existence of Riemann sum**
If f is continuous on an interval $[a, b]$, then f is integrable on $[a, b]$.

THEOREM 4.3   **General properties of the definite integral**

Linearity rule   If f and g are integrable on $[a, b]$, then so is $rf + sg$ for constants r, s.

$$\int_{a}^{b} [rf(x) + sg(x)] \, dx = r \int_{a}^{b} f(x) \, dx + s \int_{a}^{b} g(x) \, dx$$

Dominance rule   If f and g are integrable on $[a, b]$ and $f(x) \le g(x)$ throughout this interval, then

$$\int_a^b f(x)\, dx \le \int_a^b g(x)\, dx$$

Subdivision rule   For any number c such that $a < c < b$

$$\int_a^b f(x)\, dx = \int_a^c f(x)\, dx + \int_c^b f(x)\, dx$$

assuming all three integrals exist.

THEOREM 4.4   **The fundamental theorem of calculus**

If f is continuous on the interval $[a, b]$ and F is any function that satisfies $F'(x) = f(x)$ throughout this interval, then

$$\int_a^b f(x)\, dx = F(b) - F(a)$$

THEOREM 4.5   **Integration by substitution**

Let f, g, and u be differentiable functions of x such that

$$f(x) = g(u)\frac{du}{dx}$$

Then

$$\int f(x)\, dx = \int g(u)\frac{du}{dx}\, dx = G(u) + C$$

for G an antiderivative of g.

THEOREM 4.6   **Substitution with the definite integral**

Suppose f is continuous on the set of values taken on by g. If g' is continuous on $[a, b]$ and if f has an antiderivative on that interval, then

$$\int_a^b f[g(x)]g'(x)\, dx = \int_{g(a)}^{g(b)} f(u)\, du \qquad u = g(x), \quad du = g'(x)\, dx$$

provided these integrals exist.

THEOREM 4.7   **The mean value theorem for integrals**

If f is continuous on the interval $[a, b]$, there is at least one number c between a and b such that

$$\int_a^b f(x)\, dx = f(c)(b - a)$$

THEOREM 4.8   **Second fundamental theorem of calculus**

Let $f(t)$ be continuous on the interval $[a, b]$ and define the function G by the integral equation

$$G(x) = \int_a^x f(t)\, dt$$

for $a \le x \le b$. Then G is an antiderivative of f on $[a, b]$; that is,

$$G'(x) = \frac{d}{dx}\left[\int_a^x f(t)\, dt\right] = f(x)$$

over $[a, b]$.

THEOREM 4.9   Leibniz's rule

If $u(x)$ and $v(x)$ are differentiable functions of x, then

$$\frac{d}{dx}\left[\int_{v(x)}^{u(x)} f(t)\,dt\right] = f(u)\frac{du}{dx} - f(v)\frac{dv}{dx}$$

THEOREM 4.10   Error in the trapezoidal and Simpson's rules

If f has a continuous second derivative on $[a, b]$, then the error E_n in approximating $\int_a^b f(x)\,dx$ by the trapezoidal rule is

Trapezoidal error: $|E_n| \leq \dfrac{(b-a)^3}{12n^2}M$ *Where M is the maximum value of* $|f''(x)|$ *on* $[a, b]$

Moreover, if f has a continuous fourth derivative on $[a, b]$, then the error E_n in approximating $\int_a^b f(x)\,dx$ by Simpson's rule is

Simpson's error: $|E_n| \leq \dfrac{(b-a)^5}{180n^4}K$ *Where K is the maximum value of* $|f^{(4)}(x)|$ *on* $[a, b]$

CHAPTER 5

THEOREM 5.1   Bracketing theorem for exponents

Suppose b is a real number greater than 1. Then for any real number x there is a unique real number b^x. Moreover, if p and q are any two rational numbers such that $p < x < q$, then

$$b^p < b^x < b^q$$

THEOREM 5.2   Properties of exponential functions

Let x, y be real numbers, and a and b positive real numbers.

Equality rule	If $x = y$ and $b^x > 0$, then $b^x = b^y$
Inequality rules	If $x > y$ and $b > 1$, then $b^x > b^y$
	If $x > y$ and $0 < b < 1$, then $b^x < b^y$
Product rule	$b^x b^y = b^{x+y}$
Quotient rule	$\dfrac{b^x}{b^y} = b^{x-y}$
Power rules	$(b^x)^y = b^{xy}$
	$(ab)^x = a^x b^x$
	$\left(\dfrac{a}{b}\right)^x = \dfrac{a^x}{b^x}$

Limits involving exponential functions   If $b > 1$,
$$\lim_{x \to -\infty} b^x = 0 \quad \text{and} \quad \lim_{x \to +\infty} b^x = +\infty$$
$$\lim_{x \to -\infty} b^{-x} = +\infty \quad \text{and} \quad \lim_{x \to +\infty} b^{-x} = 0$$

THEOREM 5.3   Existence of an inverse

Let f be a function that is continuous and strictly monotonic on an interval I. Then f^{-1} exists and is monotone on I (increasing if f is increasing and decreasing if f is decreasing).

THEOREM 5.4   **Continuity and differentiability of inverse functions**
Let f be a one-to-one function so that it possesses an inverse.
    1. If f is continuous on a domain I, then f^{-1} is continuous on its domain.
    2. If f is differentiable at c, and $f'(c) \neq 0$, then f^{-1} is differentiable at $f(c)$.

THEOREM 5.5   **Derivative of an inverse function**
Suppose f is strictly monotonic and differentiable for all x in its domain. Then
$$(f^{-1})'(x) = \frac{1}{f'[f^{-1}(x)]}$$

THEOREM 5.6   **Basic properties of logarithmic functions**
If $b > 0$ and $b \neq 1$, then

Equality rule	If $x = y$, then $\log_b x = \log_b y$
Inequality rules	If $x > y$ and $b > 1$, then $\log_b x > \log_b y$
	If $x > y$ and $0 < b < 1$, then $\log_b x < \log_b y$
Product rule	$\log_b(xy) = \log_b x + \log_b y$
Quotient rule	$\log_b\left(\dfrac{x}{y}\right) = \log_b x - \log_b y$
Power rule	$\log_b x^p = p \log_b x$ for any real number p

THEOREM 5.7   **Change-of-base theorem**
$$\log_a x = \frac{\log_b x}{\log_b a} \qquad b > 0, \, b \neq 1$$

THEOREM 5.8   **Basic properties of the natural logarithm**
    a. $\ln 1 = 0$
    b. $\ln e = 1$
    c. $e^{\ln x} = x$ for all $x > 0$
    d. $\ln e^y = y$ for all y
    e. $\log_b x = \dfrac{\ln x}{\ln b}$ for any $b > 0$ $(b \neq 1)$
    f. $b^x = e^{x \ln b}$ for any $b > 0$ $(b \neq 1)$

THEOREM 5.9   **Derivative of $\ln u$**
If $x > 0$, then $\dfrac{d}{dx}(\ln x) = \dfrac{1}{x}$.
If u is a differentiable function of x, then $\dfrac{d}{dx}(\ln u) = \dfrac{1}{u}\dfrac{du}{dx}$ for $u > 0$.

THEOREM 5.10   **Derivative of $\ln|u|$**
If $f(x) = \ln|x|$, $x \neq 0$, then $f'(x) = \dfrac{1}{x}$.
Also, if u is a differentiable function of x, then $\dfrac{d}{dx}\ln|u| = \dfrac{1}{u}\dfrac{du}{dx}$.

THEOREM 5.11   **Derivative of e^u**
$$\frac{d}{dx}(e^x) = e^x$$

If u is a differential function of x, then $\dfrac{d}{dx}(e^u) = e^u\dfrac{du}{dx}$.

THEOREM 5.12 **Derivative of an exponential with base b**

For base b ($b > 0$, $b \neq 1$),

$$\frac{d}{dx} b^x = (\ln b)b^x$$

and if u is a differentiable function of x, then

$$\frac{d}{dx} b^u = (\ln b)b^u \frac{du}{dx} \qquad \text{for all } u$$

THEOREM 5.13 **Derivative of a natural logarithm with base b**

For base b ($b > 0$, $b \neq 1$)

$$\frac{d}{dx}(\log_b x) = \frac{1}{(\ln b)\, x} \qquad \text{for all } x > 0$$

and u is a differentiable function of x, then

$$\frac{d}{dx}(\log_b u) = \frac{1}{(\ln b)\, u} \frac{du}{dx} \qquad \text{for all } u > 0$$

THEOREM 5.14 **Limits involving natural logarithms and exponentials**

If k and n are positive integers, then

$$\lim_{x \to 0^+} \frac{\ln x}{x^n} = -\infty \qquad \lim_{x \to +\infty} \frac{\ln x}{x^n} = 0$$

$$\lim_{x \to +\infty} \frac{e^{kx}}{x^n} = +\infty \qquad \lim_{x \to +\infty} x^n e^{-kx} = 0$$

THEOREM 5.15 **Integration of e^x**

$$\int e^x \, dx = e^x + C$$

THEOREM 5.16 **Integration of $1/x$**

$$\int \frac{1}{x} \, dx = \ln|x| + C$$

THEOREM 5.17 **Integral of tangent and cotangent**

$$\int \tan x \, dx = -\ln|\cos x| + C \quad \text{and} \quad \int \cot x \, dx = \ln|\sin x| + C$$

THEOREM 5.18 **Differentiation formulas for six inverse trigonometric functions**

If u is a differentiable function of x, then

$$\frac{d}{dx}(\sin^{-1} u) = \frac{1}{\sqrt{1 - u^2}} \frac{du}{dx} \qquad \frac{d}{dx}(\cos^{-1} u) = \frac{-1}{\sqrt{1 - u^2}} \frac{du}{dx}$$

$$\frac{d}{dx}(\tan^{-1} u) = \frac{1}{1 + u^2} \frac{du}{dx} \qquad \frac{d}{dx}(\cot^{-1} u) = \frac{-1}{1 + u^2} \frac{du}{dx}$$

$$\frac{d}{dx}(\sec^{-1} u) = \frac{1}{|u|\sqrt{u^2 - 1}} \frac{du}{dx} \qquad \frac{d}{dx}(\csc^{-1} u) = \frac{-1}{|u|\sqrt{u^2 - 1}} \frac{du}{dx}$$

THEOREM 5.19 **Integrals involving the inverse trigonometric functions**

$$\int \frac{dx}{\sqrt{1 - x^2}} = \sin^{-1} x + C \qquad \text{for } |x| < 1$$

$$\int \frac{dx}{1 + x^2} = \tan^{-1} x + C \qquad \text{for all } x$$

$$\int \frac{dx}{x\sqrt{x^2 - 1}} = \sec^{-1} x + C \qquad \text{for } |x| > 1$$

THEOREM 5.20   **Properties of the logarithm as defined by $\ln x = \int_1^x \dfrac{dt}{t}$**

Let $x > 0$ and $y > 0$ be positive numbers. Then

    a. $\ln 1 = 0$

    b. $\ln xy = \ln x + \ln y$

    c. $\ln \dfrac{x}{y} = \ln x - \ln y$

    d. $\ln x^p = p \ln x$ for all rational numbers p

THEOREM 5.21   **Properties of the exponential as defined by $E(x)$**
For any numbers x and y,

    a. $E(x + y) = E(x)E(y)$

    b. $E(x - y) = \dfrac{E(x)}{E(y)}$

    c. $[E(x)]^p = E(px)$

THEOREM 5.22   **Derivative of $E(x)$**
The function defined by $E(x)$ is differentiable and

$$\frac{dE}{dx} = E(x)$$

CHAPTER 6

THEOREM 6.1   **Volume theorem of Pappus**
The solid generated by revolving a region R about a line outside its boundary (but in the same plane) has volume $V = As$, where A is the area of R and s is the distance traveled by the centroid of R.

THEOREM 6.2   **General solution of a first-order linear differential equation**
The general solution of the first-order linear differential equation

$$\frac{dy}{dx} + yP(x) = Q(x)$$

is given by

$$y = \frac{1}{I(x)}\left[\int Q(x)\,I(x)\,dx + C\right]$$

where $I(x)$ is the integrating factor $I(x) = e^{\int P(x)dx}$.

CHAPTER 7

THEOREM 7.1   **Properties of the hyperbolic functions**
$$\cosh^2 x - \sinh^2 x = 1$$

$$\sinh(-x) = -\sinh x \qquad \text{(sinh is odd)}$$
$$\cosh(-x) = \cosh x \qquad \text{(cosh is even)}$$
$$\tanh(-x) = -\tanh x \qquad \text{(tanh is odd)}$$
$$\sinh(x + y) = \sinh x \cosh y + \cosh x \sinh y$$
$$\cosh(x + y) = \cosh x \cosh y + \sinh x \sinh y$$

THEOREM 7.2   Rules for differentiating hyperbolic functions
Let u be a differentiable function of x. Then

$$\frac{d}{dx}(\sinh u) = \cosh u\, \frac{du}{dx} \qquad \frac{d}{dx}(\cosh u) = \sinh u\, \frac{du}{dx}$$

$$\frac{d}{dx}(\tanh u) = \text{sech}^2 u\, \frac{du}{dx} \qquad \frac{d}{dx}(\coth u) = -\text{csch}^2 u\, \frac{du}{dx}$$

$$\frac{d}{dx}(\text{sech}\, u) = -\text{sech}\, u \tanh u\, \frac{du}{dx} \qquad \frac{d}{dx}(\text{csch}\, u) = -\text{csch}\, u \coth u\, \frac{du}{dx}$$

THEOREM 7.3   Integration formulas involving the hyperbolic functions

$$\int \sinh x\, dx = \cosh x + C \qquad \int \cosh x\, dx = \sinh x + C$$

$$\int \text{sech}^2 x\, dx = \tanh x + C \qquad \int \text{csch}^2 x\, dx = -\coth x + C$$

$$\int \text{sech}\, x \tanh x\, dx = -\text{sech}\, x + C \qquad \int \text{csch}\, x \coth x\, dx = -\text{csch}\, x + C$$

THEOREM 7.4   Logarithmic formulas for inverse hyperbolic functions

$$\sinh^{-1}x = \ln(x + \sqrt{x^2 + 1}),\ \text{all } x \qquad \text{csch}^{-1}x = \ln\left(\frac{1}{x} + \frac{\sqrt{1 + x^2}}{|x|}\right),\quad x \neq 0$$

$$\cosh^{-1}x = \ln(x + \sqrt{x^2 - 1}),\quad x \geq 1 \qquad \text{sech}^{-1}x = \ln\left(\frac{1 + \sqrt{1 - x^2}}{x}\right),\quad 0 < x \leq 1$$

$$\tanh^{-1}x = \frac{1}{2}\ln\frac{1 + x}{1 - x},\quad |x| < 1 \qquad \coth^{-1}x = \frac{1}{2}\ln\frac{x + 1}{x - 1},\quad |x| > 1$$

THEOREM 7.5   Differentiation and integration formulas for the inverse hyperbolic functions

$$\frac{d}{dx}(\sinh^{-1}u) = \frac{1}{\sqrt{1 + u^2}}\frac{du}{dx} \qquad\qquad \int \frac{du}{\sqrt{1 + u^2}} = \sinh^{-1}u + C$$

$$\frac{d}{dx}(\cosh^{-1}u) = \frac{1}{\sqrt{u^2 - 1}}\frac{du}{dx},\quad \text{if } u > 1 \qquad \int \frac{du}{\sqrt{u^2 - 1}} = \cosh^{-1}u + C$$

$$\frac{d}{dx}(\tanh^{-1}u) = \frac{1}{1 - u^2}\frac{du}{dx},\quad \text{if } |u| < 1 \qquad \int \frac{du}{1 - u^2} = \tanh^{-1}u + C,\quad \text{if } |u| < 1$$

$$\frac{d}{dx}(\text{csch}^{-1}u) = \frac{-1}{|u|\sqrt{1 + u^2}}\frac{du}{dx} \qquad\qquad \int \frac{du}{u\sqrt{1 + u^2}} = -\text{csch}^{-1}|u| + C$$

$$\frac{d}{dx}(\text{sech}^{-1}u) = \frac{-1}{u\sqrt{1 - u^2}}\frac{du}{dx},\quad \text{if } 0 < u < 1 \qquad \int \frac{du}{u\sqrt{1 - u^2}} = -\text{sech}^{-1}u + C$$

$$\frac{d}{dx}(\coth^{-1}u) = \frac{1}{1 - u^2}\frac{du}{dx},\quad \text{if } |u| < 1 \qquad \int \frac{du}{1 - u^2} = \coth^{-1}u + C,\quad \text{if } |u| > 1$$

CHAPTER 8

THEOREM 8.1   Limit theorem for sequences
If $\lim\limits_{n\to\infty} a_n = L$ and $\lim\limits_{n\to\infty} b_n = M$, then the following limits exist and:

Linearity rule $\lim\limits_{n\to\infty}(ra_n + sb_n) = rL + sM$

Product rule $\lim\limits_{n\to\infty}(a_n b_n) = LM$

Quotient rule $\lim\limits_{n\to\infty} \dfrac{a_n}{b_n} = \dfrac{L}{M}$ provided $M \neq 0$

Root rule $\lim\limits_{n\to\infty} \sqrt[m]{a_n} = \sqrt[m]{L}$ provided $\sqrt[m]{a_n}$ is defined
for all n and $\sqrt[m]{L}$ exists

THEOREM 8.2   **Limit of a sequence**
Suppose f is a function such that $a_n = f(n)$ for $n = 1, 2, \ldots$. If $\lim\limits_{n\to\infty} f(x)$ exists and $\lim\limits_{n\to\infty} f(x) = L$, the sequence $\{a_n\}$ converges and $\lim\limits_{n\to\infty} a_n = L$.

THEOREM 8.3   **Squeeze theorem for sequences**
If $a_n \leq b_n \leq c_n$ for all $n > N$, and $\lim\limits_{n\to\infty} a_n = \lim\limits_{n\to\infty} c_n = L$, then $\lim\limits_{n\to\infty} b_n = L$

THEOREM 8.4   **BMCT; the bounded, monotonic, convergence theorem**
A monotone sequence $\{a_n\}$ converges if it is bounded and diverges otherwise.

THEOREM 8.5   **Convergence of a power sequence**
If r is a number such that $|r| < 1$, then $\lim\limits_{n\to\infty} r^n = 0$.

THEOREM 8.6   **Linearity of infinite series**
If Σa_k and Σb_k are convergent series, then so is $\Sigma(ca_k + db_k)$ for constants c, d, and
$$\Sigma(ca_k + db_k) = c\,\Sigma a_k + d\,\Sigma b_k$$

THEOREM 8.7   **Divergence of the sum of a convergent and a divergent series**
If either $\Sigma\, a_k$ or $\Sigma\, b_k$ diverges and the other converges, then the series $\Sigma\,(a_k + b_k)$ must diverge.

THEOREM 8.8   **Geometric series theorem**
The geometric series $\sum\limits_{k=0}^{\infty} ar^k$ with $a \neq 0$ diverges if $|r| \geq 1$ and converges if $|r| < 1$ with sum
$$\sum_{k=0}^{\infty} ar^k = \frac{a}{1-r}$$

THEOREM 8.9   **The divergence test**
If the series Σa_k converges, then the sequence $\{a_n\}$ converges and $\lim\limits_{n\to\infty} a_k = 0$. Thus, if $\lim\limits_{n\to\infty} a_k \neq 0$, then the series $\Sigma\, a_k$ must diverge.

THEOREM 8.10   **Convergence criterion for nonnegative terms**
A series $\Sigma\, a_k$ with $a_k \geq 0$ for all k converges if its sequence of partial sums is bounded from above and diverges otherwise.

THEOREM 8.11   **The integral test**
If $a_k = f(k)$ for $k = 1, 2, \ldots$ where f is positive, continuous, and decreasing for $x \geq 1$, then
$$\sum_{k=1}^{\infty} a_k \quad \text{and} \quad \int_1^{\infty} f(x)\, dx$$
either both converge or both diverge.

THEOREM 8.12   **The *p*-series test**

The *p*-series $\sum\limits_{k=1}^{\infty} \frac{1}{k^p}$ converges if $p > 1$ and diverges if $p \leq 1$.

THEOREM 8.13   **Direct comparison test**

Let $0 \leq a_k \leq c_k$ for all $k \geq N$ for some N.

If $\sum\limits_{k=1}^{\infty} c_k$ converges, then $\sum\limits_{k=1}^{\infty} a_k$ also converges.

Let $0 \leq d_k \leq a_k$ for all k.

If $\sum\limits_{k=1}^{\infty} d_k$ diverges, then $\sum\limits_{k=1}^{\infty} a_k$ also diverges.

THEOREM 8.14   **Limit comparison test**

Suppose $a_k > 0$ and $b_k > 0$ for all sufficiently large k and that

$$\lim_{k \to \infty} \frac{a_k}{b_k} = L$$

where L is finite and positive ($0 < L < \infty$). Then Σa_k and Σb_k either both converge or both diverge.

THEOREM 8.15   **The zero-infinity limit comparison test**

Suppose $a_k > 0$ and $b_k > 0$ for all sufficiently large k. Then

If $\lim\limits_{k \to \infty} \frac{a_k}{b_k} = 0$ and Σb_k converges, the series Σa_k converges.

If $\lim\limits_{k \to \infty} \frac{a_k}{b_k} = \infty$ and Σb_k diverges, the series Σa_k diverges.

THEOREM 8.16   **The ratio test**

Given the series Σa_k with $a_k > 0$ and suppose that $\lim\limits_{k \to \infty} \frac{a_{k+1}}{a_k} = L$

The **ratio test** states the following:

If $L < 1$, then Σa_k converges.
If $L > 1$ or if L is infinite, then Σa_k diverges.
If $L = 1$, the ratio test is inconclusive.

THEOREM 8.17   **The root test**

Given the series Σa_k with $a_k \geq 0$ and suppose that $\lim\limits_{k \to \infty} \sqrt[k]{a_k} = L$.
The **root test** states the following:
If $L < 1$, then Σa_k converges.
If $L > 1$ or if L is infinite, then Σa_k diverges.
If $L = 1$, the ratio test is inconclusive.

THEOREM 8.18   **Alternating series test**

If $a_k > 0$, then the alternating series

$$\sum_{k=1}^{\infty} (-1)^k a_k \quad \text{and} \quad \sum_{k=1}^{\infty}(-1)^{k+1} a_k$$

converge if both of the following conditions are satisfied:
   1. $\lim\limits_{k \to \infty} a_k = 0$.
   2. $\{a_k\}$ is a decreasing sequence; that is, $a_{k+1} < a_k$ for all k.

THEOREM 8.19   **The error estimate for an alternating series**
Suppose the alternating series

$$\sum_{k=1}^{\infty} (-1)^k a_k \quad \text{and} \quad \sum_{k=1}^{\infty} (-1)^{k+1} a_k$$

satisfy the conditions of the alternating series test, namely,

$$\lim_{k \to \infty} a_k = 0 \quad \text{and} \quad \{a_k\} \text{ is a decreasing sequence} \quad (a_{k+1} < a_k)$$

If the series has sum S, then

$$|S - S_n| < a_{n+1}$$

where S_n is the nth partial sum of the series.

THEOREM 8.20   **The absolute convergence test**
A series of real numbers Σa_k must converge if the related absolute value series $\Sigma |a_k|$ converges.

THEOREM 8.21   **The generalized ratio test**
Suppose $a_k \neq 0$ for $k \geq 1$ and that

$$\sum_{k=1}^{\infty} \left| \frac{a_{k+1}}{a_k} \right| = L$$

where L is a real number or ∞. Then

If $L < 1$, the series Σa_k converges absolutely and hence converges.
If $L > 1$ or if L is infinite the series Σa_k diverges.
If $L = 1$, the test fails.

THEOREM 8.22   **Convergence of a power series**

For a power series $\sum_{k=1}^{\infty} a_k x^k$, exactly one of the following is true:

1. The series converges for all x.
2. The series converges only for $x = 0$.
3. The series converges absolutely for all x in an open interval $(-R, R)$ and diverges for $|x| > R$.

The series should be checked separately at the endpoints, because it could converge absolutely, or converge conditionally, or diverge at $x = R$ and $x = -R$.

THEOREM 8.23   **The convergence set of a power series**
Let $\Sigma a_k u^k$ be a power series, and let

$$L = \lim_{k \to \infty} \left| \frac{a_{k+1}}{a_k} \right|$$

Then   If $L = \infty$, the power series converges only at $u = 0$.
If $L = 0$, the power series converges for all real u.
If $0 < L < \infty$, let $R = 1/L$. Then the power series converges absolutely for $|u| < R$ (or $-R < u < R$) and diverges for $|u| > R$. It may either converge or diverge at the endpoints $u = -R$ and $u = R$.

THEOREM 8.24   **Root test for the radius of convergence**
Let $\Sigma a_k u^k$ be a power series, and let

$$L = \lim_{k \to \infty} {}^k\sqrt{|a_k|}$$

Then   If $L = \infty$, the power series converges only at 0.
If $L = 0$, the power series converges for all real u.
If $0 < L < \infty$, let $R = 1/L$. Then the power series converges absolutely for $|u| < R$ and diverges for $|u| > R$. It may either converge or diverge at the endpoints $u = -R$ and $u = R$.

THEOREM 8.25   **Term-by-term differentiation and integration of a power series**

A power series $\sum\limits_{k=0}^{\infty} a_k u^k$ with radius of convergence $R > 0$ can be differentiated or integrated term by term on its interval of absolute convergence. More specifically, if $f(u) = \sum\limits_{k=0}^{\infty} a_k u^k$ for $|u| < R$, then for $|u| < R$ we have

$$f'(u) = \sum_{k=1}^{\infty} k a_k u^{k-1} = a_1 + 2a_2 u + 3a_3 u^2 + 4a_4 u^3 + \cdots$$

$$\int_0^x f(u)\, du = \int_0^x \left(\sum_{k=0}^{\infty} a_k u^k \right) du = \sum_{k=0}^{\infty} \left(\int_0^x a_k u^k\, du \right) = \sum_{k=0}^{\infty} \frac{a_k}{k+1} u^{k+1}$$

THEOREM 8.26   **The uniqueness theorem for power series representation**
Suppose a function f is known to have the power series representation

$$f(x) = \sum_{k=0}^{\infty} a_k (x - c)^k$$

for $-R < x - c < R$. Then there is exactly one such representation, and the coefficients a_k must satisfy

$$a_k = \frac{f^{(k)}(c)}{k!}$$

for $k = 0, 1, 2, \ldots$.

THEOREM 8.27   **Taylor's theorem**
If f and all its derivatives exist in an open interval I containing c, then for each x in I

$$f(x) = f(c) + \frac{f'(c)}{1!}(x - c) + \frac{f''(c)}{2!}(x - c)^2 + \cdots + \frac{f^{(n)}(c)}{n!}(x - c) + R_n(x)$$

where the remainder function $R_n(x)$ is given by

$$R_n(x) = \frac{f^{(n+1)}(z_n)}{(n + 1)!}(x - c)^{n+1}$$

for some z_n that depends on x and lies between c and x.

THEOREM 8.28   **Binomial series theorem**
The binomial function $(1 + x)^p$ is represented by its Maclaurin series

$$(1 + x)^p = 1 + px + \frac{p(p - 1)}{2!}x^2 + \frac{p(p - 1)(p - 2)}{3!}x^3 + \cdots = \sum_{k=0}^{\infty} \binom{p}{q} x^k$$

where $\binom{p}{q} = \dfrac{p!}{k!(p - q)!}$ for all x if p is a nonnegative integer; for $-1 < x < 1$ if $p \leq -1$; $-1 \leq x \leq 1$ if $p > 0$ and p is not an integer; and for $-1 < x \leq 1$ if $-1 < p < 0$.

CHAPTER 9

THEOREM 9.1   **Area in polar coordinates**

Let $r = f(\theta)$ define a polar curve, where f is continuous and $f(\theta) \geq 0$ on the closed interval $\alpha \leq \theta \leq \beta$. Then the region bounded by the curve $r = f(\theta)$ and the rays $\theta = \alpha$ and $\theta = \beta$ has area

$$A = \frac{1}{2} \int_\alpha^\beta r^2 \, dx = \frac{1}{2} \int_\alpha^\beta [f(x)]^2 \, dx$$

THEOREM 9.2   **Slope in polar coordinates**

If $f(\theta)$ is a differentiable function of θ, then the slope of the tangent line to the polar curve $r = f(\theta)$ at the point $P(r_0, \theta_0)$ is given by

$$m = \frac{f(\theta_0) \cos \theta_0 + f'(\theta_0) \sin \theta_0}{-f(\theta_0) \sin \theta_0 + f'(\theta_0) \cos \theta_0}$$

whenever the denominator is not zero.

THEOREM 9.3   **Parametric form of the derivative**

If a curve is described parametrically by the equations $x = x(t)$, $y = y(t)$, where x and y are differentiable functions of t, then the derivative $\dfrac{dy}{dx}$ can be expressed in terms of $\dfrac{dx}{dt}$ and $\dfrac{dy}{dt}$ by the equation

$$\frac{dy}{dx} = \frac{\dfrac{dy}{dt}}{\dfrac{dx}{dt}} = \frac{y'(t)}{x'(t)} = \frac{dy}{dt} \qquad \text{whenever } \frac{dx}{dt} \neq 0$$

THEOREM 9.4   **Arc length for parametric equations**

Let C be the curve described parametrically by the equations $x = x(t)$ and $y = y(t)$ on an interval $[a, b]$, where $\dfrac{dx}{dt}$ and $\dfrac{dy}{dt}$ are continuous, such that C does not intersect itself on the interval. Then C has arc length

$$L = \int_a^b \sqrt{\left(\frac{dx}{dt}\right)^2 + \left(\frac{dy}{dt}\right)^2} \, dt$$

THEOREM 9.5   **Formula for the area under a curve defined parametrically**

Suppose y is a monotone continuous function of x on the closed interval $[a, b]$ and that x and y are both functions of a parameter t, for $t_1 \leq t \leq t_2$. Then if $x'(t)$ is continuous on $[t_1, t_2]$, the area under the curve described parametrically by $x = x(t)$, $y = y(t)$ over $[t_1, t_2]$, is given by

$$A = \int_a^b y \, dx = \int_{t_1}^{t_2} y(t) \, x'(t) \, dt$$

THEOREM 9.6   **Reflection property of parabolas**

Let P be a point on a parabola in the plane, and let T be the tangent line to the parabola at P. Then the angle between T and the line through P parallel to the principal axis of the parabola equals the angle between T and the line connecting P to the focus.

CHAPTER 10

THEOREM 10.1   **Properties vector operations**

For any vectors **u**, **v**, and **w** in the plane and scalars s and t:

Commutativity of vector addition	$\mathbf{u} + \mathbf{v} = \mathbf{v} + \mathbf{u}$
Associativity of vector addition	$(\mathbf{u} + \mathbf{v}) + \mathbf{w} = \mathbf{u} + (\mathbf{v} + \mathbf{w})$
Associativity of scalar multiplication	$(st)\mathbf{u} = s(t\mathbf{u})$
Identity for addition	$\mathbf{u} + \mathbf{0} = \mathbf{u}$
Inverse property for addition	$\mathbf{u} + (-\mathbf{u}) = \mathbf{0}$
Vector distributivity	$(s + t)\mathbf{u} = s\mathbf{u} + t\mathbf{u}$
Scalar distributivity	$s(\mathbf{u} + \mathbf{v}) = s\mathbf{u} + s\mathbf{v}$

THEOREM 10.2   **Properties of the dot product**

If **u**, **v**, and **w** are vectors (in $\mathbb{R}^2$ or $\mathbb{R}^3$) and c is a scalar, then

Magnitude of a vector	$\mathbf{v} \cdot \mathbf{v} = \|\mathbf{v}\|^2$
Zero product	$\mathbf{0} \cdot \mathbf{v} = 0$
Commutativity	$\mathbf{v} \cdot \mathbf{w} = \mathbf{w} \cdot \mathbf{v}$
Associativity	$c(\mathbf{v} \cdot \mathbf{w}) = (c\mathbf{v}) \cdot \mathbf{w} = \mathbf{u} \cdot (c\mathbf{w})$
Distributivity	$\mathbf{u} \cdot (\mathbf{v} + \mathbf{w}) = \mathbf{u} \cdot \mathbf{v} + \mathbf{u} \cdot \mathbf{w}$

THEOREM 10.3   **Angle between two vectors**

If θ is the angle between the nonzero vectors **v** and **w**, then

$$\cos \theta = \frac{\mathbf{v} \cdot \mathbf{w}}{\|\mathbf{v}\| \, \|\mathbf{w}\|}$$

THEOREM 10.4   **Orthogonal vectors**

Nonzero vectors **v** and **w** are **orthogonal** if and only if

$$\mathbf{v} \cdot \mathbf{w} = 0$$

THEOREM 10.5   **Properties of the cross product**

If **u**, **v**, and **w** are vectors in $\mathbb{R}^3$ and s and t are scalars, then

Scalar distributivity	$(s\mathbf{v}) \times (t\mathbf{w}) = st(\mathbf{v} \times \mathbf{w})$
Vector distributivity	$\mathbf{u} \times (\mathbf{v} + \mathbf{w}) = (\mathbf{u} \times \mathbf{v}) + (\mathbf{u} \times \mathbf{w})$
	$(\mathbf{u} + \mathbf{v}) \times \mathbf{w} = (\mathbf{u} \times \mathbf{w}) + (\mathbf{v} \times \mathbf{w})$
Anticommutativity	$\mathbf{v} \times \mathbf{w} = -(\mathbf{w} \times \mathbf{v})$
Parallel vectors	$\mathbf{v} \times \mathbf{v} = \mathbf{0}$; in particular, if $\mathbf{w} = s\mathbf{v}$ then $\mathbf{v} \times \mathbf{w} = \mathbf{0}$
Zero product	$\mathbf{v} \times \mathbf{0} = \mathbf{0} \times \mathbf{v} = \mathbf{0}$

THEOREM 10.6   **Geometric property of cross product**

If **v** and **w** are nonzero vectors in $\mathbb{R}^3$, that are not multiples of one another, then $\mathbf{v} \times \mathbf{w}$ is orthogonal to both **v** and **w**.

THEOREM 10.7 **Magnitude of a cross product**
For $\mathbf{v}$ and $\mathbf{w}$ nonzero vectors in $\mathbb{R}^3$ with θ the angle between $\mathbf{v}$ and $\mathbf{w}$ ($0 \le \theta \le \pi$), then

$$\|\mathbf{v} \times \mathbf{w}\| = \|\mathbf{v}\| \, \|\mathbf{w}\| \sin \theta$$

THEOREM 10.8 **Determinant form for a triple scalar product: volume of a parallelepiped**
If $\mathbf{u} = a_1\mathbf{i} + a_2\mathbf{j} + a_3\mathbf{k}$, $\mathbf{v} = b_1\mathbf{i} + b_2\mathbf{j} + b_3\mathbf{k}$, and $\mathbf{w} = c_1\mathbf{i} + c_2\mathbf{j} += c_3\mathbf{k}$, then the triple scalar product can be found by evaluating the determinant

$$(\mathbf{u} \times \mathbf{v}) \cdot \mathbf{w} = \begin{vmatrix} a_1 & a_2 & a_3 \\ b_1 & b_2 & b_3 \\ c_1 & c_2 & c_3 \end{vmatrix}$$

THEOREM 10.9 **Existence of a plane**
Let A, B, C, and D be constants with A, B, and C not all zero. Then the graph of any equation with form

$$Ax + By + Cz + D = 0$$

is the equation of a plane with normal vector $\mathbf{N} = A\mathbf{i} + B\mathbf{j} + C\mathbf{k}$.

THEOREM 10.10 **Distance from a point to a plane in $\mathbb{R}^3$**
The distance from the point (x_0, y_0, z_0) to the plane $Ax + By + Cz + D = 0$ is given by

$$d = \left| \frac{Ax_0 + By_0 + Cz_0 + D}{\sqrt{A^2 + B^2 + C^2}} \right|$$

THEOREM 10.11 **Distance from a point to a line**
The shortest distance from the point P to the line L is given by the formula

$$d = \frac{\|\mathbf{v} \times \mathbf{QP}\|}{\|\mathbf{v}\|}$$

where $\mathbf{v}$ is a vector aligned with L and Q is any point on L.

CHAPTER 11

THEOREM 11.1 **Rules for vector limits**
If the vector functions $\mathbf{F}$ and $\mathbf{G}$ are functions of a real variable t and $h(t)$ is a scalar function such that all have finite limits as $t \to t_0$, then

Limit of a sum	$\lim\limits_{t \to t_0} [\mathbf{F}(t) + \mathbf{G}(t)] = \lim\limits_{t \to t_0} \mathbf{F}(t) + \lim\limits_{t \to t_0} \mathbf{G}(t)$
Limit of a difference	$\lim\limits_{t \to t_0} [\mathbf{F}(t) - \mathbf{G}(t)] = \lim\limits_{t \to t_0} \mathbf{F}(t) - \lim\limits_{t \to t_0} \mathbf{G}(t)$
Limit of a scalar multiple	$\lim\limits_{t \to t_0} [h(t)\mathbf{F}(t)] = \left[\lim\limits_{t \to t_0} h(t) \right] \left[\lim\limits_{t \to t_0} \mathbf{F}(t) \right]$
Limit of a dot product	$\lim\limits_{t \to t_0} [\mathbf{F}(t) \cdot \mathbf{G}(t)] = \left[\lim\limits_{t \to t_0} \mathbf{F}(t) \right] \cdot \left[\lim\limits_{t \to t_0} \mathbf{G}(t) \right]$
Limit of a cross product	$\lim\limits_{t \to t_0} [\mathbf{F}(t) \times \mathbf{G}(t)] = \left[\lim\limits_{t \to t_0} \mathbf{F}(t) \right] \times \left[\lim\limits_{t \to t_0} \mathbf{G}(t) \right]$

These limit formulas are also valid as $t \to +\infty$ or as $t \to -\infty$, assuming all limits exist.

THEOREM 11.2   **Derivative of a vector function**

The vector function $\mathbf{F}(t) = f_1(t)\mathbf{i} + f_2(t)\mathbf{j} + f_3(t)\mathbf{k}$ is differentiable whenever the component functions f_1, f_2, and f_3 are all differentiable, and in this case

$$\mathbf{F}'(t) = f_1'(t)\mathbf{i} + f_2'(t)\mathbf{j} + f_3'(t)\mathbf{k}$$

THEOREM 11.3   **Rules for differentiating vector functions**

If the vector functions $\mathbf{F}$ and $\mathbf{G}$ and the scalar function h are differentiable at t, then so are $a\mathbf{F} + b\mathbf{G}$, $h\mathbf{F}$, $\mathbf{F} \cdot \mathbf{G}$, and $\mathbf{F} \times \mathbf{G}$, and

Linearity rule	$(a\mathbf{F} + b\mathbf{G})'(t) = a\mathbf{F}'(t) + b\mathbf{G}'(t)$	for constants a, b
Scalar rule	$(h\mathbf{F})'(t) = h'(t)\mathbf{F}(t) + h(t)\mathbf{F}'(t)$	
Dot product rule	$(\mathbf{F} \cdot \mathbf{G})'(t) = (\mathbf{F}' \cdot \mathbf{G})(t) + (\mathbf{F} \cdot \mathbf{G}')(t)$	
Cross product rule	$(\mathbf{F} \times \mathbf{G})'(t) = (\mathbf{F}' \times \mathbf{G})(t) + (\mathbf{F} \times \mathbf{G}')(t)$	
Chain rule	$[\mathbf{F}(h(t))]' = h'(t)\mathbf{F}'(h(t))$	

THEOREM 11.4   **Orthogonality of a derivative**

If the nonzero vector function $\mathbf{F}(t)$ is differentiable and has constant length, then $\mathbf{F}(t)$ is orthogonal to the derivative vector $\mathbf{F}'(t)$.

THEOREM 11.5   **Kepler's second law**

The radius vector from the sun to a planet in its orbit sweeps over equal areas in equal intervals of time.

THEOREM 11.6   **Arc length of a space curve**

If C is a smooth curve defined by $\mathbf{R}(t) = x(t)\mathbf{i} + y(t)\mathbf{j} + z(t)\mathbf{k}$, on an interval $[a, b]$, then the arc length of C is given by

$$s = \int_a^b \|\mathbf{R}'(t)\| \, dt = \int_a^b \sqrt{[x'(t)]^2 + [y'(t)]^2 + [z'(t)]^2} \, dt$$

THEOREM 11.7   **Speed in terms of arc length**

Suppose an object moves with displacement $\mathbf{R}(t)$, where $\mathbf{R}'(t)$ is continuous. Then the object has speed

$$\|\mathbf{V}(t)\| = \|\mathbf{R}'(t)\| = \frac{ds}{dt} \quad \text{for } a \le t \le b$$

THEOREM 11.8   **Tangential and normal components of acceleration**

An object moving along a smooth curve with $\mathbf{T}' \ne \mathbf{0}$ has velocity $\mathbf{V}$ and acceleration $\mathbf{A}$, where

$$\mathbf{V} = \left(\frac{ds}{dt}\right)\mathbf{T} \quad \text{and} \quad \mathbf{A} = \left(\frac{d^2 s}{dt^2}\right)\mathbf{T} + \kappa\left(\frac{ds}{dt}\right)^2 \mathbf{N}$$

and where s is the arc length along the trajectory.

THEOREM 11.9   **Acceleration of an object with constant speed**

The acceleration of an object moving with constant speed is always orthogonal to the direction of motion.

CHAPTER 12

THEOREM 12.1   **Equality of mixed partials**

If $f(x, y)$ has mixed partial derivatives at (x_0, y_0) and the mixed partials are continuous in an open set containing (x_0, y_0), then

$$f_{yx}(x_0, y_0) = f_{xy}(x_0, y_0)$$

THEOREM 12.2   **Differentiability implies continuity**

If $f(x, y)$ is differentiable at (x_0, y_0), it is also continuous there.

THEOREM 12.3   **Sufficient condition for differentiability**

If f is a function of x and y where $f, f_x,$ and f_y are continuous in a disk D centered at (x_0, y_0), then f is differentiable at (x_0, y_0).

THEOREM 12.4   **The chain rule for one independent parameter**

Let $f(x, y)$ be a differentiable function of x and y, and let $x = x(t)$ and $y = y(t)$ be differentiable functions of t. Then $z = f(x, y)$ is a differentiable function of t, and

$$\frac{dz}{dt} = \frac{\partial z}{\partial x}\frac{dx}{dt} + \frac{\partial z}{\partial y}\frac{dy}{dt}$$

THEOREM 12.5   **The chain rule for two independent variables**

Suppose $z = f(x, y)$ is differentiable at (x, y) and that the partial derivatives of $x = x(u, v)$ and $y = y(u, v)$ exist at (u, v). Then the composite function $z = f[x(u, v), y(u, v)]$ is differentiable at (u, v) with

$$\frac{\partial z}{\partial u} = \frac{\partial z}{\partial x}\frac{\partial x}{\partial u} + \frac{\partial z}{\partial y}\frac{\partial y}{\partial u} \quad \text{and} \quad \frac{\partial z}{\partial v} = \frac{\partial z}{\partial x}\frac{\partial x}{\partial v} + \frac{\partial z}{\partial y}\frac{\partial y}{\partial v}$$

THEOREM 12.6   **Directional derivatives using partials**

A function $f(x, y)$ that is differentiable at $P_0(x_0, y_0)$ has a directional derivative at P_0 in every direction, and if $\mathbf{u} = u_1\mathbf{i} + u_2\mathbf{j}$, is a unit vector, the directional derivative in the direction given by

$$D_u f(x_0, y_0) = f_x(x_0, y_0)u_1 + f_y(x_0, y_0)u_2$$

THEOREM 12.7   **The gradient formula for the directional derivative**

If f is a differential function of x and y, then the directional derivative at the point $P_0(x_0, y_0)$ in the direction of the unit vector $\mathbf{u}$ is

$$D_u f(x, y) = \nabla f \cdot \mathbf{u}$$

THEOREM 12.8   **Basic properties of the gradient**

Let f and g be differentiable functions; then

Constant rule	$\nabla c = 0$	for any constant c
Linearity rule	$\nabla(af + bg) = a\nabla f + b\nabla g$	for constant a and b
Product rule	$\nabla(fg) = f(\nabla g) + g\nabla f$	
Quotient rule	$\nabla\left(\dfrac{f}{g}\right) = \dfrac{g(\nabla f) - f(\nabla g)}{g^2}$	$g \neq 0$
Power rule	$\nabla(f^n) = nf^{n-1}\nabla f$	

THEOREM 12.9   **Optimal direction property of the gradient**

Suppose f is differentiable and let ∇f_0 denote the gradient at P_0. Then, if $\nabla f_0 \neq 0$,

    a. The largest value of the directional derivative of $D_u f$ is $\|\nabla f_0\|$ and it occurs when the unit vector **u** points in the direction of ∇f_0.

    b. The smallest value of $D_u f$ is $-\|\nabla f_0\|$, and it occurs when **u** points in the direction of $-\nabla f_0$.

THEOREM 12.10   **The normal property of the gradient**

Suppose the function f is differentiable at the point P_0 and that the gradient at P_0 satisfies $\nabla f_0 \neq 0$. Then ∇f_0 is orthogonal to the level surface $f(x, y, z) = K$ at P_0.

THEOREM 12.11   **Partial derivative criteria for relative extrema**

If f has a relative extremum (maximum or minimum) at $P_0(x_0, y_0)$ and the first-order partial derivatives of f_x and f_y both exist at $P_0(x_0, y_0)$, then $f_x(x_0, y_0) = f_y(x_0, y_0) = 0$.

THEOREM 12.12   **Extreme value theorem for a function of two variables**

A function of two variables $f(x, y)$ assumes its absolute extremum on any closed, bounded set S in the plane where it is continuous. Moreover, all absolute extrema must occur either on the boundary of S or at a critical point in the interior of S.

THEOREM 12.13   **Lagrange's theorem**

Assume that f and g have continuous first partial derivatives such that f has an extremum at $P_0(x_0, y_0)$ on the smooth constraint curve $g(x, y) = c$. If $\nabla g(x_0, y_0) \neq \mathbf{0}$, then there is a number λ such that

$$\nabla f(x_0, y_0) = \lambda \nabla g(x_0, y_0)$$

THEOREM 12.14   **Rate of change of the extreme value**

Suppose E is the extreme value (maximum or minimum) of f subject to the constraint $g(x, y) = c$. Then the Lagrange multiplier λ is the rate of change of E with respect to c; that is, $\lambda = dE/dc$.

CHAPTER 13

THEOREM 13.1   **Fubini's theorem over a rectangular region**

If $f(x, y)$ is continuous over the rectangle $R: a \leq x \leq b, c \leq y \leq d$, then the double integral

$$\iint_R f(x, y)\, dA$$

is evaluated by either iterated integral; that is,

$$\iint_R f(x, y)\, dA = \int_c^d \int_a^b f(x, y)\, dx\, dy = \int_a^b \int_c^d f(x, y)\, dy\, dx$$

THEOREM 13.2   **Fubini's theorem for nonrectangular regions**

If D is a type I region, then

$$\iint_D f(x, y)\, dA = \int_a^b \int_{g_1(x)}^{g_2(x)} f(x, y)\, dy\, dx$$

whenever both integrals exist. Similarly, for a type II region,

$$\iint_D f(x, y)\, dA = \int_c^d \int_{h_1(y)}^{h_2(y)} f(x, y)\, dx\, dy$$

THEOREM 13.3 **Properties of double integrals**
Assume that all the given integrals exist.

Linearity rule   For constants a and b
$$\iint_D [af(x, y) + bg(x, y)]\, dA = a \iint_D f(x, y)\, dA + b \iint_D g(x, y)\, dA$$

Dominance rule   If $f(x, y) \geq g(x, y)$ throughout a region D, then
$$\iint_D f(x, y)\, dA \geq \iint_D g(x, y)\, dA$$

Subdivision rule   If the region of integration D can be subdivided into two subregions D_1 and D_2, then
$$\iint_D f(x, y)\, dA = \iint_{D_1} f(x, y)\, dA + \iint_{D_2} f(x, y)\, dA$$

THEOREM 13.4 **Double integral in polar coordinates**
If f is continuous in the polar region described by $a \leq r \leq b$ ($a, b \geq 0$), $\alpha \leq \theta \leq \beta$ ($0 \leq \beta - \alpha < 2\pi$), then

$$\iint_D f(x, y)\, dA = \int_\alpha^\beta \int_a^b f(r \cos \theta, r \sin \theta)\, r\, dr\, d\theta$$

THEOREM 13.5 **Fubini's theorem over a parallelepiped in space**
If $f(x, y, z)$ is continuous over a box R: $a \leq x \leq b, c \leq y \leq d, r \leq z \leq s$, then the triple integral is evaluated by the iterated integral

$$\iiint_R f(x, y, z)\, dV = \int_t^s \int_c^d \int_a^b f(x, y, z)\, dx\, dy\, dz$$

The iterated integral can be performed in any order:

$$\begin{array}{ccc} dx\, dy\, dz & dx\, dz\, dy & dz\, dx\, dy \\ dy\, dx\, dz & dy\, dz\, dx & dz\, dy\, dx \end{array}$$

THEOREM 13.6 **Triple integral over a general region**
If S is a region in space that is bounded above by the surface $z = u(x, y)$ and below by $z = v(x, y)$ as (x, y) varies over the planar region R, then

$$\iiint_S f(x, y, z)\, dV = \iint_R \int_{v(x,y)}^{u(x,y)} f(x, y, z)\, dz\, dA$$

THEOREM 13.7 **Change of variable in a double integral**
Let f be a continuous function on a region D, and let T be a one-to-one transformation that maps the region D in the uv-plane onto a region D^* in the xy-

plane under the change of variable $x = g(u, v)$, $y = h(u, v)$ where g and h are continuously differentiable on D^*. Then

$$\iint_{D^*} f(x, y) \, dy \, dx = \iint_D f[g(u, v), h(u, v)] \, |J(u, v)| \, dv \, du$$

where $J(u, v) = \begin{vmatrix} \dfrac{\partial x}{\partial u} & \dfrac{\partial x}{\partial v} \\ \dfrac{\partial y}{\partial u} & \dfrac{\partial y}{\partial v} \end{vmatrix} = \dfrac{\partial x}{\partial u} \dfrac{\partial y}{\partial v} - \dfrac{\partial y}{\partial u} \dfrac{\partial x}{\partial v} \neq 0$

is a mapping factor called the **Jacobian** for the mapping from x, y variables to u, v variables. The Jacobian is also denoted by $\left| \dfrac{\partial(x, y)}{\partial(u, v)} \right|$.

CHAPTER 14

THEOREM 14.1   **Properties of line integrals**

Let f be a given scalar function defined with respect to x on a piecewise smooth, orientable curve C. Then for any constant k:

Constant multiple $\displaystyle \int_C kf \, dx = k \int_C f \, dx$

Sum rule $\displaystyle \int_C (f_1 + f_2) \, dx = \int_C f_1 \, dx + \int_C f_2 \, dx$

where f_1 and f_2 are scalar functions defined with respect to x on C.

Opposite direction rule $\displaystyle \int_{-C} f \, dx = - \int_C f \, dx$

where $-C$ denotes the curve C traversed in the opposite direction.

Subdivision rule $\displaystyle \int_C f \, dx = \int_{C_1} f \, dx + \int_{C_2} f \, dx$

where C is subdivided into subarcs $C_1 \cup C_2$ (where $C_1 \cap C_2 = \varnothing$). This property generalizes to any finite number of subdivisions.

Similar properties hold for line integrals of the form $\displaystyle \int_C g \, dy$ or $\displaystyle \int_C h \, dz$.

THEOREM 14.2   **Cross-partials test for a conservative vector field in the plane**

Consider the vector field $\mathbf{F}(x, y) = u(x, y)\mathbf{i} + v(x, y)\mathbf{j}$, where u and v have continuous first partials in the open, simply connected region D. Then $\mathbf{F}(x, y)$ is conservative on D if and only if

$$\frac{\partial u}{\partial y} = \frac{\partial v}{\partial x} \quad \text{Throughout } D$$

THEOREM 14.3   **Fundamental theorem on line integrals**

Let $\mathbf{F}$ be a conservative vector field on the region D and let f be a scalar potential function for $\mathbf{F}$. That is, $\nabla f = \mathbf{F}$. Then, if C is any piecewise smooth curve lying entirely within D, with initial point P and terminal point Q, we have

$$\int_C \mathbf{F} \cdot d\mathbf{R} = f(Q) - f(P)$$

the line integral $\int_C \mathbf{F} \cdot d\mathbf{R}$ is independent of path in D.

THEOREM 14.4 **Closed-curve theorem for a conservative vector field**

The continuous vector field **F** is conservative in the open connected region D if and only if $\int_C \mathbf{F} \cdot d\mathbf{R} = 0$ for every piecewise-smooth closed curve C in D.

THEOREM 14.5 **Green's theorem**

Let D be a simply connected region with a positively oriented, piecewise-smooth boundary C. Then if the vector field $\mathbf{F}(x, y) = M(x, y)\mathbf{i} + N(x, y)\mathbf{j}$ is continuously differentiable on D, we have

$$\int_C (M\,dx + N\,dy) = \int\int_D \left(\frac{\partial N}{\partial x} - \frac{\partial M}{\partial y} \right) dA$$

THEOREM 14.6 **Area as a line integral**

Let D be a simply connected region in the plane with piecewise-smooth, closed boundary C. Then the area A of region D is given by the line integral

$$A = \frac{1}{2} \int_C (-y\,dx + x\,dy)$$

THEOREM 14.7 **Stokes's theorem**

Let S be an oriented surface with unit normal vector **N**, and assume that S is bounded by a closed, piecewise-smooth curve C whose orientation is compatible with that of S. If **F** is a vector field that is continuously differentiable on S, then

$$\int_C \mathbf{F} \cdot d\mathbf{R} = \int\int_S (\text{curl } \mathbf{F} \cdot \mathbf{N})\, dS$$

THEOREM 14.8 **Test for a vector to be conservative**

If **F** and curl **F** are continuous in the simply connected region D, then **F** is conservative in D if and only if curl $\mathbf{F} = \mathbf{0}$ in D.

THEOREM 14.9 **The divergence theorem**

Let D be a region in space bounded by a smooth, orientable, closed surface S. If **F** is a continuous vector field whose components have continuous partial derivatives in D, then

$$\int\int_S \mathbf{F} \cdot \mathbf{N}\, dS = \int\int\int_D \text{div } \mathbf{F}\, dV$$

where **N** is an outward unit normal to the surface S.

APPENDIX B   Selected Proofs

■ CHAIN RULE (Chapter 2)

Suppose f is a differentiable function of u and u is a differentiable function of x. Then,

$$\frac{df}{dx} = \frac{df}{du}\frac{du}{dx}$$

where $f[u(x)]$.

Proof: Define an auxiliary function g defined by

$$g(t) = \frac{f[u(x) + t] - f[u(x)]}{t} - \frac{df}{du} \quad \text{if} \quad t \neq 0 \quad \text{and} \quad g(t) = 0 \quad \text{if} \quad t = 0$$

You can verify that g is continuous at $t = 0$. Notice that for $t = \Delta u$ and $t \neq 0$,

$$g(\Delta u) = \frac{f[u(x) + \Delta u] - f[u(x)]}{\Delta u} - \frac{df}{du}$$

$$g(\Delta u) + \frac{df}{du} = \frac{f[u(x) + \Delta u] - f[u(x)]}{\Delta u}$$

$$\left[g(\Delta u) + \frac{df}{du}\right]\Delta u = f[u(x) + \Delta u] - f[u(x)]$$

We now use the definition of derivative for f.

$$\frac{df}{dx} = \lim_{\Delta x \to 0} \frac{f[u(x + \Delta x)] - f[u(x)]}{\Delta x}$$

$$= \lim_{\Delta x \to 0} \frac{f[u(x) + \Delta u)] - f[u(x)]}{\Delta x} \qquad \text{\textit{Where} } \Delta u = u(x + \Delta x) - u(x)$$

$$= \lim_{\Delta x \to 0} \frac{\left[g(\Delta u) + \dfrac{df}{du}\right]\Delta u}{\Delta x} \qquad \text{\textit{Substitution}}$$

$$= \lim_{\Delta x \to 0} \left[g(\Delta u) + \frac{df}{du}\right] \frac{\Delta u}{\Delta x}$$

$$= \lim_{\Delta x \to 0} \left[g(\Delta u) + \frac{df}{du}\right] \lim_{\Delta x \to 0} \frac{\Delta u}{\Delta x}$$

$$= \left[\lim_{\Delta x \to 0} g(\Delta u) + \lim_{\Delta x \to 0} \frac{df}{du}\right] \lim_{\Delta x \to 0} \frac{\Delta u}{\Delta x}$$

$$= \left[0 + \frac{df}{du}\right] \frac{du}{dx} \qquad \text{\textit{Because } } g \text{ \textit{is continuous at} } t = 0$$

$$= \frac{df}{du} \frac{du}{dx} \qquad\qquad\qquad\qquad\qquad\qquad\qquad\qquad\qquad \blacksquare$$

■ CAUCHY'S GENERALIZED MEAN VALUE THEOREM (Chapter 3)

Let f and g be functions that are continuous on the closed interval $[a, b]$ and differentiable on the open interval (a, b). If $g(b) \neq g(a)$ and $g'(x) \neq 0$ on (a, b), then

$$\frac{f(b) - f(a)}{g(b) - g(a)} = \frac{f'(c)}{g'(c)}$$

for at least one number c between a and b.

Proof: We begin by defining a special function, just as in the proof of the MVT as presented in Section 3.2. Specifically, let

$$F(x) = f(x) - f(a) - \frac{f(b) - f(a)}{g(b) - g(a)}[g(x) - g(a)]$$

for all x in the closed interval $[a, b]$. In the proof of the MVT in Section 3.2, we show that F satisfies the hypotheses of Rolle's theorem, which means $F'(c) = 0$ for at least one number c in (a, b). For this number c we have

$$0 = F'(c) = f'(c) - \frac{f(b) - f(a)}{g(b) - g(a)} g'(c)$$

and the result follows from this equation. ■

■ L'HÔPITAL'S THEOREM* (Chapter 3)

For any number a let f and g be functions that are differentiable on a closed interval $[a, b]$, where $g'(x) \neq 0$. Then if

$$\lim_{x \to a^+} f(x) = 0, \ \lim_{x \to a^+} g(x) = 0 \text{ and } \lim_{x \to a} \frac{f'(x)}{g'(x)} \text{ exists, then}$$

$$\lim_{x \to a^+} \frac{f(x)}{g(x)} = \lim_{x \to a^+} \frac{f'(x)}{g'(x)}$$

Proof: First, define auxiliary functions F and G by

$F(x) = f(x)$ for $a < x \leq b$ and $F(a) = 0$
$G(x) = g(x)$ for $a < x \leq b$ and $G(a) = 0$

These definitions guarantee that $F(x) = f(x)$ and $G(x) = g(x)$ for $a < x \leq b$ and that $F(a) = G(a) = 0$. Thus, if w is any number between a and b, the functions F and G are continuous on the closed interval $[a, w]$ and differentiable on the open interval (a, w). According to the Cauchy generalized mean value theorem, there exists a number t between a and w for which

$$\frac{F(w) - F(a)}{G(w) - G(a)} = \frac{F'(t)}{G'(t)}$$

$$\frac{F(w)}{G(w)} = \frac{F'(t)}{G'(t)} \qquad \textit{Because } F(a) = G(a) = 0$$

$$\frac{f(w)}{g(w)} = \frac{f'(t)}{g'(t)} \qquad \textit{Because } F(x) = f(x) \textit{ and } G(x) = g(x)$$

$$\lim_{w \to a^+} \frac{f(w)}{g(w)} = \lim_{w \to a^+} \frac{f'(t)}{g'(t)}$$

$$\lim_{w \to a^+} \frac{f(w)}{g(w)} = \lim_{t \to a^+} \frac{f'(t)}{g'(t)} \qquad \textit{Because } t \textit{ is "trapped" between } a \textit{ and } w$$

$$\lim_{x \to a^+} \frac{f(x)}{g(x)} = \lim_{x \to a^+} \frac{f'(x)}{g'(x)} \qquad ■$$

■ CONTINUITY AND DIFFERENTIABILITY OF INVERSE FUNCTIONS (Chapter 5)

Let f be a one-to-one function so that it possesses an inverse.

1. If f is continuous on a domain I, then f^{-1} is continuous on $f(I)$.
2. If f is differentiable at c, and $f'(c) \neq 0$, then f^{-1} is differentiable at $f(c)$.

Proof: **1.** Recall $y = f(x)$ if and only if $x = f^{-1}(y)$. Let I be the open interval (a, b), and let y_0 be in the open interval $(f(a), f(b))$ so that x_0 is in the open interval (a, b). To prove continuity we must show that

$$\lim_{y \to y_0} f^{-1}(y) = f^{-1}(y_0) = x_0$$

*This is a special case of l'Hôpital's rule. The other cases can be found in most advanced calculus textbooks.

Consider any interval $(x_0 - \varepsilon, x_0 + \varepsilon)$ for $\varepsilon > 0$. We must find an interval $(y_0 - \delta, y_0 + \delta)$ such that whenever y is in $(y_0 - \delta, y_0 + \delta)$, $f^{-1}(y)$ is in $(x_0 - \varepsilon, x_0 + \varepsilon)$.

Let $\delta_1 = y_0 - f(x_0 - \varepsilon)$ and $\delta_2 = f(x_0 + \varepsilon) - y_0$. If δ is the smaller of δ_1 and δ_2, it follows that if y is in $(y_0 - \delta, y_0 + \delta)$, then $f^{-1}(y)$ is in $(x_0 - \varepsilon, x_0 + \varepsilon)$, which is what we wanted to prove.

2. Let $g = f^{-1}$ and $f'[g(a)] \neq 0$. We want to show that g is differentiable.

$$g'(a) = \lim_{x \to a} \frac{g(x) - g(a)}{x - a} \qquad \textit{From the definition of derivative}$$

$$= \lim_{x \to a} \frac{y - b}{f(y) - f(b)} \qquad \textit{If } y = g(x) \textit{ then } x = f(y), \textit{ and} \\ \textit{if } b = g(a) \textit{ then } a = f(b).$$

$$= \lim_{y \to b} \frac{y - b}{f(y) - f(b)} \qquad \textit{Because f is differentiable, it is continuous,} \\ \textit{so } g = f^{-1} \textit{ is} \\ \textit{continuous by part (1). Thus, if } x \to a, \\ \textit{then } g(x) \to g(a) \textit{ so that } y \to b.$$

$$= \lim_{y \to b} \frac{1}{\dfrac{f(y) - f(b)}{y - b}}$$

$$= \frac{1}{\displaystyle\lim_{y \to b} \frac{f(y) - f(b)}{y - b}}$$

$$= \frac{1}{f'(b)}$$

Because f is differentiable, we see that g is also differentiable. ∎

■ LIMIT COMPARISON TEST (Chapter 8)

Suppose $a_k > 0$ and $b_k > 0$ for all sufficiently large k and that

$$\lim_{k \to \infty} \frac{a_k}{b_k} = L \qquad \text{where } L \text{ is finite and positive } (0 < L < \infty)$$

Then Σa_k and Σb_k either both converge or both diverge.

Proof: Assume that $\lim_{k \to \infty} \dfrac{a_k}{b_k} = L$, where $L > 0$. Using $\varepsilon = \dfrac{L}{2}$ in the definition of the limit of a sequence, we see that there exists a number N so that

$$\left| \frac{a_k}{b_k} - L \right| < \frac{L}{2} \qquad \text{whenever } k > N$$

$$-\frac{L}{2} < \frac{a_k}{b_k} - L < \frac{L}{2}$$

$$\frac{L}{2} < \frac{a_k}{b_k} \qquad < \frac{3L}{2}$$

$$\frac{L}{2} b_k < a_k \qquad < \frac{3L}{2} b_k \qquad b_k > 0$$

This is true for all $k > N$. Now we can complete the proof by using the direct comparison test. Suppose Σb_k converges. Then the series $\Sigma \frac{3L}{2} b_k$ also converges, and the inequality

$$a_k < \frac{3L}{2} b_k$$

tells us that the series Σa_k must also converge since it is dominated by a convergent series.

Similarly, if Σb_k diverges, the inequality

$$0 < \frac{L}{2} b_k < a_k$$

tells us that Σa_k dominates the divergent series $\Sigma \frac{L}{2} b_k$, and it follows that Σa_k also diverges.

Thus Σa_k and Σb_k either both converge or both diverge. ∎

■ TAYLOR'S THEOREM (Chapter 8)

If f and all its derivatives exist in an open interval I containing c, then for each x in I

$$f(x) = f(c) + \frac{f'(c)}{1!}(x - c) + \frac{f''(c)}{2!}(x - c)^2 + \cdots + \frac{f^{(n)}(c)}{n!}(x - c)^n + R_n(x)$$

where the remainder function $R_n(x)$ is given by

$$R_n(x) = \frac{f^{(n+1)}(z_n)}{(n + 1)!}(x - c)^{n+1}$$

for some z_n which depends on x and lies between c and x.

Proof: We shall prove Taylor's theorem by showing that if f and its first $n + 1$ derivatives are defined in an open interval I containing c, then for each fixed x in I

$$f(x) = f(c) + \frac{f'(c)}{1!}(x - c) + \frac{f''(c)}{2!}(x - c)^2 + \cdots + \frac{f^{(n)}(c)}{n!}(x - c)^n + \frac{f^{(n+1)}(z)}{(n + 1)!}(x - c)^{n+1}$$

where z is some number between x and c. In our proof, we shall apply Cauchy's generalized mean value theorem to the auxiliary functions F and G defined for all t in I as follows:

$$F(t) = f(x) - f(t) - \frac{f'(t)}{1!}(x - t) - \cdots - \frac{f^{(n)}(t)}{n!}(x - t)^n$$
$$G(t) = \frac{(x - t)^{n+1}}{(n + 1)!}$$

Note that $F(x) = G(x) = 0$, and thus Cauchy's generalized mean value theorem tells us

$$\frac{F'(z)}{G'(z)} = \frac{F(x) - F(c)}{G(x) - G(c)} = \frac{F(c)}{G(c)}$$

for some number z between x and c. Rearranging the sides of this equation and finding the derivatives gives

$$\frac{F(c)}{G(c)} = \frac{F'(z)}{G'(z)}$$

$$= \frac{\dfrac{-f^{(n+1)}(z)}{n!}(x-z)^n}{\dfrac{-(x-z)^n}{n!}}$$

$$= f^{(n+1)}(z)$$

$$F(c) = f^{(n+1)}(z) \, G(c)$$

$$f(x) - f(c) - \frac{f'(c)}{1!}(x-c) - \cdots - \frac{f^{(n)}(c)}{n!}(x-c)^n = f^{(n+1)}(z)\left[\frac{(x-c)^{n+1}}{(n+1)!}\right]$$

Rearranging these terms, we obtain the required equation.

$$f(x) = f(c) + \frac{f'(c)}{1!}(x-c) + \cdots + \frac{f^{(n)}(c)}{n!}(x-c)^n + f^{(n+1)}(z)\left[\frac{(x-c)^{n+1}}{(n+1)!}\right] \quad \blacksquare$$

■ SUFFICIENT CONDITION FOR DIFFERENTIABILITY (Chap. 12)

If f is a function of x and y and f, f_x, and f_y are continuous in a disk D centered at (x_0, y_0), then f is differentiable at (x_0, y_0).

Proof: If (x, y) is a point in D, we have

$$f(x, y) - f(x_0, y_0) = f(x, y) - f(x_0, y) + f(x_0, y) - f(x_0, y_0)$$

The function $f(x_0, y)$ with y fixed satisfies the conditions of the mean value theorem, so that

$$f(x, y) - f(x_0, y) = f_x(x_1, y)(x - x_0)$$

for some number x_1 between x and x_0, and similarly, there is a number y_1 between y and y_0 such that

$$f(x_0, y_0) - f(x_0, y_0) = f_y(x_0, y_1)(y - y_0)$$

Substituting these expressions, we obtain:

$$f(x, y) - f(x_0, y_0) = [f(x, y) - f(x_0, y)] + [f(x_0, y) - f(x_0, y_0)]$$

$$= [f_x(x_1, y)(x - x_0)] + [f_y(x_0, y_1)(y - y_0)]$$

$$= [f_x(x_1, y)(x - x_0)] + \underbrace{f_x(x_0, y_0)(x - x_0) - f_x(x_0, y_0)(x - x_0)}_{\text{This is zero.}}$$

$$+ [f_y(x_0, y_1)(y - y_0)] + \underbrace{f_y(x_0, y_0)(y - y_0) - f_y(x_0, y_0)(y - y_0)}_{\text{This is also zero.}}$$

$$= f_x(x_0, y_0)(x - x_0) + f_y(x_0, y_0)(y - y_0)$$

$$+ [f_x(x_1, y) - f_x(x_0, y_0)](x - x_0)$$

$$+ [f_y(x_0, y_1) - f_y(x_0, y_0)](y - y_0)$$

Let $\varepsilon_1(x, y)$ and $\varepsilon_2(x, y)$ be the functions

$$\varepsilon_1(x, y) = f_x(x_1, y) - f_x(x_0, y_0) \quad \text{and} \quad \varepsilon_2(x, y) = f_y(x_0, y_1) - f_y(x_0, y_0)$$

Then because x_1 is between x and x_0, and y_1 is between y and y_0, and the partial derivatives f_x and f_y are continuous at (x_0, y_0), we have

$$\lim_{(x,y)\to(x_0,y_0)} \varepsilon_1(x, y) = \lim_{(x,y)\to(x_0,y_0)} [f_x(x_1, y_0) - f_x(x_0, y_0)] = 0$$

$$\lim_{(x,y)\to(x_0,y_0)} \varepsilon_2(x, y) = \lim_{(x,y)\to(x_0,y_0)} [f_y(x_0, y_1) - f_y(x_0, y_0)] = 0$$

so that f is differentiable at (x_0, y_0), as required. ∎

■ CHANGE-OF-VARIABLE FORMULA FOR MULTIPLE INTEGRATION (Chapter 13)

Suppose f is a continuous function on a region D, and let D^* be the image of the domain D under the change of variable $x = g(u, v)$, $y = h(u, v)$, where g and h are continuously differentiable on D^*. Then

$$\int\int_{D^*} f(x, y)\, dy\, dx = \int\int_{D} f[g(u, v), h(u, v)] \underbrace{\left|\frac{\partial(x, y)}{\partial(u, v)}\right|}_{\text{Absolute value of Jacobian}} dv\, du$$

Proof: A proof of this theorem is found in advanced calculus, but we can provide a geometric argument that makes this formula plausible in the special case where $f(x, y) = 1$. In particular, we shall show that in order to find the area of a region D^* in the xy-plane using the change of variable $x = X(u, v)$ and $y = Y(u, v)$, it is reasonable to use the formula for area, A:

$$A = \int\int_{D^*} dy\, dx = \int\int_{D} \left|\frac{\partial(x, y)}{\partial(u, v)}\right| dv\, du$$

where D^* is the region in the uv-plane that corresponds to D.

Suppose the given change of variable has an inverse $u = u(x, y)$, $v = v(x, y)$ which transforms the region D^* in the xy-plane into a region D in the uv-plane. To find the area of D in the uv-coordinate system, it is natural to use a rectangular grid, with vertical lines $u =$ constant and horizontal lines $v =$ constant, as shown in Figure B.1a. In the xy-plane, the equations $u =$ constant and $v =$ constant will be families of parallel curves, which provide a curvilinear grid for the region D^* (Figure B.1b).

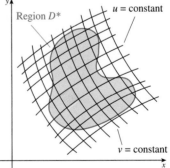

a. A rectangular grid in the uv-plane

b. Corresponding grid in the xy-plane is curvilinear.

Figure B.1

Next, let R be a typical rectangular cell in the uv-grid that covers D, and let R be the corresponding set in the xy-plane (that is, R^* is the image of R under the given change of variable). Then, as shown in Figure B.2, if R has vertices $A(\overline{u}, \overline{v})$,

$B(\bar{u} + \Delta u, \bar{v})$, $C(\bar{u}, \bar{v} + \Delta v)$, and $D(\bar{u} + \Delta u, \bar{v} + \Delta v)$, the set R^* will be the interior of a curvilinear rectangle with vertices

$$A[X(\bar{u}, \bar{v}), \quad Y(\bar{u}, \bar{v})]$$

$$B[X(\bar{u} + \Delta u, \bar{v}), \quad Y(\bar{u} + \Delta u, \bar{v})]$$

$$C[X(\bar{u}, \bar{v} + \Delta v), \quad Y(\bar{u}, \bar{v} + \Delta v)]$$

$$D[X(\bar{u} + \Delta u, \bar{v} + \Delta v), \quad Y(\bar{u} + \Delta u, \bar{v} + \Delta v)]$$

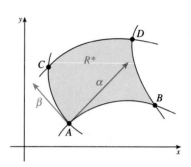

a. R is a typical rectangular cell in the grid covering D^*.

b. The image of R under the change of variable is a curvilinear rectangle R^*.

Figure B.2

Note that the curved side of R joining A to B can be approximated by the secant vector

$$\mathbf{AB} = [X(\bar{u} + \Delta u, \bar{v}) - X(\bar{u}, \bar{v})]\mathbf{i} + [Y(\bar{u} + \Delta u, \bar{v}) - Y(\bar{u}, \bar{v})]\mathbf{j}$$

and by applying the mean value theorem, we find that

$$\mathbf{AB} = \left[\frac{\partial x}{\partial u}(a, \bar{v}) \, \Delta u\right]\mathbf{i} + \left[\frac{\partial y}{\partial u}(b, \bar{v}) \, \Delta u\right]\mathbf{j}$$

for some numbers a, b between $\bar{u}$ and $\bar{u} + \Delta u$. If Δu is very small, a and b are approximately the same as $\bar{u}$, and we can approximate $\mathbf{AB}$ by the vector

$$\boldsymbol{\alpha} = \left[\frac{\partial x}{\partial u} \, \Delta u\right]\mathbf{i} + \left[\frac{\partial y}{\partial u} \, \Delta u\right]\mathbf{j}$$

where the partials are evaluated at the point $(\bar{u}, \bar{v})$. Similarly, the curved side of R joining A and C can be approximated by the vector

$$\boldsymbol{\beta} = \left[\frac{\partial x}{\partial v} \, \Delta v\right]\mathbf{i} + \left[\frac{\partial y}{\partial v} \, \Delta v\right]\mathbf{j}$$

The area of the curvilinear rectangle R^* is approximately the same as that of the parallelogram determined by $\boldsymbol{\alpha}$ and $\boldsymbol{\beta}$; that is

$$\|\boldsymbol{\alpha} \times \boldsymbol{\beta}\| = \begin{vmatrix} \mathbf{i} & \mathbf{j} & \mathbf{k} \\ \frac{\partial x}{\partial u}\Delta u & \frac{\partial y}{\partial u}\Delta u & 0 \\ \frac{\partial x}{\partial v}\Delta v & \frac{\partial y}{\partial v}\Delta v & 0 \end{vmatrix}$$

$$= \left\| \begin{vmatrix} \mathbf{i} & \mathbf{j} & \mathbf{k} \\ \frac{\partial x}{\partial u} & \frac{\partial y}{\partial u} & 0 \\ \frac{\partial x}{\partial v} & \frac{\partial y}{\partial v} & 0 \end{vmatrix} \Delta v \Delta u \right\|$$

$$= \left| \frac{\partial x}{\partial u} \frac{\partial y}{\partial v} - \frac{\partial y}{\partial u} \frac{\partial x}{\partial v} \right| \Delta v \Delta u$$

$$= \left| \frac{\partial(x, y)}{\partial(u, v)} \right| \Delta v \Delta u$$

By adding the contributions of all cells in the partition of D, we can approximate the area of D as follows:

APPROXIMATE AREA OF D = $\sum$ APPROXIMATE AREA OF CURVILINEAR RECTANGLES

$$= \sum \left| \frac{\partial'(x, y)}{\partial(u, v)} \right| \Delta v \Delta u$$

Finally, using a limit to "smooth out" the approximation, we find

$$A = \int\!\!\int_D dy\, dx = \lim \sum \left| \frac{\partial(x, y)}{\partial(u, v)} \right| \Delta v \Delta u$$

$$= \int\!\!\int_D \left| \frac{\partial(x, y)}{\partial(u, v)} \right| dv\, du \qquad \blacksquare$$

■ STOKES'S THEOREM (Chapter 14)

Let S be an oriented surface with unit normal vector $\mathbf{N}$, and assume that S is bounded by a closed, piecewise-smooth curve C whose orientation is compatible with that of S. If $\mathbf{F}$ is a continuous vector field whose components have continuous partial derivatives on an open region containing S and C, then

$$\int_C \mathbf{F} \cdot d\mathbf{R} = \int\!\!\int_S (\operatorname{curl} \mathbf{F} \cdot \mathbf{N})\, dS$$

Proof: The general proof cannot be considered until advanced calculus. However, a proof where S is a graph and $\mathbf{F}$, S, and C are "well behaved" can be given. Let S be given by $z = z(x, y)$, where (x, y) is in a region D of the xy-plane. Assume g has continuous second-order partial derivatives. Let C_1 be the projection of C in the xy-plane shown in Figure B.3. Also, let $\mathbf{F}(x, y, z) = f(x, y, z)\mathbf{i} + g(x, y, z)\mathbf{j} + h(x, y, z)\mathbf{k}$, where the partial derivatives of f, g, and h are continuous.

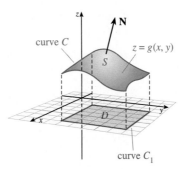

Figure B.3

We will evaluate each side of Stokes's theorem separately and show that the results for each are the same. If $x = x(t)$, $y = y(t)$ and $z = z(t)$ for $a \le t \le b$ and $\mathbf{R}(t) = x(t)\mathbf{i} + y(t)\mathbf{j} + z(t)\mathbf{k}$.

$$\int_C \mathbf{F} \cdot d\mathbf{R} = \int_a^b \left(f\frac{dx}{dt} + g\frac{dy}{dt} + h\frac{dz}{dt} \right) dt$$

$$= \int_a^b \left[f\frac{dx}{dt} + g\frac{dy}{dt} + h\left(\frac{\partial z}{\partial x}\frac{dx}{dt} + \frac{\partial z}{\partial y}\frac{dy}{dt} \right) \right] dt \qquad \textit{Chain rule}$$

$$= \int_a^b \left[\left(f + h\frac{\partial z}{\partial x} \right)\frac{dx}{dt} + \left(g + h\frac{\partial z}{\partial y} \right)\frac{dy}{dt} \right] dt$$

$$= \int_{C_1} \left(f + h\frac{\partial z}{\partial x} \right) dx + \left(g + h\frac{\partial z}{\partial y} \right) dy$$

$$= \iint_D \left[\frac{\partial}{\partial x}\left(g + h\frac{\partial z}{\partial y} \right) - \frac{\partial}{\partial y}\left(f + h\frac{\partial z}{\partial x} \right) \right] dA \qquad \textit{Green's theorem}$$

$$= \iint_D \left[\left(\frac{\partial g}{\partial x} + \frac{\partial g}{\partial z}\frac{\partial z}{\partial x} + \frac{\partial h}{\partial x}\frac{\partial z}{\partial y} + \frac{\partial h}{\partial z}\frac{\partial z}{\partial x}\frac{\partial z}{\partial y} + h\frac{\partial^2 z}{\partial x\partial y} \right) \right.$$

$$\left. - \left(\frac{\partial f}{\partial y} + \frac{\partial f}{\partial z}\frac{\partial z}{\partial y} + \frac{\partial h}{\partial y}\frac{\partial z}{\partial x} + \frac{\partial h}{\partial z}\frac{\partial z}{\partial y}\frac{\partial z}{\partial x} + h\frac{\partial^2 z}{\partial y\partial x} \right) \right] dA$$

$$= \iint_D \left(\frac{\partial g}{\partial x} + \frac{\partial g}{\partial z}\frac{\partial z}{\partial x} + \frac{\partial h}{\partial x}\frac{\partial z}{\partial y} - \frac{\partial f}{\partial y} - \frac{\partial f}{\partial z}\frac{\partial z}{\partial y} - \frac{\partial h}{\partial y}\frac{\partial z}{\partial x} \right) dA$$

We now start over by evaluating the other side of Stokes's theorem.

$$\iint_S \text{curl } \mathbf{F} \cdot dS = \iint_D \left[-\left(\frac{\partial h}{\partial y} - \frac{\partial g}{\partial z} \right)\frac{\partial z}{\partial x} - \left(\frac{\partial f}{\partial z} - \frac{\partial h}{\partial x} \right)\frac{\partial z}{\partial y} + \left(\frac{\partial g}{\partial x} - \frac{\partial f}{\partial y} \right) \right] dA$$

$$= \iint_D \left(-\frac{\partial h}{\partial y}\frac{\partial z}{\partial x} + \frac{\partial g}{\partial z}\frac{\partial z}{\partial x} - \frac{\partial f}{\partial z}\frac{\partial z}{\partial y} + \frac{\partial h}{\partial x}\frac{\partial z}{\partial y} + \frac{\partial g}{\partial x} - \frac{\partial f}{\partial y} \right) dA$$

Because these results are the same, we have

$$\int_C \mathbf{F} \cdot d\mathbf{R} = \iint_S (\text{curl } \mathbf{F} \cdot \mathbf{N})\, dS$$

■

■ DIVERGENCE THEOREM (Chapter 14)

Let D be a region in space bounded by a smooth, orientable closed surface S. If $\mathbf{F}$ is a continuous vector field whose components have continuous partial derivatives in D, then

$$\iint_S \mathbf{F} \cdot \mathbf{N}\, dS = \iiint_D \text{div } \mathbf{F}\, dV$$

where $\mathbf{N}$ is an outward unit normal to the surface S.

Proof: Let $\mathbf{F}(x, y, z) = f(x, y, z)\mathbf{i} + g(x, y, z)\mathbf{j} + h(x, y, z)\mathbf{k}$. If we state the divergence theorem using this notation for $\mathbf{F}$, we have

$$\iint_S [f(\mathbf{i} \cdot \mathbf{N}) + g(\mathbf{j} \cdot \mathbf{N}) + h(\mathbf{k} \cdot \mathbf{N})]\, dS = \iiint_D \left(\frac{\partial f}{\partial x} + \frac{\partial g}{\partial y} + \frac{\partial h}{\partial z} \right) dV$$

$$\iint_S f(\mathbf{i} \cdot \mathbf{N})\, dS + \iint_S g(\mathbf{j} \cdot \mathbf{N})\, dS + \iint_S h(\mathbf{k} \cdot \mathbf{N})\, dS = \iiint_D \frac{\partial f}{\partial x}\, dV + \iiint_D \frac{\partial g}{\partial y}\, dV + \iiint_D \frac{\partial h}{\partial z}\, dV$$

This result can be verified by proving

$$\iint_S f(\mathbf{i} \cdot \mathbf{N}) \, dS = \iiint_D \frac{\partial f}{\partial x} \, dV$$

$$\iint_S g(\mathbf{j} \cdot \mathbf{N}) \, dS = \iiint_D \frac{\partial g}{\partial y} \, dV$$

$$\iint_S h(\mathbf{k} \cdot \mathbf{N}) \, dS = \iiint_D \frac{\partial h}{\partial z} \, dV$$

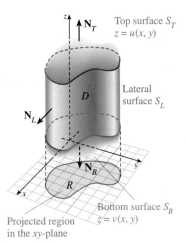

Figure B.4 A standard solid region in $\mathbb{R}^3$

Because the proof of each of these is virtually identical, if we show one, the other two can be done in a similar fashion. We will show the verification for the last of these three. We will evaluate this third integral by separately evaluating the left and right sides to show they are the same.

We will restrict our proof to a "standard region." The complete proof can then be completed by decomposing the general surface S into a finite number of "standard regions."

The standard solid region we shall consider has a top surface S_T with equation $z = u(x, y)$ and a bottom surface S_B with equation $z = v(x, y)$. We assume that both S_T and S_B project onto the region R in the xy-plane. The lateral surface S_L of the region is the set of all (x, y, z) such that $v(x, y) \leq z \leq u(x, y)$ on the boundary of R, as shown in Figure B.4.

We know that the outward unit normal (directed up) to the top surface S_T is

$$\mathbf{N}_T = \frac{-u_x \mathbf{i} - u_y \mathbf{j} + \mathbf{k}}{\sqrt{u_x^2 + u_y^2 + 1}} \qquad \text{and} \qquad dS = \sqrt{u_x^2 + u_y^2 + 1} \, dA_{xy}$$

Thus,

$$\iint_{S_T} h(\mathbf{k} \cdot \mathbf{N}_T) \, dS = \iint_R h\left(\frac{1}{\sqrt{u_x^2 + u_y^2 + 1}}\right)\left(\sqrt{u_x^2 + u_y^2 + 1} \, dA_{xy}\right)$$

$$= \iint_R h \, dA_{xy}$$

$$= \iint_R h(x, y, z) \, dA_{xy}$$

$$= \iint_R h[x, y, u(x, y)] \, dA$$

Similarly, the outward unit normal $\mathbf{N}_B$ to the bottom surface S_B is directed down, so that

$$\mathbf{N}_T = \frac{v_x \mathbf{i} - v_y \mathbf{j} - \mathbf{k}}{\sqrt{u_x^2 + u_y^2 + 1}}$$

and

$$\iint_{S_B} h(\mathbf{k} \cdot \mathbf{N}_B) \, dS = -\iint_R h \, dA_{xy}$$

$$= -\iint_R h(x, y, z) \, dA_{xy}$$

$$= -\iint_R h[x, y, v(x, y)] \, dA$$

Because the outward unit normal $\mathbf{N}_L$ is horizontal on the lateral surface S_L, it is perpendicular to $\mathbf{k}$, and

$$\iint_{S_L} h(\mathbf{k} \cdot \mathbf{N}_L) \, dS = 0$$

We now add for the surface S:

$$\iint_S h(\mathbf{k} \cdot \mathbf{N}) \, dS = \iint_{S_T} h(\mathbf{k} \cdot \mathbf{N}_T) \, dS + \iint_{S_B} h(\mathbf{k} \cdot \mathbf{N}_B) \, dS + \iint_{S_L} h(\mathbf{k} \cdot \mathbf{N}_L) \, dS$$

$$= \iint_R h[x, y, u(x, y)] \, dA_{xy} - \iint_R h[x, y, v(x, y)] \, dA_{xy} + 0$$

$$= \iint_R \{h[x, y, u(x, y)] - h[x, y, v(x, y)]\} \, dA_{zy}$$

Next, we start over by looking at the triple integral on the right side. Notice that we can describe the solid S as the set of all (x, y, z) for (x, y) in R and $v(x, y) \leq z \leq u(x, y)$. Thus,

$$\iiint_D \frac{\partial h}{\partial z} \, dV = \iint_R \left[\int_{v(x,y)}^{u(x,y)} \frac{\partial h}{\partial z}(x, y, z) \, dz \right] dA_{xy}$$

$$= \iint_R \{h[x, y, u(x, y)] - h[x, y, v(x, y)]\} \, dA_{xy}$$

We see that the left- and right-hand sides are the same, so

$$\iint_S h(\mathbf{k} \cdot \mathbf{N}) \, dS = \iiint_D \frac{\partial h}{\partial z} \, dV$$

We can now conclude that (by similar arguments for the other two parts)

$$\iint_S \mathbf{F} \cdot \mathbf{N} \, dS = \iiint_D \text{div } \mathbf{F} \, dV$$

■

APPENDIX C **Significant Digits**

Throughout this book, various computational windows appear and, in the answers to the problems, you will frequently find approximate (decimal) answers. Sometimes your answer may not exactly agree with the answer found in the back of the book. This does not necessarily mean that your answer is incorrect, particularly if your answer is very close to the given answer.

To use your calculator intelligently and efficiently, you should become familiar with its functions and practice doing problems with the same calculator, whenever possible. Read the computational windows provided throughout this text, and consult the *Owner's Manual* for your particular calculator when you have questions. In addition, there are *Technology Manuals* accompanying this text that are available for TI and HP Graphic Calculators, as well as for MATLAB and for Maple.

■ SIGNIFICANT DIGITS

Applications involving measurements can never be exact. It is particularly important that you pay attention to the accuracy of your measurements when you use a computer or calculator, because using available technology can give you a false sense of security about the accuracy in a particular problem. For example, if you measure a triangle and find that the sides are approximately 1.2 and 3.4 and then find the ratio of $1.2/3.4 \approx 0.35294117$, it appears that the result is more accurate than the original measurements! Some discussion about accuracy and significant digits is necessary.

The digits known to be correct in a number obtained by a measurement are called **significant digits**. The digits 1, 2, 3, 4, 5, 6, 7, 8, and 9 are always significant, whereas the digit 0 may or may not be significant.

1. Zeros that come between two other digits are significant, as in 203 or 10.04.
2. If the zero's only function is to place the decimal point, it is not significant, as in

$$\underbrace{0.00000}\,23 \qquad \text{or} \qquad 23,\underbrace{000}$$
$$\quad\text{Placeholders} \qquad\qquad\qquad \text{Placeholders}$$

If the decimal does more than fix the decimal point, it is not significant, as in

$$0.0023\underbrace{0} \qquad \text{or} \qquad 23,\underbrace{000}.01$$
$$\qquad\uparrow$$
$$\text{This digit is significant.} \qquad \text{These are significant.}$$

This second rule can, of course, result in certain ambiguities, such as 23,000 (measured to the *exact* unit). To avoid such confusion, we use scientific notation in this case:

$$2.3 \times 10^4 \text{ has two significant digits}$$

$$2.3000 \times 10^4 \text{ has five significant digits}$$

Numbers that come about by counting are considered to be exact and are correct to any number of significant digits.

When you compute an answer using a calculator, the answer may have 10 or more digits. In the computational windows, we generally show the 10 or 12 digits that result from the numerical calculation, but frequently the number in the answer section will have only 5 or 6 digits in the answer. It seems clear that if the first 3 or 4 nonzero digits of the answer coincide, you probably have the correct method of doing the problem.

However, you might ask why are there discrepancies and how many digits should you use when you write down your final answer? Roughly speaking, the significant digits in a number are the digits that have meaning. In order to clarify the concept, we must for the moment assume that we know the exact answer. We then assume that we have been able to compute an approximation to this exact answer. Usually, we do this by some sort of iterative process, in which the answers are getting closer and close to the exact answer. In such a process, we hope that the number of significant digits in our approximate answer are increasing at each trial. If our approximate answer is, say 6 digits long (some of those digits might even be zero), and the difference between our answer and the exact answer is 4 units or less in the last place, then the first 5 digits are significant.

For example, if the exact answer is 3.14159 and or approximate answer is 3.14162, then our answer has 5 significant digits. Note that saying that our answer is correct to 5 significant digits does not guarantee that all of those 5 digits exactly is correct to 5 significant digits does not guarantee that all of those 5 digits exactly match the first 5 digits of the exact answer. In fact, if an exact answer is 6.001 and our computed answer is 5.997, then our answer has 3 significant digits and not one of them matches the digits in the exact answer. Also note that it may be necessary for an approximation to have more digits that are actually significant for it to have a certain number of significant digits. For example, if the exact answer is 6.003 and our approximation is 5.998, then it has 3 significant digits, but only if we consider the total 4-digit number and do not strip off the last nonsignificant digit.

Again, suppose you know that all digits are significant in the number 3.456; then you know that the exact number is at most 3.4564 or at least 3.4555. Some people may say that the number 3.456 is correct to 3 decimal places. This is the same as saying that it has 4 significant digits.

Why bother with significant digits? If you multiply (or divide) two numbers with the same number of significant digits, then the product will generally be at least twice as long, but will have roughly the same number of significant digits as the original factors. You can then dispense with the unneeded digits. In fact, to keep them would be misleading about the accuracy of the result.

Frequently, we can make an educated guess of the number of significant digits in an answer. For example, if we compute an iterative approximation such as

$$2.3123, 2.3125, 2.3126, 2.31261, 2.31262, \ldots$$

we would generally conclude that the answer is 2.3126 to 5 signficant digits. Of course, we may very well be wrong, and if we went on iterating the answer might end up as 2.4.

■ ROUNDING AND RULES OF COMPUTATION USED IN THIS BOOK

In hand and calculator computations, rounding a number is done to reduce the number of digits displayed and make the number easier to comprehend. In addition, if you suspect that the digit in the last place is not significant, then you might be tempted to round and remove this last digit. This can lead to error. For example, if the computed value is 0.64 and the true value is known to be between 0.61 and 0.67, then the computed value has only 1 significant digit. However, if we round it to 0.6 and the true value is really 0.66, then 0.6 is not correct to even 1 significant digit. In the interest of making the text easier to read, we have used the following rounding procedure.

ROUNDING PROCEDURES   To round off numbers:

1. Increase the last retained digit by 1 if the remainder is greater than or equal to 5; or
2. Retain the last digit unchanged if the remainder is less than 5.

Elaborate rules for computation of approximate data can be developed when needed (in chemistry, for example), but in this text we will use three simple rules:

RULES FOR SIGNIFICANT DIGITS   *Addition-subtraction*: Add or subtract in the usual fashion, and then round off the result so that the last digit retained is in the column farthest to the right in which both given numbers have significant digits.

Multiplication-Division: Multiply or divide in the usual fashion, and then round off the results to the smaller number of significant digits found in either of the given numbers.

Counting numbers: Numbers used to count or whole numbers used as exponents are considered to be correct to any number of significant digits.

ROUNDING RULE

We use the following rounding procedure in problems requiring rounding by involving several steps: *Round only once, at the end. That is, do not work with rounded results, since round-off errors can accumulate.*

■ CALCULATOR EXPERIMENTS

You should be aware that you are much better than your calculator at performing certain computations. For example, almost all calculators will fail to give the correct answer to

$$(10.0 \text{ EE} + 50.0) + 911.0 - (10.0 \text{ EE} + 50.0)$$

Calculators will return the value of 0, while you know at a glance that the answer is 911.0. We must reckon with this poor behavior on the part of calculators, which is called *loss of accuracy due to catastrophic cancellation*. In this case, it is easy to catch the error immediately, but what if the computation is so complicated (or hidden by other computations) that we do not see the error?

First, we want to point out that the order in which you perform computations can be very important. For example, most calculators will correctly conclude that

$$(10.0 \text{ EE} + 50.0) - (10.0 \text{ EE} + 50.0) + 911.0 = 911$$

There are other cases besides catastrophic cancellation where the order in which a computation is performed will substantially affect the result. For example, you may not be able to calculate

$$(10.0 \text{ EE} + 50.0)*(911.0 \text{ EE} + 73.0)/(20.0 \text{ EE} + 60.0)$$

but by rearranging the factors as

$$((10.0 \text{ EE} + 50.0)/(20.0 \text{ EE} + 60.0))*(911.0 \text{ EE} + 73.0)$$

should provide the correct answer of 4.555 EE 65. So, for what do we need to watch? Try not to subtract two numbers that are close to each other in magnitude. If you must, then be aware that you may obtain an inaccurate result. When you have a sequence of multiplications and divisions in a string, try to arrange the factors so that in each partial result up to that point, the intermediate answer stays as close to 1.0 as possible.

Second, since all computations a calculator performs are done with a finite number of digits, it is unable to do exact computations involving nonterminating decimals. This enables us to see how many digits the calculator actually uses when it computes a result. For example,

$$(7.0/17.0)*(17.0) - 7.0$$

should give the result, but on most calculators it does not. The size of the answer gives an indication of how many digits "Accuracy" the calculator uses internally. That is, the calculator may display decimal numbers that have 10 digits, but use 12 digits internally. If the answer to the above computation is something similar to 1.0 EE—12, then the calculator is using 12 digits internally.

■ TRIGONOMETRIC EVALUATIONS

In many problems you will be asked to compute the values of trigonometric functions such as the sine, cosine, or tangent. In calculus, trigonometric arguments are usually assumed to be measured in radians. You must make sure the calculator is in radian mode. If it is in radian mode, then the sine of a small number will almost be equal to that number. For example,

$$\sin(0.00001) = 0.00001 \cdots$$

If not, then you are not using radian mode—make sure you know how to put your calculator in radian mode.

■ GRAPHING BLUNDERS

When you are using the graphing features, you must always be careful to choose reasonable scales for the domain (horizontal scale) and range (vertical scale). If the scale is too large, you may not see important wiggles. if the scale is too small, you may not see important behavior elsewhere in the plane. Of course, knowing the techniques of graphing discussed in Chapter 3 will prevent you from making such blunders. Some calculators may have trouble with curves that jump suddenly at a point. An example of such a curve would be

$$y = \frac{e^x}{x}$$

which jumps at the origin. Try plotting this curve with your calculator using different horizontal and vertical scales, making sure that you understand how your calculator handles such graphs.

APPENDIX D   Short Table of Integrals

Each formula is numbered for easy reference. The numbers in this short table are not sequential, because this short table is truncated from the table of integrals found in the *Student Mathematics Handbook*.

BASIC FORMULAS

1. **Constant rule** $\int 0\, du = c$

2. **Power rule** $\int u^n\, du = \frac{u^{n+1}}{n+1};\quad n \neq -1$

   $\int u^n\, du = \ln|u|;\quad n = -1$

3. **Exponential rule** $\int e^u\, du = e^u$

4. **Logarithmic rule** $\int \ln|u|\, du = u \ln|u| - u$

Trigonometric rules

5. $\int \sin u\, du = -\cos u$

6. $\int \cos u\, du = \sin u$

7. $\int \tan u\, du = -\ln|\sec u|$

8. $\int \cot u\, du = \ln|\sin u|$

9. $\int \sec u\, du = \ln|\sec u + \tan u|$

10. $\int \csc u\, du = \ln|\csc u - \cot u|$

11. $\int \sec^2 u\, du = \tan u$

12. $\int \csc^2 u\, du = -\cot u$

13. $\int \sec u \tan u\, du = \sec u$

14. $\int \csc u \cot u\, du = -\csc u$

Exponential rule

15. $\int a^u\, du = \frac{a^u}{\ln a}\quad a > 0, a \neq 1$

Hyperbolic rules

16. $\int \cosh u\, du = \sinh u$

17. $\int \sinh u\, du = \cosh u$

18. $\int \tanh u\, du = \ln \cosh u$

19. $\int \coth u\, du = \ln|\sinh u|$

20. $\int \operatorname{sech} u\, du = \tan^{-1}(\sinh u)$

21. $\int \operatorname{csch} u\, du = \ln\left|\tanh \frac{u}{2}\right|$

Inverse rules

22. $\int \frac{du}{\sqrt{a^2 - u^2}} = \sin^{-1}\frac{u}{a}$

23. $\int \frac{du}{\sqrt{u^2 - a^2}} = \cosh^{-1}\frac{u}{a}$

24. $\int \frac{du}{a^2 + u^2} = \frac{1}{|a|} \tan^{-1}\frac{u}{a}$

25. $\int \frac{du}{a^2 - u^2} = \begin{cases} \frac{1}{a} \tanh^{-1}\frac{u}{a} & \text{if } \left|\frac{u}{a}\right| < 1 \\ \frac{1}{a} \coth^{-1}\frac{u}{a} & \text{if } \left|\frac{u}{a}\right| > 1 \end{cases}$

26. $\int \frac{du}{u\sqrt{u^2 - a^2}} = \frac{1}{a} \sec^{-1}\left|\frac{u}{a}\right|$

27. $\int \frac{du}{u\sqrt{a^2 - u^2}} = -\frac{1}{a} \operatorname{sech}^{-1}\left|\frac{u}{a}\right|$

28. $\int \frac{du}{\sqrt{1 + u^2}} = \sinh^{-1} u$

29. $\int \frac{du}{u\sqrt{1 + u^2}} = -\operatorname{csch}^{-1}|u|$

INTEGRALS INVOLVING $au + b$

30. $\displaystyle\int (au + b)^n du = \frac{(au + b)^{n+1}}{(n + 1)a}$

31. $\displaystyle\int u(au + b)^n du = \frac{(au + b)^{n+2}}{(n + 2)a^2} - \frac{b(au + b)^{n+1}}{(n + 1)a^2}$

32. $\displaystyle\int u^2(au + b)^n du = \frac{(au + b)^{n+3}}{(n + 3)a^3} - \frac{2b(au + b)^{n+2}}{(n + 2)a^3} + \frac{b^2(au + b)^{n+1}}{(n + 1)a^3}$

33. $\displaystyle\int u^m(au + b)^n du = \begin{cases} \dfrac{u^{m+1}(au + b)^n}{m + n + 1} + \dfrac{nb}{m + n + 1}\displaystyle\int u^m(au + b)^{n-1} du \\[2ex] \dfrac{u^m(au + b)^{n+1}}{(m + n + 1)a} - \dfrac{mb}{(m + n + 1)a}\displaystyle\int u^{m-1}(au + b)^n du \\[2ex] \dfrac{-u^{m+1}(au + b)^{n+1}}{(n + 1)b} + \dfrac{m + n + 2}{(n + 1)b}\displaystyle\int u^m(au + b)^{n+1} du \end{cases}$

34. $\displaystyle\int \frac{du}{au + b} = \frac{1}{a}\ln|au + b|$

35. $\displaystyle\int \frac{u\,du}{au + b} = \frac{u}{a} - \frac{b}{a^2}\ln|au + b|$

36. $\displaystyle\int \frac{u^2\,du}{au + b} = \frac{(au + b)^2}{2a^3} - \frac{2b(au + b)}{a^3} + \frac{b^2}{a^3}\ln|au + b|$

37. $\displaystyle\int \frac{u^3\,du}{au + b} = \frac{(au + b)^3}{3a^4} - \frac{3b(au + b)^2}{2a^4} + \frac{3b^2(au + b)}{a^4} - \frac{b^3}{a^4}\ln|au + b|$

INTEGRALS INVOLVING $u^2 + a^2$

55. $\displaystyle\int \frac{du}{u^2 + a^2} = \frac{1}{a}\tan^{-1}\frac{u}{a}$

56. $\displaystyle\int \frac{u\,du}{u^2 + a^2} = \frac{1}{2}\ln(u^2 + a^2)$

57. $\displaystyle\int \frac{u^2\,du}{u^2 + a^2} = u - a\tan^{-1}\frac{u}{a}$

58. $\displaystyle\int \frac{u^3\,du}{u^2 + a^2} = \frac{u^2}{2} - \frac{a^2}{2}\ln(u^2 + a^2)$

59. $\displaystyle\int \frac{du}{u(u^2 + a^2)} = \frac{1}{2a^2}\ln\left(\frac{u^2}{u^2 + a^2}\right)$

60. $\displaystyle\int \frac{du}{u^2(u^2 + a^2)} = -\frac{1}{a^2 u} - \frac{1}{a^3}\tan^{-1}\frac{u}{a}$

61. $\displaystyle\int \frac{du}{u^3(u^2 + a^2)} = -\frac{1}{2a^2 u^2} - \frac{1}{2a^4}\ln\left(\frac{u^2}{u^2 + a^2}\right)$

INTEGRALS INVOLVING $u^2 - a^2$, $u^2 > a^2$

74. $\displaystyle\int \frac{du}{u^2 - a^2} = \frac{1}{2a}\ln\left|\frac{u - a}{u + a}\right|$ or $-\frac{1}{a}\coth^{-1}\frac{u}{a}$

75. $\displaystyle\int \frac{u\,du}{u^2 - a^2} = \frac{1}{2}\ln|u^2 - a^2|$

76. $\displaystyle\int \frac{u^2\,du}{u^2 - a^2} = u + \frac{a}{2}\ln\left|\frac{u - a}{u + a}\right|$

77. $\displaystyle\int \frac{u^3\,du}{u^2 - a^2} = \frac{u^2}{2} + \frac{a^2}{2}\ln|u^2 - a^2|$

78. $\displaystyle\int \frac{du}{u(u^2 - a^2)} = \frac{1}{2a^2}\ln\left|\frac{u^2 - a^2}{u^2}\right|$

79. $\displaystyle\int \frac{du}{u^2(u^2 - a^2)} = \frac{1}{a^2 u} + \frac{1}{2a^3}\ln\left|\frac{u - a}{u + a}\right|$

80. $\displaystyle\int \frac{du}{u^3(u^2 - a^2)} = \frac{1}{2a^2 u^2} - \frac{1}{2a^4}\ln\left|\frac{u^2}{u^2 - a^2}\right|$

INTEGRALS INVOLVING $a^2 - u^2$, $u^2 < a^2$

93. $\displaystyle\int \frac{du}{a^2 - u^2} = \frac{1}{2a} \ln\left(\frac{a + u}{a - u}\right)$ or $\dfrac{1}{a} \tanh^{-1}\dfrac{u}{a}$

94. $\displaystyle\int \frac{u\,du}{a^2 - u^2} = -\frac{1}{2} \ln|a^2 - u^2|$

95. $\displaystyle\int \frac{u^2\,du}{a^2 - u^2} = -u + \frac{a}{2} \ln\left|\frac{a + u}{a - u}\right|$

96. $\displaystyle\int \frac{u^3\,du}{a^2 - u^2} = -\frac{u^2}{2} - \frac{a^2}{2} \ln|a^2 - u^2|$

97. $\displaystyle\int \frac{du}{u(a^2 - u^2)} = \frac{1}{2a^2} \ln\left|\frac{u^2}{a^2 - u^2}\right|$

98. $\displaystyle\int \frac{du}{u^2(a^2 - u^2)} = -\frac{1}{a^2 u} + \frac{1}{2a^3} \ln\left|\frac{a + u}{a - u}\right|$

99. $\displaystyle\int \frac{du}{u^3(a^2 - u^2)} = -\frac{1}{2a^2 u^2} + \frac{1}{2a^4} \ln\left|\frac{u^2}{a^2 - u^2}\right|$

100. $\displaystyle\int \frac{du}{(a^2 - u^2)^2} = \frac{u}{2a^2(a^2 - u^2)} + \frac{1}{4a^3} \ln\left|\frac{a + u}{a - u}\right|$

101. $\displaystyle\int \frac{u\,du}{(a^2 - u^2)^2} = \frac{1}{2(a^2 - u^2)}$

102. $\displaystyle\int \frac{u^2\,du}{(a^2 - u^2)^2} = \frac{u}{2(a^2 - u^2)} - \frac{1}{4a} \ln\left|\frac{a + u}{a - u}\right|$

103. $\displaystyle\int \frac{u^3\,du}{(a^2 - u^2)^2} = \frac{a^2}{2(a^2 - u^2)} + \frac{1}{2} \ln|a^2 - u^2|$

104. $\displaystyle\int \frac{du}{u(a^2 - u^2)^2} = \frac{1}{2a^2(a^2 - u^2)} + \frac{1}{2a^4} \ln\left|\frac{u^2}{a^2 - u^2}\right|$

105. $\displaystyle\int \frac{du}{u^2(a^2 - u^2)^2} = \frac{-1}{a^4 u} + \frac{u}{2a^4(a^2 - u^2)} + \frac{3}{4a^5} \ln\left|\frac{a + u}{a - u}\right|$

106. $\displaystyle\int \frac{du}{u^3(a^2 - u^2)^2} = \frac{-1}{2a^4 u^2} + \frac{1}{2a^4(a^2 - u^2)} + \frac{1}{a^6} \ln\left|\frac{u^2}{a^2 - u^2}\right|$

INTEGRALS INVOLVING $\sqrt{au + b}$

135. $\displaystyle\int \frac{du}{\sqrt{au + b}} = \frac{2\sqrt{au + b}}{a}$

136. $\displaystyle\int \frac{u\,du}{\sqrt{au + b}} = \frac{2(au - 2b)}{3a^2} \sqrt{au + b}$

137. $\displaystyle\int \frac{u^2\,du}{\sqrt{au + b}} = \frac{2(3a^2 u^2 - 4abu + 8b^2)}{15a^3} \sqrt{au + b}$

138. $\displaystyle\int \frac{du}{u\sqrt{au + b}} = \begin{cases} \dfrac{1}{\sqrt{b}} \ln\left|\dfrac{\sqrt{au + b} - \sqrt{b}}{\sqrt{au + b} + \sqrt{b}}\right| \\[2ex] \dfrac{2}{\sqrt{-b}} \tan^{-1}\sqrt{\dfrac{au + b}{-b}} \end{cases}$

139. $\displaystyle\int \frac{du}{u^2\sqrt{au + b}} = -\frac{\sqrt{au + b}}{bu} - \frac{a}{2b} \int \frac{du}{u\sqrt{au + b}}$

140. $\displaystyle\int \sqrt{au + b}\,du = \frac{2\sqrt{(au + b)^3}}{3a}$

141. $\displaystyle\int u\sqrt{au + b}\,du = \frac{2(3au - 2b)}{15a^2} \sqrt{(au + b)^3}$

142. $\displaystyle\int u^2\sqrt{au + b}\,du = \frac{2(15a^2 u^2 - 12abu + 8b^2)}{105a^3} \sqrt{(au + b)^3}$

INTEGRALS INVOLVING $\sqrt{u^2 + a^2}$

168. $\displaystyle\int \sqrt{u^2 + a^2}\,du = \frac{u\sqrt{u^2 + a^2}}{2} + \frac{a^2}{2} \ln|u + \sqrt{u^2 + a^2}|$

169. $\displaystyle\int u\sqrt{u^2 + a^2}\,du = \frac{(u^2 + a^2)^{3/2}}{3}$

170. $\displaystyle\int u^2\sqrt{u^2 + a^2}\,du = \frac{u(u^2 + a^2)^{3/2}}{4} - \frac{a^2 u\sqrt{u^2 + a^2}}{8} - \frac{a^4}{8} \ln|u + \sqrt{u^2 + a^2}|$

171. $\displaystyle\int u^3\sqrt{u^2 + a^2}\,du = \frac{(u^2 + a^2)^{5/2}}{5} - \frac{a^2(u^2 + a^2)^{3/2}}{3}$

172. $\displaystyle\int \frac{du}{\sqrt{u^2 + a^2}} = \ln|u + \sqrt{u^2 + a^2}|$ or $\sinh^{-1}\dfrac{u}{a}$

173. $\int \dfrac{u\,du}{\sqrt{u^2 + a^2}} = \sqrt{u^2 + a^2}$

174. $\int \dfrac{u^2\,du}{\sqrt{u^2 + a^2}} = \dfrac{u\sqrt{u^2 + a^2}}{2} - \dfrac{a^2}{2}\ln|u + \sqrt{u^2 + a^2}|$

175. $\int \dfrac{u^3\,du}{\sqrt{u^2 + a^2}} = \dfrac{(u^2 + a^2)^{3/2}}{3} - a^2\sqrt{u^2 + a^2}$

176. $\int \dfrac{du}{u\sqrt{u^2 + a^2}} = -\dfrac{1}{a}\ln\left|\dfrac{a + \sqrt{u^2 + a^2}}{u}\right|$

177. $\int \dfrac{du}{u^2\sqrt{u^2 + a^2}} = -\dfrac{\sqrt{u^2 + a^2}}{a^2 u}$

178. $\int \dfrac{du}{u^3\sqrt{u^2 + a^2}} = -\dfrac{\sqrt{u^2 + a^2}}{2a^2 u^2} + \dfrac{1}{2a^3}\ln\left|\dfrac{a + \sqrt{u^2 + a^2}}{u}\right|$

INTEGRALS INVOLVING $\sqrt{u^2 - a^2}$

196. $\int \dfrac{du}{\sqrt{u^2 - a^2}} = \ln|u + \sqrt{u^2 - a^2}|$

197. $\int \dfrac{u\,du}{\sqrt{u^2 - a^2}} = \sqrt{u^2 - a^2}$

198. $\int \dfrac{u^2\,du}{\sqrt{u^2 - a^2}} = \dfrac{u\sqrt{u^2 - a^2}}{2} + \dfrac{a^2}{2}\ln|u + \sqrt{u^2 - a^2}|$

199. $\int \dfrac{u^3\,du}{\sqrt{u^2 - a^2}} = \dfrac{(u^2 - a^2)^{3/2}}{3} + a^2\sqrt{u^2 - a^2}$

200. $\int \dfrac{du}{u\sqrt{u^2 - a^2}} = \dfrac{1}{a}\sec^{-1}\left|\dfrac{u}{a}\right|$

201. $\int \dfrac{du}{u^2\sqrt{u^2 - a^2}} = \dfrac{\sqrt{u^2 - a^2}}{a^2 u}$

202. $\int \dfrac{du}{u^3\sqrt{u^2 - a^2}} = \dfrac{\sqrt{u^2 - a^2}}{2a^2 u^2} + \dfrac{1}{2a^3}\sec^{-1}\left|\dfrac{u}{a}\right|$

203. $\int \sqrt{u^2 - a^2}\,du = \dfrac{u\sqrt{u^2 - a^2}}{2} - \dfrac{a^2}{2}\ln|u + \sqrt{u^2 - a^2}|$

204. $\int u\sqrt{u^2 - a^2}\,du = \dfrac{(u^2 - a^2)^{3/2}}{3}$

205. $\int u^2\sqrt{u^2 - a^2}\,du = \dfrac{u(u^2 - a^2)^{3/2}}{4} + \dfrac{a^2 u\sqrt{u^2 - a^2}}{8} - \dfrac{a^4}{8}\ln|u + \sqrt{u^2 - a^2}|$

206. $\int u^3\sqrt{u^2 - a^2}\,du = \dfrac{(u^2 - a^2)^{5/2}}{5} + \dfrac{a^2(u^2 - a^2)^{3/2}}{3}$

INTEGRALS INVOLVING $\sqrt{a^2 - u^2}$

224. $\int \dfrac{du}{\sqrt{a^2 - u^2}} = \sin^{-1}\dfrac{u}{a}$

225. $\int \dfrac{u\,du}{\sqrt{a^2 - u^2}} = -\sqrt{a^2 - u^2}$

226. $\displaystyle\int \frac{u^2\,du}{\sqrt{a^2-u^2}} = -\frac{u\sqrt{a^2-u^2}}{2} + \frac{a^2}{2}\sin^{-1}\frac{u}{a}$

227. $\displaystyle\int \frac{u^3\,du}{\sqrt{a^2-u^2}} = \frac{(a^2-u^2)^{3/2}}{3} - a^2\sqrt{a^2-u^2}$

228. $\displaystyle\int \frac{du}{u\sqrt{a^2-u^2}} = -\frac{1}{a}\ln\left|\frac{a+\sqrt{a^2-u^2}}{u}\right|$

229. $\displaystyle\int \frac{du}{u^2\sqrt{a^2-u^2}} = -\frac{\sqrt{a^2-u^2}}{a^2 u}$

230. $\displaystyle\int \frac{du}{u^3\sqrt{a^2-u^2}} = -\frac{\sqrt{a^2-u^2}}{2a^2u^2} - \frac{1}{2a^3}\ln\left|\frac{a+\sqrt{a^2-u^2}}{u}\right|$

231. $\displaystyle\int \sqrt{a^2-u^2}\,du = \frac{u\sqrt{a^2-u^2}}{2} + \frac{a^2}{2}\sin^{-1}\frac{u}{a}$

232. $\displaystyle\int u\sqrt{a^2-u^2}\,du = -\frac{(a^2-u^2)^{3/2}}{3}$

233. $\displaystyle\int u^2\sqrt{a^2-u^2}\,du = -\frac{u(a^2-u^2)^{3/2}}{4} + \frac{a^2 u\sqrt{a^2-u^2}}{8} + \frac{a^4}{8}\sin^{-1}\frac{u}{a}$

234. $\displaystyle\int u^3\sqrt{a^2-u^2}\,du = \frac{(a^2-u^2)^{5/2}}{5} - \frac{a^2(a^2-u^2)^{3/2}}{3}$

INTEGRALS INVOLVING cos au

311. $\displaystyle\int \cos au\,du = \frac{\sin au}{a}$

312. $\displaystyle\int u\cos au\,du = \frac{\cos au}{a^2} + \frac{u\sin au}{a}$

313. $\displaystyle\int u^2\cos au\,du = \frac{2u}{a^2}\cos au + \left(\frac{u^2}{a} - \frac{2}{a^3}\right)\sin au$

314. $\displaystyle\int u^3\cos au\,du = \left(\frac{3u^2}{a^2} - \frac{6}{a^4}\right)\cos au + \left(\frac{u^3}{a} - \frac{6u}{a^3}\right)\sin au$

315. $\displaystyle\int u^n\cos au\,du = \frac{u^n\sin au}{a} - \frac{n}{a}\int u^{n-1}\sin au\,du$

316. $\displaystyle\int u^n\cos au\,du = -\frac{u^n\sin au}{a} + \frac{nu^{n-1}}{a^2}\cos au - \frac{n(n-1)}{a^2}\int u^{n-2}\cos au\,du$

317. $\displaystyle\int \cos^2 au\,du = \frac{u}{2} + \frac{\sin 2au}{4a}$

INTEGRALS INVOLVING sin au

342. $\displaystyle\int \sin au\,du = -\frac{\cos au}{a}$

343. $\displaystyle\int u\sin au\,du = \frac{\sin au}{a^2} - \frac{u\cos au}{a}$

344. $\displaystyle\int u^2\sin au\,du = \frac{2u}{a^2}\sin au + \left(\frac{2}{a^3} - \frac{u^2}{a}\right)\cos au$

345. $\int u^3 \sin au \, du = \left(\frac{3u^2}{a^2} - \frac{6}{a^4}\right) \sin au + \left(\frac{6u}{a^3} - \frac{u^3}{a}\right) \cos au$

346. $\int u^n \sin au \, du = -\frac{u^n \cos au}{a} + \frac{n}{a} \int u^{n-1} \cos au \, du$

347. $\int u^n \sin au \, du = -\frac{u^n \cos au}{a} + \frac{nu^{n-1} \sin au}{a^2} - \frac{n(n-1)}{a^2} \int u^{n-2} \sin au \, du$

348. $\int \sin^2 au \, du = \frac{u}{2} - \frac{\sin 2\,au}{4a}$

349. $\int u \sin^2 au \, du = \frac{u^2}{4} - \frac{u \sin 2\,au}{4a} - \frac{\cos 2au}{8a^2}$

350. $\int \sin^3 au \, du = -\frac{\cos au}{a} + \frac{\cos^3 au}{3a}$

INTEGRALS INVOLVING sin *au* and cos *au*

373. $\int \sin au \cos au \, du = \frac{\sin^2 au}{2a}$

374. $\int \sin pu \cos qu \, du = -\frac{\cos(p-q)u}{2(p-q)} - \frac{\cos(p+q)u}{2(p+q)}$

375. $\int \sin^n au \cos au \, du = \frac{\sin^{n+1} au}{(n+1)a}$

376. $\int \cos^n au \sin au \, du = -\frac{\cos^{n+1} au}{(n+1)a}$

377. $\int \sin^2 au \cos^2 au \, du = \frac{u}{8} - \frac{\sin 4au}{32a}$

INTEGRALS INVOLVING tan *au*

403. $\int \tan au \, du = -\frac{1}{a} \ln|\cos au| = \frac{1}{a} \ln|\sec au|$

404. $\int \tan^2 au \, du = \frac{\tan au}{a} - u$

405. $\int \tan^3 au \, du = \frac{\tan^2 au}{2a} + \frac{1}{a} \ln|\cos au|$

406. $\int \tan^n au \, du = \frac{\tan^{n-1} au}{(n-1)a} - \int \tan^{n-2} au \, du$

407. $\int \tan^n au \sec^2 au \, du = \frac{\tan^{n+1} au}{(n+1)a}$

INTEGRALS INVOLVING INVERSE TRIGONOMETRIC FUNCTIONS

445. $\int \cos^{-1}\frac{u}{a} \, du = u \cos^{-1}\frac{u}{a} - \sqrt{a^2 - u^2}$

446. $\int u \cos^{-1}\frac{u}{a} \, du = \left(\frac{u^2}{2} - \frac{a^2}{4}\right) \cos^{-1}\frac{u}{a} - \frac{u\sqrt{a^2 - u^2}}{4}$

447. $\int u^2 \cos^{-1}\frac{u}{a} \, du = \frac{u^3}{3} \cos^{-1}\frac{u}{a} + \frac{(u^2 + 2a^2)\sqrt{a^2 - u^2}}{9}$

448. $\int \frac{\cos^{-1}(u/a)}{u} \, du = \frac{\pi}{2} \ln|u| - \int \frac{\sin^{-1}(u/a)}{u} \, du$

449. $\int \frac{\cos^{-1}(u/a)}{u^2} \, du = -\frac{\cos^{-1}(u/a)}{u} + \frac{1}{a} \ln\left|\frac{a + \sqrt{a^2 - u^2}}{u}\right|$

450. $\int \left(\cos^{-1}\frac{u}{a}\right)^2 du = u\left(\cos^{-1}\frac{u}{a}\right)^2 - 2u - 2\sqrt{a^2 - u^2} \cos^{-1}\frac{u}{a}$

451. $\int \sin^{-1}\frac{u}{a} \, du = u \sin^{-1}\frac{u}{a} + \sqrt{a^2 - u^2}$

452. $\int u \sin^{-1}\frac{u}{a} \, du = \left(\frac{u^2}{2} - \frac{a^2}{4}\right) \sin^{-1}\frac{u}{a} + \frac{u\sqrt{a^2 - u^2}}{4}$

453. $\int u^2 \sin^{-1}\frac{u}{a} \, du = \frac{u^3}{3}\sin^{-1}\frac{u}{a} + \frac{(u^2 + 2a^2)\sqrt{a^2 - u^2}}{9}$

454. $\int \frac{\sin^{-1}(u/a)}{u} \, du = \frac{u}{a} + \frac{(u/a)^3}{2\cdot 3\cdot 3} + \frac{1\cdot 3(u/a)^5}{2\cdot 4\cdot 5\cdot 5} + \frac{1\cdot 3\cdot 5(u/a)^7}{2\cdot 4\cdot 6\cdot 7\cdot 7} + \cdots$

455. $\int \frac{\sin^{-1}(u/a)}{u^2} \, du = -\frac{\sin^{-1}(u/a)}{u} - \frac{1}{a}\ln\left|\frac{a + \sqrt{a^2 - u^2}}{u}\right|$

456. $\int \left(\sin^{-1}\frac{u}{a}\right)^2 du = u\left(\sin^{-1}\frac{u}{a}\right)^2 - 2u + 2\sqrt{a^2 - u^2}\,\sin^{-1}\frac{u}{a}$

457. $\int \tan^{-1}\frac{u}{a} \, du = u\tan^{-1}\frac{u}{a} - \frac{a}{2}\ln(u^2 + a^2)$

458. $\int u\tan^{-1}\frac{u}{a} \, du = \frac{1}{2}(u^2 + a^2)\tan^{-1}\frac{u}{a} - \frac{au}{2}$

459. $\int u^2 \tan^{-1}\frac{u}{a} \, du = \frac{u^3}{3}\tan^{-1}\frac{u}{a} - \frac{au^2}{6} + \frac{a^3}{6}\ln(u^2 + a^2)$

INTEGRALS INVOLVING e^{au}

483. $\int e^{au} \, du = \frac{e^{au}}{a}$

484. $\int ue^{au} \, du = \frac{e^{au}}{a}\left(u - \frac{1}{a}\right)$

485. $\int u^2 e^{au} \, du = \frac{e^{au}}{a}\left(u^2 - \frac{2u}{a} + \frac{2}{a^2}\right)$

486. $\int u^n e^{au} \, du = \frac{u^n e^{au}}{a} - \frac{n}{a}\int u^{n-1} e^{au} \, du = \frac{e^{au}}{a}\left(u^n - \frac{nu^{n-1}}{a} + \frac{n(n-1)u^{n-2}}{a^2} - \cdots \frac{(-1)^n n!}{a^n}\right)$ if $n = $ positive integer

487. $\int \frac{e^{au}}{u} \, du = \ln|u| + \frac{au}{1\cdot 1!} + \frac{(au)^2}{2\cdot 2!} + \frac{(au)^3}{3\cdot 3!} + \cdots$

488. $\int \frac{e^{au}}{u^n} \, du = \frac{-e^{au}}{(n-1)u^{n-1}} + \frac{a}{n-1}\int \frac{e^{au}}{u^{n-1}} \, du$

489. $\int \frac{du}{p + qe^{au}} = \frac{u}{p} - \frac{1}{ap}\ln|p + qe^{au}|$

490. $\int \frac{du}{(p + qe^{au})^2} = \frac{u}{p^2} + \frac{1}{ap(p + qe^{au})} - \frac{1}{ap^2}\ln|p + qe^{au}|$

491. $\int \frac{du}{pe^{au} + qe^{-au}} = \begin{cases} \dfrac{1}{a\sqrt{pq}}\tan^{-1}\left(\sqrt{\dfrac{p}{q}}e^{au}\right) \\[2mm] \dfrac{1}{2a\sqrt{-pq}}\ln\left|\dfrac{e^{au} - \sqrt{-q/p}}{e^{au} + \sqrt{-q/p}}\right| \end{cases}$

492. $\int e^{au}\sin bu \, du = \frac{e^{au}(a\sin bu - b\cos bu)}{a^2 + b^2}$

493. $\int e^{au}\cos bu \, du = \frac{e^{au}(a\cos bu + b\sin bu)}{a^2 + b^2}$

INTEGRALS INVOLVING $\ln|u|$

499. $\int \ln|u| \, du = u\ln|u| - u$

500. $\int (\ln|u|)^2 \, du = u(\ln|u|)^2 - 2u\ln|u| + 2u$

501. $\int (\ln|u|)^n \, du = u(\ln|u|)^n - n\int (\ln|u|)^{n-1} \, du$

502. $\int u\ln|u| \, du = \frac{u^2}{2}\left(\ln|u| - \frac{1}{2}\right)$

APPENDIX E   Answers to Selected Problems

CHAPTER 1

PROBLEM SET 1.1, Page 8

*Many problems in this book are labeled ■ **What Does This Say?** These problems solicit answers in your own words or a statement for you to rephrase as given statement in your own words. For this reason, it seems inappropriate to include the answers to these questions in the answer section.*

5. $\frac{1}{3}$ **7.** π **9.** 2   **11.** 0

13. a.

b.

c.

d. There is no unique tangent line.

15. 4π **17.** $\frac{187}{512} \approx 0.3652$

PROBLEM SET 1.2, Page 19

1. a. $(-3, 4)$ **b.** $3 \le x \le 5$ **c.** $-2 \le x < 1$ **d.** $(2, 7]$

3. a.   **b.**

c.   **d.**

5. a. $d = 4$; $M = (3, 0)$ **b.** $d = 2\sqrt{5}$; $M = (0, 4)$

7. a. $d = 5$; $M = \left(1, -\frac{1}{2}\right)$ **b.** $d = \sqrt{2}$; $M = \left(-\frac{3}{2}, -\frac{3}{2}\right)$

9. $\{0, 1\}$ **11.** $\{-2, 7\}$ **13.** $\left\{\dfrac{-b \pm \sqrt{b^2 + 12c}}{6}\right\}$

15. $\{6, -10\}$ **17.** $\{-2, 5\}$ **19.** $\{\ \}$; no solution

21. $\left\{\dfrac{7\pi}{6}, \dfrac{11\pi}{6}\right\}$ **23.** $\left\{\dfrac{3\pi}{4}, \dfrac{5\pi}{4}, \dfrac{\pi}{3}, \dfrac{5\pi}{3}\right\}$ **25.** $\left\{\dfrac{2\pi}{3}\right\}$

27. $\left(-\infty, -\dfrac{5}{3}\right)$ **29.** $\left(-\dfrac{5}{3}, 0\right)$ **31.** $(2, 7]$

33. $[-1, 3]$ **35.** $(-\infty, 0) \cup \left(\dfrac{1}{2}, 5\right)$ **37.** $[7.999, 8.001]$

39. a. $\dfrac{\pi}{6}$ **b.** $\dfrac{\pi}{4}$ **41. a.** $\dfrac{\pi}{3}$ or $60°$ **b.** $\dfrac{\pi}{6}$ or $30°$

43. Length is 4 cm.

45. a. $\dfrac{\sqrt{2}}{2}$ **b.** $-\sqrt{2}$ **c.** $-\sqrt{3}$

47. a. 1.5574   **b.** -0.0584 **c.** 0.9656

49. $(x + 1)^2 + (y - 2)^2 = 9$ **51.** $x^2 + (y - 1.5)^2 = 0.0625$

53.

55.

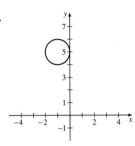

57. $\dfrac{\sqrt{2} - \sqrt{6}}{4}$ **59.** $2 - \sqrt{3}$

PROBLEM SET 1.3, Page 24

3. $2x + y - 5 = 0$ **5.** $2y - 1 = 0$

7. $x + 2 = 0$ **9.** $8x - 7y - 56 = 0$

11. $3x + y - 5 = 0$ **13.** $8x - 3y - 17 = 0$

15. $4x + y + 3 = 0$

17. $m = -\dfrac{3}{5}$; $(-5, 0)$, $(0, -3)$ **19.** $m = \dfrac{3}{2}$; $(2, 0)$, $(0, -3)$

21. $m = \dfrac{1}{5}$; $(0, 0)$ **23.** no slope (slope undefined); $(-3, 0)$

   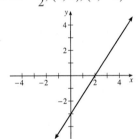

25. Point $(6, 6)$ with $5x + 2y - 11 = 0$; $8x - 3y + 1 = 0$; $8x - 3y - 30 = 0$; $5x + 2y - 42 = 0$. Answer is not unique. Another solution can be generated using the point $(2, 16)$.

27. a. -38.2 **b.** $-\dfrac{160}{9}$ **c.** -40

29.

31. Let t = time (in years) and V = value (in dollars). Consider ordered pairs (t, V).
$V = 200{,}000 - 19{,}000\,t$; in 4 years, $V = 124{,}000$.

33. a. $(3, 1)$, $(1, 11)$, and $(-3, -5)$; also draw parallelograms

35. 289 vehicles

PROBLEM SET 1.4, Page 39

1. $D:(-\infty, +\infty)$; $f(-2) = -1$; $f(1) = 5$; $f(0) = 3$

3. $D:(-\infty, +\infty)$; $f(1) = 6$; $f(0) = -2$; $f(-2) = 0$

5. $D:(-\infty, -3) \cup (-3, +\infty)$; $f(2) = 0$; $f(0) = -2$; $f(-3)$ is undefined

7. $D:(-\infty, -2] \cup [0, +\infty)$; $f(-1)$ is undefined; $f\left(\dfrac{1}{2}\right) = \dfrac{\sqrt{5}}{2}$; $f(1) = \sqrt{3}$

9. $D:(-\infty, +\infty)$; $f(-1) = \sin 3 \approx 0.1411$; $f\left(\dfrac{1}{2}\right) = 0$; $f(1) = -\sin 1 \approx -0.8415$

11. $D:(-\infty, +\infty)$; $f(3) = 4$; $f(1) = 2$; $f(0) = 4$

13. 9   **15.** $10x + 5h$ **17.** -1 **19.** $\dfrac{-1}{x(x + h)}$

21. a. Not equal **b.** Equal   **23. a.** Not equal   **b.** Equal

25. a. Neither   **b.** Odd   **27. a.** Even   **b.** Even

29. $(f \circ g)(x) = \sin(1 - x^2)$
$(g \circ f)(x) = 1 - \sin^2 x = \cos^2 x$

31. $(f \circ g)(u) = u$; $(g \circ f)(u) = u$

33. $(f \circ g)(x) = \cot x$; $(g \circ f)(x) = \tan(1/x)$

35. a. $u(x) = \tan x$; $g(u) = u^2$ **b.** $u(x) = x^2$; $g(u) = \tan u$

37. a. $u(x) = \dfrac{x + 1}{2 - x}$;   **b.** $u(x) = \dfrac{2x}{1 - x}$;
$g(u) = \sin u$ $g(u) = \tan u$

39.   **41.**

43.   **45.**

47.   **49.**

51.

53. $R(a, g(a))$, $S(x_0, g(x_0))$

55. a. \$4,500   **b.** \$371

57. a. $I = \dfrac{30}{t^2(6 - t)^2}$

b. $\dfrac{6}{5}$ or 1.2 candles; $15 \cdot 2^{-5}$ or 0.46875 candles

59. a. $(-\infty, 0) \cup (0, +\infty)$

b. $[1, p]$ for some positive integer p determined by the rat's ability to do the experiment.

c. 7 min   **d.** $n = 12$

e. Mathematically, yes, because the limit is 3, but practically, no, because n has an upper bound.

61. a. $625t^2 + 25t + 900$ **b.** \$6,600   **c.** 4 hours

PROBLEM SET 1.5, Page 47

1. 0   **3.** 6   **5.** 7   **7.** 6

9. 2   **11.** 2   **13.** 15   **15.** 10

17. 8   **19.** 2   **21.** -1

25. 1.00   **27.** 5.00   **29.** -0.17 **31.** Does not exist

33. -0.32 **35.** 0.00   **37.** 0.64   **39.** Does not exist

41. 1.00   **43.** 3.14   **45.** 0.00   **47.** 0.67

49. -0.06 **51.** 3.00   **53.** 1.00   **55.** 2.00

57. 0.00

59. a. $-32t + 40$ **b.** 40 ft/s
c. After 3 seconds; -56 ft/s   **d.** $t = 1.25$ sec

61. 228   **63.** 0

65. a. -1 **b.** 0
c. Oscillates widely at the origin; cannot determine the limit.

PROBLEM SET 1.6, Page 54

1. -9 **3.** -8 **5.** $-\dfrac{1}{2}$ **7.** 2   **9.** $\dfrac{\sqrt{3}}{9}$

11. 4   **13.** -1 **15.** $\dfrac{1}{9}$ **17.** $\dfrac{1}{2}$ **19.** 1

21. 2   **23.** 1   **25.** $-\dfrac{1}{9}$ **27.** 0   **29.** 0

35. -1 **37.** 1   **39.** -1 **41.** 0   **51.** $\dfrac{1}{6}$

53. $\dfrac{1}{2}$ **55.** Does not exist   **57.** 4   **59.** 8   **61.** 3   **63.** $-3x^{-2}$

PROBLEM SET 1.7, Page 66

1. Continuous; domain $0 \leq t < 24$, where t is the number of hours after midnight

3. Not continuous; $p \geq 0$, where p is the selling price of ATT stock; p quoted in eighth of a dollar

5. Not continuous; domain $m \geq 0$, where m is the number of miles traveled on the trip

7. No suspicious points; no points of discontinuity

9. Suspicious points: $x = 0$, $x = 1$; discontinuous at $x = 0$, $x = 1$

11. Suspicious point: $x = 0$; discontinuous at $x = 0$

13. Suspicious points: $t = 0$, $t = -1$; discontinuous at $t = 0$, $t = -1$

15. Suspicious point: $x = 1$; no points of discontinuity

17. Suspicious point: $x = \frac{\pi}{2} + n\pi$; discontinuous at $x = \frac{\pi}{2} + n\pi$

19. Suspicious points: $t = n\pi$; discontinuous at $t = n\pi$

21. $f(2) = 3$ **23.** $f(2) = \pi$

25. No value possible   **27.** Yes

29. Yes   **31.** No

33. Yes   **49.** $a = 1; b = -\frac{18}{5}$

51. $a = 1; b = \frac{1}{2}$ **53.** $a = 5; b = 5$

55. $x = 1.618$ **57.** $x = -0.414$

59. $x = 1.116$ **61.** $-\frac{1}{6}$

PROBLEM SET 1.8, Page 74

1. $|f(x) - L| = |(2x - 5) - (-3)|$
$= |2x - 2|$
$= 2|x - 1|$
$< 2\delta = \varepsilon$ if $|x - 1| < \delta$

Choose $\delta = \frac{\varepsilon}{2}$.

3. Doubter wins;
$|f(x) - L| = |(3x + 1) - 5|$
$= |3x - 4|$

Choose $\varepsilon = \frac{1}{4}$ and no δ can be found.

5. $|f(x) - L| = |(x^2 + 2) - 6|$
$= |x^2 - 4|$
$= |x - 2||x + 2|$
Note: If $|x - 2| < 1$ ($\delta < 1$), then $1 < x < 3$, so we note that $|x + 2| < 5$. Thus,
$|f(x) - L| < 5|x - 2|$
$\leq 5\delta = \varepsilon$ if $|x - 2| < \delta$

Choose $\delta = \min\left(1, \frac{\varepsilon}{5}\right)$.

7. $|f(x) - L| = |(x + 3) - 5|$
$= |x - 2|$
$< \delta = \varepsilon$ if $|x - 2| < \delta$
Choose $\delta = \varepsilon$.

9. $|f(x) - L| = |(3x + 7) - 1|$
$= |3x + 6|$
$= 3|x + 2|$
$< 3\delta = \varepsilon$ if $|x + 2| < \delta$

Choose $\delta = \frac{\varepsilon}{3}$.

11. $|f(x) - L| = |(x^2 + 2) - 6|$
$= |x^2 - 4|$
$= |x - 2||x + 2|$
$< 4\delta = \varepsilon$
If $\delta < 1$, then $-1 < x - 2 < 1$, so $1 < x < 3$; thus, $|x + 2| < 5$.
Choose $\delta = \min\left(1, \frac{\varepsilon}{5}\right)$, then $|x - 2| < \frac{\varepsilon}{2}$
and $|x + 2| < 5$, so $|f(x) - L| < 5 \cdot \frac{\varepsilon}{5} = \varepsilon$.

CHAPTER 1 REVIEW

Each chapter review begins with a proficiency examination. Calculus cannot be reduced to formulas and vocabulary, but your study of calculus should begin by understanding its basic tools; that is, you should know the basic concept before solving problems. It is suggested that you write out each of the answers to the concepts problems in your own hand before continuing with the practice problems. We provide all the answers to the practice problems to help you with your study of the chapter.

Practice Problems, Page 75

22. a. $6x + 8y - 37 = 0$
  b. $3x + 10y - 41 = 0$
  c. $3x - 28y - 12 = 0$
  d. $2x + 5y - 24 = 0$
  e. $4x - 3y + 8 = 0$

23. a.   **b.**

  c.   **d.**

e.

24. $x = -\frac{3}{2}, 1$

25. Algebraically they are the same, but they are not equal because they do not have the same domain.
Domain of f: $(-\infty, 0] \cup (1, +\infty)$
Domain of g: $(1, +\infty)$

26. $(f \circ g)(x) = \sin(\sqrt{1 - x^2})$;   **27.** $C = 25N\left(\frac{3N + 4}{2N - 5}\right)$
$(g \circ f)(x) = |\cos x|$

28. a. $\frac{3}{2}$ **b.** $\frac{1}{4}$ **c.** $-\frac{1}{4}$ **d.** 0

29. $A = -1$, $B = 1$

30. $f(x) = x + \sin x - \frac{1}{\sqrt{x + 3}}$

$f(0) = -\frac{1}{3} < 0$ and $f(\pi) > 0$; there is at least one root by the root location theorem.

Supplementary Problems, Page 76

1. $P = 30$; $A = 30$ **3.** $P = 10 + 2\sqrt{73}$; $A = 40$

5. $(x - 5)^2 + (y - 4)^2 = 16$ **7.** $5x - 3y + 3 = 0$

9. a. $y - 6 = \frac{5}{3}(x - 5)$

$y - 1 = -\frac{1}{4}(x + 2)$

$y + 2 = -\frac{7}{5}(x - 3)$

b. The point of intersection is $\left(\frac{34}{23}, \frac{3}{23}\right)$.

11. The highest point is 1,024 ft.

13. 1   **15.** $-\frac{1}{2}$ **17.** 3   **19.** $2x + 1$

21. $A = -1$ and $B = 1$

23. a. 15 in.   **b.** 21 in.   **c.** 29 in.   **d.** 19 in.

25. a. $(-\infty, 300) \cup (300, +\infty)$ **b.** $0 \le x \le 100$
c. 120   **d.** 300   **e.** 60%

27. a. 9π **b.** 6

29. a. $V = 16\pi$; $S = 24\pi$ **b.** $V = 15\pi$; $S = 3\sqrt{34}\pi + 6\pi$

33. $c = -\frac{4}{5}$; x-intercepts are $(2, 0)$, $(-2, 0)$

35. a. Between 7.5 °C and 5.8 °C; probably about 7.2 °C or 7.3 °C.
b. About 1.8 or 1.9 seconds

37. $s = \sqrt{67t^2 - 35t + 49}$; after 4 hours, $s \approx 31$ km

39. They will catch the spy in $\frac{1}{2}$ hr. In $\frac{1}{2}$ hr, the spy will have gone 36 km further, so the spy just makes it.

41. Take it on the 12th day.

45. a. Publisher B **b.** Publisher B
c. $D = (\text{profit } A - \text{profit } B)$
$$= \begin{cases} 0.6x \text{ for } x \le 4,000 \\ 35,600 - 0.3x \text{ for } 4,000 \le x \le 30,000 \\ -3,900 - 0.05x \text{ for } x \ge 30,000 \end{cases}$$
John should go with A when $D > 0$, go with B when $D < 0$, and break even when $D = 0$.
d. Break even is 12,000 copies.

47. When one zooms in *very* close to $x = 2$, one sees a sharp peak, or "cusp," which is missed by most graphs. There is no tangent at $x = 2$.

49. Solutions for PUTNAM EXAMINATION PROBLEMS can be found in the *American Mathematical Monthly*. We believe the library research to find the solution to these problems is as valuable as the interpretation of the solution when it is found. Consequently, we will simply provide the volume number in which the original problem and solution appeared. This problem is found in Vol. 67 of *American Mathematical Monthly*.

CHAPTER 2

PROBLEM SET 2.1, Page 93

3. 0   **5.** 2
7. 0   **9.** 0; all x
11. 3; all t **13.** $6r$; all r
15. $2x - 1$; all x **17.** $2s - 2$; all s
19. $\frac{\sqrt{5x}}{2x}$; all $x > 0$ **21.** $y = 3x - 7$
23. $3s - 4y + 1 = 0$ **25.** $x + 25y - 7 = 0$
27. $x + 5y - 68 = 0$ **29.** $216t - 6y - 215 = 0$
31. 2   **33.** 0
35. a. -3.9 **b.** -4

37.

$y' = 0$ at $x = \frac{1}{2}$
Horizontal tangent is
$y = -\frac{1}{4}$

39. a. $f'(x) = -4x$ **b.** $y = 4$ **c.** $\left(\frac{2}{3}, \frac{28}{9}\right)$

41. a.

43. 4   **45.** $\frac{1}{4}$

47. $y = Ax^2$, so $y' = 2Ax$; at $x = c$, we have $y = Ac^2$. The point is (c, Ac^2), and the slope of the line is $m = 2Ac$. The equation of the tangent line is $y - Ac^2 = 2Ac(x - c)$. The x-intercept $(y = 0)$ is $x = \frac{c}{2}$. The y-intercept $(x = 0)$ is $y = -Ac^2$.

49. a. $2x + 3$ **b.** $2x$; 3

  c. $f'(x) = g'(x) + h'(x)$

51.

53.

55. a.

(51)

(52)

(53)

(54)

  b. The graph is increasing where the derivative is positive and the graph is decreasing where the derivative is negative.

57. $f'(x)$ does not exist.

PROBLEM SET 2.2, Page 102

1. (3) 0; (4) 1; (5) 2; (6) $4x$; (7) $-2x$; (8) $-2x$

3. (15) $2x - 1$; (16) $-2t$; (17) $2s - 2$; (18) $-\frac{1}{2x^2}$; (19) $\frac{\sqrt{5x}}{2x}$;

  (20) $\frac{1}{2}(x + 1)^{-1/2}$

5. a. $12x^3$ **b.** -1 **7. a.** $3x^2$ **b.** 1

9. $2t + 2t^{-3} - 20t^{-5}$ **11.** $-14x^{-3} + \frac{2}{3}x^{-1/3}$

13. $1 - x^{-2} + 14x^{-3}$ **15.** $-32x^3 - 12x^2 + 2$

17. $\dfrac{22}{(x + 9)^2}$ **19.** $4x^3 + 12x^2 + 8x$

21. $f'(x) = 5x^4 - 15x^2 + 1$; $f''(x) = 20x^3 - 30x$; $f'''(x) = 60x^2 - 30$; $f^{(4)}(x) = 120x$

23. $f'(x) = 4x^{-3}$; $f''(x) = -12x^{-4}$; $f'''(x) = 48x^{-5}$; $f^{(4)}(x) = -240x^{-6}$

25. $18x - 14$ **27.** $7x + y + 9 = 0$

29. $6x + y - 6 = 0$ **31.** $x - 6y + 5 = 0$

33. $\left(\dfrac{4}{3}, -\dfrac{1}{27}\right)$, $(1, 0)$ **35.** $\left(\dfrac{3}{2}, \dfrac{4}{27}\right)$

37. $(1, -2)$; derivative does not exist at $x = 0$.

39. No horizontal tangent line

41. a. $\dfrac{2(x^3) - 3x^2(2x - 3)}{x^6} = \dfrac{-4x^3 + 9x^2}{x^6}$

  $= \dfrac{x^2(-4x + 9)}{x^6} = \dfrac{-4x + 9}{x^4}$

  b. $-3x^{-4}(2x - 3) + x^{-3}(2)$
    $= -6x^{-3} + 9x^{-4} + 2x^{-3}$
    $= -4x^{-3} + 9x^{-4}$

  c. $-4x^{-3} + 9x^{-4}$

  d. Note that the results of parts **a, b,** and **c** are all equal.

43. $2x - y - 2 = 0$

45. a. $4x + y - 1 = 0$ **b.** $x = 0$

47. $(0, 0)$, $(4, 64)$ **49.** No   **51.** Yes

53. k = degree of the polynomial function + 1; that is, the $(k + 1)$th derivative is 0.

PROBLEM SET 2.3, Page 110

1. 2   **3.** $\dfrac{3}{2}$ **5.** $\dfrac{5}{2}$ **7.** 0

9. $\sin 1$ **11.** 1

13. $\cos x - \sin x$ **15.** $2t - \sin t$

17. $2x \cos x - x^2 \sin x$ **19.** $2 \sin t \cos t$

21. $-x^{1/2}\sin x + \dfrac{1}{2} x^{-1/2}\cos x - x \csc^2 x + \cot x$

23. $\dfrac{x \cos x - \sin x}{x^2}$ **25.** $\dfrac{t \sec^2 t - \tan t}{t^2}$

27. $\dfrac{\sec^2 x - 2x \sec^2 x + 2 \tan x}{(1 - 2x)^2}$

29. $\dfrac{t \cos t + 2 \cos t - \sin t - 2}{(t + 2)^2}$

31. $\dfrac{1}{\cos x - 1}$ **33.** $\dfrac{2 \cos x - \sin x - 1}{(2 - \cos x)^2}$

35. $\dfrac{-2}{(\sin x - \cos x)^2}$ **37.** $-\sin x$

39. $-\sin \theta$ **41.** $2 \sec^2\theta \tan \theta$

43. $\sec^3\theta + \sec \theta \tan^2\theta$ **45.** $-\sin x - \cos x$

47. $\csc^3 y - 2 \csc^2 y \cot y + \csc y \cot^2 y$

49.

The graphs are almost the same.

```
Y₁₈(sin (X+.1)-s
in (X))/.1
Y₂₈cos X
Xmin=0
Xmax=2π
Xscl=1.5707963...
Ymin=-1.2
Ymax=1.2
Yscl=.5
```

51. $y - 1 = 2\left(x - \dfrac{\pi}{4}\right)$ **53.** $y - \dfrac{1}{2} = \dfrac{\sqrt{3}}{2}\left(x - \dfrac{\pi}{6}\right)$

55. $y = 2x$ **57.** $y - \dfrac{\pi}{6} = \left(\dfrac{3 - \pi\sqrt{3}}{6}\right)\left(x - \dfrac{\pi}{3}\right)$

59. $\dfrac{d^2y}{dx^2} + y = 0$ **61.** $A = 0; B = -\dfrac{3}{2}$

PROBLEM SET 2.4, Page 117

1. 1   **3.** -3 **5.** $\dfrac{13}{4}$ **7.** -1

9. 4   **11.** -1 **13.** -6

15. a. $v(t) = 2t - 2$ **b.** $a(t) = 2$

c. Advancing on $(1, 2]$; retreating on $[0, 1)$; total distance traveled is 2 units.

d. Always accelerating on $[1, 2]$

17. a. $v(t) = 3t^2 - 18t + 15$

b. $a(t) = 6t - 18$

c. Advancing on $[0, 1) \cup (5, 6]$; retreating on $(1, 5)$; total distance traveled is 46 units.

d. Accelerating on $(3, 6]$; decelerating on $[0, 3)$

19. a. $v(t) = -2t^{-2} - 2t^{-3}$

b. $a(t) = 4t^{-3} + 6t^{-4}$

c. Always retreating; total distance traveled is 20/9 units.

d. Accelerating on $[1, 3]$

21. a. $v(t) = -3 \sin t$ **b.** $a(t) = -3 \cos t$

c. Advancing on $(\pi, 2\pi]$; retreating on $[0, \pi)$; total distance traveled is 12 units.

d. Accelerating on $\left(\dfrac{\pi}{2}, \dfrac{3\pi}{2}\right)$; decelerating on $\left[0, \dfrac{\pi}{2}\right) \cup \left(\dfrac{3\pi}{2}, 2\pi\right]$

23. a. -6

b. Scores will be steadily decreasing.

25. 136 units

27. a. 9.8 m/min   **b.** 9.8 m

29. a. 64 ft/s   **b.** 336 ft

c. $-32t + 64$ **d.** -160 ft/s

31. 30 ft   **33.** 144 ft

35. $v_0 = 24$ ft/s; height of cliff is 126 ft

37. a. $200t + 400$ **b.** 1,400

c. Increase by 1,500

39. a. 0.2 ppm/yr   **b.** 0.15 ppm

c. 0.25 ppm

41. 91 thousand/hr

43. a. 20   **b.** 0.39

45. 7.5%

47. a. $\dfrac{-3t^2 + 12t}{5 - t^3 + 6t^2} \cdot 100$ **b.** Between 2nd and 3rd wk

49. The slower car is traveling at $15\sqrt{3} \approx 26$ mi/h

51. $\dfrac{dV}{ds} = 3s^2$; it is 50% of the surface area.

53. $\dfrac{dP}{dV} = \dfrac{-kT}{(V - B)^2} + \dfrac{2A}{V^3}$

PROBLEM SET 2.5, Page 126

3. $6(3x - 2)$ **5.** $\dfrac{-8x}{(x^2 - 9)^3}$

7. $-2x \sin(x^2 + 7)$

9. a. $5u^4$ **b.** 3   **c.** $15(3x - 1)^4$

11. a. $15u^{14}$ **b.** $6x + 5$ **c.** $15(6x + 5)(3x^2 + 5x - 7)^{14}$

13. a. $2 \sin x\cos^2 x - \sin^3 x$ **b.** $-\sin^2\theta\sin x$

15. $4 \cos(4\theta + 2)$ **17.** $2x\tan x^2 + 2x^3\sec^2 x^2$

19. $2x(\cos^2 x^2 - \sin^2 x^2)$

21. $2x(2x^2 + 1)^3(x^2 - 2)^4(18x^2 - 11)$

23. $2t(\cos t^2 - t^2\cos t^2 - \sin t^2)$

25. $3(t^2 - 1)^2[2t \cos(3t + 2) - t^2\sin(3t + 2) + \sin(3t + 2)]$

27. $\dfrac{7x}{(2x^2 - 1)^{1/2}(3x^2 + 2)^{3/2}}$

29. a. $x \sin x^2(\cos x^2)^{-3/2}$ **b.** $\dfrac{\tan x}{|\cos x|}$

31. $\dfrac{2x\sqrt{x} + 1}{3\sqrt{x}(x^2 + 2\sqrt{x})^{2/3}}$ **33.** $y - 3 = \dfrac{2}{3}(x - 2)$

35. $y - \dfrac{1}{16} = 0$ **37.** $y = 0$

39. $x = \dfrac{2}{9}$ **41.** $x = 1$ or $x = 7$

43. a. $f'(x) = 2(x + 3)(x - 2)(2x + 1); -3, 2, -\dfrac{1}{2}$

b. $f''(x) = 12x^2 + 12x - 22; \dfrac{-3 \pm 5\sqrt{3}}{6}$

45. a. -500π cm³/hr   **b.** -200π cm²/hr

47. $4,222.80/hr

49. −6 (decreasing demand)

51. a. $\dfrac{2}{x}$ **b.** $-\dfrac{1}{x}$

   c. $-\dfrac{1}{2x}$ **d.** $\dfrac{3}{(2x+1)(1-x)}$

53. 1.28 lux/s

55. b. 48π km/min

57. $y - 3 = -6(x + 3)$ **59.** $g'(2) = -24$

61. $\dfrac{d}{dx} f[f'(x)] = f'[f'(x)] \cdot f''(x)$

PROBLEM SET 2.6, Page 134

1. $-\dfrac{x}{y}$ **3.** $-\dfrac{y}{x}$

5. $-\dfrac{2x + 3y}{3x + 2y}$ **7.** $-\dfrac{(x + y)^2}{(x + y)^2 + 1}$

9. $-\dfrac{y^2}{x^2}$ **11.** $\dfrac{1 - \cos(x + y)}{1 + \cos(x + y)}$

13. $\dfrac{2x - y \sin xy}{x \sin xy}$

15. a. $-\dfrac{2x}{3y^2}$ **b.** $-\dfrac{2x}{3(12 - x^2)^{2/3}}$

17. a. y^2 **b.** $\dfrac{1}{(5 - x)^2}$

19. $y - 3 = \dfrac{2}{3}(x + 2)$ **21.** $y - \pi = (1 + \pi)x$

23. 0   **25.** $\dfrac{5}{4}$ **27.** $x = 1$ **29.** $-\dfrac{49}{100}y^{-3}$

31. $-4y^{-3}$ **33. a.** $-\dfrac{a^2v}{b^2u}$ **b.** $-\dfrac{b^2u}{a^2v}$

35. The line is $4a + 3b = 0$; points may vary.

41. $(\sqrt{2}, 0), \left(-\dfrac{2\sqrt{3}}{9}, -\dfrac{\sqrt{15}}{9}\right), \left(-\dfrac{2\sqrt{3}}{9}, \dfrac{\sqrt{15}}{9}\right)$

43. $x - y^2 = 9$ or $1 - 2yy' = 9$;
since $y^2 = x - 9$, we see two
possibilities are $y = \pm\sqrt{x - 9}$.

49. $\theta = \dfrac{\pi}{3} \left(\theta = \dfrac{2\pi}{3} \text{ is not a solution because } 0 \le \theta \le \dfrac{\pi}{2}.\right)$

PROBLEM SET 2.7, Page 141

1. $\dfrac{dy}{dt} = -3$ **3.** $\dfrac{dy}{dt} = 1{,}000$ **5.** $\dfrac{dx}{dt} = 15$

7. $\dfrac{dy}{dt} = \dfrac{4}{5}$ **9.** $\dfrac{dx}{dt} = \dfrac{30}{13}$ **11.** $\dfrac{dF}{dt} = -3$

13. $-10\sqrt{3} \approx -5.77$ units/s

15. $\dfrac{2}{\pi} \approx 0.637$ ft/s   **17.** $34,000 per year   **19.** -30 lb/in.^{2}/s

23. $\dfrac{dr}{dt} = \dfrac{-5}{64\pi} \approx -0.0249$ in./min; $\dfrac{dS}{dt} = -2.5$ in.^{2}/mi

25. $\dfrac{dV}{dt} = 19.2\pi \approx 60.319$ cm^3/min

27. 7.2 ft/s   **29.** 0.13 ft/min   **31.** 7.5 ft/min

33. −200 ft/s   **35.** 30 ft/s

37. a. If $s = \sqrt{(50t)^2 + (250 - 25t)^2}$, then

   $\dfrac{ds}{dt} = \dfrac{1}{s}[2500t - 50(250 - 25t)]$

   or $\dfrac{3{,}125t - 6{,}250}{\sqrt{3{,}125t^2 - 12{,}500t + 62{,}500}}$

   b. $t = 2$ hr
   c. $100\sqrt{5} \approx 224$ mi

39. 60 rad/hr or $\dfrac{180}{\pi} \approx 57°/$min   **41.** $\dfrac{5\pi}{4} \approx 3.927$ mi/hr

43. 8.875 knots at 2 P.M.; 10.417 knots at 5 P.M.

45. The water level is falling at about $\dfrac{32}{441\pi} \approx 0.023$ in./min.

47. a. $\cot \theta = \dfrac{x}{150}$ **b.** 0.27 rad/sec

   c. $\dfrac{d\theta}{dt} = \dfrac{v}{150}$; as v increases, so does $\dfrac{d\theta}{dt}$ and it becomes hard to see the seals.

PROBLEM SET 2.8, Page 152

1. a. 4.123105626   **b.** 4.125

3. a. 1.967989671   **b.** 1.97

5. a. 0.4714045208   **b.** 0.47

7. a. 1.4641   **b.** 1.4

9. a. 0.9949874371   **b.** 0.995

11. a. −0.00999983333   **b.** −0.01

13. a. 0.706399321   **b.** 0.7063

15. 0.003   **17.** −0.15

19. 0.00325   **21.** $6x^2\, dx$

23. $x^{-1/2}\, dx$ **25.** $(\cos x - x \sin x)\, dx$

27. $\dfrac{3x \sec^2 3x - \tan 3x}{2x^2}\, dx$ **29.** $(x^2 - 1)^{-1/2}(2x^2 - 1)\, dx$

33. 217.69 approx; 217.7155882 calculator; error is 0.0255882.

35. Within approx. 6%   **37.** Within approx. 3%

39. 0.05 ppm   **41.** −12,000 units

43. 28.3725 in.^{3}

45. Pulse rate decreases about 2 beats every 3 min.

47. Approx. 2% error

49. Decrease by about 7 particles/unit area

51. a. $472.70   **b.** $468.70

53. a. $\dfrac{4}{5}x + 3$ **b.** $4.00

   c. $11.80   **d.** $11.40

PROBLEM SET 2.9, Page 158

1. 3.072   **3.** 1.443   **5.** 2.006

7. −0.000   **9.** 0.453   **13.** 0.322

15. −2.5468   **17.** −2.79632   **19.** 0.876726

21. If $x_0 = 2$, then $x_1 = 0$ and it is impossible to continue. More formally,

$$\left|\frac{f(x)f''(x)}{[f'(x)]^2}\right| = \left|\frac{(1-x^{-1})(-2x^{-3})}{x^{-4}}\right|$$
$$= \left|\frac{-2x^{-3} + 2x^{-4}}{x^{-4}}\right| = |-2x + 2| = 2|x-1|$$

When $x_0 = 2$, $2|x-1|$ is not less than 1, so Newton's method fails.

23. Fails because $f'\left(\frac{4}{3}\right) = 0$, so we cannot form

$$x_{n+1} = x_n - \frac{f(x_n)}{f'(x_n)}.$$

25. 1.53981

27. Find one of the following roots: −1.16137, 1.27506.

29. −2.346407142

31. We need to find one of the following roots: 0.01672 or 1.78105. (*Note:* t is not negative.)

35. $K = \frac{1}{3}$

37. $A = \frac{20}{81}$

39. They are all the same, because $x_{n+1} = x_n + \frac{0}{f'(x)} = x_n$

41. $x_{n+1} = 2x_n - x_n^2 N$; $\frac{1}{2.355673} \approx 0.4245071$

CHAPTER 2 REVIEW

Practice Problems, Page 160

15. $3x^2 + \frac{3}{2}x^{1/2} - 2\sin 2x$

16. $\frac{-4x^7(\sqrt{3}x^3 - 6)}{(\sqrt{3}x^3 + 3)^5}$

17. $\frac{-x\cos(3 - x^2)}{[\sin(3 - x^2)]^{1/2}}$

18. $\frac{-y}{x + 3y^2}$

19. 0

20. $\frac{18(x - y)(x + 2y)}{(x - 4y)^3}$

21. $1 - 6x$

22. $y - 8 = 14(x - 1)$

23. Tangent: $y - \frac{1}{2} = \frac{\pi}{4}(x - 1)$

Normal: $y - \frac{1}{2} = -\frac{4}{\pi}(x - 1)$

24. 2π ft^2/s   **25.** 2.89571

Supplementary Problems, Page 161

1. $4x^3 + 6x - 7$

3. $\frac{-4x}{(x^2 - 1)^{1/2}(x^2 - 5)^{3/2}}$

5. $\frac{4x - y}{x - 2}$ or $\frac{2x^2 - 8x + 5}{(x - 2)^2}$

7. $-4\left(\sqrt{3x} + \frac{3}{x^2}\right)^{-5}\left[\frac{\sqrt{3}}{2\sqrt{x}} - \frac{6}{x^3}\right]$ or

$$\frac{24x^{-3} - 6(3x)^{-1/2}}{[(3x)^{1/2} + 3x^{-2}]^5} \text{ or } \frac{2x^7(4\sqrt{3} - x^{5/2})}{9(x^{5/2} + \sqrt{3})^5}$$

9. $10x^9(3x^2 + 1)(x^2 + 1)^9$ **11.** $\frac{(x^3 + 1)^4(46x^3 + 1)}{3x^{2/3}}$

13. $8x^3(x^4 - 1)^9(2x^4 + 3)^6(17x^4 + 8)$

15. $\frac{-\sin\sqrt{x}}{4\sqrt{x}(x\cos\sqrt{x})^{1/2}}$

17. $5(x^{1/2} + x^{1/3})^4\left(\frac{1}{2}x^{-1/2} + \frac{1}{3}x^{-2/3}\right)$ or

$$\frac{5x^{2/3}(x^{1/6} + 1)^4(3x^{1/6} + 2)}{6}$$

19. $(\cos x)(\cos(\sin x))$ **21.** $\frac{2x^{1/2}y^{1/2} - y^{1/2}}{x^{1/2}}$

23. $\frac{1 - y\cos(xy)}{x\cos(xy) - 1}$

25. $20x^3 - 60x^2 + 42x - 6$ **27.** $-\frac{2}{9}\left[\frac{3y^3 + 4x^2}{y^5}\right]$

29. $y = -3$ **31.** $y = -\frac{\pi}{2}\left(x - \frac{\pi}{2}\right)$

33. $x + y - 2 = 0$ **35.** $y - 1 = 4(x - 1)$

37. Tangent: $y - 1 = 12(x - 1)$

Normal: $y - 1 = -\frac{1}{12}(x - 1)$

39. $(3x^2 - 7)(2\cos t - t\sin t) + 6x(\sin t + t\cos t)^2$

41. $f'(x) = 4x^3 + 4x^{-5}$
$f''(x) = 12x^2 - 20x^{-6}$
$f'''(x) = 24x + 120x^{-7}$
$f^{(4)}(x) = 24 - 840x^{-8}$

43. $\frac{-4x^3}{(x^4 - 2)^{4/3}(x^4 + 1)^{2/3}}$

45. $\frac{dy}{dx} = \frac{x + 2y}{y - 2x}$; $\frac{d^2y}{dx^2} = \frac{5y^2 - 20xy - 5x^2}{(y - 2x)^3}$

47. Tangent: $x - y + 2 = 0$; normal: $x + y = 0$

49. 0.864321

51. "The change in tax rate with respect to time"; or "the derivative of the tax rate"

53. $3x^2[2(x^3 - 1)^2 + 3)]$ **55.** $36x(3x^2 + 1)$

57. $\sin\frac{1}{x} - \frac{1}{x}\cos\frac{1}{x}$ at $x \neq 0$; the derivative does not exist at $x = 0$.

59. 75 mi/hr   **61.** −36 cm^2/hr

63. 2.4×10^6 m/s^2 **65.** -1.8π mm^2/s

67. a. $C(x) = 2\left[\left(\frac{1,500}{x} + x\right)\right] + \frac{4,800}{x}$
$= 7,800x^{-1} + 2x$

b. Cost decreases by approximately $1.16.

69. By implicit differentiation we obtain $a = \frac{dv}{dt} = -\frac{kx}{m}$. Thus, $F = ma = m\left(-\frac{kx}{m}\right) = -kx$.

71. −100.9 ft/s   **73.** $-\frac{42}{5} = -8.4$ in.^{3}/m

77. See *American Mathematical Monthly*, Vol. 45.

CHAPTER 3

PROBLEM SET 3.1, Page 175

1. Maximum, 26; minimum, -34
3. Maximum, 0; minimum, -4
5. Maximum, 1; minimum, $-\frac{1}{8}$
7. Maximum, 0; minimum, -2
9. Maximum, 1; minimum, 0
11. Maximum, $\frac{5}{4}$; minimum, 0.41067 (approx.)
15. Maximum, 1; minimum, 0
17. Maximum, 0; minimum, -5
19. Maximum, 20; minimum, -20
21. Maximum, 76; minimum, -32
23. Maximum, $\frac{5}{6}$; minimum, $\frac{1}{6}$
25. Maximum, 0; minimum, $-\sqrt[6]{108} \approx -2.1822$
27. Not continuous on $[0, 2\pi]$
29. Maximum, 13; minimum, 5
31. $f(0) = 0$ 33. $g(3) = 3$ 35. $f\left(-\frac{1}{2}\right) = \frac{9}{4}$
39. **a, b,** and **d,** no such functions exist.
    c. Any continuous function will suffice.
43. $s'(0) = 60$ 45. 3 and 6
47. Maximum is 1,323 when $x = 21$ and $y = 63$.

PROBLEM SET 3.2, Page 181

3. 1   5. $\frac{\sqrt{21}}{3} \approx 1.5275$

7. $\sqrt[3]{1.25} \approx 1.0772$ 9. $\frac{9}{4}$

11. $-1 + \sqrt{3} \approx 0.7321$ 13. $\sin^{-1}\left(\frac{2}{\pi}\right) \approx 0.6901$

15. Not differentiable   17. Rolle's theorem applies.
19. $f(-8) \neq f(8)$; cannot be applied
21. Not continuous   23. Rolle's theorem applies.
25. The function $\tan x$ is continuous on $[u, v]$ and differentiable on (u, v). This implies that $\frac{\tan v - \tan u}{v - u} = \sec^2 a$ for some $u < a < v$. Because $\sec^2 a \geq 1$, $|\tan v - \tan u| \geq |v - u|$.
27. No, f is not differentiable at $x = 0$ on $(-2, 2)$.
29. No, f is not continuous at $x = 0$.
31. **b.** 0

33. $f'(x) = -\frac{1}{x^2}$, which is always negative; however, $\frac{f(b) - f(a)}{b - a} = \frac{-1}{ab}$ is always positive when $a < 0 < b$, so there is no such number w.

PROBLEM SET 3.3, Page 190

3.

5.

7.

9.

11.

13. **a.** $x = 0$, $x = -2$
    b. Increasing on $(-\infty, -2) \cup (0, +\infty)$; decreasing on $(-2, 0)$
    c. Critical points: $(0, 1)$, relative minimum; $(-2, 5)$, relative maximum
    d.

15. **a.** $x = \frac{5}{3}$, $x = -25$
    b. Increasing on $(-\infty, -25) \cup \left(\frac{5}{3}, +\infty\right)$ decreasing on $\left(-25, \frac{5}{3}\right)$
    c. Critical points: $\left(\frac{5}{3}, -9481\right)$, relative minimum; $(-25, 0)$, relative maximum
    d.

17. a. $x = 0$, $x = 4$

   b. Increasing on $(-\infty, 0) \cup (4, +\infty)$; decreasing on $(0, 4)$

   c. Critical points: $(4, -156)$, relative minimum; $(0, 100)$, relative maximum

   d.

19. a. $x = -1$, $x = 3$

   b. Increasing on $(-1, 3)$; decreasing on $(-\infty, -1) \cup (3, +\infty)$

   c. Critical points: $\left(-1, -\frac{1}{2}\right)$, relative minimum; $\left(3, \frac{1}{6}\right)$, relative maximum

   d.

21. a. $t = -1$, $t = 3$

   b. Increasing on $(-\infty, -1) \cup (3, +\infty)$; decreasing on $(-1, 3)$

   c. Critical points: $(3, -32)$, relative minimum; $(-1, 0)$, relative maximum

   d.

23. a. $x = 1$, $x = \dfrac{16}{3}$;

   b. Increasing on $(-\infty, 1) \cup \left(\dfrac{16}{3}, +\infty\right)$;

   decreasing on $\left(1, \dfrac{16}{3}\right)$

   c. Critical points: $\left(\dfrac{16}{3}, -\dfrac{1,225}{27}\right)$, relative minimum; $(1, 36)$, relative maximum

   d.

25. a. $x = 0$

   b. Increasing on $(0, +\infty)$; decreasing on $(-\infty, 0)$

   c. Critical point: $(0, 1)$, relative minimum

   d.

27. a. $x = 0$, $x = 1$

   b. Increasing on $(-\infty, 0) \cup (1, +\infty)$; decreasing on $(0, 1)$

   c. Critical points: $(1, -3)$, relative minimum; $(0, 0)$, relative maximum

   d.

29. a. $x = \dfrac{7\pi}{6}$, $x = \dfrac{11\pi}{6}$

   b. Increasing on $\left(\dfrac{7\pi}{6}, \dfrac{11\pi}{6}\right)$;

   decreasing on $\left(0, \dfrac{7\pi}{6}\right) \cup \left(\dfrac{11\pi}{6}, 2\pi\right)$

   c. Critical points: $\left(\dfrac{7\pi}{6}, -5.3972\right)$, relative minimum; $\left(\dfrac{11\pi}{6}, -4.0275\right)$, relative maximum

   d.

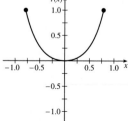

31. a. $x = 0$

   b. Increasing on $\left(0, \dfrac{\pi}{4}\right)$;

   decreasing on $\left(-\dfrac{\pi}{4}, 0\right)$

   c. Critical point: $(0, 0)$, relative minimum

   d.

33. a. $x = 25\pi^2$, $x = 75\pi^2$

   b. Increasing on $(0, 25\pi^2) \cup (75\pi^2, 100\pi^2)$; decreasing on $(25\pi^2, 75\pi^2)$

c. Critical points: $(75\pi^2, -1)$, relative minimum; $(25\pi^2, 1)$, relative maximum

d.

37. Relative minimum at $x = 1$

39. Relative minimum at $x = 4$

41. Relative maximum at $x = -3$; relative minimum at $x = \frac{1}{2}$; neither at $x = 1$

45. $a = -\frac{9}{25}$, $b = \frac{18}{5}$, $c = 3$

49.

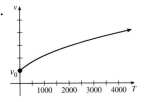

51. $A = -16$, $B = 24$, $C = 0$, $D = -15$; relative maximum at $x = 0$; neither at $x = 2$

53. Neither at $x = -\frac{B}{A}$; relative minimum at $x = -\frac{2B}{5A}$; neither at $x = 0$

55. Critical points: $(0, 0)$ and $(-0.71, 0.30)$

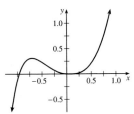

61. True

63. False; counterexamples vary.

65. False; counterexamples vary.

67. False; counterexamples vary.

PROBLEM SET 3.4, Page 201

5. Critical point: $(-18, -1)$, relative minimum; increasing on $(-18, +\infty)$; decreasing on $(-\infty, -18)$; concave up on $(-\infty, +\infty)$

7. Critical points: $(-3, 20)$, relative maximum; $(3, -16)$, relative minimum; increasing on $(-\infty, -3) \cup (3, +\infty)$; decreasing on $(-3, 3)$; inflection point: $(0, 2)$; concave up on $(0, +\infty)$; concave down on $(-\infty, 0)$

9. Critical points: $(-3, -11)$, relative maximum; $(3, 13)$, relative minimum; increasing on $(-\infty, -3) \cup (3, +\infty)$; decreasing on $(-3, 0) \cup (0, 3)$; concave up on $(0, +\infty)$; concave down on $(-\infty, 0)$

11. Critical points: $(0, 26)$, relative maximum; $(-6.38, -852.22)$, relative minimum; $(1.88, -6.47)$, relative minimum; increasing on $(-6.38, 0) \cup (1.88, +\infty)$; decreasing on $(-\infty, -6.38) \cup (0, 1.88)$; inflection points: $(-4, -486)$, $(1, 9)$; concave up on $(-\infty, -4) \cup (1, +\infty)$; concave down on $(-4, 1)$

13. Critical points: $(-3, -9)$, relative maximum; $(1, -1)$, relative minimum; increasing on $(-\infty, -3) \cup (1, +\infty)$; decreasing on $(-3, -1) \cup (-1, 1)$; concave up on $(-1, +\infty)$; concave down on $(-\infty, -1)$

15. Critical point: $(0, 0)$, relative minimum; increasing on $(0, +\infty)$; decreasing on $(-\infty, 0)$; concave up on $(-\infty, +\infty)$

17. Critical points: $(0, 0)$, point of inflection; $\left(\frac{1}{4}, \frac{1}{256}\right)$, relative maximum; increasing on $\left(-\infty, \frac{1}{4}\right)$; decreasing on $\left(\frac{1}{4}, +\infty\right)$; points of inflection: $(0, 0)$, $\left(\frac{1}{6}, \frac{1}{432}\right)$; concave up on $\left(0, \frac{1}{6}\right)$; concave down on $(-\infty, 0) \cup \left(\frac{1}{6}, +\infty\right)$

19. Critical points: $(0, 0)$, point of inflection; $(0.84, -1.8)$, relative minimum; increasing on $(0.84, +\infty)$; decreasing on $(-\infty, 0.84)$; points of inflection: $(0, 0)$, $(0.62, 0)$; concave up on $(-\infty, 0) \cup (0.62, +\infty)$; concave down on $(0, 0.62)$

21. Critical points: $\left(-1, -\dfrac{1}{2}\right)$, relative minimum; $\left(1, \dfrac{1}{2}\right)$, relative maximum; increasing on $(-1, 1)$; decreasing on $(-\infty, -1) \cup (1, +\infty)$; points of inflection: $(0, 0)$, $\left(\sqrt{3}, \dfrac{\sqrt{3}}{4}\right)$, $\left(-\sqrt{3}, \dfrac{\sqrt{3}}{4}\right)$; concave up on $(-\sqrt{3}, 0) \cup (\sqrt{3}, +\infty)$; concave down on $(-\infty, -\sqrt{3}) \cup (0, \sqrt{3})$

23. Critical points: $(0, 0)$, relative maximum; $(15.4, -444.4)$, relative minimum; increasing on $(-\infty, 0) \cup (15.4, +\infty)$; decreasing on $(0, 15.4)$; inflection point is $(3.9, -140)$; concave up on $(3.9, +\infty)$; concave down on $(-\infty, 3.9)$

25. Critical points: $\left(\dfrac{\pi}{12}, 1.13\right)$, relative maximum; $\left(\dfrac{5\pi}{12}, 0.44\right)$, relative minimum; increasing on $\left(0, \dfrac{\pi}{12}\right) \cup \left(\dfrac{5\pi}{12}, \pi\right)$; decreasing on $\left(\dfrac{\pi}{12}, \dfrac{5\pi}{12}\right)$; inflection points: $\left(\dfrac{\pi}{4}, 0.79\right)$, $\left(\dfrac{3\pi}{4}, 2.4\right)$; concave up on $\left(\dfrac{\pi}{4}, \dfrac{3\pi}{4}\right)$; concave down on $\left(0, \dfrac{\pi}{4}\right) \cup \left(\dfrac{3\pi}{4}, \pi\right)$

27. No critical points; decreasing on $(0, \pi)$; inflection points: $(0.52, 0.65)$, $(1.57, 0)$, $(2.62, -0.65)$; concave up on $(0.52, 1.57) \cup (2.62, 2\pi)$; concave down on $(0, 0.52) \cup (1.57, 2.62)$

33. $y' = 2Ax + B$ and $y'' = 2A$; concave up if $y'' > 0$ or $2A > 0$ or $A > 0$; concave down if $y'' < 0$ or $2A < 0$ or $A < 0$

37. Maximum deflection at $x = \dfrac{2\ell}{3}$

39. Maximum marginal cost is -2 at $x = 0$; minimum marginal cost is -58 at $x = 2$.

41. **a.** $-(2)^2 + 6(2)^2 + 13(2) = 42$
$-\dfrac{1}{3}(2)^3 + \dfrac{1}{2}(2)^2 + 25(2) = 49\dfrac{1}{3}$

b. $N(x) = -x^3 + 6x^2 + 13x - \dfrac{1}{3}(4 - x)^3$
$+ \dfrac{1}{2}(4 - x)^2 + 25(4 - x)$

c. $N'(x) = 0$ when $x = 2.5$, so the optimum time for the break is 10:30 A.M.

45. Critical points: $(-0.31, -5.21)$, relative minimum; $(2.20, -11.32)$, relative maximum; $(0.36, -4.76)$, relative minimum inflection points: $(0, -5)$, $\left(\dfrac{3}{2}, -\dfrac{137}{16}\right)$

47. Critical points: $(2.08, -3.12)$, $(4.37, -13.29)$, $(5.03, -25.34)$; inflection points: $(-5.68, -28.57)$, $(-2.54, -2.77)$, $(0.60, 3.32)$, $(3.74, -10.31)$

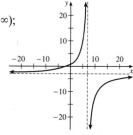

PROBLEM SET 3.5, Page 211

1. 0   **3.** 3   **5.** -1 **7.** $-\dfrac{3}{2}$

9. 0   **11.** $+\infty$ **13.** $\dfrac{1}{14}$ **15.** 0

17. $\dfrac{15}{7}$ **19.** -64 **21.** 1   **23.** 0

25. $+\infty$ **27.** $-\infty$ **29.** $+\infty$ **31.** $+\infty$

33. 1   **35.** $+\infty$

37. Asymptotes: $x = 7$, $y = -3$; graph rising on $(-\infty, 7) \cup (7, +\infty)$; concave up on $(-\infty, 7)$; concave down on $(7, +\infty)$; no critical points; no points of inflection

39. Asymptotes: $x = 3$, $y = 6$; graph falling on $(-\infty, 3) \cup (3, +\infty)$; concave up on $(3, +\infty)$; concave down on $(-\infty, 3)$; no critical points; no points of inflection

41. Asymptotes: $x = 0$; graph falling on $(-\infty, 0) \cup (0, +\infty)$; concave up on $(-\infty, -\sqrt[3]{2})$ and $(0, +\infty)$; concave down on $(-\sqrt[3]{2}, 0)$; critical point $(1, 3)$ is a relative minimum; point of inflection is $(-\sqrt[3]{2}, -2\sqrt[3]{4})$

43. Asymptotes: $x = 2$, $y = 1$; graph falling on $(-\infty, 2)$ $\cup$ $(2, +\infty)$; concave up on $(-\sqrt[3]{4}, 0)$ and $(2, +\infty)$; concave down on $(-\infty, -\sqrt[3]{4})$, and $(2, +\infty)$; critical point is $\left(0, -\dfrac{1}{3}\right)$; points of inflection $\left(0, -\dfrac{1}{8}\right), \left(-\sqrt[3]{4}, \dfrac{1}{4}\right)$

45. Asymptotes: $x = -4$, $x = 1$, $y = 0$; graph falling on $(-\infty, -4) \cup (-4, 1) \cup (1, +\infty)$; concave up on $(-4, -1)$, $(1, +\infty)$; concave down on $(-\infty, -4)$, $(-1, 1)$; no critical points; point of inflection is $(-1, 5)$

47.

49.

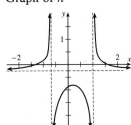

55. Solution 2 is incorrect; need to divide by the highest power of x (x^2 in this example).

57. **a.** $+\infty$ **b.** $+\infty$ **c.** $-\infty$ **d.** $-\infty$ **e.** $+\infty$

59. **a.** $\displaystyle\lim_{x \to +\infty} f(x) = \dfrac{a}{r}$; $f\left(\dfrac{at - cr}{br - as}\right) = \dfrac{a}{r}$

   b. Vertical asymptote

   c. Graph of g Graph of h

PROBLEM SET 3.6, Page 218

5.

7.

9.

11.

13.

15.

17.

19.

21.

For Problems 23–43, in addition to showing the requested information, as an aid to graphing, we show the critical points and inflection points with coordinates rounded to the nearest tenth unit.

23. Relative maximum at $x = -2$; relative minimum at $x = 0$; inflection point at $x = -1$; critical points: $(-2, 5)$, $(0, 1)$; inflection point: $(-1, 3)$

25. Relative maximum at $x = 0$; relative minimums at $x = \pm 3$; inflection points at $x = \pm\sqrt{3}$; critical points: $(-3, 0)$, $(0, 81)$, $(3, 0)$; inflection points: $(-1.7, 36)$, $(1.7, 36)$

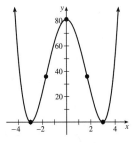

27. Relative maximum at $x = -3$; relative minimum at $x = 3$; critical value at $x = 0$ (neither; it is a vertical asymptote); critical points: $(-3, -11)$, $(3, 13)$; no inflection points

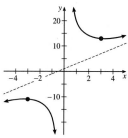

29. Relative maximum at $x = 3$; relative minimum at $x = -1$; inflection point at $x = 1$; critical points: $(-1, 0)$, $(3, 32)$; inflection point: $(1, 16)$

31. Relative minimum at $x = -3/2$; inflection point at $x = -2/3$, 1; critical points: $(-1.5, -32.1)$, $(1, 7)$; inflection points: $(-0.67, -16.1)$

33. Relative maximum at $x = 0$; relative minimum at $x = 14/5$; inflection point at $x = -7/5$; critical points: $(0, 0)$, $(2.8, -8.3)$; inflection point: $(-1.4, 10.5)$

35. Relative maximum at $x = 0$; relative minimum at $x = 4$; critical value at $x = 2$ (neither; it is a vertical asymptote); critical points: $(0, 0)$, $(4, 8)$; no inflection points

37. Relative maximum at $x = 5\pi/6$; relative minimum at $x = \pi/6$; inflection point at $x = \pi/2$; critical points: $(0.5, -0.3)$, $(2.6, 3.5)$; inflection point: $(1.6, 1.6)$

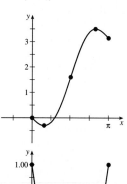

39. Relative minimum at $x = \pi/2$; critical point: $(1.6, 0)$

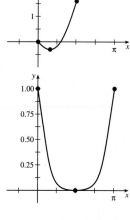

41. Inflection point: $(0, 0)$

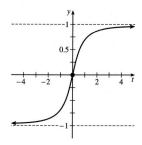

43. Critical values; $x = \pm\pi$ (neither; vertical asymptotes); inflection points at $x = 0$, $\pm 2\pi$; $(0, 0)$, $(6.2, 0)$, $(-6.2, 0)$

45.

47.

49. False; counterexamples vary.

51. False; counterexamples vary.

PROBLEM SET 3.7, Page 226

3. 8 ft × 8 ft

5. a. 80 ft × 80 ft   **b.** 80 ft × 160 ft

7. $360, when $x = 30$ **9.** 35 in. × 14 in. × 5 in.

11. $r = \dfrac{\sqrt{2R}}{2}$ and $h = \sqrt{2}R$ **13.** $r = \dfrac{2R}{3}$ and $h = \dfrac{H}{3}$

17. The largest box is 2 ft × 2 ft × 6 ft.

19. The minimum time is $\dfrac{\sqrt{5}}{3}$ hours or 44.72 minutes. He has 5 minutes and 17 seconds to defuse the bomb.

21. The minimum value for L is 14.283 (when $x \approx 7.395$).

23. The maximum area is $64\sqrt{2}$ (when $s = 2$).

25. $r = \sqrt[3]{\dfrac{3V}{5\pi}}$ **27.** 4 ft × 4 ft

29. $x = \dfrac{\dfrac{Md}{2m}}{\sqrt{1 - \dfrac{M^2}{4m^2}}} = \dfrac{Md}{\sqrt{4m^2 - M^2}}$

31. $R = r$ **33.** $d = 2\sqrt{2}$ ft ≈ 3 ft

35. 8 ft   **37.** Minimized at $T \approx 3.96$ °C

PROBLEM SET 3.8, Page 236

1. $P(x) = -\dfrac{5}{8}x^2 + \dfrac{65}{2}x - 98$; $x = 26$

3. $P(x) = \dfrac{-2(3x^2 - 145x + 450)}{5(x + 30)}$; $x = 20$

5. Maximum average cost of $25 when $x = 4$

7. a. $R(x) = \dfrac{380x - x^2}{20}$; $C(x) = 5x + \dfrac{x^2}{50}$;

$\quad P(x) = -0.07x^2 + 14x$

b. Maximum profit of $700 when $x = 100$ and priced at $14

9. Order 400 cases each time.

11. a. $x = 8$

b. Increasing if $\dfrac{128}{x^2} - 2 > 0$; this is true on $[0, 8)$.

$\quad$ Decreasing if $\dfrac{128}{x^2} - 2 < 0$; this is true on $(8, +\infty)$.

c.

15. The price should be $41 (assuming only $1 price increases are possible; otherwise the price is $40.83).

17. Lower the fare by $250.

19. Plant 20 additional trees for a total of 80 trees.

21. Plant 62 grapevines (an additional 12 grapevines). Note that we cannot plant 12.5 additional grapevines (the maximum). If we check, we obtain the same value for both 12 and 13, but why plant 13 when 12 gives the same result?

23. a. Maximum when $x = 80$ or when $p = 20$; R is increasing on $(0, 20)$ and decreasing on $(20, 20\sqrt{3})$.

b.

25. $\theta = \dfrac{\pi}{6}$ **27.** $r = \sqrt[3]{\dfrac{v_0}{2\pi}}$

29. The maximum value of V is $\dfrac{4}{27}Ar_0^3$, which occurs at $r = \dfrac{2}{3}v_0$.

31. a. 3 machines   **b.** $1,866.67

PROBLEM SET 3.9, Page 245

3. 8   **5.** $\dfrac{19}{5}$ **7.** 10   **9.** Does not exist

11. $\dfrac{1}{2}$ **13.** 0   **15.** $\dfrac{1}{2}$ **17.** 3

19. 3   **21.** 2   **23.** 0   **25.** 2

27. $\dfrac{1}{2}$ **29.** $-\infty$ **31.** $+\infty$ **33.** 0

35. 2   **37.** 0   **39.** $\dfrac{Ct\cos(\beta t)}{2\beta}$

PROBLEM SET 3.10, Page 251

1. $2x + C$ **3.** $x^2 + 3x + C$

5. $t^4 + t^3 + C$ **7.** $2u^3 - 3\sin u + C$

9. $\tan\theta + C$ **11.** $-2\cos\theta + C$

13. $\dfrac{2}{5}u^{5/2} - \dfrac{2}{3}u^{3/2} - \dfrac{1}{9}u^{-9} + C$

15. $\dfrac{1}{3}x^3 + \dfrac{2}{5}x^{5/2} + C$ **17.** $-t^{-1} + \dfrac{1}{2}t^{-2} - \dfrac{1}{3}t^{-3} + C$

19. $\dfrac{4}{5}x^5 + \dfrac{20}{3}x^3 + 25x + C$

21. $-x^{-1} - \dfrac{3}{2}x^{-2} + \dfrac{1}{3}x^{-3} + C$

23. $\dfrac{1}{3}x^3 + \dfrac{3}{2}x^2$ **25.** $\dfrac{4}{3}x^3 - 2x^2 + x + \dfrac{8}{3}$

27. a. $F(x) = 2\sqrt{x} - 4x + 2$

b. 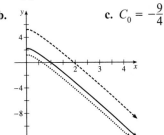   **c.** $C_0 = -\dfrac{9}{4}$

29. $249   **31.** 10,128 people

33. $k = 20$ ft/s^2 **35.** 4,167 mi/hr^2

CHAPTER 3 REVIEW

Practice Problems, Page 252

14. 2   **15.** $-\dfrac{1}{2}$ **16.** 0   **17.** 0

18. Relative maximum: $(-3, 29)$; relative minimum: $(1, -3)$; inflection point: $(-1, 13)$

19. Relative maximum: $(6.8, 38.3)$; inflection points: $(0, 0)$, $(-13.5, -96.4)$

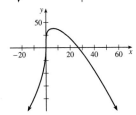

20. Relative maximum: $(\pi, 2)$;
relative minimum: $(0, -2)$,
$(2\pi, -2)$; inflection points:
$\left(\dfrac{\pi}{3}, -\dfrac{1}{4}\right)$, $\left(\dfrac{5\pi}{3}, -\dfrac{1}{4}\right)$

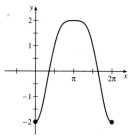

21. Relative maximum: $\left(0, \dfrac{1}{4}\right)$;
vertical asymptotes at $x = \pm 2$

22.

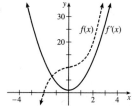

23. Maximum of 5.00512, where $x = 0.4$;
minimum of 4, where $x = 1$

24. 19 in. $\times$ 19 in. $\times$ 10 in.

25. The population will increase by 1,200, but the approximation is $\Delta P \approx 1,500$.

Supplementary Problems, Page 252

1.

3.

5.

7.

9.

11.

13.

15. Maximum $f(0) = 12$;
minimum $f(2) = -4$

17. 0   **19.** $-\dfrac{1}{2}$ **21.** 0

23. Does not exist   **25.** 1   **27.** 9

29. 0   **31.** $\dfrac{5}{2}x^2 - 6x + C$ **33.** $-\dfrac{1}{2}x^{-2} + C$

35. The red curve f is the function, the blue curve g is the derivative.

39. Radius is $P_0(\pi + 4)^{-1}$; length is $P_0(\pi + 4)^{-1}$; width is 2.

41. a^2 **43.** 35 trees; 6,125 peaches

45. 3 weeks; profit is \$1,225.

47. Price is \$60 (90 units) for a maximum profit of \$5,600.

49. 9 machines   **53.** $y = -x + \sqrt{2}$ **57.** $x = \dfrac{R}{\sqrt{2}}$

59. $f'(x) > 0$ when $x < -\dfrac{1}{3}$
and $x > 1$; $f'(x) < 0$ when
$-\dfrac{1}{3} < x < 1$; $f'(x) = 0$ when
$x = 1, -\dfrac{1}{3}$; $f''(x) = 0$ when
$x = \dfrac{1}{3}$

```
Y₁⊟X^3-X²-X+1
Y₂⊟nDeriv(Y₁,X,X
)
Y₃⊟nDeriv(Y₂,X,X
)
Xmin=-1.5 Ymin=-9
Xmax=2    Ymax=8
Xscl=.5   Yscl=2
```

61. $f'(x) > 0$ when
$x < -0.876123$ or
$x > 0.876123$; $f'(x) < 0$
when $-0.876123 < x$
< 0.876623; $f'(x) = 0$ when
$x = \pm0.876123$; $f''(x) \neq 0$

```
Y₁⊟X^3-X+1/X+1
Y₂⊟nDeriv(Y₁,X,X
)
Y₃⊟nDeriv(Y₂,X,X
)
Xmin=-2 Ymin=-20
Xmax=2  Ymax=20
Xscl=1  Yscl=10
```

63. When $x = 0.460355$

65. **a.** 27 mi/hr   **b.** 55 mi/hr

67. **a.** Estimate $r = 310$ **b.** 313.33

69. See *American Mathematical Monthly*, Vol. 48.

71. See *American Mathematical Monthly*, Vol. 92.

CHAPTER 4

PROBLEM SET 4.1, Page 264

1. 6 **3.** 120 **5.** 225 **7.** 9,800

9. $\frac{1}{2}$ **11.** 3 **13. a.** 3.5 **b.** 3.25

15. a. 2.71875 **b.** 2.523475 **17.** 0.795

19. 1.269 **21.** 1.2033 **23.** 18 **25.** 68

27. 2

29. False; the given area is a trapezoid.

$A = \frac{1}{2}[Ca + Cb](b - a) = \frac{1}{2}C(b^2 - a^2)$ not $\frac{1}{2}C(b - a)$

31. True; the graph represents the top half of a circle with center at the origin and radius 1. Therefore, the area is $\pi/2$.

33. True, since the graph of an even function is symmetric with respect to the y-axis.

37. a. $\frac{14}{3}$ **b.** $g(1) = \frac{2}{3}$, $g(2) = \frac{16}{3}$; $g(2) - g(1) = \frac{14}{3}$

c. Yes

39. By the tabular approach, we find the area (for $n = 64$) to be 21.83594.

41. By the tabular approach, we find the area (for $n = 256$) is 0.5990286; from Problem 17 the approximate area is 0.795, so these differ by about 0.2.

PROBLEM SET 4.2, Page 275

1. 2.25 **3.** 10.75 **5.** −0.88 **7.** 1.18

9. 28.88 **11.** 1.896 **13.** $-\frac{1}{3}$ **15.** 1.5

17. $-\frac{1}{2}$ **19.** $\frac{1}{2}$ **21.** $\int_{-2}^{4} f(x)\,dx = 1$; $\int_{-2}^{4} g(x)\,dx = 1$

23. 10 **25.** 35.5 **29.** 1.1 **31.** 3.41364 **35. c.** 5

PROBLEM SET 4.3, Page 285

1. 140 **3.** $16 + 8a$ **5.** $\frac{15}{4}a$ **7.** $\frac{3}{8}$

9. a. $\frac{5}{8} + \pi^2$ **b.** $1 + \sqrt{\pi}$

11. $-\frac{1}{10}$ **13.** $\frac{226}{15}$ **15.** $\frac{\pi}{4}$

17. a. 1 **b.** 1 **19. a.** $\frac{16}{3}$ **b.** $\frac{16}{3}$

21. a. $\frac{45}{2}$ **b.** $\frac{45}{2}$ **c.** 45

23. $\frac{1}{10}(2x + 3)^5 + C$ **25.** $\frac{3}{5}(x - 27)^{5/3} + C$

27. $\frac{x^3}{3} - \frac{1}{3}\sin 3x + C$ **29.** $\cos(4 - x) + C$

31. $\frac{1}{6}(t^{3/2} + 5)^4 + C$

33. a. $\frac{1}{36}(3x^2 - 5)^6 + C$

b. $\frac{1}{63}(3x - 5)^7 + \frac{5}{54}(3x - 5)^6 + C$ or

$\frac{1}{378}(3x - 5)^6(18x + 5) + C$

35. a. $\frac{1}{6}(2x^2 + 1)^{3/2} + C$

b. $\frac{1}{10}(2x + 1)^{5/2} - \frac{1}{6}(2x + 1)^{3/2} + C$ or

$\frac{1}{15}(3x - 1)(2x + 1)^{3/2} + C$

37. a. $\frac{1}{3}(x^2 + 4)^{3/2} + C$

b. $\frac{1}{5}(x^2 + 4)^{5/2} - \frac{4}{3}(x^2 + 4)^{3/2} + C$ or

$\frac{1}{15}(3x^2 - 8)(x^2 + 4)^{3/2} + C$

39. $\frac{1}{4}\sin^4 t + C$ **41.** $\frac{2}{3}$

43. $\frac{3 - \sqrt{3}}{2}$ **45.** $\frac{16}{3}$ **47.** $\frac{5}{2}$

49. The integrand $(\sqrt{x})$ is undefined on $(-4, 0)$ and therefore can not be integrated.

53. $\frac{3\pi^2 + 8}{8}$ **55.** 0 **57.** 0

59. a. T **b.** T **c.** F

61. a. It turns around when $t = 2$.
b. It turns around at $s = -3$.

63. $\frac{3}{2}\left(\frac{x - 1}{x + 1}\right)^{1/3} + C$

PROBLEM SET 4.4, Page 293

7. $x^2 + y^2 = C$ **9.** $x^{3/2} - y^{3/2} = C$

11. $3y^2 + 2(1 - x^2)^{3/2} = C$ **13.** $x^{3/2} + 3y^{1/2} = C$

15. $\cos x + \sin y = C$ **17.** $xy = C$

19. $x = Cy$

21. $\frac{dQ}{dt} = kQ$, where Q is the number of bacteria at time t ($Q > 0$).

23. $\frac{dT}{dt} = C(T - T_0)$, where T is the temperature at time t and T_0 is the surrounding temperature.

25. $\frac{dQ}{dt} = kq(P - Q)$, where Q is the number of people who have caught the disease by time t.

27. Family of curves: $2x - 3y = C$;
orthogonal trajectories:
$2Y + 3X = K$

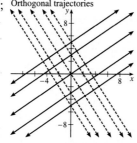
Orthogonal trajectories

29. Family of curves: $y = x^3 + C$;
orthogonal trajectories:

$Y = \frac{1}{3}X^{-1} + K$

Orthogonal trajectories

31. Family of curves: $xy^2 = C$;
orthogonal trajectories:
$X^2 - Y^2/2 = -K$

Orthogonal trajectories

33. a.

b.

c.

d.

e.

f.
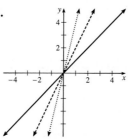

a and d are orthogonal trajectories;
b and e are orthogonal trajectories;
c and f are orthogonal trajectories.

35. About 28 min

37. a. $v(1.61) \approx 98.5$ ft/s

b. $s = 351.56$ ft when $t \approx 4.6875$ sec

39. a. In 1990 ($t = 0$) the population was 33,000.

b. In 1999 ($t = 9$) the population will be 42,000.

41. Value increases by \$2,820 during the next 20 days.

43. It will be 20 years, or, in other words, 10 years from now.

45. No; the stopping distance is 199.9, so the camel is toast.

47. 171.875 calories/s

49. a. $\dfrac{dh}{dt} = -\dfrac{4.8}{2,304}\sqrt{h} = -\dfrac{1}{480}\sqrt{h}$　　**b.** 39 min

PROBLEM SET 4.5, Page 301

1. $\frac{1}{2}\sqrt[3]{30} \approx 1.55$, which is between 1 and 2

3. $\sqrt{5} \approx 2.24$, which is between 1 and 5

5. Mean value theorem does not apply, because the function is not continuous.

7. $F(x) = 2x^2 + 9x + C$; $F'(x) = 4x + 9$

9. $F(x) = \frac{4}{5}x^{5/4} - 4x - \frac{16\sqrt{2}}{5} + 16$; $F'(x) = x^{1/4} - 4$

11. $F(x) = -\frac{1}{6}(1 - 3x)^{-3} - \frac{1}{24}$; $F'(x) = \dfrac{1}{(1 - 3x)^3}$

13. $A = 25$; $c = 5$　　**15.** $A = \frac{38}{3}$; $c = \dfrac{-3 \pm \sqrt{39}}{3} \approx 1.08$

17. $A = 1.839$; $c = \pm 0.744$

19. 1.5　　**21.** $\dfrac{4 - 2\sqrt{2}}{\pi} \approx 0.3729$

23. $\dfrac{4}{3}$　　**25.** -10

27. -25.375　　**29.** $\dfrac{3\pi}{4}$

31. $\cos x^2$　　**33.** $\dfrac{\sin(1 - t)}{t - 2} - \dfrac{3\sin 3t}{3t + 1}$

37. 18.7 °C　　**39.** $f(2) = \frac{1}{7}$

PROBLEM SET 4.6, Page 308

1. Trapezoidal, 2.344; Simpson's, 2.3333; actual value, $\frac{7}{3}$

3. a. 0.78279　　**b.** 0.78539

5. a. 2.03787　　**b.** 2.04860

9. 0.79 ± 0.05　　**11.** 0.727

13. 8.5

15. a. 164　　**b.** 18

17. a. 184　　**b.** 22

19. 3.1   **21.** 578   **23.** 494 m^2 **25.** $\dfrac{475}{6} \approx 79$

27. a. The error term involves $f^{(4)}(x)$, which is zero for a cubic, so the Simpson error is 0.

   b. The difference is that $f^{(4)}(x)$ is unbounded near $x = 2$.

29. 11.25

PROBLEM SET 4.7, Page 317

1. Vertical strip;

$$\int_1^{7/2} [(-x^2 + 6x - 5) - \left(\frac{3}{2}x - \frac{3}{2}\right)]\, dx = \frac{125}{48}$$

3. Horizontal strip;

$$\int_0^5 [0 - (y^2 - 5y)]\, dy = \frac{125}{6}$$

5. Vertical strip;

$$\int_0^\pi \sin x \, dx + \int_\pi^{2\pi} (-\sin x)\, dx = 4$$

Should also show a graph in Problems 7–23.

7. 1   **9.** $\dfrac{1}{12}$

11. $\dfrac{8}{3}$ **13.** $\dfrac{324}{5}$

15. $\dfrac{9}{2}$ **17.** $\dfrac{253}{12}$

19. $\dfrac{5}{2}$ **21.** $\dfrac{323}{12}$

23. $32\dfrac{3}{4}$

25. a. $0.75   **b.** 0

27. a. $75.00   **b.** $432

31. $\dfrac{16}{3} \approx \$5.33$ **33.** $\dfrac{128}{3} \approx \$42.67$

35. π **37. a.** 9 years   **b.** $12,150

39. a. It will be profitable for 12 years.

   b. $1,008

41. a. $20   **b.** 400

43. a. $R(q) = \frac{1}{4}(10 - q)^2 q$; $R'(q) = \frac{1}{4}(10 - q)(10 - 3q)$

   b. $q = 2$

   c. $p = 16$ when $q = 2$; consumer's surplus is $8.67

45. Consumer's surplus is $\dfrac{8}{3}$ units.

CHAPTER 4 REVIEW

Practice Problems, Page 319

19. $-\dfrac{3}{5}$ **20.** $x^5\sqrt{\cos(2x + 1)}$

21. $\dfrac{17}{3}$ **22.** $\dfrac{5}{2}$

23. $\dfrac{1}{2}$ **24.** 0

25. a. 36   **b.** $\dfrac{5}{12}$ **26.** 0

27. $v(t) = t^2 + t + 2$; $s(t) = \dfrac{t^3}{3} + \dfrac{t^2}{2} + 2t + 4$

28. a. $x = 5$ **b.** 1,250

29. $-y^{-1} = -\dfrac{1}{3}\cos 3x + C$ or

   $y = 3 \sec 3x + C$

30. a. $n = 26$ **b.** $n = 4$

Supplementary Problems, Page 320

1. 25   **3.** 6

5. 1,710   **7.** $\dfrac{6 - 2\sqrt{2}}{3}$

9. $\sqrt{3} - 1$ **11.** 0.810063

13. $\dfrac{1}{3}(x - 1)^3 + C$ **15.** $x + C$

17. $\dfrac{x^3(x^2 + 1)^{3/2}}{3} + C$

19. $-\dfrac{1}{15}(1 - 5x^2)^{3/2} + C$

21. 60

23. $3x^8\cos^4 x^3 - 2x^5 \cos^4 x^2$

25. $\dfrac{10}{3}$ **27.** $9 - 2\sqrt{6} \approx 4.1010$

29. $\dfrac{1}{20}$ **31.** $3 - \sqrt{3} \approx 1.2679$

33. $x = \dfrac{1}{1 - y} + C$ or $y = 1 - \dfrac{1}{x - C}$

35. $\tan y + \cot x = C$

37. $y^3 = 3x + C$

39. $\sin y^3 = -\dfrac{3}{2}\cos x^2 + C$

41. $\dfrac{4}{\pi}(\sqrt{2} - 1) \approx 0.5274$

43. 1.9541 (exact value is 2)

45. 0.9089   **47.** 0.9096

49. 0.2158 ($n = 6$)   **51.** 1.0141

53. -6.25 m/s^2 **55.** $776.48

57. $2.67   **59.** $x = 27$

61. $d = 10$ ft/s^2; $v_0 = 30$ ft/s;
   $s_0 = 45$ ft; $s_1 = 125$ ft

63. a. 5   **b.** $6,374.26

65. $76.80 increase   **67.** $20,700

73. See *American Mathematical Monthly*, Vol. 77.

75. See *American Mathematical Monthly*, Vol. 65.

CHAPTER 5

PROBLEM SET 5.1, Page 332

1.

3.

5. 31

7. 0.736 806 299 727

9. 13.463 738 035

11. 200.336 809 974

13. 9,783.225 895 91

15. 38,523.625 435 7

17. 2, −1

19. 3

21. 2, $-\dfrac{5}{3}$

23. $-\dfrac{3}{2}$

25. a. $b^x = 1$ when $b = 1$; algebraic

b. $b^x = 0$ when $b = 0$, $x > 0$; algebraic

27. a.
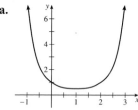

b. $(0, 1)$; $y \to +\infty$ as $x \to \pm\infty$

c. $E_{min} = 0.5$

29. $10,081.44

31. $2,456.19

33. a. 30.12%   **b.** 77.69%   **c.** 7.81%

35. $659.51

37. 108 °F

PROBLEM SET 5.2, Page 343

1. f and g are inverses.

3. Not inverses

5. Not inverses

7. $f^{-1} = \{(5, 4), (3, 6), (1, 7), (4, 2)\}$

9. $g^{-1}(x) = \sqrt{x + 5}$

11. $h^{-1}(x) = \dfrac{3x + 6}{2 - 3x}$

13. 0   **15.** 2   **17.** −2   **19.** 3.5

21. $\dfrac{3}{10}$ **23.** 4   **25.** 0.231 049 06

27. −1.391 662 509   **29.** $3^6 = 729$

31. 1   **33.** 2   **35.** $\dfrac{1}{\sqrt{1 - x^2}}$

37. 9

39.

$f^{-1}(x) = -\sqrt{x}$

41.
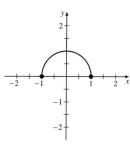

f^{-1} does not exist.

Inverse is drawn by reflecting in the line $y = x$.

43.

45. $k = -1.498$; depth is 3 m.

47. 11 years, 202 days

49. First National Bank is better.

51. 5.71%

PROBLEM SET 5.3, Page 350

1. $y' = 3e^{3x}$

3. $y' = \dfrac{12x^3 + 5}{3x^4 + 5x}$

5. $y' = 2x + 2^x \ln 2$

7. $y' = e^x + exe^{-1}$

9. $y' = 2xe^{x^2}$

11. $y' = -4e^{-4x} - 2e^{3-2x}$

13. $f'(t) = (2t + 1)e^{t^2+t+5}$

15. $f'(u) = e^{2u} + e^{-2u}$

17. $f'(x) = 2xe^{-x} - x^2e^{-x}$

19. $g'(t) = \dfrac{6t + 7}{(3t + 5)^2} e^{2t}$

21. $g'(t) = 2(e^{\sqrt{t}} - t)\left(\dfrac{e^{\sqrt{t}}}{2\sqrt{t}} - 1\right)$

23. $f'(u) = \dfrac{1}{u \ln u}$

25. $y' = \dfrac{\cos x - \sin x}{\sin x + \cos x}$

27. $y' = e^{-x}(1 - x)$

29. $y' = \dfrac{2x - ye^{xy}}{xe^{xy}}$

31. $\dfrac{dy}{dx} = \dfrac{1 - ye^{xy}}{xe^{xy} + \dfrac{2}{y}}$

37. $y' = y\left[\dfrac{10}{2x - 1} - \dfrac{1}{2(x - 9)} - \dfrac{2}{x + 3}\right]$

39. $y' = y\left[6x - \dfrac{6x^2}{x^3 + 1} + \dfrac{8}{4x - 7}\right]$

41. $y' = \frac{y}{x}\ln x$ **43.** $y' = y\left[\frac{1}{2\sqrt{x}}\ln|\sin x| + \sqrt{x}\cot x\right]$

45. $y' = y[2x\ln x + x]$

47. $y' = y[\ln|\sin x| + x\cot x]$

49. $y = 1$ **51.** $y = x$

53. $y = e$ **55.** $y = -2x + 2$

57. $y = \dfrac{1 - 3\ln 2}{8}x + \dfrac{3}{8}\ln 2$ or $y = -0.135x + 0.260$

59. $y = \dfrac{1}{32}(1 - \ln 4)(x - 4) + \dfrac{\ln 2}{4}$

61. $y - 9 = 240(x - 1)$ **63.** $y = 0$

PROBLEM SET 5.4, Page 356

1. c **3.** b

5. a. $D = (-\infty, +\infty)$; or the set $\mathbb{R}$

  b. None; the graph is always rising.

  c. None; intercept $\left(0, \frac{1}{3}\right)$.

  d. Concave up everywhere; no inflection points

7. a. $D = (0, +\infty)$

  b. None; the graph is rising for $x > 1$ and falling for $0 < x < 1$.

  c. Relative minimum at $(1, 1)$; no intercepts

  d. Concave up everywhere; no inflection points

9. a. $D = (-\infty, +\infty)$; or the set $\mathbb{R}$

  b. $x = 1$; the graph is rising on $(-\infty, 1)$; falling on $(1, +\infty)$.

  c. Relative maximum at $(1, e^{-1})$; intercept $(0, 0)$

  d. Concave up on $(2, +\infty)$; concave down on $(-\infty, 2)$; inflection point at $(2, 2e^{-2})$

11. a. $D = (0, +\infty)$

  b. $x = e^2$; the graph is rising on $(0, e^2)$; and falling on $(e^2, +\infty)$.

  c. Relative maximum at (e^2, e^{-1}); intercept $(1, 0)$

d. Concave down on $(0, e^{8/3})$, concave up on $(e^{8/3}, +\infty)$; inflection point $\left(e^{8/3}, \frac{4}{3}e^{-4/3}\right)$

13. a. $D = (-\infty, +\infty)$; or the set $\mathbb{R}$

  b. $x = 0$; the graph is rising on $(-\infty, 0)$; falling on $(0, +\infty)$

  c. Relative maximum at $(0, 1)$; intercept $(0, 1)$

  d. Concave up on $(-\infty, -2^{-1/2})$ and on $(2^{-1/2}, +\infty)$; concave down on $(-2^{-1/2}, 2^{1/2})$; points of inflection $(-2^{-1/2}, e^{-1/2})$, $(2^{-1/2}, e^{-1/2})$

15. a. $D = (-\infty, 0) \cup (0, 1)$

  b. None; the graph is rising on $(0, 1)$ and falling on $(-\infty, 0)$.

  c. None; intercepts $\left(\dfrac{-1 + \sqrt{5}}{2}, 0\right)$ and $\left(\dfrac{-1 - \sqrt{5}}{2}, 0\right)$

  d. Concave down on $(-\infty, 0)$ and on $(0, 2 - \sqrt{2})$; concave up on $(2 - \sqrt{2}, 1)$; point of inflection at $x = 2 - \sqrt{2}$

17. a. $D = (-\infty, +\infty)$; or the set $\mathbb{R}$

  b. The graph is rising on $(0, \infty)$ and falling on $(-\infty, 0)$.

  c. Relative minimum at $(0, 2)$; intercept $(0, 2)$

  d. Concave up everywhere; no inflection points.

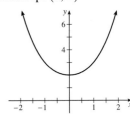

19. a. $D = (0, +\infty)$

  b. $x = 1$; graph is falling on $(0, 1)$ and rising on $(1, \infty)$.

  c. Relative minimum at $(1, 0)$; intercept $(1, 0)$

  d. Concave up on $(0, e)$, concave down on (e, ∞); inflection point at $(e, 1)$.

21. a. $S'(x) = \frac{1}{2}(e^x - (-1)e^{-x}) = C(x)$

    $C'(x) = \frac{1}{2}(e^x + (-1)e^{-x}) = S(x)$

b.

$y = \cosh x$

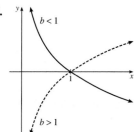

$y = \sinh x$

23.

25. Min, $f(1) = e \approx 2.71$;

max, $f(2) = \frac{1}{2}e^2 \approx 3.695$

27. Max, $f\left(\frac{\sqrt{2}}{2}\right) = \frac{1}{\sqrt{2e}} \approx 0.43$;

min, $f\left(-\frac{\sqrt{2}}{2}\right) = \frac{-1}{\sqrt{2e}} \approx -0.43$

29. 0   **31.** 0   **33.** e^{-2} **35.** e^2 **37.** 1

39. e

41. $G'(x) = (ABk)\exp(-kx - Be^{-kx})$

$G'(x) \neq 0$, so there are no critical points

$G''(x) = (ABk)\exp(-kx - Be^{-kx})(-k + Bke^{-kx})$

$G''(x) = 0$ when $e^{-kx} = \frac{1}{B}$, or $x = \frac{1}{k}\ln B$

43. Minimum, $g(e^{-1}) = 1 - e^{-1} \approx 0.6321$;

maximum, $g(4) = 8\ln 2 + 1 \approx 6.5452$

45. a. $e^{0.2} \approx 1.22$ **b.** 2%

47. $f(t) = Ae^{-kt}$

a. $f'(t) = -Ake^{-kt}$

b. $100\dfrac{f'(t)}{f(t)} = 100\left[\dfrac{-Ake^{-kt}}{-Ae^{-kt}}\right] = -100k$

49. a. 406 copies   **b.** 368 copies

51. 208 years from now

53. a. $v(t) = x'(t) = e^{-t}\left(\dfrac{1}{2\sqrt{t}} - \sqrt{t}\right)$

$a(t) = x''(t) = e^{-t}\left(\sqrt{t} - \dfrac{1}{\sqrt{t}} - \dfrac{1}{4t\sqrt{t}}\right)$

b. $T = 0.5$; $x(0.5) \approx 0.43$

c. Total distance is 0.49 unit.

55. $f(\pi) = 1$

PROBLEM SET 5.5, Page 362

1. $\frac{1}{5}e^{5x} + C$ **3.** $\frac{1}{2}\ln|2x + 1| + C$

5. $\frac{x^2}{2} + C$ **7.** $\frac{au^3}{3} - \ln|u| + e^u + C$

9. $-\frac{1}{2}e^{1-x^2} + C$

11. $-\frac{1}{3}\ln|1 - x^3| + \frac{1}{2}e^{x^2} + C$

13. $\frac{1}{4}\ln(2x^2 + 3) + C$

15. $2x + 11\ln|x - 5| + C$

17. $\frac{2}{3}e^{x\sqrt{x}} + C$ **19.** $\frac{2^{3+u}}{\ln 2} + C$

21. $\frac{1}{2}(\ln x)^2 + C$ **23.** $2\ln(\sqrt{x} + 7) + C$

25. $\ln(e^t + 1) + C$ **27.** $\frac{1}{2}\ln(5 + 2\sin x) + C$

29. $2\ln|\sin \sqrt{x}| + C$

31. $-\ln|\sin x + \cos x| + C$

33. $\frac{5}{6}\ln 3 \approx 0.92$ **35.** 0

37. $e - \sqrt{e} \approx 1.07$ **39.** $\frac{1}{2}\ln 2 \approx 0.3466$

41. $2.9\ln\left(\frac{e}{2} + \frac{1}{2}\right) \approx 1.79833$

43. $\frac{1}{4}$ **45.** $\frac{3 - 2\sqrt{2}}{\ln 2} \approx 0.2475$

47. $\frac{1}{15}\left(e^{12} - \frac{1}{e}\right) \approx 10{,}850$

49. $\frac{2}{\pi}\ln 2 \approx 0.44$ **51.** $\ln|\ln x| + C$

53. $\frac{3 + e^4}{2} \approx 28.8$ **55.** 4,207

57. $1.5 - 2\ln 2 \approx 0.11$ **59.** $\frac{8}{5}$

PROBLEM SET 5.6, Page 372

3. a. $\frac{\pi}{3}$ **b.** $-\frac{\pi}{3}$ **5. a.** $-\frac{\pi}{4}$ **b.** $\frac{5\pi}{6}$

7. a. $-\frac{\pi}{3}$ **b.** π **9.** $\frac{\sqrt{3}}{2}$ **11.** 3

13. $-\frac{2\sqrt{6}}{5} \approx -0.9798$ **15.** $\frac{1}{\sqrt{-x^2 - x}}$

17. $\frac{x}{(2 + x^2)\sqrt{x^2 + 1}}$ **19.** $\frac{6(\sin^{-1}2x)^2}{\sqrt{1 - 4x^2}}$

21. $\frac{1}{(1 + 4x^2)\sqrt{\tan^{-1}2x}}$ **23.** $\frac{1}{\cos^{-1}x\sqrt{1 - x^2}}$

25. $\frac{-1}{1 + x^2}$ **27.** $\frac{-\sin x}{|\sin x|}$

29. $\dfrac{1 - \sin^{-1}y - \dfrac{y}{1 + x^2}}{\dfrac{x}{\sqrt{1 - y^2}} + \tan^{-1}x}$

31. $\dfrac{1}{4}\tan^{-1}\left(\dfrac{x}{4}\right) + C$

33. $\dfrac{\sqrt{2}}{2}\sin^{-1}\left(\dfrac{x\sqrt{10}}{5}\right) + C$

35. $\ln(x^2 + 4x + 5) + \tan^{-1}(x + 2) + C$

37. $\dfrac{1}{2}\ln(x^2 + x + 1) - \dfrac{1}{\sqrt{3}}\tan^{-1}\left[\dfrac{2x + 1}{\sqrt{3}}\right] + C$

39. $-\sqrt{4 - 2x - x^2} + \sin^{-1}\left(\dfrac{x + 1}{\sqrt{5}}\right) + C$

41. $\tan^{-1}(1 + x) + C$

43. $\dfrac{\pi}{6}$ **45.** $\dfrac{\pi}{6} - \dfrac{1}{2}\tan^{-1}\left(\dfrac{1}{2}\right)$

47. $\dfrac{\pi}{12}$ **49.** $\dfrac{2x}{x^2 + 1}$

51. $\dfrac{\sqrt{1 - x^2}}{x}$ **53.** 1   **57.** $\dfrac{\pi}{12}$

59. Relative minimum at $x = \sqrt{ab}$;
relative maximum at $x = -\sqrt{ab}$

61.   **63.**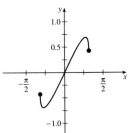

65. $3\sqrt{17} \approx 12.4$ ft

PROBLEM SET 5.7, Page 377

1. Let $L(x) = \displaystyle\int_1^x \dfrac{dt}{t}$. Then we have
$$L(xy) = L(x) + L(y) \text{ and } L(x^r) = rL(x)$$
In particular,
$$L(2^{-N}) = -NL(2) < 0$$
since
$$L(2) = \int_1^2 \dfrac{dt}{t} > 0$$
As $N \to +\infty$, $2^{-N} \to 0$ and $L(2^{-N}) \to -\infty$.
Thus,
$$\lim_{x \to 0^+} \ln x = -\infty$$

3. $n = 18$

5. a. $F'(x) = \dfrac{p}{x}$;
$G(x) = p \ln x$, so $G'(x) = \dfrac{p}{x} = F'(x)$.
Therefore, $F(x) = G(x) + C$.

b. If $x = 1$, then
$$0 = p \cdot 0 + C, \text{ so } C = 0$$
Thus, $F(x) = G(x)$
$$\ln x^p = p \ln x$$

9. It is clear that
$$\ln 2 < \ln e < \ln 3$$
$$e^{\ln 2} < e^{\ln e} < e^{\ln 3}$$
$$2 < e < 3$$

CHAPTER 5 REVIEW

Practice Problems, Page 379

17. a. $2xe^{-\sqrt{x}} - \dfrac{1}{2}x^{3/2}e^{-\sqrt{x}}$ **18. a.** $\dfrac{3}{\sqrt{1 - (3x + 2)^2}}$

b. $\dfrac{\ln 1.5}{x(\ln 3x)^2}$ **b.** $\dfrac{2}{1 + 4x^2}$

19. $\dfrac{dy}{dx} = y\left[\dfrac{2x}{(x^2 - 1)\ln(x^2 - 1)} - \dfrac{1}{3x} + \dfrac{9}{1 - 3x}\right]$

20. Relative minimum at $(-1, -2e)$;
relative maximum at $(3, 6e^{-3})$;
points of inflection at
$x = 2 \pm \sqrt{5}$; intercepts
$(0, -3)$, $(\pm\sqrt{3}, 0)$;
asymptote, $y = 0$

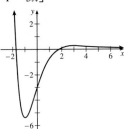

21. a. $\dfrac{9}{8}$ **b.** $\dfrac{(\ln x)^2}{2} + C$ **c.** $-\dfrac{1}{2}\ln|\cos 2x| + C$

22. a. e^4 **b.** Does not exist   **c.** 1

23. $\dfrac{1}{2}e^2 - e + \dfrac{1}{2} \approx 1.47624$

24. a. 11 yr 208 days   **b.** 11 yr 180 days
c. 11 yr 166 days

25. \$140

Supplementary Problems, Page 379

1. a. 1.504 077   **b.** 16.444 647   **c.** 1.107 149

3. a. $\dfrac{3}{5}$ **b.** $\dfrac{63}{65}$

5. a. $\sqrt{13}$ **b.** $\dfrac{\pi^2}{4}$

7. a. 16   **b.** $\dfrac{2\ln 3}{2\ln 3 - \ln 2} \approx 1.4084$

9. a. $f^{-1}(x) = \ln(1 + x^2)$

b. $f^{-1}(x) = \dfrac{5 + 7x}{x - 1}$

11. $f^{-1}(x) = \dfrac{b - xd}{cx - a}$; domain is $\left\{x \mid x \neq \dfrac{a}{c}\right\}$

13. $\dfrac{dy}{dx} = (4x + 5)e^{2x^2 + 5x - 3}$ **15.** $\dfrac{dy}{dx} = 3^{2 - x}(1 - x \ln 3)$

17. $\dfrac{dy}{dx} = \dfrac{y(1 + xye^{xy})}{x(1 - yxe^{xy})}$ **19.** $\dfrac{dy}{dx} = e^{\sin x}\cos x$

21. $\dfrac{dy}{dx} = \dfrac{e^{-x}}{x \ln 5}(1 - x \ln 3x)$ **23.** $\dfrac{dy}{dx} = \dfrac{2x^2 + 2xy^2 - 1}{2y - 2x - 2y^2}$

25. $\dfrac{dy}{dx} = \dfrac{\sin^{-1}x - x\dfrac{1}{\sqrt{1 - x^2}}}{(\sin^{-1}x)^2} + \dfrac{1}{x^2}\left(\dfrac{x}{1 + x^2} - \tan^{-1}x\right)$

27. $\dfrac{dy}{dx} = \cos x(\sin^{-1}x) + \dfrac{\sin x}{\sqrt{1 - x^2}} + \cot^{-1}x - \dfrac{x}{1 + x^2}$

29. $y = 2x - \dfrac{1}{2}$ **31.** $y = 1$

33. $\dfrac{dy}{dx} = y\left[-\ln 5 + \dfrac{3(2x - 1)}{x^2 - x} - \dfrac{12(2x^2 - 1)}{2x^3 - 3x}\right]$

35. $\dfrac{dy}{dx} = 2y\left[\ln(x^2 + 1) + \dfrac{2x^2}{x^2 + 1}\right]$

37. $\dfrac{dy}{dx} = 2y\left[\ln(3x^2 + 2) + \dfrac{6x^2}{3x^2 + 2}\right]$

39. Domain $(0, +\infty)$;
relative minimum at $(e^{-1/2}, -0.09)$;
point of inflection at $x = e^{-1.5}$;
intercept $(1, 0)$;
defined only for $x > 0$

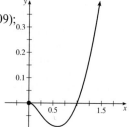

41. Domain $(-\infty, -1) \cup (1, +\infty)$;
no extreme points;
no points of inflection;
no intercepts;
asymptotes $y = 0$, $x = \pm 1$

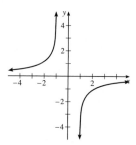

43. $\dfrac{1}{2}\ln(x^2 + 2x + 5) + C$

45. $\dfrac{1}{\sqrt{7}}\tan^{-1}\left(\dfrac{x}{\sqrt{7}}\right) + C$

47. $\ln 1.5$ **49.** $\dfrac{22}{3}$

51. $2e^{\sqrt{x}} + C$ **53.** $e^x - \ln(e^x + 1) + C$

55. $\ln|\cos x + \sin x| + C$

57. $\sin^{-1}x + x + C$ **59.** $\dfrac{1}{2}\ln|\sec x + \tan x| + C$

61. $\dfrac{1}{3}\tan^{-1}x^3 + C$ **63.** $\tan^{-1}(\ln x) + C$

65. **a.** e^4 **b.** 0   **67.** **a.** 0   **b.** 0

69. $\dfrac{1}{2 \ln 2}$ **71.** $\dfrac{1}{2}\ln 2$

73. Relative maximum at $x = \dfrac{-b - \sqrt{b^2 - 4b}}{2}$;
relative minimum at $x = \dfrac{-b + \sqrt{b^2 - 4b}}{2}$

75. **a.** \$1,075.71   **b.** \$1,070.52

77. 20π mi/min   **79.** $-\dfrac{1}{1 + x^2}$

81. The body had been in the freezer for 35.5536 hours, so Siggy had been put into the freezer on Wednesday morning at about 1:30 A.M. André was in the slammer, so Boldfinger must have done it.

83. First National Bank

89. 0.64   **91.** 0.75

93. See *American Mathematical Monthly*, Vol. 46.

95. See *American Mathematical Monthly*, Vol. 58.

CHAPTER 6

PROBLEM SET 6.1, Page 393

1. 9   **3.** $\dfrac{1}{30}$ **5.** 2   **7.** $36\sqrt{3}$

9. $\dfrac{128\sqrt{3}}{15}$ **11.** $\dfrac{\sqrt{3}}{4}\left(1 - \dfrac{\pi}{4}\right)$

13. **a.** Disk: $\pi \displaystyle\int_0^4 (4 - x)^2\, dx$ **b.** Shell: $2\pi \displaystyle\int_0^4 x(4 - x)\, dx$

c. Washer: $\pi \displaystyle\int_0^4 [(5 - x)^2 - 1]\, dx$

or shell: $2\pi \displaystyle\int_0^4 (x + 1)(4 - x)\, dx$

15. **a.** Shell: $2\pi \displaystyle\int_0^2 y\sqrt{4 - y^2}\, dy$ **b.** Disk: $\pi \displaystyle\int_0^2 (4 - y^2)\, dy$

c. Washer: $\pi \displaystyle\int_0^2 [(1 + \sqrt{4 - y^2})^2 - 1]\, dy$

or shell: $2\pi \displaystyle\int_0^2 (x + 1)\sqrt{4 - x^2}\, dx$

17. **a.** Washer: $\pi \displaystyle\int_0^1 (x - x^4)\, dx$

b. Shell: $2\pi \displaystyle\int_0^1 (x^{3/2} - x^3)\, dx$

or washer: $\pi \displaystyle\int_0^1 (y - y^4)\, dy$

19. **a.** Washer: $\pi \displaystyle\int_0^1 [(x^3 + 2x + 1)^2 - 1]\, dx$

b. Shell: $2\pi \int_1^4 x(x^3 + 2x)\, dx$

21. 144   **23.** 18   **25.** $\dfrac{81}{10}$ **27.** $\dfrac{9}{2}$

29. $\dfrac{\pi}{2}$ **31.** π **33.** $\dfrac{\pi^8}{7} + \dfrac{\pi^7}{3} + \dfrac{\pi^6}{5} \approx 2{,}555$

35. $\dfrac{2\pi}{35}$ **37.** 2π **39.** $\dfrac{4\pi}{3}$ **41.** $\dfrac{\pi}{10}$

43. $\dfrac{\pi}{2}$ **45.** $\dfrac{\pi}{4}$ **47.** $\dfrac{47\pi}{210}$ **49.** $\dfrac{419\pi}{15}$

51. 28π **53.** $\dfrac{16}{3}$ **55.** $\dfrac{8\pi}{3}$

57. $90{,}000{,}000 \text{ ft}^3$ **59.** If $\Delta x = 0.5$, sum is 284.375;
if $\Delta x = 0.25$, sum is 260.4063;
if $\Delta x = 0.1$, sum is 246.295

61. 10.045   **65.** About the x-axis is $\dfrac{4}{3}\pi ab^2$;

about the y-axis is $\dfrac{4}{3}\pi a^2 b$

67. $V = \dfrac{\pi}{3}(2R^3 - 3R^2h + h^3)$

69. $V = R^2 h_2 \pi - \dfrac{1}{3}\pi(2h_1^3 + h_2^3)$

PROBLEM SET 6.2, Page 401

1. $3\sqrt{10}$ **3.** $2\sqrt{5}$ **5.** $-\dfrac{2}{3} + \dfrac{10}{3}\sqrt{5}$

7. $\dfrac{331}{120}$ **9.** $\dfrac{123}{32}$

11. 9.29 (needs numerical integration)

13. $\dfrac{14}{3}$

15. a. $S = 2\pi \int_1^3 \left(\dfrac{1}{3}x^3 + \dfrac{1}{4x}\right)\left(\dfrac{x^{-2}}{4} + x^2\right)dx$

$\qquad = \dfrac{1{,}505\pi}{18}$

b. $S = 2\pi \int_1^3 x\left(x^2 + \dfrac{4}{x^2}\right)dx = 2\pi\left(20 + \dfrac{1}{4}\ln 3\right)$

17. $12\pi\sqrt{5}$ **19.** $\dfrac{515\pi}{64} \approx 25.28$

21. $3\pi\sqrt{10}$ **23.** $\pi\left[\dfrac{28\sqrt{3}}{5} - \dfrac{16}{15}\right]$

25. 6 units   **27.** 36 units

29. 8.632601 ($n = 20$)   **35.** $S = 4\pi^2 rR$

PROBLEM SET 6.3, Page 413

5. 12,750 ft-lb   **7.** $\dfrac{10}{3}$ ft-lb

9. 6,500 ft-lb   **11.** 2,000 ft-lb

13. 192 lb   **15.** 460.8 lb

17. $9{,}056\sqrt{2}$ lb   **19.** $\left(0, -\dfrac{18}{5}\right)$

21. $\left(\dfrac{1}{\ln 2}, \dfrac{1}{4\ln 2}\right)$ **23.** $\left(\dfrac{7}{3}, \dfrac{1}{2}\ln 2\right)$

25. $\dfrac{200\pi}{3}$ **27.** $\dfrac{32}{3}\pi + 8\pi^2$

29. $\left(\dfrac{4}{3}, 1\right)$ **31.** 4 ergs

33. 0 ft-lb   **35.** 345,800 ft-lb

37. $7{,}920\pi$ ft-lb   **39.** 592.8 lb

41. 278.2 lb   **43.** 23,400,000 lb

45. $I_x = \dfrac{64}{16}, I_y = \dfrac{256}{7}$ **47.** $\dfrac{2}{3}\sqrt{6}$

49. a. For $V = 500$, $h = -0.64$
b. For $V = 800$, $h = 0.87$

51. Use method of disks: $V = \pi \int_0^r x^2\, dx = \dfrac{1}{3}\pi r^3$

53. $\dfrac{\pi L^3}{4}$

PROBLEM SET 6.4, Page 425

1. $y = Ce^{3x}$ **3.** $y = -\ln|C - x|$
5. $y = Cx$ **7.** $y = \sin^{-1}(\sin x + C)$
9. $y = Ce^x - 10$
11. a. ii   **b.** i   **c.** v   **d.** iv   **e.** iii

13. $y = \dfrac{2}{7}x^{3/2} + \dfrac{1}{3}x + Cx^{-2}$

15. $y = \dfrac{2}{x}\ln x + \dfrac{C}{x}$ **17.** $y = \dfrac{1}{2}xe^{-2x} + \dfrac{C}{xe^{2x}}$

19. $y = \dfrac{4}{x}$ **21.** $y^2 = x^2 + C$

23. $\dfrac{1}{2}y = x^2 + C$ **25.** About 11,000 yr old

27. $1,902 billion   **29.** About 8,241,820

31. a. About 70 min   **b.** 94 lb
33. It has no effect.   **35.** 2,500; (2488.707549)
37. He will land safely.

43. a. $v = \dfrac{mg}{k} + e^{-kt/m}\left(v_0 - \dfrac{gm}{k}\right)$

b. $s(t) = \dfrac{mg}{k}t + \dfrac{m}{k}\left(v_0 - \dfrac{gm}{k}\right)(1 - e^{-kt/m}) + s_0$

CHAPTER 6 REVIEW

Practice Problems, Page 429

13. E   **14.** A, B, F, and G
15. F and G   **16.** C and D
17. A and F   **18.** B and G

19. a. $\frac{32}{3}$ **b.** $\frac{256\pi}{5}$ **c.** $\frac{128\pi}{3}$

20. $\frac{256}{3}$ **21.** $\frac{13\sqrt{13}}{27} - \frac{8}{27}$

22. $\frac{\pi}{6}(5^{3/2} - 1) \approx 5.33$ **23.** $y = \frac{x+1}{e^x}[\ln|x+1| + 1]$

24. $k_{min} = 1.3$ lb/gal; $k_{max} = 2$ lb/gal; $t \approx 238$ min

25. $\left(\frac{13}{25}, \frac{9}{175}\right)$

Supplementary Problems, Page 429

1. $\frac{81\pi}{2}$ **3.** $\frac{8\pi}{45}$

5. 64   **7.** $\left(-\frac{1}{2}, \frac{2}{5}\right)$

9. 250 in.-lb   **11.** 24,047 ft-lb

13. $\frac{4}{3}\pi a^3$ **15.** $2\pi r h$

17. 4,680 ft-lb   **19.** 30,264 ft-lb

21. 192π lb   **23.** 9,360 lb

25. 2,662.4 lb

27. a. $mg(s - s_0)$ **b.** $P = mg\left(v_0 t - \frac{1}{2}gt^2\right)$;

$K = \frac{1}{2}m(v_0 - gt)^2$

29. $P(t) = A + (P_0 - A)e^{k\sin t}$

31. $\left(2, \frac{1}{3}\right)$ **33.** $\pi b^2\left(\frac{r^3}{3a^2} - r + \frac{2}{3}a\right)$

35. 17,500 ft-lb   **37.** 135 lb

39. $F(t) = \frac{1}{2}t + \frac{2}{3}$ **41.** $6,176\pi$ ft-lb

43. 10.34 cm, 11.12 cm, and 5.66 cm

45. $x(y) = ye^y + C$ **47.** $\frac{35\pi}{3}$ ft-lb

49. 0.6431

51. $62.4B\left[\frac{1}{2}Dh + \frac{h^2}{3}\right]$, where $h = \frac{1}{2}\sqrt{4A^2 - B^2}$

53. $2\sqrt{2}\pi$ **55.** 235.5π

57. $\left(\frac{b}{3}, \frac{a}{3}\right)$ **59. a.** 51.7%   **b.** 17.44 yr

61. Approx. 12,190,000; 35 yr

63. $2\pi(3 - \sqrt{5})$ **65.** $\frac{\pi}{4}$

67. $\frac{\sqrt{3}}{16}(e^2 - 1)$ **69.** $3a + \frac{b^2}{8a}\ln 2$

71. See *American Mathematical Monthly*, Vol. 46.

CUMULATIVE REVIEW, Page 435

5. $\frac{7}{5}$ **7.** $\frac{1}{2}$ **9.** 0   **11.** 1

13. 1   **15.** $6(2x - 1)^2(x^2 + 1)^2(3x - 4)$

17. $\frac{\cos x + x\sin x}{(x + \cos x)^2}$ **19.** $-6\csc^2 3x\cot 3x$

21. $\frac{10x + 3}{5x^2 + 3x - 2}$ **23.** 5

25. $\sqrt{10} - 3$ **27.** $\ln(e^x + 2) + C$

29. 1.812   **31.**

33. $\frac{24\sqrt{3} - 32\sqrt{2} + 27}{3} \approx 7.77$

35. $y = \frac{2\sqrt{2}(\pi - 4)}{\pi^2}$

37. $y = \frac{-x(\ln x)^2}{2} + Cx$ **39.** $y = -\ln(\cos x + e^{-5} - 1)$

41. $e - 1$ **43.** $\frac{d\theta}{dt} = \frac{17}{164} \approx 0.1$ rad/s

45. 79.6 lb salt

CHAPTER 7

PROBLEM SET 7.1, Page 446

1. $\frac{-1}{16x(x - 1)} + C$ **3.** $\frac{1}{2}(\ln x)^2 + C$

5. $e^{\sin x} + C$ **7.** $\frac{1}{9}\tan^{-1}\left(\frac{t^3}{3}\right) + C$

9. $\ln(x^4 - 2x^2 + 3) + C$ **11.** $\ln|x^2 + 4x + 3| + C$

13. Formula 201; $\frac{\sqrt{x^2 - a^2}}{a^2 x} + C$

15. Formula 502; $\frac{x^2}{2}\left(\ln|x| - \frac{1}{2}\right) + C$

17. Formula 484; $\frac{e^{ax}}{a}\left(x - \frac{1}{a}\right) + C$

19. Formula 174;

$\frac{1}{2}x\sqrt{x^2 + 1} - \frac{1}{2}\ln|x + \sqrt{x^2 + 1}| + C$

21. Formula 173; $\frac{1}{4}\sqrt{4x^2 + 1} + C$

23. Formula 492;

$\frac{-e^{-4x}(4\sin 5x + 5\cos 5x)}{41} + C$

25. $\frac{\ln|bx + 1|}{b} + C$ **27.** $\frac{(x + 1)^4(4x - 1)}{20} + C$

29. $\frac{xe^{4x}}{4} - \frac{e^{4x}}{16} + C$ **31.** $\sin^{-1}\left(\frac{x + 2}{3}\right) + C$

33. $x\ln^3|x| - 3x\ln^2|x| + 6x\ln|x| - 6x + C$

35. $\sin^{-1}\left(\dfrac{x}{3}\right) + C$

37. $\dfrac{9 \ln(\sqrt{9 + x^2} + x)}{2} + \dfrac{x\sqrt{9 + x^2}}{2} + C$

39. $\sqrt{4x^2 + 1} - \ln\left|\dfrac{1 + \sqrt{4x^2 + 1}}{2x}\right| + C$

41. $-\dfrac{1}{6}\sin^5 x \cos x - \dfrac{5}{24}\sin^3 x \cos x + \dfrac{5}{16}x - \dfrac{5}{32}\sin 2x + C$

43. $\dfrac{x(9 - x^2)^{3/2}}{4} + \dfrac{27x\sqrt{9 - x^2}}{8} + \dfrac{243}{8}\sin^{-1}\left(\dfrac{x}{3}\right) + C$

47. $\dfrac{\sin^5 x}{5} + C$

49. $\dfrac{x}{8} - \dfrac{\sin 4x}{32} + C$ or $-\dfrac{\sin x \cos^3 x}{4} + \dfrac{\sin x \cos x}{8} + \dfrac{x}{8} + C$

55. $4\left[\dfrac{x^{1/2}}{2} - x^{1/4} + \ln(x^{1/4} + 1)\right] + C$

57. $4x^{1/2} - 3x^{1/3} + 3x^{1/6} - \dfrac{3}{2}\ln(2x^{1/6} + 1) + C$

59. $\dfrac{1}{e^x + e^{-x}} + C$ **61.** $\dfrac{1}{2}$ square units

63. $\dfrac{9\pi}{2}(9 - \ln 10) \approx 94.6825$

65. $\dfrac{1}{2}\sqrt{5} + \dfrac{1}{4}\ln(2 + \sqrt{5}) \approx 1.4789$

67. $\dfrac{9\sqrt{5}\pi}{16} - \dfrac{\pi \ln(\sqrt{5} + 2)}{32} \approx 3.08097$

PROBLEM SET 7.2, Page 453

1. $-\dfrac{xe^{-2x}}{2} - \dfrac{e^{-2x}}{4} + C$ **3.** $\dfrac{x^2}{2}\ln x - \dfrac{x^2}{4} + C$

5. $x\sin^{-1}x + \sqrt{1 - x^2} + C$ **7.** $\sqrt{x}\ln x - 2\sqrt{x} + C$

9. $\dfrac{x^2}{4} + \dfrac{x}{4}\sin 2x + \dfrac{1}{8}\cos 2x + C$

11. $\dfrac{x^3}{3}\ln x - \dfrac{x^3}{9} + C$ **13.** $-\dfrac{2}{15}(1 - e^x)^{3/2}(3e^x + 2) + C$

15. $\dfrac{32}{3}\ln 2 - \dfrac{28}{9} \approx 4.28245$

17. $e - 2 \approx 0.71828$ **19.** $\dfrac{1}{4}(e^{2\pi} - 1) \approx 133.623$

23. $\dfrac{1}{2}\cos^2 x - \cos^2 x \ln|\cos x| + C$

25. $-(2 + \cos x)\ln(2 + \cos x) + (2 + \cos x) + C$

27. $\dfrac{1}{2}(x - \sin x \cos x) + C$ **29.** $\dfrac{x^{n+1}}{n + 1}\ln x - \dfrac{x^{n+1}}{(n + 1)^2} + C$

31. $400 - 1{,}000e^{-3/2} \approx 177$ **33.** $2\pi(1 - 3e^{-2}) \approx 3.73217$

35. **a.** $\pi e - 2\pi$ **b.** $\dfrac{\pi}{2}(e^2 + 1)$

37. $(0.6774, 1.2715)$ **39.** $\dfrac{-x^2\cos x + 2x\sin x + \cos x}{x^2 + 1}$

41. $f(\pi) = -3$ **43.** $v = \dfrac{mg}{k} + \dfrac{v_0 - mg/k}{e^{kt/m}}$

45. 0.07 **47.** $1.558nRt$

PROBLEM SET 7.3, Page 463

1. $-\dfrac{1}{3x} + \dfrac{1}{3(x - 3)}$ **3.** $3 - \dfrac{1}{x}$

5. $\dfrac{4}{x} - \dfrac{8}{2x + 1}$ **7.** $-\dfrac{1}{x^2} + \dfrac{3}{x} - \dfrac{2}{(x + 1)^2} + \dfrac{1}{x + 1}$

9. $-\dfrac{4}{9x^2} + \dfrac{17}{27x} - \dfrac{13}{9(x + 3)^2} + \dfrac{10}{27(x + 3)}$

11. $\dfrac{1}{4(1 - x)} + \dfrac{1}{4(1 + x)} + \dfrac{1}{2(1 + x^2)}$

13. $-\dfrac{1}{3}\ln|x| + \dfrac{1}{3}\ln|x - 3| + C$

15. $3x - \ln|x| + C$ **17.** $4\ln|x| - 4\ln|2x + 1| + C$

19. $-\dfrac{1}{x} - 9\ln|x| + 5\ln|x - 1| + 6\ln|x + 1| + C$

21. $x - \dfrac{5}{3}\ln|x + 2| + \dfrac{2}{3}\ln|x - 1| + C$

23. $x + \dfrac{1}{2}\ln|x - 1| - \dfrac{1}{2}\ln|x + 1| - \tan^{-1}x + C$

25. $\ln|x + 1| + \dfrac{1}{x + 1} + C$

27. $-\dfrac{1}{2}\ln|x| + \dfrac{1}{3}\ln|x + 1| + \dfrac{1}{6}\ln|x - 2| + C$

29. $-\ln|x + 1| - \dfrac{2}{x + 2} + \ln|x + 2| + C$

31. $2\ln|x + 3| + 3\ln|x - 1| + C$

33. Let $u = x^3 - x^2 + 4x - 4$ to obtain
$\ln|x^3 - x^2 + 4x - 4| + C$ or use partial fractions to obtain
the equivalent form $\ln|x - 1| + \ln|x^2 + 4| + C$.

37. $-\dfrac{1}{7}\ln(2e^x + 1) + \dfrac{1}{7}\ln|e^x - 3| + C$

39. $\dfrac{1}{1 + \cos x} + C$ **41.** $\ln|\tan x + 4| + C$

43. $-2\tan^{-1}x^{1/4} - \ln|x^{1/4} - 1| + \ln(x^{1/4} + 1) + C$

45. $\dfrac{1}{5}\ln\left|3\tan\dfrac{x}{2} + 1\right| - \dfrac{1}{5}\ln\left|\tan\dfrac{x}{2} - 3\right| + C$

47. $-\ln|\sin x + \cos x| + C$

49. $\ln|\sec x + \tan x| - \ln|\cos x| + C$ or $-\ln(1 - \sin x) + C$

51. $\left[\tan\left(\dfrac{x}{2}\right) - 2\right]^{-1} + C$

53. $\dfrac{1}{2}[\ln|3 - \ln x| - \ln|1 - \ln x|] + C$

55. $\ln 2 \approx 0.6931$ **57.** $\pi\left(\dfrac{11}{180} + \dfrac{2}{27}\ln\dfrac{5}{8}\right) \approx 0.0826$

59. $128\pi \ln 2 - \dfrac{256}{3}\pi \approx 10.6484$

61. $t \approx 6.4$ days; the spy is captured.

PROBLEM SET 7.4, Page 467

1. $\dfrac{1}{2x^2(x - 1)^2}$ **3.** $\dfrac{1}{4}\ln|\sec 2x^2 + \tan 2x^2| + C$

5. $\ln|\sin e^x| + C$ **7.** $-\ln|\cos(\ln x)| + C$

9. $3 \ln|\sec t + \tan t| - 2 \ln|\cos t| + C$

11. $\frac{1}{2} \tan^{-1} e^{2x} + C$

13. $x + \frac{1}{2} \ln (x^2 + 9) - \frac{8}{3} \tan^{-1}\left(\frac{x}{3}\right) + C$

15. $x - 2 \ln|e^x - 1| + C$ **17.** $\frac{2}{3} \sin^{-1} t^3 + C$

19. $x - \frac{1}{2} \ln(e^{2x} + 1) + C$ **21.** $\tan^{-1}(x + 1) + C$

23. $\frac{2}{\sqrt{3}} \tan^{-1}\left(\frac{2x + 1}{\sqrt{3}}\right) + C$ **25.** $x \tan^{-1}x - \frac{1}{2}\ln(x^2 + 1) + C$

27. $\frac{1}{2} e^{-x}\sin x - \frac{1}{2} e^{-x}\cos x + C$

29. $x \cos^{-1}(-x) + \sqrt{1 - x^2} + C$ or
$x \sin^{-1}x + \frac{\pi x}{2} + \sqrt{1 - x^2} + C$

31. $-\cos x + \frac{\cos^3 x}{3} + C$ **33.** $\frac{1}{5} \cos^5 x - \frac{1}{3}\cos^3 x + C$

35. $-\frac{1}{6} \sin^5 x \cos x + \frac{7}{24} \sin^3 x \cos x - \frac{1}{16}x - \frac{1}{32} \sin 2x + C$

37. $-\frac{1}{9} \cos^9 x + \frac{2}{7} \cos^7 x - \frac{1}{5} \cos^5 x + C$

39. $\frac{1}{6} \tan^6 x + \frac{1}{8} \tan^8 x + C$

41. $\sqrt{1 - x^2} - \ln\left|\frac{1 + \sqrt{1 - x^2}}{x}\right| + C$

43. $\sqrt{2x^2 - 1} + \frac{3}{\sqrt{2}} \ln|\sqrt{2x^2 - 1} + \sqrt{2}x| + C$

45. $\ln|x| - \ln|\sqrt{x^2 + 1} + 1| + C$

47. $5 \sin^{-1}\left(\frac{2x - 2}{\sqrt{2}}\right) - 2\sqrt{4x - 2 - x^2} + C$

49. $\ln|\sqrt{1 + \sin^2 x} + \sin x| + C$

51. π **53.** $\frac{\sqrt{3}}{6} \approx 0.2887$

55. $\frac{5\sqrt{7} + 16}{216} \approx 0.1353$ **57.** $\frac{1,792 - 64\sqrt{2}}{15} \approx 113.43$

59. $-\frac{1}{2} \ln(\sqrt{5} - 2\sqrt{2} + \sqrt{10} - 2) - \frac{1}{2}\sqrt{2} + \sqrt{5} \approx 1.8101$

61. $\frac{8}{15} - \frac{43\sqrt{2}}{120} \approx 0.0266$ **63.** $\frac{\pi}{4} - \frac{2}{3} \approx 0.1187$

65. $\ln(\sqrt{1 + e^{2x}} + e^x) + C$

67. $\frac{4}{\sqrt{3}} \tan^{-1}\left(\frac{2x + 1}{\sqrt{3}}\right) - \ln(x^2 + x + 1) + 3 \ln|x| + C$

69. $5 \ln|x - 7| + \frac{2}{x + 2} + C$ **71.** $3 \ln|x + 1| - \frac{2}{x + 1} + C$

73. $3 \ln|x + 2| + 2 \ln|x| + \frac{1}{x} + C$

75. $-\frac{1}{2}\ln|x + 1| + 2 \ln|x + 2| - \frac{3}{2} \ln|x + 3| + C$

77. $\frac{1}{13} \ln\left|\frac{5 + \tan\frac{x}{2}}{1 - 5 \tan\frac{x}{2}}\right|$

79. $\frac{1}{6} \cos^3 1 - \frac{1}{2} \cos 1 + \frac{1}{3} \approx 0.09$

83. $\frac{4 \ln(\sqrt{2} + 1)}{\pi} \approx 1.122\ 19$

85. 4   **87.** $\frac{324}{5}\pi \approx 203.58$

89. $(0.71, 0.12)$

PROBLEM SET 7.5, Page 476

3. $\frac{1}{2}$ **5.** Diverges   **7.** 10

9. Diverges   **11.** $\frac{1}{10}$ **13.** $\frac{5}{2}$

15. $\frac{1}{9}$ **17.** Diverges   **19.** $2e^{-1}$

21. $5e^{10}$ **23.** Diverges   **25.** 2

27. Diverges   **29.** Diverges   **31.** 0

33. $\frac{5}{4}$ **35.** 2   **37.** -1

39. 1   **41.** 2   **43.** $\frac{1}{4}$

45. 100,000 millirads   **47.** 4

49. Converges for $p < 1; I = \frac{1}{1 - p}$

51. Diverges   **53.** 8

55. **a.** 5   **b.** $\cos 2t + \sin 2t$ **c.** $-3t + 2e^t$

d. $3 \cos 2t + \frac{5}{2} \sin 2t - \frac{3}{2} e^t + \frac{3}{2} e^{-t}$

57. **a.** $\frac{6}{(s + 2)^4}$ **b.** $\frac{s + 3}{(s + 3)^2 + 4}$ **c.** $5te^t$

d. $4e^{-2t}(\cos t - \sin t)$

PROBLEM SET 7.6, Page 484

1. 3.6269   **3.** -0.7616 **5.** 1.1995

7. 0.9624   **9.** 1.6667   **11.** 0.6481

13. $3 \cosh 3x$

15. $(4x + 3)\sinh(2x^2 + 3x)$

17. $-\frac{1}{x^2} \cosh\left(\frac{1}{x}\right)$ **19.** $\frac{3x^2}{\sqrt{1 + x^6}}$

21. $\sec x$ **23.** $\sec x$

25. $\frac{\sqrt{x^2 + 1}\, \cosh^{-1}x - \sqrt{x^2 + 1}\, \sinh^{-1}x}{\sqrt{x^4 - 1}(\cosh^{-1}x)^2}$

27. $\cosh^{-1}x$

29. $\sqrt{y^2 - 1}\left[\cosh^{-1}y - \frac{e^{2x}}{\sqrt{x^2 + 1}} - e^{2x}\sinh^{-1}x\right]$

31. $-\cosh\left(\frac{1}{x}\right) + C$ **33.** $\ln|\sinh x| + C$

35. $\frac{1}{3} \cosh^{-1}\left(\frac{3t}{4}\right) + C$ or $\frac{1}{3} \ln(3t + \sqrt{9t^2 - 16}) + C$

37. $\sinh^{-1}(\sin x) + C$ or $\ln(\sin x + \sqrt{1 + \sin^2 x}) + C$

39. $\frac{1}{3}\tanh^{-1}x^3 + C$ or $\frac{1}{6}\ln\left|\frac{x^3 + 1}{x^3 - 1}\right| + C$

41. $\frac{1}{2}\ln\frac{2}{3}$

43. $\cosh^{-1}e^2 - \cosh^{-1}e \approx 1.0311$ or
$\ln(e^2 + \sqrt{e^4 - 1}) - \ln(e + \sqrt{e^2 - 1})$

45. $\frac{e^2 - 1}{2(e^2 + 1)} \approx 0.3808$ **53. b.** $y = \cosh 2x + \sinh 2x$

55. $(e - e^{-1})a$ **57.** $\frac{\pi}{2}(e^2 - e^{-2} + 2) \approx 17.68$

CHAPTER 7 REVIEW

Practice Problems, Page 485

14. a. 0.5493 **b.** $\frac{4}{3}$ **c.** 0.5493

15. $2\sqrt{x^2 + 1} + 3\sinh^{-1}x + C$ or
$2\sqrt{x^2 + 1} + 3\ln(x + \sqrt{x^2 + 1}) + C$

16. $-\frac{1}{2}x\cos 2x + \frac{1}{4}\sin 2x + C$

17. $-\frac{1}{2}\cosh(1 - 2x) + C$ **18.** $\sin^{-1}\left(\frac{x}{2}\right) + C$

19. $\frac{1}{2}\ln|x - 1| + \frac{1}{4}\ln(x^2 + 1) + \frac{1}{2}\tan^{-1}x + C$

20. $\frac{1}{2}x^2 + \frac{1}{2}\ln|x^2 - 1| + C$

21. $6\ln 2 - \frac{9}{4} \approx 1.9089$ **22.** $\frac{1}{9}\left(\ln\frac{5}{8} + \frac{3}{2}\right) \approx 0.1144$

23. $\frac{1}{2}\ln\frac{2}{3} = -0.2027$ **24.** $\frac{2\sqrt{2} - 1}{3} \approx 0.6095$

25. $\frac{1}{4}$ **26.** Diverges

27. Diverges   **28.** $\frac{1}{2}$

29. $\frac{1}{(1 - 4x^2)\sqrt{\tanh^{-1}2x}}$ **30.** $6\pi - 2\pi\sqrt{5} \approx 4.7999$

Supplementary Problems, Page 485

1. $\frac{1}{1 - x^2}$ **3.** e^{-2x}

5. $\sinh x + x\cosh x + (e^x - e^{-x})\cosh(e^x + e^{-x})$

7. $2\sin^{-1}\left(\frac{x}{2}\right) - \frac{x}{2}\sqrt{4 - x^2} + C$

9. $-\frac{1}{x} + \ln\left|\frac{x - 2}{x}\right| + C$ **11.** $4x^{1/4} - 4\ln|1 + x^{1/4}| + C$

13. $\frac{1}{3}x^3\tan^{-1}x - \frac{1}{6}x^2 + \frac{1}{6}\ln(x^2 + 1) + C$

15. $2\sin^{-1}\left(\frac{e^x}{2}\right) + \frac{1}{2}e^x\sqrt{4 - e^{2x}} + C$

17. $\frac{1}{15}\left(1 + \frac{1}{x^2}\right)^{3/2}\left(2 - \frac{3}{x^2}\right)$ **19.** $-2\sqrt{1 - \sin x} + C$

21. $\frac{x}{2}\sin(\ln x) - \frac{x}{2}\cos(\ln x) + C$

23. $\ln(e^{2x} + 4e^x + 1) - x + C$

25. $\frac{x^2}{6} + \frac{x^3}{3}\cot^{-1}x - \frac{1}{6}\ln|1 + x^2| + C$

27. $\frac{1}{3}\ln|x^3 + 6x + 1| + C$

29. $2\cos\sqrt{x + 2} + 2\sqrt{x + 2}\sin\sqrt{x + 2} + C$

31. $\frac{1}{4}\ln(x^4 + 4x^2 + 3) + C$

33. $\sqrt{5 - x^2} + \sqrt{5}\ln\left|\frac{\sqrt{5 - x^2} - \sqrt{5}}{x}\right| + C$

35. $\frac{\sqrt{x^2 + 4}}{3}(x^2 - 8) + C$

37. $\frac{\pi}{2}$ **39.** $1 - \frac{\pi}{4}$ **41.** $-\tan^{-1}(\cos x) + C$

43. a. True   **b.** True   **45.** 6

47. For $n = 4$, $L(1,000) \approx 321$; for $n = 20$, $L(1,000) \approx 201$;
and for $n = 10,000$ (by computer), $L(1,000) \approx 177$

49. $(0.647, 1)$ **51.** 2.848

53. $\frac{16\sqrt{2}}{15} \approx 1.5085$ **55.** $\frac{\pi^2}{2} - \pi\tan^{-1}\left(\frac{1}{16}\right)$

57. $\pi e^2 - \frac{1}{16}\pi e^{-2} + \frac{1}{16}\pi \approx 23.3832$

61. $3|a| + \frac{b^2}{8|a|}\ln 2$

65. $\frac{x(9 - x^2)^{5/2}}{6} + \frac{15x(9 - x^2)^{1/2}}{8} + \frac{405\sqrt{9 - x^2}}{16}$
$+ \frac{3,645}{16}\sin^{-1}\left(\frac{x}{3}\right) + C$

71. Diverges

73. See *American Mathematical Monthly*, Vol. 87.

CHAPTER 8

PROBLEM SET 8.1, Page 499

3. $0, 2, 0, 2, 0$ **5.** $1, \frac{1}{2}, \frac{1}{3}, \frac{1}{4}, \frac{1}{5}$

7. $\frac{4}{3}, \frac{7}{4}, 2, \frac{13}{6}, \frac{16}{7}$ **9.** $256, 16, 4, 2, \sqrt{2}$

11. $1, 3, 13, 183, 33673$ **13.** 5   **15.** -7

17. 0   **19.** $\frac{1}{2}$ **21.** 4   **23.** 0

25. 1   **27.** 1   **29.** 1   **31.** $\frac{1}{2}$

33. 1   **35.** 0

37. Bounded below by 0; decreasing

39. Bounded below by 4; decreasing

41. Bounded below by 0; decreasing

43. Diverges by oscillation   **45.** Sequence is unbounded

47. 6.25%, $100\left(\frac{1}{2}\right)^n$%

49. $N = 99$ **51.** $N = 1,000$

PROBLEM SET 8.2, Page 507

3. 5   **5.** 3   **7.** Diverges

9. $\frac{3}{20}$ **11.** $\frac{1}{e^{0.2} - 1} \approx 4.5167$ **13.** $-\frac{2}{45}$

15. $\frac{1}{3}$ **17.** $\frac{16}{63}$ **19.** $2(2 + \sqrt{2})$

21. $\frac{3\sqrt{2} + 4}{2}$ **23.** 1   **25.** 1

27. Diverges   **29.** 1   **31.** $\frac{1}{99}$

33. $\frac{52}{37}$ **35. a.** $A = B = 1$ **b.** $\frac{1}{2}$

37. 0   **39.** 9.14   **41.** $\frac{583}{120}$

43. $\frac{1}{a}$ **45.** 2   **47.** 1,500 rev

49. 3 ft   **51.** $10,000   **53.** 30.8 units

55. 33 trustees   **59. b.** $\frac{3}{4n^2 + 8n + 3}$ **65.** $\frac{1}{4}$

PROBLEM SET 8.3, Page 515

3. Converges   **5.** Diverges   **7.** Converges

9. Diverges   **11.** Converges   **13.** Diverges

15. Diverges   **17.** Diverges   **19.** Diverges

21. Converges   **23.** Converges   **25.** Converges

27. Converges   **29.** Diverges   **31.** Diverges

33. Converges   **35.** Converges   **37.** Diverges

39. Diverges   **41.** Converges   **43.** Diverges

45. Converges   **47.** $p > 1$ **49.** $p > 1$

51. $p > 1$

53. b. $N > 100$

c. $N > 100$ gives an actual error of 0.009 95 (compared with a guarantee of 0.01)

PROBLEM SET 8.4, Page 521

3. Geometric, converges   **5.** Geometric, diverges

7. p-series, diverges   **9.** p-series, converges

11. Geometric, diverges   **13.** Converges

15. Diverges   **17.** Diverges   **19.** Converges

21. Converges   **23.** Converges   **25.** Diverges

27. Converges   **29.** Converges   **31.** Converges

33. Converges   **35.** Diverges   **37.** Converges

39. Converges   **41.** Converges   **43.** Diverges

45. Converges   **47.** Converges   **49.** Converges

51. Diverges   **53.** Converges   **55.** Converges

PROBLEM SET 8.5, Page 528

3. Converges   **5.** Diverges   **7.** Converges

9. Converges   **11.** Diverges   **13.** Converges

15. Converges   **17.** Converges   **19.** Diverges

21. Converges   **23.** Converges   **25.** Converges

The test used in Problems 27–44 may vary.

27. Diverges; direct comparison test

29. Converges; direct comparison test or ratio test

31. Diverges; ratio test

33. Converges; ratio test

35. Converges; limit comparison test or ratio test

37. Diverges; direct comparison test

39. Converges; root test

41. Converges; direct comparison test

43. Converges; root test

45. $0 < x < 1$ **47.** $-1.5 \le x \le 0.5$ **49.** $x > 0$

51. $0 < x < \frac{1}{a}$

PROBLEM SET 8.6, Page 537

5. Conditionally convergent   **7.** Divergent

9. Absolutely convergent   **11.** Conditionally convergent

13. Absolutely convergent   **15.** Absolutely convergent

17. Absolutely convergent   **19.** Conditionally convergent

21. Conditionally convergent **23.** Conditionally convergent

25. Divergent   **27.** Conditionally convergent

29. Conditionally convergent **31.** Absolutely convergent

33. a. $S_4 = \frac{5}{8} = 0.625$; $|E_4| = \frac{1}{120} \approx 0.00833$

b. 0.632

35. a. $S_4 = \frac{20}{243} \approx 0.08230$; $|E_4| = \frac{1}{729} \approx 0.001372$

b. 0.083

37. a. $S_4 = -\frac{104}{625} \approx -0.1664$; $|E_4| = \frac{1}{3,125} \approx 0.000\,32$

b. -0.167

39. $-1 \le x < 1$ **41.** $-1 \le x \le 1$

43. $-1 < x < 1$ **45.** $|E_n| < \frac{1}{36}$

47. $|E_n| < \dfrac{7}{27}$

49. Converges (it is a series of positive terms)

55. a. Diverges **b.** Converges absolutely

57. $a_k = \dfrac{1}{k}$

PROBLEM SET 8.7, Page 547

1. $R = 1; (-1, 1)$ **3.** $R = 1; (-1, 1)$

5. $R = \dfrac{1}{3}; \left(\dfrac{8}{3}, \dfrac{10}{3}\right)$ **7.** $R = \dfrac{4}{3}; \left(-\dfrac{13}{3}, -\dfrac{5}{3}\right)$

9. $R = 0, x = 1$ **11.** $R = 2; (-1, 3)$

13. $R = \dfrac{1}{3}; \left[1, \dfrac{5}{3}\right)$ **15.** $R = 7; (-7, 7)$

17. $R = 0, x = 0$ **19.** $R = 1; (-1, 1]$

21. $R = \infty; (-\infty, \infty)$ **23.** $R = 0, x = 0$

25. $R = \infty; (-\infty, \infty)$ **27.** $R = \dfrac{1}{5\sqrt[4]{3}}; \left(\dfrac{-1}{5\sqrt[4]{3}}, \dfrac{1}{5\sqrt[4]{3}}\right)$

29. $R = 1; (-2, 0)$ **31.** $(0, 2)$

33. $\left(-\dfrac{1}{a}, \dfrac{1}{a}\right)$ **35.** $\displaystyle\sum_{k=0}^{\infty} k2^{-k}x^{k-1}$

37. $\displaystyle\sum_{k=0}^{\infty} k(k + 2)x^{k-1}$ **39.** $\displaystyle\sum_{k=0}^{\infty} \dfrac{1}{2^k(k + 1)} x^{k+1}$

41. $\displaystyle\sum_{k=0}^{\infty} \dfrac{k + 2}{k + 1} x^{k+1}$ **45.** $|x| < R^{1/p}$

47. $|x| > 1$ **49.** $R = \infty$

PROBLEM SET 8.8, Page 562

3. $\displaystyle\sum_{k=0}^{\infty} \dfrac{(2x)^k}{k!}$ **5.** $\displaystyle\sum_{k=0}^{\infty} \dfrac{x^{2k}}{k!}$

7. $\displaystyle\sum_{k=0}^{\infty} \dfrac{(-1)^k x^{4k+2}}{(2k + 1)!}$ **9.** $\displaystyle\sum_{k=0}^{\infty} \dfrac{(-1)(ax)^{2k+1}}{(2x + 1)!}$

11. $\displaystyle\sum_{k=0}^{\infty} \dfrac{(-1)^k (2x^2)^{2k}}{(2k)!}$ **13.** $\displaystyle\sum_{k=0}^{\infty} \dfrac{(-1)^k x^{2k+2}}{(2k)!}$

15. $x^2 + 2x + 1$ **17.** $\displaystyle\sum_{k=0}^{\infty} \dfrac{x^{k+1}}{k!}$

19. $\displaystyle\sum_{k=0}^{\infty} \left[\dfrac{x^k}{k!} + \dfrac{(-1)^k x^{2k+1}}{(2k + 1)!}\right] = 1 + 2x + \dfrac{x^2}{2!} + \dfrac{x^4}{4!} + \cdots$

21. $\displaystyle\sum_{k=0}^{\infty} (-4)^k x^k$ **23.** $\displaystyle\sum_{k=0}^{\infty} (-1)^k \dfrac{x^k}{a^{k+1}}$

25. $\ln 3 + \displaystyle\sum_{k=0}^{\infty} \dfrac{(-1)^k}{3^{k+1}} \cdot \dfrac{x^{k+1}}{k + 1}$

27. $\displaystyle\sum_{k=0}^{\infty} \dfrac{(-1)^k 2^{2k+1} x^{2k+1}}{2k + 1}$ **29.** $\displaystyle\sum_{k=0}^{\infty} \dfrac{(-1)^k x^{2k}}{k!}$

31. $f(x) = e + e(x - 1) + \dfrac{e(x - 1)}{2!} + \dfrac{e(x - 1)^3}{3!} + \cdots$

33. $f(x) = \cos\dfrac{\pi}{3} - \left(x - \dfrac{\pi}{3}\right)\sin\dfrac{\pi}{3}$
$$- \dfrac{\left(x - \dfrac{\pi}{3}\right)^2}{2!} \cos\dfrac{\pi}{3} + \dfrac{\left(x - \dfrac{\pi}{3}\right)^3}{3!} \sin\dfrac{\pi}{3} + \cdots$$

35. $f(x) = x + \dfrac{x^3}{3} + \dfrac{2x^5}{15} + \dfrac{17x^7}{315} + \cdots$

37. $f(x) = (x - 2)^3 + 4(x - 2)^2 + 5(x - 2) - 3$

39. $f(x) = \displaystyle\sum_{k=0}^{\infty} \dfrac{(-1)^{k+1}(x - 5)^k}{3^{k+1}}$
$$= -\dfrac{1}{3}\left[1 + \left(\dfrac{x - 5}{-3}\right) + \left(\dfrac{x - 5}{-3}\right)^2 + \left(\dfrac{x - 5}{-3}\right)^3 + \cdots\right]$$

41. $f(x) = \displaystyle\sum_{k=0}^{\infty} \left(-\dfrac{2}{3}\right)^k (x - 2)^k$
$$= 1 + \left[-\dfrac{2}{3}(x - 2)\right] + \left[-\dfrac{2}{3}(x - 2)\right]^2$$
$$+ \left[-\dfrac{2}{3}(x - 2)\right]^3 + \cdots$$

43. $1 + \dfrac{1}{2}x - \dfrac{1}{8}x^2 + \dfrac{1}{16}x^3 - \dfrac{5}{128}x^4 + \cdots; (-1, 1)$

45. $1 + \dfrac{2x}{3} - \dfrac{x^2}{9} + \dfrac{4x^3}{81} + \cdots; (-1, 1)$

47. $x + \dfrac{x^3}{2} + \dfrac{3x^5}{8} + \dfrac{5x^7}{16} + \cdots; (-1, 1)$

51. $\displaystyle\sum_{k=0}^{\infty} \dfrac{x^{2k+1}}{(2k + 1)!}$ **53.** $n = 4$

55. $f(x) = \dfrac{1}{1 + \dfrac{x}{2}} + \dfrac{\dfrac{1}{2}}{1 - \dfrac{x}{2}} = \displaystyle\sum_{k=0}^{\infty} \left[\dfrac{1}{2^{k+1}} + \dfrac{(-1)^k}{2^k}\right] x^k$

57. $f(x) = \dfrac{1}{1 - x} + \dfrac{-\dfrac{1}{2}}{1 - \dfrac{x}{2}} = \displaystyle\sum_{k=0}^{\infty} \left[-\dfrac{1}{2^{k+1}} + 1\right] x^k$

59. $f(x) = \dfrac{4}{3(x + 2)} + \dfrac{1}{6(x - 1)} - \dfrac{1}{2(x + 1)}$
$$= \displaystyle\sum_{k=0}^{\infty} \left[\dfrac{2}{3}\left(-\dfrac{1}{2}\right)^k - \dfrac{1}{6} - \dfrac{1}{2}(-1)^k\right] x^k$$

61. $\dfrac{1}{2} \displaystyle\sum_{k=0}^{\infty} (-1)^k \dfrac{x^{4k+2}}{(2k + 1)!}$ **63.** $\dfrac{1}{2} \displaystyle\sum_{k=0}^{\infty} (-1)^k \dfrac{(1 + 2^{2k})x^{2k}}{(2k)!}$

65. $\displaystyle\sum_{k=0}^{\infty} [(-1)^k 2^{k+1} + 2^{k+1} + 1] \dfrac{x^{k+1}}{k + 1}$

67. $\displaystyle\sum_{k=0}^{\infty} \dfrac{x^k}{(k + 1)!}; \lim_{x \to 0} g(x) = 1$

69. $|R_{2n+1}| = \dfrac{|\cos\alpha||x|^{2n+2}}{(2n + 2)!} \le \dfrac{|x|^{2n+2}}{(2n + 2)!}$ for $0 \le \alpha \le x$

71. a. $P_5\left(x - 2x^3 + \dfrac{2x^5}{3}\right)$

b. $\dfrac{4x^7}{45} < 0.000\,70$ on $\left[-\dfrac{1}{2}, \dfrac{1}{2}\right]$

c. Same as above

d. The actual maximum error was $0.000\,682\,2$, so the preceding estimate was excellent.

73. $\displaystyle\sum_{k=0}^{\infty} \frac{1}{2}(k+2)(k+1)x^k$ **75.** $\displaystyle\sum_{k=0}^{\infty} \frac{1}{k+1.2} \cdot \frac{1}{k!}$

CHAPTER 8 REVIEW

Practice Problems, Page 565

31. 0   **32.** $-\dfrac{3}{2}$ **33.** e

34. Converges to $e^e - 1$ **35.** Diverges (divergence test)

36. Diverges (integral test)

37. Converges absolutely (p-test)

38. Convergence interval is $(-1, 1)$

39. $\displaystyle\sum_{k=0}^{\infty} \frac{(-1)^k(2x)^{2k+1}}{(2k+1)!}$ **40.** $-\dfrac{2}{5}\displaystyle\sum_{k=0}^{\infty}\left(\dfrac{2}{5}\right)^k\left(x-\dfrac{1}{2}\right)^k$

Supplementary Problems, Page 566

1. Diverges   **3.** Converges to e^{-2}

5. Converges to 1   **7.** Converges to $\dfrac{5}{3}$

9. Converges to 0   **11.** Converges to 0

13. Converges to e^4 **15.** Converges to 0

17. $\dfrac{1}{3}$ **19.** $\dfrac{e}{3-e}$ **21.** $\dfrac{232}{77}$ **23.** $\dfrac{15-e}{9(6-e)}$

25. $-\dfrac{1}{\ln 2}$ **27.** $\dfrac{1}{4}$

29. Diverges   **31.** Diverges   **33.** Converges

35. Converges   **37.** Converges   **39.** Converges

41. Diverges   **43.** Converges   **45.** Converges

47. Diverges   **49.** Conditionally convergent

51. Diverges   **53.** Converges conditionally

55. Converges absolutely

57. Converges conditionally

59. $(-3, 3)$ **61.** $[-1, 1]$

63. $[-1 - \sqrt{2}, -1 + \sqrt{2}]$ **65.** $[0, 1]$

67. $(-\infty, \infty)$ **69.** $[-1, 1]$

71. $\displaystyle\sum_{k=0}^{\infty} \frac{(-3)^k x^{k+2}}{k!}$ **73.** $\displaystyle\sum_{k=0}^{\infty} \frac{(\ln 3)^k x^k}{k!}$

75. $\displaystyle\sum_{k=0}^{\infty} [2(-3)^k + 3]\, x^k$

77. $e^{-1/2} \approx 0.6065$ **79.** $\dfrac{410{,}993}{33{,}300}$

81. $\tan x = x + \dfrac{x^3}{3} + \dfrac{2x^5}{15} + \cdots; \qquad |x| < \dfrac{\pi}{2}$

$\ln(\cos x) = -\dfrac{x^2}{2} - \dfrac{x^4}{12} - \dfrac{x^6}{45} - \cdots$

85. 0.396 884 13   **89.** 0.048 790

91. 8 terms for error $< 10^{-6}$; with 3 terms the approximate error is 0.0004.

93. $|x| < 0.187$

95. a. $a_n + \dfrac{n(n-1)}{2}d$ **b.** $\dfrac{a(1-r^n)}{1-r}$

c. $\dfrac{a}{1-r}$ for $|r| < 1$

97. See *American Mathematical Monthly*, Vol. 84.

CHAPTER 9

PROBLEM SET 9.1, Page 575

	Polar form	Rectangular form
3.	$\left(4, \dfrac{\pi}{4}\right), \left(-4, \dfrac{5\pi}{4}\right);$	$(2\sqrt{2}, 2\sqrt{2})$
5.	$\left(-5, \dfrac{5\pi}{3}\right), \left(5, \dfrac{2\pi}{3}\right);$	$\left(-\dfrac{5}{2}, \dfrac{5\sqrt{3}}{2}\right)$
7.	$\left(\dfrac{3}{2}, \dfrac{7\pi}{6}\right), \left(-\dfrac{3}{2}, \dfrac{\pi}{6}\right);$	$\left(\dfrac{-3\sqrt{3}}{4}, -\dfrac{3}{4}\right)$
9.	$(1, \pi), (-1, 0);$	$(-1, 0)$
11.	$(0, \pi - 3), (0, 2\pi - 3);$	$(0, 0)$

13. $\left(2, \dfrac{2\pi}{3}\right), \left(-2, \dfrac{5\pi}{3}\right)$ **15.** $\left(2\sqrt{2}, \dfrac{5\pi}{4}\right), \left(-2\sqrt{2}, \dfrac{\pi}{4}\right)$

17. $\left(\sqrt{58}, \tan^{-1}\dfrac{7}{3}\right), \left(-\sqrt{58}, \tan^{-1}\dfrac{7}{3} + \pi\right)$

19. $\left(2, \dfrac{11\pi}{6}\right), \left(-2, \dfrac{5\pi}{6}\right)$

21. a. United States   **b.** India   **c.** Greenland
    d. Canada

23. $x^2 + (y - 2)^2 = 4$ **25.** $x^2 + y^2 = (x^2 + y^2 + y)^2$

27. $x = 1$ **29.** $x^2 + 2y^2 = 2$

31.

33.

35.

37.

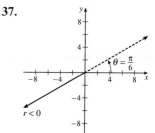

39. Yes   **41.** No   **43.** Yes   **45.** Yes
47. No   **49.** No   **51.** No

Answers vary in Problems 53–59.

61. a. $d = \dfrac{\sqrt{232 - 42\sqrt{2} - 42\sqrt{6}}}{2} \approx 4.1751$

   b. $\sqrt{r_1^2 + r_2^2 - 2r_1r_2\cos(\theta_2 - \theta_1)}$

PROBLEM SET 9.2, Page 584

5. a. Rose (4 petals)   **b.** Lemniscate
   c. Circle   **d.** Rose (16 petals)
   e. None   **f.** Lemniscate
   g. Rose (3 petals)   **h.** Cardioid

7.

9.

11.

13.

15.

17.

19.

21.

23.

25.

27.

29.

31.

33.

35.

37.

39.

41.

43.

45.

47.

49.

51.

53.

57.

59.

61.

63.

65.

73. b.

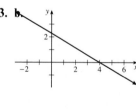

19. $(0, 0)$, $\left(\dfrac{16}{5}, 2\pi - \sin^{-1}\dfrac{4}{5}\right)$ or $(3.2, 5.356)$

21. $(0, 0)$, $\left(1, \dfrac{\pi}{2}\right)$, $\left(\dfrac{3}{5}, \pi - \cos^{-1}\dfrac{4}{5}\right)$ or $(0.6, 0.6435)$

23. $\left(2, \dfrac{\pi}{3}\right)$, $\left(2, \dfrac{5\pi}{3}\right)$ **25.** No intersection points

27. $\left(\sqrt{2}, \dfrac{\pi}{4}\right)$, $\left(\sqrt{2}, \dfrac{7\pi}{4}\right)$ **29.** $\left(2, \dfrac{\pi}{6}\right)$, $\left(2, \dfrac{5\pi}{6}\right)$

31. $\dfrac{\pi}{24} + \dfrac{\sqrt{3}}{16}$ **33.** $\dfrac{\sqrt{3}}{4}$

35. $\dfrac{\pi}{8} + \dfrac{1}{4}$ **37.** $\dfrac{16}{5}\pi^3$

39. $\pm\sqrt{3}$ **41.** $-\dfrac{\sqrt{3}}{3}$

43. $-\dfrac{2}{\pi}$ **45.** $-\dfrac{2}{3}$

47. $\dfrac{2}{\sqrt{3}}$ **49.** $\left(\dfrac{3a}{2}, \dfrac{\pi}{3}\right)$, $\left(\dfrac{3a}{2}, \dfrac{5\pi}{3}\right)$

51. $\left(2\sin\dfrac{\pi}{8}, \dfrac{\pi}{8}\right) \approx (0.77, 0.39)$

$\left(2\sin\dfrac{5\pi}{8}, \dfrac{5\pi}{8}\right) \approx (1.85, 1.96)$

53. $\dfrac{\pi a^2}{4}$ **55.** $2a^2 - \dfrac{a^2\pi}{4}$

57. 4π **59.** $4\pi + 12\sqrt{3}$

63. a. $-\cot\theta$ **b.** $\dfrac{1 - \cos\theta}{\sin\theta}$ **c.** $\dfrac{1}{3}$

PROBLEM SET 9.4, Page 602

3. $y = x - 2$; $1 \le x \le 3$ **5.** $y = \dfrac{4x}{3} - \dfrac{x^2}{225}$, $0 \le x \le 180$

7. $y = \dfrac{2}{3}x + \dfrac{4}{3}$, $2 \le x \le 5$ **9.** $y = x - 2$, $1 \le x \le 3$

11. $y = x^{2/3}$, $x \ge 0$ **13.** $x^2 + y^2 = 9$

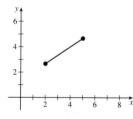

PROBLEM SET 9.3, Page 593

5. $(0, 0)$, $\left(4\sqrt{2}, \dfrac{\pi}{4}\right)$ **7.** $\left(2, \dfrac{\pi}{6}\right)$, $\left(2, \dfrac{5\pi}{6}\right)$

9. $\left(2, \dfrac{\pi}{4}\right)$, $\left(2, \dfrac{5\pi}{4}\right)$ **11.** $(0, 0)$, $(2, 0)$, $(2, \pi)$

13. $(0, 0)$, $\left(2, \dfrac{\pi}{4}\right)$ **15.** $(2, 0)$, $(2, \pi)$

17. $(0, 0)$, $\left(\dfrac{\sqrt{2}}{2}, \dfrac{\pi}{6}\right)$, $\left(\dfrac{\sqrt{2}}{2}, \dfrac{5\pi}{6}\right)$

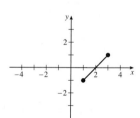

15. $(x - 1)^2 + (y + 2)^2 = 1$

17. $\dfrac{y^2}{9} - \dfrac{x^2}{16} = 1$

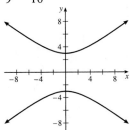

19. $y = 3x,\ x \geq 1$

21. $y = ex,\ x \geq 1$

23. $y = \ln x$

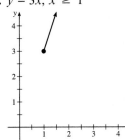

25. $\dfrac{dy}{dx} = 2t^2;\ \dfrac{d^2y}{dx^2} = 2$

27. $\dfrac{dy}{dx} = \dfrac{\cos 2t}{2e^{4t}};$

$\dfrac{d^2y}{dx^2} = \dfrac{-\sin 2t - 2\cos 2t}{4e^{8t}}$

29. $\dfrac{dy}{dx} = -\dfrac{b}{a}\cot t;\ \dfrac{d^2y}{dx^2} = \dfrac{-b}{a^2\sin^3 t}$

31. $\dfrac{dy}{dx} = 2(x - 1)$ **33.** $\dfrac{dy}{dx} = e^{2t}$ **35.** $\dfrac{2}{3}$

37. $\dfrac{\pi - 2}{8}$ **39.** $\dfrac{1}{2}(1 - \ln 2)$ **41.** $\dfrac{1}{27}(22^{3/2} - 8)$

43. $4 + \dfrac{1}{2}\ln\dfrac{3}{2}$ **45.** $\ln(4\sqrt{3} + 7)$ **47.** $\dfrac{b}{16a^2}(16a^2 - x^2)$

49. 12 **51.** $\dfrac{2\pi}{3}$ **53.** $\sqrt{2}$

59. a. 15.865 **b.** 161.557 **c.** 126.645

61. $x(\theta) = f(\theta)\cos\theta;\ y(\theta) = f(\theta)\sin\theta$

PROBLEM SET 9.5, Page 611

3.

5.

7.

9.

11.

13.

15.

17.

19.

21.

23.

25. $y^2 = 10\left(x - \dfrac{5}{2}\right)$

27. $(y - 2)^2 = -16(x + 1)$ **29.** $(x + 2)^2 = 24(y + 3)$

31. $(x + 3)^2 = -\dfrac{1}{3}(y - 2)$

33. $y^2 = -12(x - 3)$ **35.** $x^2 = 18\left(y + \dfrac{9}{2}\right)$

37. $y^2 = 8(x + 2)$

39. $r = \dfrac{8}{1 + \cos\theta}$

41. $r = \dfrac{4}{1 - \sin\theta}$

43. $r\sin^2\theta = 4\cos\theta$

45. $4r^2\cos^2\theta = r\sin\theta - 3$

47. $(0, 0)$

49. Tangent: $(y + 2) = -(x - 1)$
perpendicular: $(y + 2) = (x - 1)$

51. $3x + y = 5$

53. $x^2 = -6(y + 3)$

55. $\dfrac{9}{4}$ m from the vertex

63. $A = 4c^2$

PROBLEM SET 9.6, Page 623

5.

7.

9.

11.

13.

15.

17.

19.

21.

23.

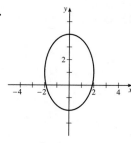

25. $\dfrac{x^4}{4} + \dfrac{(y - 5)^2}{9} = 1$

27. $\dfrac{x^2}{8} + \dfrac{y^2}{4} = 1$

29. $x^2 - y^2 = 1$

31. $\dfrac{x^2}{16} + \dfrac{y^2}{9} = 1$

33. $\dfrac{(x - 2)^2}{9} + \dfrac{(y - 1)^2}{25} = 1$

35. $\dfrac{y^2}{4} - \dfrac{x^2}{32} = 1$

37. $\dfrac{x^2}{9} - \dfrac{(y + 3)^2}{7} = 1$

39.

41.

43. $5x - 6y + 28 = 0$

45. $\left(\pm\sqrt{3}, -\dfrac{1}{2}\right)$

47. $\dfrac{4}{3}\pi ab^2$

49. $8\pi^2$

51. $\dfrac{x^2}{81} - \dfrac{y^2}{81} = 1$

53. $\dfrac{(x - x_0)^2}{a^2} - \dfrac{(y - y_0)^2}{b^2} = 1$, and $x \geq x_0 + a$

55. $12\sqrt{3} - 6\ln(2 + \sqrt{3}) \approx 12.882\,8$

57. **a.** 24π **b.** $24\sqrt{3}\pi$

59. Maximum distance is 9.46×10^7 mi;
minimum distance is 9.14×10^7 mi.

61. $r = \dfrac{3}{2\cos\theta - 1}; \left(3.54, \dfrac{\pi}{8}\right)$

CHAPTER 9 REVIEW

Practice Problems, Page 626

27. **a.** Parabola   **b.** Hyperbola
c. Circle   **d.** Circle
e. Line   **f.** Parabola
g. Four-leaved rose   **h.** Cardioid

28. Parabola   **29.** Circle

30. Ellipse

31. Hyperbola

17.

19.

32. Lemniscate

33. Limaçon

21.

23.

34. $\frac{a^2}{4}(\pi - 2)$

Horizontal tangents at
(2.2, 2.2), (−0.6, 0.6),
(2.2, −2.2), (−0.6, −0.6)

Supplementary Problems, Page 627

25.

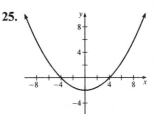

27. $r = \dfrac{4}{2\cos\theta + 3\sin\theta}$

1.

3.

Horizontal tangent at (2, $3\pi/2$)

29. $r^2 - 3r\cos\theta = 5$

31. $r^2 = \theta$

33. $\tan\theta = m$

35. $r = 2a\cos\theta$

37. $\dfrac{x^2}{4} - \dfrac{y^2}{9} = 1$

39. $x^2 = -20y$

5.

7.

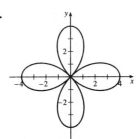

41. $\dfrac{x^2}{16} - \dfrac{y^2}{48} = 1$

43. $\dfrac{(x-6)^2}{4} - \dfrac{y^2}{5} = 1$

45. $\dfrac{(x+5)^2}{1} - \dfrac{(y-4)^2}{3} = 1$

47. $\dfrac{4\left(x - \frac{1}{2}\right)^2}{25} + \dfrac{(y-3)^2}{4} = 1$

49. (0, 0), (2, 0)

9.

11.

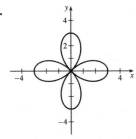

51. $(0, 0), \left(\dfrac{2+\sqrt{2}}{2}, \dfrac{\pi}{4}\right), \left(\dfrac{2-\sqrt{2}}{2}, \dfrac{5\pi}{4}\right)$

53. (2.24, 0.464)

55. $\left(1, \dfrac{\pi}{12}\right), \left(1, \dfrac{5\pi}{12}\right)$

57. (0, 0), (a, 0), (a, π)

59. 8π

61. $\dfrac{1}{2}$

63. $a^2\left(\dfrac{2\pi}{3} - \dfrac{\sqrt{3}}{2}\right)$

13.

15.

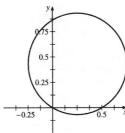

65. $\dfrac{1}{8}(e^{4\pi} - 1)$

67. π

69. 0.905

71.

73. a. $y = x - a\left(\frac{\pi}{2} - 2\right)$ **b.** $y = 2a$ **c.** $x = 2a\pi$

75. $(19, 2), (3, 0)$ **77.** $3\pi a^2$

83. -1 **85.** $\dfrac{-9 - 6\sqrt{2}}{4\sqrt{2}}$

87. a. 2 **b.** Circle area is π; cardioid area is $\dfrac{3\pi}{2}$.

89. $\dfrac{x^2}{1} + \dfrac{y^2}{9} = \dfrac{L^2}{16}$ **91.** $\dfrac{4(a - b)b}{a}$

93. $\dfrac{(x - 5)^2}{0.1736} - \dfrac{y^2}{24.8267} = 1$

95. See *American Mathematical Monthly*, Vol. 83.

CHAPTER 10

PROBLEM SET 10.1, Page 637

1.   **3.**

5.   **7.**

9. $2\mathbf{i}$; 2 **11.** $4\mathbf{i} + 2\mathbf{j}$; $2\sqrt{5}$ **13.** $\dfrac{1}{\sqrt{2}}\mathbf{i} + \dfrac{1}{\sqrt{2}}\mathbf{j}$

15. $\dfrac{3}{5}\mathbf{i} - \dfrac{4}{5}\mathbf{j}$ **17.** $s = 6, t = 24$ **19.** $s = -1, t = -5$

21. $17\mathbf{i} - 18\mathbf{j}$ **23.** $35\mathbf{i} - 35\mathbf{j}$ **25.** $x = 3, y = 2$

27. $x = -1 + \sqrt{7}, y = 1 + \sqrt{7}$ or $x = -1 - \sqrt{7}, y = 1 - \sqrt{7}$

29. $\dfrac{\sqrt{3}}{2}\mathbf{i} + \dfrac{1}{2}\mathbf{j}$ **31.** $\dfrac{4}{\sqrt{17}}\mathbf{i} - \dfrac{1}{\sqrt{17}}\mathbf{j}$ **33.** $\dfrac{5}{\sqrt{26}}\mathbf{i} + \dfrac{1}{\sqrt{26}}\mathbf{j}$

35. $(3, 10)$ **37.** $(3, -5), (7, -3)$ **39.** $\|v\| = \sqrt{\cos^2\theta + \sin^2\theta} = 1$

43. a. Points on the circle with center (x_0, y_0) and radius 1

b. Points on or inside the circle with center (x_0, y_0) and radius 2

45. $a = -2t, b = t, c = t$, for any t

47. $-6\mathbf{i} + 3\mathbf{j}$

49. Horizontal component is $60 \cos 40°$ or 45.96 ft/s; vertical component is $60 \sin 40°$ or 38.56 ft/s.

51. $\left(\dfrac{5}{2} - 5\sqrt{3}\right)\mathbf{i} - \left(13 - \dfrac{5}{2}\sqrt{3}\right)\mathbf{j}$

PROBLEM SET 10.2, Page 000

1.

$d = \sqrt{149}$

3.

$d = \sqrt{382}$

5. $x^2 + y^2 + z^2 = 1$

7. $x^2 + (y - 4)^2 + (z + 5)^2 = 9$

9. $(0, 1, -1)$; 2 **11.** $(3, -1, 1)$; 1

13. B   **15.** E   **17.** A   **19.** G   **21.** I

23. Isosceles, but not right

25. Right triangle, but not isosceles

29.   **31.**

33.   **35.**

37.   **39.**

41. Ellipsoid; traces are ellipses.

43. Hyperboloid of one sheet; trace in the xy-plane is an ellipse; traces in the xz-plane and yz are hyperbolas.

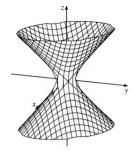

45. Elliptic paraboloid; trace in the xy-plane is a single point $(0, 0, 0)$; trace in the yz-plane is a parabola; trace in the xz-plane is a parabola.

47. Elliptic cone; trace in the xy-plane is a single point $(0, 0, 0)$; trace in the yz-plane is a pair of lines; trace in the xz-plane is a pair of lines.

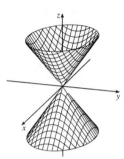

49. $\left(x + \frac{1}{2}\right)^2 + \left(y - \frac{5}{2}\right)^2 + z^2 = \frac{23}{2}$

51. $\left(\frac{1}{3}, \frac{7}{3}, \frac{13}{3}\right)$

PROBLEM SET 10.3, Page 655

3. $-2\mathbf{i} + 2\mathbf{j} + \mathbf{k}$; 3

5. $-4\mathbf{i} - 4\mathbf{j} - 4\mathbf{k}$; $4\sqrt{3}$

7. -16 **9.** 5 **11.** Yes **13.** Yes

15. $\sqrt{3}$ **17.** 14 **19.** $-4\mathbf{i} - 16\mathbf{j} + 7\mathbf{k}$

21. $\sqrt{321}$ **23.** No **25.** No **27.** 11

29. 0 **31.** 1.23 or 71°

33. 1.98 or 114° **35.** $\mathbf{k}$; 1

37. $-\frac{6}{13}(2\mathbf{j} - 3\mathbf{k})$; $\frac{6}{\sqrt{13}}$ **39.** $\pm\mathbf{j}$

41. $\pm\frac{1}{\sqrt{2}}(\mathbf{i} - \mathbf{k})$ **43.** $s(2\mathbf{i} + 3\mathbf{j} - 2\mathbf{k})$ where $s < 0$

45. $x = -1, y = -1, z = 4$

47. $a = \frac{3}{2}$ **49.** 35°, 66°, 114°

51. a. 4 **b.** $\frac{2}{3\sqrt{7}}$ **c.** $\frac{9}{2}$ **d.** $-\frac{7}{2}$

53. $2\sqrt{6}$ **55.** 8 units

57. 868 lb **59.** 25,000 ft-lb

63. 50 **65.** $\mathbf{v} = \mathbf{0}$, and $\mathbf{w}$ can be any vector.

PROBLEM SET 10.4, Page 663

1. $\mathbf{k}$ **3.** $-2\mathbf{i} + 4\mathbf{j} + 3\mathbf{k}$

5. $-2\mathbf{i} + 25\mathbf{j} + 14\mathbf{k}$ **7.** $-2\mathbf{i} + 16\mathbf{j} + 11\mathbf{k}$

9. $-14\mathbf{i} - 4\mathbf{j} - \mathbf{k}$ **11.** $\frac{\sqrt{3}}{2}$

13. $\frac{\sqrt{3}}{2}$ **15.** $\frac{3}{77}\sqrt{33}$

17. $\frac{1}{\sqrt{14}}(\mathbf{i} + 3\mathbf{j} - 2\mathbf{k})$ **19.** $\frac{1}{\sqrt{386}}(-16\mathbf{i} + 7\mathbf{j} + 9\mathbf{k})$

21. $\sqrt{26}$ **23.** $2\sqrt{59}$

25. $\frac{1}{2}\sqrt{3}$ **27.** $\frac{3}{2}\sqrt{3}$

29. a. Does not exist **b.** Scalar

31. a. Scalar **c.** Vector

33. 5 **35.** 8 **39. a.** No **b.** No **c.** Yes

41. $t = 0$

43. $(\mathbf{u} \times \mathbf{v}) \times \mathbf{w} \neq \mathbf{u} \times (\mathbf{v} \times \mathbf{w})$; cross product is not associative

45. $\mathbf{w} = \mathbf{0}$ **47.** $-40\sqrt{3}\,\mathbf{i}$

PROBLEM SET 10.5, Page 673

3. $2x - y + 3z - 5 = 0$ **5.** $3x - 2y + 2z - 12 = 0$

7. $\frac{x - 1}{3} = \frac{y + 1}{-2} = \frac{z + 2}{5}$;
$x = 1 + 3t, y = -1 - 2t, z = -2 + 5t$

9. $\frac{x - 1}{1} = \frac{y + 1}{2} = \frac{z - 2}{1}$; $x = 1 + t, y = -1 + 2t, z = 2 + t$

11. $\frac{x - 1}{1} = \frac{y + 3}{-3} = \frac{z - 6}{-5}$; $x = 1 + t, y = -3 - 3t, z = 6 - 5t$

13. $\frac{x}{11} = \frac{y - 4}{-3} = \frac{z + 3}{5}$; $x = 11t, y = 4 - 3t, z = -3 + 5t$

15. $x = 3, y = -1 + t, z = 0$

17. $(0, -6, -3), (8, 0, -1), (12, 3, 0)$

19. $(0, 4, 9), (8, 0, -3), (6, 1, 0)$

21. Parallel **23.** Parallel **25.** $(1, 2, 3)$

27. $\frac{2}{\sqrt{38}}, \frac{-3}{\sqrt{38}}, \frac{-5}{\sqrt{38}}$; 1.24 or 71°, 2.08 or 119°, 2.52 or 144°

29. $\frac{1}{\sqrt{2}}, \frac{-4}{5\sqrt{2}}, \frac{3}{5\sqrt{2}}$; 0.79 or 45°, 2.17 or 124°, 1.13 or 65°

31. $\frac{1}{\sqrt{91}}, \frac{-3}{\sqrt{91}}, \frac{9}{\sqrt{91}}$; 1.47 or 84°, 1.89 or 108°, 0.34 or 19°

33. $2x + 4y - 3z + 5 = 0$ **35.** $2y - 3z + 6 = 0$

37. $z = 0$ **39.** $\pm\frac{1}{\sqrt{21}}(4\mathbf{i} + 2\mathbf{j} + \mathbf{k})$

41. $\pm\frac{1}{\sqrt{29}}(2\mathbf{i} + 4\mathbf{j} - 3\mathbf{k})$ **45.** $\pm\frac{1}{3}(2\mathbf{i} - 2\mathbf{j} + \mathbf{k})$

47. $\frac{x - 1}{2} = \frac{y - 4}{-5} = \frac{z - 1}{-3}$ **49.** $x + 2y + z - 1 = 0$

51. $3x + 5y + 2z - 9 = 0$ **55.** 1.18 or 68°

57. $\dfrac{x}{14} = \dfrac{y-1}{2} = \dfrac{z+1}{15}$ **59.** $\dfrac{x}{8} = \dfrac{y}{-5} = \dfrac{z+5}{19}$

61. $\dfrac{3}{\sqrt{61}}, \dfrac{-6}{\sqrt{61}}, \dfrac{-4}{\sqrt{61}}$; 67°, 140°, 121°

63. The lines intersect at (x_0, y_0, z_0) and are perpendicular to each other.

45. $\dfrac{4}{\sqrt{30}}$ **46.** $\dfrac{6}{\sqrt{26}}$

47. $\dfrac{5\sqrt{6}}{\sqrt{35}}$ **48.** 168.4 mi/hr

49. $75\sqrt{3}$ ft-lb

PROBLEM SET 10.6, Page 677

1. 0   **3.** $\dfrac{31}{13}$ **5.** $\dfrac{19}{\sqrt{10}}$ **7.** $\dfrac{1}{\sqrt{3}}$

9. $\sqrt{6}$ **11.** $\dfrac{|4a^2 - 3a|}{\sqrt{5a^2 + 1}}$ **13.** $\dfrac{7}{\sqrt{14}}$ **15.** $\dfrac{3}{\sqrt{35}}$

17. $\dfrac{4\sqrt{3}}{\sqrt{14}}$ **19.** $\dfrac{\sqrt{65}}{3}$ **21.** $\dfrac{4|a|\sqrt{5}}{3}$

23. $(x + 2)^2 + (y - 3)^2 + (z - 7)^2 = 36$

25. $\sqrt{5,435} \approx 73.72$

27. $(3y + z + 3)^2 + (3x - 4z - 3)^2 + (x + 4y + 3)^2 = 650$

29. $\dfrac{65}{\sqrt{122}}$ **31.** $\dfrac{1}{3}\sqrt{6}$

33. a. $d = \dfrac{|D_1 - D_2|}{\sqrt{A^2 + B^2 + C^2}}$ **b.** $\dfrac{2}{\sqrt{6}}$

CHAPTER 10 REVIEW

Practice Problems, Page 679

34. a. $13\mathbf{i} - 12\mathbf{j} + 2\mathbf{k}$ **b.** 1

c. $\dfrac{12}{13}(3\mathbf{i} - 2\mathbf{j})$ **d.** $\dfrac{12}{\sqrt{14}}$

35. a. -8 **b.** $14\mathbf{i} + 6\mathbf{j} + 2\mathbf{k}$

36. a. 40

    b. Not possible to cross multiply a scalar and a vector

    c. $25\mathbf{i} - 10\mathbf{j} - 15\mathbf{k}$

    d. Not possible because dot product is a scalar

37. $\dfrac{x}{1} = \dfrac{y+2}{-6} = \dfrac{z-1}{4}$ **38.** $2x + 3z - 11 = 0$

39. $\dfrac{x + \frac{13}{2}}{5} = \dfrac{y-5}{-3} = \dfrac{z}{-1}$ **40.** $17x + 19y + 13z - 25 = 0$

41. $\dfrac{x-1}{2} = \dfrac{y-2}{-3} = \dfrac{z+1}{3}$

42. $\dfrac{-2}{\sqrt{14}}, \dfrac{3}{\sqrt{14}}, \dfrac{1}{\sqrt{14}}$; 2.13 or 122°, 0.64 or 37°, 1.30 or 74°

43. a. Skew lines   **b.** $(2, 2, 3)$

44. a. 6   **b.** $\sqrt{2}$

Supplementary Problems, Page 680

1. $8\sqrt{2} + \sqrt{14}$ **3.** 125°, 26°, 30°

5. $\dfrac{x-1}{3} = \dfrac{y+2}{1} = \dfrac{z-3}{-1}$;

    $x = 1 + 3t, \; y = -2 + t, \; z = 3 - t$;

    Points may vary: $(-2, -3, 4), (7, 0, 1)$.

7. $\dfrac{x-1}{2} = \dfrac{z}{1}, \; y = 4$; $x = 1 + 2t, \; y = 4, \; z = t$

    Points may vary: $(3, 4, 1), (-1, 4, -1)$.

9. $\dfrac{x-3}{8} = \dfrac{y-4}{-7} = \dfrac{z+1}{3}$ **11.** $\dfrac{x-2}{14} = \dfrac{y-3}{8} = \dfrac{z+1}{13}$

13. $z = 0$ **15.** $3x + 4y - z + 13 = 0$

17. $5x - 2y + 3z - 32 = 0$ **19.** $3x + 2y - 11z + 19 = 0$

21. $\sqrt{14}$; $-\mathbf{i} - 3\mathbf{j} + 4\mathbf{k}$; $18\mathbf{i} - \mathbf{j} - 7\mathbf{k}$

23. $\sqrt{38}$; $6\mathbf{i} - 5\mathbf{j} + 5\mathbf{k}$; $7\mathbf{i} - 5\mathbf{j}$

25. 0; $\mathbf{k}$ **27.** 6; $-2\mathbf{i} + 4\mathbf{j} + 3\mathbf{k}$

29. 2; $6\mathbf{i} + 3\mathbf{j} - 4\mathbf{k}$

31. a. $14\mathbf{i} + 7\mathbf{j} + 20\mathbf{k}$ **b.** $\sqrt{94}$

    c. $\dfrac{1}{3}\mathbf{i} + \dfrac{1}{6}\mathbf{j} - \dfrac{5}{6}\mathbf{k}$ **d.** $\dfrac{5}{\sqrt{21}}$

33. $\dfrac{-3}{\sqrt{46}}, \dfrac{6}{\sqrt{46}}, \dfrac{1}{\sqrt{46}}$ **35.** $\pm\left(\dfrac{3}{\sqrt{19}}\mathbf{i} + \dfrac{1}{\sqrt{19}}\mathbf{j} + \dfrac{3}{\sqrt{19}}\mathbf{k}\right)$

37. $\sqrt{74}$

39. $(0, 14, -10), (21, 0, 25), (6, 10, 0)$

41. $(3, -2, 1)$ **43.** $2x - z + 13 = 0$

45. $\dfrac{1}{7}\sqrt{497}$ **47.** $1{,}250\sqrt{3}$

49. $(\|\mathbf{v}\|\mathbf{w} + \|\mathbf{w}\|\mathbf{v}) \cdot (\|\mathbf{v}\|\mathbf{w} - \|\mathbf{w}\|\mathbf{v}) = 0$

51. 25°, 65°, 90°   **53.** $x + y + z = a$

55. $\dfrac{9}{2}\sqrt{2}$ **57.** $\dfrac{\sqrt{26}}{2}$

59. $2x - 3y - 7z = 0$ **61.** $\dfrac{x+1}{1} = \dfrac{y-2}{1}, \; z = 0$

63. $\pm\left(\dfrac{6}{\sqrt{37}}\mathbf{i} - \dfrac{1}{\sqrt{37}}\mathbf{j}\right)$

65. This set of vectors is the line $x = a + At, \; y = b + Bt,$ $z = c + Ct$

81. See *American Mathematical Monthly*, Vol. 46.

83. See *American Mathematical Monthly*, Vol. 90.

CHAPTER 11

PROBLEM SET 11.1, Page 690

1. $t \neq 0$

3. $t \neq (2n+1)\dfrac{\pi}{2}$

5. $t \neq \dfrac{n\pi}{2}$

7. $t > 0$

9.

11.

13.

15.

17.

19.

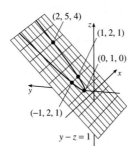

25. $t\mathbf{i} + t^2\mathbf{j} + 2\mathbf{k}$

27. $2t\mathbf{i} + (1-t)\mathbf{j} + \sin t\mathbf{k}$

29. $t^2\mathbf{i} + t\mathbf{j} + \sqrt{9 - t^2 - t^4}\,\mathbf{k}$

31. $(7t - 3)\mathbf{i} - 10\mathbf{j} + \left(2t^2 - \dfrac{3}{t}\right)\mathbf{k}$

33. $3t - 2t^2$

35. $(1-t)\sin t$

37. $-t^2 e^t\mathbf{i} + (t^2\sin t)\mathbf{j} + (2te^t + 5\sin t)\mathbf{k}$

39. $(4te^t + t - t^2 + 10\sin t)\mathbf{i} + (2t^2 e^t + 1)\mathbf{k}$

41. $t^2 e^t - t^3 e^t - 2e^t - \dfrac{5\sin t}{t}$

43. $3\mathbf{i} + e^2\mathbf{j}$

45. $3\mathbf{i} - \dfrac{1}{3}\mathbf{j} + 2\mathbf{k}$

47. $\mathbf{i} + e\mathbf{k}$

49. $2\mathbf{i} - 3\mathbf{j} + e\mathbf{k}$

51. all real t

53. $t \neq 0,\ t \neq -1$

55. $t \neq 0$

PROBLEM SET 11.2, Page 700

1. $\mathbf{F}'(t) = \mathbf{i} + 2t\mathbf{j} + (1 + 3t^2)\mathbf{k}$

3. $\mathbf{F}'(s) = (1 + \ln s)\mathbf{i} + \left(\dfrac{5}{s}\right)\mathbf{j} - e^s\left(\ln s + \dfrac{1}{s}\right)\mathbf{k}$

5. $\mathbf{F}'(t) = 2t\mathbf{i} - t^{-2}\mathbf{j} + 2e^{2t}\mathbf{k}$;
$\mathbf{F}''(t) = 2\mathbf{i} + 2t^{-3}\mathbf{j} + 4e^{2t}\mathbf{k}$

7. $\mathbf{F}'(s) = \cos s\mathbf{i} - \sin s\mathbf{j} + 2s\mathbf{k}$
$\mathbf{F}''(s) = -\sin s\mathbf{i} - \cos s\mathbf{j} + 2\mathbf{k}$

9. $f'(x) = -9x^2 - 2x$

11. $g'(x) = \dfrac{4x}{\sqrt{1 + 4x^2}}$

13. $\mathbf{V}(t) = \mathbf{i} + 2t\mathbf{j} + 2\mathbf{k};\ \mathbf{V}(1) = \mathbf{i} + 2\mathbf{j} + 2\mathbf{k};$
$\|\mathbf{V}(1)\| = 3$ in the direction $\dfrac{1}{3}\mathbf{i} + \dfrac{2}{3}\mathbf{j} + \dfrac{2}{3}\mathbf{k};$
$\mathbf{A}(t) = 2\mathbf{j};\ \mathbf{A}(1) = 2\mathbf{j}$

15. $\mathbf{V}(t) = -\sin t\mathbf{i} + \cos t\mathbf{j} + 3\mathbf{k};$
$\mathbf{V}\left(\dfrac{\pi}{4}\right) = -\dfrac{\sqrt{2}}{2}\mathbf{i} + \dfrac{\sqrt{2}}{2}\mathbf{j} + 3\mathbf{k};$
$\left\|\mathbf{V}\left(\dfrac{\pi}{4}\right)\right\| = \sqrt{10}$ in the direction $-\dfrac{1}{2\sqrt{5}}\mathbf{i} + \dfrac{1}{2\sqrt{5}}\mathbf{j} + \dfrac{3}{\sqrt{10}}\mathbf{k};$
$\mathbf{A}(t) = -\cos t\mathbf{i} - \sin t\mathbf{j};\ \mathbf{A}\left(\dfrac{\pi}{4}\right) = -\dfrac{\sqrt{2}}{2}\mathbf{i} - \dfrac{\sqrt{2}}{2}\mathbf{j}$

17. $\mathbf{V}(t) = e^t\mathbf{i} - e^{-t}\mathbf{j} + 2e^{2t}\mathbf{k};\ \mathbf{V}(\ln 2) = 2\mathbf{i} - \dfrac{1}{2}\mathbf{j} + 8\mathbf{k};$
$\|\mathbf{V}(\ln 2)\| = \dfrac{\sqrt{273}}{2}$ in the direction
$\dfrac{4}{\sqrt{273}}\mathbf{i} - \dfrac{1}{\sqrt{273}}\mathbf{j} + \dfrac{16}{\sqrt{273}}\mathbf{k};\ \mathbf{A}(t) = e^t\mathbf{i} + e^{-t}\mathbf{j} + 4e^{2t}\mathbf{k};$
$\mathbf{A}(\ln 2) = 2\mathbf{i} + \dfrac{1}{2}\mathbf{j} + 16\mathbf{k}$

19. $\mathbf{F}'(0) = 2\mathbf{j};\ \mathbf{F}'(1) = 2\mathbf{i} + 2\mathbf{j} + 5\mathbf{k};\ \mathbf{F}'(-1) = -2\mathbf{i} + 2\mathbf{j} + \mathbf{k}$

21. $\mathbf{F}'(0) = \mathbf{i};\ \mathbf{F}'(2) = \dfrac{1}{25}\mathbf{i} + \dfrac{12}{25}\mathbf{j} + \dfrac{44}{25}\mathbf{k}$

23. $\mathbf{F}'\left(\dfrac{\pi}{2}\right) = -\mathbf{j} + a\mathbf{k};\ \mathbf{F}'(\pi) = -\mathbf{i} + a\mathbf{k}$

25. $\dfrac{t^2}{2}\mathbf{i} - \dfrac{1}{3}e^{3t}\mathbf{j} + 3t\mathbf{k} + \mathbf{C}$

27. $(t\ln|t| - t)\mathbf{i} - \dfrac{t^2}{4}(2\ln|t| - 1)\mathbf{j} + (3t\ln|t| - 3t)\mathbf{k} + \mathbf{C}$

29. $\left(\dfrac{t^2}{2}\ln|t| - \dfrac{t^2}{4}\right)\mathbf{i} - \cos(1 - t)\mathbf{j} + \dfrac{t^2}{2}\mathbf{k} + \mathbf{C}$

33. $\mathbf{i} + 2\mathbf{j} - 3\mathbf{k}$

35. $2\sqrt{14}$

37. $[6t + 2\cos(2 - t)]\mathbf{i} + 9\sin 3t\mathbf{j} - (3t^{-2} - 4e^{2t})\mathbf{k}$

39. $\mathbf{R}(t) = e^t\mathbf{i} + \left(\dfrac{t^3}{3} - 1\right)\mathbf{j}$

41. $\dfrac{1}{3}(2\sqrt{2} - 1)\mathbf{i} + \dfrac{\pi}{4}\mathbf{j}$

PROBLEM SET 11.3, Page 708

1. $T_f = 4.6$ sec; $R = 481$ ft

3. $T_f = 129.9$ sec; $R = 73{,}175$ m

5. $T_f = 1.9$ sec; $R = 41$ ft

7. $T_f = 1.5$ sec; $R = 148$ ft

9. $\mathbf{V}(t) = \sqrt{5}\mathbf{u}_r;\ \mathbf{A}(t) = \mathbf{0}$

11. $\mathbf{V}(t) = (2\cos 2t)\mathbf{u}_r + (2\sin 2t)\mathbf{u}_\theta$
$\mathbf{A}(t) = (-4\sin 2t)\mathbf{u}_r + (8\cos 2t)\mathbf{u}_\theta$

13. $\mathbf{V}(t) = -10\sin(2t + 1)\mathbf{u}_r + 10[1 + \cos(2t + 1)]\mathbf{u}_\theta$
$\mathbf{A}(t) = -20[2\cos(2t + 1) + 1]\mathbf{u}_r - 40\sin(2t + 1)\mathbf{u}_\theta$

15. 140 m/s   **17.** 21.7° or 68.3°

19. Maximum height is 35.64 ft; range is 225.93 ft; the distance to the fence is 217.47 ft.

21. 3.45 sec   **23.** 5.5 sec

25. 23.53 ft

27. $\mathbf{V}(t) = (2 \cos t)\mathbf{u}_r + (9t^2 + 6t^2 \sin t)\mathbf{u}_\theta$

$\mathbf{A}(t) = (-2 \sin t - 27t^4 - 18t^4 \sin t)\mathbf{u}_r$
$+ (18t + 12t \sin t + 12t^2 \cos t)\mathbf{u}_\theta$

29. aw **31.** aw^2 **33.** 1.82 sec; 56.7 ft

PROBLEM SET 11.4, Page 719

1. $\mathbf{T}(t) = \dfrac{2}{\sqrt{4 + 9t^2}}\mathbf{i} + \dfrac{3t}{\sqrt{4 + 9t^2}}\mathbf{j}$

$\mathbf{N}(t) = \pm\left[\dfrac{-3t}{\sqrt{4 + 9t^2}}\mathbf{i} + \dfrac{2}{\sqrt{4 + 9t^2}}\mathbf{j}\right]$

3. $\mathbf{T}(t) = \dfrac{\cos t - \sin t}{\sqrt{2}}\mathbf{i} + \dfrac{\cos t + \sin t}{\sqrt{2}}\mathbf{j}$

$\mathbf{N}(t) = \pm\left[\dfrac{\sin t + \cos t}{\sqrt{2}}\mathbf{i} + \dfrac{\sin t - \cos t}{\sqrt{2}}\mathbf{j}\right]$

5. $\mathbf{T}(t) = \dfrac{-\sin t}{\sqrt{2}}\mathbf{i} + \dfrac{\cos t}{\sqrt{2}}\mathbf{j} + \dfrac{1}{\sqrt{2}}\mathbf{k}$

$\mathbf{N}(t) = \pm[\cos t\mathbf{i} + \sin t\mathbf{j}]$

7. $\mathbf{T}(t) = \dfrac{1}{\sqrt{1 + 4t^4}}\mathbf{i} + \dfrac{2t^2}{\sqrt{1 + 4t^4}}\mathbf{k}$

$\mathbf{N}(t) = \pm\left[\dfrac{-2t^2}{\sqrt{1 + 4t^4}}\mathbf{i} + \dfrac{1}{\sqrt{1 + 4t^4}}\mathbf{k}\right]$

9.

Length is $4\sqrt{5}$.

11.

Length is $\dfrac{3}{2}\pi\sqrt{2}$.

13.
Length is $\sqrt{41}\pi$.

15. $\kappa = 0$ **17.** $\kappa = \dfrac{3}{5\sqrt{10}} \approx 0.19$

19. $\kappa = \dfrac{2|a|}{[1 + (2ac + b)^2]^{3/2}}$ **21.** $\kappa = 0.875$

23. $\kappa = 1$ **25.** $\kappa = \dfrac{1}{2\sqrt{2}}$

29. $\mathbf{T}\left(\dfrac{\pi}{3}\right) = \dfrac{1}{\sqrt{10}}\mathbf{i} - \dfrac{3}{\sqrt{10}}\mathbf{j}$; $\mathbf{N}\left(\dfrac{\pi}{3}\right) = \dfrac{3}{\sqrt{10}}\mathbf{i} + \dfrac{1}{\sqrt{10}}\mathbf{j}$

31. a. $\mathbf{T}(\pi) = \dfrac{-1}{\sqrt{2}}\mathbf{i} + \dfrac{1}{\sqrt{2}}\mathbf{k}$ **b.** $\kappa = \dfrac{1}{2}$ **c.** $L = \sqrt{2}\pi$

33. Maximum curvature (of 24) occurs at $(0, 3)$, $(0, -3)$

35. At $x = 0$, $\rho = \dfrac{1}{6}$; at $x = \pm1$, $\rho = \dfrac{1}{24}$

37. $x = 2 + 2t$, $y = -1 - t$, $z = 1 + 2t$

39. $\kappa = \dfrac{2\sqrt{9t^4 + 9t^2 + 1}}{(1 + 4t^2 + 9t^4)^{3/2}}$ **41.** $\kappa = \dfrac{2}{(1 + 4x^2)^{3/2}}$

43. $\kappa = \dfrac{2|x|^3}{(1 + x^4)^{3/2}}$ **45.** $\kappa = \dfrac{1}{\sqrt{2}e^\theta}$

PROBLEM SET 11.5, Page 726

1. $A_T = \dfrac{4t}{\sqrt{1 + 4t^2}}$; $A_N = \dfrac{2}{\sqrt{1 + 4t^2}}$

3. $A_T = \dfrac{t}{\sqrt{t^2 + 1}}$; $A_N = \dfrac{t^2 + 2}{\sqrt{t^2 + 1}}$

5. $A_T = \dfrac{4t}{\sqrt{2 + 4t^2}}$; $A_N = \dfrac{2}{\sqrt{1 + 2t^2}}$

7. $A_T = \dfrac{15 \sin t \cos t}{\sqrt{1 + 15 \sin^2 t}}$; $A_N = \dfrac{4}{\sqrt{1 + 15 \sin^2 t}}$

9. $A_T = 0$; $A_N = 4$

11. $A_T = \dfrac{2\sqrt{399}}{5} \approx 7.99$; $A_N = 0.4$

13. Pressure at highest point is $\dfrac{3\omega^2}{16}$ lb/ft^2; smallest value for ω is 4 ft/s.

15. a. 3,536.5 lb   **b.** $\theta = 44.7°$

17. $\omega \approx 14$ rev/min

19. $A_T = \dfrac{4t}{\sqrt{4t^2 + 5}}$; $A_N = 2\sqrt{\dfrac{5}{4t^2 + 5}}$

21. $A_T = \sqrt{3}e^t$; $A_N = \sqrt{2}e^t$ **23. a.** $A_N = \dfrac{W}{g}(60\pi^2\omega^2)$

       b. $\omega = 4.83$ rev/min

25. $\mathbf{A} = -g\mathbf{j}$; $\mathbf{V} = v_0\cos \alpha\mathbf{i} + (-gt + v_0\sin \alpha)\mathbf{j}$

$\mathbf{R} = (v_0\cos \alpha)t\mathbf{i} + \left[-\dfrac{gt^2}{2} + (v_0\sin \alpha)t\right]\mathbf{j}$

$t = \dfrac{v_0\sin \alpha}{g}$ for maximum height; at this height,

$\|\mathbf{V}\| = \sqrt{v_0^2\cos^2\alpha + (-gt + v_0\sin \alpha)^2}$

$\mathbf{A}_T = 0$, and $\mathbf{A}_N = v_0\sqrt{\dfrac{2 \cos \alpha \sin \alpha - \sin^2\alpha}{2g}}$

29. About 36,000 km

CHAPTER 11 REVIEW

Practice Problems, Page 729

24.

Length is $2\pi\sqrt{10}$.

25. $\mathbf{F}'(t) = \dfrac{1}{(1+t)^2}\mathbf{i} + \dfrac{t\cos t - \sin t}{t^2}\mathbf{j} - (\sin t)\mathbf{k}$

$\mathbf{F}''(t) = \dfrac{-2}{(1+i)^3}\mathbf{i} + \dfrac{2\sin t - 2t\cos t - t^2\sin t}{t^3}\mathbf{j} - (\cos t)\mathbf{k}$

26. $(3 - 6\ln 2)\mathbf{i} + \dfrac{45}{4}\mathbf{j} + \left(6\ln 2 - \dfrac{9}{4}\right)\mathbf{k}$

27. $(e^t - t)\mathbf{i} - \left(\dfrac{t^4}{12} + 2\right)\mathbf{j} + \left(\dfrac{3}{2}t^2 + 3t\right)\mathbf{k}$

28. $\mathbf{V} = \mathbf{i} + 2\mathbf{j} + e^t(t+1)\mathbf{k}$

$\mathbf{A} = e^t(t+2)\mathbf{k}$

$\dfrac{ds}{dt} = \sqrt{5 + e^{2t}(t+1)^2}$

29. $\mathbf{T} = \dfrac{2t}{\sqrt{4t^2+18}}\mathbf{i} + \dfrac{3}{\sqrt{4t^2+18}}\mathbf{j} - \dfrac{3}{\sqrt{4t^2+18}}\mathbf{k}$

$\mathbf{N} = \dfrac{3}{\sqrt{2t^2+9}}\mathbf{i} - \dfrac{t}{\sqrt{2t^2+9}}\mathbf{j} + \dfrac{t}{\sqrt{2t^2+9}}\mathbf{k}$

$\kappa = \dfrac{3}{(2t^2+9)^{3/2}}$

$\mathbf{A}_T = \dfrac{2\sqrt{2}\,t}{\sqrt{2t^2+9}}; \mathbf{A}_N = \dfrac{6}{\sqrt{2t^2+9}}$

30. a. $\dfrac{625}{64} \approx 9.8$ ft

b. Time of flight is $\dfrac{25}{16} \approx 1.6$ sec; range is $\dfrac{625\sqrt{3}}{16} \approx 67.7$ ft.

Supplementary Problems, Page 730

1. $2\mathbf{k}$

3. $-5\mathbf{k}$

5. $\mathbf{i} - \mathbf{j}$

7. $\mathbf{F}'(t) = e^t(t+1)\mathbf{i} + 2t\mathbf{j}$
$\mathbf{F}''(t) = e^t(t+2)\mathbf{i} + 2\mathbf{j}$

9. $\mathbf{F}'(t) = -2t^{-2}\mathbf{i} - 2\mathbf{j} + e^{-t}(1-t)\mathbf{k}$
$\mathbf{F}''(t) = 4t^{-3}\mathbf{i} + e^{-t}(t-2)\mathbf{k}$

11. $\mathbf{F}'(t) = (2t + ae^{at})\mathbf{i} + e^{-at}(1-at)\mathbf{j} + ae^{at+1}\mathbf{k}$
$\mathbf{F}''(t) = (2 + a^2e^{at})\mathbf{i} + e^{-at}(a^2t - 2a)\mathbf{j} + a^2e^{at+1}\mathbf{k}$

13.

15.

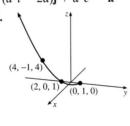

(4, −1, 4)

(2, 0, 1) (0, 1, 0)

17.

19. $\dfrac{\mathbf{F}(t)\cdot\mathbf{F}'(t)}{\|\mathbf{F}(t)\|}$

21. $\dfrac{\|\mathbf{F}\|^2\mathbf{F}' - (\mathbf{F}\cdot\mathbf{F}')\mathbf{F}}{\|\mathbf{F}\|^3}$

23. 0

25. $(e - e^{-1})\mathbf{i} + 6\mathbf{k}$

27. $e^t(t-1)\mathbf{i} + \left(\dfrac{1}{2}\cos 2t\right)\mathbf{j} + \dfrac{t^3}{3}\mathbf{k} + \mathbf{C}$

29. $e^t(t-1)\mathbf{i} + \dfrac{1}{4}t^2(2\ln t - 1)\mathbf{j} + \dfrac{3}{2}t^2\mathbf{k} + \mathbf{C}$

31. $\mathbf{V} = \mathbf{i} - \mathbf{j}; \mathbf{A} = 0; \dfrac{ds}{dt} = \sqrt{2}$

33. $\mathbf{V} = (\sin t + t\cos t)\mathbf{i} + e^{-t}(1-t)\mathbf{j} + \mathbf{k}$;
$\mathbf{A} = (2\cos t - t\sin t)\mathbf{i} + e^{-t}(t-2)\mathbf{j}$;
$\dfrac{ds}{dt} = \sqrt{\sin^2 t + t\sin 2t + t^2\cos^2 t + e^{-2t}(1-t)^2 + 1}$

35. $\mathbf{T} = \dfrac{1}{\sqrt{2}}\mathbf{i} - \dfrac{1}{\sqrt{2}}\mathbf{j}$;

$\mathbf{N} = \dfrac{1}{\sqrt{2}}\mathbf{i} + \dfrac{1}{\sqrt{2}}\mathbf{j}$

37. $\mathbf{T} = \left(-\dfrac{4}{5}\sin t\right)\mathbf{i} - \dfrac{3}{5}\mathbf{j} + \left(\dfrac{4}{5}\cos t\right)\mathbf{k}$

$\mathbf{N} = (-\cos t)\mathbf{i} + (\sin t)\mathbf{k}$

39. $\mathbf{A}_T = \dfrac{4t + e^{2t}}{\sqrt{4t^2 + 4 + e^{2t}}}$;

$A_N = 2\sqrt{\dfrac{t^2e^{2t} - 2te^{2t} + 2e^{2t} + 4}{4t^2 + 4 + e^{2t}}}$

$\kappa = \dfrac{2\sqrt{t^2e^{2t} - 2te^{2t} + 2e^{2t} + 4}}{(4t^2 + 4 + e^{2t})^{3/2}}$

41. $A_T = 0; A_N = 4\sqrt{2}; \kappa = \dfrac{1}{8}$

43. $\kappa = \dfrac{1}{2}$

45. $\kappa = \dfrac{e}{\sqrt{2}} \approx 1.92$

47. $\kappa = \dfrac{1}{6}$

49. $t \neq 1$

51. $\mathbf{F}(t) = (2t - \sin t + 1)\mathbf{i} + \left(\dfrac{3}{2}t^2 + \cos t - 1\right)\mathbf{j} + \left(\dfrac{t^4}{24\pi} + \dfrac{t^2}{2}\right)\mathbf{k}$

53. *Answers may vary.*

$\mathbf{T}(s) = \dfrac{1}{\sqrt{5}}\left[-\sin\left(\dfrac{s}{a}\right)\mathbf{i} + \cos\left(\dfrac{s}{a}\right)\mathbf{j} + 2\mathbf{k}\right]$

$\mathbf{N}(s) = \pm\left[\cos\left(\dfrac{s}{a}\right)\mathbf{i} + \sin\left(\dfrac{s}{a}\right)\mathbf{j}\right]$

55. At $t = 0$, $R = \dfrac{b^2}{a}$; at $t = \dfrac{\pi}{2}$, $R = \dfrac{a^2}{b}$

57. a. $\mathbf{V} = -e^{-t}(\cos t + \sin t)\mathbf{i} + e^{-t}(\cos t - \sin t)\mathbf{j} - e^{-t}\mathbf{k}$;
speed $= \|\mathbf{V}\| = \sqrt{3}e^{-t}$;
$\mathbf{A} = (2e^{-t}\sin t)\mathbf{i} - (2e^{-t}\cos t)\mathbf{j} + e^{-t}\mathbf{k}$

b. $\kappa = \dfrac{1}{3}\sqrt{2}\,e^t$

59. $A_T = 0; A_N = aw^2$ **61.** 18,150 lb

63.

$x = t$
$y = 0$

65. Maximum velocity is 11.6 m/s.

67. Yes

69. $\mathbf{F}'(x) = (\sin x)\mathbf{i} - (\cos 2x)\mathbf{j} + e^{-x}\mathbf{k}$

71. $\mathbf{F}(t) = \left(\dfrac{t^2}{2} + 1\right)\mathbf{i} + \left(\dfrac{t^2}{2} + 2\right)\mathbf{j} - \left(\dfrac{t^2}{2} + 3\right)\mathbf{k}$

73. $\mathbf{F}(t) = \dfrac{1}{2}(3 - \cos 2t)\mathbf{i}$

$\qquad + \dfrac{1}{2}[e^t(\sin t + \cos t) - 1]\mathbf{j} - [3\ln(t + 1) + 3]\mathbf{k}$

75. See *American Mathematical Monthly*, Vol. 46.

77. See *American Mathematical Monthly*, Vol. 53.

CUMULATIVE REVIEW, Page 736

5. $y' = \cosh^{-1} x + \dfrac{x}{\sqrt{x^2 - 1}}$ 　　　**7.** $\dfrac{1}{6}x^2\left(\ln x - \dfrac{1}{2}\right) + C$

9. $\dfrac{1}{2}\sec x \tan x - \dfrac{1}{2}\ln|\sec x + \tan x| + C$

11. $\tan^{-1}(\sinh x) + C$

13. $\dfrac{1}{5}\left[-\dfrac{1}{x} - \dfrac{\sqrt{5}}{5}\tan^{-1}\left(\dfrac{x}{\sqrt{5}}\right)\right] + C$ 　**15.** $\sin^{-1}(x - 1) + C$

17. $4(x - 5) + 14(y - 1) - 2(z - 2) = 0$
$\qquad$ or $2x + 7y - z - 15 = 0$

19. Diverges

21. Diverges

23. Diverges

25. Converges

27. a. $5e^{-1}$ 　　**b.** $\dfrac{\pi}{2}$

29. $\mathbf{F}'(t) = 2\mathbf{i} - 3e^{-3t}\mathbf{j} + 4t^3\mathbf{k}$
$\qquad \mathbf{F}''(t) = 9e^{-3t}\mathbf{j} + 12t^2\mathbf{k}$

31. $\mathbf{T} = \dfrac{(2\cos 2t)\mathbf{i} + (-2\sin 2t)\mathbf{j} + 3\mathbf{k}}{\sqrt{13}}$
$\qquad \mathbf{N} = \pm[\sin 2t\,\mathbf{i} + \cos 2t\,\mathbf{j}]$

33. a. $f(x) = x^2 e^{-x^2} = \displaystyle\sum_{k=0}^{\infty} \dfrac{(-1)^k x^{2k+2}}{k!}$

$\qquad$ **b.** 0.1894

35. a.

b.

37. $y = 8x + 10;\ y = 2$

39. $v = 4.3726$ mi/s $\approx 15{,}741$ mi/hr

CHAPTER 12

PROBLEM SET 12.1, Page 745

1. a. 0 　　**b.** 0 　　**c.** 0 　　**d.** 2 　　**e.** 48 　　**f.** $2t^3$
$\quad$ **g.** $t^4 + t^5$ 　　**h.** $t - t^2$

3. a. 0 　　**b.** $1 - e^2$ 　　**c.** $e^{-2} + 1$
$\quad$ **d.** $2x^3 e^{2x} + 3x^2 e^{2x} + 2x$
$\quad$ **e.** $e^2 + 2y$ 　　**f.** $4z(z^2 - 2)$

9. Domain: $x > y$; range: $f(x, y) > 0$

11. Domain: $\dfrac{y}{x} \geq 0,\ x \neq 0$; range: $f(x, y) \geq 0$

13. Domain: $u\sin v \geq 0$; range: $f(x, y) \geq 0$

15. Domain: $y \neq 2$; range: $f(x, y) > 0$

17. Domain: $x^2 + y^2 < 9$; range: $f(x, y) > 0$

19.

21.

23.

25.

27.

29.

31. An ellipsoid; the traces in the planes parallel to the coordinate planes are ellipses.

33. A hyperboloid of two sheets whose axis is the x-axis with vertices $(\pm 3, 0, 0)$. The traces in the xz- and xy-planes are hyperbolas. If $|k| > 3$, the trace in $x = k$ is an ellipse. If $|k| < 3$, the trace does not exist.

35. A hyperbolic paraboloid. In the xy-plane, a pair of lines is intersecting at $(0, 0)$. Traces in planes parallel to xy-plane are hyperbolas, which open in the y-direction above and in the x-direction below. The traces in planes parallel to the xz- and yz-planes are parabolas.

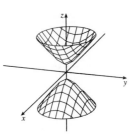

37. A hyperboloid of two sheets whose axis is the z-axis with vertices at $(0, 0, \pm 1)$. The traces in the xz- and yz-planes are hyperbolas. If $|k| > 1$, the traces in $z = k$ are ellipses. If $|k| < 1$, there is no trace in $z = k$.

39. C   **41.** E   **43.** F

45.

47.

49.

51.

53.

55.

57. a. Production more than doubles.
   b. Production will increase more slowly (less than doubles).
   c. Production will double.

59. Q exactly doubles; Q exactly triples.

61. $P(T, V) = \dfrac{kT}{V}$; the level curves are lines through the origin.

63. $P(x, y, z) = -\dfrac{x^2}{5} + \dfrac{y^2}{20} - \dfrac{xy}{20} + 60x + 50y$

PROBLEM SET 12.2, Page 754

3. 5   **5.** -2 **7.** 1   **9.** 1
11. 0   **13.** 1   **15.** 1   **17.** 50
19. 4   **21.** 10   **23.** Does not exist
25. 1   **27.** -1 **29.** 1

Paths shown in Problems 31 and 33 may vary.

31. Let $x = 0$, then $\lim\limits_{(x,y)\to(0,0)} f(x, y) = -1$;
   let $y = 0$, then $\lim\limits_{(x,y)\to(0,0)} f(x, y) = \pm\infty$.
   Therefore, the limit does not exist.

33. Let $x = 0$, then $\lim\limits_{(x,y)\to(0,0)} f(x, y) = 0$;
   let $x = y$, then $\lim\limits_{(x,y)\to(0,0)} f(x, y) = \dfrac{1}{2}$.
   Therefore, the limit does not exist.

35. a. If $x = 0$, $\lim\limits_{(x,y)\to(0,0)} \dfrac{0}{y^6} = 0$; if $y = 0$, $\lim\limits_{(x,y)\to(0,0)} \dfrac{0}{x^2} = 0$;
   if $y = kx$, $\lim\limits_{(x,y)\to(0,0)} \dfrac{k^3 x^2}{1 + k^6 x^4} = 0$.

   b. If $y^3 = x$, $\lim\limits_{(x,y)\to(0,0)} \dfrac{x^2}{2x^2} = \dfrac{1}{2}$.

   Because $\dfrac{1}{3} \neq 0$, the function is not continuous.

37. a. 1.1
   b. Along the x-axis, $y = 0$ and $f(x, 0) \to 1$; along the y-axis, $x = 0$ and $f(0, y) \to 2$.

39. $B = 0$ **43.** If $\sqrt{x^2 + y^2} < \delta$, then (for $x = 0$)
   $|x + y^2 - 0| \leq |x| + y^2 < 2\delta$
   Choose $\delta = \dfrac{\varepsilon}{2}$.

45. If $\sqrt{(x - 1)^2 + (y + 1)^2} < \delta$, then (for $x = 1$)
   $\left| \dfrac{x^2 - y^2}{x + y} - 2 \right| = |x - y - 2| = |(x - 1) - (y + 1)|$
   $\leq |x - 1| + |y + 1| < \delta$. Choose $\delta = \varepsilon$.

PROBLEM SET 12.3, Page 762

3. $f_x = 3x^2 + 2xy + y^2$; $f_y = x^2 + 2xy + 3y^2$; $f_{xx} = 6x + 2y$; $f_{yx} = 2x + 2y$

5. $f_x = \dfrac{1}{y}$; $f_y = -\dfrac{x}{y^2}$; $f_{xx} = 0$; $f_{yx} = -\dfrac{1}{y^2}$

7. $f_x = \dfrac{2}{2x + 3y}$; $f_y = \dfrac{3}{2x + 3y}$; $f_{xx} = \dfrac{-4}{(2x + 3y)^2}$; $f_{yx} = \dfrac{-6}{(2x + 3y)^2}$

9. a. $f_x = 2x \cos x^2 \cos y$; $f_y = -\sin x^2 \sin y$
   b. $f_x = 2x \cos y \cos(x^2 \cos y)$; $f_y = -x^2 \sin y \cos(x^2 \cos y)$

11. $f_x = \dfrac{3x}{\sqrt{3x^2 + y^4}}$; $f_y = \dfrac{2y^3}{\sqrt{3x^2 + y^4}}$

13. $f_x = x(x + 2)e^{x+y} \cos y$; $f_y = x^2 e^{x+y}(\cos y - \sin y)$

15. $f_x = \dfrac{y}{\sqrt{1 - x^2 y^2}}$; $f_y = \dfrac{x}{\sqrt{1 - x^2 y^2}}$

17. $f_x = y^2 + yz$; $f_y = 2xy + xz + z^3$; $f_z = xy + 3yz^2$

19. $f_x = z^{-1}$; $f_y = 2yz^{-1}$; $f_z = -z^{-2}(x + y^2)$

21. $f_x = \dfrac{1}{x + y^2 + z^3}$; $f_y = \dfrac{2y}{x + y^2 + z^3}$; $f_z = \dfrac{3z^2}{x + y^2 + z^3}$

23. $z_x = \dfrac{-2x}{9z}$; $z_y = \dfrac{y}{2z}$ **25.** $z_x = \dfrac{6xy}{2z - y^3}$; $z_y = \dfrac{3x^2 + 3y^2 z}{2z - y^3}$

27. $z_x = -\dfrac{z}{x} - \dfrac{1}{2x^{3/2}\cos(xz)}$; $z_y = \dfrac{-2y}{x \cos(xz)}$

29. $f_x = -(x + 1)^2$; $f_y = (y + 1)^2$

31. $-\dfrac{3}{5}$ **33.** $f_{xx} = -f_{yy} = 6y$

35. $f_{xx} = -f_{yy} = e^x \sin y$ **37. a.** -4 **b.** 4

39. $f_{xy} = f_{yx} = -2xy^3 \cos(xy^2) - 2y \sin(xy^2)$

41. $2(\sin z - x \cos z)$ **43. a.** $-0.67\sigma(T - t)m^{-1.67}$
   b. $\sigma m^{-0.67}$
   c. $-\sigma m^{-0.67}$

45. a. $\dfrac{\partial V}{\partial T} = \dfrac{k}{P}$ **b.** $\dfrac{\partial V}{\partial P} = -\dfrac{V}{P}$

   c. $\dfrac{\partial P}{\partial V} \cdot \dfrac{\partial V}{\partial T} \cdot \dfrac{\partial T}{\partial P} = -\dfrac{P}{V} \cdot \dfrac{k}{P} \cdot \dfrac{V}{k} = -1$

47. a. 9 **b.** 14

49. This does not violate the mixed partials theorem because f_x, f_y, f_{xy}, f_{yx} are not all continuous at $(0, 0)$.

51. a. $\delta = \dfrac{b}{a^2}$

PROBLEM SET 12.4, Page 772

1. $3x + y - \sqrt{10}z = 0$ **3.** $2x + 4y - z - 4 = 0$

5. $x - y + 4z - \pi = 0$ **7.** $10xy^3\, dx + 15x^2 y^2\, dy$

9. $y \cos(xy)\, dx + x \cos(xy)\, dy$

11. $-\dfrac{y}{x^2}\, dx + \dfrac{1}{x}\, dy$ **13.** $ye^x\, dx + e^x\, dy$

15. $9x^2\, dx - 8y^3\, dy + 5\, dz$

17. $2z^2\cos(2x - 3y)\, dx - 3z^2\cos(2x - 3y)\, dy + 2z \sin(2x - 3y)\, dz$

19. $f(x, y) = xy^3 + 3xy^2$; $\dfrac{\partial f}{\partial x} = y^3 + 3y^2$; $\dfrac{\partial f}{\partial y} = 3xy^2 + 6xy$;
   all are continuous, so f is differentiable.

21. $f(x, y) = x^3 y^2$; $f_x = 3x^2 y^2$; $f_y = 2x^2 y$; all are continuous, so f is differentiable.

23. 37.04; actual is 37.085 445 65

25. 0; actual is 0

27. 2.69; actual is 2.690 696 279

29. $z = 9$ **31. c.** $\dfrac{1}{2}(1 - x - y)$

33. The maximum possible error is $1.14.

35. a. $R(x, y) = 4{,}000x - 500x^2 + 3{,}000y - 450y^2$
   b. Estimate the change in revenue to be $180.

37. 11% **39.** 0.036

41. Profit is increasing at $24/week.

43. -0.0014 **45.** Not continuous at $(0, 0)$

47. Increases by 1%

PROBLEM SET 12.5, Page 779

5. a. $8e^{8t} + 8e^{2t}$
   b. $(4 + y^2)(2e^{2t}) + 2xy(3e^{3t}) = 8e^{2t} + 8e^{8t}$

7. a. $\dfrac{3 \sin^3(3t)}{\cos^2(3t)} + 6 \sin 3t$

   b. $\dfrac{-3 \sin^3(3t)}{\cos^2(3t)} + \dfrac{6 \sin(3t)}{\cos^2(3t)} = \dfrac{3 \sin^2(3t)}{\cos^2(3t)} + 6 \sin 3t$

9. a. $\dfrac{\partial F}{\partial u} = 2u \sin^2 v + 2u - 4v$

   $\dfrac{\partial F}{\partial v} = 2u^2 \sin v \cos v - 4u + 8v$

   b. $\dfrac{\partial F}{\partial u} = 2x \sin v + 2y \sin(-2) = 2u \sin^2 v - 2(u + 2v)$

   $\dfrac{\partial F}{\partial v} = 2xu \cos v - 4y = (2u \sin v)(u \cos v) - 4(u - 2v)$
   $= 2u^2 \sin v \cos v - 4(u - 2v)$

11. a. $\dfrac{\partial F}{\partial u} = v^2 + v$; $\dfrac{\partial F}{\partial v} = 2uv + u$

   b. $\dfrac{\partial F}{\partial u} = \dfrac{1}{x}v^2 e^{uv^2} + \dfrac{1}{y}ve^{uv} = v^2 + v$

   $\dfrac{\partial F}{\partial v} = \dfrac{1}{x}2uve^{uv^2} + \dfrac{1}{y}ue^{ub} = 2uv + u$

13. $\dfrac{\partial w}{\partial s} = \dfrac{\partial w}{\partial x} \cdot \dfrac{\partial x}{\partial s} + \dfrac{\partial w}{\partial y} \cdot \dfrac{\partial y}{\partial s} + \dfrac{\partial w}{\partial z} \cdot \dfrac{\partial z}{\partial s}$

   $\dfrac{\partial w}{\partial t} = \dfrac{\partial w}{\partial x} \cdot \dfrac{\partial x}{\partial t} + \dfrac{\partial w}{\partial y} \cdot \dfrac{\partial y}{\partial t} + \dfrac{\partial w}{\partial z} \cdot \dfrac{\partial z}{\partial t}$

15. $\dfrac{\partial w}{\partial s} = \dfrac{\partial w}{\partial x} \cdot \dfrac{\partial x}{\partial s} + \dfrac{\partial w}{\partial y} \cdot \dfrac{dy}{\partial s} + \dfrac{\partial w}{\partial z} \cdot \dfrac{\partial z}{\partial s}$

   $\dfrac{\partial w}{\partial t} = \dfrac{\partial w}{\partial x} \cdot \dfrac{\partial x}{\partial t} + \dfrac{\partial w}{\partial y} \cdot \dfrac{dy}{\partial t} + \dfrac{\partial w}{\partial z} \cdot \dfrac{\partial z}{\partial t}$

   $\dfrac{\partial w}{\partial u} = \dfrac{\partial w}{\partial x} \cdot \dfrac{\partial x}{\partial u} + \dfrac{\partial w}{\partial y} \cdot \dfrac{dy}{\partial u} + \dfrac{\partial w}{\partial z} \cdot \dfrac{\partial z}{\partial u}$

17. $\cos(xyz)[-3yz - xze^{1-t} + 4xy]$

19. $e^{x^3+yz}\left[\dfrac{-6x^2}{t^2} + 2ty + \dfrac{2z}{2t-3}\right]$

21. $\dfrac{\partial w}{\partial r} = \dfrac{2s}{2-z} + \dfrac{t\cos(rt)}{2-z} = \dfrac{2s + t\cos(rt)}{2-z}$

$\dfrac{\partial w}{\partial t} = \dfrac{r\cos(rt)}{2-z} + \dfrac{(x+y)(2st)}{(2-z)^2}$

$\phantom{\dfrac{\partial w}{\partial t}} = \dfrac{(2-z)[r\cos(rt)] + 2st(x+y)}{(2-z)^2}$

23. a. $\dfrac{2}{x^2y^2} = \dfrac{1}{2}z^2$ **b.** $\dfrac{4}{x^3y}$ **c.** $\dfrac{4}{xy^3}$

25. a. $\dfrac{2z^3}{x^2y^2}$ **b.** $\dfrac{2z^2(x+z)}{x^4}$ **c.** $\dfrac{2z^2(y+z)}{y^4}$

27. a. $\dfrac{\sec^2 y \cos x}{4z^3}$ **b.** $\dfrac{2z^2 \sin x - \cos^2 x}{4z^2}$

c. $\dfrac{4z^3 \sec^2 y \tan y - \sec^4 y}{4z^3}$

29. $\dfrac{\partial^2 z}{\partial u^2} = a^2 \dfrac{\partial^2 z}{\partial x^2}$, $\dfrac{\partial^2 z}{\partial v^2} = b^2 \dfrac{\partial z}{\partial y^2}$

31. Both the volume and the surface area are decreasing.

41. Let $u = x^2 + y^2$;

a. $2f'(x^2 + y^2) + 4x^2 f''(x^2 + y^2)$

b. $2f'(x^2 + y^2) + 4y^2 f''(x^2 + y^2)$

c. $4xy\, f''(x^2 + y^2)$

47. $u_x = \dfrac{u^2 - uv - ux + vy}{x^2 + y^2 - ux - uy - vx + vy}$

$v_x = \dfrac{v^2 - uv - uy - vx}{x^2 + y^2 - ux - uy - vx + vy}$

PROBLEM SET 12.6, Page 791

1. $(2x - 2y)\mathbf{i} - 2x\mathbf{j}$

3. $\left(-\dfrac{y}{x^2} + \dfrac{1}{y}\right)\mathbf{i} + \left(\dfrac{1}{x} - \dfrac{x}{y^2}\right)\mathbf{j}$

5. $e^{3-v}(\mathbf{i} - u\mathbf{j})$

7. $\cos(x + 2y)(\mathbf{i} + 2\mathbf{j})$

9. $e^{y+3z}(\mathbf{i} + x\mathbf{j} + 3x\mathbf{k})$

11. $\dfrac{\sqrt{2}}{2}$

13. $\dfrac{5\sqrt{2}}{8}$

15. 0

17. $\pm\dfrac{1}{\sqrt{3}}(\mathbf{i} - \mathbf{j} + \mathbf{k})$; $x - y + z - 3 = 0$

19. $\pm\dfrac{1}{\sqrt{3}}(\mathbf{i} + \mathbf{j} - \mathbf{k})$; $x + y - z - \dfrac{\pi}{2} = 0$

21. $\pm\dfrac{1}{\sqrt{3}}(\mathbf{i} - \mathbf{j} + \mathbf{k})$; $x - y + z = 0$

23. $\pm\dfrac{1}{\sqrt{46}}(3\mathbf{i} + 6\mathbf{j} + \mathbf{k})$; $3x + 6y + z - 3 = 0$

Answers to Problems 25–33 may vary.

25. a. $3\mathbf{i} - 2\mathbf{j}$; $\sqrt{13}$ **b.** $3\mathbf{i} + 2\mathbf{j}$; $\sqrt{13}$

27. a. $\mathbf{i} + \mathbf{j}$; $27\sqrt{2}$ **b.** $\mathbf{i} + \mathbf{j}$; $27\sqrt{2}$

29. $2a^2\mathbf{i} + 2b^2\mathbf{j} + 2c^2\mathbf{k}$; $2\sqrt{a^4 + b^4 + c^4}$

31. $\mathbf{i} + 2\mathbf{j}$; $\dfrac{1}{\sqrt{5}}$ **33.** $10\mathbf{i} + 4\mathbf{j} + 10\mathbf{k}$; $6\sqrt{6}$

35. $\pm\dfrac{1}{\sqrt{a^2 + b^2}}(a\mathbf{i} + b\mathbf{j})$

37. $\pm\dfrac{1}{\sqrt{b^4 x_0^2 + a^4 y_0^2}}(b^2 x_0 \mathbf{i} + a^2 y_0 \mathbf{j})$

39. $1 + \sqrt{3}$ **41.** $\dfrac{-6e}{\sqrt{17}}$ **43.** $\dfrac{11\sqrt{3}}{15}$

45. $2\sqrt{3}$ in the direction $\dfrac{1}{\sqrt{3}}(\mathbf{i} + \mathbf{j} + \mathbf{k})$

47. She turns in the direction $\dfrac{3}{2}\mathbf{i} - \dfrac{5}{2}\mathbf{j}$.

49. 8.06   **51.** $\dfrac{50}{\sqrt{40}}(2\mathbf{i} - 6\mathbf{j})$

53. $y = y_0\left(\dfrac{x}{x_0}\right)^{b/a}$

55. The spy walks along the parabola $x = 6 - \dfrac{5}{16}(y-1)^2$ from (1, 5) to (6, 1), a distance of 6.7 ft; he reaches the hole in about 1 min 40 sec, which is plenty of time for a cup of tea before Chapter 13!

PROBLEM SET 12.7, Page 802

5. (2, 3) is a rel. min.   **7.** (0, 0) is a rel. max.

9. (0, 0) is a rel. min.

11. $(\sqrt{3}, 0)$ is a rel. max. $(-\sqrt{3}, 0)$ is a saddle pt.

13. $(-1, 0)$ and $(1, 0)$ are saddle pts; $(0, -1)$ and $(0, 1)$ are rel. max.; $(0, 0)$ is a rel. min.

15. $(2^{-1/3}, 2^{-1/3})$ is a rel. min.

17. $(-2, 0)$ and $(0, 3)$ are saddle points; $(-2, 3)$ is a rel. max.; $(0, 9)$ is a rel. min.

19. $\left(\dfrac{3}{2}, 2\right)$ is a saddle point.

21. Maximum of 18 at $(0, -3)$; minimum of $-\dfrac{22}{3}$ at $\left(2, -\dfrac{1}{3}\right)$

23. Maximum of 1 at any point on the boundary; minimum of e^{-1} at $(-1, 0)$

25. Maximum of 16 at $(0, 2)$; minimum of 0 at $(0, 0)$

27. $y = 1.02x + 0.80$ **29.** $y = -0.58x - 0.60$

33. Maximum profit at (20, 20)

35. Min. at $x = y = z = \sqrt[3]{V_0}$ **37.** Min. at (2, 2, 8)

39. Price the first type at \$3,000 and the second at \$4,500.

41. $y = 0.78x + 0.19$; GPA 3.13

43. a. $Y = \ln y$, $X = \ln x$, $K = \ln k$

b. Linear fit is $T = -1.6099 + 1.49996A$; so $k = e^K = 0.1999 \approx 0.2$ and $m \approx 1.5$ as Kepler predicted.

49. a. relative minimum   **b.** saddle point

PROBLEM SET 12.8, Page 813

1. $f\left(\frac{5}{4}, \frac{5}{4}\right) = \frac{25}{16}$
　　　　　　　　3. $f\left(\frac{6}{5}, \frac{12}{5}\right) = \frac{44}{5}$

5. $f(1, 1) = f(-1, -1) = 2$

7. $f(0, 2) = f(0, -2) = -4$

9. For x between 0 and 2π, $f\left(\frac{15\pi}{8}, \frac{17\pi}{8}\right) \approx 1.8478$.

11. $f\left(\frac{2}{7}, -\frac{4}{7}, \frac{6}{7}\right) = \frac{8}{7}$

13. $f\left(\frac{5}{7}, -\frac{5}{7}, \frac{5}{7}\right) = \frac{25}{7}$; there is no maximum value.

15. Maximum is $10\sqrt{3}$ at $\left(\frac{10}{\sqrt{3}}, -\frac{10}{\sqrt{3}}, \frac{10}{\sqrt{3}}\right)$

17. The distance is 0 because $(0, 0, 0)$ is on the given plane, regardless of the values of A, B, and C.

19. $\left(\frac{1}{3}, \frac{1}{6}, \frac{1}{6}\right)$

21. Maximum is 324 for $x = 3$, $y = 6$, and $z = 3$.

23. Minimum temperature is $\frac{200}{3}$.

25. 80 yd by 80 yd　　　　**27.** $r = 1$ and $h = 4$

29. Spend \$2,000 on development and \$6,000 on promotion.

31. 10 acre-feet of water and 3 acre-feet of fertilizer

33. The largest box is 18 in. by 18 in. by 36 in.

35. Minimum of $\frac{56}{3}$ at $\left(\frac{2}{3}, \frac{10}{3}, \frac{8}{3}\right)$

37. Maximum of $\frac{121}{24}$ at $\left(\frac{5}{4}, \frac{16}{5}, \frac{5}{6}\right)$

39. a. Spend \$3,000 on development and \$5,000 on promotion.

　　b. The profit will increase about \$130.61.

　　c. \$4,000 on development and \$6,000 on promotion

　　d. $\lambda = 0$

41. $x = \frac{a}{\sqrt{3}}$, $y = \frac{b}{\sqrt{3}}$, and $z = \frac{c}{\sqrt{3}}$; $V = \frac{abc}{3\sqrt{3}}$

CHAPTER 12 REVIEW

Practice Problems, Page 815

32. $(1 - x^2y^2)^{-3/2}$　　　　**33.** $6\pi^2$

34. a. $\nabla f(1, 2, -1) = \mathbf{i} + 3\mathbf{k}$

　　b. $-\frac{2}{\sqrt{5}}$　　　　**c.** $\mathbf{i} + 3\mathbf{k}$; $\sqrt{10}$

35. Along the line $x = 0$, the limit is 0, but along the line $y = 0$, the limit is 0.5.

36. $f_x = -1/x$, $f_y = 1/y$, $f_{yy} = -1/y^2$, $f_{xy} = 0$

37. $(x + y + z)^2$　　　　**38.** $-32(1 + \sqrt{3}) \approx -87.4$

39. Critical points are $(0, 0)$ or any point on the circle $x^2 + y^2 = 1$.

40. Maximum of 12 at $(1, \pm\sqrt{3})$; minimum of 3 at $(-2, 0)$

Supplementary Problems, Page 816

1. The closed disc $x^2 + y^2 \leq 16$

3. $-1 \leq x \leq 1$, $-1 \leq y \leq 1$

5. $f_x = 1$, $f_y = -1$　　**7.** $f_x = 2xy - x^{-2}y \cos(y/x)$
　　　　　　　　　　　　　　　$f_y = x^2 + x^{-1} \cos(y/x)$

9. $f_x = 6x^2y + 3y^2 - x^{-2}y$; $f_y = 2x^3 + 6xy + x^{-1}$

11.

$\begin{array}{l}\text{—— } c = 2 \\ \cdots\cdots\ c = -2\end{array}$

Level curves　　　　　　　Surface

You need to show the level curves only.

13.

$\begin{array}{l}\text{—— } c = 1 \\ \cdots\cdots\ c = 2\end{array}$

Level curve for $c = -1$ is undefined. **Show level curves only.**

15. a. Level surface for $c = 1$:　**b.** Level surface for $c = 2$:

17. $\frac{1}{2}$　　**19.** 0

21. Along the line $x = 0$, the limit is -1; along the line $y = 0$ the limit is 1; the limit does not exist.

23. Along the line $x = 0$, the limit is -1; along the line $y = 0$ the limit is 1; the limit does not exist.

25. $ye^t(t^{-1} - t^{-2}) + (x + 2y)\sec^2 t$

27. $\frac{\partial z}{\partial u} = \left(\tan\frac{x}{y} + \frac{x}{y}\sec^2\frac{x}{y}\right)v + \left(-\frac{x^2}{y^2}\sec^2\frac{x}{y}\right)\left(\frac{1}{v}\right)$

　　$\frac{\partial z}{\partial v} = \left(\tan\frac{x}{y} + \frac{x}{y}\sec^2\frac{x}{y}\right)u + \left(-\frac{x^2}{y^2}\sec^2\frac{x}{y}\right)\left(-\frac{u}{v^2}\right)$

29. $\frac{\partial z}{\partial x} = -e^{x-z}$; $\frac{\partial z}{\partial y} = -e^{y-z}$

31. $\frac{\partial z}{\partial x} = \frac{2xe^{2z} - z^2e^{2z} - 2}{-2z - 2(x - y)(2x - z^2)e^{2z}}$;

　　$\frac{\partial z}{\partial y} = \frac{2xe^{2z} - z^2e^{2z}}{2z + 2(x - y)(2x - z^2)e^{2z}}$

33. $\dfrac{\partial z}{\partial x} = \dfrac{z}{3z + 1}$, $\dfrac{\partial z}{\partial y} = \dfrac{2z}{3z + 1}$

35. $f_x = \dfrac{y}{\sqrt{1 - x^2y^2}}$; $f_y = \dfrac{x}{\sqrt{1 - x^2y^2}}$

$\quad f_{xx} = \dfrac{xy^3}{(1 - x^2y^2)^{3/2}}$; $f_{yx} = (1 - x^2y^2)^{-3/2}$

37. $f_x = 2xe^{x^2+y^2}$; $f_y = 2ye^{x^2+y^2}$;

$\quad f_{xx} = 2(2x^2 + 1)e^{x^2+y^2}$; $f_{yx} = 4xye^{x^2+y^2}$

39. $f_x = 3x^2e^{3y/z^2}$; $f_y = \dfrac{3x^3e^{3y/z^2}}{z^2}$; $f_{xx} = 6xe^{3y/z^2}$; $f_{yx} = \dfrac{9x^2e^{3y/z^2}}{z^2}$

41. $f_x = 3x^2y^2\sqrt{z} + 2x\cos(x^2 + y \ln z)$

$\quad f_y = 2x^3y\sqrt{z} + (\ln z)\cos(x^2 + y \ln z)$

$\quad f_{xx} = 6xy^2\sqrt{z} + 2\cos(x^2 + y \ln z) - 4x^2\sin(x^2 + y \ln z)$

$\quad f_{yx} = 6x^2y\,\sqrt{z} - \sin(x^2 + y \ln z)(2x \ln z)$

43. Tangent plane: $16x - 7y - 9 = 0$;

$\quad$ Normal line: $-16(x - 1) + 7(y - 1) = 0$ or $\dfrac{x - 1}{16} = \dfrac{y - 1}{-7}$

$\quad$ and $z = 1$

45. Relative minimum at $(3, -1)$

47. Relative maximum at $\left(\dfrac{2}{3}, \dfrac{2}{3}\right)$; saddle points at $(0, 1)$, $(1, 1)$, and $(1, 0)$

49. Relative maximum at $(0, 3)$; relative minimum at $(2, 9)$; saddle points at $(0, 9)$, and $(2, 3)$

51. $\dfrac{dz}{dt} = 4x - 12xyt - 6y^2$

53. $\dfrac{\partial z}{\partial x} = e^{(u^2-v^2)}[8xu^2 + 4x - 12vx]$

$\quad \dfrac{\partial z}{\partial y} = e^{(u^2-v^2)}(12yu^2 + 6y + 8uvy)$

55. $m = -1$

57. $2x + 2y - z + 1 = 0$; $x = 2t$, $y = 1 + 2t$, $z = 3 - t$

59. Answers may vary; $g(x, y, z) = x^2y + y^2z + xz^2$

61. $\left[\dfrac{2}{1 + x^2 + y^2}\right]\left(\dfrac{2xt}{1 + t^2}\right) + \left[\dfrac{2y}{1 + x^2 + y^2} - \dfrac{2}{1 + y^2}\right]e^t$

63. $-\dfrac{4}{\sqrt{5}}(3 + 4 \ln 2)$

65. a. $-3\sqrt{6}$ **b.** $-6\mathbf{i} + \mathbf{j} + 7\mathbf{k}$

67. $x = 6$, $y = 3$, $z = 3$ **69.** $\sqrt{6}$

71. a. $y = 11.54x + 44.45$ **b.** 102.15

73. $24xy^2z^3\sin(x^2 + y^3 + z^4)$

75. $-\dfrac{2}{3}$

77. $\pm\left(\dfrac{2}{3}\mathbf{i} + \dfrac{2}{3}\mathbf{j} - \dfrac{1}{3}\mathbf{k}\right)$

79. $-\left[\dfrac{\sin^2(x + z)\cos(x + y) + \sin^2(x + y)\cos(x + z)}{\sin^3(x + z)}\right]$

81. Relative minimum of 18 at $(2, 3)$

83. Minimum at $x = \dfrac{a}{(a^2 + b^2 + c^2)}$,

$\quad y = \dfrac{b}{(a^2 + b^2 + c^2)}$, and $z = \dfrac{c}{(a^2 + b^2 + c^2)}$

89. $\theta = 2$, $r^2 = A$ **91. a.** 10π **b.** 6π

93. 0.64 cm^3 has been removed.

95. The sum is $\sqrt{k}$.

97. See *The College Mathematics Journal*, May 1991, p. 227.

99. See *American Mathematical Monthly*, Vol. 74.

101. See *American Mathematical Monthly*, Vol. 45.

CHAPTER 13

PROBLEM SET 13.1, Page 828

1. 32   **3.** 24   **5.** 24   **7.** $\dfrac{7}{6}$

9. -1 **11.** $4 \ln 2$ **13.** 1   **15.** 8

17. $\dfrac{a^3b}{2} + \dfrac{ab^3}{2}$ **19.** $\dfrac{32}{9}$ **21.** 2

23. 3   **25.** $\dfrac{2^{n+2} - 1}{(n + 1)(n + 2)}$

29. $\displaystyle\int_0^a \int_0^c f(x, y)\, dy\, dx$ **31.** $1,400 \displaystyle\int_a^b \int_c^d f(x, y)\, dA$

33. $\dfrac{\ln 2}{2}$ **37.** $\dfrac{5}{3}$; answers vary from 1 to 3.

39. $\dfrac{2\pi}{3}$

PROBLEM SET 13.2, Page 836

3. $\dfrac{32}{3}$ **5.** $\dfrac{2}{3}$ **7.** $3\pi - 2\sqrt{3}$

9. $\dfrac{27}{2}$ **11.** $\dfrac{5}{12}$ **13.** $\dfrac{1}{6}\sin^3 2 \approx 0.1253$

15. $\dfrac{1}{2}$ **17.** 5   **19.** $\dfrac{5}{12}$ **21.** 13

23. $\dfrac{2}{3} + 2 \ln 2 \approx 2.0530$ **25.** $2e - 4 \approx 1.4366$

27. a. $\displaystyle\int_0^4 \int_0^{4-x} xy\, dy\, dx = \dfrac{32}{3}$ **b.** $\displaystyle\int_0^4 \int_0^{4-y} xy\, dx\, dy = \dfrac{32}{3}$

29. a. $\displaystyle\int_0^1 \int_x^{2x} e^{y-x}\, dy\, dx = e - 2$

b. $\displaystyle\int_0^1 \int_{y/2}^y e^{y-x}\, dx\, dy + \int_1^2 \int_{y/2}^1 e^{y-x}\, dx\, dy = e - 2$

31. a. $\displaystyle\int_0^1 \int_{-x^2}^{x^2} dy\, dx = \dfrac{2}{3}$

b. $2\displaystyle\int_0^1 \int_{\sqrt{y}}^1 dx\, dy = \dfrac{2}{3}$

33. a. $\displaystyle\int_0^{2\sqrt{3}}\int_{y^2/6}^{\sqrt{16-y^2}} dx\, dy = \frac{8\pi}{3} + \frac{2\sqrt{3}}{3}$

b. $\displaystyle\int_0^2\int_0^{\sqrt{6x}} dy\, dx + \int_2^4\int_0^{\sqrt{16-x^2}} dy\, dx = \frac{8\pi}{3} + \frac{2\sqrt{3}}{3}$

35.

$\displaystyle\int_0^2\int_{x/2}^1 f(x,y)\, dy\, dx$

37.

$\displaystyle\int_0^2\int_{x^2}^{2x} f(x,y)\, dy\, dx$

39.
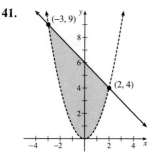
$\displaystyle\int_0^1\int_0^{3x} f(x,y)\, dy\, dx$
$\displaystyle + \int_1^2\int_0^{4-x^2} f(x,y)\, dy\, dx$

41.
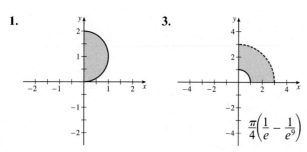
$\displaystyle\int_0^4\int_{-\sqrt{y}}^{\sqrt{y}} f(x,y)\, dx\, dy$
$\displaystyle + \int_4^9\int_{-\sqrt{y}}^{6-y} f(x,y)\, dx\, dy$

43. $\dfrac{2}{3}$ **45.** $\dfrac{128\sqrt{2}}{15} \approx 12.0679$ **47.** $\dfrac{4}{3}$

49. $\dfrac{3}{8}$ **51.** 20   **53.** $\dfrac{8}{3}$

55. The integral is between 1.17 and 2.31.

PROBLEM SET 13.3, Page 844

1.
3.

$\dfrac{\pi}{4}\left(\dfrac{1}{e} - \dfrac{1}{e^9}\right)$

5.

$\dfrac{32\pi}{3}$

7.
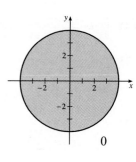
0

9. 16π **11.** 6π **13.** 4π **15.** $\dfrac{\pi}{2}$

17. $\dfrac{1}{6}(2\pi + 3\sqrt{3})$ **19.** $\dfrac{5\pi}{4} - 2$ **21.** π

23. $\dfrac{a^4\pi}{4}$ **25.** $\pi \ln 2$ **27.** $2\pi a(1 - \ln 2)$

29. 0   **31.** $\pi(e^9 - 1)$

33. $\dfrac{1}{4}(6\pi \ln 3 + 4\pi \ln 2 - 4\pi) \approx 4.2131$

35. 8π **37.** $\dfrac{8}{3}$

39. $2\displaystyle\int_0^{\pi/4}\int_0^{a \sin\theta} r\, dr\, d\theta = \dfrac{1}{8}a^2(\pi - 2)$

41. $\dfrac{256\pi}{3}$ **43.** $\dfrac{\pi}{4}$ **45.** $\dfrac{\pi}{8}$ **47.** $\dfrac{3\pi}{4} - 2$

49. $\dfrac{15\pi}{4}$ **51.** $\dfrac{\sqrt{2}\pi}{4}$

PROBLEM SET 13.4, Page 853

1. $4\sqrt{21}$ **3.** $\dfrac{\pi}{6}(17^{3/2} - 1)$ **5.** $\dfrac{7}{4}$

7. $2\sqrt{17} + \dfrac{1}{2}\ln(4 + \sqrt{17})$

9. $8\sqrt{65} + \ln(\sqrt{65} + 8)$ **11.** $\dfrac{\pi}{6}(5^{3/2} - 1)$

13. 2π **15.** $8\pi - 16$

17. $15\sqrt{2} + \dfrac{5}{2}\ln(2\sqrt{2} + 3)$ **19.** $\dfrac{\pi}{6}(37^{3/2} - 1)$

23. $\dfrac{D^2\sqrt{A^2 + B^2 + C^2}}{2ABC}$ **25.** $\dfrac{3\sqrt{3}\pi a^2}{4}$

27. $8\displaystyle\int_0^{\pi/2}\int_0^a \dfrac{a}{\sqrt{a^2 - r^2}} r\, dr\, d\theta = 4\pi a^2$

29. $2\pi rh$ **31.** 36π

33. $\displaystyle\int_0^1\int_0^y \sqrt{e^{-2x} + 1}\, dx\, dy$

35. $\displaystyle\int_0^{2\pi}\int_0^{\sqrt{\pi/2}} r\sqrt{4r^2\sin r^2 + 1}\, dr\, d\theta$

37. $\displaystyle\int_0^3\int_0^x \sqrt{(2x + 5y)^2 + (2y + 5x)^2 + 1}\, dy\, dx$

39. $4|u|\sqrt{u^2 + 1}$ **41.** $\sqrt{9u^4 + 1}$

43. $\dfrac{\pi}{3}(6^{3/2} - 8) \approx 7.01$ **45.** $4\pi^2 ab$

PROBLEM SET 13.5, Page 863

3. 45   **5.** 45   **7.** $\dfrac{68}{9}$ **9.** $-\dfrac{15}{\pi}$

11. $\dfrac{1}{8}(5 - e^2)$ **13.** $6\pi - 18 \ln 2$

15. 8   **17.** $\dfrac{1}{720}$ **19.** 0   **21.** $\dfrac{e^2}{2} - e$

23. $\dfrac{1}{6}$ **25.** $\dfrac{4\pi}{3}$ **27.** 4π

29. $\displaystyle\int_0^1 \int_y^1 \int_0^y f(x, y, z)\, dz\, dx\, dy$

31. $\displaystyle\int_0^2 \int_0^{\sqrt{4-z^2}} \int_0^{\sqrt{4-y^2-z^2}} f(x, y, z)\, dx\, dy\, dz$

33. 32π **35.** 32π **37.** 15   **39.** $\dfrac{4}{3}\pi r^3$

41. $\dfrac{4}{3}\pi abc$

43. $\displaystyle\int_0^b \int_0^{a(1-y/b)} \int_0^{c(1-x/a-y/a)} dz\, dx\, dy$

$\displaystyle\int_0^a \int_0^{b(1-x/a)} \int_0^{c(1-x/a-y/a)} dz\, dy\, dx$

$\displaystyle\int_0^a \int_0^{c(1-x/a)} \int_0^{b(1-x/a-z/c)} dy\, dz\, dx$

$\displaystyle\int_0^c \int_0^{a(1-z/c)} \int_0^{b(1-x/a-z/c)} dy\, dx\, dz$

$\displaystyle\int_0^c \int_0^{b(1-z/c)} \int_0^{a(1-y/b-z/c)} dx\, dy\, dz$

$\displaystyle\int_0^b \int_0^{c(1-y/b)} \int_0^{a(1-y/b-z/c)} dx\, dz\, dy$

47. $\displaystyle\int_1^2 \int_{-1}^1 \int_0^1 xyz^2w^2\, dx\, dy\, dz\, dw = \dfrac{14}{9}$

PROBLEM SET 13.6, Page 872

5. $\left(\dfrac{3}{2}, 2\right)$ **7.** $\left(1, \dfrac{8}{5}\right)$ **9.** $\left(\dfrac{1}{4}, \dfrac{108}{135}\right)$ **11.** $(1, 1, 1)$

13. $\left(0, \dfrac{24}{5\pi}\right)$ **15.** $\left(7, \dfrac{5}{3}\right)$

17. $\left(\dfrac{4 \ln 2 - 2}{\ln^2 2}, \dfrac{\ln 2}{3}\right)$

19. a. $\left(0, \dfrac{3a}{2\pi}\right)$ **b.** $\left(-\dfrac{8a}{3\pi^2}, \dfrac{4a}{3\pi}\right)$

21. $\left(\dfrac{3(e^4 + 1)}{4(e^2 + 1)}, \dfrac{e^2 - 1}{e^2 + 1}\right) = (4.971, 0.762)$ **23.** $\dfrac{32}{945}$

25. $\left(0, \dfrac{21}{20}\right)$ **27.** $(1.38, 0)$

29. b. $(0, 0, 0)$ and $I_Z = \dfrac{8}{45} a^3 b^3 c^3 (a^2 + b^2)$

31. $\dfrac{a^4 \pi}{64}$

33. $\displaystyle\int_0^{2\pi} \int_0^a r^2\cos^2\theta\,(r\, dr\, d\theta) = \dfrac{a^4\pi}{4} = \dfrac{ma^2}{4}$

35. $4 \displaystyle\int_0^a \int_0^{(b/a)\sqrt{a^2 - x^2}} y^2\, dy\, dx = \dfrac{\pi ab^3}{4} = \dfrac{mb^2}{4}$

37. $\left(\dfrac{3a}{8}, \dfrac{3a}{8}, \dfrac{3a}{8}\right)$ **39.** $1 - \dfrac{5}{2}e^{-1} \approx 0.0803$

41. 0.0902   **43.** 0.4731

45. $3(e - 2)$ **47.** 0

49. $\dfrac{\sqrt{10}a}{5}$ **53.** $\dfrac{hl}{12}(h^2 + l^2)$ **55.** $4\pi^2 ab$

PROBLEM SET 13.7, Page 882

3. a. $(1.41, 0.79, 1.00)$ **b.** $(1.73, 0.79, 0.96)$

5. a. $(2.45, -0.96, 1.73)$ **b.** $(3.00, -0.96, 0.96)$

7. a. $(2.24, 1.11, 3.00)$ **b.** $(3.74, 1.11, 0.64)$

9. a. $(-1.50, 2.60, -3.00)$ **b.** $(4.24, 2.09, 2.36)$

11. a. $(1.41, 1.41, 3.14)$ **b.** $(3.72, 0.79, 0.57)$

13. a. $(-0.42, 0.91, 3.00)$ **b.** $(3.16, 2.00, 0.32)$

15. a. $(1.50, 0.87, -1.00)$ **b.** $(1.73, 0.52, -1.00)$

17. a. $(0.50, 0.00, 1.00)$ **b.** $(0.00, 0.52, 1.00)$

19. a. $(-0.06, 0.13, -0.99)$ **b.** $(0.14, 2.00, -0.99)$

21. $z = r^2\cos 2\theta$ **23.** $9r^2\cos^2\theta - 4r^2\sin^2\theta + 36z^2 = 0$

 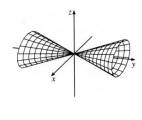

25. $9 - r^2\sin^2\theta = z^2$ **27.** $\phi = \dfrac{\pi}{4}$

29. $\rho = 1/\sqrt{2}$

31. $\rho = 2$

33. $z = 2xy$

35. $z = x^2 - y^2$

37. $xz = 1$

39. $\dfrac{16}{3}$ **41.** 2π **43.** 8π

45. $\left(\dfrac{x}{a}\right)^2 + \left(\dfrac{y}{b}\right)^2 + \left(\dfrac{z}{c}\right)^2 = r^2$

47. $\dfrac{a^6}{3}$ **49.** $\left(0, 0, \dfrac{27}{4}\right)$

51. $\dfrac{16\pi\sqrt{2}}{5}$ **53.** 6π

55. $\dfrac{7\pi}{2}$ **57.** $\dfrac{5\pi}{2}$

59. Because water pours in at the rate of 25 ft³/min, it takes 8.84 minutes to fill the cave to nose level. So he drowns, you say? Nonsense! Any spy worth his or her salt can hold his or her breath for a little more than a minute. The spy frees his hands, stands (to buy more time), hops to the door, pulls up the lever (to stop the water), and opens the door.

63. $\dfrac{8\pi}{5}$

PROBLEM SET 13.8, Page 889

1. $u - v$ **3.** 2   **5.** $4uv^3 + 4u^3v$

7. $-2e^{2u}$ **9.** -9 **11.** ue^{uv}

13.

15.

17. $u\,du\,dv$ **19.** 0   **21.** 0   **25.** $\dfrac{5}{6}$ **27.** $\dfrac{625}{6}$

29. $\dfrac{25}{2}\left(\tan^{-1}5 - \dfrac{1}{10}\ln 26\right) \approx 13.1$ **31.** $\dfrac{1}{2}$

33. π **35. a.** 1   **b.** 0   **37.** r

39. $49\ln 7 - \dfrac{75}{2}\ln 5 - 27\ln 3 + 6 \approx 11.3331$

41. $\dfrac{1}{2}(\ln 5)(\ln 13) \approx 2.064$

CHAPTER 13 REVIEW

Practice Problems, Page 891

23. $\dfrac{\sqrt{3}}{2} - 1 + e^{-\sqrt{3}/2}$ **24.** 0   **25.** 36

26. $\dfrac{\pi}{4}\sin 1$ **27.** 8π

28. $\displaystyle\int_0^4 \int_0^{\sqrt{(4x-x^2)/2}} \int_{x^2+2y^2}^{4x} dz\,dy\,dx = 2\pi\sqrt{2}$

29. $\dfrac{128\pi}{15}$ **30.** $\dfrac{1}{3}\left(e^2 + 8e^{-1} - 3\right)$

Supplementary Problems, Page 892

1.

$\dfrac{3}{2}$

$\displaystyle\int_0^3 \int_{y/3}^1 x^2 y^2\,dx\,dy$

3.

$\dfrac{\pi}{4}\ln 2;$

$\displaystyle\int_0^1 \int_1^2 \dfrac{1}{x^2 + y^2}\,dy\,dx$

$+ \displaystyle\int_1^2 \int_x^2 \dfrac{1}{x^2 + y^2}\,dy\,dx$

5.

$\dfrac{8\sqrt{2} - 4}{15};$

$\displaystyle\int_0^1 \int_0^1 x\sqrt{x^2 + y}\,dy\,dx$

7.

$-\dfrac{4}{21};$

$\displaystyle\int_{-1}^0 \int_0^{\sqrt{1-y^2}} y\sqrt{x}\,dx\,dy$

9.

$\dfrac{1 - \cos 1}{12}$;

$\displaystyle\int_0^1 \int_0^{\sqrt{y}} x^3 \sin y^3 \, dx \, dy$

11. $\dfrac{1}{3}(e - 1)$ **13.** 10   **15.** $\dfrac{2\pi^4}{3}(2 - \sqrt{2})$

17. $\dfrac{31}{30}$ **19.** $\dfrac{81\pi}{8}$ **21.** 12π

23. $\dfrac{\pi}{n + 1}(2^{2n+2})$ **25.** 0   **27.** 0

29. $\dfrac{\pi}{m - 1}a^{2(1-m)}$ **31.** 11

33. π **35.** π **37.** $\dfrac{8\pi}{5}$

39. $\displaystyle\int_0^1 \int_z^1 \int_{z^2/x}^x f(x, y, z) \, dy \, dx \, dz$

41. $\dfrac{1}{3}(e^8 - 8e)$ **43.** $\displaystyle\int_{-1}^1 \int_{x^2}^{2-x} f(x, y) \, dy \, dx$

45. $\sqrt{3} - \dfrac{\pi}{3}$ **47.** $\pi + 3\sqrt{3}$

49. $\dfrac{abc}{6}$ **51.** $\dfrac{a^4}{8}$ **53.** $\sqrt{2}\,\pi$

55. $\dfrac{4\pi}{3}$ **57.** $\dfrac{\pi}{2}$ **59.** $\dfrac{2\pi}{3}(27 - 16\sqrt{2})$

61. $\dfrac{2\pi a^3}{3}(1 - \cos \phi)$

63. a. $\dfrac{75\pi k}{2}$ **b.** 105π **c.** $\dfrac{1{,}275\pi}{32}$

65. $\dfrac{\pi H}{6}(H^2 + R^2)^{3/2}$ **67.** 8

69. $u - 2v = 0;\ 2v - u = 5;\ v + 2u = 0;\ v + 2u = 5$

71. a. $-2xy$ **b.** $\dfrac{-1}{2xy}$ **c.** 1

73. $\dfrac{1}{540}$ **75.** $\dfrac{4(2 - \sqrt{2})}{3\pi}$

77. a. $\dfrac{\pi a^2 b}{2}$ **b.** $\left(0, 0, \dfrac{b}{2}\right)$

83. $4\displaystyle\int_{\pi/12}^{\pi/4} \int_{\sqrt{2}a}^{2a\sqrt{\sin 2\theta}} \rho r \, dr \, d\theta$

85. $(0, 0, 0)$

87. $\left(\dfrac{1 - \ln 2}{4 - \pi}, \dfrac{1 - \ln 2}{4 - \pi}, \dfrac{1 - \ln 2}{4 - \pi}\right)$

89. See *American Mathematical Monthly*, Vol. 49.

91. See *American Mathematical Monthly*, Vol. 65.

CHAPTER 14

PROBLEM SET 14.1, Page 905

3.

5.

7.

9. div $\mathbf{F} = \dfrac{1}{\sqrt{x^2 + y^2}}$;

curl $\mathbf{F} = \mathbf{0}$

11. div $\mathbf{F} = 2$; curl $\mathbf{F} = \mathbf{0}$ **13.** 0; **0**

15. 7; $\mathbf{j} - 3\mathbf{k}$ **17.** $2 - 2e^{-6}$; $-3\mathbf{i} + 3e^{-6}\mathbf{k}$

19. $\cos x - \sin y$; **0**   **21.** 0; **0**

23. $\dfrac{1}{\sqrt{x^2 + y^2}}$; **0**   **25.** $a + b$; **0**

27. $2x + 2y + 2z$; **0**   **29.** $x + y + z$; $-y\mathbf{i} - z\mathbf{j} - x\mathbf{k}$

31. $yz + 2x^2y^2z^2 + 3y^2z^2$;
$(2yz^3 - 2x^2y^2z)\mathbf{i} + xy\mathbf{j} + (2xy^2z^2 - xz)\mathbf{k}$

33. 3; $\mathbf{i} + \mathbf{j} + \mathbf{k}$ **35.** Harmonic

37. Harmonic   **39.** $6x\mathbf{j} - 3y\mathbf{k}$

41. $3x + 2z$ **43.** $6xyz^2 + 2xy^3$

45. 0; **B** is solenoidal.

51. Let $\omega = \omega_1\mathbf{i} + \omega_2\mathbf{j} + \omega_3\mathbf{k}$, where ω_1, ω_2, and ω_3 are constants.

a. $(\omega_2 z - \omega_3 y)\mathbf{i} + (\omega_3 x - \omega_1 z)\mathbf{j} + (\omega_1 y - \omega_2 x)\mathbf{k}$

b. 0; 2ω

53. II

PROBLEM SET 14.2, Page 914

3. $\dfrac{4}{3}$ **5.** 1   **7.** $\dfrac{26}{3}$

9. a. $-\dfrac{1}{3}$ **b.** $-\dfrac{1}{3}$ **11.** $-\dfrac{16}{3}$ **13.** $\dfrac{77}{15}$

15. $-\dfrac{7}{60}$ **17.** 12   **19.** 12

21. a. $\dfrac{\pi^2}{8}$ **b.** $\dfrac{\pi^2}{8}$ **23. a.** $\dfrac{5}{2}$ **b.** $\dfrac{11}{2}$

25. 0   **27.** 9   **29.** $-\dfrac{1}{3}$ **31.** 0

33. $\dfrac{-1}{\sqrt{2}}$ **35.** 2π **37.** 16   **39.** $\dfrac{1}{2}$

41. 42   **43.** $\dfrac{5}{2}$ **45.** 27,750 ft-lb

PROBLEM SET 14.3, Page 922

5. Conservative; x^2y^3 **7.** Not conservative

9. Not conservative   **11. a.** -2π **b.** -4 **c.** -2π

13. a. 0   **b.** 32   **c.** 32   **15.** x^2y; 1

17. $x^2 - xy + \dfrac{1}{3}y^3$; $\dfrac{1}{3}$ **19.** $e^{-x}\cos xy + \sin 2x$; 0.1081

21. $\dfrac{13}{4}$ **23.** 8   **25.** $\dfrac{3\pi}{2} - 2$ **27.** 8

29. 32   **31.** -2.492

33. $\dfrac{\partial P}{\partial y} = \dfrac{\partial N}{\partial z} = xe^{xy}$; $\dfrac{\partial M}{\partial z} = \dfrac{\partial P}{\partial x} = ye^{xy}$;

$\dfrac{\partial N}{\partial x} = \dfrac{\partial M}{\partial y} = ze^{xy}$; conservative

35. $\dfrac{\partial P}{\partial y} = \dfrac{\partial N}{\partial z} = 2yz$; $\dfrac{\partial M}{\partial z} = \dfrac{\partial P}{\partial x} = 2xz$;

$\dfrac{\partial N}{\partial x} = \dfrac{\partial M}{\partial y} = 2xy$; conservative

37. $\dfrac{\partial P}{\partial y} = \dfrac{\partial N}{\partial z} = x + 3y^2$; $\dfrac{\partial M}{\partial z} = \dfrac{\partial P}{\partial x} = y$;

$\dfrac{\partial N}{\partial x} = \dfrac{\partial M}{\partial y} = 2xy + z$; conservative

39. a. $f = \dfrac{KmM}{r}$

b. $KmM\left[\dfrac{1}{\sqrt{a_2^2 + b_2^2 + c_2^2}} - \dfrac{1}{\sqrt{a_1^2 + b_1^2 + c_1^2}}\right]$

41. 0

45. a. $f = xy^2 - x^2z + c(y, z)$

b. $c(y, z) = yz + c(z)$

c. $f = xy^2 - x^2z + yz$

PROBLEM SET 14.4, Page 931

1. 0   **3.** 3   **5.** 0   **7.** -6π

9. 0   **11.** 16   **13.** 2π **15.** 4π

17. $\dfrac{15}{2}$ **19.** $-\dfrac{\pi a^4}{4}$

25. 0   **27.** 0   **29.** 160π **31.** 1

33. To the spy's surprise and relief, he finds that the Death Force is a conservative field. It does not matter which path he takes, the work will be the same! Because he wants to get out of the room as quickly as possible, he walks in a straight line from (0, 0) to (5, 4) and leaves.

PROBLEM SET 14.5, Page 939

1. 8π **3.** 0   **5.** 16π **7.** $4\sqrt{2}$

9. 0   **11.** $\dfrac{160\sqrt{6}}{3}$ **13.** $\dfrac{\pi}{2}$

15. $\dfrac{\pi}{60}(391\sqrt{17} + 1) \approx 84.4635$ **17.** 36π **19.** $\dfrac{4\pi}{3}$

21. $\dfrac{7\pi\sqrt{2}}{4}$ **23.** $-\dfrac{57}{8}$ **25.** $\dfrac{4\pi}{3}$ **27.** π

29. $\dfrac{1}{8}(2\sqrt{5} + \ln(2 + \sqrt{5})$ **31.** $-\dfrac{1}{2}\sqrt{17} - \dfrac{1}{8}\ln(4 + \sqrt{17})$

33. $25\sqrt{6}$ **35.** $\dfrac{\pi}{6}(5\sqrt{5} - 1)$ **37.** $\dfrac{\sqrt{3}}{2}$

PROBLEM SET 14.6, Page 947

1. 18π **3.** $\dfrac{9}{2}$ **5.** -8π **7.** -18

9. 0   **11.** -2π **13.** -3π **15.** $-\dfrac{1}{2}$

17. 0   **19.** -16π **21.** $\dfrac{3}{2}$ **23.** 0

PROBLEM SET 14.7, Page 955

1. $\dfrac{64\pi}{3}$ **3.** $\dfrac{128}{3}$ **5.** 3   **7.** 24π

9. $\dfrac{13}{3}$ **11.** $\dfrac{243\pi}{2}$ **13.** 0   **15.** 12π

17. $\dfrac{\pi}{4}$ **19.** $\dfrac{9}{2}\pi a^4$ **21.** $4\pi a^4$

23. b. 6   **25.** 0

CHAPTER 14 REVIEW

Practice Problems, Page 962

23. $xyz + C$

24. div $\mathbf{F} = 2xy - ze^{yz}$; curl $\mathbf{F} = ye^{yz}\mathbf{i} - \dfrac{1}{2}\mathbf{j} - x^2\mathbf{k}$

25. -2 **26.** $4\pi\sqrt{2}$ **27.** 0   **28.** 0

29. $f = \dfrac{m\omega^2}{2}\|R\|^2$ **30.** 0

Supplementary Problems, Page 962

1. Conservative; $f(x, y) = 2x - 3y$

3. Conservative; $f(x, y) = xy^{-3} + \sin y$

5. Not conservative   **7.** -7

9. $-\dfrac{31}{32} + \sin 4 - \sin 1$ **11.** $\dfrac{5}{2}$

13. div $\mathbf{F} = 3$; curl $\mathbf{F} = \mathbf{0}$ **15.** div $\mathbf{F} = \dfrac{2}{r}$; curl $\mathbf{F} = \mathbf{0}$

17. $\pi\cos\pi^2$ **19.** $-\dfrac{3\pi}{4} - 6$

21. $\sqrt{2}$ **23.** $\dfrac{5}{6}$

25. $2\pi^2 - 2\pi$ **27.** 0

29. 4π **31.** $\dfrac{6\pi\sqrt{2}}{5}$ **33.** $\dfrac{2a-3b}{2abc}$ **35.** 0

37. $\dfrac{3}{4}$ **39.** $\dfrac{3}{2}$ **41.** -1 **43.** $\dfrac{5}{6}$

45. $\ln\left(\dfrac{c+d}{a+b}\right)$ **47.** $3x^2y + 2xy^2 - 5x - 6y = 0$

51. div $\mathbf{F} = 0$, so $\mathbf{F}$ is solenoidal   **55.** 0

57. a. $f(x, y) = -\dfrac{1+y^2}{2x^2} - \dfrac{y^2}{2}$

  b. $-\dfrac{134}{18}$; C cannot cross the y-axis.

59. $\dfrac{5}{4} + \ln\dfrac{16}{72}$

61. $2\pi c$

63. 0 **65.** 0 **67.** $\dfrac{\pi}{4} - \dfrac{1}{2}\ln 2$

69. $\dfrac{q}{\varepsilon}$ **73.** $\dfrac{16\pi}{3}$ **75.** 21

79. The minimum value is maximized when N is chosen to be 5. If both Puritys "play" properly, the Green Purity chooses $N = 5$, the Red Purity chooses $x = -N \pm 1$ (that is, -4 or -6), and the resulting head start is approximately 30 min.

However, the spy reneges on his deal and subdues a rather surprised Red Purity. The Green Purity asks, "How did you know?" The spy smiles smugly and says, "The woman who set those traps to kill me knows some math. You don't and your sister does." The Red Purity snarls, "So she wins because I'm smarter. I'll remember that next time, and, believe me, there will be a next time."

CUMULATIVE REVIEW, page 969

5. $f_x = e^{y/x}(2x - y)$; $f_y = xe^{y/x}$; $f_{xy} = e^{y/x}\left(1 - \dfrac{y}{x}\right)$

7. $f_x = 2y\sin x\cos x - y\sin xy$; $f_y = \sin^2 x - x\sin xy$; $f_{xy} = \sin 2x - xy\cos xy - \sin xy$

9. $f_x = \dfrac{x^2 - 2xy - y^2}{(x-y)^2}$; $f_y = \dfrac{x^2 + 2xy - y^2}{(x-y)^2}$; $f_{xy} = \dfrac{-4xy}{(x-y)^3}$

11. $\dfrac{49{,}152}{13}$ **13.** $\dfrac{4\pi}{15}$ **15.** $e^2 - 3$ **17.** π

19. 8 **21.** 0 **23.** $x = y = z = \sqrt[3]{V_0}$

25. $\dfrac{\pi}{4} + 2$ **27.** $\dfrac{\pi}{6}[17^{3/2} - 1]$

29. $\mathbf{F}$ is conservative; $W = 0$

APPENDIX F Credits

CHAPTER 1

pp. 2, 3 Quotation from "The Calculus According to Newton and Leibniz," in *The Historical Development of the Calculus* (New York: Springer-Verlag, 1979).

p. 7 Global modeling illustration from *Scientific American*, March 1991.

p. 20 Journal problem (No. 75) by Murray Klamkin reprinted from *The Mathematics Student Journal*, Vol. 28, 1980, issue 3, p. 2.

p. 26 Journal problem (No. 41) reprinted from *Ontario Secondary School Mathematics Bulletin*, Vol. 18, 1982, issue 2, p. 7.

p. 41 Journal problem (No. 66) reprinted from *The Mathematics Student Journal*, Vol. 28, 1980, issue 3, p. 2.

p. 79 Putnam examination problem (No. 49), 1959, reprinted by permission from The Mathematical Association of America.

p. 79 Putnam examination problem (No. 50) 1960, reprinted by permission from The Mathematical Association of America.

p. 80 Guest essay, "Calculus Was Inevitable," by John L. Troutman.

CHAPTER 2

p. 104 Journal problem (No. 65) by Michael W. Ecker from *The AMATYC Review*, Vol. 6, 1984, issue 1, p. 55.

p. 136 Journal problem (No. 50) by Bruce W. King from *The Pi Mu Epsilon Journal*, Vol. 7, 1981, p. 346.

p. 161 Newspaper clipping from *The Wall Street Journal*, June 6, 1986.

p. 163 Putnam examination problem (No. 74) 1946, reprinted by permission from The Mathematical Association of America.

p. 163 Putnam examination problem (No. 75) 1939, reprinted by permission from The Mathematical Association of America.

p. 163 Putnam examination problem (No. 76) 1946, reprinted by permission from The Mathematical Association of America.

p. 164 Group research project from Diane Schwartz from Ithaca College, Ithaca, N.Y.

CHAPTER 3

p. 192 Journal problem (No. 68) from *Mathematics Magazine*, Vol. 55, 1982, p. 300.

p. 202 Problem (No. 42) from a paper "The Mechanics of Bird Migration," by C. J. Pennycuick, published by *Ibis III*, 1969, pp. 525–556.

p. 212 Journal problem (No. 55) by Michael G. Murphy from the *College Mathematics Journal*, Vol. 22, May 1991, p. 221.

p. 212 Journal problem (No. 56) from *Parabola*, Vol. 20, issue 1, 1984.

p. 226 Journal problem (No. 7) from *Parabola*, Vol. 19, issue 1, 1983, p. 22.

p. 238 Problem (No. 30) adapted from "Flight of Birds in Relation to Energetics and Wind Directions," by V. A. Tucker and K. Schmidt-Koenig, *The Auk*, Vol. 88, 1971, pp. 97–107.

p. 253 Journal problem (No. 35) from the *Mathematics Teacher*, December 1990, p. 718.

p. 255 Putnam examination problem (No. 68), 1938, reprinted by permission from The Mathematical Association of America.

p. 255 Putnam examination problem (No. 69) 1941, reprinted by permission from The Mathematical Association of America.

p. 255 Putnam examination problem (No. 70) 1986, reprinted by permission from The Mathematical Association of America.

p. 255 Putnam examination problem (No. 71) 1985, reprinted by permission from The Mathematical Association of America.

p. 256 Group research project from Elgin Johnston of "The Venerable Cooper," Quantum, May 1990. This group research project comes from research done at Iowa State University as part of a National Science Foundation grant.

CHAPTER 4

p. 258 Asian integration from *Mathematics*, by David Bergamini, 1963, p. 108. Reprinted by permission of Time, Incorporated.

p. 260 Software output from *Converge* by John R. Mowbray, JEMware, 567 South King Street, Suite 178, Honolulu, HI 96813-3076 (808-523-4811).

p. 286 Journal problem (No. 63) by Murray Klamkin from the *College Mathematics Journal*, September 1989, p. 343.

p. 289 Photograph of scattering experiment from *Scientific American*, May 1991.

p. 307 Quotation from "A Short Account of the History of Mathematics," as quoted in *Mathematical Circles Adieu* by Howard Eves (Boston: Prindle, Weber & Schmidt, Inc., 1977).

p. 308 Graph from *The Wall Street Journal*, February 26, 1986.

p. 322 Putnam examination problem (No. 73), 1970, reprinted by permission from The Mathematical Association of America.

p. 322 Putnam examination problem (No. 74), 1951, reprinted by permission from The Mathematical Association of America.

p. 322   Putnam examination problem (No. 75), 1958, reprinted by permission from The Mathematical Association of America.

p. 322   Guest essay, "Kinematics of Jogging," by Ralph Boas.

CHAPTER 5

pp. 374–375   Quotation about Bernoulli from Leonhard Euler in *Elements of Algebra*.

p. 381   Putnam examination problem (No. 93), 1939, reprinted by permission from The Mathematical Association of America.

p. 381   Putnam examination problem (No. 94), 1940, reprinted by permission from The Mathematical Association of America.

p. 381   Putnam examination problem (No. 95), 1951, reprinted by permission from The Mathematical Association of America.

p. 381   Putnam examination problem (No. 96), 1961, reprinted by permission from The Mathematical Association of America.

p. 382   Group research project from Peter D. Taylor of Queen's University, Kingston, Ontario.

CHAPTER 6

p. 433   Putnam examination problem (No. 71), 1939, reprinted by permission from The Mathematical Association of America.

p. 433   Putnam examination problem (No. 72), 1938, reprinted by permission from The Mathematical Association of America.

p. 434   Group research project from *MAA Notes*, Vol. 17, 1991, "Priming the Calculus Pump: Innovations and Resources," by Marcus S. Cohen, Edward D. Gaughan, R. Arthur Knoebel, Douglas S. Kurtz, and David J. Pengelley.

CHAPTER 7

p. 477   Journal problem (No. 52) by Peter Lindstrom from the *College Mathematics Journal*, Vol. 24, No. 4, September 1993, p. 343.

p. 487   Putnam examination problem (No. 72), 1968, reprinted by permission from The Mathematical Association of America.

p. 487   Putnam examination problem (No. 73), 1968, reprinted by permission from The Mathematical Association of America.

p. 487   Putnam examination problem (No. 74), 1985, reprinted by permission from The Mathematical Association of America.

p. 488   Group research project adapted from a computer project used at the U.S. Coast Guard Academy.

CHAPTER 8

p. 567   Putnam examination problem (No. 97), 1984, reprinted by permission from The Mathematical Association of America.

p. 567   Putnam examination problem (No. 98), 1977, reprinted by permission from The Mathematical Association of America.

p. 568   Group research project from David Pengelley, Marcus Cohen, Edward D. Gaughan, Arthur Knoebel, and Douglas S. Kurtoro, Department of Mathematical Sciences, of New Mexico State University, Las Cruces, NM 88004.

CHAPTER 9

p. 628   Putnam examination problem (No. 94), 1974, reprinted by permission from The Mathematical Association of America.

p. 628   Putnam examination problem (No. 95), 1976, reprinted by permission from The Mathematical Association of America.

p. 628   Putnam examination problem (No. 96), 1984, reprinted by permission from The Mathematical Association of America.

p. 629   Group research project from Steve Hilbert, Ithaca College, Ithaca, New York.

CHAPTER 10

p. 682   Putnam examination problem (No. 81), 1939, reprinted by permission from The Mathematical Association of America.

p. 682   Putnam examination problem (No. 82), 1959, reprinted by permission from The Mathematical Association of America.

p. 682   Putnam examination problem (No. 83), 1983, reprinted by permission from The Mathematical Association of America.

p. 682   Group research project from *MAA Notes*, Vol. 17, 1991, "Priming the Calculus Pump: Innovations and Resources," by Marcus S. Cohen, Edward D. Gaughan, R. Arthur Knoebel, Douglas S. Kurtz, and David J. Pengelley.

CHAPTER 11

p. 686   Photograph of double helix of DNA, courtesy of *Scientific American*, October 1985, p. 60, "DNA" by Gary Felsenfield.

p. 705   Photograph of an earth satellite, courtesy AT & T Photo Center.

p. 727   Photograph of a Ferris wheel, courtesy Eugene Gordon.

p. 732   Putnam examination problem (No. 75), 1939, reprinted by permission from The Mathematical Association of America.

p. 732 Putnam examination problem (No. 76), 1947, reprinted by permission from The Mathematical Association of America.

p. 732 Putnam examination problem (No. 77), 1946, reprinted by permission from The Mathematical Association of America.

p. 733 Quotation by Johannes Kepler from *The World of Mathematics*, Vol. I, James R. Newman, (New York: Simon & Schuster, 1952), p. 220.

p. 733 Guest essay, "The Simulation of Science," by Howard Eves. This article is reprinted by permission from *Great Moments in Mathematics Before 1650,* published by The Mathematical Association of America, 1983, p. 194.

CHAPTER 12

p. 738 Computer-generated graph of Mount St. Helens, courtesy of Bill Lennox, Humboldt State University.

p. 741 Three-dimensional curves, Stanford Graphics image courtesy of Visual Numerics, Houston, TX.

p. 741 Typographical map, courtesy of U.S. Geological Survey.

p. 742 Weather forcast map, courtesy of Accu-Weather, Inc.

p. 818 Problem No. 97 adapted from "Hidden Boundaries in Constrained Max–Min Problems," by Herbert R. Bailey from *The College Mathematics Journal*, May, 1991, p. 227.

p. 819 Photograph of soap bubbles from *Scientific American*, "The Geometry of Soap Films and Soap Bubblers," by Frederick Almgren, Jr., and Jean Taylor.

p. 819 Putnam examination problem (No. 99) 1967, reprinted by permission from The Mathematical Association of America.

p. 819 Putnam examination problem (No. 100) 1946, reprinted by permission from The Mathematical Association of America.

p. 819 Putnam examination problem (No. 101) 1938, reprinted by permission from The Mathematical Association of America.

p. 819 Group research project is from *MAA Notes*, Vol. 17, 1991, "Priming the Calculus Pump: Innovations and Resources," by Marcus S. Cohen, Edward D. Gaughan, R. Arthur Knoebel, Douglas S. Kurtz, and David J. Pengelley.

CHAPTER 13

p. 895 Putnam examination problem (No. 89) 1942, reprinted by permission from The Mathematical Association of America.

p. 895 Putnam examination problem (No. 90) 1957, reprinted by permission from The Mathematical Association of America.

p. 895 Putnam examination problem (No. 91) 1958, reprinted by permission from The Mathematical Association of America.

p. 896 Photograph of an Apollo spacecraft, courtesy NASA.

p. 896 Group research project is from *MAA Notes*, Vol. 17, 1991, "Priming the Calculus Pump: Innovations and Resources," by Marcus S. Cohen, Edward D. Gaughan, R. Arthur Knoebel, Douglas S. Kurtz, and David J. Pengelley.

CHAPTER 14

p. 964 Photograph of an earth satellite, courtesy NASA.

p. 965 Putnam examination problem (No. 82), 1948, reprinted by permission from The Mathematical Association of America.

p. 966 Guest essay, "Continuous vs. Discrete Mathematics," by William Lucas.

NOTE: Portraits of Newton, Leibniz, Euler, Lagrange, Laplace, Gauss, Cauchy, Hamilton, Fermat, Weirstrass, and Rieman are based upon portraits from the David Eugene Smith Collection of the Rare Book and Manuscript Library, Columbia University.

INDEX